Hoover's Handbook of

Private Companies
2016

HOOVERS™
A D&B COMPANY

Austin, Texas

Copyright © 2016 by Mergent, Inc. All rights reserved. No part of this book may be reproduced or transmitted in any form or by any means, electronic or mechanical, including by photocopying, facsimile transmission, recording, rekeying, or using any information storage and retrieval system, without permission in writing from Hoover's, except that brief passages may be quoted by a reviewer in a magazine, in a newspaper, online, or in a broadcast review.

10 9 8 7 6 5 4 3 2 1

Publishers Cataloging-in-Publication Data
Hoover's Handbook of Private Companies 2016
    Includes indexes.
    ISBN: 978-1-63053-407-3
    ISSN 1073-6433

    1. Business enterprises — Directories. 2. Corporations — Directories.
HF3010 338.7

U.S. AND WORLD BOOK SALES

Mergent Inc.

580 Kingsley Park Drive
Fort Mill, SC
29715
Phone: 800-342-5647
e-mail: orders@mergent.com
Web: www.mergentbusinesspress.com

Mergent Inc.

CEO: Jonathan Worrall

Executive Managing Director: John Pedernalis

Executive Vice President of Sales: Fred Jenkins

Managing Director of Relationship Management: Chris Henry

Managing Director of Print Products: Thomas Wecera

MERGENT CUSTOMER SERVICE

Support and Fulfillment Manager: Melanie Horvat

ABOUT MERGENT INC.

Mergent, Inc. is a leading provider of business and financial data on global publicly listed companies. Based in the U.S, the company maintains a strong global presence, with offices in New York, Charlotte, San Diego, London, Tokyo and Melbourne.

Founded in 1900, Mergent operates one of the longest continuously collected databases of: descriptive and fundamental information on domestic and international companies; pricing and terms and conditions data on fixed income and equity securities; and corporate action data. In addition, Mergent's Indxis subsidiary develops and licenses equity and fixed income investment products based on its proprietary investment methodologies. Our licensed products have over $9 billion in assets under management and are offered by major investment management firms. The Indxis calculation platform is the chosen technology for some of the world's largest index companies. Its index calculation and pricing distribution protocols are used to administer index rules and distribute real-time pricing data .

Abbreviations

AFL-CIO – American Federation of Labor and Congress of Industrial Organizations

AMA – American Medical Association

AMEX – American Stock Exchange

ARM – adjustable-rate mortgage

ASP – application services provider

ATM – asynchronous transfer mode

ATM – automated teller machine

CAD/CAM – computer-aided design/computer-aided manufacturing

CD-ROM – compact disc – read-only memory

CD-R – CD-recordable

CEO – chief executive officer

CFO – chief financial officer

CMOS – complementary metal oxide silicon

COO – chief operating officer

DAT – digital audiotape

DOD – Department of Defense

DOE – Department of Energy

DOS – disk operating system

DOT – Department of Transportation

DRAM – dynamic random-access memory

DSL – digital subscriber line

DVD – digital versatile disc/digital video disc

DVD-R – DVD-recordable

EPA – Environmental Protection Agency

EPS – earnings per share

ESOP – employee stock ownership plan

EU – European Union

EVP – executive vice president

FCC – Federal Communications Commission

FDA – Food and Drug Administration

FDIC – Federal Deposit Insurance Corporation

FTC – Federal Trade Commission

GATT – General Agreement on Tariffs and Trade

GDP – gross domestic product

HMO – health maintenance organization

HR – human resources

HTML – hypertext markup language

ICC – Interstate Commerce Commission

IPO – initial public offering

IRS – Internal Revenue Service

ISP – Internet service provider

kWh – kilowatt-hour

LAN – local-area network

LBO – leveraged buyout

LCD – liquid crystal display

LNG – liquefied natural gas

LP – limited partnership

Ltd. – limited

mips – millions of instructions per second

MW – megawatt

NAFTA – North American Free Trade Agreement

NASA – National Aeronautics and Space Administration

NASDAQ – National Association of Securities Dealers Automated Quotations

NATO – North Atlantic Treaty Organization

NYSE – New York Stock Exchange

OCR – optical character recognition

OECD – Organization for Economic Cooperation and Development

OEM – original equipment manufacturer

OPEC – Organization of Petroleum Exporting Countries

OS – operating system

OSHA – Occupational Safety and Health Administration

OTC – over-the-counter

PBX – private branch exchange

PCMCIA – Personal Computer Memory Card International Association

P/E – price to earnings ratio

RAID – redundant array of independent disks

RAM – random-access memory

R&D – research and development

RBOC – regional Bell operating company

RISC – reduced instruction set computer

REIT – real estate investment trust

ROA – return on assets

ROE – return on equity

ROI – return on investment

ROM – read-only memory

S&L – savings and loan

SEC – Securities and Exchange Commission

SEVP – senior executive vice president

SIC – Standard Industrial Classification

SOC – system on a chip

SVP – senior vice president

USB – universal serial bus

VAR – value-added reseller

VAT – value-added tax

VC – venture capitalist

VoIP – Voice over Internet Protocol

VP – vice president

WAN – wide-area network

Contents

Companies Profiled vi

About *Hoover's Handbook of Private Companies 2016* xiv

Using Hoover's Handbooks xv

A List-Lover's Compendium 1a

    The 200 Largest Companies by Sales in *Hoover's Handbook of Private Companies 2016* 2a

    The 200 Largest Employers in *Hoover's Handbook of Private Companies 2016* 4a

    The Top 100 Companies by Net Income in *Hoover's Handbook of Private Companies 2016* 6a

    The Top 100 Companies by Total Assets in *Hoover's Handbook of Private Companies 2016* 7a

The Companies 1

Index of Company Executives 657

Companies Profiled

A C & T CO INC 1
A G EQUIPMENT COMPANY 1
A-1 SPECIALIZED SERVICES & SUPPLIES INC...1
AAA COOPER TRANSPORTATION 1
ABINGTON MEMORIAL HOSPITAL INC...........1
ABINGTON RELDAN METALS LLC 2
ACADIAN AMBULANCE SERVICE INC. 2
ACME TRUCK LINE INC. 3
ACTION CAPITAL CORPORATION 3
ACTIONET INC. 3
ACTIONTEC ELECTRONICS INC. 3
ADAC PLASTICS INC. 4
ADELPHI UNIVERSITY 4
ADENA HEALTH SYSTEM 5
ADVANTAGE ELECTRIC SERVICES LLC 5
ADVOCATE HEALTH AND HOSPITALS
    CORPORATION 6
ADVOCATE HEALTH AND HOSPITALS
    CORPORATION 6
AEROTEK INC. 6
AFFILIATED FOODS MIDWEST COOPERATIVE
    INC. 7
AG GEORGIA FARM CREDIT 7
AGMARK LLC 7
AGRI-AFC LLC 7
AGSOUTH FARM CREDIT ACA 8
AHS HOSPITAL CORP. 8
AKAL SECURITY INC. 8
ALABAMA FARMERS COOPERATIVE INC. 8
ALASKA NATIVE TRIBAL HEALTH
    CONSORTIUM 9
ALASKA PERMANENT FUND CORPORATION 9
ALBANY MEDICAL CENTER 10
ALBANY MEDICAL CENTER HOSPITAL 11
ALBERICI CONSTRUCTORS INC. 11
ALBERICI CORPORATION 11
ALBERICI GROUP INC. 12
ALBERT EINSTEIN MEDICAL ASSOCIATES ...12
ALBERT EINSTEIN MEDICAL CENTER 12
ALDRIDGE ELECTRIC INC. 12
ALEXANDRIA INOVA HOSPITAL 13
ALL POINTS COOPERATIVE 13
ALL SAINTS HEALTH CARE SYSTEM INC. 13
ALLEGIS GROUP INC. 13
ALLEN LUND COMPANY LLC 14
ALLIANCE FOR SUSTAINABLE ENERGY LLC ...14
ALLIED BUILDING STORES INC. 15
ALLINA HEALTH SYSTEM 15
ALRO STEEL CORPORATION 15
ALSCO INC. 16
ALTA COLLEGES INC. 16
AMERICA CHUNG NAM (GROUP) HOLDINGS
    LLC 16
AMERICAN ASSOCIATED PHARMACIES 17
AMERICAN BAR ASSOCIATION 17
AMERICAN BUREAU OF SHIPPING INC 18
AMERICAN CHEMICAL SOCIETY 18
AMERICAN FEDERATION OF LABOR & CON-
    GRESS OF INDUSTRIAL ORGANZATIO........19
AMERICAN FEDERATION OF STATE COUNTY &
    MUNICIPAL EMPLOYEES 20
AMERICAN FURNITURE WAREHOUSE CO INC 20
AMERICAN INSTITUTE OF CERTIFIED PUBLIC
    ACCOUNTANTS 21
AMERICAN INSTITUTES FOR RESEARCH IN
    THE BEHAVIORAL SCIENCES 21
AMERICAN LEBANESE SYRIAN ASSOCIATED
    CHARITIES INC. 22
AMERICAN MEDICAL ASSOCIATION INC 22
AMERICAN PETROLEUM INSTITUTE INC 23
AMERICAN SOCIETY FOR THE PREVENTION OF
    CRUELTY TO ANIMALS (INC) 23
AMERICAN SYSTEMS CORPORATION 23
AMERICAN UNIVERSITY 24
AMERICARES FOUNDATION INC. 25
AMERICA'S HOME PLACE INC. 17
AMES CONSTRUCTION INC. 25
ANCHORAGE SCHOOL DISTRICT 25

ANDERSEN CONSTRUCTION COMPANY..........26
ANDERSON AND DUBOSE INC...................26
ANMED HEALTH 26
ANN & ROBERT H. LURIE CHILDREN'S HOSPI-
    TAL OF CHICAGO 26
ANNE ARUNDEL COUNTY BOARD OF
    EDUCATION 27
ANNE ARUNDEL MEDICAL CENTER INC.........27
API GROUP INC. 28
APPLE AMERICAN GROUP LLC 29
APPLE HOSPITALITY REIT INC 29
APPLIED CARD SYSTEMS INC. 29
APPLIED RESEARCH ASSOCIATES INC. 29
APRO LLC 30
ARBITECH LLC 30
ARCTIC SLOPE REGIONAL CORPORATION 30
ARKANSAS CHILDREN'S HOSPITAL 31
ARKANSAS ELECTRIC COOPERATIVES INC....32
ARNOLD MACHINERY COMPANY 32
ARROW HEAD REGIONAL MEDICAL CENTER .32
ASHLAND HOSPITAL CORPORATION 33
ASI COMPUTER TECHNOLOGIES INC 33
ASPIRUS INC. 34
ASPIRUS WAUSAU HOSPITAL INC. 34
ASSOCIATED ELECTRIC COOPERATIVE INC. ..34
ASSOCIATED FOOD STORES INC. 35
ASSOCIATED GROCERS OF NEW ENGLAND
    INC. 35
ASSOCIATED WHOLESALE GROCERS INC. 36
ASSOCIATION OF UNIVERSITIES FOR
    RESEARCH IN ASTRONOMY INC. 37
ASTRONAUTICS CORPORATION OF AMERICA .37
ATALANTA CORPORATION 38
ATLANTIC BROADBAND FINANCE LLC............39
ATLANTIC HEALTH SYSTEM INC. 39
ATLANTIC METHANOL PRODUCTION COMPANY
    LLC 39
ATLANTICARE REGIONAL MEDICAL CENTER .40
ATLAS OIL COMPANY 40
AUGUSTANA HEALTH CARE CENTER OF APPLE
    VALLEY 40
AUSABLE VALLEY COMMUNITY MENTAL
    HEALTH FOUNDATION 40
AVERITT EXPRESS INC. 40
AVERITT INCORPORATED 41
AVI SYSTEMS INC. 41
AVI-SPL HOLDINGS INC. 41
AVIO INC. 42
AXEL JOHNSON INC. 42
AZUSA PACIFIC UNIVERSITY 42
BABSON COLLEGE 43
BAER'S FURNITURE CO. INC. 43
BALL STATE UNIVERSITY 44
BALTIMORE CITY PUBLIC SCHOOL SYSTEMS
    (INC) 44
BALTIMORE WASHINGTON MEDICAL SYSTEM
    INC. 45
BANNER HEALTH 45
BAPTIST HEALTH 46
BAPTIST HEALTH SOUTH FLORIDA INC. 47
BAPTIST HEALTH SYSTEM INC. 48
BAPTIST HEALTHCARE SYSTEM INC. 48
BAPTIST HOSPITAL OF MIAMI INC. 48
BAPTIST MEMORIAL HEALTH CARE
    CORPORATION 49
BAPTIST MEMORIAL HOSPITAL 50
BAR-ILAN UNIVERSITY IN ISRAEL 50
BARD COLLEGE 50
BARRICK ENTERPRISES INC. 51
BARRY UNIVERSITY INC. 51
BARRY-WEHMILLER GROUP INC. 51
BARTON MALOW COMPANY 52
BARTON MALOW ENTERPRISES INC. 53
BATELLE MEMORIAL INSTITUTE 53
BATON ROUGE GENERAL MEDICAL CENTER .53
BATTELLE MEMORIAL INSTITUTE INC 54
BAUER BUILT INC. 55
BAY MEDICAL CENTER 55

BAY REGIONAL MEDICAL CENTER..............56
BAYHEALTH MEDICAL CENTER INC. 56
BAYLOR UNIVERSITY MEDICAL CENTER.........56
BAYSIDE FUEL OIL DEPOT CORP 57
BAYSTATE HEALTH SYSTEM HEALTH
    SERVICES INC. 57
BEACON HEALTH SYSTEM INC. 58
BEALL'S INC. 58
BEARING DISTRIBUTORS INC. 59
BEAVER STREET FISHERIES INC. 59
BECK & MASTEN PONTIAC-GMC INC 60
BECK SUPPLIERS INC. 60
BECKMAN RESEARCH INSTITUTE OF THE CITY
    OF HOPE 60
BEEBE MEDICAL CENTER INC. 61
BELAIRE HEALTH CARE CENTER INC. 61
BELLIN HEALTH SYSTEMS INC. 61
BELLIN MEMORIAL HOSPITAL INC. 61
BELOIT HEALTH SYSTEM INC. 62
BEN-TREI LTD. 62
BENCO DENTAL SUPPLY CO. 63
BENTLEY UNIVERSITY 63
BERGELECTRIC CORP. 64
BERGEN REGIONAL MEDICAL CENTER L.P. ...64
BERKLEE COLLEGE OF MUSIC INC. 65
BERKSHIRE MEDICAL CENTER INC............65
BERRY COMPANIES INC. 66
BEST WESTERN INTERNATIONAL INC...........66
BETH ISRAEL DEACONESS MEDICAL CENTER
    INC. 67
BETH ISRAEL MEDICAL CENTER 67
BETHCO CORPORATION 68
BETHESDA HOSPITAL INC. 68
BI-MART ACQUISITION CORPORATION 68
BI-RITE RESTAURANT SUPPLY CO. INC. 69
BIG RIVER RESOURCES GALVA LLC 69
BIG RIVER RESOURCES LLC 69
BIG RIVER RESOURCES WEST BURLINGTON
    LLC 69
BIG RIVER UNITED ENERGY LLC. 69
BIG RIVERS ELECTRIC CORPORATION..........70
BIG-D CONSTRUCTION CORP. 70
BILL HILLARY & CHELSEA CLINTON
    FOUNDATION 70
BILLINGS CLINIC 70
BIOURJA TRADING LLC 71
BIRKEY'S FARM STORE INC. 71
BJT INC. 72
BLACK & VEATCH CONSTRUCTION INC. 73
BLACK & VEATCH CORPORATION 73
BLACK & VEATCH HOLDING COMPANY 74
BLACK & VEATCH INTERNATIONAL
    COMPANY 74
BLANCHARD VALLEY FARMERS COOPERATIVE
    INC. 74
BLARNEY CASTLE OIL CO. 75
BLESSING HOSPITAL 75
BLOOD SYSTEMS INC. 76
BLUE CROSS AND BLUE SHIELD OF ARIZONA
    INC. 76
BLUE TEE CORP. 77
BLUEBONNET ELECTRIC COOPERATIVE 78
BOARD OF COOPERATIVE EDUCATIONAL SER-
    VICES OF NASSAU COUNTY 78
BOARD OF EDUCATION FOR THE CITY OF
    SAVANNAH AND THE COUNTY OF CH 78
BOARD OF EDUCATION OF CARROLL
    COUNTY 78
BOARD OF EDUCATION OF FREDERICK COUN-
    TY MD (INC) 79
BOARD OF EDUCATION-MEMPHIS CITY
    SCHOOLS 79
BOCA RATON REGIONAL HOSPITAL INC. 79
BODDIE-NOELL ENTERPRISES INC. 79
BOGOPA ENTERPRISES INC. 79
BON SECOURS HEALTH SYSTEM INC 80
BON SECOURS-MEMORIAL REGIONAL MED-
    ICAL CENTER INC. 80

Companies Profiled (continued)

BOND BROS. INC. ...81
BONGARDS' CREAMERIES ...81
BORGESS MEDICAL CENTER ...81
BOSTON MEDICAL CENTER CORPORATION ...81
BOWEN ENGINEERING CORPORATION ...82
BOY SCOUTS OF AMERICA ...82
BRANDEIS UNIVERSITY ...83
BRAZOS ELECTRIC POWER COOPERATIVE INC. ...83
BROADWAY MANOR NURSING HOME ...84
BROCKTON HOSPITAL INC. ...84
BRONSON METHODIST HOSPITAL INC. ...84
BRONX LEBANON HOSPITAL CENTER (INC) ...85
BROOKHAVEN MEMORIAL HOSPITAL MEDICAL CENTER IN. ...86
BROOKLYN HOSPITAL CENTER ...86
BROWN'S SUPER STORES INC. ...87
BRUCE OAKLEY INC. ...87
BRUCKNER TRUCK SALES INC. ...87
BRYAN MEDICAL CENTER ...88
BUCKEYE POWER INC. ...88
BUCKNELL UNIVERSITY ...89
BUNKERS INTERNATIONAL CORP. ...89
BURLINGTON HEALTH CARE CENTER (66) INC. ...89
C & K MARKET INC. ...89
C.D. SMITH CONSTRUCTION INC. ...90
C.R. ENGLAND INC. ...90
CADENCE MCSHANE CONSTRUCTION COMPANY LLC ...91
CAJUN CONSTRUCTORS INC. ...91
CAJUN INDUSTRIES LLC ...91
CALCOT LTD. ...92
CALIBRE SYSTEMS INC. ...92
CALIFORNIA COMMUNITY FOUNDATION ...92
CALIFORNIA INDEPENDENT SYSTEM OPERA-TOR CORPORATION ...93
CANDID COLOR SYSTEMS INC. ...93
CANNERY CASINO RESORTS LLC ...93
CAPE COD HEALTHCARE INC. ...93
CAPE COD HOSPITAL ...94
CAPITAL DISTRICT PHYSICIANS' HEALTH PLAN INC. ...94
CAPITAL HEALTH SYSTEM INC. ...95
CAREALLIANCE HEALTH SERVICES ...96
CAREGROUP INC. ...97
CARILION NEW RIVER VALLEY MEDICAL CENTER ...97
CARITAS NORWOOD HOSPITAL INC. ...98
CARLE FOUNDATION HOSPITAL ...98
CARLETON COLLEGE ...99
CARNEGIE MELLON UNIVERSITY ...99
CAROLINA CARE CENTER OF CHERRYVILLE INC. ...100
CAROLINA FARM CREDIT ACA ...100
CAROLINA HEALTHCARE CENTER OF CUMBERLAND LP ...100
CARPENTER CONTRACTORS OF AMERICA INC. ...100
CARSON OIL CO. INC. ...101
CARSON TAHOE REGIONAL HEALTHCARE ...101
CARTER-JONES COMPANIES INC. ...101
CARY OIL CO. INC. ...101
CASCADE ENGINEERING INC. ...102
CASH-WA DISTRIBUTING CO. OF KEARNEY INC. ...102
CATAMOUNT CONSTRUCTORS INC. ...103
CATHOLIC MEDICAL CENTER ...103
CATHOLIC MEDICAL MISSION BOARD INC ...103
CATHOLIC RELIEF SERVICES - UNITED STATES CONFERENCE OF CATHOLIC ...104
CDM CONSTRUCTORS INC. ...104
CEDARS-SINAI MEDICAL CENTER ...104
CEDARWOOD-YOUNG COMPANY ...105
CENTERLIGHT HEALTHCARE INC. ...105
CENTIMARK CORPORATION ...105
CENTRA HEALTH INC. ...106
CENTRAL ARKANSAS RADIATION THERAPY INSTITUTE INC. ...106
CENTRAL CONTINUING CARE INC. ...107
CENTRAL CRUDE INC ...107
CENTRAL DUPAGE HOSPITAL ASSOCIATION ...107
CENTRAL ELECTRIC POWER COOPERATIVE INC. ...107
CENTRAL GROCERS INC. ...108
CENTRAL IOWA HOSPITAL CORP ...108
CENTRAL IOWA POWER COOPERATIVE ...108
CENTRAL MAINE HEALTH VENTURES INC. ...108
CENTRAL MICHIGAN UNIVERSITY ...109

CENTRAL REFRIGERATED SERVICE INC. ...109
CENTRO MEDICO DEL TURABO INC. ...109
CERES SOLUTIONS LLP ...109
CERTCO INC. ...110
CFJ PROPERTIES LLC ...110
CGB ENTERPRISES INC. ...110
CH2M HILL COMPANIES LTD. ...111
CHALMETTE REFINING L.L.C. ...113
CHAPMAN UNIVERSITY ...113
CHARLES C PARKS CO INC ...113
CHARLES COUNTY BOARD OF EDUCATION ...114
CHARLESTON AREA MEDICAL CENTER INC. ...114
CHARLOTTE HEALTH CARE CENTER (68) INC ...114
CHARTER MANUFACTURING COMPANY INC. ...115
CHATHAM COUNTY BOARD OF EDUCATION ...115
CHECKERED FLAG MOTOR CAR COMPANY INC. ...115
CHENEGA CORPORATION ...116
CHERRY CENTRAL COOPERATIVE INC. ...116
CHILDFUND INTERNATIONAL USA ...116
CHILDRENS HOSPITAL MEDICAL CENTER OF AKRON ...119
CHILDREN'S HOSPITAL CENTRAL CALIFORNIA ...117
CHILDREN'S HOSPITAL OF ORANGE COUNTY ...117
CHILDREN'S HOSPITAL OF THE KINGS DAUGHTERS INC ...117
CHILDREN'S MEDICAL CENTER OF DALLAS ...117
CHILDREN'S NATIONAL MEDICAL CENTER ...118
CHILTON HOSPITAL ...119
CHRISTIAN BROTHERS INVESTMENT SERVICES INC. ...120
CHRISTIAN HOSPITAL NORTHEAST NORTHWEST ...120
CHRISTIANA CARE HEALTH SERVICES INC. ...121
CHRISTUS HEALTH ...121
CHRISTUS HEALTH CENTRAL LOUISIANA ...122
CHRISTUS SANTA ROSA HEALTH CARE CORPORATION ...122
CHUGACH ALASKA CORPORATION ...122
CIC GROUP INC. ...123
CIMA ENERGY LTD. ...123
CITATION OIL & GAS CORP. ...123
CITIZENS ENERGY GROUP ...124
CITRUS VALLEY HEALTH PARTNERS INC. ...125
CITRUS VALLEY MEDICAL CENTER INC. ...125
CITY OF HOPE NATIONAL MEDICAL CENTER ...125
CITY OF HUNTSVILLE ELECTRIC SYSTEMS ...125
CITY PUBLIC SERVICES OF SAN ANTONIO ...126
CITY UTILITIES OF SPRINGFIELD MO ...126
CITYSERVICEVALCON LLC ...127
CLAPP S NURSING CENTER INC. ...127
CLARE ROSE INC. ...127
CLAREMONT HEALTH SYSTEM INC ...127
CLASSIC STAR GROUP LP ...128
CLAY ELECTRIC COOPERATIVE INC. ...128
CLAYCO INC. ...128
CLEVELAND CONSTRUCTION INC. ...129
CLIFTONLARSONALLEN LLP ...129
CLUNE CONSTRUCTION COMPANY L.P. ...130
COAST CITRUS DISTRIBUTORS ...130
COAST ELECTRIC POWER ASSOCIATION ...131
COASTAL FEDERAL CREDIT UNION ...131
COASTAL PACIFIC FOOD DISTRIBUTORS INC. ...131
COBB ELECTRIC MEMBERSHIP CORPORATION ...132
COBORN'S INCORPORATED ...132
COC PROPERTIES INC. ...132
COLLEGE ENTRANCE EXAMINATION BOARD ...133
COLLEGE OF THE HOLY CROSS ...133
COLONIAL SAVINGS F.A. ...134
COLORADO SEMINARY ...134
COLSA CORPORATION ...134
COLUMBIA COLLEGE CHICAGO ...135
COLUMBIA PROPERTY TRUST INC. ...135
COLUMBIA ST MARYS HOSPITAL MILWAUKEE ...135
COMMAND TRANSPORTATION LLC ...136
COMMUNITY ASPHALT CORP. ...136
COMMUNITY CARE INC. ...136
COMMUNITY HEALTH CHOICE INC. ...136
COMMUNITY HEALTH NETWORK INC. ...136
COMMUNITY HEALTH SYSTEM ...137

COMMUNITY HOSPITAL OF THE MONTEREY PENINSULA ...138
COMMUNITY MEMORIAL HEALTH SYSTEM ...138
COMPASSION INTERNATIONAL INC ...139
CONCORD HOSPITAL INC. ...139
CONCORDIA UNIVERSITY ...139
CONNECTICUT CHILDREN'S MEDICAL CENTER ...140
CONNECTICUT STATE UNIVERSITY SYSTEM ...140
CONNEXUS ENERGY ...141
CONSIGLI CONSTRUCTION CO INC. ...141
CONSOLIDATED GRAIN & BARGE COMPANY ...141
CONSUMER PRODUCT DISTRIBUTORS INC. ...142
CONSUMERS UNION OF UNITED STATES INC ...142
CONTI ENTERPRISES INC. ...143
CONTINUUM ENERGY SERVICES L.L.C. ...143
CONTRACK INTERNATIONAL INC. ...144
CONTRACTORS STEEL COMPANY ...144
CONWAY HOSPITAL INC. ...144
COOK CHILDREN'S MEDICAL CENTER ...144
COOPERATIVE ELEVATOR CO. ...145
COOPERATIVE FOR ASSISTANCE AND RELIEF EVERYWHERE INC. ...145
COOPERATIVE PRODUCERS INC. ...145
COOPERATIVE REGIONS OF ORGANIC PRODUCER POOLS ...145
COPLEY HEALTH CARE PARTNERSHIP ...146
CORE CONSTRUCTION GROUP LTD. ...146
CORE CONSTRUCTION INC. ...146
CORPORATE TRAVEL CONSULTANTS INC ...147
CORPORATION FOR PUBLIC BROADCASTING ...147
COUNTRYMARK COOPERATIVE HOLDING CORPORATION ...147
COUNTY OF MARICOPA ...148
COUNTY OF TARRANT ...148
COVENANT HEALTH SYSTEM ...148
COVENANT MEDICAL CENTER INC ...148
COVERALL NORTH AMERICA INC. ...149
CREATIVE MANAGEMENT INC ...149
CREIGHTON UNIVERSITY ...149
CREST INDUSTRIES LLC (DE) ...150
CREST OPERATIONS LLC ...150
CROSSLAND CONSTRUCTION COMPANY INC. ...150
CROWDER CONSTRUCTION COMPANY INC. ...151
CROWN BATTERY MANUFACTURING COMPANY ...151
CROZER-KEYSTONE HEALTH SYSTEM ...152
CSAA INSURANCE GROUP ...152
CSC SUGAR LLC ...152
CSI LEASING INC. ...153
CTSC LLC ...153
CUMBERLAND COUNTY HOSPITAL SYSTEM INC. ...153
CUMBERLAND COUNTY SCHOOLS ...154
CYCLE LINK (U.S.A.) INC. ...154
CYSTIC FIBROSIS FOUNDATION ...154
D REYNOLDS COMPANY LLC ...155
D W W CO. INC. ...155
D/L COOPERATIVE INC. ...155
DAIRYAMERICA INC. ...156
DAKOTA ELECTRIC ASSOCIATION ...156
DAKOTA SUPPLY GROUP INC. ...156
DANA-FARBER CANCER INSTITUTE INC. ...156
DANBURY HOSPITAL DEVELOPMENT FUND INC ...157
DANIS BUILDING CONSTRUCTION COMPANY ...158
DARTMOUTH-HITCHCOCK CLINIC ...158
DATS TRUCKING INC. ...158
DAVIDSON'S INC. ...159
DBSI INC ...159
DCR SYSTEM HOUSE INC. ...159
DCR WORKFORCE INC. ...159
DE PAUL UNIVERSITY ...159
DEACONESS HEALTH SYSTEM INC. ...160
DEACONESS HOSPITAL INC ...160
DECATUR MEMORIAL HOSPITAL ...161
DEKALB COUNTY BOARD OF EDUCATION ...162
DEKALB COUNTY PUBLIC LIBRARY ...162
DEKALB MEDICAL CENTER INC. ...162
DELI MANAGEMENT INC. ...163
DELTA DENTAL OF TENNESSEE ...163
DENNIS K BURKE INC ...163
DEPAUW UNIVERSITY ...163
DESERET GENERATION AND TRANSMISSION CO-OPERATIVE ...164

Companies Profiled (continued)

DEVCON CONSTRUCTION INCORPORATED ..164
DEVEREUX FOUNDATION ...164
DFB PHARMACEUTICALS INC ...165
DIALYSIS CLINIC INC. ...166
DICKINSON COLLEGE ...166
DIMENSIONS HEALTH CORPORATION ...166
DIMEO CONSTRUCTION COMPANY ...167
DIRECT RELIEF ...167
DOCTORS' HOSPITAL ...168
DOCTOR'S ASSOCIATES INC. ...167
DON FORD SANDERSON INC ...168
DOOLEY'S PETROLEUM INC ...169
DORCHESTER FARMERS COOPERATIVE ...169
DOYLESTOWN HOSPITAL HEALTH AND WELL-NESS CENTER INC. ...169
DPR CONSTRUCTION INC. ...169
DRAKE UNIVERSITY ...170
DREXEL UNIVERSITY ...170
DRISCOLL CHILDREN'S HOSPITAL ...171
DTJ HOLDINGS INC. ...171
DUCON TECHNOLOGIES INC. ...172
DUPONT HOSPITAL FOR CHILDREN ...172
DUQUESNE UNIVERSITY OF THE HOLY SPIRIT ...172
DURHAM PUBLIC SCHOOLS ...172
DUVAL COUNTY PUBLIC SCHOOLS ...173
DYNASTY FARMS INC. ...173
E-Z MART STORES INC. ...173
E. C. BARTON & COMPANY ...173
EAST BATON ROUGE PARISH SCHOOL DISTRICT ...174
EAST JEFFERSON GENERAL HOSPITAL ...174
EAST TENNESSEE CHILDREN'S HOSPITAL ASSOCIATION INC. ...174
EAST TENNESSEE STATE UNIVERSITY ...175
EAST TEXAS MEDICAL CENTER REGIONAL HEALTHCARE SYST ...175
EASTERN BAG AND PAPER COMPANY INCORPORATED ...176
EASTERN MICHIGAN UNIVERSITY ...177
EASTERN SHIPBUILDING GROUP INC. ...177
EASTERN VIRGINIA MEDICAL SCHOOL ...177
ED STAUB & SONS PETROLEUM INC. ...178
EDUCATIONAL CREDIT MANAGEMENT CORPORATION ...178
EDWARD HOSPITAL ...178
EFFINGHAM EQUITY ...178
EIDE BAILLY LLP ...178
EISENHOWER MEDICAL CENTER ...179
EISNERAMPER LLP ...180
EL DORADO FURNITURE CORP ...180
ELECTRIC POWER BOARD OF THE METROPOL-ITAN GOVERNMENT OF NASHVILLE ...181
ELECTRIC POWER RESEARCH INSTITUTE INC. ...181
ELECTRIC RELIABILITY COUNCIL OF TEXAS INC. ...182
ELLIOT HOSPITAL OF THE CITY OF MANCHESTER ...182
ELLIS HOSPITAL ...183
ELMHURST MEMORIAL HOSPITAL INC ...184
ELWYN ...184
EMBRY-RIDDLE AERONAUTICAL UNIVERSITY INC. ...185
EMERSON HOSPITAL ...185
EMILY DICKINSON MUSEUM ...186
EMJ CORPORATION ...186
EMPIRE SOUTHWEST LLC ...186
EMPLOYERS RESOURCE MANAGEMENT COMPANY ...187
ENERGYUNITED ELECTRIC MEMBERSHIP CORPORATION ...187
EP ENERGY LLC ...187
EPIC AVIATION LLC ...187
ERIE COUNTY MEDICAL CENTER CORP. ...188
ERM-NA HOLDINGS CORP. ...188
ERP OPERATING LIMITED PARTNERSHIP ...188
ESTES EXPRESS LINES INC. ...188
EVANGELICAL COMMUNITY HOSPITAL ...189
EWING IRRIGATION PRODUCTS INC. ...189
EXCELITAS TECHNOLOGIES CORP. ...190
FAIRFIELD MEDICAL CENTER ...190
FAIRFIELD UNIVERSITY ...190
FAIRLEIGH DICKINSON UNIVERSITY ...191
FAIRVIEW HEALTH SERVICES ...192
FAITH TECHNOLOGIES INC. ...193
FAMILY EXPRESS CORPORATION ...193
FAMILY HEALTH INTERNATIONAL INC ...193
FARM CREDIT SERVICES ILLINOIS ACA ...194

FARM CREDIT SERVICES OF AMERICA PCA/FLCA ...194
FARM CREDIT WEST ...194
FARMERS CO-OPERATIVE ELEVATOR COMPANY ...194
FARMERS COOPERATIVE COMPANY ...194
FARMERS COOPERATIVE SOCIETY ...195
FARMERS GRAIN TERMINAL INC. ...195
FARMERS' SUPPLY COMPANY INC. ...195
FATHER FLANAGAN'S BOY'S HOME INC ...195
FATHER MURRAY NURSING CENTER ...195
FAYETTE COMMUNITY HOSPITAL INC. ...196
FCTG HOLDINGS INC. ...196
FEED THE CHILDREN INC. ...196
FERMI RESEARCH ALLIANCE LLC ...197
FERRIS STATE UNIVERSITY ...197
FERROUS PROCESSING AND TRADING COMPANY ...197
FINANCIAL INDUSTRY REGULATORY AUTHORITY INC. ...197
FIRELANDS REGIONAL HEALTH SYSTEM ...198
FIRST COOPERATIVE ASSOCIATION ...199
FIRST ELECTRIC CO-OPERATIVE CORPORATION ...199
FIRSTFLEET INC. ...199
FIVE STAR COOPERATIVE ...199
FLEMING GANNETT INC ...200
FLETCHER ALLEN HEALTH CARE INC. ...201
FLINT ELECTRIC MEMBERSHIP CORPORATION ...202
FLORIDA CLINICAL PRACTICE ASSOCIATION INC. ...202
FLORIDA HOSPITAL MEDICAL GROUP INC. ..202
FLORIDA HOSPITAL WATERMAN INC. ...202
FLOYD HEALTHCARE MANAGEMENT INC ...203
FOOD FOR THE POOR INC. ...203
FORCE 3 INC. ...204
FORDHAM UNIVERSITY ...204
FOREX CAPITAL MARKETS L.L.C. ...205
FORGE INDUSTRIES INC. ...205
FOX HEAD INC. ...205
FOXWORTH GALBRAITH LUMBER COMPANY ...206
FRANCIS SAINT MEDICAL CENTER ...206
FRANCISCAN ALLIANCE INC. ...207
FRANKLIN AND MARSHALL COLLEGE ...207
FRANKLIN HOSPITAL ...208
FRAZIER INDUSTRIAL COMPANY (INC) ...208
FREDERICK MEMORIAL HOSPITAL INC. ...209
FREEMAN HEALTH SYSTEM ...209
FREMAR L.L.C. ...210
FRESH MARK INC. ...210
FRESNO COMMUNITY HOSPITAL AND MEDICAL CENTER ...211
FROEDTERT MEMORIAL LUTHERAN HOSPITAL INC ...211
FRUIT GROWERS SUPPLY COMPANY INC ...211
GAINESVILLE REGIONAL UTILITIES (INC) ...212
GALLAUDET UNIVERSITY ...212
GALLUP INC. ...213
GARDEN PALS INC. ...213
GARFF ENTERPRISES INC. ...214
GAVI FUND ...214
GEHAN HOMES LTD. ...214
GELBER GROUP LLC ...214
GENESIS HEALTH SYSTEM ...215
GENESIS HEALTHCARE SYSTEM ...215
GENESIS HEALTHCARE SYSTEM ...215
GENICA CORPORATION ...216
GENPACT LIMITED ...216
GEORGIA REGENTS UNIVERSITY ...216
GEORGIA SOUTHERN UNIVERSITY ...216
GEORGIA TECH FOUNDATION INC. ...217
GEORGIA TRANSMISSION CORPORATION ...217
GERBER CHILDRENSWEAR LLC ...218
GERRITY'S SUPER MARKET INC. ...218
GILLETTE CHILDREN'S SPECIALTY HEALTHCARE ...218
GLASS MTN. PUMICE INC ...219
GLENDALE ADVENTIST MEDICAL CENTER INC ...219
GLOBAL HEALTH SOLUTIONS INC ...219
GLOBAL TRADING ENTERPRISES LLC ...219
GOLD-EAGLE COOPERATIVE ...220
GOLDEN GRAIN ENERGY LLC ...220
GOOD SAMARITAN HOSPITAL ...220
GOOD SAMARITAN HOSPITAL CORVALLIS ...220
GOOD360 ...220
GOODFELLOW BROS. INC. ...221

GOODWILL INDUSTRIES OF SOUTHEASTERN WISCONSIN INC. ...221
GPM INVESTMENTS LLC ...221
GRACE HEIGHTS HEALTH AND REHABILITATION CENTRE ...222
GRAEBEL COMPANIES INC. ...222
GRAHAM ENTERPRISE INC. ...223
GRAND STRAND REGIONAL MEDICAL CENTER LLC ...223
GRAND VIEW HOSPITAL ...223
GRANDVIEW HEALTH HOME ...223
GRANITE SCHOOL DISTRICT ...224
GRANITE TELECOMMUNICATIONS LLC ...224
GREAT NORTHERN CORPORATION ...224
GREENSTONE FARM CREDIT SERVICES ACA ...224
GREENWICH HOSPITAL ASSOCIATION INC ..225
GROSSMONT HOSPITAL CORPORATION ...225
GROUP O INC. ...225
GROVE SERVICES INC. ...226
GROWMARK INC. ...226
GRUNLEY CONSTRUCTION CO. INC. ...227
GUARANTEE ELECTRICAL COMPANY ...227
GUEST SERVICES INC. ...227
GUILDNET INC. ...228
GUILFORD COUNTY SCHOOL SYSTEM ...228
GWINNETT HOSPITAL SYSTEM INC. ...228
H. J. RUSSELL & COMPANY ...228
H. LEE MOFFITT CANCER CENTER & RESEARCH INSTITUTE HOSPITAL INC ...229
HABITAT FOR HUMANITY INTERNATIONAL INC. ...230
HACKENSACK UNIVERSITY MEDICAL CENTER ...230
HACKLEY HOSPITAL ...231
HAGGEN INC. ...232
HAMPTON WOODS HEALTH & REHABILITATION CENTER ...232
HARFORD COUNTY BOARD OF EDUCATION (INC) ...232
HARLAND M. BRAUN & CO. INC. ...232
HARLEE MANOR INC. ...233
HARRISON MEDICAL CENTER ...233
HARTFORD HOSPITAL ...233
HATCH MOTT MACDONALD GROUP INC. ...233
HATTIESBURG CLINIC PROFESSIONAL ASSOCIATION ...234
HAWKINS CONSTRUCTION COMPANY ...234
HAWTHORNE MACHINERY CO. ...234
HAYS MEDICAL CENTER INC. ...235
HDR ENGINEERING INC. ...235
HEALTH FIRST INC. ...235
HEALTH PARTNERS PLANS INC. ...236
HEALTH QUEST SYSTEMS INC. ...236
HEALTH RESEARCH INC. ...237
HEALTHEAST CARE SYSTEM ...237
HEARTLAND HEALTH ...237
HEARTLAND REGIONAL MEDICAL CENTER ..237
HENDRICK MEDICAL CENTER ...238
HENRY FORD HEALTH SYSTEM ...238
HENRY MAYO NEWHALL MEMORIAL HOSPITAL ...239
HENRY MODELL & COMPANY INC. ...239
HENSEL PHELPS CONSTRUCTION CO. ...240
HERSHEY ENTERTAINMENT & RESORTS COMPANY ...241
HF MANAGEMENT SERVICES LLC ...241
HICKMAN WILLIAMS & COMPANY ...241
HIGH INDUSTRIES INC. ...242
HIGH POINT REGIONAL HEALTH SYSTEM ...242
HIGH POINT SOLUTIONS INC. ...243
HIGH STEEL STRUCTURES LLC ...243
HILAND DAIRY FOODS COMPANY. LLC ...243
HILL PHYSICIANS MEDICAL GROUP INC ...244
HILL/AHERN FIRE PROTECTION LLC ...244
HILLCO LTD. ...245
HINES INTERESTS LIMITED PARTNERSHIP ...245
HINSHAW & CULBERTSON LLP ...246
HOAG MEMORIAL HOSPITAL PRESBYTERIAN ...246
HOLIDAY BUILDERS INC. ...247
HOLLAND COMMUNITY HOSPITAL INC ...247
HOLLINGSWORTH OIL CO. INC. ...248
HOLMES REGIONAL MEDICAL CENTER INC ...248
HOLTEC INTERNATIONAL CORPORATION ...249
HOLY CROSS HEALTH INC. ...249
HOLY CROSS HOSPITAL INC. ...249
HOLY SPIRIT HOSPITAL OF THE SISTERS OF CHRISTIAN CHARITY ...250

Companies Profiled (continued)

HOMELAND ENERGY SOLUTIONS LLC 250
HOOSIER ENERGY RURAL ELECTRIC COOPERATIVE INC 250
HORIZON RESOURCES 251
HORRY TELEPHONE COOPERATIVE INC. 251
HOSPITAL OF CENTRAL CONNECTICUT 251
HOSPITAL THE DANBURY INC 252
HOUSING AUTHORITY OF THE CITY OF TAMPA 252
HOUSTON SAM STATE UNIVERSITY 252
HOVENSA LLC 253
HPS LLC 253
HUGHES SATELLITE SYSTEMS CORPORATION 253
HUMAX USA INC. 253
HUNTER ROBERTS CONSTRUCTION GROUP LLC 254
HUNTINGTON CABELL HOSPITAL INC 254
HURLEY MEDICAL CENTER INC. 254
HURON HEALTH CARE CENTER INC 254
HY-VEE INC. 255
HYDROCARBON EXCHANGE CORP. 255
ILLINOIS INSTITUTE OF TECHNOLOGY 256
ILLINOIS MUNICIPAL ELECTRIC AGENCY 256
IMMACULATE MARY HOME 256
IMMIXGROUP INC. 256
IMMIXTECHNOLOGY INC. 257
IMPERIAL IRRIGATION DISTRICT 257
INDEPENDENT PHARMACY COOPERATIVE 257
INDEPENDENT SCHOOL DISTRICT 1 OF TULSA COUNTY 258
INDIANA UNIVERSITY FOUNDATION INC. 258
INDIANA UNIVERSITY HEALTH BLOOMINGTON INC. 258
INDIANA UNIVERSITY HEALTH INC. 259
INDYNE INC. 260
INFINITE ENERGY INC. 260
INLAND COUNTIES REGIONAL CENTER INC. 260
INNOVATIVE AG SERVICES CO. 260
INOVA HEALTH CARE SERVICES 261
INSTITUTE FOR DEFENSE ANALYSES INC 261
INSTITUTE OF INTERNATIONAL EDUCATION INC. 261
INTELLIGENT SOFTWARE SOLUTIONS INC. 261
INTERBOND CORPORATION OF AMERICA 262
INTERBOND HOLDING CORP. 262
INTERMOUNTAIN HEALTH CARE INC 262
INTERNATIONAL BROTHERHOOD OF TEAMSTERS 264
INTERNATIONAL RELIEF AND DEVELOPMENT INC. 265
INTERNET CORPORATION FOR ASSIGNED NAMES AND NUMBERS 265
INVACARE CORPORATION (TW) 266
IOWA HEALTH SYSTEM 266
ISO NEW ENGLAND INC. 267
ITA GROUP INC 267
J & H OIL COMPANY 268
J M SMITH CORPORATION 268
J. D. STREETT & COMPANY INC. 269
J. H. FINDORFF & SON INC. 269
J. P. CULLEN & SONS INC. 269
J.D. ABRAMS L.P. 269
J.H. WILLIAMS OIL COMPANY INC. 270
JACKSON ELECTRIC MEMBERSHIP CORPORATION 270
JACKSON ENERGY AUTHORITY 270
JACO OIL COMPANY 271
JAMES M D HOFFMAN 271
JAMES MADISON UNIVERSITY INC. 271
JAMESON MEMORIAL HOSPITAL 272
JEFFERSON HOMEBUILDERS INC. 272
JEFFERSON HOSPITAL ASSOCIATION INC. 272
JEFFERSON UNIVERSITY PHYSICIANS 273
JERSEY CITY MEDICAL CENTER INC 273
JET PEP INC. 273
JET SPECIALTY INC. 273
JEWISH COMMUNAL FUND 274
JFK HEALTH SYSTEM INC. 274
JOERIS GENERAL CONTRACTORS LTD. 274
JOHN C. LINCOLN HEALTH NETWORK 274
JOHN D ARCHBOLD MEMORIAL HOSPITAL 275
JOHN F KENNEDY CENTER FOR THE PERFORMING ARTS 275
JOHN SNOW INCORPORATED 276
JOHN T. MATHER MEMORIAL HOSPITAL OF PORT JEFFERSON NEW YORK INC. 276
JOHNSON & JOHNSON PATIENT ASSISTANCE FOUNDATION INC 277
JOHNSON & WALES UNIVERSITY INC 277
JOHNSTON ENTERPRISES INC. 277
JORDAN CF INVESTMENTS LLP 277
JUPITER MEDICAL CENTER INC. 278
K & M TIRE INC. 278
KADLEC REGIONAL MEDICAL CENTER 279
KAISER FOUNDATION HOSPITALS INC. 279
KALEIDA HEALTH 280
KAMO ELECTRIC COOPERATIVE INC. 281
KANSAS STATE UNIVERSITY 281
KBS REAL ESTATE INVESTMENT TRUST III INC. 282
KBS STRATEGIC OPPORTUNITY REIT INC. 282
KELLSTROM AEROSPACE LLC 282
KENERGY CORP. 283
KENNEDY HEALTH SYSTEM INC. 283
KENNEDY KRIEGER INSTITUTE INC. 284
KENNEDY MEMORIAL HOSPITAL UNIVERSITY MEDICAL CENTER INC 285
KENNESTONE HOSPITAL INC 285
KENT COUNTY MEMORIAL HOSPITAL 285
KENT GENERAL HOSPITAL INC 286
KENTUCKY MEDICAL SERVICES FOUNDATION INC. 286
KETTERING MEDICAL CENTER 286
KEY COOPERATIVE 287
KEY FOOD STORES CO-OPERATIVE INC. 287
KEYSTOPS LLC 288
KGBO HOLDINGS INC 288
KIMBALL HILL INC 288
KING COUNTY PUBLIC HOSPITAL DISTRICT NO 2 288
KINGSBROOK JEWISH MEDICAL CENTER INC 289
KIRBY - SMITH MACHINERY INC. 289
KIRBY RISK CORPORATION 289
KISATCHIE CORPORATION 290
KITCHELL CORPORATION 290
KLAMATH FALLS INTERCOMMUNITY HOSPITAL AUTHORITY 291
KMM TELECOMMUNICATIONS 291
KNIGHTS OF COLUMBUS 291
KNOUSE FOODS COOPERATIVE INC. 292
KNOX COUNTY HOSPITAL 292
KOOTENAI HOSPITAL DISTRICT 293
KPH HEALTHCARE SERVICES INC. 293
KRAMM HEALTHCARE CENTER INC 293
KRUEGER INTERNATIONAL INC. 293
KUTZTOWN MANOR INC 294
KWIK TRIP INC. 294
KYUNGSHIN-LEAR SALES AND ENGINEERING LLC 295
LAFAYETTE GENERAL MEDICAL CENTER INC 295
LAFAYETTE PARISH SCHOOL BOARD 296
LAHEY CLINIC HOSPITAL INC. 296
LAKE COUNTY SCHOOLS 296
LAKE HOSPITAL SYSTEM INC. 296
LAKELAND REGIONAL HEALTH SYSTEM 297
LAKELAND REGIONAL HEALTH SYSTEMS INC. 297
LAKELAND REGIONAL MEDICAL CENTER INC. 297
LAKESIDE INDUSTRIES INC. 298
LANE INDUSTRIES INCORPORATED 298
LANSING BOARD OF WATER AND LIGHT 298
LATEX CONSTRUCTION COMPANY INC 299
LAUREN ENGINEERS & CONSTRUCTORS INC. 299
LAWRENCE & MEMORIAL HOSPITAL INC. 299
LEE COUNTY ELECTRIC COOPERATIVE INC. 300
LEE LEWIS CONSTRUCTION INC. 300
LEE MEMORIAL HOSPITAL 300
LEGACY EMANUEL HOSPITAL & HEALTH CENTER 301
LEGACY HEALTH 301
LEHIGH UNIVERSITY 302
LEHIGH VALLEY HEALTH NETWORK INC. 302
LEON COUNTY SCHOOL BOARD 303
LESTER E. COX MEDICAL CENTERS 303
LEWIS ENERGY GROUP L.P. 304
LEXA INTERNATIONAL CORPORATION 304
LICKING MEMORIAL HEALTH SYSTEMS 304
LIFEBRIDGE HEALTH INC. 305
LIFEWAY CHRISTIAN RESOURCES OF THE SOUTHERN BAPTIST CONVENTION 305
LINCOLN GLEN MANOR 306
LINCOLN PUBLIC SCHOOLS INC 306
LITTLE ROCK SCHOOL DISTRICT 306
LITTLE SIOUX CORN PROCESSORS LLC 307
LLOG EXPLORATION COMPANY L.L.C. 307
LODGING RLJ TRUST L P 307
LONG BEACH MEMORIAL MEDICAL CENTER 307
LONG ISLAND UNIVERSITY 308
LOOP LLC 308
LOS ANGELES COUNTY OFFICE OF EDUCATION 308
LOS ANGELES DEPARTMENT OF WATER AND POWER 309
LOUISIANA CHILDRENS MEDICAL CENTER INC 309
LOUISIANA WHOLESALE DRUG COMPANY INC. 309
LOYOLA MARYMOUNT UNIVERSITY INC 309
LOYOLA UNIVERSITY MARYLAND INC. 310
LOYOLA UNIVERSITY MEDICAL CENTER 310
LUCILE SALTER PACKARD CHILDREN'S HOSPITAL AT STANFORD 310
LUKOIL PAN AMERICAS LLC 310
LUMBER PRODUCTS AN OREGON CORPORATION 311
M & H ENTERPRISES INC. 311
M. M. FOWLER INC. 311
M.G. OIL COMPANY 311
MACK-CALI REALTY L. P. 311
MACOMB OAKLAND REGIONAL CENTER INC 312
MAGNOLIA REHABILITATION & NURSING CENTER 312
MAIN LINE HOSPITALS INC. 312
MAINE MEDICAL CENTER 313
MAINEGENERAL HEALTH 313
MAINEGENERAL MEDICAL CENTER 314
MAINLINE INFORMATION SYSTEMS INC. 314
MAKE CORPORATION 314
MANAGEMENT AND TRAINING CORPORATION 314
MANAGEMENT SCIENCES FOR HEALTH INC. 315
MAP INTERNATIONAL (INC.) 315
MAR-JAC POULTRY INC. 315
MARCH OF DIMES FOUNDATION 316
MARIETTA MEMORIAL HOSPITAL INC 316
MARIST COLLEGE 316
MARITZ HOLDINGS INC. 317
MARJAM SUPPLY CO. INC. 318
MARKET AMERICA INC. 318
MARQUETTE UNIVERSITY 319
MARS SUPER MARKETS INC 319
MARSHALL NURSING SERVICES INC 319
MARSHALL UNIVERSITY 319
MARSHFIELD CLINIC INC. 320
MARTIN & BAYLEY INC. 321
MARTIN'S POINT HEALTH CARE INC. 321
MARYLAND AND VIRGINIA MILK PRODUCERS COOPERATIVE ASSOCIATION INC 322
MARYLAND SOUTHERN ELECTRIC COOPERATIVE INC 322
MASONIC HOMES OF CALIFORNIA INC 323
MASSACHUSETTS HIGHER EDUCATION ASSISTANCE CORPORATION 323
MASSACHUSETTS PORT AUTHORITY 323
MATTINGLY FOODS INC. 323
MAXIFACIAL DENTAL SURGERY 324
MAXIM HEALTHCARE SERVICES INC. 324
MAXOR NATIONAL PHARMACY SERVICES CORPORATION 324
MAXYIELD COOPERATIVE 325
MAYER ELECTRIC SUPPLY COMPANY INC. 325
MAYO CLINIC HEALTH SYSTEM-FRANCISCAN MEDICAL CENTER INC. 326
MAYVILLE ENGINEERING CO INC 326
MCCARTHY BUILDING COMPANIES INC. 326
MCCARTHY HOLDINGS INC. 327
MCLAREN REGIONAL MEDICAL CENTER 327
MCLEOD REGIONAL MEDICAL CENTER OF THE PEE DEE INC. 327
MCNAUGHTON-MCKAY ELECTRIC CO. 327
MCNEILUS STEEL INC. 328
MED AMERICA HEALTH SYSTEMS CORPORATION 328
MEDCO L.L.C. 328
MEDICAL FACULTY ASSOCIATES INC. 328
MEGLOBAL AMERICAS INC. 329

Companies Profiled (continued)

MEMORIAL HEALTH SERVICES CORPORATION...329
MEMORIAL HEALTH SYSTEM OF EAST TEXAS...329
MEMORIAL HEALTH UNIVERSITY MEDICAL CENTER INC...330
MEMORIAL HERMANN HEALTH SYSTEM...331
MEMORIAL HERMANN HEALTHCARE SYSTEM...331
MERCY CORPS...332
MERCY HEALTH CENTER INC...332
MERCY HEALTH SERVICES INC...332
MERCY HEALTH SERVICES IOWA CORP...332
MERCY HOSPITAL AND MEDICAL CENTER...332
MERCY HOSPITAL OF BUFFALO...333
MERCY HOSPITAL ROGERS...333
MERCY HOSPITAL SPRINGFIELD...333
MERCY HOSPITALS EAST COMMUNITIES...334
MERCY MEDICAL CENTER...334
MERCY MEDICAL CENTER INC...334
MERCY MEDICAL CENTER INC...334
MERITER HEALTH SERVICES INC...335
MERITER HOSPITAL INC...336
MERITUS HEALTH INC...336
MESSER CONSTRUCTION CO...336
METHODIST HOSPITAL OF SOUTHERN CALIFORNIA...337
METHODIST HOSPITALS OF DALLAS INC...338
METROPOLITAN UTILITIES DISTRICT OMAHA NEBRASKA...338
MFA INCORPORATED...339
MFA OIL COMPANY...339
MIAMI UNIVERSITY...339
MIAMI VALLEY HOSPITAL...340
MICHIGAN MILK PRODUCERS ASSOCIATION...341
MICHIGAN TECHNOLOGICAL UNIVERSITY...341
MIDDLE TENNESSEE STATE UNIVERSITY...342
MIDDLESEX HOSPITAL...342
MIDMICHIGAN HEALTH...343
MIDMICHIGAN MEDICAL CENTER-MIDLAND...343
MIDWEST ENERGY INC...343
MILES HEALTH CARE INC...343
MILLER ELECTRIC COMPANY...344
MILTON HERSHEY SCHOOL & SCHOOL TRUST...344
MILWAUKEE PUBLIC SCHOOLS...344
MINERS INCORPORATED...344
MINNESOTA SOYBEAN PROCESSORS...345
MISSION HOSPITAL INC...345
MISSION HOSPITAL REGIONAL MEDICAL CENTER INC...346
MISSISSIPPI COUNTY ELECTRIC COOPERATIVE INC...346
MISSOURI BAPTIST MEDICAL CENTER...346
MISSOURI STATE UNIVERSITY...346
MISSOURI VALLEY PETROLEUM INC...347
MMR CONSTRUCTORS INC...347
MMR GROUP INC...347
MNP CORPORATION...348
MOBILE INFIRMARY ASSOCIATION...348
MONMOUTH MEDICAL CENTER INC...348
MONMOUTH UNIVERSITY...349
MONOGRAM FOOD SOLUTIONS LLC...350
MONTANA STATE UNIVERSITY INC...350
MONTCLAIR STATE UNIVERSITY...350
MOORE REGIONAL HOSPITAL...351
MORSE OPERATIONS INC...351
MORTGAGE INVESTORS CORPORATION...351
MORTON PLANT HOSPITAL ASSOCIATION INC...352
MOUNT AUBURN HOSPITAL...352
MOUNT CARMEL HEALTH SYSTEM...352
MOUNT CLEMENS REGIONAL MEDICAL CENTER INC...353
MULTICARE HEALTH SYSTEM...353
MUNSON MEDICAL CENTER...354
MUNSTER MEDICAL RESEARCH FOUNDATION INC...354
MUSCOGEE COUNTY SCHOOL DISTRICT...354
MUSCULOSKELETAL TRANSPLANT FOUNDATION INC...354
MUSTANG FUEL CORPORATION...355
MV TRANSPORTATION INC...355
NACA LOGISTICS (USA) INC...356
NATIONAL CHRISTIAN CHARITABLE...356
NATIONAL EDUCATION ASSOCIATION OF THE UNITED STATES...356

NATIONAL FROZEN FOODS CORPORATION...356
NATIONAL GRAPE CO-OPERATIVE ASSOCIATION INC...357
NATIONAL MARROW DONOR PROGRAM INC.358
NATIONAL PUBLIC RADIO INC...358
NATIONAL RIFLE ASSOCIATION OF AMERICA...358
NATIONAL RURAL ELECTRIC COOPERATIVE ASSOCIATION...359
NATIONAL UNIVERSITY...359
NATIONWIDE CHILDREN'S HOSPITAL...360
NCH CORPORATION...361
NEBRASKA METHODIST HOSPITAL INC...362
NEIGHBORHOOD REINVESTMENT CORPORATION...362
NEMOURS FOUNDATION...363
NEW ENGLAND PETROLEUM LIMITED PARTNERSHIP...363
NEW HANOVER REGIONAL MEDICAL CENTER AUXILIARY INC...363
NEW JERSEY INSTITUTE OF TECHNOLOGY (INC)...364
NEW PRIME INC...365
NEW YORK BLOOD CENTER INC...365
NEW YORK COMMUNITY TRUST AND COMMUNITY FUNDS INC...366
NEW YORK METHODIST HOSPITAL...366
NEW YORK POWER AUTHORITY...366
NEW YORK SOCIETY FOR THE RELIEF OF THE RUPTURED & CRIPPLED...367
NEW YORK STATE CATHOLIC HEALTH PLAN INC...367
NEWARK BETH ISRAEL MEDICAL CENTER INC...368
NEWPORT NEWS PUBLIC SCHOOL DISTRICT...369
NJVC LLC...369
NOBLIS INC...369
NORDIC PCL CONSTRUCTION INC...369
NORKUS ENTERPRISES INC...369
NORTH CAROLINA ELECTRIC MEMBERSHIP CORPORATION...370
NORTH CENTRAL COOPERATIVE INC...370
NORTH CENTRAL FARMERS ELEVATOR...370
NORTH DAKOTA MILL & ELEVATOR ASSOCIATION INC...371
NORTH DAKOTA UNIVERSITY SYSTEM FOUNDATION...371
NORTH KANSAS CITY HOSPITAL...371
NORTH LA COUNTY REGIONAL CENTER INC371
NORTH MEMORIAL HEALTH CARE...371
NORTH MISSISSIPPI HEALTH SERVICES INC...372
NORTH MISSISSIPPI MEDICAL CENTER INC...373
NORTH PACIFIC PAPER CORPORATION...373
NORTHBAY HEALTHCARE GROUP...374
NORTHEAST GEORGIA MEDICAL CENTER INC...374
NORTHEAST HEALTH SYSTEMS INC...374
NORTHEAST HOSPITAL CORPORATION...375
NORTHERN TIER ENERGY LP...375
NORTHERN VIRGINIA ELECTRIC COOPERATIVE...376
NORTHSHORE UNIVERSITY HEALTHSYSTEM...376
NORTHSIDE HOSPITAL INC...377
NORTHSTAR GROUP SERVICES INC...377
NORTHWEST DAIRY ASSOCIATION...378
NORTHWEST FARM CREDIT SERVICES ACA.378
NORTHWESTERN MEMORIAL HOSPITAL...379
NOVA SOUTHEASTERN UNIVERSITY INC...379
NOVELART MANUFACTURING COMPANY...380
NOVO CONSTRUCTION INC...380
NYSARC INC...380
O. C. TANNER COMPANY...382
O. C. TANNER RECOGNITION COMPANY...382
OAKLAND UNIVERSITY...382
OBERLIN COLLEGE...383
OCEAN BEAUTY SEAFOODS LLC...383
OCEAN DUKE CORPORATION...384
OCHSNER CLINIC FOUNDATION...384
OCLC ONLINE COMPUTER LIBRARY CENTER INCORPORATE...384
ODOM CORPORATION...385
OHIO STATE UNIVERSITY RESEARCH FOUNDATION...385
OHIOHEALTH CORPORATION...386
OLE' MEXICAN FOODS INC...386

OLMSTED MEDICAL CENTER...387
OMNI CABLE CORPORATION...387
ON-SITE FUEL SERVICE INC...388
OPEN SOCIETY INSTITUTE...388
OPERATION BLESSING INTERNATIONAL RELIEF AND DEVELOPMENT CORPORAT.388
ORANGE COUNTY HEALTH AUTHORITY...388
ORANGE COUNTY TRANSPORTATION AUTHORITY SCHOLARSHIP FOUNDATION IN...388
OREGON HEALTH & SCIENCE UNIVERSITY MEDICAL GROUP...389
OREGON UNIVERSITY SYSTEM...390
ORLANDO HEALTH INC...390
OROVILLE HOSPITAL...391
OSC SPORTS INC...391
OSF HEALTHCARE SYSTEM...392
OTTER PRODUCTS LLC...393
OUR LADY OF LOURDES MEDICAL CENTER INC...393
OUR LADY OF LOURDES REGIONAL MEDICAL CENTER INC...394
OUR LADY OF THE LAKE HOSPITAL INC...394
OVERLAKE HOSPITAL ASSOCIATION...395
OVERLAKE HOSPITAL MEDICAL CENTER...395
OWENSBORO HEALTH INC...395
O'BRIEN & GERE LIMITED...380
O'CONNOR HOSPITAL...381
O'NEIL INDUSTRIES INC...381
PACE UNIVERSITY...396

PACIFIC COAST PRODUCERS...396
PACIFIC HIDE & FUR DEPOT...396
PALMETTO HEALTH...397
PAN AMERICAN HEALTH ORGANIZATION INC...397
PAPER CONVERTING MACHINE COMPANY...397
PARKLAND COMMUNITY HEALTH PLAN...398
PARKS XANTERRA & RESORTS INC...398
PARKVIEW FOUNDATION INC...398
PARKWEST MEDICAL CENTER...398
PARSONS ENVIRONMENT & INFRASTRUCTURE GROUP INC...399
PARTNERSHIP FOR SUPPLY CHAIN MANAGEMENT INC...399
PATERSON PUBLIC SCHOOL DISTRICT...399
PATTON BOGGS LLP...399
PAXTON MEDIA GROUP LLC...400
PCL CONSTRUCTION ENTERPRISES INC...400
PCL INDUSTRIAL CONSTRUCTION CO...400
PDS TECH INC...400
PEACEHEALTH...401
PEARCE INDUSTRIES INC...402
PENINSULA REGIONAL MEDICAL CENTER.402
PEPPER CONSTRUCTION COMPANY...402
PEPPER CONSTRUCTION GROUP LLC...402
PEREZ TRADING COMPANY INC...402
PERISHABLE DISTRIBUTORS OF IOWA LTD.403
PETERSBURG MOTOR COMPANY INC...403
PETR-ALL PETROLEUM CONSULTING CORP.403
PETRO STAR INC...403
PETROCARD INC...403
PETROLEUM TRADERS CORPORATION...404
PHELPS MEMORIAL HOSPITAL ASSOCIATION...404
PHILLIPS AND JORDAN INCORPORATED...405
PHOENIX CHILDREN'S HOSPITAL INC...405
PIEDMONT HEALTH CARE AUTHORITY...406
PIGGLY WIGGLY ALABAMA DISTRIBUTING CO. INC...406
PIKEVILLE MEDICAL CENTER INC...406
PINNACLE HEALTH HOSPITAL...407
PINNACLE HEALTH HOSPITALS...407
PITT COUNTY MEMORIAL HOSPITAL INCORPORATED...407
PITT-OHIO EXPRESS LLC...407
PJM INTERCONNECTION LLC...408
PLACID HOLDING COMPANY...409
PLACID REFINING COMPANY LLC...409
PLAINS COTTON COOPERATIVE ASSOCIATION...409
PLAN INTERNATIONAL INC...410
POLK COUNTY SCHOOL DISTRICT...410
POMP'S TIRE SERVICE INC...410
POPULATION SERVICES INTERNATIONAL...410
PORT OF HOUSTON AUTHORITY...411
POTANDON PRODUCE L.L.C...411
POWER ENGINEERS INCORPORATED...411
POWERSOUTH ENERGY COOPERATIVE...412
PRAIRIE FARMS DAIRY INC...412

Companies Profiled (continued)

PREMIER PURCHASING PARTNERS L.P. 413
PRESBYTERIAN HOSPITAL 413
PRESBYTERIAN INTERCOMMUNITY HOSPITAL
   INC. 413
PRESBYTERIAN MEDICAL CENTER OF THE
   UNIVERSITY OF PENNSYLVANIA HE........413
PRESIDENT AND FELLOWS OF MIDDLEBURY
   COLLEGE 413
PRESSURE VESSEL SERVICE INC. 414
PRIDGEON & CLAY INC. 414
PRINCE GEORGE'S COUNTY PUBLIC
   SCHOOLS 415
PRINCE WILLIAM COUNTY PUBLIC
   SCHOOLS 415
PRINCETON HEALTHCARE SYSTEM A NEW
   JERSEY NONPROFIT CORPORATION 415
PRO PETROLEUM INC. 415
PRODUCERS RICE MILL INC. 415
PRODUCTION TOOL SUPPLY COMPANY LLC.416
PROHEALTH CARE INC 416
PROTESTANT MEMORIAL MEDICAL CENTER
   INC. 417
PROVIDENCE COLLEGE 417
PROVIDENCE HOSPITAL 418
PROVIDENCE HOSPITAL 418
PSCU INCORPORATED 419
PUBLIC BROADCASTING SERVICE 419
PUBLIC HEALTH SOLUTIONS 420
PUBLIC UTILITIES BOARD 420
PULSE ELECTRONICS INC. 420
PYCO INDUSTRIES INC. 421
QUAKER VALLEY FOODS INC. 421
QUALITY OIL COMPANY LLC 421
QUEEN OF THE VALLEY MEDICAL CENTER..422
QUINNIPIAC UNIVERSITY 422
R. E. MICHEL COMPANY 423
R. L. JORDAN OIL COMPANY OF NORTH
   CAROLINA INC. 423
R. M. PARKS INC. 424
R.S. HUGHES COMPANY INC. 424
RADY CHILDREN'S HOSPITAL-SAN DIEGO ...424
RALEY'S 425
RAPPAHANNOCK ELECTRIC COOPERATIVE..426
RARITAN BAY MEDICAL CENTER. 426
RAYBURN COUNTRY ELECTRIC COOPERATIVE
   INC 427
RAYMOURS FURNITURE COMPANY INC. 427
RDO EQUIPMENT CO 428
READING HOSPITAL 428
REDNER'S MARKETS INC. 429
REGIONS HOSPITAL FOUNDATION 430
REID HOSPITAL & HEALTH CARE SERVICES
   INC. 430
REIF OIL COMPANY 431
RENFRO CORPORATION 431
REPLACEMENT PARTS INC. 431
RESEARCH TRIANGLE INSTITUTE INC 431
REX HEALTHCARE INC. 432
REX HOSPITAL INC. 433
RHODE ISLAND HOSPITAL 433
RICELAND FOODS INC. 433
RICH PRODUCTS CORPORATION 434
RICHMOND SCHOOL INC. 434
RIGGINS INC. 435
RIP GRIFFIN TRUCK SERVICE CENTER INC. ...435
RIVER CITY PETROLEUM INC. 435
RIVER VALLEY COOPERATIVE 435
RIVERSIDE HEALTHCARE ASSOCIATION
   INC. 435
RIVERSIDE HOSPITAL INC. 436
ROBERT WOOD JOHNSON UNIVERSITY
   HOSPITAL 436
ROBERTS DAIRY COMPANY LLC 437
ROBINSON OIL CORPORATION 438
ROCHESTER CITY SCHOOL DISTRICT 438
ROCHESTER GENERAL HOSPITAL INC. 438
ROCHESTER INSTITUTE OF TECHNOLOGY
   (INC) 438
ROCKFORD MEMORIAL HOSPITAL 439
ROCKHILL MENNONITE HOME 439
ROCKVIEW DAIRIES INC. 439
ROGERS PETROLEUM INC. 440
RONILE INC. 440
ROPER HOSPITAL INC. 440
ROSE INTERNATIONAL INC. 440
ROSELAND PARTNERS L.L.C. 441
ROSEN HOTELS AND RESORTS INC. 441
ROTH STAFFING COMPANIES L.P 441
ROUSE'S ENTERPRISES L.L.C. 442

RUMSEY ELECTRIC COMPANY 442
RUSAL AMERICA CORP. 442
RUSH UNIVERSITY MEDICAL CENTER..........442
RUSH-COPLEY MEDICAL CENTER INC. 443
RUSSELL & SMITH FORD INC. 443
RUSSELL SIGLER INC. 443
RUTLAND HOSPITAL INC. 444
RYAN LLC 444
S.D. DEACON CORP. 445
SABRA HEALTH CARE REIT INC. 446
SACRED HEART HOSPITAL INC. 446
SADDLEBACK MEMORIAL MEDICAL
   CENTER 446
SAINT AGNES MEDICAL CENTER 447
SAINT ALPHONSUS REGIONAL MEDICAL
   CENTER INC. 447
SAINT ELIZABETH MEDICAL CENTER INC....448
SAINT ELIZABETH REGIONAL MEDICAL
   CENTER 448
SAINT EUGENE MEDICAL CENTER 449
SAINT FRANCIS HOSPITAL AND MEDICAL CEN-
   TER FOUNDATION INC. 449
SAINT FRANCIS HOSPITAL INC. 450
SAINT JOSEPH REGIONAL MEDICAL CENTER-
   SOUTH BEND CAMPUS INC 450
SAINT JOSEPH'S HOSPITAL OF MARSHFIELD
   INC. 450
SAINT JOSEPH'S UNIVERSITY 450
SAINT LOUIS UNIVERSITY 451
SAINT LUKE'S HOSPITAL OF BETHLEHEM
   PENNSYLVANIA 451
SAINT LUKE'S HOSPITAL OF KANSAS CITY...451
SAINT TAMMANY PARISH HOSPITAL SERVICE
   DISTRICT 1 452
SAINT TAMMANY PARISH SCHOOL BOARD ...452
SAINT THOMAS HEALTH SERVICES INC. 452
SAINT THOMAS HOSPITAL 453
SALEM HOSPITAL 453
SALEM-KEIZER SCHOOL DISTRICT 24 J 453
SAM LEVIN INC. 453
SAM SWOPE AUTO GROUP LLC 454
SAMARITAN'S PURSE 454
SAMPSON-BLADEN OIL COMPANY
   INCORPORATED 454
SAN ANDREAS REGIONAL CENTER 454
SAN BERNARDINO COUNTY SCHOOL
   DISTRICT 455
SANFORD CLINIC NORTH 455
SANFORD HEALTH 455
SANFORD NORTH 455
SANTA BARBARA COTTAGE HOSPITAL
   FOUNDATION 455
SANTA ROSA MEMORIAL HOSPITAL INC 455
SAPP BROS. INC. 456
SAPP BROS. PETROLEUM INC. 456
SARAH BUSH LINCOLN HEALTH CENTER......456
SARGENT ELECTRIC COMPANY 457
SATTERFIELD AND PONTIKES CONSTRUCTION
   INC. 457
SAVE THE CHILDREN FEDERATION INC. 457
SAWNEE ELECTRIC MEMBERSHIP
   CORPORATION 458
SCHAUMBOND GROUP INC. 458
SCHOOL BOARD OF BREVARD COUNTY 458
SCHOOL BOARD OF ORANGE COUNTY
   FLORIDA 458
SCHOOL DISTRICT 1J MULTNOMAH COUNTY
   OREGON (INC) 459
SCHWAB CHARITABLE FUND 459
SCIENCE AND ENGINEERING SERVICES
   LLC 459
SCIENTIFIC RESEARCH CORP 459
SCL HEALTH - FRONT RANGE INC. 459
SCOTT & WHITE HEALTH PLAN 460
SCOTT EQUIPMENT COMPANY L.L.C.............460
SCOTTSDALE HEALTHCARE CORP. 460
SCOTTSDALE HEALTHCARE HOSPITALS 461
SCRIPPS HEALTH 461
SEACOAST NURSING AND REHABILITATION
   CENTER INC 462
SEALASKA CORPORATION 462
SEALY & SMITH FOUNDATION 463
SEATTLE CANCER CARE ALLIANCE 463
SEATTLE CHILDREN'S HOSPITAL 463
SEATTLE UNIVERSITY 464
SECURITIES INVESTOR PROTECTION
   CORPORATION 465
SECURITY FINANCE CORPORATION OF
   SPARTANBURG 465

SECURITY GROUP INC. 465
SECURITY HEALTH PLAN OF WISCONSIN
   INC. 465
SELECT ENERGY SERVICES LLC 466
SELECTRANSPORTATION RESOURCES LLC..466
SELLEN CONSTRUCTION CO. INC. 466
SEMINOLE ELECTRIC COOPERATIVE INC.....466
SENTARA HEALTHCARE 467
SENTARA RMH MEDICAL CENTER 468
SERVCO PACIFIC INC. 469
SES HOLDINGS LLC 469
SETON HALL UNIVERSITY 469
SEYFARTH SHAW LLP 470
SGT INC. 470
SHAMROCK FOODS COMPANY 471
SHAMROCK TRADING CORPORATION...........471
SHANDS JACKSONVILLE MEDICAL CENTER
   INC. 471
SHARI'S MANAGEMENT CORPORATION 472
SHARP CHULA VISTA MEDICAL CENTER.......472
SHARP CHULA VISTA MEDICAL CENTER.......472
SHARP HEALTHCARE 473
SHARP MEMORIAL HOSPITAL 474
SHAWMUT WOODWORKING & SUPPLY 474
SHAWNEE MISSION MEDICAL CENTER 475
SHAWNEE MISSION UNIFIED SCHOOL
   DISTRICT 512 475
SHEA HOMES LIMITED PARTNERSHIP A CALI-
   FORNIA LIMITED PARTNERSHIP 476
SHELBY COUNTY BOARD OF EDUCATION.....476
SHEPHERD CENTER INC. 476
SHEPHERD ELECTRIC COMPANY
   INCORPORATED 477
SHEPPARD AND ENOCH PRATT FOUNDATION
   INC. 477
SHI INTERNATIONAL CORP. 477
SHIRES HOUSING INC. 478
SHORE MEMORIAL HOSPITAL 478
SHRIEVE CHEMICAL COMPANY 479
SIGNAL INTERNATIONAL LLC 479
SIGNATURE CONSULTANTS LLC 479
SIGNATURE HEALTHCARE CORPORATION 479
SILVER BLUFF LLC 479
SILVER CROSS HOSPITAL AND MEDICAL
   CENTERS 480
SILVER TOWNE L.P. 480
SINAI HOSPITAL OF BALTIMORE INC 480
SINGING RIVER HEALTH SYSTEM 481
SLOAN IMPLEMENT COMPANY INC............481
SMDC MEDICAL CENTER 482
SMO INCORPORATED 482
SNAKE RIVER SUGAR COMPANY 482
SNAPPING SHOALS ELECTRIC TRUST 482
SOMERSET TIRE SERVICE INC. 482
SOUTH DAKOTA STATE UNIVERSITY 483
SOUTH DAKOTA WHEAT GROWERS 483
SOUTH MIAMI HOSPITAL INC. 484
SOUTH MISSISSIPPI ELECTRIC POWER 484
SOUTH NASSAU COMMUNITIES HOSPITAL
   INC 484
SOUTH SHORE HOSPITAL INC. 485
SOUTH TEXAS ELECTRIC COOPERATIVE
   INC. 485
SOUTHCO DISTRIBUTING COMPANY 485
SOUTHCOAST HOSPITALS GROUP INC. 485
SOUTHEAST MISSOURI HOSPITAL
   ASSOCIATION 486
SOUTHEAST PETRO DISTRIBUTORS INC.......486
SOUTHERN BAPTIST HOSPITAL OF FLORIDA
  486
SOUTHERN MAINE HEALTH CARE 486
SOUTHERN METHODIST UNIVERSITY INC.....486
SOUTHERN NEW HAMPSHIRE MEDICAL
   CENTER 487
SOUTHERN NEW HAMPSHIRE UNIVERSITY..488
SOUTHERN OHIO MEDICAL CENTER 488
SOUTHERN PIPE & SUPPLY COMPANY 488
SOUTHFRESH AQUACULTURE LLC.............488
SOUTHLAND INDUSTRIES 488
SOUTHWEST CATHOLIC HEALTH NETWORK
   CORPORATION 489
SOUTHWEST LOUISIANA ELECTRIC MEMBER-
   SHIP CORPORATION 490
SOUTHWEST RESEARCH INSTITUTE INC......490
SOUTHWEST WASHINGTON HEALTH SYS ...491
SOUTHWIND NURSING AND REHABILITATION
   CENTER INC. 491
SPAW GLASS HOLDING L.P. 491
SPECTRUM HEALTH HOSPITALS................491

Companies Profiled (continued)

SPECTRUM HEALTH PRIMARY CARE PARTNERS DBA 491
SPECTRUM HEALTH SYSTEM............492
SPF ENERGY INC. 493
SPORTS INC. 493
SRC TEC INC. 493
SRI INTERNATIONAL 493
ST AGNES HOSPITAL OF FOND DU LAC WISC INC 494
ST BARNABAS MEDICAL CENTER INC............494
ST FRANCIS HOSPITAL 495
ST JOHN MEDICAL CENTER INC............495
ST JOHNS HOSPITAL SISTERS OF THE THIRD ORDER OF ST FRANCIS 496
ST JOHN'S UNIVERSITY NEW YORK 495
ST JOSEPH OF THE PINES INC 496
ST LUKE'S METHODIST HOSPITAL INC 496
ST PATRICK HOSPITAL CORPORATION 497
ST PETER'S MEDICAL CENTER 497
ST. ALBANS COOPERATIVE CREAMERY INC .498
ST. ALEXIUS MEDICAL CENTER 498
ST. ALEXIUS MEDICAL CENTER 498
ST. ANTHONY'S MEDICAL CENTER 499
ST. BERNARD'S HOSPITAL INC. 499
ST. CLOUD HOSPITAL 499
ST. DOMINIC-JACKSON MEMORIAL HOSPITAL 500
ST. JOHN HEALTH SYSTEM INC. 500
ST. JOHN'S UNIVERSITY 500
ST. JOSEPH HEALTH SYSTEM............500
ST. JOSEPH HOSPITAL OF ORANGE 501
ST. JOSEPH'S HOSPITAL AND MEDICAL CENTER 502
ST. JOSEPH'S HOSPITAL HEALTH CENTER ..502
ST. JOSEPH'S HOSPITAL INC. 502
ST. JUDE CHILDREN'S RESEARCH HOSPITAL INC. 503
ST. JUDE HOSPITAL 503
ST. LUKE'S EPISCOPAL-PRESBYTERIAN HOSPITALS 504
ST. LUKE'S HEALTH SYSTEM FOUNDATION .504
ST. LUKE'S HOSPITAL OF DULUTH 504
ST. LUKE'S REGIONAL MEDICAL CENTER LTD............505
ST. MARY MEDICAL CENTER 505
ST. MARY'S HOSPITAL & MEDICAL CENTER INC 505
ST. MARY'S MEDICAL CENTER 506
ST. MARY'S MEDICAL CENTER 506
ST. OLAF COLLEGE............506
ST. PETER'S HEALTH PARTNERS 506
ST. VINCENT HEALTHCARE............507
ST. VINCENT HOSPITAL 507
ST. VINCENT HOSPITAL OF THE HOSPITAL SISTERS OF THE THIRD ORDER............507
ST. VINCENT'S BIRMINGHAM............507
ST. VINCENT'S MEDICAL CENTER 508
ST. VINCENT'S MEDICAL CENTER INC 508
STAN BOYETT & SON INC. 508
STANDARD ELECTRIC COMPANY 508
STANFORD HEALTH SERVICES 508
STANLEY STEEMER INTERNATIONAL INC. ...508
STAPLE COTTON CO-OPERATIVE ASSOCIATION 509
STAR OF THE WEST MILLING COMPANY.......509
STEEL RESOURCES LLC 510
STEIN FIBERS LTD. 510
STEPHEN GOULD CORPORATION............510
STEPHENSON WHOLESALE COMPANY INC. ..511
STEVENS INSTITUTE OF TECHNOLOGY (INC) 511
STEVENS TRANSPORT INC. 512
STEWARD HEALTH CARE SYSTEM LLC 512
STEWART BUILDERS INC. 513
STEWART'S SHOPS CORP. 513
STG INC. 514
STM INDUSTRIES INC. 514
STORMONT-VAIL HEALTHCARE INC. 514
STRACK AND VAN TIL SUPER MARKET INC ..515
STRIKE LLC 515
STURDY MEMORIAL HOSPITAL INC. 515
SUFFOLK CONSTRUCTION COMPANY INC. ...516
SUFFOLK UNIVERSITY 516
SUMMA HEALTH SYSTEM 517
SUMMIT ELECTRIC SUPPLY CO. INC 518
SUMMIT HEALTH 519
SUMMIT MATERIALS LLC 519
SUN COAST RESOURCES INC. 519
SUN MAR MANAGEMENT SERVICES............520

SUN-MAID GROWERS OF CALIFORNIA............520
SUNDT CONSTRUCTION INC. 520
SUNFLOWER ELECTRIC POWER CORP 520
SUNKIST GROWERS INC. 521
SUNRUN INSTALLATION SERVICES INC. 522
SUNSWEET GROWERS INC. 522
SUPERIOR BULK LOGISTICS INC. 523
SUPERIOR OIL COMPANY INC 523
SUTTER GOULD MEDICAL FOUNDATION............523
SUTTER MEDICAL FOUNDATION 524
SWEDISH HEALTH SERVICES 524
SWEDISHAMERICAN HOSPITAL 525
SWINERTON BUILDERS 525
SWINERTON INCORPORATED 525
SYRACUSE UNIVERSITY 526
TALLAHASSEE MEMORIAL HEALTHCARE INC. 527
TAUBER OIL COMPANY 527
TEAM INDUSTRIES INC. 528
TEKNOR APEX COMPANY 528
TEKSYSTEMS INC. 529
TELAMON CORPORATION 529
TEMPLE UNIVERSITY HEALTH SYSTEM INC.529
TEMPLE UNIVERSITY-OF THE COMMONWEALTH SYSTEM OF HIGHER EDUCATION 530
TENASKA MARKETING VENTURES............531
TERRACON CONSULTANTS INC. 531
TEXAS A&M FOUNDATION 531
TEXAS AROMATICS LP 531
TEXAS CHRISTIAN UNIVERSITY INC 532
TEXAS COUNTY AND DISTRICT RETIREMENT SYSTEM 532
TEXAS GUARANTEED STUDENT LOAN CORPORATION............532
TEXAS HEALTH HARRIS METHODIST HOSPITAL FORT WORTH............533
TEXAS STATE UNIVERSITY 533
THE AEROSPACE CORPORATION............534
THE ALICE BYRD TAWES NURSING HOME INC 535
THE AMALGAMATED SUGAR COMPANY LLC .535
THE AMERICAN MUSEUM OF NATURAL HISTORY............535
THE ANNENBERG FOUNDATION 536
THE ASSOCIATED PRESS............536
THE BIG TEN CONFERENCE INC 537
THE BOLDT GROUP INC............537
THE BRANCH GROUP INC 537
THE BROAD INSTITUTE INC 537
THE BROTHER'S BROTHER FOUNDATION....537
THE CALIFORNIA ENDOWMENT 538
THE CARLE FOUNDATION 538
THE CARTER-JONES LUMBER COMPANY 538
THE CATHOLIC UNIVERSITY OF AMERICA....539
THE CHILDRENS HOSPITAL LOS ANGELES..540
THE CHILDREN'S HOSPITAL CORPORATION539
THE CHILDREN'S HOSPITAL OF ALABAMA ...540
THE CHRISTIAN BROADCASTING NETWORK INC 541
THE CLEVELAND FOUNDATION............541
THE COMMUNITY HOSPITAL GROUP INC.....541
THE COOPER HEALTH SYSTEM 541
THE CORPORATION OF GONZAGA UNIVERSITY 542
THE CORPORATION OF MERCER UNIVERSITY 543
THE DAVID AND LUCILE PACKARD FOUNDATION............543
THE DELONG CO INC 543
THE DREES COMPANY 544
THE FIRST DISTRICT ASSOCIATION 544
THE FISHEL COMPANY............544
THE FLORIDA SCHOOL CHOICE FUND 545
THE G W VAN KEPPEL COMPANY 545
THE GARDEN CITY CO-OP INC 545
THE GEORGE J FALTER COMPANY 546
THE GOLUB CORPORATION 546
THE HEALTHCARE AUTHORITY FOR BAPTIST HEALTH AND AFFILIATE OF UAB 547
THE HENRY M JACKSON FOUNDATION FOR THE ADVANCEMENT OF MILITARY M.......547
THE HOWARD UNIVERSITY 547
THE HUMANE SOCIETY OF THE UNITED STATES 547
THE INGALLS MEMORIAL HOSPITAL............548
THE JACKSON LABORATORY 549
THE JEFFERSON COUNTY ASSISTED HOUSING CORPORATION............549

THE JERRY BROWN CO INC 549
THE JEWISH GUILD FOR THE BLIND............550
THE JUDGE GROUP INC 550
THE KLEINFELDER GROUP INC 550
THE LANCASTER GENERAL HOSPITAL 551
THE LANE CONSTRUCTION CORP 552
THE LEGAL AID SOCIETY 552
THE MARY IMOGENE BASSETT HOSPITAL...552
THE MEDICAL CENTER 553
THE MEDICAL COLLEGE OF WISCONSIN INC 553
THE MERCHANTS COMPANY............553
THE METHODIST HOSPITAL 553
THE METHODIST HOSPITALS INC 554
THE METROHEALTH SYSTEM............555
THE MIDDLE TENNESSEE ELECTRIC MEMBERSHIP CORPORATION............556
THE MITRE CORPORATION 556
THE MOSES H CONE MEMORIAL HOSPITAL.557
THE NEW LIBERTY HOSPITAL DISTRICT OF CLAY COUNTY MISSOURI 557
THE NEW SCHOOL 558
THE NEW YORK AND PRESBYTERIAN HOSPITAL 558
THE NEW YORK INDEPENDENT SYSTEM OPERATOR INC 559
THE NEWTRON GROUP L L C 559
THE NORTH CAROLINA MUTUAL WHOLESALE DRUG COMPANY 560
THE NORTH HIGHLAND COMPANY 560
THE NORTH HIGHLAND HOLDING COMPANY INC 561
THE NORWALK HOSPITAL ASSOCIATION 561
THE OLTMANS CONSTRUCTION CO 561
THE PARADIES SHOPS LLC 561
THE PENNSYLVANIA HOSPITAL OF THE UNIVERSITY OF PENNSYLVANIA HEAL............562
THE PEPPER COMPANIES INC 562
THE PEW CHARITABLE TRUSTS 562
THE PLAZA GROUP INC 563
THE PRIDDY FOUNDATION............563
THE RESEARCH FOUNDATION OF STATE UNIVERSITY OF NEW YORK 563
THE ROCKEFELLER UNIVERSITY FACULTY AND STUDENTS CLUB INC 564
THE RUDOLPH/LIBBE COMPANIES INC........564
THE SALVATION ARMY 565
THE SALVATION ARMY 565
THE SALVATION ARMY NATIONAL CORPORATION............565
THE SAVANNAH COLLEGE OF ART AND DESIGN INC 566
THE SCOULAR COMPANY............566
THE SCRIPPS RESEARCH INSTITUTE 567
THE SHEPHERD GOOD HOSPITAL INC.........568
THE SOUTHEASTERN CONFERENCE............568
THE STAMFORD HOSPITAL 568
THE SUNDT COMPANIES INC 568
THE SUSAN G KOMEN BREAST CANCER FOUNDATION INC 569
THE TOLEDO HOSPITAL 569
THE TRUSTEES OF THE SMITH COLLEGE 570
THE UNIVERSITY OF ARIZONA MEDICAL CENTER 570
THE UNIVERSITY OF CHICAGO MEDICAL CENTER 571
THE UNIVERSITY OF DAYTON 571
THE UNIVERSITY OF HARTFORD............572
THE UNIVERSITY OF TULSA 572
THE VALLEY HOSPITAL INC 573
THE WALDINGER CORPORATION 573
THE WALSH GROUP LTD 574
THE WALTERS GROUP 574
THE WASHINGTON UNIVERSITY 574
THE WATERBURY HOSPITAL............575
THE WHITING-TURNER CONTRACTING COMPANY 576
THE WICHITA STATE UNIVERSITY 577
THE WILLS GROUP INC 577
THEDACARE INC. 577
THOMAS JEFFERSON UNIVERSITY............578
THOMAS JEFFERSON UNIVERSITY HOSPITALS INC. 579
THUNDERCAT TECHNOLOGY LLC 579
TIAA REAL ESTATE ACCOUNT 579
TIFFIN MOTOR HOMES INC. 580
TIFT REGIONAL MEDICAL CENTER FOUNDATION INC. 580
TOM LANGE COMPANY INC. 580

Companies Profiled (continued)

TORRANCE HEALTH ASSOCIATION INC. 581
TORRANCE MEMORIAL MEDICAL CENTER ..581
TOURO COLLEGE & UNIVERSITY SYSTEM 581
TOURO INFIRMARY 582
TOWNSHIP HIGH SCHOOL DISTRICT 211
  FOUNDATION 582
TRAMMO INC. 582
TRANS-SYSTEM INC. 583
TRANSPERFECT TRANSLATIONS
  INTERNATIONAL INC. 583
TRAYLOR BROS. INC. 584
TREE TOP INC. 584
TRI STAR ENERGY LLC 585
TRI-WEST LTD 585
TRIMEGA PURCHASING ASSOCIATION 585
TRINITY HEALTH-MICHIGAN 586
TRINITY MOTHER FRANCES HEALTH SYSTEM
  FOUNDATION 586
TROUT-BLUE CHELAN-MAGI INC. 586
TROY UNIVERSITY 587
TRUE VALUE COMPANY 587
TRUMAN ARNOLD COMPANIES 588
TRUMAN MEDICAL CENTER
  INCORPORATED 589
TRUSTEES OF BOSTON COLLEGE 589
TRUSTEES OF MEASE HOSPITAL INC. 590
TRUSTEES OF THE ESTATE OF BERNICE
  PAUAHI BISHOP 590
TRUSTEES OF TUFTS COLLEGE INC. 591
TUDOR INVESTMENT CORPORATION 591
TURTLE & HUGHES INC. 591
U G N INC 592
U.R.M. STORES INC. 592
U.S. VENTURE INC. 593
UMASS MEMORIAL COMMUNITY MEDICAL
  GROUP INC. 593
UMASS MEMORIAL HEALTH CARE INC. 594
UMASS MEMORIAL HOSPITALS INC. 594
UMASS MEMORIAL MEDICAL CENTER 594
UNDERWRITERS LABORATORIES INC. 594
UNION BANK AND TRUST COMPANY 595
UNION COUNTY BOARD OF EDUCATION 596
UNION HOSPITAL INC. 596
UNIPRO FOODSERVICE INC 596
UNITED COOPERATIVE 597
UNITED DAIRYMEN OF ARIZONA 597
UNITED ELECTRIC SUPPLY COMPANY INC. 598
UNITED FOOD AND COMMERCIAL WORKERS
  UNIONS AND FOOD EMPLOYERS BEN 598
UNITED HEALTH SERVICES HOSPITAL INC. ..598
UNITED METHODIST RETIREMENT & HEALTH
  CARE CENTER INC 599
UNITED NEGRO COLLEGE FUND INC. 599
UNITED NETWORK FOR ORGAN SHARING 600
UNITED REGIONAL HEALTH CARE SYSTEM
  INC. 600
UNITED SPACE ALLIANCE LLC 601
UNITED STATES BEEF CORPORATION 601
UNITED STATES FUND FOR UNICEF 601
UNITED STATES GOLF ASSOCIATION 602
UNITED STATES OLYMPIC COMMITTEE 602
UNITED STEEL PAPER AND FORESTRY RUBBER
  MANUFACTURING ENERGY ALLI................603
UNITED STUDENT AID FUNDS INC 603
UNIVERSAL COOPERATIVES INC. 603
UNIVERSITY AL HEALTH SVC FNDN PC 603
UNIVERSITY CORPORATION FOR ATMOSPHER-
  IC RESEARCH 603
UNIVERSITY HOSPITALS HEALTH SYSTEM
  INC. 604
UNIVERSITY MEDICAL CENTER INC 605
UNIVERSITY OF CHICAGO 605
UNIVERSITY OF CINCINNATI MEDICAL CENTER
  LLC 605
UNIVERSITY OF COLORADO 605
UNIVERSITY OF GEORGIA 606
UNIVERSITY OF ILLINOIS FOUNDATION 606
UNIVERSITY OF IOWA HOSPITALS AND
  CLINICS 606
UNIVERSITY OF KENTUCKY RESEARCH
  FOUNDATION 607
UNIVERSITY OF MAINE SYSTEM 607
UNIVERSITY OF MARYLAND MEDICAL SYSTEM
  CORPORATION 607
UNIVERSITY OF MINNESOTA PHYSICIANS 608
UNIVERSITY OF MISSISSIPPI 608
UNIVERSITY OF MONTANA SYSTEM 608
UNIVERSITY OF NEBRASKA FOUNDATION 609

UNIVERSITY OF NORTH CAROLINA
  HOSPITALS 609
UNIVERSITY OF NORTH DAKOTA 610
UNIVERSITY OF NORTH TEXAS SYSTEM 610
UNIVERSITY OF OKLAHOMA FOUNDATION
  INC 610
UNIVERSITY OF PITTSBURGH 610
UNIVERSITY OF PUGET SOUND 611
UNIVERSITY OF RHODE ISLAND.....................611
UNIVERSITY OF RICHMOND..............................611
UNIVERSITY OF SAN DIEGO 612
UNIVERSITY OF SAN FRANCISCO INC 613
UNIVERSITY OF SCRANTON 613
UNIVERSITY OF SOUTH FLORIDA 614
UNIVERSITY OF SOUTHERN MISSISSIPPI 614
UNIVERSITY OF ST. THOMAS 615
UNIVERSITY OF TENNESSEE 615
UNIVERSITY OF THE PACIFIC 615
UNIVERSITY OF WASHINGTON INC. 616
UNIVERSITY OF WISCONSIN FOUNDATION ..617
UNIVERSITY OF WISCONSIN SYSTEM 617
UNIVERSITY OF WYOMING 618
UNIVERSITY PHYSICIANS HEALTHCARE 618
UNIVERSITY SYSTEM OF NEW HAMPSHIRE .618
UNMC PHYSICIANS 619
USS POSCO INDUSTRIES 619
UTAH HOUSING CORPORATION 620
UTAH STATE UNIVERSITY 620
VALLEY MEDICAL FACILITIES INC. 620
VALLEY PRESBYTERIAN HOSPITAL 620
VALUE DRUG COMPANY 620
VANGUARD CHARITABLE ENDOWMENT
  PROGRAM 621
VASSAR BROTHERS HOSPITAL 621
VASSAR COLLEGE INC 621
VCC LLC 622
VENTURE ELECTRICAL CONTRACTORS INC. 622
VERST GROUP LOGISTICS INC. 622
VIKING YACHT COMPANY 622
VILLANOVA UNIVERSITY IN THE STATE OF
  PENNSYLVANIA 623
VIRGINIA COMMUNITY COLLEGE SYSTEM
  OFFICE 624
VIRGINIA WEST UNIVERSITY FOUNDATION
  INC 624
VIRGINIA WEST UNIVERSITY HOSPITALS
  INC 624
VIRTUA MEMORIAL HOSPITAL BURLINGTON
  COUNTY INC. 624
VIZIO INC. 625
VOLUNTEER ENERGY COOPERATIVE 625
W. DOUGLASS DISTRIBUTING LTD..................626
W. K. KELLOGG FOUNDATION 626
W.S. BADCOCK CORPORATION 626
WABASH VALLEY POWER ASSOCIATION INC 627
WADA FARMS MARKETING GROUP LLC.........627
WAKE COUNTY PUBLIC SCHOOL SYSTEM 627
WAKE FOREST BAPTIST MEDICAL CENTER..628
WAKEFERN FOOD CORP. 628
WALSH BROTHERS INCORPORATED 629
WALSH CONSTRUCTION COMPANY 629
WALTON CONSTRUCTION COMPANY LLC 629
WALTON ELECTRIC MEMBERSHIP
  CORPORATION 629
WALTON FAMILY FOUNDATION INC.................630
WARREN DISTRIBUTION INC. 630
WARREN RURAL ELECTRIC COOPERATIVE
  CORPORATION 630
WASHINGTON COUNTY BOARD OF
  EDUCATION 630
WASHINGTON REGIONAL MEDICAL
  CENTER 631
WATKINS AND SHEPARD TRUCKING INC.......631
WATONWAN FARM SERVICE INC 632
WAUKESHA MEMORIAL HOSPITAL INC. 632
WAUKESHA-PEARCE INDUSTRIES INC. 632
WAYNE J. GRIFFIN ELECTRIC INC. 633
WEBSTER UNIVERSITY 633
WELCH FOODS INC. A COOPERATIVE.............634
WELLMONT HEALTH SYSTEM 634
WELLS REAL ESTATE INVESTMENT TRUST
  II 635
WELSPUN PIPES INC. 635
WESLEYAN UNIVERSITY (INC) 635
WEST TEXAS GAS INC. 636
WEST VIRGINIA UNITED HEALTH SYSTEM
  INC. 636
WESTAT INC. 636
WESTERN CONSOLIDATED COOPERATIVE ...637

WESTERN FARMERS ELECTRIC
  COOPERATIVE 637
WESTERN MARYLAND HEALTH SYSTEM
  REHAB 638
WESTERN OREGON UNIVERSITY......................638
WESTERN STATES FIRE PROTECTION
  COMPANY INC 638
WESTERN WASHINGTON UNIVERSITY 638
WEXFORD HEALTH SOURCES INC. 639
WHEATON FRANCISCAN 639
WHEATON FRANCISCAN HLTHCRE-FRANKLIN
  INC 639
WHEATON FRANCISCAN SERVICES INC.........639
WHEELING HOSPITAL INC. 640
WHEELING-NISSHIN INC. 640
WHITE COUNTY MEDICAL CENTER 640
WICKED FASHIONS INC. 641
WIDENER UNIVERSITY......................................641
WILBUR SMITH ASSOCIATES INC. 642
WILBUR-ELLIS COMPANY 642
WILDLIFE CONSERVATION SOCIETY 643
WILLIAM MARSH RICE UNIVERSITY INC 643
WILLIS-KNIGHTON MEDICAL CENTER.............644
WILMED NURSING CARE CENTER....................644
WINCHESTER MEDICAL CENTER AUXILIARY
  INC. 644
WINCO HOLDINGS INC. 644
WINSTON-SALEM/FORSYTH COUNTY
  SCHOOLS 645
WINTHROP-UNIVERSITY HOSPITAL INC 645
WISCONSIN ALUMNI RESEARCH
  FOUNDATION 646
WITHLACOOCHEE RIVER ELECTRIC
  COOPERATIVE INC 646
WITHLACOOCHEE RIVER ELECTRIC
  COOPERATIVE INC 646
WOLVERINE POWER SUPPLY COOPERATIVE
  INC. 646
WOMAN'S HOSPITAL FOUNDATION INC 647
WOMEN & INFANTS HOSPITAL OF RHODE
  ISLAND 647
WORLD FINER FOODS INC 647
WORLD OF JEANS & TOPS 648
WORLD WILDLIFE FUND INC............................648
WORLEY & OBETZ INC......................................649
WOROCO MANAGEMENT LLC...........................649
WRIGHT STATE UNIVERSITY.............................649
WTG GAS PROCESSING L.P. 650
WYCKOFF HEIGHTS MEDICAL CENTER..........650
WYOMING MEDICAL CENTER INC. 651
XANTERRA HOLDING CORP 651
XANTERRA INC. 651
XAVIER UNIVERSITY...651
YAKIMA VALLEY MEMORIAL HOSPITAL
  ASSOCIATION INC 652
YESHIVA UNIVERSITY 652
YORK HOSPITAL 653
YOSEMITE FARM CREDIT ACA 653
YOUNG LIFE 653
YUMA REGIONAL MEDICAL CENTER INC 654
Z GALLERIE 654
ZEN-NOH GRAIN CORPORATION 655
ZOOLOGICAL SOCIETY OF SAN DIEGO.........655

About Hoover's Handbook of Private Companies 2016

Finding current relevant information about non-public companies can be a challenge, as many of these organizations see secrecy as a competitive strategy. In this edition of *Hoover's Handbook of Private Companies*, we have done for you the tough work of compiling these hard-to-find facts.

We consider this volume to be one of the premier sources of business information on privately held enterprises in the US. It features the facts on 900 of the largest and most influencial of those enterprises. Entries feature overviews of company operations, up to five years of financial information, product information, and lists of company executives as found in Hoover's huge database of company information. Some larger and more visable companies will feature an additional History section.

HOOVER'S ONLINE FOR BUSINESS NEEDS

In addition to Hoover's widely used MasterList and Handbooks series, comprehensive coverage of more than 40,000 business enterprises is available in electronic format on our website at www.hoovers.com. Our goal is to provide our customers with the fastest path to business with insight and actionable information about companies, industries, and key decision makers, along with the powerful tools to find and connect to the right people to get business done. Hoover's has partnered with other presigious business information and service providers to bring you all the right business information, services, and links in one place.

We welcome the recognition we have received as a provider of high-quality company information — online, electronically, and in print — and continue to look for ways to make our products more available and more useful to you.

Hoover's Handbook of Private Companies is one of our four-title series of handbooks that covers, literally, the world of business. The series is available as an indexed set, and also includes *Hoover's Handbook of American Business, Hoover's Handbook of World Business,* and *Hoover's Handbook of Emerging Companies.* This series brings you information on the biggest, fast-growing, and most influential enterprises in the world.

We believe that anyone who buys from, sells to, invests in, lends to, competes with, interviews with, or works for a company should know all there is to know about that enterprise. Taken together, this book and the other Hoover's products and resources represent the most complete source of basic corporate information readily available to the general public.

HOW TO USE THIS BOOK

This book has four sections:

1. "Using Hoover's Handbooks" describes the contents of our profiles and explains the ways in which we gather and compile our data.

2. "A List-Lover's Compendium" contains lists of the largest and fastest-growing private companies. The lists are based on the information in our profiles, or compiled from well-known sources.

3. The company profiles section makes up the largest and most important part of the book — 900 profiles of major private enterprises, arranged alphabetically.

4. Three indexes complete the book. The first sorts companies by industry groups, the second by headquarters location. The third index is a list of all the executives found in the Executives section of each company profile.

Using Hoover's Handbooks

SELECTION OF THE COMPANIES PROFILED

The 900 enterprises profiled in this book include the largest and most influential companies in America. Among them are:

- private companies, from the giants (Cargill and Koch) to the colorful and prominent (Bad Boy Entertainment and L.L. Bean)
- mutuals and cooperative organizations owned by their customers (State Farm Insurance, Ace Hardware, Ocean Spray Cranberries)
- not-for-profits (Red Cross, Kaiser Permanente, Smithsonian Institution)
- joint ventures (Motiva Enterprises, Dow Corning)
- partnerships (PricewaterhouseCoopers, Baker & McKenzie)
- universities (Columbia, Harvard, University of California)
- government-owned corporations (US Postal Service and New York City's Metropolitan Transportation Authority)
- and a selection of other enterprises (National Basketball Association, AFL-CIO, Texas Lottery Commission).

ORGANIZATION

The profiles are presented in alphabetical order. You will find the commonly used name of the enterprise at the beginning of the profile; the full, legal name is found in the Locations section. If a company name is also a person's name, such as Henry Ford Health System or Mary Kay, it will be alphabetized under the first name; if the company name starts with initials, for example, L.L. Bean or S.C. Johnson, look for it under the combined initials (in the above examples, LL and SC, respectively).

Basic financial data are listed under the heading Historical Financials. The annual financial information contained in the profiles is current through fiscal year-ends occuring as late as October 2014. We have included certain nonfinancial developments , such as officer changes, through December 2014.

OVERVIEW

In the first section of the profile, we have tried to give a thumbnail description of the company and what it does. The description will usually include information on the company's strategy, reputation, and ownership. We rec-

ommend that you read this section first.

HISTORY

This extended section, which is available for some of the larger and more well-known companies, reflects our belief that every enterprise is the sum of its history and that you have to know where you came from in order to know where you are going. While some companies have limited historical awareness, we think the vast majority of the enterprises in this book have colorful backgrounds. We have tried to focus on the people who made the enterprises what they are today. We have found these histories to be full of twists and ironies; they make fascinating reading.

EXECUTIVES

Here we list the names of the people who run the company, insofar as space allows. In the few cases where available, we have shown the ages and pay of key officers. In some instances the published data is for the previous year, although the company has announced promotions or retirements since year-end. The pay represents cash compensation, including bonuses, but excludes stock option programs.

Although companies are free to structure their management titles any way they please, most modern corporations follow standard practices. The ultimate power in any corporation lies with the shareholders, who elect a board of directors, usually including officers or "insiders" as well as individuals from outside the company. The chief officer, the person on whose desk the buck stops, is usually called the chief executive officer (CEO). Often, he or she is also the chairman of the board.

As corporate management has become more complex, it is common for the CEO to have a "right-hand person" who oversees the day-to-day operations of the company, allowing the CEO plenty of time to focus on strategy and long-term issues. This right-hand person is usually designated the chief operating officer (COO) and is often the president of the company. In other cases one person is both chairman and president.

A multitude of other titles exists, including chief financial officer (CFO), chief administrative officer, and vice chairman. We have always tried to include the CFO, the chief legal officer, and the chief human resources or personnel officer.

The people named in the Executives section are indexed at the back of the book.

The Executives section also includes the name of the company's auditing (accounting) firm, where available.

LOCATIONS

Here we include the company's full legal name and its headquarters, street address, telephone and fax numbers, and Web site, as available. The back of the book includes an index of companies by headquarters locations.

In some cases we have also included information on the geographic distribution of the company's business, including sales and profit data. Note that these profit numbers, like those in the Products/Operations section below, are usually operating or pretax profits rather than net profits. Operating profits are generally those before financing costs (interest income and payments) and before taxes, which are considered costs attributable to the whole company rather than to one division or part of the world. For this reason the net income figures (in the Historical Financials section) are usually much lower, since they are after interest and taxes. Pretax profits are after interest but before taxes.

Headquarters for companies that are incorporated in Bermuda, but whose operational headquarters are in the US, are listed under their US address.

PRODUCTS/OPERATIONS

This section contains selected lists of products, services, brand names, divisions, subsidiaries, and joint ventures. We have tried to include a company's major lines and most familiar brand names.

The nature of this section varies by company and the amount of information contained in Hoover's storehouse of business information. If the company publishes sales and profit information by type of business, we have included it.

COMPETITORS

In this section we have listed companies that compete with the profiled company. This feature is included as a quick way to locate similar companies and compare them. The universe of competitors includes all public companies and all private companies with sales in excess of $500 million. In a few instances we have identified smaller private companies as key competitors.

HISTORICAL FINANCIALS

Here we have tried to present as much data about each enterprise's financial performance as we could compile in the allocated space. The information varies somewhat from industry to industry and is less complete in the case of private companies that do not release data. (We have always tried to provide annual sales and employment, although in some instances those numbers are simply not available). There are a few industries, venture capital and investment banking, for example, for which revenue numbers are not reported as a rule. In the case of private companies that do not publicly disclose financial information, we have statistics when reliable sources are available.

The following information is generally present.

A five-year table, with relevant annualized compound growth rates, covers:

- Sales — fiscal year sales (year-end assets for most financial companies)
- Net income — fiscal year net income (before accounting changes)
- Net profit margin — fiscal year net income as a percent of sales (as a percent of assets for most financial firms)
- Employees — fiscal year-end or average number of employees

The information on the number of employees is intended to aid the reader interested in knowing whether a company has a long-term trend of increasing or decreasing employment. As far as we know, we are the only company that publishes this information in print format.

The numbers on the left in each row of the Historical Financials section give the month and the year in which the company's fiscal year actually ends. Thus, a company with a March 31, 2010, year-end is shown as 3/10. The last item in the Financials section is a graph, which for private companies shows net income, or, if that is unavailable, sales.

Key year-end statistics are included in this section for insurance companies and companies required to file reports with the SEC. They generally show the financial strength of the enterprise, including:

- Debt ratio (long-term debt as a percent of shareholders' equity)
- Return on equity (net income divided by the average of beginning and ending common shareholders' equity)
- Cash and cash equivalents
- Current ratio (ratio of current assets to current liabilities)
- Total long-term debt (including capital lease obligations)
- Fiscal year sales for financial institutions

Hoover's Handbook of

Private Companies

A List-Lover's Compendium

The 200 Largest Companies by Sales in Hoover's Handbook of Private Companies 2016

Rank	Company	Sales ($ bil.)	Rank	Company	Sales ($ bil.)	Rank	Company	Sales ($ bil.)
1	UNITED NETWORK FOR ORGA	$35,112	61	BON SECOURS HEALTH SYSTEM INC	$3,085	122	SUFFOLK CONSTRUCTION COMP	$1,761
2	MAKE CORPORATION	$22,725	62	EP ENERGY LLC	$3,084	123	WHEATON FRANCISCAN SERVICE	$1,754
3	CANDID COLOR SYSTEMS INC.	$21,742	63	RALEY"S	$3,054	124	COUNTY OF MARICOPA	$1,751
4	VENTURE ELECTRICAL CONTRACT	$16,837	64	NEW YORK POWER AUTHORITY	$3,030	125	SOUTHWEST CATHOLIC HEALTH	$1,748
5	KAISER FOUNDATION HOSPITALS	$14,795	65	MCCARTHY BUILDING COMPANIES	$2,992	126	ASI COMPUTER TECHNOLOGIES INC	$1,747
6	WAKEFERN FOOD CORP.	$11,456	66	AXEL JOHNSON INC.	$2,982	127	NYSARC INC.	$1,747
7	TRAMMO INC.	$11,315	67	RICH PRODUCTS CORPORATION	$2,859	128	SPECTRUM HEALTH HOSPITALS	$1,743
8	ALLEGIS GROUP INC.	$10,440	68	IOWA HEALTH SYSTEM	$2,841	129	ALBERICI GROUP INC.	$1,736
9	GROWMARK INC.	$10,372	69	MEMORIAL HERMANN HEALTHCARE	$2,841	130	ALBERICI CORPORATION	$1,736
10	TENASKA MARKETING VENTURES	$10,310	70	WILBUR-ELLIS COMPANY	$2,812	131	RDO EQUIPMENT CO	$1,698
11	HOVENSA LLC	$10,048	71	TEMPLE UNIVERSITY-OF THE COM	$2,724	132	LEHIGH VALLEY HEALTH NETWORK.	$1,694
12	U.S. VENTURE INC.	$9,089	72	PETROLEUM TRADERS CORPORA	$2,670	133	THE CARLE FOUNDATION	$1,691
13	THE PRIDDY FOUNDATION	$8,792	73	CEDARS-SINAI MEDICAL CENTER	$2,658	134	SWINERTON INCORPORATED	$1,682
14	ASSOCIATED WHOLESALE GROCER.	$8,380	74	SCRIPPS HEALTH	$2,655	135	SWINERTON BUILDERS	$1,675
15	HY-VEE INC.	$8,014	75	FRANCISCAN ALLIANCE INC.	$2,625	136	INOVA HEALTH CARE SERVICES	$1,664
16	CFJ PROPERTIES LLC	$7,672	76	THE METHODIST HOSPITAL	$2,616	137	NATIONWIDE CHILDREN"S HOSP	$1,658
17	ZEN-NOH GRAIN CORPORATION	$7,550	77	ERP OPERATING LIMITED PART	$2,615	138	C.R. ENGLAND INC.	$1,629
18	CGB ENTERPRISES INC.	$7,228	78	LEXA INTERNATIONAL CORPOR	$2,598	139	WALSH CONSTRUCTION COMPANY	$1,627
19	CONSOLIDATED GRAIN & BARGE CO	$7,093	79	UNIVERSITY OF MARYLAND MEDL	$2,571	140	AHS HOSPITAL CORP.	$1,625
20	MORTGAGE INVESTORS CORPORA	$6,746	80	IMMACULATE MARY HOME	$2,569	141	ATLANTIC HEALTH SYSTEM INC.	$1,625
21	HILL/AHERN FIRE PROTECTION LLC	$5,669	81	STANFORD HEALTH SERVICES	$2,511	142	DAIRYAMERICA INC.	$1,618
22	CHALMETTE REFINING L.L.C.	$5,648	82	TRINITY HEALTH-MICHIGAN	$2,476	143	NORDIC PCL CONSTRUCTION INC.	$1,617
23	ST. JOSEPH HEALTH SYSTEM	$5,632	83	THE WASHINGTON UNIVERSITY	$2,472	144	PCL CONSTRUCTION ENTERPRISES	$1,617
24	NORTHERN TIER ENERGY LP	$5,556	84	CAREGROUP INC.	$2,449	145	ALRO STEEL CORPORATION	$1,614
25	CH2M HILL COMPANIES LTD.	$5,468	85	SHAMROCK FOODS COMPANY	$2,434	146	GENPACT LIMITED	$1,600
26	AEROTEK INC.	$5,269	86	J M SMITH CORPORATION	$2,370	147	RUSH UNIVERSITY MEDICAL CEN	$1,584
27	ADVANTAGE ELECTRIC SERVICES	$5,241	87	UNIVERSITY HOSPITALS HEALTH	$2,326	148	STEWART"S SHOPS CORP.	$1,577
28	BANNER HEALTH	$5,085	88	ARCTIC SLOPE REGIONAL CORPOR	$2,297	149	ORLANDO HEALTH INC.	$1,577
29	INTERMOUNTAIN HEALTH CARE INC	$5,042	89	ST JOSEPH OF THE PINES INC	$2,286	150	GLOBAL HEALTH SOLUTIONS INC	$1,574
30	SHI INTERNATIONAL CORP.	$5,003	90	TRUMAN ARNOLD COMPANIES	$2,259	151	SAPP BROS. INC.	$1,567
31	PLACID REFINING COMPANY LLC	$4,929	91	HENSEL PHELPS CONSTRUCTION	$2,249	152	MULTICARE HEALTH SYSTEM	$1,564
32	PLACID HOLDING COMPANY	$4,929	92	CITY PUBLIC SERVICES OF SAN ANT	$2,213	153	FATHER MURRAY NURSING CENTER	$1,563
33	OCHSNER CLINIC FOUNDATION	$4,830	93	NORTHWEST DAIRY ASSOCIATION	$2,207	154	FCTG HOLDINGS INC.	$1,535
34	BATELLE MEMORIAL INSTITUTE	$4,796	94	SCHAUMBOND GROUP INC.	$2,200	155	MFA INCORPORATED	$1,511
35	BATTELLE MEMORIAL INSTITUTE	$4,770	95	OREGON HEALTH & SCIENCE UNIV	$2,170	156	AUGUSTANA HEALTH CARE CENTER	$1,505
36	TAUBER OIL COMPANY	$4,769	96	KNIGHTS OF COLUMBUS	$2,116	157	SOUTH DAKOTA WHEAT GROWERS	$1,499
37	LUKOIL PAN AMERICAS LLC	$4,746	97	MEMORIAL HEALTH SERVICES CORP	$2,094	158	AFFILIATED FOODS MIDWEST COOP	$1,478
38	BIOURJA TRADING LLC	$4,622	98	CONTINUUM ENERGY SERVICES	$2,093	159	BLUE CROSS AND BLUE SHIELD OF	$1,472
39	UNIVERSITY OF WASHINGTON INC	$4,563	99	API GROUP INC.	$2,049	160	MFA OIL COMPANY	$1,471
40	HENRY FORD HEALTH SYSTEM	$4,517	100	VIZIO INC.	$2,006	161	SHAMROCK TRADING CORPORATION	$1,469
41	ALASKA PERMANENT FUND CORP	$4,441	101	UNIVERSITY OF PITTSBURGH	$2,006	162	SPECTRUM HEALTH SYSTEM	$1,446
42	THE SALVATION ARMY NATIONAL	$4,316	102	OHIOHEALTH CORPORATION	$2,000	163	EPIC AVIATION LLC	$1,439
43	SENTARA HEALTHCARE	$4,299	103	PRIESTES EXPRESS LINES INC.	$1,958	164	BALTIMORE CITY PUBLIC SCHOOL	$1,432
44	THE NEW YORK AND PRESBYTERIAN	$4,265	105	ASSOCIATED FOOD STORES INC.	$1,957	165	SEACOAST NURSING AND REHAB	$1,422
45	WINCO HOLDINGS INC.	$4,104	106	NEW YORK STATE CATHOLIC HEAL	$1,921	166	ROCKHILL MENNONITE HOME	$1,417
46	THE WHITING-TURNER CONTRACTY	$3,782	107	OSF HEALTHCARE SYSTEM	$1,893	167	HDR ENGINEERING INC.	$1,416
47	ADVOCATE HEALTH AND HOSPITALS	$3,645	108	INDIANA UNIVERSITY HEALTH INC.	$1,890	168	TRUE VALUE COMPANY	$1,412
48	KWIK TRIP INC.	$3,640	109	BAPTIST MEMORIAL HEALTH CARE	$1,884	169	KGBO HOLDINGS INC	$1,387
49	BLACK & VEATCH HOLDING CO	$3,563	110	PRAIRIE FARMS DAIRY INC.	$1,879	170	NORTHWESTERN MEMORIAL HOSP	$1,380
50	TEKSYSTEMS INC.	$3,551	111	SCHOOL BOARD OF ORANGE COUN	$1,877	171	MARYLAND AND VIRGINIA MILK PR	$1,373
51	UNIVERSITY OF WISCONSIN SYS	$3,539	112	UNITED SPACE ALLIANCE LLC	$1,860	172	PEACEHEALTH	$1,372
52	THE GOLUB CORPORATION	$3,473	113	BECK & MASTEN PONTIAC-GMC INC	$1,839	173	A-1 SPECIALIZED SERVICES & SUPP	$1,359
53	THE WALSH GROUP LTD	$3,462	114	DPR CONSTRUCTION INC.	$1,836	174	TEMPLE UNIVERSITY HEALTH SYS	$1,356
54	ALLINA HEALTH SYSTEM	$3,421	115	COC PROPERTIES INC.	$1,830	175	D/L COOPERATIVE INC.	$1,334
55	FAIRVIEW HEALTH SERVICES	$3,370	116	CARY OIL CO. INC.	$1,829	176	BARRY-WEHMILLER GROUP INC.	$1,333
56	MEMORIAL HERMANN HEALTH SYS	$3,285	117	PRO PETROLEUM INC.	$1,815	177	COUNTRYMARK COOPERATIVE HOLD	$1,326
57	MCCARTHY HOLDINGS INC.	$3,229	118	HUGHES SATELLITE SYSTEMS COR	$1,808	178	CAPITAL DISTRICT PHYSICIANS"	$1,315
58	LOS ANGELES DEPARTMENT OF W&P	$3,126	119	INVACARE CORPORATION (TW)	$1,801	179	AVIO INC.	$1,310
59	SANFORD HEALTH	$3,106	120	OREGON UNIVERSITY SYSTEM	$1,782	180	THE DELONG CO INC	$1,307
60	UNIVERSITY OF CHICAGO	$3,092	121	COMMUNITY HEALTH NETWORK INC.	$1,763	181	THE UNIVERSITY OF CHICAGO MED	$1,295

The 200 Largest Companies by Sales in Hoover's Handbook of Private Companies 2016 (continued)

Rank	Company	Sales ($ bil.)
182	MILWAUKEE PUBLIC SCHOOLS	$1,293
183	BAPTIST HEALTHCARE SYSTEM INC.	$1,290
184	BAYSTATE HEALTH SYSTEM HEALTH	$1,286
185	BEALL"S INC.	$1,273
186	PAN AMERICAN HEALTH ORGANIZ	$1,269
187	GRANDVIEW HEALTH HOME	$1,262

Rank	Company	Sales ($ bil.)
188	COASTAL PACIFIC FOOD DISTRIBU	$1,260
189	BETH ISRAEL MEDICAL CENTER	$1,257
190	NORTHSIDE HOSPITAL INC.	$1,254
191	WESTERN OREGON UNIVERSITY	$1,252
192	THOMAS JEFFERSON UNIVERSITY	$1,250
193	GPM INVESTMENTS LLC	$1,250

Rank	Company	Sales ($ bil.)
194	COBORN"S INCORPORATED	$1,247
195	STEWARD HEALTH CARE SYSTEM	$1,241
196	UNIPRO FOODSERVICE INC	$1,239
197	THE MITRE CORPORATION	$1,235
198	SUNKIST GROWERS INC.	$1,234
199	MAXIM HEALTHCARE SERVICES INC.	$1,227
200	WAKE COUNTY PUBLIC SCHOOL SYS	$1,224

The 200 Largest Employers in
Hoover's Handbook of Private Companies 2016

The 200 Largest Employers in
Hoover's Handbook of Private Companies 2016 (continued)

Rank	Company	Employees
1	KAISER FOUNDATION HOSPITALS	175668
2	DAKOTA ELECTRIC ASSOCIATION	100000
3	ALLEGIS GROUP INC.	85000
4	HY-VEE INC.	62000
5	THE SALVATION ARMY NATIONAL	60000
6	BANNER HEALTH	35000
7	MAXIM HEALTHCARE SERVICES INC.	35000
8	HEARTLAND HEALTH	32000
9	UNIVERSITY OF WISCONSIN SYSTEM	31992
10	UNIVERSITY HOSPITALS HEALTH SYI	30000
11	LIFE CARE CENTERS OF AMERICA I	29000
12	NYSARC INC.	28000
13	UNIVERSITY OF WASHINGTON INC	27228
14	PROGRESS WEST HEALTHCARE	27000
15	ALLINA HEALTH SYSTEM	26400
16	CH2M HILL COMPANIES LTD.	26000
17	OREGON UNIVERSITY SYSTEM	26000
18	SCHOOL BOARD OF ORANGE COU	25000
19	CHRISTUS HEALTH	25000
20	INTERMOUNTAIN HEALTH CARE INC	23000
21	HENRY FORD HEALTH SYSTEM	23000
22	SENTARA HEALTHCARE	22000
23	THE GOLUB CORPORATION	21741
24	ST. JOSEPH HEALTH SYSTEM	21500
25	STAFF FORCE INC.	20000
26	BON SECOURS HEALTH SYSTEM INC	19000
27	IOWA HEALTH SYSTEM	18923
28	ESSENTIA HEALTH	18177
29	FAIRVIEW HEALTH SERVICES	18000
30	PRINCE GEORGE"S COUNTY PUBLIC	18000
31	WHEATON FRANCISCAN SERVICES	18000
32	OCEAN BEAUTY SEAFOODS LLC	18000
33	UNIVERSITY OF GEORGIA	17800
34	INDIANA UNIVERSITY HEALTH INC.	17242
35	WAKE COUNTY PUBLIC SCHOOL SY	17000
36	SPECTRUM HEALTH SYSTEM	16996
37	MEMORIAL HERMANN HEALTHCARE	16505
38	THE SALVATION ARMY	16168
39	UNIVERSITY OF SOUTH FLORIDA	16165
40	DEKALB COUNTY BOARD OF EDUCA	16000
41	THE NEW YORK AND PRESBYTERIAN	15078
42	OHIOHEALTH CORPORATION	15000
43	AKAL SECURITY INC.	15000
44	ADVANCE SERVICES INC.	14200
45	MILWAUKEE PUBLIC SCHOOLS	14154
46	WINCO HOLDINGS INC.	14000
47	MEMORIAL HERMANN HEALTH SYS	14000
48	RALEY"S	14000
49	THE METHODIST HOSPITAL	14000
50	OREGON HEALTH & SCIENCE UNI	14000
51	ESTES EXPRESS LINES INC.	14000
52	HOSPITAL SISTERS HEALTH SYSTEM	14000
53	ALSCO INC.	13585
54	SCRIPPS HEALTH	13445
55	INOVA HEALTH CARE SERVICES	13000
56	SHARP HEALTHCARE	13000
57	DUVAL COUNTY PUBLIC SCHOOLS	13000
58	BODDIE-NOELL ENTERPRISES INC.	13000
59	BAPTIST HEALTHCARE SYSTEM INC.	12601
60	MV TRANSPORTATION INC.	12389
61	BOARD OF EDUCATION-MEMPHIS SC	12015
62	UNIVERSITY OF MARYLAND MEDICAL	12000
63	CAREGROUP INC.	12000
64	LEHIGH VALLEY HEALTH NETWORK	12000
65	BALTIMORE CITY PUBLIC SCHOOL	12000
66	STEWARD HEALTH CARE SYSTEM LLC	12000
67	ST. PETER"S HEALTH PARTNERS	12000
68	UNIVERSITY OF TENNESSEE	12000
69	PULSE ELECTRONICS INC.	12000
70	PAN-O-GOLD BAKING CO.	12000
71	THE ROMAN CATHOLIC ARCHBISHOP	12000
72	METHODIST LE BONHEUR HEALTHC	11459
73	SPECTRUM HEALTH HOSPITALS	11000
74	ST. MARYS DEAN VENTURES INCOR	11000
75	WAKE FOREST UNIVERSITY BAPTIST	11000
76	UNDERWRITERS LABORATORIES INC	10846
77	OCHSNER CLINIC FOUNDATION	10500
78	KWIK TRIP INC.	10500
79	UNITED SPACE ALLIANCE LLC	10500
80	PALMETTO HEALTH	10200
81	BEALL"S INC.	10100
82	MCLAREN HEALTH CARE CORPOR	10003
83	ORLANDO HEALTH INC.	10000
84	MERCY HOSPITALS EAST COMMUNI	10000
85	THOMAS JEFFERSON UNIVERSITY	10000
86	UMASS MEMORIAL HEALTH CARE INC	10000
87	FARM CREDIT SERVICES OF AMERICA	10000
88	COOPERATIVE FOR ASSISTANCE AND	10000
89	PDS TECH INC.	10000
90	UMASS MEMORIAL HOSPITALS INC.	10000
91	ON TIME STAFFING LLC	10000
92	BAPTIST MEMORIAL HEALTH CARE	9877
93	CATHOLIC BISHOP OF CHICAGO	9604
94	THE WASHINGTON UNIVERSITY	9600
95	MANAGEMENT AND TRAINING	9500
96	BAPTIST HEALTH SOUTH FLORIDA	9374
97	DARTMOUTH-HITCHCOCK CLINIC	9300
98	LESTER E. COX MEDICAL CENTERS	9100
99	TEMPLE UNIVERSITY-OF THE COM.	9061
100	SCHOOL BOARD OF BREVARD COU	9031
101	FRANCISCAN ALLIANCE INC.	9000
102	KALEIDA HEALTH	9000
103	NORTHSHORE UNIVERSITY HEALTH	9000
104	FRANCISCAN MISSIONARIES OF OUR	9000
105	CHRISTIANA CARE HEALTH SERVICES	8800
106	UNIVERSITY OF MISSISSIPPI	8700
107	NCH CORPORATION	8500
108	RICH PRODUCTS CORPORATION	8400
109	PITT COUNTY MEMORIAL HOSPITAL	8373
110	AVERITT INCORPORATED	8210
111	AVERITT EXPRESS INC.	8208
112	BETH ISRAEL MEDICAL CENTER	8100
113	ACCENTCARE INC.	8060
114	LOS ANGELES DEPARTMENT OF WAT	8000
115	CEDARS-SINAI MEDICAL CENTER	8000
116	NORTHSIDE HOSPITAL INC.	8000
117	MOUNT CARMEL HEALTH SYSTEM	8000
118	THE RESEARCH FOUNDATION OF	8000
119	PRINCE WILLIAM COUNTY PUBLIC	8000
120	RIVERSIDE HEALTHCARE ASSOCIAT	8000
121	THE CHILDREN"S HOSPITAL CORP	8000
122	GUILFORD COUNTY SCHOOL SYSTEM	8000
123	GRANITE SCHOOL DISTRICT	8000
124	RIVERSIDE HOSPITAL INC.	8000
125	LEGACY HEALTH	8000
126	UNIVERSITY OF IOWA HOSPITALS	7638
127	WAKE FOREST BAPTIST MEDICAL CEN	7612
128	EAST TEXAS MEDICAL CENTER REGI	7600
129	TEMPLE UNIVERSITY HEALTH SYSTEM	7573
130	MAXIFACIAL DENTAL SURGERY	7500
131	HARTFORD HOSPITAL	7500
132	SAINT LOUIS UNIVERSITY	7500
133	GEORGIA REGENTS UNIVERSITY	7500
134	DIVERSIFIED MAINTENANCE SYSTEMS	7500
135	BATTELLE MEMORIAL INSTITUTE INC	7457
136	SUMMA HEALTH SYSTEM	7406
137	AHS HOSPITAL CORP.	7300
138	ANNE ARUNDEL COUNTY BOARD OF	7200
139	SANFORD NORTH	7200
140	HACKENSACK UNIVERSITY MEDICAL	7175
141	CROZER-KEYSTONE HEALTH SYSTEM	7100
142	HERSHEY ENTERTAINMENT & RESORT	7100
143	BLACK & VEATCH HOLDING COMPANY	7017
144	COBORN"S INCORPORATED	7000
145	THE MITRE CORPORATION	7000
146	ALBANY MEDICAL CENTER	7000
147	BAPTIST HEALTH	7000
148	HILLCO LTD.	7000
149	SANFORD CLINIC NORTH	7000
150	THE MOSES H CONE MEMORIAL HOSI	7000
151	PARKVIEW HEALTH SYSTEM INC.	7000
152	UNIVERSITY OF WYOMING	7000
153	YOUNG MEN"S CHRISTIAN ASSOCIAT	7000
154	LINCOLN PUBLIC SCHOOLS INC	6950
155	SWEDISH HEALTH SERVICES	6916
156	MARSHFIELD CLINIC INC.	6900
157	HEALTH FIRST INC.	6900
158	WINSTON-SALEM/FORSYTH COUNTY	6841
159	EAST BATON ROUGE PARISH SCHOOL	6800
160	READING HEALTH SYSTEM	6800
161	JFK HEALTH SYSTEM INC.	6735
162	PEACEHEALTH	6690
163	MULTICARE HEALTH SYSTEM	6510
164	C.R. ENGLAND INC.	6500
165	BETH ISRAEL DEACONESS MEDICAL	6500
166	SCOTTSDALE HEALTHCARE CORP.	6500
167	CSAA INSURANCE GROUP	6500
168	MIDMICHIGAN HEALTH	6500
169	CARE NEW ENGLAND HEALTH SYSTEM	6500
170	EDWARD-ELMHURST HEALTHCARE	6500
171	TALLAHASSEE MEMORIAL HEALTH	6430
172	BALL STATE UNIVERSITY	6426
173	MERCY HEALTH SPRINGFIELD COMM	6300
174	VIRGINIA WEST UNIVERSITY HOSP	6267
175	CFJ PROPERTIES LLC	6250
176	SAINT ELIZABETH MEDICAL CENTER	6227
177	CUMBERLAND COUNTY SCHOOLS	6210
178	RHODE ISLAND HOSPITAL	6200
179	YORK HOSPITAL	6200
180	CONTRACK INTERNATIONAL INC.	6200

SOURCE: HOOVER'S, INC., DATABASE, DECEMBER 2015

The 200 Largest Employers in
Hoover's Handbook of Private Companies 2016 (continued)

Rank	Company	Employees
181	INDEPENDENT SCHOOL DISTRICT 1	6115
182	WELLMONT HEALTH SYSTEM	6114
183	HDR ENGINEERING INC.	6111
184	DEACONESS HEALTH SYSTEM INC.	6086
185	SIMPLIFIED BUSINESS SOLUTIONS	6008
187	NATIONWIDE CHILDREN"S HOSPITAL	6000

Rank	Company	Employees
188	ST. LUKE"S HEALTH SYSTEM FOUNDA	6000
189	FLETCHER ALLEN HEALTH CARE INC.	6000
190	LIFEBRIDGE HEALTH INC.	6000
191	THE METROHEALTH SYSTEM	6000
192	UNIVERSITY OF NORTH CAROLINA H	6000
193	NORTH MISSISSIPPI HEALTH SERVIC	6000

Rank	Company	Employees
194	MIAMI VALLEY HOSPITAL	6000
195	WINTHROP-UNIVERSITY HOSPITAL	6000
196	NORTH MISSISSIPPI MEDICAL CENT.	6000
197	CENTRA HEALTH INC.	6000
198	CHILDREN"S NATIONAL MEDICAL CEN	6000
199	BAPTIST MEMORIAL HOSPITAL	6000
200	DEVEREUX FOUNDATION	6000

The Top 100 Companies by Net Income in
Hoover's Handbook of Private Companies 2016

Rank	Company Headquarters	Net Income ($bil)
1	ALASKA PERMANENT FUND CORPORATION	$4,520
2	CANDID COLOR SYSTEMS INC.	$2,535
3	INTERMOUNTAIN HEALTH CARE INC	$1,546
4	MAKE CORPORATION	$1,400
5	THE SALVATION ARMY NATIONAL CORPORATION	$1,350
6	THE WASHINGTON UNIVERSITY	$918
7	SENTARA HEALTHCARE	$862
8	BANNER HEALTH	$855
9	STAPLE COTTON CO-OPERATIVE ASSOCIATION	$807
10	LUDWIG INSTITUTE FOR CANCER RESEARCH	$761
11	THE METHODIST HOSPITAL	$684
12	VANGUARD CHARITABLE ENDOWMENT PROGRAM	$608
13	LLOG EXPLORATION COMPANY L.L.C.	$601
14	THE NEW YORK AND PRESBYTERIAN HOSPITAL	$595
15	THE PEW CHARITABLE TRUSTS	$585
16	UNIVERSITY OF PITTSBURGH	$570
17	SECURITIES INVESTOR PROTECTION CORPORATION	$512
18	UNIVERSITY OF WISCONSIN SYSTEM	$503
19	TIAA REAL ESTATE ACCOUNT	$490
20	TUDOR INVESTMENT CORPORATION	$486
21	KAISER FOUNDATION HOSPITALS INC	$429
22	UNIVERSITY OF WASHINGTON INC	$425
23	STANFORD HEALTH SERVICES	$416
24	THE DAVID AND LUCILE PACKARD FOUNDATION	$413
25	OPEN SOCIETY INSTITUTE	$376
26	ALLINA HEALTH SYSTEM	$374
27	PREMIER PURCHASING PARTNERS L.P.	$371
28	IOWA HEALTH SYSTEM	$369
29	WALTON FAMILY	$369
30	CHALMETTE REFINING L.L.C.	364
31	ST. JOSEPH HEALTH SYSTEM	$353
32	DEKALB COUNTY BOARD OF EDUCATION	$351
33	UNITED NETWORK FOR ORGAN SHARING	$341
34	EMILY DICKINSON MUSEUM	$334
35	ADVANTAGE ELECTRIC SERVICES LLC	$329
36	PRODUCERS RICE MILL INC.	$327
37	UNIVERSITY OF WISCONSIN FOUNDATION	$324
38	SCRIPPS HEALTH	$312
39	OHIOHEALTH CORPORATION	$304
40	NEW YORK COMMUNITY TRUST AND COMMUNITY FUNDS INC	$302
41	ATLANTIC HEALTH SYSTEM INC.	$292
42	UNIVERSITY OF RICHMOND	$287
43	LOUISIANA CHILDRENS MEDICAL CENTER INC	$280
44	THE TRUSTEES OF GRINNELL COLLEGE	$265
45	JOHN TEMPLETON FOUNDATION	$261
46	SWARTHMORE COLLEGE	$253
47	FAIRVIEW HEALTH SERVICES	$249
48	CITATION OIL & GAS CORP.	$248
49	CYSTIC FIBROSIS FOUNDATION	$247
50	PRESIDENT & TRUSTEES OF WILLIAMS COLLEGE	$245
51	UNIVERSITY HOSPITALS HEALTH SYSTEM INC.	$244
52	COASTAL CAROLINA UNIVERSITY	$244
53	NORTHERN TIER ENERGY LP	$242
54	NORTHWEST FARM CREDIT SERVICES ACA	$237
55	MEMORIAL HERMANN HEALTH SYSTEM	$231
56	GRANITE TELECOMMUNICATIONS LLC	$229
57	WINCO HOLDINGS INC.	$226
58	LEHIGH VALLEY HEALTH NETWORK INC.	$225
59	BIG RIVER RESOURCES LLC	$224
60	OREGON HEALTH & SCIENCE UNIVERSITY MEDICAL GROUP	$221
61	TEXAS A M UNIVERSITY 12TH MAN FOUNDATION	$215
62	AMERICAN LEBANESE SYRIAN ASSOCIATED CHARITIES INC.	$210
63	THE SALVATION ARMY	$207
64	GEORGIA TECH FOUNDATION INC.	$207
65	WISCONSIN ALUMNI RESEARCH FOUNDATION	$206
66	INOVA HEALTH CARE SERVICES	$200
67	UNIVERSITY OF ILLINOIS FOUNDATION	$196
68	THE SALVATION ARMY	$192
69	GENPACT LIMITED	$191
70	TEXAS A & M UNIVERSITY SYSTEM HEALTH SCIENCE	$186
71	UNIVERSITY OF COLORADO	$186
72	HILL/AHERN FIRE PROTECTION LLC	$186
73	IMMACULATE MARY HOME	$185
74	CENTRAL DUPAGE HOSPITAL ASSOCIATION	$184
75	UNIVERSITY OF CHICAGO	$182
76	TEMPLE UNIVERSITY-OF THE COMMONWEALTH SYSTEM	$182
77	MILTON HERSHEY SCHOOL & SCHOOL TRUST	$180
78	THE NOBLE SAMUEL ROBERTS FOUNDATION INC	$176
79	SCHWAB CHARITABLE FUND	$173
80	SPECTRUM HEALTH HOSPITALS	$171
81	UNITED SPACE ALLIANCE LLC	$168
82	GROWMARK INC.	$167
83	NEWTON-WELLESLEY HEALTH CARE SYSTEM INC.	$165
84	TEXAS SCOTTISH RITE HOSPITAL FOR CHILDREN FOUNDA	$164
85	BETHESDA HOSPITAL INC.	$157
86	FARM CREDIT WEST	$156
87	THE TRUSTEES OF THE SMITH COLLEGE	$155
88	THE ELI AND EDYTHE BROAD FOUNDATION	$155
89	POMONA COLLEGE	$154
90	KUTZTOWN MANOR INC	$154
91	SAINT EUGENE MEDICAL CENTER	$152
92	IMPERIAL IRRIGATION DISTRICT	$152
93	EP ENERGY LLC	$148
94	UNIVERSITY OF THE PACIFIC	$147
95	SEYFARTH SHAW LLP	$147
96	ELKHART COUNTY COMMUNITY FOUNDATION	$145
97	SPECTRUM HEALTH SYSTEM	$143
98	NATIONAL CHRISTIAN CHARITABLE	$142
99	UNIVERSITY OF MARYLAND MEDICAL SYSTEM CORP	$139
100	THE SAN FRANCISCO FOUNDATION	$139

SOURCE: HOOVER'S INC., DATABASE, DECEMBER 2015

The Top 100 Companies by Total Assets in Hoover's Handbook of Private Companies 2016

Rank	Company Headquarters	Net Income ($bil)	Rank	Company Headquarters	Net Income ($bil)
1	ALASKA PERMANENT FUND CORPORATION	$49,797	51	FRANCISCAN ALLIANCE INC.	$4,009
2	ERP OPERATING LIMITED PARTNERSHIP	$22,951	52	SCRIPPS HEALTH	$3,992
3	KAISER FOUNDATION HOSPITALS INC	$22,753	53	IOWA HEALTH SYSTEM	$3,952
4	TIAA REAL ESTATE ACCOUNT	$22,409	54	THE SALVATION ARMY	$3,919
5	FARM CREDIT SERVICES OF AMERICA PCA/FLCA	$21,274	55	UNIVERSITY OF TENNESSEE	$3,885
6	KNIGHTS OF COLUMBUS	$20,534	56	MEMORIAL HERMANN HEALTHCARE SYSTEM	$3,826
7	TEXAS COUNTY AND DISTRICT RETIREMENT SYSTEM	$17,829	57	UNIVERSITY OF MARYLAND MEDICAL SYSTEM CORPOR	$3,814
8	SHIRES HOUSING INC.	$15,191	58	APPLE HOSPITALITY REIT INC	$3,780
9	THE SALVATION ARMY NATIONAL CORPORATION	$14,511	59	CEDARS-SINAI MEDICAL CENTER	$3,689
10	LOS ANGELES DEPARTMENT OF WATER AND POWER	$12,520	60	VANGUARD CHARITABLE ENDOWMENT PROGRAM	$3,626
11	THE WASHINGTON UNIVERSITY	$10,800	61	THE CALIFORNIA ENDOWMENT	$3,562
12	EP ENERGY LLC	$10,194	62	ALLINA HEALTH SYSTEM	$3,533
13	CITY PUBLIC SERVICES OF SAN ANTONIO	$10,084	63	HENRY FORD HEALTH SYSTEM	$3,525
14	UNIVERSITY OF WASHINGTON INC	$10,040	64	THE SALVATION ARMY	$3,514
15	MILTON HERSHEY SCHOOL & SCHOOL TRUST	$9,942	65	LLOG EXPLORATION COMPANY L.L.C.	$3,485
16	UNIVERSITY OF CHICAGO	$9,704	66	CITIZENS ENERGY GROUP	$3,457
17	NORTHWEST FARM CREDIT SERVICES ACA	$9,605	67	OREGON HEALTH & SCIENCE UNIVERSITY MEDICAL GROUP	$3,358
18	NEW YORK POWER AUTHORITY	$9,331	68	FARM CREDIT SERVICES ILLINOIS ACA	$3,338
19	ST. JOSEPH HEALTH SYSTEM	$9,027	69	UNIVERSITY HOSPITALS HEALTH SYSTEM INC.	$3,338
20	INTERMOUNTAIN HEALTH CARE INC	$8,682	70	MASSACHUSETTS PORT AUTHORITY	$3,322
21	UNIVERSITY OF WISCONSIN SYSTEM	$8,556	71	DEKALB COUNTY PUBLIC LIBRARY	$3,297
22	BANNER HEALTH	$8,227	72	WESTERN OREGON UNIVERSITY	$3,186
23	TRUSTEES OF THE ESTATE OF BERNICE PAUAHI BISHOP	$7,703	73	SCHWAB CHARITABLE FUND	$3,176
24	WILLIAM MARSH RICE UNIVERSITY INC	$7,365	74	SANFORD HEALTH	$3,151
25	THE NEW YORK AND PRESBYTERIAN HOSPITAL	$7,364	75	OHIOHEALTH CORPORATION	$3,121
26	FARM CREDIT WEST	$6,926	76	UNIVERSITY OF WISCONSIN FOUNDATION	$3,101
27	THE METHODIST HOSPITAL	$6,583	77	TENNESSEE ENERGY ACQUISITION CORPORATION	$3,088
28	UNIVERSAL SERVICE ADMINISTRATIVE COMPANY	$6,491	78	EMILY DICKINSON MUSEUM	$3,059
29	UNIVERSITY OF PITTSBURGH	$6,225	79	FAIRVIEW HEALTH SERVICES	$3,037
30	THE PEW CHARITABLE TRUSTS	$6,199	80	NORTHWESTERN MEMORIAL HOSPITAL	$3,019
31	THE DAVID AND LUCILE PACKARD FOUNDATION	$6,194	81	THE ROCKEFELLER UNIVERSITY FACULTY AND STU$	$3,006
32	VENTURE ELECTRICAL CONTRACTORS INC.	$6,185	82	TRINITY HEALTH-MICHIGAN	$3,001
33	ADVOCATE HEALTH AND HOSPITALS CORPORATION	$6,053	83	TRUSTEES OF TUFTS COLLEGE INC.	$2,991
34	ADVOCATE HEALTH AND HOSPITALS CORPORATION	$6,053	84	ASSOCIATED ELECTRIC COOPERATIVE INC.	$2,988
35	SENTARA HEALTHCARE	$5,854	85	TRI-COUNTY METROPOLITAN TRANSPORTATION DISTRICT	$2,978
36	COUNTY OF MARICOPA	$5,050	86	CH2M HILL COMPANIES LTD.	$2,941
37	SCHOOL BOARD OF ORANGE COUNTY FLORIDA	$4,989	87	UNION BANK AND TRUST COMPANY	$2,863
38	COLUMBIA PROPERTY TRUST INC.	$4,739	88	ST. JUDE CHILDREN"S RESEARCH HOSPITAL INC.	$2,860
39	SOUTHERN NEVADA WATER AUTHORITY	$4,677	89	ADVANTAGE ELECTRIC SERVICES LLC	$2,841
40	HUGHES SATELLITE SYSTEMS CORPORATION	$4,665	90	AMERICAN LEBANESE SYRIAN ASSOCIATED CHARITIES INC.	$2,824
41	MEMORIAL HERMANN HEALTH SYSTEM	$4,481	91	ALLEGIS GROUP INC.	$2,816
42	OREGON UNIVERSITY SYSTEM	$4,352	92	MEMORIAL HEALTH SERVICES CORPORATION	$2,805
43	GREENSTONE FARM CREDIT SERVICES ACA	$4,317	93	BON SECOURS HEALTH SYSTEM INC	$2,799
44	UNIVERSITY OF RICHMOND	$4,293	94	HOVENSA LLC	$2,770
45	TEMPLE UNIVERSITY-OF THE COMMONWEALTH SYSTEM OF	$4,278	95	RUSH UNIVERSITY MEDICAL CENTER	$2,727
46	MACK-CALI REALTY L. P.	$4,192	96	MULTICARE HEALTH SYSTEM	$2,722
47	LODGING RLJ TRUST L P	$4,128	97	STANFORD HEALTH SERVICES	$2,711
48	PSECU SERVICES INC.	$4,119	98	CHRISTUS HEALTH	$2,696
49	TRUSTEES OF BOSTON COLLEGE	$4,100	99	WAKE COUNTY PUBLIC SCHOOL SYSTEM	$2,655
50	THE CHILDREN"S HOSPITAL CORPORATION	$4,026	100	CAREGROUP INC.	$2,641

SOURCE: FORBES, NOVEMBER 2015

Hoover's Handbook of

Private Companies

The Companies

A C & T CO INC

Auditors: FLURIE SLICK & KINNETT CPAS

LOCATIONS

HQ: A C & T CO INC
11535 HOPEWELL RD, HAGERSTOWN, MD
217402178
Phone: 800 458-3835
Web: WWW.ACANDT.COM

HISTORICAL FINANCIALS

Company Type: Private

Income Statement

FYE: June 30

	REVENUE ($ mil.)	NET INCOME ($ mil.)	NET PROFIT MARGIN	EMPLOYEES
06/11	310	2	0.9%	300
06/10	244	6	2.5%	—
Annual Growth	26.8%	(54.8%)	—	—

2011 Year-End Financials

Return on assets: 2.4%   Cash ($ mil.): 2
Return on equity: 0.9%
Current ratio: 1.10

A G EQUIPMENT COMPANY

LOCATIONS

HQ: A G EQUIPMENT COMPANY
3401 W ALBANY ST, BROKEN ARROW, OK 740121174
Phone: 918 250-7386
Web: WWW.AGEQUIPMENTCOMPANY.COM

HISTORICAL FINANCIALS

Company Type: Private

Income Statement

FYE: June 30

	REVENUE ($ mil.)	NET INCOME ($ mil.)	NET PROFIT MARGIN	EMPLOYEES
06/14	402	29	7.4%	370
06/13	362	34	9.6%	—
06/12	315	17	5.6%	—
06/11	237	0	—	—
Annual Growth	19.1%	—	—	—

2014 Year-End Financials

Return on assets: 5.7%   Cash ($ mil.): 97
Return on equity: 7.4%
Current ratio: 1.00

A-1 SPECIALIZED SERVICES & SUPPLIES INC.

Auditors: MEENA JERATH CPA MED MBA

LOCATIONS

HQ: A-1 SPECIALIZED SERVICES & SUPPLIES INC.
2707 STATE RD, CROYDON, PA 190216969
Phone: 215 788-9200

HISTORICAL FINANCIALS

Company Type: Private

Income Statement

FYE: December 31

	REVENUE ($ mil.)	NET INCOME ($ mil.)	NET PROFIT MARGIN	EMPLOYEES
12/10	1,359	7	0.6%	66
12/09	1,205	2	0.2%	—
Annual Growth	12.7%	171.1%	—	—

2010 Year-End Financials

Return on assets: 12.6%   Cash ($ mil.): 8
Return on equity: 0.6%
Current ratio: 0.40

AAA COOPER TRANSPORTATION

They might not give you a map like that other AAA but AAA Cooper Transportation can freight your cargo from point A to point B. A non-union regional less-than-truckload (LTL) freight hauler AAA Cooper (ACT) operates in a dozen southeastern US states as well as Puerto Rico; it also maintains facilities in Chicago and a few other industrial crossroads. (LTL carriers combine freight from multiple shippers into a single truckload.) ACT operates a fleet of approximately 2400 tractors and 6000 trailers. ACT also offers freight brokerage services and dedicated contract carriage.

Geographic Reach

ACT operates more than 70 facilities in the Southeast Southwest Midwest and Puerto Rico. It has nearly 40 maintenance facilities nationwide and partners with carriers to extend its coverage into Canada and Mexico. The company's international partnerships allow it for operate across the Caribbean Latin America Europe Asia Africa and Australia.

Operations

The company's five primary service offerings are LTL Services dedicated services international Services (including port services) managed services and fleet maintenance services. Its port services provide services to the port the shipper and the customer. It transloads the goods from the container to its trailer or dock and returns the container to the port. Its fleet maintenance services provide maintenance services for all types of diesel engines including the CAT VOLVO International Detroit and Cummins brands. The company's distribution operations offer assembly operations manufacturing plant transfers warehouse transfers wholesale distribution and retail distribution.

Sales and Marketing

ATC serves a range of sectors including Automotive Manufacturing Automotive Parts Heavy Equipment Parts Building Materials Retail and HVAC. ACT customers include Schneider Logistics Volvo Logistics Mastio & Company GlobalTranz Technicolor John Deere and Nissan.

Strategy

As part of its growth strategy ACT seeks to offer new services and expand into new geographies. In 2014 the company launched a new Managed Services offering adding Truckload Brokerage and Parcel Audit to its services.

In 2013 the company opened a service center at Corpus Christi Texas.

Company Background
The ATC was founded in 1955.

EXECUTIVES

Vice President Administration Chief Financial Officer Treasurer and Corporate Secretary, Steve Roy
Senior Vice President Finance, Mark Griffis
National Account Manager, Bob Menas
National Account Manager, Teresa L Riggs
Vice President, Steven (Steve) Aronhalt
Vice President Of Information Technology, Paul Turner
Vice President Information Services, Dan Christian
National Account Manager, Michelle Combs
National Account Manager, David Hunt
Vice President Sales and Operations, Clay Scofield
Vice President, Steve Aronhalt

LOCATIONS

HQ: AAA COOPER TRANSPORTATION
1751 KINSEY RD, DOTHAN, AL 363035877
Phone: 334 793-2284
Web: WWW.AAACOOPER.COM

PRODUCTS/OPERATIONS

Selected Services
Company branding
Specialized equipment
International LTL
LTL
Port
  Consolidation
  Drayage
  Transloading

COMPETITORS

ArcBest	Saia
Averitt Express	Southeastern Freight
Estes Express	Lines
FedEx Freight	UPS Freight
Old Dominion Freight	YRC Worldwide
R+L Carriers	

HISTORICAL FINANCIALS

Company Type: Private

Income Statement

FYE: December 29

	REVENUE ($ mil.)	NET INCOME ($ mil.)	NET PROFIT MARGIN	EMPLOYEES
12/13	575	20	3.6%	4,193
12/12*	553	20	3.8%	—
01/12	520	7	1.5%	—
01/11	468	0	—	—
Annual Growth	7.0%	—	—	—

*Fiscal year change

2013 Year-End Financials

Return on assets: 2.2%   Cash ($ mil.): —
Return on equity: 3.6%
Current ratio: 1.40

ABINGTON MEMORIAL HOSPITAL INC

Abington Memorial Hospital brings health care to residents of southeastern Pennsylvania. The not-for-profit community hospital has some 670 beds.

In addition to general medical and surgical care the hospital offers specialized care centers for cancer and cardiovascular conditions operates high-tech orthopedic and neurological surgery units and serves as a regional trauma care facility. It also runs an inpatient pediatric unit in affiliation with The Children's Hospital of Philadelphia. Abington Memorial also known as Abington Health operates the neighboring 125-bed Lansdale Hospital and several area outpatient facilities.

Operations

The not-for-profit community hospital has some 670 beds and employs about 1400 physicians. Its specialty units include the Pilla Heart Center the Rosenfeld Cancer Center the Diamond Stroke Center as well as a level II trauma center and institutes for senior health and bariatric surgeries. Abington Memorial is affiliated with several medical schools including the Temple University School of Medicine and offers residency programs and postgraduate medical education.

In addition to its hospitals Abington Memorial operates an extensive outpatient care facility named Abington Health Center-Warminster. The Warminster facility is located in Bucks County and features an inpatient hospice center. Other outpatient facilities include Abington Health Center-Schilling (in Willow Grove) Abington Health Center-Blue Bell and Abington Physicians at Montgomeryville.

Altogether the organization's facilities handle 677000 outpatient visits and 33000 inpatient admissions each year.

Additionally Abington Memorial operates a nursing school and a clinical research center.

Geographic Reach

Abington Memorial provides care to residents of southeastern Pennsylvania. The hospital serves Montgomery Bucks and Philadelphia counties.

Strategy

Abington Memorial began using the Abington Health moniker to reflect its larger network of facilities after it acquired Lansdale Hospital which was previously known as Central Montgomery Medical Center from Universal Health Services in 2008. Abington Memorial has since invested in a number of improvements at the acquired hospital. The main Abington Memorial facility has also been enhanced including a new hybrid operating room for cardiac procedures in 2013.

Mergers and Acquisitions

In 2013 Abington Memorial acquired a home health agency the North Penn Visiting Nurse Association (NPVNA). The purchase expanded the geographic reach of Abington Memorial's home health operations.

Company Background

Abington Memorial first opened its doors in 1914.

EXECUTIVES

President Abington Hospitals, Margaret M. (Meg) McGoldrick
Chief Medical Officer, John J. Kelly
Executive Vice President Of Information Technology, Jan Seip
Vice President Human Resources, Hans Kim
Vice President, Lisa Durst
Vice President It, John Peniston
Vice President Professional Services And Quality Assurance, Gary R Candia
Medical Director, Gerry Cleary
Medical Director of Labor and Delivery, Amy Mackey
Executive Vice President Sales East, Del Humenik
Nursing Director, Barbara (Barb) Wadsworth
Vice President Legal, Deborah Datte
Occupational Therapy Director, Eileen Jameson
Secretary To Director Of Material Management, Joanne Jones

Secretary, Desiree Barber
Auditors: WITHUMSMITHBROWN PC MORNSTOWN

LOCATIONS

HQ: ABINGTON MEMORIAL HOSPITAL INC
1200 OLD YORK RD, ABINGTON, PA 190013788
Phone: 215 481-2000

PRODUCTS/OPERATIONS

Selected Facilities
Abington Health Center — Blue Bell Campus (Blue Bell PA)
Abington Health Center — Schilling Campus (Willow Grove PA)
Abington Health Center — Warminster Campus (Warminster PA)
Abington Memorial Hospital (Abington PA)
Abington Physicians at Montgomeryville (North Wales PA)
Lansdale Hospital (Lansdale PA)

COMPETITORS

Albert Einstein Healthcare Network
Aria Health
Crozer-Keystone Health System
Doylestown Hospital
Grand View
Jefferson Health System
Memorial Hospital (PA)
Mercy Health System
Moses Taylor Hospital
North Philadelphia Health System
TUHS
Tenet Healthcare
University of Pennsylvania Health System
Virtua Memorial

HISTORICAL FINANCIALS
Company Type: Private

Income Statement
FYE: June 30

	REVENUE ($ mil.)	NET INCOME ($ mil.)	NET PROFIT MARGIN	EMPLOYEES
06/13	708	20	2.9%	4,018
06/10	783	16	2.1%	—
06/09	704	(36)	—	—
Annual Growth	0.1%	—	—	—

2013 Year-End Financials
Return on assets: 13.1%
Return on equity: 2.9%
Current ratio: 0.40
Cash ($ mil.): 64

ABINGTON RELDAN METALS LLC

LOCATIONS

HQ: ABINGTON RELDAN METALS LLC
550 OLD BORDENTOWN RD, FAIRLESS HILLS, PA 190304510
Phone: 215 335-3200
Web: WWW.ARMETALS.COM

HISTORICAL FINANCIALS
Company Type: Private

Income Statement
FYE: December 31

	REVENUE ($ mil.)	NET INCOME ($ mil.)	NET PROFIT MARGIN	EMPLOYEES
12/10	380	17	4.5%	102
12/09	354	15	4.3%	—
12/08	726	0	—	—
Annual Growth	—	3146.6%	—	—

2010 Year-End Financials
Return on assets: —
Return on equity: 4.5%
Current ratio: 0.90
Cash ($ mil.): 2

ACADIAN AMBULANCE SERVICE INC.

From ground to air and back again Acadian Ambulance Service is all about getting Southerners to the hospital safe and sound. The company provides ground and air medical transportation service to millions of residents in Louisiana Mississippi and Texas. Along with its ground ambulances the company operates a handful of helicopter ambulances through affiliate Metro Aviation. Its many subsidiaries provide a broad array of additional services including telemedicine (remote patient monitoring) paramedic training services chartered transportation and emergency medical services to offshore oil projects. Established in 1971 Acadian Ambulance Service is owned by its employees through a private stock option plan.

Operations

Acadian's fleet includes more than 400 ground ambulances helicopters and fixed-wing aircraft. The company divides its business into six operating segments. Its eponymous ambulance unit includes emergency and non-emergency medical transport on the ground. Air Med Services provides the same thing through the air via six helicopters one Lear jet equipped for internationally flights and two turbo prop jets for cross-country use. It trains emergency medical services personnel from across the country at its National EMS Academy with seven Louisiana locations and two in Texas and offers chartered flights throughout North America through its Executive Aircraft Charter Service. Acadian Monitoring Service provides medical security and fire monitoring for homes and businesses as well as hosted monitoring for security system providers and GPS-based vehicle and asset tracking. Safety Management Systems LLC includes specially trained paramedics (for off-shore oil rigs and other local work) safety technicians and consultants and fire-prevention specialists along with regulatory and compliance training.

Strategy

The company has expanded its operations through the years through occasional acquisitions. In 2013 it purchased Care Ambulance in New Orleans expanding its service in Orleans and Jefferson parishes. In 2013 Acadian's Safety Management Systems lead the company into international operations when it established on office in Alberta Canada. Though it's foreign soil SMS personnel won't be in completely foreign territory as they serve Alberta's oil and gas extraction industry just like they do in Texas and Louisiana.

Mergers and Acquisitions

In 2013 it purchased Care Ambulance in New Orleans expanding its service in Orleans and Jefferson parishes. Building its business in Texas in late 2012 Acadian acquired StarPlus EMS in McKinney. The purchase expanded the firm's presence in North Texas and added 50 employees eight ambulances and three wheelchair vans to Acadian's Texas fleet. In 2011 it purchased Central Texas EMS an emergency and non-emergency transport services provider in three counties as well as Humble-based NorthStar EMS which extended operations in Harris and Montgomery counties.

EXECUTIVES

Executive Vice President And Chief Administrative Officer, John Zuschlag
Vice President Fleet Operations, Justin Back
Senior Vice President Operations, Daniel (Dan) Lennie
Regional Vice President, Mike Burney
Executive Vice President and Chief Administrative Officer, John (Jack) Zuschlag
Vice President Talent Acquisition, Mark Hatfield
Auditors: ERNST & YOUNG LLP NEW ORLEAN

LOCATIONS

HQ: ACADIAN AMBULANCE SERVICE INC.
130 E KALISTE SALOOM RD, LAFAYETTE, LA 705088308
Phone: 337 291-3333
Web: WWW.ACADIAN.COM

PRODUCTS/OPERATIONS

Selected Subsidiaries

Acadian Ambulance Service
Acadian Monitoring Services
Air Med Services LLC
Executive Aircraft Charter Service
National EMS Academy
Safety Management Systems LLC

COMPETITORS

Air Methods	Rural/Metro
CHC Group	Safe Ride Services
Envision Healthcare	Wackenhut Services
LogistiCare	

HISTORICAL FINANCIALS

Company Type: Private

Income Statement

	REVENUE ($ mil.)	NET INCOME ($ mil.)	NET PROFIT MARGIN	EMPLOYEES
12/11	380	9	2.4%	2,385
12/10	358	7	2.0%	—
12/09	1,264	0	0.0%	—
Annual Growth	(45.1%)	21794.4%	—	—

2011 Year-End Financials

Return on assets: 1.2%   Cash ($ mil.): 5
Return on equity: 2.4%
Current ratio: 0.90

ACME TRUCK LINE INC.

Auditors: LAPORTE A PROFESSIONAL ACCOUN

LOCATIONS

HQ: ACME TRUCK LINE INC.
200 WESTBANK EXPY, GRETNA, LA 700535615
Phone: 504 368-2510
Web: WWW.ACMETRUCK.COM

HISTORICAL FINANCIALS

Company Type: Private

Income Statement

FYE: December 31

	REVENUE ($ mil.)	NET INCOME ($ mil.)	NET PROFIT MARGIN	EMPLOYEES
12/13	330	13	4.0%	3,200
12/12	346	19	5.7%	—
12/11	302	18	6.2%	—
12/10	199	0	—	—
Annual Growth	18.3%	—	—	—

2013 Year-End Financials

Return on assets: 14.4%   Cash ($ mil.): 17
Return on equity: 4.0%
Current ratio: 1.50

ACTION CAPITAL CORPORATION

Auditors: MCGREGOR & COMPANY LLP COLUM

LOCATIONS

HQ: ACTION CAPITAL CORPORATION
230 PEACHTREE ST NW # 910, ATLANTA, GA 303031534
Phone: 404 524-3181
Web: WWW.ACTIONCAPITAL.COM

HISTORICAL FINANCIALS

Company Type: Private

Income Statement

FYE: December 31

	ASSETS ($ mil.)	NET INCOME ($ mil.)	INCOME AS % OF ASSETS	EMPLOYEES
12/13	125	6	4.9%	17
12/12	109	5	5.1%	—
12/11	113	3	3.5%	—
12/10	108	0	—	—
Annual Growth	5.2%	—	—	—

ACTIONET INC.

ActioNet provides information technology services such as custom software development computer security assessment network design consulting project management systems integration and design and training. Customers come from industries such as manufacturing retail transportation telecommunications financial services and the public sector. ActioNet was founded in 1998 by president and CEO Ashley Chen. Key customers have included Qwest the Department of Energy and the Department of Labor.

Geographic Reach

ActioNet is based in Vienna Virginia and has offices in the Washington D.C. where many of its federal agency clients are as well as more far flung locations such as New Orleans Honolulu and Guam. The company has employees in 35 states.

Strategy

Part of ActioNet's strategy is to be where the action in. When your client include federal agencies such as U.S. Department of Commerce Department of Defense Department of Energy Depart-

ment of Transportation and several others that means being in and around the Beltway. The company has new offices in Washington D.C. and in Tysons Corner Virginia.

ActioNet partners with a range of technology companies to offer complementary and comprehensive IT services to clients. Its primary partners are BMC Microsoft Terremark Hewlett-Packard ServiceNow Amazon Symantec and Cisco Systems.

EXECUTIVES

Senior Vice President Strategic Programs, Michael L Genebach
V Pres, Brian J Orourke
Vice President Civilian Programs, Anthony R Adoremos
Jr Vice President Global Operations, Gerald (Jerry) Greer
Vice President of Health Services, David (Dave) Collignon
Vice President of Applied Innovation, Tom Boyce

LOCATIONS

HQ: ACTIONET INC.
2600 PARK TWR DR STE 1000, VIENNA, VA 22180
Phone: 703 204-0090
Web: WWW.ACTIONET.COM

COMPETITORS

Amadeus Consulting	Leidos
CACI International	Lockheed Martin
Computer Sciences Corp.	ManTech
HP Enterprise Services	Northrop Grumman
IBM Global Services	Unisys

HISTORICAL FINANCIALS

Company Type: Private

Income Statement

FYE: December 31

	REVENUE ($ mil.)	NET INCOME ($ mil.)	NET PROFIT MARGIN	EMPLOYEES
12/13	298	23	8.0%	1,352
12/08	23	3	13.4%	—
12/07	15	1	11.9%	—
12/06	1,392	0	—	—
Annual Growth	(19.7%)	—	—	—

2013 Year-End Financials

Return on assets: —   Cash ($ mil.): 22
Return on equity: 8.0%
Current ratio: 2.30

ACTIONTEC ELECTRONICS INC.

Actiontec Electronics aims to broaden your approach to networking. The company makes gateways routers modems and other broadband connection equipment used to create wireless home networks. Its fiber optic routers allow broadband television and other content to be distributed to multiple devices throughout the home over coaxial cables. Actiontec sells its equipment through partnerships with broadband service providers and equipment makers such as Qwest Verizon Cisco and Entropic. It also sells directly through retailers including Amazon.com Best Buy and Wal-Mart.

Geographic Reach

The company's US offices are located in Sunnyvale California and Colorado Springs Colorado.

Actiontec also has international offices in Shanghai China and Taipei Taiwan.

Operations

Actiontec's products including Gigabit Ethernet fiber routers high speed bonded VDSL2 gateways 4G LTE routers DSL modems and whole-home networking solutions are uses by some of North America's largest telecom carriers.

Sales and Marketing

Major customers include Micronics Apple Sasktel BellAliant Century Link and Telus.

Strategy

The company has strategically positioned itself to capitalize on the proliferation of wireless home networks and entertainment devices offering a product portfolio that encompasses IP-based video services DSL modems wireless networking devices and network adapters. Actiontec's zControl home automation controller lets the user manage electronics such as lights thermostats and garage door openers from an Internet-enabled computer mobile phone or TV.

In 2013 Actiontec launched its first product in its Whole Home Wireless portfolio —WCB3000 Wi-Fi Wireless Network Adapter using MoCA. It also introduced the first wireless display receiver for Intel WiDi 4.1 for 4th Generation Intel Core Processor Based Systems enabling users with an Intel WiDi or Miracast-certified device to beam their screens to their big screen HDTV in realtime.

That year the company's ScreenBeam Pro was chosen by Microsoft as a premier wireless display receiver for Windows 8.1 devices.

In 2012 Actiontec rolled out its Multi-band MoCA (Multimedia over Coax) Network Adapter that supports all three pay TV segments in the same device. The adapter leverages MoCA technology to deliver robust and reliable Pay-TV services to every corner of the home.

Company Background

The company was founded by CEO Dean Chang in 1993.

EXECUTIVES

Vice President, Chuang Li

LOCATIONS

HQ: ACTIONTEC ELECTRONICS INC.
760 N MARY AVE, SUNNYVALE, CA 940852908
Phone: 408 752-7700
Web: WWW.ACTIONTEC.COM

PRODUCTS/OPERATIONS

Selected Products
Fiber Routers
VDSL2 Modem Routers
DSL Modem Routers
Wireless Display
Wireless Video Networking
Wireless Data Networking
Wireless Network Extenders
MoCA Network Adapters
Powerline Network Kits
Home Services

COMPETITORS

Belkin	NETGEAR
Buffalo Technology	SMC Networks
D-Link	ZyXEL Communications

HISTORICAL FINANCIALS

Company Type: Private

Income Statement

FYE: December 31

	REVENUE ($ mil.)	NET INCOME ($ mil.)	NET PROFIT MARGIN	EMPLOYEES
12/10	162	1	1.1%	350
12/07	183	0	—	—
12/06	1,449	0	—	—
Annual Growth	—	225.5%	—	—

2010 Year-End Financials

Return on assets: 31.6% Cash ($ mil.): 23
Return on equity: 1.1%
Current ratio: 0.70

ADAC PLASTICS INC.

ADAC Plastics which does business as ADAC Automotive has a handle on what automakers need. The company (privately owned by the Teets and Hungerford families) supplies automakers and tier 1 suppliers worldwide with door handles and components exterior trim and marker lighting. Other products include cowl vent grilles and fuel filler doors. Services provided by ADAC Automotive include design molding painting and assembly. Its ADAC Technologies subsidiary is a leading supplier of plastic moldings subassemblies and decorative finishes. It is part of the VAST (Vehicle Access Systems Technology) Alliance along with fellow automotive suppliers STRATTEC SECURITY and WITTE Automotive of Velbert Germany.

Geographic Reach

ADAC Plastics operates seven facilities in Michigan and in Brazil China Germany Japan and Korea. The VAST marketing alliance owns and operates manufacturing facilities in the US Mexico Germany the Czech Republic Brazil Japan and Korea.

Operations

ADAC Plastics manufactures products that include latching systems lock sets door handle components exterior trim and lighting products.

Sales and Marketing

Major customers include Chrysler Ford General Motors Honda and Nissan among others.

Strategy

Responding to the resurgence of the US auto manufacturing industry in 2013 ADAC Plastics completed a $18 million expansion of its Muskegon paint facility.

With this new upgrade complete the company announced plans to decommission its painting facility in the Port City Industrial Park by the end of 2014.

Company Background

During the late-2000's economic downturn of the automotive industry in the US VAST helped mitigate the losses for ADAC Plastics by generating revenues outside of North America especially in developing vehicle manufacturing markets such as Asia and South America.

The company started as A-Line Plastics in 1972. It became ADAC Plastics in 1975.

EXECUTIVES

Treasurer, Bill Powers
Auditors: CROWE HORWATH LLP GRAND RAPID

LOCATIONS

HQ: ADAC PLASTICS INC.
5920 TAHOE DR SE, GRAND RAPIDS, MI 495467123
Phone: 616 957-0311
Web: WWW.ADACPLASTICS.COM

PRODUCTS/OPERATIONS

Selected Products
Access Systems
Door handles (interior and exterior)
Liftgate handles
Tailgate handles
Trunk release handles
Lighting
Fog lights
Interior lighting
License lamps
Reflectors
Side markers
Turn signals
Trim
Antenna modules
Cowl vent grilles
Fuel filler doors
License modules

COMPETITORS

Cascade Engineering	Magna International
Engineering Solid Solutions	North American Lighting
Grote Industries	Peterson Manufacturing
Hella	SportPaint
Johnson Controls	Truck-Lite
Lear Corp	

HISTORICAL FINANCIALS

Company Type: Private

Income Statement

FYE: December 31

	REVENUE ($ mil.)	NET INCOME ($ mil.)	NET PROFIT MARGIN	EMPLOYEES
12/12	226	7	3.2%	800
12/07	177	25	14.6%	—
12/06	177	3	2.2%	—
12/05	1,820	0	—	—
Annual Growth	—	—	—	—

2012 Year-End Financials

Return on assets: 7.5% Cash ($ mil.): —
Return on equity: 3.2%
Current ratio: 1.00

ADELPHI UNIVERSITY

It may not house an oracle but Adelphi University hopes to provide answers to students' questions about their future. Founded in 1896 the university has about 7700 students enrolled at its four campuses located in New York (Garden City Hauppage Manhattan and the Hudson Valley). Adelphi University a private institution offers graduate undergraduate and continuing education programs in areas including business management education nursing and social work. Its Swirbul Library contains about 600000 books and documents and 33000 audiovisual materials. The school counts Nextel co-founder Brian McAuley US Chamber of Commerce CEO Thomas Donahue and author Alice Hoffman among its alumni.

Operations

Arts and Sciences and Nursing and the two most popular degree fields at Adelphi. Average annual tuition is about $32000 and the school has an impressive student to teacher ratio of 10 to 1.

Geographic Reach

Students from 43 states and 45 nations attend Adelphi.

Strategy

Given the popularity of its nursing programs and continued growth in the health care field Adelphi is expanding both it physical space for nursing with a new 100000-square-foot College of Nursing and Public Health building and its degrees by adding a Master of Science in Healthcare Informatics online degree in 2013.

Company Background

Adelphi University began in 1863 as the Adelphi Academy a private prep school in Brooklyn.

EXECUTIVES

Assistant Vice President, Lisa Araujo
Vice President For Enrollment Management, Lauren Mounty
Vice President Of Administration, Julianna Claase
Vice President For Communications, Christian Vaupel
Assistant Secretary To The Board Of Trustees, Mary Aldridge
Co Chairman, Andrew (Andy) Lackmann
Board Member, Henry Greenberg
Auditors: GRANT THORNTON LLP MELVILLE

LOCATIONS

HQ: ADELPHI UNIVERSITY
1 S AVE LVH 310 310 LVH, GARDEN CITY, NY 11530
Phone: 516 877-3000
Web: WWW.LIBRARIES.ADELPHI.EDU

PRODUCTS/OPERATIONS

Schools & Colleges
College of Arts and Sciences
Gordon F. Derner Institute of Advanced Psychological Studies
Honors College
School of Business
School of Education
School of Nursing and Public Health
School of Social Work
University College

HISTORICAL FINANCIALS

Company Type: Private

Income Statement   FYE: August 31

	REVENUE ($ mil.)	NET INCOME ($ mil.)	NET PROFIT MARGIN	EMPLOYEES
08/14	210	23	11.1%	1,400
08/13	195	13	7.0%	—
08/10	175	13	7.4%	—
08/09	157	0	—	—
Annual Growth	6.0%			

2014 Year-End Financials

Return on assets: 9.4%   Cash ($ mil.): 10
Return on equity: 11.1%
Current ratio: —

ADENA HEALTH SYSTEM

Adena Health System hopes to be an Eden for those seeking health care. The system serves the residents of some 10 counties in southern and central Ohio centered on the city of Chillicothe. Its main facility is the 261-bed Adena Regional Medical Center which provides general medical and surgical care as well as specialty care in a number of areas including cardiology women's health oncology and rehabilitation. The health system also features two smaller hospitals outpatient clinics surgery centers and a counseling center among other facilities. The history of the Adena Health System goes back to 1895 when a group of local women established an emergency hospital in the wake of a fatal train wreck.

Operations

Adena Health System facilities include three hospitals (located in Chillicothe Waverly and Greenfield) and five regional clinics with a total of 311 beds. Other facilities include Adena Cancer Center Adena Home Care and Hospice and Adena Rehabilitation and Wellness Center.

Geographic Reach

Adena Health caters to the Ohio communities of Chillicothe Circleville Greenfield Jackson Oak Hill Pike Piketon Washington Court House and Waverly.

Financial Performance

In 2013 the system increased its revenue by 6% to $1 billion (over $976 million in 2013) due to an increase in bills submitted to Medicare Medicaid individuals and insurance providers.

Strategy

Like most hospital systems Adena Health is always looking to expand the services it offers patients and add locations. In 2014 it opened a new occupational health facility and an inpatient palliative care unit at its Adena Regional Medical Center.

EXECUTIVES

President and CEO, Mark H. Shuter, age 55
Interim CFO, Dawn Bennett Johnson
Chief Medical Officer, John Fortney
Chief Nursing Officer, Judith (Judi) Henson
Chief Strategic Information Officer, Linn Weimer
Division Chair WomenÂ's and ChildrenÂ's, Sathish Jetty
VP Adena Regional Medical Center, Nick Alexander
VP Adena Medical Group, Michael Glanzman
COO, Eric Cecava
Rph, Mark Unger
Medical Director, Kort M Gronbach
Operating Room Director, Jeff Collins
Director Of Radiology Services, Dave Zanni
Vice President, Peggy Depugh-landrum
Chairman, David Strickland
Vice Chairman, Tom White
Treas, Tony Colby

LOCATIONS

HQ: ADENA HEALTH SYSTEM
272 HOSPITAL RD, CHILLICOTHE, OH 456019031
Phone: 740 779-7360
Web: WWW.ADENA.ORG

PRODUCTS/OPERATIONS

Selected Services
Behavioral Health
Colon and Rectal Services
Endocrinology and Diabetes
Endoscopy Home Care
Hospitalist Laboratory
Occupational Health
Pain Management
Radiology
Rehabilitation Services
Sleep Urology
Surgery and Procedures
Wound Care

Selected Facilities
Adena Counseling Center (Chillicothe)
Adena Health Center - Jackson
Adena Health Center - Oak Hill
Adena Health Center - Waverly
Adena Health Center - Western Avenue (Chillicothe)
Adena Health Pavilion (Chillicothe)
Adena Home Care Services (Chillicothe)
Adena Pike Medical Center (Waverly)
Adena Medical Office Building (Chillicothe)
Adena Regional Medical Center (Chillicothe)
Adena Rehabilitation & Wellness Center (Chillicothe)
Adena Urgent Care Centers (Chillicothe and Waverly)
Greenfield Area Medical Center

COMPETITORS

Catholic Health Initiatives
Fairfield Medical Center
Licking Memorial Health Systems
Mercy Health (OH)
Mount Carmel Health
Nationwide Children's Hospital
OhioHealth

HISTORICAL FINANCIALS

Company Type: Private

Income Statement   FYE: December 31

	REVENUE ($ mil.)	NET INCOME ($ mil.)	NET PROFIT MARGIN	EMPLOYEES
12/09	315	15	5.0%	2,700
12/07	252	9	3.8%	—
12/06	231	16	7.2%	—
12/05	207	0	—	—
Annual Growth	11.1%			

2009 Year-End Financials

Return on assets: —   Cash ($ mil.): 70
Return on equity: 5.0%
Current ratio: 0.50

ADVANTAGE ELECTRIC SERVICES LLC

Auditors: PLANTE & MORAN PLLC TRAVERSE

LOCATIONS

HQ: ADVANTAGE ELECTRIC SERVICES LLC
2238 TRAVERSEFIELD DR, TRAVERSE CITY, MI 496869251
Phone: 231 929-4900
Web: WWW.ADVANTAGEMI.COM

HISTORICAL FINANCIALS

Company Type: Private

Income Statement   FYE: December 31

	REVENUE ($ mil.)	NET INCOME ($ mil.)	NET PROFIT MARGIN	EMPLOYEES
12/12	5,240	329	6.3%	35
12/08	10	1	10.1%	—
12/06	13	1	7.9%	—
12/05	818	0	—	—
Annual Growth	—	—	—	—

2012 Year-End Financials

Return on assets: 5.0%   Cash ($ mil.): 1,320
Return on equity: 6.3%
Current ratio: 3.00

ADVOCATE HEALTH AND HOSPITALS CORPORATION

LOCATIONS

HQ: ADVOCATE HEALTH AND HOSPITALS CORPORATION
3975 HIGHLAND AVE, DOWNERS GROVE, IL 605151515
Phone: 630 572-9393
Web: WWW.ADVOCATEHEALTH.COM

HISTORICAL FINANCIALS
Company Type: Private

Income Statement
FYE: December 31

	REVENUE ($ mil.)	NET INCOME ($ mil.)	NET PROFIT MARGIN	EMPLOYEES
12/12	3,645	419	11.5%	4,110
12/01	2,014	114	5.7%	—
Annual Growth	5.5%	12.5%	—	—

2012 Year-End Financials
Return on assets: 15.8% Cash ($ mil.): 271
Return on equity: 11.5%
Current ratio: 0.40

ADVOCATE HEALTH AND HOSPITALS CORPORATION

Advocate Lutheran General Hospital also known simply as Lutheran General provides acute and long-term medical and surgical care to the residents of Park Ridge Illinois and the surrounding northern suburban Chicago area. As one of the largest hospitals in the region Lutheran General boasts nearly 640 beds and a Level I trauma center. Its operations also include a complete children's hospital and pediatric critical care center. Lutheran General serves as a teaching hospital and its specialized programs include oncology cardiology women's health emergency medicine and hospice care. Lutheran General is part of the Advocate Health Care network.

Geographic Reach

The hospital system is the primary academic referral hospital for northwest Chicago and north Greater Chicago.

Operations

Lutheran General the sixth largest hospital in the Chicago area is a not-for-profit faith-based organization related to the Evangelical Lutheran Church in America and the United Church of Christ. With some 1150 physicians representing more than 50 specialties and subspecialties Advocate Lutheran General saw 62500 patients in its emergency department in 2012.

That year the company reported more than 29000 admissions 19000 surgeries and more than 4000 births.

Strategy

Increase its services to meet specific demographics in 2012 Lutheran General opened a new South Asian Cardiovascular Center in the Midwest; it also launched Expressions a program aimed at helping seniors in the early stages of Alzheimer's disease.

That year thee hospital introduced a new Pet Therapy program to the Adult Oncology unit. It also launched of its neuroendovascular program to expand Lutheran General's acute stroke care to provide advanced acute stroke care to patients throughout the northern Chicago area.

Company Background

Lutheran General serves those who live in the northern suburban Chicago area specifically Park Ridge Illinois.

The hospital was founded in 1897.

EXECUTIVES

Vice President Patient Care Services CNE, Barb Weber
Secretary Martha Lehman cordts Rowena Brown evans, Bridget Moriarity

LOCATIONS

HQ: ADVOCATE HEALTH AND HOSPITALS CORPORATION
1775 DEMPSTER ST, PARK RIDGE, IL 600681143
Phone: 847 723-6105
Web: WWW.ADVOCATEHEALTH.COM

Selected Hospitals
Advocate BroMenn Medical Center
Advocate Children's Hospital - Oak Lawn
Advocate Children's Hospital - Park Ridge
Advocate Christ Center for Breast Care
Advocate Christ Medical Center
Advocate Christ Medical Center - Physical Rehabilitation Center Center for Hearing and Sleep Center
Advocate Christ Outpatient Center
  Advocate C
Advocate Condell Medical Center
Advocate Eureka Hospital
Advocate Good Samaritan Hospital
Advocate Good Shepherd Hospital
Advocate Illinois Masonic Medical Center
Advocate Lutheran General Hospital
Advocate South Suburban Hospital
Advocate Trinity Hospital

PRODUCTS/OPERATIONS

Selected Services
Adult Day Hospital
Adult Down Syndrome Center
Anticoagulation Center
Behavioral Health
Caldwell Breast Center
Cancer Care
Center for Fetal Care
Children's Services
The Comprehensive Continence Center
Emergency Services
Heart and Vascular
Hyperbaric Treatment
Interventional Radiology
Joint Reconstruction & Replacement
Nutrition Services Opthamology
Outpatient Testing Prep Instructions
Pain Management Center
Rehabilitation
Senior Services
Sleep Disorders
Surgical Services
The Center for Robotic Surgery
Women's Services
Wound Care

COMPETITORS

Children's Hopsital of Chicago
Gottleib Memorial Hospital
NorthShore University HealthSystem
Northwest Community Healthcare
Northwestern Lake Forest Hospital
Northwestern Memorial HealthCare
Rush System for Health
University of Chicago Medical Center

HISTORICAL FINANCIALS
Company Type: Private

Income Statement
FYE: December 31

	REVENUE ($ mil.)	NET INCOME ($ mil.)	NET PROFIT MARGIN	EMPLOYEES
12/12	692	102	14.8%	4,818
12/02	2,603	(6)	—	—
Annual Growth	(12.4%)	—	—	—

2012 Year-End Financials
Return on assets: 25.7% Cash ($ mil.): 271
Return on equity: 14.8%
Current ratio: 0.70

AEROTEK INC.

Aerotek a unit of staffing powerhouse Allegis Group offers commercial and technical staffing services throughout North America. Through several divisions Aerotek staffs workers such as engineers mechanics scientists and technical professionals as well as administrative staff members general laborers and tradespeople. The company also provides training and support services. Along with aerospace auto and engineering companies Aerotek's clients include companies from the construction energy manufacturing health care and finance industries.

Geographic Reach

The company has more than 200 office locations across the US Canada Europe (including the UK Germany and the Netherlands) and Singapore.

Strategy

Aerotek has expanded its operations over the years through organic growth and acquisitions especially in niche markets such as the biotechnology health care clinical research chemical and plastics sectors. Despite the economic downturn demand within these industries has been consistent along with engineering giving Aerotek some continuity during the recession. Aerotek has also widened its client focus to include the niche market of minority and woman-owned companies.

EXECUTIVES

VP Technical and Professional Services, Mark Cooper
President, Todd M. Mohr
CFO, Thomas B. (Tom) Kelly
SVP Operations, John Flanigan
Regional VP Northeast, John Rudy
Regional VP Midwest, Marty Schager
Regional VP Central, Mike Hansen
Regional VP West, Tony Bartolucci
Regional VP Northwest, Brooks Wells
VP Canada, Bryan Toffey
Regional VP Southwest, Brad Kennedy
Regional VP Mid-Atlantic, Jeff Colvin
Regional VP Southeast, Greg Jones
Vice President of Human Resources, Tanya Axenson
Auditors: PRICEWATERHOUSECOOPERS LLP B

LOCATIONS

HQ: AEROTEK INC.
7301 PARKWAY DR, HANOVER, MD 210761159
Phone: 410 694-5100
Web: WWW.AEROTEK.COM

PRODUCTS/OPERATIONS

Selected Industries
Accounting and Finance

Administrative
Aerospace & Defense
Architecture
Automotive
Aviation
Call Center
Clinical Research
Construction
Energy
Engineering
Environmental
Labor
Manufacturing
Mortgage
Scientific

COMPETITORS

AMN Healthcare	MSX International
Adecco	ManpowerGroup
Bryant Bureau	On Assignment
CDI	Pinnacle Staffing
COMFORCE	Randstad Holding
Kelly Services	Robert Half
Kforce	

HISTORICAL FINANCIALS

Company Type: Private

Income Statement

FYE: December 31

	REVENUE ($ mil.)	NET INCOME ($ mil.)	NET PROFIT MARGIN	EMPLOYEES
12/13	5,268	0	—	4,200
12/12	5,119	307	6.0%	—
12/11	4,481	226	5.0%	—
12/10	3,446	0	—	—
Annual Growth	15.2%	—	—	—

2013 Year-End Financials

Return on assets: 1.2% Cash ($ mil.): 8
Return on equity: —
Current ratio: 3.20

AFFILIATED FOODS MIDWEST COOPERATIVE INC.

Affiliated Foods Midwest Cooperative is a wholesale food distribution cooperative that supplies more than 800 independent grocers in some 15 states in the Midwest. From its handful of distribution centers in Kansas Nebraska and Wisconsin the co-op distributes fresh produce meats deli items baked goods dairy products and frozen foods as well as general merchandise and equipment. It distributes goods under the Shurfine brand (from Topco Associates) and IGA labels. Additionally Affiliated Foods Midwest provides marketing merchandising and warehousing support services for its members. The cooperative was formed in 1931 to make wholesale purchases for a group of retailers in Nebraska.

Geographic Reach

Norfolk Nebraska-based Affiliated Foods Midwest Cooperative has distribution centers in Norfolk Elwood Kansas and Kenosha Wisconsin. It serves customers in 15 states across the Midwest.

Financial Performance

Affiliated Foods Midwest rang up an estimated $1.6 billion in sales in fiscal 2013 (ended June).

EXECUTIVES

Vice President Of Information Technology, Linda Mattson
Vice President Of Sales And Marketing, Angie McLean
Senior Vice President Sales, Louis Stinebaugh
Vice President Information Technology, Mattson Linda
Vice President, Jeannie Wesemann
Senior Vice President Credit Investigations, Mike Ruge
Vice President, Timothy (Tim) Goetsch
Auditors: BKD LLP LINCOLN NEBRASKA

LOCATIONS

HQ: AFFILIATED FOODS MIDWEST COOPERATIVE INC.
  1301 W OMAHA AVE, NORFOLK, NE 687015872
Phone: 402 371-0555
Web: WWW.AFMIDWEST.COM

PRODUCTS/OPERATIONS

Selected Private-Label Brands
CharKing
ChuckWagon (pet food)
Clear Value
Cow Belle Creamery (ice cream)
Domestix (household products)
Full Circle (organic natural products)
IGA
PAWS Premium (pet products)
Shurfine
TopCare (OTC drugs health and beauty)
Valu Time
Wide Awake Coffee Co. (coffee)
World Classics Trading Company

COMPETITORS

Associated Wholesale Grocers	Kroger
C&S Wholesale	McLane
Central Grocers	SUPERVALU
Certco	Wal-Mart
Dearborn Wholesale Grocers	

HISTORICAL FINANCIALS

Company Type: Private

Income Statement

FYE: June 28

	REVENUE ($ mil.)	NET INCOME ($ mil.)	NET PROFIT MARGIN	EMPLOYEES
06/14	1,477	2	0.2%	850
06/13	1,391	2	0.2%	—
06/12	1,486	2	0.2%	—
06/11	1,356	0	—	—
Annual Growth	2.9%	—	—	—

2014 Year-End Financials

Return on assets: 3.0% Cash ($ mil.): 19
Return on equity: 0.2%
Current ratio: 0.40

AG GEORGIA FARM CREDIT

Auditors: PRICEWATERHOUSECOOPERS LLP FO

LOCATIONS

HQ: AG GEORGIA FARM CREDIT
  468 PERRY PKWY, PERRY, GA 310692861
Phone: 478 987-8300
Web: WWW.AGGEORGIA.COM

HISTORICAL FINANCIALS

Company Type: Private

Income Statement

FYE: December 31

	ASSETS ($ mil.)	NET INCOME ($ mil.)	INCOME AS % OF ASSETS	EMPLOYEES
12/11	1,135	7	0.7%	116
12/10	1,177	19	1.7%	—
12/09	1,122	18	1.7%	—
12/08	1,070	0		—
Annual Growth	2.0%	—	—	—

2011 Year-End Financials

Return on assets: — Sales ($ mil.): 71
Return on equity: 10.6%

AGMARK LLC

Auditors: LINDBURG VOGEL PIERCE FARIS H

LOCATIONS

HQ: AGMARK LLC
  118 W MAIN ST, BELOIT, KS 674202745
Phone: 785 738-9641
Web: WWW.FARMWAYCOOP.COM

HISTORICAL FINANCIALS

Company Type: Private

Income Statement

FYE: January 31

	REVENUE ($ mil.)	NET INCOME ($ mil.)	NET PROFIT MARGIN	EMPLOYEES
01/14	399	20	5.1%	27
01/13	442	18	4.1%	—
01/12	489	25	5.2%	—
01/10	329	0	—	—
Annual Growth	4.9%	—	—	—

2014 Year-End Financials

Return on assets: — Cash ($ mil.): —
Return on equity: 5.1%
Current ratio: 0.10

AGRI-AFC LLC

Auditors: WEAR HOWELLSTRICKLAND QUINN

LOCATIONS

HQ: AGRI-AFC LLC
  121 SOMERVILLE RD NE, DECATUR, AL 356012659
Phone: 256 560-2848
Web: WWW.AGRI-AFC.COM

HISTORICAL FINANCIALS

Company Type: Private

Income Statement

FYE: July 31

	REVENUE ($ mil.)	NET INCOME ($ mil.)	NET PROFIT MARGIN	EMPLOYEES
07/14	343	13	3.8%	165
07/13	328	10	3.1%	—
07/11	281	8	2.9%	—
07/10	224	0	—	—
Annual Growth	11.2%	—	—	—

2014 Year-End Financials

Return on assets: —
Return on equity: 3.8%
Current ratio: 0.70

Cash ($ mil.): —

AGSOUTH FARM CREDIT ACA

Auditors: PRICEWATERHOUSECOOPERS LLP FO

LOCATIONS

HQ: AGSOUTH FARM CREDIT ACA
26 S MAIN ST, STATESBORO, GA 304585256
Phone: 912 764-9091
Web: WWW.AGSOUTHFC.COM

HISTORICAL FINANCIALS

Company Type: Private

Income Statement

FYE: December 31

	ASSETS ($ mil.)	NET INCOME ($ mil.)	INCOME AS % OF ASSETS	EMPLOYEES
12/13	1,594	49	3.1%	226
12/12	1,583	42	2.7%	—
12/11	1,599	33	2.1%	—
12/10	1,639	0	—	—
Annual Growth	(0.9%)	—	—	—

2013 Year-End Financials

Return on assets: —
Return on equity: 56.0%

Sales ($ mil.): 89

AHS HOSPITAL CORP.

Auditors: PRICEWATERHOUSECOOPERS LLP F

LOCATIONS

HQ: AHS HOSPITAL CORP.
475 SOUTH ST, MORRISTOWN, NJ 079606459
Phone: 973 660-3100
Web: WWW.ATLANTICHEALTH.ORG

HISTORICAL FINANCIALS

Company Type: Private

Income Statement

FYE: December 31

	REVENUE ($ mil.)	NET INCOME ($ mil.)	NET PROFIT MARGIN	EMPLOYEES
12/13	1,624	291	18.0%	7,300
12/12	1,498	140	9.4%	—
12/08	637	(138)	—	—
12/07	960	0	—	—
Annual Growth	9.2%	—	—	—

2013 Year-End Financials

Return on assets: —
Return on equity: 18.0%
Current ratio: 1.60

Cash ($ mil.): 218

AKAL SECURITY INC.

Unarmed? Akal Security provides contract security guard services for customers in the US and abroad. Akal's Judicial Security division specializes in security services for protecting federal courthouses in 40 states. It also transports prisoners and illegal aliens for homeland security efforts. In addition Akal supplies security officers for detention facilities and military installations and offers electronic security surveillance and access control system design installation and integration. The company serves federal agencies as well as commercial clients and state and local government facilities. Clients have included the US Army the Department of Homeland Security the US Marshals Service and NASA.

Since its startup in 1980 funded by a $1200 loan from a co-founder Akal Security has expanded its footprint from serving businesses and communities in New Mexico to clients in Arizona California Louisiana and Texas. Its international arm protects both US government and multinational corporate officials in some 20 countries worldwide.

Alak's growth builds upon a series of progressively significant contracts. Among them the company furnishes security to 14 NASA locations including White Sands Test Facility (near Las Cruces New Mexico) the Kennedy and Johnson Space Centers and NASA headquarters in Washington D.C. The company's Homeland Security Division is contracted by the federal Justice Prisoner and Alien Transportation Systems (JPATS). In a similar vein Alak's air security officers support the air fleet of the US Marshals Service within the Bureau of Immigration and Customs Enforcement.

Success however has also spurred a redeployment of resources from non-core operations. In early 2009 the company sold its Hawaiian commercial business to Stockholm security giant Securitas for about $2 million. Some 300 employees in Hawaii left Akal for Securitas Security Services USA. The sale excluded Akal's federal government contracts and commercial business outside of Hawaii.

The company was founded by members of a Sikh community. Sikhism with its roots in India is traditionally seen as the religion of warriors protecting those who cannot defend themselves. The word akal meaning timeless and immortal is integral to Sikh tradition.

EXECUTIVES

Vice President Of Operations, Brian Beckwith
Vice President of Information Technology and Data Systems, Dave Welliver
Auditors: PULASKOS CPAS PC ALBUQUERQUE

LOCATIONS

HQ: AKAL SECURITY INC.
7 INFINITY LOOP, ESPANOLA, NM 875326737
Phone: 505 753-7832
Web: WWW.AKALSECURITY.COM

PRODUCTS/OPERATIONS

Selected Services

Aviation security services (airport programs)
Investigations (US and international corporate clients)
Personal protection (US corporate executives)
Security officer services (guarding programs)
Security systems integration (design installation and integration of electronic security surveillance and access control systems)
Security training programs (Akal Training Academy)
Third country national personnel (trained former military personnel from Asia and Africa)

COMPETITORS

AlliedBarton Security
Command Security
D&D Security Training
Guardsmark
Securitas Security Services North America
Tyco Fire & Security
Walden Security

HISTORICAL FINANCIALS

Company Type: Private

Income Statement

FYE: December 31

	REVENUE ($ mil.)	NET INCOME ($ mil.)	NET PROFIT MARGIN	EMPLOYEES
12/11	461	3	0.8%	15,000
12/10	466	2	0.5%	—
12/09	698	0	0.0%	—
Annual Growth	(18.7%)	29351.6%	—	—

2011 Year-End Financials

Return on assets: 0.4%
Return on equity: 0.8%
Current ratio: 0.90

Cash ($ mil.): —

ALABAMA FARMERS COOPERATIVE INC.

Alabama Farmers Cooperative (AFC) provides farmers in the Yellowhammer state with a range of agricultural supplies and services. The co-op offers animal feed crop fertilizer and home-gardening items such as seed and hand tools as well as grain storage and hardware. AFC comprises 37 member associations including about 90 retail locations. Expanding through joint ventures it boasts one of the largest farmer-owned agriculture businesses in the southeastern US. Its Bonnie Plants is one of the biggest suppliers of vegetable and herb plants for home gardeners. BioLogic makes forage products for wild game. AFC supplies the foodservice industry with fresh fish through its SouthFresh Farms catfish farm.

Geographic Reach

AFC based in Alabama serves the southeastern US.

Operations

The cooperative operates through more than half a dozen divisions including Feed Farm & Home; Universal Seed & Supply/ECS; Bonnie Plants; BioLogic/Mossy Oak; Agri-AFC LLC; and SouthFresh Farms.

It has about 90 retail outlets located in Florida Georgia Alabama and Mississippi. Among them more than 60 are co-op stores and the balance operates under the Agri-AFC banner name.

Sales and Marketing

AFC serves customers through a network of sales representatives.

Financial Performance

AFC has been ranked as one of Alabama's top 25 privately owned companies boasting sales totaling more than $450 million.

Company Background

Founded in 1936 the co-op was originally known as the Tennessee Valley Fertilizer Cooperative. It changed its name in 1960 to reflect its statewide reach.

EXECUTIVES

Vice President of Grain, John (Jack) Gamble

LOCATIONS

HQ: ALABAMA FARMERS COOPERATIVE INC.
121 SOMERVILLE RD NE, DECATUR, AL 356012659
Phone: 256 353-6843
Web: WWW.ALAFARM.COM

PRODUCTS/OPERATIONS

Selected Divisions
Agri-AFC LLC
BioLogic/Mossy Oak
Bonnie Plants
Feed Farm & Home
SouthFresh Farms
Universal Seed & Supply/ECS

COMPETITORS

Ag Processing Inc.	Monrovia Nursery
Andersons	Orscheln Farm and Home
CHS	Scoular
Color Spot Nurseries	Southern States
DeBruce Grain	Tennessee Farmers
Farmers Cooperative	Co-op
Company	Watonwan Farm Service
GROWMARK	West Central Co-op
Heartland Co-op	

HISTORICAL FINANCIALS

Company Type: Private

Income Statement   FYE: July 31

	REVENUE ($ mil.)	NET INCOME ($ mil.)	NET PROFIT MARGIN	EMPLOYEES
07/13	592	17	2.9%	3,000
07/11	450	9	2.0%	—
07/10	400	8	2.0%	—
07/09	393	0	—	—
Annual Growth 10.8%				—

2013 Year-End Financials

Return on assets: 5.3%   Cash ($ mil.): 4
Return on equity: 2.9%
Current ratio: 0.70

ALASKA NATIVE TRIBAL HEALTH CONSORTIUM

The Alaska Native Tribal Health Consortium (ANTHC) brings good health to Alaska Natives. The company is a not-for-profit statewide health care organization managed by regional tribal governments and their respective regional health organizations. The organization connects disparate medical providers by providing a range of health programs and services including community health care public health advocacy and education initiatives health research (including water and sanitation) and medical supply distribution. The 150-bed Alaska Native Medical Center (ANMC) a native-owned hospital is jointly managed by ANTHC and Southcentral Foundation a regional health corporation based in the Cook Inlet region.

Geographic Reach

ANTHC and ANMC are located in Anchorage Alaska. The organization provides services throughout the state.

Operations

ANMC's services are reserved primarily for Alaska Native Tribal groups with the exception of its Urgent Care centers and Emergency Room.

(Emergency rooms are compelled to take patients of all types under US fair care guidelines.) The hospital handles about 8000 patient admissions each year as well as 300000 outpatient and 57000 emergency room visits. It also conducts some 11000 surgeries and 1600 births. ANMC has about 100 physicians.

The organization's primary mission is to improve the health of Alaska natives through health sanitation technology and advocacy services. It conducts a number of community outreach programs and it works to create a continuum of care for its members so they can move smoothly through the health care process (including initial specialist and follow-up care visits). The hospital is the regional hub of that health care continuum offering general and specialist care in a range of fields. ANTHC also operates outpatient care centers and it operates an extensive telemedicine network (allow providers to care for and consult with patients in outlying areas).

ANTHC provides administrative support to Alaska's Tribal health groups and it supports state legislative efforts such as the reauthorization of the Indian Health Care Improvement Act. The consortium formed in 1997 also works to improve the Alaskan health system by participating in strategic summit meetings and sponsoring electronic health record initiatives.

Financial Performance

The company's 2014 revenues stood at $643 million about 33% of which came from patient revenues. Other major operating segments include compact revenue (25% of sales) and grant and project income (17%).

Strategy

Infrastructure and service expansions are a key means of growth for ANTHC.

In 2015 ANTHC awarded Neeser Construction Inc. a contract to build the new ANMC patient housing facility on the Alaska Native Health Campus in Anchorage. The building will house patients and their families travelling to ANMC for medical care. The a new patient housing facility is expected to open in fall 2016. It will have 202 private rooms and six floors with a dedicated floor for new families.

In 2015 Alaska Governor Walker introduced legislation declaring his plan for Medicaid reform and expansion. ANTHC supports the Governor's efforts to expand Medicaid coverage to more than 41000 Alaskans.

Company Background

In 2012 ANMC expanded its maternal child health and neurosurgery departments due to increasing patient populations in the Anchorage area. In 2010 the medical center opened the only Level II trauma center in Alaska making it a referral hospital for major trauma cases.

The organization has also improved its health care technology resources; it expanded the use of electronic health records at ANMC in 2012 and it is expanding its telemedicine operations (as telemedicine is becoming an increasingly popular way for specialists to see patients without the expense of a personal visit). It has increased other community outreach efforts as well such as smoking cessation and behavioral health programs.

EXECUTIVES

CEO and Director, Don Kashevaroff
Vice Chair, Lincoln A. Bean Sr.
Chairman and President, Ray Alstrom
COO, Susan Childers
Chief Financial Officer, Garvin Federenko
Chief Executive Officer, Roald Helgesen
Chief Information Officer, Stewart Ferguson
CEO and Director, Don Kashevaroff
Director, Robert J. Henrichs
Director, Andrew (Andy) Jimmie, age 78

Director, Evelyn Beeter
Director, Mike Zacharof
Director, H. Sally Smith
Director, Linda Clement
Director, Emily Hughes
Director, Katherine Gottlieb
Vice Chair, Lincoln A. Bean Sr.
Director, Bernice Kaigelak
Director, Charlene Nollner
Director, Andrew (Andy) Teuber
Auditors: MIKUNDA COTTRELL & CO CPA'S A

LOCATIONS

HQ: ALASKA NATIVE TRIBAL HEALTH CONSORTIUM
4000 AMBASSADOR DR, ANCHORAGE, AK 995085909
Phone: 907 729-1900

PRODUCTS/OPERATIONS

2014 Sales

		$ mil.	% of total
Patient revenue	213	33	
Compact revenue	161	25	
Grant & project revenue	109	17	
Warehouse revenue	22	3	
Investment income	4	1	
Other 133	21		
Total		643	100

Selected Services
Ear Nose Throat
Emergency and Trauma
Family Medicine
Imaging and Laboratory Services
Internal Medicine Clinic
Maternal Fetal Medicine
OB/GYN Services
Oncology
Orthopedics Clinic
Pediatric ICU
Pediatrics
Pharmacy Services
Pregnancy and Childbirth
Primary Care Services
Respiratory Care

COMPETITORS

HCA	South Peninsula
Immediate Care	Hospital
PeaceHealth	Tenet Healthcare
Providence Health &	
Services	

HISTORICAL FINANCIALS

Company Type: Private

Income Statement   FYE: September 30

	REVENUE ($ mil.)	NET INCOME ($ mil.)	NET PROFIT MARGIN	EMPLOYEES
09/13	459	21	4.6%	1,850
09/12	447	21	4.9%	—
09/11	427	24	5.8%	—
09/10	414	0	—	—
Annual Growth 3.5%				—

2013 Year-End Financials

Return on assets: 14.7%   Cash ($ mil.): 87
Return on equity: 4.6%
Current ratio: 1.00

ALASKA PERMANENT FUND CORPORATION

Auditors: KPMG LLP ANCHORAGE AK

LOCATIONS

HQ: ALASKA PERMANENT FUND CORPORATION
801 W 10TH ST STE 302, JUNEAU, AK 998011878
Phone: 907 796-1500

HISTORICAL FINANCIALS
Company Type: Private

Income Statement FYE: June 30

	ASSETS ($ mil.)	NET INCOME ($ mil.)	INCOME AS % OF ASSETS	EMPLOYEES
06/13	49,797	4,520	9.1%	36
06/12	45,043	192	0.4%	—
06/11	45,240	6,885	15.2%	—
06/10	37,052	0	—	—
Annual Growth	10.4%	—	—	—

ALBANY MEDICAL CENTER

Albany Medical Center (AMC) provides upscale medical care in upstate New York. Serving residents of northeastern New York and western New England the health system has at its heart the 730-bed Albany Medical Center Hospital. The general medical-surgical facility also provides specialty care in such areas as oncology rehabilitation and organ transplantation. AMC also features a children's hospital an outpatient surgery center and a group medical practice. It employs some 400 full-time physicians. Its Albany Medical College is one of the nation's first private medical schools. It offers undergraduate and graduate medical degrees and residency programs as well as fellowships and continuing medical education.

Operations

AMC's assets includes a biomedical research enterprise and one of the region's largest physicians practices with more than 400 doctors. Its physicians have extensive training and experience in 34 subspecialties of pediatric medicine. The system's subsidiaries include the Albany Medical Center Kidskeller Corporation a not-for-profit day care facility and Madison Avenue Services Corporation a taxable corporation.

AMC is affiliated with several community physician groups including Albany Vascular Group Capital Cardiology Associates and Capital Region Orthopaedic Group.

In 2013 the system reported some 33000 admissions 581000 outpatient visits 28000 surgical cases and 68000 emergency department visits.

Geographic Reach

AMC offers services in 25 counties in northeastern New York and western New England. In addition to treating patients at the main site in Albany providers also treat patients at community-based locations throughout the region including Clifton Park Latham Malta North Greenbush Delmar and others.

Sales and Marketing

HMOs account for around a third of net patient revenue while Medicare and Medicaid represent about 20% and 15% respectively.

Financial Performance

The company's revenues grew by 3% to $752 million in 2013 (versus $728 million in 2012) due to an increase in net patient revenue; this was partially offset by declines in interest income dividends and other revenue. Net income grew 21% to $63 million in 2013 as net realized gains on sales of

securities and impairment charges rose. Other gains were made in pension-related changes and net unrealized gains and losses in investments.

Cash flow from operations fell 55% that year to $37 million as more was used in receivables and other liabilities.

Strategy

AMC grows through organic expansion partnerships and product initiatives. The company is in the midst of a $360 million expansion including a new patient tower with more than 100 beds and increased intensive care resources. The project — expected to last several years —will also increase Albany Medical Center Hospital's bed count to more than 700.

In 2014 The Neurology Group and The Endocrine Group joined AMC's Albany Med Faculty Physician Group.

AMC and Union Graduate College joined forces in 2013 to offer a new joint degree combining medical school with an MBA.

That year AMC and Saratoga Hospital formed a joint venture and opened the $17.5 million Malta Med Emergent Care to provide area residents an alternative to hospital emergency rooms for all but the most serious medical circumstances.

On the product innovation side in 2013 AMC introduced advanced imaging technologies in a pair of its new Patient Pavilion operating rooms that provide for greater precision and patient safety during brain and spinal surgeries.

Also that year the company opened a Chronic Kidney Disease Clinic as the sole source for comprehensive care for 6000 people in its service area suffering from the slow loss of kidney function.

AMC also engages in research and development of new pharmaceuticals through partnerships with companies like Aegis Therapeutics with which it is developing an anti-obesity peptide to benefit patients with type 2 diabetes. The college's research department is also studying brain mapping techniques as well as Alzheimer's disease vascular disease and cancer and multiple sclerosis treatments.

Company Background

AMC which produced Nobel prize winners in both 2009 and 2011 annually awards its own $500000 prize the largest monetary award in medicine and biomedical research in the US. In 2010 combined federal-state entities awarded the center $10 million the center's largest grant since its founding which will be used to expand research labs at Albany Medical College.

AMC's status as the Capital Region's reigning health care giant was toppled by the 2011 merger of four locals hospitals to form St. Peter's Health Partners with nearly 12000 employees vs. 6000 at AMC. Post merger the newly-merged group has nearly 50% of the Capital Region market while AMC has 25%. While AMC is no longer the area's largest hospital as the region's trauma center and only medical school it continues to draw many patients from outside the four-county area.

Albany Medical College was formed in 1839; the hospital's predecessor was formed in 1849. The two combined under the AMC umbrella in 1982.

EXECUTIVES

President and CEO, James J. Barba
COO, Gary J. Kochem
EVP and CFO, William C. Hasselbarth
EVP and CIO, George T. Hickman
EVP IDS and Hospital Systems General Director, Steven M. Frisch
EVP Policy Planning and Communications, Kim Fine
SVP Hospital Business Services and COO Hospital, Bernadette Pedlow
Dean and EVP Health Affairs, Vincent Verdile
SVP and Chief Nursing Officer, Mary Ellen Plass

Senior Vice President and Chief Compliance Officer, Noel Hogan
Medical Director, Dennis McKenna
Assistant Vice President For Communications, Tania Allard
Vice President Finance, Cooper Matthew
Assistant Vice President, Kenneth (Ken) Urquhart
Director Of Radiology, Howell Morris
Physical Therapy Director, Louann Kuntz
Vice President For Communications, Jeffrey Gordon
Vice President Human Resources, Thomas (Thom) Murphy
Assistant Vice President Development, James (Jamie) Kellerhouse
Upper Management Vice President, Garry Robinson
Vice President Patient Financial Seervices, Carol McDonald
Vice President, Julia Mason
Vice President Of Facility Operations, Don Stichter
Director Of Radiology, Rupal Chopra
Vice President Information System, Dennis Delisle
Vice President, Cris Harris
Vice President Operations and Finance, Laura O'Brien
Vice President, Anjali Singla
Vice President, Michael Gruenthal
Senior Vice President of Integrated Delivery Systems and Hospital Director, Stephen (Steve) Frisch
Director Of Pharmacy, Michael (Mel) Belemjamin
Chairman, Robert Cushing
Secretary, Kathy Fields
Auditors: KPMG LLP ALBANY NY

LOCATIONS

HQ: ALBANY MEDICAL CENTER
43 NEW SCOTLAND AVE, ALBANY, NY 122083478
Phone: 518 262-3125
Web: WWW.AMC.EDU

PRODUCTS/OPERATIONS

2013 Sales

	% of total
Net patient service	96
Inter-institutional	1
Interest & dividends	-
Other	2
Net assets released from restrictions	1
Total	**100**

2013 Net Patient Service Revenue

	% of total
Health maintenance organizations	32
Medicare	19
Medicaid	15
Blue Cross and Blue Shield	14
Commercial carriers	9
No fault & worker's compensation	5
Private pay	2
Other third-party payors	4
Total	**100**

Selected Services
Cancer center
Children' s Hospital
Center for Donation and Transplant
Diabetes service
Emergency medical services
Hearing center
HIV medicine
Pain management
Perinatal
Physical therapy
Radiology
Rheumatology
Surgical
Trauma center
Women' s wellness center

COMPETITORS

Berkshire Health Systems

St. Joseph' s Hospital Health Center

Ellis Hospital
SUNY Upstate Medical
  University
Southwestern Vermont
  Health Care

St. Peter' s Health
  Partners
United Health Services
  Hospitals

HISTORICAL FINANCIALS
Company Type: Private

Income Statement
FYE: December 31

	REVENUE ($ mil.)	NET INCOME ($ mil.)	NET PROFIT MARGIN	EMPLOYEES
12/13	980	115	11.7%	7,000
12/12	935	76	8.1%	—
/ 0	0		—	—
Annual Growth	—	—	—	—

2013 Year-End Financials
Return on assets: 5.8%   Cash ($ mil.): 117
Return on equity: 11.7%
Current ratio: 0.60

ALBANY MEDICAL CENTER HOSPITAL

Auditors: KPMG LLP ALBANY NY

LOCATIONS
HQ: ALBANY MEDICAL CENTER HOSPITAL
  43 NEW SCOTLAND AVE, ALBANY, NY 122083478
Phone: 518 262-3125
Web: WWW.AMC.EDU

HISTORICAL FINANCIALS
Company Type: Private

Income Statement
FYE: December 31

	REVENUE ($ mil.)	NET INCOME ($ mil.)	NET PROFIT MARGIN	EMPLOYEES
12/09	604	15	2.5%	1,568
12/08	525	3	0.7%	—
12/06	510	13	2.6%	—
12/05	480	0	—	—
Annual Growth	5.9%	—	—	—

2009 Year-End Financials
Return on assets: —   Cash ($ mil.): 38
Return on equity: 2.5%
Current ratio: 0.60

ALBERICI CONSTRUCTORS INC.

LOCATIONS
HQ: ALBERICI CONSTRUCTORS INC.
  8800 PAGE AVE, SAINT LOUIS, MO 631146106
Phone: 314 733-2000
Web: WWW.ALBERICI.COM

HISTORICAL FINANCIALS
Company Type: Private

Income Statement
FYE: December 31

	REVENUE ($ mil.)	NET INCOME ($ mil.)	NET PROFIT MARGIN	EMPLOYEES
12/13	578	0	—	2,000
12/12	489	0	—	—
12/11	543	0	—	—
12/10	551	0	—	—
Annual Growth	1.6%	—	—	—

2013 Year-End Financials
Return on assets: 19.0%   Cash ($ mil.): 77
Return on equity: —
Current ratio: 0.90

ALBERICI CORPORATION

Alberici helped shape the St. Louis skyline; it now sets its sights —or its construction sites — across North America. As the parent company of Alberici Constructors the company encompasses a group of enterprises with a presence in North America Central America South America and Europe. Operations include construction services building materials and steel fabrication and erection units. Alberici offers general contracting design/build construction management demolition and specialty contracting services while also offering facilities management. Founded in 1918 the Alberici family still holds the largest share of the employee-owned firm.

Operations

The company boasts more than a dozen operating companies in the US Canada and Mexico that serve the automotive energy health care industrial manufacturing and wastewater treatment markets. Its Gunther-Nash subsidiary provides construction services to the mining industry. Another division Vertegy specializes in construction consulting for green and sustainable projects.

Geographic Reach

Alberici is active throughout North America and has offices in St. Louis Missouri; Detroit Michigan; Atlanta Georgia; Topeka Kansas; Burlington and Cambridge Ontario; Saskatoon Saskatchewan; and Léon Mexico.Sales and MarketingAlberici serves a range of different companies including those that are automotive building energy healthcare heavy industrial industrial process mining infrastructure or water-related. Some of Alberici's completed projects include casinos for Ameristar modernization and new facilities for Anheuser-Busch and factories for Boeing. Nearly 80% of its revenue comes from repeat clients.

Financial Performance

While full financial information was not available for the privately held company Alberici reports that its annual revenue typically exceeds $1 billion. In 2013 the company took home $1.9 billion and was ranked the 46th largest contractor in the US by the Engineering News-Record.In 2012 the company reported more than $530 million in industrial-related revenue thanks to a recovering economy supporting demand for major industrial projects in the US and Canada.

Strategy

In recent years the heavy construction firm has pursued acquisitions to better diversify its business both geographically and by entering new specialty markets. In 2013 for example Alberici purchased contractor Flintco LLC to broaden its reach into new markets in the southern and southwestern regions of the US. In early 2012 Alberici acquired a water treatment facility specialist to expand its service offerings in the water plant construction market.

Alberici has also become a recognized contractor in recent years which could help give the company a higher profile and thus more exposure to new potential clients. In 2013 the Associated General Contractors of St. Louis awarded Alberici with top prizes at its 16th Annual Keystone Awards for the company's work on the Seabrook Gates Complex and the Knights of Columbus Child Development Center. To date Alberici has won 14 Keystone Awards more than any other general contractor.So far its high standing hasn't hurt business. In July 2014 Alberici was chosen to lead in the engineering procurement and construction of a major air quality improvement project —with the goal of installing environmental controls and reducing sulfur dioxide emissions by 90% —at one of the generating stations owned and operated by Alliant Energy's Wisconsin utility Wisconsin Power and Light Company.

Mergers and Acquisitions

Expanding it range of capabilities in January 2012 Alberici acquired water treatment facility specialist CAS Construction. The addition of CAS which has built facilities throughout the central and western US strengthens Alberici's capabilities in the water market. The company was renamed CAS Constructors.

In early 2013 Alberici closed on its acquisition of Flintco LLC a century-old Native American-owned contractor based in Tulsa Oklahoma. With offices in Oklahoma New Mexico Texas Arkansas and California Flintco presented an attractive geographic diversification opportunity for Alberici.

EXECUTIVES
Evp, Michael W (Mel) Burke

LOCATIONS
HQ: ALBERICI CORPORATION
  8800 PAGE AVE, SAINT LOUIS, MO 631146106
Phone: 314 733-2000
Web: WWW.ALBERICI.COM

PRODUCTS/OPERATIONS

Selected Markets
Automotive
Building
Energy
Green building
Health care
Industrial
Manufacturing/Food and Beverage
Mining infrastructure
Steel fabrication
Water and Wastewater Treatment

Selected Subsidiaries and Brands
Alberici Global Group GmbH
  Alberici Constructors Ltd. (Canada)
  Alberici Construcciones S.A. de C.V. (Mexico)
Alberici Group Inc.
  Alberici Constructors Inc.
  Alberici Global Automotive Constructors (automotive construction)
  Alberici Healthcare Constructors
  Alberici Industrial LLC
  CAS Construction LLC (water wastewater)
  Flintco LLC (Native American-owned contractor)
  Gunther-Nash Inc. (shaft slope and tunnel construction for mining industry)
  Hillsdale Fabricators (steel fabrication)
  Kienlen Constructors (structural concrete structural steel)
  Vertegy (green building consulting)

COMPETITORS
Barton Malow   Jacobs Engineering

Bechtel	McCarthy Building
Black & Veatch	Parsons Corporation
DPR Construction	Peter Kiewit Sons'
Fluor	TIC Holdings
Hensel Phelps	Tutor Perini
Construction	Walbridge Aldinger
Hoffman Corporation	Walsh Group
Hunt Construction	Zachry Inc.

HISTORICAL FINANCIALS
Company Type: Private

Income Statement
FYE: December 31

	REVENUE ($ mil.)	NET INCOME ($ mil.)	NET PROFIT MARGIN	EMPLOYEES
12/13	1,736	0	—	2,080
12/12	772	0	—	—
12/11	713	0	—	—
Annual Growth	56.0%	—	—	—

2013 Year-End Financials
Return on assets: 14.9% Cash ($ mil.): 178
Return on equity: —
Current ratio: 1.10

ALBERICI GROUP INC.

LOCATIONS
HQ: ALBERICI GROUP INC.
   8800 PAGE AVE, SAINT LOUIS, MO 631146106
Phone: 314 733-2000

HISTORICAL FINANCIALS
Company Type: Private

Income Statement
FYE: December 31

	REVENUE ($ mil.)	NET INCOME ($ mil.)	NET PROFIT MARGIN	EMPLOYEES
12/13	1,736	0	—	2,000
12/12	629	0	—	—
12/11	565	0	—	—
12/10	565	0	—	—
Annual Growth	45.4%	—	—	—

2013 Year-End Financials
Return on assets: 14.9% Cash ($ mil.): 151
Return on equity: —
Current ratio: 0.90

ALBERT EINSTEIN MEDICAL ASSOCIATES INC.

LOCATIONS
HQ: ALBERT EINSTEIN MEDICAL ASSOCIATES INC.
   5501 OLD YORK RD STE 1, PHILADELPHIA, PA
   191413018
Phone: 215 456-7890
Web: WWW.EINSTEIN.EDU

HISTORICAL FINANCIALS
Company Type: Private

Income Statement
FYE: June 30

	REVENUE ($ mil.)	NET INCOME ($ mil.)	NET PROFIT MARGIN	EMPLOYEES
06/09	670	0	—	5,251
06/08	693	33	4.9%	—
06/07	785	63	8.0%	—
06/06	718	0	—	—
Annual Growth	(2.3%)	—	—	—

2009 Year-End Financials
Return on assets: 28.2% Cash ($ mil.): 82
Return on equity: —
Current ratio: 0.30

ALBERT EINSTEIN MEDICAL CENTER

Auditors: PRICEWATERHOUSECOOPERS LLP PH

LOCATIONS
HQ: ALBERT EINSTEIN MEDICAL CENTER
   5501 OLD YORK RD STE 1, PHILADELPHIA, PA
   191413098
Phone: 215 456-8710
Web: WWW.ALBERTEINSTEINMEDICALCENTER.COM

HISTORICAL FINANCIALS
Company Type: Private

Income Statement
FYE: June 30

	REVENUE ($ mil.)	NET INCOME ($ mil.)	NET PROFIT MARGIN	EMPLOYEES
06/11	744	52	7.1%	—
06/10	713	(38)	—	—
06/09	635	23	3.7%	—
06/01	345	0	—	—
Annual Growth	8.0%	—	—	—

2011 Year-End Financials
Return on assets: — Cash ($ mil.): 13
Return on equity: 7.1%
Current ratio: 0.30

ALDRIDGE ELECTRIC INC.

Aldridge Electric powers up the Windy City and other parts of the Midwest. The electrical contractor divides its business into six main areas: airport industrial power drilling highway and transit. It works on projects ranging from Chicago's subway system to its airport runways. Additional activities include services for street lighting traffic signals high-voltage cabling and splicing and foundation drilling. Aldridge Electric has worked for clients such as Commonwealth Edison Company and Exelon Corporation. It sister companies in the family-owned AldridgeGroup include Aldridge Construction GFS Construction and Woodward Brothering.

Operations
Aldridge Electric has more than 1200 pieces of equipment.

It is the general contractor and subcontractor of choice for the multi-million dollar O'Hare Modernization Program (OMP) intended to reduce delays and improve efficiency at the Chicago international airport. Aldridge completed several OMP contracts involving the construction extension and relocation of several runways in addition to the installation of taxiway lights and navigational equipment.

The company is also participating in a $130 million project the Oak Glen Substation a two-circuit 34.5-kV to 69-kV collection substation on the site of Oak Glen Wind Farm near Blooming Prairie Minnesota. It was selected to provide electrical service and maintenance lighting DelDOT Intelligent Traffic Management Systems (ITMS) bridge monitoring instrumentation and the design and installation of a sand-bypass system over the main span of on a new cable stay bridge.

Aldridge Electric's drilling division has enjoyed a robust backlog due to the growing demand in the wind energy market. The division has worked to drill foundations for wind turbines and transmission lines that criss-cross the US.

Ownership
Aldridge Electric is owned by CEO Ken Aldridge the grandson of company's founder.

Company Background
Leonard "Len" Aldridge started the business in 1932 and incorporated it in 1952.

EXECUTIVES
Vice President Utility Division, Daniel Galovich

LOCATIONS
HQ: ALDRIDGE ELECTRIC INC.
   844 E ROCKLAND RD, LIBERTYVILLE, IL 600483358
Phone: 847 680-5200
Web: WWW.ALDRIDGE-ELECTRIC.COM

PRODUCTS/OPERATIONS

Selected Divisions and Services
Airport
   Approach lighting systems
   Control system
   Electrical vaults
   Hangar facility electrical
   High-voltage cable pulling splicing and terminating
   Hold pad perimeter lighting and limit lighting
   Parking lot lighting
   Parking structure rehabilitation
   Runway and taxiway lighting
   Site utility work
   Terminal rehabilitation work
   Traffic management and control
Drilling
   Bridge foundations
   Building structure foundations
   Communication tower foundations
   Drilled shafts for sewer lift stations
   Drilling for earth-retention systems
   High-mast lighting tower foundations
   Sign foundations
   Transmission line foundations
Highway
   Closed-loop detection
   High-mast lighting
   Highway lighting
   Intelligent transportation systems
   Lighting systems design/build
   Municipal street lighting
   RTMS detection systems
   Subdivision street lighting
   Surveillance camera systems
   Surveillance systems
   Traffic interconnect systems
   Traffic signal systems
   Variable message signs
Industrial
   Design/build capabilities
   Electrical maintenance and renovations

Electrical power distribution and lighting for new construction and existing facilities
Energy conservation upgrades and retrofits
Fire alarm and security
Movable bridge power lighting and control systems
Process control systems
Supervisory control and data acquisition systems
Tenant build-out
Voice data communication systems and CCTV
Power
Design/build
Fiber optic cabling
Interconnect yard construction
Project management
Overhead elerical construction
Substation construction
Solar panal installation
Turbine wiring
Underground electrical construction
Transit
Catenary systems
Communications systems
Traction power 3rd rail systems
Train control
Affiliates in the AldridgeGroup
Aldridge Canada
GFS Construction LLC
Woodward Brothering

COMPETITORS

Bayview Electric Company
EEI
EMCOR
Faith Technologies
Integrated Electrical Services
Kelso-Burnett
Mass Electric
Motor City Electric

HISTORICAL FINANCIALS

Company Type: Private

Income Statement — FYE: March 31

	REVENUE ($ mil.)	NET INCOME ($ mil.)	NET PROFIT MARGIN	EMPLOYEES
03/11	208	2	1.0%	500
03/10	272	10	3.8%	—
Annual Growth	(23.2%)	(79.8%)	—	—

2011 Year-End Financials

Return on assets: 6.3%
Return on equity: 1.0%
Current ratio: 1.50
Cash ($ mil.): 12

ALEXANDRIA INOVA HOSPITAL

Inova Alexandria Hospital provides medical surgical and therapeutic services in northeastern Virginia. The hospital was founded in 1872 and became part of the not-for-profit Inova Health System in 1997. Inova Alexandria Hospital has about 320 beds. The hospital offers specialty services such as heart and cancer treatment women's and children's health care emergency medicine vascular procedures interventional radiology and sleep disorder and heartburn treatment services. The Inova Health System provides health care services in northern Virginia through a network of hospitals clinics assisted living centers and other provider facilities.

EXECUTIVES

Vice President, Patrick Walters
Medical Records Director, Bonnie Greek

LOCATIONS

HQ: ALEXANDRIA INOVA HOSPITAL
4320 SEMINARY RD, ALEXANDRIA, VA 223041535
Phone: 703 504-3000
Web: WWW.INOVA.ORG

COMPETITORS

Ascension Health
Bon Secours Health
HCA
Johns Hopkins Health System
MedStar Health

HISTORICAL FINANCIALS

Company Type: Private

Income Statement — FYE: December 31

	REVENUE ($ mil.)	NET INCOME ($ mil.)	NET PROFIT MARGIN	EMPLOYEES
12/08	276	24	9.0%	1,750
12/06	247	22	9.2%	—
12/05	233	22	9.8%	—
12/01	180	0	—	—
Annual Growth	6.2%	—	—	—

2008 Year-End Financials

Return on assets: 3.5%
Return on equity: 9.0%
Current ratio: 1.90
Cash ($ mil.): 2

ALL POINTS COOPERATIVE

All Points Cooperative provides agricultural support services to farmers and ranchers in central Nebraska. The cooperative offers seed energy fuel agronomy storage and purchasing services along with financial credit marketing and purchasing assistance for its member/farmers. Its agronomy services include fertilizer application soil sampling and crop planning and management. Its energy division offers bulk fuel bulk oil heating oil and propane delivery. It also operates retail outlets including two Ampride Convenience Stores and the Trustworthy Feed and Hardware Store. In addition to its headquarters in Gothenburg Nebraska All Points has cooperative operations in 12 other communities.

EXECUTIVES

Director, Ed Oberg
Vice Chairman, Jeff Beattie
Director, Tim Easterday
Director, Seth Gruber
Director, Jeffrey Huffman
Director, Fred Nisley
Director, Bruce Rickertson

LOCATIONS

HQ: ALL POINTS COOPERATIVE
120 8TH ST, GOTHENBURG, NE 691381006
Phone: 308 537-7141
Web: WWW.ALLPOINTS.COOP

COMPETITORS

ADM
AGRI Industries
Ag Processing Inc.
Andersons
Bartlett and Company
CHS
Cargill
DeBruce Grain
GROWMARK
Land O' Lakes Purina Feed
NC Hybrids
Scoular

HISTORICAL FINANCIALS

Company Type: Private

Income Statement — FYE: September 30

	REVENUE ($ mil.)	NET INCOME ($ mil.)	NET PROFIT MARGIN	EMPLOYEES
09/12	236	7	3.2%	150
09/08	192	10	5.6%	—
09/06	91	0	—	—
09/05	0	0	—	—
Annual Growth	—	—	—	—

2012 Year-End Financials

Return on assets: 2.2%
Return on equity: 3.2%
Current ratio: 0.30
Cash ($ mil.): 3

ALL SAINTS HEALTH CARE SYSTEM INC.

LOCATIONS

HQ: ALL SAINTS HEALTH CARE SYSTEM INC.
3801 SPRING ST, MOUNT PLEASANT, WI 534051667
Phone: 262 687-4011

HISTORICAL FINANCIALS

Company Type: Private

Income Statement — FYE: June 30

	REVENUE ($ mil.)	NET INCOME ($ mil.)	NET PROFIT MARGIN	EMPLOYEES
06/08	406	(15)	—	2,680
06/05	0	0	99.6%	—
06/04	0	0	99.8%	—
06/03	323	0	—	—
Annual Growth	4.7%	—	—	—

ALLEGIS GROUP INC.

Clients in need of highly skilled technical and other personnel might want to take the pledge of Allegis. The group is one of the world's largest staffing and recruitment firms. Among its companies are Aerotek (engineering automotive and scientific professionals) Stephen James Associates (recruitment for accounting financial and cash management positions) and TEKsystems (information technology staffing and consulting). Other Allegis units include sales support outsourcer MarketSource. Chairman Jim Davis helped found the company (originally known as Aerotek) in 1983 to provide contract engineering personnel to two clients in the aerospace industry.

Geographic Reach

The company operates through more than 300 offices worldwide including its corporate headquarters in Hanover Maryland. Outside of the US the company has operations in Canada Europe the Middle East the Pacific Rim Puerto Rico and the UK.

Operations

Allegis Group has more than 12000 internal employees including 3000 dedicated recruiters and

130000 contract employees working with customers around the world.

Strategy

The company has expanded its geographical footprint and improved its position in specialist staffing markets through the use of acquisitions.

Mergers and Acquisitions

Allegis Group acquired Talent2 during fiscal 2014. Talent2's strong presence in the Asia Pacific region combined with Allegis Group's dominant position in North America will help both organizations to better serve clients needs.

EXECUTIVES

CEO, Michael (Mike) Salandra
CFO, Paul J. Bowie
CIO, Mercedes Kelch
President - International Operations, Chris Hartman
V President-tax, Michael (Mel) Bison
Senior Vice President RPO Operations, Gil Smith
Vice President Information Technology, Chuck Masters
Vice President State Government Affairs, Cheryl Ann Stewart
Vice President Human Resources, Connie Lee
Vice President Global Accounts Director, Bob Nappi
Chairman, James C. (Jim) Davis
Auditors: PRICEWATERHOUSECOOPERS LLP BA

LOCATIONS

HQ: ALLEGIS GROUP INC.
7301 PARKWAY DR, HANOVER, MD 210761159
Phone: 410 579-3000
Web: WWW.ALLEGISGROUP.COM

PRODUCTS/OPERATIONS

Selected Subsidiaries
Aerotek
  Aerotek Automotive
  Aerotek Aviation LLC
  Aerotek Canada
  Aerotek CE
  Aerotek Commercial Staffing
  Aerotek E&E
  Aerotek Energy Services
  Aerotek Germany
  Aerotek Netherlands
  Aerotek Professional Services
  Aerotek Scientific LLC
  Aerotek United Kingdom
Allegis Group Canada
Allegis Group Europe
Allegis Group India
Allegis Group Services
InSearch Worldwide
Major Lindsey & Africa
MarketSource Inc
Stephen James Associates
TEKsystems
  TEKsystems Canada
  TEKsystems Germany
  TEKsystems Netherlands
  TEKsystems United Kingdom

COMPETITORS

ASG Renaissance	Kelly Services
Adecco	Korn/Ferry
CDI	ManpowerGroup
Curran Partners	RDL Corporation
ExecuNet	Randstad Holding
Heidrick & Struggles	Robert Half
Horton International	Snelling Staffing
Innovative Management Solutions Group	Volt Information

HISTORICAL FINANCIALS
Company Type: Private

Income Statement
FYE: December 31

	REVENUE ($ mil.)	NET INCOME ($ mil.)	NET PROFIT MARGIN	EMPLOYEES
12/13	10,440	0	—	85,000
12/12	9,544	0	—	—
12/11	8,275	438	5.3%	—
12/10	6,405	0	—	—
Annual Growth 17.7%	—	—	—	—

2013 Year-End Financials
Return on assets: 1.2%
Return on equity: —
Current ratio: 2.70
Cash ($ mil.): 511

ALLEN LUND COMPANY LLC

The Allen Lund Company (ALC) knows loads; it matches shippers' loads with a network of truckload and less-than-truckload (LTL) carriers. (LTL carriers collect consolidate and haul freight from multiple shippers.) The brokerage firm arranges the transport of dry refrigerated (predominantly produce) and flatbed cargo. It operates from 30 offices throughout more than 20 US states. ALC Logistics ALC Perishable Logistics and ALC International (an international division) assist shippers in managing transportation costs tracking and tracing shipments managing appointments and executing freight forward management services overseas. The company was founded in 1976 by Allen Lund and his wife Kathie Lund.

Geographic Reach

The company's international division provides transportation services worldwide along with transportation to and from the US including Puerto Rico Hawaii Alaska and ground transportation for Canada and Mexico.

Operations

ALC has a Logistics & Software division ALC Logistics.

Strategy

In an effort to expand its operation in 2012 the company opened a new office in Joplin Missouri and another in McAllen Texas which mainly focuses on handling heavy haul flatbed particularly in and out of Mexico. In addition the company opened four additional offices in 2012.

Mergers and Acquisitions

In an effort to grow its business in early 2014 ALC acquired Wisconsin based Northern Freight Service Inc. a company provides truckload LTL and intermodal services to the customers ranging from small shippers to FORTUNE 500 shippers.

EXECUTIVES

Vice President Of Business Development, Doug Clark
National Accounts Manager, Fred Huberlie
National Accounts Manager Atlanta Branch, Jim Scazzero
Vice President Support Operations, Kenny Lund
Vice President Sales and Branch Operations, Ed Lund
National Accounts Manager, Dennis Connors

LOCATIONS

HQ: ALLEN LUND COMPANY LLC
4529 ANGELES CREST HWY # 300, LA CANADA FLINTRIDGE, CA 910113247
Phone: 818 790-1110

PRODUCTS/OPERATIONS

Selected Services
Software and Logistics
  LTL Freight
  Scheduling
  Spot Pricing and Bid Management
  Truck Load
Transportation Services
  Dry Van
  Flatbed Trucking
  International Freight Shipping
  LTL Freight
  Refrigerated Transportation

COMPETITORS

C.H. Robinson Worldwide	Ryder System
CEVA Logistics	Universal Truckload Services
Menlo Worldwide	

HISTORICAL FINANCIALS
Company Type: Private

Income Statement
FYE: December 31

	REVENUE ($ mil.)	NET INCOME ($ mil.)	NET PROFIT MARGIN	EMPLOYEES
12/13	421	1	0.3%	310
12/12*	355	3	0.9%	—
10/12	313	3	1.0%	—
10/11	313	0	—	—
Annual Growth 15.9%	—	—	—	—
*Fiscal year change				

2013 Year-End Financials
Return on assets: 4.6%
Return on equity: 0.3%
Current ratio: 2.00
Cash ($ mil.): 4

ALLIANCE FOR SUSTAINABLE ENERGY LLC

LOCATIONS

HQ: ALLIANCE FOR SUSTAINABLE ENERGY LLC
15013 DENVER WEST PKWY, GOLDEN, CO 804013111
Phone: 303 275-3000

HISTORICAL FINANCIALS
Company Type: Private

Income Statement
FYE: September 30

	REVENUE ($ mil.)	NET INCOME ($ mil.)	NET PROFIT MARGIN	EMPLOYEES
09/13	382	4	1.1%	1,678
09/11	532	6	1.2%	—
09/10	443	6	1.4%	—
Annual Growth (4.8%)	(12.3%)	—	—	—

2013 Year-End Financials
Return on assets: 17.6%
Return on equity: 1.1%
Current ratio: 1.20
Cash ($ mil.): 2

ALLIED BUILDING STORES INC.

Auditors: HEARD MCELROY & VESTAL SHREV

LOCATIONS

HQ: ALLIED BUILDING STORES INC.
850 KANSAS LN, MONROE, LA 712034776
Phone: 318 699-9100
Web: WWW.ALLIEDBUILDINGSTORES.COM

HISTORICAL FINANCIALS

Company Type: Private

Income Statement

FYE: August 31

	REVENUE ($ mil.)	NET INCOME ($ mil.)	NET PROFIT MARGIN	EMPLOYEES
08/14	487	0	0.0%	125
08/13	503	0	0.0%	—
08/12	456	0	0.0%	—
08/11	440	0	—	—
Annual Growth	3.4%	—	—	—

2014 Year-End Financials

Return on assets: 6.8%
Return on equity: —
Current ratio: 0.90
Cash ($ mil.): 3

ALLINA HEALTH SYSTEM

Allina Health System (aka Allina Hospitals and Clinics) is a not-for-profit health care system that goes all in to protect people's #1 asset –their good health. The health system owns and operates more than a dozen hospitals a network of nearly one hundred clinics and specialty centers and a whole bunch of pharmacies. Its vast system of provider locations serve residents throughout Minnesota and western Wisconsin providing disease prevention programs along with specialized inpatient and outpatient services. Allina's Aspen Medical Group division also operates a range of outpatient clinics providing primary and specialty care.

Geographic Reach

The health care system's hospitals are located in Burnsville Champlin Coon Rapids Edina Inver Grove Heights Maplewood Plymouth St. Paul Shakopee and Woodbury in Minnesota and in River Falls in Wisconsin.

Operations

Allina has 13 hospitals (about 1800 beds) more than 90 clinics and 16 pharmacies. The largest hospital in the group is Abbott Northwestern Hospital (600 beds) followed by United Hospital which has about 570 beds. Five of Allina's hospitals are in the Minneapolis/St. Paul metropolitan area (where the system has more than a 30% share of the health care market) five are scattered throughout the rest of Minnesota and one is in western Wisconsin. The health system reported more than 100000 inpatient admissions in 2014 1.3 million outpatient admissions more than 300000 emergency care visits more than 15000 births and more than 3.5 million clinic visits.

Regina Hospital has a 57-bed acute care hospital a 61-bed skilled care nursing home and a 134-bed assisted living facility. It also operates three outpatient multi-specialty clinics. Located in Minneapolis/St. Paul District One Hospital provides a broad range of health care services to Faribault and the surrounding communities.

In 2013 Allina contributed more than $541 million in charity care.

Strategy

The system's wide-ranging locations combined with its huge number of facilities have prompted Allina to embark on a multi-year initiative to install electronic medical records (EMR) at all of its hospitals and clinics. The installation gives medical providers the ability to track a patient's progress through any of the myriad health care settings operated by Allina. The EMR also gives patients access to coordinated care between the different providers as well as the ability to see portions of their medical records and lab results online. Patients can also schedule appointments and make use of a number of health and wellness tools all via the Internet.

Allina is the first Minnesota health care organization to earn the Davies Award the industry's preeminent award for health information technology.

Despite Allina's already hefty size the system has a partnership with retail clinic provider MinuteClinic which offers basic health care at CVS Health stores. The hospital also has a multi-year collaboration with HealthPartners designed to reduce total medical costs at both hospitals.

In 2013 Courage Center and Allina merged Sister Kenny Rehabilitation Institute and Courage Center. The merger of the two entities (which focus on the health and well-being of people with disabilities) served Allina's goal of expanding its network.

EXECUTIVES

System VP; President Mercy Hospital, Sara Criger
EVP Clinics and Home Care Services, Robert A. Wieland
CEO, Penny Ann Wheeler
System VP; President Abbott Northwestern Hospital, Ben Bache-Wiig
System VP; President United Hospital, Thomas (Tom) O'Connor
EVP Administration and CFO, Duncan P. Gallagher
EVP Hospital and Specialty Services, Daniel McGinty
Medical Director, Kurt Belk
Vice President Operations, Cheryl Hermann
Medical Director for Quality, Steven (Steve) Bergeson
Vice President, Brian Prokosch
Director Of Pharmacy, Jill Strykowski
Pharmacy Manager, Lee Mork
Vice President Of Human Resources, Margaret Butler
Vice President Of Marketing, Cathy Runck
Vice President, John Lesser
Director Of Pharmacy, Scott Skelton
Clinic Manager, Shawnee Strand
Director Of Nursing, Karen Tennis
Chairman, Mark S. Jordahl
Treasurer, Scott Roby
Treasurer, Anne Uttermark
Auditors: KPMG LLP MINNEAPOLIS MN

LOCATIONS

HQ: ALLINA HEALTH SYSTEM
2925 CHICAGO AVE, MINNEAPOLIS, MN 554071321
Phone: 612 262-5000
Web: WWW.ALLINAHEALTH.ORG

PRODUCTS/OPERATIONS

Selected Services

Care at home
Chronic and advanced illness
Clinics
Home oxygen and medical equipment
Hospitals
Lab services
Medical Services
Medical transportation
Pharmacies
Providers
Specialty services
Urgent care

Selected Hospitals

Abbott Northwestern Hospital (Minneapolis MN)
Buffalo Hospital (Buffalo MN)
Cambridge Medical Center (Cambridge MN)
District One Hospital (Faribault MN)
Mercy Hospital (Coon Rapids MN)
New Ulm Medical Center (New Ulm MN)
Owatonna Hospital (Owatonna MN)
Phillips Eye Institute (Minneapolis MN)
Regina Hospital (Hastings MN)
River Falls Area Hospital (River Falls WI)
St. Francis Regional Medical Center (Shakopee MN)
United Hospital (St. Paul MN)
Unity Hospital (Fridley MN)

COMPETITORS

Bethesda Hospital
Catholic Health Initiatives
CentraCare Health
Children's Hospitals and Clinics of Minnesota
Fairview Health
Hazelden Betty Ford
HealthEast Care System
Mayo Clinic
Methodist Hospital (MN)
North Memorial Health Care
Park Nicollet Health Services
Regions Hospital
St. John's Hospital (Minnesota)
University of Minnesota Medical Center

HISTORICAL FINANCIALS

Company Type: Private

Income Statement

FYE: December 31

	REVENUE ($ mil.)	NET INCOME ($ mil.)	NET PROFIT MARGIN	EMPLOYEES
12/13	3,420	374	10.9%	26,400
12/12	3,246	154	4.8%	—
12/11	2,743	225	8.2%	—
12/09	2,978	0	—	—
Annual Growth	3.5%	—	—	—

2013 Year-End Financials

Return on assets: —
Return on equity: 10.9%
Current ratio: 1.00
Cash ($ mil.): 132

ALRO STEEL CORPORATION

Alro Steel runs its service centers like a grocery store for metals keeping what customers need in easy reach. The service center operator which has a dozen facilities in the US Northeast Midwest and Southeast provides processing services such as aluminum circle cutting CNC flame cutting forming and machining. The company carries an extensive inventory of steel products along with industrial tools and supplies. It also offers plastic sheet rod tube and film through its Alro Plastics division and distributes industrial tools and materials through subsidiary Alro Industrial Supplies.

Geographic Reach

Alro Steel has more than 50 facilities in 12 US states (Florida Illinois Indiana Kentucky Michigan Missouri New York North Carolina Ohio Oklahoma Pennsylvania and Wisconsin).

Operations

Led by its steel activities Alro Steel operates several other businesses: Alro Metals Service Center Alro Metals Plus (steel bars plates and sheet and brass copper aluminum and other products); Alro Plastics (fiberglass acrylics nylon urethanes and other); and Alro Industrial Supplies (threading milling boring holemaking reaming and other machinery and equipment).

Sales and Marketing

The company distributes metals industrial supplies and plastics through its online store.

Strategy

Alro Steel is expanding its operations to meet demand.

In 2014 the company expanded its presence in Greensboro North Carolina by opening a 42000-sq.-ft. facility. It plans to potentially double the work force there within five years.

In 2013 it opened a new 70000 sq. ft. facility in St. Louis to provide regional manufacturers with Alro's broad range of metal products and extensive processing capabilities. That year the company also opened a new 98000 sq. ft. facility in Imperial Pennsylvania to serve manufacturers in western and central Pennsylvania and northern West Virginia.

Company Background

The company was established in 1948.

EXECUTIVES

President and COO, Mark Alyea

LOCATIONS

HQ: ALRO STEEL CORPORATION
3100 E HIGH ST, JACKSON, MI 492036413
Phone: 517 787-5500
Web: WWW.ALRO.COM

COMPETITORS

Carlisle Companies	Mill Steel
Central Steel & Wire	Peerless Steel
Contractors Steel	Tyco
Flame Metals Processing	

HISTORICAL FINANCIALS

Company Type: Private

Income Statement				FYE: May 31
	REVENUE ($ mil.)	NET INCOME ($ mil.)	NET PROFIT MARGIN	EMPLOYEES
05/14	1,613	0	—	2,000
05/13	1,553	0	—	—
05/12	1,605	0	—	—
05/11	1,348	0	—	—
Annual Growth	6.2%	—	—	—

2014 Year-End Financials

Return on assets: 3.8%   Cash ($ mil.): 88
Return on equity: —
Current ratio: 2.80

ALSCO INC.

Alsco has built a big business outfitting its customers in uniforms linens and related products. Operating from some 150 branches in about 10 countries worldwide the company (whose name stands for American linen supply company) rents and sells uniforms linens towels and clean room garments to more than 140000 customers in North America. It also manages janitorial services provides washroom supplies and launders and

sterilizes garments. Alsco serves the automotive food processing restaurant medical and IT industries as well as the federal government. Founded in 1889 by George Steiner the company is owned and operated by the Steiner family.

Geographic Reach

Utah-based Alsco has locations in Australia Brazil Canada China Germany Italy New Zealand Singapore Switzerland Thailand and the US.

Strategy

Alsco heavily promotes its green cleaning solutions and the company has focused on international expansion in recent years. In 2014 the company expanded its uniform and linen services in Texas with a branch in San Antonio and service centers in Austin Houston and Waco.

In addition to uniforms and linens Alsco supplies promotional products for trade shows conventions golf outings sales meetings and other special events and occasions.   800x600

Company Ownership

Alsco is owned and operated by the family of its founder George Steiner. It was formerly known at Steiner Corp.

EXECUTIVES

Co Chief Executive Officer, Robert Stephens
Vice President National Linen Division, Steve Larson

LOCATIONS

HQ: ALSCO INC.
505 E SOUTH TEMPLE, SALT LAKE CITY, UT 841021004
Phone: 801 328-8831
Web: WWW.ALSCO.COM

PRODUCTS/OPERATIONS

Selected Products and Services

Clean room garments
Gown room management
Hospitality/restaurant apparel
Laundry services
Linens
Mats
Mops
Napkins
Restroom service
Towels
Uniform rental and sales
Vacuum filters
Washroom supplies

COMPETITORS

ARAMARK	ISS A/S
Angelica Corporation	Rentokil Initial
Berendsen	ServiceMaster
Cintas	Sodexo USA
Crothall Healthcare	Superior Uniform Group
Diversey	Swisher Hygiene
Ecolab	Tranzonic
G&K Services	UniFirst
Healthcare Services	

HISTORICAL FINANCIALS

Company Type: Private

Income Statement				FYE: December 31
	REVENUE ($ mil.)	NET INCOME ($ mil.)	NET PROFIT MARGIN	EMPLOYEES
12/13	633	33	5.2%	13,585
12/12	614	35	5.8%	—
12/11	556	43	7.8%	—
12/10	544	0	—	—
Annual Growth	5.1%	—	—	—

2013 Year-End Financials

Return on assets: —   Cash ($ mil.): 32
Return on equity: 5.2%
Current ratio: 1.40

ALTA COLLEGES INC.

Auditors: DELOITTE & TOUCHE LLP DENVER

LOCATIONS

HQ: ALTA COLLEGES INC.
7604 TECH WAY STE 400, DENVER, CO 80237
Phone: 303 691-5700
Web: WWW.WESTWOOD.EDU

HISTORICAL FINANCIALS

Company Type: Private

Income Statement				FYE: September 30
	REVENUE ($ mil.)	NET INCOME ($ mil.)	NET PROFIT MARGIN	EMPLOYEES
09/10	413	11	2.9%	2,500
09/09	380	13	3.6%	—
09/08	1,951	0	0.0%	—
Annual Growth	(54.0%)	20799.2%	—	—

2010 Year-End Financials

Return on assets: Cash ($ mil.): 9
Return on equity: 2.9%
Current ratio: 0.70

AMERICA CHUNG NAM (GROUP) HOLDINGS LLC

Ever wondered where all that paper and plastic to be recycled goes? If this company is any indication a lot of it —some 10 million tons —goes to China. The company sells recovered fiber sources to Chinese paper mills where they can be converted into fiberboard cardboard and packaging. It also collects and exports a number of grades of post-consumer plastics. The company sources its materials through exclusive relationships with recycling facilities waste management companies and distribution centers. Founder Yan Cheung owns the company.

Operations

America Chung Nam makes and supplies recovered paper recyclable plastics (including PET HDPE LDPE) ferrous and non-ferrous metals and livestock feed ingredients (including canola meal and fish meal).It annually exports more 10 million tons of recovered paper from North America Europe and Asia.

The company's main customer for fiber is Nine Dragons a paper mill company founded by American Chung Nam's founders.

Geographic Reach

The company has operations in North America Asia and Europe. It has offices in the US (Jersey City Los Angeles and Wilmington North Carolina) Europe (the Netherlands and the UK) and Asia (China and Japan).

Strategy

America Chung Nam supplies fiber materials to Nine Dragons Paper China's largest packaging manufacturer. Nine Dragons (also owned by the owner of American Chung Nam) converts these products into the packaging material that is used to ship various Chinese products to consumers across the world. Once delivered the packaging is ready for recycling and export back to China. In 2013 Nine Dragons operated 35 production lines and had an annual capacity of 14 million metric tons.

The strong relationships with Nine Dragons other paper mills suppliers and transportation partners help the company to adapt to a changing marketplace. In addition to expanding into the recycled plastics market the company is looking for new opportunities in other segments of the recoverable materials market including ferrous and nonferrous metals.

Company Background

America Chung Nam was founded in 1990 by Yan Cheung and Ming Chung Liu. Recognizing the demand for packaging materials driven by China's product exports and having a ready source for fiber materials through America Chung Nam Cheung established Nine Dragons Paper in 1996.

EXECUTIVES

Chief Executive Officer Worldwide Marketing, Peter Wang

Deputy CEO Asia Pacific Region, Teresa Cheung

President and CEO, Yan Cheung

LOCATIONS

HQ: AMERICA CHUNG NAM (GROUP) HOLDINGS LLC
1163 FAIRWAY DR, CITY OF INDUSTRY, CA
917892846
Phone: 909 839-8383
Web: WWW.ACNI.NET

COMPETITORS

Caraustar Recovered	International Paper
Fiber Group	Weyerhaeuser
Guanwei Recycling	

HISTORICAL FINANCIALS

Company Type: Private

Income Statement

FYE: December 31

	REVENUE ($ mil.)	NET INCOME ($ mil.)	NET PROFIT MARGIN	EMPLOYEES
12/09	1,125	16	1.5%	250
12/08	1,363	7	0.6%	—
Annual Growth	(17.5%)	112.4%	—	—

2009 Year-End Financials

Return on assets: 10.8%   Cash ($ mil.): 18
Return on equity: 1.5%
Current ratio: 1.20

AMERICA'S HOME PLACE INC.

America's Home Place builds custom homes on its customers' land. The company builds single-family detached houses with more than 100 custom floor plans and designs. Its two- to five-bedroom cabin chalet ranch two-story and split-level houses range in price from about $80000 to more than $300000. Sizes start at about 900 sq. ft. and go up to to 4000 sq. ft. America's Home Place operates nearly 40 home building and model centers in the southeastern US. Buyers typically already own their land from a single lot to many acres. The company also assists buyers who are not landowners in locating available property. President Barry Conner owns the company he founded in 1972.

Customizable home options include choice of flooring lighting roofing siding cabinets and countertops. The company uses products with such brand names as Armstrong (flooring) CertainTeed (roofing and siding) Sherwin-Williams (paint) and Whirlpool (appliances).

America's Home Place traditionally services its customers at retail outlets where buyers select their design carpet paint tile and window options. However the company added to its marketing strategy to begin providing model centers which feature full-sized model homes plus product and sales centers. The company builds its homes in Florida Georgia Louisiana Mississippi North Carolina South Carolina and Tennessee.

America's Home Place does not offer financing. However it does have relationships with several preferred lenders that are recommended to homebuyers.

EXECUTIVES

Vice President Technology, Alan Cooper
District Vice President, Phil Lelievre
Assistant Vice President, Leah Bagwell
Division President, Chris Strawn
DVP, Ron Meares

LOCATIONS

HQ: AMERICA' S HOME PLACE INC.
2144 HILTON DR, GAINESVILLE, GA 305016172
Phone: 770 532-1128
Web: WWW.AMERICASHOMEPLACE.COM

COMPETITORS

Beazer Homes	Lennar
CalAtlantic	M.D.C.
D.R. Horton	NVR
David Weekley Homes	PulteGroup
KB Home	

HISTORICAL FINANCIALS

Company Type: Private

Income Statement

FYE: December 31

	REVENUE ($ mil.)	NET INCOME ($ mil.)	NET PROFIT MARGIN	EMPLOYEES
12/12	155	7	4.6%	275
12/11	125	4	3.7%	—
12/07	173	8	4.9%	—
12/06	184	0	—	—
Annual Growth	(2.9%)	—	—	—

2012 Year-End Financials

Return on assets: 7.2%   Cash ($ mil.): 3
Return on equity: 4.6%
Current ratio: 0.20

AMERICAN ASSOCIATED PHARMACIES

Auditors: GANT CROFT ASSOCIATES PC

LOCATIONS

HQ: AMERICAN ASSOCIATED PHARMACIES
211 LNNIE E CRAWFORD BLVD, SCOTTSBORO, AL
357697408
Phone: 256 574-6819

HISTORICAL FINANCIALS

Company Type: Private

Income Statement

FYE: December 31

	REVENUE ($ mil.)	NET INCOME ($ mil.)	NET PROFIT MARGIN	EMPLOYEES
12/13	498	0	0.0%	75
12/12	476	0	0.1%	—
12/11	439	1	0.3%	—
12/10	375	0	—	—
Annual Growth	9.9%	—	—	—

2013 Year-End Financials

Return on assets: 9.5%   Cash ($ mil.): 30
Return on equity: —
Current ratio: 0.30

AMERICAN BAR ASSOCIATION

The world's largest voluntary professional organization American Bar Association (ABA) promotes improvements in the American justice system and develops guidelines for the advancement of the legal profession and education. The association provides law school accreditation continuing education legal information and other services to assist legal professionals. The ABA's roster of about 400000 members includes lawyers judges court administrators law librarians and law school professors and students. The organization cannot discipline lawyers nor enforce its rules; it can only develop guidelines. The ABA was founded in 1878.

Operations

The ABA releases books magazines journals and newsletters in various formats through its ABA Publishing division. Popular materials run the gamut of topics including administrative practices for lobbyists immigration law guides for criminal lawyers and leadership and empowerment for women lawyers. Publications are sold through the ABA's online store.

Financial Analysis

The ABA's fiscal 2013 revenue was essentially unchanged vs. the prior year while net income rose 57% over the same period as investment returns rose.

HISTORY

One hundred lawyers from 21 states met in Saratoga New York in 1878 and drafted the constitution for the American Bar Association. As the ABA grew over the next hundred years it came to influence the direction of legal education and the nomination and confirmation of judicial candidates. This brought the ABA into the political arena where its stance on controversial issues politicized the group and opened it to charges of partisan bias.

Its activities also have led to lawsuits (imagine that) including a 1993 suit by the Massachusetts School of Law claiming that the ABA's law school accreditation practices impinged on the university's right to set school policy. The US Justice Department agreed saying the ABA's requirements raised costs without improving educational quality so in 1995 the association changed its accreditation process.

Its influence over judicial nominations took a beating in 1997 when the Senate Judiciary Committee announced that it would no longer await ABA pronouncements before acting on a nomination. The ABA's accreditation process came under fire again in 1998 when the government agency that oversees educational accreditation agencies threatened to penalize or terminate the ABA unless its accreditation policies complied with federal law. Supreme Court Justice Clarence Thomas levied his own attack in 1999 by charging that the ABA's political platforms compromised its objectivity in reviewing judicial nominations.

EXECUTIVES

General Committee Vice Chair Of The Aba, Tatenda Chitemerere

LOCATIONS

HQ: AMERICAN BAR ASSOCIATION
321 N CLARK ST FL 14, CHICAGO, IL 606547598
Phone: 312 988-5000
Web: WWW.AMERICANBAR.ORG

PRODUCTS/OPERATIONS

2011 Revenues

	$ mil.	% of total
Membership dues	75	37
Gifts and grants	59	29
Meeting fees	27	13
Publications	12	6
Royalties	7	3
Investment income	6	3
Advertising	3	2
Designated reserve for operations	3	2
Rental income	3	2
Accreditation fees	1	1
Net assets released from restrictions	1	1
Other	2	1
Total	**205**	**100**

Selected Committees Forums and Other Groups

Coalition for Justice
Commission on Domestic Violence
Commission on Mental and Physical Disability Law
Commission on Racial and Ethnic Diversity in the Profession
Death Penalty Moratorium Project
Division for Public Services
Forum Committee on Affordable Housing
Forum Committee on Entertainment and Sports Industries
Law Student Division
Lawyers' Professional Liability
Office of the President
Pro Bono and Public Service
Section of Administrative Law and Regulatory Practice
Section of Business Law
Senior Lawyers Division
Special Committee on Gun Violence
Standing Committee on Election Law
Standing Committee on Judicial Independence
Young Lawyers Division

HISTORICAL FINANCIALS

Company Type: Private

Income Statement
FYE: August 31

	REVENUE ($ mil.)	NET INCOME ($ mil.)	NET PROFIT MARGIN	EMPLOYEES
08/13	206	39	19.1%	900
08/12	146	9	6.2%	—
08/11	140	10	7.7%	—
08/10	140	0	—	—
Annual Growth	**13.5%**	**—**	**—**	**—**

2013 Year-End Financials

Return on assets: 5.3%
Return on equity: 19.1%
Current ratio: 0.40
Cash ($ mil.): 26

AMERICAN BUREAU OF SHIPPING INC

One of the world's largest ship classification societies American Bureau of Shipping (ABS) offers inspection and analysis services to verify that vessels are mechanically and structurally fit. The not-for-profit company's surveyors examine ships in major ports throughout the world assessing whether the vessels comply with ABS rules for design construction and maintenance. Additionally its engineers consult with shipbuilders on proposed designs and repairs. The not-for-profit company operates from more than 150 offices in about 70 countries. For-profit subsidiaries ABS Group offers risk management consulting services while ABS Nautical Systems provides fleet management software. ABS was founded in 1862.

Geographic Reach

Houston-based ABS operates through a network of 150 offices in 70 countries. Its main divisional offices reside in China Singapore the UK and the US. The organization's technology headquarters is in Houston and it has research centers in Singapore China Korea Canada and Brazil.

Strategy

ABS's strategy for growth includes building upon its core capabilities in inspection integrity management and project quality management services. These services have also been the foundation for growth in the fast-growing regions of the Middle East and the Asia-Pacific. Recent initiatives include the formation of ABS Global Gas Solutions Team to leverage the organization's liquid natural gas and liquified petroleum gas capabilities in 2013. Also in 2013 ABS made significant investments in Singapore to strengthen its engineering and survey capabilities and lay the foundation for strategic global initiatives in the region.

ABS's efforts are meeting with some success: its classed fleet surpassed the 200 million gross tons in 2013. In June of 2013 the organization classed the world's largest container ship the Maersk McKinney Møller.

Additionally ABS Group invested in building its presence in Europe with added business development resources in London and the acquisition of Safetec Nordic AS in Trondheim Norway. The investment positioned ABS Group to capitalize on projects in the North Sea from both Norway and Aberdeen.

In 2012 ABS opened a new energy technology center in Korea and extended its services in Singapore an important region for catering to the deepwater sector.

EXECUTIVES

EVP and COO, Tony Nassif
President and COO ABS Americas Division, James Watson
Chairman President and CEO, Christopher J. (Chris) Wiernicki
EVP Energy Project Development, Kenneth (Ken) Richardson
President and COO ABS Greater China Division, Eric Kleess
President and COO ABS Pacific Division, Derek Novak
President and COO ABS Europe Division, Kirsi Tikka
SVP and CTO, Howard Fireman
VP Global Gas Solutions, Patrick Janssens
Vice President and Division President Americas, Robert (Bob) Gilman
Regional Vice President North America, Stephen (Steve) Gumpel
Vice President Marketing, Susan (Sue) Gonzalez
Vice President for the Eastern Region of Europe, Demetri Stroubakis
Auditors: KIMBRELL & ASSOCIATES SUGAR L

LOCATIONS

HQ: AMERICAN BUREAU OF SHIPPING INC
16855 NORTHCHASE DR, HOUSTON, TX 770606010
Phone: 281 877-5800
Web: WWW.EAGLE.ORG

PRODUCTS/OPERATIONS

Selected Services

Casualty Response
Certification (Marine and Container)
Classification
Environmental
Statutory
Training
Type Approval

COMPETITORS

Accenture	Cotecna Inspection
BSI Group	Lloyd's Register
Booz Allen	Norske Veritas
Bureau Veritas	SGS
ClassNK	

HISTORICAL FINANCIALS

Company Type: Private

Income Statement
FYE: December 31

	REVENUE ($ mil.)	NET INCOME ($ mil.)	NET PROFIT MARGIN	EMPLOYEES
12/12	1,134	155	13.7%	3,000
12/11	726	143	19.8%	—
12/09	648	180	27.9%	—
12/03	159	0	—	—
Annual Growth	**24.4%**	**—**	**—**	**—**

2012 Year-End Financials

Return on assets: —
Return on equity: 13.7%
Current ratio: 1.00
Cash ($ mil.): 136

AMERICAN CHEMICAL SOCIETY

This group has a lot of chemistry. With more than 163000 members the American Chemical Society (ACS) is the world's largest scientific society. It provides information career development and educational resources to member chemists chemical engineers and technicians. ACS also publishes dozens of magazines journals and books and its Chemical Abstracts Service provides access to an online database o more than 70 million literature and research summaries from around the world. ACS also serves as an advocate for its members on public policy issues. The ACS Member Insurance Program provides insurance plans to members. The not-for-profit organization was founded in 1876 and chartered by Congress in 1937.

Geographic Reach

Based in Washington D.C. the ACS's international membership exceeds 24000 and represents more than 100 countries. More than 60% of the content and articles published in ACS journals and abstracts originates from outside the US. The society hosts an annual International Chemistry Olympiad.

Financial Performance

The ACS's revenue increased 2% in 2012 versus 2011 to just shy of $500 million. The increase was driven by a 3% rise in proceeds from electronic services the organization's largest source of income.

EXECUTIVES

Executive Director and CEO, Thomas M. (Tom) Connelly, age 63

Treasurer and CFO, Brian Bernstein

President ACS Publications Division, Brian Crawford

Director Member and Scientific Advancement Division, Denise Creech

President Chemical Abstracts Service (CAS), Manuel Guzman

Director Education Division, Mary Kirchhoff

CIO Washington IT Operations, John Sullivan

President, Diane Grob Schmidt

Vice President Sales and Marketing, Brandon Nordin

Department Head, Chris Pruitt

Vice President Business Development and Publisher Chemical and Engineering News, Kevin Davies

Vice President Science and Technology, Gary Calabrese

Chair, Pat N. Confalone

LOCATIONS

HQ: AMERICAN CHEMICAL SOCIETY
1155 16TH ST NW, WASHINGTON, DC 200364892
Phone: 202 872-4600
Web: WWW.PORTAL.ACS.ORG

PRODUCTS/OPERATIONS

2012 Revenue

	$ mil.	% of total
Electronic services	403	81
Dues	12	2
Membership insurance premiums refunds & fees	11	2
Printed services	10	2
Registration fees & booth sales	10	2
Investment income	10	2
Advertising	8	2
Net assets released from restriction	26	5
Other	6	1
Total	**499**	**100**

HISTORICAL FINANCIALS

Company Type: Private

Income Statement

FYE: December 31

	REVENUE ($ mil.)	NET INCOME ($ mil.)	NET PROFIT MARGIN	EMPLOYEES
12/08	451	(38)	—	2,000
12/05	411	26	6.4%	—
12/04	408	56	13.9%	—
12/03	421	0	—	—
Annual Growth	1.4%	—	—	—

2008 Year-End Financials

Return on assets: —
Return on equity: (-8.5%)
Current ratio: 1.20
Cash ($ mil.): 29

AMERICAN FEDERATION OF LABOR & CONGRESS OF INDUSTRIAL ORGANZATIO

Talk about spending a long time in labor: The AFL-CIO (American Federation of Labor and Congress of Industrial Organizations) has been focused on the task for more than a century. The AFL-CIO is an umbrella organization for more than 55 autonomous national and international unions. Altogether the AFL-CIO represents more than 12 million workers —from actors and airline pilots to marine engineers and machinists. It fights to improve wages and working conditions. The organization charters 50-plus state federations and about 500 central labor councils. Union members generally receive about 30% higher pay and more benefits than non-members. The AFL-CIO was created in 1955 by the merger of the AFL and the CIO.

Geographic Reach

Headquartered in Washington DC the AFL-CIO maintains regional offices and field staff nationwide. Through affiliations the group enjoys a global reach.

Operations

The AFL-CIO's executive council comprises about 55 executives. It monitors executive pay through its Executive PayWatch reports and case studies.

As part of the organization's emphasis on corporate responsibility it devotes blogs reports videos and other mediums to discuss the retail environment such as the dominance of Wal-Mart.

Strategy

The organization's membership has been decreasing due in part to the decline in manufacturing jobs and the increased use of temporary workers and automation. The AFL-CIO's 12.2 million members include 3.2 million members of Working America its community affiliate.

To strengthen and unify unions the AFL-CIO and the National Education Association (NEA) partnered to allow local NEA affiliates to join the federation at the local and state levels through affiliation with the national AFL-CIO. These local affiliates are called Directly Affiliated NEA locals (DANLs). In fiscal 2013 there were 39 DANLs across half a dozen states as well as the District of Columbia that altogether had a total of 38475 members.

To extend its reach further the AFL-CIO is affiliated with the Belgium-based International Trade Union Confederation (ITUC) which is a global union network. ITUC represents some 175 million workers across 150-plus countries and territories with about 310 national affiliates.

Company Background

Despite aggressive plans to increase recruiting the Teamsters and the Service Employees International Union (SEIU) left the AFL-CIO in 2005 over the issues of plummeting membership and the future course of the labor movement. They took 3.3 million members with them.

HISTORY

The American Federation of Labor (AFL) was formed in 1886 in Columbus Ohio by the merger of six craft unions and a renegade craft section of the Marxist-oriented Knights of Labor. Samuel

Gompers a New York cigar factory worker who headed the AFL until his death in 1924 initiated the AFL's pragmatic focus: to work within the economic system to increase wages improve working conditions and abolish child labor.

Gompers' successes incensed employers whose arsenal supported by the US courts and public opinion included injunctions government-backed police forces to crush strikes and the Sherman Anti-Trust Act (used to assail union monopoly powers).

WWI's production needs boosted AFL membership to 4 million by 1919. Labor clashes with management were widespread in the 1920s amid the fear of Bolsheviks. As part of open-shop drives employers replaced strikers with southern African-Americans and Mexican workers.

The Great Depression brought more supportive public and pro-labor laws including the National Industrial Recovery Act (NIRA 1933) which allowed union organizing and collective bargaining. After NIRA was declared unconstitutional the Wagner Act (1936) restated many of NIRA's provisions and established the legal basis for unions.

Union power split in 1935 when AFL coal miner John L. Lewis began organizing unskilled workers. Lewis and his allies expelled from the AFL formed the Congress of Industrial Organizations (CIO 1938) and enjoyed success in unionizing the auto steel textile and other industries. By 1946 the AFL and CIO had 9 million and 5 million members respectively.

Amid postwar concern over rising prices communist infiltration and union corruption Congress passed the Taft-Hartley Act in 1947 (which outlawed closed shops). The new climate of hostility led the AFL (headed by plumber George Meany) and the CIO (headed by autoworker Walter Reuther) to merge in 1955. The AFL-CIO soon expelled the Teamsters and other unions on charges of corruption. (The Teamsters reaffiliated in 1987.)

AFL-CIO membership jumped after President Kennedy gave federal employees the right to unionize (1962); state county and municipal workers soon followed.

Union membership which peaked in the mid-1940s with more than a third of the US labor force was particularly hurt by a jump in imported goods in the 1970s and automation's triumph over manual labor in the 1980s. Legislation supported by the AFL-CIO included a law requiring 60 days' notice for plant closings (1988) and the Family Medical Leave Act (1993). But labor lost its battle against NAFTA (North American Free Trade Agreement) which it feared would export jobs to Mexico.

In 1995 John Sweeney former head of the Service Employees International Union (SEIU) became president of the AFL-CIO in its first contested election. Under Sweeney the union spent $35 million in advertising in 1996 to draw attention to issues. After years with little focus on organizing in 1997 the AFL-CIO launched a massive campaign to organize construction hospital and hotel workers in Las Vegas and committed a third of its budget to recruiting and reorganizing. It supported the Teamsters' successful strike against UPS in 1997 and in 1998 threw its weight behind the Air Line Pilots Association's walkout on Northwest Airlines. It approved a restructuring plan in 1999 and the next year spent significant time and money rallying members all across the US in support of losing presidential candidate Al Gore. In 2002 AFL-CIO announced its pledge of $750 million to create affordable housing in New York City.

At the group's 2005 convention the Teamsters and the SEIU broke ranks over Sweeney's inability to stem the tide of falling membership. They joined a rival group Change to Win Coalition led by SEIU's Andrew Stern.

In September 2009 Richard Trumka was elected president of the AFL-CIO.

EXECUTIVES

Secretary, Eileen Bridegroom
Secretary, Brenda Chase
Auditors: CALIBRE CPA GROUP PLLC WASHIN

LOCATIONS

HQ: AMERICAN FEDERATION OF LABOR & CONGRESS OF INDUSTRIAL ORGANZATIO
815 16TH ST NW, WASHINGTON, DC 200064101
Phone: 202 637-5000
Web: WWW.AFLCIO.ORG

PRODUCTS/OPERATIONS

Selected Departments
Accounting
Campaigns
Civil Human and Women's Rights
Digital Strategies
Facilities Management
Government Affairs
Human Resources
Information Technology
International
Meetings and Travel
Office of General Counsel
Office of Investment
Organizing
Policy
Political
Public Affairs
Support Services

HISTORICAL FINANCIALS

Company Type: Private

Income Statement

FYE: June 30

	REVENUE ($ mil.)	NET INCOME ($ mil.)	NET PROFIT MARGIN	EMPLOYEES
06/13	158	(9)	—	380
06/11*	168	6	3.8%	—
08/09	0	0	—	—
06/08	150	0	—	—
Annual Growth	0.9%	—	—	—

*Fiscal year change

2013 Year-End Financials

Return on assets: 23.8%   Cash ($ mil.): 16
Return on equity: (-5.9%)
Current ratio: 0.80

AMERICAN FEDERATION OF STATE COUNTY & MUNICIPAL EMPLOYEES

American Federation of State County and Municipal Employees AFL-CIO (AFSCME) finds strength in its numbers. The 1.6 million member labor union represents public sector employees in industries such as health care education social services transportation and public works. The group advocates and seeks legislative change for issues relating to social and economic justice in the workplace. AFSCME has more than 3400 local unions in some 45 states the District of Columbia and Puerto Rico. The union is a member of The American Federation of Labor-Congress of Industrial Organizations (AFL-CIO). AFSCME began in

1932 as the Wisconsin State Administrative Clerical Fiscal and Technical Employees Association.

AFSCME supports its members by publishing and providing several magazines newsletters manuals and guides. These include AFSCME Works PrimeTime Preventing Workplace Violence: A Union Representative's Guidebook Safe Jobs Now: A Guide to Health and Safety in the Workplace and AFSCME Local Union Election Manual. The group operates its own blog named GreenLine.

EXECUTIVES

President, Lee A. Saunders
Secretary and Treasurer, Laura Reyes
Vice President Operations, Ken Allen
Treasurer, Tom McGraw
Auditors: BOND BEEBE PC BETHESDA MD

LOCATIONS

HQ: AMERICAN FEDERATION OF STATE COUNTY & MUNICIPAL EMPLOYEES
1625 L ST NW, WASHINGTON, DC 200365665
Phone: 202 429-1000

PRODUCTS/OPERATIONS

Selected Issues
Budget and taxes
Privatization
Women
Health care
Health and safety
Pension security

HISTORICAL FINANCIALS

Company Type: Private

Income Statement

FYE: December 31

	REVENUE ($ mil.)	NET INCOME ($ mil.)	NET PROFIT MARGIN	EMPLOYEES
12/13	181	32	17.7%	450
12/12	160	(15)	—	—
12/08*	2	0	—	—
06/08	2	0	—	—
Annual Growth	104.7%	—	—	—

*Fiscal year change

2013 Year-End Financials

Return on assets: —   Cash ($ mil.): 14
Return on equity: 17.7%
Current ratio: —

AMERICAN FURNITURE WAREHOUSE CO INC

Tony the Tiger hawking home furnishings might give some marketers pause but the combination seems to work for American Furniture Warehouse. American Furniture's television commercials often spotlight white-haired president and CEO Jake Jabs (who has become a well-known personality in the state as well as in the home furnishings industry) accompanied by baby exotic animals mostly tigers. The company sells furniture electronics and decor at discounted prices. It boasts about a dozen retail locations in Colorado and Arizona and sells through its website which also features bridal and gift registries. The company has built a reputation as a home-spun local furniture retailer. Jabs bought the company in 1975.

Geographic Reach
American Furniture has locations in the Colorado cities of Aurora Englewood Centennial

Lakewood Thornton Westminster Colorado Springs Firestone/Longmont Fort Collins Glenwood Springs Pueblo and Grand Junction. In Arizona it has locations in Phoenix Gilbert and Glendale. It serves customers in the neighboring states of Wyoming Utah Kansas Nevada and New Mexico.

Strategy
In 2013 the company made its first move outside Colorado when it opened a 630000-sq.-ft. store in Gilbert Arizona (near Phoenix). It opens another store –in Glendale Arizona –in late 2014. American Furniture hopes to net $3.4 million in direct revenue from the Glendale store during its first year in operation. The furniture retailer also has an eye on expanding into north Scottsdale.

Financial Performance
American Furniture's 2013 sales reached more than $390 million.

EXECUTIVES

Sec-treas, Lori Tielke
Auditors: BAUERLE AND COMPANY DENVER C

LOCATIONS

HQ: AMERICAN FURNITURE WAREHOUSE CO INC
8820 AMERICAN WAY, ENGLEWOOD, CO 801127056
Phone: 303 799-9044
Web: WWW.AFWONLINE.COM

PRODUCTS/OPERATIONS

Selected Products
Decorative accessories
Electronics
Furniture
  Bedroom
  Chairs
  Dining room
  Home office
  Indoor/outdoor
  Living room
  Occasional tables
  Sectionals
  Sofas
  Youth bedroom
Lighting
Mattresses
Rugs

COMPETITORS

Ashley Furniture	Pier 1 Imports
Big Lots	Rooms To Go
Costco Wholesale	Sears
J. C. Penney	Target Corporation
Kmart	Wal-Mart

HISTORICAL FINANCIALS

Company Type: Private

Income Statement

FYE: March 31

	REVENUE ($ mil.)	NET INCOME ($ mil.)	NET PROFIT MARGIN	EMPLOYEES
03/14	413	12	3.0%	1,900
03/13	353	11	3.2%	—
03/12	326	10	3.3%	—
03/11	306	0	—	—
Annual Growth	10.5%	—	—	—

2014 Year-End Financials

Return on assets: 4.7%   Cash ($ mil.): 2
Return on equity: 3.0%
Current ratio: 0.10

AMERICAN INSTITUTE OF CERTIFIED PUBLIC ACCOUNTANTS

When you add it all up the American Institute of Certified Public Accountants (AICPA) makes perfect sense. One of the nation's leading non-profit professional associations the AICPA has more than 400000 members from more than 145 countries who are involved in public accounting business education law and government. The group which generates just more than half of its revenues from membership dues promotes awareness of the accounting profession; identifies financial trends; sets certification licensing and professional standards; and provides information and advice to CPAs. The AICPA distributes its information through websites conferences and forums and publications.

Geographic Reach

The AICPA has offices in New Jersey New York North Carolina and Washington DC.

Operations

The organization develops and grades the Uniform CPA Examination and offers specialty credentials for CPAs who focus on personal financial planning; forensic accounting; business valuation; and information management and technology assurance. Through a joint venture with the Chartered Institute of Management Accountants it has established the Chartered Global Management Accountant designation which sets a new standard for global recognition of management accounting.

The AICPA members represent many areas of practice including business and industry public practice government education and consulting.

Financial Performance

The AICPA's 2014 revenues increased by 4% due to growth in membership dues revenues as a result of a higher membership base and an increase in revenues from professional development and member service conferences and contributions.Net income decreased by 44% due to loss from pensions and postretirement benefits.Operating cash flow increased by 151% as a result of higher cash received from members and customers.

Strategy

The institute's Chartered Global Management Accountant (CGMA) designation is designed to reverse a shortage of PhD accounting faculty at US colleges and universities.

To better serve the public in a time of rapid technological innovation increasing business complexity and regulatory scrutiny the AICPA has launched the Enhancing Audit Quality initiative.The AICPA and its joint venture partner (the Chartered Institute of Management Accountants) have also launched a competency framework that raises the skills of CGMAs in the marketplace.

Company Background

Other initiatives in recent years have included private business financial reporting rebuilding investor confidence and the implementation of the Sarbanes-Oxley Act.

In 2012 the institute launched the CPA Examination internationally in six countries and administered more than 7000 sections in Bahrain Brazil Japan Kuwait Lebanon and the United Arab Emirates.

The AICPA was founded in 1887.

EXECUTIVES

SVP Management Accounting and Global Markets, Arleen R. Thomas
President and CEO, Barry C. Melancon
VP Business Reporting and Member Specialization, Anthony J. Pugliese
SVP Public Practice & Global Alliances, Susan S. Coffey
SVP Congressional and Political Affairs, Mark G. Peterson
SVP Strategy People & Innovation, Lawson Carmichael
CFO, Tim LaSpaluto
Senior Vice President Marketing Develo, Todd Conard
Vice President Students Academics and Membership, Susan (Sue) Pierson
Vice President Information Technology, Hemchandra Nerkar
Vice President Technology Studies, John Hudson
Vice President Member Learning and Competency, Clar Rosso
Vice President Academics Professional Pathways and Inclusion, Jeannie Patton
Vice Chair, Kimberly N. Ellison-Taylor
Chairman, Tim L. Christen
Treasurer, Adell Battle
General Counsel Secretary, Michael (Mel) Buddendeck
Auditors: JH COHN LLP ROSELAND NJ

LOCATIONS

HQ: AMERICAN INSTITUTE OF CERTIFIED PUBLIC ACCOUNTANTS
220 LEIGH FARM RD, DURHAM, NC 277078110
Phone: 919 402-0682
Web: WWW.AICPA.ORG

PRODUCTS/OPERATIONS

2014 Revenue

	$ mil.	% of total
Dues	124	53
Professional development & membership service conference	43	18
Professional examinations	23	10
Publications	21	9
Investment & other income	19	9
Contributions	2	1
Total	**235**	**100**

HISTORICAL FINANCIALS

Company Type: Private

Income Statement

FYE: July 31

	REVENUE ($ mil.)	NET INCOME ($ mil.)	NET PROFIT MARGIN	EMPLOYEES
07/13	219	15	6.9%	400
07/09	199	(13)	—	—
07/08	209	9	4.7%	—
Annual Growth	1.0%	8.9%	—	—

2013 Year-End Financials

Return on assets: 16.3%   Cash ($ mil.): 35
Return on equity: 6.9%
Current ratio: —

AMERICAN INSTITUTES FOR RESEARCH IN THE BEHAVIORAL SCIENCES

The American Institutes for Research (AIR) lives and breathes to enhance human performance. The not-for-profit organization conducts behavioral and social science research on topics related to education and educational assessment health international development and work and training. Clients including several federal agencies use AIR's research in developing policies. As a major ongoing initiative the organization provides tools to improve education both in the US and internationally particularly in disadvantaged areas. John C. Flanagan who developed the Critical Incident Technique personnel-selection tool to identify human success indicators in the workplace founded the organization in 1946.

Geographic Reach

Begun as a small research group affiliated with the University of Pittsburgh AIR's corporate headquarters and business offices are located in Washington DC. The group maintains about a dozen offices in the US. Domestic offices are located in San Mateo and Sacramento California; Atlanta Georgia; Honolulu Hawaii; Chicago and Naperville Illinois; Indianapolis Indiana; Baltimore Frederick and Silver Spring Maryland; Portland Oregon; Columbus Ohio; Chapel Hill North Carolina; New York New York; and Waltham Massachusetts. AIR also operates nearly 10 international offices located in Egypt Honduras Kyrgyzstan Liberia Tajikistan Cote d'Ivoire and Zambia.

Operations

AIR has organized its group into six program areas: Analysis of Longitudinal Data in Education Research Assessment Education Healthand Social Development Workforce and International Development Evaluation and Research.

AIR's assessment program focuses on score reports and online reporting tools to translate large-scale testing data on student achievement into a benchmark for school performance. International human and social development programs aim to improve the quality of life and education in developing areas. It works to achieve this through teacher and school administrator training curriculum development and teaching materials coupled with mobilizing health communications HIV/AIDS education and raising awareness about such issues as child labor exploitation. Working with governments private health care providers and the general public AIR's health programs design implement and evaluate the impact of health care policies.

Strategy

The National Center for Education Statistics a key source for statistical data about education and AIR team up to develop large-scale databases for policymaking. Among various efforts AIR designs surveys and assessments develops questionnaires and tests items as well as informational materials. It also helps in producing The Condition of Education the agency's chief report. The organization's successes include campaigns that address public health emergencies such as the flu and H1N1 and the prevention of HIV/AIDS heart disease and birth defects.

Adding to its educational research capabilities AIR has pursued a number of strategic alliances and acquisitions. In 2015 SEDL joined forced with AIR. The combined organizations will have new and enhanced capabilities around for example disability research as well as an increased capacity to conduct large-scale randomized control trials and provide technical assistance to diverse populations across a broader geographic area.

In 2015 AIR awarded a $500000 grant to Impact Network a nonprofit seeking to make high-quality education in Zambia sustainable.In 2014 AIR launched the Education Policy Center.

Company Background

In 2011 the National Center for Analysis of Longitudinal Data in Educational Research (CALDER) began operating as a joint project of AIR. CALDER examines how public policies and community conditions impact teacher-student results. A year earlier AIR acquired Learning Point Associates a Chicago-based firm that delivers research in the educational sector. Its clients include state education agencies single-school districts private foundations and for-profit organizations.

EXECUTIVES

Vice President Education Human Development, Hans Bos
Vice President of IT, Bob Holstein
Vice President Education Human Development, Mark Schneider
Auditors: RUBINO & COMPANY BETHESDA MA

LOCATIONS

HQ: AMERICAN INSTITUTES FOR RESEARCH IN THE BEHAVIORAL SCIENCES
1000 THMAS JFFERSON ST NW, WASHINGTON, DC 200073835
Phone: 202 403-5000
Web: WWW.AIR.ORG

PRODUCTS/OPERATIONS

Selected Program Areas
Education
Education assessment
Health
Human development
International development
Work & training

HISTORICAL FINANCIALS

Company Type: Private

Income Statement

	REVENUE ($ mil.)	NET INCOME ($ mil.)	NET PROFIT MARGIN	EMPLOYEES
12/13	356	24	6.8%	1,589
12/12	326	22	6.9%	—
12/11	300	13	4.3%	—
12/10	285	0	—	—
Annual Growth	7.7%	—	—	—

FYE: December 31

2013 Year-End Financials

Return on assets: —
Return on equity: 6.8%
Current ratio: 1.30

Cash ($ mil.): 30

AMERICAN LEBANESE SYRIAN ASSOCIATED CHARITIES INC.

Auditors: DELOITTE & TOUCHE LLP MEMPHIS

LOCATIONS

HQ: AMERICAN LEBANESE SYRIAN ASSOCIATED CHARITIES INC.
501 SAINT JUDE PL, MEMPHIS, TN 381051905
Phone: 901 578-2150
Web: WWW.STJUDE.ORG

HISTORICAL FINANCIALS

Company Type: Private

Income Statement

	REVENUE ($ mil.)	NET INCOME ($ mil.)	NET PROFIT MARGIN	EMPLOYEES
06/13	976	210	21.5%	1,200
06/12	780	72	9.3%	—
06/11	1,066	444	41.7%	—
06/10	869	0	—	—
Annual Growth	3.9%	—	—	—

FYE: June 30

2013 Year-End Financials

Return on assets: 1.9%
Return on equity: 21.5%
Current ratio: —

Cash ($ mil.): 35

AMERICAN MEDICAL ASSOCIATION INC

The AMA knows whether there's a doctor in the house. The American Medical Association (AMA) prescribes the standards for the medical profession. The membership group's activities include advocacy for physicians promoting ethics standards in the medical community and improving health care education. Policies are set by the AMA's House of Delegates comprised of elected representatives. The AMA is also a publisher of books for physicians and provides an online physician network through a partnership with Medfusion sells medical malpractice insurance and helps doctors fight legal claims. Founded in 1847 by a physician to establish a code of medical ethics AMA has nearly 225000 members.

Financial Performance

The AMA's revenue declined 4% in 2012 versus 2011 to about $274 million largely due to a material drop in print advertising sales and a downturn in coding book sales. Publishing-related revenue declined by more than $9 million mainly due to the $10 million drop in ad revenues. Continued growth in site licensing helped to offset revenue losses from print subscriptions and reprints. Print book sales fell $9.8 million in 2012 as migration to online products continued. Current Procedural Terminology royalties and online product revenues partially offset the decline in print book sales up $4.5 million in total. Proceeds from membership dues increased 3% in 2012 over 2011 to account for 14% of total revenue. Indeed membership increased more than 3% in 2012 compared with 2011 to approach 225000. Despite the uptick in its ranks AMA membership is still below 2009 when it boasted 228000 members.

Net income increased 8% over the same period due to the decline in cost of goods sold and selling expenses. Cash provided by operating activities increased 11% from $26.2 million in 2011 to $37.6 million in 2012.

Strategy

During this time of historical change for the nation's health care system the AMA's five-year strategic plans emphasizes three core areas of focus: improving health outcomes; accelerating change in medical education; and enhancing physician satisfaction and practice sustainability by shaping delivery and payment models. The group has been an active and vocal participant concerning health care and insurance reform both huge issues in recent years. National campaigns such as the "Voice for the Uninsured" waged by the AMA call attention to deficiencies in our health care system. It is also stridently against Medicare cuts.

As part of the AMA affiliated groups have sprouted to support the association and fund some of its efforts. The American Medical Association Alliance is a large grassroots group established to support and represent physician spouses. The AMA Foundation founded in 1950 funds medical education research and service through its focus on health care. AMA extends its reach internationally through its AMA Office of International Medicine established in 1978.

EXECUTIVES

Senior Vice President Human Resources and Corporate Services, Robert (Bob) Davis
SVP and CFO, Denise M. Hagerty
VP and Chief Medical Information Officer, Michael L. Hodgkins
SVP and Chief Communication and Marketing Officer, Rodrigo A. Sierra
COO, Bernard L. Hengesbaugh
SVP Chief Health and Science Officer, Modena H. Wilson
CEO, James L. Madara
SVP and Editor-in-Chief Scientific Publications, Howard C. Bauchner
SVP and Publisher Periodic Publications, Thomas J. Easley
SVP and General Manager Business Services, Mary G. Henderson
Group VP and CIO, Craig Ethridge
President, Steven J. Stack
Vice President, Deborah Harvey
Vice President, Thomas (Thom) Healy
Vice President, Robert (Bob) Hobart
Vice President Of Government Affairs, Cynthia Brown
Vice President Public Relations, Brenda Craine
Vice President, John (Jack) Harrison
Vice President, Robin Menes
Vice President, Cae Lawler
Secretary, Barbara (Barb) Barzansky

LOCATIONS

HQ: AMERICAN MEDICAL ASSOCIATION INC
330 N WABASH AVE # 39300, CHICAGO, IL 606113586
Phone: 312 464-5000
Web: WWW.AMA-ASSN.ORG

PRODUCTS/OPERATIONS

2012 Sales

	$ mil.	% of total
Royalties &credentialing products	83	30
Books newsletters &online products	39	14
Membership dues	38	14
Insurance commissions	36	13
Advertising	19	7
Periodical online	17	6
Grants & other	10	4
Investment income	9	4
Periodical printsubscriptions	9	4
Other publishing	9	3
Other	0	1
Total	**273**	**100**

HISTORICAL FINANCIALS
Company Type: Private

Income Statement
FYE: December 31

	REVENUE ($ mil.)	NET INCOME ($ mil.)	NET PROFIT MARGIN	EMPLOYEES
12/13	258	(6)	—	1,150
12/08*	3	(0)	—	—
06/06	1	(0)	—	—
12/05	0	0	—	—
Annual Growth	—	—	—	—

*Fiscal year change

2013 Year-End Financials
Return on assets: 14.4% Cash ($ mil.): 7
Return on equity: (-2.7%)
Current ratio: 0.30

AMERICAN PETROLEUM INSTITUTE INC

The American Petroleum Institute (API) is a trade association for the oil and natural gas industry. The group represents more than 625 corporate members including such industry giants as BP and Exxon Mobil as well as small independent companies with offices in more than 20 state capitals and overseas. Besides serving as an advocate in legislative regulatory and media arenas the API compiles data on industry operations. The organization's members come from several segments of the petroleum industry including upstream (exploration and production) downstream (refining and marketing) pipeline operations marine transportation and oil field service. The API was founded in 1919.

Operations

Recent hot issues for the API and its members include the Keystone XL Pipeline and hydraulic fracturing (aka fracking). Indeed in 2013 and 2014 API launched TV radio and online ads in key states in support of the approval of the Keystone XL pipeline.

Geographic Reach

While the organization's focus in primarily domestic Washington D.C.-based API has offices in Beijing Singapore Dubai and Brazil (Rio de Janeiro) as well as an office in Houston.

EXECUTIVES

Vice President Regulatory and Economic Policy, Kyle Isakower
Vice President Communications, Linda Rozett
Vice President Sales, David (Dave) Lax
Executive Vice President Government Affairs, Louis Finkel
Director Media Relations, Eric Wohlschlegel
Vice President General Counsel and Corporate Secretary, Stacy Linden
Vice President, J Elder
Chairman, Ryan M. Lance, age 53
Auditors: TATE & TRYON WASHINGTON DC

LOCATIONS

HQ: AMERICAN PETROLEUM INSTITUTE INC
1220 L ST NW STE 900, WASHINGTON, DC
200054070
Phone: 202 682-8000
Web: WWW.RECYCLEOIL.ORG

HISTORICAL FINANCIALS
Company Type: Private

Income Statement
FYE: December 31

	REVENUE ($ mil.)	NET INCOME ($ mil.)	NET PROFIT MARGIN	EMPLOYEES
12/13	224	0	0.4%	250
12/09	197	19	9.6%	—
12/08	204	(10)	—	—
12/07	1,529	0	—	—
Annual Growth (27.4%)	—	—	—	—

2013 Year-End Financials
Return on assets: — Cash ($ mil.): 17
Return on equity: 0.4%
Current ratio: 0.70

AMERICAN SOCIETY FOR THE PREVENTION OF CRUELTY TO ANIMALS (INC)

This group watches out for Fidos Fluffies and other furry friends all across the country. The ASPCA (American Society for the Prevention of Cruelty to Animals) is a nonprofit organization dedicated to promoting the humane treatment of non-humans. The society's aim is to save the lives of homeless pets and help victims of animal cruelty. It engages in education public awareness and government advocacy efforts and supports the work of independent humane societies throughout the US. It provides medical services and animal placement from facilities in New York City. The privately-funded organization was established in 1866 by Henry Bergh.

Financial Performance

The ASPCA generated nearly $148 million in revenue in 2011. About two-thirds of the society's revenue came from contributions grants and memberships. The remainder is generated by campaigns bequests trust income animal health services fees and royalties and licenses among other sources. The ASPCA spends money on programs (including animal health services and anti-cruelty programs) community outreach grants sponsorships and communications.

Strategy

In 2013 the society opened the ASPCA Behavioral Rehabilitation Center at St. Hubert's Animal Welfare Center in Madison New Jersey. The new rehab center is dedicated to helping animal victims of cruelty.

To help it help animals the ASPCA enlists the help of corporate partners to assist in funding its efforts. Bank of America Fresh Step Lowe's and Subaru donate a portion of their sales to the group. Other donors have included Google UnitedHealth Group Verizon Johnson & Johnson The Gap PepsiCo The McGraw Hill Companies Nestl @nd many others.

EXECUTIVES

EVP and COO, Stephen Musso
Science Advisor, Stephen L. Zawistowski
SVP Community Outreach, Julie Morris
President and CEO, Matthew Bershadker

SVP Adoption Center, Gail Buchwald
SVP Development, Todd Hendricks
SVP Center for People Development, Art Rios
SVP Anti-Cruelty Group, Stacy Wolf
SVP Government Relations, Nancy Perry
SVP and Chief Legal Officer, Beverly Jones
SVP Animal Health Services, Jed Rogers
SVP Operations, Sarah Goodstine
Treasurer, Fredrik Gradin
Vice President Of Shelter Research And Development, Emily Weiss
Vice Chairman, Frederick Tanne
Chairman, Tim F. Wray
Auditors: KPMG LLP NEW YORK NY

LOCATIONS

HQ: AMERICAN SOCIETY FOR THE PREVENTION OF CRUELTY TO ANIMALS (INC)
424 E 92ND ST, NEW YORK, NY 101286804
Phone: 212 876-7700
Web: WWW.ASPCA.ORG

PRODUCTS/OPERATIONS

Selected Programs and Services
Animal Health Services
  Animal Behavior Center
  Animal Poison Control Center
  Bergh Memorial Animal Hospital
  Grief counseling
  Mobile spay/neuter clinic outreach
  Veterinary outreach
Anti-cruelty Initiatives
  Field services
  Government relations
  Humane law enforcement
Community Outreach
  Animal-assisted therapy
  ASPCA Equine Fund
  ASPCA Onyx and Breezy Shefts Adoption Center
  ASPCA Partnership
  ASPCA's Meet Your Match
  ASPCAPro.org
  Disaster readiness
  Mobile adoption center

COMPETITORS

Trupanion

HISTORICAL FINANCIALS
Company Type: Private

Income Statement
FYE: December 31

	REVENUE ($ mil.)	NET INCOME ($ mil.)	NET PROFIT MARGIN	EMPLOYEES
12/13	171	(1)	—	350
12/08	127	34	26.8%	—
12/05	66	19	29.5%	—
12/04	0	0	—	—
Annual Growth	—	—	—	—

2013 Year-End Financials
Return on assets: 8.0% Cash ($ mil.): 14
Return on equity: (-0.8%)
Current ratio: 1.60

AMERICAN SYSTEMS CORPORATION

American Systems provides government and commercial clients with IT management and consulting services including custom engineering and application development. Its consulting division advises clients on such issues as network access and identity management data security and process optimization. The company also provides managed technical support and staffing. American Systems works with government customers to develop systems related to command and control logistics and national security functions. Its commercial-focused operations serve the energy financial services retail and telecom industries among others.

Geographic Reach

The company has 16 offices along the Eastern Seaboard and in Arizona and California.

Operations

American Systems' government unit serves every branch of the US military as well as government agencies ranging from the Federal Aviation Administration to the Department of Agriculture. Its commercial unit on the other hand has served such companies as AT&T The Coca-Cola Company and The Home Depot.

Mergers and Acquisitions

The company's acquisition of Science Applications International Corporation's (SAIC's) Test & Evaluation (T&E) business unit strengthened American Systems' T&E capabilities and expanded the company's offerings to include testing scientific engineering logistic administrative and ancillary support.

EXECUTIVES

Vice President, John (Jack) Manning
Vice President Operations, William Killham
Vice President, Byron Johns
Vice President of IDIQ Service Center Proposal Development, Ruth Bowers
Vice President and Director, Steve Bonwich
Vice President Operations and Human Resources, Bob Hedgpeth
Vice President Of Capture Management, Kristen Murphy
Vice President And Director Engineering Solutions, Cari Smiley
Vice President Of Government Services, Gary Ager
Senior Vice President, Doug Gosnell
Vice President and General Manager of Professional Services, Hyuk Byun
Vice President Human Resources, Christine Braccio
Auditors: DELOITTE & TOUCHE LLP MCLEAN

LOCATIONS

HQ: AMERICAN SYSTEMS CORPORATION
14151 PK MADOW DR STE 500, CHANTILLY, VA 20151
Phone: 703 968-6300
Web: WWW.AMERICANSYSTEMS.COM

PRODUCTS/OPERATIONS

Selected Mergers and Acquisitions
FY2012
Science Applications International Corporation's (SAIC's) Test & Evaluation (T&E) business unit (undisclosed price; Raleigh NC; testing and evaluation services)

COMPETITORS

Alion
Allen Corporation of America
Booz Allen
CACI International
Computer Sciences Corp.
General Dynamics Information Technology
HP Enterprise Services
IBM Global Services
Jacobs Engineering
Kratos Defense & Security Solutions
Leidos
Lockheed Martin Information Systems
ManTech
Northrop Grumman Info Systems
Unisys
Ventera

HISTORICAL FINANCIALS
Company Type: Private

Income Statement
FYE: December 31

	REVENUE ($ mil.)	NET INCOME ($ mil.)	NET PROFIT MARGIN	EMPLOYEES
12/13	324	5	1.6%	1,480
12/12	242	10	4.3%	—
12/11	250	16	6.7%	—
12/10	273	0	—	—
Annual Growth	5.8%	—	—	—

2013 Year-End Financials
Return on assets: 9.0%
Return on equity: 1.6%
Current ratio: 1.40
Cash ($ mil.): 2

AMERICAN UNIVERSITY

Fulfilling the vision of George Washington for a national university in the country's capital American University was chartered by an Act of Congress in 1893 as a private independent co-educational institution under the auspices of the United Methodist Church. Today the school offers a broad range of undergraduate and graduate degree programs to more than 12000 students from 140 countries. Its student-teacher ratio is 12:1. American University has schools devoted to arts and sciences business communications international service public affairs and law. It is one of the top producers of Peace Corps volunteers serving overseas. Nine US presidents have served on American University's Board of Trustees.

Operations

American University is known for what else political activism (it has been named most politically active university in the nation by Princeton Review). But you don't have to be pursuing a degree in political science to attend American University; the school offers about 60 undergraduate degrees 50 master's and 10 doctoral degrees.

The school's research centers and institutes include projects focused on chemistry social sciences art design and business behavior. Its academic centers explore research areas that range from social media to war crimes and global peace.

Financial Performance

American University recognized total revenue growth of 2% in fiscal 2014 due to increases in revenue from net tuition and fees and federal grants and contracts. About 48% of net tuition and fees revenue in fiscal 2014 was funded by federal student financial aid programs (including loan grant and work-study programs).

Strategy

In 2013 the school completed a $34 million expansion of its North Hall located on the northwest corner of its main campus. The the new space will provide 360 beds with shared living rooms for upperclassmen plus an 8000-sq. ft. fitness center. A three-story addition to Nebraska Hall also added 150 new beds in apartment-style units.

Company Background

In 2010 American University ended a seven year fund-raising campaign that raised $211 million to support a number of campus initiatives. The money is being used to strengthen the school's academic programs develop new facilities and help secure American University's financial future.

The school was founded in 1893.

EXECUTIVES

V Pres, Gail Hanson
CFO; VP and Treasurer, Douglas Kudravetz
CIO, David G. Swartz
Provost, Scott A. Bass
President, Cornelius M. Kerwin
Vice President Sales Marketing Financial Advisor, Susan (Sue) Gordon
Department Chairman, Jonathan Loesberg
Vice President, Paula Warrick
Assistant Vice President External Relations and Auxiliary Services, Linda Argo
Assistant Vice President, Jeff Watts
Department Chair Public Administration and Policy, David (Dave) Pitts
Director Media Relations, Maggie Barrett
Assistant Vice President Campaigns And Planning, Peter (Pete) Edleman
Vice President Of Communication, Terry Flannery
Vice President Marketing, Julie Zito
Assistant Vice President Creative Services, Kevin Grasty
Assistant Vice President Housing and Dining Programs, Chris Moody
Assistant Vice President Campus Life A, Robert (Bob) Hradsky
Chairman, Jeffrey A. Sine
Vice Chairman, Jack C. Cassell
Board Member, Walter Calahan
Board Member, Richard (Dick) Harrington
Board Member, Chris Usher
Board Member, Abelardo Morell
Board Member, Acey Harper
Board Member, Harry Callahan
Board Member, Lucian Perkins
Assistant Treasurer, Robert Carter
Auditors: PRICEWATERHOUSECOOPERS LLP BA

LOCATIONS

HQ: AMERICAN UNIVERSITY
4400 MASSACHUSETTS AVE NW, WASHINGTON, DC 200168200
Phone: 202 885-1000
Web: WWW.AMERICAN.EDU

PRODUCTS/OPERATIONS

Selected Schools and Colleges
College of Arts and Sciences (CAS)
Kogod School of Business (Kogod)
School of Communication (SOC)
School of International Service (SIS)
School of Professional and Extended Studies (SPExS)
School of Public Affairs (SPA)
Washington College of Law (WCL)

HISTORICAL FINANCIALS
Company Type: Private

Income Statement
FYE: April 30

	REVENUE ($ mil.)	NET INCOME ($ mil.)	NET PROFIT MARGIN	EMPLOYEES
04/13	507	90	17.9%	2,000
04/12	605	55	9.1%	—
04/09	54	(108)	—	—
04/08	398	0	—	—
Annual Growth	5.0%	—	—	—

2013 Year-End Financials
Return on assets: —
Return on equity: 17.9%
Current ratio: —
Cash ($ mil.): 57

AMERICARES FOUNDATION INC.

AmeriCares Foundation provides emergency medical aid around the world. The not-for-profit charitable organization helps victims of natural disasters and supports long-term humanitarian programs by collecting medical supplies in the US and overseas and delivering them to places where they are needed. AmeriCares has provided aid in more than 90 countries worldwide. In the US the organization offers medical assistance runs a camp for kids with HIV/AIDS and conducts HomeFront a program that renovates housing for the needy in parts of Connecticut and New York. Robert C. Macauley founded AmeriCares in 1982.

Geographic Reach

The company has presence in US Latin America Caribbean Asia and Eurasia Africa and Middle East.

Financial Performance

AmeriCares' revenue decreased 9% to $572 million in 2014 due to a decline in public support and loss on investments.

EXECUTIVES

President and CEO, Curtis R. (Curt) Welling, age 64
SVP Communications & Marketing, Carol Shattuck
SVP Development and Communications, Carolyn O'Brien
SVP Global Program Operations, Chrisoph Gorder
Director Corporate Relations, Geoff Kneisel
Director Logistics, Peter Tokarczyk
SVP Human Resources, Kevin R. Gilrain
Medical Director, Frank Bia
VP; Managing Director AmeriCares India, Purvish M. Parikh
Director Communications, Peggy Atherlay
SVP Finance and Technology, Katherine A. Sears
Auditors: GRANT THORNTON LLP NEW YORK

LOCATIONS

HQ: AMERICARES FOUNDATION INC.
88 HAMILTON AVE, STAMFORD, CT 069023100
Phone: 203 658-9500
Web: WWW.AMERICARES.ORG

HISTORICAL FINANCIALS

Company Type: Private

Income Statement
FYE: June 30

	REVENUE ($ mil.)	NET INCOME ($ mil.)	NET PROFIT MARGIN	EMPLOYEES
06/13	621	(38)	—	125
06/12	526	5	1.1%	—
06/11	671	(0)	—	—
06/10	795	0	—	—
Annual Growth	(7.9%)	—	—	—

2013 Year-End Financials
Return on assets: —
Return on equity: (-6.2%)
Current ratio: 0.50
Cash ($ mil.): 4

AMES CONSTRUCTION INC.

Ames Construction aims right for the heart of heavy construction. The company is a general contractor providing heavy civil and industrial construction services to the transportation mining and power industries mainly in the West and Midwest. The family-owned company works on highways airports bridges rail lines mining facilities power plants and other infrastructure projects. Ames also performs flood control environmental remediation reclamation and landfill work. Additionally the firm builds golf courses and undertakes commercial and residential site development projects. Ames typically partners with other companies to perform the engineering and design portion of construction jobs.

Geographic Reach

Ames Construction has offices in the US in Minnesota Arizona California Colorado Nevada and Utah as well as in Canada.

Operations

Some of Ames Construction's project include the Arlington Power Plant Dry Fork Station Unit 1 Site Work and Substructure Construction Rentech ClearFuels Cortez Hills Mine and Mills Site and Airport Extension Projects such as its MSP International Airport work.

Strategy

Ames Construction is also known to take on subcontracting work. It contributed to the construction of the new Minnesota Twins ballpark. Ames also is serving as subcontractor and partner in a joint venture with Fluor and Balfour Beatty Rail that is undertaking the $1 billion design/build portion of a rail line project for the Denver Regional Transit District. The contract involves designing and constructing electrified commuter rail lines stations and a vehicle maintenance facility. The joint venture will also operate and maintain the system for a period of 40 years. All lines are expected to be in service by 2016.

Having earned the contract in 2013 Ames Construction is the construction manager general contractor (CMGC) contracting team for the Winona Bridge the first Minnesota Department of Transportation project to use the CMGC procurement method.

EXECUTIVES

Vice President Of Engineering, John Tripi
Regional Vice President of Engineering, Robert (Bob) Gillis
Vice President Engineering, Jeff Williamson
Vice President Of Engineering, Butch Trebesch
Vice President Design Build, Richard Fahland
Vice President Director Manager IT IS, Tony W Meyers
Auditors: CLIFTONLARSONALLEN LLP MINNEA

LOCATIONS

HQ: AMES CONSTRUCTION INC.
14420 COUNTY ROAD 5, BURNSVILLE, MN 553066997
Phone: 952 435-7106
Web: WWW.AMESCONSTRUCTION.COM

Selected Locations
Arizona
California
Canada
Colorado
Minnesota
Nevada
Utah

PRODUCTS/OPERATIONS

Selected Markets
Commercial
  Commercial site development
  Environmental remediation/ landfills
  Residential site development
Mining
  Contract mining
  Leach pad construction
  Mine development
  Mine infrastructure
  Mine reclamation/remediation
  Mine tailings dam
Power
  Coal fired
  Combined-cycle/natural gas
  Nuclear
  Transmission
  Wind
Transportation
  Airports
  Bridges
  Highways
  Railroads
Water resources
  Dams reservoirs and flood control
  Wastewater/water treatment
  Water delivery
  Water retention structures

COMPETITORS

American Civil Constructors Holdings
Balfour Beatty Construction
Clyde Companies
Granite Construction
Meadow Valley
Peter Kiewit Sons'
SEMA Construction
Skanska USA Civil
Sterling Construction
Tutor-Saliba

HISTORICAL FINANCIALS

Company Type: Private

Income Statement
FYE: November 30

	REVENUE ($ mil.)	NET INCOME ($ mil.)	NET PROFIT MARGIN	EMPLOYEES
11/14*	1,074	26	2.4%	2,200
12/12	582	5	1.0%	—
11/10	685	18	2.7%	—
11/09	712	0	—	—
Annual Growth	8.6%	—	—	—

*Fiscal year change

2014 Year-End Financials
Return on assets: 8.3%
Return on equity: 2.4%
Current ratio: 0.80
Cash ($ mil.): 42

ANCHORAGE SCHOOL DISTRICT

Auditors: BDO USA LLP ANCHORAGE ALASK

LOCATIONS

HQ: ANCHORAGE SCHOOL DISTRICT
5530 E NTHRN LIGHTS BLVD, ANCHORAGE, AK 99504
Phone: 907 742-4000
Web: WWW.ASDK12.ORG

HISTORICAL FINANCIALS
Company Type: Private

Income Statement
FYE: June 30

	REVENUE ($ mil.)	NET INCOME ($ mil.)	NET PROFIT MARGIN	EMPLOYEES
06/13	858	(0)	—	5,039
06/12	834	(8)	—	—
06/11	822	(2)	—	—
06/10	774	0	—	—
Annual Growth	3.5%	—	—	—

ANDERSEN CONSTRUCTION COMPANY

Andersen Construction Company focuses on commercial and industrial construction in the Western US. The group which introduced concrete tilt-up construction to the Pacific Northwest builds everything from parking structures to medical facilities manufacturing plants and industrial complexes. It also works on institutional projects for the government and education markets. Other projects include tenant improvements seismic upgrades and remediation construction. The company provides construction management (which accounts for 80% of its work) as well as general contracting and design/build delivery. It also offers startup and commissioning services. Chairman and CEO Andy Andersen founded the company in 1950.

Andersen Construction has offices in Oregon and Idaho. It has built and renovated more than 35 Bank of America branches throughout the Pacific Northwest constructed a computer chip manufacturing facility for Hewlett-Packard and worked on the Cole M. Rivers Hatchery the largest fish hatchery on the West Coast. Projects under way include an expansion and renovation of the Shriners Hospitals For Children in Portland.

As a green builder Andersen Construction incorporates LEED standards into its design/build plans and is a founding member of the Oregon Natural Step Network an international network that follows a scientific framework that helps businesses individuals and organizations achieve sustainability.

EXECUTIVES

President, David Andersen
CFO, Bill Eckhardt
Information Systems Manager, Tim Ashman
Chairman, H. A. (Andy) Andersen
VP Operations, Martin Cloe
Director of Business Development, Steve Tinney
VP Development Services, Bob Durgan
VP Construction, Bob Okano
Chief Estimator, Brian Knudsen
Owner, Don Hynes
Senior Vice President Adventist Medical Center, Thomas Russell
Auditors: THOMPSON KESSLER WIEST & BORQU

LOCATIONS

HQ: ANDERSEN CONSTRUCTION COMPANY
6712 N CUTTER CIR, PORTLAND, OR 972173933
Phone: 503 283-6712
Web: WWW.ANDERSEN-CONST.COM

PRODUCTS/OPERATIONS

Selected Services
Commercial development (acquisition due diligence financing land entitlements leasing master planning and permitting)
Construction management
Design/build
Estimating
General contracting
Green building
Preconstruction
Startup and commissioning

COMPETITORS

Absher	PCL Construction
GLY Construction	Enterprises
Hoffman Corporation	Skanska USA Building
Howard S. Wright	Swinerton Builders
Construction	Turner Corporation
M. A. Mortenson	

HISTORICAL FINANCIALS
Company Type: Private

Income Statement
FYE: January 31

	REVENUE ($ mil.)	NET INCOME ($ mil.)	NET PROFIT MARGIN	EMPLOYEES
01/14	329	0	0.1%	150
01/11	278	1	0.4%	—
01/06	198	0	0.5%	—
01/05	274	0	—	—
Annual Growth	—	—	—	—

2014 Year-End Financials
Return on assets: 13.5%   Cash ($ mil.): 8
Return on equity: 0.1%
Current ratio: 0.10

ANDERSON AND DUBOSE INC.

You might say this company keeps the Big Mac big and the Happy Meals happy. Anderson-DuBose Pittsburgh is a leading wholesale distributor that supplies food and non-food items to McDonald's and Chipotle fast-food restaurants in Ohio Pennsylvania New York and West Virginia. It serves about 500 Golden Arches locations with frozen meat and fish dairy products and paper goods and packaging as well as toys for Happy Meals. One of the largest black-owned companies in the US Anderson-DuBose was started in 1991 by Warren Anderson and Stephen DuBose who purchased control of a McDonald's distributorship from Martin-Brower. Anderson became sole owner in 1993 when he bought out his partner's stake in the business.
Auditors: PRICEWATERHOUSECOOPERS LLP CL

LOCATIONS

HQ: ANDERSON AND DUBOSE INC.
5300 TOD AVE SW, WARREN, OH 444819767
Phone: 440 248-8800
Web: WWW.ANDERSON-DUBOSE.COM

COMPETITORS

Golden State Foods	Meadowbrook Meat
Gordon Food Service	Company
Keystone Foods	Reinhart FoodService
MAINES	Sysco
Martin-Brower	US Foods

HISTORICAL FINANCIALS
Company Type: Private

Income Statement
FYE: December 30

	REVENUE ($ mil.)	NET INCOME ($ mil.)	NET PROFIT MARGIN	EMPLOYEES
12/11	372	1	0.3%	100
12/10	341	1	0.5%	—
12/09	757	0	—	—
Annual Growth	—	7130.5%	—	—

ANMED HEALTH

Auditors: DIXON HUGHES PLLC ASHEVILLE

LOCATIONS

HQ: ANMED HEALTH
800 NH FANT ST, ANDERSON, SC 29621
Phone: 864 261-1000
Web: WWW.ANMEDHEALTH.ORG

HISTORICAL FINANCIALS
Company Type: Private

Income Statement
FYE: December 31

	REVENUE ($ mil.)	NET INCOME ($ mil.)	NET PROFIT MARGIN	EMPLOYEES
12/13*	463	93	20.1%	2,600
09/12	512	55	10.9%	—
09/09	419	(13)	—	—
12/08	0	0	—	—
Annual Growth	357.5%	—	—	—

*Fiscal year change

2013 Year-End Financials
Return on assets: 3.2%   Cash ($ mil.): 40
Return on equity: 20.1%
Current ratio: 1.60

ANN & ROBERT H. LURIE CHILDREN'S HOSPITAL OF CHICAGO

When it comes to caring for kids Ann & Robert H. Lurie Children's Hospital of Chicago has the Windy City covered. Founded in 1882 the not-for-profit hospital provides a full range of pediatric services with acute and specialty care. Lurie Children's provides services through its main hospital campus with about 300 beds and outpatient centers in Chicago's Lincoln Park neighborhood and through more than a dozen suburban outpatient centers and outreach partner locations in the greater Chicago area. A leader in pediatric research the hospital operates the Children's Hospital of Chicago Research Center and is the pediatric teaching facility of Northwestern University's Feinberg School of Medicine.

Operations

Lurie Children's serves roughly 150000 patients each year and employs some 1350 pediatric specialists with expertise in 70 different specialties. The hospital is one of only about a dozen children's hospitals nationwide to perform more than 1000 liver transplants. The center performs on average 50 solid organ and 50 stem cell transplants annually.

A major research center Lurie Children's is one of nearly 30 interdisciplinary research centers and institutes belonging to the hospital's academic partner –Feinberg School of Medicine. Its research arm Stanley Manne Children's Research Institute employs some 200 physician-scientists and research investigators who in 2014 were awarded more than $40 million in external funding.

Geographic Reach

Based in Chicago Lurie Children's has cared for patients from throughout the US and about 50 countries around the globe.

Financial Performance

Lurie Children's saw revenues increase by 8% to $826 million in fiscal 2014 (ended August). That growth was attributed to a rise in patient care revenues and other earnings. Net income increased 198% to $128 million that year largely due to the higher revenue as well as strong investment returns.

Cash flow from operations rose 36% to $124.5 million in fiscal 2014.

Strategy

The hospital has all-private rooms even in the neonatal intensive care unit; private rooms are said to speed healing by reducing hospital-acquired infection and minimize noise. Lurie Children's is working to enhance its specialist services and has upgraded its information technology systems. In 2013 it implemented a Voalte system that allows nurses to communicate through rapid-response systems including text messages and high-definition voice calls. Also that year it opened the first pediatric gender identity clinic. In 2015 the hospital acquired the fourth-generation da Vinci Xi robotic system for use in minimally invasive surgery.

In 2014 Lurie Children's Health Partners (composed of Lurie Children's and two groups of pediatricians) launched the Clinically Integrated Network the first health care network in Chicago to focus exclusively on children and their families. Its areas of focus include care coordination obesity asthma immunizations and child development.

EXECUTIVES

President and CEO, Patrick M. Magoon
Chief Human Resource Officer, Robert Powell
Chief Marketing and Managed Care Officer, Maureen Murphy
CFO, Paula Noble
Communications and Media Strategist, Kathleen Keenan
President Children's Memorial Foundation, Thomas J. Sullivan
Head Division Hematology Oncology and Stem Cell Transplant, Morris Kletzel
Head Kidney Diseases (Nephrology), Craig B. Langman
Division Head Neurology, Leon G. Epstein
Head Division Rheumatology, Marisa S. Klein-Gitelman
Auditors: ERNST & YOUNG US LLP CHICAGO

LOCATIONS

HQ: ANN & ROBERT H. LURIE CHILDREN' S HOSPITAL OF CHICAGO
225 E CHICAGO AVE, CHICAGO, IL 606112991
Phone: 312 227-4000
Web: WWW.LURIECHILDRENS.ORG

Selected Illinois Locations
Lurie Children' s at Cadence Health (Winfield)
Main Hospital (Chicago)
Outpatient Center in Arlington Heights (Arlington Heights)
Outpatient Center in Glenview (Glenview)
Outpatient Center in Lake Forest (Lake Forest)

Outpatient Center in Lincoln Park (Chicago)
Outpatient Center in New Lenox (New Lenox)
Outpatient Center in Westchester (Westchester)
Outpatient Services in Grayslake (Grayslake)
Outpatient Services in Gurnee (Gurnee)
Outpatient Services in Lincoln Square (Chicago)
Pediatrics - Uptown (Chicago)
Rehabilitation Services at Westbrook (Westchester)

PRODUCTS/OPERATIONS

2014 Sales

	% of total
Patient care revenues	85
Grants gifts & endowment income	8
Other revenues	7
Total	**100**

Selected Services

Adolescent Medicine
Allergy and Immunology
Anesthesiology
Audiology
Autonomic Medicine
Brain Tumor
Cancer and Blood Disorders
Cardiology (Heart Center)
Child Abuse Pediatrics
Child and Adolescent Psychiatry
Clinical Nutrition
Convenient Care
Critical Care
Cystic Fibrosis
Dentistry and Oral Surgery
Dermatology
Emergency Medicine
Endocrinology
Epilepsy
Fetal Health
Gastroenterology Hepatology and Nutrition (Digestive Disorders)
Gender and Sex Development
General Pediatric Surgery
General Pediatrics
Genetics Birth Defects and Metabolism
Heart Failure and Transplants
HIV/AIDS Prevention
Infectious Diseases
Intestinal Transplants
Kidney Diseases
Kidney Transplants
Liver Transplants
Medical Imaging (Radiology)
Neonatology
Neurology
Neurosurgery
Occupational Therapy
Ophthalmology
Orthopaedic Surgery
Orthotics/Prosthetics
Otolaryngology (ENT)
Palliative Care
Pathology and Laboratory Medicine
Physical Therapy
Plastic and Reconstructive Surgery
Pulmonary Medicine
Rehabilitative Services
Rheumatology
Speech-Language Pathology
Spina Bifida Center
Sports Medicine
Stem Cell Transplants
Transitioning to Adult Care
Transplantation
Urology

COMPETITORS

Advocate Health Care	NorthShore University
Advocate Lutheran	HealthSystem
General Hospital	Northwestern Lake
Alexian Brothers	Forest Hospital
Health System	Northwestern Memorial
Covenant Ministries	HealthCare
HCA	Rush System for Health
Loyola University	SSM Health Care
Health System	Sinai Health System
Mercy Hospital and	University of Chicago
Medical Center	Medical Center

HISTORICAL FINANCIALS

Company Type: Private

Income Statement

FYE: August 31

	REVENUE ($ mil.)	NET INCOME ($ mil.)	NET PROFIT MARGIN	EMPLOYEES
08/13	694	28	4.2%	2,800
08/10	599	52	8.8%	—
08/09	533	(5)	—	—
08/08	410	0	—	—
Annual Growth 11.1%		—	—	—

2013 Year-End Financials

Return on assets: 11.0%   Cash ($ mil.): 92
Return on equity: 4.2%
Current ratio: 1.80

ANNE ARUNDEL COUNTY BOARD OF EDUCATION

Auditors: CLIFTON GUNDERSON LLP BALTIMO

LOCATIONS

HQ: ANNE ARUNDEL COUNTY BOARD OF EDUCATION
2644 RIVA RD, ANNAPOLIS, MD 214017427
Phone: 410 222-5000
Web: WWW.AACPS.ORG

HISTORICAL FINANCIALS

Company Type: Private

Income Statement

FYE: June 30

	REVENUE ($ mil.)	NET INCOME ($ mil.)	NET PROFIT MARGIN	EMPLOYEES
06/13	1,147	3	0.3%	7,200
06/04	712	0	0.1%	—
06/03	701	50	7.1%	—
Annual Growth 5.1%		(23.0%)		

2013 Year-End Financials

Return on assets: 3.8%   Cash ($ mil.): 166
Return on equity: 0.3%
Current ratio: —

ANNE ARUNDEL MEDICAL CENTER INC.

The ill and infirm get the royal treatment at Anne Arundel Medical Center. The full-service acute-care hospital serves the residents of Anne Arundel Calvert Prince George's and Queen Anne counties in Maryland. With about 425 beds the hospital administers care for women's health oncology pediatrics (it has a level III neonatal intensive care unit) neurology orthopedics and cardiovascular care. The medical center also has weight loss sleep disorder and rehabilitation centers. Anne Arundel which opened its doors in 1902 and is part of the Anne Arundel Health System has expanded its service offerings through various affiliations with regional specialty and primary care clinics. It also has a partnership with Johns Hopkins Medicine.

Operations

With more than 1000 staff members Anne Arundel handles some 26000 inpatient visits and 102000 outpatient visits per year. It also manages more than 5000 births and 93000 emergency room visits.

Johns Hopkins and the not-for-profit Anne Arundel share some services faculty and patients through their collaboration. They also operate a joint outpatient urgent-care facility. Additionally the two organizations work together to perform clinical research projects and conduct physician graduate medical education programs.

Geographic Reach

In addition to its 57-acre Annapolis campus Anne Arundel has outpatient centers in Bowie Kent Island Odenton Pasadena and Waugh Chapel.

Sales and Marketing

In 2014 Medicare payments accounted for about one-third of net patient revenues.

Financial Performance

In 2014 revenue grew 3% to $591 million as net patient services revenues increased. However net income fell 23% to $42 million due to a decline in non-operating income (investment earnings). Cash flow from operations spike 188% to $56 million as cash generated from patient receivables prepaid expenses and other sources rose.

Strategy

Anne Arundel has in recent years added new facilities to better keep up with a continued growth in demand for health care services throughout its service area. In 2015 it opened the second phase of its Pasadena Pavilion adding physical therapy orthopedics and sports medicine capabilities. It also opened a new FastCare walk-in clinic in a grocery store/pharmacy in Annapolis. In 2014 the system opened an outpatient mental health clinic in Annapolis which provides services for patients 13 years of age and older.

In 2013 Anne Arundel opened a training center –the James and Sylvia Earl Simulation to Advance Innovation and Learning (SAIL) Center –to enhance its medical education programs and improve the quality and safety of care in the region. It also opened the Hackerman-Patz House that year to provide an affordable and convenient housing option for families of patients.

Also in 2013 the organization was designated as a Medicare accountable care organization (ACO) by the US government. ACOs work to coordinate care for Medicare patients to improve quality and reduce expenses.

EXECUTIVES

R V Pres, Joseph (Jo) Moser
Auditors: ERNST & YOUNG LLP BALTIMORE

LOCATIONS

HQ: ANNE ARUNDEL MEDICAL CENTER INC.
2001 MEDICAL PKWY, ANNAPOLIS, MD 214013280
Phone: 443 481-1000
Web: WWW.ANNEARUNDELDIAGNOSTICS.COM

PRODUCTS/OPERATIONS

Selected Centers and Services
Blood Donor Center
Breast Center
Cardiac Cath Lab
Chest Pain Center
DeCesaris Cancer Institute
Diabetes Wound and Hyperbaric Center
Diagnostic Imaging
Heart and Vascular Institute
Joint Center
Laboratory

Pediatrics
Rehabilitation
Research Institute
Sleep Disorder Center
Spine Center
Stroke Center
Surgery
Women' s and Children' s Center

COMPETITORS

Ascension Health	Johns Hopkins Medicine
Bon Secours Health	LifeBridge Health
Dimensions Healthcare	MedStar Health
Franklin Square Hospital Center	Sinai Hospital of Baltimore
GBMC	St. Agnes HealthCare
Harbor Hospital	University of Maryland Medical System
Johns Hopkins Health System	

HISTORICAL FINANCIALS

Company Type: Private

Income Statement

FYE: June 30

	REVENUE ($ mil.)	NET INCOME ($ mil.)	NET PROFIT MARGIN	EMPLOYEES
06/13	493	16	3.4%	1,890
06/11	445	24	5.4%	—
06/10	413	20	4.9%	—
06/09	0	0	—	—
Annual Growth	—	—	—	—

2013 Year-End Financials

Return on assets: 18.6%
Return on equity: 3.4%
Current ratio: 0.20

Cash ($ mil.): 26

API GROUP INC.

Holding company APi Group has a piece of the action in two main sectors: fire protection systems and industrial and specialty construction services. APi boasts about 40 subsidiaries which operate as independent companies across the US (nearly half of them in Minnesota) the UK and Canada. Services provided by the company's construction subsidiaries include HVAC and plumbing system installation; electrical industrial and mechanical contracting; industrial insulation; and garage door installation. Safety-focused units install a host of fire sprinkler detection security and alarm systems. The family-owned company was founded in 1926 by Reuben Anderson father of chairman Lee Anderson.

Geographic Reach

Minnesota-based APi Group operates companies throughout North America and the UK.

Sales and Marketing

APi Group serves several sectors such as security and defense education commercial industrial medical oil and gas and residential.

Operations

Through its various companies APi Group is involved in engineering designing constructing and installing LEED green-building certification program projects. Its divisions include Architectural Roofing and Mechanical Classic Industrial Services APi Construction APi Distribution and Industrial Fabricators among others.

Strategy Although APi Group companies are independent they often pool resources and work together to service clients.

Mergers and Acquisitions The highly acquisitive APi Group regularly acquires new companies to strengthen its growing group.

In 2013 the company's Western States Fire Protection (WSFP) acquired Advanced Fire an Oklahoma City-based fire-suppression company that specializes in military work. Buying Advanced Fire extends the company's reach in the fire protection industry and boosts its market share within Oklahoma City and the surrounding area. APi Group's Delta Fire Systems acquired Idaho's 3-D Fire which provides full-fire-system design fabrication installation testing and certification capabilities for commercial and private projects.APi Group previous purchases include Dynamic Fire Protection LLC (DFP) Omlid & Swinney Fire Protection and Security Canada-based Fire Stop Enterprises Ohio-based 3S and Kansas-based mainline pipeline contractor Jomax Construction.

EXECUTIVES

Vice President of Construction, Mark Udager
Auditors: MCGLADREY & PULLEN LLP MINNE

LOCATIONS

HQ: API GROUP INC.
1100 OLD HIGHWAY 8 NW, SAINT PAUL, MN 551126447
Phone: 651 636-4320
Web: WWW.APIGROUPINC.COM

PRODUCTS/OPERATIONS

Selected Subsidiaries
Fire Protection Systems
  Alliance Fire Protection Inc.
  APi National Service Group
  Davis-Ulmer Sprinkler Company
  Delta Fire Systems Inc.
  Grunau Company
  Halon Banking Systems
  International Fire Protection Inc.
  Island Fire Sprinkler Inc.
  Reliance Fire Protection
  Rich Fire Protection Co Inc.
  Security Fire Protection Company
  United States Fire Protection Company
  VFP Fire Systems Inc.
  Viking Automatic Sprinkler Company
  Vipond Fire Protection Inc. (Canada)
  Vipond Fire Protection Ltd. (UK)
  Western States Fire Protection Inc.
Industrial and Specialty Construction Services
  3S Incorporated
  Anco Products Inc.
  APi CAD Services
  APi Construction Company
  APi Distribution Inc.
  APi Electric
  APi Supply Inc.
  Classic Industrial Services Inc.
  Doody Mechanical Inc.
  Garage Door Store
  Grunau Company Inc.
  Industrial Contractors Inc.
  Industrial Fabricators Inc.
  Jamar Company
  Jomax Construction Co.
  LeJeune Steel Company
  NYCO Inc.
  Tessier' s Inc.
  Twin City Garage Door Company
Low Voltage
  APi Systems Group Inc.
  APi Systems Integrators
  Vipond Systems Group

COMPETITORS

Comfort Systems USA	John E. Green
EMCOR	TDIndustries
Integrated Electrical Services	Team
Irex	Turner Industries
	Tyco Fire & Security

HISTORICAL FINANCIALS
Company Type: Private

Income Statement
FYE: December 31

	REVENUE ($ mil.)	NET INCOME ($ mil.)	NET PROFIT MARGIN	EMPLOYEES
12/13	2,049	93	4.6%	4,237
12/12	1,731	62	3.6%	—
12/11	1,484	52	3.6%	—
12/10	1,238	0	—	—
Annual Growth	18.3%	—	—	—

2013 Year-End Financials
Return on assets: 3.9%
Return on equity: 4.6%
Current ratio: 1.10

Cash ($ mil.): 19

APPLE AMERICAN GROUP LLC

This company must really enjoy casual dining in its neighborhood. Apple American Group is the largest franchisee of Applebee's with about 450 Applebee's Neighborhood Grill & Bar locations in about two dozen states. The #1 casual dining chain in the US Applebee's restaurants offer a full-service menu of beef chicken and seafood entrees along with a wide selection of appetizers. Apple American's restaurants are found from coast to coast with large concentrations in the Midwest (Ohio Indiana Pennsylvania) and on the West Coast (California Washington). Founded in 1998 by CEO Greg Flynn Apple American is controlled by private equity firm Weston Presidio Service.

Strategy

As a franchise operator the company benefits from the fact that its eateries carry a well-known brand backed by by the national marketing muscle of Applebee's parent DineEquity. It pays for the privilege of operating Applebee's restaurants in the form of royalties and franchise fees. The company also agrees to abide by operating agreements designed to ensure consistency in food and service quality. Locally Apple American's restaurants compete for business against a wide range of independent operators as well as such national chains as Chili's (owned by Brinker International) and Outback Steakhouse (OSI Restaurant Partners).

Apple American has been rapidly building its base of casual dining eateries; it has more than doubled its locations since 2010. It operates via a decentralized business model where each geographic region is managed by a market president who has wide latitude in decision-making.

EXECUTIVES
Vice President of Real Estate, Patrick J (Paddy) Eulberg
Vice President Of Real Estate, Patrick Eulberg
Auditors: PRICEWATERHOUSECOOPERS LLP CL

LOCATIONS
HQ: APPLE AMERICAN GROUP LLC
6200 OAK TREE BLVD # 250, CLEVELAND, OH 441316933
Phone: 216 525-2775
Web: WWW.APPLEAMERICAN.COM

Selected Locations
Alabama
California

Colorado
Delaware
Georgia
Idaho
Indiana
Maine
Massachusetts
Minnesota
Nevada
New Hampshire
New Jersey
New Mexico
New York
Ohio
Oregon
Pennsylvania
Rhode Island
Vermont
Washington
West Virginia
Wisconsin

COMPETITORS
Acapulco/El Torito Restaurants
Black Angus Steakhouse
Brinker
Carlson Restaurants
Cheesecake Factory
Cracker Barrel
Darden
Denny's
Eat' n Park
Lone Star Steakhouse
Marie Callender
OSI Restaurant Partners
Red Robin
Ruby Tuesday
Texas Roadhouse

HISTORICAL FINANCIALS
Company Type: Private

Income Statement
FYE: December 29

	REVENUE ($ mil.)	NET INCOME ($ mil.)	NET PROFIT MARGIN	EMPLOYEES
12/13	1,098	17	1.6%	5,500
12/09	479	19	4.0%	—
12/08	431	9	2.3%	—
12/07	339	0	—	—
Annual Growth	21.7%	—	—	—

2013 Year-End Financials
Return on assets: 2.4%
Return on equity: 1.6%
Current ratio: 0.20

Cash ($ mil.): 20

APPLE HOSPITALITY REIT INC

Auditors: ERNST & YOUNG LLP RICHMOND V

LOCATIONS
HQ: APPLE HOSPITALITY REIT INC
814 E MAIN ST, RICHMOND, VA 232193306
Phone: 804 344-8121
Web: WWW.APPLEREITNINE.COM

HISTORICAL FINANCIALS
Company Type: Private

Income Statement
FYE: December 31

	ASSETS ($ mil.)	NET INCOME ($ mil.)	INCOME AS % OF ASSETS	EMPLOYEES
12/14	3,779	6	0.2%	6
12/13	1,491	115	7.7%	—
12/12	1,526	75	4.9%	—
12/11	1,700	0	—	—
Annual Growth	30.5%	—	—	—

APPLIED CARD SYSTEMS INC.

Applied Card Systems is the servicing arm for Applied Bank a subprime consumer lender that issues secured and unsecured credit cards to customers with little or no credit history. Applied Card Systems processes payments from and provides customer service to more than 500000 holders of subprime Visa and MasterCard accounts. Applied Card Systems also services credit card accounts for third-party issuers primarily small and midsized financial institutions. Chairman Rocco Abessinio is the founder of both Applied Card Bank and Applied Card Systems which was formed in 1987. The company has offices in Florida and Pennsylvania.

Applied Card Systems owns and occupies the former headquarters of American Media publishers of the National Enquirer. Acquired in 2007 the Boca Raton Florida site had been closed since 2001 when anthrax sent to the publishing company killed an employee. The building underwent decontamination before being reopened.

Parent company Applied Bank whose main business is providing credit cards nationwide has two traditional bank branches in Delaware.

EXECUTIVES
Vice President, John (Jack) MacConnell

LOCATIONS
HQ: APPLIED CARD SYSTEMS INC.
5401 BROKEN SOUND BLVD NW, BOCA RATON, FL 334873512
Phone: 561 995-8820
Web: WWW.APPLIEDCARD.COM

COMPETITORS
Asset Acceptance Capital
Asta Funding
Encore Capital Group
PRA Group

HISTORICAL FINANCIALS
Company Type: Private

Income Statement
FYE: December 31

	REVENUE ($ mil.)	NET INCOME ($ mil.)	NET PROFIT MARGIN	EMPLOYEES
12/09	162	21	13.5%	126
12/08	251	145	57.9%	—
12/07	1,520	0	0.0%	—
Annual Growth	(67.4%)	23844.9%	—	—

2009 Year-End Financials
Return on assets: —
Return on equity: 13.5%
Current ratio: 20.50

Cash ($ mil.): 169

APPLIED RESEARCH ASSOCIATES INC.

Applied Research Associates (ARA) has defense down to a science. The research and engineering contractor develops tests and manages software and equipment for the aerospace and defense civil and commercial sectors. From more than 70 offices laboratories and testing and manufacturing facilities primarily in the US ARA provides expertise in system analysis blast testing environmental site characterization pavement evaluation robotic vehicles and other technologies and technical fields. The federal government including various US Department of Defense agencies is ARA's primary client. Founded in 1979 the company is owned by its employees.

Operations

Through its Vermont-based Vertek division ARA has undertaken such projects as the development of a remotely controlled robotic system useful for addressing such emergency needs as neutralizing bombs cleaning hazardous waste and fire fighting. The company had also developed a patented technology that creates fuel for turbine and diesel engines from plants and algae.

EXECUTIVES

Svp Security Engineering And Manager Applied Sciences Sector, Joseph L (Jo) Smith
Senior Vice President, James L Drake
Executive Vice President, Lawrence A Twisdale
Senior Vice President and Manager Gulf Coast Sector, Glen McDonald
Vice President of The Southeast Division, William (Bill) Ratliff
Senior Vice President Strategy Development, George Ullrich
Vice President, Jack McChesney
Senior Vice President and Manager Transportation Infrastructure and Environmental Sector, Curt A Beckemeyer
Vice President and Manager Software Systems and Modeling Sector, Allen (Al) York
Vice President, Larry Ghormely
Co Chairman, Cornelius J Higgins, age 75
Auditors: KPMG LLP ALBUQUERQUE NM

LOCATIONS

HQ: APPLIED RESEARCH ASSOCIATES INC.
4300 SAN MATEO BLVD NE A220, ALBUQUERQUE, NM 871101229
Phone: 505 883-3636
Web: WWW.ARA.COM

COMPETITORS

CACI International
ComGlobal Systems
Epsilon Systems
General Dynamics Information Technology
Honeywell Technology Solutions
Innovative Technology Application
Leidos
Lockheed Martin Information Systems
Northrop Grumman Info Systems
ORION International Technologies
Photon Research Associates
Quantum Research
Symvionics
Technology Service Corporation

HISTORICAL FINANCIALS
Company Type: Private

Income Statement
FYE: September 30

	REVENUE ($ mil.)	NET INCOME ($ mil.)	NET PROFIT MARGIN	EMPLOYEES
09/13	213	6	2.9%	1,235
09/12	226	2	1.2%	—
09/11	232	5	2.6%	—
09/08	196	0	—	—
Annual Growth	1.7%	—	—	—

2013 Year-End Financials
Return on assets: 1.4% Cash ($ mil.): 29
Return on equity: 2.9%
Current ratio: 1.60

APRO LLC

Auditors: HOLTHOUSE CARLIN & VAN TRIGT L

LOCATIONS

HQ: APRO LLC
17311 S MN ST, GARDENA, CA 90248
Phone: 310 323-3992

HISTORICAL FINANCIALS
Company Type: Private

Income Statement
FYE: December 31

	REVENUE ($ mil.)	NET INCOME ($ mil.)	NET PROFIT MARGIN	EMPLOYEES
12/12	968	22	2.3%	100
12/11	488	8	1.7%	—
12/10	551	7	1.4%	—
12/09	296	0	—	—
Annual Growth	48.4%	—	—	—

2012 Year-End Financials
Return on assets: 0.7% Cash ($ mil.): 29
Return on equity: 2.3%
Current ratio: 2.30

ARBITECH LLC

There's nothing arbitrary about Arbitech's business model. Arbitech sells a variety of new and used computer equipment made by such companies as Avaya Cisco Systems Hewlett-Packard IBM Microsoft Nortel and VMware. The company's wide range of products include PCs networking equipment servers storage systems components memories and software. In addition to new equipment the company deals in open-box discontinued and refurbished inventory a niche typically not served by other large distributors and resellers of computer products. Arbitech was co-founded in 2000 by CEO Torin Pavia and one of the company's partners William Poovey.

Arbitech has added services such as full configuration and online ordering and tracking to encourage more business from its partners. Rather than selling directly to the end user the company sells through partnerships with other resellers and distributors. By focusing on products that are most in demand and using a worldwide network of suppliers Arbitech is able to offer products at a price that provides higher profit margins for the company as well as its customers.

The company has jumped onto the virtualization bandwagon by expanding its sales of products for data centers primarily to the small and midsized business (SMB) market. In order to round out its server and storage center offerings Arbitech has inked a deal with Eaton to distribute its line of backup power enclosures and power distribution products.

EXECUTIVES

Vice President business Initatives, Jimmy Whalen
Executive Vice President, Doug Kari
Vice President Of Sales Asia, James Kim
Vice President Finance, Jim Binford
Vice President Purchasing, Ariel Gabriel
Vice President Purchasing And Operations, Stuart Jeffries
Executive Vice President, Clarissa Zulick
Auditors: JLK ROSENBERGER LLP IRVINE

LOCATIONS

HQ: ARBITECH LLC
15330 BARRANCA PKWY, IRVINE, CA 926182215
Phone: 949 376-6650
Web: WWW.ARBITECH.COM

COMPETITORS

Arrow Electronics   SYNNEX
Avnet   Tech Data
Ingram Micro   Westcon

HISTORICAL FINANCIALS
Company Type: Private

Income Statement
FYE: December 31

	REVENUE ($ mil.)	NET INCOME ($ mil.)	NET PROFIT MARGIN	EMPLOYEES
12/09	191	0	—	74
12/08	180	0	—	—
12/05	153	8	5.5%	—
Annual Growth	5.7%	—	—	—

2009 Year-End Financials
Return on assets: 2.1% Cash ($ mil.): —
Return on equity: —
Current ratio: 0.70

ARCTIC SLOPE REGIONAL CORPORATION

The Inupiat people have survived the rigors of the Arctic for centuries and now they're surviving in the business world. The Inupiat-owned Arctic Slope Regional Corporation (ASRC) is the largest locally owned and operated business in Alaska. It gets the bulk of its sales from energy services (ASRC Energy Services) and petroleum refining and marketing unit (Petro Star). Other operations include construction (ASRC Construction Holding) governmental services (ASRC Federal Holding) economic development (Alaska Growth Capital BIDCO) local services (Eskimos Inc.) and tourism (Tundra Tours).

Geographic Reach

ASRC represents 11000 members/shareholders in eight villages on the North Slope of Alaska: Anaktuvuk Pass Atqasuk Barrow Kaktovik Nuiqsut Point Hope Point Lay and Wainwright. ASRC has its head office in Barrow with a major administrative office in Anchorage. It has other subsidiary offices in the Lower 48 states.

Operations

ASRC owns title to nearly 5 million acres of land on Alaska's North Slope which contain a high potential for oil gas coal and base metal sulfides. It also owns subsurface and surface rights to certain lands.

The company seeks to adhere to traditional Inupiat values of protecting the land the environment and the native culture while developing economic programs.

It operates in four diverse major business segments: petroleum refining and marketing government services energy services and construction industries. Petro Star Inc. has two refineries (strategically positioned along the Trans-Alaska Pipeline) and serves Interior Alaska South Central Alaska Kodiak and Dutch Harbor.

ASRC Federal Holding Company provides professional and technical services to the federal government (aviation space and missile defense base operations resource and development engineering IT financial management and other).

ASRC Energy Services offers oilfield engineering operations maintenance construction fabrication regulation and permitting and other services to oil and gas companies.

ASRC Construction Holding Company provides construction services to commercial and government clients in Alaska the lower-48 the Gulf of Mexico and in other countries.

Alaska Growth Capital BIDCO offers economic development finance including small business loans and investments in economically challenged areas of Alaska.

LRS Inc. provides help to increase well flow output as well as well work-over and well production support.

Financial Performance

ARSC has distributed more than $543 million in dividends to shareholders since 1972. Since 2005 ARSC has distributed $16 million each year in benefits to its shareholders in the form of educational scholarships and community support funding as well as for training and development activities.

Strategy

The company's strategic plan for 2012 to 2017 calls for ASRC to diversify its holdings to reach $225 million in sustainable earnings before interest and taxes (including a sustainable $55 dividend) and to achieve this goal through minimal debt a favorable tax position and by making cash available to acquire new businesses inside and outside of Alaska. It is looking for a successful acquisition strategy to diversify revenue streams increase earnings and generate new job opportunities for ASRC's shareholders.In 2014 Royal Dutch Shell and the ASRC formed a new company —Arctic Inupiat Offshore LLC which includes six village corporations on the North Slope. The agreement with the Shell subsidiary Shell Gulf of Mexico Inc. gives the Alaska Native company the option of acquiring an overriding royalty interest from Shell's drilling on leases in the Chukchi Sea.

Company Background

ASRC is owned by Inupiat Eskimo shareholders.

ASRC was set up to own and manage 5 million acres on Alaska's North Slope after the Alaska Native Claims Settlement Act in 1971 cleared the way for oil development in the area.

In 2010 ASRC protested the US Fish and Wildlife Service's designation of Alaskan North Slope oil-producing areas as a critical habitat for endangered polar bears claiming it would cost ASRC millions of dollars in lost oil revenues. In 2011 it led a coalition of Native groups to sue the Department of the Interior over this issue.

In 2012 ASRC Construction Holding expanded into southeast Alaska with the acquisition of native-Alaskan owned McGraw's Custom Construction.

EXECUTIVES

EVP Lands and Natural Resources, Richard K. Glenn
President and CEO, Rex A. Rock
Chairman and EVP Shareholder Community Programs, Crawford Patkotak
EVP and General Counsel, Denali Kemppel
EVP and COO, Butch Lincoln
EVP and CFO, Charlie Kozak
Vice President Application Development, Tara Sweeney
Vice President Tax, Mark Hamilton
Vice President, Teresa Imm
Senior Vice President For Enterprise Support, Lisa Young
Vice Chairman, George Sielak

LOCATIONS

HQ: ARCTIC SLOPE REGIONAL CORPORATION
3900 C ST STE 801, ANCHORAGE, AK 995035963
Phone: 907 339-6000
Web: WWW.ASRC.COM

PRODUCTS/OPERATIONS

Selected Businesses
Energy Services
  ASRC Energy Services Inc.
  Arctic Inupiat Offshore LLC.
Petroleum Refining and Marketing
  Petro Star Inc.
Government Services
  ASRC Federal Holding Company
Construction
  ASRC Construction Holding Company LLC
Resource Development
  Little Red Services
  Petrochem

COMPETITORS

Alaska Communications Systems	Noble
Baker Hughes	Schlumberger
Halliburton	T-Mobile USA
Nabors Industries	Tesoro

HISTORICAL FINANCIALS

Company Type: Private

Income Statement

FYE: December 31

	REVENUE ($ mil.)	NET INCOME ($ mil.)	NET PROFIT MARGIN	EMPLOYEES
12/08	2,297	151	6.6%	6,000
12/07	1,777	207	11.7%	—
12/06	1,700	206	12.1%	—
12/05	1,566	0	—	—
Annual Growth	**13.6%**	**—**	**—**	**—**

2008 Year-End Financials

Return on assets: —
Return on equity: 6.6%
Current ratio: 0.80

Cash ($ mil.): 302

ARKANSAS CHILDREN'S HOSPITAL

As the only pediatric medical center in the state Arkansas Children's Hospital (ACH) serves the youngest Razorbacks from birth to age 21. The not-for-profit hospital with its 370 beds specializes in childhood cancer pediatric orthopedics and neonatology. Besides acute care services it operates more than 80 specialty clinics and outpatient centers. One of the US's largest pediatric hospitals ACH is also engaged in teaching and medical research through its affiliation with the University of Arkansas for Medical Sciences. Its Arkansas Children's Hospital Research Institute focuses on biological mechanisms underlying birth defects diabetes-related complications and childhood diseases.

Geographic Reach

Based in Little Rock Arkansas on a campus that extends nearly 30 city blocks ACH serves children nationwide as one of the largest pediatric hospitals in the US. It has several locations across Arkansas in Little Rock Jonesboro and Lowell.

Operations

ACH each year performs more than 14500 operations and boasts 55000-plus emergency depart-

ment visits nearly 330000 outpatient visits and about 14800 inpatient admissions.

ACH's Circle of Friends clinic treats more than 20000 patients annually. The clinic which opened in 2008 provides primary care as well as a broad range of specialty care services related to endocrinology dermatological conditions hemophilia and tuberculosis.

The hospital also offers community outreach services that include help for children of domestic abuse and wellness programs as well as a number of clinics to support those with eating disorders and diabetes.

As a prime destination for treatment ACH also runs Angel One Transport an intensive care medical transportation system that brings critically ill and injured infants children and adolescents as well as adult burn patients from throughout Arkansas and the surrounding states to ACH. It also boasts a high risk obstetric transport program in partnership with the University of Arkansas for Medical Sciences.

ACH has a staff of 500 physicians including 95 residents in pediatrics and pediatric specialties. Its mobile clinics annually serve more than 6000 patients and provide more than $3 million in dental treatment.

Financial Performance

The hospital gets about 82% of its net sales from net patient service revenues.

Strategy

In 2015 ACH announced plans to build a $184 million hospital in Springdale. The 24-bed hospital will be located on 37 acres of land near Arvest Ballpark. The hospital is targeted to be completed in 2018.

In 2013 ACH inked a contract with Aetna health insurance under which patients with Aetna health insurance will be able to seek in-network care at ACH. The contract allows the company to reach more families throughout the region.Company Background

The hospital opened a new $121 million south wing in mid-2012 that added more than 50 inpatient beds to the hospital's capacity. The nearly 260000-sq.-ft. four-story building features telemedicine technology (for remote patient care) new trauma rooms a dedicated orthopedics suite and a decontamination unit.

To its benefit ACH became the state's only pediatric Level I trauma center in 2010 after receiving a four-year designation from the Arkansas Department of Health. The designation means that the hospital is equipped for and capable of taking care of children with the most severe of traumas. Level I trauma centers serve as referral locations for hospitals that are unable to provide the same level of care.

EXECUTIVES

President CEO and Director, Jonathan R. (Jon) Bates
COO, Scott R. Gordon
Director; President Arkansas Children's Hospital Research Institute, Richard F. Jacobs
SVP and CIO, Darrell T. Leonhardt
SVP and CFO, Gena G. Wingfield
SVP and COO, David T. Berry
President ACH Foundation, Fred Scarborough
Senior Vice President Chief Quality Officer, Jayant K. Deshpande
Senior Vice President Medical Director, W. Robert Morrow
Infection Control Director, Craig Gilliam
Director Of Health Information, Marilyn Ambrose
Radiology Director, Karen Craig
Vice President - Patient Accounts, Carol Hudgens
Director Of Pharmacy, Marita Nazarian
Cost Analysis Vice President, Cindy L Hill
Director Of Nursing, Rebecca Kersten

Vice President Patient Care Services, Katie Lea
Nursing Director, Gail Wilson
Nursing Director, Carrie Lee
Director Of Nursing, Leslie Bradley
Senior Vice President, Katherine Friend
Nursing Director, Amy Allen
Pharmd, Alvin Simmons
Vice President Of Facilities, Larry Beckius
Vice President Clinical Excellence and
 Innovation, Tammy Webb
Vice President Managed Care Business
 Development, Beth Petlak
Vice President, Curtis Summers
Vice President and General Counsel, Rhonda
 Thornton
Vice President of Quality and Patient Safety,
 Pamela (Pam) Brown
Secretary to Vice President Human Resources,
 Charlotte Johnson
Secretary, Tarina Goodwin
Secretary, Shashi Dyamenahalli
Auditors: DELOITTE TAX LLP HOUSTON TX

LOCATIONS

HQ: ARKANSAS CHILDREN' S HOSPITAL
 1 CHILDRENS WAY, LITTLE ROCK, AR 722023500
Phone: 501 364-1100
Web: WWW.ARCHILDRENS.ORG

PRODUCTS/OPERATIONS

Selected Services
Ambulatory Surgery
Audiology
Center for Good Mourning
Cleft Clinic
Dennis Developmental Center
Dental Clinic
ECMO
Gastroenterology Clinic
Genetic and Metabolic Clinic
Infectious Diseases
Neuroscience Unit
Physical Medicine & Rehab Outreach Clinics
Sleep Disorders Center
Volunteer Services
WHAM (Wellness Health Action & Motivation) Clinic

COMPETITORS

Arkansas Heart Hospital
Baptist Health (Arkansas)
Children' s Healthcare of Atlanta
Children' s Medical Center of Dallas
Children' s Mercy Hospital
Children' s National Medical Center
Cook Children' s Health Care System
Dell Children' s Medical Center
East Tennessee Children' s Hospital
Jefferson Regional Medical Center of Arkansas
Methodist Healthcare
Shriners Hospitals For Children
St. Joseph' s Mercy Health Center
St. Jude Children' s Research Hospital
St. Vincent Health System
Texas Children' s Hospital
Universal Health Services
White County Medical Center

HISTORICAL FINANCIALS
Company Type: Private

Income Statement

	REVENUE ($ mil.)	NET INCOME ($ mil.)	NET PROFIT MARGIN	EMPLOYEES
				FYE: June 30
06/11	509	48	9.5%	3,700
06/10	513	42	8.4%	—
06/08	1	(0)	—	—
06/06	0	0	—	—
Annual Growth	—	—	—	—

Return on assets: —   Cash ($ mil.): 66
Return on equity: 9.5%
Current ratio: 2.30

ARKANSAS ELECTRIC COOPERATIVES INC.

Auditors: BKD LLP LITTLE ROCK ARKANSA

LOCATIONS

HQ: ARKANSAS ELECTRIC COOPERATIVES INC.
 1 COOPERATIVE WAY, LITTLE ROCK, AR 722095493
Phone: 501 570-2361
Web: WWW.AECC.COM

HISTORICAL FINANCIALS
Company Type: Private

Income Statement

	REVENUE ($ mil.)	NET INCOME ($ mil.)	NET PROFIT MARGIN	EMPLOYEES
				FYE: December 31
12/13	416	32	7.7%	840
12/12	438	35	8.0%	—
12/11	357	18	5.1%	—
12/10	313	0	—	—
Annual Growth	10.0%	—	—	—

2013 Year-End Financials
Return on assets: 3.1%   Cash ($ mil.): 71
Return on equity: 7.7%
Current ratio: 2.90

ARNOLD MACHINERY COMPANY

Arnold Machinery helps keep construction on the move. Through its many divisions the company distributes construction mining industrial and material handling equipment as well as farm machinery throughout the US. Arnold Machinery also offers used equipment and provides repair and maintenance rebuild exchange and rental services. The company's divisions include General Implement Distributors Mining Equipment Construction Equipment and Material Handling. Arnold Machinery operates about 20 branch facilities covering some 15 states in the Western US.

Strategy

Since its founding the company has expanded geographically and built its product offerings by acquiring complementary businesses. Arnold Machinery continues to acquire other distributors in its territory and to expand its facilities in many markets.

Company Background

L. E. "Doc" Arnold and Floyd Stannard founded predecessor company Stannard­-Arnold Machinery Company in 1929. The company's name was changed to Arnold Machinery Company upon the resignation of Stannard later that year.

EXECUTIVES

President and CEO, Russ Fleming
President Material Handling Division, Rex Mecham

Aftermarket Manager Material Handling Division,
 Kirk Reese
President General Implement Distributors,
 Wendell Nelson
Corporate VP; President Mining Division, John
 Ragsdale
Vice President Of Technical Services, Billy Greenlee
Chairman, Alvin Richer
Auditors: GRANT THORNTON LLP SALT LAKE

LOCATIONS

HQ: ARNOLD MACHINERY COMPANY
 2955 W 2100 S, SALT LAKE CITY, UT 841191207
Phone: 801 972-4000
Web: WWW.ARNOLDMACHINERY.COM

COMPETITORS

Cashman Equipment	NES Rentals
Cummins	Sunbelt Rentals
Empire Southwest	United Rentals

HISTORICAL FINANCIALS
Company Type: Private

Income Statement

	REVENUE ($ mil.)	NET INCOME ($ mil.)	NET PROFIT MARGIN	EMPLOYEES
				FYE: September 30
09/13	294	12	4.3%	450
09/12	306	13	4.3%	—
09/11	235	11	4.8%	—
09/10	191	0	—	—
Annual Growth	15.4%	—	—	—

2013 Year-End Financials
Return on assets: 3.7%   Cash ($ mil.): 5
Return on equity: 4.3%
Current ratio: 0.10

ARROW HEAD REGIONAL MEDICAL CENTER

Find yourself dehydrated after searching the Inland Empire deserts for arrowheads? Arrowhead Regional Medical Center (ARMC) can fix you up. The San Bernardino County owned and operated hospital provides a range of health services from general medical and surgical care to emergency services rehabilitation inpatient psychiatric care pediatric and women's health services. It also serves as a Level II trauma center a regional burn center and medical training facility. ARMC with some 460 beds (370 inpatient and 90 behavioral) opened in 1999 to replace the aging San Bernardino County Hospital. The hospital also offers outpatient services on its main campus and at area clinics.

Geographic Reach

The company serves patients in San Bernardino Riverside Inyo and Mono counties in California. ARMC's main facility campus in Colton includes an outpatient services complex. It also runs three primary care Family Health Centers in the nearby towns of Fontana Rialto and San Bernadino as well as wound care and elder care clinics.

Operations

Along with a full range of health care services ARMC offers about 10 residency programs including emergency and family medicine general surgery geriatrics orthopedics neurosurgery and gynecology. The hospital trains about 170 residents each year and also provides training programs for nurses pharmacists clinical laboratory scientists and radiologic technologists.

The ARMC emergency room handles about 140000 visits each year. The hospital's inpatient capacity handles about 25000 patients annually while its outpatient centers see some 250000 patients.

The Medical Center's Internal Medicine Primary Care Clinic offers services for individuals ranging in age from 18 to 100. Its Outpatient Care facility offers more than 60 different specialty services including pediatrics geriatrics orthopedics surgery internal medicine women's health and rehabilitation services.

ARMC's two Breath Mobiles provide pediatric asthma care management at sites throughout San Bernardino County.

Financial Performance

ARMC's revenues dropped by 1% to $385 million in 2012 due to a decline in net patient service revenues.However net income decreased by 63% to $12 million in 2012 due to higher operating expenses (salaries benefits and purchased services) partially offset by a rise in non-operating revenues due to an increase in state funding.

Strategy

To better serve the needs of patients in its service territory ARMC looks to expand services in high-demand areas.

To enable doctors and technologists to provide a vastly expanded number of procedures for cardiac patients neurology patients and those requiring interventional radiology in 2013 ARMC opened its new Dual Purpose Interventional Lab (medical suite).That year it also opened a new and larger Westside Family Health Center which was expanded from 12 to 21 exam rooms in a new colocation facility in Rialto. It also expanded its Breath Mobile service to the High Desert with service to sites including Adelanto Apple Valley Barstow Hesperia Phelan Victorville and Trona.

Company Background

An increase in cases of asthma (particularly among children) in the Central Valley led ARMC to expand its Breathmobile program an asthma clinic on wheels that travels to schools throughout San Bernadino County in 2010.

The hospital is also enhancing stationary outpatient care clinics. It added the ARMC Medical Office Building to its main campus in 2011; the center includes physician practices and an internal medicine clinic.

EXECUTIVES

Director Of Nursing, Michelle Sayre
Physical Therapy Director, Johnson Gill
Vice chairman Department of Medical Imaging, Ha Le

LOCATIONS

HQ: ARROW HEAD REGIONAL MEDICAL CENTER
400 N PEPPER AVE, COLTON, CA 923241801
Phone: 909 580-1000

PRODUCTS/OPERATIONS

Selected Services
Audiology
Breast Cancer Clinic
Cardiology
Child Health Disability Program
Dialysis Center
Emergency Medicine
Family and Elder Care
Internal Medicine
Level II Trauma Center
Oncology/Infusion Therapy
Ophthalmology
Orthopedics
Pediatric Clinic
Psychiatric Emergency Services
Radiation Oncology
Rehabilitation Clinic
Surgery
Women's Health

COMPETITORS

Anaheim Regional	HCA
Medical Center	Loma Linda University
Cedars-Sinai Medical	Medical Center
Center	Memorial Health
Children' s Hospital of	Services
Orange County	St. Jude Medical
City of Hope	Center
Community Hospital of	Tenet Healthcare
San Bernardino	Trinity Health (Novi)
Dignity Health	

HISTORICAL FINANCIALS

Company Type: Private

Income Statement

FYE: June 30

	REVENUE ($ mil.)	NET INCOME ($ mil.)	NET PROFIT MARGIN	EMPLOYEES
06/09	225	25	11.3%	2,500
06/04	439	3	0.8%	—
06/03	313	(1)	—	—
06/02	313	0	—	—
Annual Growth	(4.6%)	—	—	—

2009 Year-End Financials

Return on assets: 5.0%   Cash ($ mil.): 33
Return on equity: 11.3%
Current ratio: 1.10

ASHLAND HOSPITAL CORPORATION

LOCATIONS

HQ: ASHLAND HOSPITAL CORPORATION
2201 LEXINGTON AVE, ASHLAND, KY 411012843
Phone: 606 408-4000
Web: WWW.KDMC.COM

HISTORICAL FINANCIALS

Company Type: Private

Income Statement

FYE: September 30

	REVENUE ($ mil.)	NET INCOME ($ mil.)	NET PROFIT MARGIN	EMPLOYEES
09/13	465	(0)	—	4,200
09/12	530	50	9.4%	—
/	0	0	—	—
Annual Growth	—	—	—	—

2013 Year-End Financials

Return on assets: 10.8%   Cash ($ mil.): 23
Return on equity: (-0.1%)
Current ratio: 0.30

ASI COMPUTER TECHNOLOGIES INC

ASI Computer Technologies is a wholesale distributor of computer software hardware and accessories. It offers more than 15000 products including PCs modems monitors networking equipment and data storage devices. The company sells to resellers retailers systems integrators and equipment makers from offices and facilities in the US Canada and Mexico. Its vendor partners include companies the likes of AMD Intel Microsoft and Western Digital. ASI's services include custom systems integration and contract assembly. It also markets PCs and notebooks under its own brands: Pegatron IQ and Nspire. The company was established in 1987 by president and owner Cristine Liang.

Geographic Reach

Based in California ASI operates nationwide as well as in Mexico and Canada. To support its business the wholesaler operates regional offices in Atlanta Chicago Dallas Houston Los Angeles Miami Portland and in Kansas and New Jersey. Its Canadian offices are in Montreal Toronto and Vancouver. In Mexico ASI has offices in Monterrey Nuevo Laredo and Torreon.

Financial Performance

ASI reported $1.5 billion in sales in 2013 up from about $1.4 billion in 2012.

Strategy

The wholesale distributor regularly adds to its products portfolio through distribution agreements with multiple partners. In 2014 ASI partnered with Huawei a manufacturer of telecommunications equipment in China to distribute Huawei's IP network infrastructure communications and storage products through its resellers in North America. Also in 2014 the company partnered with Belkin a maker of USB devices and other products to distribute its full line of products. Previously in 2013 it inked a deal with computer hardware maker Rosewill to carry the company's computer cases power supplies networking cables and computer accessories which range from entry-level lines to high-end items.

The company supports its comprehensive products menu with value-added services that range from ISO 9001-certified integration system design and process validation kitting private labeling and custom packaging.

To its benefit ASI is the largest privately-held woman-owned business in California and the third largest of its kind in the nation. It holds certificates as a minority supplier and woman-owned business.

Sales and Marketing

ASI's diverse portfolio of products and services allow it to service a broad customer base which includes VARs system integrators retailers DMRs and OEM accounts.

EXECUTIVES

President of ASI Computer Systems, Dave Wirth
Commercial Insurance Specialist Executive Vice President, Orlando Lopez
Auditors: MARCUM LLP SAN FRANCISCO CA

LOCATIONS

HQ: ASI COMPUTER TECHNOLOGIES INC
48289 FREMONT BLVD, FREMONT, CA 945386510
Phone: 510 353-1960
Web: WWW.ASIPARTNER.COM

PRODUCTS/OPERATIONS

Selected Products
Accessories
Cables
Cameras
Cases
CD-ROM drives
Central processing units
Controller cards
DVD drives
Fans
Floppy drives
Hard drives
Keyboards
Memory
Mice
Modems

Monitors
Motherboards
MP3 players
Multimedia products
Network connectivity products
Notebooks
Optical drives
PCs
Power supplies
Printers
Projectors
Removable drives and media
Scanners
Software
Sound cards
Speakers
Storage devices
Tape back-up products
Video cards
Zip drives

COMPETITORS

ASCII Group	Ingram Micro
Agilysys	MTM Technologies
Arrow Electronics	Merisel
Avnet	MicroAge
Avnet Technology	New Age Electronics
Solutions	SED International
CompuCom	SHI International
Continental Resources	SYNNEX
D & H Distributing	Softmart
En Pointe	Supercom
Flextronics	Tech Data

HISTORICAL FINANCIALS
Company Type: Private

Income Statement
FYE: December 31

	REVENUE ($ mil.)	NET INCOME ($ mil.)	NET PROFIT MARGIN	EMPLOYEES
12/13	1,746	17	1.0%	700
12/04	1,057	12	1.2%	—
12/03	982	13	1.3%	—
12/02	865	0	—	—
Annual Growth	6.6%	—	—	—

2013 Year-End Financials
Return on assets: 5.4% Cash ($ mil.): 28
Return on equity: 1.0%
Current ratio: 1.10

ASPIRUS INC.

Aspirus aspires to provide care for Midwesterners in need. The health system provides a comprehensive range of health and medical services to residents in a 14-county region of central and northern Wisconsin as well as Michigan's Upper Peninsula. Aspirus operates the Aspirus Wausau Hospital a 325-bed multi-specialty regional health center and seven smaller community hospitals. Its hospitals and network of community clinics provide specialized primary and emergency care. Aspirus also operates imaging centers hospice services home health care long-term care facilities and an outpatient dialysis center.

Operations

Other facilities in Aspirus' network include the 25-bed Aspirus Medford Hospital the Catholic Aspirus Langlade Hospital specialist hospital Riverview Family Clinic and 25-bed critical care access hospitals Aspirus Ontonagon and NORTH-STAR. In all it operates four hospitals in Michigan and four in Wisconsin as well as 50 clinics home health and hospice care helicopter transport nursing homes and pharmacies.

Sales and Marketing

Aspirus takes payments from most health plans and payers in the region in which it operates. It also contracts directly with employers and community business coalitions.

Mergers and Acquisitions

Michigan-based NORTHSTAR Health System became an Aspira subsidiary in 2014. It added a 25-bed critical access hospital as well as clinics to Aspira's network.

EXECUTIVES

Physical Therapy, Nathan Weiler
Senior Vice President Of Legal Services And General Counsel For Aspirus, Cari Logemann
Director Of Nursing, Amy Brushwood
Clinic Manager, Gail Koss
Medical Director of Informatics, Larry Gordon
Vice President Finance and Compliance, Lori Peck
Senior Vice President Of Legal Services, Pete Hessert
Vice President Marketing and Planning, Rick Nevers
Director Of Hospice Services, Laura Pearson
Vice President of Information Technology Chief Information Officer, Todd Richardson
Clinic Manager, Jody Baeseman
Director Of Operating Room, Patty Aho
Director Of Nursing, Pam Wildberg
Director Of Nursing, Patti Klingen
Director of Hospice Services, Laura Samak
Auditors: ERNST & YOUNG LLP MILWAUKEE

LOCATIONS

HQ: ASPIRUS INC.
333 PINE RIDGE BLVD, WAUSAU, WI 544014187
Phone: 715 298-3213
Web: WWW.ASPIRUS.ORG

Selected FacilitiesU.P. of MichiganAspirus Grand View Aspirus Keweenaw HospitalAspirus Ontonagon HospitalNORTHSTAR Health System WisconsinAspirus Wausau HospitalAspirus Langlade HospitalAspirus Medford HospitalRiverview Hospital

PRODUCTS/OPERATIONS

Selected Services
Alzheimer' s & Memory Disorders
Anesthesia Services
Angioplasty
Anticoagulation Clinic
Cardiac Electrophysiology
Cardiac Rehab
Cardioversion
Dentistry
Oral & Maxillofacial Surgery
Prosthodontics
Psychiatry
Psychology
Pulmonary Medicine
Sleep Disorders

COMPETITORS

Dean Health Systems Inc.
Howard Young Health Care
Luther Midelfort
ThedaCare Inc.
University of Wisconsin Hospital and Clinics

HISTORICAL FINANCIALS
Company Type: Private

Income Statement
FYE: June 30

	REVENUE ($ mil.)	NET INCOME ($ mil.)	NET PROFIT MARGIN	EMPLOYEES
06/14	562	78	13.9%	3,900
06/13	536	47	8.9%	—
06/12	529	26	4.9%	—
06/11	503	0	—	—
Annual Growth	3.8%	—	—	—

2014 Year-End Financials
Return on assets: 1.8% Cash ($ mil.): 77
Return on equity: 13.9%
Current ratio: 1.80

ASPIRUS WAUSAU HOSPITAL INC.

Auditors: ERNST & YOUNG LLP MINNEAPOLIS

LOCATIONS

HQ: ASPIRUS WAUSAU HOSPITAL INC.
425 PINE RIDGE BLVD # 1, WAUSAU, WI 544014123
Phone: 715 847-2121
Web: WWW.ASPIRUS.ORG

HISTORICAL FINANCIALS
Company Type: Private

Income Statement
FYE: June 30

	REVENUE ($ mil.)	NET INCOME ($ mil.)	NET PROFIT MARGIN	EMPLOYEES
06/10	319	33	10.4%	3,500
06/09	295	(8)	—	—
06/08	1,606	0	—	—
Annual Growth	—34903.2%	—	—	—

2010 Year-End Financials
Return on assets: 1.8% Cash ($ mil.): 41
Return on equity: 10.4%
Current ratio: 2.40

ASSOCIATED ELECTRIC COOPERATIVE INC.

Associated Electric Cooperative makes the connection between power and cooperatives. The utility provides transmission and generation services to its six member/owner companies which in turn provide power supply services to 51 distribution cooperatives in three Midwest states. (The distribution cooperatives have a combined customer count of about 875000 people.) Associated Electric operates 9645 miles of power transmission lines and has about 5895 MW of generating capacity from interests in primarily coal- and gas-fired power plants and from wholesale energy transactions with other regional utilities.

Geographic Reach

The cooperative is engaged in the wholesale transmission business with more than 70 investor-owned and municipal utilities electric cooperatives power marketing firms and regional transmission organizations. Associated Electric supplies wholesale power to 39 distribution cooperatives in Missouri three in southeast Iowa and nine in northeast Oklahoma.

Financial Performance

In 2012 Associated Electric's revenues dropped by 0.2% due to lower sales volume was the result of mild winter temperatures in 2012 that tamped down demand.

Despite the decrease in net sales the company's net income grew by 8% in 2012 thanks to lower operating expenses.

Strategy

The company is also looking to increase power generated from renewable sources in order to meet tightening emission regulations. It has contracted hydropower sources and it also gets wind energy from Missouri's first utility-scale wind farms the fourth of which the 150 MW Lost Creek Wind Farm. In 2012 Associated Electric signed a long-term power purchase agreement for 314 MW of power from BP Wind Energy's proposed Flat Ridge 2 Wind farm in Kansas boosting the cooperative's total wind power capacity to 600MW.

To meet growing demand the company is also growing its fossil-fueled power assets. In 2013 the city of New Madrid approved an option for Associated Electric to buy New Madrid Unit 1 power plant before their existing agreement ends in 2022.

In 2011 Associated Electric completed a 540 MW combined-cycle natural gas plant adjacent to its existing Chouteau Power Plant in Pryor Oklahoma boosting that location's overall capacity to 1062 MW.

Company BackgroundSix generation and transmission cooperatives/owners formed Associated Electric in 1961 to provide them with a wholesale power supply.

EXECUTIVES

CEO and General Manager, James J. Jura
CIO, Ronald H. Murphy
CFO, David W. McNabb
Director Engineering and Operations, Roger S. Clark
Director Power Production, Kenneth S. Wilmot
Vice President Of Information Systems, Dale Reinhart
Chairman, Emery O. Geisendorfer
Vice Chairman, John B. Killgore
Auditors: KPMG LLP KANSAS CITY MO

LOCATIONS

HQ: ASSOCIATED ELECTRIC COOPERATIVE INC.
2814 S GOLDEN AVE, SPRINGFIELD, MO 658073213
Phone: 660 261-4211
Web: WWW.AECI.ORG

PRODUCTS/OPERATIONS

Member Transmission and Distribution Cooperatives
Central Electric Power Cooperative
KAMO Power
M&A Electric Power Cooperative
Northeast Missouri Electric Power Cooperative
NW Electric Power Cooperative Inc.
Sho-Me Power Electric Cooperative

COMPETITORS

Ameren
Empire District Electric
Great Plains Energy
Southern Union
Westar Energy
Xcel Energy

HISTORICAL FINANCIALS

Company Type: Private

Income Statement — FYE: December 31

	REVENUE ($ mil.)	NET INCOME ($ mil.)	NET PROFIT MARGIN	EMPLOYEES
12/13	1,129	41	3.7%	600
12/12	1,081	50	4.7%	—
12/11	1,083	46	4.3%	—
12/10	1,055	0	—	—
Annual Growth	2.3%	—	—	—

2013 Year-End Financials
Return on assets: 10.0%   Cash ($ mil.): 89
Return on equity: 3.7%
Current ratio: 0.80

ASSOCIATED FOOD STORES INC.

This business makes sure there's plenty of grub for the Wild West. Associated Food Stores (AFS) is a leading regional cooperative wholesale distributor that supplies groceries and other products to some 500 independent supermarkets in about eight Western states. It also offers support services for its member-owners including market research real estate analysis store design technology procurement and training. In addition AFS owns a stake in Western Family Foods a grocery wholesalers' partnership that produces Western Family private-label goods. The co-op formed in 1940 also operates 40-plus corporate stores in Utah under five different banners including Fresh Market.

Geographic Reach

Salt Lake City-based Associated Food Stores has operations in Arizona Colorado Idaho Montana Nevada Oregon Utah and Wyoming. The

Operations

In addition to its wholesale business AFS's retail arm —Associated Retail Operations —owns and operates corporate stores in Utah under five different formats and banners: Macey's; Fresh Market; Dan's Fresh Market in Salt Lake City; Lin's Fresh Market; and Dick's Fresh Market. The retail business accounts for about 35% of AFS's annual revenue.

The grocery distributor supplies independent supermarkets with over 3600 products. Products comprise a wide array including baking breakfast cereals frozen foods household supplies and even pet food and supplies. In early 2013 Associated closed its distribution centers in Helena and Billings Montana and consolidated warehouse operations for its nearly 100 Montana and Wyoming customers at its facility in Farr West Utah.

Financial Performance

While privately-owned Associated Food Stores doesn't report its financial results the company logged an estimated $2.2 billion in sales in fiscal 2013 (ended March) versus $2.1 billion in sales the previous year.

EXECUTIVES

Vice President Of Maintence, Norm Johnson
Rph, Denise Kunkel
Vice President Centerstore Associated Food Store, Kevin Fitz
Vice President, Troy Thomas
Director of Pharmacy Operations, Shawna Hanson
Treasurer, Bob Obray
Auditors: DELOITTE & TOUCHE LLP SALT L

LOCATIONS

HQ: ASSOCIATED FOOD STORES INC.
1850 W 2100 S, SALT LAKE CITY, UT 841191304
Phone: 801 973-4400
Web: WWW.AFSTORES.COM

PRODUCTS/OPERATIONS

Selected Brands
Western Family
Full Circle
Shur Saving

Selected Retail Banners
Dan' s Fresh Market
Dick' s Fresh Market
Fresh Market
Lin' s Fresh Market
Macey' s

COMPETITORS

AMCON Distributing
C&S Wholesale
GSC Enterprises
Kroger
McLane
SUPERVALU
Safeway
URM Stores
Unified Grocers
Wal-Mart

HISTORICAL FINANCIALS

Company Type: Private

Income Statement — FYE: March 31

	REVENUE ($ mil.)	NET INCOME ($ mil.)	NET PROFIT MARGIN	EMPLOYEES
03/13	1,957	2	0.1%	300
03/12	2,011	5	0.3%	—
03/11	1,953	(6)	—	—
03/10	1,785	0	—	—
Annual Growth	3.1%	—	—	—

2013 Year-End Financials
Return on assets: —   Cash ($ mil.): 105
Return on equity: 0.1%
Current ratio: 0.40

ASSOCIATED GROCERS OF NEW ENGLAND INC.

AGNE gets the products you want on to grocers' shelves. Associated Grocers of New England (AGNE) is a leading wholesale grocery distributor. The retailer-owned organization supplies more than 650 independent grocers and convenience stores in six New England states and the Upstate New York and Albany area. AGNE supplies customers with baked goods fresh produce and meat as well as general grocery items and other merchandise. The grocery distributor also offers such retail support services as advertising marketing and merchandising. AGNE's retail arm operates about a half a dozen supermarkets under the Harvest Market Sully's Superette and Vista Foods banners. The cooperative was formed in 1946.

Geographic Reach

The New Hampshire-based company serves stores in Connecticut Maine Massachusetts New Hampshire Rhode Island and Vermont and the Upstate New York/Albany area.

Financial Peformance

AGNE rings up more than $475 million in annual sales.

Strategy

The 2011 liquidation of rival Associated Grocers of Maine which distributed products to hundreds of small independent grocery stores in Maine boosted AGNE's business in the state. To meet increasing demand AGNE is expanding its distribution facility in Pembroke New Hampshire. The 105000-square-foot addition to the existing 380000-square-foot facility is slated for completion by the end of 2014. It features an automated product movement system to reduce the "number of touches" and increase efficiency. The wholesaler has been gradually increasing its retail store operation in recent years with the purchase of individual member stores in its market area.

Mergers and Acquisitions

In a move to expand its retail coverage AGNE acquired Bi-Wise Market of Allentown New Hampshire in January 2014. In 2012 AGNE acquired Sully's Superette also in New Hampshire.

AGNE's acquisition of New Hampshire-based Manchester Wholesale Distributors (in 2009) helped boost sales during the economic downturn as did improved performance at its Associated Convenience Grocers division. Manchester Wholesale Distributors supplied convenience stores and food service operators throughout New Hampshire.

EXECUTIVES

President CEO of Associated Grocers of New England, Michael C. (Mike) Bourgoine
Manager Warehousing, James (Jim) Johnson
Manager Center Store Purchasing, Karen St. Louis
General Manager Convenience Store Division, Stephen Felton
SVP Sales and Retail Development, Michael J. (Mike) Violette
Director Retail Programs, Curt O'Hara
Director Information Technology, Kenneth (Ken) Peperissa
Manager Sales and Purchasing Bakery and Deli, William Carter
Vice President Wholesale Merchandising and Procurement, Allan Hulse
Manager Sales and Purchasing Produce, Lenny Miner
Director, Terry P. Appleby
Director, James G. (Jim) Crosby

LOCATIONS

HQ: ASSOCIATED GROCERS OF NEW ENGLAND INC.
11 COOPERATIVE WAY, PEMBROKE, NH 032753251
Phone: 603 223-6710
Web: WWW.AGNE.COM

Service Areas
New Hampshire
Vermont
Massachusetts
Connecticut
Rhode Island
Maine
Upstate New York/Albany area

PRODUCTS/OPERATIONS

Departments
Private label
Grocery
Meat/ Seafood
Products
Deli/Bakery
Dairy/Frozen/ Ice Cream

COMPETITORS

Bozzuto' s	McLane
C&S Wholesale	Pine State Trading
Dole & Bailey Inc.	SUPERVALU
Hannaford Bros.	Shaw' s

HISTORICAL FINANCIALS
Company Type: Private

Income Statement
FYE: March 30

	REVENUE ($ mil.)	NET INCOME ($ mil.)	NET PROFIT MARGIN	EMPLOYEES
03/13	480	0	0.1%	625
03/09	340	0	0.2%	
03/08	315	0	0.1%	
03/07	1,996	0	—	
Annual Growth	—	—	—	—

2013 Year-End Financials
Return on assets: 2.6%   Cash ($ mil.): 8
Return on equity: 0.1%
Current ratio: 0.60

ASSOCIATED WHOLESALE GROCERS INC.

Associated Wholesale Grocers (AWG) knows its customers can't live on bread and milk alone. The second-largest retailer-owned cooperative in the US (behind Wakefern Food Corporation) AWG supplies more than 2900 retail outlets in more than 30 states from nine distribution centers. In addition to its wholesale grocery operation AWG offers a variety of business services to its members including marketing and merchandising programs shelf management insurance and store design. AWG was founded by a group of independent grocers in 1924.

HISTORY

About 20 Kansas City Kansas-area grocers met in a local grocery in 1924 and organized the Associated Grocers Company to get better deals on purchases and advertising. They elected J. C. Harline president and each chipped in a few hundred dollars to make their first purchases. It took a while to find a manufacturer who would sell directly to them; a local soap maker was finally convinced and others gradually followed.

In 1926 the group was incorporated as Associated Wholesale Grocers (AWG). It outgrew two warehouses in four years finally moving to a 16000-sq.-ft. facility big enough to add new lines and more products. Membership doubled between 1930 and 1932 as grocers moved from ordering products a year ahead to the new wholesale concept and members took seriously the slogan: "Buy Sell Buy Some More." They met every week to plan how to sell their products and buyer and advertising manager Harry Small gave sales presentations and advertising ideas (his trade-in plan for old brooms sold more than two train-carloads of brooms in two weeks). Heavy newspaper advertising also paid off; AWG topped $1 million in sales in 1933.

The cooperative made its first acquisition in 1936 buying Progressive Grocers a warehouse in Joplin Missouri; a second warehouse named Associated Grocers was acquired the next year in Springfield Missouri. AWG continued building and expanding warehouses and annual sales were at $11 million by 1951.

Louis Fox became CEO in 1956. Fox maximized year-end rebates for members led several acquisitions and formed a new subsidiary for financing stores and small shopping centers where AWG members had a presence (Supermarket Developers). Sales increased nearly 15-fold to over $200 million in his first 15 years.

James Basha who succeeded Fox when he retired in 1984 saw sales reach $2.4 billion by the time of his own retirement in 1992.

Basha was followed by former COO Mike DeFabis once a deputy mayor of Indianapolis. DeFabis orchestrated several acquisitions including 41 Kansas City-area stores —most of which were quickly bought by members —from bankrupt Food Barn Stores in 1994 and 29 Oklahoma stores and a warehouse from Safeway spinoff Homeland Stores in 1995 (members bought all the stores).

AWG's non-food subsidiary Valu Merchandisers was established in 1995; its new Kansas warehouse began shipping health and beauty aids and housewares the following year to help members battle big discounters. Members narrowly defeated

a proposal in late 1996 to convert the cooperative into a public company. Proponents promptly petitioned for a second vote which was defeated early the next year.

AWG veteran Doug Carolan succeeded DeFabis in 1998 becoming only the fifth CEO in the cooperative's history. The company bought five Falley's and 33 Food 4 Less stores in Kansas and Missouri from Fred Meyer in 1998 for $300 million. In a break with tradition AWG began operating the stores rather than selling them to members.

In 2000 after a months-long labor dispute with the Teamsters was resolved Carolan left AWG. The company's CFO Gary Phillips was named president and CEO later that year. In 2001 the company debuted a new format ALPS (Always Low Price Stores) —small stores that carry a limited selection of grocery top-sellers. Also that year AWG's Kansas City division began distributing to more than 10 new stores that had formerly been served by Fleming at the time the #1 US wholesale food distributor.

In 2002 supermarket operator Homeland Stores which operates stores in Oklahoma emerged from bankruptcy as a fully owned subsidiary of AWG. AWG formed a new subsidiary Associated Retail Grocers to oversee Homeland and its Falley's chain.

As a result of the 2003 sale of Fleming Companies' wholesale distribution business AWG picked up food distribution centers in Nebraska (two) Oklahoma (one) and Tennessee (two) and general-merchandise distribution centers in Tennessee and Kansas.

Introducing a "dollar" section in its stores in 2004 proved successful leading AWG to expand the category to more than 1000 food and non-food items. The following year it merged the corporate offices of its Homeland and Food 4 Less chains.

AWG took steps to expand its capacity and its territory in 2007 when it acquired a distribution center in Fort Worth from Albertsons. The cooperative also took on supply operations for Albertsons locations in Arkansas Louisiana and Texas.

In 2009 AWG acquired the assets of Little Rock Arkansas-based Affiliated Foods Southwest in 2009 adding about a dozen new stores.

During 2010 the firm introduced a paperless coupon program.

In December 2011 AWG sold its corporate supermarkets to a group of employees. The corporate stores included 76 retail locations operating under the Homeland United of Oklahoma and Country mart banners in Oklahoma and the Super Saver banner in northern Texas.

In late 2012 AWG completed a 35000-square-foot addition to its corporate headquarters in Kansas City. The location is also home to AWG's Kansas City distribution centers and its Valu Merchandisers division.

EXECUTIVES

Vice President Corporate Controller, Gary Koch
EVP Division Operations, David Smith
Senior Vice President Grocery Products, Dan Funk
Vice President Of Sales, Joe Busch
Senior Vice President Distribution, Richard (Dick) Kearns
Svp And Division Manager Fort Worth, Linda Lawson
Vice President Store Engineering, John (Jack) Crumley
Vice President Corporate Human Resources, Susan (Sue) Ott
Vice President Investor, Lisa Fox
Director Of Pharmacy, Joseph Maslak
Senior Vice President Springfield, Tim Bellanti
Vice President, Don Ketter
Vice President, Gary Jennings
Senior Vice President Gen Concl, Frances Puhl

Senior Vice President Finance, David (Dave) Carl
Vice President and General Manager Limited
  Assortment stores, Mike Danes
Senior Vice President and Division Manager
  Kansas City, Bill Quade
Senior Vice President and Division Manager
  Kansas City, Bob Pickerill
Senior Vice President Perishables, Jerry Edney
Senior Vice President and Division Manager Gulf
  Coast, Bob Durand
Auditors: GRANT THORNTON LLP KANSAS CIT

LOCATIONS

HQ: ASSOCIATED WHOLESALE GROCERS INC.
  5000 KANSAS AVE, KANSAS CITY, KS 661061135
Phone: 913 288-1000
Web: WWW.AWGINC.COM

Selected States Served
Alabama
Arizona
Arkansas
Colorado
Florida
Georgia
Idaho
Illinois
Indiana
Iowa
Kansas
Kentucky
Louisiana
Michigan
Minnesota
Mississippi
Missouri
Montana
Nebraska
New Mexico
North Carolina
North Dakota
Ohio
Oklahoma
South Carolina
South Dakota
Tennessee
Texas
Utah
Virginia
West Virginia
Wisconsin
Wyoming

COMPETITORS

Affiliated Foods
Affiliated Foods
  Midwest
Alex Lee
Associated Grocers
  Inc.
C&S Wholesale
Central Grocers
Dearborn Wholesale
  Grocers

GSC Enterprises
H. T. Hackney
McLane
SUPERVALU
SpartanNash
Wakefern Food
Wal-Mart

HISTORICAL FINANCIALS

Company Type: Private

Income Statement

	REVENUE ($ mil.)	NET INCOME ($ mil.)	NET PROFIT MARGIN	EMPLOYEES
12/13	8,380	192	2.3%	5,500
12/12	7,852	175	2.2%	—
12/11	7,766	169	2.2%	—
12/10	7,251	0	—	—
Annual Growth	4.9%			

FYE: December 28

2013 Year-End Financials

Return on assets: 5.1%
Return on equity: 2.3%
Current ratio: 0.40

Cash ($ mil.): 59

ASSOCIATION OF UNIVERSITIES FOR RESEARCH IN ASTRONOMY INC.

There is nothing quasi-scientific about this aura. The Association of Universities for Research in Astronomy (AURA) is a consortium of universities and not-for-profit organizations devoted to the study of space. The organization was founded to create astronomical observing facilities for use by qualified researchers and to serve the community by offering public outreach education and dissemination of information. AURA was founded in 1957 and operates astronomical observatories at 34 US institutions and six international affiliates including Harvard University Ohio State University and the University of Toronto.

EXECUTIVES

Vice President for Administration, Deborah (Deb) Narcisso
Auditors: CLIFTONLARSONALLEN LLP CALVE

LOCATIONS

HQ: ASSOCIATION OF UNIVERSITIES FOR RESEARCH IN ASTRONOMY INC.
  1212 NEW YORK AVE NW # 450, WASHINGTON, DC 200053987
Phone: 202 483-2101
Web: WWW.AURA-ASTRONOMY.ORG

PRODUCTS/OPERATIONS

Member Institutions
Boston University / 1993
California Institute of Technology / 1972
Carnegie Institution of Washington / 1997
Georgia State University / 2008
Harvard University / 1957
Indiana University / 1957
Instituto de Astrofísica de Canarias / 2005
Iowa State University / 1992
Johns Hopkins University / 1982
Kiepenheuer-Institut für Sonnenphysik / 2005
Massachusetts Institute of Technology / 1981
Michigan State University / 1997
Montana State University / 2005
New Mexico State University / 1999
Ohio State University / 1957
Pennsylvania State University / 1990
Pontificia Universidad Catolica de Chile / 1997
Princeton University / 1959
Rutgers University / 1999
SUNY - Stony Brook / 1986
Swinburne University / 2008
Universidad de Chile / 1992
University of Arizona / 1972
University of California at Berkeley / 2007
University of California at Santa Cruz / 1957
University of Chicago / 1957
University of Colorado / 1977
University of Florida / 2002
University of Hawaii / 1978
University of Illinois at Urbana-Champaign / 1980
University of Maryland / 1986
University of Michigan / 1957
University of Minnesota / 1995
University of North Carolina at Chapel Hill / 1995
University of Texas at Austin / 1972
University of Toronto / 2004
University of Virginia / 2003
University of Washington / 1986
University of Wisconsin / 1957
Yale University / 1958

HISTORICAL FINANCIALS

Company Type: Private

Income Statement

	REVENUE ($ mil.)	NET INCOME ($ mil.)	NET PROFIT MARGIN	EMPLOYEES
09/13	238	2	0.9%	1,000
09/10	197	(2)	—	—
09/09	180	(0)	—	—
09/08	0	0	—	—
Annual Growth	—	—	—	—

FYE: September 30

2013 Year-End Financials

Return on assets: 14.8%
Return on equity: 0.9%
Current ratio: —

Cash ($ mil.): 40

ASTRONAUTICS CORPORATION OF AMERICA

Sometimes it's hard to know which way is up but Astronautics Corporation of America gives good directions. The company makes maintains and repairs electronic components and systems that enable manned and unmanned planes ships land vehicles and spacecraft to orient themselves in time and space. Its lineup runs from integrated avionics navigation and network server systems to electronic flight bags and instruments mission and display processors and inertial navigation systems. More than 150000 aircraft rely on the hardware. Astronautics' customers include the US Departments of Defense and Homeland Security as well as NASA Boeing Lockheed Martin and Sikorsky.
  Operations
  Subsidiary Kearfott Corporation constitutes Astronautics' Guidance & Navigation Division. The subsidiary makes navigation systems and motion and control components for use on all types of aircraft. In 2014 it expanded its operations to supply navigation systems for unmanned aircraft aka drones.
  Geographic Reach
  Astronautics has two manufacturing plants in Milwaukee and a satellite office in Phoenix. Kearfott's manufacturing plants are located in New Jersey North Carolina and Tamaulipas Mexico.
  Astronautics also operates in Israel through Astronautics C.A. Ltd and in Russia through AKE.
  Strategy
  Since its formation in 1959 the company has sought to lead the avionics industry through its state-of-the-industry products and operations. Astronautics has grown through its success in winning US government contracts from repair of horizontal situation video display interfaces to repair and modification of steering computers. Some of its projects have included upgrading the C-130 fleet of transport aircraft for the Brazilian air force providing equipment for new Airbus aircraft and providing network server systems for the Federal Express fleet.

EXECUTIVES

CFO, Steven Givant
Vice President Engineering, Dan Olson
Vice President, Michael Garten

Vice President Of Engineering, Dan Jinar
Auditors: BDO SELDMAN LLP MILWAUKEE W

LOCATIONS

HQ: ASTRONAUTICS CORPORATION OF AMERICA
4115 N TEUTONIA AVE, MILWAUKEE, WI 532096731
Phone: 414 449-4000
Web: WWW.ASTRONAUTICS.COM

PRODUCTS/OPERATIONS

Selected Products

Air
  Computers
  Airborne file server
  Air data computers
  Digital air data computers
  Mission and display processor
  Displays
  Electronic flight bag/pilot information displays
  Electronic warfare displays
  Engine instrument and caution advisory system displays
  Engine performance indicator
  Integrated flight deck displays
  Multi-function color displays
  Flight controls
  Unmanned aerial vehicle (UAV) servo actuators
  Flight instruments
  Attitude director indicators
  Electronic flight instruments
  Horizontal situation indicator
  Integrated avionics
  Mission and display systems
  Navigation systems
  Attitude heading reference systems
  Digital attitude heading reference systems
  High accuracy inertial navigation system
Land
  Components
  Accelerometer triad assembly
  Inertial single axis accelerometer
  Displays
  Dash boards for tanks
  Fire
  Fire control computer
  Fire control systems
  Line-of-sight stabilization and data link subsystem
  Line-of-sight stabilization system
  Navigation
  Land navigation systems
  Miniature land navigation system
  Modular azimuth positioning system
Sea
  Displays
  Operating and control console
  Navigation
  Seaborne navigation system
  Ship integrated navigation system
Space
  High accuracy inertial navigation systems for the Space Shuttle
  Inertial single axis accelerometer
  Inertial measurement unit for tactical applications
  Space qualified inertial reference unit
  Two-axis rate assembly

COMPETITORS

BAE SYSTEMS
CIC International
Elbit Systems
L-3/IS
Moog

Parker-Hannifin
Raven Industries
Raytheon
Rockwell Collins
United Technologies

HISTORICAL FINANCIALS
Company Type: Private

Income Statement
FYE: May 31

	REVENUE ($ mil.)	NET INCOME ($ mil.)	NET PROFIT MARGIN	EMPLOYEES
05/08	235	19	8.3%	1,550
05/07	233	20	8.9%	—
05/06	353	0	—	—
Annual Growth	—23275.9%			

2008 Year-End Financials
Return on assets: 6.2%   Cash ($ mil.): 2
Return on equity: 8.3%
Current ratio: 0.90

ATALANTA CORPORATION

Atalanta Corporation helps customers outfit any wine and cheese soirée. The company is a top specialty food importer that markets 2500 different products such as gourmet cheeses deli and canned meats and frozen seafood. Its menu of products also includes pastas rices and grains as well as coffee and a line of kosher foods. Atalanta's brands include Casa Diva Celebrity Zerto Del Destino Maria Brand Martel and Atalanta. Importing products from Europe Asia and South America Atalanta sells primarily to restaurants and other foodservice operators grocery stores and specialty food retailers. Founded in 1945 the company is controlled by the Gellert family and led by chairman George Gellert.

Geographic Reach

New Jersey-based Atalanta has 10 offices in the US in Georgia Massachusetts Illinois Connecticut Texas California and Florida and three offices abroad in Europe. It boasts a presence on three continents.

Operations

The multinational food importer specializes in sourcing and providing meat cheese groceries fruit juice concentrates seafood grains pasta rice baked products and coffee.

Atalanta operates in Europe through its 50%-owned Lemarco S.A. business in Romania which is focused on agricultural commodities such as sugar grains oilseeds and vegetable oils. Sugar is imported from some of the world's largest international trading companies and shipped to Lemarco. Besides Lemarco Atalanta's international businesses include Atalanta Furniture SRL and Atalanta Nova SRL.

Sales and Marketing

Atalanta serves several sectors such as retailers foodservice operators restaurants and manufacturers. It boasts sales agents in every major commercial center globally.

Strategy

Inking exclusive deals gives Atalanta an edge against competitors. The company entered an agreement in 2012 with Belgium's Chimay Trappist Cheeses to become the exclusive importer for the product in North America. Chimay Peres Trappistes is one of only three Trappist cheesemakers worldwide. It also inked a deal in 2012 to become the exclusive North American importer of Lazzaroni's historical range of Italian biscuits.

Mergers and Acquisitions

Atalanta aims to purchase equity interests in suppliers and trading companies worldwide.

To maintain a foothold in the West Coast markets Atalanta in 2013 acquired H&J Trading Company. The company's Maria Brand of artichokes capers peppers and other grocery items have earned a following among the foodservice and retail markets.

Company Ownership

Atalanta is controlled and led by the Gellert family. Atalanta is one of a handful of companies operated by Gellert Global Group. The group specializes in importing food products. Sister companies to Atalanta include Camerican International Swiss

Chalet Fine Foods WePackItAll and Monarch Seafood among others.

Company Background

The company is named for ancient Greek goddess Atalanta known for her hunting skills and speed.

EXECUTIVES

Vice President Operations Logistics, Joseph (Jo) Denicholas
Vice President, Al Pish
Vice President Management Information Systems, Carrol Stitt
Auditors: MC GLADREY & PULLEN LLP NEW

LOCATIONS

HQ: ATALANTA CORPORATION
1 ATLANTA PLZ STE 3, ELIZABETH, NJ 072062120
Phone: 908 351-8000
Web: WWW.ATALANTA1.COM

PRODUCTS/OPERATIONS

Selected Brands
Atalanta
Casa Diva
Celebrity
Chimay Trappist Cheeses (North American imports only)
Del Destino
Maria Brand
Martel
Zerto

Selected Products
Cheeses and accompaniments
Coffee
Desserts and baked goods
Frozen seafood
Fish
Fruit juice concentrate
Groceries
Meat
Pasta rice and grains
Specialty cheeses

COMPETITORS

Allied International Corporation of VA
American Milk Products
Boar's Head
Cento
DPI Specialty Foods

European Imports
KeHE Distributors
Millbrook Distribution Services
World Finer Foods

HISTORICAL FINANCIALS
Company Type: Private

Income Statement
FYE: December 31

	REVENUE ($ mil.)	NET INCOME ($ mil.)	NET PROFIT MARGIN	EMPLOYEES
12/09	384	8	2.3%	150
12/07	348	10	3.1%	—
12/06	0	0	—	—
Annual Growth	—	—	—	—

2009 Year-End Financials
Return on assets: —   Cash ($ mil.): 7
Return on equity: 2.3%
Current ratio: 0.40

ATLANTIC BROADBAND FINANCE LLC

LOCATIONS

HQ: ATLANTIC BROADBAND FINANCE LLC
1 BATTERYMARCH PARK # 405, QUINCY, MA
021697454
Phone: 617 786-8800
Web: WWW.ATLANTICBB.COM

HISTORICAL FINANCIALS

Company Type: Private

Income Statement
FYE: December 31

	REVENUE ($ mil.)	NET INCOME ($ mil.)	NET PROFIT MARGIN	EMPLOYEES
12/10	316	46	14.6%	662
12/09	301	39	13.0%	—
Annual Growth	5.1%	17.5%	—	—

2010 Year-End Financials
Return on assets: 4.7%   Cash ($ mil.): 9
Return on equity: 14.6%
Current ratio: 0.40

ATLANTIC HEALTH SYSTEM INC.

Got a gash or gout in the Garden State? Atlantic Health System has more than 1600 beds for you to get better in. The not-for-profit Atlantic Health System (AHS) operates five acute care hospital providing general medical and surgical services to residents of northern New Jersey. Its flagship Morristown Medical Center serves as a regional trauma center and provides specialty care in a number of areas including oncology pediatrics and cardiac care. The system's Overlook Medical Center houses the Atlantic Neuroscience Institute; home to the Comprehensive Stroke Center. Its smaller Newton Medical Center serves patients in two New Jersey counties as well as counties in Pennsylvania and New York.

Operations
The system's corporate health division provides employee assistance programs as well as a full range of corporate-related medical services including physicals smoking cessation work injury and travel medicine services. Its corporate clients include pharmaceutical companies manufacturing operations and municipal governments.

In addition to its hospitals AHS operates home care and hospice units that serve Essex Morris Somerset and Union counties. It also serves as the official health care provider for the New York Jets football team which has named its corporate headquarters and training facility the Atlantic Health Jets Training Center.

AHS provides educational that includes continuing medical education classes and residency programs in pharmacy and nursing to keep its medical staff current on medical technologies and techniques. Annually the hospital system teaches more than 250 medical residents through about a dozen residency programs in emergency and family medicine surgery and pediatrics among others.

It is affiliated with Mount Sinai School of Medicine and the Mount Sinai Hospital giving AHS access to the major university hospital's resources.

Strategy
AHS is growing by acquiring other hospitals in northern New Jersey. In 2014 it acquired Pompton Plains-based Chilton Memorial Hospital (now Chilton Medical Center) and affiliated Chilton Health Network sites. The purchase added 260 beds plus related outpatient clinics. AHS became a three-hospital system in early 2011 when Newton Medical Center then known as Newton Memorial Hospital moved under the AHS umbrella. The deal expanded access to outpatient and preventative care throughout the region increased specialty care options and allowed for the improvement of facilities at the Newton campus.

EXECUTIVES

President Chilton Medical Center, Stephanie Bloom
Medical Director, Theodor Feigelman
Vice President, Kevin Shanley
Vice President Of Regulatory Affairs, Ashish Shah
Vp; President Morristown Medical Center, David J (Dave) Shulkin
Vice President Of Human Resources And Cao, Andrew L (Andy) Kovach
Vice President Government Affairs, Madeline Ferraro
Vice Chairman, Anne S Rooke
Auditors: PRICEWATERHOUSECOOPERS LLP F

LOCATIONS

HQ: ATLANTIC HEALTH SYSTEM INC.
475 SOUTH ST, MORRISTOWN, NJ 079606459
Phone: 973 660-3100
Web: WWW.ATLANTICHEALTH.ORG

PRODUCTS/OPERATIONS

Selected Operations
Atlantic Home Care
Atlantic Hospice
Atlantic Neuroscience Institute (Overlook Hospital)
Carol G. Simon Cancer Center (Morristown and Overlook hospitals)
Chilton Medical Center
Gagnon Cardiovascular Institute (Morristown Hospital)
Goryeb Children's Hospital
Morristown Medical Center
Newton Medical Center
Overlook Medical Center

COMPETITORS

Barnabas Health
Children's Specialized Hospital
Chilton Medical Center
Community Health Systems
East Orange General Hospital
JFK Health System
JFK Medical Center
Newark Beth Israel Medical Center
Raritan Bay Medical Center
Robert Wood Johnson University Hospital at Rahway
Saint Barnabas Medical
St. Joseph's Healthcare System
The Valley Hospital
Trinitas Regional Medical Center

HISTORICAL FINANCIALS

Company Type: Private

Income Statement
FYE: December 31

	REVENUE ($ mil.)	NET INCOME ($ mil.)	NET PROFIT MARGIN	EMPLOYEES
12/13	1,624	291	18.0%	221
12/09	0	0	—	—
12/03	883	6	0.8%	—
Annual Growth	6.3%	45.3%	—	—

2013 Year-End Financials
Return on assets: 10.5%   Cash ($ mil.): 218
Return on equity: 18.0%
Current ratio: 1.60

ATLANTIC METHANOL PRODUCTION COMPANY LLC

Atlantic Methanol Production Company (AMPCO) must have adopted "Waste not want not" as its motto. It tries not to waste the natural gas that is a by-product of its parent companies' production processes. A joint venture between Noble Energy (45% ownership) Marathon Oil (45%) and SONAGAS the National Gas Company of Equatorial Guinea (10%) the company operates one of the largest methanol plants in the world. The plant off the coast of Equatorial Guinea produces about 1 million tons of methanol annually — 2% of the global market. AMPCO also distributes using three vessels and five terminals in Europe and US where it sells most of its production.

Geographic Reach
AMPCO's plant located on Bioko Island in Equatorial Guinea has the capacity to produce 3000 metric tons per day of methanol. It maintains storage at its production site at Punta Europa in Equatorial Guinea as well as in the US (Louisiana and Texas) the Netherlands and the UK.

Operations
The global demand for methanol is about 60 million metric tons per year of which Equitorial Guinea supplies 2% from its single plant. Methanol is used as an intermediate in the manufacture of several everyday products including adhesive resins for plywood and pressboard polyester fibers and packaging paints and coatings plastics and fuels and fuel additives. Some of methanol's fastest growth areas are in the acetic acid and fuels areas including biodiesel. Other applications include using methanol for fuel cells.

Feedstock for AMPCO's plant is supplied from natural gas production from the Alba field in Equatorial Guinea (operated by Marathon Oil and Noble Energy) under a contract that runs through 2026.

Sales and Marketing
The company manages its marketing and sales from its US-based headquarters in Houston. It markets in Europe through an agent solvadis methanol in Frankfurt Germany.

Financial Performance
While no separate financials are available Noble Energy reported that 2013 net income derived by Noble Energy and AMPCO increased primarily due to a 19% jump in the average realized sales price of methanol.

Strategy
AMPCO is reporting an increase in demand from Asia the US and Western Europe for methanol. There is also an expanding demand for methanol in the oilfield services sector along the coast of West Africa. To keep up with demand in 2013 AMPCO contracted with Mitsui O.S.K. Lines for two new methanol carriers.

Company Background
Noble Energy Marathon Oil and SONAGAS formed the JV in 1997.

EXECUTIVES

President and General Manager, Paul Moschell
Manager Human Resources and Administration, Arthur (Budd) Buschmann
Chairman, W. Ken Keag
Vice Chairman, Juan A. Ndong
Vice President Marketing, Edson Jones
Manager Finance and Administration, Jim O'Casek
Vice President Operations and Resident Manager, Pedro Arasa
Vice Chairman, Juan Antonio
Vice Chairman President and General Manager, Paul Moschell
Vice Chairman, Juan A. Ndong
Vice Chairman, Juan Antonio
Auditors: UHY LLP HOUSTON TEXAS

LOCATIONS

HQ: ATLANTIC METHANOL PRODUCTION COMPANY LLC
12600 NORTHBOROUGH DR # 150, HOUSTON, TX 770673200
Phone: 281 872-8324
Web: WWW.ATLANTICMETHANOL.COM

COMPETITORS

Celanese
Eastman Chemical
LyondellBasell
Methanex
OCI Partners LP

HISTORICAL FINANCIALS
Company Type: Private

Income Statement
FYE: December 31

	REVENUE ($ mil.)	NET INCOME ($ mil.)	NET PROFIT MARGIN	EMPLOYEES
12/10	254	65	25.8%	342
12/08	341	122	35.8%	—
12/07	1,405	0	—	—
Annual Growth	(43.4%)	10372.8%	—	—

2010 Year-End Financials
Return on assets: 2.1%
Return on equity: 25.8%
Current ratio: 0.90
Cash ($ mil.): 22

ATLANTICARE REGIONAL MEDICAL CENTER

LOCATIONS

HQ: ATLANTICARE REGIONAL MEDICAL CENTER
65 W JIMMIE LEEDS RD, POMONA, NJ 082409102
Phone: 609 652-1000
Web: WWW.ATLANTICARE.ORG

HISTORICAL FINANCIALS
Company Type: Private

Income Statement
FYE: December 31

	REVENUE ($ mil.)	NET INCOME ($ mil.)	NET PROFIT MARGIN	EMPLOYEES
12/08	560	(58)	—	249
12/05	457	51	11.3%	—
Annual Growth	6.9%	—	—	—

2008 Year-End Financials
Return on assets: 10.9%
Return on equity: (-10.5%)
Current ratio: 0.70
Cash ($ mil.): 7

ATLAS OIL COMPANY

Auditors: ERNST & YOUNG LLP DETROIT M

LOCATIONS

HQ: ATLAS OIL COMPANY
24501 ECORSE RD, TAYLOR, MI 481801641
Phone: 313 292-5500
Web: WWW.ATLASOIL.COM

HISTORICAL FINANCIALS
Company Type: Private

Income Statement
FYE: December 31

	REVENUE ($ mil.)	NET INCOME ($ mil.)	NET PROFIT MARGIN	EMPLOYEES
12/08	1,153	1	0.1%	110
12/07	717	1	0.1%	—
Annual Growth	60.7%	50.3%	—	—

2008 Year-End Financials
Return on assets: —
Return on equity: 0.1%
Current ratio: 0.50
Cash ($ mil.): 3

AUGUSTANA HEALTH CARE CENTER OF APPLE VALLEY

LOCATIONS

HQ: AUGUSTANA HEALTH CARE CENTER OF APPLE VALLEY
14650 GARRETT AVE, SAINT PAUL, MN 551247543
Phone: 952 431-7700
Web: WWW.AUGUSTANACARE.ORG

HISTORICAL FINANCIALS
Company Type: Private

Income Statement
FYE: September 30

	REVENUE ($ mil.)	NET INCOME ($ mil.)	NET PROFIT MARGIN	EMPLOYEES
09/09	1,505	30	2.0%	280
09/05	6	(0)	—	—
Annual Growth	287.7%	—	—	—

2009 Year-End Financials
Return on assets: —
Return on equity: 2.0%
Current ratio: 2.90
Cash ($ mil.): 1

AUSABLE VALLEY COMMUNITY MENTAL HEALTH FOUNDATION

LOCATIONS

HQ: AUSABLE VALLEY COMMUNITY MENTAL HEALTH FOUNDATION
1199 HARRIS AVE, TAWAS CITY, MI 487639681
Phone: 989 362-8636
Web: WWW.AVCMH.ORG

HISTORICAL FINANCIALS
Company Type: Private

Income Statement
FYE: June 30

	REVENUE ($ mil.)	NET INCOME ($ mil.)	NET PROFIT MARGIN	EMPLOYEES
06/09*	436	(29)	—	400
09/07	13	(0)	—	—
09/06	13	(0)	—	—
09/05	12	0	—	—
Annual Growth	141.9%	—	—	—

*Fiscal year change

2009 Year-End Financials
Return on assets: 0.1%
Return on equity: (-6.7%)
Current ratio: 0.20
Cash ($ mil.): —

AVERITT EXPRESS INC.

Small loads add up at Averitt Express. The company provides less-than-truckload (LTL) freight transportation service. (LTL carriers combine freight from multiple shippers into a single trailer.) It operates a fleet of about 4100 tractors and 12250 trailers from a network of 80 terminals. Averitt Express directly serves the southern US and Mexico and it provides service elsewhere in North America through partnerships with other carriers such as Lakeville Motor Express and DATS. The company also offers truckload and expedited freight transportation along with logistics warehousing and international freight forwarding. Customers have included Home Depot Shoe Carnival and V.F. Corporation.

Geographic Reach

Averitt Express has a total of roughly 140 facilities that serve thousands of points throughout the Southern US (in about 20 states) Canada Mexico and the Caribbean.

Strategy

The company aims to grow from solely a LTL carrier based in the Southeast to an international transportation and logistics company. To this end it continues to strategically broaden its geographic reach and range of services. Averitt Express over the years has launched a new business unit zeroing in on retailers in need of distribution services. The new unit Averitt Retail Distribution Services offers customized delivery services catering to the unique requirements of retailers and is targeting retailers needing delivery in large Southern markets.

EXECUTIVES

President and CEO, Gary D. Sasser

EVP and COO, Wayne Spain
EVP Sales and Marketing, Phil Pierce
EVP and CFO, George Johnson
Regional Sales Vice President, Ted Vanhyfte
Auditors: DUNCAN WHEELER & WILKERSON P

LOCATIONS

HQ: AVERITT EXPRESS INC.
1415 NEAL ST, COOKEVILLE, TN 385014328
Phone: 931 526-3306
Web: WWW.AVERITTEXPRESS.COM

PRODUCTS/OPERATIONS

Selected Services

Cross-border/domestic offshore (Canada Mexico Puerto
  Rico/Virgin Islands)
Dedicated
Expedited
Intermodal
International ocean/air (ocean/air Asia-Memphis
  Express)
LTL (regional nationwide distribution/consolidation)
Portside
Retail specialized services
Transportation management
Truckload (dry van flatbed brokerage)
Warehousing

COMPETITORS

AAA Cooper Transportation	Old Dominion Freight R+L Carriers
ArcBest	Schneider National
C.H. Robinson Worldwide	Southeastern Freight Lines
Estes Express	Swift Transportation
FedEx Freight	UPS Freight
J.B. Hunt	YRC Worldwide

HISTORICAL FINANCIALS

Company Type: Private

Income Statement
FYE: December 31

	REVENUE ($ mil.)	NET INCOME ($ mil.)	NET PROFIT MARGIN	EMPLOYEES
12/13	1,000	39	4.0%	8,208
12/12	957	39	4.2%	—
12/11	917	30	3.3%	—
12/10	819	0	—	—
Annual Growth	6.8%	—	—	—

2013 Year-End Financials
Return on assets: 2.5%   Cash ($ mil.): 1
Return on equity: 4.0%
Current ratio: 1.60

AVERITT INCORPORATED

Auditors: DUNCA WHEELER & WILKERSON P

LOCATIONS

HQ: AVERITT INCORPORATED
1415 NEAL ST, COOKEVILLE, TN 385014328
Phone: 931 526-3306
Web: WWW.AVERITTEXPRESS.COM

HISTORICAL FINANCIALS

Company Type: Private

Income Statement
FYE: December 31

	REVENUE ($ mil.)	NET INCOME ($ mil.)	NET PROFIT MARGIN	EMPLOYEES
12/13	1,012	48	4.8%	8,210
12/12	964	47	4.9%	—
12/11	924	32	3.5%	—
12/10	832	0	—	—
Annual Growth	6.7%	—	—	—

2013 Year-End Financials
Return on assets: 2.6%   Cash ($ mil.): 2
Return on equity: 4.8%
Current ratio: 1.50

AVI SYSTEMS INC.

AVI Systems knows that a CEO's message is only as good as its transmission. The employee-owned company designs installs and services audiovisual systems in boardrooms classrooms hospitals hotels places of worship and sports arenas primarily in the Midwest. It specializes in broadcast and cable sales and training video production and post-production videoconferencing and rental and staging systems. AVI runs more than 15 regional offices as well as a help desk that offers remote monitoring and emergency on-site service. It also provides IT engineering support for larger-scale national or international installations. AVI was founded in 1974 by chairman and former CEO Joe Stoebner.

Geographic Reach

With offices in the upper Midwest and on the West coast Minnesota-based AVI boasts a regional presence and a national reach.

Operations

Having become one of the nation's top five audio visual integrators AVI is authorized to install equipment from leading audiovisual equipment manufacturers such as Audio-Technica U.S. ClearOne Communications NEC Display Solutions and Samsung Electronics America.

Sales and Marketing

The company serves a variety of sectors such as universities schools service firms non-profit organizations and large companies the likes of Best Buy AT&T Carlson Companies Sprint ConAgra and Target.

Financial Performance

The fast-growing audiovisual tech company's revenue increased by more than 53% between 2010 and 2012 to $137.3 million driven by acquisitions and organic growth. The firm is benefiting from the growing popularity –indeed necessity –of audiovisual collaboration amongst employees.

Strategy

AVI not only integrates systems for others it has also begun integrating itself. Several subsidiaries including AVI Midwest and Televideo San Diego have traded their names for the AVI Systems banner. Also the company has worked to roll out its own line of digital signage and asset management products.

Ownership

AVI became a completely employee-owned company in 2009.

EXECUTIVES

President and CEO, Jeff Stoebner
CFO, Randi Borth

Chairman, Joe Stoebner
Auditors: EIDE BAILLY LLP BISMARCK NOR

LOCATIONS

HQ: AVI SYSTEMS INC.
9675 W 76TH ST STE 200, EDEN PRAIRIE, MN 553443707
Phone: 952 949-3700
Web: WWW.AVISYSTEMS.COM

Selected Locations
California
Colorado
Illinois
Iowa
Michigan
Minnesota
Missouri
Nebraska
North Dakota
Ohio
South Dakota
Texas
Wisconsin

COMPETITORS

ACT Teleconferencing	IVCi
AT Conference	PSAV Presentation Services
AVI-SPL	

HISTORICAL FINANCIALS

Company Type: Private

Income Statement
FYE: March 31

	REVENUE ($ mil.)	NET INCOME ($ mil.)	NET PROFIT MARGIN	EMPLOYEES
03/14	172	9	5.7%	233
03/13	143	7	5.0%	—
03/12	111	6	5.6%	—
03/11	89	0	—	—
Annual Growth	24.4%	—	—	—

2014 Year-End Financials
Return on assets: 4.9%   Cash ($ mil.): 15
Return on equity: 5.7%
Current ratio: 1.90

AVI-SPL HOLDINGS INC.

Auditors: ERNST & YOUNG LLP TAMPA FL

LOCATIONS

HQ: AVI-SPL HOLDINGS INC.
6301 BENJAMIN RD STE 101, TAMPA, FL 336345115
Phone: 813 884-7168
Web: WWW.AVISPL.COM

HISTORICAL FINANCIALS

Company Type: Private

Income Statement
FYE: December 31

	REVENUE ($ mil.)	NET INCOME ($ mil.)	NET PROFIT MARGIN	EMPLOYEES
12/12	580	9	1.6%	1,500
12/11	555	5	1.1%	—
12/10	505	(0)	—	—
12/09	421	0	—	—
Annual Growth	11.2%	—	—	—

2012 Year-End Financials
Return on assets: 11.4%   Cash ($ mil.): 4
Return on equity: 1.6%
Current ratio: 0.80

AVIO INC.

LOCATIONS
HQ: AVIO INC.
270 SYLVAN AVE STE 130, ENGLEWOOD CLIFFS, NJ
076322520
Phone: 201 816-2720

HISTORICAL FINANCIALS
Company Type: Private

Income Statement
FYE: December 31

	REVENUE ($ mil.)	NET INCOME ($ mil.)	NET PROFIT MARGIN	EMPLOYEES
12/12	1,310	7	0.6%	34
12/05	293	0	0.2%	—
12/04	387	8	2.1%	—
12/03	1,817	0	—	—
Annual Growth	—	—	—	—

2012 Year-End Financials
Return on assets: 12.3%
Return on equity: 0.6%
Current ratio: 0.60
Cash ($ mil.): 42

AXEL JOHNSON INC.

The Johnson family of Stockholm Sweden has an investment arm that stretches across the ocean. Axel Johnson owns and operates North American businesses on behalf of the Johnson dynasty. The investment firm focuses on several industries such as energy medical device manufacturing and water treatment. Its portfolio includes Sprague Energy Parkson Corp. and Kinetico Incorporated. Axel Johnson's companies boast about $4 billion in annual revenues. Axel Johnson along with Axel Johnson AB and AXFast are all affiliated with Sweden-based Axel Johnson Group but are independent. Established in 1873 the Johnson family of companies is in its fourth generation of family ownership.

Operations

Axel Johnson which was formed in 1920 is a long-term investor that typically holds on to its companies for about 20 years. Some companies have been a part of Axel Johnson's portfolio for more than 40 years. Two of its holdings Parkson and Kinetico are part of Axel Johnson's AxWater Group which was formed in 2000.

Strategy

Through NewtrAX Axel Johnson makes minority investments in smaller businesses. NewtrAX has stakes in Cadence a manufacturer of cutting and piercing instruments used for the medical and industrial applications. It also owns portions of wood reclamation company Mountain Lumber Co. and Walk2Campus a real estate management and acquisition company. The company in late 2011 invested some $15 million in ConforMIS which develops and markets customized medical devices for the treatment of osteoarthritis and joint damage.

Financial Performance

Following the economic downturn the company has seen sales increase for several years. Axel Johnson's revenue rose by 6% in 2012 to $4.2 billion as compared to 2011. Energy product sales generated the largest portion of the company's revenue. The results were powered by higher commodity prices and growth at Kinetico Cadence and Mountain Lumber; the first two along with Con-

forMis and Walk2Campus reported record sales in 2012.

EXECUTIVES
Vice President and Managing Director Corporate Development, Clare Peeters
Vice President Tax, Timothy (Tim) Grier
Vice President Finance and Administration, Sally Sarsfield
Vice President and Managing Director, Peter (Pete) Harris
Auditors: ERNST & YOUNG LLP NEW YORK N

LOCATIONS
HQ: AXEL JOHNSON INC.
155 SPRING ST FL 6, NEW YORK, NY 100125254
Phone: 646 291-2445
Web: WWW.AXELJOHNSON.COM

PRODUCTS/OPERATIONS

Selected Portfolio Companies
Cadence Incorporated
ConforMIS Inc.
Decisyon Inc.
Kinetico Incorporated
Mountain Lumber Company
Parkson Corporation
Sprague Energy Corp.
Walk2Campus Holdings LLC

COMPETITORS

CCMP Capital	KKR
Court Square Capital Partners	Menlo Ventures
Enterprise Partners	Sevin Rosen

HISTORICAL FINANCIALS
Company Type: Private

Income Statement
FYE: December 31

	REVENUE ($ mil.)	NET INCOME ($ mil.)	NET PROFIT MARGIN	EMPLOYEES
12/10	2,982	15	0.5%	1,200
12/09	2,598	11	0.5%	—
Annual Growth	14.8%	26.0%	—	—

2010 Year-End Financials
Return on assets: —
Return on equity: 0.5%
Current ratio: 0.80
Cash ($ mil.): 9

AZUSA PACIFIC UNIVERSITY

An evangelical Christian institution Azusa Pacific University (APU) has an enrollment of about 10300 undergraduate graduate and doctoral students. It offers approximately 70 fields of undergraduate study and about 40 graduate degree programs (including eight doctoral programs) as well as a number of certificate and credentialing programs. Undergraduate students are required to complete ministry and service credits every semester; options include participating in ministries international service experience and doing volunteer work. APU traces its roots to 1899 and the Training School for Christian Workers the West Coast's first bible college.

Operations

APU has a student-to-faculty ratio of 12:1 and employs more than 1200 full-time part-time and adjunct faculty members. Full-time undergraduate

tuition totaled some $32500 in fiscal 2015. (Nearly 90% of undergraduate students receive some sort of financial aid.) In addition to theology the university's major programs include business sciences liberal arts music nursing education and visual and performing arts. It offers online programs to supplement classes held at its main campus and regional branch locations. In 2014 ASU awarded about 3000 degrees.

The university's three libraries contain more than 386000 books and media items 128000 e-books 92000 electronic journals 1600 print periodicals and 110 databases.

Geographic Reach

In addition to its two main campuses (known as the East Campus and the West Campus) in Azusa a community located in the San Gabriel Valley northeast of Los Angeles the university has six regional centers in Southern California.

Financial Performance

APU's annual budget runs at some $232 million. It has an endowment of about $59 million.

Strategy

Five-year strategic plans (reaching through 2016) include improving resources for internal communication; enhancing support infrastructure for grants research and teaching; and increasing student and faculty diversity. APU is also working to restructure its curriculum.

EXECUTIVES
President, Jon R. Wallace
EVP, David E. Bixby
EVP, John C. Reynolds
Provost, Mark E. Stanton
SVP and CFO, Bob Johansen
Vice President for Enrollment Mangement, David (Dave) Dufault-Hunter
Vice President Emeritus Estate Planning, Hank Bode
Associate Vice President of University Relations, David (Dave) Peck
Vice President, Wanda Calnon
Vice President Business Affairs Chief Financial Officer, Robert L (Bob) Johansen
Vice President, Marcela Rojas
Vice Chair, Steve Perry
Secretary Undergraduate Office of School of Business and Management, Cindy Richmond
Auditors: CAPIN CROUSE LLP BREA CA

LOCATIONS
HQ: AZUSA PACIFIC UNIVERSITY
901 E ALOSTA AVE, AZUSA, CA 917022701
Phone: 626 969-3434
Web: WWW.APU.EDU

Selected Locations
Azusa CA
Los Angeles CA
Murrieta CA
Orange CA
Oxnard CA
San Bernardino CA
San Diego CA
Victorville CA

PRODUCTS/OPERATIONS

Selected Schools
American Language and Culture Institute
Azusa Pacific Online University
Center for Global Learning and Engagement
College of Liberal Arts and Sciences
School of Adult and Professional Studies
School of Behavioral and Applied Sciences
School of Business and Management
School of Education
School of Music
School of Nursing
School of Theology
School of Visual and Performing Arts
University Libraries

Selected Academic Programs

Adult and Professional Studies
Behavioral and Applied Sciences
Business and Management
Education
Liberal Arts and Sciences
Music and the Arts
Nursing
Theology

COMPETITORS

Ave Maria University	Lipscomb University
Biola University	Mercer University
Emory University	SMU
Fuller Theological Seminary	Seton Hall University

HISTORICAL FINANCIALS

Company Type: Private

Income Statement
FYE: June 30

	REVENUE ($ mil.)	NET INCOME ($ mil.)	NET PROFIT MARGIN	EMPLOYEES
06/13	281	1	0.4%	1,344
06/11	270	26	9.7%	—
06/10	227	8	3.8%	—
06/09	0	0	—	—
Annual Growth	—	—	—	—

2013 Year-End Financials

Return on assets: 4.4%
Return on equity: 0.4%
Current ratio: 0.20

Cash ($ mil.): 13

BABSON COLLEGE

Babson students could babble on and on about business management. With an enrollment of more than 3000 students Babson College is lauded as one of the nation's leading business schools. The school's undergraduate programs combine liberal arts with business curriculum; it also grants master's degrees in business administration entrepreneurship and other fields. Babson students in their first year receive the practical experience of creating for-profit ventures. Babson's entrepreneurship program has been ranked at the top of such programs in publications including Entrepreneur and U.S. News & World Report.

Geographic Reach

Babson College's main campus is located in Babson Park near Wellesley Massachusetts. Its students come from across the US and 70 international countries.

Operations

While the F.W. Olin Graduate School of Business grants Master of Business Administration (MBA) degrees and customized Master of Science degrees the Arthur M. Blank Center for Entrepreneurship offers graduate and undergraduate courses in entrepreneurial leadership.

In addition to undergraduate and graduate degree programs Babson conducts collaborative research programs that connect students with scholars and area business leaders.

Financial Performance

Operating revenue rose 4% to about $178 million in fiscal 2013 from higher student tuition and fee earnings as well as income from auxiliary activities room and board services and other educational and non-educational programs. The increase was offset somewhat by a dip in contributions and grants and investment income.

Undergraduate tuition runs at some $43500 per year.

Strategy

Babson College is expanding and improving its undergraduate curriculum with the goal of integrating management and liberal arts focuses. In 2013 it began rolling out new guidelines that aim to increase the undergraduate programs' focus on social environmental and economic concerns as well as on creativity and entrepreneurship.

To increase entrepreneurship opportunities for students in 2012 Babson extended its Butler Venture Accelerator program to its San Francisco campus. Also that year the college widened international entrepreneurship opportunities by partnering with Shiv Nadar University to provide programs in India. In 2013 Babson launched a new Master's Degree in Entrepreneurial Leadership; it also opened a new innovation lab focused on supporting female entrepreneurs.

Company Background

Babson was founded in 1919 (as Babson Institute) by philanthropist educator and businessman Roger Babson.

EXECUTIVES

Vice President Human Resources, Donna Bonaparte
Vice President Of Global And Career Education, Emily Wang
One Year Mba Vice President, Roberto Tietzsch
Co Executive Vice President, Shatiek Gatlin
Vice President of Marketing, Marc Labbe
Executive Vice President, Erin Janklow
Co President Healthcare and Life Sciences Club, Yash Shah
Night Glo Vice President of Sales, Caitlin Howard-Gomez
Academic Affairs Vice President, Nicole Wark
Vice President Finance And Contracts, Richard (Dick) Speer
Managing Director Leveraged Finance, Jeffrey McLane
Vice President of Communication, Amelie Bushong
Vice President, Seth Kurlinski
Vice President Of Communications, Jiamei Chen
Vice President Of Sales, Shafaat Khan
Vice President Of Membership And Events, Eric Burns
Vice President, Shanza Sheikh
Vice President Marketing, Vaibhav Shah
Vice President Of Finance, Hanna Letts
Vice President Of Finance, Shruthi Harve
Vice President Of Events, Ashwin Mysore
Vice President and O'Mahony S. (2014), Victor Seidel
Vice President, Daniel Chang
Vice President Marketing, Nidhi Purohit
Vice President Of Silkroad Activity Coordinator, Yin Chen
Graduate Vice President, Raunak Rajan
Vice President Finance, Jesus Herrera
Vice President Of Communications, Brooke Greiner
Vice President Marketing, Tyler Geertsen
Vice President Of Events, Takuo Urushihara
Vice President for Governance, Jane (Ginny) Edmonds
Sga Vice President Of Finance, Anthony Vasquez
Vice President Of Communications, Lena Wu
Vice President Of The Evening Program, Emily Robertson
Vice President Of Sales, James (Jamie) Pidhurney
Associate Vice President and Director Human Resources, Charles Anderson
Vice President Of Marketing, Daquan Oliver
Vice President of Finance Eric Fudeman, Craig Wing
Vice President Blended Learning Program, Diego Pacheco
Vice President for Strategic Initiatives, Steven (Steve) Moore

Vice President MSEL and MSA Programs, Katie Chaput
Vice Chair, Amy Weil
Executive Board Member, Kyle Shute
Babson College Republicans Treasurer, Zachary (Zach) Jacobson
Auditors: PRICEWATERHOUSECOOPERS LLP BO

LOCATIONS

HQ: BABSON COLLEGE
231 FOREST ST, BABSON PARK, MA 02457
Phone: 781 235-1200
Web: WWW.BABSONATHLETICS.COM

PRODUCTS/OPERATIONS

2012 Sales

	$ mil.	% of total
Program service fees	160	90
Net released assets	7	4
Endowment spending	6	4
Contributions & grants	2	2
Investment income	0	-
Total	**177**	**100**

Selected Academic Divisions

Accounting And Law
Arts And Humanities
Economics
Entrepreneurship
Finance
History And Society
Management
Marketing
Math And Science
Technology Operations And Information Management

HISTORICAL FINANCIALS

Company Type: Private

Income Statement
FYE: June 30

	REVENUE ($ mil.)	NET INCOME ($ mil.)	NET PROFIT MARGIN	EMPLOYEES
06/14	192	47	24.6%	750
06/13	177	43	24.4%	—
06/11	202	14	7.1%	—
06/10	176	0	—	—
Annual Growth	2.2%	—	—	—

2014 Year-End Financials

Return on assets: 10.5%
Return on equity: 24.6%
Current ratio: —

Cash ($ mil.): 41

BAER'S FURNITURE CO. INC.

Having assembled a furniture portfolio full of big-name brands Baer's Furniture counts the likes of Lexington Home Brands and Bernhardt as family. Family-owned Baer's Furniture operates about 15 mid-priced to high-end retail furniture showrooms and two warehouses in South Florida. The company offers furnishings (living room dining room bedroom and office furniture) bedding rugs and accessories made by popular manufacturers that are designed to fit the budgets of shoppers who have a little cash tucked away. The chain was founded in 1945 by Melvin and Lucile Baer in South Bend Indiana. Their sons Robert now the company's CEO and Allan company president moved the business to Florida in 1968.

Geographic Reach

Based in Pompano Beach Florida Baer's serves consumers throughout Florida as well as in South America and the Caribbean. The furniture retailer operates 15 stores and two warehouses across Florida.

Operations

Within its portfolio of living room bedroom dining room home office mattresses entertainment and outdoor furniture Baer's features brands that include Tommy Bahama Home Serta and Broyhill.

Financial Performance

Baer's stores rang up an estimated $143.2 million in sales in 2012 an 8.5% increase versus 2011.

Sales and Marketing

Baer's ships its furniture and decor items worldwide and sells its products online and through several Florida stores.

Strategy

Furniture retailers including Baer's were hard hit by the recession and housing crisis in the US. (Florida along with Arizona and California suffered more than most other states.) Furniture sales typically follow real estate sales trends and Baer's exposure to the Florida market led to losses. To cope with declining sales and deflation in furniture prices the company cut costs by outsourcing customer service overseas among other measures.

Now with housing posting a comeback Baer's is looking to grow by opening new stores. In 2015 it aims to open a new store in Winter Garden following the opening of a pair of stores in Central Florida.

EXECUTIVES

V Pres, Jerome I Baer
V Pres, Ira J Baer, age 53

LOCATIONS

HQ: BAER' S FURNITURE CO. INC.
1589 NW 12TH AVE, POMPANO BEACH, FL
330691734
Phone: 954 946-8001
Web: WWW.BAERS.COM

Selected Florida Locations
Altamonte Springs
Stuart
North Palm Beach
West Palm Beach
Boca Raton
Tamarac
Fort Lauderdale
Dania Beach
Pembroke Pines
Pinecrest
Naples
Fort Myers
Port Charlotte
Sarasota
West Melbourne

PRODUCTS/OPERATIONS

Selected Product Categories
Bedroom
Living Room
Kids' Bedroom
Dining Room
Home Office
Entertainment
Accent Tables
Mattresses
Outdoor

Selected Brands
Better Homes and Gardens
Bernhardt
Broyhill
HGTV Home
Hooker
Hunter Douglas
Lexington Home Brands
Pulaski
Serta

Sherrill
Tempur- Pedic
Tommy Bahama Home
Tommy Bahama Outdoor

COMPETITORS

Ashley Furniture	Norwalk Furniture
Bassett Furniture	Pier 1 Imports
El Dorado Furniture	Rooms To Go
Ethan Allen	W.S. Badcock
Havertys	Z Gallerie

HISTORICAL FINANCIALS
Company Type: Private

Income Statement FYE: December 31

	REVENUE ($ mil.)	NET INCOME ($ mil.)	NET PROFIT MARGIN	EMPLOYEES
12/13	160	10	6.6%	437
12/12	143	9	6.6%	—
12/11	138	7	5.3%	—
12/06	0	0	—	—
Annual Growth	—	—	—	—

2013 Year-End Financials
Return on assets: —
Return on equity: 6.6%
Current ratio: 0.10
Cash ($ mil.): 1

BALL STATE UNIVERSITY

Students at this university are on the ball. Ball State University (BSU) has an enrollment of about 21000 undergraduate and graduate students. It offers about 180 undergraduate majors more than 100 master's degree programs and 17 doctoral six associate and two specialist degrees in seven academic colleges. It has a Teachers College as well as colleges of applied sciences and technology; architecture and planning; business; communication information and media; fine arts; and sciences and humanities. Notable alumni include late night talk show host David Letterman and Garfield comic strip creator Jim Davis.

Geographic Reach

BSU has students from 48 states two US territories about 43 countries and every Indiana county.

Operations

The university's 731-acre campus in Muncie Indiana includes 106 academic administrative auxiliary and residential buildings valued at more than $1 billion.

The institution enrolls more than 675 international students. Out-of-state students make up 13% of on-campus enrollment. BSU has a student-to-faculty ratio of 16:1.

Modern initiatives include harnessing geothermal energy to power the campus and raising scholarship money to attract more students from outside of Indiana. Renovation and new construction of buildings were part of a multi-year effort to upgrade the campus infrastructure that concluded in 2012.

In 2013 BSU launched three free online classes.

Financial Performance

The university generates more than 30% of its revenues from tuition and fees net of scholarship allowances. BSU's 6% increase in revenues in 2012 was due to increase in student tuition and fees and increased enrollment. Auxiliary enterprises revenues including housing and dining net revenues increased by $3.7 million as the result of rate increases and increased occupancy in apartments and residence halls partially offset by a de-

cline in scholarship allowances from government and private sources.Net income increased by 13% in 2012 due to higher investment returns and capital appropriations partially offset by rise in operating expenses.

Company Background

The institution traces its origins to a private teacher's college in 1899. Officially founded in 1918 BSU became a university in 1965.

Glass jars filled with pickles apple butter and stewed tomatoes were part of the university's foundation. The family that gave us Ball canning jars and other glass containers donated the land for the original campus.

EXECUTIVES

VP Academic Affairs and Provost, Terry S. King
VP Information Technology, Philip Repp
President, Paul W. Ferguson
Associate Vice President For Emerging Media, David (Dave) Ferguson
Associate Vice President Facilities Planning and Management, John (Jack) Branies
Vice President Bus Affairs, Randy Howard
Vice Chairman, Frank Hancock
Chairman, Rick Hall
Secretary, Courtney Lyon
Auditors: STATE BOARD OF ACCOUNTS INDIA

LOCATIONS

HQ: BALL STATE UNIVERSITY
2000 W UNIVERSITY AVE, MUNCIE, IN 473060002
Phone: 765 289-1241
Web: WWW.CMS.BSU.EDU

PRODUCTS/OPERATIONS

Colleges
College of Applied Sciences and Technology
College of Architecture and Planning
College of Communication Information and Media
College of Fine Arts
College of Sciences and Humanities
Honors College
Miller College of Business
Teachers College
University College

HISTORICAL FINANCIALS
Company Type: Private

Income Statement FYE: June 30

	REVENUE ($ mil.)	NET INCOME ($ mil.)	NET PROFIT MARGIN	EMPLOYEES
06/07	224	43	19.4%	6,426
06/06	219	24	11.1%	—
06/05	277	0	0.0%	—
Annual Growth	(10.2%)	53178.7%	—	—

2007 Year-End Financials
Return on assets: 12.3%
Return on equity: 19.4%
Current ratio: 1.10
Cash ($ mil.): 23

BALTIMORE CITY PUBLIC SCHOOL SYSTEMS (INC)

LOCATIONS

HQ: BALTIMORE CITY PUBLIC SCHOOL SYSTEMS (INC)
200 E NORTH AVE, BALTIMORE, MD 212025910
Phone: 410 396-8700
Web: WWW.BSFA.ORG

HISTORICAL FINANCIALS

Company Type: Private

Income Statement

FYE: June 30

	REVENUE ($ mil.)	NET INCOME ($ mil.)	NET PROFIT MARGIN	EMPLOYEES
06/13	1,432	(4)	—	12,000
06/12	1,480	(18)	—	—
06/02	988	(23)	—	—
Annual Growth	3.4%	—	—	—

2013 Year-End Financials

Return on assets: —
Return on equity: (-0.3%)
Current ratio: —

Cash ($ mil.): 147

BALTIMORE WASHINGTON MEDICAL SYSTEM INC.

Auditors: GRANT THORNTON LLP PHILADELPH

LOCATIONS

HQ: BALTIMORE WASHINGTON MEDICAL SYSTEM INC.
301 HOSPITAL DR, GLEN BURNIE, MD 210615803
Phone: 410 787-4000
Web: WWW.MYBWMC.ORG

HISTORICAL FINANCIALS

Company Type: Private

Income Statement

FYE: June 30

	REVENUE ($ mil.)	NET INCOME ($ mil.)	NET PROFIT MARGIN	EMPLOYEES
06/13	337	(3)	—	2,676
06/11	3	0	5.6%	—
06/10*	3	0	5.5%	—
12/09	0	0	—	—
Annual Growth	823.1%	—	—	—

*Fiscal year change

2013 Year-End Financials

Return on assets: 13.7%
Return on equity: (-1.1%)
Current ratio: 1.70

Cash ($ mil.): 37

BANNER HEALTH

Hoist this Banner high! Banner Health is one of the largest secular not-for-profit health systems in the US. The organization operates 28 acute-care hospitals (with roughly 4000 beds). It also operates clinics nursing homes clinical laboratories ambulatory surgery centers home health agencies and other healthcare-related organizations including physician practices and a captive insurance company. Banner Health participates in medical research in areas such as Alzheimer's disease and spinal cord injuries through its Banner Sun Health Research division. The company which has almost 300000 members provides services in seven states

in the western US; its largest concentration of facilities is in Arizona.

Operations

Banner Health is one of the first not-for-profit hospital operators to reinsure its employees through its captive insurance company Samaritan Insurance Funding. By offering this service Banner Health is able to diversify its risk improve cash flow and lower life insurance costs by about half a million dollars a year.

The multi-specialty system also operates a health plan in Arizona for Medicare-eligible patients. Its MediSunONE plan includes Medicare and Medicare Part D. The company has joined forces with Aetna in what is called an accountable care collaboration (ACO). An ACO uses technology and a team-based approach to care for the hospital's patients. Doctors and hospitals assume accountability for patient outcomes and are rewarded financially for achieving higher quality greater efficiency and overall better patient outcomes. The partnership also includes a new product called Aetna Whole Health that allows Banner's patients access to a line of Aetna services including their own electronic patient record.

The system's specialty centers include Banner Alzheimer's Institute Banner Concussion Center Banner Heart Hospital and the Western States Burn Center. In addition Banner Health trains 270 doctors per year at Banner Good Samaritan and Northern Colorado Medical Center.

Banner Health also partners with M.D. Anderson Cancer Center to operate a comprehensive cancer center in Phoenix. Services include medical oncology radiation oncology surgical oncology pathology laboratory diagnostic imaging as well as other supportive clinical services. M.D. Anderson has clinical oversight for all aspects of care delivery.

Education looms large on Banner Health's list of priorities –the hospital operates one of the country's largest simulation education centers at its Banner Corporate Center-Mesa. Simulation education is an expanding field in which medical students use computerized mannequins to improve their surgical and medical skills. The school's research has paid off and with Scottsdale Healthcare Osborn Medical Center Banner Health invented the Sapien Transcatheter Heart Valve an artificial heart valve that can replace a diseased aortic heart valve without the open heart surgery that previously was required.In 2013 Banner Health provided $520 million for community benefit.

Geographic Reach

Banner Health operates in Alaska Arizona California Colorado Nebraska Nevada and Wyoming.

Financial Performance

Banner Health's income is generally derived through three channels: third-party payers such as commercial insurance managed care agreements Medicare and Medicaid and a small portion of self-pay patients as well as by borrowing funds and receiving philanthropic donations.

Its revenues grew by 5% in 2013 from $4.9 million to $5.1 million. Prudent investing boosted net income by 39% from $615 to $855.

Strategy

The health system has grown through construction. Banner Health is nearly always engaged in some sort of construction renovation or upgrade at its numerous facilities. The organization has more than $1 billion in construction projects in progress or completed in recent years. The system has expanded its facilities at Banner Baywood Medical Center Banner Del E. Webb Medical Center Banner Desert Medical Center Banner Thunderbird Medical Center Cardon Children's Medical Center and McKee Medical Center.

Banner Health is constructing a Fort Collins facility on a 28-acre campus which is scheduled to

open in 2015 with a two-story hospital featuring an emergency department a 24-bed inpatient unit labor and delivery rooms medical imaging women's services surgical services and lab services.

In 2014 Arizona Banner Health completed a $62.6 million 111000-sq. ft. expansion project of the outpatient cancer facility adding three linear accelerators 30 clinic exam rooms and 13 infusion bays. It also allowed for the expansion of the Laboratory Intake Center and the Welcome Center and includes the Cox Center for Integrative Oncology and Cancer Prevention; and completed a $161 million expansion project which includes the addition of a new tower an expanded emergency department and expanded surgical obstetrical and medical imaging capabilities.

In 2014 Banner Network Colorado and Humana announced a new Accountable Care agreement covering individuals and families purchasing insurance in Weld and Larimer counties through Connect for Health Colorado and through Humana commercial health maintenance organization health plans for small employers.In 2013 Banner Health opened Banner Goldfield Medical Center to provide patient-centered care to the communities of Apache Junction and Gold Canyon.

Mergers and Acquisitions

Banner Health does occasionally pick up a new hospital through acquisition. For instance in 2015 the company acquired The University of Arizona Health Network (now Banner - University Medicine). As a result University Medicine is the new academic medicine division of Banner Health which includes three academic medical centers: Banner - University Medical Center Tucson Banner - University Medical Center Phoenix and Banner - University Medical Center South.

In 2014 Banner Health acquired Casa Grande Regional Medical Center and renamed it as the Banner Casa Grande Medical Center.

Company BackgroundBanner Good Samaritan Medical Center first opened its doors as a 20-bed hospital in 1911. The medical center which is four months older than the state of Arizona marked its 100th anniversary in October 2011.

EXECUTIVES

EVP and Chief Administrative Officer, Ronald R. (Ron) Bunnell
SVP and Chief Marketing Officer, Alexandra Morehouse-Reynolds
President CEO and Director, Peter S. Fine, age 63
EVP and Chief Medical Officer, John Hensing
EVP University Medicine, Kathy Bollinger
CEO Northern Colorado Service Area (Banner Fort Collins Medical Center McKee Medical Center North Colorado Medical Center), Richard O. (Rick) Sutton
EVP Community Delivery, Rebecca (Becky) Kuhn
Interim CEO Fairbanks Memorial Hospital/Denali Center, Sheldon G. Stadnyk
CEO Banner University Medical Center South and Banner University Medical Center Tucson, Tom Dickson
CEO Banner Baywood Medical Center; CEO Banner Heart Hospital, Julie Nunley
President Western Region, Jim Ferando
CEO East Morgan County Hospital, Linda Thorpe
President Arizona East Division, Todd S. Werner, age 47
SVP and CFO, Dennis Dahlen
CEO Banner Boswell Medical Center, Dave Cheney
President Arizona West Division, Rob Gould
CEO Pharmacy Services, Pam Nenaber
CEO Banner Baywood Medical Center and Banner Heart Hospital, Laura Robertson
CEO Banner Medical Group, Jim Brannon
CEO Platte County Memorial Hospital, Shelby Nelson

CEO Cardon Children's Medical Center, Rhonda Anderson

CEO Banner Thunderbird Medical Center, Deb Krmpotic

CEO Banner Research, Eric (Bill) Reiman

EVP Strategic Growth; CEO Banner Health Network, Chuck Lehn

CEO Banner Del E. Webb Medical Center, Debbie Flores

CEO University Medical Center Phoenix, Steve Narang

CEO Banner Ironwood Medical Center and Banner Goldfield Medical Center, Sharon Lind

President and CEO Banner Health Foundation; President and CEO Banner Alzheimer's Foundation, Andy Kramer Petersen

President and CEO University Medical Group, Jason Krupp

SVP Information Technology and CIO, Ryan Smith

CEO Banner Casa Grande Medical Center, Rona Curphy

CEO Banner Estrella Medical Center, Courtney Ophaug

CEO Banner Gateway Medical Center and Banner MD Anderson Cancer Center, Lamont Yoder

CEO Banner Home Care/Hospice, Lynn Rosenbach

CEO Banner Surgery Centers, Robert Thunberg

CEO Banner Lassen Medical Center, Catherine Harshbarger

CEO Banner Churchill Community Hospital, Hoyt Skabelund

CEO Washakie Medical Center, Jay Stallings

CEO Ogallala Community Hospital, Drew Dostal

CEO Banner Behavioral Health Hospital, Brian Beutin

VP and CEO Banner Health Network, Lisa Stevens Anderson

Chief Medical Officer Banner Health Network, Nishant (Shaun) Anand

CEO Page Hospital, Brian Kellar

CEO Sterling Regional MedCenter, Jeff Shelton

Vice President Human Resources Banner Me, Diane Ekstrand

Vice President Ethics and Compliance, David (Dave) Ledbetter

Vice President Of Materials Management, Doug Bowen

Director Of Infection Control, Marti Reich

Vice President Of Information Services, Steve Eiss

Director Of Nursing, Jennifer Kramer

Vice President Information Services, Frank Wallace

Vice President Brand Services, Julie Sherman

Assistant Vice President Information Technology, Michael Cherry

Vice President Of Marketing, Steven Kisiel

Vice President Of Clinical Operations, Maggie Row

Vice President, Therese Valadez

Vice President Management, Laura Brunner

Medical Director, Clinton Clarke

Vice President Of Information Technology, Mary Hubenthal

Vice President, Tricia Barger

Vice President, Samantha Endsley

Vice President, Diahann Groves

Medical Librarian, Bryan Nugent

Director Of Hospice Services, Amberly Molosky

Director Of Nursing, Angela Bonkowski

Vice President Organizational Performance, Twila Burdick

Vice President, Brian Smit

Medical Director Of Minimally Invasive Gynecology, Patrick (Paddy) Wilson

Director Of Clinical Services, Kristina Day

Director Of Nursing Medical Specialty Services, Susan Eubanks

Vice President Operations, Lillian Ruedrich

Vice President Business Health, Rebecca Havlisch

Medical Director, Carol Williams

Vice President Technology and Materials, Deb Dahl

Medical Records Director, Carol Robinson

Senior Vice President General Counsel, David (Dave) Bixby

Executive Vice President and Chief Administrative Officer, Ron Bunnell

Director, Christopher H. (Chris) Volk

Chairman, Larry S. Lazarus

Secretary, Krista Finlayson

Secretary, William (Bill) Shumway

Secretary, Laura Snow

Treasurer, Brenda Schaefer

Treasurer, Paul Nolde-morrissey

Auditors: ERNST & YOUNG LLP PHOENIX AZ

LOCATIONS

HQ: BANNER HEALTH
1441 N 12TH ST, PHOENIX, AZ 850062887
Phone: 602 747-4000
Web: WWW.BANNERHEALTH.COM

Selected Facilities
Alaska
  Fairbanks Memorial Hospital
  Tanana Valley Clinic
Arizona
  Banner Baywood
  Banner Boswell
  Banner Del E. Webb
  Banner Desert
  Banner Estrella
  Banner Gateway
  Banner Good
  Samaritan
  Banner Heart
  Banner Ironwood
  Banner MD Anderson Cancer Center
  Banner Thunderbird
  Banner University Medical Center
  Cardon Children' s
  Page Hospital
California
  Banner Lassen Community Hospital
Colorado
  East Morgan County Hospital
  North Colorado Medical Center
  McKee Medical Center
  Sterling Regional MedCenter
Nebraska
  Ogallala Community Hospital
Nevada
  Banner Churchill Community Hospital
Wyoming
  Community Hospital
  Platte County Memorial Hospital
  Washakie Medical Center

PRODUCTS/OPERATIONS

2013 Sales

	$ mil.	% of total
Patient service revenues	4,412	87
Medical insurance premiums	439	8
Other	233	5
Total	**5,085**	**100**

COMPETITORS

Community Health Systems	Poudre Valley Health System
Dignity Health	Providence Health & Services
HCA	
Iasis Healthcare	Scottsdale Healthcare
Inova	St. Joseph Health System
John C. Lincoln Health Network	Tenet Healthcare
Memorial Health System of East Texas	Texas Health Resources
Northern Arizona Healthcare	Wyoming Medical Center
Phoenix Children' s Hospital	Yuma Regional Medical Center

HISTORICAL FINANCIALS
Company Type: Private

Income Statement
FYE: December 31

	REVENUE ($ mil.)	NET INCOME ($ mil.)	NET PROFIT MARGIN	EMPLOYEES
12/13	5,085	854	16.8%	35,000
12/12	4,878	614	12.6%	—
12/11	4,741	0	0.0%	—
12/10	4,863	0	—	—
Annual Growth	**1.5%**	**—**	**—**	**—**

2013 Year-End Financials

Return on assets: 2.3%   Cash ($ mil.): 133
Return on equity: 16.8%
Current ratio: 0.70

BAPTIST HEALTH

For those seeking medical salvation Baptist Health may be the answer to their prayers. The organization provides health services through about 175 points of care scattered throughout in Arkansas. Its facilities include seven hospitals and a number of rehabilitation facilities family clinics and therapy and wellness centers. Arkansas Health Group a division of Baptist Health runs more than 20 physician clinics across the state. Specialized services include cardiology women's health orthopedics rehabilitation and home and hospice care. Baptist Health's Parkway Village is a 90-acre retirement community for active seniors located close to Baptist Health Medical Center - Little Rock.

Geographic Reach

Baptist Health serves patients across Arkansas. Baptist Health's hospitals include Baptist Health Extended Care Hospital Baptist Health Medical Center – Arkadelphia Baptist Health Medical Center - Heber Springs Baptist Health Medical Center - Little Rock Baptist Health Medical Center - North Little Rock Baptist Health Medical Center – Stuttgart and Baptist Health Medical Center - Hot Spring County.

Operations

In addition to its hospitals the company has 47 physician clinics 20 therapy centers and 53 other centers and service locations. Its Baptist Health Mobile Health Unit travels the state to provide a temporary facility for health screenings health education and first-aid (emergent care) services.

Along with the standard roster of health care services Baptist Health also offers Little Rock residents nine programs of health care study through its Baptist Health Schools Little Rock division. The school coordinates with Arkansas Tech University to offer Baptist Health RN graduates an online option to complete their Bachelor of Science in Nursing degree. Its average enrollment is about 900 students each semester.Sales and Marketing

Baptist Health works with a number of insurance policies and organizations including Aetna AMCO PPO Arkansas Blue Cross and Blue Shield Arkansas Municipal League Care Improvement Plus CIGNA Coventry/First Health PPO and GEHA.

Strategy

The hospital system has been growing to meet the needs of its customers. In 2013 it began leasing Hot Spring County Medical Center in Malvern. The 72-bed acute care hospital was renamed Baptist Health Medical Center Hot Spring County. Baptist Health also bought nearly 40 acres in Conway and began construction on a medical center to serve Faulkner county.

To improve operating efficiency in 2013 Baptist Health formed a new organization –Baptist Health Physician Partners a clinical integration program with more than 200 physician partners.

EXECUTIVES

Director Of Pharmacy, John (Jack) Norris
Medical Director, Nancy Rector
Vp Of Marketing, Mark Lowman
Vice President Patient Care Services, Jill Massiet
Vice President Internal Audit, Sid Gipson
Vice President of Administrative Services, Todd Hart
Vice President of Long Term Care, Marsha Cunningham
Director Of Health Information, Lynn Matheny
Vice President of Human Resources, Anthony Kendall
Auditors: BKD LLP LITTLE ROCK ARKANSA

LOCATIONS

HQ: BAPTIST HEALTH
9601 INTRSTATE 630 EXIT 7, LITTLE ROCK, AR 722057299
Phone: 501 202-2000
Web: WWW.BAPTIST-HEALTH.COM

Selected Locations in Arkansas
Arkansas Health Group (statewide)
BH Extended Care (Little Rock)
BHMC Arkadelphia
BHMC Heber Springs
BHMC Hot Spring County
BHMC Little Rock
BHMC North Little Rock
BHMC Stuttgart
Baptist Health Rehabilitation Institute (Little Rock)
Parkway Village (Little Rock)

PRODUCTS/OPERATIONS

Selected Services
Behavioral Health
Cardiac Rehab
Diabetes Treatment & Management
Eye Center
Hospice & Home Health
Home Infusion Services
Imaging Services
Laboratory
MedFlight
Men's Health
Pastoral Care
Sleep Disorder
Transplant
Weight Loss Program
Wound Care Center

COMPETITORS

Arkansas Children's Hospital
Arkansas Heart Hospital
Baxter Regional Medical Center
Conway Regional Health System
Jefferson Regional Medical Center of Arkansas
Saline Memorial
Sparks Health System
St. Joseph's Mercy Health Center
St. Vincent Health System
White County Medical Center

HISTORICAL FINANCIALS

Company Type: Private

Income Statement

	REVENUE ($ mil.)	NET INCOME ($ mil.)	NET PROFIT MARGIN	EMPLOYEES
12/13	836	71	8.6%	7,000
12/09	924	64	7.0%	—
12/08	860	(204)	—	—
Annual Growth	(0.5%)	—	—	—

FYE: December 31

2013 Year-End Financials

Return on assets: —
Return on equity: 8.6%
Current ratio: 1.00
Cash ($ mil.): 51

BAPTIST HEALTH SOUTH FLORIDA INC.

Baptist Health South Florida (BHSF) has a good grip on Miami's health. The faith-based not-for-profit enterprise operates seven acute-care hospitals a children's hospital and a vascular institute in the Miami area. Its flagship facility Baptist Hospital with more than 680 beds provides a comprehensive range of medical and surgical services. The system also includes South Miami Hospital with 460 beds as well as several smaller inpatient facilities in surrounding communities. In all BHSF hospitals contain about 1500 beds. In addition to inpatient services the organization provides ambulatory surgery primary and urgent care diagnostic imaging rehabilitation and home health services.

Operations

BHSF includes two diagnostic imaging centers 13 satellite diagnostic imaging centers and 16 urgent care centers.

Financial Performance

BHSF saw a slight increase in revenue net income and cash flow for 2013 based on increased patient revenues.

Strategy

The system's strategic goals focus on organic expansion through new construction and additions but also by acquisitions and through select partnerships when they meet its purposes. Additionally the health system works to improve patient care through medical equipment and information technology upgrades.

Mergers and Acquisitions

As part of an ongoing wave of consolidation among hospital operators BHSF has agreed to merge with another South Florida-based health care organization the not-for-profit Bethesda Health. Bethesda operates two hospitals in Boynton Beach. After a two-year transition period the partnership between the systems is expected to officially occur in October 2017.

EXECUTIVES

EVP and CFO, Ralph E. Lawson
President and CEO, Brian E. Keeley
CEO and Executive Medical Director Miami Cancer Institute, Michael J. Zinner
EVP and Chief Administrative Officer, George W. Foyo
EVP and COO, D. Wayne Brackin
EVP and Chief Physician Executive, Jack A. Ziffer
Director of Radiology Services Nuclear Medicine Director, Lloyd Maciver
Vice President Of Cardiology, Carol Mascioli
Vice President of Information Technology, Mimi Taylor
Corporate Vice President Real Estate, Kathy Moorman
Assistant Vice President of Finance Senior Corporate Controller, Matt Arsenault
Corporate Assistant Vice President Managed Care and Network Development, Cheryse Burgos Santos
Vice President, Randall Lee
Assistant Vice President Organizational Learning, Tom Land
Vice President and Chief Nursing Officer, Tina Jones

Assistant Vice President Human Resources Operations, Frank Voytek
Vice President of Marketing, Felica Carreras
Corp Vice President Of Strategic Planning Physician, Ana Lopez
Director of HIM, Kay Heiden
Director Of Pharmacy, Radhan Gopalani
Vice President, Ryan Ner
Vice President Of Professional Development, Barby Debenedetti
Corporate Vice President, Suzzanne Quintero
Director Of Nursing Services, Nada Wakim
Assistant Vice President Quality PI and Accreditation, Andrea Lavallee
Pharmacy Manager, Ayse Ozdamar
Vice President Government Relations, Phillis Oeters
Vice President Nursing, Sandra Hyatt
Medical Director, James (Jamie) Benenati
Corporate Vice President Hospitality Business Relations, Ben Mollere
Medical Director, Roberto Hernando
Director Of Nursing, Vernon Bartholomew
Medical Director, Daniel Mandri
Assistant Vice President Employee Health Wellness Advantage, Maribeth Rouseff
Pharmacy Manager, Aixa Rey
Assistant Vice President Finance and Accounting Operations, Karla Medina
Assistant Vice President Marketing And Public Relations, Christine Kotler
Chairman, Rev. William W. White
Chapter Treasurer, Arely Rego
Auditors: DELOITTE TAX LLP TAMPA FL

LOCATIONS

HQ: BAPTIST HEALTH SOUTH FLORIDA INC.
6855 S RED RD STE 600, SOUTH MIAMI, FL 331433518
Phone: 305 596-1960
Web: WWW.BAPTISTHEALTH.NET

PRODUCTS/OPERATIONS

2013 Sales

	$ mil.	% of total
Managed Care	1,655	69
Medicare	278	12
Medicaid	122	5
Other	331	14
Total		**100**

Selected Florida Facilities
Baptist Hospital of Miami (Kendall)
  Baptist Cardiac & Vascular Institute
  Baptist Children's Hospital
Doctors Hospital (Coral Gables)
Homestead Hospital (Homestead)
Mariners Hospital (Tavernier)
South Miami Hospital (South Miami)
West Kendall Baptist Hospital (Kendall)

Selected Services
Addiction treatment
Behavorial medicine
Blood conservation program
Cancer services
Cardiovascular services
Care and counseling services
Children's health
Community wellness
Critical care center
Diabetes
eICU LifeGuard
Emergency
Endoscopy
Executive health
Gamma knife center
Heart surgery
Home care
Hyperbaric services
Imaging
Intensive care unit
International services
Interventional/surgical Services

Laboratory
Maritime medical services
Neonatal
Neuroscience
Nutrition counseling services
Occupational health
Online appointments
Orthopedics
Outpatient/diagnostic services
Pain center
Pastoral care
Pediatric
Pelvic health
Physical and speech therapy
Pregnancy and childbirth
Progressive care unit
Prostate cancer
Pulmonary services
Radiation oncology
Rehabilitation services
Robotic surgery
Senior services
Sleep diagnostic center
Sports medicine and orthopedic programs
Stroke services
Surgery
Weight-loss surgery
Wellness Center
Women' s health
Wound care

COMPETITORS

Adventist Health System Sunbelt Healthcare
Boca Raton Regional Hospital
Broward Health
HCA
Holy Cross Hospital Fort Lauderdale
Jackson Health System
Lakeland Regional Medical Center
Miami Children' s Hospital
Mount Sinai Medical Center of Florida
South Broward Hospital District
Tenet Healthcare
The Cleveland Clinic
University of Miami Hospital

HISTORICAL FINANCIALS

Company Type: Private

Income Statement

FYE: September 30

	REVENUE ($ mil.)	NET INCOME ($ mil.)	NET PROFIT MARGIN	EMPLOYEES
09/09*	616	121	19.7%	9,374
12/08	2	(1)	—	—
09/06	1,517	136	9.0%	—
09/05	1,459	0	—	—
Annual Growth	(19.4%)	—	—	—

*Fiscal year change

2009 Year-End Financials

Return on assets: —
Return on equity: 19.7%
Current ratio: —

Cash ($ mil.): 18

BAPTIST HEALTH SYSTEM INC.

Auditors: WARREN AVERETT LLC

LOCATIONS

HQ: BAPTIST HEALTH SYSTEM INC.
1130 22ND ST S STE 1000, BIRMINGHAM, AL
352052881
Phone: 205 715-5000
Web: WWW.BHSALA.COM

HISTORICAL FINANCIALS

Company Type: Private

Income Statement

FYE: December 31

	REVENUE ($ mil.)	NET INCOME ($ mil.)	NET PROFIT MARGIN	EMPLOYEES
12/13	553	61	11.0%	4,300
12/12	528	(15)	—	—
12/11*	587	(34)	—	—
06/10	602	0	—	—
Annual Growth	(2.1%)	—	—	—

*Fiscal year change

2013 Year-End Financials

Return on assets: 4.9%
Return on equity: 11.0%
Current ratio: 0.60

Cash ($ mil.): 4

BAPTIST HEALTHCARE SYSTEM INC.

Baptist Healthcare System which goes by Baptist Health wants to keep all its followers healthy. The system owns eight acute -care hospitals one a long-term facility in Kentucky with a total capacity of more than 2100 beds. The not-for-profit health system's largest facility is Baptist Hospital East a 520-bed hospital in Louisville that provides a wide range of health services with special expertise in cardiology rehabilitation and women's health. In addition to its owned facilities Baptist Healthcare manages Hardin Memorial a 300-bed hospital located in Elizabethtown and Russell County Hospital with 25 beds. Founded as a single hospital in Louisville in 1924 the growing hospital system rebranded as Baptist Health in 2012.

Strategy

Baptist Health is expanding its network with the aim of covering more of rural western Kentucky. In 2012 it acquired Trover Health System based in Madisonville which operates a 410-bed medical center and eight outpatient clinics in western Kentucky. Later in the year Baptist Health acquired the Pattie A. Clay Regional Medical Center in Richmond. Both hospitals were renamed following their acquisition becoming Baptist Health Madisonville and Baptist Health Richmond respectively.

In 2014 the system joined with Community Hospital Corporation and Oak Tree Hospital to offer long-term acute care services at 32-bed ContinueCARE Hospital formerly Baptist Health Corbin. That year it also opened a new clinic in Muhlenberg County.

Along with inpatient acute care services Baptist Healthcare offers home health care services runs two outpatient surgery centers provides urgent care through a handful of clinics and operates a regional physicians' practice group. It also runs a community-based not-for-profit health care plan Bluegrass Family Health operating across the state and into parts of Indiana and Tennessee.

EXECUTIVES

Vice President of Human Resources, David (Dave) Rhodes
Vice President Human Resources, Steve Rudolf
Vice President Marketing, Carla Conklin
Executive Vice President, Scott Childers
Clinic Manager, Sean Sullivan
Director Of Pharmacy, Paul Lucas
Vice President of Marketing and Business Development, Patti Mason
Vice President Customer Care, Bonnie Schrock
Medical Director, Jeffrey Reynolds
Vice President Of Nursing, Polly Bechtold
Auditors: ERNST & YOUNG US LLP COLUMBUS

LOCATIONS

HQ: BAPTIST HEALTHCARE SYSTEM INC.
2701 EASTPOINT PKWY, LOUISVILLE, KY 402234166
Phone: 502 896-5000
Web: WWW.BHSI.COM

PRODUCTS/OPERATIONS

Selected Facilities and Operations (Kentucky)

Hospitals
  Managed
  Baptist Health Corbin
  Baptist Health La Grange
  Baptist Health Lexington
  Baptist Health Louisville
  Baptist Health Richmond
  Baptist Health Madisonville
  Baptist Health Paducah
  ContinueCARE Hospital (Corbin)
  Owned
  Hardin Memorial Hospital (Elizabethtown)
  Russell County Hospital (Russell Springs)
Other operations
  Baptist East Milestone Wellness Center (Louisville)
  Baptist Express Care (various Walmarts in state)
  Baptist Medical Associates (medical practice group Louisville area)
  Baptist Urgent Care (Louisville)
  Bluegrass Family Health (provider-sponsored insurance)

COMPETITORS

Appalachian Regional Healthcare
Catholic Health Initiatives
Jewish Hospital & St. Mary' s HealthCare
Kindred Healthcare
Norton Healthcare
Pikeville Medical Center
University Health Care
University of Kentucky Chandler Hospital

HISTORICAL FINANCIALS

Company Type: Private

Income Statement

FYE: August 31

	REVENUE ($ mil.)	NET INCOME ($ mil.)	NET PROFIT MARGIN	EMPLOYEES
08/12	1,290	90	7.0%	12,601
08/11	1,317	96	7.3%	—
08/10	1,231	75	6.2%	—
08/09	1,448	0	—	—
Annual Growth	(3.8%)	—	—	—

2012 Year-End Financials

Return on assets: —
Return on equity: 7.0%
Current ratio: 0.40

Cash ($ mil.): 152

BAPTIST HOSPITAL OF MIAMI INC.

Baptist Hospital of Miami can treat many vices for Miami residents. The flagship facility of the Baptist Health South Florida health system provides residents of the city with a full range of health care services including pediatric cancer home health rehabilitation neurology and cardiovascular care. The hospital has more than 680 beds and includes the Baptist Children's Hospital which offers a pediatric emergency room and a neonatal intensive care unit. Baptist Hospital of Miami also includes the Baptist Cardiac & Vascular Institute a regional cancer program and a diabetes care center. Baptist Hospital of Miami was founded in 1960.

Operations

Baptist Children's Hospital offers 24-hour emergency care as well as two intensive care units and specialist services including pediatric cancer care. Baptist Hospital of Miami also contains the Baptist Cardiac and Vascular Institute which conducts treatment and research programs. The hospital's international care unit provides services to patients from the Caribbean Latin America and other regions. Other specialist divisions include a sleep diagnostic center and a spine care facility as well as a maternity ward. Baptist Hospital of Miami also operates several wellness centers.

As part of Baptist Health South Florida the Baptist Hospital of Miami is part of a network of six hospitals including South Miami Hospital Doctors Hospital and the West Kendall Baptist Hospital. In addition the health system includes outpatient care clinics including emergency surgery imaging and primary care centers.

Strategy

Controlling expenses through data management quality and wellness initiatives and other measures becomes increasingly important for the hospital and its affiliates as the cost of medical care in the US market continues to skyrocket. Maintaining an efficient organization is also imperative as the level of charity care provided by the system's facilities continues to rise in the face of economic difficulties.

As the largest hospital in the Baptist Health system Baptist Hospital of Miami takes a leading role in technology programs such as medical equipment and data management system upgrades. The Baptist Health network is in the process of installing an electronic health record (EHR) system to connect patient records across its facilities.

In 2012 Baptist Hospital of Miami launched a $90 million construction effort to expand the Cardiac and Vascular Institute. The new expanded institute facility will open in 2016 and will include centers for aneurysm treatment structural heart therapy and endovascular therapy. The project also includes expansion efforts on the hospital's surgery center which will have enhanced capabilities for neurological cardiac and robotic surgery procedures.

EXECUTIVES

Vice President Chief Nursing Officer, Becky Montesino
Pharmacy Manager, Ydelia Eger
Ambulatory Services Director, David Reinhardt
Vice President Operations, Jeanette Stone
Director Of Nursing, Alex Mendez

LOCATIONS

HQ: BAPTIST HOSPITAL OF MIAMI INC.
8900 N KENDALL DR, MIAMI, FL 331762197
Phone: 786 596-1960
Web: WWW.BAPTISTHEALTH.NET

PRODUCTS/OPERATIONS

Selected Centers and Services
Baptist Cardiac & Vascular Institute (Heart Care)
Baptist Children's Hospital (Pediatrics)
Breast Care
Cancer Services
Center for Spine Care
Children's Cancer Services
Children's Emergency Center
Clinical Research Trials
Community Wellness
Critical Care/eICU LifeGuard
Diabetes Care

Diagnostic Imaging
Emergency Services
Endoscopy
Gynecology
Home Care
Intensive Care
International Services
Interventional
Maternity
Neonatal Intensive Care Unit
Neuroscience Center
Neurosurgery
Orthopedic Services
Pain Management
Physical & Speech Therapy
Pulmonary Services
Rehabilitation Services
Robotic Surgery
Senior Services
Sleep Diagnostic Center
Spine Care
Stroke Services
Surgery
Women's Services

COMPETITORS

Broward Health
H. Lee Moffitt Cancer Center & Research Institute
HCA
Jackson Health System
Larkin Community Hospital
Miami Children's Hospital
Mount Sinai Medical Center of Florida
South Broward Hospital District
University of Miami Hospital

HISTORICAL FINANCIALS
Company Type: Private

Income Statement
FYE: September 30

	REVENUE ($ mil.)	NET INCOME ($ mil.)	NET PROFIT MARGIN	EMPLOYEES
09/13	846	99	11.7%	4,200
09/12	916	71	7.8%	—
09/08	908	81	9.0%	—
09/04	674	0	—	—
Annual Growth	2.5%	—	—	—

2013 Year-End Financials

Return on assets: 4.8% Cash ($ mil.): —
Return on equity: 11.7%
Current ratio: 0.70

BAPTIST MEMORIAL HEALTH CARE CORPORATION

Serving portions of Tennessee Mississippi and Arkansas Baptist Memorial Health Care consists of more than a dozen acute care and specialty hospitals and a network of clinic home health care and hospice operations. The health system has more than 2300 beds with more than half of which are located in the greater Memphis area. Its flagship facility is 700-bed Baptist Memorial Hospital-Memphis a tertiary care facility offering advanced care in numerous medical specialties including cardiovascular disease and pediatrics. Via an affiliation with Baptist College of Health Sciences the organization provides undergraduate education in a number of health care fields including nursing and medical radiography.

Geographic Reach

Baptist Memorial Health Care's main hospital campus is located on Memphis's east side. There are other network facilities in the city and its suburbs include smaller community centers in western Tennessee northern Mississippi and eastern Arkansas.

Operations

The company has more than 4000 affiliated physicians. It includes Baptist Medical Group a multispecialty physician group with more than 500 doctors; home hospice and psychiatric care; minor medical centers and clinics; a network of surgery rehabilitation and other outpatient centers; and an education system highlighted by the Baptist College of Health Sciences.

In 2014 Baptist Memorial Health Care had 84300 discharges; 349400 emergency room visits; more than 50000 surgical procedures; and delivered more 10700 babies.

In addition to health care and education services the system operates a bereavement camp (named Camp Good Grief) for family members and friends to come to terms with the loss of loved ones. It also conducts research in medical fields including cardiovascular care endocrinology oncology emergency care and pulmonary medicine.

Financial Performance

Baptist Memorial Health Care's revenues increased by 3% in 2014 due to higher net patient service revenues and other revenues. Medicare accounted for 35% of net patient service revenues; self-pay 23%; commercial and Blue Cross 20%; managed care 10%; and Medicaid 9% The company's net income dropped by 72% in 2014 due to higher operating expenses which included salaries and benefits and professional fees. Net unrealized losses on investments also contributed to the decline.Operating cash flow increased by 10% due to a change in net patient accounts receivable.

Company Background

To improve its pediatric care operations in 2013 the organization's physician practice organization (Baptist Medical Group) acquired River City Pediatrics. The purchase established Baptist Memorial Health Care's first pediatric group practice operation in Memphis.

The organization is expanding its cancer care network and in 2013 Baptist Memorial Health Care broke ground on the Baptist Cancer Center the first such institution in the Memphis area. To further strengthen its oncology programs in 2012 Baptist Memorial Health Care formed a cancer research and education affiliation with Vanderbilt University Medical Center.

The company was formed in 1912 with the establishment of its main hospital. The flagship hospital is where Elvis Presley was pronounced dead in 1977.

EXECUTIVES

Radiology Director, Johnny Stanford
Vice President Of Finance, Bill Griffin
Executive Vice President, Bob Gordon
Director Of Medical Records, Karen Miller
Radiology Director, Beth Turner
Director Of Surgery, Beret Felleson-ilko
Executive Vice President Cao, Robert Gordon
Vpfinance Operations, David (Dave) Barham
Vice President Chief Medical Officer, Richard (Dick) Drewry
Occupational Therapy Director, Lindsay Stencel
Vice President Community Health Education, George Weiss
Assistant Vice President Information Technology, Susan (Sue) Butler
Vice President of Information Technology, Val Lopez
Auditors: DELOITTE & TOUCHE LLP MEMPHIS

LOCATIONS

HQ: BAPTIST MEMORIAL HEALTH CARE
CORPORATION
350 N HUMPHREYS BLVD, MEMPHIS, TN 381202177
Phone: 901 227-2727
Web: WWW.BAPTISTONLINE.ORG

PRODUCTS/OPERATIONS

Selected Facilities

Baptist Memorial Hospital-Booneville (Booneville
Mississippi)

Baptist Memorial Hospital-Collierville (Collierville
Tennessee)

Baptist Memorial Hospital-DeSoto (Southaven
Mississippi)

Baptist Memorial Hospital-Golden Triangle (Columbus
Mississippi)

Baptist Memorial Hospital-Huntingdon (Huntingdon
Tennessee)

Baptist Memorial Hospital-Memphis (Memphis
Tennessee)

Baptist Memorial Hospital-North Mississippi (Oxford
Mississippi)

Baptist Memorial Hospital-Tipton (Covington Tennessee)

Baptist Memorial Hospital-Union City (Union City
Tennessee)

Baptist Memorial Hospital-Union County (New Albany
Mississippi)

Baptist Memorial Hospital for Women (Memphis
Tennessee)

Baptist Memorial Restorative Care Hospital (Memphis
Tennessee)

Baptist Rehabilitation-Germantown (Germantown
Tennessee)

NEA Baptist Memorial Hospital (Jonesboro Arkansas)

COMPETITORS

Cookeville Regional	St. Jude Children' s
Medical Center	Research Hospital
Methodist Healthcare	Tenet Healthcare
North Mississippi	UT Medical Group
Health Services	
Shelby County Health	
Care	

HISTORICAL FINANCIALS

Company Type: Private

Income Statement

FYE: September 30

	REVENUE ($ mil.)	NET INCOME ($ mil.)	NET PROFIT MARGIN	EMPLOYEES
09/13	1,884	27	1.5%	9,877
09/12	161	1	0.8%	—
09/10	136	(1)	—	—
09/09	124	0	—	—
Annual Growth	**97.4%**	—	—	—

2013 Year-End Financials

Return on assets: 1.9%   Cash ($ mil.): 102
Return on equity: 1.5%
Current ratio: 1.00

BAPTIST MEMORIAL HOSPITAL

When most of us think of Memphis we think of
Elvis Presley. When doctors think of Memphis they
think of Elvis and Baptist Memorial Hospital-Memphis. As the flagship facility of Baptist Memorial
Health Care the 710-bed hospital often simply
called Baptist Memphis offers patients the full spectrum of health care services including cancer treatment orthopedics surgical services and neurology.
The campus also features the Baptist Heart Insti-

tute for cardiovascular care and research a pediatric emergency room a skilled nursing facility and
the Plaza Diagnostic Pavilion for outpatient health
care. Baptist Memphis established in 1979 is one
of the state's highest volume hospitals.

Operations

Doctors at the hospital see more than 27000 admissions 54000 emergency department visits and
nearly 116000 outpatient visits each year. The
emergency department houses more than 30 treatment bays. In addition Baptist Memphis' skilled
nursing center includes 30 beds. The hospital also
operates a 30-bed rehabilitation hospital and a
165000 sq. ft. heart institute for diagnostic and
surgical cardiac care. The facility boasts advanced
surgical systems including the CyberKnife radiation system for cancerous and non-cancerous
tumor removal.

EXECUTIVES

Operating Room Director, Tracy Godsey
Medical Records Director, Janet Chapman
Occupational Therapy Director, Lindsay Stencel

LOCATIONS

HQ: BAPTIST MEMORIAL HOSPITAL
6019 WALNUT GROVE RD, MEMPHIS, TN 381202113
Phone: 901 226-5000
Web: WWW.BAPTISTONLINE.ORG

COMPETITORS

Methodist Healthcare	St. Jude Children' s
Parkwest Medical	Research Hospital
Center	Tenet Healthcare
Shelby County Health	
Care	

HISTORICAL FINANCIALS

Company Type: Private

Income Statement

FYE: September 30

	REVENUE ($ mil.)	NET INCOME ($ mil.)	NET PROFIT MARGIN	EMPLOYEES
09/13	504	17	3.4%	6,000
09/12	697	15	2.2%	—
09/03	429	26	6.1%	—
09/02	377	0	—	—
Annual Growth	**2.7%**	—	—	—

2013 Year-End Financials

Return on assets: 1.3%   Cash ($ mil.): 13
Return on equity: 3.4%
Current ratio: 1.30

BAR-ILAN UNIVERSITY IN ISRAEL

Auditors: GRANT THORNTON LLP NEW YORK

LOCATIONS

HQ: BAR-ILAN UNIVERSITY IN ISRAEL
160 E 56TH ST FL 5, NEW YORK, NY 100223609
Phone: 212 906-3900
Web: WWW.AMERICANFRIENDSOFBIU.NET

HISTORICAL FINANCIALS

Company Type: Private

Income Statement

FYE: September 30

	REVENUE ($ mil.)	NET INCOME ($ mil.)	NET PROFIT MARGIN	EMPLOYEES
09/13	343	(30)	—	30
09/08	330	38	11.5%	—
Annual Growth	**0.8%**	—	—	—

2013 Year-End Financials

Return on assets: 13.5%   Cash ($ mil.): 26
Return on equity: (-8.8%)
Current ratio: 0.60

BARD COLLEGE

Although Shakespeare might appreciate the curriculum Bard College is not named for the Bard of
Avon but for founder John Bard. The institution
of higher learning is an independent nonsectarian
residential coeducational four-year college of the
liberal arts and sciences. Bard's total enrollment of
1900 includes some 600 graduate students. First-
year students are required to take a three-week
Workshop in Language and Thinking that emphasizes the connection between expression and
thought. Students must also complete a year-long
senior project that is reviewed by faculty members.

Operations

In the Bard system more than 1900 undergraduates study at the main Annandale campus and
600 graduate students study in Bard programs as
well as 1000 students in high schools and college
preparation schools. Total enrollment for Bard and
its global affiliates is about 5000 students.Bard offers BA degrees in about 50 academic programs
and a five-year BS/BA degree in economics and
finance. The Bard College Conservatory of Music
offers a five-year program in which students pursue a Bachelor of Music and a BA in a non-music
field. In addition to offering AA and BA degrees
through high schools and early colleges the Bard
Prison Initiative offers similar options at six prisons in New York State.Bard's graduate degree
programs include in curatorial studies economic
theory and policy environmental policy climate science and policy and music. It also offers MAs
M.Phils and PhDs in the decorative arts design
history and material culture. It has 293 faculty
members 92% of which hold a terminal degree.In
2012 Bard charged $31600 tuition and fees of
$950. It also had a $350 million endowment. The
college enrolled students from 38 US states and 25
countries.

Geographic Reach

It addition to its US operations (Annandale-on-
Hudson New York New York City and Boston)
Bard confers degrees (in tandem with the host
school) at St. Petersburg State University Russia
(Smolny College); the American University of Central Asia in Kyrgyzstan; Bard College Berlin Germany; and Al-Quds University in the West Bank
Palestine. It also has operations in Budapest Hungary.

Strategy

In 2014 Bard announced plans to launch the
Levy Economics Institute's Master of Science in
Economic Theory and Policy Program as well as
a 3+2 dual-degree option for undergraduates.

Expanding its network in 2013 German university ECLA of Bard become Bard College Berlin. In
2012 Longy School of Music joined Bard and be-

came the Longy School of Music of Bard College.Expanding its curriculum in 2013 Bard launched the Center for Moving Image Arts focused on undergraduate education and in bringing various aspects of film culture (archival development educational initiatives public screenings and publications) under one umbrella.

Company Background

Among Bard's distinguished faculty are three Grammy Award winners six MacArthur Fellows 14 National Science Foundation Grant recipients 29 Guggenheim Fellows and recipients of the French Legion of Honor Tony Award and Pulitzer Prize.

Donald Fagen and Walter Becker of the band Steely Dan both attended Bard (Fagen is an alum; Becker did not graduate) and penned the song "My Old School" as a sardonic tribute to their alma mater.

The institution was founded in 1860 by John Bard in association with Episcopal Church leaders in New York City.

EXECUTIVES

Vice President Dean Of The College, Michele D Dominy
Director Of Admissions, Frank Corliss
Managing Director, Susan Tveekrem
Vice President for Administration, Deanna Cochran
Auditors: LAMBRIDES ARNOLD MOULTHROP LLP

LOCATIONS

HQ: BARD COLLEGE
30 CAMPUS RD, ANNANDALE ON HUDSON, NY 125049800
Phone: 845 758-7518
Web: WWW.CLEMENTE.BARD.EDU

HISTORICAL FINANCIALS

Company Type: Private

Income Statement

FYE: June 30

	REVENUE ($ mil.)	NET INCOME ($ mil.)	NET PROFIT MARGIN	EMPLOYEES
06/10	181	(5)	—	525
06/09	164	0	—	—
06/08	873	0	0.0%	—
Annual Growth	(54.4%)	—	—	—

2010 Year-End Financials

Return on assets: —
Return on equity: (-3.0%)
Current ratio: —
Cash ($ mil.): —

BARRICK ENTERPRISES INC.

Auditors: DOEREN MAYHEW TROY MICHIGAN

LOCATIONS

HQ: BARRICK ENTERPRISES INC.
4307 DELEMERE CT, ROYAL OAK, MI 480731809
Phone: 248 549-3737
Web: WWW.BARRICK.COM

HISTORICAL FINANCIALS

Company Type: Private

Income Statement

FYE: December 31

	REVENUE ($ mil.)	NET INCOME ($ mil.)	NET PROFIT MARGIN	EMPLOYEES
12/13	800	2	0.4%	35
12/12	811	2	0.4%	—
12/07	0	0	—	—
12/06	0	0	—	—
Annual Growth	—	—	—	—

2013 Year-End Financials

Return on assets: 1.4%
Return on equity: 0.4%
Current ratio: 1.50
Cash ($ mil.): 6

BARRY UNIVERSITY INC.

Barry University is a Catholic institution of Dominican heritage based in South Florida. With a student-faculty ratio of about 14:1 the liberal arts university annually enrolls about 3000 undergraduate students and some 4000 graduate students. The university's academic division includes two colleges (the College of Arts and Sciences and the College of Health Sciences) and seven schools. It offers more than 100 specializations and programs for undergraduate graduate and doctoral studies. Barry University also offers about 35 non-degree and certificate programs. Barry University was founded by the Adrian Dominican Sisters in 1940.

Geographic Reach

Barry University enrolls students from throughout the US and some 75 international countries. Its main campus consists of 120 acres in Miami Shores Florida. Its School of Adult and Continuing Education has satellite offices in 16 Florida counties. Other Barry University Schools have between two and five campus/satellite locations while the Andreas School of Law is located solely in Orlando.

Operations

The university's programs cover a range of subjects including art business communication education human studies law medicine nursing psychology social work and theology. Its professional study programs combined with graduate and undergraduate majors bring Barry University's total enrollment to some 9000 students.

Strategy

Barry University is focused on several key initiatives including creating excellence in its academic programs through evaluation and enhancement efforts; forming student-centered learning communities to increase retention and engagement; and ensuring financial growth through measures including building community relationships increasing fundraising efforts and implementing right-sizing and best practice strategies. Other improvement efforts relate to diversity community service and governance.

EXECUTIVES

Associate Vice President Student Services, Eileen McDonough
Vice President of Human Resources, Jennifer (Jen) Boyd-Pugh
Associate Vice President Officer Cmpsite Coordinator DN Cont Ed, Carol Sodano
Auditors: CAPIN CROUSE LLP GREENWOOD I

LOCATIONS

HQ: BARRY UNIVERSITY INC.
11300 NE 2ND AVE, MIAMI SHORES, FL 331616695
Phone: 305 899-3050
Web: WWW.BARRY.EDU

PRODUCTS/OPERATIONS

Selected Colleges and Schools

Adrian Dominican School of Education
College of Arts and Sciences
College of Health Sciences
D. Inez Andreas School of Business
Dwayne O. Andreas School of Law
Ellen Whiteside McDonnell School of Social Work
Frank J. Rooney School of Adult and Continuing Education
School of Human Performance and Leisure Sciences
School of Podiatric Medicine

HISTORICAL FINANCIALS

Company Type: Private

Income Statement

FYE: June 30

	REVENUE ($ mil.)	NET INCOME ($ mil.)	NET PROFIT MARGIN	EMPLOYEES
06/13	223	6	3.1%	1,407
06/10	151	12	8.1%	—
06/09	147	8	5.7%	—
06/08	0	0	—	—
Annual Growth	—	—	—	—

2013 Year-End Financials

Return on assets: 6.0%
Return on equity: 3.1%
Current ratio: 0.50
Cash ($ mil.): 41

BARRY-WEHMILLER GROUP INC.

With Barry-Wehmiller you get the whole package. The company manufactures and supplies packaging corrugating paper converting filling and labeling automation equipment for a broad range of industries. It conducts business around the world through a group of 60 companies including Accraply (labeling machinery) Barry-Wehmiller Company (bottle washers and pasteurizers); HayssenSandiacre and Thiele Technologies (packaging systems); PneumaticScaleAngelus (bottle fillers and cappers); and FleetwoodGoldcoWyard (conveyor systems). Other divisions manufacture paper converting machinery and offer engineering/design consulting services.

Geographic Reach

Barry-Wehmiller has operations in about 30 countries in some 100 locations spanning Asia Australia Europe and the Americas.

Operations

The company operates through three segments and ten divisions: Packaging Automation Equipment (Accraply BW Container Systems Hayssen Flexible Systems Pneumatic Scale Angelus Synerlink and Thiele Technologies); Engineering & IT Consulting (Barry-Wehmiller International and Design Group); and Paper Systems Equipment (BW Papersystems and Paper Converting Machine Company).

Sales and Performance

Barry-Wehmiller's manufacturing technology and services serve a wide range of industries including packaging paper converting sheeting corrugating engineering and IT consulting.

Financial Performance

Through its aggressive acquisition strategy and the opening of new locations Barry-Wehmiller generated revenues of about $2 billion in 2014. The company has seen 18% compound revenue growth since 1987.

Strategy

Barry-Wehmiller's mantra is expansion through organic growth and acquisitions. The company has purchased more than 65 companies over approximately 25 years creating a mosaic of time and money-saving products and services in locations around the globe. In the same vein its businesses' operations are built upon lean manufacturing practices whereby employees are empowered and resources optimized to contribute to the end product's value.

Mergers and Acquisitions

In 2014 Barry-Wehmiller acquired Körber AG's Papersystems companies (E.C.H. Will GmbH Pemco Inc. and Kugler-Womako GmbH) making BW Papersystems the world's leading supplier of sheeting and sheet packaging machinery with the widest range of applications for the paper converting manufacturing and packaging industries.

In 2013 this unit acquired the PTC software business of ENSER Corporation allowing it to more effectively service ENSER's existing PTC customers. Several months later Barry-Wehmiller entered the French market for the first time when it acquired Arcil SA a Paris-based supplier of packaging technology for the fresh dairy and food industry. The acquisition opened up the firm's packaging platform to six separate operating companies and escalated its reach within the growing global yogurt industry.

Company Background

In 2012 the company expanded its engineering IT consulting platform by buying Kansas-based Customer Driven Technology (CDT) a reseller of advanced IT and enterprise products for engineering and manufacturing companies. CDT provides products and services to address the rapidly changing landscape of product development product lifecycle management and global project collaboration.

Originally a provider of conveying equipment to St. Louis malt houses Barry-Wehmiller was founded by Thomas Barry and Alfred Wehmiller in 1885. Ownership passed from the Wehmiller family to the Chapman family in 1963 and the Chapmans continue as the majority owners.

EXECUTIVES

Chairman and CEO, Robert H. (Bob) Chapman, age 69
VP CFO and Director, James W. (Jim) Lawson
CIO, Craig Hergenroether
CTO, Robert Richards
Auditors: ERNST & YOUNG LLP ST LOUIS M

LOCATIONS

HQ: BARRY-WEHMILLER GROUP INC.
8020 FORSYTH BLVD, SAINT LOUIS, MO 631051707
Phone: 314 862-8000
Web: WWW.BWDESIGNGROUP.COM

PRODUCTS/OPERATIONS

Selected Operations
Engineering/Consulting
Barry-Wehmiller Design Group Inc. (high-speed complex automated manufacturing and packaging system design)
Barry-Wehmiller International Resources (IT consulting and engineering services)
Converting equipment
Paper Converting Machine Company (PCMC)
Coaters
Narrow web in-line printing systems

Nonwovens converting equipment
Tissue converting equipment
Wide web flexo printing coating and laminating
Corrugating equipment
MarquipWardUnited Inc. (corrugating sheeting and finishing equipment)
Packaging equipment
Accraply Inc. (packaging label machinery)
Arcil SA (supplier of packaging technology)
FleetwoodGoldcoWyard (conveyer systems)
HayssenSandiacre (form/fill/seal packaging machinery)
PneumaticScaleAngelus (fillers cappers seamers and labelers)
Thiele Technologies Inc. (packaging systems)

Selected Markets
Corrugated paperboard and folded carton
Dairy
Food and beverage
Household
Medical and biotech
Packaging
Personal care
Pharmaceutical
Tissue and nonwovens

COMPETITORS

Bradman Lake	STT Enviro
Gilbreth	Sencorp Inc
Industria Macchine	Tetra Laval
Automatiche	Traco Manufacturing
Kl\u0131ckner-Werke	

HISTORICAL FINANCIALS
Company Type: Private

Income Statement
FYE: September 30

	REVENUE ($ mil.)	NET INCOME ($ mil.)	NET PROFIT MARGIN	EMPLOYEES
09/12	1,332	69	5.2%	4,500
09/11	1,240	0	—	—
09/10	1,097	0	—	—
09/09	976	0	—	—
Annual Growth	10.9%			

2012 Year-End Financials
Return on assets: 10.0% Cash ($ mil.): 109
Return on equity: 5.2%
Current ratio: 0.90

BARTON MALOW COMPANY

Barton Malow scores by building end zones and home plates. The construction management and general contracting firm which has built its share of sporting facilities also focuses on projects such as schools hospitals offices and plants. Across the US and Mexico the company offers design/build and program management services ranging from the pre-planning stage to completion. Projects have included the Detroit Institute of Arts and Cultural Center and the Baltimore Orioles stadium. Affiliate Barton Malow Design provides architecture and engineering services while Barton Malow Rigging installs process equipment and machinery. Carl Osborn Barton founded the employee-owned firm as C.O. Barton Company in 1924.

Geographic Reach

Michigan-based Barton Malow operates about a dozen offices mostly in the East Coast. The firm also has an office in San Luis Potosi Mexico.

Financial Performance

Barton Malow's annual revenue exceeds $1 billion.

Strategy

Headquartered in a Detroit suburb Barton Malow has historically maintained a healthy relationship with the steel and auto industries. The company has expanded into new sectors and geographic markets however. It serves the federal market through its Florida-based L.C. Gaskins Construction Company.

In 2014 the firm was selected as the construction manager for a new Major League Soccer (MLS) stadium in Orlando Florida. Other recent projects include a new events center in Detroit and a Facility for Rare Isotope Breams at Michigan State University.

Company Ownership

The family of CEO Ben Maibach III a third-generation Barton Malow executive owns a controlling interest in the company.

EXECUTIVES

Senior Vice President, Alex Ivanikiw
Vice President Central Region, Todd Ketola
Vice President Central Region, Michael (Mel) Stobak
Vp Human Resources, Jim Nahrgang
Vice President Eastern Region and Virginia, Carrie Shaeffer
Vice President, John Wieland
Senior Vice President Sports Facilities, Harvey Oliva
Vice President Central Region, Dan Kovoch
Vice President National Sports, Len Moser
Svp Southeast Region, Rod Creach
Vice President, Joe Benvenuto
Vice President Baltimore Operations, Bob Grottenthaler
Vice President, Mike Stobak
Auditors: GRANT THORNTON LLP SOUTHFIEL

LOCATIONS

HQ: BARTON MALOW COMPANY
26500 AMERICAN DR, SOUTHFIELD, MI 480342252
Phone: 248 436-5000
Web: WWW.BARTONMALOW.COM

Selected Locations
Atlanta
Baltimore
Charlottesville
Chicago
Columbus
Fairfax
Jacksonville
Oak Park
Orlando
Richmond
Southfield

PRODUCTS/OPERATIONS

Selcted Services
Architecture and planning
Building Information Management (BIM)
Concrete trade services
Construction management
Design/build
Facility audits
Facility services
 Administration
 Engineering
 Maintenance repair and operations
General contracting
Interior design
Interior trade services
Preconstruction
Program management
Rigging
Special projects
Technology consulting

COMPETITORS

Alberici	KBR Building Group
Clark Enterprises	M. A. Mortenson
Fluor	McCarthy Building
Gilbane	Skanska USA Building

H.J. Russell
Hensel Phelps
  Construction
Hunt Construction

Turner Corporation
Walbridge Aldinger
Walsh Group
Whiting-Turner

HISTORICAL FINANCIALS

Company Type: Private

Income Statement

FYE: March 31

	REVENUE ($ mil.)	NET INCOME ($ mil.)	NET PROFIT MARGIN	EMPLOYEES
03/14	1,078	2	0.3%	1,200
03/13	1,005	3	0.3%	—
Annual Growth	7.3%	(20.9%)	—	—

2014 Year-End Financials

Return on assets: 13.4%   Cash ($ mil.): 61
Return on equity: 0.3%
Current ratio: 0.60

BARTON MALOW ENTERPRISES INC.

Auditors: GRANT THORNTON LLP SOUTHFIEL

LOCATIONS

HQ: BARTON MALOW ENTERPRISES INC.
  26500 AMERICAN DR, SOUTHFIELD, MI 480342252
Phone: 248 436-5000

HISTORICAL FINANCIALS

Company Type: Private

Income Statement

FYE: March 31

	REVENUE ($ mil.)	NET INCOME ($ mil.)	NET PROFIT MARGIN	EMPLOYEES
03/14	1,078	7	0.7%	1,415
03/13	1,005	6	0.7%	
03/12	1,164	(14)	—	
03/11	0	0	—	
Annual Growth	—	—	—	—

2014 Year-End Financials

Return on assets: 13.2%   Cash ($ mil.): 68
Return on equity: 0.7%
Current ratio: 0.70

BATELLE MEMORIAL INSTITUTE

LOCATIONS

HQ: BATELLE MEMORIAL INSTITUTE
  2555 INTERNATIONAL ST, COLUMBUS, OH
  432284604
Phone: 800 201-2011
Web: WWW.BATTELLE.ORG

HISTORICAL FINANCIALS

Company Type: Private

Income Statement

FYE: September 30

	REVENUE ($ mil.)	NET INCOME ($ mil.)	NET PROFIT MARGIN	EMPLOYEES
09/13	4,795	(7)	—	3
09/12	5,228	(20)	—	
Annual Growth	(8.3%)	—	—	

2013 Year-End Financials

Return on assets: 1.3%   Cash ($ mil.): 112
Return on equity: (-0.2%)
Current ratio: 2.00

BATON ROUGE GENERAL MEDICAL CENTER

The first hospital founded in Louisiana's capital Baton Rouge General Medical Center is a not-for-profit full-service community hospital offering patients general medical and surgical care. Through the hospital's two locations Bluebonnet and Mid City Baton Rouge General also provides specialty services for cancer heart and neonatal care. In addition the nearly 530-bed health care facility provides services in areas such as burn treatment diabetes sleep disorders and behavioral health. Baton Rouge General Medical Center is the flagship facility of General Health System.

Geographic Reach

Through the hospital's two locations Bluebonnet and Mid City Baton Rouge General Medical Center also provides specialty services for cancer heart and neonatal care. Baton Rouge General is affiliated with and also serves as a satellite campus of Tulane University School of Medicine.

Operations

Baton Rouge General Medical Center is affiliated with and also serves as a satellite campus of Tulane University School of Medicine. In addition to serving as a satellite campus for Tulane medical students in the Leadership Education Advocacy and Discovery Academy program Baton Rouge General Medical Center also offers a Family Medicine Residency Program an Internal Medicine Residency Program a Sports Medicine Fellowship Program a School of Nursing and a School of Radiologic Technology. In 2012 the Center had more than 1000 physicians and about 950 nurses on its medical staff and served 153000 patients and had about 91000 emergency department visits. Financial PerformanceIn 2012 Baton Rouge General Medical Center reported gross revenues of $820 million and a net income of $10 million.

Strategy

The Center is expanding its infrastructure to keep up with demand. In 2014 Baton Rouge General Medical Center and Lane Regional Medical Center opened a $4.5 million state-of-the-art Radiation Oncology Center in Zachary Louisiana. In 2013 Baton Rouge General Medical Center announced plans to add two floors and 64 beds to an existing patient tower at the Bluebonnet campus a project that will cost an estimated $24 million and which will be completed by early 2015.

In 2013 Baton Rouge General Medical Center completed the steel beam structure for the hospital's patient tower expansion project.

In 2012 the Center initiated OneVision a program aimed at investing in minimally invasive technology and strengthening its physician network. That year it also opened the Behavioral Wellness Center at Jackson.Company BackgroundIn 2011 Baton Rouge General Medical Center broke ground on a $40 million expansion at the Bluebonnet campus. The project included a new five-story medical office building with 105000 sq. ft. of space and four large operating rooms. Part of the hospital's larger Bluebonnet expansion project the new construction projects follow the surgical services expansion and new heart and vascular tower. The surgical expansion included the addition of four new operating rooms equipped with an innovative hybrid build out and minimally invasive robotics.

The Center which has been an accredited teaching hospital since 1991 first opened its doors in 1900.

EXECUTIVES

Clinic Supervisor, Jessi Lassetter

LOCATIONS

HQ: BATON ROUGE GENERAL MEDICAL CENTER
  3600 FLORIDA BLVD, BATON ROUGE, LA 708063842
Phone: 225 387-7000
Web: WWW.BRGENERAL.ORG

PRODUCTS/OPERATIONS

Selected Products and Services
Birth Center
Cancer
Heart & Vascular
Pediatrics
Emergency Room (ER)
Behavioral Health
Burn
Gastroenterology
Hyperbarics & Wound Care
Imaging/Radiology
Neurosciences
Orthopedics
Rehabilitation/Therapy
Seniors
Weight Loss
Wellness
Clinical Trials
Limbs For Life
Sleep Center

COMPETITORS

Lane Regional Medical
  Center
Our Lady of the Lake
  RMC

River Parishes
  Hospital
Woman's Hospital

HISTORICAL FINANCIALS

Company Type: Private

Income Statement

FYE: September 30

	REVENUE ($ mil.)	NET INCOME ($ mil.)	NET PROFIT MARGIN	EMPLOYEES
09/13	382	6	1.8%	394
09/09	304	0	0.2%	—
09/08*	281	2	0.9%	—
12/05	0	0	—	
Annual Growth	—	—	—	—

*Fiscal year change

2013 Year-End Financials

Return on assets: 14.5%   Cash ($ mil.): 71
Return on equity: 1.8%
Current ratio: 0.50

BATTELLE MEMORIAL INSTITUTE INC

When you use a copier hit a golf ball or listen to a CD you're using technologies developed by Battelle Memorial Institute. The not-for-profit is one of the world's largest research enterprises with more than 22000 scientists engineers and staff serving corporate and government clients. Research areas include national security energy and health and life sciences. Battelle owns facilities in the US Asia and Europe and manages six Department of Energy-sponsored labs: Brookhaven National Laboratory Oak Ridge National Laboratory Idaho National Laboratory and Pacific Northwest National Laboratory. The institute was established by the family of steel industry pioneer Gordon Battelle in 1929.

Geographic Reach

The company's headquarters are located in Columbus Ohio. Battelle has about 130 locations globally.

Operations

Battelle's major subsidiaries include Battelle Arabia Battelle India Battelle Japan Battelle Ventures Bluefin Robotics and Winner Water Services.

Sales and Marketing

The company serves the national security health and life sciences and energy and environmental industries. Battelle's major customer group includes government and commercial organizations in Laboratory Management National Security Health & Pharmaceutical Energy & Environment Consumer & Industrial and STEM Education.

Strategy

Battelle is in the process of building an advanced research-and-development facility that will expand its global footprint and capacity to provide advanced science and technology solutions for the agriculture food and health care industries. The new facility will augment Battelle's established global scientific expertise in formulation development toxicology and biotechnology programs that help agriculture and food customers accelerate product development and meet multi-national regulatory requirements.

Mergers and Acquisitions

In 2014 Battelle acquired Healthcare Accreditation Colloquium (HAC). The HAC will be renamed The Healthcare Colloquium and operate as a subsidiary of Battelle

HISTORY

Company Background

Battelle Memorial Institute was founded with a $1.5 million trust willed by Gordon Battelle who died in 1923. Battelle was a champion of research for the advancement of humankind and before taking his father's place as president of several Ohio steel mills he had funded a former university professor's successful work to extract useful chemicals from mine waste. Battelle's mother upon her death in 1925 left the institute an additional $2.1 million. The institute opened in 1929.

The institute took on perhaps the most important project in its history in 1944 when it helped an electronics company's patent lawyer Chester Carlson find practical uses for his invention called xerography. Eventually Battelle developed the first photocopy machine and in 1955 it sold the patent rights for the machine to Haloid (now Xerox) in exchange for royalties.

During WWII Battelle worked on uranium refining for the Manhattan Project and in the early 1950s it established the world's first private nuclear research facility. The company also set up operations in Germany and Switzerland.

The tax man came knocking in 1961 questioning the tax-free status of some of Battelle's activities. The organization eventually had to pay $47 million. In 1965 Battelle developed a coin with a copper core and a copper-and-nickel-alloy cladding for the US Treasury.

As the result of a ruling that reinterpreted a clause in Gordon Battelle's will in 1975 the institute gave $80 million to philanthropic enterprises. This ruling coupled with the taxes that the organization was still unaccustomed to paying forced Battelle to re-examine its strategy.

Battelle co-developed the Universal Product Code (the bar code symbol found today on nearly all consumer goods packaging) in the 1970s. The institute also landed a lucrative contract from the US Department of Energy (DOE) to manage its commercial nuclear waste isolation program.

In 1987 Battelle chose Douglas Olesen —a 20-year veteran of the institute —to replace retiring CEO Ronald Paul. The company signed an extension with the DOE in 1992 to run its Pacific Northwest Laboratory (which it has operated since 1965).

An Ohio court in 1997 approved a seven-page agreement with the institute outlining the key principles that must be followed according to Gordon Battelle's will. This agreement replaced the 1975 decree and ended more than 20 years of scrutiny by the state attorney general's office.

In 1998 the DOE contracted Brookhaven Science Associates —a partnership between the State University of New York and Battelle —to operate Brookhaven National Laboratory. That year a Battelle contract to dispose of Vietnam War-era napalm drew national attention when subcontractor Pollution Control Industries backed out of the project citing safety concerns. Under Battelle's direction Houston-based GNI Group took the 3.4 million gallons of napalm off the US Navy's hands.

Battelle and the University of Tennessee in 1999 won a five-year contract to operate the US government's Oak Ridge National Laboratory. That year the institute made several breakthroughs in cancer research including FDA approval to test an inhalation delivery system for treating lung cancer.

In 2000 the company spun off OmniViz (data mining software) and Battelle Pulmonary Therapeutics (pulmonary and drug delivery technology) as wholly owned subsidiaries. In 2001 Battelle chose former Kodak EVP and CTO Carl Kohrt to replace Olesen. (Kohrt retired in January 2009 and was replaced by Jeffrey Wadsworth who has worked for the company since 2002.)

Battelle and several partners including BWX Technologies Washington Group International and Electric Power Research Institute won a 10-year contract in 2004 to operate Idaho National Laboratory a research facility established to focus on nuclear energy research and related technologies.

With offices in Japan and South Korea Battelle expanded its international reach to include India in 2008. The company formed a partnership in 2007 with oil and gas company PETRONAS to operate a renewable energy lab in Kuala Lumpur Malaysia.

Battelle underwent a leadership change in 2009 when Jeffrey Wadsworth took over as CEO replacing Carl Kohrt who retired.

EXECUTIVES

Sr V Pres, Russell Austin
President National Security, Stephen E. Kelly
President and CEO, Jeffrey (Jeff) Wadsworth, age 66
EVP Global Laboratory Operations, Ronald D. (Ron) Townsend
President Energy Health and Environmental business, Marty Toomajian
EVP and CFO, Dave Evans
President and CEO Winner Water Services, Carolyn Kotsol
Vice President, Victoria Loewengart
Vice President Operations, John (Jack) Folkerts
Vice President And Product Line Manager, Dennis Nelson
Vice President And General Manager, Lisa A Mccauley
Vice President Marketing And Communicati, Patrick (Paddy) Jarvis
Ph D Vice President Health Policy Battelle Memorial Institute, Sudip Parikh
Vice President Agrifood, David Nothmann
Vice President Account Manager, Michael Kuhlman
Vice President and Division Leader Global Laborary Operations, Paul Kearns
Vice President for Systems Integration Services, Michael (Mel) Janus
Vice President Account Manager, James McNeely
Vice President Of Business Development, Bradley Ashbrook
Vice President Business Development, Michael (Mel) Brooker
Senior Vice President Human Resources, Thomas Snowberger
Vice President Strategic Development, Robert Wilkins
Vice President navy and Special Operations Market Sector, Fred Byus
Vice President and Senior Relationship Manager Special Programs, Justin J Jackson
Evice President Global Laboratory Operations, Ron Townsend
Vice President, David (Dave) Robinson
Vice President and Manager, John (Jack) Wade
Senior Vice President Business and Economic Development, Alexander (Al) Fischer
Chairman, John K. Welch
Treasurer, Hornback Randi
Secretary, Tiffani Gollihue
Auditors: DELOITTE & TOUCHE LLP COLUMBU

LOCATIONS

HQ: BATTELLE MEMORIAL INSTITUTE INC
505 KING AVE, COLUMBUS, OH 432012681
Phone: 614 424-6424
Web: WWW.BATTELLE.ORG

PRODUCTS/OPERATIONS

Selected Laboratories and Research Facilities
Battelle Biomedical Research Center (West Jefferson OH)
Battelle Eastern Science and Technology Center (Aberdeen MD)
Battelle Frederick Operations (Maryland)
Battelle Geneva Operations (Switzerland)
Brookhaven National Laboratory (Upton NY)
Human Factors Transportation Center (Seattle)
Idaho National Laboratory (Idaho Falls)
Lawrence Livermore National Laboratory (Livermore CA)
Marine Science Laboratory (Sequim WA)
National Renewable Energy Laboratory (Golden CO)
Oak Ridge National Laboratory (Tennessee)
Battelle Duxbury Operations (Massachusetts)
Pacific Northwest National Laboratory (Richland WA)

Selected Inventions
Exploded-tip paintbrush (nylon brush for Wooster Brush Co. 1950)
Golf ball coatings (1965)
Heat Seat (microwaveable stadium cushion 1990s)
Holograms (work began in the 1970s)
Insulin injection pen (for Eli Lilly 1990s)
Oil spill outline monitor (1992)
PCB-cleaning chemical process (1992)
Photocopy machine (with Haloid 1940s)
Plastic breakdown process (1990s)
"Sandwich" coins (copper/copper-and-nickel-alloy cladding design for US Treasury 1965)
SenSonic toothbrush (with Teledyne/WaterPik 1990s)

Smart cards (cards embedded with tiny computer chips that store information 1980s)
Universal Product Code (co-creator; bar code 1970s)

COMPETITORS

Argonne National Laboratory	Institute for Defense Analyses
Berkeley Lab	SwRI
Charles Stark Draper Laboratory	

HISTORICAL FINANCIALS
Company Type: Private

Income Statement
FYE: September 30

	REVENUE ($ mil.)	NET INCOME ($ mil.)	NET PROFIT MARGIN	EMPLOYEES
09/14	4,769	(111)	—	7,457
09/13	4,795	(7)	—	—
09/12	5,228	(24)	—	—
09/11	5,499	0	—	—
Annual Growth	(4.6%)	—	—	—

2014 Year-End Financials
Return on assets: 1.0% Cash ($ mil.): 105
Return on equity: (-2.3%)
Current ratio: 1.50

BAUER BUILT INC.

Bauer Built ensures its customers are well-treaded. The company owns about 30 automotive tire and service centers throughout the Midwest more than 10 wholesale distribution centers seven tire retread plants and three rim and wheel reconditioning centers. It delivers petroleum products (including gasoline ethanol biodiesel and kerosene) throughout eastern Minnesota and western Wisconsin as well as operates a car wash in Durand Wisconsin. Bauer Built was founded in 1944 by Sam Bauer the father of president Jerome "Jerry" Bauer as Bauer Oil Co. It got into the retread business in 1950. Employees own about 30% of the company; the Bauer family holds the remainder.

Looking to grow its operations the company acquired Jansky's Tire Service a local business based in Manitowoc Wisconsin in 2010. As part of the deal Jansky's was converted to a Bauer Built Tire & Service Center. Bauer Built plans to continue gradually expanding its bricks-and-mortar presence in order to increase revenues.

To add more depth to its leadership team and establish a controlled succession plan the company reorganized its management in 2009. As part of the shake-up EVP of marketing and logistics Tad Bauer was named COO and EVP of Bauer Built's tire division. EVP of sales and manufacturing Jim Fenn became EVP of marketing and logistics; VP of sales Todd Weber was tapped as EVP of tire sales; and tire center manager Joe Weber took over as sales VP.

EXECUTIVES
Vice President Logistic, Ted Bauer
Vice President Marketing, Larry Hildebrandt

LOCATIONS
HQ: BAUER BUILT INC.
1111 W PROSPECT ST, DURAND, WI 547361061
Phone: 715 672-8300
Web: WWW.BAUERBUILT.COM

COMPETITORS

American Tire	TBC

Distributors	TCI Tire Centers
Discount Tire	Wal-Mart
Pep Boys	Wingfoot Commercial
Pomp' s Tire Service	Tire Systems
Sears	

HISTORICAL FINANCIALS
Company Type: Private

Income Statement
FYE: December 31

	REVENUE ($ mil.)	NET INCOME ($ mil.)	NET PROFIT MARGIN	EMPLOYEES
12/08	191	3	1.8%	450
12/06	171	2	1.5%	—
12/05	182	2	1.6%	—
12/04	161	0	—	—
Annual Growth	4.3%	—	—	—

2008 Year-End Financials
Return on assets: 4.1% Cash ($ mil.): —
Return on equity: 1.8%
Current ratio: 0.40

BAY MEDICAL CENTER

Bay Medical Center is a 320-bed regional hospital located in the Florida panhandle. the center provides general medical and surgical services. The hospital's specialized services and programs include an open-heart surgery program a cancer center women's and children's health and emergency care. It also operates centers for sleep disorder and childhood communication disorders. Bay Medical Center has a staff of more than 300 physicians. The hospital also operates outpatient facilities for primary care and diagnostics. Bay Medical Center is operated by a joint venture between Sacred Heart Health System and LHP Hospital Group.

Geographic Reach

From its main location in Panama City the hospital serves residents of seven counties in northwestern Florida. In addition to the main hospital campus Bay Medical has diagnostic and rehab facilities in Panama City Beach and in Lynn Haven along with HealthPlex Fitness a wellness facility.

Operations

Bay Medical Center features a level II trauma center. The hospital's cardiovascular surgery center features 16 suites and conducts some 10000 procedures annually including about 400 open-heart surgeries.

Most of Bay Medical Center's revenue comes from commercial and government insurance plan reimbursements. It also provides care to some self-pay customers. For low-income and uninsured patients the hospital typically provides some $30 million in charity and uncompensated care each year.

Company Background

In 2012 Sacred Heart Health System and LHP Hospital Group formed a joint venture that will lease and operate the Bay Medical Center for 40 years. The transaction allows Bay Medical Center to retire all of its debt obligations; it also gives the hospital access to broader purchasing power and clinical resources. Its governing board will consist of representatives from LHP and Sacred Heart; the hospital will also have an independent board of trustees to oversee day-to-day operations.

Facility expansion measures at Bay Medical Center have included a new chest pain observation unit opened in 2013. Previously he hospital constructed a new patient tower to expand capacity and provide more private (single-patient) rooms for cus-

---

tomers. The $60 million expansion project added 144 new patient rooms as well as lobby and cafeteria spaces and was completed in 2010. The tower also included new ICU surgery neurological nursing and orthopedic specialty units. The company divested some outpatient facilities to help offset construction expenses as well as to pay down debt.

The hospital was formed in 1949.

EXECUTIVES
Vice President Of Human Resources, Donna Baird
Occupational Therapy Director, Gail Darnell
Medical Director Chief Of Staff Chief Marketing Officer, Wm Bone
Respiratory Therapy Director, Dennis Arnold
Radiology Medical Director, Emily Billingsley
Director Of Radiology, Glen Bailey
Medical Director For The Emergency Department, Frederick (Fred) Epstein

LOCATIONS
HQ: BAY MEDICAL CENTER
615 N BONITA AVE, PANAMA CITY, FL 324013623
Phone: 850 769-1511
Web: WWW.BAYMEDICAL.ORG

PRODUCTS/OPERATIONS

Selected Centers and Services
Blood Donor Center
Cancer Center
Diabetes Services
Diagnostic Services
Emergency Medicine
Family Birthing Center
HealthPlex Fitness
Heart and Vascular Institute
Hyperbaric Medicine
Infusion Therapy
Interventional Radiology
Pediatrics
Rehabilitation
Sleep Lab
Stroke Care
Surgical Services
Women' s Services
Wound Healing

COMPETITORS

Adventist Health System Sunbelt Healthcare
Baptist Health System
H. Lee Moffitt Cancer Center & Research Institute
HCA
Jackson County Hospital of Florida
Munroe Regional Health System
Tallahassee Memorial HealthCare
UF&Shands

HISTORICAL FINANCIALS
Company Type: Private

Income Statement
FYE: September 30

	REVENUE ($ mil.)	NET INCOME ($ mil.)	NET PROFIT MARGIN	EMPLOYEES
09/10	219	(5)	—	2,000
09/09	231	4	1.9%	—
09/08	966	0	0.0%	—
Annual Growth	(52.3%)	—	—	—

2010 Year-End Financials
Return on assets: 7.8% Cash ($ mil.): 42
Return on equity: (-2.7%)
Current ratio: 2.20

BAY REGIONAL MEDICAL CENTER

McLaren Bay Region provides a full range of medical services for the residents at the tip of Saginaw Bay in eastern Michigan. A part of McLaren Health Care the hospital's main campus has more than 400 beds and provides general medical and surgical care as well as specialty care in areas such as cardiovascular disease neuroscience oncology rehabilitation orthopedics and women's health. It also features an emergency room and Level II trauma center and provides home health and hospice care. A second campus McLaren Bay Special Care Hospital is a long-term acute care hospital serving patients requiring hospital stays of longer than 25 days. The regional provider also provides outpatient and home health services.

Geographic Reach

McLaren Bay Region has about 45 offices in Michigan counties including Auburn Bay Davison Essexville Lake Orion and Pinconning.

Operations

In addition to its two acute care centers McLaren Bay Region operates outpatient centers including the Nickless Volunteer Clinic which provides primary care for uninsured and underinsured residents of Bay County.

The hospital system has one of the largest multidisciplinary research programs in the state. It works with international pharmaceutical and device companies –as well as universities foundations and agencies –to create new and improved treatments for illnesses including cancers and infectious diseases.

Going hand-in-hand with clinical trials is teaching and McLaren Bay Region offers a roster of residency programs for up-and-coming medical professionals. The hospital works with Michigan State University's colleges of Human Medicine and Osteopathic Medicine.

Strategy

McLaren Bay Region is looking to expand its geographic reach in eastern Michigan. It is also widening its range of specialist services in areas such as oncology cardiovascular care and orthopedic rehabilitation. The organization launched a new cancer rehabilitation program in 2012; it also opened a new outpatient heart center featuring cardiac diagnostic capabilities in Mt. Pleasant.

Company Background

McLaren Bay Region was formed after the merging of four hospitals during the 1970s and 1980s with the idea of developing a full continuum of health services for Northeast Michigan. It changed its name to McLaren Bay Region from Bay Regional Medical Center in 2012.

EXECUTIVES

President CEO, Philip A. Incarnati
President and CEO, Alice Gerard
VP Finance and CFO, Brian Kay
Administrative Assistant, Jodi Reetz
Auditors: PLANTE & MORAN PLLC EAST LAN

LOCATIONS

HQ: BAY REGIONAL MEDICAL CENTER
1900 COLUMBUS AVE, BAY CITY, MI 487086831
Phone: 989 894-3000
Web: WWW.BAYREGIONAL.ORG

PRODUCTS/OPERATIONS

Selected Centers and Services
Bariatrics
Behavioral Health
Blood Conservation
Cancer Services
Cardiac
Diabetes
Diagnostic Imaging
Dialysis Services
Emergency Care
EMS
Family BirthPlace
Fitness Centers
Free Clinics
Health Insurance
Home Care
Implantable Hearing Solutions
Infectious Disease
Infusion Center
Intensive Care
Internal Medicine
Laboratory and Pathology
Lifeline
Medical Library
Medical Supplies & Equipment
Neurosciences
Nutritional Counseling
Ophthalmology
Orthopedics
Pain Management
Pediatrics
Primary Care
Proton Therapy
Pulmonary and Respiratory
Rehabilitation and Therapy
Robotic Surgery
Sleep Medicine
Stroke Center
Surgical and Endoscopy Services
Trauma
Urology
Walk-in Clinics
Women's Services
Wound Care

COMPETITORS

Ascension Health	Hurley Medical Center
Covenant HealthCare	Munson Healthcare
Crittenton Hospital	Select Medical
Detroit Medical Center	Sparrow Health System
Genesys Health System	St. John Health
Genesys Regional	University of Michigan
Medical Center	Health System
Henry Ford Health	
System	

HISTORICAL FINANCIALS
Company Type: Private

Income Statement
FYE: September 30

	REVENUE ($ mil.)	NET INCOME ($ mil.)	NET PROFIT MARGIN	EMPLOYEES
09/14	278	19	6.9%	2,000
09/13	251	31	12.6%	—
09/12	278	22	8.1%	—
09/11	271	0	—	—
Annual Growth	0.8%	—	—	—

2014 Year-End Financials

Return on assets: 3.9%   Cash ($ mil.): 11
Return on equity: 6.9%
Current ratio: 0.80

BAYHEALTH MEDICAL CENTER INC.

Auditors: GRANT THORNTON LLP PHILADELPH

LOCATIONS
HQ: BAYHEALTH MEDICAL CENTER INC.
640 S ST, DOVER, DE 19901
Phone: 302 422-3311
Web: WWW.BAYHEALTH.ORG

HISTORICAL FINANCIALS
Company Type: Private

Income Statement
FYE: June 30

	REVENUE ($ mil.)	NET INCOME ($ mil.)	NET PROFIT MARGIN	EMPLOYEES
06/14	511	86	17.0%	2,790
06/13	482	85	17.8%	—
06/12	490	22	4.7%	—
06/11	442	0	—	—
Annual Growth	4.9%	—	—	—

2014 Year-End Financials

Return on assets: 5.3%   Cash ($ mil.): 33
Return on equity: 17.0%
Current ratio: 1.10

BAYLOR UNIVERSITY MEDICAL CENTER

Baylor University Medical Center at Dallas is the flagship institution of the Baylor Health Care System. The medical center (known as Baylor Dallas) serves more than 300000 patients annually with more than 1000 inpatient beds and some 1200 physicians. It offers general medical and surgical services to specialty care in a wide range of fields including oncology cardiovascular disease and neuroscience. The hospital also features a Level I trauma center neonatal ICU and organ transplantation center. Founded in 1903 the Baylor Dallas campus includes the Charles A. Sammons Cancer Center and the Baylor Research Institute which conducts basic and clinical research across numerous medical specialties.

Operations

The Baylor University Medical Center campus consists of 20 specialty centers for treating a range of medical conditions. Primary facilities include the Charles A. Sammons Cancer Center Neuroscience Center Annette C. and Harold C. Simmons Transplant Institute James M. and Dorothy D. Collins Womens and Children's Center and the George Truett James Orthopaedic Institute as well as a top trauma center digestive care program and heart and vascular unit. The Heart and Vascular Institute conducts more than 50 research studies a year.

Strategy

The hospital received a boost in 2011 when Texas A&M's Health Science Center struck an affiliation with Baylor Health Care System. The two parties agreed to make Baylor Dallas a primary teaching hospital for A&M's third and fourth-year medical students. No hospital in the Baylor Health Care System held such a designation after it became independent from Baylor University in 1997.

As one of only two adult Level 1 trauma centers in the region Baylor Dallas has worked to bolster its emergency services to keep up with increasing demand. To this end it has broadened its Level 1 trauma capabilities increased the size of its minor emergency care area and added more patient care areas. The Riggs Emergency Department treats some 67000 patients each year.

Baylor Dallas' transplant program is considered a national leader in solid organ transplantation and in partnership with the program at Baylor All Saints Medical Center is one of only three programs worldwide to have performed more than 3000 adult liver transplants. The program is also known for its kidney pancreas heart and lung small bowel and blood and marrow transplants.

EXECUTIVES

Vice President Finance and Corporate Controller, James (Jamie) Pool

Senior Vice President General Counsel, Stephen (Steve) Boyd

LOCATIONS

HQ: BAYLOR UNIVERSITY MEDICAL CENTER
2001 BRYAN ST STE 2200, DALLAS, TX 752013024
Phone: 214 820-0111
Web: WWW.BAYLORHEALTH.EDU

Selected Locations
A. Webb Roberts Hospital
Baylor Charles A. Sammons Cancer Center
Baylor Jack and Jane Hamilton Heart and Vascular Hospital
Carr P. Collins Hospital
Erik and Margaret Jonsson Medical and Surgical Hospital
George W. Truett Memorial Hospital
Karl and Esther Hoblitzelle Memorial Hospital
Baylor Specialty Hospital
Our Children' s House at Baylor

PRODUCTS/OPERATIONS

Selected Speciality Centers
Baylor Cancer Hospital
Baylor Center for Pain Management
Baylor Diagnostic Imaging Centers
Baylor George Truett James Orthopaedic Institute
Baylor Geriatric and Senior Center
Baylor Heart and Vascular Institute
Baylor Heart Failure Program
Baylor Motion and Sports Performance Center
Baylor Neuroscience Center
Baylor Radiosurgery Center
Baylor Ruth Collins Diabetes Center
Baylor Sammons Bone Tumor Center
Baylor Sammons Lung Cancer Center
Baylor Spine Center
Baylor SportsCare
Comprehensive Wound Center
Darlene G. Cass Women' s Imaging Center
Digestive Care Services
Ernie' s Appearance Center
Gastrointestinal and Endoscopy Laboratory
Hereditary Cancer Risk Program
Infectious Disease Center
James M. and Dorothy D. Collins Women and Children' s Center
Kimberly H. Courtwright and Joseph W. Summers Institute of Metabolic Disease
Louise Gartner Center for Hyperbaric Medicine
Martha Foster Lung Care Center
Non-invasive Heart and Vascular Laboratory
Reuben H. Adams Family Health Center
Simply Mom' s Mother and Baby Boutique
Sleep Center
TINY TOTS Clinic
Virginia R. Cvetko Cancer Patient Education Center
Visual Function Testing Center
W.H. and Peggy Smith Baylor Sammons Breast Center
Weight Loss Surgery Program

COMPETITORS

CHRISTUS Health	Presbyterian Hospital
Children' s Medical	of Dallas
Center of Dallas	Southwestern Medical
Dynacq Healthcare	Center
Harris Methodist Fort	Texas Health Denton
Worth Hospital	Texas Health Resources
Parkland Health &	The Methodist Health
Hospital System	System

HISTORICAL FINANCIALS
Company Type: Private

Income Statement
FYE: June 30

	REVENUE ($ mil.)	NET INCOME ($ mil.)	NET PROFIT MARGIN	EMPLOYEES
06/09	1,072	0	—	5,003
06/08	155	16	10.3%	—
06/06	937	114	12.2%	—
06/05	906	0	—	—
Annual Growth	4.3%	—	—	—

2009 Year-End Financials
Return on assets: 5.7%   Cash ($ mil.): —
Return on equity: —
Current ratio: —

BAYSIDE FUEL OIL DEPOT CORP

A tree isn't the only thing that has grown in Brooklyn. So has Bayside Fuel Oil Depot which provides heating oil to customers in New York through its own four Brooklyn terminals and from two other locations the 149th Street terminal in the Bronx and the Western Nassau terminal in Nassau County. The company was founded in 1937 as a retail distributor of heating oil by Sergio Allegretti In 1965 Bayside Fuel became a wholesale oil terminal operator. It sold its retail business in 2001. Vincent Allegretti the grandson of the company's founder runs the business.

The founder's sons Victor and Alfred helped run the business for many years. During the 1970s the third generation of Allegretti's joined the family business. Sergio's grandsons (Bartolo Sergio and Vincent) took up management positions.

EXECUTIVES

Vice President, Bart Allegretti

LOCATIONS

HQ: BAYSIDE FUEL OIL DEPOT CORP
1776 SHORE PKWY, BROOKLYN, NY 112146546
Phone: 718 372-9800

COMPETITORS

Benit Fuel	richland partners
Mirabito Fuel	

HISTORICAL FINANCIALS
Company Type: Private

Income Statement
FYE: December 31

	REVENUE ($ mil.)	NET INCOME ($ mil.)	NET PROFIT MARGIN	EMPLOYEES
12/12	276	(3)	—	36
12/05	195	1	0.6%	—
12/04	152	1	0.7%	—
12/03	146	0	—	—
Annual Growth	7.4%	—	—	—

2012 Year-End Financials
Return on assets: 3.9%   Cash ($ mil.): 4
Return on equity: (-1.2%)
Current ratio: 1.10

BAYSTATE HEALTH SYSTEM HEALTH SERVICES INC.

Patients in need of medical care can dock at this bay. Not-for-profit Baystate Health is the largest health care services provider in western Massachusetts. The system operates five acute-care and specialty hospitals with a total of approximately 1000 beds including the flagship Baystate Medical Center which operates a Level 1 Trauma Center and a specialized children's hospital. Baystate Health also offers ancillary medical services such as cancer care respiratory care infusion therapy visiting nurse and hospice services through its regional clinics and agencies. The system controls for-profit health plan provider Health New England as well as clinical pathology firm Baystate Reference Laboratories.

Operations

Baystate Medical Center accounts for more than 700 of the system's beds. Its other four acute care hospitals are Baystate Franklin Medical Center (89 beds) Baystate Wing Hospital (74 beds) Baystate Noble Hospital (97 beds) and Baystate Mary Lane Hospital (25 beds). The system also runs a physicians group Baystate Medical Practices which operates more than two dozen physician practices in several surrounding counties and towns. Other outpatient centers include surgery centers imaging and radiology clinics and neighborhood health centers. Altogether its facilities serve a population of 750000 western New England residents and admit more than 45000 inpatients perform some 34000 surgeries handle about 4500 births and conduct 1.4 million outpatient visits each year.

Baystate Health provides academic and community educational programs as well as conducting basic clinical and biomedical research. For instance the Baystate Medical Center is a teaching hospital that serves as the western campus of the Tufts University School of Medicine. Baystate Health also partners with a number of regional colleges to offer nursing programs.

In the research realm Tufts and Baystate Health work on biomedical studies through the Tufts Clinical and Translational Science Institute. Baystate Medical Center also has a partnership with the University of Massachusetts that forms the Pioneer Valley Life Sciences Institute. Areas of research include clinical care quality of care and diabetes and metabolism. The Baystate Health system receives about $10 million per year in research funding from the National Institutes of Health and other agencies.

Geographic Reach

Baystate Health has some 60 locations serving western Massachusetts including Berkshire Franklin Hampden Hampshire and Worcester counties.

Sales and Marketing

Patient service revenue accounts for a majority (about 60%) of the hospital system's sales; Medicare and Medicaid reimbursements make up 57% of patient service payments. Other sources include commercial insurers and private-pay customers.

Financial Performance

In fiscal 2015 (ended September) Baystate Health revenues grew 17% to $1.2 billion; this was driven by a growth in premiums as well as net patient service revenue. However that year the system reported a net loss of $78 million due to higher medical claims and capitation as well as losses on investments and pension adjustments.

Following net income's suit cash flow from operations dropped 38% to $51 million in fiscal 2015.

Strategy

Baystate Health has been conducting expansion and renovation efforts at its facilities in recent years including medical technology and information system upgrades. The system's largest effort was the construction of a $300 million clinical building on the Baystate Medical Center Campus.

Other facilities and divisions are undergoing expansion as well: The system is adding new space to house a pharmacy and nearly 100 modern inpatient rooms at its flagship campus while a new surgical center is being added to Baystate Franklin Medical Center in Greenfield. Baystate Medical Practices continues to grow by adding new practices on a regular basis. Baystate Health is also upgrading its medical equipment and its information technology systems.

Mergers and Acquisitions

Baystate Health acquired Noble Hospital (now Baystate Noble Hospital) a 97-bed not-for-profit community hospital in 2015. The year before that it added another acute care facility when it bought the 74-bed Wind Memorial Hospital (now Baystate Wing Hospital) from UMass Memorial Healthcare.

EXECUTIVES

SVP Community Hospitals CFO and Treasurer, Dennis W. Chalke
VP Facilities and Guest Services, Michael F. Moran
President and CEO Health New England Inc., Maura C. McCaffrey
CEO Baycare Health Partners, Stephen J. Sweet
VP and Chief Information Officer, Joel L. Vengco
President and CEO, Mark A. Keroack
SVP COO and Chief Nursing Office Baystate Medical Center, Nancy Shendell-Falik
President Baystate Medical Practices and Chief Physician Executive, John R. Schreiber
President Eastern Region, Charles E. Cavagnaro
Vice President, Doug Neal
Medical Director, Sudeep Aulakh
Medical Director, Alice Abbott
Medical Director, Algernon Anatol
Vice President, Lawrence Emerson
Medical Director, Deborah Abell
Director Physician Recruitment, John (Jack) Larson
Secretary, Nancy Melanson
Auditors: ERNST & YOUNG LLP BOSTON MAS

LOCATIONS

HQ: BAYSTATE HEALTH SYSTEM HEALTH SERVICES INC.
280 CHESTNUT ST, SPRINGFIELD, MA 011991000
Phone: 413 794-9939
Web: WWW.BAYSTATEHEALTH.ORG

Selected Locations

Baystate Medical Center (Springfield)
Baystate Children's Hospital (Springfield)
Baystate Franklin Medical Center (Greenfield)
Baystate Mary Lane Hospital (Ware)
Baystate Noble Hospital (Westfield)
Baystate Wing Hospital (Palmer)
Outpatient Centers
Baystate Home Infusion & Respiratory Services
Baystate Medical Practices
Baystate Radiology and Imaging (BRI)
Baystate Reference Laboratories (BRL)
Baystate Visiting Nurse Association & Hospice
Brightwood Health Center
Chestnut Surgery Center
D' Amour Center for Cancer Care
High Street Center (adult and pediatrics)
Mason Square Neighborhood Health Center
Neurodiagnostics & Sleep Center
Orthopedic Surgery Center
Wesson Women & Infants Health Center

PRODUCTS/OPERATIONS

2015 Sales

	% of total
Net patient service revenue	57
Premiums	39
Other	4
Total	**100**

Selected Services

Ambulance
Anesthesiology
Behavioral health services
Birthing services
Cancer
Cardiovascular
Emergency medicine
Endoscopy
Home care and home medical supplies
Hospital medicine
Neurosciences
Obstetrics and gynecology
Pain management center
Pathology
Pediatrics
Radiology
Rehabilitation care
Reproductive medicine
Sleep program
Surgery
Weight management
Women' s health

COMPETITORS

Berkshire Health Systems	Partners HealthCare
Cambridge Health Alliance	Shriners Hospitals For Children
Cape Cod Healthcare	Southcoast Hospitals Group
CareGroup	Steward Health Care
Harrington Memorial Hospital	Universal Health Services

HISTORICAL FINANCIALS

Company Type: Private

Income Statement

FYE: September 30

	REVENUE ($ mil.)	NET INCOME ($ mil.)	NET PROFIT MARGIN	EMPLOYEES
09/07	1,286	125	9.7%	5,000
09/06	1,209	83	6.9%	—
09/05	0	0	—	—
09/04	0	0	—	—
Annual Growth	—	—	—	—

2007 Year-End Financials

Return on assets: 5.4%
Return on equity: 9.7%
Current ratio: 0.70
Cash ($ mil.): 61

BEACON HEALTH SYSTEM INC.

Auditors: ERNST & YOUNG LLP CHICAGO IL

LOCATIONS

HQ: BEACON HEALTH SYSTEM INC.
615 N MICHIGAN ST, SOUTH BEND, IN 466011033
Phone: 575 647-1000
Web: WWW.BEACONHEALTHSYSTEM.ORG

HISTORICAL FINANCIALS

Company Type: Private

Income Statement

FYE: December 31

	REVENUE ($ mil.)	NET INCOME ($ mil.)	NET PROFIT MARGIN	EMPLOYEES
12/14	913	61	6.8%	—
12/13	820	136	16.7%	—
Annual Growth	11.3%	(54.9%)	—	—

2014 Year-End Financials

Return on assets: 6.6%
Return on equity: 6.8%
Current ratio: 1.80
Cash ($ mil.): 96

BEALL'S INC.

Residents of the Sun Belt have been known to leave their homes with Beall's on. The retail holding company operates through subsidiaries Beall's Department Stores Beall's Outlet and Burke's Outlet Stores in a dozen states. The multi-brand retailer has more than 530 department and outlet stores (about 200 are in Florida) located throughout states in the southern and western US including Arizona California Georgia Louisiana and Texas. Products range from off-price clothing and footwear for men and women to cosmetics gifts and housewares. Each chain has its own online shopping destination. The family-owned company was founded in 1915 by the grandfather of chairman Robert Beall (pronounced "bell").

Geographic Reach

Beall's trio of chain's operate stores in Alabama Arkansas Arizona California Florida Georgia Kentucky Louisiana Mississippi Nevada New Mexico North Carolina South Carolina Tennessee Texas Virginia and West Virginia.

Operations

Beall's Inc. oversees operations of its three operating companies. Beall's Florida operates some 190 stores in the Sunshine State. Beall's Outlet operates about 300 stores in Arizona Florida Texas and Georgia while Burke's Outlet operates more than 190 stores in 16 states.

Financial Performance

Privately-owned Beall's rings ups more than $1 billion in sales annually.

Strategy

The company has aspirations to transform itself into a major discount retailer much like its larger rivals TJX and Ross Stores. To that end the company plans to add new stores outside its traditional markets with an eye on establishing a national retail presence. Targets include adding 30 to 50 stores a year for the next several years and raising brand awareness beyond Florida.

With many of its stores in Arizona Florida and California (three of the states hit hardest by the housing crisis and deep recession) Beall's Inc. should have been in a heap of retail trouble. However its largest chain —Beall's Outlet –proved to be quite popular during this recession. Indeed the budget-priced outlet chain outperformed its two sister chains as well as more moderately priced department stores. The retailer has also benefited from the demise of other retailers including Goody's Linens 'n Things and Mervyn's.

The three operating companies share resources provided by Beall's Inc. such as distribution finance loss prevention and information systems. Conversely each chain is responsible for its purchasing product development real estate and advertising activities.

Company Background

Stores operating under the Bealls name in Alabama New Mexico and Texas are owned by Stage Stores and are not affiliated with Beall's Inc.

EXECUTIVES

Vice President Merchandise Process, Ron Friese
Dvp Store Systems, Louann Brekhus
Divisional Vice President Development, Rick Dreiling
Auditors: CHRISTOPHER SMITH LEONARD B

LOCATIONS

HQ: BEALL' S INC.
1806 38TH AVE E, BRADENTON, FL 342084700
Phone: 941 747-2355
Web: WWW.BEALLSINC.COM

PRODUCTS/OPERATIONS

Selected Retail Operations

Bealls Department Stores (Florida)
Bealls Outlet (deep-discount outlet stores in Arizona Florida Georgia)
Burke' s Outlet (11 southern states)

COMPETITORS

Bed Bath & Beyond	Ross Stores
Costco Wholesale	Sears
Dillard' s	Stage Stores
J. C. Penney Company	TJX Companies
Kohl' s	Target Corporation
Macy' s	The Gap
Nordstrom	Wal-Mart

HISTORICAL FINANCIALS

Company Type: Private

Income Statement   FYE: August 3

	REVENUE ($ mil.)	NET INCOME ($ mil.)	NET PROFIT MARGIN	EMPLOYEES
08/13*	1,273	10	0.8%	10,100
07/12	1,232	14	1.1%	—
07/11	1,166	15	1.3%	—
07/10	1,123	0	—	—
Annual Growth	4.2%	—	—	—

*Fiscal year change

2013 Year-End Financials

Return on assets: 9.6%   Cash ($ mil.): 47
Return on equity: 0.8%
Current ratio: 0.20

BEARING DISTRIBUTORS INC.

Bearing Distributors Inc. (BDI) began as a regional Midwestern distributor of replacement parts to OEMs. Among the world's largest industrial suppliers today the company also provides maintenance and repair services as well as training and inventory management. Its offerings include bearings electrical power products material handling systems and motion control products hydraulic and pneumatic systems and fluid power components. BDI serves customers in automotive to power generation industries and from mining to food and beverage paper processing and package handling operations. Founded in 1935 the company a unit of Forge Industries has locations dotting North America Europe and Asia.

Geographic Reach

BDI operates more than 200 global branches spanning 12 countries including the US Canada Mexico Europe and Asia. Its distribution centers reside in Cleveland Ohio; Montreal and Mississauga Canada; Budapest Hungary; Tianjin China; Suzhou China; and Bangalore India.

Strategy

BDI grows its business through acquisitions and organic growth. As part of this strategy in early 2015 it purchased Munnell & Sherrill an industrial distribution company based in the Pacific Northwest with locations in Oregon Washington and Northern California.

In 2013 BDI opened a new branch in Flint Michigan to serve customers in central and southeastern Michigan. That year it also relocated a branch in Maine and a branch in Detroit to better serve its expanding customer base.

EXECUTIVES

President and COO, John Ruth
Manager Product Group Specialist, David Strovers
Manager Conveying Equipment, Dan Paustian
Vice President Midwest Region and Marketing, William (Bill) Shepard

LOCATIONS

HQ: BEARING DISTRIBUTORS INC.
8000 HUB PKWY, CLEVELAND, OH 441255788
Phone: 216 642-9100
Web: WWW.BDI-USA.COM

PRODUCTS/OPERATIONS

Selected Products

Adhesive sealant and lubricant products
  Adhesives
  Cleaners
  Epoxies
  Hand cleaners
  Lube systems
  Lubricants
  Micro poly
  Paints
  Sealants
  Silicones
  Solvents
  Thread lockers
  Thread repair
Bearings
  Ball and roller bearings
  Lubricated bearings
  Mounted bearing units
  Specialty bearings
Bulk chemicals
  Adhesives
  Metalworking fluids
  Surface treatment
Electrical Products
  Clutches and brakes
  DC SCR drives
  Electric motors
  Tachometers
Fluid power components
  Components
  Hydraulic cylinders and actuators
  Hydraulic and pumps
  Pressure gauges
  PVC fittings
  Temperature gauges
  Valves (ball butterfly hydraulic and pneumatic)
Industrial hose and fittings
  High pressure hose
  Hydraulic fittings
  PVC fittings
  Quick disconnect fittings
  Tube fittings
Linear motion control
  Electromechanical actuators
  Linear accelerators
  Linear actuators
Material handling products and systems
  Belt fasteners idlers and lacers
  Conveyors
  Conveyor components

Drive components
Mechanical power transmission
  Belts
  Chain attachments
  Couplings
  Drive systems
  Gears
  Speed reducers

COMPETITORS

Applied Industrial Technologies	MRC Global
DXP Enterprises	Milk Specialties Company
HD Supply	THG Corporation
Industrial Distribution Group	W.W. Grainger
Lewis-Goetz	WESCO International

HISTORICAL FINANCIALS

Company Type: Private

Income Statement   FYE: December 31

	REVENUE ($ mil.)	NET INCOME ($ mil.)	NET PROFIT MARGIN	EMPLOYEES
12/08	528	5	1.1%	850
12/07	502	13	2.6%	—
12/06	2,099	0	—	—
Annual Growth	—44021.8%	—	—	—

2008 Year-End Financials

Return on assets: 7.6%   Cash ($ mil.): 5
Return on equity: 1.1%
Current ratio: 0.80

BEAVER STREET FISHERIES INC.

After more than 60 years of fishing Beaver Street Fisheries can tell a tale or two of the one that got away. It's a top supplier of fish and other seafood products to wholesalers retailers and food service operators. Sourcing its products from more than 50 countries family-owned Beaver Street Fisheries offers one of the largest selections of seafood in the US. It boasts a variety of fresh and frozen seafood —including octopus shrimp and turtle —sold under its flagship Sea Best brand as well as the HF's and Island Queen names. Beaver Street Fisheries also imports lamb from New Zealand and sells Silver Fern-brand pork and beef via its Florida-New Zealand Lamb & Meat unit.

Operations

Beaver Street Fisheries has expanded its products portfolio in recent years through the efforts of its sister companies Bahamas Food Service and Tropic Seafood. Based in Nassau Bahamas the company's food service operation specializes in food distribution as one of the largest full-line food service distributors in the Bahamas. The company's Tropic Seafood business concentrates on lobster tail and seafood processing in the Bahamas. Specifically it processes lobster tails conch and other seafood items under the Island Queen and Island Prince brand names for sale worldwide.

The company maintains 8 million cubic feet of freezer space in Jacksonville Florida and offers 27 loading bays to facilitate a speedy dock turnaround process. It also has a network of cold storage facilities works with carriers to ensure national and international delivery within 48 hours.

Strategy

The food service operation specializes in food distribution as one of the largest full-line food service distributors in the Bahamas. In 2012 it working to double the size of its warehouse in Nassau while also fine-tuning the company's automation labor and transportation processes. Beaver Street Fisheries hopes to automate the workforce management processes in Nassau so that it can boost order volume without greatly expanding its employee count there.

Company Background

Alfred and Hans Frisch started the business as a retail fish shop in 1950. It established the Sea Best brand in 1979.

EXECUTIVES

Vice President Risk Management, Harry Frisch
Executive Vice President, Mark Frisch

LOCATIONS

HQ: BEAVER STREET FISHERIES INC.
1741 W ST BEAVER, JACKSONVILLE, FL 32209
Phone: 904 354-5661
Web: WWW.BEAVERSTREETFISHERIES.COM

PRODUCTS/OPERATIONS

Selected Products
Fish and other seafood
  Albacore tuna
  Black cod
  Bluefish
  Calamari
  Catfish
  Clams
  Cod
  Conch
  Crab
  Crawfish
  Flounder
  Grouper
  Haddock
  Halibut
  Lake perch
  Langostinos
  Lobster
  Mackerel
  Mahi mahi
  Marlin
  Mullet
  Mussels
  Ocean catfish
  Ocean perch
  Orange roughy
  Oysters
  Pollock
  Salmon
  Scallops
  Sea bass
  Sea trout
  Shark
  Shrimp
  Snails/escargot
  Snapper
  Sole
  Squid
  Surimi
  Swordfish
  Tilapia
  Whiting
  Yellowfin tuna
  Value-added
  Breaded seafood
  Crab cakes
  Crab patties
  Crabmeat stuffing
  Deviled crab
  Lobster tails
  Paella mix
  Salted fish
  Smoked fish
Other
  Alligator
  Beef
  Frog legs
  Lamb
  Octopus
  Pork
  Turtle

COMPETITORS

American Seafoods	Mims Meat
Brown Packing Company	Niman Ranch
Colorado Boxed Beef	North Pacific Seafoods
Del Monte Capitol Meat	Ocean Beauty Seafoods
Fishhawk Fisheries	Pacific Seafood Group
Florida Fresh Seafood	Pioneer Wholesale Meat
Corp.	Red Chamber Co.
Fossil Farms	Ronald A. Chisholm
Freedman Meats	Limited
Gorton' s	SYSCO Newport Meat
Harvest Meat Company	Company
High Liner Foods	Smithfield Foods
Icelandic Group	Trident Seafoods
JBS USA	Wolverine Packing
Jim Pattison Group	
Maid-Rite Steak	
Company	

HISTORICAL FINANCIALS
Company Type: Private

Income Statement
FYE: May 28

	REVENUE ($ mil.)	NET INCOME ($ mil.)	NET PROFIT MARGIN	EMPLOYEES
05/11	450	13	3.0%	200
05/10	442	19	4.4%	—
05/09	741	0	0.0%	—
Annual Growth	(22.0%)	41071.0%	—	—

2011 Year-End Financials
Return on assets: 6.2%   Cash ($ mil.): 19
Return on equity: 3.0%
Current ratio: 1.80

BECK & MASTEN PONTIAC-GMC INC

LOCATIONS

HQ: BECK & MASTEN PONTIAC-GMC INC
11300 FM 1960 RD W, HOUSTON, TX 770653698
Phone: 281 469-5222
Web: WWW.BECKMASTENNORTH.COM

HISTORICAL FINANCIALS
Company Type: Private

Income Statement
FYE: December 31

	REVENUE ($ mil)	NET INCOME ($ mil.)	NET PROFIT MARGIN	EMPLOYEES
12/13	1,839	4	0.3%	137
12/12	158	2	1.5%	
12/11	153	4	2.8%	
12/10	143	0	—	
Annual Growth	134.3%	—	—	—

2013 Year-End Financials
Return on assets: 0.1%   Cash ($ mil.): 19
Return on equity: 0.3%
Current ratio: 0.50

BECK SUPPLIERS INC.

More than willing to be at the beck and call of its customers Beck Suppliers provides its clients in Ohio with fuel oil diesel gasoline kerosene and propane. The company annually delivers more than 70 million gallons of fuel at its 58 Sunoco and 28 Marathon gas stations in northwestern Ohio. Beck Suppliers also operates 25 Friendship Food Stores. The company's truck fleet delivers diesel fuel oil gasoline kerosene and propane for farm construction and industrial purposes as well as home heating oil and propane for residential use. Beck Suppliers also operates car washes under the Oasis brand and has a construction division that builds convenience stores gas stations and car washes.

EXECUTIVES

President, Doug Beck
VP Friendship Food Stores, Brian Beck
Treasurer, Dean Beck
VP Operations, Ed Willman
Accounting, Bill Taylor
Project Engineer, Lee Beckman
Ace Check Cashing, Aaron Taylor
Webmaster, Adam Miller

LOCATIONS

HQ: BECK SUPPLIERS INC.
1000 N FRONT ST, FREMONT, OH 434201921
Phone: 419 332-5527
Web: WWW.FRIENDSHIPFOODSTORES.COM

COMPETITORS

Benit Fuel	Sapp Bros Petroleum
Lykins	

HISTORICAL FINANCIALS
Company Type: Private

Income Statement
FYE: December 31

	REVENUE ($ mil.)	NET INCOME ($ mil.)	NET PROFIT MARGIN	EMPLOYEES
12/09	252	1	0.5%	250
12/08	316	0	0.2%	—
12/07	1,300	0	—	—
Annual Growth	—	7165.1%	—	—

2009 Year-End Financials
Return on assets: 1.6%   Cash ($ mil.): 1
Return on equity: 0.5%
Current ratio: 0.50

BECKMAN RESEARCH INSTITUTE OF THE CITY OF HOPE

LOCATIONS

HQ: BECKMAN RESEARCH INSTITUTE OF THE CITY OF HOPE
1500 DUARTE RD, DUARTE, CA 910103012
Phone: 626 359-8111

HISTORICAL FINANCIALS

Company Type: Private

Income Statement
FYE: September 30

	REVENUE ($ mil.)	NET INCOME ($ mil.)	NET PROFIT MARGIN	EMPLOYEES
09/13	300	39	13.0%	250
09/09	239	30	12.9%	—
09/08	253	33	13.2%	—
09/07	70	0	—	—
Annual Growth	27.5%	—	—	—

2013 Year-End Financials

Return on assets: 5.8%   Cash ($ mil.): 70
Return on equity: 13.0%
Current ratio: 0.90

BEEBE MEDICAL CENTER INC.

Sea shells on the sea shore can be found near Beebe Medical Center. The health care provider offers emergency inpatient long-term care women's health and other medical services to residents of Sussex County Delaware. The hospital is located in the town of Lewes near Rehoboth Beach. It has approximately 210 beds and offers specialized services including cardiology orthopedic rehabilitation and oncology treatments. Beebe Medical Center offers outpatient services including wound care diabetes management surgery radiology and sleep disorder diagnosis. It also operates senior care centers home health agencies medical laboratories and a nursing school.

Operations

Beebe Medical Center has a staff of some 1400 health professionals including about 300 doctors. It handles some 50000 emergency room visits per year. In addition to the primary hospital facilities the health care provider operates the Beebe Health Campus (outpatient services) and the nearby Millville Emergency Center (a summertime clinic near Bethany Beach).

Strategy

Beebe Medical Center has expanded its facilities over the years to better serve area residents. It began an expansion aiming to double enrollment of the nursing school in 2012. Construction efforts at the main hospital facility include a new emergency and critical care wing added in 2008.

Company Background

Beebe Medical Center was founded in 1916 by two brothers Dr. James Beebe and Dr. Richard Beebe. The Beebe School of Nursing opened in 1921 and the outpatient Beebe Health Campus was completed in 2003.

EXECUTIVES

Director Of Pharmacy, Samuel Roberts
Vice President Management, Gerald (Jerry) Smith
Vice President Of Operations, Donna Streletzky
Medical Records Director, Steven D (Steve) Berlin

LOCATIONS

HQ: BEEBE MEDICAL CENTER INC.
424 SAVANNAH RD, LEWES, DE 199581462
Phone: 302 645-3300

Selected Delaware Locations
Beebe Health Campus (Rehoboth Beach)
Beebe Lab Express (Milton)
Beebe School of Nursing (Lewes)

Diabetes Management and Wound Care Center (Long Neck)
Georgetown Professional Park (Georgetown)
Gull House Adult Activities Center (Lewes)
Home Health Agency (Lewes)
Millville Walk-in Health Center (Millville)
Sleep Disorders Center (Rehoboth Beach)
Tunnell Cancer Center (Rehoboth Beach)

PRODUCTS/OPERATIONS

Selected Services
Bariatric
Cancer care
Cardiac & vascular
Community health
Diabetes management
Emergency
Home health
Hospitalist program
Imaging
Integrative health
Orthopedics
Rehabilitation
Senior care
Sleep Disorder
Surgical
Walk-in Healthcare
Wellness
Women' s Health
Wound Care

COMPETITORS

Anne Arundel Medical Center
AtlantiCare
Christiana Care
Crozer-Keystone Health System
Inspira Health Network
Shore Memorial Hospital

HISTORICAL FINANCIALS

Company Type: Private

Income Statement
FYE: June 30

	REVENUE ($ mil.)	NET INCOME ($ mil.)	NET PROFIT MARGIN	EMPLOYEES
06/13	275	16	5.9%	1,600
06/10	259	15	5.9%	—
06/09*	234	0	—	—
04/09	0	0	—	—
Annual Growth	—	—	—	—

*Fiscal year change

2013 Year-End Financials

Return on assets: 18.3%   Cash ($ mil.): 28
Return on equity: 5.9%
Current ratio: 0.60

BELAIRE HEALTH CARE CENTER INC.

LOCATIONS

HQ: BELAIRE HEALTH CARE CENTER INC.
2065 LYON ST, GASTONIA, NC 280526230
Phone: 704 867-7300
Web: WWW.BELAIREHEALTHREHAB.COM

HISTORICAL FINANCIALS

Company Type: Private

Income Statement
FYE: September 30

	REVENUE ($ mil.)	NET INCOME ($ mil.)	NET PROFIT MARGIN	EMPLOYEES
09/09	833	99	11.9%	120
09/04	5	0	2.7%	—
09/03	5	(0)	—	—
09/02	5	0	—	—
Annual Growth	107.2%	—	—	—

2009 Year-End Financials

Return on assets: —   Cash ($ mil.): —
Return on equity: 11.9%
Current ratio: 2.20

BELLIN HEALTH SYSTEMS INC.

Auditors: WIPFLI LLP GREEN BAY WISCON

LOCATIONS

HQ: BELLIN HEALTH SYSTEMS INC.
744 S WEBSTER AVE, GREEN BAY, WI 543013505
Phone: 920 433-3500
Web: WWW.BELLIN.ORG

HISTORICAL FINANCIALS

Company Type: Private

Income Statement
FYE: September 30

	REVENUE ($ mil.)	NET INCOME ($ mil.)	NET PROFIT MARGIN	EMPLOYEES
09/14	460	34	7.4%	2,300
09/10	348	30	8.8%	—
09/09	323	13	4.0%	—
09/08	767	0	—	—
Annual Growth	—	—	—	—

2014 Year-End Financials

Return on assets: 3.0%   Cash ($ mil.): 80
Return on equity: 7.4%
Current ratio: 2.40

BELLIN MEMORIAL HOSPITAL INC.

LOCATIONS

HQ: BELLIN MEMORIAL HOSPITAL INC.
744 S WEBSTER AVE, GREEN BAY, WI 543013581
Phone: 920 433-3500
Web: WWW.BELLIN.ORG

HISTORICAL FINANCIALS

Company Type: Private

Income Statement

FYE: September 30

	REVENUE ($ mil.)	NET INCOME ($ mil.)	NET PROFIT MARGIN	EMPLOYEES
09/13	363	28	7.8%	1,725
09/09	288	14	5.1%	—
09/08*	267	14	5.3%	—
06/08	9	0	—	—
Annual Growth	106.8%	—	—	—

*Fiscal year change

2013 Year-End Financials

Return on assets: 3.5% Cash ($ mil.): 54
Return on equity: 7.8%
Current ratio: 2.30

BELOIT HEALTH SYSTEM INC.

Beloit Wisconsin: Home of the world's largest can of chili the Beloit Snappers and... Beloit Health System. Its Beloit Memorial Hospital acute care facility provides medical care to the city's residents and surrounding areas. Specialty services include emergency medicine cardiology home care and occupational health. Its NorthPointe integrative medicine campus provides traditional and alternative medical approaches including massage Tai Chi and yoga. Beloit Health also provides primary care and specialized services through numerous outreach medical centers and operates an assisted living complex called Riverside Terrace. Beloit Health is affiliated with the University of Wisconsin Hospital and Clinics.

Geographic Reach

In addition to Beloit Memorial Hospital Beloit Health also has half a dozen primary care clinics in northern Illinois and southern Wisconsin.

Operations

In 2012 Beloit Health operated 103 beds admitted 3995 patients has 39853 emergency room visits and conducted 4447 surgical procedures more than 755600 outpatient procedures and more than 659390 laboratory tests.

The company operates a hospitalist program (doctors who specialize in caring for hospitalized patients) to help streamline patient care and improve operational efficiency. Beloit Clinic offers a range of medical care to the residents of this region. Darien Clinic provides healthcare services such as physical exams diagnosis of illness developing treatment plans the order and interpretation of lab tests and the writing of prescriptions. The Janesville Clinic offers specialized services such as Occupational Health Services Physical Therapy and Counseling Care therapists. Beloit Health also offers its services through the Sports Medicine Center (Occupational Health Sports and Family Medicine Center); West Side Clinic (primary care services); Clinton Clinic (primary care clinic); NorthPointe Health and Wellness Campus (from diagnostic services to immediate and primary care to a medically integrated health and fitness center); NorthPointe Terrace - Assisted Living (assisted living center); and Riverside Terrace (a Residential Care Apartment Complex).

Financial Performance

The company's reported $191 million in revenues in 2012. The majority of revenues came from net patient revenues (Medicare accounted for 47% of net patient revenues; insurance 33%).

That year Beloit Health reported net income of $91 million.

Strategy

Beloit Health has spent nearly $12 million to expand its emergency room to meet increasing patient demand. The three-phase project which was completed in 2013 added more than 15 treatment rooms a larger ambulance garage bigger waiting areas and improved technology.

To expand and improve its cancer treatment options (and in partnership with University of Wisconsin) in 2013 the company broke ground on new Beloit Health System Cancer Center. The new cancer center will be built on a five-acre parcel of land on the corners of Milwaukee Road and Lee Lane in front of Beloit Health System's Occupational Health Sports and Family Clinic.

To streamline its administration operations in 2012 Beloit Health launched the Electronic Medical Records project to replace the expensive and more inefficient paper-based filing system.

Company Background

In 2010 Beloit Memorial Hospital partnered with Beloit Clinic and become a new integrated health system with the name of Beloit Health System.

The company was founded in 1970.

LOCATIONS

HQ: BELOIT HEALTH SYSTEM INC.
1969 W HART RD, BELOIT, WI 535112298
Phone: 608 364-5011
Web: WWW.BELOITHEALTHSYSTEM.ORG

PRODUCTS/OPERATIONS

2012 Revenues Payor Sources

	% of total
Medicare	47
Insurance	33
Medical Assistance	15
Other	5
Total	**100**

Selected Services

AlertLine Personal Response Program
Ambulatory Surgery
At-Home Healthcare
Audiology
Breastfeeding Class
Cancer Center
Cardiac Rehabilitation - Heart and Vascular Center
Cardiology Center
Community Links
Counseling Care Center
Counseling Care Center: Alcohol and Drug Addictions
Counseling Care Center: Contact Us
Counseling Care Center: Employee Assistance Program
Counseling Care Center: Forms & Resources
Counseling Care Center: Group Therapy
Critical Care
Diabetes Care Services
Dialysis Center
Dietitians & Nutritional Counseling
Education
Emergency Medical Services
Enterostomal Services
Family Care Center - Birthing Services
First Choice Benefits Management
Gastroenterology
Heart Health Physicians
Incontinence Services
Integrative Medicine Program
Intermediate Care
Joint Replacement Center
Laboratory Services
Library
Medical Imaging/Mammography
Medical Outpatient Care Center
Multicare Center
Neurology Services
Occupational Health and Wellness
Outreach Medical Centers
Patient Accounts
Patient and Family Services
Pharmacy
Physical Medicine and Rehabilitation Department
Pulmonary Rehab Center
Sibling Classes - Big Brother Big Sister
Sleep Disorders
Surgical Services
Vascular Care and Ultrasound
Volunteer Services

COMPETITORS

Centegra Health System
Columbia St. Mary's
Dean Health Systems Inc.
FHN
KishHealth
Meriter Health Services
Ministry Health Care
Rockford Health System
Stoughton Hospital
SwedishAmerican Health System
University of Wisconsin Hospital and Clinics

HISTORICAL FINANCIALS

Company Type: Private

Income Statement

FYE: December 31

	REVENUE ($ mil.)	NET INCOME ($ mil.)	NET PROFIT MARGIN	EMPLOYEES
12/12	193	7	3.9%	1,400
12/11	187	(1)	—	—
Annual Growth	3.3%	—	—	—

2012 Year-End Financials

Return on assets: 12.6% Cash ($ mil.): 25
Return on equity: 3.9%
Current ratio: 0.50

BEN-TREI LTD.

LOCATIONS

HQ: BEN-TREI LTD.
4605 E 91ST ST, TULSA, OK 741372852
Phone: 918 496-5115
Web: WWW.BENTREI.COM

HISTORICAL FINANCIALS

Company Type: Private

Income Statement

FYE: June 30

	REVENUE ($ mil.)	NET INCOME ($ mil.)	NET PROFIT MARGIN	EMPLOYEES
06/08	378	6	1.7%	18
06/07	181	1	0.8%	—
06/05	0	0	—	—
06/04	50	0	—	—
Annual Growth	65.2%	—	—	—

2008 Year-End Financials

Return on assets: 4.3% Cash ($ mil.): 2
Return on equity: 1.7%
Current ratio: 0.40

BENCO DENTAL SUPPLY CO.

Benco Dental Supply is a one-stop shop for the tooth doc. Through regional showrooms and distribution centers Benco provides dental and dentistry supplies to more than 30000 dental professionals throughout the US. Its offerings include dental hand pieces furniture and disposable supplies. Its BencoNET division develops and distributes custom computers and proprietary programming and networking systems for dentists. Other services include dental office design practice consulting financing and real estate planning wealth management and equipment repairs.

Geographic Reach

Benco Dental's main headquarters and showroom is located in Pittston Pennsylvania. It also operates another CenterPoint Experience (large-scale) showroom in Costa Mesa California and it has a network of about 50 smaller regional showrooms and five distribution centers (in Pittston; Dallas; Fort Wayne Indiana; Jacksonville Florida; and Reno Nevada) across the US that serve customers in all 50 US states.

Although most of its operations are in the US the company also ships products to overseas customers.

Operations

Benco offerings range from large equipment to small supplies made by a broad range of manufacturers. The company supplies more than 80000 products including dental cement impression supplies and curing lights made by manufacturers such as 3M Dentsply Sybron (Kerr) Hu-Friedy and more. It also sells products under its own Benco Dental brand.

Support services include offers inventory management services and hand piece equipment and upholstery repair.

Benco Dental's practice management services include staff recruitment assistance product training programs for dentists peer-to-peer networking solutions and continuing medical education programs.

Sales and Marketing

Benco markets its products and services directly to dental practices. It also increasing the number of orders placed through its online ordering system (Painless) and it promotes services to dentists through affiliations with dental organizations and associations (including the American Academy of Dental Group Practice and the American Association of Orthodontists). The company has more than 400 sales representatives. To support sales it also has about 300 factory-trained service technicians.

Financial Performance

Benco increased net sales by 9% in 2012 due to new product sales launches and increased sales of existing products in fields including 3D imaging equipment and digital sensors.

Strategy

Benco tends to expand its operations through organic growth initiatives including offering new products and services to a wider customer base. In addition the company grows through acquisitions in key growth regions. The company launched 14 Benco branded products during 2012 as well as 3800 new products made by its vendor partners. It also added about 50 new sales reps that year to meet rising customer demands. The company estimated that it grew market share to some 11% of the US market that year (placing itself among the top three dental supply distributors).

Benco increased sales to community health centers that year through its partnership with PSS. To expand its educational programs in 2012 the company also formed a partnership with the Kois Center which offers a nine-course program on topics including aesthetic and restorative dentistry.

To reach additional customers and expand its capacity the company opened its fifth distribution center —a 120000-sq. ft. facility in Reno Nevada — in 2011. It also opened a new sales branch office in Los Angeles to serve the Southern California market in 2012.

Benco Dental moved into its CenterPoint headquarters and showroom in Pittston Pennsylvania in early 2010. The facility is one of the largest dental equipment showrooms in the US with exhibits including more than two dozen dental rooms 14 digital X-ray units three sterilization centers and other oral surgery and orthodontic units as well as an office design concept suite and a training and education center. Following the success of that location the company opened a second CenterPoint Experience showroom in Costa Mesa California in 2012.

Ownership

Benco is named after founder Benjamin Cohen who started the company in 1930. The Cohen family controls the company.

EXECUTIVES

Vice President, Michael (Mel) McElaney
Auditors: COHEN & COMPANY CLEVELAND OH

LOCATIONS

HQ: BENCO DENTAL SUPPLY CO.
295 CENTERPOINT BLVD, PITTSTON, PA 186406136
Phone: 800 462-3626
Web: WWW.BENCO.COM

Selected Distribution Center Locations
Dallas Texas
Fort Wayne Indiana
Jacksonville Florida
Pittston Pennsylvania
Reno Nevada

PRODUCTS/OPERATIONS

Selected Brands
Large Equipment
  A-dec
  Belmont
  BIOLASE
  Cadent
  Gendex
  Instrumentarium
  Marus
  Midmark
  Pelton & Crane
  Sirona
  Soredex
  Vatech
Small Equipment
  Accutron
  Aceton
  Air Techniques
  Cadent
  KaVo
  Midmark
  Midwest
  Tuttnauer
  W&H
Supplies and technology (Benco brands)
  BencoNET
  BluChip rewards
  BluPrint (dental impression material)
  fas-TRACT
  HD
  Iris (dental pit and fissure sealant)
  Natural Extensions (nitrile gloves)
  Painless
  ValuGrip (latex gloves)
  Vision XR (oral x-ray film)
  XLR8 (dental equipment)
  Z3

COMPETITORS

Burkhart Dental	Henry Schein
Cardinal Health	McKesson
DENTSPLY	Owens & Minor
Darby Dental	Patterson Companies
Discus Dental	Sybron Dental

HISTORICAL FINANCIALS
Company Type: Private

Income Statement
FYE: January 4

	REVENUE ($ mil.)	NET INCOME ($ mil.)	NET PROFIT MARGIN	EMPLOYEES
01/14*	620	8	1.4%	1,120
12/12	600	7	1.2%	—
12/07	389	5	1.3%	—
12/06	344	0	—	—
Annual Growth 8.8%			—	—

*Fiscal year change

2014 Year-End Financials
Return on assets: 9.9%
Return on equity: 1.4%
Current ratio: 0.70
Cash ($ mil.): —

BENTLEY UNIVERSITY

Bentley University is not the Rolls-Royce of universities but is fairly prestigious nevertheless. It offers undergraduate graduate and doctoral degree programs to its nearly 5670 enrolled students from 82 countries. The university also offers professional development and certificate programs for executives and corporations. The focus at Bentley is on business; the school was a pioneer in integrating information technology into the business curriculum. In the belief that businesspeople need a broad education Bentley requires a liberal arts core of classes in behavioral and social sciences English and other subjects in the humanities as well as math and natural sciences.

Geographic Reach

Bentley University is situated on about 165 acres in Waltham west of Boston. In partnership with Bahrain Institute of Banking and Finance Bentley launched its "Bentley in Bahrain" degree program in 2002 expanding its campus to students in Bahrain and surrounding Gulf States in the Middle East. It also has a campus in San Francisco

Operations

The university has a student-faculty ratio of 14:1 with 78% of its faculty holding doctoral degrees. It offers 23 majors and 36 minors in business the arts and sciences. Tuition and fees are about $44020 per year.

Bentley offers numerous on-campus activities outside its academic and research functions. These include cultural events athletics the arts volunteering and more than 100 student organizations.

Strategy

Bentley is working to implement what it calls a fused curriculum where courses are taught by faculty from both the business and the arts and sciences sides academia. As part of the movement it offers an 11-month MBA that pulls from multiple disciplines.

Seeing a market for students on the West Coast in 2013 Bentley opened a campus in San Francisco.

Company Background

Harry Bentley founded the institution as the Bentley School of Accounting and Finance in 1917.

Bentley's university designation and name change occurred in 2008.

EXECUTIVES

Vice President Business Finance Treas, Paul Clemente
President, Gloria Cordes Larson
VP Academic Affairs and Provost, Michael J. Page
VP Administration and Finance, Kenneth B. Cody
Dean Arts and Sciences, Daniel L. Everett
VP Student Affairs and Dean of Students, J. Andrew Shepardson
Dean Business and Graduate School; Director Bentley Microfinance Initiative, Roy A. (Chip) Wiggins
CIO, Phillip G. Knutel
Business Systems Analyst I Office of Vice President for Enrollment Mgmnt, Jillian Proia
Senior Business Systems Analyst Office of Vice President for Enrollment Mgmnt, Jay DeFrank
Department Chair, Patrick (Paddy) Scholten
Vice President Publications Elect, Jean Bedard
Vice President Enrollment Management, Joann McKenna
Vice President, Gerald A (Jerry) Madek
Vice President Student Affairs, Kathleen Yorkis
Senior Vice President Liberty Mutual, Roxanne Martinez
Financial Vice President, Maggie Russo
Vice Chairman, Robert P. (Bob) Badavas, age 62
Chairman Board of Trustees, Steven P. Manfredi
Secretary, Danielle Lerose
Assistant Treasurer, James Fuerst
Treasurer, Hao LA
Auditors: KPMG LLP BOSTON MA

LOCATIONS

HQ: BENTLEY UNIVERSITY
175 FOREST ST, WALTHAM, MA 024524713
Phone: 781 891-2000

HISTORICAL FINANCIALS
Company Type: Private

Income Statement
FYE: June 30

	REVENUE ($ mil.)	NET INCOME ($ mil.)	NET PROFIT MARGIN	EMPLOYEES
06/14	202	48	23.7%	911
06/13	192	40	21.0%	—
06/12	185	(21)	—	—
06/11	183	0	—	—
Annual Growth	3.3%	—	—	—

2014 Year-End Financials
Return on assets: 12.2%   Cash ($ mil.): 29
Return on equity: 23.7%
Current ratio: —

BERGELECTRIC CORP.

One of the nation's top electrical contractors Bergelectric provides design/build and design/assist services on projects that include office buildings public-sector facilities bioscience labs entertainment complexes hotels data centers and hospitals. Its projects also consist of parking garages water treatment plants residential towers and correctional facilities. The company boasts expertise in building information modeling fire alarms and security and telecommunications and data infrastructure. Bergelectric operates mainly in the western and southeastern US from about a dozen offices.

Geographic Reach

From its headquarters in Los Angeles Bergelectric maintains a presence in California through a handful of offices in San Diego Los Angeles Orange County Sacramento and Ventura. It also serves as an electrical contractor in half a dozen cities including Austin Texas; Denver Colorado; Las Vegas Nevada; Orlando Florida; Phoenix Arizona; Portland Oregon; and Raleigh North Carolina.

Operations

The electrical company keeps a lengthy list of projects past and current. More recent projects have included the San Ysidro Land Port of Entry Lackland Ambulatory Care Center Northwest Water Reclamation Facility Naval Hospital Camp Pendleton Fort Riley Community Replacement Hospital Wilshire Boulevard Temple California Health Care Facility Visitors Center at King Gillette Ranch Variety Special Education School Greenlaw Partners and Sandy High School.

The company has more than $550 million in backlog.

Strategy

The company is also focused on green initiatives completing Leadership in Energy and Environmental Design (LEED) construction projects for the likes of Sony the FBI the EPA and the University of Oregon. To this end the company formed the Fire-Alarm/Security Division which provides projects and clients with comprehensive electrical services for such fire alarm projects as the Morongo Casino & Hotel Pechanga Hotel & Casino and San Manuel Indian Bingo & Casino.

Bergelectric has extended the reach of its traditional electrical contracting operations by expanding into new markets including sustainable building structures and renewable energy systems such as wind farms. Through a partnership with telecommunications firm Teo Bergelectric provides communications services to wind energy producers. As part of the agreement Bergelectric designs and installs fiber connections and equipment while Teo supplies phones switches and other hardware.

To simplify the integration of complex systems Bergelectric established a national Technology Systems group which serves to consolidate all of the company's existing low-voltage divisions under one management umbrella. The move aims to differentiate Bergelectric from the traditionally fragmented industry of electrical and systems components.

Company Background
Bergelectric was founded in 1946.

EXECUTIVES

Senior Vice President, Alan Mashburn
EVP Bergelectric, Tom Anderson
Vice President, Douglas Crumby
Senior Vice President Operations, William (Bill) Wingerning
Auditors: MOSS LEVY & HARTZHEIM LLP B

LOCATIONS

HQ: BERGELECTRIC CORP.
5650 W CENTINELA AVE, LOS ANGELES, CA 900451501
Phone: 310 337-1377
Web: WWW.BERGELECTRIC.COM

Selected Locations
Agoura Hills CA
Austin TX
Costa Mesa CA
Denver
Durham NC
Escondido CA
Los Angeles
North Las Vegas NV
Orlando FL
Portland OR
Rancho Cordova CA
Tempe AZ

COMPETITORS

Cupertino Electric	MYR Group
EMCOR	Morrow-Meadows
Fisk Electric	Rex Moore
Henkels & McCoy	Rosendin Electric
Integrated Electrical Services	Sachs Electric

HISTORICAL FINANCIALS
Company Type: Private

Income Statement
FYE: January 31

	REVENUE ($ mil.)	NET INCOME ($ mil.)	NET PROFIT MARGIN	EMPLOYEES
01/14	525	4	0.9%	2,100
01/13	478	3	0.6%	—
01/12	394	23	6.0%	—
01/11	403	0	—	—
Annual Growth	9.2%	—	—	—

2014 Year-End Financials
Return on assets: 4.6%   Cash ($ mil.): 7
Return on equity: 0.9%
Current ratio: 1.40

BERGEN REGIONAL MEDICAL CENTER L.P.

Bergen Regional Medical Center (BRMC) is not just the biggest hospital in Paramus New Jersey — it's one of the biggest in the state. BRMC provides acute care long-term care and behavioral health care services to the residents of northeastern New Jersey. The not-for-profit medical center with approximately 1190 beds also offers specialized services including orthopedics cardiology neurology emergency medicine and surgery as well as substance abuse treatment and hospice services. About half of the facility is devoted to long-term nursing care; and about 325 beds serve behavioral health patients.

Geographic Reach
BRMC serves patients from Bergen County as well as surrounding counties. The hospital is located on a 65-acre campus in Paramus New Jersey.

Operations
The 575-bed long-term care division is New Jersey's largest licensed nursing home. Residents receive nursing care and have access to round-the-clock medical care; they also participate in community and recreational activities. Other specialist units include BRMC's Evergreen Substance Abuse Treatment Center which provides comprehensive treatment –including inpatient detoxification and intensive outpatient programs –to about 15000 patients annually.Through an affiliation with the University of Medicine and Dentistry of New Jersey the medical center also trains medical students. The BRMC Clinic is the hospital's outpatient care center which provides ambulatory care in about 20 specialist fields.BRMC is a safety net provider meaning that it takes care of elderly mentally impaired uninsured or underinsured patients who cannot afford care elsewhere. This causes the hospital to see a high number of Medicare and Medicaid patients as well as to provide a high volume of charity (unreimbursed) care.As a complement to its long term care and behavioral health/substance abuse expertise Bergen Regional also offers acute medical services including an

emergency department surgical suites physical rehabilitation a pharmacy ans a laboratory radiologic services (including digital mammography) and more than 20 ambulatory specialties available through the BRMC Clinic.In 2012 the hospital reported more than 16000 emergency department visits.StrategyWith the contract between Bergen County and the for-profit operator of BRMC expiring in 2017 and with the hospital in recent years receiving poor marks from the federal government as well as in private rankings of healthcare facilities nationwide in 2014 the County Executive called for a study of the embattled Paramus-based acute care center. The Bergen County Executive created a seven-person task force to urgently study the needs of and future options for BRMC which has been hit by a 2012 lawsuit claiming non-payment of bills and other allegations of financial impropriety.Company BackgroundIn 2011 an agreement was made that extended the affiliation with the University of Medicine and Dentistry of New Jersey by allowing psychiatry graduate students to enter a training program at BRMC as part of their postgraduate education.BRMC is owned by Bergen County but it is managed by a for-profit company.

EXECUTIVES

Vice President Of Facilities, Herman Lindenbaum
Director Of Nursing, Grace Vickerie
Vice President Behavioral Health Services,
  Thomas (Thom) Rosamilia
Medical Director, Stephen H Jacobs
Director Of Admissions, Kathleen Wallace
Medical Director, Dana Banu
Vice President Of Information Technology, Debbie
  Greenip
Vice Chairman and Executive Vice President, Ehud
  Fried

LOCATIONS

HQ: BERGEN REGIONAL MEDICAL CENTER L.P.
  230 E RIDGEWOOD AVE, PARAMUS, NJ 076524142
Phone: 201 967-4000
Web: WWW.BERGENREGIONAL.COM

PRODUCTS/OPERATIONS

Selected Services
Accessing Mental Health & Addiction Services
Acute Care
Acute Rehabilitation Services
Ambulatory Outpatient Services
Behavioral Health Services
Critical and Emergency Care
Long Term Care

COMPETITORS

Barnabas Health	Monmouth Medical
Englewood Hospital and	Center
Medical Center	Newark Beth Israel
Hackensack University	Medical Center
Medical Center	Nyack Hospital
JFK Health -	Robert Wood Johnson
Muhlenberg Campus	University Hospital
JFK Medical Center	Somerset Medical
Jersey City Medical	Center
Center	The Valley Hospital
Meridian Health	Valley Health System

HISTORICAL FINANCIALS
Company Type: Private

Income Statement				FYE: December 31
	REVENUE ($ mil.)	NET INCOME ($ mil.)	NET PROFIT MARGIN	EMPLOYEES
12/12	197	(1)	—	1,856
12/08	146	(78)	—	—
Annual Growth	7.8%	—	—	—

2012 Year-End Financials
Return on assets: 3.9%   Cash ($ mil.): —
Return on equity: (-0.6%)
Current ratio: 0.70

BERKLEE COLLEGE OF MUSIC INC.

If you get accepted to this school you've no doubt hit a high note in your musical career. Berklee College of Music the largest independent music college in the world offers bachelor's degrees in a dozen majors including film scoring jazz composition music education music production and engineering performance and songwriting. Located in Boston the school has some 4000 students and 522 faculty members. Notable alumni include Branford Marsalis Quincy Jones Melissa Etheridge and Steely Dan vocalist Donald Fagen. Pianist Lawrence Berk founded the college in 1945. The school was named after his son Lee Berk who served as Berklee president from 1979 to 2004.

More than a quarter of Berklee's undergraduate students are from outside the US representing some 70 countries. This gives Berklee the distinction of having the highest percentage of international undergraduates of any college in the nation.

The school's Berkleeshares.com is a file-sharing Web site offering free online music lessons developed by school faculty and alumni. Berklee also has five internet music channels produced by its students.

EXECUTIVES

President, Roger H. Brown, age 59
VP Technology and Education Outreach, David S. Mash
Dean Professional Writing Division, Kari Juusela
Dean Professional Performance Division, Matt Marvuglio
Chief Financial Officer Vice President for Finance and Administration, Richard M. Hisey
Director of Admissions, Michael (Mel) Moyes
Auditors: KPMG LLP BOSTON MA

LOCATIONS

HQ: BERKLEE COLLEGE OF MUSIC INC.
  1140 BOYLSTON ST, BOSTON, MA 022153693
Phone: 617 266-1400
Web: WWW.BERKLEE.EDU

PRODUCTS/OPERATIONS

Selected Majors
Composition
Contemporary Writing and Production
Film Scoring
Jazz Composition
Music Business/Management
Music Education
Music Production and Engineering
Music Synthesis
Music Therapy
Performance
Professional Music
Songwriting

Selected Academic Departments
Music Technology
  Music Production and Engineering
  Music Synthesis
Professional Education
  Liberal Arts
  Music Business/Management

Music Education
Music Therapy
Professional Music
Professional Performance
  Bass
  Brass
  Ear Training
  Ensembles
  Guitar
  Percussion
  Piano
  Strings
  Voice
  Woodwinds
Professional Writing
  Composition
  Contemporary Writing and Production
  Film Scoring
  Harmony
  Jazz Composition
  Songwriting

HISTORICAL FINANCIALS
Company Type: Private

Income Statement				FYE: May 31
	REVENUE ($ mil.)	NET INCOME ($ mil.)	NET PROFIT MARGIN	EMPLOYEES
05/13	225	11	5.3%	—
05/11	220	21	9.6%	—
05/09	171	0	—	—
05/07	127	0	—	—
Annual Growth	10.0%			

2013 Year-End Financials
Return on assets: 35.0%   Cash ($ mil.): 24
Return on equity: 5.3%
Current ratio: 0.10

BERKSHIRE MEDICAL CENTER INC.

LOCATIONS

HQ: BERKSHIRE MEDICAL CENTER INC.
  725 NORTH ST, PITTSFIELD, MA 012014124
Phone: 413 447-2000
Web: WWW.BERKSHIREMEDICALCENTER.NET

HISTORICAL FINANCIALS
Company Type: Private

Income Statement				FYE: September 30
	REVENUE ($ mil.)	NET INCOME ($ mil.)	NET PROFIT MARGIN	EMPLOYEES
09/13	342	31	9.2%	1,375
09/12	339	43	12.8%	—
09/09	326	(1)	—	—
09/06	210	0	—	—
Annual Growth	7.2%	—	—	—

2013 Year-End Financials
Return on assets: 3.2%   Cash ($ mil.): 31
Return on equity: 9.2%
Current ratio: 1.00

BERRY COMPANIES INC.

Savoring the fruit of its labor Berry Companies makes a living bulldozing big jobs. The employee-owned business runs eight divisions; each independently sells and rents new and used construction and material handling equipment. Berry Cos. specialize in graders tractors loaders excavators cranes rollers construction and woodworking supplies concrete equipment and small tools. The company's five distribution dealerships include White Star Machinery (Kansas); Bobcat of Dallas and Houston (Texas); K.C. Bobcat (Missouri); and Bobcat of the Rockies (Colorado). Berry Cos. also operates Berry Tractor and Equipment Berry Material Handling and Superior Broom (makes self-propelled road construction brooms).

The company has more than 20 locations in five states: Colorado Kansas Missouri Oklahoma and Texas. Each operating division runs autonomously and handles a lineup including equipment by Bobcat Komatsu Terex Yale by NACCO Bomag and Superior Broom.

Berry Co.'s strategy for expansion has captured a significant share of the heavy machinery market that supplies contractors governmental agencies and commercial builders. In early 2011 the company absorbed the operations of Colorado Machinery a Bobcat distributor into its Bobcat of the Rockies division which further expands the company's distribution network in that region. In 2009 it purchased Bobcat Operations of Conley Lott Nichols which gives it an even greater share in the north Texas market.

The construction equipment distribution business is fueled by the residential and non-residential construction industry which took a major beating during the Great Recession. As the industry recovers and Berry Cos. expands it has the advantage of being able to buy equipment to stock multiple outlets. Its regional locations grow by building a strong customer loyalty for repeat business based on reputation and service.

Weathering half a century of business is something to respect. Berry Cos. got its start when Fred Berry Jr. and his brother Paul bought the Sam H. Denney Road Machinery Co. in 1957 and renamed it Berry Tractor & Equipment Co. Seeing the wide open market for repairing Kansas' unpaved roads the material men (Fred and Paul) moved into dealing in motor graders.

EXECUTIVES

Vice President Technology, Bob Young
Vice President, Steve Meadows
Executive Vice President, Dan Scheer
Vice President Bobcat Operations, John Engels
Treasurer, Judy Worrell
Auditors: KENNEDY & COE LLC WICHITA K

LOCATIONS

HQ: BERRY COMPANIES INC.
3223 N HYDRAULIC ST, WICHITA, KS 672193893
Phone: 316 838-3321
Web: WWW.BERRYCOMPANIESINC.COM

PRODUCTS/OPERATIONS

Selected Subsidiaries
Berry Material Handling
Berry Tractor and Equipment Co.
Bobcat Dallas/Fort Worth/ Longview
Bobcat of Houston
Bobcat of the Rockies
K.C. Bobcat
Superior Broom
White Star

COMPETITORS

Briggs Equipment	NES Rentals
H&E Equipment	Sunbelt Rentals
HOLT Texas	United Rentals
Hertz	Van Keppel
IBT Inc.	Victor L. Phillips
Mustang CAT	

HISTORICAL FINANCIALS
Company Type: Private

Income Statement   FYE: March 31

	REVENUE ($ mil.)	NET INCOME ($ mil.)	NET PROFIT MARGIN	EMPLOYEES
03/13	229	3	1.5%	520
03/09	178	0	0.3%	—
03/08	203	2	1.3%	—
03/07	1,240	0	—	—
Annual Growth	—	—	—	—

2013 Year-End Financials

Return on assets: 3.5%   Cash ($ mil.): 4
Return on equity: 1.5%
Current ratio: 0.30

BEST WESTERN INTERNATIONAL INC.

Western hospitality has really spread. Begun in 1946 by hotelier M. K. Guertin and named for its California origins Best Western has more than 4000 independently owned and operated hotels throughout the globe (including nearly 2200 in North America) making it the world's largest hotel brand (by number of rooms). Hotels sport its flag in about 100 countries and territories; Australia and the UK have the most outside the US. The company has more than 80 Best Western Premier luxury branded hotels which offer upscale amenities and services in North America Asia and Europe. Best Western is organized as a not-for-profit membership association with most of its sales coming from monthly fees and annual dues.

Geographic Reach

The company has hotel properties all over the world. Part of the company's strategic plan is ongoing global expansion. In addition to Asia the Middle East and Eastern Europe the company is targeting emerging markets such as Africa New Zealand Russia and South America for growth.

Sales and Marketing

Best Western attracts travelers through its marketing efforts including print and television advertising. It launched a program to reward members of its global Best Western Rewards loyalty program by matching the elite status of other hotel loyalty programs free of charge.

Strategy

While the travel industry has been facing hard times as a result of the economic downturn Best Western claims that its hotels benefited from companies looking to cut costs by moving their hotel business to the mid-market sector. For example Best Western requires its hoteliers to provide complimentary Internet and local phone calls.

EXECUTIVES

President and CEO, David T. Kong
SVP and CFO, Mark Straszynski
SVP and Chief Marketing Officer, Dorothy Dowling
SVP International Operations, Suzi MacDonald Yoder
VP Information Systems Operations, David Velasquez
VP and Chief Digital Officer, Greg Adams
Vice President Operations, Ron A Pohl
Vice President Human Resources, Barbara (Barb) Bras
Senior Vice President International Operations, Suzi Yoder
Vice President Operations, Ron Pohl
Chairman, Terry Porter
Vice Chairman, Terrance (Terry) Bichsel
Auditors: MUKAI GREENLEE & COMPANY PC

LOCATIONS

HQ: BEST WESTERN INTERNATIONAL INC.
6201 N 24TH PKWY, PHOENIX, AZ 850162023
Phone: 602 957-4200
Web: WWW.BESTWESTERN.COM

Sales Office Locations
Atlanta
Bangkok
Beijing
Bogota
Buenos Aires
Chicago
Dallas
Dubai
Hong Kong
London
Los Angeles
Mexico City
Miami
Milan
New York City
Orlando
Rio de Janeiro
Sao Paolo
San Diego
Santiago
Seattle
Seoul
Singapore
St. Louis
Sydney
Tel-Aviv
Tokyo
Toronto
Washington DC.

PRODUCTS/OPERATIONS

Selected Hotels
Best Western
Brighton Inn (Brighton CO)
City Center Hotel (Philadelphia)
Courtesy Inn (Anaheim CA)
Kirkwood Inn (Saint Louis MO)
Mardi Gras Hotel & Casino (Las Vegas)
Plaza Hotel & Stuites at Medical Center (Houston)
Roehampton Hotel & Suites (Toronto MO)
West Deptford Inn (Thorofare NJ)
Victoria Place (London)
Best Western Plus
Hawthorne Terrace Hotel (Chicago)
Pioneer Square Hotel (Seattle)
Rio Grand Inn (Albuquerque NM)
Best Western Premier
Royal Saint Michel (Paris)

COMPETITORS

Accor	La Quinta
Carlson Hotels	Marriott
Choice Hotels	Red Lion Hotels
Extended Stay America Inc.	Scandic Hotels
	Sunburst Hospitality
Hilton Worldwide	USFS
InterContinental Hotels	Wyndham Worldwide

HISTORICAL FINANCIALS

Company Type: Private

Income Statement
FYE: November 30

	REVENUE ($ mil.)	NET INCOME ($ mil.)	NET PROFIT MARGIN	EMPLOYEES
11/07	220	(2)	—	1,015
11/06	205	2	1.2%	
11/05	1,260	0	—	
Annual Growth	—	—	—	—

2007 Year-End Financials

Return on assets: 15.8% Cash ($ mil.): 22
Return on equity: (-1.4%)
Current ratio: 0.90

BETH ISRAEL DEACONESS MEDICAL CENTER INC.

When a Boston Red Sox player gets slugged he may very well end up at Beth Israel Deaconess Medical Center (BIDMC). Though it's the official hospital for this Major League Baseball team it's perhaps better known for being a teaching hospital of Harvard Medical School. BIDMC has about 650 beds and provides general medical and surgical care as well as outpatient services at its facilities. In addition to a Level I trauma center BIDMC offers specialized care in such areas as organ transplantation breast cancer care and cardiac surgery. Beth Israel Deaconess Medical Center traces its roots to Deaconess Hospital founded in 1896 and Beth Israel Hospital established in 1916.

Operations

BIDMC has 1200 physicians on its active medical staff (including some 800 full-time staff physicians). Most of these physicians hold faculty appointments at Harvard Medical School.

Along with helping students become doctors BIDMC provides clinical education to students in nursing social work radiologic technology ultrasound and nuclear medicine and physical occupational speech and respiratory therapies.

The Carl J. Shapiro Institute for Education and Research provides medical students and physicians in training with an onsite centralized educational facility.

Financial Performance

The hospital is very active in medical research and consistently ranks among the top four recipients of biomedical research funding from the National Institutes of Health totaling nearly $200 million annually. BIDMC researchers oversee more than 850 active sponsored projects and 500 clinical trials. The health system is also home to the Harvard-Thorndike Laboratory the nation's oldest clinical research laboratory.

Strategy

BIDMC affiliates with Milton Hospital to share resources and staff. Hospital systems that coordinate can take advantage of each others' resources stretching their dollars further under the global payment system. The medical center formed another affiliation with Brockton Hospital to improve specialist and medical training programs at the 360-bed Brockton Hospital facility.

Being on the forefront of medical education goes hand-in-hand with using cutting-edge technology

and BIDMC does just that with its Carl J. Shapiro Simulation and Skills Center (SASC) administers training for learners at all levels and from all disciplines using progressive and simulation teaching methods to replicate real-life patient care situations from routine procedures to acute management crises. The SASC features a range of technologically advanced educational resources including realistic models simulators virtual reality experiences computer-based materials ultrasound technology and the world's largest collection of filmed operations

Mergers and Acquisitions

BIDMC's staff numbers could grow significantly if talks between it and rival The Lahey Clinic to merge are successful. Though neither hospital has signed anything definite a merger would fit with the industry's current trend toward consolidation as health systems prepare themselves for upcoming health care reform initiatives.

One impetus for consolidating their operations could be changes to how providers are paid; hospitals and doctors are increasingly being forced to use global payment systems in which they are given an annual amount of funding to use for patient care (rather than the current system of being paid based on services performed).

EXECUTIVES

CIO, John D. Halamka, age 52
SVP Finance and CFO, Steven Fischer
President and CEO Affiliated Physicians Group, John Christoforo
Chief Department of Medicine, Mark L. Zeidel
President CEO and Director, Kevin Tabb
Chief Nursing Officer and SVP Patient Care Services, Marsha Maurer
President and CEO Beth Israel Deaconess Hospital - Needham, John Fogarty
Interim President and CEO Beth Israel Deaconess Hospital - Milton, Doris Sinkevich
Vp Research Operations, Randy Mason
Director Media Relations, Jerry Berger
Chairman, Stephen B. Kay

LOCATIONS

HQ: BETH ISRAEL DEACONESS MEDICAL CENTER INC.
330 BROOKLINE AVE, BOSTON, MA 022155400
Phone: 617 667-7000
Web: WWW.BIDMC.ORG

PRODUCTS/OPERATIONS

Selected Facilities

item 1
Beth Israel Deaconess HealthCare-Chelsea
Beth Israel Deaconess HealthCare-Chestnut Hill
Beth Israel Deaconess HealthCare-Lexington
Beth Israel Deaconess Hospital-Milton
Beth Israel Deaconess Hospital-Needham
Beth Israel Deaconess Hospital-Plymouth

COMPETITORS

Boston Medical Center
Brigham and Women's Hospital
Cambridge Health Alliance
Care New England
CareGroup
Children's Hospital Boston
Dana-Farber
Massachusetts General Hospital
Newton-Wellesley Hospital
Northeast Health System
Partners HealthCare
Southcoast Hospitals Group
Spaulding Rehabilitation Hospital
Steward Health Care

HISTORICAL FINANCIALS

Company Type: Private

Income Statement
FYE: September 30

	REVENUE ($ mil.)	NET INCOME ($ mil.)	NET PROFIT MARGIN	EMPLOYEES
09/13	1,051	56	5.4%	6,500
09/12	1,081	49	4.6%	—
Annual Growth	(2.7%)	13.0%	—	—

2013 Year-End Financials

Return on assets: 16.6% Cash ($ mil.): 158
Return on equity: 5.4%
Current ratio: 1.30

BETH ISRAEL MEDICAL CENTER

Residents of New York City's Lower East Side look to Beth Israel Medical Center to keep them healthy. A member of Continuum Health Partners the tertiary care medical facility has more than 1100 inpatient beds at two facilities in the New York area –its main location in Manhattan and another in Brooklyn. It also operates outpatient care centers and physician offices. Along with its patient care operations Beth Israel Medical Center maintains medical residency programs through its affiliation with Yeshiva University's Albert Einstein College of Medicine. The hospital also conducts institutional medical research with Rockefeller University and offers a nursing degree through its Phillips Beth Israel School of Nursing.

Geographic Reach

The hospital's main campus in Manhattan is known as the Beth Israel Medical Center-Petrie Campus. The Brooklyn location is known as Beth Israel Brooklyn; prior to 2012 the campus was known as the Beth Israel Medical Center-Kings Highway Division.

Operations

The main campus in Petrie has about 900 beds and hosts several major specialist units while the Brooklyn location has more than 210 beds and provides general medicine surgery radiology and intensive care services. Outpatient centers include the Phillips Ambulatory Care Center in Manhattan and the Beth Israel Ambulatory Surgi-Center in Brooklyn which provide diagnostic and ambulatory surgery services. Another affiliated clinic the Continuum Center for Health and Healing provides primary and specialty care as well as alternative services including acupuncture. The Beth Israel Medical Group operates several primary and specialty care physician clinics in Manhattan.

Altogether the Beth Israel Medical Center facilities handle about 59000 inpatient encounters annually. It also manages about 107000 emergency room visits 3500 births 11000 inpatient surgeries and 21000 outpatient surgeries. The center employs about 2300 medical and dental staff members.

Strategy

Continuum Health is investing in upgrades to Beth Israel Medical Center's facilities. For instance it added a new endoscopy suite at the Brooklyn campus in 2012. The main Petrie campus is renovating its emergency room and various inpatient units are increasing quality programs.

In 2012 a major expansion project was launched at the Continuum Center for Health and Healing to expand access to outpatient care for area residents; the program will add services including dermatology cardiology and podiatry. In addition the hospital opened a new cancer center in Manhattan in 2010 and a deluxe unit for high-income patients having orthopedic and other surgeries in 2008. Continuum Health is also upgrading some of Beth Israel Medical Center's IT functions including its radiology data management systems.

EXECUTIVES

Vice President Real Estate And Facilities, Kenneth (Ken) Holden
Clinical Director, Paul Rinaldi
Vice President Managed Care and Network Development, Ruth Levin
Senior Vice President Business Development, Marc Hall
Executive Vice President And Chief Operating Officer, Richard (Dick) Freeman
Managing Director, Nicole Nembhard
Vice President of Sales, Barbara (Barb) King
Senior Vice President Revenue cycle man, Mitchell (Mitch) Leone
Vice President, Hope Bellingham
Vice President Risk Management, Joanne Coffin
Senior Vice President Medical Affairs and Medical Director, David (Dave) Bernard
Occupational Medicine, Sabrina Perry
Secretary, Ivette Ortega
Auditors: PRICEWATERHOUSECOOPERS LLP NE

LOCATIONS

HQ: BETH ISRAEL MEDICAL CENTER
10 NATHAN D PERLMAN PL, NEW YORK, NY 100033881
Phone: 212 420-2000
Web: WWW.BETHISRAELNY.ORG

PRODUCTS/OPERATIONS

Selected Centers and Services
AIDS Services
Allergy and Immunology
Anesthesiology
Appel-Venet Comprehensive Breast Service
Asian Services
Beth Israel ALS Center
Beth Israel Hernia Center
Beth Israel Medical Group
Betty & Morton Yarmon Stroke Center
Brief Psychotherapy Research Program
Cancer Center (Oncology)
Center for Blood Management and Bloodless Medicine and Surgery
Center for Endovascular Surgery
Center for Health and Healing
Craniofacial and Cleft Palate Center
Cystic Fibrosis Center
Dermatology
Endocrinology and Metabolism
Epilepsy
Friedman Diabetes Institute
Genetics
Geriatrics
Heart Institute (Cardiology)
Hematology
Hospice
Hyman Newman Institute for Neurology and Neurosugery (INN)
The Chris and Morton P. Hyman Patient Care Unit
Hyperhidrosis Program
Incontinence
Integrative Medicine
Interventional Neuroradiology
Israeli Health Program
Karpas Health Information Center
Latino Health Institute
Live Well New York
Louis Armstrong Center for Music and Medicine:
Lung Nodule Center
Maternity Services
Methadone Maintenance Treatment Program
Midwifery
Nephrology
Neurology

Orthopedics
Ostomy Program
Pain Medicine and Palliative Care
Pediatrics
Phillips Beth Israel School of Nursing
Primary Care
Psychiatry
Pulmonary and Critical Care Medicine
Radiation Oncology
Radiology
Rheumatology
Senior Health
Sleep Health
Speech-Language and Learning Center
Spine Institute
Sports Medicine
Stroke Centers
Styuvesant Square Chemical Dependency Services
Surgery
Urology
Vascular and Birthmarks Institute of New York
Women's Health
Women's Heart NY
Wound Healing Center

COMPETITORS

Bronx-Lebanon Hospital
Catholic Healthcare System
Kingsbrook Jewish Medical Center
Lutheran HealthCare
Maimonides Medical Center
MediSys Health Network
Memorial Sloan-Kettering
Montefiore Medical
NYU Hospital for Joint Diseases
New York City Health and Hospitals
NewYork-Presbyterian Healthcare
North Shore-Long Island Jewish Health System
SUNY Downstate

HISTORICAL FINANCIALS
Company Type: Private

Income Statement
FYE: December 31

	REVENUE ($ mil.)	NET INCOME ($ mil.)	NET PROFIT MARGIN	EMPLOYEES
12/09	1,256	15	1.2%	8,100
12/08	932	(59)	—	—
Annual Growth	34.8%	—	—	—

2009 Year-End Financials
Return on assets: —
Return on equity: 1.2%
Current ratio: 0.40
Cash ($ mil.): 98

BETHCO CORPORATION

Auditors: LOEB & TROPER LLP NEW YORK

LOCATIONS

HQ: BETHCO CORPORATION
612 ALLERTON AVE, BRONX, NY 104677404
Phone: 718 519-4238

HISTORICAL FINANCIALS
Company Type: Private

Income Statement
FYE: December 31

	REVENUE ($ mil.)	NET INCOME ($ mil.)	NET PROFIT MARGIN	EMPLOYEES
12/11	551	(5)	—	—
12/10	484	10	2.2%	—
12/09	5	2	46.3%	—
12/07	5	0	—	—
Annual Growth	224.0%	—	—	—

2011 Year-End Financials
Return on assets: —
Return on equity: (-0.9%)
Current ratio: 0.60
Cash ($ mil.): 37

BETHESDA HOSPITAL INC.

LOCATIONS

HQ: BETHESDA HOSPITAL INC.
2815 S SEACREST BLVD, BOYNTON BEACH, FL 334357995
Phone: 561 737-7733
Web: WWW.BETHESDAWEB.COM

HISTORICAL FINANCIALS
Company Type: Private

Income Statement
FYE: September 30

	REVENUE ($ mil.)	NET INCOME ($ mil.)	NET PROFIT MARGIN	EMPLOYEES
09/13	316	156	49.6%	1,604
09/12	256	5	2.3%	—
09/09	293	(54)	—	—
09/08	251	0	—	—
Annual Growth	4.7%	—	—	—

2013 Year-End Financials
Return on assets: 2.0%
Return on equity: 49.6%
Current ratio: 11.40
Cash ($ mil.): 81

BI-MART ACQUISITION CORPORATION

Auditors: DELOITTE & TOUCHE LLP PORTLAN

LOCATIONS

HQ: BI-MART ACQUISITION CORPORATION
220 SENECA RD, EUGENE, OR 974022725
Phone: 541 344-0681
Web: WWW.BIMART.COM

HISTORICAL FINANCIALS
Company Type: Private

Income Statement
FYE: February 23

	REVENUE ($ mil.)	NET INCOME ($ mil.)	NET PROFIT MARGIN	EMPLOYEES
02/08	721	10	1.4%	3,300
02/07	694	11	1.7%	—
02/06	665	6	1.0%	—
02/05	648	0	—	—
Annual Growth	3.6%	—	—	—

2008 Year-End Financials
Return on assets: 6.4%
Return on equity: 1.4%
Current ratio: 0.20
Cash ($ mil.): 3

BI-RITE RESTAURANT SUPPLY CO. INC.

Bi-Rite Restaurant Supply which does business as BiRite Foodservice Distributors is a leading food service supplier serving the San Francisco Bay area and Northern California. The company distributes a full line of food equipment and supplies including meat and dairy items seafood frozen foods dry groceries cleaning supplies china kitchen equipment and disposables. Its customers include restaurant operators hotels universities and hospitals. The company's international arm supplied food to the Middle East and Asia. A member of the UniPro Foodservice cooperative the family-owned company was founded in 1966 by cousins Victor and John Barulich.

Geographic Reach

Brisbane-based Bi-Rite's coverage area ranges from Cloverdale in Northern California east to Reno (Nevada) and South to Fresno and Monterey. Beyond California the company supplies food and equipment to Afghanistan Jordan Kuwait Turkey China Japan South Korea Singapore Thailand Vietnam and several other territories.

Mergers and Acquisitions

In December 2012 the company acquired family-owned A&B Produce which supplies food to restaurants throughout the San Francisco Bay area.

EXECUTIVES

Executive Vice President Of Purchasing, Tom Whiteside
Vice President Sales, Mike Pendergast
Vice President Human Resources, Natasha Eltringham

LOCATIONS

HQ: BI-RITE RESTAURANT SUPPLY CO. INC.
123 S HILL DR, BRISBANE, CA 940051203
Phone: 415 656-0187
Web: WWW.BIRITE.COM

PRODUCTS/OPERATIONS

Selected Product Categories
Disposables
Equipment & supply
Food
Fresh cut produce
Fresh next-day protein
Fresh seafood
Janitorial

COMPETITORS

Dot Foods
Golden State Foods
Jacmar
MAINES

McLane Foodservice
Sysco
US Foods

HISTORICAL FINANCIALS

Company Type: Private

Income Statement

	REVENUE ($ mil.)	NET INCOME ($ mil.)	NET PROFIT MARGIN	EMPLOYEES
12/13	279	6	2.5%	230
12/12	258	4	1.8%	—
12/11	255	4	1.8%	—
12/10	271	0	—	—
Annual Growth	0.9%	—	—	—

FYE: December 31

2013 Year-End Financials

Return on assets: 3.1%
Return on equity: 2.5%
Current ratio: 2.20
Cash ($ mil.): 4

BIG RIVER RESOURCES GALVA LLC

Auditors: CHRISTIANSON & ASSOCIATES PLL

LOCATIONS

HQ: BIG RIVER RESOURCES GALVA LLC
1100 SE 2ND ST, GALVA, IL 614348907
Phone: 309 932-2033
Web: WWW.BIGRIVERRESOURCES.COM

HISTORICAL FINANCIALS

Company Type: Private

Income Statement

	REVENUE ($ mil.)	NET INCOME ($ mil.)	NET PROFIT MARGIN	EMPLOYEES
12/14	334	59	17.8%	60
12/13	361	31	8.8%	—
12/12	310	(0)	—	—
12/11	371	0	—	—
Annual Growth	(3.4%)	—	—	—

FYE: December 31

2014 Year-End Financials

Return on assets: 0.7%
Return on equity: 17.8%
Current ratio: 3.10
Cash ($ mil.): 41

BIG RIVER RESOURCES LLC

Auditors: CHRISTIANSON & ASSOCIATES PLLP

LOCATIONS

HQ: BIG RIVER RESOURCES LLC
15210 103RD ST, WEST BURLINGTON, IA 526558697
Phone: 319 753-1100
Web: WWW.BIGRIVERRESOURCES.COM

HISTORICAL FINANCIALS

Company Type: Private

Income Statement

	REVENUE ($ mil.)	NET INCOME ($ mil.)	NET PROFIT MARGIN	EMPLOYEES
12/14	1,184	224	18.9%	202
12/13	1,292	107	8.3%	—
12/12	1,135	2	0.2%	—
12/11	1,162	0	—	—
Annual Growth	0.6%	—	—	—

FYE: December 31

2014 Year-End Financials

Return on assets: 2.7%
Return on equity: 18.9%
Current ratio: 2.00
Cash ($ mil.): 97

BIG RIVER RESOURCES WEST BURLINGTON LLC

Auditors: CHRISTIANSON & ASSOCIATES PLLP

LOCATIONS

HQ: BIG RIVER RESOURCES WEST BURLINGTON LLC
15210 103RD ST, WEST BURLINGTON, IA 526558697
Phone: 319 753-1100
Web: WWW.BIGRIVERRESOURCES.COM

HISTORICAL FINANCIALS

Company Type: Private

Income Statement

	REVENUE ($ mil.)	NET INCOME ($ mil.)	NET PROFIT MARGIN	EMPLOYEES
12/14	346	60	17.5%	73
12/13	395	26	6.7%	—
12/12	381	0	0.1%	—
12/11	412	0	—	—
Annual Growth	(5.6%)	—	—	—

FYE: December 31

2014 Year-End Financials

Return on assets: 6.4%
Return on equity: 17.5%
Current ratio: 0.90
Cash ($ mil.): 24

BIG RIVER UNITED ENERGY LLC

Auditors: CHRISTIANSON & ASSOCIATES PLLP

LOCATIONS

HQ: BIG RIVER UNITED ENERGY LLC
3294 VINE RD, DYERSVILLE, IA 520408714
Phone: 563 875-5500
Web: WWW.BIGRIVERRESOURCES.COM

HISTORICAL FINANCIALS

Company Type: Private

Income Statement

	REVENUE ($ mil.)	NET INCOME ($ mil.)	NET PROFIT MARGIN	EMPLOYEES
12/14	356	74	21.0%	50
12/13	378	34	9.2%	—
12/12	320	4	1.4%	—
12/10	254	0	—	—
Annual Growth	8.8%	—	—	—

FYE: December 31

2014 Year-End Financials

Return on assets: 0.9%
Return on equity: 21.0%
Current ratio: 0.40
Cash ($ mil.): 1

BIG RIVERS ELECTRIC CORPORATION

Auditors: KPMG LLP PHILADELPHIA PA

LOCATIONS

HQ: BIG RIVERS ELECTRIC CORPORATION
201 3RD ST, HENDERSON, KY 424202979
Phone: 270 827-2561
Web: WWW.BIGRIVERS.COM

HISTORICAL FINANCIALS
Company Type: Private

Income Statement
FYE: December 31

	REVENUE ($ mil.)	NET INCOME ($ mil.)	NET PROFIT MARGIN	EMPLOYEES
12/13	562	8	1.5%	599
12/12	568	11	2.0%	—
12/11	561	5	1.0%	—
12/10	527	0	—	—
Annual Growth	2.2%	—	—	—

2013 Year-End Financials

Return on assets: 6.2%
Return on equity: 1.5%
Current ratio: 1.80

Cash ($ mil.): 95

BIG-D CONSTRUCTION CORP.

Big-D builds big things. With offices in Utah Arizona California and Wyoming the construction firm offers design/build services to customers in about 20 states. Big-D focuses on projects for clients in such industries as manufacturing health care hospitality food processing and distribution manufacturing and retail. The company's Signature Group builds high-end luxury homes as well as and condominiums spas and other special projects in resort communities. Clients have included SYSCO and Marriott. The company also operates a concrete division devoted to architectural structural and parking garage projects. Big-D was founded in 1967 by Dee Livingood. His family continues to lead the company.

Big-D has been courting more government projects as a way to weather the economic downturn which has put a halt on many commercial jobs. Among those public projects is the Utah Museum of Natural History at The University of Utah and the Wallace F. Bennett Federal Building in Salt Lake City. Big-D also is focusing on developing its eco-friendly construction business.

EXECUTIVES

Chairman and CEO, Jack Livingood
SVP and CFO, Larry Worrell
SVP Operations, Forrest McNabb
President Big-D Construction, Rob Moore
President Big-D Pacific, Ken Mitchell
President Big-D Signature, Scott Dansie
Vice President, Rich Hazel
Auditors: GRANT THORNTON LLP SALT LAKE

LOCATIONS

HQ: BIG-D CONSTRUCTION CORP.
404 W 400 S, SALT LAKE CITY, UT 841011108
Phone: 801 415-6000
Web: WWW.BIG-D.COM

Selected Markets
Arizona
Arkansas
California
Colorado
Georgia
Hawaii
Idaho
Montana
Nevada
New Mexico
North Carolina
North Dakota
Oklahoma
Oregon
South Dakota
Tennessee
Texas
Utah
Washington

PRODUCTS/OPERATIONS

Selected Services
Construction management
Design/build
Field services
Architectural concrete
Finish carpentry
Rough framing
Structural concrete
General contracting
Green and Leadership in Energy and Environmental Design

Selected Industry Specializations
Commercial/public spaces (governmental educational and office complexes; mixed-use projects)
Food processing and distribution
Health care
Hospitality and resort
Manufacturing
Retail

COMPETITORS

Bechtel	Jaynes Companies
Hensel Phelps Construction	Layton
	Okland Construction
J.F. Shea	Swinerton
Jacobsen Construction	

HISTORICAL FINANCIALS
Company Type: Private

Income Statement
FYE: December 31

	REVENUE ($ mil.)	NET INCOME ($ mil.)	NET PROFIT MARGIN	EMPLOYEES
12/13	640	0	—	433
12/12	541	0	—	—
12/11	554	0	—	—
12/10	259	0	—	—
Annual Growth	35.1%	—	—	—

2013 Year-End Financials

Return on assets: 14.7%
Return on equity: —
Current ratio: 1.20

Cash ($ mil.): 44

BILL HILLARY & CHELSEA CLINTON FOUNDATION

Auditors: BKD LLP LITTLE ROCK AR

LOCATIONS

HQ: BILL HILLARY & CHELSEA CLINTON FOUNDATION
1200 PRSIDENT CLINTON AVE, LITTLE ROCK, AR 722011749
Phone: 501 748-0471
Web: WWW.CLINTONMUSEUMSTORE.COM

HISTORICAL FINANCIALS
Company Type: Private

Income Statement
FYE: December 31

	REVENUE ($ mil.)	NET INCOME ($ mil.)	NET PROFIT MARGIN	EMPLOYEES
12/10	321	17	5.4%	400
12/09	252	13	5.5%	—
12/05	0	0		
Annual Growth	—	303.3%	—	—

2010 Year-End Financials

Return on assets: —
Return on equity: 5.4%
Current ratio: 7.00

Cash ($ mil.): 69

BILLINGS CLINIC

Billings Clinic is an integrated health care system that serves the residents of Big Sky Country. Through a group of more than 320 doctors and other providers the clinic caters to some 570000 people in Billings Montana and in surrounding communities. It offers 50-plus specialties such as emergency and trauma cancer orthopedics birthing cardiovascular neurosciences dialysis and pediatrics. Its operations include a more than 285-bed hospital and the organization's main clinic. Additionally Billings Clinic operates the 90-bed Aspen Meadows Retirement Community and provides support services to several regional community hospitals. The not-for-profit health care system is owned by the community.

Geographic Reach

As the largest health care organization in the area Billings Clinic's service area comprises 40 counties and extends more than 120000 miles in Montana Wyoming and the western Dakotas.

Operations

With its vast service area the health care system provides a MedFlight advanced life support fixed-wing aircraft service that transports critically ill or injured patients from rural communities. The service averages 700 flights per year.

As part of its operations Billings Clinic runs a Level II emergency and trauma center 14-suite family birthing center Level III neonatal intensive care unit inpatient cancer care unit and a 15-bed transitional care unit. The health care system's cancer center provides both inpatient and outpatient care in Billings and the surrounding four-state region.

Billings Clinic is governed by a 12-member board consisting of mostly community members but also a pair of doctors and a physician CEO.

In 2014 Billings Clinic's Community Benefit totaled $37.6 million including $14.8 million in financial assistance (charity care) provided to 5744 patients.

Strategy

Billings Clinic works with pharmaceutical sponsors on a variety of clinical research trials in various phases and indications. To this end it operates a research center with more than 20 years of experience in the areas of basic and clinical research. The center has participated in more than 200 clinical research studies with the help of some 5000 volunteer subjects since 1988.

The health care system has been growing. In 2014 it completed construction of a 24-bed Intensive Care Unit located on the second floor of the hospital directly above the Emergency and Trauma Center. That year Billings Clinic also opened a second ExpressCare retail clinic in the Albertsons store and opened two new major cardiac facilities.

In 2014 Billings Clinic began offering anew non-invasive surgery for the brain using Gamma Knife Perfexion an advanced technology for stereotactic radiosurgery.

Company Background

It expanded its capacity for infusions in 2012 when its Billings Clinic Cody location opened an infusion center. In late 2012 the organization also opened a new Stillwater Billings Clinic medical facility which combines Stillwater Community Hospital and Billings Clinic Columbus and integrates the billing process for the two health care facilities.

The Billings Clinic evolved from the general practice of Dr. Arthur J. Movius who founded his Billings practice in 1911.

EXECUTIVES

CEO and Director, Nicholas J. Wolter
VP and CIO, Chris Stevens
Physician in Chief, Mark C. Rumans
President Billings Clinic Foundation, Jim Duncan
VP Hospital Operations, Lu Byrd
CFO, Connie F. Prewitt
Vice President Strategic Development and Corporate Compliance Officer, Kristianne Wilson
Director Of Radiology, Douglas (Doug) Bell
Ambulatory Services Director, Jackie Hines
Vp Clinic Operations, Peggy Wharton
Director Of Patient Relations, Karrie Cleveland
Director Of Medical Records, Lorraine Jelle
Treasurer and Director, J. Scott Millikan
Vice Chairman, David Brown
Secretary, Starla Harrington
Auditors: BKD LLP COLORADO SPRINGS CO

LOCATIONS

HQ: BILLINGS CLINIC
2800 10TH AVE N, BILLINGS, MT 591010703
Phone: 406 657-4000
Web: WWW.BILLINGSCLINIC.COM

PRODUCTS/OPERATIONS

Selected Services
Advance Medical Directives
Allergy Asthma Immunology
Aspen Meadows - Skilled Nursing and Assisted Living
Anticoagulation Clinic
Breast Center
Cancer Center
Cardiovascular Services
Cardiovascular Surgery
Children's Services
Continence Center
Community Training Center
Cosmetic Surgery
da Vinci Surgical System
Dermatology Center
Diabetes Management Center

Diagnostic Imaging
Diabetes
Dialysis Center
Eldercare Solutions
Emergency & Trauma Center
Emmi Educational Videos
Employer Services - Occupational Health
Endocrinology
Eye Center
Facial Plastic Surgery
Family Medicine
Family Birth Center
Gastroenterology
General Surgery
Genetic Counseling
Geriatric Assessment Program
Gynecologic Cancer
Heart Services
Heart Surgery
Home Oxygen & Medical Equipment
Hospitalist Program
Infectious Diseases
Insurance Finder
Internal Medicine
Laboratory Services
LifeFit
Maternal-Fetal Medicine
MedFlight Air Ambulance
Mental Health Services
Metabolism Center
Mohs Surgery
Nutrition Services
Neurosciences
Obstetrics & Gynecology
Occupational Health - Employer Services
Ophthalmology
Orthopedics & Sports Medicine
Palliative Care
Pediatrics
  Pediatric Center
  Pediatric Cancer
  Pediatric Diabetes
  Pediatric Gastroenterology
  Pediatric Pulmonology
  Rehabilitation (Therapy)
Pharmacy
Physical Medicine & Rehabilitation
Plastic Surgery
Primary Care for Adults
Pulmonary Rehabilitation Program
Radiology Services
Reproductive Medicine and Fertility Care
Robotic Surgery
SameDay Care
Senior Services
Sleep Disorders Center
Sports Medicine
Sports Specific Camps
Stroke Care
Surgery Center
Transitional Care Unit
Urology Services
Vascular Surgery
Vein Clinic
Women's Free Screenings
Women's and Children's Services

Selected Affiliate Hospitals and Clinics
Beartooth Billings Clinic - Red Lodge
Colstrip Medical Center - Colstrip
Daniels Memorial Healthcare - Scobey
Livingston HealthCare - Livingston
North Big Horn Hospital - Lovell
Pioneer Medical Center - Big Timber
Roundup Memorial Healthcare - Roundup
Sheridan Memorial Hospital Association
Stillwater Billings Clinic

COMPETITORS

Glendive Medical Center
St. Alexius Medical Center
St. James Healthcare
St. Patrick Hospital
Wyoming Medical Center

HISTORICAL FINANCIALS
Company Type: Private

Income Statement — FYE: June 30

	REVENUE ($ mil.)	NET INCOME ($ mil.)	NET PROFIT MARGIN	EMPLOYEES
06/13	560	14	2.6%	3,300
06/11	533	28	5.4%	—
06/10	494	25	5.2%	—
06/09	658	0	—	—
Annual Growth	(4.0%)	—	—	—

2013 Year-End Financials

Return on assets: 8.7%
Return on equity: 2.6%
Current ratio: 0.60
Cash ($ mil.): 38

BIOURJA TRADING LLC

Auditors: CARR RIGGS & INGRAM LLC HOUST

LOCATIONS

HQ: BIOURJA TRADING LLC
1080 ELDRIDGE PKWY # 1175, HOUSTON, TX 770772575
Phone: 832 775-9000
Web: WWW.BIOURJA.COM

HISTORICAL FINANCIALS
Company Type: Private

Income Statement — FYE: December 31

	REVENUE ($ mil.)	NET INCOME ($ mil.)	NET PROFIT MARGIN	EMPLOYEES
12/13	4,622	26	0.6%	32
12/12	2,992	11	0.4%	—
12/11	3,842	13	0.4%	—
12/10	2,157	0	—	—
Annual Growth	28.9%	—	—	—

2013 Year-End Financials

Return on assets: 2.3%
Return on equity: 0.6%
Current ratio: 0.90
Cash ($ mil.): 15

BIRKEY'S FARM STORE INC.

Auditors: CLIFTONLARSONALLEN LLP CHAMP

LOCATIONS

HQ: BIRKEY'S FARM STORE INC.
2102 W PARK CT, CHAMPAIGN, IL 618212986
Phone: 217 892-8255
Web: WWW.BIRKEYS.COM

HISTORICAL FINANCIALS

Company Type: Private

Income Statement

FYE: December 31

	REVENUE ($ mil.)	NET INCOME ($ mil.)	NET PROFIT MARGIN	EMPLOYEES
12/13	394	16	4.1%	350
12/12	355	15	4.3%	—
12/11	280	13	4.7%	—
12/10	245	0	—	—
Annual Growth	**17.1%**	—	—	—

2013 Year-End Financials

Return on assets: 2.7% Cash ($ mil.): —
Return on equity: 4.1%
Current ratio: —

BJT INC.

A wholesaler of Southern comfort Mutual Distributing distributes alcoholic and nonalcoholic beverages in North Carolina. The company started in 1946 operates from seven locations across the state. Alcoholic beverage brands handled by Mutual Distributing include domestic and imported wine labels by Wyndham Estate Robert Mondavi Moet & Chandon and Folie a Deux and beers by Anchor Tecate Heineken and Sapporo. The company distributes bottled waters too such as Evian Perrier San Pellegrino and Fiji. Mutual Distributing caters to retail customers (supermarkets convenience stores and specialty package outlets restaurants and hotels) in every county in North Carolina.

The company's growth is spurred in part by increasing consumer interest in new alcoholic beverage categories such as moscatos (a sweet low-in-alcohol wine) and ready-to-drink wine-based cocktails coupled with the availability of lower-priced wines at many retail grocery chains. To maintain sales momentum Mutual Distributing has extended its already vast lineup in such categories as well as added labels from local and regional wine and beer producers.

Simultaneously the company has managed the upswing in demand by expanding its warehouse in Charlotte and upgrading its IT infrastructure. Its improved offerings and operations are intended to both strengthen relationships with regional and national chains and build market share.

EXECUTIVES

Vice President of Sales, William (Bill) Riley

LOCATIONS

HQ: BJT INC.
2233 CAPITAL BLVD, RALEIGH, NC 276041421
Phone: 919 828-3842
Web: WWW.MUTUALDISTRIBUTING.COM

PRODUCTS/OPERATIONS

List of Brands

Beer
Amstel
Anchor
Asahi
Ayinger
Bavaria
Bitburger
Bohemia
Caguama
Carolina
Carta Blanca
Charleston
Cottonwood
Del Mar
Dos Equis
Export 33
Grady's Grog
Harpoon
Heineken
Hoegaarden
Kingfisher
Lindemans
Mackeson
Maisels
Mendocino
Moosehead
Moretti
Murphy's
Orion
Peroni
Pinkus
Samuel Smith
Sapporo
Saranac
Sol
St Pauli Girl
Tecate
Tsingtao
Utica Club
Warsteiner
Weihenstephan
Non-alcoholic brands
Acqua Panna
Evian
Perrier
San Pellegrino
Zing Zang
Wine
Acacia
Alice White
Allegrini
Almaden
Andes Peak
Anselmi
Arbor Mist
Artesa
Avia
Avalon
Banrock Station
Barossa
Bertani
Benton-Lane
Biltmore
Black Box
Blackstone
Blue Nun
Bolla
Boutinot
Brancaia
Brolio
Burgess
Candoni
Canei
Carneros Creek
CH LaMothe
Chateau Morrisette
Childress Vineyards
Chocovine
Citra
CK Mondavi
Claude Jourdon
Cline
Clos du Bois
Coastal Vintners Pinecroft
Colombo
Concha y Toro
Condesa de LeGanza
Cooks
Covey Run
Cribari
Cypress Bend Vineyards
Deloach
Di Majo
Dry Sack
Dubonnet
Dyed In The Wool
Dynamite Vineyards
Edna Valley
Estancia
Estrella
Fabre Montmayou
Faustino
Ferrari Carano
Firesteed
Fisheye
Florio
Folie a Deux
Fonterutoli
Four Graces
Francis F. Copola
Franciscan
Freixenet
Frescobaldi
Gato
Gelisi Antonio
Girard
Glen Ellen
Goats do Roam
Gotham
Grahams
Grant Burge
Grgich
Groth Hakutsuru
Hardy's
Hess
Hogue
Hinnant Family Vineyards
Inglenook
J Lohr
J Roget
Jacobs Creek
Jewel
Joel Gott
Kenwood
Kijafa
Kim Crawford
Korbel
Kressmann
Kris
L Felipe Edwards
La Terre
La Vieille Ferme
Le Faux Frog
LeJon
Liberty School
Lillet
Little Boomey
Los Cardos
Los Vascos
Lost Vineyards
Louis Latour
Lucente
Lucky Duck
Manischewitz
Mahoney Vineyards
Marco Negri
Marcus James
Mark West
Marques de Caceres
Martini & Rossi
Matchbook
Mateus
Melini
Merryvale
Mezzacorona
Moet & Chandon
Mogen David
Mondoro
Monkey Bay
Montevina
Motovino
Mumm
Napa Cellars
Nathanson Creek
Nobilo
Noilly Prat
Oak Creek
Oak Leaf
Oak Vineyard
Old North State
Opus One
Palladio
Papio
Patient-Cottat
Patton Valley Vineyards
Paul Masson
Pedroncelli
Penfolds
Perrin
Picket Fence
Placido
Rabbit Ridge
Ramon Bilbao
Ravenswood

Raymond
Real
Renee Barbier
Reynold's
Rex Goliath
RH Phillips
Riunite
Robert Mondavi
Rocca delle Macie
Rodney Strong
Rosemount
Rosenblum
Ruffino
Rutherford Hill
Saintsbury
Salmon Harbor
Sandeman
Santa Margherita
Santa Rita
Santi
Sartori
Schmitt Sohne
Sebastiani
Sebastopol
Sho Chiku Bai
Silver Oak
Sonoma Cutrer
St Jacobs
Simi
St Supery
Stags Leap
Stephen Vincent
Stock
Straccali
Sutter Home
Sycamore Lane
SXS (Step by Step)
Takara
Talus
Taylor
Tiefenbrunner
Tiziano
Toad Hollow
Toasted Head
Tommasi
Tosti
Trackers Crossing
Trapiche
Tribuno
Trinchero
Trinity Oaks
Twin Fin
Valley Of The Moon
Vendange
Veramonte
Veuve du Vernay
Villa Maria
Volpaia
Walnut Crest
Warres
Woodbridge
Wyndham Estate
Yellowtail
Zaca Mesa
Zonin

COMPETITORS

Constellation Brands
Gambrinus
Glazer's
National Distributing
National Wine &
 Spirits
Southern Wine &
 Spirits
The Charmer Sunbelt
 Group

HISTORICAL FINANCIALS
Company Type: Private

Income Statement
FYE: December 31

	REVENUE ($ mil.)	NET INCOME ($ mil.)	NET PROFIT MARGIN	EMPLOYEES
12/09	200	6	3.1%	650
12/08	191	7	4.1%	—
12/06	172	4	2.4%	—
12/05	158	0	—	—
Annual Growth	6.1%	—	—	—

BLACK & VEATCH CONSTRUCTION INC.

LOCATIONS

HQ: BLACK & VEATCH CONSTRUCTION INC.
 8400 WARD PKWY, KANSAS CITY, MO 641142031
Phone: 913 458-2000
Web: WWW.BV.COM

HISTORICAL FINANCIALS
Company Type: Private

Income Statement
FYE: December 26

	REVENUE ($ mil.)	NET INCOME ($ mil.)	NET PROFIT MARGIN	EMPLOYEES
12/08	365	7	2.1%	44
12/07	182	(5)	—	—
12/06	275	10	3.8%	—
Annual Growth	15.3%	(13.8%)	—	—

2008 Year-End Financials
Return on assets: 12.5%
Return on equity: 2.1%
Current ratio: 0.30
Cash ($ mil.): 29

2009 Year-End Financials
Return on assets: 3.6%
Return on equity: 3.1%
Current ratio: 0.20
Cash ($ mil.): —

BLACK & VEATCH CORPORATION

One of the US's largest private companies Black & Veatch (BV) is a leading global engineering consulting and construction firm specializing in infrastructure development for the energy water environmental federal and telecommunications markets. BV offers environmental consulting operations and maintenance security design and consulting management consulting and IT services. With offices worldwide it has worked on coal nuclear and combustion turbine plants; drinking water and coastal water operations; and wireless and broadband installation. Clients include Sumitomo Corp. and Southern Water. The company was founded in 1915 in Kansas City Missouri by engineers E. B. Black and Tom Veatch.

Geographic Reach

Kansas-based Black & Veatch has more than 100 offices worldwide and has completed projects in more than 100 countries. The firm primarily operates in the US Europe and Asia.

Operations

BV is organized around key markets which include energy telecommunications water management consulting and projects for the federal government.

The group's operations in the global water markets impact water quality and quantity throughout the water cycle: from source to treatment to delivery to wastewater collection and treatment. A key player in water treatment and wastewater treatment design BV's water division works with utilities governments and industries worldwide. The company is seeing an increase in water projects following the economic recession which stifled the flow of capital.

Financial Performance

Black & Veatch posted $3.3 billion in revenue in 2012. The firm managed more than $1.8 billion in general contracting projects during the year.

Strategy

BV's telecommunications operations are growing quickly as communications infrastructure is being improved around the world. Clients include wireless and wireline operators satellite networks public safety agencies municipalities utilities and various government agencies including the departments of energy defense and Homeland Security and the EPA and FAA. The business will continue to grow thanks to the Sprint/Samsung mobile network upgrade project. BV is working to provide wireless site development services to support the infrastructure project.

The company's energy division which accounts for about 40% of revenues is another growing segment. Clients are busy with new projects to meet the growing demand for energy. BV is involved in major US transmission line work as well as power plant projects in places such as China India and the Middle East. Indeed in 2012 BV expanded its operations in India to meet the country's growing infrastructure requirements.

EXECUTIVES

CEO Energy Business, O. H. (Dean) Oskvig
CFO, Karen L. Daniel, age 55
President Federal Services Division, William R. (Bill) Van Dyke
President Telecommunications, Martin G. Travers
President Water Business, Cindy Wallis-Lage
Chief Administrative Officer; President Administrative Division, James R. (Jim) Lewis
SVP B&V Energy Asia Middle East India Europe and B&V Water Asia Pacific, Hoe Wai Cheong
President Management Consulting, John Chevrette
Chairman President & CEO, Steven L. Edwards
President Construction & Procurement, John E. Murphy
Associate Vice President Project Director nuclear Const., Richard (Dick) Hirsch
Vice President, John (Jack) Johnson
Vice President, Lisa Terry
Vice President Of Finance, Jerry Myers
Vice President Of Customer Information Technology, Mike Prescher
Associate Vice President, Adrienne Mickells
Vice President and Director Human Resources, Craig Anderson
Senior Vice President, Ernie Wright
Senior Vice President Energy Finance, Dave Mendelsohn
Vice President Senior Division Legal Counsel, Dennis Schapker
Vice President Tax Counsel, Jeffrey (Jeff) Stamm
Vice President, Bob Kolb
Vice President and Senior Project Manager Energy, Javid Talib
Vice President, Matthew Webber
Associate Vice President National Practice Leader Automation Services, Dave Roberts
Associate Vice President Energy, Tom O'Brien
Vice President Marketing, Don Graf
Associate Vice President Chief Civil Structural Engineer, Brian Schmidt
General Manager Executive Vice President Safety, Shawn King
Senior Vice President Director Nuclear, Steven Rus
Assistant Vice President Bangkok Office Manager, Tom Christensen
Associate Vice President Project Manager, David (Dave) Lefebvre
Associate Vice President, Norman Song

Vice President of Enterprise Management Solutions, John (Jack) Achenbach
Associate Vice President, Christopher (Chris) Mueller
Associate Vice President and Division Counsel, Curtis Martin
Senior Vice President Global Energy Business, John Gustke
Vice President, Cindy McGlynn
Vice President, Steven Canney
Assistant Vice President Telecommunications Division, Christopher (Chris) Ruddle
Associate Vice President, Andrew Byers
Associate Vice President Asset Management Services, David (Dave) Brill
Associate Vice President And Project Manager For Global Energy Business, Mark Mcdermott
Vice President, T Pintcke
Secretary To Managing Director, Archana Vaidya
Board Member, Brent Ferren

LOCATIONS

HQ: BLACK & VEATCH CORPORATION
11401 LAMAR AVE, OVERLAND PARK, KS 662111598
Phone: 913 458-2000
Web: WWW.BV.COM

PRODUCTS/OPERATIONS

Market Sectors
Energy
  Air quality control
  Coal
  Combustion turbine
  Gas oil and chemicals
  Hydropower
  IGCC
  Nuclear
  Power delivery
  Renewables
Environmental
  Air quality
  Compliance management
  Due diligence
  Field studies/investigations
  Permitting
  Prevention plans
  Remediation
  Watershed analysis and restoration
  Water/wastewater
Federal
  Civil works
  Disaster support
  Facilities
  Federal design-build
  Management programs
  Security
Management consulting
  Integrated strategy development
  Process improvement
  Technology application services
Services
  Asset management
  Climate change solutions
  Construction
  Design/build
  Engineering and design
  Engineering consulting
  Infrastructure planning
  Management consulting
  Procurement
  Program management
  SAP services
  Smart utility
  Water spares
Telecommunications
  Broadband wireline
  Cyber and physical security
  Site acquisition services
  Telecom for smart utilities
  Utility automation
  Utility telecommunications
  Wireless
Water
  Conveyance systems and tunneling services
  Drinking water
  Hydropower
  River and coastal management

Wastewater
Water resources

COMPETITORS

AECOM	Halcrow Group
ARCADIS	Louis Berger
Amec Foster Wheeler	MWH Global
Balfour Beatty	McDermott
Infrastructure	Michael Baker
Bechtel	Mott MacDonald
Burns & McDonnell	Parsons Brinckerhoff
Burns and Roe	Parsons Corporation
CH2M HILL	SNC-Lavalin
Costain	TIC Holdings
EA Engineering	Tetra Tech
Fluor	Zachry Inc.
HNTB Companies	

HISTORICAL FINANCIALS
Company Type: Private

Income Statement
FYE: December 31

	REVENUE ($ mil.)	NET INCOME ($ mil.)	NET PROFIT MARGIN	EMPLOYEES
12/09	1,163	58	5.0%	4,065
12/08	1,267	16	1.3%	—
12/07	1,287	33	2.6%	—
12/06	1,075	0	—	—
Annual Growth	2.6%	—	—	—

2009 Year-End Financials
Return on assets: 11.7%
Return on equity: 5.0%
Current ratio: —
Cash ($ mil.): 16

BLACK & VEATCH HOLDING COMPANY

Auditors: KPMG LLP KANSAS CITY MISSOUR

LOCATIONS

HQ: BLACK & VEATCH HOLDING COMPANY
11401 LAMAR AVE, OVERLAND PARK, KS 662111598
Phone: 913 458-2000
Web: WWW.BV.COM

HISTORICAL FINANCIALS
Company Type: Private

Income Statement
FYE: December 27

	REVENUE ($ mil.)	NET INCOME ($ mil.)	NET PROFIT MARGIN	EMPLOYEES
12/13	3,562	148	4.2%	7,017
12/12	3,279	134	4.1%	—
12/11	2,560	104	4.1%	—
12/10	2,265	0	—	—
Annual Growth	16.3%	—	—	—

2013 Year-End Financials
Return on assets: 14.1%
Return on equity: 4.2%
Current ratio: 0.70
Cash ($ mil.): 758

BLACK & VEATCH INTERNATIONAL COMPANY

Auditors: KPMG LLP KANSAS CITY MO

LOCATIONS

HQ: BLACK & VEATCH INTERNATIONAL COMPANY
8400 WARD PKWY, KANSAS CITY, MO 641142031
Phone: 913 458-2000
Web: WWW.BV.COM

HISTORICAL FINANCIALS
Company Type: Private

Income Statement
FYE: December 31

	REVENUE ($ mil.)	NET INCOME ($ mil.)	NET PROFIT MARGIN	EMPLOYEES
12/09	711	43	6.1%	283
12/08	711	43	6.1%	—
12/07	1	(0)	—	—
12/06	1	0	—	—
Annual Growth	754.9%	—	—	—

2009 Year-End Financials
Return on assets: 11.8%
Return on equity: 6.1%
Current ratio: 0.10
Cash ($ mil.): 39

BLANCHARD VALLEY FARMERS COOPERATIVE INC.

Supporting local farmers gives Blanchard Valley Farmers Cooperative (BVFC) roots and reach. Founded in 1989 BVFC has about 1700 area members. The co-op owns more than a dozen locations including four agronomy stations two seasonal grain facilities a farm and garden store and two petroleum sites. Member-farmers benefit from the co-op's array of products and services including seed feed fertilizer grain crop storage crop applications and farming equipment sales and rental. The feed store also sells mulch birdseed and pet supplies as well as conducts soil testing and arranges seeding and fertilizer programs. BVFC's petroleum locations offer gasoline and home-heating oil among several products.

BVFC's terminal elevator at Fostoria is one of Ohio's largest grain facilities. Its installation and capacity weighing in at 8.77 million bushels allows farmers depositing grain to get through the facility more quickly and store more grain until markets are favorable for selling. In 2011 the co-op handled nearly 27 million bushels throughout all locations.

BVFC's capacity is the result of an expansion during 2010 and 2011 that added two new receiving pits a 30000-bph Hawthorne-Servingleg several massive enclosed-belt conveyors a new 73000-bushel grain bin and new scalehouse and probe. The probe allows the facility to reroute and expedite truck traffic.

Financially BVFC has reportedly averaged a 5% increase through grain marketing. Its cost of operation takes a 1% cut out of total revenue; the remaining revenue is distributed to members. Since 2004 BVFC has averaged more than nine cents per bushel to members.

The co-op's future faces increased competition from large and small rivals such as ADM and Cargill ethanol plants and neighbor co-op Central Ohio Farmers. At the same time farmers who have had better yields at high higher prices have purchased more efficient equipment to plant and harvest crops. As a result the co-op's facilities are pressured to handle more bushels faster. Few growers are also accounting for a higher percentage of business making investment decisions that serve members in far-flung areas more difficult. BVFC in early 2012 began mulling a merger with another cooperative Luckey Farmers. A merger is anticipated to strengthen the co-ops' product offerings and marketing opportunities and provide a more stable cost structure.

EXECUTIVES

Vice President Marketing, Gale Berry
Vice President Marketing, Jeffrey (Jeff) Hassler
Vice President Marketing, Brice Berry
Auditors: BALESTRA HARR & SCHERER CPAS

LOCATIONS

HQ: BLANCHARD VALLEY FARMERS COOPERATIVE INC.
6566 COUNTY ROAD 236, FINDLAY, OH 458409769
Phone: 419 423-2611
Web: WWW.BVFCOOP.COM

PRODUCTS/OPERATIONS

Selected Services
Customer accounting
Feed
Grain
Petroleum
Seasonal grain

COMPETITORS

ADM
Ag Processing Inc.
CHS
Cargill
GROWMARK
Luckey Farmers

HISTORICAL FINANCIALS

Company Type: Private

Income Statement — FYE: December 31

	REVENUE ($ mil.)	NET INCOME ($ mil.)	NET PROFIT MARGIN	EMPLOYEES
12/13	321	8	2.5%	122
12/12	335	5	1.6%	—
12/11	292	7	2.5%	—
12/10	196	0	—	—
Annual Growth	17.9%	—	—	—

2013 Year-End Financials
Return on assets: 15.7%   Cash ($ mil.): 5
Return on equity: 2.5%
Current ratio: 0.10

BLARNEY CASTLE OIL CO.

While kissing the Blarney stone has a reputation for reliably making people loquacious Blarney Castle Oil and Propane has a reputation for reliably supplying its customers with fuels. The family-owned company transports petroleum products to customers through about 10 office locations in Michigan. Its products include agricultural and commercial fuels (diesel and gasoline) commercial and industrial lubricants and coolants home heating oil fuel oil and propane. Blarney Castle Oil and Propane also operates 90 convenience stores under the EZ Mart brand name.

To ensure a continuous fuel supply Blarney Castle has wholesale supply contracts with half dozen major oil companies including BP Exxon Mobil Marathon and Shell. Originally a Texaco (now Chevron) distributor the company became a multi-brand distributor following the withdrawal of Texaco from the Michigan market in the late 1970s.

The family-owned company was founded in 1933 by Dennis McCarthy and two of his brothers and is still managed by family members

EXECUTIVES

Vice President, William McCarthy
Auditors: HUNGERFORD ALDRIN NICHOLS &

LOCATIONS

HQ: BLARNEY CASTLE OIL CO.
12218 WEST ST, BEAR LAKE, MI 496149432
Phone: 231 864-3111
Web: WWW.BLARNEYCASTLEOIL.COM

COMPETITORS

Crystal Flash Energy   Vesco Oil
PetroLiance

HISTORICAL FINANCIALS

Company Type: Private

Income Statement — FYE: March 31

	REVENUE ($ mil.)	NET INCOME ($ mil.)	NET PROFIT MARGIN	EMPLOYEES
03/14	525	5	1.1%	700
03/13	513	6	1.2%	—
03/12	501	4	0.8%	—
03/11	415	0	—	—
Annual Growth	8.2%	—	—	—

2014 Year-End Financials
Return on assets: 1.5%   Cash ($ mil.): 7
Return on equity: 1.1%
Current ratio: 1.50

BLESSING HOSPITAL

Blessing Hospital is a not-for-profit acute care medical center that provides a wide range of health services to residents in areas of western Illinois northeast Missouri and southeast Iowa. Through its main campus location it provides primary and emergency care as well as specialty services including diagnostics and surgery. The hospital is home to centers of excellence in the treatment of cancer heart and cardiovascular ailments wound care and women's health issues. Blessing Hospital provides outpatient and behavioral health services at a nearby campus. It also operates family practice centers and provides home and hospice care services. It is part of the Blessing Health System.

Operations

Blessing Health System includes two hospitals a physician group medical specialty operations a foundation and a four-year nursing education program.

Blessing Hospital boasts a medical staff of more than 240 physicians with an additional 2000 health care personnel. Its operations consist of a behavioral center body motion center breast center cancer center heart and vascular center sleep center and wound center as well as family practice centers.

The hospital typically sees more than 13400 inpatients and 245000 outpatients each year.

Geographic Reach

Blessing Hospital serves those who reside in western Illinois southeast Iowa and northeast Missouri.

Strategy

Blessing Hospital is working to boost its range of tertiary (acute specialty care) services to keep residents in the area from heading to larger towns more than 150 miles away. To this end it has built up its cardiac services and brought in a robotic surgical system.

EXECUTIVES

Assistant Director of Pharmacy; Director; Pharmacy Manager, Lori Stratton
Vice President Human Resources, Joellen Randall
Director Icu Coronary Care Unit, Debbie Mcginnis
Associate Medical Director, Chris Solaro
Vice President Innovation and Integration, Connie Schroeder
Auditors: GRAY HUNTER STENN LLP QUINCY

LOCATIONS

HQ: BLESSING HOSPITAL
BROADWAY AT 11TH ST, QUINCY, IL 62301
Phone: 217 223 1200
Web: WWW.BLESSINGHEALTHSYSTEM.ORG

PRODUCTS/OPERATIONS

Selected Services
Bariatric Services
Behavioral Center
Blessing FastCare Clinic
Body Motion Center
Breast Center
Cancer Center
Emergency Center
Heart & Vascular Center
Home Care
Hospice & Palliative Care
Hospital Medicine Program
Maternity Care
Nutrition Services
Orthopedic Surgical Services
Pain Management Service
Radiology
Rehabilitation Services
Renal Dialysis Services
Sleep Center
Surgical Services
Wound Center

COMPETITORS

Advocate BroMenn   Memorial Health System
Hospital Sisters   St. John's Hospital
Health System   (Illinois)

HISTORICAL FINANCIALS

Company Type: Private

Income Statement — FYE: September 30

	REVENUE ($ mil.)	NET INCOME ($ mil.)	NET PROFIT MARGIN	EMPLOYEES
09/13	303	31	10.5%	2,500
09/12	289	14	5.1%	—
09/08	238	(2)	—	—
09/07	230	0	—	—
Annual Growth	4.7%	—	—	—

2013 Year-End Financials
Return on assets: 3.7%   Cash ($ mil.): 66
Return on equity: 10.5%
Current ratio: 2.00

BLOOD SYSTEMS INC.

As one might assume from its name Blood Systems collects and provides blood to hospitals. The not-for-profit Blood Systems collects blood and provides blood products and services to more than 500 hospitals in about 20 states. Its network of blood bank facilities are operated through its United Blood Services and Blood Centers of the Pacific subsidiaries. Blood Systems also provides blood donor testing services through its Creative Testing Solutions (CTS) facilities. Its BioCARE division distributes plasma derivative products used in medical procedures.

Operations

Blood Systems gets more than half of revenues from blood component service fees made by the blood centers. Laboratory testing services (CTS) and sales of pharmaceutical products (BioCARE) make up most of the rest of sales.

The Blood Systems Research Institute conducts transfusion medicine research including investigational work on transfusion-transmitted diseases (such as HIV and HCV) and infectious diseases such as the West Nile Virus. It also prepares stem cells for research and therapeutic purposes.

The organization's community blood centers include LifeStream (active in Southern California) Blood Centers of the Pacific (Northern California) Bonfils Blood Center (Colorado) and Inland Northwest Blood Center (the Spokane Washington region). The CTS division tests more than 2.6 million blood donations annually from its facilities in Phoenix Dallas and Tampa. Another division Blood Systems Laboratories specializes in identifying antibodies in blood and stem cell processing.

Geographic Reach

Blood Systems has about 50 donor centers in Arizona California Colorado Idaho Louisiana Mississippi Montana Nevada New Mexico North Dakota South Dakota Texas Washington and Wyoming (through the United Blood Services and Blood Centers of the Pacific units). The company also has about 20 BioCARE locations and a handful of CTS and research labs scattered across the US.

Financial Performance

Blood Systems reported revenues of $743 million in 2013 a 1% increase over the previous year due to higher sales of laboratory testing services and pharmaceutical products. The company reported a net loss of $11 million that year (versus net income of $22.7 million in 2012) due to higher expenses related to the costs of blood collection pharmaceutical supplies and testing products.

Strategy

Blood Systems primarily operates in the western and midwestern US and tends to grow by entering new hospital service contracts in strategic markets. In addition the company is working to improve its IT systems to give customers better access to its blood supplies. It also invests in facility and equipment upgrades as well as product research and development efforts to improve quality.

In 2013 BioCARE opened CanyonCARE Rx a full-service pharmacy that specializes in hemophilia von Willebrand disease and other blood disorders. The division also established four new group purchasing organization (GPO) contracts a key focus area for BioCARE as it looks to expand its customer base.

Company Background

The company which was founded in 1943 as the Salt River Valley Blood Bank is governed by a voluntary board of directors consisting of community and medical industry leaders.

EXECUTIVES

EVP and General Counsel, Scott M. Nelson
EVP and Chief Quality Officer, Mary Beth Bassett
EVP Business Services, Patrick Holt
Vice President Planning And Development, Michael Lamb
Medical Director, Hany Kamel
Vice President Procedures, Dennis Harpool
Vice President Of Donor Services, Terrina Yamamoto
Vice President Blood Systems Laboratories, Sally Caglioti

LOCATIONS

HQ: BLOOD SYSTEMS INC.
6210 E OAK ST, SCOTTSDALE, AZ 852571101
Phone: 480 946-4201
Web: WWW.BLOODSYSTEMS.ORG

PRODUCTS/OPERATIONS

2013 Sales

	$ mil.	% of total
Blood component service fees	323	44
Laboratory testing services	208	28
Sales of pharmaceutical products	174	23
Other services & income	37	5
Total	**743**	**100**

Selected Services

Blood Centers
  Blood Components
  Component Therapy
  Commonly Ordered Derivatives
  Modified Blood Components
Laboratory Services
  Donor Counseling
  Histocompatibility Laboratory (HLA)
  Immunohematology Reference Laboratory (IRL)
Special Collections
  Directed Donation
  Perioperative Blood Salvage
  Pre-operative Autologous Donation (PAD)
  Stem Cell Processing
  Therapeutic (Clinical) Apheresis
Transfusion Medicine
  Blood Management Services
  Compatibility Services

COMPETITORS

CSL	New York Blood Center
Daxor	Puget Sound Blood
FFF Enterprises	Center
Grifols Inc.	Red Cross
HemaCare	SeraCare Life Sciences

HISTORICAL FINANCIALS

Company Type: Private

Income Statement

FYE: December 31

	REVENUE ($ mil.)	NET INCOME ($ mil.)	NET PROFIT MARGIN	EMPLOYEES
12/13	743	65	8.8%	3,900
12/12	488	21	4.4%	—
12/11	67	0	1.2%	—
12/10	476	0	—	—
Annual Growth	**15.9%**	**—**	**—**	**—**

2013 Year-End Financials

Return on assets: 4.1%
Return on equity: 8.8%
Current ratio: 1.30
Cash ($ mil.): 19

BLUE CROSS AND BLUE SHIELD OF ARIZONA INC.

Blue Cross Blue Shield of Arizona (BCBSAZ) provides health insurance products and services to more than 1.3 million Arizonans. The not-for-profit company offers a variety of managed care plans to small and large employer groups individuals and families including PPO HMO and high-deductible health plans. It also provides dental vision and prescription drug coverage as well as supplemental health plans for Medicare beneficiaries. Additionally BCBSAZ's HealthyBlue wellness and disease management programs give members information and services that encourage healthy lifestyles. Founded in 1939 the company is an independent licensee of the Blue Cross and Blue Shield Association.

Operations

The company's statewide PPO network includes 90% of Arizona's doctors and hospitals.

Geographic Reach

BCBSAZ serves customers throughout the state of Arizona from its offices in Chandler Flagstaff Phoenix and Tucson. It has a contracted network of some 21000 physicians and dentists located across the state as well.

Sales and Marketing

The company offers insurance services to individuals and families seniors employers brokers and consultants and health care professionals through agents.

Its Alliance Network includes contracted hospitals and doctors that are part of Banner Health and Scottsdale Healthcare. Its Select Network comprises contracted hospitals and doctors that are part of Phoenix Children's Hospital Dignity Health IASIS Healthcare and Abrazo Health.

Strategy

The company has been revamping many of its health plan offerings revising coverage terms and lowering premiums in an effort to attract more customers. In addition BCBSAZ has launched marketing campaigns targeting Arizona's Hispanic community which makes up 30% of the state's population.

To help reduce skyrocketing costs plaguing the health care industry the company has also been enhancing its HealthyBlue wellness program offering which promotes preventative care and fitness and allows for personalized online health assessment and coaching services. In 2014 it partnered with Phoenix Children's Hospital to open the state's first childhood obesity clinic; some 25% of Arizona's children are categorized as either overweight or obese.

BCBSAZ is also expanding. In 2013 BCBSAZ affiliate Blue Cross Blue Shield of Arizona Advantage began to expand its physician network to better serve Scottsdale-area residents. Through a contract with Scottsdale Healthcare Hospitals and Scottsdale Health Partners members of a Blue Medicare Advantage (HMO) plan can select doctors within the Banner Health Network or Scottsdale Health Partners.

EXECUTIVES

Vice President Finance, Bill Arthur
President and CEO, Richard L. (Rich) Boals
EVP External Operations, Susan H. Navran
EVP Internal Operations, Sandra Lee Gibson
CIO, Elizabeth A. Messina

SVP and CFO, Karen Abraham
SVP Health Services and Chief Medical Officer,
  Vishu Jhaveri
SVP Strategy Sales and Marketing, Jeff Stelnik
CEO Blue Cross Blue Shield of Arizona
  Advantage, Dave Firdaus
Vp Strategy & Informatics, Matthew (Matt)
  Wandoloski
Vice President Chief Technology Officer Of
  Information Technology, Gerard Farmer
Vice President Operations, Andrew Mason
Vice President Of Network Management, Marcus
  Montoya
Information Technology Quality Assurance Vice
  President, Diana Crowell
Vice President Of Marketing, Marty Laurel
Vice President, Sue Glawe
Medical Director, Laura Dodson
Vice President Of Medical Management, Cynthia
  Walls
Vice President Quality Improvement Accreditation
  Product, Tina Trout
Medical Director Vice President, Daniel (Dan)
  Aspery
Vice President Pharmacy Benefit Management,
  Chris Hogan
Senior Vice President and Chief Service Officer, H
  Chandler
Chairman, Harry A. Papp
Vice Chairman, Alton J. Washington
Vice President Treasurer, Kathryn Baker

LOCATIONS

HQ: BLUE CROSS AND BLUE SHIELD OF ARIZONA
  INC.
  2444 W LAS PALMARITAS DR, PHOENIX, AZ
  850214860
Phone: 602 864-4100
Web: WWW.AZBLUE.COM

PRODUCTS/OPERATIONS

Selected Plans
Family and Individual Medical Plans
  BlueBasic Plus PPO
  BlueEssential Plus PPO
  BlueOptimum Plus PPO
  BluePortfolio Plus (high deductible PPO with HSA)
  BlueValue Plus PPO
  Medicare Part D
  Medicare Supplement
Group Medical Plans
  BlueAlliance benefit
  BluePreferred PPO
  BluePreferred HSA Plus (high deductible PPO with
  HSA)
  BlueSelect HMO
  Dental plans
  Eyewear plans
  GeoBlue Expat

COMPETITORS

Aetna	Humana
Banner Health	Southwest Catholic
CIGNA HealthCare of	Health Network
Arizona	UnitedHealth Group
First Dental Health	Western Dental
Health Net	Services

HISTORICAL FINANCIALS
Company Type: Private

Income Statement   FYE: December 31

	ASSETS ($ mil.)	NET INCOME ($ mil.)	INCOME AS % OF ASSETS	EMPLOYEES
12/09	1,059	64	6.1%	1,278
12/08	975	71	7.4%	—
Annual Growth	8.6%	(9.9%)	—	—

BLUE TEE CORP.

Handling a variety of steel products and scrap materials suits Blue Tee to a tee. The holding company which operates through two primary subsidiaries distributes steel building materials and scrap metal. Blue Tee's Brown-Strauss Steel subsidiary is one of the largest distributors of wide flange beam and structural steel products (beams pipe and tubing) in North America. The metal distributor's other primary business is Azcon a leading scrap processor broker and mill services management company which handles scrap metal sales rail cars and other steel parts.Geographic Reach

The company has major offices in Denver Kansas City Longview (Washington) New York City Phoenix Salt Lake City and Stockton and Fontana (California). It has additional locations in Alton Chicago and Sterling (Illinois); Austin Texas; Duluth Minnesota; and Sharpsburg Pennsylvania.

In Canada Blue Tee has offices in Edmonton Calgary Grande Prairie Grimshaw Kamloops Prince George and Red Deer.
  Operations
Azcon is a major scrap processor broker and mill services management company. Brown-Strauss Steel distributes steel products.

Azcon buys collects warehouses and distributes a wide variety of rail and track accessories for the railroad industry across North America. Its core businesses include Processing Yard Mill Scrap Management and Brokerage. Other product lines include Relaying and Re-rolling Rail Railroad Equipment and Railroad Parts. Brown-Strauss Steel's focus is on the distribution of new steel (wide flange beam and structural steel tubing) across the US.
  Sales and Marketing
Blue Tee serves a range of industries including construction forestry road building mining farming power oil and gas solid waste water waste management highway transportation environmental and groundwater monitoring.
  Strategy
The company is focusing its resources developing Azcon and Brown-Strauss Steel. Brown-Strauss is looking to grow its product offerings to include structural tubing; it also plans to expand its facilities. In this regard in 2012 Blue Tee Corp (through Brown-Strauss) purchased a 69190 sq. ft. industrial building in Aurora Colorado from The Lowenberg Corp. for $6 million.
  Company Background
Blue Tee is owned by its employees through an employee stock ownership plan.

In 2011 Blue Tee divested subsidiaries GEFCO (an OEM of portable drilling rigs and other industrial equipment) and STECO (transfer and dump-truck trailers) to Astec Industries for about $30.8 million.

The move to axe its GEFCO and STECO subsidiaries followed another sale. Blue Tee sold its pump parts subsidiary Texas-based Standard Alloys to German pump manufacturer KSB in mid-2010.

The Blue Tee holding company was founded in 1986. Azcon was formed in 1863 and Brown-Strauss Steel was established in 1905.

EXECUTIVES

President Chief Executive Officer, William M. Kelly,
  age 64
Executive Vice President - Finance and Secretary,
  David P. Alldian
Group VP Metals Operations, Richard A. Secrist Jr.
Controller and Assistant Secretary, Thomas Caruso

Executive Director Benefit Plans, Annette Marino
  D'Arienzo
President, Mike Calvert
EVP, Ryan Secrist
VP; President Azcon, Ronnie Hirsch
Auditors: DELOITTE & TOUCHE LLP NEW YO

LOCATIONS

HQ: BLUE TEE CORP.
  250 PARK AVE S RM 203, NEW YORK, NY 100031495
Phone: 212 598-0880
Web: WWW.BLUETEE.COM

PRODUCTS/OPERATIONS

Selected Subsidiaries
Azcon Corporation (ferrous and nonferrous scrap; rail
  cars locomotives and parts; relay and reroll rail)
Brown-Strauss Steel (steel distribution including angles
  beams channels pipe and tubing)

Selected Azcon Services
Barge Services
Brokerage Services
Demolition Services
Foundries - Scrap Management
Industrial Plants - Scrap Management
Mill Service
Mine Services
Railroad Industry Services
Steel Mills - Scrap Management

Selected Brown-Strauss Steel Products and Services
Products:
Structural Angle
Structural Channels
Structural Pipe
Structural Tubing
Wide Flange Beams
Services:
Cambering
Inventory Stocking program
Length/cutting optimization program
Mill Brokerage
Saw Cutting
Track Torch Cutting

COMPETITORS

A. M. Castle	Reliance Steel
APi Group	Russel Metals
Dover Corp.	Ryerson
Metals USA	TTX
OmniSource	Wescast Industries
Pacesetter Steel	
RTI International	
Metals	

HISTORICAL FINANCIALS
Company Type: Private

Income Statement   FYE: December 31

	REVENUE ($ mil.)	NET INCOME ($ mil.)	NET PROFIT MARGIN	EMPLOYEES
12/10	809	14	1.8%	900
12/09	564	(10)	—	—
Annual Growth	43.4%	—	—	—

2010 Year-End Financials

Return on assets: 10.5%   Cash ($ mil.): 8
Return on equity: 1.8%
Current ratio: 0.10

BLUEBONNET ELECTRIC COOPERATIVE INC.

Bluebonnet Electric Cooperative's mission has echoes of the late Lady Bird Johnson's quest to spread bluebonnets and other wildflower seeds along Texas' highways. In this case the cooperative spreads power to homes and businesses in rural central and southeast Texas. One of the largest power distribution cooperatives in the state Bluebonnet Electric serves more than 81000 customers in 14 counties (a service area of more than 3800 square miles). The member-owned company which was formed in 1939 operates approximately 11000 miles of transmission and distribution lines and 19 substations. It purchases its wholesale power supply at 21 Lower Colorado River Authority-owned substations.

A long Texas drought caused a dust buildup on several of the co-op's insulators prompting a number of pole-top fires in late 2008 and early 2009. The utility is retrofitting the insulators to avoid a recurrence of the problem and ensure uninterrupted service.

Higher-than-normal summer heat drove up power demand in 2010. This resulted in Bluebonnet Electric reporting higher revenues and an improved net profit.

The heat and drought continued in 2011 and helped fuel a major wildfire in Bastrop over the Labor Day weekend. Bluebonnet Electric was subsequently confronted with a lawsuit which blamed it for the wildfire that destroyed almost 1600 homes (high winds brought down tree limbs on the coop's power lines sparking the blaze). The coop's executives ponted out that the trees which triggered the fire were on private property outside of the utility's easement and that Bluebonnet Electric could not be reasonably blamed for the conflagration.

In late 2011 the company lowered its electric rates to reflect lower natural gas commodity prices (natural gas accounts for 90% of the fuel Bluebonnet Electric uses to generate power).

In 1964 in order to avoid confusion with the Lower Colorado River Authority the utility originally known as the Lower Colorado River Electric Cooperative changed its name to Bluebonnet Electric Cooperative.

EXECUTIVES

Chairman, Richard Schmidt
CEO and General Manager, Mark Rose
General Manager, Elizabeth Kana
Secretary Treasurer and Director, James B. Kershaw
Assistant Secretary Assistant Treasurer and Director, Byron Balke
Vice Chairman, Ben Flencher
Chief Operating Officer, Johnny Sanders
Chief Engineer, Will Holford
Secretary Treasurer and Director, James B. Kershaw
Assistant Secretary Assistant Treasurer and Director, Byron Balke
Vice Chairman, Ben Flencher
Director, Kenneth (Ken) Mutscher
Director, Lyle L. Wolz
Director, Robert Mikeska
Director, Milton Shaw
Auditors: BOLINGER SEGARS GILBERT & MO

LOCATIONS

HQ: BLUEBONNET ELECTRIC COOPERATIVE INC.
155 ELECTRIC AVE, BASTROP, TX 78602
Phone: 800 842-7708

HISTORICAL FINANCIALS
Company Type: Private

Income Statement
FYE: December 31

	REVENUE ($ mil.)	NET INCOME ($ mil.)	NET PROFIT MARGIN	EMPLOYEES
12/13	201	6	3.3%	265
12/12	188	5	2.9%	—
12/11	199	5	2.9%	—
12/10	191	0	—	—
Annual Growth	1.7%	—	—	—

2013 Year-End Financials
Return on assets: —
Return on equity: 3.3%
Current ratio: 0.60
Cash ($ mil.): 8

BOARD OF COOPERATIVE EDUCATIONAL SERVICES OF NASSAU COUNTY

Auditors: RS ABRAMS AND CO LLP ISLAND

LOCATIONS

HQ: BOARD OF COOPERATIVE EDUCATIONAL SERVICES OF NASSAU COUNTY
71 CLINTON RD STE 100, GARDEN CITY, NY 115304728
Phone: 516 396-2500
Web: WWW.NASSAUBOCES.ORG

HISTORICAL FINANCIALS
Company Type: Private

Income Statement
FYE: June 30

	REVENUE ($ mil.)	NET INCOME ($ mil.)	NET PROFIT MARGIN	EMPLOYEES
06/10	307	3	1.2%	3,059
06/09	303	9	3.1%	—
06/05	243	0	0.3%	—
06/04	236	0	—	—
Annual Growth	4.5%	—	—	—

2010 Year-End Financials
Return on assets: 1.4%
Return on equity: 1.2%
Current ratio: —
Cash ($ mil.): 87

BOARD OF EDUCATION FOR THE CITY OF SAVANNAH AND THE COUNTY OF CH

Auditors: KRT CPAS PC SAVANNAH GEORG

LOCATIONS

HQ: BOARD OF EDUCATION FOR THE CITY OF SAVANNAH AND THE COUNTY OF CH
208 BULL ST, SAVANNAH, GA 314013997
Phone: 912 395-1000
Web: WWW.SAVANNAH.CHATHAM.K12.GA.US

HISTORICAL FINANCIALS
Company Type: Private

Income Statement
FYE: June 30

	REVENUE ($ mil.)	NET INCOME ($ mil.)	NET PROFIT MARGIN	EMPLOYEES
06/14	447	36	8.1%	4,781
06/13	415	4	1.1%	—
06/12	405	(43)	—	—
06/11	423	0	—	—
Annual Growth	1.9%	—	—	—

BOARD OF EDUCATION OF CARROLL COUNTY

Auditors: CLINTONLARSONALLEN LLP BALTI

LOCATIONS

HQ: BOARD OF EDUCATION OF CARROLL COUNTY
125 N COURT ST STE 101, WESTMINSTER, MD 211575192
Phone: 410 751-3000
Web: WWW.CARROLLK12.ORG

HISTORICAL FINANCIALS
Company Type: Private

Income Statement
FYE: June 30

	REVENUE ($ mil.)	NET INCOME ($ mil.)	NET PROFIT MARGIN	EMPLOYEES
06/13	372	0	0.3%	2,500
06/12	375	10	2.7%	—
06/07	0	0	—	—
06/06	298	0	—	—
Annual Growth	3.2%	—	—	—

2013 Year-End Financials
Return on assets: 2.1%
Return on equity: 0.3%
Current ratio: 0.20
Cash ($ mil.): 7

BOARD OF EDUCATION OF FREDERICK COUNTY MD (INC)

Auditors: WOODEN & BENSON BALTIMORE MA

LOCATIONS

HQ: BOARD OF EDUCATION OF FREDERICK COUNTY MD (INC)
191 S EAST ST, FREDERICK, MD 217015918
Phone: 301 644-5000
Web: WWW.FCPS.ORG

HISTORICAL FINANCIALS
Company Type: Private

Income Statement

	REVENUE ($ mil.)	NET INCOME ($ mil.)	NET PROFIT MARGIN	EMPLOYEES
06/13	550	3	0.7%	3,500
06/12	543	(5)	—	—
06/05	0	0	—	—
06/03	0	0	—	—
Annual Growth	—	—	—	—

FYE: June 30

BOARD OF EDUCATION- MEMPHIS CITY SCHOOLS

LOCATIONS

HQ: BOARD OF EDUCATION-MEMPHIS CITY SCHOOLS
160 S HOLLYWOOD ST, MEMPHIS, TN 381124801
Phone: 901 416-5300

HISTORICAL FINANCIALS
Company Type: Private

Income Statement

	REVENUE ($ mil.)	NET INCOME ($ mil.)	NET PROFIT MARGIN	EMPLOYEES
06/13	1,157	(12)	—	12,015
06/12	1,169	(2)	—	—
06/11*	1,173	(5)	—	—
12/09	449	0	—	—
Annual Growth	37.1%	—	—	—

FYE: June 30

*Fiscal year change

2013 Year-End Financials

Return on assets: —
Return on equity: (-1.1%)
Current ratio: —
Cash ($ mil.): 177

BOCA RATON REGIONAL HOSPITAL INC.

LOCATIONS

HQ: BOCA RATON REGIONAL HOSPITAL INC.
800 MEADOWS RD, BOCA RATON, FL 334862304
Phone: 561 395-7100
Web: WWW.BRRH.COM

HISTORICAL FINANCIALS
Company Type: Private

Income Statement

	REVENUE ($ mil.)	NET INCOME ($ mil.)	NET PROFIT MARGIN	EMPLOYEES
06/13	362	21	6.0%	1,917
06/05	263	13	5.2%	—
06/04	0	0	—	—
06/03	226	0	—	—
Annual Growth	4.8%	—	—	—

FYE: June 30

2013 Year-End Financials

Return on assets: 10.7%
Return on equity: 6.0%
Current ratio: 0.70
Cash ($ mil.): —

BODDIE-NOELL ENTERPRISES INC.

Boddie-Noell Enterprises (BNE) is a hearty competitor in the fast-food business. The company is one of the largest franchise operators of Hardee's a fast-food chain owned by CKE Restaurants with about 330 locations the four southeastern states of Kentucky North Carolina South Carolina and Virginia. In addition the company owns The Highway Diner restaurant concept. BNE is also involved in real estate development through BNE Land & Development. The family owned company was started in 1962 by Carleton Noell and his nephews Nick and Mayo Boddie.

Geographic Reach

BNE owns 334 Hardee's locations throughout Kentucky North Carolina South Carolina and Virgina.

Strategy

The company previously owned the Texas Steakhouse & Saloon concept but it sold that operation in late 2012 to CB Holding owner of Charlie Brown's Steakhouse. BNE made the divestiture to focus solely on its Hardee's franchises.

EXECUTIVES

Vice President Purchasing, Tim Lane
Vice President Information Systems, Bob Larimer
Vice President, Nanette Herbert
Vice President Is, Kathy Trusch
Vice President, David (Dave) Schmitt
Auditors: THOMAS JUDY & TUCKER PA R

LOCATIONS

HQ: BODDIE-NOELL ENTERPRISES INC.
1021 NOELL LN, ROCKY MOUNT, NC 278041761
Phone: 252 937-2000
Web: WWW.BNEINC.COM

PRODUCTS/OPERATIONS

Selected Operations
Restaurants
  Hardee's
  The Highway Diner
Other
  BNE Land & Development (commercial and resort real estate development)
  Rose Hill Conference Center (Rocky Mount NC)

COMPETITORS

Biglari Holdings	Chick-fil-A
Bojangles'	DavCo Restaurants
Burger King	McDonald's
Carolina Restaurant	Sonic Corp.
Group	Wendy's
Carrols	YUM!

HISTORICAL FINANCIALS
Company Type: Private

Income Statement

	REVENUE ($ mil.)	NET INCOME ($ mil.)	NET PROFIT MARGIN	EMPLOYEES
12/13	369	16	4.5%	13,000
12/12	395	13	3.5%	—
12/11	395	(9)	—	—
12/10	389	0	—	—
Annual Growth	(1.7%)	—	—	—

FYE: December 30

2013 Year-End Financials

Return on assets: 3.7%
Return on equity: 4.5%
Current ratio: 0.90
Cash ($ mil.): 36

BOGOPA ENTERPRISES INC.

LOCATIONS

HQ: BOGOPA ENTERPRISES INC.
650 FOUNTAIN AVE, BROOKLYN, NY 112085306
Phone: 718 346-6500
Web: WWW.MYFOODBAZAAR.COM

HISTORICAL FINANCIALS
Company Type: Private

Income Statement

	REVENUE ($ mil.)	NET INCOME ($ mil.)	NET PROFIT MARGIN	EMPLOYEES
12/10	312	6	2.1%	1,200
12/06	294	6	2.1%	—
12/04	1,163	0	0.0%	—
Annual Growth	(19.7%)	469.2%	—	—

FYE: December 31

2010 Year-End Financials

Return on assets: 8.2%
Return on equity: 2.1%
Current ratio: 0.30
Cash ($ mil.): 3

BON SECOURS HEALTH SYSTEM INC

Bon Secours Health System provides succor to the sick and injured. The Roman Catholic health care organization sponsored by the Bon Secours Ministries is home to about 20 hospitals with some 4400 licensed acute care beds. First founded in 1919 the organization's facilities are in six states in the eastern US from New York to Florida. In addition to its acute care hospitals the not-for-profit health care system operates a psychiatric hospital numerous nursing homes and assisted-living facilities as well as hospices and home health care agencies. Its Global Ministry Initiative provides outreach for health care and social services in developing countries particularly Haiti Peru and South Africa.

Geographic Reach

Headquartered in Marriottsville Maryland the system has hospitals in Kentucky Maryland New York South Carolina and Virginia and long-term care facilities in Florida New York and Virginia.

Sales and Marketing

In fiscal 2014 (ended August) Medicare and Medicaid payments accounted for 35% of total net patient revenue.

Financial Performance

Revenue increased 3% to $3.5 billion in fiscal 2014 (ended August) as net patient service revenues increased. Despite that growth higher operating costs led to a decline in net income which fell 57% to $143.5 million.

Cash flow from operations slipped 6% to $190.4 million that year as a result of the lower net income as well as a change in working capital.

Strategy

Bon Secours plans to continue to grow its operations in existing and new communities targeting expansion in ambulatory care elderly services and home health and hospice. The health system has opened several new ambulatory care centers in existing service territories and it is conducting renovation and expansion efforts at some of its hospital facilities.

Bon Secours has also initiated information technology restructuring efforts; it has developed a new clinical information management system (electronic medical records) ConnectCare which is being implemented at its facilities in gradual stages.

EXECUTIVES

President CEO and Director, Richard J. (Rich) Statuto, age 58
VP Information Systems and CIO, Skip Hubbard
EVP, Mark S. Nantz
EVP, Janice Burnett
CEO Bon Secours Baltimore Health System, Samuel L. Ross
CEO Bon Secours St. Francis Health System, R. Craig McCoy
CEO Bon Secours Charity, Mary Leahy
Senior Vice President Sponsorship, Pat Heath
Senior Vice President Of Mission, Pam Phillips
Vice President, Jennifer Scholtz
Medical Director the Womens Center, James A (Jamie) Marquardt
Clinical Director, Deborah Pope
Vice President Philanthropy And Development, Julie Mercer
Medical Director Of Inpatient Psychiatry, Bruce R Stevens
Vice President Cardiology, Shadi Shalakhti
Director Of Admissions, Sharon Balinsky
Vice President of Surgical Services, Pat Fowler

Vice President Ancillary Amb Services, Johnna S Reed
Vice President Women's Surgery SF Eastside, Rose Leo
Vice President Revenue Cycle, Sheila Kuenzle
Acting Vice President Revenue Cycle, Steve Friedman
Vice President Mission, Elizabeth Keith
Medical Director, Robert (Bob) Sprague
Vice President Military Affairs, Bill Barrett
Vice President Ambulatory Services, Kyle Moore
Director, Charles H. Brown
Treasurer, Pamela Schmidt
Auditors: KPMG LLP BALTIMORE MD

LOCATIONS

HQ: BON SECOURS HEALTH SYSTEM INC
1505 MARRIOTTSVILLE RD, MARRIOTTSVILLE, MD 211041301
Phone: 410 442-5511
Web: WWW.BSHSI.COM

Selected Facilities
Florida
  Bon Secours St. Petersburg Health System
  Bon Secours - Maria Manor Nursing Care and Rehabilitation Center
  Bon Secours Place at St. Petersburg
  Bon Secours St. Petersburg Home Care Services
Kentucky
  Bon Secours Kentucky Health System
  Our Lady of Bellefonte Hospital (Ashland)
Maryland
  Bon Secours Baltimore Health System
  Bon Secours Hospital
  Bon Secours Washington Village
  Community Institute of Behavioral Sciences
  Hollins Terrace/Benet House
New York
  Bon Secours Charity Health System
  Bon Secours Community Hospital (Port Jervis)
  Good Samaritan Hospital (Suffern)
  St. Anthony Community Hospital (Warwick)
  Bon Secours New York Health System
  Schervier Nursing Care Center (Riverdale)
Pennsylvania
  Altoona Regional Health System (joint venture)
South Carolina
  Bon Secours St. Francis Health System Inc.
  St. Francis Hospital (Downtown and Eastside Campuses Greenville)
  Roper St. Francis Healthcare (Charleston joint venture)
Virginia
  Bon Secours Hampton Roads Health System
  Bon Secours Maryview Nursing Care Center (Suffolk)
  DePaul Medical Center (Norfolk)
  Mary Immaculate Hospital (Newport News)
  Maryview Medical Center (Portsmouth)
  Province Place (Norfolk and Portsmouth)
  St. Francis Nursing Care Center (Newport News)
  Bon Secours Richmond Health System (joint venture)
  Memorial Regional Medical Center (Mechanicsville)
  Richmond Community Hospital
  St. Francis Medical Center (Midlothian)
  St. Mary's Hospital (Richmond)

Selected Affiliations
Cosponsoring Congregational Relationships
  Bernardine Sisters of the Third Order of St. Francis (Newport News Virginia)
  Sisters of Charity of Saint Elizabeth of Convent Station (New Jersey and New York)
Affiliated Organizations
  Health Corporation of Virginia (Richmond)
  Medical Society of South Carolina and Carolinas Health Care System (Charleston)
  Life Care Services (Florida and Virginia)

PRODUCTS/OPERATIONS

2014 Sales

	$ mil.	% of total
Net Patient Service Revenue	3,328	96
Other revenue	133	4
Total	**3,461**	**100**

COMPETITORS

Adventist HealthCare	HCA
Albany Medical Center	Highlands Health
Albert Einstein Healthcare Network	Inova
	Johns Hopkins Medicine
Appalachian Regional Healthcare	MedStar Health
	MediSys Health Network
Carilion Clinic	New York City Health and Hospitals
Catholic Health Initiatives	Novant Health
Centra Health Inc.	Riverside Health
Christiana Care	System (Virginia)
Community Health Systems	Sentara Healthcare
	St. Agnes HealthCare
Conemaugh Health System	University of Maryland Medical System
Franklin Square Hospital Center	University of Miami Hospital
GBMC	Virginia Hospital Center
Greenville Hospital System	

HISTORICAL FINANCIALS
Company Type: Private

Income Statement
FYE: August 31

	REVENUE ($ mil.)	NET INCOME ($ mil.)	NET PROFIT MARGIN	EMPLOYEES
08/10	3,084	(41)	—	19,000
08/09	2,895	(291)	—	—
Annual Growth	6.6%	—	—	—

2010 Year-End Financials

Return on assets: 5.5%   Cash ($ mil.): 180
Return on equity: (-1.3%)
Current ratio: 1.20

BON SECOURS-MEMORIAL REGIONAL MEDICAL CENTER INC.

LOCATIONS

HQ: BON SECOURS-MEMORIAL REGIONAL MEDICAL CENTER INC.
8260 ATLEE RD STE 1203, MECHANICSVILLE, VA 231161844
Phone: 804 764-1253
Web: WWW.BONSECOURS.COM

HISTORICAL FINANCIALS
Company Type: Private

Income Statement
FYE: August 31

	REVENUE ($ mil.)	NET INCOME ($ mil.)	NET PROFIT MARGIN	EMPLOYEES
08/13	363	10	2.8%	1,975
08/06	114	(0)	—	—
08/05	199	18	9.0%	—
08/03	164	0	—	—
Annual Growth	8.3%	—	—	—

2013 Year-End Financials

Return on assets: 4.2%   Cash ($ mil.): 165
Return on equity: 2.8%
Current ratio: 10.00

BOND BROS. INC.

LOCATIONS

HQ: BOND BROS. INC.
145 SPRING ST, EVERETT, MA 021494517
Phone: 617 387-3400
Web: WWW.BONDBROTHERS.COM

HISTORICAL FINANCIALS
Company Type: Private

Income Statement
FYE: October 31

	REVENUE ($ mil.)	NET INCOME ($ mil.)	NET PROFIT MARGIN	EMPLOYEES
10/08	407	8	2.2%	350
10/07	348	0	—	—
10/06	336	0	—	—
Annual Growth	10.2%	147994.5%	—	—

2008 Year-End Financials
Return on assets: 17.6%
Return on equity: 2.2%
Current ratio: 1.20
Cash ($ mil.): 31

BONGARDS' CREAMERIES

Auditors: EIDE BAILLY LLP MINNEAPOLIS

LOCATIONS

HQ: BONGARDS' CREAMERIES
13200 COUNTY ROAD 51, NORWOOD, MN 553689743
Phone: 952 466-5521
Web: WWW.BONGARDS.COM

HISTORICAL FINANCIALS
Company Type: Private

Income Statement
FYE: December 31

	REVENUE ($ mil.)	NET INCOME ($ mil.)	NET PROFIT MARGIN	EMPLOYEES
12/07	355	7	2.1%	350
12/06	252	(2)	—	—
12/05	249	(7)	—	—
12/04	252	0	—	—
Annual Growth	12.1%	—	—	—

2007 Year-End Financials
Return on assets: 3.7%
Return on equity: 2.1%
Current ratio: 0.30
Cash ($ mil.): 2

BORGESS MEDICAL CENTER

Borgess Medical Center is part of the Borgess Health Alliance which is a member of the Ascension Health network. The general acute care facility which serves residents of southwestern Michigan houses more than 420 beds. It has a comprehensive offering of medical and surgical services including specialty care in areas such as cancer heart disease neuroscience and orthopedics. Borgess Medical Center also serves as a Level II trauma center and features a research institute a sleep disorders clinic a weight loss surgery center no-wait emergency room and outpatient facilities. The hospital was founded in 1889 by a local priest.

Operations

Borgess Medical Center sees more than 60000 visitors at its emergency and trauma facilities each year. Its specialist surgical facilities include operating rooms with comprehensive monitoring services for brain surgery spinal surgery and other complex procedures. The facility also serves as a regional behavioral health center. Its Stryker Center features extensive cardiovascular and neurological diagnosis and treatment resources as well as radiology pharmacy and same-day surgery units.

EXECUTIVES

Medical Director, Paul Lange
Medical Director, John Spitzer
Vp Human Resources, Laura Lentenbrink
Medical Director, Mark Kanzawa
Director of Pharmacy, Philip Early
Medical Director, Rashmikant Kothari
Board Member, Lawrence Cain
Auditors: DELOITTE TAX LLP CINCINNATI

LOCATIONS

HQ: BORGESS MEDICAL CENTER
1521 GULL RD, KALAMAZOO, MI 490481666
Phone: 269 226-7000
Web: WWW.BORGESS.COM

PRODUCTS/OPERATIONS

Selected Centers and Services
Behavioral Health
Birthing Center
Brain & Spine
Breast Care Centers
Cancer & Oncology
Cardiology Group
Critical Care
Dietary Services
Emergency & Trauma
Fibroid Center
Henry Ford
Inpatient Services
Laboratory Services
Osteoporosis Centers
Palliative Care
Radiology
Rehabilitation Services
Sleep Disorders
Vascular
Women's Services

COMPETITORS

Bronson Health Care
Covenant HealthCare
Gerber Memorial
McLaren Health Care
Memorial Hospital & Health System

Sheridan Community Hospital
Sparrow Health System
Spectrum Health
Trinity Health (Novi)

HISTORICAL FINANCIALS
Company Type: Private

Income Statement
FYE: June 30

	REVENUE ($ mil.)	NET INCOME ($ mil.)	NET PROFIT MARGIN	EMPLOYEES
06/10	455	(6)	—	2,200
06/09	414	(5)	—	—
06/08	1,203	0	—	—
Annual Growth	—	—	—	—

2010 Year-End Financials
Return on assets: —
Return on equity: (-1.4%)
Current ratio: 0.30
Cash ($ mil.): 19

BOSTON MEDICAL CENTER CORPORATION

Located in Boston's South End neighborhood Boston Medical Center (BMC) offers a full spectrum of health care services from prenatal care and obstetrics to surgery and rehabilitation. BMC is also the city's largest provider of indigent care spending millions of dollars annually on care for uninsured patients and offering free screenings and other community outreach programs. The not-for-profit hospital boasts nearly 500 licensed beds more than 700 physicians and includes a Level 1 trauma center acute rehabilitation facilities and neonatal and pediatric intensive care units. The center is the primary teaching hospital of Boston University's School of Medicine.

Operations

BMC also operates Boston HealthNet a network affiliation of the medical center Boston University School of Medicine and more than a dozen community health centers. Boston HealthNet provides outreach prevention primary care and specialty care and dental services at sites located throughout the community.

Hand-in-hand with being a major teaching hospital is engaging in extensive medical research. BMC oversees more than 590 research and service projects and conducts both biomedical and clinical research programs exploring infectious disease cardiology vascular biology Parkinson's disease geriatrics and endocrinology among other areas. With Boston University BMC also operates a 16-acre research and business park called BioSquare that serves as a collaborative center for the development and commercialization of new biomedical technologies.

In 2015 BMC had more than 712 000 outpatient clinic visits 204000 outpatient ancillary visits 125000 emergency department visits and 24000 admissions.

Sales and Marketing

In addition to its medical and research services BMC provides health insurance through its BMC HealthNet Plan a managed care plan that has more than 240000 Medicaid and low-cost health plan members. The center markets its services through social media.

Financial Performance

BMC received more than $119 million in sponsored research funding in fiscal 2015; it oversees 594 research and service projects separate from research activities at Boston University School of Medicine.

Strategy

In late 2014 BMC's Center for Regenerative Medicine and Boston University were awarded a $2.7 million grant from the National Heart Lung and Blood Institute to establish a stem cell repository that researchers across the US can access for free. The first-of-its-kind repository will help promote stem cell research particularly in the area of lung disease.

EXECUTIVES

Vice President Information Technology, Michael (Mel) Krugman
SVP Finance and CFO, Richard Silveria

President and CEO, Kate E. Walsh
SVP and Chief Nursing Officer, Nancy Gaden
SVP and Chief Medical Officer, Ravin Davidoff
COO, Alastair Bell
President and CEO Faculty Practice Foundation,
William Creevy
**SVP Quality Safety and Technology; Chief Quality
Officer,** Stanley Hochberg
Medical Director, Brendan Magauran
Senior Director Of Pharmacy, David (Dave)
Twitchell
**Vice President Planning Budgeting and
Information,** Marvin Cook
Director of Pharmacy, Patricia (Pat) Hite
Vice President Information Technology, Joanna
Norbrun
Director Of Radiology, Deb Clements
Pharmacy Manager, Chirag Desai
Vice President, Anthony Rossetti
Associate Vice President for Human Resources,
Manuel Monteiro
Vice President Administrative Services, Peter
(Pete) Fiedler
Vice President, Mary Glover
**Associate Vice President for Financial and
Business Affairs and Assistant Treasurer Medical
Campus,** William (Bill) Gasper
Treasurer, Marybeth Begley

LOCATIONS

HQ: BOSTON MEDICAL CENTER CORPORATION
1 BOSTON MEDICAL CTR PL # 1, BOSTON, MA
021182908
Phone: 617 414-5000
Web: WWW.BMC.ORG

PRODUCTS/OPERATIONS

Selected Services and Programs

Alzheimer' s Disease Center
Anesthesiology
Boston HealthNet
Boston University Affiliated Physicians
Boston University Cosmetic and Laser Center
Cardiovascular Center
Care Management
Dermatology
Diabetes
Elders Living at Home Program
Emergency Medicine
Facial Plastic and Reconstructive Surgery
General Internal Medicne / Primary Care
Geriatrics
Head and Neck Cancer Center of Excellence
Hematology & Medical Oncology
Immigrant & Refugee Health Program
Integrative Medicine
LocoMotor Training
Mattapan Community Health Center
Melanoma Program
Neurosurgery
Nursing
Ophthalmology
Oral and Maxillofacial Surgery
Pediatrics - bWell Center
  Pediatrics
Rehabilitation Therapies
Renal Medicine
South End Community Health Center
Special Kids Special Help
Thoracic Surgery
Transplant Surgery
Uphams Corner Health Center
Urology
Vascular Center
Vascular and Endovascular Surgery
Weight Loss Surgery (Bariatric Surgery)
Whittier Street Health Center

COMPETITORS

Beth Israel Deaconess Medical Center
Brigham and Women' s Hospital
Cambridge Health Alliance
Care New England
CareGroup

Children' s Hospital Boston
Dana-Farber
Massachusetts General Hospital
Newton-Wellesley Hospital
Northeast Health System
Partners HealthCare
Shriners Hospitals For Children
Spaulding Rehabilitation Hospital
St. Elizabeth' s Medical Center
Steward Health Care

HISTORICAL FINANCIALS

Company Type: Private

Income Statement

FYE: September 30

	REVENUE ($ mil.)	NET INCOME ($ mil.)	NET PROFIT MARGIN	EMPLOYEES
09/13	893	6	0.8%	4,200
09/12	886	2	0.3%	—
09/09	1,004	(12)	—	—
09/08	1,103	0	—	—
Annual Growth	(4.1%)	—	—	—

2013 Year-End Financials

Return on assets: 14.3%
Return on equity: 0.8%
Current ratio: 0.80
Cash ($ mil.): 139

BOWEN ENGINEERING CORPORATION

Bowen Engineering understands the elements of earth wind and water. The company provides engineering and construction services for water wastewater earthwork concrete industrial power and underground utility projects. It operates through three divisions: Power and industrial; private water; and public works. The company which has offices in Indiana Tennessee and Ohio offers design/build general contracting and construction management services to public and private clients. Bowen Engineering was founded in 1967 by Robert Bowen. The Bowen family continues to lead the company.

Bowen is expanding. In 2009 the company moved its headquarters to Indianapolis —a move that positioned Bowen for growth.

The company has worked an many projects including the Indiana University central power plant and the Tennessee Valley Authority Kingston Fossil plant. Most recently Bowen has recently been awarded contracts to work on wind power projects in Indiana.

EXECUTIVES

Vice President, Jim Ankrum
Senior Vice President, Jeff Chinn
Vice President Of Operations, Ed Storrs
Vice President P E, Bill Matthews
Vice President Business Development, Tom Kyner
Senior Vice President, Todd Lemen
**Vice President Business Development Gulf Coast
Operations,** Steve Blackmon
Auditors: BLUE & CO LLC CARMEL IN

LOCATIONS

HQ: BOWEN ENGINEERING CORPORATION
8802 N MERIDIAN ST, INDIANAPOLIS, IN 462605380
Phone: 219 661-9770
Web: WWW.BOWENENGINEERING.COM

PRODUCTS/OPERATIONS

Selected Services

Mechanical
  Process mechanical equipment
  Process piping
  Process boilermaker ductwork
  Process instrumentation
Site-Civil
  Excavation
  Concrete
Structural
  Structural steel
  Engineered structures

COMPETITORS

Black & Veatch
CH2M HILL
F.A. Wilhelm
Garney Holding
Hagerman Construction
Hunt Construction

HISTORICAL FINANCIALS

Company Type: Private

Income Statement

FYE: September 30

	REVENUE ($ mil.)	NET INCOME ($ mil.)	NET PROFIT MARGIN	EMPLOYEES
09/09	365	16	4.4%	700
09/08	288	17	6.0%	—
09/07	60	0	—	—
Annual Growth	—42515.9%	—	—	—

2009 Year-End Financials

Return on assets: 10.0%
Return on equity: 4.4%
Current ratio: 0.30
Cash ($ mil.): 19

BOY SCOUTS OF AMERICA

Scouts enter dens as Tigers and eventually take flight as Eagles. Boy Scouts of America (BSA) one of the nation's largest youth organizations has about 2.6 million youth members and more than 1 million adult leaders in its ranks. BSA offers educational and character-building programs emphasizing leadership citizenship personal development and physical fitness. In addition to traditional scouting programs (Tiger Cub Webelos and Boy Scouts ranging up to Eagle rank) it offers the Venturing program for boys and girls ages 14-21. BSA generates revenue through membership and council fees food and magazine sales and contributions. The organization was founded by Chicago publisher William Boyce in 1910.

Operations

BSA's group membership is supported through about 300 local Boy Scout councils. Additionally it hosts a National Scout Jamboree each year to bring all scouts together. The organization also operates a high-adventure base in West Virginia. The bases offer scouts a range of outdoor activities including backpacking camping canoeing and diving. The West Virginia location serves as the organization's permanent location for its annual Jamboree. BSA operates also bases in Florida Minnesota and New Mexico.

BSA also publishes Boys' Life monthly magazine which boasts more than 1 million subscribers and Scouting magazine for adults registered in Cub Scouting Boy Scouting Varsity Scouting and Venturing.

Financial Analysis

BSA's revenue increased 24% in 2013 to $283 over 2012's $229 million. The uptick was due to a bump in fees (44% of total revenue) primarily from the 2013 National Scout Jamboree as well as from contributions and bequests.

Strategy

BSA boasts programs that remain popular but in recent years membership growth has slowed with the recession and other societal forces including video games social media and other entertainment.

In 2013 Cub Scout membership (which accounts for more than 50% of total youth membership) dipped by about 7% while the ranks of the Boy Scouts decreased by 3%. Overall total youth membership declined by about 6% for the year continuing its downward trend. To boost membership and grow its organization BSA developed a strategic plan that involves reaching out to new groups of parents and students. To this end it has developed and maintained relationships with civic religious and fraternal organizations across the US including those that serve African-American Asian and Latino families. It has also analyzed Generation X and Millennial parents to determine how to best bring scouting to their families.

EXECUTIVES

Deputy Chief Scout Executive and COO, Gary P. Butler
National President, Robert M. Gates
CFO, Michael Ashline
Chief Scout Executive, Michael Surbaugh
Auditors: PRICEWATERHOUSCOOPER LLP DALL

LOCATIONS

HQ: BOY SCOUTS OF AMERICA
1325 W WALNUT HILL LN, IRVING, TX 750383096
Phone: 972 580-2000
Web: WWW.SCOUTING.ORG

PRODUCTS/OPERATIONS

2013 Youth Membership

	No.
Cub Scout-Age	1,417,034
Boy Scout	826,045
Venturers	192,080
Explorers	114,894
Varsity Scouts	62,902
Total	**2,612,955**

2013 Revenue

	$ mil.	% of total
Fees	123	44
Net investment gain	82	29
Contributions & bequests	37	13
Supply operations	28	10
Magazines	0	-
Other (includes trading post sales)	10	4
Total	**282**	**100**

HISTORICAL FINANCIALS

Company Type: Private

Income Statement

FYE: December 31

	REVENUE ($ mil.)	NET INCOME ($ mil.)	NET PROFIT MARGIN	EMPLOYEES
12/10	310	90	29.0%	2,800
12/09	287	145	50.5%	—
Annual Growth	8.0%	(37.9%)	—	—

2010 Year-End Financials

Return on assets: 16.6% Cash ($ mil.): 42
Return on equity: 29.0%
Current ratio: —

BRANDEIS UNIVERSITY

Brandeis University offers more than 40 undergraduate majors and more than 30 master's and doctoral degree programs. Located just west of Boston it comprises the College of Arts and Sciences the Graduate School of Arts and Sciences the International Business School the Heller School for Social Policy and Management the Lown School for Near Eastern and Judaic Studies and the Rabb School of Continuing Studies. The university has an enrollment of more than 5000 students; the student/faculty ratio is 9-to-1. A nonsectarian Jewish community-sponsored institution Brandeis University was founded in 1948 and is named after the late Justice Louis Brandeis of the US Supreme Court.

EXECUTIVES

Interim President and Provost; Dean Heller School for Social Policy and Management, Lisa M. Lynch
Provost and Chief Academic Officer, Steve A. N. Goldstein
CIO and Vice Provost for Library and Technology Services, John Unsworth
Dean International Business School, Bruce Magrid
SVP Finance and CFO, Marianne Cwalina
SVP and Chief of Staff, David A. Bunis
Dean College of Arts and Sciences, Susan J. Birren
Vice President, Karen Muncaster
Vice President for Operations, James (Jamie) Gray
Vice President, Ziqian LU
Assistant Vice President Corporate and Foundation Relations, Michael (Mel) Dettelbach
Vice President For Enrollment Development, Carolina Figueroa
Senior Vice President Chief Operating Officer, Steven Mano
Interim Senior Vice President for Communications, Judy Glasser
Senior Vice President and General Counsel, Judith (Judi) Sizer
Executive Vice President Chief Operating Officer, Peter French
Executive Vice President, Arlene Carey
Chair Department of Computer Science, Timothy (Tim) Hickey
Vice President, Peter Walton
Associate Vice President Campaign, Susan Krinsky
Vice President Campus Operations, Mark Collins
Vice President, Shirel Guez
Senior Vice President Institutional Advancement, Nancy Winship
Vice President, Shourya Veeraganti
Vice President Marketing Of Ascend Brandeis Chapter, Huan Zhou
Vice President, Shen Wang
Chair, Malcolm L. Sherman
Treasurer, Helen Berger
Assistant Treasurer, Jiaying Zhang
Assistant Treasurer, Heather Yoon
Secretary, Eleanor Fruchter
Treasurer, Ean Silbar
Secretary, Briana McCalmon-bailey
Secretary, Megan Shin
Assistant Treasurer, Harry Greenberg
Treasurer, Rohan Lal
Secretary, George Velonias
Auditors: KPMG LLP BOSTON MA

LOCATIONS

HQ: BRANDEIS UNIVERSITY
415 SOUTH ST MS110, WALTHAM, MA 024532700
Phone: 781 736-8317
Web: WWW.CYC.BRANDEIS.EDU

HISTORICAL FINANCIALS

Company Type: Private

Income Statement

FYE: June 30

	REVENUE ($ mil.)	NET INCOME ($ mil.)	NET PROFIT MARGIN	EMPLOYEES
06/13	305	77	25.5%	1,200
06/10	323	(24)	—	—
06/09	248	(173)	—	—
Annual Growth	5.3%	—	—	—

2013 Year-End Financials

Return on assets: — Cash ($ mil.): 26
Return on equity: 25.5%
Current ratio: —

BRAZOS ELECTRIC POWER COOPERATIVE INC.

Brazos means "arms" in Spanish and the generation and transmission arms of Brazos Electric Power Cooperative reach across 68 Texas counties. It serves 16 member/owner distribution cooperatives and one municipality in Northern and Central Texas. Brazos Electric Power annually generates (through its four power stations) and/or accesses from other power marketers some 3655 MW of electric power. The cooperative's members include Comanche Electric Cooperative Association Heart of Texas Electric Co-op (McGregor) Mid-South Synergy (Navasota) United Coop Services (Cleburne) and Wise Electric (Decatur).

Brazos Electric Power is the largest generation and transmission cooperative in Texas. Its service region stretches from the Greater Houston area to Lubbock in the Texas Panhandle.

The cooperative is managed by a board of directors on which each of its member cooperatives has a representative. The board's ongoing strategy is to find ways to generate buy and transmit power at low costs and with high reliability.

Benefitting from federal government support in 2010 the co-op was selected by USDA Rural Development's Rural Utilities Service to get a $438.9 million loan guarantee to allow it to build 237 miles of new transmission lines and improve 52 miles of existing transmission lines.

Founded in 1941 Brazos Electric Power was the state's first electricity generation and transmission cooperative.

EXECUTIVES

Vice President Technology, Lynn Gustafson
Managing Director, Steve Dillon
Vice President, David Murphy
Secretary, Lois Anderson

LOCATIONS

HQ: BRAZOS ELECTRIC POWER COOPERATIVE INC.
2404 LA SALLE AVE, WACO, TX 767063928
Phone: 254 750-6500
Web: WWW.BRAZOSELECTRIC.COM

Brazos Electric Power Cooperative has operations in 68 counties in northern and Central Texas.

PRODUCTS/OPERATIONS

Member/Owners
Barlett Electric Cooperative
BEPC
Comanche Electric Cooperative
Cooke County Electric Cooperative
CoServ Electric
Fort Belknap Electric Cooperative
Hamilton County Electric Cooperative
Heart of Texas Electric Cooperative
HILCO Electric Cooperative
J-A-C Electric Cooperative
Mid-South Synergy
Navarro County Electric Cooperative
Navasota Valley Electric Cooperative
South Plains Electric Cooperative
Tri-County Electric Cooperative
United Cooperative Services
Wise Electric Cooperative

COMPETITORS

AEP
CenterPoint Energy
El Paso Electric
Energy Future
Entergy
LCRA

HISTORICAL FINANCIALS
Company Type: Private

Income Statement
FYE: December 31

	REVENUE ($ mil.)	NET INCOME ($ mil.)	NET PROFIT MARGIN	EMPLOYEES
12/09	963	56	5.9%	366
12/99	307	6	2.3%	—
12/98	286	0	0.3%	—
12/97	278	0	—	—
Annual Growth	10.9%	—	—	—

2009 Year-End Financials
Return on assets: —
Return on equity: 5.9%
Current ratio: 0.10
Cash ($ mil.): 1

BROADWAY MANOR NURSING HOME

LOCATIONS

HQ: BROADWAY MANOR NURSING HOME
1622 E BROADWAY ST, MUSKOGEE, OK 744034601
Phone: 918 683-2851
Web: WWW.BROADWAYMANORHEALTHCARE.COM

HISTORICAL FINANCIALS
Company Type: Private

Income Statement
FYE: June 30

	REVENUE ($ mil.)	NET INCOME ($ mil.)	NET PROFIT MARGIN	EMPLOYEES
06/09*	494	(6)	—	100
12/00	3	0	18.5%	—
Annual Growth	87.3%	—	—	—

*Fiscal year change

2009 Year-End Financials
Return on assets: —
Return on equity: (-1.4%)
Current ratio: 2.10
Cash ($ mil.): —

BROCKTON HOSPITAL INC.

Signature Healthcare Brockton Hospital is a not-for-profit acute medical facility that serves southeastern Massachusetts. The hospital has 245 beds including about 30 beds in its skilled nursing unit. Its emergency department sees more than 62000 patients per year. Specialized services include radiation oncology cardiac care pediatrics orthopedics and joint replacement and inpatient and outpatient psychiatry. It is a community-based teaching hospital and part of the Signature Healthcare network. Brockton Hospital also formed a clinical affiliation with Beth Israel Deaconess Medical Center in 2013.

Geographic Reach

Signature Healthcare Brockton serves about 460000 people residing in more than 20 communities in southeastern Massachusetts.

Operations

Through the affiliation with Beth Israel Deaconess Brockton Hospital has access to Harvard-affiliated specialists as well as resources that will help to improve its residency and teaching programs. Brockton Hospital has also provided certain services in affiliation with Tufts Medical Center such as pediatric care.

The Signature Healthcare organization also includes affiliated primary care physician practices specialty outpatient clinics and a nursing school. Its Signature Medical Group operates practices in fields including primary diagnostic and urgent care as well as women's health.

Strategy

Signature Healthcare forms collaborative agreements with other providers to enhance medical services in the region. It also works to enhance its offerings by developing new services and programs in high-demand fields such as diabetes care and obesity treatment as well as diagnostic and orthopedic capabilities. In addition Signature Healthcare is working to reduce medical errors enhance employee productivity and increase consumer health awareness through the implementation of electronic health record (EHR) systems.

Company Background

Signature Healthcare Brockton Hospital was founded in 1896 as Brockton Hospital. It changed its name from Brockton Health to Signature Healthcare in 2008.

EXECUTIVES

Director Of Health Information, Debbie Mellace
Auditors: PRICEWATERHOUSECOOPERS LLP BO

LOCATIONS

HQ: BROCKTON HOSPITAL INC.
680 CENTRE ST, BROCKTON, MA 023023395
Phone: 508 941-7000
Web: WWW.SIGNATURE-HEALTHCARE.ORG

PRODUCTS/OPERATIONS

Selected Services
Acupuncture
Anesthesiology
Behavioral health
Cancer care
Cardiac care
Cardiac rehab
Concussion/Traumatic brain injury program
Critical care
CT scan
Diabetes information
Endoscopy
Emergency care
Eye services
Family practice
Gastroenterology
Hospitalists
Imaging
Infection control
Internal medicine
Laboratory
Maternal-Newborn Pavilion
MRI
Neurology
Nuclear medicine
Nurse midwifery services
Nutrition
Obstetrics/gynecology
Occupational therapy
Orthopedics
Otoplasty
Outpatient care
Pain management
Pediatrics
Perinatology
Physical therapy
Plastic surgery
Primary care
Radiology and medical imaging
Radiation therapy center/Vantage oncology
Respiratory therapy
Speech therapy
Stress test
Stroke center
Surgery
Transitional care
Ultrasound
Urgent care
Vascular lab
Weight and wellness center
Wound care

COMPETITORS

Boston Medical Center
CareGroup
Lahey Health System
McLean Hospital
Northeast Health System
Partners HealthCare
Steward Health Care

HISTORICAL FINANCIALS
Company Type: Private

Income Statement
FYE: September 30

	REVENUE ($ mil.)	NET INCOME ($ mil.)	NET PROFIT MARGIN	EMPLOYEES
09/14	236	(15)	—	1,500
09/13	211	19	9.3%	—
09/12	222	19	8.9%	—
09/09	200	0	—	—
Annual Growth	3.3%	—	—	—

2014 Year-End Financials
Return on assets: 7.2%
Return on equity: (-6.6%)
Current ratio: 1.20
Cash ($ mil.): 19

BRONSON METHODIST HOSPITAL INC

From your leg bone to your knee bone; your neck bone to your head bone Bronson Methodist Hospital has the specialists to cure what ails you. The 435-bed hospital is the flagship facility of the Bronson Healthcare Group a not-for-profit health care system. Bronson Methodist provides care in just about every specialty including orthopedics surgery and oncology. The hospital also contains specialist units for critical care (level I trauma center) neurology (primary stroke center) cardiology

(Chest pain emergency center) women's health (BirthPlace) and pediatrics (children's hospital).

Geographic Reach

Bronson Methodist serves patients throughout southwestern Michigan from its main facility in Kalamazoo.

Operations

In addition to providing general emergency and specialty inpatient care to privately insured or self-paying customers the hospital serves a large percentage of Medicaid patients and provides charity care to uninsured patients. Altogether Bronson Methodist's charity and community outreach program contributions total more than $55 million annually.

The hospital contains the Bronson Children's Hospital which offers burn and wound neonatal development and newborn pulmonary services among others.

Strategy

All of the hospital's inpatient rooms are private; this transition was made to reduce infection rates and increase privacy for Bronson Methodist patients.

Bronson Methodist began participation in the bundled payment program of the Centers for Medicare and Medicaid Services in 2013. The program is designed to improve the quality of care delivery for Medicare patients by changing the way that providers are reimbursed for services.

EXECUTIVES

Vice President System Quality Standards, Cheryl Knapp

Director Of Radiology, Brook Ward

LOCATIONS

HQ: BRONSON METHODIST HOSPITAL INC
601 JOHN ST STE E-012, KALAMAZOO, MI
490075346
Phone: 269 341-7654
Web: WWW.BRONSONHEALTH.COM

PRODUCTS/OPERATIONS

Selected Services
Anticoagulation
Bereavement
Breast Health
Burn
Cancer Care
Critical Care
Diabetes
Flu
Heart and Vascular
Home Health
Hyperbaric Oxygen Therapy
Infusion
Laboratory
Medical and Surgical Weight Management
Neurosciences
Nutrition
Occupational Health
Orthopedics
Palliative Care
Pediatrics
Pharmacy
Pregnancy and Childbirth
Rehabilitation
Respiratory Care
Sleep
Surgery
Stomal Therapy
Testing and Imaging
Trauma and Emergency
Women's Health
Wound

COMPETITORS

Ascension Health	Holland Hospital
Borgess Health	Spectrum Health
Bronson Battle Creek	Trinity Health (Novi)
Community Hospital	Zeeland Community
Elkhart General	Hospital

Healthcare System
Hayes Green Beach
Memorial Hospital

HISTORICAL FINANCIALS
Company Type: Private

Income Statement FYE: December 31

	REVENUE ($ mil.)	NET INCOME ($ mil.)	NET PROFIT MARGIN	EMPLOYEES
12/12	422	39	9.4%	2,861
12/09	524	41	7.9%	—
12/08	491	(1)	—	—
12/07	487	0	—	—
Annual Growth	(2.8%)	—	—	—

2012 Year-End Financials

Return on assets: —
Return on equity: 9.4%
Current ratio: 2.20

Cash ($ mil.): —

BRONX LEBANON HOSPITAL CENTER (INC)

Bronx-Lebanon Hospital Center cares for patients in the central and south Bronx no doubt while rooting for the Yankees a few blocks away. The health care provider maintains more than 970 beds across its two campuses as well as psychiatric and nursing home facilities. Hospital specialty units include chest pain orthopedic cancer and women's health centers. Bronx-Lebanon also manages a network of about 70 owned and affiliated medical practices (under the BronxCare brand). This network includes primary care doctors and specialty clinics as well as rehabilitation facilities. The hospital is also a primary teaching hospital for the Albert Einstein College of Medicine.

Geographic Reach

The hospital system's 37 locations serve residents of central and south Bronx in New York.

Operations

Aside from its two major hospitals Bronx-Lebanon operates a psychiatric facility a pair of specialized long-term care facilities and the Bronx-Care network of medical practices that include Dr. Martin Luther King Jr. Health Center and a 51-unit facility to house seniors and low-income residents. Bronx-Lebanon cares for those with mental or substance abuse problems through the Family Wellness Center. It also operates a 240-bed Special Care Center and the 90-bed Highbridge Woodycrest Center to provide long term health care to geriatric AIDS and disabled residents. Its ER Department responds to about 141000 patient visits a year.

Sales and Marketing

In 2013 the company spent about $144000 on advertising.

Financial PerformanceThe Hospital Center is supported primarily by patient service fees paid by Medicaid Medicare and commercial insurance carriers. In 2013 the Medicaid contributed 63% of the revenue whereas Medicare contributed 28% and the rest 9% was contributed other third-party insurance carriers.

In 2013 Bronx-Lebanon's net revenues increased by about 5% due to a rise in patient service revenues and grants partially offset by a decrease in auxiliary services.

The company's net income increased by more than 790% in 2013 as the result of an increase in

revenues. Bronx-Lebanon's operating cash flows increased by 53% thanks to higher income.

Strategy

Bronx-Lebanon emphasizes its role as a community health care provider not only through its BronxCare network but through a number of community outreach and service efforts including school-based programs mobile health units free health screening and even a weekly live television show that discusses health issues.

To accommodate the growing population in and around the Bronx the hospital system has expanded in recent years with a new children's wing for inpatient and outpatient services; a nine-story ambulatory care facility; and an extensive emergency room modernization. Bronx-Lebanon also maintains a short stay observation unit in the emergency room area to monitor and evaluate patients in cardiac distress prior to admission or discharge.

Bronx-Lebanon is one of many hospital organizations to have joined a regional health information organization (RHIO) to allow medical professionals to access a patient's medical records at any number of health care locations. Other members of the Bronx RHIO include Montefiore Medical Center Jacobi Medical Center St. Barnabas Hospital and Hebrew Home at Riverdale.

Bronx-Lebanon is also one of the few hospitals in New York that is fully computerized with a complete inpatient and outpatient electronic medical record.

The hospital center's expansion plans include a $42 million 60000 sq. ft ambulatory care facility and a $34 million 56000 sq. ft. life recovery center for chemical dependency services.

In 2014 the company completed the construction of its Health and Wellness Center a new state-of-the-art outpatient facility with general and specialty services and new treatment rooms and diagnostic equipment. It also completed the construction of its Life Recovery Center to combine inpatient outpatient and residential services for individuals suffering from chemical dependency.The company also expanded its Emergency room adding a new 11-bay treatment area.In the same year it also relocated and expanded its main Dentistry Practice adding 39 dental chairs (a 50% increase).

EXECUTIVES

Vice President Rcm, George Irizarry
Medical Director, Soni Mathew
Director Of Operating Room, Lydia Cosme
Vice President, Milton Gumbs
Assistant Vice President Patient Care Services, Prissana Alston
Vice President, Clarett Forbes
Vice President Finance, Victor Demarco
Auditors: LOEB & TROPER LLP NEW YORK N

LOCATIONS

HQ: BRONX LEBANON HOSPITAL CENTER (INC)
1276 FULTON AVE, BRONX, NY 104563499
Phone: 718 590-1800
Web: WWW.BRONX-LEB.ORG

PRODUCTS/OPERATIONS

Selected Services
Anesthesiology
Asthma
 Adult
 Pediatric
Cardiology
Dentistry
Diabetes
 Adult
 Pediatric
Ear Nose & Throat
Gastroenterology
Hematology & Oncology

Neonatology
Neurology
Ophthalmology
Orthopaedics
Pediatrics
Physical Medicine
Psychiatry
Radiology
Special Care Center
Urology & Men' s Health

Selected Academic Affiliations

Albert Einstein College of Medicine
Bronx Community College
Hostos Community College
Lehman College City University of New York
State University of New York at Stony Brook

COMPETITORS

Beth Israel Medical Center
Catholic Healthcare System
Continuum Health Partners
Lenox Hill Hospital
Maimonides Medical Center
Memorial Sloan-Kettering
Montefiore Medical
New York City Health and Hospitals
NewYork-Presbyterian Healthcare
North Shore-Long Island Jewish Health System
Winthrop-University Hospital

HISTORICAL FINANCIALS

Company Type: Private

Income Statement

	REVENUE ($ mil.)	NET INCOME ($ mil.)	NET PROFIT MARGIN	EMPLOYEES
12/09	709	22	3.1%	4,000
12/08	489	(45)	—	—
12/07	634	21	3.4%	—
12/06	513	0	—	—
Annual Growth	11.4%	—	—	—

2009 Year-End Financials

Return on assets: 6.8%
Return on equity: 3.1%
Current ratio: 0.60
Cash ($ mil.): 67

BROOKHAVEN MEMORIAL HOSPITAL MEDICAL CENTER INC.

Brookhaven Memorial Hospital Medical Center is an acute-care facility with more than 300 beds that serves patients primarily in Suffolk County on Long Island New York. The not-for-profit community hospital's Emergency Trauma and Chest Pain Pavilion is one of the largest emergency rooms on Long Island. Founded in 1956 Brookhaven Memorial also offers behavioral health services including inpatient and outpatient mental health and alcohol treatment services. In addition to hospital services the medical center operates two community health clinics and a specialty center that provides hemodialysis women's imaging and home health and hospice services.

Geographic Reach
The medical center serves those who reside in the Suffolk County area of Long Island New York which consists of 28 communities.

Operations

Brookhaven Memorial Hospital Medical Center comprises a main campus Level II Trauma Center/Emergency Room a pair of community multidisciplinary health centers and a downtown Patchogue facility for its hemodialysis program home health and hospice services and ambulatory women's imaging center. Its emergency department treats more than 70000 patients.

It operates the South Brookhaven Family Health Center in Patchogue and Shirley on a contractual basis along with Suffolk County Department of Health. Brookhaven Memorial logs the largest number of visits in the town of Patchogue.

Strategy
Brookhaven Memorial has been expanding and entering new markets. Brookhaven Memorial in 2014 embarked on a $60-million expansion project for its new Knapp Cardiac Center which spans some 60000 sq. ft. It also opened a Bellport Primary Care Center in 2014 to provide primary medicine to an underserved community.

EXECUTIVES

Vice President Operations, Satheesh Joseph
Auditors: BDO USA LLP NEW YORK NY

LOCATIONS

HQ: BROOKHAVEN MEMORIAL HOSPITAL MEDICAL CENTER INC.
101 HOSPITAL RD, EAST PATCHOGUE, NY 117724870
Phone: 631 654-7100
Web: WWW.BROOKHAVENHOSPITAL.ORG

Selected Locations

Brookhaven Center for Wound Care and Hyperbaric Medicine - Patchogue New York
Brookhaven Family Medicine - Patchogue New York
Brookhaven Hemodialysis Center - Patchogue New York
Brookhaven Home Care - Patchogue New York
Brookhaven Hospice - Patchogue New York
Brookhaven Memorial Hospital Medical Center - Patchogue New York
Brookhaven Outpatient Imaging - Patchogue New York
Cardiac Rehabilitation - Patchogue New York
Diabetes Wellness Center - Patchogue New York
South Brookhaven Health Center East - Shirley New York
South Brookhaven Health Center West - Patchogue New York

PRODUCTS/OPERATIONS

Selected Services
Medical Services
Behavioral Health
Cancer Care
Cardiology Department
Family Medicine
Long Island Orthopaedic and Spine Specialists
Laboratory
Neuroscience Center
Pain Management
Radiology Imaging
Respiratory Care
Surgery /
Women' s Im
Specialized Services
Bariatric and Wellness Program
Case Management
Community Health Centers
Coumadin Management Center
Diabetes Wellness Center
Hemodialysis Center
Home Health Agency
Hospice
Nutrition
Physical Rehabilitation
Sleep Center
Speech-Language Pathology
Support Groups
Wound Care / Hyperbaric Medicine

COMPETITORS

CSH
Catholic Health Services of Long Island

Catholic Healthcare System
Continuum Health Partners
Memorial Sloan-Kettering
New York City Health and Hospitals
North Shore-Long Island Jewish Health System

HISTORICAL FINANCIALS

Company Type: Private

Income Statement

	REVENUE ($ mil.)	NET INCOME ($ mil.)	NET PROFIT MARGIN	EMPLOYEES
12/09	298	(2)	—	2,100
12/06	269	6	2.6%	—
12/05	230	1	0.6%	—
12/04	230	0	—	—
Annual Growth	5.3%	—	—	—

2009 Year-End Financials

Return on assets: —
Return on equity: (-0.8%)
Current ratio: —
Cash ($ mil.): 18

BROOKLYN HOSPITAL CENTER

The Brooklyn Hospital Center has been taking care of ailing Kings County residents since before Brooklyn was a borough. Established in 1845 (before Brooklyn became part of New York City) the hospital houses some 460 beds and is a member of the NewYork-Presbyterian Healthcare System. It provides general medical and surgical care as well as a wide variety of specialty medical services including dialysis pediatrics obstetrics and cardiovascular care. The Brooklyn Hospital Center is affiliated with Weill Medical College of Cornell University. The hospital also operates a network of outpatient clinics providing primary and specialty care throughout the borough.

Operations
Each year the Brooklyn Hospital Center handles about 65000 ER visits 19000 inpatient stays and 150000 outpatient care visits. It has a medical staff of about 600 doctors. The hospital also conducts nursing and medical education programs.

Financial Performance
The Brooklyn Hospital Center has an annual operating budget of about $380 million.

Strategy
The Brooklyn Hospital Center is striving to increase the quality of its clinical programs and upgrade its infrastructure. It also aims to retain a quality medical staff and increase the hospitals educational and research activities.

Company Background
The Brooklyn Hospital Center filed for bankruptcy protection in 2005 when expensive expansion projects that didn't pay off as well as malpractice litigation left the company in more debt than it could manage. The hospital emerged from bankruptcy in 2007.

EXECUTIVES

Svp And Cfo, Joseph J Guarracino
VP and Acting CFO, Patrick S. Semenza
Assistant Vice President Finance, Rubin Diaz
Vice President Chief Development Officer, Debbie Niederhoffer
Senior Vice President And Chief Nursing Officer, Patricia Winston
Assistant Vice President, Elizabeth Bonetti

Vice President Physician Services Revenue
Enhancement And Analytics, Karen Milano
Vice Chairman Department Of Surgery And
Surgical Residency Program Director, Armand
Asarian
Auditors: ERNST & YOUNG LLP NEW YORK

LOCATIONS

HQ: BROOKLYN HOSPITAL CENTER
121 DEKALB AVE, BROOKLYN, NY 112015493
Phone: 718 250-8000
Web: WWW.TBH.ORG

PRODUCTS/OPERATIONS

Selected Services
Bariatric Surgery
Cancer Care
Dental Care and Oral Surgery
Dialysis Services
Emergency Medicine
Family Medicine
The Family Medicine Residency
Geriatric Care
Home Health Services
Imaging and Radiology
Inpatient Hospitalist Care
Obstetrics and Gynecology
Orthopaedic Surgery
Pediatrics
Pediatric Cancer Care
Pediatric Emergency Services
Pediatric and Neonatal Critical Care
Sleep Center
Spine and Neurosurgery
Stroke Center
TeleHealth
Vascular Surgery
Wound Care

COMPETITORS

Brookdale University Hospital
Catholic Healthcare System
Continuum Health Partners
Kingsbrook Jewish Medical Center
Maimonides Medical Center
Montefiore Medical
New York City Health and Hospitals
North Shore-Long Island Jewish Health System
SUNY Downstate
Winthrop-University Hospital

HISTORICAL FINANCIALS

Company Type: Private

Income Statement FYE: December 31

	REVENUE ($ mil.)	NET INCOME ($ mil.)	NET PROFIT MARGIN	EMPLOYEES
12/12	384	5	1.4%	3,300
12/11	379	10	2.6%	
12/10	388	5	1.5%	
12/09	0	0	—	
Annual Growth	7201.2%	—	—	—

2012 Year-End Financials

Return on assets: —
Return on equity: 1.4%
Current ratio: 0.80

Cash ($ mil.): 17

BROWN'S SUPER STORES INC.

LOCATIONS

HQ: BROWN' S SUPER STORES INC.
700 DELSEA DR, WESTVILLE, NJ 080931229
Phone: 856 933-7000
Web: WWW.UPLIFTSOLUTIONS.ORG

HISTORICAL FINANCIALS

Company Type: Private

Income Statement FYE: December 29

	REVENUE ($ mil.)	NET INCOME ($ mil.)	NET PROFIT MARGIN	EMPLOYEES
12/07	312	2	0.7%	2,200
12/06	373	1	0.4%	
12/05*	0	0	—	
01/05	248	0	—	
Annual Growth	8.0%	—	—	—

*Fiscal year change

2007 Year-End Financials

Return on assets: 6.8%
Return on equity: 0.7%
Current ratio: 0.20

Cash ($ mil.): 4

BRUCE OAKLEY INC.

From little acorns mighty Oakleys grow. Bruce
Oakley provides road and river (barge) transportation of dry bulk commodities as well as grain storage and bulk fertilizer sales. The company's trucking division which uses both end-dump and
pneumatic tank trailers serves the continental US
and Canada. Overall Bruce Oakley operates some
450 trailers. It maintains about half a dozen ports
in Arkansas Louisiana and Missouri on the
Arkansas Mississippi and Red rivers and the company's river barge transportation unit operates on
those and other inland and intracoastal waterways.
Grain storage services are available in five ports in
Arkansas. Bruce Oakley was founded in 1968.

Additionally the company offers farm supplies
including feed vet supplies fencing hay salt and
lime. Its Oakley Beebe facility which can warehouse 2000 tons of bagged product provides bagging and spreading services for its wholesale fertilizer.

Bruce Oakley is in the thick of it when it comes
to what Louisiana farmers decide to grow —corn
or soy beans. Because corn is more marketable
and easier to harvest farmers have traditionally
chosen it over soybeans even though it draws a
lower price per bushel. Soy beans which are not
as hearty as corn require more immediate transport after harvest over much longer distances (250
miles to market compared to corn's 65 miles).

EXECUTIVES

Vice President, Shane Smith
Vice President, Bruce Oakley

LOCATIONS

HQ: BRUCE OAKLEY INC.
3700 LINCOLN AVE, NORTH LITTLE ROCK, AR
721146448
Phone: 501 945-0875
Web: WWW.BRUCEOAKLEY.COM

PRODUCTS/OPERATIONS

Selected Products and Services
Bagging
Barges
Bulk fertilizer
Grain and grain storage
Oakley vessel freight
River ports and stevedoring
Trucking

COMPETITORS

American Commercial Lines
Bulkmatic
Comcar
GrainCorp
Groendyke Transport
Kansas City Southern
Superior Bulk Logistics

HISTORICAL FINANCIALS

Company Type: Private

Income Statement FYE: September 25

	REVENUE ($ mil.)	NET INCOME ($ mil.)	NET PROFIT MARGIN	EMPLOYEES
09/08	1,160	31	2.8%	670
09/07	526	11	2.2%	
Annual Growth	120.2%	170.9%		

2008 Year-End Financials

Return on assets: 0.9%
Return on equity: 2.8%
Current ratio: 0.80

Cash ($ mil.): 3

BRUCKNER TRUCK SALES INC.

Auditors: BROWN GRAHAM & COMPANY AMARI

LOCATIONS

HQ: BRUCKNER TRUCK SALES INC.
9471 E INTERSTATE 40, AMARILLO, TX 791186960
Phone: 806 376-6273
Web: WWW.BRUCKNERTRUCK.COM

HISTORICAL FINANCIALS

Company Type: Private

Income Statement FYE: June 30

	REVENUE ($ mil.)	NET INCOME ($ mil.)	NET PROFIT MARGIN	EMPLOYEES
06/14	490	10	2.1%	550
06/10	200	2	1.1%	
06/09	229	4	1.9%	
06/08	1,193	0	—	
Annual Growth	(13.8%)	—	—	—

2014 Year-End Financials

Return on assets: 2.9%
Return on equity: 2.1%
Current ratio: 0.50

Cash ($ mil.): 33

BRYAN MEDICAL CENTER

Bryan Medical Center is the centerpiece of a not-for-profit health care system serving residents of Lincoln Nebraska and surrounding communities. The medical center which operates as part of Bryan Health features two acute-care hospitals (Bryan East and Bryan West) housing a combined 670 beds. In addition to providing general medical and surgical care it serves as a regional trauma center and provides specialty care in areas such as cancer orthopedics and cardiology. The Bryan Health organization also includes a rural hospital and several outpatient clinics and it provides medical training home health care services and wellness programs.

OperationsIn addition to Bryan Medical Center the Bryan Health organization operates the Crete Area Medical Center a 25-bed community hospital. Outpatient facilities include the Bryan Heart Institute (cardiology and cardiothoracic surgery) the Bryan Physician Network (family practice urgent care and specialist locations) and Bryan LifePointe (wellness and fitness programs). In addition the network includes the Bryan College of Health Sciences which provides bachelor's and master's degrees in nursing and health professional fields and the Bryan Foundation. It also conducts community education activities.

In the latest year for which data is available the hospital had 5912 inpatient visits; 6650 outpatient surgeries; and 68352 emergency department visits.Geographic ReachBryan Medical Center serves patients throughout Nebraska as well as portions of neighboring states including Kansas Iowa and Missouri with clinics in more than 30 communities including Lincoln Columbus and Hastings.

Sales and Marketing

Bryan Medical Center advertises through magazines and through the Internet.

Strategy

In 2015 the hospital became the first in Nebraska to utilize the CardioMEMS HF System a miniaturized and wireless monitoring device to manage heart failure and reduce hospital admissions. That year it also began using the Kiva VCF Treatment System for the treatment of patients with vertebral compression fractures.

Company BackgroundThe BryanLGH system was formed through the 1997 combination of Bryan Memorial Hospital (named after populist firebrand William Jennings Bryan) and Lincoln General Hospital. Bryan Health is part of the Heartland Health Alliance a group of about 40 Nebraska hospitals that work together to improve rural health care services through shared services and best practices.

In 2012 the health organization rebranded itself to reflect its expanded position in the region's health care market.BryanLGH Medical Center was renamed Bryan Medical Center and the broader health organization changed its name from the BryanLGH Health System to simply Bryan Health.

EXECUTIVES

Vp Medical Affairs, John J Trapp, age 54
Infection Control Director, Larry Krebsbach
Vice President, Cathy Parker
Respiratory Therapy Director, Marcy Wyrens
Vice President, Ken Foster
Pharmacy Manager, Penny Drews
Director of Radiology, Albert (Al) Owusu-ansah

LOCATIONS

HQ: BRYAN MEDICAL CENTER
   1600 S 48TH ST, LINCOLN, NE 685061283
Phone: 402 481-3190
Web: WWW.BRYANHEALTH.COM

PRODUCTS/OPERATIONS

Selected Services
Bariatrics
Cardiac Services
Cancer
Cardiothoracic Surgery
Childbirth/Family Birthplace
Corporate & Community Wellness
Diabetes Center
Early Detection
Emergency Department
Heart Valve Center of Excellence
Hospitalists
Independence Center
Inpatient Rehabilitation
Neuroscience
Mental Health
Orthopedics
Outpatient Specialty Clinic
Radiation Oncology
Radiology
Rehabilitation/Therapy
Robotic Surgery
Sleep Medicine
StarCare Air Ambulance
Substance Abuse
Trauma Center
Urgent Care
Vascular Services
Women's & Children's

COMPETITORS

Catholic Health Initiatives
Children's Hospital & Medical Center
Madonna Rehabilitation Hospital
Methodist Health System
Nebraska Medical Center

HISTORICAL FINANCIALS

Company Type: Private

Income Statement

FYE: December 31

	REVENUE ($ mil.)	NET INCOME ($ mil.)	NET PROFIT MARGIN	EMPLOYEES
12/13*	273	48	17.7%	3,970
05/13	462	77	16.7%	
05/12	481	(4)	—	
05/11	478	0	—	
Annual Growth	(17.0%)	—	—	—

*Fiscal year change

2013 Year-End Financials

Return on assets: 5.0%
Return on equity: 17.7%
Current ratio: 3.00
Cash ($ mil.): 122

BUCKEYE POWER INC.

It has cost a few bucks to generate power but the effort has been well worth it for Buckeye Power an electricity generation and transmission cooperative that provides electricity to 24 distribution companies in Ohio and one in Michigan. Together they serve about 400000 homes and businesses in 77 of Ohio's 88 counties. The company was established by Ohio's rural electric co-ops to produce and transmit electric power for member systems throughout the state. Buckeye Power contracts with other Ohio electric companies to use their transmission systems to transmit power to its member electric distribution cooperatives.

Buckeye Power owns two of the three generating units at the Cardinal Generating Station on the Ohio River and contracts with other Ohio electric companies to use their transmission systems to transmit power to its member electric distribution cooperatives.

Buckeye Power is owned by 25 electric distribution cooperatives in Ohio (24 of the cooperatives are based in the state). A 25th Midwest Energy Cooperative based in Cassopolis Michigan serves about 1000 members in parts of Fulton and Williams counties in northwestern Ohio. Their coops' combined service areas cover 40% of the Michigan primarily its rural regions.

A super derecho storm in June 2012 with its very strong winds caused at least $12 million of damage to electric infrastructure in 21 counties across Ohio.

In addition to transmitting energy from traditional power plants Buckeye Power is looking to access a range of renewable sources and conservation measures to help the state meet its green energy goals. Its green portfolio includes contracts with a 150 MW wind energy farm biogas/landfill generation projects and a hydropower deal with the New York Power Authority. It also offers 100 kW-hour blocks of renewable power to members who wish to support environmental and energy goals by buying green power as well as a range of efficiency options (smart bulbs energy audits etc.) to individual customers.

Buckeye Power was formed by Ohio's electric cooperatives in 1959 as a statewide generation and transmission co-op. In the 1960s Buckeye Power and American Electric Power's Ohio Power unit teamed up to build the Cardinal Generating Station 1200 MW coal-fired power plant.

EXECUTIVES

Vice President of Engineering and Power Supply, Pat O'Loughlin
Treasurer, Nicholas Baker
Auditors: BDO USA LLP CHICAGO ILLINO

LOCATIONS

HQ: BUCKEYE POWER INC.
   6677 BUSCH BLVD, COLUMBUS, OH 432291101
Phone: 614 781-0573
Web: WWW.BUCKEYEPOWER.COM

COMPETITORS

AEP
FirstEnergy
Ohio Valley Electric

HISTORICAL FINANCIALS

Company Type: Private

Income Statement

FYE: June 30

	REVENUE ($ mil.)	NET INCOME ($ mil.)	NET PROFIT MARGIN	EMPLOYEES
06/13	639	26	4.1%	300
06/12	626	31	5.0%	—
06/11	580	32	5.7%	—
06/10	538	0	—	—
Annual Growth	5.9%	—	—	—

2013 Year-End Financials

Return on assets: 9.1%
Return on equity: 4.1%
Current ratio: 0.40
Cash ($ mil.): 25

BUCKNELL UNIVERSITY

Just getting into Bucknell University is an accomplishment. The highly selective private liberal arts school accepts only about 10% of applicants each year. Students who do get in some 3600 of them from around the world have the option to specialize in more than 50 majors and 60 minors. Bucknell confers both undergraduate and master's degrees in the liberal arts sciences engineering and music. It also offers programs in pre-law and pre-med. Bucknell tuition and fees total more than $58000; more than half of the student body typically receives financial aid. The school's student-to-faculty ratio is 10-to-1.

Geographic Background

In fiscal year 2013 Bucknell enrolled students from 46 states and 63 countries. The minority student enrollment is more than 500 with more than 175 foreign students.

Operations

Some 86% of undergraduates live on campus. Bucknell has more than 350 full-time faculty members of which about 97% hold PhD or equivalent terminal degrees. Some 62% of faculty are tenured.

The university's Bertrand Library houses more than 800000 books.

Financial Performance

Bucknell's revenue increased by 4% in fiscal year 2013 thanks to higher net tuition and fees and an increase in net investment income from endowments. The university reported $74 million of net income in fiscal year 2013 (compared to a loss in 2012) due to stronger non-operating net investment income and post retiree credits and an increase in income from grants and capital gifts.

Company Background

Bucknell was founded in 1846 as the University at Lewisburg.

EXECUTIVES

Vice President, Matthew McAnear
Vice President Of Campus Environment, Lynn Pierson
Vice President Of Finance, Matthew Garman
Vice President, Julie Kohn
Vice President Of Administration, Clinton Kittrell
Vice President, Sean Coyne
Vice President Marketing and Market Research, LaVonne Poteet
Treasurer, Chelsea Brinkman
Secretary, Kelly Sprague
Secretary, Rebecca Howell
Service Chair, Ava Ginsberg
Treasurer, Dan Hart
Treasurer, Charlotte Clegg
Secretary, Maura Higgins
Treasurer, Billy Raska
Auditors: KPMG LLP HARRISBURG PA

LOCATIONS

HQ: BUCKNELL UNIVERSITY
1 DENT DR, LEWISBURG, PA 178372029
Phone: 570 577-2000
Web: WWW.BUCKNELL.EDU

HISTORICAL FINANCIALS
Company Type: Private

Income Statement
FYE: June 30

	REVENUE ($ mil.)	NET INCOME ($ mil.)	NET PROFIT MARGIN	EMPLOYEES
06/14	206	92	45.0%	1,500
06/13	196	74	37.8%	—
06/12	189	(28)	—	—
06/11	184	0	—	—
Annual Growth	3.8%	—	—	—

2014 Year-End Financials
Return on assets: 11.1% Cash ($ mil.): 9
Return on equity: 45.0%
Current ratio: —

BUNKERS INTERNATIONAL CORP.

LOCATIONS

HQ: BUNKERS INTERNATIONAL CORP.
1071 S SUN DR STE 3, LAKE MARY, FL 327462405
Phone: 407 328-7757
Web: WWW.BUNKERSINTERNATIONAL.COM

HISTORICAL FINANCIALS
Company Type: Private

Income Statement
FYE: December 31

	REVENUE ($ mil.)	NET INCOME ($ mil.)	NET PROFIT MARGIN	EMPLOYEES
12/08	436	1	0.4%	100
12/07	319	1	0.4%	—
12/01	436	0	0.0%	—
Annual Growth	0.0%	92.3%	—	—

2008 Year-End Financials
Return on assets: — Cash ($ mil.): 2
Return on equity: 0.4%
Current ratio: 1.10

BURLINGTON HEALTH CARE CENTER (66) INC.

LOCATIONS

HQ: BURLINGTON HEALTH CARE CENTER (66) INC.
1987 HILTON RD, BURLINGTON, NC 272172968
Phone: 336 226-0848
Web: WWW.ALAMANCEREHAB.COM

C & K MARKET INC.

Family-owned C&K Market operates about 45 supermarkets in southern Oregon and northern California mostly under the name Ray's Food Place but also under Shop Smart and C&K banners. The Shop Smart warehouse-style stores focus on value-priced groceries and household goods. Most of C&K's stores are situated in small rural communities. C&K Market was founded in 1957 by Raymond "Ray" Nidiffer. Stung by competition from large national discounters including Wal-Mart and Costco the regional chain filed for bankruptcy in late 2013 and closed 15 supermarkets and sold 15 pharmacies.

Bankruptcy

C&K Market filed a voluntary petition for Chapter 11 bankruptcy protection in November 2013 blaming competition from larger chains legacy costs underperforming stores and debt issues. C&K expects to emerge from bankruptcy in May 2014.

Geographic Reach

The Oregon-based grocer operates about 45 stores in Oregon and northern California.

Financial Performance

C&K's stores rang up an estimated $480 million in sales in 2012.

Strategy

Traditionally C&K has focused on serving small rural communities. However as more rural shoppers travel to buy groceries at larger grocery chains and mega-stores its sales have declined. Indeed in its bankruptcy filing C&K said most of its stores are within 40 miles of "a large discount grocery operation such as Wal-Mart of Costco." By closing about a third of its grocery stores and selling its freestanding pharmacies the chain hopes to remain viable. The store closings resulted in a workforce reduction of about 20%. The company sold its 15 Pharmacy Express stores in late 2013 to focus on its core grocery business.

Prior to its Chapter 11 filing C&K was experimenting with new store formats. In late 2012 it launched a new everyday low price grocery banner called Lo Buck$. The 40000-square-foot store features a "wall of values" and has a large Hispanic foods section. It also serves up natural and organic items fresh meat and produce.

Ownership

C&K Market is a family-owned company.

EXECUTIVES

Chairman of the Board, Doug Nidiffer
President Chief Executive Officer, Greg Sandeno

HISTORICAL FINANCIALS
Company Type: Private

Income Statement
FYE: September 30

	REVENUE ($ mil.)	NET INCOME ($ mil.)	NET PROFIT MARGIN	EMPLOYEES
09/09	1,165	88	7.6%	160
09/04	9	0	5.0%	—
09/03	9	0	5.3%	—
09/02	9	0	—	—
Annual Growth	99.4%	—	—	—

2009 Year-End Financials
Return on assets: — Cash ($ mil.): —
Return on equity: 7.6%
Current ratio: 2.90

Executive Vice President Chief Financial & Administrative Officer, Elizabeth Bauer
Executive Vice President Chief Information Officer, Alan Nidiffer
Vice President Merchandising & Marketing, Terry Spencer
Vice President Finance, Becky Olsen
Vice President Operations, Rocky Campbell ??????
Vice President
Vice President Controller, Jimmy Martini
Vice President Operations Taking over the operational reigns from Greg Sandeno, Rocky Campbell
Vice President Human Resources & General Counsel, Kate Wilkinson
Auditors: JONES & ROTH PC EUGENE OREG

LOCATIONS

HQ: C & K MARKET INC.
  615 5TH ST, BROOKINGS, OR 974159199
Phone: 541 469-3113
Web: WWW.CKMARKET.COM

PRODUCTS/OPERATIONS

2013 Stores

	No.
Ray's Food Place	37
Shop Smart Food Warehouse	7
C&K Market	1
Total	**45**

COMPETITORS

7-Eleven	Safeway
Albertsons	Target Corporation
Costco Wholesale	Wal-Mart
Fred Meyer Stores	

HISTORICAL FINANCIALS
Company Type: Private

Income Statement
FYE: December 31

	REVENUE ($ mil.)	NET INCOME ($ mil.)	NET PROFIT MARGIN	EMPLOYEES
12/10	457	3	0.8%	2,322
12/09	467	5	1.1%	—
12/07	1,513	0	0.0%	—
Annual Growth	(32.9%)	1737.3%	—	—

2010 Year-End Financials
Return on assets: 3.6%   Cash ($ mil.): 6
Return on equity: 0.8%
Current ratio: 0.10

C.D. SMITH CONSTRUCTION INC.

One of the Midwest's top contractors C.D. Smith Construction works on commercial institutional and industrial projects. It builds manufacturing retail correctional health care and education facilities as well as water treatment plants. The company offers general contracting and design/build services and also provides specialty contracting services such as steel erection masonry and concrete work carpentry and demolition. Charles D. Smith grandfather of president Gary Smith founded the company in 1936.

C.D. Smith Construction has added Leadership in Energy and Environmental Design (LEED) Green Building services to its offerings. The company is a U.S. Green Building Council member and has LEED Accredited Project Managers to assist throughout the entire certification process. LEED promotes a whole-building approach to sustainability by recognizing performance in five key areas of human and environmental health

EXECUTIVES

Vice President, Tom Baker
Secretary and Safety Director, Patrick (Paddy) Smith
Auditors: GRANT THORNTON LLP MILWAUKEE

LOCATIONS

HQ: C.D. SMITH CONSTRUCTION INC.
  889 E JOHNSON ST, FOND DU LAC, WI 549352933
Phone: 920 924-2900
Web: WWW.CDSMITH.COM

COMPETITORS

Boldt	J.H. Findorff & Son
C. G. Schmidt	Market & Johnson
C. R. Meyer	R.A. Smith National
Edward Kraemer & Sons	Sonag Company
Hagerman Construction	Walsh Group
Hunzinger Construction	

HISTORICAL FINANCIALS
Company Type: Private

Income Statement
FYE: September 30

	REVENUE ($ mil.)	NET INCOME ($ mil.)	NET PROFIT MARGIN	EMPLOYEES
09/13	252	0	—	440
09/12	252	0	—	—
09/11	0	0	—	—
09/10	0	0	—	—
Annual Growth	—	—	—	—

2013 Year-End Financials
Return on assets: 9.9%   Cash ($ mil.): 44
Return on equity: —
Current ratio: 1.20

C.R. ENGLAND INC.

The world's top refrigerated trucking company and one of North America's largest transportation firms C.R. England hauls refrigerated and dry cargo throughout the US. The family-owned company also serves parts of Canada and through alliances points in Mexico. C.R. England's fleet includes more than 3500 Freightliner Peterbilt Volvo and International tractors and 5500 trailers. Besides for-hire freight hauling C.R. England offers dedicated contract carriage in which drivers and equipment are assigned to a customer long-term; logistics services including freight brokerage; and intermodal railroad service.

Operations

The company's operations include national US US regional and Mexican truckload service as well as dedicated (customized) truck contracts and intermodal service.

In addition to freight brokerage C.R. England's England Logistics unit offers intermodal service for refrigerated cargo in which customers' containerized freight is shuttled between truck and railroad facility. The logistics unit also arranges the transportation of less-than-truckload quantities of freight and provides ground transportation of ocean containers for shipping lines.

This unit also provides global logistics – international shipping and freight forwarding solutions); supply chain management (freight man-

agement) and carrier services (factoring solutions fuel discounts tire discounts and other services).

C.R. England's business also benefits from operating five truck driving schools in the US and a course on becoming a freight broker. The school helps improve driver safety as well as provides a pool of qualified truck drivers for hire.

Strategy

Greening its fleet in 2014 C. R. England announced a multi-year liquefied natural gas (LNG) bulk fueling agreement with Shell. C.R. England will replace existing diesel trucks with LNG-powered trucks servicing southern California the most mature US market for fueling LNG-powered trucks.

The company is focusing on innovation in its intermodal and dedicated operations. The intermodal division has more than 1000 TempStack 53 ft. temperature-controlled containers which can be double-stacked on the flatcars of its partner railroad reducing customer costs increasing shipping capacity and efficiency and lowering fuel costs.

C.R. England is also beefing up its trucking operations working to deliver faster more secure shipments for its customers in its National and Regional divisions.

Its Mexico operations offer multiple border crossings and full-service connection yards to move shipments across the U.S. and Mexico border. In 2012 it boosted its regional division by introducing a new Texas regional service to meet the demands of larger volumes that move into and out of Mexico and across Texas.

Company Background

C.R. England was founded in 1920 by Chester Rodney England and is run by his descendants.

EXECUTIVES

President Mexico Division, David (Dave) Akers
EVP Maintenance, Todd D. England
EVP Operations Support, Corey D. England
CEO, Chad England
President, Josh England
COO, Brandon Harrison
EVP Corporate Sales and Marketing, David A. Kramer
COO, Zach England
Corporate VP Compliance and Safety, Dustin England
President National and Regional, Sam Scott
President Intermodal, Coby Bullard
President Dedicated, Tracy Brown
CFO, TJ McGeean
Vice President Of National Fleet Management, Ryan Holm
Vice President Of Marketing, May Philip
Vice President Of Maintenance, Douglas Kading
Vice President Operations Dedicated, Rick Bowman
Senior Vice President Corporate Sales Marketing, Mike Bunnell
CVP Recruiting Training And Safety, Thom Pronk
Senior Vice President Human Resources, Wayne Cederholm
Vice President Information Technology, Rich Farr
Vice President Dedicated Sales, Stuart (Stu) Rosenlund
Vice President of Dedicated Operations, Bob Walters
Corporate Vice President Driver Recruiting and Development, Spencer Angerbauer
Senior Vice President and Litagation Counsel, Nelson Hayes
Vice President Intermodal Sales, Ricky Stover
Co-Chairman, Daniel E. (Dan) England, age 67
Co-Chairman, Dean D. England
Auditors: TANNER LLC SALT LAKE CITY UT

LOCATIONS

HQ: C.R. ENGLAND INC.
4701 W 2100 S, SALT LAKE CITY, UT 841201223
Phone: 801 974-2712
Web: WWW.CRENGLAND.COM

PRODUCTS/OPERATIONS

Selected Operations
Trucking
National - Long haul truckload service
Mexico - Shipments in and out of Mexico
Regional - Short haul truckload service positioned in
the West Midwest and Texas and surrounding areas
(AR LA OK)
Dedicated - Tailor-made services dedicating trucks and
drivers to specific customer needs
Intermodal - Expedited priority rail service using
TempStack 53' refrigerated containers
England Logistics

COMPETITORS

C.H. Robinson Worldwide	Landstar System
Central Refrigerated Service	Marten Transport
	Menlo Worldwide
Covenant Transportation	Navajo Shippers
	Prime Inc.
Crete Carrier	Stevens Transport
Frozen Food Express	Swift Transportation
J.B. Hunt	Willis Shaw Express
KLLM Transport Services	

HISTORICAL FINANCIALS

Company Type: Private

Income Statement
FYE: December 31

	REVENUE ($ mil.)	NET INCOME ($ mil.)	NET PROFIT MARGIN	EMPLOYEES
12/13	1,628	37	2.3%	6,500
12/12	1,579	56	3.6%	—
12/11	1,315	55	4.3%	—
12/07	829	0	—	—
Annual Growth	11.9%	—	—	—

2013 Year-End Financials
Return on assets: 3.2% Cash ($ mil.): 24
Return on equity: 2.3%
Current ratio: 1.00

CADENCE MCSHANE CONSTRUCTION COMPANY LLC

With a certain cadence Cadence McShane Construction has been right in step with the top contractors in the US. A part of development and construction group The McShane Companies it provides general construction construction management and design/build services for commercial institutional and industrial projects in Texas and the central US. The firm is known for its school and community projects throughout Texas. It also provides services to the manufacturing office multi-family residential government hospitality and retail markets. Recent projects include a 730000 sq. ft Port of Houston distribution center for First Industrial Realty. Cadence McShane was founded in 1995.

EXECUTIVES

Vice President; Finance Vice President; Finance, Ellen Hilgendorf
Vice President Business Development Cadence Mcshane Corporation, Glenn Denham
Vice President General Manager, Srinath Pai Kasturi
Vice President, Roger Pavlovich
Vice President Houston Office, Rodney Bowers
Auditors: WARADY & DAVIS LLP DEERFIELD

LOCATIONS

HQ: CADENCE MCSHANE CONSTRUCTION COMPANY LLC
14860 MONTFORT DR STE 270, DALLAS, TX 752546719
Phone: 972 239-2336
Web: WWW.CADENCEMCSHANE.COM

Cadence McShane has offices Austin Houston and Dallas Texas.

PRODUCTS/OPERATIONS

Selected Project Areas
Community/Religious (churches)
Cultural (museums libraries)
Educational (K-12 schools and higher education)
Health care (medical centers labs medical suites and offices)
Hospitality (hotels)
Industrial (distribution assembly manufacturing)
Institutional (federal state county and municipal)
Offices (single-story to mid-rise)
Parking structures
Residential (multi-residence condominium complexes townhomes senior living)
Retail (shopping centers parking structures)

COMPETITORS

Austin Industries	Hunt Construction
Beck Group	Manhattan Construction
FaulknerUSA	Spawglass Holding
Gilbane Building Company	Structure Tone Southwest
Harvey Builders	Turner Corporation
Hensel Phelps Construction	

HISTORICAL FINANCIALS

Company Type: Private

Income Statement
FYE: September 30

	REVENUE ($ mil.)	NET INCOME ($ mil.)	NET PROFIT MARGIN	EMPLOYEES
09/10	158	1	0.8%	120
09/09	259	4	1.9%	—
09/07	724	0	—	—
Annual Growth	—	322.0%	—	—

2010 Year-End Financials
Return on assets: 14.9% Cash ($ mil.): 7
Return on equity: 0.8%
Current ratio: 1.00

CAJUN CONSTRUCTORS INC

Auditors: HANNIS T BOURGEOIS LLP CPAS

LOCATIONS

HQ: CAJUN CONSTRUCTORS INC
15635 AIRLINE HWY, BATON ROUGE, LA 708177318
Phone: 225 753-5857
Web: WWW.CAJUNCONSTRUCTORS.NET

HISTORICAL FINANCIALS

Company Type: Private

Income Statement
FYE: September 30

	REVENUE ($ mil.)	NET INCOME ($ mil.)	NET PROFIT MARGIN	EMPLOYEES
09/14	431	10	2.5%	1,000
09/13	275	10	4.0%	—
09/12	207	14	6.7%	—
09/11	61	0	—	—
Annual Growth	91.6%			

2014 Year-End Financials
Return on assets: 13.1% Cash ($ mil.): 16
Return on equity: 2.5%
Current ratio: 0.20

CAJUN INDUSTRIES LLC

Offering a mixed gumbo of services Cajun Industries builds oil refineries power plants process plants water-treatment plants and other industrial and infrastructure projects primarily in Louisiana and Texas. Subsidiary Cajun Constructors provides a full range of services from design/build to maintenance; Cajun Deep Foundations offers drilling piles installation and related services. Cajun Maritime focuses on marine coastal and oilfield services including construction repair and power distribution. Cajun Equipment Services manages a fleet of trucks and trailers that transport heavy and specialized loads. Chairman and owner Lane Grigsby founded the company as Cajun Contractors and Engineers in 1973.

The group is typically engaged in a variety of public and private projects including the expansion of the Port Arthur Refinery in Texas to become the largest refinery in the US. Cajun won several cleanup and reconstruction projects in New Orleans following Hurricane Katrina; these included helping to pump floodwater out of the city and rebuilding the Industrial Canal levee. It was also awarded several projects to construct floodwalls in the area.

Cajun is licensed to perform construction in more than 20 states.

EXECUTIVES

Senior Vice President Public Works Projects Constructors, Euclid Michel
President, Mike Moran
CEO, Todd Grigsby
Vice President, Michael (Mel) Bates
Vice President Of Marketing, John (Jack) English
Auditors: HANNIS T BOURGEOIS LLP CPAS

LOCATIONS

HQ: CAJUN INDUSTRIES LLC
15635 AIRLINE HWY, BATON ROUGE, LA 708177318
Phone: 225 753-5857
Web: WWW.CAJUNUSA.COM

PRODUCTS/OPERATIONS

Selected Divisions
Cajun Constructors Inc.
Cajun Deep Foundations LLC
Cajun Equipment Services LLC
Cajun Maritime LLC

Selected Services
ASME code work
Bridge construction and repair
Building construction
Coastal restoration

Dock facility construction and repair
Deep foundation work
  Drill shafts
  Driven piles
  Earth retention
  Marine piles
Design/build
Emergency response
Hauling
Maintenance
Marsh and marine power transmission and distribution
Oilfield construction
Paving
Pipeline installation and repair
Plant dismantling and relocation
Procurement
Project management
Retrofits
Stevedoring
Structural steel erection
Turnarounds
Water quality

COMPETITORS

Bechtel	Jacobs Engineering
Boh Bros Construction	KBR
Eby	Performance
Fluor	Contractors

HISTORICAL FINANCIALS

Company Type: Private

Income Statement

	REVENUE ($ mil.)	NET INCOME ($ mil.)	NET PROFIT MARGIN	EMPLOYEES
09/14	476	11	2.5%	1,500
09/13	317	9	3.1%	—
09/12	246	18	7.4%	—
09/11	497	0	—	—
Annual Growth	(1.4%)	—	—	—

FYE: September 30

2014 Year-End Financials

Return on assets: —
Return on equity: 2.5%
Current ratio: 0.20
Cash ($ mil.): 27

CALCOT LTD.

With a crop of nearly 1400 members in Arizona California New Mexico and Texas Calcot is one of the top cotton-marketing cooperatives in the US. Members of the co-op which started in 1927 primarily grow premium-grade Far Western cottons including California Upland Pima and San Joaquin Acala varieties. The company operates six warehousing locations and sells between 1 million and 2 million bales of cotton per year. Approximately 85% of Calcot's annual harvest is exported to textile mills worldwide mostly in Pacific Rim countries. Calcot and three other major US co-ops together comprise Amcot a worldwide cotton marketer.

The company expanded into Texas in 2005 adding growers of FiberMax cotton to its member list. The next year it acquired SWIG (Southwestern Irrigated Cotton Growers) which expanded its reach into New Mexico and western Texas. Calcot is the nation's largest supplier of Far Western cottons.

EXECUTIVES

Vice President Sales, John (Jack) Burch
Assistant VP Call Pool Operations and Economics, Jarral Neeper, age 52
CFO, Roxanne F. Wang
Assistant Vice President Sales, Claud Acker
Vice President Sales, John Burch
Chairman, Greg Wuertz
Auditors: EADIE & PAYNE LLP REDLANDS/O

LOCATIONS

HQ: CALCOT LTD.
1900 E BRUNDAGE LN, BAKERSFIELD, CA 933072789
Phone: 661 327-5961
Web: WWW.CALCOT.COM

COMPETITORS

Cargill	JB Cotton
Cotton Inc.	King Ranch
Dunavant Enterprises	Plains Cotton
International Cotton Marketing	Plexus Cotton
	Staplcotn
J.G. Boswell Co.	Weil Brothers Cotton

HISTORICAL FINANCIALS

Company Type: Private

Income Statement

	REVENUE ($ mil.)	NET INCOME ($ mil.)	NET PROFIT MARGIN	EMPLOYEES
08/14	172	3	1.9%	150
08/13	195	1	0.8%	—
08/12	306	5	1.7%	—
08/11	399	0	—	—
Annual Growth	(24.4%)	—	—	—

FYE: August 31

2014 Year-End Financials

Return on assets: 1.8%
Return on equity: 1.9%
Current ratio: 0.40
Cash ($ mil.): 4

CALIBRE SYSTEMS INC.

When it comes to information technology CALIBRE aims to please. The employee-owned company provides information technology and management services to government and commercial clients in the US. It specializes in data analytics modeling and simulation financial and cost management land management logistics and strategic planning among other areas. To expand its capabilities the company partners with a host of technology firms consulting firms educational institutions and other enterprises including AT&T IBM KPMG and George Mason University. CALIBRE operates from a handful of US offices as well as onsite at customer facilities.

Geographic Reach CALIBRE has offices in Virginia as well as Alabama Florida and Texas. Its consultants however work on-site at customer locations across the US and in Afghanistan Kuwait and Qatar.

Sales and Marketing The company's primary client base is agencies of the federal government such as the Department of Defense the Department of Transportation the Army the Navy and the Air Force; it also serves associations and not-for-profits (Disabled American Veterans American Institute of Architects) and commercial entities (Boeing ManTech Del Monte and Audi of America.

Strategy
CALIBRE's strategic growth plan is to expand its business development in its core markets of defense energy and the environment in the US Southeast.

In 2012 the company teamed up with Veterans Green Jobs to advance training and employment opportunities for military veterans across the US.

Company Background
CALIBRE was founded in 1989.

EXECUTIVES

Vice President Information Technology, Timothy O'Connor
Vice President Energy Environment and Infrastructure Division., Philip Rizzi
Vice President Manager Director, Ted Majer
Vice President of Performance Improvement Programs, Richard (Dick) Formica
Senior Vice President of Strategy Development, Craig College
Vice President of Human Resources, Laura Weil
Executive Vice President and Chief Administrative Officer, Rob Larrick
Auditors: ARGY WILTSE & ROBINSON PC

LOCATIONS

HQ: CALIBRE SYSTEMS INC.
6354 WALKER LN STE 300, ALEXANDRIA, VA 223103252
Phone: 703 797-8500
Web: WWW.CALIBRESYS.COM

PRODUCTS/OPERATIONS

Selected Services
Data Analytics
Energy Environment and Safety Management
Financial and Cost Management
Installation and Land Management
Logistics and Acquisition Management
Program Management and Decision Support
Strategic Planning
Technology Solutions
Training Modeling and Simulation Services

COMPETITORS

Alion	HP Enterprise Services
Booz Allen	Lockheed Martin
CACI International	Information Systems
Computer Sciences Corp.	ManTech
Computer Technology Associates	Unisys

HISTORICAL FINANCIALS

Company Type: Private

Income Statement

	REVENUE ($ mil.)	NET INCOME ($ mil.)	NET PROFIT MARGIN	EMPLOYEES
02/11	157	10	6.5%	682
02/09	108	6	5.7%	—
02/08	1,037	0	0.0%	—
Annual Growth	(46.6%)	757.3%	—	—

FYE: February 28

2011 Year-End Financials

Return on assets: 3.7%
Return on equity: 6.5%
Current ratio: 0.50
Cash ($ mil.): 14

CALIFORNIA COMMUNITY FOUNDATION

California Community Foundation supports not-for-profit organizations and public institutions in the Los Angeles area. The organization performs its function by offering funding for health and human services affordable housing early childhood education and community arts and culture. The 24th Street Theatre Antelope Valley Hospital and

Community Arts Partnership are among the organizations to have received the foundation's grant funding. In times of emergency it has also pitched in to help groups in other areas. California Community Foundation was founded in 1915.By 2015 the foundation hopes to have helped others find affordable housing and quality education access health care and discover the arts and culture.

EXECUTIVES

Vice President Civic Engagement, Maria Blanco
Vice President Civic Engagement Public Policy, Efrain Escobedo
Vice President External and Donor Relations, Carol Bradford
Vice President Charitable Business Development, Nichole Baker
Auditors: KMPG LLP LOS ANGELES CALIFOR

LOCATIONS

HQ: CALIFORNIA COMMUNITY FOUNDATION
221 S FIGUEROA ST STE 400, LOS ANGELES, CA 900123760
Phone: 213 413-4130
Web: WWW.CALFUND.ORG

HISTORICAL FINANCIALS

Company Type: Private

Income Statement				FYE: June 30
	ASSETS ($ mil.)	NET INCOME ($ mil.)	INCOME AS % OF ASSETS	EMPLOYEES
06/13	1,315	119	9.1%	60
06/12	1,091	70	6.5%	—
06/11	1,242	139	11.2%	—
06/10	1,120	0	—	—
Annual Growth	5.5%	—	—	—

2013 Year-End Financials

Return on assets: —
Return on equity: 39.8%
Sales ($ mil): 300

CALIFORNIA INDEPENDENT SYSTEM OPERATOR CORPORATION

The California Independent System Operator (California ISO) manages a 25627-mile power transmission system (about 80% of California's power grid) balancing wholesale supply to meet retail demand. The enterprise directs the flow of electricity along long-distance high-voltage power lines that connect California with neighboring states as well as with Mexico and Canada. It manages the transmission lines and supervises maintenance but the transmission systems are owned and maintained by individual utilities. The not-for-profit public benefit corporation also acts as a transmission planner.

Geographic Reach

The company handles an about 35% of the electric load in the Western US including the high-voltage long-distance power lines that make up 80% of California's power grid and a small part of Nevada's.

Operations

California ISO also keeps its eye on about 760 powers plants with about 60000 MW of capacity which serve some 30 million California customers. As the control center for the California power grid the company matches buyers and sellers of electricity facilitating nearly 30000 market transactions every day to ensure enough power is on hand to meet demand. It delivers over 260 million MWhs of electricity annually and oversees more than 270000 miles of high-voltage power lines.

In 2013 the ISO power grid produce a new record of 4196 MW.

Sales and Marketing

The company maintains partnership with more than 100 client organizations for a modern and reliable operation of the bulk power grid at the least wholesale cost.

Strategy

The ISO identifies and approves improvements to be made to the grid by individual transmission owners in order to meet state and federal standards for reliability.

To diversify California's power base the corporation has opened up its system to integrate the storage of electricity from alternative sources such as solar wind hydro batteries and flywheels. By 2020 in order to meet stringent carbon emission regulations it is aiming to have 33% of the power on its grid generated by renewable sources (mainly wind solar hydro and biomass).

The ISO is also looking replace the power delivered to about 1.4 million consumers by Southern California Edison's permanent shut-down in 2013 of the San Onofre Nuclear Generating Station.

In 2013 ISO Board approved a transition agreement for Merced Irrigation District to join the California ISO grid. The deal when final will take the number of community-owned municipal utilities participating in the ISO as transmission members to nine.

Company Background

The organization was formed by the state government in 1996. The Independent System Operator assumed computerized command of California's wholesale power grid in 1998.

EXECUTIVES

Vice President Operations, Eric Schmitt
Vice President Technology, Petar Ristanovic
Area Vice President, Chris McIntosh
Board Member, Andrew Ulmer
Auditors: PRICEWATERHOUSECOOPERS LLP SA

LOCATIONS

HQ: CALIFORNIA INDEPENDENT SYSTEM OPERATOR CORPORATION
250 OUTCROPPING WAY, FOLSOM, CA 956308773
Phone: 916 351-4400
Web: WWW.CAISO.COM

HISTORICAL FINANCIALS

Company Type: Private

Income Statement				FYE: December 31
	REVENUE ($ mil.)	NET INCOME ($ mil.)	NET PROFIT MARGIN	EMPLOYEES
12/07	200	46	23.0%	530
12/06	189	41	21.7%	—
12/05	131	0	0.0%	—
Annual Growth	23.5%	34621.9%	—	—

2007 Year-End Financials

Return on assets: —
Return on equity: 23.0%
Current ratio: 1.00
Cash ($ mil.): 220

CANDID COLOR SYSTEMS INC.

LOCATIONS

HQ: CANDID COLOR SYSTEMS INC.
1300 METROPOLITAN AVE, OKLAHOMA CITY, OK 731082042
Phone: 405 947-8747
Web: WWW.OKLAHOMAPARTYPICS.COM

HISTORICAL FINANCIALS

Company Type: Private

Income Statement				FYE: July 31
	REVENUE ($ mil.)	NET INCOME ($ mil.)	NET PROFIT MARGIN	EMPLOYEES
07/07	21,742	2,534	11.7%	300
07/05	22	1	8.3%	—
07/04	21	2	10.9%	—
07/03	21	0	—	—
Annual Growth	467.2%	—	—	—

2007 Year-End Financials

Return on assets: —
Return on equity: 11.7%
Current ratio: 1.70
Cash ($ mil.): 2

CANNERY CASINO RESORTS LLC

LOCATIONS

HQ: CANNERY CASINO RESORTS LLC
9107 W RUSSELL RD, LAS VEGAS, NV 891481243
Phone: 702 507-5700
Web: WWW.CANNERYCASINO.COM

HISTORICAL FINANCIALS

Company Type: Private

Income Statement				FYE: December 31
	REVENUE ($ mil.)	NET INCOME ($ mil.)	NET PROFIT MARGIN	EMPLOYEES
12/10	513	(15)	—	1,860
12/09	509	(23)	—	—
12/08	1,235	0	0.0%	—
Annual Growth	(35.5%)	—	—	—

2010 Year-End Financials

Return on assets: 1.6%
Return on equity: (-2.9%)
Current ratio: 1.20
Cash ($ mil.): 55

CAPE COD HEALTHCARE INC.

There once was a man from Nantucket who broke his leg when he stepped in a bucket. Falmouth Hospital took care of the man and helped him devise a get-well plan and in the end he was hooked on Cape Cod Healthcare. Cape Cod Healthcare is a not-for-profit healthcare organization that includes two acute-care hospitals (Cape Cod Hospital and Falmouth Hospital) with a total of some 350 beds. It also operates a home health services agency (Visiting Nurse Association) primary and specialized care clinics medical labs a 130-bed skilled nursing and rehabilitation facility and a 60-unit assisted living facility. The health care system has a staff of more than 450 physicians.

Strategy

Cape Cod Healthcare has improved its finances in recent years through a number of cost-cutting measures including employee layoffs and process improvements.

While Cape Cod Healthcare enjoys a strong market share in the Cape Cod region it also struggles with seasonal fluctuations and high Medicare and Medicaid numbers within its patient load. As such the company could be impacted by health reform measures that would decrease Medicare reimbursement levels in future years. Cape Cod Healthcare plans to continue its efforts to control costs and increase efficiencies to keep its operations nimble and keep pace with the changing health care environment.

EXECUTIVES

Senior Vice President Chief Legal Officer, Michael (Mel) Jones
Senior Vice President, Jeff Dykens
Senior Vice President, Jack D Lipomi
Senior Vice President Marketing Communications and Business Development, Patrick J (Paddy) Kane
Senior Vice President of Development, Mary Franco
Director Of Nursing, Paula Cronin
Vice President Patient Financial Services, Victor Oliveira
Senior Vice President Human Resources, Emily Schorer
Senior Vice President Development, Kevinh Ralp
Auditors: PRICEWATERHOUSECOOPERS LLP BO

LOCATIONS

HQ: CAPE COD HEALTHCARE INC.
27 PARK ST, HYANNIS, MA 026015230
Phone: 508 862-5030
Web: WWW.CAPECODHEALTHCARE.COM

PRODUCTS/OPERATIONS

Selected Massachusetts Facilities
Bourne Health Center
Cape Cod Hospital (Hyannis)
Davenport Mugar Cancer Center (Hyannis)
Falmouth Hospital
 Clark Cancer Center
Fontaine Medical Center (Harwich)
Heritage at Falmouth
JLM Care Center (Falmouth)
Mashpee Health Center
Sandwich Health Center
Wilkins Outpatient Medical Complex (Hyannis)

COMPETITORS

Baystate Health	Partners HealthCare
Boston Medical Center	Southcoast Hospitals
Cambridge Health	Group
Alliance	Steward Health Care
Care New England	Universal Health
CareGroup	Services
Milford Regional	Winchester Healthcare
Medical Center	
Northeast Health	
System	

HISTORICAL FINANCIALS
Company Type: Private

Income Statement
FYE: September 30

	REVENUE ($ mil.)	NET INCOME ($ mil.)	NET PROFIT MARGIN	EMPLOYEES
09/13	724	45	6.2%	1,850
09/12	680	80	11.9%	—
09/11	648	37	5.7%	—
09/09	587	0	—	—
Annual Growth	5.4%	—	—	—

2013 Year-End Financials
Return on assets: 8.7%   Cash ($ mil.): 40
Return on equity: 6.2%
Current ratio: 0.50

CAPE COD HOSPITAL

Get too much sun or eat too much lobster while visiting Cape Cod? Never fear Cape Cod Hospital can treat whatever ails you. Cape Cod Hospital a subsidiary of Cape Cod Healthcare is a 260-bed acute care hospital that serves the Cape Cod Massachusetts area. Its specialty services include pediatrics maternity care cancer treatment and infectious disease therapeutics. The not-for-profit Cape Cod Hospital also includes a specialty cardiovascular center a psychiatry unit a surgical pavilion and a diagnostic imaging facility as well as outpatient medical offices.

Operations

Cape Cod Hospital's emergency department treats about 85000 patients each year. The medical center also performs more than 12500 surgeries and 1000 birth procedures each year as well as about 2 million laboratory tests. Its 20-bed Cape Psych Center provides inpatient and outpatient mental and behavioral services. The campus also includes more than a dozen medical offices buildings and a community health center. Cape Cod Hospital's staff includes about 300 physicians.

Geographic Reach

Cape Cod Hospital is located on a 40-acre campus on the shoreline of Hyannis Massachusetts.

Strategy

To keep its facilities modern and efficient in 2015 the company opened a new emergency center located adjacent to the existing emergency center. The 18-month $22 million project added 25000 sq. ft. of space and 72 patient treatment rooms.

In 2013 Cape Cod Hospital reopened the renovated and expanded Intensive Care Unit. That project cost $4.9 million and doubled the size of the original area.

To control the cost of providing hospital care parent Cape Cod Healthcare has also been expanding its outpatient and ambulatory care services. It is adding new urgent care centers and surgery centers both near the hospital and in surrounding communities.

Company Background

Cape Cod Hospital was established in Hyannis in 1920.

EXECUTIVES

Senior Vice President Managed Care, Jack D Lipomi
Ambulatory Services Director, Robin Grace
Medical Director, Kelsey Rezendes
Vice President, Stephanie Nadolny
Nursing Director, Joanie Drushella

Medical Director, Timothy (Tim) Herrick
Auditors: PRICEWATERHOUSECOOPERS LLP BO

LOCATIONS

HQ: CAPE COD HOSPITAL
27 PARK ST, HYANNIS, MA 026015203
Phone: 508 862-7575
Web: WWW.CAPECODORTHO.COM

PRODUCTS/OPERATIONS

Selected Services
Allergy and Immunology
Behavioral Health
Blood Center
Dermatology
Foot Care & Surgery
Hand Surgery
Orthopedics
Pregnancy & Birth
Sports Medicine
Women' s Health

COMPETITORS

Baystate Health	Northeast Health
Boston Medical Center	System
Cambridge Health	Partners HealthCare
Alliance	Southcoast Hospitals
Care New England	Group
CareGroup	Steward Health Care
Children' s Hospital	Sturdy Memorial
Boston	Universal Health
Milford Regional	Services
Medical Center	Winchester Healthcare

HISTORICAL FINANCIALS
Company Type: Private

Income Statement
FYE: September 30

	REVENUE ($ mil.)	NET INCOME ($ mil.)	NET PROFIT MARGIN	EMPLOYEES
09/13	407	19	4.8%	1,700
09/12	427	52	12.3%	—
09/11	409	29	7.1%	—
09/08	352	0	—	—
Annual Growth	3.0%	—	—	—

2013 Year-End Financials
Return on assets: 9.0%   Cash ($ mil.): 24
Return on equity: 4.8%
Current ratio: 1.30

CAPITAL DISTRICT PHYSICIANS' HEALTH PLAN INC.

Capital District Physicians' Health Plan (CDPHP) is an independent not-for-profit health plan serving some 448000 members in two dozen New York counties. It offers employer-sponsored and individual managed care plans (including HMO PPO and consumer-directed plans) as well as a Medicare Advantage plan for seniors. The company's coverage include full coverage for some preventative medical services as well as options for covering prescription drugs dental work and vision services. CDPHP also provides wellness programs that help members with weight loss smoking cessation and chronic disease management.

Geographic Reach

CDPHP serves customers in 24 New York counties: Albany Broome Chenango Columbia

Delaware Dutchess Essex Fulton Greene Hamilton Herkimer Madison Montgomery Oneida Orange Otsego Rensselaer Saratoga Schenectady Schoharie Tioga Ulster Warren and Washington.

Operations

In addition to its commercial and Medicare offerings CDPHP provides health plans under several state-subsidized insurance programs including Family Health Plus and Child Health Plus (intended for residents who don't qualify for Medicaid) and Healthy NY (intended for small businesses and sole proprietors). Altogether the CDPHP provider network includes more than 10000 physicians and facilities.

The company's classifies its products in three lines of business: Health Maintenance Organization (HMO) products (which includes Healthy New York Medicare Choices Medicaid Child Health Plus and Family Health Plus) provided by CDPHP; Preferred Provider Organization (PPO) products (which include PPO High Deductible PPO Medicare Choices Exclusive Provider Organization -EPO- and High Deductible EPO products) provided by CDPHP Universal Benefits Inc.; and the Administrative Services Organization (ASO) plans (which includes ASO and self-insured plans) provided by Capital District Physicians' Healthcare Network Inc. In 2013 CDPHP's membership increased by about 38000.

Financial Performance

CDPHP reported a 13% increase in revenues in 2013 due to an increase in membership and in earned premiums. The company suffered a loss of $43 million in 2013 (a decrease of more than 375%) due to an increase in claims and general expenses.

Strategy

CDPHP's self-proclaimed strategy is to use the majority of its premium income to pay out medical claims while maintaining necessary reserve levels to keep its solid financial performance and to comply with federal medical loss-ratio guidelines. It earmarks a small amount of income for operational expenses as well as to fund growth and wellness initiatives.

In mid-2014 the company teamed upewith Independent Health to build innovative products tools and services for providers employers and individuals across New York State. The partnership will focus on developing new tools technology and products along with recruiting new physicians.

In the early 2013 the company opened a new CDPHP Service Center location at Latham New York and a health and fitness center inside an Albany supermarket.

CDPHP also works to lower medical expenses by partnering with other regional care and plan providers.Company Background

In 2011 CDPHP partnered with Trendshift in 2011 to provide a new group funding management system for employers.

An association of local Albany physicians founded CDPHP in 1984.

EXECUTIVES

Medical Director, Kirk Panneton
Vice President Internal Operations, Patricia Lushkevich
Svp Medical Affairs And Chief Medical Officer, Bruce D Nash
Physical Therapy Center Health Care Pt, Abigail Andrews
Physical Therapy, Jennifer Miller
Physical Therapy, Benjamin Robinson
Vice President Of Underwriting, Robert Little
Physical Therapy, Lori Pietryka
Physical Therapy, Anna Rocci
Physical Therapy, Deborah Santulli
Legal Secretary, David Benyo
Physical Therapy, Melissa Bertolozzi

Vice President State Programs, Sheila Nelson
Physical Therapy, Cristie Holland
Physical Therapy, Richard Escano
Vice President Core Application Configuration And Change Management Office, Andy Prior
Vice President Medicare Products, Kevin Mowll
Vice President, John Demers
Physical Therapy, Gretchen Meier
Physical Therapy, Elizabeth Toombs
Vice President Medical Affairs, Tracy Langlais
Occupational Medicine, Eckardt Johanning
Physical Therapy, Amanda McLenithan
Physical Therapy, Pamela Gabel
Physical Therapy, Andrew Whalen
Physical Therapy, Jennifer Szymanski
Vice President Engineering, Tom Holladay
Physical Therapy, Kevin Stafford
Physical Therapy, Margaret Runge
Physical Therapy, Kristin Banse
Physical Therapy, Aniruddha Gadre
Physical Therapy, Amy Smith
Physical Therapy, Arthur Finkelstein
Physical Therapy, Doris Nieves
Physical Therapy, Kellie Fox
Senior Vice President Government and External Relations, Robert (Bob) Hinckley
Senior Vice President, Cynthia Wicks
Vice President Application Management, Sigrid Cerio
Vice President Enterprise Application Solutions, Umesh Rege
Medical Director, Nancy Schuster
Executive Vice President, April Braman
Medical Director, Symansky Martin
Vice Chairman, Gary Wilson
Board Member, James Leyhane
Auditors: PRICEWATERHOUSECOOPERS LLP BO

LOCATIONS

HQ: CAPITAL DISTRICT PHYSICIANS' HEALTH PLAN INC.
500 PATROON CREEK BLVD, ALBANY, NY 122065006
Phone: 518 641-3700
Web: WWW.CDPHP.COM

PRODUCTS/OPERATIONS

Selected Products
Dental and Vision Health Plans
  CVS ExtraCare Health Card
  Delta Dental
Government Plans
  Child Health Plus
  Family Health Plus
  Medicaid Select Plan
  Medicare Choices (HMO)
Group Health Plans
  Embrace Health
  Exclusive Provider Organization (EPO)
  Group Medicare
  High Deductible Health Plans (HDHP)
  Health Maintenance Organization (HMO)
  Healthy Direction
  Lifestyle Riders
  Preferred Provider Organization (PPO)
  Transitional Health Plans
  Health Funding Arrangements
  Flexible Spending Accounts
  Health Reimbursement Arrangement
  Health Savings Account
Individual Health Plans
  Healthy New York
  Non-Group Health Plans

COMPETITORS

Aetna
Anthem
CIGNA
EmblemHealth
Fidelis Care New York
Humana
Independent Health
MVP Health Plan
UnitedHealth Group

excellus bluecross blueshield rochester region healthnow new york inc

HISTORICAL FINANCIALS
Company Type: Private

Income Statement
FYE: December 31

	REVENUE ($ mil.)	NET INCOME ($ mil.)	NET PROFIT MARGIN	EMPLOYEES
12/13	1,314	22	1.7%	700
12/09	1,037	33	3.2%	—
12/03	818	(1)	—	—
12/02	719	0	—	—
Annual Growth	5.6%	—	—	—

2013 Year-End Financials
Return on assets: 13.5%   Cash ($ mil.): 61
Return on equity: 1.7%
Current ratio: 0.70

CAPITAL HEALTH SYSTEM INC.

Capital Health System (CHS) serves the residents of New Jersey's capital city through two hospitals. Together they have about 430 beds. The not-for-profit organization offers emergency surgical and acute health care and it serves as a hands-on teaching facility to nursing and medical students. It also operates outpatient care facilities. CHS primarily serves residents of Mercer County and parts of Bucks County in central New Jersey. Capital Health System offers centers for maternal and pediatric health neurology emergency and trauma services oncology orthopedics mental health surgery and sleep diagnostics.

Operations

CHS's main hospital is the Capital Health Regional Medical Center in Trenton which includes a regional stroke and cerebrovascular center a level II trauma center a neurological emergency department (the first of its kind in the country) and a emergency mental health center that serves as a county referral center for behavioral care. CHS' second hospital is the 223-bed Capital Health Medical Center-Hopewell facility which also includes a designated stroke center. It also operates the Capital Health-Hamilton outpatient care center and the Capital Health-Mercer satellite emergency care clinic.Geographic ReachCHS primarily serves patients in central New Jersey (in Mercer and Bucks county). Its Capital Health Medical Center-Hopewell is located in Hopewell while its Capital Health Regional Medical Center is located in Trenton New Jersey. Capital Health also has an outpatient facility in Hamilton Township.

Strategy

Capital Health System has been making headlines with breakthroughs in treatment over the past few years. In 2014 for example the Capital Institute for Neurosciences at Capital Health performed the first clinical trial procedure of chemotherapy treatment on brain tumors using a catheter that was inserted through the patient's leg. Also that year the Capital Health Medical Center in Hopewell became the first and only hospital in the Mercer and Bucks county region to be awarded a Chest Pain Center accreditation from the Society of Cardiovascular Patient Care (SCPC). CHS has also been expanding its facilities in recent years to accommodate its patients and offer more care services. In 2013 Capital Health's Institute for Neurosciences opened a new outpatient office in Philadelphia to meet the needs of patients traveling to CHS' hospitals for neurological services. In addition the Raritan Bay Medical Center joined the institute's network of affiliated centers in 2013; the group of hospitals is working collaboratively to improve access to advanced diagnostic and treatment technologies for neurology patients. In 2012 it opened a new primary care center in Mountain View.

The company has also upgraded its surgical equipment in recent years adding a da Vinci surgical suite and a CyberKnife robotic surgery system which are used for minimally invasive and non-invasive surgical procedures as well as the TREVO and Solitaire clot retrieval devices for neurosurgery procedures.

Company Background
CHS was formed through the merger of Helene Fuld Medical Center and Mercer Medical Center in 1997.

EXECUTIVES
Physical Therapy Director, Janice J Pesco
Vp Patient Services And Chief Nursing Officer, Eileen Horton
Medical Director Stereotactic Radiosurgery Program, Timothy (Tim) Chen
Vice President Marketing Assistant, Carmen Salter
Vice President Chief Administrative Officer, David (Dave) Dafilou
Auditors: WITHUMSMITHBROWN PC MORNSTOWN

LOCATIONS
HQ: CAPITAL HEALTH SYSTEM INC.
750 BRUNSWICK AVE, TRENTON, NJ 086384143
Phone: 609 394-6000
Web: WWW.CAPITALHEALTH.ORG

PRODUCTS/OPERATIONS

Selected Facilities
Capital Health (Hamilton NJ)
Capital Health Medical Center-Hopewell (Pennington NJ)
Capital Health Regional Medical Center (Trenton NJ)
Satellite Emergency Department at Capital Health (Mercer NJ)

Selected Services
Brain and Spine
Oncology
Digestive Health
Trauma and Emergency Services
Orthopedics
Maternity
Sleep Medicine
Surgery

COMPETITORS
CentraState Healthcare System
Community Medical Center
Hunterdon Healthcare
Inspira Health Network
JFK Medical Center
Kennedy Health System
Kimball Medical Center
Meridian Health
Monmouth Medical Center
Princeton HealthCare
Robert Wood Johnson University Hospital
Shore Memorial Hospital
Somerset Medical Center
The Cooper Health System
Virtua Health

HISTORICAL FINANCIALS
Company Type: Private

HISTORICAL FINANCIALS
Company Type: Private

Income Statement
FYE: December 31

	REVENUE ($ mil.)	NET INCOME ($ mil.)	NET PROFIT MARGIN	EMPLOYEES
12/12	538	(58)	—	3,000
12/08	0	0	—	
12/06	419	28	6.8%	
12/05	1,096	0	—	
Annual Growth	—	—	—	—

2012 Year-End Financials
Return on assets: 12.1%
Return on equity: (-10.8%)
Current ratio: 1.30
Cash ($ mil.): 9

CAREALLIANCE HEALTH SERVICES

CareAlliance Health Services (doing business as Roper St. Francis Healthcare) knows that St. Francis may be the patron saint of animals but its medical centers are more concerned with humans. The company operates four hospitals —the 370-bed Roper Hospital the 200-bed Bon Secours St. Francis Hospital the 85-bed Mount Pleasant Hospital and the Roper Rehabilitation Hospital. Besides providing home health services it also operates outpatient emergency primary care and diagnostic facilities. Roper St. Francis Healthcare serves Charleston South Carolina and surrounding communities. Its Roper St. Francis Physician Partners is one of the region's largest physician practices.

Operations
The health system comprises Roper Hospital Bon Secours St. Francis Hospital Roper St. Francis Mount Pleasant Hospital Roper St. Francis Foundation and Roper St. Francis Physicians Network. Altogether it boasts three acute care hospitals with 655-plus beds one specialty hospital 15 centers for outpatient services three industrial medicine sites five emergency rooms and two urgent care centers.

Roper St. Francis Healthcare has a medical staff of some 800 physicians. The Roper St. Francis Physician Partners organization has more than 230 physicians who offer primary and specialty care including family practice internal medicine and pediatrics.

Geographic Reach
Altogether Roper St. Francis Healthcare operates about 90 facilities in seven counties in the lowcountry region of South Carolina.

Strategy
The health system in 2014 signed an agreement with Trendlines Lab to collaborate on the development of new medical device inventions as well as low-cost solutions for clinical problems. The partnership will work to create devices that will address unmet needs identified by physicians and other health care providers.

Company Background
Roper St. Francis Healthcare was formed through the merger of Roper Hospital and Bon Secours St. Francis Hospital in 1998.

Roper St. Francis Physician Partners was formed through the 2009 combination of Roper St. Francis Physicians' Network and Lowcountry Medical Associates.

EXECUTIVES
President and CEO, David L. Dunlap
VP and CIO, Mike Taylor
Vice President of Medical Affairs & Chief Medical Officer, Steven Shapiro
SVP and CFO, Bret Johnson
CEO Roper Hospital and SVP Operations, Matthew Severance
CEO Roper St. Francis Mount Pleasant Hospital and VP Operations, John Sullivan
CEO Bon Secours St. Francis Hospital and SVP Operations, Allen Carroll
Chairman Roper St. Francis Foundation, John B. Holloway
Vice Chairman Roper St. Francis Foundation, Charles T. Cole
Vice President Nursing & Senior Nurse Executive Bon Secours St. Francis, Pennie Peralta
CEO RSF Physician Partners & RSFH Vice President & Chief Strategy Officer, Douglas Bowling
Pharmacy Manager, Thomas Baxley
Interim Chief Nursing Officer Vice President Nursing Roper Hospital, Susan (Sue) Bennett
Medical Director Corporate Health, Edward (Ed) Galaid
Vice President Human Resources, Melanie Stith
Director Of Pharmacy, Holly Balcer
Senior Vice President Of Sales And Marketing, Carolyn Cantey
Vice President of Nursing and Senior Nurse Executive, Lisa Irvin
Director of Pharmacy, Phil Creger
Vice President Of Nursing, P Floyd
Vice President For System Development, Doug Bowling
Vice President, Dana Stephens
Chairman of the Board, Pierre Manigault
Board Member, David Ellison
Auditors: DELOITTE & TOUCHE LLP CHARLO

LOCATIONS
HQ: CAREALLIANCE HEALTH SERVICES
315 CALHOUN ST STE 107, CHARLESTON, SC 294011115
Phone: 843 724-2000

Selected South Carolina Facilities
Hospitals
Mt. Pleasant Hospital Campus - Mount Pleasant
Roper Hosp
Roper Rehabilitation Hospital
St. Franci
Outpatient Centers
After Hours Care - James Island
Kiawah-Seabrook Medical & Urgent Care
Roper Hosp
Roper Hospital Ambulatory Surgery & Pain Management - James Island
Roper Hosp
Roper Hosp
Roper Hosp
Roper Hosptial Diagnostics - Goose Creek
Roper Hosptial Diagnostics - James Island
Roper Hosp
Roper Hospital Diagnostics - Moncks Corner
Roper Hospital Imaging - Wesley Drive
Roper Hospital Imaging - Wingo Way

COMPETITORS
Beaufort Memorial Hospital
Conway Medical Center
Georgetown Hospital System
Grand Strand Regional Medical Center
HCA
Medical University of South Carolina
Tenet Healthcare

Income Statement FYE: December 31

	REVENUE ($ mil.)	NET INCOME ($ mil.)	NET PROFIT MARGIN	EMPLOYEES
12/12	729	18	2.5%	5,000
12/09	682	56	8.3%	—
12/08	618	(51)	—	—
12/06	1,658	0	—	—
Annual Growth	(12.8%)	—	—	—

2012 Year-End Financials

Return on assets: 6.7% Cash ($ mil.): 35
Return on equity: 2.5%
Current ratio: 0.90

CAREGROUP INC.

Thanks to CareGroup there's well-bein' in Beantown. CareGroup serves Massachusetts residents through its flagship facility the 672-bed Beth Israel Deaconess Medical Center (BIDMC) and five other hospital campuses. With more than 1100 beds total the system provides a comprehensive range of general acute care as well as specialty care in a number of areas including orthopedics obstetrics diabetes and cardiovascular disease. In addition to its hospitals CareGroup operates a network of outpatient clinics and physician practices in the Boston area. It is also heavily involved in biomedical research and medical education.

Geographic Reach

All of CareGroup's facilities are located in the Boston Massachusetts area.

Operations

The not-for-profit CareGroup organization operates six hospitals: BIDMC and its Beth Israel Deaconess Hospital-Needham and Beth Israel Deaconess Hospital-Milton (90 beds) satellite centers as well as the Beth Israel Deaconess New England Baptist Hospital and the Mount Auburn Hospital (213 beds). BIDMC and its two satellite hospitals employ 1250 physicians and handle some 49865 inpatient and more than 557800 outpatient visits each year. In 2014 BIDMC became the sole corporate member of Jordan Health Systems Inc. and its affiliates now known as Beth Israel Deaconess Hospital – Plymouth Inc.

BIDMC and the system's Mount Auburn Hospital are both teaching facilities for Harvard University's medical school while New England Baptist is affiliated with the medical schools of Harvard and Tufts University. BIDMC's biomedical research division receives roughly $200 million annually from the National Institutes of Health to help fund its research programs. BIDMC researchers conduct more than 850 active sponsored projects and 200 clinical trials. Research partners include the Dana-Farber Cancer Institute and the Joslin Diabetes Center. The BIDMC campus also includes the Harvard-Thorndike Laboratory which conducts clinical and medical lab research and has one of the most competitive residency and fellowship programs in the country.

Sales and Marketing

As its patient volume has continued to remain stable or even increase in recent years CareGroup has sought to expand and establish new clinical relationships with suburban providers in order to create a strong referral base in the communities surrounding Boston. Framingham's MetroWest Medical Center and BIDMC are establishing a car-

diac service line while Mount Auburn is establishing its own primary care network.

CareGroup promotes its services through television print and outdoor advertising as well as direct mail and physician marketing campaigns.

Financial Performance

In 2014 net revenue increased by 11% due to higher net patient revenues driven by the net amount realized by patients third-party payors and other services rendered. BIDMC contributed 13% of CareGroup's total revenue. Medicare contributed 31%; Medicaid 12%; Blue Cross 21%; Commercial insurance and managed care 27%; Patient 6%; and Other 3% of the total revenue. CareGroup's net income in 2014 grew by 11% due to higher net sales. Cash from operating activities increased by 37%.

Strategy

CareGroup also known as CareGroup Healthcare System administers care to its member facilities in the form of consulting administrative and financial support. Though it offers such support services to its facilities each hospital operates autonomously with its own government and operational authority.

The system looks to grow by forming new affiliation agreements with area care providers as well as by expanding and improving services at existing facilities. By partnering with hospitals and clinics CareGroup aims to form a regional care organization to improve care management efficiency and quality for area residents.

BIDMC has formed partnerships with other outstanding institutions and the partners. These include Beth Israel Deaconess Hospital-Milton Beth Israel Deaconess Hospital-Needham Beth Israel Deaconess Hospital-Plymouth Anna Jaques Hospital Cambridge Health Alliance Lawrence General Hospital Signature Healthcare Beth Israel Deaconess HealthCare Community Care Alliance Atrius Health and Hebrew Rehabilitation Center. Research funding totals over $229.8 million annually. BIDMC researchers run more than 850 active sponsored projects and 500 funded and nonfunded clinical trials. In 2014 New England Baptist Hospital and BIDMC formed a strategic relationship for orthopedic care.

Company Background

To expand its specialist services in 2013 the group launched construction of a new cancer center and surgical pavilion on the Beth Israel Deaconess Hospital-Needham campus.

BIDMC added a second satellite hospital when it formed an affiliation with Milton Hospital (now Beth Israel Deaconess Hospital-Milton) in 2012. The following year BIDMC entered an agreement to bring another Massachusetts medical center Jordan Hospital into the group. Through the affiliation Jordan Hospital will retain its independent management team and board of directors.

CareGroup was formed through the 1997 union of several Boston-area health care organizations.

EXECUTIVES

Vice President, Joan Joan Pickett Pickett
Senior Vice President Marketing, Lynn Sullivan
Vice President Marketable Securities, Aliza L Samuels
Auditors: KPMG LLP BOSTON MASSACHUSETT

LOCATIONS

HQ: CAREGROUP INC.
375 LONGWOOD AVE FL 7, BOSTON, MA 022155395
Phone: 617 667-1715
Web: WWW.CAREGROUP.ORG

PRODUCTS/OPERATIONS

Selected Massachusetts Hospitals
Beth Israel Deaconess Medical Center (Boston)

Beth Israel Deaconess Hospital-Milton
Beth Israel Deaconess Hospital-Needham
Mount Auburn Hospital (Cambridge)
New England Baptist Hospital (Boston)

COMPETITORS

Baystate Health	Massachusetts General
Boston Medical Center	Hospital
Brigham and Women's	Milford Regional
Hospital	Medical Center
Cambridge Health	Partners HealthCare
Alliance	Southcoast Health
Cape Cod Healthcare	St. Elizabeth's
Children's Hospital	Medical Center
Boston	Steward Health Care
Lahey Health System	Winchester Healthcare

HISTORICAL FINANCIALS
Company Type: Private

Income Statement FYE: September 30

	REVENUE ($ mil.)	NET INCOME ($ mil.)	NET PROFIT MARGIN	EMPLOYEES
09/12	2,448	131	5.4%	12,000
09/11	2,380	46	2.0%	—
Annual Growth	2.9%	179.5%	—	—

2012 Year-End Financials

Return on assets: — Cash ($ mil.): 284
Return on equity: 5.4%
Current ratio: 1.50

CARILION NEW RIVER VALLEY MEDICAL CENTER

LOCATIONS

HQ: CARILION NEW RIVER VALLEY MEDICAL CENTER
2900 LAMB CIR STE 150, CHRISTIANSBURG, VA 240736341
Phone: 540 731-2000
Web: WWW.CARILIONCLINIC.ORG

HISTORICAL FINANCIALS
Company Type: Private

Income Statement FYE: September 30

	REVENUE ($ mil.)	NET INCOME ($ mil.)	NET PROFIT MARGIN	EMPLOYEES
09/13	896	116	12.9%	800
09/05	30	2	6.5%	—
09/04	115	18	16.0%	—
09/03	88	0	—	—
Annual Growth	26.1%	—	—	—

2013 Year-End Financials

Return on assets: 4.3% Cash ($ mil.): —
Return on equity: 12.9%
Current ratio: 1.00

CARITAS NORWOOD HOSPITAL INC.

Caritas Norwood Hospital cares for hearts (and other body parts) of people in the greater Boston area. Operating as Norwood Hospital the facility is a community hospital with some 265 beds that serves patients in Norwood Massachusetts and surrounding towns. Founded in 1902 the acute care hospital has a medical staff of more than 460 that provides area residents with emergency and general health care and medical transport services. Norwood Hospital is also home to specialized programs including behavioral health services cancer treatment cardiology obstetrics/gynecology orthopedic medicine pediatrics rehabilitation sleep disorder treatment and surgery. Norwood Hospital is part of the Steward Health Care System.

Operations

Norwood Hospital conducts a number of community health outreach programs including a cardiovascular disease education program a diabetes awareness program and a healthy nutrition program. The facility boasts a robotic assisted orthopedic surgery program and a newly constructed pain management center and cardiac catheterization lab.

The medical center had more than 41000 emergency department visits; 11000 inpatient visits; 126000 outpatient visits; and some 490 births in 2014.

Sales and Marketing

Norwood Hospital serves a population of about 300000 people in Norwood and about 15 other area communities.

EXECUTIVES

Medical Records Director, Melanie Altruda
Senior Vice President of Operations, William (Bill) Fleming
Auditors: FEELEY & DRISCOLL PC BOSTON

LOCATIONS

HQ: CARITAS NORWOOD HOSPITAL INC.
800 WASHINGTON ST STE 1, NORWOOD, MA 020623487
Phone: 781 769-4000

PRODUCTS/OPERATIONS

Selected Services
Behavioral Health
Cancer Care
Cardiac and Vascular
Diabetes
Digestive Diseases
Ear Nose and Throat
Emergency Medicine
General Surgery
Geriatrics
MAKOplasty® Services
Maternity Services
Neurosciences
Orthopedics
Pain Management
Pediatrics
Primary Care
Pulmonary Medicine
Radiology
Rehabilitation & Physical Therapy
Sleep Medicine
Urology
Weight Loss Surgery
Women' s Health

COMPETITORS

Boston Medical Center
Cambridge Health
Northeast Health System

Alliance
CareGroup
Children' s Hospital Boston
Harrington Memorial Hospital
Partners HealthCare
South Shore Health
Sturdy Memorial

HISTORICAL FINANCIALS
Company Type: Private

Income Statement
FYE: September 30

	REVENUE ($ mil.)	NET INCOME ($ mil.)	NET PROFIT MARGIN	EMPLOYEES
09/09	159	4	2.7%	1,800
09/08	151	(3)	—	—
09/06	153	15	9.8%	—
09/05	150	0	—	—
Annual Growth	1.6%	—	—	—

2009 Year-End Financials

Return on assets: —
Return on equity: 2.7%
Current ratio: 0.30

Cash ($ mil.): 7

CARLE FOUNDATION HOSPITAL

Carle Foundation Hospital is a 393-bed acute-care facility that serves the residents of east central Illinois. The hospital includes the region's only Level I trauma center as well as a Level III perinatal center a neonatal ICU and centers devoted to cardiac and cancer care. It also runs a handful of specialty centers in the region. Carle Foundation Hospital is the primary teaching hospital for the University of Illinois College of Medicine at Urbana-Champaign. It is controlled by the not-for-profit Carle Foundation; sister company Carle Physician Group which boasts more than 400 physicians representing 80 specialties is one of the nation's largest private physician groups.

Operations

The hospital averages more than 22000 annual patient admissions and treats 63000-plus emergency room patients. It offers services related to bariatrics stroke sports medicine women's health and heart and cancer care.

Geographic Reach

Carle Foundation Hospital's service area spans 14 communities across east-central Illinois.

Sales and Marketing

Revenue increased 12% to $2 billion in 2014 as patient service earnings and rental income grew. However due to an increase in medical benefits of insured and pension-related changes net income fell 65% to $112 million that year.

Despite the lower net income cash flow from operations rose 20% to $193 million on changes in medical claims payable as well as an increase in cash generated fro third-party payor settlements.

Strategy

Construction has been key to Carle Foundation Hospital's growth in recent years. The hospital built a $6 million center for children with hearing loss; the center houses the Expanding Children's Hearing Opportunities Center and the Carle Auditory Oral School. Carle Foundation Hospital Research Institute opened an $11-million Biomedical Research Center that houses hospital and University of Illinois staff conducting research in breast cancer gastrointestinal and cardiovascular disease and neuroscience.

The hospital in 2013 added a $200 million seven-story patient tower that houses the heart and vascular institute. The new patient capacity replaced patient beds in older parts of the hospital and provides for future growth opportunities. Carle Foundation Hospital now plans to build a new facility to address the region's needs for increased orthopedic and sports medicine services.

In 2015 Crawford Memorial Hospital and Carle Foundation Hospital entered into an affiliation agreement. Crawford's 25-bed facility joined Carle's network of rural care centers to better provide care for patients in the area.

EXECUTIVES

Vice President Information Technology Chief Information Officer, Rick Rinehart
Vice President Marketing, Jeff Ingrum
President and CEO, James C. Leonard
Medical Director, Robert T Kiskaddon
Vice President Of Facility, Scott Harding
Medical Director, Douglas Filipov
Director Of Nursing, Edith Matesic
Rph, Chris Howard
Occupational Medicine, Laura Shanks
Vice President Human Resources, Phil Kubow
Vice President, Lauren Schmid
Vice President, Bonnie Standley
Operating Room Director, Julie Cox
Vice President Human Resources, Philip Cohen
Vice President Information Management And Analytics, Cheryl Gerow
Radiology Director, Tim Sapyta
Secretary, Cora Musial
Executive Board Member, Annett Schmit
Board Member, Sean Grambart
Auditors: ERNST & YOUNG US LLP INDIANAP

LOCATIONS

HQ: CARLE FOUNDATION HOSPITAL
611 W PARK ST, URBANA, IL 618012529
Phone: 217 326-2900
Web: WWW.CARLE.ORG

PRODUCTS/OPERATIONS

2014 Sales

	% of total
Net premium revenue-health insurance	63
Net patient service revenue	34
Rental income	1
Net assets released from restrictions	-
Other	2
Loss on the disposal of property & equipment	-
Total	**100**

Selected Medical Services

Bariatrics
Cancer
Cancer
Cardiology & Heart Surgery
Diabetes & Endocrinology
Ear Nose & Throat
Gastroenterology & GI Surgery
Geriatrics
Gynecology
Heart
Nephrology
Neurology & Neurosurgery
Sports Medicine
Stroke
Women' s Health

COMPETITORS

Advocate BroMenn
Decatur Memorial Hospital
Hospital Sisters Health System
Iroquois Memorial Hospital
Memorial Health System
Morris Hospital
OSF Healthcare System
Sarah Bush Lincoln Health Center
Silver Cross Hospital
St. Elizabeth Regional Health
St. John' s Hospital (Illinois)
Union Hospital (Indiana)

HISTORICAL FINANCIALS

Company Type: Private

Income Statement

FYE: December 31

	REVENUE ($ mil.)	NET INCOME ($ mil.)	NET PROFIT MARGIN	EMPLOYEES
12/12*	462	106	23.0%	2,500
06/09	365	30	8.4%	—
06/08	383	36	9.6%	—
Annual Growth	3.8%	23.7%	—	—

*Fiscal year change

CARLETON COLLEGE

Curiosity is key at Carleton College. In addition to providing a traditional undergraduate liberal arts education the school encourages critical thinking and creativity at its campus in southern Minnesota. It has an enrollment of some 2000 students and a student-to-teacher ratio of 9:1. The college confers Bachelor of Arts degrees in more than 35 academic majors with a focus on fields including biology chemistry physics mathematics and computer science. The school offers education and foreign language certification and pre-professional programs as well. Carleton College was founded in 1866 by the Minnesota Conference of Congregational Churches under the name of Northfield College.

Geographic Reach

Students attending Carleton College come from nearly all 50 US states as well as more than 40 countries. The college's campus consists of more than 1000 acres in Northfield Minnesota; about 90% of its students live on campus. Carleton College also has a number of cross-cultural and off-campus study programs including study abroad programs in 45 countries.

Operations

The school which says it approaches learning with humility and conviction in addition to a sense of humor consistently ranks near the top of liberal arts colleges with graduates who go on to earn doctorates particularly in the fields of physics astronomy biology chemistry and geology. It also sits near the top of the list of schools with students awarded National Science Foundation Fellowships. Carleton also ranks among top small colleges with graduates serving in the Peace Corps.

In addition to the usual student organizations like the chess club and Christian students club Carleton has unique offerings such as juggling and random acts of kindness clubs. It also has nationally recognized recreational options such as Quiz Bowl and Ultimate Frisbee teams.

Financial Performance

Carleton College reported a 53% decrease in revenues in 2012 due to losses on investments.

Strategy

To fulfill its mission of providing high-level undergraduate programs Carlton College is working to enhance its curriculum strengthen student diversity and prepare students for post-graduation education or careers. In addition the school is working to increase its endowment invest in facility improvements and establish collaborative relationships with other universities and institutions.

EXECUTIVES

VP and Treasurer, Frederick A. (Fred) Rogers
Director Information Technology Services, Joel Cooper
Dean of the College, Shelby J. Boardman

President, Robert A. Oden Jr.
Dean of Admissions, Paul Thiboutot
VP External Relations, Kristine Cecil
Dean of Students, Hudlin Wagner
Vice President Treasurer, Barb Silk
President Spouse, Jane Poskanzer
Chief Investment Officer, Jason Matz
President Manager, Stephanie Huston
President Emeritus, Stephen Lewis
President Professor of Political Science, Steven Poskanzer
Auditors: CLIFTONLARSONALLEN LLP MINNE

LOCATIONS

HQ: CARLETON COLLEGE
1 N COLLEGE ST, NORTHFIELD, MN 550574044
Phone: 507 222-4000
Web: WWW.APPS.CARLETON.EDU

HISTORICAL FINANCIALS

Company Type: Private

Income Statement

FYE: June 30

	REVENUE ($ mil.)	NET INCOME ($ mil.)	NET PROFIT MARGIN	EMPLOYEES
06/14	233	108	46.4%	650
06/13	188	66	35.3%	—
06/12	110	(8)	—	—
06/11	232	0	—	—
Annual Growth	0.1%	—	—	—

2014 Year-End Financials

Return on assets: 1.3%	Cash ($ mil.): 33
Return on equity: 40.4%	
Current ratio: —	

CARNEGIE MELLON UNIVERSITY

If you can't act maybe Carnegie Mellon University can help. The university is known around the world for churning out award-winning actors from its highly regarded drama school. Drama isn't all Carnegie teaches though the school has seven colleges and schools that offer academic programs in areas such as psychology computer science engineering biology and public policy. It has more than 12000 students and 5000 faculty and staff and it has a relatively small student-teacher ratio of 10:1. Carnegie Mellon was founded by philanthropist and industrialist Andrew Carnegie who established the Carnegie Technical Schools in 1900 for the sons and daughters of Pittsburgh's blue-collar workers.

Geographic Reach

The school has locations in Pittsburgh (its main campus); Australia; Japan; Silicon Valley California; Singapore; Mexico; Greece; Portugal; and Doha Qatar.

Operations

Along with its undergraduate and graduate degree programs Carnegie offers working adults a chance to continue their learning through the Professional & Distance Learning arm of the school. Students there can hone their international business management skills and bone up on information technology health systems and human resources among other topics.

Carnegie prides itself on its innovation efforts and to support them operates about 120 research institutes and centers across its campus. Carnegie's CyLab is one of the largest university-based cyber-

security education and research centers in the country. Cylab focuses on seven primary areas of research and development spanning a wide range of technologies and systems and users.

Carnegie in 2012 established the Wilton E. Scott Institute for Energy Innovation a research and education initiative focused on improving energy efficiency and developing new clean and affordable energy sources. It also launched Initiative for Digital Entertainment Analytics which conducts research into questions raised by the emergence of digital distribution channels for entertainment content.

Financial Performance

The university experienced growth of 11% in 2012 due to increased retention in undergraduate programs and growth in graduate program tuition and international programs. The growth was also due to increase in investment income and income from auxiliary service.

However Carnegie experienced a 84% decline in net income in 2012 due to increases in operating expenses dining vendor expenses and software and maintenance licenses. Its bottom line was also hurt by a decrease in revenue from non-operating activities.

Company Background

Carnegie Tech merged with the Mellon Institute of Research to become Carnegie Mellon University in 1967.

EXECUTIVES

President and Trustee, Jared L. Cohon, age 67
EVP Provost and Chief Academic Officer; Interim CFO, Mark S. Kamlet
VP and CFO, Deborah Moon
Dean Heinz College, Ramayya Krishnan
Chief Investment Officer, Charles A Kennedy
CIO, Steven K. (Steve) Huth
Dean Carnegie Institute of Technology School of Engineering, James H. Garrett
Dean College of Fine Arts, Dan Martin
Dean Dietrich College of Humanities and Social Sciences, John Lehoczky
Dean Mellon College of Science, Fred Gilman
Dean School of Computer Science, Randall E. (Randy) Bryant
Dean Tepper School of Business, Robert M. Dammon
President Chemical Engineering, Alexandra Grande
President Manager Business Administration, Neil Sanyal
President Information Systems, Sandeep Movva
President Business Administration, Shawn Alwani
Assoc Vice President Chief Human Resources Officer, Barbara (Barb) Smith
Assoc Vice President Financial Planning, BARBARA (Barb) MORYCZ
Senior Management (Senior Vice President General Manager Director), Gretchen Beck
Vice President, Randall Feenstra
Associate Vice President, Tim McNulty
Associate Vice President Chief Human Resources Officer, Dianne Kenney
Assistant Vice President for Marketing Communications, Marilyn Kail
Vice President of Operations, Eric Apeagyei
Senior Vice President Of Business Affairs At Viacom Productions, David Lavin
Vice President Of Technology, Neel Kishan
Vice President of Mentorship, Adrian Galarza
Department Head, Patsy McCarthy
Vice President, Zach Weinberg
Director Finance Vice President University Advancement Univ Advancement, Carolyn J Wolfe
Vice President, Chinmayi Bhavanishankar
Divisional (Vice President for Education), Donora Craighead
Vice President for Research, Farnam Jahanian
Divisional Vice President Bh, Linda Anderson

Vice President, Missy Demme
Contracts Manager Associate Vice President for Re, Lynn Young
Assistant Vice President For Research Compliance, Ann Mathias
Department Head, Stephen Garoff
Regional Vice President Bh, Noboru Matsuda
Executive Vice President, Harrison Apple
Vice President, Robert (Bob) Sekerka
Assistant Vice President for Marketing Communicati, Marilyn Kai
Vice President, Egon Balas
Vice President, Mike Trick
Vice President, Gerard Cornuejols
Associate Vice President Campus Design Facility Development, Ralph Horgan
Vice President Of Finance, Lapah Mofor
Vice President Of Technology, Daniel Dallala
Vice President Of Finance, Peter Tran
Vice President Of Finance, Jorge Carvallo
Assistant Vice President Internationa, Carrie Nelson
Vice President Of Finance, Sam Phong
Vice President of Technology Education, Silvio Tannert
Vice President Finance, Maneesh Lekkala
Co Vice President of Finance, Sahil Jain
Vice President Of Education Technology, Georgia Tech
Vice President Of Finance, Kevin Gallagher
Vice President of Finance and Technology, Daniel (Dan) Robinson
Vice President Of Corporate Finance, Mark Flemming
Vice President of Cross Campus Collaboration, Moises Morgenstern
Associate Vice President For Individual Giving, Pamela (Pam) Eager
Assistant Vice President Marketing, Alan (Al) Montgomery
Co Director, Carl Olson
Associate Vice President Government Relations, Timothy (Tim) McNulty
Vice Chairman, James E. (Jim) Rohr, age 67
Chairman, Raymond J. (Ray) Lane, age 68
Vice Chairman, E. Kears Pollock
Treasurer, Jay Calhoun
Treasurer, Michelle Martin
Assistant Treasurer, Amy Faber
Secretary, Alice Yochum
Secretary, Amanda Bodnar
Secretary, Maria Wilkin
Assistant Secretary, Karen Khan
Auditors: PRICEWATERHOUSECOOPERS LLP P

LOCATIONS

HQ: CARNEGIE MELLON UNIVERSITY
5000 FORBES AVE, PITTSBURGH, PA 152133890
Phone: 412 268-8746
Web: WWW.CMU.EDU

Selected Locations
Adelaide Australia
Athens Greece
Aveiro and Coimbra Portugal
Doha Qatar
Kobe Japan
Lisbon Portugal
Los Angeles
Madeira Portugal
Minho and Porto Portugal
Mexico
Silicon Valley
Singapore

PRODUCTS/OPERATIONS

Selected Schools
Carnegie Institute of Technology
School of Computer Science
College of Fine Arts
College of Humanities & Social Sciences
H. John Heinz III College

Mellon College of Science
Tepper School of Business

HISTORICAL FINANCIALS
Company Type: Private

Income Statement
FYE: June 30

	REVENUE ($ mil.)	NET INCOME ($ mil.)	NET PROFIT MARGIN	EMPLOYEES
06/13	1,106	182	16.5%	4,913
06/12	1,061	44	4.2%	—
06/11	956	278	29.1%	—
06/10	899	0	—	—
Annual Growth	7.1%	—	—	—

2013 Year-End Financials
Return on assets: —
Return on equity: 16.5%
Current ratio: —
Cash ($ mil.): 141

CAROLINA CARE CENTER OF CHERRYVILLE INC.

Auditors: F WESLEY TALTON JR CPA PA

LOCATIONS

HQ: CAROLINA CARE CENTER OF CHERRYVILLE INC.
111 HARRILSON RD, CHERRYVILLE, NC 280219541
Phone: 704 435-4161
Web: WWW.CAROLINACARECENTER.COM

HISTORICAL FINANCIALS
Company Type: Private

Income Statement
FYE: September 30

	REVENUE ($ mil.)	NET INCOME ($ mil.)	NET PROFIT MARGIN	EMPLOYEES
09/09	733	55	7.5%	130
09/02	5	0	7.0%	—
09/01	5	0	5.0%	—
09/00	4	0	—	—
Annual Growth	74.1%	—	—	—

2009 Year-End Financials
Return on assets: —
Return on equity: 7.5%
Current ratio: 2.60
Cash ($ mil.): —

CAROLINA FARM CREDIT ACA

Auditors: PRICEWATERHOUSECOOPERS LLP AT

LOCATIONS

HQ: CAROLINA FARM CREDIT ACA
146 VICTORY LN, STATESVILLE, NC 286258507
Phone: 704 873-1761
Web: WWW.CAROLINAFARMCREDIT.COM

HISTORICAL FINANCIALS
Company Type: Private

Income Statement
FYE: December 31

	ASSETS ($ mil.)	NET INCOME ($ mil.)	INCOME AS % OF ASSETS	EMPLOYEES
12/09	1,331	20	1.5%	208
12/08	1,448	24	1.7%	—
Annual Growth	(8.1%)	(15.9%)	—	—

2009 Year-End Financials
Return on assets: —
Return on equity: 21.1%
Sales ($ mil.): 95

CAROLINA HEALTHCARE CENTER OF CUMBERLAND LP

Auditors: RSM MCGLADREY CHARLOTTE NC

LOCATIONS

HQ: CAROLINA HEALTHCARE CENTER OF CUMBERLAND LP
4600 CUMBERLAND RD, FAYETTEVILLE, NC 283062412
Phone: 910 429-1690
Web: WWW.CAROLINA-HEALTH.COM

HISTORICAL FINANCIALS
Company Type: Private

Income Statement
FYE: September 30

	REVENUE ($ mil.)	NET INCOME ($ mil.)	NET PROFIT MARGIN	EMPLOYEES
09/09	1,019	62	6.2%	150
09/03	6	(0)	—	—
Annual Growth	132.0%	—	—	—

2009 Year-End Financials
Return on assets: —
Return on equity: 6.2%
Current ratio: 0.70
Cash ($ mil.): —

CARPENTER CONTRACTORS OF AMERICA INC.

Carpenter Contractors of America has been working with wood for more than half of a century. The company manufactures roof trusses and wall panels and supplies building materials through its manufacturing facilities in Florida. The company also has offices in North Carolina and Illinois where it operates under the name R&D Thiel. The company's products and services are used in both residential and commercial construction. In 1955 brothers Robert and Donald Thiel founded the company as R&D Thiel in Belvidere Illinois. Carpenter Contractors of America filed for Chapter 11 bankruptcy in 2010.

EXECUTIVES

Chairman and CEO, Donald Thiel
VP Finance Secretary and Treasurer, Terrance B.
 (Terry) Smith
President Chicago, Donald W. (Don) Reiter
President, Billy D. (Bill) Fritsch

LOCATIONS

HQ: CARPENTER CONTRACTORS OF AMERICA INC.
 3900 AVE D NW, WINTER HAVEN, FL 33880
Phone: 863 294-6449
Web: WWW.RDTHIEL.COM

COMPETITORS

Putnam Lumber & Export   Roberts Lumber Company
Robbins Manufacturing
 Company

HISTORICAL FINANCIALS

Company Type: Private

Income Statement

FYE: February 3

	REVENUE ($ mil.)	NET INCOME ($ mil.)	NET PROFIT MARGIN	EMPLOYEES
02/07	353	12	3.5%	1,000
02/02	183	8	4.4%	—
02/01*	174	8	4.6%	—
01/00	159	0	—	—
Annual Growth	12.1%	—	—	—

*Fiscal year change

2007 Year-End Financials

Return on assets: 1.5%   Cash ($ mil.): 28
Return on equity: 3.5%
Current ratio: 2.40

CARSON OIL CO. INC.

LOCATIONS

HQ: CARSON OIL CO. INC.
 3125 NW 35TH AVE, PORTLAND, OR 972101637
Phone: 503 829-5441
Web: WWW.CARSONOIL.COM

HISTORICAL FINANCIALS

Company Type: Private

Income Statement

FYE: December 31

	REVENUE ($ mil.)	NET INCOME ($ mil.)	NET PROFIT MARGIN	EMPLOYEES
12/07	361	1	0.5%	300
12/06	284	1	0.6%	—
12/05*	256	1	0.7%	—
09/98	59	0	—	—
Annual Growth	22.3%	—	—	—

*Fiscal year change

2007 Year-End Financials

Return on assets: 3.1%   Cash ($ mil.): 2
Return on equity: 0.5%
Current ratio: 0.80

CARSON TAHOE REGIONAL HEALTHCARE

Carson Tahoe Regional Healthcare which includes the Carson Tahoe Regional Medical Center (CTRMC) serves Nevada's Carson Valley and its surrounding areas. The not-for-profit CTRMC boasts about 220 beds and provides a wide range of services such as acute general surgical specialty and outpatient care. The medical center also includes a rehabilitation center cardiovascular center surgical unit free-standing cancer center emergency room and women and children's center. Carson Tahoe Regional Healthcare also operates smaller urgent care behavioral health physical therapy and outpatient care centers in Carson City and nearby communities.

Geographic Reach

Carson Tahoe Health System's network of healthcare facilities services and programs are located in and around Northern Nevada and Eastern California.

OperationsThe health system operates in 22 locations and serves a population of 250000. It has more than 240 board-certified physicians with expertise in more than 35 medical specialties.Altogether Carson Tahoe Health System boasts three hospitals two urgent care facilities and several medical support facilities. Its multiple outpatient locations include a fully-accredited cancer center an emergent care facility primary care clinics a pair of urgent care clinics and three retail care clinics. Carson Tahoe Health's Behavioral Health Services division provides a diagnosis/multi disciplinary team approach to treating seniors adults adolescents and children experiencing behavioral and addictive disorders. It provides a broad range of inpatient and outpatient services that includes individual group and family counseling support groups medical model detoxification services and a 14-21 day addictive disorders rehabilitation program.StrategyThe health system works to regularly add to its roster of services. In 2013 it expanded its Carson Tahoe Center for Wound Healing on the second floor of its Carson Tahoe Specialty Medical Center. The center provides the latest advanced treatments to help those with non-healing wounds. Carson Tahoe Health System also added a new cardiology office in Reno in 2013. Sales and MarketingAs part of its marketing efforts Carson Tahoe Health System launched Toast an online blog at www.ToastCarsonTahoe.com that shares health tips fashion advice recipes and lifestyle articles.

Company Background

The health system was established in 1949.

EXECUTIVES

V Pres, Cathy Dinaue
Vice President Of Finance, Ann Beck
Assistant Secretary, Timothy (Tim) McFarren
Auditors: BKD LLP ST LOUIS MO

LOCATIONS

HQ: CARSON TAHOE REGIONAL HEALTHCARE
 1600 MEDICAL PKWY, CARSON CITY, NV 897034625
Phone: 775 445-8000
Web: WWW.CARSONTAHOE.COM

PRODUCTS/OPERATIONS

Selected Services

Behavioral Health Services Inpatient
Cancer Center
Carson Tahoe Cardiology Locations
Carson Tahoe Surgery Center

Dayton Medical Building
Eagle Medical Center
Holbrook Therapy
Minden Medical Center
Regional Medical Center
Sierra Surgery Hospital
Specialty Medical Center
Therapy at N. Roop Prof. Center
Urgent & Emergent Care
Walmart Clinics
Womens Health/Cardiology

COMPETITORS

Dignity Health   Universal Health
HCA   Services
Sutter Health

HISTORICAL FINANCIALS

Company Type: Private

Income Statement

FYE: December 31

	REVENUE ($ mil.)	NET INCOME ($ mil.)	NET PROFIT MARGIN	EMPLOYEES
12/12	186	4	2.4%	1,500
12/09	195	18	9.4%	—
12/08	163	(8)	—	—
12/06	164	0	—	—
Annual Growth	2.1%	—	—	—

2012 Year-End Financials

Return on assets: 2.9%   Cash ($ mil.): 4
Return on equity: 2.4%
Current ratio: 1.60

CARTER-JONES COMPANIES INC.

Auditors: SS&G AKRON OH

LOCATIONS

HQ: CARTER-JONES COMPANIES INC.
 601 TALLMADGE RD, KENT, OH 442407331
Phone: 330 673-6100
Web: WWW.CARTERLUMBER.COM

HISTORICAL FINANCIALS

Company Type: Private

Income Statement

FYE: December 31

	REVENUE ($ mil.)	NET INCOME ($ mil.)	NET PROFIT MARGIN	EMPLOYEES
12/13	956	10	1.1%	3,225
12/12	808	3	0.5%	—
12/11	671	1	0.3%	—
12/10	652	0	—	—
Annual Growth	13.6%	—	—	—

2013 Year-End Financials

Return on assets: 3.3%   Cash ($ mil.): 11
Return on equity: 1.1%
Current ratio: 1.10

CARY OIL CO. INC.

Auditors: BATCHELOR TILLERY & ROBERTS L

LOCATIONS

HQ: CARY OIL CO. INC.
110 MACKENAN DR STE 300, CARY, NC 275117901
Phone: 919 462-1100
Web: WWW.CARYOIL.COM

HISTORICAL FINANCIALS

Company Type: Private

Income Statement

FYE: December 31

	REVENUE ($ mil.)	NET INCOME ($ mil.)	NET PROFIT MARGIN	EMPLOYEES
12/13	1,829	3	0.2%	50
12/12	1,647	2	0.2%	—
12/11	1,608	2	0.1%	—
12/10	1,177	0	—	—
Annual Growth	15.8%	—	—	—

2013 Year-End Financials

Return on assets: —
Return on equity: 0.2%
Current ratio: 0.90

Cash ($ mil.): 2

CASCADE ENGINEERING INC.

Ideas about plastic parts cascade down from Cascade Engineering's collection of companies ending up as practical components for many applications. The company manufactures and markets under the Cascade and other brands plastic injection molded products as well as parts for OEMs in the automotive truck material handling waste and recycling and home and office industries. Its auto lineup includes interior and exterior trim HVAC cases and ducts and acoustical parts along with heavy truck fairings fenders and grills. Catering to resource conservation markets Cascade also makes and services an eco-lineup comprising building-mountable wind turbines waste collection bins and water filtration systems.

Geographic Reach

Cascade Engineering serves its customers through 15 facilities spanning North America and Europe.

Operations

Cascade Engineering's operations are divided into 13 strategic business units serving the markets of automotive commercial truck and bus solid waste and recycling furniture material handling consumer products consulting and renewable energy. These units include CK Technologies Cascade Engineering Automotive Americas Cascade Engineering Automotive Europe Cascade Cart Solutions Xtreme RFID Capturit Cascade Engineering Commercial Products Invisible Waste Services Noble Polymers Decade Products Cascade Renewable Energy Cascade Consulting Group and Triple Quest.

Strategy

For growth the company has pursued a variety of public programs such as the Environmental Protection Agency's set-aside fund that supports job creation through green manufacturing. It launched a line of pink trash carts in 2010 garnering market awareness for breast cancer research as well as for the company.

In agriculture Cascade has partnered with an Israel company to form Decade Products a joint venture that manufactures harvesting bins touted as labor-saving for West Coast citrus and onion farm-

ers. Fueling its renewable energy efforts Cascade has retrofitted a warehouse to accommodate an assembly line for wind turbine rotors used on top of houses. Research and development dollars are also being put into producing the Swift brand of lighter less expensive turbines.

Company Background

The company was founded by chairman and CEO Fred P. Keller in 1973.

EXECUTIVES

Vice President of Manufacturing, Judy Bland
Vice President Of Operations, Scott Suits
Senior Vice President New Business Development and Managing Director Cascade Engineering Europe, Lance Tennant
Auditors: BDO GRAND RAPIDS MI

LOCATIONS

HQ: CASCADE ENGINEERING INC.
3400 INNOVATION CT SE, GRAND RAPIDS, MI 495122085
Phone: 616 975-4800
Web: WWW.CASCADENG.COM

PRODUCTS/OPERATIONS

Selected Products and Brands

Automotive (acoustics chassis and powertrain interior and exterior trim)
Automotive aftermarket (portable consumer electronic devices for cars and trucks)
Commercial truck and bus (interior exterior functional systems)
Compounded polymers (thermoplastic polyolefins elastomers nanocomposites specialty polymers)
Furniture (seating products)
Material handling (reusable plastic containers and pallets)
Renewable energy (SWIFT wind turbine)
RFID systems tags and software
Solid waste and recycling (EcoCart)
Valet trash (Invisible Waste Services)
Water (HydrAid BioSand water filter)

COMPETITORS

ADAC Plastics	Key Plastics
Delphi Automotive Systems	Lear Corp
Fisher & Company	Nypro
Johnson Controls	Visteon

HISTORICAL FINANCIALS

Company Type: Private

Income Statement

FYE: August 30

	REVENUE ($ mil.)	NET INCOME ($ mil.)	NET PROFIT MARGIN	EMPLOYEES
08/14	358	0	—	1,200
08/13*	238	0	—	—
09/12	238	0	—	—
08/11	238	0	—	—
Annual Growth	14.7%			

*Fiscal year change

2014 Year-End Financials

Return on assets: 14.5%
Return on equity: —
Current ratio: 0.60

Cash ($ mil.): 1

CASH-WA DISTRIBUTING CO. OF KEARNEY INC.

This company keeps the Quik-E Marts in merchandise. Cash-Wa Distributing supplies food produce beverages equipment cleaning supplies and more to foodservice operators and convenience stores throughout Nebraska and in all or parts of 10 surrounding states. It operates three distribution centers and serves more than 6500 customers with an inventory of some 20000 items. The family-owned and -operated company was formed in 1934 as a candy and tobacco wholesaler and was purchased by the Henning family in 1957. Cash-Wa Distributing is a member of the UniPro distribution cooperative.

Operations

The company's operations include a fleet of some 175 trucks and a larger number of refrigerated trailers. It also has three truck and trailer shops.

Geographic Reach

Cash-Wa Distributing's market area includes all or part of Nebraska Kansas Missouri Iowa Minnesota Montana North and South Dakota Wyoming Oklahoma and Colorado. It has sales offices in Hays Kansas; Omaha and Sidney Nebraska; and Rapid City South Dakota and distribution centers in Aberdeen South Dakota and Kearney and Lincoln Nebraska.

Sales & Marketing

The company's customer segments include convenience stores restaurants health care facilities and schools.

EXECUTIVES

National Accounts Manager, Linda Rechtine

LOCATIONS

HQ: CASH-WA DISTRIBUTING CO. OF KEARNEY INC.
401 W 4TH ST, KEARNEY, NE 688457825
Phone: 308 237-3151
Web: WWW.CASHWA.COM

COMPETITORS

AMCON Distributing	MAINES
Affiliated Foods	McLane
Midwest	Meadowbrook Meat Company
Associated Wholesale Grocers	Performance Food Group
C&S Wholesale	Reinhart FoodService
Core-Mark	Sysco
Farner-Bocken	US Foods

HISTORICAL FINANCIALS

Company Type: Private

Income Statement

FYE: November 30

	REVENUE ($ mil.)	NET INCOME ($ mil.)	NET PROFIT MARGIN	EMPLOYEES
11/13*	377	6	1.8%	539
12/12	398	11	3.0%	—
12/11	306	5	1.8%	—
Annual Growth	10.9%	8.1%	—	—

*Fiscal year change

2013 Year-End Financials

Return on assets: 2.8%
Return on equity: 1.8%
Current ratio: 0.60

Cash ($ mil.): —

CATAMOUNT CONSTRUCTORS INC.

A solid foundation is tantamount to Catamount's success. The company provides general contracting services for the construction of commercial industrial health care institutional and residential developments around the US. It offers services from conceptualization and design-build to construction management. Subsidiary CC Residential specializes in midrise multifamily residences including condominiums apartments and mixed-use developments. Catamount Constructors boasts a high customer return rate; it has provided services for such return clients as CarMax Walgreen and Chase Bank. CEO Geoff Wormer and other executives Kurt Kenchel Jeff Sidwell and Jeff Cochran founded the company in 1997.

Catamount Constructors has offices in metropolitan Denver and Atlanta two areas where it completes most of its projects.

EXECUTIVES

Vice President, Thomas J Harper
Vice President, Kurt T Kenchel
Vice President, Thomas (Thom) Harper
SEC Treas, Jeffrey (Jeff) Cochran
Auditors: EKS&H LLLP DENVER COLORADO

LOCATIONS

HQ: CATAMOUNT CONSTRUCTORS INC.
1527 COLE BLVD STE 100, LAKEWOOD, CO
804013411
Phone: 303 679-0087

COMPETITORS

A.G. Spanos
Boran Craig Barber
 Engel
Edward Rose
Imperial Construction
 Group

J.E. Dunn Construction
 Group
Peter Kiewit Sons'
Skanska USA Building
The Grupe Company
Turner Construction

HISTORICAL FINANCIALS

Company Type: Private

Income Statement

FYE: December 31

	REVENUE ($ mil.)	NET INCOME ($ mil.)	NET PROFIT MARGIN	EMPLOYEES
12/13	319	(0)	—	142
12/08	226	4	1.9%	—
12/07	183	7	4.1%	—
12/06	156	0	—	—
Annual Growth	—	—	—	—

2013 Year-End Financials

Return on assets: 15.9%
Return on equity: (-0.3%)
Current ratio: 0.30
Cash ($ mil.): 15

CATHOLIC MEDICAL CENTER

Catholic Medical Center is a 330-bed hospital serving southern New Hampshire. Services include cancer treatment surgery rehabilitation treatments for sleep disorders and emergency medical services. Catholic Medical Center (CMC) offers about 40 medical specialties through divisions including The Mom's Place (a birthing facility) and the New England Heart Institute. CMC has partnered with its community to extend health care and dental care to the uninsured and the homeless and has established a health clinic geared to help refugees being resettled in the area.

Operations
CMC employs some 500 physicians. The hospital operates about a dozen outpatient and urgent care centers in its service territory as well as outreach programs including the Parish Nurse Program the Poisson Dental Facility the Westside Neighborhood Health Center and the Healthcare for the Homeless Project. As a not-for-profit institution CMC contributed some $74 million in community benefits during 2013.

Geographic Reach
The hospital serves residents in and around Manchester New Hampshire as well as patients from across the state. Its primary service area includes the communities of Allenstown Auburn Bedford Candia Deerfield Dunbarton Goffstown Hooksett Manchester and New Boston.

Financial Performance
The hospital reported net patient service revenues of some $284 million in 2012 with Medicare and Medicaid policy reimbursements accounting for $94 million of sales.

Strategy
CMC focuses on enhancing and expanding its service offerings for area residents. It opened a heart and vascular intervention unit within the hospital facility in 2013 for instance and added neurology services as a new specialist offering. The hospital also expands by forming clinical care partnerships with other area medical centers.

In 2011 CMC canceled plans to merge with Dartmouth-Hitchcock Medical Center although the hospitals continue to collaborate at CMC's Special Care Nursery and D-H's Norris Cotton Cancer Center. CMC and Dartmouth-Hitchcock cited evolving changes in health care reforms behind their decision not to merge. The partnership was opposed by the New Hampshire attorney general on the grounds that it would violate state law and needed court approval.

Company Background
CMC was founded in 1974 through the merger of two Catholic-sponsored Manchester hospitals: Notre Dame Hospital and Sacred Heart Hospital.

EXECUTIVES

President and CEO, Alyson Pitman Giles
Vice President Of Emergency Services, Lu Mulla
Director Of Pharmacy, Barbara Case
Vice President Of Sales, Daniel Bouvier
Vice President Human Resources, Margo Campagna
Director of Infection Control, Karen Kennett
Vice President Human Resources, Jennifer (Jen) Torosian
Vice President Of Human Resources, Janet Troski
Vice President Operations, Bob Duhaime
Vice President Emergency Services, Lu Mula
Auditors: BAKER NEWMAN & NOYES PORTLAND

LOCATIONS

HQ: CATHOLIC MEDICAL CENTER
100 MCGREGOR ST, MANCHESTER, NH 031023770
Phone: 603 663-6888
Web: WWW.CATHOLICMEDICALCENTER.ORG

PRODUCTS/OPERATIONS

Selected Centers and Services
Behavioral Health Services
Breast Care Center
Cancer Care
Cholesterol Management Center
Community Health Services
Diabetes Resources Institute
Diagnostic Imaging
Emergency Department
Laboratory
New England Heart Institute
New England Sleep Center
Obesity Treatment Center
Primary Care Locations
Rehabilitation Services
Respiratory Services
Surgical Care Group
Surgical Services
The Mom's Place
The Wellness Center
Urgent Care at Bedford
Wound Care Center

COMPETITORS

Beth Israel Deaconess
 Medical Center
Boston Medical Center
Brigham and Women's
 Hospital
Cambridge Health
 Alliance
CareGroup
Caritas Holy Family
 Hospital

Concord Hospital
Elliot Health System
Exeter Health
 Resources
Frisbie Memorial
 Hospital
HealthSouth
Southern New Hampshire
 Medical Center

HISTORICAL FINANCIALS

Company Type: Private

Income Statement

FYE: June 30

	REVENUE ($ mil.)	NET INCOME ($ mil.)	NET PROFIT MARGIN	EMPLOYEES
06/13	322	29	9.1%	1,500
06/10	277	11	4.2%	—
06/09	241	(1)	—	—
06/08	88	0	—	—
Annual Growth 29.6%				

2013 Year-End Financials

Return on assets: 12.0%
Return on equity: 9.1%
Current ratio: 1.00
Cash ($ mil.): 85

CATHOLIC MEDICAL MISSION BOARD INC

Auditors: MARKS PANETH & SHRON LLP NEW

LOCATIONS

HQ: CATHOLIC MEDICAL MISSION BOARD INC
10 W 17TH ST, NEW YORK, NY 100115765
Phone: 212 242-7757
Web: WWW.CMMB.ORG

HISTORICAL FINANCIALS

Company Type: Private

Income Statement

FYE: September 30

	REVENUE ($ mil.)	NET INCOME ($ mil.)	NET PROFIT MARGIN	EMPLOYEES
09/13	526	44	8.4%	38
09/11	305	47	15.5%	—
09/10	179	(4)	—	—
09/08	207	0	—	—
Annual Growth 20.5%				

2013 Year-End Financials

Return on assets: 0.4%
Return on equity: 8.4%
Current ratio: —
Cash ($ mil.): 2

CATHOLIC RELIEF SERVICES - UNITED STATES CONFERENCE OF CATHOLIC

Auditors: MCGLADREY LLP GAITHERSBURG M

LOCATIONS

HQ: CATHOLIC RELIEF SERVICES - UNITED STATES CONFERENCE OF CATHOLIC
228 W LEXINGTON ST, BALTIMORE, MD 212013443
Phone: 410 625-2220
Web: WWW.CRS.ORG

HISTORICAL FINANCIALS

Company Type: Private

Income Statement

FYE: September 30

	REVENUE ($ mil.)	NET INCOME ($ mil.)	NET PROFIT MARGIN	EMPLOYEES
09/13	639	8	1.3%	5,879
09/12	701	(15)	—	—
09/11	822	(6)	—	—
09/10	918	0	—	—
Annual Growth	(11.4%)	—	—	—

2013 Year-End Financials

Return on assets: 14.2%   Cash ($ mil.): 74
Return on equity: 1.3%
Current ratio: 0.60

CDM CONSTRUCTORS INC.

Auditors: PRICEWATERHOUSECOOPERS LLP BO

LOCATIONS

HQ: CDM CONSTRUCTORS INC.
50 HAMPSHIRE ST, CAMBRIDGE, MA 021391548
Phone: 617 452-6000
Web: WWW.CDMVIETNAM.COM

HISTORICAL FINANCIALS

Company Type: Private

Income Statement

FYE: December 28

	REVENUE ($ mil.)	NET INCOME ($ mil.)	NET PROFIT MARGIN	EMPLOYEES
12/13	402	13	3.4%	500
12/12	392	10	2.8%	—
12/11*	360	10	2.9%	—
01/11	341	0	—	—
Annual Growth	5.6%	—	—	—

*Fiscal year change

2013 Year-End Financials

Return on assets: 13.5%   Cash ($ mil.): 31
Return on equity: 3.4%
Current ratio: 0.90

CEDARS-SINAI MEDICAL CENTER

Many a star has been born literally at Cedars-Sinai Medical Center. The 886-bed teaching and research hospital is located right where Los Angeles meets Beverly Hills and West Hollywood and has tended to the medical needs of a number of celebrities since its founding in 1902. However the center is also a major teaching hospital for UCLA's David Geffen School of Medicine and is engaged in hundreds of research programs in areas such as cancer neuroscience and genetics. It also includes two multi-specialty physician associations Cedars-Sinai Medical Group and Ceders-Sinai Health Associates and operates a number of community health centers and outreach programs (such as mobile health clinics).

Operations

The not-for-profit hospital's more than 2100 physicians represent just about every clinical specialty out there. Cedars-Sinai is consistently listed as a top-ranked hospital by U.S. News & World Report in such specialties as cancer cardiology endocrinology gastrointestinal disorders gynecology heart surgery kidney disease neurology orthopaedics and respiratory disorders.

Cedars-Sinai is the only private hospital with a Level 1 trauma center in Los Angeles County; as such the hospital sees about 1600 trauma patients a year. The hospital also provides a number of outpatient services.

Federal funding from the National Institutes of Health and other sources have provided the hospital with some $40 million towards research. Cedars-Sinai currently has some 1300 research projects.

The hospital sees some 660000 outpatient visits and 85000 emergency department visits each year.

Geographic Reach

Cedars-Sinai's hospital is located in Los Angeles; it has an administrative office in Beverly Hills California.

Financial Performance

Revenues from patient care and other sources totaled nearly $2.77 billion in fiscal 2015 while net income amounted to $472.9 million.

Strategy

To meet increasing patient demand and expand its capacity for research projects Cedars-Sinai added nearly 7000 sq. ft. of space to house the Cedars-Sinai Biobank and Translational Research Core Facility in 2015. The previous year it opened a new clinic dedicated to the evaluation of heart and vascular disease patients for participation in stem cell medical studies.

EXECUTIVES

Senior Vice President Legal Affairs, Peter (Pete) Braveman
Senior Vice President System Development, Richard (Dick) Jacobs
President and CEO, Thomas M. (Tom) Priselac
SVP Finance and CFO, Edward M. Prunchunas
SVP Clinical Care Services and COO, Mark R. Gavens
SVP Academic Affairs and Chief Academic Officer, Shlomo Melmed
SVP Medical Affairs and Chief Medical Officer, Michael L. Langberg
SVP Enterprise Information Systems and CIO, Darren Dworkin
VP Nursing and Chief Nursing Officer, Linda Burnes Bolton
Medical Director, Matthew T Wilson
Vice President Legal Affairs, James (Jamie) Laur
Director of Operating Room Anesthesia, Jan Decker
Medical Director GenRISK Adult Genetic, Ora Gordon
Nursing Director Women's And Children's Psych, Mary Cirricione
Senior Vice President Medical Network, Thomas D (Thom) Gordon
Medical Director, Spencer Koerner
Senior Vice President Community Relations, Arthur (Art) Ochoa
Vice President of Patient Financial Services, Patricia (Pat) Kittell
Director of Radiology, Lynne Roy
Vice Chairman, Marc H. Rapaport
Chairman, Vera S. Guerin
Auditors: ERNST & YOUNG US LLP IRVINE

LOCATIONS

HQ: CEDARS-SINAI MEDICAL CENTER
8700 BEVERLY BLVD, WEST HOLLYWOOD, CA 900481804
Phone: 310 423-3277
Web: WWW.CEDARS-SINAI.EDU

PRODUCTS/OPERATIONS

Selected Centers and Services

Ambulatory Care Center
Cedars-Sinai Center for Chest Disease
Cedars-Sinai Center for Digestive Diseases
Cedars-Sinai Heart Institute
Cedars-Sinai Institute Spine Center
Cedars-Sinai Health Associates (affiliated independent physician association)
Cedars-Sinai Medical Group (multi-specialty physicians group)
Cedars-Sinai Orthopedic Center
Diagnostic imaging center
Emergency department and trauma center
Hospice services
Kidney and pancreas transplant center
Neuroscience services
Pediatric services
Psychiatry and mental health services
Samuel Oschin Comprehensive Cancer Institute
Surgical services
Organ and bone marrow transplantation
Radiation therapy
Radiology
Stroke program
Pain management services
Women's health services

COMPETITORS

Adventist Health
Brotman Medical Center
Childrens Hospital Los Angeles
City of Hope
Community Health Systems
Dignity Health
Eisenhower Medical Center
Glendale Adventist Medical Center
Glendale Memorial Hospital
Golden State Health Centers
Good Samaritan Hospital (IN)
HCA
Hollywood Presbyterian Medical Center
Los Angeles County Health Department
Newhall Memorial Hospital
Pasadena Hospital Association
Providence Health System Southern California
Providence Saint Joseph Medical Center
Scripps health
Tenet Healthcare
UCSF Medical
White Memorial Medical Center

HISTORICAL FINANCIALS

Company Type: Private

Income Statement
FYE: June 30

	REVENUE ($ mil.)	NET INCOME ($ mil.)	NET PROFIT MARGIN	EMPLOYEES
06/11	2,658	210	7.9%	8,000
06/10	2,309	152	6.6%	—
Annual Growth	15.1%	37.7%	—	—

2011 Year-End Financials

Return on assets: —
Return on equity: 7.9%
Current ratio: 0.40

Cash ($ mil.): 303

CEDARWOOD-YOUNG COMPANY

Auditors: DOUGHERTY & COMPANY PASADENA

LOCATIONS

HQ: CEDARWOOD-YOUNG COMPANY
14620 JOANBRIDGE ST, BALDWIN PARK, CA
917061750
Phone: 626 962-4047
Web: WWW.ALLANCOMPANY.COM

HISTORICAL FINANCIALS

Company Type: Private

Income Statement
FYE: December 31

	REVENUE ($ mil.)	NET INCOME ($ mil.)	NET PROFIT MARGIN	EMPLOYEES
12/13	365	2	0.8%	275
12/12	393	3	0.9%	—
12/11	456	4	1.1%	—
12/10	391	0	—	—
Annual Growth	(2.3%)	—	—	—

2013 Year-End Financials

Return on assets: 3.1%
Return on equity: 0.8%
Current ratio: 2.90

Cash ($ mil.): 7

CENTERLIGHT HEALTHCARE INC.

Auditors: LOEB & TROPER LLP NEW YORK N

LOCATIONS

HQ: CENTERLIGHT HEALTHCARE INC.
1250 WATERS PL STE 602, BRONX, NY 104612732
Phone: 718 515-8600
Web: WWW.CENTERLIGHTHEALTHCARE.ORG

HISTORICAL FINANCIALS

Company Type: Private

Income Statement
FYE: December 31

	REVENUE ($ mil.)	NET INCOME ($ mil.)	NET PROFIT MARGIN	EMPLOYEES
12/13	687	(13)	—	4,000
12/10	288	3	1.2%	—
12/09	258	5	2.0%	—
12/08	456	0	—	—
Annual Growth	8.5%	—	—	—

2013 Year-End Financials

Return on assets: 5.7%
Return on equity: (-2.0%)
Current ratio: 1.60

Cash ($ mil.): 77

CENTIMARK CORPORATION

Shout it from the rooftops Centimark is one of the largest commercial and industrial roofing contractors in North America. The company provides roof installation inspection repair and emergency leak service. Centimark typically works on flat roofs using EPDM rubber thermoplastic bitumen metal and coatings. Top customers have included NASA and the US Army Corps of Engineers. Its QuestMark division offers commercial industrial and retail flooring do-it-yourself (DIY) products and floor maintenance and cleaning products. The company which has about 80 offices throughout North America.

Geographic Reach

Pittsburgh Pennsylvania-based Centimark also does business in Canada through subsidiary Centimark Ltd. which has offices in Calgary Edmonton Toronto and Vancouver.

Operations

The company offers roof and floor services roof replacement roof repairs floor repairs emergency services preventative maintenance programs energy efficient solutions safety options and accessories online project management and DIY floor products. Centimark also provides systems such as thermoplastic solutions sprayed polyurethane foams roof coatings modified bitumen and built-up roofing metal products and steep slope products. In addition it engages in the online retail of flooring products such as patch and repair and maintenance/floor care products and coatings.

QuestMark a division of Centimark offers materials for commercial retail and industrial floors. It specializes in DiamondQuest polished concrete flooring epoxy flooring floor repair materials floor maintenance and floor cleaning products.

Centimark's Asset Management service provides extensive roof surveys roof life expectancy models return-on-investment analysis for roof repairs and evaluations for roof repair or roof replacement.

Sales and Marketing

The company serves customers in different segments including retail industrial general contractors and education.

Financial Performance

Centimark's 2014 sales totaled $485 million.

Strategy

In response to customer demand for more energy-efficient options Centimark has been increasing its use of spray polyurethane foam (which adds insulation and a waterproof barrier to roofs). The company also installs electricity-producing photovoltaic solar panels onto roofs. Other green options available from Centimark include skylights and garden roofs.

The company also tries to stay ahead of the pack with technological innovations such as its MyCentimark service. The online resource allows property owners to view invoices work authorizations before-and-after photos and recommendations for future roof maintenance. In 2014 the company launched a tablet and smartphone app that allows customers to request service and find the nearest Centimark office based on their current location.

Company Background

Chairman and CEO Edward Dunlap founded Centimark as an industrial cleaning business in 1967. Centimark is owned by its employees.

EXECUTIVES

Vice President Online Applications, Joe Filtz
Chairman and CEO, Edward B. Dunlap
President and COO, Timothy M. Dunlap
EVP and Northern Group Director, Robert J. Rudzik
EVP and Western Group Director, Steven M. Ferencz
EVP National and Regional Sales, John T. Godwin
EVP and CFO, John L. Heisey
EVP and Southern Group Director, Sherman L. Gaskins
EVP and QuestMark Flooring Group Director, John P. Scanlon
EVP and Eastern Group Director, Mark A. Cooper
EVP and Canada Group Director CentiMark Ltd, Robert T. Penney
SVP and Southern Group Director, Keith Battenfield
EVP Service, Kenneth W. Zmich
Vice President Of Human Resources, Landon Connolly
National Account Manager, David (Dave) Conaghan
National Account Manager, Robert Marinkoski
National Account Manager, Carl Nece
Executive Vice President, John (Jack) Rudzik
Executive Vice President, Robert Marshall
National Account Manager, Josh Canning
National Account Manager, Bill Shanko
National Accounts Manager, Darren Dicenso
Senior Vice President, Michael (Mel) Rew
Vice President Saftey Risk Mngmt, Jeffrey (Jeff) Mccarthy
National Account Manager, Tom Blaylock
Vice President Of Litigation Department, John (Jack) Liekar
Auditors: SCHNEIDER DOWNS & CO INC P

LOCATIONS

HQ: CENTIMARK CORPORATION
12 GRANDVIEW CIR, CANONSBURG, PA 153178533
Phone: 724 743-7777
Web: WWW.CENTIMARKLTD.COM

PRODUCTS/OPERATIONS

Selected Operations
CentiMark (roofing)
CentiMark ltd. (Canada roofing)
QuestMark (flooring)

Selected Systems
Roof Systems
EPDM
Green Roofing
Metal Roofs
Modified Bitumen and Built-Up Roofs
Roof Coatings
SPF
Steep Slope
TPO & PVC
Floor Systems
Chemical Resistant Systems
Decorative Broadcast

Decorative Concrete
Electric Static Dissipative
Heavy Duty Resurfacer
High Build Coating
Polished Concrete
Thin Mil

COMPETITORS

Armstrong World Industries	Duro-Last Roofing
Cabral Roofing & Waterproofing	Garcia Roofing Holland Roofing
D. C. Taylor	Pickens Roofing Tecta America

HISTORICAL FINANCIALS
Company Type: Private

Income Statement
FYE: April 30

	REVENUE ($ mil.)	NET INCOME ($ mil.)	NET PROFIT MARGIN	EMPLOYEES
04/14	508	42	8.3%	2,400
04/13	484	38	8.0%	—
04/12	474	38	8.1%	—
04/11	404	0	—	—
Annual Growth	7.9%	—	—	—

2014 Year-End Financials
Return on assets: 3.1%   Cash ($ mil.): 85
Return on equity: 8.3%
Current ratio: 2.30

CENTRA HEALTH INC.

Centra Health is a constellation of hospitals and medical practices targeting the health care needs of residents in central and southern Virginia. At the not-for-profit entity's core are two acute care facilities in Lynchburg: the 358-bed Lynchburg General which is the region's main emergency center and specializes in orthopedic pediatric and cardiac care; and Virginia Baptist a 161-bed facility focused on surgery women's health infant care mental health and rehabilitation. Centra also operates a nearby community hospital and an array of primary care physician practices home health agencies retirement centers and other physical and behavioral health businesses.

Operations

In addition to Lynchburg General and Virginia Baptist Centra's acute care facilities include Southside Community Hospital (Farmville). Southside Community Hospital serves as a central acute care and birthing facility for an eight-county region. Centra also operates the Bedford Memorial Hospital through a partnership with Carilion Health System; it plans to buy out Carilion's shares in the partnership.

Outside of its acute care operations Centra Health administers senior care services through The Summit assisted living and independent living facilities. The Summit offers senior residents private apartments medical care and personal assistance. Centra also operates a network of treatment centers for patients of all ages with behavioral and psychiatric disorders. The network includes facilities that specialize in treating children and adolescents with emotional and behavioral disorders.

Altogether the network handles more than 300000 patient visits each year including more than 90000 emergency room visits and more than 5000 cardiac procedures. Its hospitals have a medical staff of about 500 doctors who perform more than 6300 inpatient and 9300 outpatient surgeries annually. Centra also operates the Centra Medical Group which includes about 140 primary care and specialist physicians.

Geographic Reach

Centra Health serves Lynchburg and surrounding communities in central Virginia including Farmville (located in Prince Edward County) Bedford Danville/Gretna and Moneta/Smith Mountain Lake Virginia.

Strategy

Centra Health is expanding its breadth of services as well as its network of facilities. Recent additions include new behavioral health facilities and an expansion of Bedford Memorial's orthopedic center. In 2015 it announced plans to buy out Carilion Clinic's shares of Bedford Memorial Hospital and the Oakwood Health and Rehabilitation Center for $11 million.

Company Background

Centra Health was founded in 1987 through the merger of Lynchburg General and Virginia Baptist. Southside Community Hospital joined the network in 2006.

EXECUTIVES

Chairman Centra Foundation, George A. Hurt
President and CEO, E. W. Tibbs
VP and CEO Centra Southside Community Hospital, William L. Bass
Medical Director, John Paul (Jack) Jones
Medical Director, Ken Fore
Chairman, Walker P. Sydnor
Vice Chairman, Amy G. Ray
Secretary of Nursing Services, Jackie Anderson
Auditors: DIXON HUGHES PLLC ASHEVILLE

LOCATIONS

HQ: CENTRA HEALTH INC.
1920 ATHERHOLT RD, LYNCHBURG, VA 245011120
Phone: 434 200-4700
Web: WWW.CENTRAHEALTH.COM

PRODUCTS/OPERATIONS

Selected Facilities
Bedford Memorial Hospital (Bedford Virginia; partnership with Carilion Health System)
Lynchburg General Hospital (Lynchburg Virginia)
Virginia Baptist Hospital (Lynchburg Virginia)
Southside Community Hospital (Farmville Virginia)
Physician Practices
 Altavista Medical Center (Altavista Virginia)
 Big Island Medical Center (North Big Island Virginia)
 Brookneal Family Medical Center (Brookneal Virginia)
 Gretna Medical Center (Gretna Virginia)
 Lynchburg Family Medicine Center (Lynchburg Virginia)
Other Facilities
 Bridges Treatment Center (Lynchburg Virginia)
 Fairmont Crossing Health and Rehabilitation Center (Amherst Virginia)
 Guggenheimer Health and Rehabilitation Center (Lynchburg Virginia)
 Piedmont Psychiatric Center (Lynchburg Virginia)
 Rivermont Schools (regional)
 The Summit (regional)

COMPETITORS

Alleghany Regional Hospital	Martha Jefferson Hospital
Bon Secours Health	Mary Washington Healthcare
Carilion Clinic	
Clinch Valley Medical Center	Montgomery Regional Hospital
Danville Regional Medical Center	Sentara Healthcare
HealthSouth	University of Virginia Health System
Henrico Doctors' Hospital	

HISTORICAL FINANCIALS
Company Type: Private

Income Statement
FYE: December 31

	REVENUE ($ mil.)	NET INCOME ($ mil.)	NET PROFIT MARGIN	EMPLOYEES
12/09	534	16	3.1%	6,000
12/08	419	33	7.9%	—
12/04	331	10	3.3%	—
12/03	313	0	—	—
Annual Growth	9.3%	—	—	—

2009 Year-End Financials
Return on assets: —   Cash ($ mil.): 21
Return on equity: 3.1%
Current ratio: 0.30

CENTRAL ARKANSAS RADIATION THERAPY INSTITUTE INC.

Auditors: HUDSON CISNE & CO LLP LITTLE

LOCATIONS

HQ: CENTRAL ARKANSAS RADIATION THERAPY INSTITUTE INC.
4 SAINT VINCENT CIR, LITTLE ROCK, AR 722055402
Phone: 501 664-8573
Web: WWW.CARTI.COM

HISTORICAL FINANCIALS
Company Type: Private

Income Statement
FYE: June 30

	REVENUE ($ mil.)	NET INCOME ($ mil.)	NET PROFIT MARGIN	EMPLOYEES
06/13	352	15	4.5%	175
06/10	139	5	4.1%	—
06/09	128	0	—	—
06/08	857	0	—	—
Annual Growth	(16.3%)	—	—	—

2013 Year-End Financials
Return on assets: 3.8%   Cash ($ mil.): —
Return on equity: 4.5%
Current ratio: 1.40

CENTRAL CONTINUING CARE INC.

LOCATIONS

HQ: CENTRAL CONTINUING CARE INC.
1287 NEWSOME ST, MOUNT AIRY, NC 270305439
Phone: 336 786-2133

HISTORICAL FINANCIALS

Company Type: Private

Income Statement

FYE: September 30

	REVENUE ($ mil.)	NET INCOME ($ mil.)	NET PROFIT MARGIN	EMPLOYEES
09/09	723	(8)	—	135
09/98	3	0	4.5%	—
Annual Growth 61.6%	—	—	—	—

2009 Year-End Financials

Return on assets: —
Return on equity: (-1.1%)
Current ratio: 3.70

CENTRAL CRUDE INC

Auditors: MCELROY QUIRK & BURCH

LOCATIONS

HQ: CENTRAL CRUDE INC
4187 HIGHWAY 3059, LAKE CHARLES, LA 706153310
Phone: 713 783-2167
Web: WWW.CENTRALCRUDE.COM

HISTORICAL FINANCIALS

Company Type: Private

Income Statement

FYE: March 31

	REVENUE ($ mil.)	NET INCOME ($ mil.)	NET PROFIT MARGIN	EMPLOYEES
03/09	637	1	0.2%	50
03/08	635	0	0.1%	—
03/06	985	0	—	—
Annual Growth (13.5%)	3231.6%	—	—	—

2009 Year-End Financials

Return on assets: —
Return on equity: 0.2%
Current ratio: 0.90

CENTRAL DUPAGE HOSPITAL ASSOCIATION

Central DuPage Hospital attends to the health needs of Windy City suburbanites. Located in DuPage County just west of Chicago the hospital has more than 310 beds and provides general medical and surgical care including specialty care in areas such as oncology cardiovascular disease neuroscience and orthopedics. The hospital is the focal point of a network of health services that include a physician medical group home health care services occupational care and about half a dozen urgent care centers. Central DuPage Hospital opened its doors in 1964.

Geographic Reach

DuPage County is a highly-populated community west of Chicago (and Cook County).

Operations

Central DuPage Hospital merged with neighboring Delnor Health System to create a new health system in 2011 called Cadence Health Foundation. The two facilities still operate independently with their own charitable money-raising foundations. Their affiliated community health operations were also moved into the system.

At the hospital network's urgent care centers which it calls Convenient Care Centers patients are able to obtain treatment for minor illnesses and injuries such as the flu and fractures as well as after-hours care. The idea behind the centers is to direct patients to the appropriate location for care rather than places such as expensive emergency rooms.StrategyThough it may not be the largest of hospitals Central DuPage has worked hard to keep up with the industry's technological advances and has an electronic medical records system that allows physicians to securely access a patient's clinical information from remote locations enabling them to spend less time filling out paperwork and more time providing medical care. The hospital also has a medication barcoding system that is used to confirm that patients receive the right medications at the right time reducing medical errors and improving patient outcomes which can lead to government-paid incentives.Additionally nurses are able to electronically enter patient information at a patient's bedside through a computerized patient charting system reducing errors through lapse of memory as nurses make rounds of dozens of patients.Central DuPage is also the first hospital in the county to use the da Vinci robotic surgical system to perform delicate prostate and gynecological procedures. Finally the hospital operates a telephone monitoring system for homebound patients to keep the hospital team aware of any issues prior to home visits.Company BackgroundThe hospital is one in the region that conducts clinical trials to help further our understanding of diseases and how they can be better treated. Some of its clinical trial areas include cardiology neonatal intensive care neuroscience oncology and many others.

EXECUTIVES

Vice President Medical Affairs, Kevin Most
Director Of Pharmacy, Elaine Rodriguez
Vice President, Jeffrey (Jeff) Huml
Medical Director, Qamar Jalil
Occupational Medicine, Robin Robinson
Vice President Treasurer, Brett Tande
Executive Vice President And Chief Information Officer, Dan Kinsella
Director Of Operating Room, Maura Trilla
Nursing Director, Colleen Drolshagen
Medical Records Director, Debra Czink
Medical Director, Konstantin Dzamashvili
Medical Director of Behavioral Health Services, Danesh Alam
Medical Director Of Laboratory, Beth Johnson
Vice President Patient Care Services and Chief Nursing Officer, Deb O'Donnell
Auditors: CROWE HORWATH LLP CHICAGO IL

LOCATIONS

HQ: CENTRAL DUPAGE HOSPITAL ASSOCIATION
25 N WINFIELD RD, WINFIELD, IL 601901295
Phone: 630 933-1600
Web: WWW.CDH.ORG

PRODUCTS/OPERATIONS

Selected Facilities

Cadence Health Foundation
Cadence Physician Group
Central DuPage Business Health (occupational health services)
Central DuPage Hospital
Central DuPage Physician Group
CNS Home Health and Hospice
Convenient Care Centers (urgent care)
HealthLab

COMPETITORS

Adventist Health System Sunbelt Healthcare
Advocate Health Care
Alexian Brothers Health System
Covenant Ministries
Elmhurst Memorial Healthcare
Gottleib Memorial Hospital
Loyola University Health System
Northwest Community Healthcare
Rush System for Health
St. Bernard Hospital and Health Care Center
University of Chicago Medical Center
Wheaton Franciscan Services

HISTORICAL FINANCIALS

Company Type: Private

Income Statement

FYE: June 30

	REVENUE ($ mil.)	NET INCOME ($ mil.)	NET PROFIT MARGIN	EMPLOYEES
06/13	849	184	21.7%	1,600
06/12	773	112	14.5%	—
06/11	667	25	3.9%	—
06/10	633	0	—	—
Annual Growth 10.2%	—	—	—	—

2013 Year-End Financials

Return on assets: 12.3%
Return on equity: 21.7%
Current ratio: 1.40
Cash ($ mil.): 4

CENTRAL ELECTRIC POWER COOPERATIVE INC.

LOCATIONS

HQ: CENTRAL ELECTRIC POWER COOPERATIVE INC.
121 GREYSTONE BLVD, COLUMBIA, SC 292108002
Phone: 803 779-4975
Web: WWW.CEPCI.ORG

HISTORICAL FINANCIALS

Company Type: Private

Income Statement

FYE: December 31

	REVENUE ($ mil.)	NET INCOME ($ mil.)	NET PROFIT MARGIN	EMPLOYEES
12/13	1,198	0	0.0%	44
12/09	1,037	1	0.2%	—
12/08	896	1	0.2%	—
12/07	777	0	—	—
Annual Growth 7.5%	—	—	—	—

2013 Year-End Financials

Return on assets: 10.4%
Return on equity: —
Current ratio: 1.10
Cash ($ mil.): 11

CENTRAL GROCERS INC.

In a city of big stores Central Grocers helps neighborhood markets stay afloat. Founded in 1917 the cooperative wholesale food distributor is owned by some 225 members. It supplies 40000 food items and general merchandise to more than 400 independent grocery stores serving several states such as Illinois Indiana Iowa Michigan and Wisconsin. Central Grocers distributes products under both national brands and its own Centrella brand which is marketed exclusively to its member stores. The co-op also operates about 30 stores under a handful of banner names including Strack & Van Til Town & Country Key Market and the low-cost Ultra Foods chain.

Operations

As part of its business Central Grocers caters to its customers with the help of a fleet of 100 refrigerated trucks 300 dry trailers and about 70 Freightliner tractors.

Strategy

Central Grocers the 7th largest grocery cooperative in the US boasts the second-largest market share in the Chicago area. It specializes in serving Chicago independent supermarkets. Central Grocers supplies them with a comprehensive menu of groceries produce fresh meat service deli items frozen foods ice cream and items from its own Centrella brand.

Central Grocers expanded its distribution center by 15000-sq.-ft. to 940000-sq.-ft. of storage capacity in 2011. The reason for expansion was due to demand for produce and fresh meats.

Financial Performance

While privately-owned Central Grocers doesn't report financial results. The co-op rings up an estimated $2 billion in sales and it returns (in the form of dividends) to its members about $243 million.

Sales and Marketing

Central Grocers services a wide variety of store formats and ethnic groups including Hispanic Italian and African Americans. Besides older and smaller 5000-sq.-ft. stores its clients include large-scale warehouse discount stores that measure 75000 sq. ft. and large conventional stores that average 70000 sq. ft.

EXECUTIVES

Vice President Warehouse Operations, John Coari
Director of Health and Safety, Thomas H (Thom) Pirro

LOCATIONS

HQ: CENTRAL GROCERS INC.
2600 HAVEN AVE, JOLIET, IL 604338467
Phone: 815 553-8800
Web: WWW.CENTRAL-GROCERS.COM

PRODUCTS/OPERATIONS

Selected Products
Fresh meat
Frozen foods
Groceries
Ice cream
Produce
Service deli items

COMPETITORS

ALDI	Kroger
Albertsons	Meijer
Alex Lee	SUPERVALU
Associated Wholesale	Safeway
Grocers	Schnuck Markets
C&S Wholesale	Wal-Mart
Certco	Winkler
Dearborn Wholesale	
Grocers	

HISTORICAL FINANCIALS
Company Type: Private

Income Statement
FYE: July 28

	REVENUE ($ mil.)	NET INCOME ($ mil.)	NET PROFIT MARGIN	EMPLOYEES
07/07	1,197	(10)	—	2,300
07/06	1,108	5	0.5%	—
07/05	1,103	4	0.4%	—
07/04	1,047	0	—	—
Annual Growth	4.5%	—	—	—

2007 Year-End Financials
Return on assets: —
Return on equity: (-0.9%)
Current ratio: 0.20
Cash ($ mil.): —

CENTRAL IOWA HOSPITAL CORP

LOCATIONS

HQ: CENTRAL IOWA HOSPITAL CORP
1200 PLEASANT ST, DES MOINES, IA 503091406
Phone: 515 241-6212

HISTORICAL FINANCIALS
Company Type: Private

Income Statement
FYE: December 31

	REVENUE ($ mil.)	NET INCOME ($ mil.)	NET PROFIT MARGIN	EMPLOYEES
12/12	720	75	10.5%	3,495
12/09	633	44	7.0%	—
12/08	412	(15)	—	—
12/05	519	0	—	—
Annual Growth	4.8%	—	—	—

2012 Year-End Financials
Return on assets: —
Return on equity: 10.5%
Current ratio: 1.80
Cash ($ mil.): 48

CENTRAL IOWA POWER COOPERATIVE

Keeping a sharp eye out for the well-being of Iowa's citizens Central Iowa Power Cooperative provides electricity transmission and generation services to 13 member distribution cooperatives (12 rural electric cooperatives and one municipal cooperative) which in turn serve about 320000 residential and 7000 industrial and commercial customers. Central Iowa Power's member distribution cooperatives deliver power to commercial businesses farmsteads industrial parks manufacturers urban residences and other customers in a service area that stretches 300 miles diagonally across the state from Shenandoah in the southwest to the Mississippi River in the east.

The power cooperative serves 58 of of Iowa's 99 counties and 12 of its 17 cities with populations of more than 25000.

More than 95% of the electric power provided by Central Iowa Power to its member cooperatives is generated in Iowa by coal gas hydroelectric nuclear oil and renewable energy power plants. An active advocate for reducing carbon dioxide emissions about 40% of its total power generation is fueled by non carbon-fuel sources (primarily nuclear and wind). In 2008 Central Iowa Power signed a 10-year contact to buy 42MW of wind power from FPL Energy's Story County Wind Energy Center.

HISTORY

h

EXECUTIVES

Vice President Of Information Technology, Paul Hofman
Auditors: LWBJ LLP WEST DES MOINES IA

LOCATIONS

HQ: CENTRAL IOWA POWER COOPERATIVE
1400 HIGHWAY 13, CEDAR RAPIDS, IA 524039060
Phone: 319 366-8011
Web: WWW.CIPCO.NET

HISTORICAL FINANCIALS
Company Type: Private

Income Statement
FYE: December 31

	REVENUE ($ mil.)	NET INCOME ($ mil.)	NET PROFIT MARGIN	EMPLOYEES
12/13	193	12	6.3%	117
12/09	185	23	12.9%	—
12/08	164	6	4.0%	—
12/06	140	0	—	—
Annual Growth	4.6%	—	—	—

2013 Year-End Financials
Return on assets: 10.1%
Return on equity: 6.3%
Current ratio: 2.20
Cash ($ mil.): 20

CENTRAL MAINE HEALTH VENTURES INC.

Auditors: KPMG LLP BOSTON MA

LOCATIONS

HQ: CENTRAL MAINE HEALTH VENTURES INC.
300 MAIN ST, LEWISTON, ME 042407027
Phone: 207 795-0111
Web: WWW.CMMC.ORG

HISTORICAL FINANCIALS
Company Type: Private

Income Statement
FYE: June 30

	REVENUE ($ mil.)	NET INCOME ($ mil.)	NET PROFIT MARGIN	EMPLOYEES
06/13	319	(11)	—	275
06/10	314	(4)	—	—
06/09	291	4	1.6%	—
06/08	29	0	—	—
Annual Growth	61.3%	—	—	—

2013 Year-End Financials
Return on assets: 22.5%
Return on equity: (-3.6%)
Current ratio: 0.30
Cash ($ mil.): 22

CENTRAL MICHIGAN UNIVERSITY

Academic advancement is central at Central Michigan University (CMU). The university offers more than 200 academic programs for undergraduate graduate and professional coursework through eight colleges including business communication and fine arts medicine and education and human services. The university enrolls more than 20000 students at the main campus in Mt. Pleasant. The institution also enrolls another 7000 students online and at 50 locations throughout North America. In addition CMU offers study abroad programs in 40 countries.

Operations

CMU has 1000 faculty members and a student-to-faculty ratio of about 21:1. It has 22 residence halls. The university also has division I athletic programs for men and women. Its CMU Public Broadcasting unit operates 10 television and seven radio stations.

Financial Strategy

CMU has pioneer in distance learning since 1971 when it was one of the first universities to provide education off campus and directly to students and adults. In 2014 it had nearly 40 locations in the US and Canada including on more than 20 military bases.

Company Background

Notable alumni include former US Senator Robert P. Griffin and actor Jeff Daniels.

CMU was founded in 1892 as a teachers' college.

EXECUTIVES

Interim Associate Vice President University Communications, Sherry Knight
Vice President Enrollment and Student Services, Steven (Steve) Johnson
Vice President Of Chapter Development, Katie Frankhart
Associate Vice President Institutional D, Carolyn Dunn
Vice Chairman, John D Hurd
Secretary, Jody Dittenber
Secretary, Maxine Davis
Secretary, Sue Blubaugh
Executive Board Member, Brittnee Nicolle
Secretary, William (Bill) Cron
Auditors: PLANTE MORAN PLLC PORTAGE M

LOCATIONS

HQ: CENTRAL MICHIGAN UNIVERSITY
1200 S FRANKLIN ST, MOUNT PLEASANT, MI 488592001
Phone: 989 774-4000
Web: WWW.MEDIA.CMICH.EDU

PRODUCTS/OPERATIONS

Selected Colleges and Schools
College of Business Administration
College of Communication and Fine Arts
College of Education and Human Services
College of Graduate Studies
College of Health Professions
College of Humanities and Social and Behavioral Sciences
College of Medicine
College of Science and Technology
Global Campus & Online

HISTORICAL FINANCIALS
Company Type: Private

Income Statement
FYE: June 30

	REVENUE ($ mil.)	NET INCOME ($ mil.)	NET PROFIT MARGIN	EMPLOYEES
06/14	348	19	5.7%	2,388
06/13	319	32	10.1%	—
06/12	321	6	1.9%	—
06/11	329	0	—	—
Annual Growth	1.9%	—	—	—

2014 Year-End Financials
Return on assets: 19.4%
Return on equity: 5.7%
Current ratio: 0.60
Cash ($ mil.): 43

CENTRAL REFRIGERATED SERVICE INC.

No matter the weather conditions trucking company Central Refrigerated Service stays cool when it's on the move. The carrier provides temperature-controlled transportation and dry cargo services for major food suppliers and retailers across the US. It specializes in providing a wide array of offerings from private fleet conversion to inner city and solo driver deliveries to long haul truckload transportation services. Central Refrigerated operates a fleet of about 1800 tractors and 2700 refrigerated trailers or reefers. The company was acquired by truckload carrier Swift Transportation in mid-2013.

Change of Company Type

Central Refrigerated was owned by Jerry Moyes who also owns Swift Transportation. In August 2013 Swift acquired Central Refrigerated for $225 million in order to bolster its refrigerated transport and temperature-controlled offerings.

Operations Central Refrigerated Service estimates that 95% of its loads are food products. Through its Central Logistics division the company provides truckload capacity brokerage and dedicated fleet services.

Company Background Founded in 2002 as a unit of Central Freight Lines Central Refrigerated Service expanded that year by buying the assets of bankrupt Simon Transportation Services another Moyes-controlled company. Central Refrigerated Service was spun off from Central Freight Lines at the end of 2002.

EXECUTIVES

CEO, Jon F. Isaacson
VP Sales and Pricing, Tork A. Fulton
Southern California and Southwest Sales Manager, Brian Kilpatrick
Director Sales National Accounts, Charlie Bringle
Southeast Sales Manager, Mike Bailey
Director Customer Service, Mike Cafarelli
CFO, Bob Baer
Sales Manager, Al Aldrich
Sales Manager, Archie Tucker
Sales Manager, Joe Weber

LOCATIONS

HQ: CENTRAL REFRIGERATED SERVICE INC.
5175 W 2100 S, SALT LAKE CITY, UT 841201252
Phone: 801 924-7000
Web: WWW.CENTRALREFRIGERATED.COM

COMPETITORS
C.R. England	Marten Transport
Covenant	Prime Inc.
Transportation	Stevens Transport
Crete Carrier	Werner Enterprises
Frozen Food Express	Willis Shaw Express
KLLM Transport Services	

HISTORICAL FINANCIALS
Company Type: Private

Income Statement
FYE: December 31

	REVENUE ($ mil.)	NET INCOME ($ mil.)	NET PROFIT MARGIN	EMPLOYEES
12/08	406	9	2.4%	1,650
12/07	361	6	1.8%	—
12/06	0	0	—	—
Annual Growth	—	—	—	—

CENTRO MEDICO DEL TURABO INC.

LOCATIONS

HQ: CENTRO MEDICO DEL TURABO INC.
AVE MUNOZ MARIN, CAGUAS, PR 00725
Phone: 787 653-3099

HISTORICAL FINANCIALS
Company Type: Private

Income Statement
FYE: December 31

	REVENUE ($ mil.)	NET INCOME ($ mil.)	NET PROFIT MARGIN	EMPLOYEES
12/13	436	(6)	—	1,400
12/10	418	1	0.4%	—
12/09	396	(3)	—	—
12/08	1,866	0	—	—
Annual Growth	(25.2%)	—	—	—

2013 Year-End Financials
Return on assets: 16.4%
Return on equity: (-1.4%)
Current ratio: 0.70
Cash ($ mil.): 14

CERES SOLUTIONS LLP

Ceres Solutions is a growth business. The agricultural partnership provides farmers in about a dozen Indiana counties with crop farming support services and supplies. It sells stores and distributes such goods as fertilizers and fuel (gasoline propane home-heating). The company's agronomy services include field mapping crop and pest management soil sampling and yield analysis. Ceres Solutions also offers crop-financing programs sells crop insurance and provides marketing services. Its Green Notes newsletter offers the state's farmers market and technical advice and analysis.

Ceres Solutions which was formed in 2007 through the merger of three agricultural cooperatives —Westland Growers and AgroKey. It operates primarily in the western region of Indiana through about 30 agronomy office locations an energy office and its main office which is located in Crawfordsville Indiana.

EXECUTIVES

VP Agronomy, Dan Weber
CEO, Jeffrey (Jeff) Troike
Chairman, Shan Del Unger
VP Energy and Special Projects, Howard Jones
Secretary and Director, Bob Hall
Vice Chairman, Dale Johnson
Sales Manager, Andrew Nagel
Controller, Don Conder
Vice President of Finance, Jeffrey Moore
Controller, Kevin Benner
Controller, Laura Blackledge
Director, Rex Marchino
Director, Alan Meyer
Secretary and Director, Bob Hall
Vice Chairman, Dale Johnson
Director, Alan McDonald
Director, John Taylor
Director, Randy Waling
Director, Dennis Foster
Director, Joe Irwin
Director, Allan Clauser Jr.
Director, Mark Nesbitt
Auditors: BLUE & CO LLC SEYMOUR IN

LOCATIONS

HQ: CERES SOLUTIONS LLP
2112 INDIANAPOLIS RD, CRAWFORDSVILLE, IN
479333137
Phone: 765 362-6108
Web: WWW.CERESLLP.COM

COMPETITORS

ADM	Cargill
Ag Processing Inc.	GROWMARK
CHS	Premier AG Co-Op Inc.

HISTORICAL FINANCIALS
Company Type: Private

Income Statement
FYE: July 31

	REVENUE ($ mil.)	NET INCOME ($ mil.)	NET PROFIT MARGIN	EMPLOYEES
07/14	412	22	5.4%	125
07/13	402	25	6.4%	—
07/12	399	22	5.6%	—
07/11	329	0	—	—
Annual Growth	7.8%	—	—	—

2014 Year-End Financials
Return on assets: 8.4%
Return on equity: 5.4%
Current ratio: 0.90
Cash ($ mil.): 16

CERTCO INC.

Certco has built a business serving about 200 independent grocers in Minnesota Wisconsin Iowa and Illinois. The food distribution cooperative offers customers an inventory of more than 57000 items including bakery goods frozen foods meat products produce and general merchandise. It distributes products under the Shurfine Shurfresh and Top Care labels. Additionally Certco offers its member-operators such services as advertising accounting client data services warehousing merchandising store planning and design and other business support services. The cooperative was founded in 1930 as Central Wisconsin Cooperative Food Stores.
Geographic Reach

Based in Madison Wisconsin Certco operates in Minnesota and Wisconsin with an extended reach into parts of Iowa and Illinois.
Operations
To support its business Certco operates a nearly 1 million-sq.-ft. distribution center. Its brands include Shurfine Shurfresh Value Time Full Circle Topco and Top Care.
Sales and Marketing
Many of Certco's clients are Fortune 500 companies. It distributes the national brands of major companies such as Kraft General Mills Procter & Gamble and Johnson & Johnson. The company also distributes specialty items under the names Amy's Hodgson Mills Bob's Red Mill and Annie's that are only available through direct-store-delivery suppliers.
Company Background
Certco was established in 1930 when five Madison-area retailers formed an alliance to boost their combined purchasing muscle.

EXECUTIVES

President and General Manager, Randall (Randy) Simon
Director Sales, David (Dave) Ryman
CIO, Steve Baus
Director Deli/Bakery and Meat Departments, Mike McCulloch
Auditors: SATTELL JOHNSON APPEL MENOMON

LOCATIONS

HQ: CERTCO INC.
5321 VERONA RD, FITCHBURG, WI 537116050
Phone: 608 278-2246
Web: WWW.CERTCOINC.COM

PRODUCTS/OPERATIONS

Selected Brands
Full Circle
Shurfine
Shurfresh
Top Care
Topco
Value Time

Selected Services
Advertising
Client data services
Retail accounting
Retail meetings/seminars
Retail support
Retail technology
Store planning & design
Trade shows
Value added services
Warehouses
Web architecture

COMPETITORS

Affiliated Foods Midwest	Dearborn Wholesale Grocers
Associated Wholesale Grocers	Kroger
	Roundy' s
C&S Wholesale	Winkler
Central Grocers	

HISTORICAL FINANCIALS
Company Type: Private

Income Statement
FYE: April 26

	REVENUE ($ mil.)	NET INCOME ($ mil.)	NET PROFIT MARGIN	EMPLOYEES
04/14	640	5	0.9%	325
04/13	607	5	0.9%	—
04/12	569	5	0.9%	—
04/11	525	0	—	—
Annual Growth	6.8%	—	—	—

2014 Year-End Financials
Return on assets: 4.6%
Return on equity: 0.9%
Current ratio: 0.80
Cash ($ mil.): 11

CFJ PROPERTIES LLC

Auditors: KPMG LLP SALT LAKE CITY UTAH

LOCATIONS

HQ: CFJ PROPERTIES LLC
5508 LONAS DR, KNOXVILLE, TN 379093221
Phone: 801 624-1000
Web: WWW.CRYSTALINNS.COM

HISTORICAL FINANCIALS
Company Type: Private

Income Statement
FYE: January 31

	REVENUE ($ mil.)	NET INCOME ($ mil.)	NET PROFIT MARGIN	EMPLOYEES
01/09	7,672	157	2.1%	6,250
01/07	6,769	50	0.7%	
Annual Growth	6.5%	77.6%	—	—

2009 Year-End Financials
Return on assets: 1.5%
Return on equity: 2.1%
Current ratio: 0.40
Cash ($ mil.): 37

CGB ENTERPRISES INC.

The farmer in the delta relies on CGB Enterprises. Located in Louisiana near the shores of Lake Pontchartrain and the mouth of the Mississippi River the agricultural company provides US farmers with a range of services including grain handling storage and merchandising. It offers inland grain transportation by barge rail and truck and also markets and sells seeds agricultural chemicals and insurance. CGB's Consolidated Terminals and Logistics Co. (CTLC) subsidiary provides transportation logistics and bulk commodity services for both agricultural and non-agricultural customers. The company operates more than 95 locations across the US. Japanese trading conglomerates ITOCHU and ZEN-NOH own CGB.
Geographic Reach
From its headquarters in the city of Mandeville Louisiana CGB operates its business through more than 95 locations nationwide including 74 grain elevators across the Midwest. It boasts grain facilities in nearly 10 states including Nebraska Oklahoma Arkansas Iowa Illinois Indiana Ohio Kentucky and Missouri. The company's fertilizer operations span Ohio Illinois Arkansas and Michigan.
Sales and Marketing
Besides its core services of inland grain transportation via barge rail and truck CGB markets and sells seeds agricultural chemicals and insurance as part of its operations.
Strategy
CGB has expanded its CTLC business in recent years. To give the unit an extended reach CTLC now serves the transportation bulk commodity and logistics needs of a global base of customers rather than just CGB's core businesses.

CGB also regularly invests in its own holdings. The company is constructing a rail shipment facility in Defiance Ohio to boost its production capacity and existing transportation system. In 2014 CGB began building a new facility on the Ohio River near Brandenburg Kentucky.

Mergers and Acquisitions

In mid-2014 CGB Enterprises acquired a grain storage facility in Savage Minnesota from Ceres Global Ag Corp. Under the terms of the deal Ceres will lease back 3.5 million bushels of storage capacity from CGB for a six-year term. The purchase of the grain storage facility in Savage brings new customers to CGB which also plans to expand its fertilizer diversified services and other divisions in the Minnesota market. Also CGB acquired Oklahoma's W.B. Johnston Grain (WBJ) in April 2014. WBJ operates 19 grain elevators in Oklahoma and Texas including two grain terminals.

Strengthening its foothold on the Mississippi River CGB acquired the grain and fertilizer assets of Twomey based in Smithshire Illinois. The deal consummated in 2011 added valuable loading capacity on the river and offered CGB with a solid customer base in northwestern Illinois.

Company Ownership

CGB is owned by a pair of Japanese trading conglomerates: ITOCHU and ZEN-NOH.

EXECUTIVES

President CEO, Kevin D. Adams
General Manager Diversified Services, Rodney L. Clark
General Manager Agri Financial Services, Alan Singleton
Manager BioEnergy Services, Steve Burbrink
Manager Information Systems, Sean Goodgion
General Manager Feed Ingredients, Marc Cruse
Director of Sales & Marketing, Brent Mahana
Vice President Manager Director, Cindi Ernest
Vice President Administration, Mike Merkel
Vice President, Osamu Yako
Vice President Human Resources, Mark Berry
Vice President And Controller, Michael (Mel) Smith
Auditors: KPMG LLP NEW ORLEANS LA

LOCATIONS

HQ: CGB ENTERPRISES INC.
1127 HWY 190 E SERVICE RD, COVINGTON, LA
704334929
Phone: 985 867-3500
Web: WWW.CGB.COM

PRODUCTS/OPERATIONS

Selected Business Units
Feed Ingredients
Fertilizer
Financial Services
Grain
Marine
Premium Grains
Risk Management
Soybean Processing
Terminals & Logistics

COMPETITORS

ADM	Crosby Tugs
Ag Processing Inc.	Jimmy Sanders
Alabama Farmers	Kirby Corporation
Cooperative	Southern States
Canal Barge Company	Tennessee Farmers
Cargill	Co-op

HISTORICAL FINANCIALS

Company Type: Private

Income Statement

FYE: May 31

	REVENUE ($ mil.)	NET INCOME ($ mil.)	NET PROFIT MARGIN	EMPLOYEES
05/14	7,227	53	0.7%	1,250
05/13	6,212	30	0.5%	—
05/12	6,108	53	0.9%	—
05/11	5,202	0	—	—
Annual Growth	**11.6%**	—	—	—

2014 Year-End Financials

Return on assets: 0.7%
Return on equity: 0.7%
Current ratio: 0.30
Cash ($ mil.): 16

CH2M HILL COMPANIES LTD.

CH2M HILL's name is a bit tricky but the engineering and construction firm is all up front. The firm (named for its founders Cornell Howland Hayes and Merryfield) operates five main market-oriented divisions: Environment and Nuclear Water Transportation Energy and Industrial and Urban Environments. CH2M Hill's top client is the US Government which contributes more than one-fifth of the company's annual revenue. Public sector clients include the US Department of Energy and the Department of Defense. CH2M HILL also works for state and local governments building water and wastewater systems airports highways and other transportation projects. Founded in 1946 the firm is owned by its employees.

Operations

Since reorganizing its business lines in January 2015 CH2M HILL operates five business segments based on market type: Environment and Nuclear Energy Water Transportation and Industrial and Urban Environments. The Environment and Nuclear division which made up 25% of total revenue in 2014 provides consulting design build engineering operations and maintenance construction management and program management services. The segment is comprised of the Environmental business the Government Facilities and Infrastructure business and the Nuclear business.

Its Energy division (20% of revenue) provides similar construction and design services as the company's Environmental and Nuclear segment. The division is comprised of the Oil Gas and Chemicals business as well as the Power business. The Water division (23% of revenue) works on various water-related projects for the wastewater drinking water industrial water conveyance and storage water resources and ecosystem management and intelligent water services markets. CH2M HILL's Transportation division (18% of revenue) provides horizontal and vertical infrastructure development services for the Aviation Highway and Bridge Ports and Maritime and Transit and Rail market sectors. The Industrial and Urban Environments division (15% of revenue) provides similar design and construction services to the company's Energy division and is made up of the Industrial and Advanced Technology business the Buildings business and the Urban Environments business.

In 2014 CH2M HILL derived 33% of its total revenues from fixed price and guaranteed maximum price contracts.

Geographic Reach

Colorado-based CH2M HILL gets about 70% of its revenue from the US while about 10% comes from the UK. The remainder comes from Asia Australia/New Zealand Canada Europe Latin America and the Middle East and Africa: some 120 countries in all.

Sales and Marketing

The company's clients include US federal and foreign government agencies state and local governments private sector companies and utilities. The US government (and federally-regulated agencies) is the company's largest client generating approximately 21% of total revenues in 2014.

Financial Performance

CH2M HILL has experienced slowly declining revenue since 2012. The firm's revenue fell by 8% to $5.47 billion in 2014 mostly due to declines in its Energy and Industrial and Urban Environments divisions. The Energy division drove most of the total revenue declines shrinking by 29% after the business completed four of its domestic design-build power plant projects. The Industrial and Urban Environments business also shrank by 14% due to lower demand for new projects in the US electronics and manufacturing industries and because of a decline in planning support services in the Middle East for US armed forces. Further adding to its revenue decline the company decided that it would no longer pursue fixed-price design-build contracts in the Government Facilities sector. Lower revenue and higher impairment losses on goodwill and intangibles in 2014 led HC2M HILL to a net loss of $318.30 million (compared to a $131.15 million profit in 2013). Cash from operations also declined by 43% mostly due to lower cash earnings.

Strategy

CH2M HILL announced in 2014 that it would be restructuring the company to improve efficiency reduce risk and create more opportunity for profitable growth. The restructuring aims to gain over $100 million in operational efficiencies and will include cutting the company's workforce by about 5% (about 1200 people). As part of this plan the company in January 2015 organized its business into five key integrated markets and six core regions in order to more effectively serve the infrastructure needs of its clients: Energy Environment & Nuclear Industrial & Urban Environment Transportation and Water. Reducing its dependence on the US Federal Government the company decided in 2014 that it would no longer pursue fixed-price design-build contracts in the Government Facilities sector. It's also begun to do more projects abroad. In 2015 for example the company partnered with the Singapore Public Utilities Board (PUB) and Singapore Cooperation Enterprise to provide technical and integrated water management services to the Rajasthan state government for the four-million-person city of Jaipur India. CH2M HILL occasionally acquires similar businesses to bolster its own service lines. In 2014 it purchased certain assets of Canada-based TERA Environmental Consultants an employee-owned environmental consulting firm that specializes in environmental assessment planning siting and permitting as well licensing services for the oil & gas pipeline and electrical transmission industries. Company Background

In November 2011 the company acquired Halcrow Group a London-based specialist in environmental infrastructure and transport projects for an estimated $192 million. The deal helped boost CH2M HILL's facilities and infrastructure revenues and expanded the company's global reach adding Halcrow's extensive client list and about 100 offices worldwide.

In 2011 CH2M HILL expanded its public transit business when it acquired the state and local government transit consulting business of Booz Allen Hamilton.

The company which is owned by its employees was founded in 1946.

EXECUTIVES

EVP Chief Operational Excellence Officer and Chief Delivery Officer, Michael A. Szomjassy, age 64, $500,011 total compensation

Vice President CH2M HILL OMI, Elisa Speranza

EVP Client Solutions and Sales, Lisa Glatch, age 52, $328,852 total compensation

EVP and CFO, Gary L. McArthur, age 55, $223,080 total compensation

EVP and Chief Human Resources Officer, John A. Madia, age 59, $453,003 total compensation

President Global Business Groups, Gregory T. (Greg) McIntyre, age 56

SVP and Regional Managing Director Middle East North Africa and India, Neil Reynolds

EVP Sales and Risk, Frank C. Gross

President Water Business Group, Peter G. Nicol

SVP and Regional Managing Director Latin America, Manuel E. Aguirre, age 56

Corporate VP and President Global Regions, Mark D. Fallon

Chairman and CEO, Jacqueline C. Hinman, age 53, $889,919 total compensation

Corporate VP and Global President Transportation, Terry A. Ruhl

Global President Environment and Nuclear, Chris Shea

SVP and Regional Managing Director United States, Patrick O'Keefe

SVP and Managing Director Tunnels and Earth Engineering, Martin Knights

SVP and Managing Director Operations Management Services, Steve Meininger

SVP and Regional Managing Director Asia/Pacific, Steven J. Nye

Acting Regional Managing Director Europe, Mark Thurston

EVP General Counsel and Corporate Secretary, Thomas M. (Tom) McCoy, age 64

Business Group President Industrial and Urban Environments, Thomas L. Pennella

SVP and Regional Managing Director - Canada, Alan Cary

Vice President, Didier Menard

Senior Vice President Of Corporate Development, Matthew (Matt) Mcgowan

Vice President, Sidney A (Sid) Faas

Vice President Of Information Systems, Rick Robertson

Executive Vice President Marketing, Gail Chamberlain

Regional Vice President Project Delivery, Gary Wood

Senior Vice President, Ken Miller

Vice President for National Security Programs, Rob Hood

Executive Vice President Marketing, Henry (Hal) Abiera

Vice President of Technology Systems, Kathryn Benson

Vice President Bd for Strategic Carbon and Energy Management, Ronald (Ron) Rudolph

Division Executive Vice President, Courtney Brown

Executive Vice President Marketing, Erika Powell

Vice President Navy and Utility Programs, James (Jamie) Kovalcik

Executive Vice President Marketing, Grace Wachira

Vice President Sales, William (Bill) Hannah

Executive Vice President Marketing, Gary Colgan

Vice President Of Information Systems, Donna Riley

Vice President Of Information Technology, Kristina Nygaard

Vice President Creative, Rosemarie Gumba

Vice President Bd Energy And Chemicals, Sun Pao

Senior Vice President Operations Energy And Chemicals, Pete Wiggin

Vice President, Mike Tilchin

Vice President of Technology, Cathy Zou

Vice President, Tony Omobono

Vice President, Christopher (Chris) Thomas

Senior Vice President; Managing Director Strategic Consulting, Scott Haskins

Vice President, Russell Bowen

Senior Vice President, Craig Pierrotti

Vice President Of Information Technology, Rick Riker

Vice President, Pete Butler

Vice President, Scott Yenzer

Vice President of Municipal Services, Rick Hirsekorn

Executive Vice President Marketing, James (Jamie) Gorham

Vice President Sales, Andrew Barash

Executive Vice President Marketing, James (Jamie) Maughan

Vice President, Alan (Al) Ispass

SeniorVice President Corporate Secretary and Chief Legal Officer, Mark Boedigheimer

Vice President Sales, Aaron Hall

Vice President Sales, Anja Schoenberger

Vice President of Information Technology, Birsen Zeyrek

Senior Vice President, Jhan Schmitz

Executive Vice President Marketing, Gregg Thompson

Vice President, David Hackworth

Vice President Of Operations, Randy Bender

Executive Vice President Marketing, Gregg Hughes

Vice President Of Marketing, Joseph Arnold

Vice President Of Business Development, Karen Wiemelt Karen Wiemelt

Vice President Of Information Technology, Louise Lella

Vice President Of Finance, David (Dave) Bechler

Vice President, Steve Gelman

Vice President, Meg Ibison

Vice President Of Information Technology, Tim Constantine

Vice President Of Tax, John-Bauer Martinez

Senior Vice President, George Powell

Executive Vice President Marketing, Emilio Candanoza

Vice President Director Of Aviation, Jerry Farrar

Senior Vice President, Jan Walstrom

Regional Sales Vice President, James (Jamie) Mcpherson

Vice President Sales, Alan Teare

Vice President, Gwendolyn Buchholz

Vice President Of Information Technology, Thomas Higgins

Vice President, Ted Garrish

Regional Business Group Manager Vice President, Rod Brauer

Executive Vice President Marketing, Gerald Simpson

Vice President Of Information Systems, Michael Fiaksel

Vice President Engineering, Tom Heinemann

Vice President And Area Manager, Deron Huck

Executive Vice President Marketing, Ileana Ruiz

Group Vice President Finance, Steven (Steve) Betts

Executive Vice President Marketing, Fair Yeager

Vice President International Government Affairs, Theresa Loar

Technology Vice President, Korkud Egrican

Vice President, Gary Swanson

Vice President, Scott Weikert

Executive Vice President Marketing, Imad Feghali

Executive Vice President Marketing, Gretchen Engel

Executive Vice President Marketing, Ginger Moore

Vice President, Jonathan Goldstick

Vice President Site Management, Saeed Khan

Vice President Finance, Todd Heskett

Executive Vice President Marketing, Jay McRae

Executive Vice President Marketing, Elizabeth (Beth) Bryant

Vice President, Leofwin Clark

Vice President, Laurens Tak

Vice President, George Gunn

Executive Vice President Marketing, Howard Thomas

Senior Vice President, Michael Rengel

Vice President Sales, Benjamin Romero

Executive Vice President Marketing, Greg Eldridge

Vice President, Joe Cazares

Vice President Business Development And Nuclear Business Group, Cathy Hickey

Executive Vice President, Gerard Orozco

Executive Vice President, Mike Bracken

Vice President Sales, Angela Lee

Executive Vice President Marketing, Iosefa Matagi

Vice President, Tom Price

Vice President Tunnels, Mark Johnson

Vice President North West Regional Business Manager, Vicki Bogenberger

Senior Vice President Latin America Region Energy And Chemicals, Jose Montalvo

Vice President ??? International, Dan Baublis

Vice President Of Information Technology, Stuart Jeffcoat

Vice President And Business Manager, Brent Diemer

Vice President Of Community Investment And Director Of Ch2m Hill Foundation, Ellen Sandberg

Vice President, Jerry Notte

Vice President, Elizabeth French

Global Vice President And Director Of Wastewater Market Segment, Liliana Maldonado

Senior Vice President, Keith Ogden

Vice President, Jim Hunter

Vice President Program Manager, Robert Hayden

Vice President Senior Program Manager, Daniel Wetstein

Vice President (Business Development), Chris Coggans

Vice President International Operations Director, Matthew (Matt) Radek

Executive Vice President Marketing, Emilee Edginton

Vice President Sales, Anne Lynch

Vice President, Paul Wobma

Vice President of Water Supply, Bill Bellamy

Vice President Product Marketing, Morgan Hanscom

Vice President of Information Technology, Jonathan (Jon) James

Vice President Information Technology, Dana Raughton

Vice President Waste Management Market Segment Director, John J (Jack) Wood

Regional Vice President Project Delivery, Ted Constantine

Vice President, Mel Hatcher

Board Member, Bill Farmer

Board Member, Paul Davis

Assistant Treasurer, Allan Chow

Board Member, Don Lewissecretary

Secretary, Franklin Judy

Board Member, Hank Postrozny

Auditors: KPMG LLP DENVER COLORADO

LOCATIONS

HQ: CH2M HILL COMPANIES LTD.
9191 S JAMICA ST, ENGLEWOOD, CO 801125946
Phone: 303 771-0900
Web: WWW.CH2M.COM

2014 Sales

	% of total
US	70
International	30
Total	**100**

PRODUCTS/OPERATIONS

2014 Sales

	$ mil.	% of total
Environment and Nuclear	1,377	24
Water	1,243	23
Energy	1,055	20
Transportation	947	18
Facilities and Urban Environment	789	15
Total	**5,413**	**100**

Selected Subsidiaries

CH2M HILL Alaska Inc.
CH2M HILL Canada Inc.
CH2M HILL Constructors Inc.
CH2M Hill Energy Ltd.
CH2M HILL Engineers Inc.
CH2M HILL Hanford Inc.
CH2M HILL Inc.
CH2M HILL International Ltd.
Halcrow Group Ltd.
HEBL Inc.

COMPETITORS

AECOM	Jacobs Engineering
Amec Foster Wheeler	KBR
Balfour Beatty	MWH Global
Bechtel	Parsons Brinckerhoff
Black & Veatch	Parsons Corporation
ERM	Tetra Tech
Fluor	Tutor Perini

HISTORICAL FINANCIALS

Company Type: Private

Income Statement

FYE: December 31

	REVENUE ($ mil.)	NET INCOME ($ mil.)	NET PROFIT MARGIN	EMPLOYEES
12/14	5,468	(318)	—	26,000
12/13	5,931	131	2.2%	—
12/12	6,224	98	1.6%	—
12/11	5,555	0	—	—
Annual Growth	**(0.5%)**	**—**	**—**	**—**

2014 Year-End Financials

Return on assets: 9.7%   Cash ($ mil.): 131
Return on equity: (-5.8%)
Current ratio: 1.00

CHALMETTE REFINING L.L.C.

Auditors: DELOITTE & TOUCHE LLP NEW ORL

LOCATIONS

HQ: CHALMETTE REFINING L.L.C.
  500 W SAINT BERNARD HWY, CHALMETTE, LA
  700434821
Phone: 504 279-9481
Web: WWW.CHALMETTEREFINING.COM

HISTORICAL FINANCIALS

Company Type: Private

Income Statement

FYE: December 31

	REVENUE ($ mil.)	NET INCOME ($ mil.)	NET PROFIT MARGIN	EMPLOYEES
12/07	5,647	364	6.4%	600
12/06	5,020	423	8.4%	—
12/05	3,462	264	7.6%	—
12/04	3,130	0	—	—
Annual Growth	**21.7%**	**—**	**—**	**—**

2007 Year-End Financials

Return on assets: —   Cash ($ mil.): 302
Return on equity: 6.4%
Current ratio: 0.50

CHAPMAN UNIVERSITY

Chapman University enrolls 7000 students at campuses throughout California as well as in Washington State. From its main campus in Orange California the university offers traditional undergraduate graduate and professional programs at seven colleges and schools. It also confers bachelor and master's degrees and teaching credentials to non-traditional students at its two-dozen satellite campuses. The university offers some 50 undergraduate majors and 40 graduate programs. It has 650 faculty members and a student-to-teacher ratio of 15:1. Chapman University includes Brandman University a distance learning program for some 10000 working adults that operates two dozen locations and offers online courses.

Financial Performance

Chapman University reported a 9% increase in revenues to $304 million in 2011 due to higher income from tuition fees gifts grants and bequests. Net income also increased 27% to $70 million due to increased endowment returns offset slightly by increased general educational and auxiliary expenses.

Strategy

Chapman University is expanding programs to widen opportunities for students. In 2011 the School of Law launched a new business law program and in 2013 the Argyros School of Business and Economics opened a new financial center for real-time student investor trading and portfolio management training. Facilities expansions include the construction of a new center for the arts and a new health sciences campus; both projects were launched in 2012.

Company Background

Chapman University was founded in 1861 as Hesperian College; it was re-named Chapman College in 1934 in honor of philanthropist Charles C. Chapman.

EXECUTIVES

Vice President, Rebecca Haber
Vice President of Finance, Ernest Wang
Vice President, Brenton Burke
Vice President For Public Relations, Jesse Richards
Vice President Finance, Hannah Brown
Financial Management Vice President, Lisa Aniston
Vice President Recruitment, Carrie Ferrando
Vice President Strategic Marketing and Communications, Mark Woodland
Board Member, Nicole Michaelis
Secretary, Brendan Le
Secretary, Sarah Price
Auditors: KPMG LLP LOS ANGELES CA

LOCATIONS

HQ: CHAPMAN UNIVERSITY
  1 UNIVERSITY DR, ORANGE, CA 928661005
Phone: 714 744-7099
Web: WWW.CHAPMAN.EDU

PRODUCTS/OPERATIONS

Selected Colleges and Schools

College of Educational Studies
College of Performing Arts
George L. Argyros School of Business and Economics
Lawrence and Kristina Dodge College of Film and Media Arts
Schmid College of Science and Technology
School of Law
Wilkinson College of Humanities and Social Sciences

HISTORICAL FINANCIALS

Company Type: Private

Income Statement

FYE: May 31

	REVENUE ($ mil.)	NET INCOME ($ mil.)	NET PROFIT MARGIN	EMPLOYEES
05/14	380	78	20.6%	3,300
05/13	356	78	22.1%	—
05/12	369	75	20.3%	—
05/11	303	0	—	—
Annual Growth	**7.8%**	**—**	**—**	**—**

2014 Year-End Financials

Return on assets: 11.5%   Cash ($ mil.): 41
Return on equity: 20.6%
Current ratio: 0.70

CHARLES C PARKS CO INC

The Charles C. Parks Company is a grocery distributor that primarily supplies convenience stores in more than half a dozen Southern states. It distributes a variety of food items and dry goods as well as beverages cigarettes candy and general merchandise. The company also offers support programs for in-store delis and other quick-service food operations. Carl C. Parks Jr. started the family-run business in 1934.

EXECUTIVES

SVP Sales, Gary Pickett
President, Crockett Parks III
Warehouse Manager, Donnie Vaughn
Manager Transportation, Jamie Davenport
CFO, Tom Cripps
EVP and COO, Bo Lanier
Sales Manager, Chris Pizzini
Food Service Director, Chuck Watkins
Purchasing Manager, Tim Flick
Information Technology Manager, David Lowery
Novelty Manager, Mike Pike
Auditors: LATTIMORE BLACK MORGAN AND CAI

LOCATIONS

HQ: CHARLES C PARKS CO INC
  500 N BELVEDERE DR, GALLATIN, TN 370665408
Phone: 615 452-2406
Web: WWW.CHARLESCPARKS.COM

COMPETITORS

Alex Lee	H. T. Hackney
Atlantic Dominion	McLane
Core-Mark	S. Abraham & Sons
Eby-Brown	SUPERVALU

HISTORICAL FINANCIALS

Company Type: Private

Income Statement

FYE: April 30

	REVENUE ($ mil.)	NET INCOME ($ mil.)	NET PROFIT MARGIN	EMPLOYEES
04/13	275	0	0.2%	145
04/12	268	(0)	—	—
04/11	264	0	0.1%	—
04/10	292	0	—	—
Annual Growth	**(2.0%)**	**—**	**—**	**—**

2013 Year-End Financials

Return on assets: 0.3% Cash ($ mil.): —
Return on equity: 0.2%
Current ratio: 2.50

CHARLES COUNTY BOARD OF EDUCATION

Auditors: CLIFTONLARSONALLEN LLP BALTI

LOCATIONS

HQ: CHARLES COUNTY BOARD OF EDUCATION
5980 RADIO STATION RD, LA PLATA, MD 206463337
Phone: 301 932-6610
Web: WWW.CCBOE.COM

HISTORICAL FINANCIALS
Company Type: Private

Income Statement

	REVENUE ($ mil.)	NET INCOME ($ mil.)	NET PROFIT MARGIN	EMPLOYEES
06/14	403	5	1.3%	5,000
06/13	393	9	2.5%	—
06/12	365	8	2.3%	—
06/10	355	0	—	—
Annual Growth	3.2%	—	—	—

FYE: June 30

2014 Year-End Financials

Return on assets: 2.4% Cash ($ mil.): 62
Return on equity: 1.3%
Current ratio: —

CHARLESTON AREA MEDICAL CENTER INC.

CAMC Health System is a catalyst for care in Charleston. The health network includes flagship facility Charleston Area Medical Center (CAMC) which is the largest hospital in West Virginia and consists of three campuses with some 840 beds total. The system also includes the CAMC Health Education and Research Institute which coordinates education programs for medical students from West Virginia University. In addition the health system operates smaller rural hospital CAMC Teays Valley and several urgent care and family practice clinics. CAMC Health System operates an online medical information system and physician services company Integrated Health Care Providers.

OperationsThe three campuses of CAMC include CAMC General Hospital CAMC Memorial Hospital and CAMC Women and Children's Hospital all of which are located in Charleston. Specialty services at the hospitals include cardiology kidney transplants trauma and pediatrics. The CAMC Institute conducts graduate and continuing education courses; it also connects education and health care through clinical research projects in areas such as cancer and cardiovascular clinical science studies. The Teays Valley Hospital is a 70-bed facility located in nearby Hurricane West Virginia.

CAMC General Hospital is home to the highest level Trauma Center nationally-accredited Medical Rehabilitation and Stroke Centers The Center for Joint Replacement Neurosciences Center one of two Facial Surgery Centers Charleston's only accredited Sleep Center and West Virginia's only kidney transplant program affiliated with the Cleveland Clinic. CAMC Memorial Hospital hosts one of highest volume heart programs in the US which performs 8000 procedures in the cardiac catheterization labs and more than 1600 open-heart bypass surgeries a year.CAMC Women and Children's Hospital facilitates the birth of more than 3000 babies (including many high-risk births) per year.

Teays Valley Hospital is a not-for-profit 70-bed hospital. More than 100 doctors are authorized to practice at the hospital.

CAMC serves as a clinical training site for 700 additional learners per year through educational affiliations with regional colleges and universities.

Sales and Marketing

Commercial insurance providers and other third parties accounted for more than half of CAMC's net patient revenue in 2013; Medicare and Medicaid account for 30% and 13% respectively.

Financial Performance

The company's revenue grew by 4% to $969 million in 2013 due to higher net patient revenues and investment income. Net income fell 8% to $86 million though as expenses including salaries and employee benefits rose. Cash flow from operations dropped 48% to $33 million both as a result of the lower net income and an increase in cash used in short-term trading investments.

Strategy

In 2013 CAMC teamed up with The Ohio State University University of Michigan and West Virginia University to raise awareness and educate the community about cervical cancer. Community Awareness Resources and Education (CARE) is one of OSU Cancer Center's programs sponsored by the National Cancer Institute that focuses on an important health disparity among an underserved Appalachian population.

The following year CAMC teamed with Alliance Oncology a division of Alliance HealthCare Services to work on establishing a department of radiation therapy at CAMC Cancer Center.

Upgrading its infrastructure in 2013 Teays Valley Hospital completed a $3.7 million ICU expansion project.

EXECUTIVES

Director Of Utilization Review, Janice Kiser
Director Of Operating Room, Marcy Myers
Operating Room Director, Glen Martin
Respiratory Therapy Director, Chuck Menders
Infection Control Director, Terrie Lee
Director of Radiology, Michael E (Mel) Anton
Interim Vice President for Medical Affairs, Joan Phillips
Medical Director, Bruce Horswell
Vice President Finance, Steve Bell
Occupational Therapy Director, Peter (Pete) Americo
Vice Chairperson, Mark James
Secretary, Marshall Mcmullen
Auditors: DELOITTE TAX LLP CHICAGO IL

LOCATIONS

HQ: CHARLESTON AREA MEDICAL CENTER INC.
501 MORRIS ST, CHARLESTON, WV 253011326
Phone: 304 348-5432
Web: WWW.CAMC.ORG

PRODUCTS/OPERATIONS

2013 Net Patient Revenue

	% of total
Commercial insurance & other third-party payment programs	51
Medicare	30
Medicaid	13
Self-pay	1
PEIA	5
Total	**100**

2013 Sales

	% of total
Net patient revenue less provision for bad debts	91
Investment income	5
Other revenue	4
Net assets released from restrictions	-
Total	**100**

Selected Service Areas

Behavioral health
Cancer
Cardiac
Children's medicine
Craniofacial surgery
Endoscopy
Fertility
Gynecology
Hemophilia
Kidney transplant
Orthopedics
Palliative care
Perinatal
Plastic surgery
Stroke
Trauma
Urology
Vascular

COMPETITORS

Charleston Hospital	WVUHS
Ohio Valley Medical Center	Weirton Medical Center
Princeton Community Hospital	West Virginia University Hospitals
St. Mary's Medical Center	

HISTORICAL FINANCIALS
Company Type: Private

Income Statement

	REVENUE ($ mil.)	NET INCOME ($ mil.)	NET PROFIT MARGIN	EMPLOYEES
12/13	861	54	6.3%	4,000
12/07	703	9	1.3%	—
12/06	703	38	5.5%	—
12/05	406	0	—	—
Annual Growth	—	—	—	—

FYE: December 31

2013 Year-End Financials

Return on assets: 5.6% Cash ($ mil.): 28
Return on equity: 6.3%
Current ratio: 0.80

CHARLOTTE HEALTH CARE CENTER (68) INC

LOCATIONS

HQ: CHARLOTTE HEALTH CARE CENTER (68) INC
1735 TODDVILLE RD, CHARLOTTE, NC 282142436
Phone: 704 394-4001
Web: WWW.CHARLOTTEHEALTHREHAB.COM

HISTORICAL FINANCIALS
Company Type: Private

Income Statement
FYE: September 30

	REVENUE ($ mil.)	NET INCOME ($ mil.)	NET PROFIT MARGIN	EMPLOYEES
09/09	923	51	5.6%	125
09/04	7	0	7.8%	—
09/03	6	0	8.7%	—
09/02	6	0	—	—
Annual Growth	105.3%	—	—	—

2009 Year-End Financials
Return on assets: —
Return on equity: 5.6%
Current ratio: 2.70
Cash ($ mil.): —

CHARTER MANUFACTURING COMPANY INC.

Charter Manufacturing's magna carta calls for it to make steel products. The family-owned company manufactures such steel products as special bar quality (SBQ) bar rod wire and stainless steel rod. The company also supplies precision cold-rolled custom profiles and engineered components including driveline engine and transmission parts for the automotive industry. It operates primarily in the US but also in Europe and Asia through subsidiaries Charter Steel (general steel products) Charter Wire (precision cold-rolled custom profiles flat wire and standard shapes) Charter Dura-Bar (cast iron bar and bronze alloys) and Charter Automotive (engineered components for automotive applications).

Geographic Reach

Charter Manufacturing serves customers around the world and has plants in the US (Illinois North Carolina Ohio Pennsylvania and Wisconsin) China (one plant) and the UK (two plants).

Operations

The company manufactures special bar quality bar rod and wire as well as precision cold-rolled custom profiles flat wire and standard shapes and engineered components for use in engines transmissions and drivelines. Charter Steel is an integrated producer of special bar quality bar rod and wire products has an annual coil-making capacity of 1.2 million tons; Charter Dura-Bar is a leading producer of continuous cast iron bar stock and a distributor (through Dura-Bar Metal Services) of Dura-Bar products and bronze alloys; Charter Wire supplies precision cold-rolled custom profiles flat wire and standard shapes; while Charter Automotive supplies of engineered components for engine driveline and transmission applications.

Sales and Marketing

Charter Manufacturing sells its products through its operating subsidiaries and sales representatives.

Strategy

The company is looking to expand both geographically and in terms of product offerings. Growing its global footprint in 2012 the company expanded its European operations with the purchase of a 57000 sq.-ft. manufacturing plant in Burntwood UK. The expansion strengthens Charter Automotive's position as a global supplier to OEM automotive and powertrain industries and helps it meet the growing demands of customers in Europe and elsewhere.

Mergers and Acquisitions

In 2012 the company acquired Wells Manufacturing Company (owner of Dura-Bar and DuraBar Metal Services). The acquired assets (which added a fourth division to Charter Manufacturing's family of companies –Charter Dura-Bar) focus on producing specialty iron bar and distributing bronze alloy products.

Company Background

Facing tough market conditions Charter Automotive closed part of its steelmaking operations in Milwaukee Wisconsin in 2010. The company ceased making steel dipsticks and tubes for cars and trucks as part of a wider response to global market trends. The company which kept its engine components operations elsewhere in Milwaukee active sold the Heather Avenue plant idled by this move.

Charter Manufacturing was established in 1936 and is owned by the family of founder Alfred Mellowes.

EXECUTIVES
Vice President and General Manager Charter Specialty Steel, Charles (Chas) Mellowes
Vice President Of Human Resources, Samantha Inks
Auditors: DELOITTE & TOUCHE LLP MILWAU

LOCATIONS
HQ: CHARTER MANUFACTURING COMPANY INC.
1212 W GLEN OAKS LN, MEQUON, WI 530923357
Phone: 262 243-4700
Web: WWW.CHARTERMFG.COM

PRODUCTS/OPERATIONS

Selected Operating Units
Charter Automotive
Charter Dura-Bar
Charter Steel
Charter Wire

Selected Mergers and Acquisitions

COMPETITORS

AK Steel Holding Corporation	Nucor
Federal-Mogul	Republic Steel
Gerdau Ameristeel	Timken
	United States Steel

HISTORICAL FINANCIALS
Company Type: Private

Income Statement
FYE: December 31

	REVENUE ($ mil.)	NET INCOME ($ mil.)	NET PROFIT MARGIN	EMPLOYEES
12/10	903	74	8.3%	2,000
12/09	517	2	0.4%	—
Annual Growth	74.4%	3354.5%	—	—

2010 Year-End Financials
Return on assets: 13.7%
Return on equity: 8.3%
Current ratio: 1.00
Cash ($ mil.): 85

CHATHAM COUNTY BOARD OF EDUCATION

Auditors: ROBINSON GRIMES & COMPANY P

LOCATIONS
HQ: CHATHAM COUNTY BOARD OF EDUCATION
208 BULL ST, SAVANNAH, GA 314013997
Phone: 912 395-1000
Web: WWW.INTERNET.SAVANNAH.CHATHAM.K12.GA.US

HISTORICAL FINANCIALS
Company Type: Private

Income Statement
FYE: June 30

	REVENUE ($ mil.)	NET INCOME ($ mil.)	NET PROFIT MARGIN	EMPLOYEES
06/11	423	10	2.5%	4,800
06/07	373	20	5.4%	—
06/06	330	10	3.3%	—
06/05	1,736	0	—	—
Annual Growth	—	—	—	—

2011 Year-End Financials
Return on assets: 1.1%
Return on equity: 2.5%
Current ratio: —
Cash ($ mil.): 51

CHECKERED FLAG MOTOR CAR COMPANY INC.

LOCATIONS
HQ: CHECKERED FLAG MOTOR CAR COMPANY INC.
5225 VIRGINIA BEACH BLVD, VIRGINIA BEACH, VA 234621899
Phone: 757 490-1111
Web: WWW.HONDA.CHECKEREDFLAG.COM

HISTORICAL FINANCIALS
Company Type: Private

Income Statement
FYE: December 31

	REVENUE ($ mil.)	NET INCOME ($ mil.)	NET PROFIT MARGIN	EMPLOYEES
12/07	362	(0)	—	700
12/06	378	1	0.5%	—
12/05	365	44	12.3%	—
12/04	338	0	—	—
Annual Growth	2.4%	—	—	—

2007 Year-End Financials
Return on assets: 0.6%
Return on equity: —
Current ratio: 0.10
Cash ($ mil.): 3

CHENEGA CORPORATION

An Alaska Native Corporation Chenega Corporation has gone from landowner to business titan. Representing the Chenega people residing in the central Alaskan Prince William Sound region it operates mostly through its subsidiaries. Chenega Integrated Systems and Chenega Technology Services offer information technology security training manufacturing research and development network engineering and military operation support services. Chenega Corporation's clients have included the Department of Defense Department of Homeland Security and EPA.

Geographic Reach

The company's headquarters are located in Anchorage Alaska. Chenega Corporation and its subsidiaries operate in 45 states and 11 countries.

Strategy

Government contracts are a source of revenue growth. Chenega Corporation began to participate in the Government Services marketplace in 1997. By 2012 it was performing on more than 158 prime contracts and 100 principal sub-contracts through a combination of competitive and negotiated best-value awards.

Ownership

The corporation is owned by about 140 Native Alaskan shareholders.

EXECUTIVES

Vice President and Director, Lloyd Kompkoff
Vice President Human Resources, Peggy O'Keefe
Senior Vice President Of Finance, Tom Reed
Auditors: MCGLADREY LLP FREDERICK MARY

LOCATIONS

HQ: CHENEGA CORPORATION
3000 C ST STE 301, ANCHORAGE, AK 995033975
Phone: 907 277-5706
Web: WWW.CHENEGA.JOBS

PRODUCTS/OPERATIONS

Selected Services
Base operations and maintenance
Environmental management
Information technology
Intel and military operations
Light manufacturing
Logistics support
Telecommunications
Tourism and hospitality
Training services
Security services

COMPETITORS

Akal Security
Arctic Slope Regional
  Corporation
Computer Sciences
  Corp.
HP Enterprise Services

Halliburton
IBM Global Services
Parsons Corporation
TKC Communications
chugach alaska

HISTORICAL FINANCIALS
Company Type: Private

Income Statement
FYE: September 30

	REVENUE ($ mil.)	NET INCOME ($ mil.)	NET PROFIT MARGIN	EMPLOYEES
09/12	1,099	8	0.8%	4,500
09/11	1,108	28	2.6%	—
09/10	1,115	28	2.6%	—
09/09	1,077	0	—	—
Annual Growth	0.7%	—	—	—

2012 Year-End Financials
Return on assets: 6.8%   Cash ($ mil.): 2
Return on equity: 0.8%
Current ratio: 1.70

CHERRY CENTRAL COOPERATIVE INC.

Serving as a central hub for cherry pickers' crops Cherry Central Cooperative is a fruit marketing co-operative that consists of more than a dozen member cooperatives representing hundreds of growers in Michigan New York Utah Washington Wisconsin and Ontario. It processes cherries cranberries apples and other fruit products including the Indian Summer brand of apple and cherry juices and ciders. Its Oceana Foods unit makes dried fruit sold under the Traverse Bay label while its Dunkley International subsidiary makes fruit-processing equipment. Cherry Central's products are sold to retail foodservice and ingredient customers. The cooperative was formed in 1973.

Geographic Reach

From its base in Traverse City Michigan Cherry Central Cooperative directs fruit-growing activities in Michigan New York Utah Washington and Wisconsin serving customers nationwide in Canada and globally.

Operations

Besides its namesake cherry operations Cherry Central supplies customers with apples blueberries cranberries strawberries pomegranate arils and asparagus. The company makes Traverse Bay-brand dried fruit through its Shelby Michigan based Oceana Foods business. The cooperative makes equipment to process fruit at its Dunkley International subsidiary headquartered in Kalamazoo Michigan.

Strategy

To entice customers to continue to buy its products Cherry Central has been working to go to market with new shelf-stable and alternative products. Through a partnership inked in mid-2012 with Vancouver-based EnWave Corporation Cherry Central has been evaluating and testing EnWave's Radiant Energy Vacuum (REV) technology. The cooperative anticipates that the collaboration will fuel the development and subsequent launch of a premium dehydrated cherry snack product as well as cherry and apple powders marketed as an alternative to conventional fruit purees. As part of the agreement Cherry Central licenses the REV technology for commercial distribution of these products.

Cherry Cooperative in 2012 expanded its membership to Canada when it brought onboard Norfolk Cherry Company Limited located in Simcoe Ontario. The move boosts the cooperative's market share of tart/sour cherry production.

Sales and Marketing

The cooperative organization sells products to retailers ingredient customers and foodservice operators such as schools hospitals restaurants cafeterias hotels and airlines.

EXECUTIVES

Vice President, Roy Hackert, age 81
Auditors: DENNIS GARTLAND & NIERGARTH

LOCATIONS

HQ: CHERRY CENTRAL COOPERATIVE INC.
1771 N US 31 S, TRAVERSE CITY, MI 496858748
Phone: 231 946-1860
Web: WWW.CHERRYCENTRAL.COM

PRODUCTS/OPERATIONS

Selected Frozen Ingredients
Apples
Blueberries
Cranberries
Damson Plums
Dark Sweet Cherries
Red Tart Cherries

Selected Frozen Fruit Varieties
Diced
Juice concentrate
IQF (Individually Quick Frozen)
Pitted or punch pitted
Pureed
Sliced
Solid or sugar pack
Whole

Selected Private Label and Co-pack Products
Applesauce
Formulas
Juice Flavors
Packaging

Selected Brands
Indian Summer
Traverse Bay Fruit Co.

COMPETITORS

California Giant
Chiquita Brands
Dole Food
Donio Produce
Encore Fruit Marketing
Fazio Marketing
Fresh Del Monte
  Produce
Graceland Fruit
Greenridge Fruit
Jasper Wyman & Son
Knouse Foods
Naturipe Farms
Pacific Coast
  Producers

Pro-Fac
Red Jacket Orchards
Seneca Foods
Shoreline Fruit
Sun World
  International
Sun-Maid
SunOpta
SunnyRidge Farm
Sunsweet Growers
Tree Top
Welch's

HISTORICAL FINANCIALS
Company Type: Private

Income Statement
FYE: April 30

	REVENUE ($ mil.)	NET INCOME ($ mil.)	NET PROFIT MARGIN	EMPLOYEES
04/14	169	1	0.6%	115
04/13	185	1	0.6%	—
04/12	154	0	0.5%	—
04/11	144	0	—	—
Annual Growth	5.5%	—	—	—

2014 Year-End Financials
Return on assets: 2.0%   Cash ($ mil.): —
Return on equity: 0.6%
Current ratio: 0.40

CHILDFUND INTERNATIONAL USA

ChildFund International (CFI) serves the little ones. The worldwide non-profit organization provides education medical care food and safe water to more than 13 million children —of all faiths —in about 30 countries in Africa Asia the Caribbean Eastern Europe Latin America and the US. It works in areas of early childhood development education family income generation nutrition and sanitation. The group also tries to get child soldiers away from the military and reintegrated into daily life. Founded in 1938 as China's Children Fund the group changed its name to Christian Children's Fund in 1951. In 2009 it again renamed itself ChildFund International.

Since its founding as an organization focused on orphans and orphanages CFI has become an international child development organization. More than 500000 sponsored children receive monthly contributions through the group; about 350000 of those sponsorships are supported by donors in the US. CFI also publishes newsletters booklets and studies on the effects of poverty and violence on children.

EXECUTIVES

VP Communications and Public Affairs, Cheri W. Dahl
President and CEO, Anne Lynam Goddard
Chief Financial Officer Vice President Finance & Operations, James M. Tuite
Chairman, Charles M. Caravati Jr.
Executive Vice President Programs, Isam M. Ghanim
Interim VP Global Programs, Dula C. James
VP People and Culture, Diane H. Willis
VP Marketing and Strategic Resources, Mike Pressendo
VP Global Programs, Anne Scott
Director Communications, Cynthia Price
Manager Communications, Ellie Whinnery
Chief Information Officer Vice President Information Technology, Scott Lemler
Executive Vice President CAO, Steve Stirling
Director, A. Hugh Ewing III
Director, Karen Hein
Director, Velma McBride Murry
Director, Thomas A. Siegfried
Director, Thomas Weisner
Director, Paul Hirschbiel
Auditors: MCGLADREY LLP VIENNA VA

LOCATIONS

HQ: CHILDFUND INTERNATIONAL USA
2821 EMERYWOOD PKWY, RICHMOND, VA 232943726
Phone: 804 756-2700
Web: WWW.CHILDFUND.ORG

HISTORICAL FINANCIALS
Company Type: Private

Income Statement
FYE: June 30

	REVENUE ($ mil.)	NET INCOME ($ mil.)	NET PROFIT MARGIN	EMPLOYEES
06/12	230	3	1.5%	160
06/11	228	12	5.3%	—
06/10	215	4	2.2%	—
06/09	217	0	—	—
Annual Growth	1.9%	—	—	—

2012 Year-End Financials
Return on assets: —
Return on equity: 1.5%
Current ratio: 1.30
Cash ($ mil.): 32

CHILDREN'S HOSPITAL CENTRAL CALIFORNIA

LOCATIONS

HQ: CHILDREN'S HOSPITAL CENTRAL CALIFORNIA
9300 VALLEY CHILDRENS PL, MADERA, CA 936368761
Phone: 559 353-3000
Web:
WWW.WAYSTOGIVE.CHILDRENSCENTRALCAL.ORG

HISTORICAL FINANCIALS
Company Type: Private

Income Statement
FYE: September 30

	REVENUE ($ mil.)	NET INCOME ($ mil.)	NET PROFIT MARGIN	EMPLOYEES
09/13*	542	103	19.0%	1,800
06/05	457	(24)	—	—
09/02	219	0	0.3%	—
09/01	0	0	—	—
Annual Growth	—	—	—	—

*Fiscal year change

2013 Year-End Financials
Return on assets: 10.9%
Return on equity: 19.0%
Current ratio: 0.80
Cash ($ mil.): 113

CHILDREN'S HOSPITAL OF ORANGE COUNTY

Auditors: KPMG LLP SEATTLE WA

LOCATIONS

HQ: CHILDREN'S HOSPITAL OF ORANGE COUNTY
1201 W LA VETA AVE, ORANGE, CA 928684203
Phone: 714 997-3000
Web: WWW.CHOC.COM

HISTORICAL FINANCIALS
Company Type: Private

Income Statement
FYE: June 30

	REVENUE ($ mil.)	NET INCOME ($ mil.)	NET PROFIT MARGIN	EMPLOYEES
06/13	548	29	5.3%	3,200
06/10	408	69	16.9%	—
06/09	337	8	2.4%	—
06/05	1,553	0	—	—
Annual Growth	(12.2%)	—	—	—

2013 Year-End Financials
Return on assets: 13.2%
Return on equity: 5.3%
Current ratio: 0.60
Cash ($ mil.): 169

CHILDREN'S HOSPITAL OF THE KINGS DAUGHTERS INC

LOCATIONS

HQ: CHILDREN'S HOSPITAL OF THE KINGS DAUGHTERS INC
601 CHILDRENS LN, NORFOLK, VA 235071910
Phone: 757 668-7000
Web: WWW.CHKD.ORG

HISTORICAL FINANCIALS
Company Type: Private

Income Statement
FYE: June 30

	REVENUE ($ mil.)	NET INCOME ($ mil.)	NET PROFIT MARGIN	EMPLOYEES
06/13	337	50	15.0%	1,211
06/12	312	41	13.3%	—
06/08	254	26	10.3%	—
06/05	0	0	—	—
Annual Growth	—	—	—	—

2013 Year-End Financials
Return on assets: 8.4%
Return on equity: 15.0%
Current ratio: 0.80
Cash ($ mil.): 34

CHILDREN'S MEDICAL CENTER OF DALLAS

Sick kiddos in North Texas who need specialized care don't have to travel far to find it. Children's Medical Center of Dallas (operating as Children's Health) treats children with various medical needs from birth to age 18. Specialties include craniofacial deformities cystic fibrosis gastroenterology cancer and heart disease. Children's is also a major pediatric center for heart kidney bone marrow and other transplant procedures. The not-for-profit hospital has about 600 beds and is the pediatric teaching facility for UT Southwestern Medical. Children's also operates a network of about 20 primary care and specialty clinics in and around Dallas in addition to its two full-service campuses.

Operations

The Children's system serves patients through two full-service hospitals a specialty care center in Southlake and a network of primary care offices called MyChildren's located throughout the Metroplex. As the primary pediatric teaching facility for UT Southwestern Children's supports a three-year residency program for physicians and academic fellowships in numerous subspecialties.

Children's Health's Dallas campus operates the city's only pediatric emergency room and the region's only pediatric-centered teaching hospital. It was also the first Level I trauma center for pediatrics in the state. Together the Dallas and Plano hospital campuses serve some 800000 patients annually and provide more than 50 sub-specialty programs. Additionally the organization provides primary health care services to the county's children living in under-served areas; some of these care services are provided through academic programs for doctors in training.

The system's research and development areas includes cancer cardiothoracic neonatology kidney disease infectious disease pharmacology sickle cell disease and psychiatry. It also provides Level IV Neonatal Intensive Care Unit.

In 2014 Children's logged some 173000 patient visits in its emergency departments in Dallas and Plano.

Geographic Reach

Children's main hospital campuses are in Dallas and Plano Texas. It has a handful of specialty centers and 16 primary care locations in the Dallas suburbs and area communities including Southlake.

Financial Performance

Children's receives revenues from a mix of third-party payers including HMOs and PPOs as well as Medicaid and Medicare and the state Children's Health Insurance Program (CHIP). It also relies heavily on private donations and fundraising efforts but provides a hefty amount of charity care each year for the region's uninsured children.

Strategy

Children's introduced its Children's Health brand in 2014. The new identity serves to reflect its operations as an integrated health system beyond the two primary campus locations.

At any given time it seems that Children's is building or opening one facility or another. In 2015 it opened the nation's second Pitt Hopkins Syndrome clinic treating a rare genetic condition that can cause development delays intellectual disabilities breathing issues and seizures.

Mergers and Acquisitions

In 2015 the system bought Our Children's House which provides rehabilitative and transitional care to children with special needs from Baylor Scott & White. Children's took over operations of Our Children's House's inpatient and outpatient facilities as well as eight outpatient clinics.

Company Background

In the four-year period between 2001 and 2005 the center spent more than $250 million on new construction and expansion projects. It opened a 72-bed Children's Legacy Hospital in nearby Plano in 2008 and in 2009 Children's completed construction of a new $150 million tower on its main Dallas campus to house its heart center cancer center and neonatal intensive care unit.

The company was founded in 1913.

EXECUTIVES

EVP and Chief Administrative Officer Corporate Services, Michele Chulick
Chief Clinical Officer and EVP, W. Robert (Bob) Morrow
EVP Population Health and Business Development, Peter W. Roberts
President ChildrenÂ's Medical Center Dallas Foundation and EVP ChildrenÂ's Health System Texas, Kern Wildenthal
President and CEO, Christopher J. Share
President and COO, Douglas G. Share
Respiratory Therapy Director, Sandra McDermott
Vice President Of Marketing, Judy Watkins
Medical Librarian, Albi Calman
Pharmacy Manager, Bill Oden
Medical Director Anesthesiology LGY Campus, William (Bill) Jones
Director of Radiology, Eric McDaniel
Vice President Of Public Affairs, Elizabeth F Mackay
Vice President Human Resources, Kimberly Besse
Vice President of Facilities Development and Operations Administration, Daniel (Dan) Carney
Vice President Of Quality, Michelle Slovak

Vice President Finance and Treasury, Mitch Mulvehill
Occupational Medicine, Michele Hurt
Director Of Nursing, Ramonda Busby
Senior Vice President Strategy and Physician Organizations, Pat Wining
Medical Director Pediatric Pain Management Service, Alan (Al) Farrow
Secretary To Engineering, Heather Pepe
Secretary Pharmacy, Rena McCarver
Auditors: ERNST & YOUNG

LOCATIONS

HQ: CHILDREN' S MEDICAL CENTER OF DALLAS
1935 MEDICAL DISTRICT DR, DALLAS, TX
752357701
Phone: 214 456-7000
Web: WWW.CHILDRENS.COM

Children's Medical Center Selected Locations
Chase Bank Building Specialty Center (Dallas)
Children' s Medical Center and Ambulatory Care Pavilion at Legacy (Plano)
Children' s Medical Center of Dallas Main Campus
Dallas Ambulatory Care Pavilion
Irving Specialty Center
Mesquite Specialty Center
MyChildren' s Primary Care (about 16 locations)
Pediatric Urology Clinic at Rockwall
Southlake Specialty Care Center
Walnut Hill Urology Clinic

PRODUCTS/OPERATIONS

Children's Medical Center Selected Services
Allergy/Immunology/Asthma
Audiology
Cystic fibrosis
Day surgery
Dentistry
Dermatology
Diabetes
Ear/Nose/Throat
Endocrinology
Gastroenterology
General surgery
Genetics/Metabolism
International adoption medicine
Laboratory services
Neurology
Nutrition
Obesity program
Occupational therapy
Ophthalmology
Orthodontics
Orthopaedics
Physical therapy
Plastic Surgery
Pulmonary function lab
Pulmonology
Radiology
Rheumatology
Sickle cell treatment
Sleep disorders
Speech therapy
Trauma
Urology

COMPETITORS

Baylor University Medical Center	HCA
Cook Children' s Health Care System	Parkland Health & Hospital System
Dell Children' s Medical Center	Tenet Healthcare Texas Children' s Hospital

HISTORICAL FINANCIALS
Company Type: Private

Income Statement
FYE: December 31

	REVENUE ($ mil.)	NET INCOME ($ mil.)	NET PROFIT MARGIN	EMPLOYEES
12/08	744	(4)	—	5,318
12/06	579	130	22.4%	—
Annual Growth	13.3%	—	—	—

Return on assets: 7.6%   Cash ($ mil.): 43
Return on equity: (-0.6%)
Current ratio: 1.20

CHILDREN'S NATIONAL MEDICAL CENTER

Along with the National Archives and the National Mall Children's National Medical Center is a US capital city gem. Its flagship Children's Hospital which was founded in 1870 is an acute care facility with some 310 beds. It serves as a regional referral center for pediatric trauma cancer and other kinds of complex pediatric cases. Additionally it operates eight outpatient centers in DC and the Delmarva peninsula that provide specialized medical services (such as chemotherapy and outpatient surgery) and community health clinics that offer primary care to children and adolescents. Children's National Health Network links more than 900 community-based pediatricians with the specialists and services of the center.

Operations

Children's National treats more than 300000 patients from around the world each year. It performs more than 17000 surgeries and provides more than 460000 outpatient visits annually. The company serves as the regional referral center for pediatric emergency trauma cancer cardiac critical care neonatology orthopedic surgery sports medicine neurology and neurosurgery. Every year it hosts 150 subspecialty fellows in 30 fellowship programs more than 100 pediatric residents 750 rotating residents and 300 medical students.

In the realm of research Children's National has more than 475 projects investigating diseases including brain and spinal cord injuries obesity and type 2 diabetes renal disease and autism. More than half of its funding for research comes from federal agencies including 40% from the National Institutes of Health.

Geographic Reach

Children's National operates in 30 locations in the District of Columbia and in Virginia Maryland Delaware and West Virginia.

Financial Performance

Revenue totaled $1 billion in 2014.

Strategy

The system continues to expand to provide improved access to health care in the region. Pediatric Specialists of Virginia is a private practice launched in 2013 to provide quality specialty care to families in northern Virginia. It was established by Children's National and INOVA Health Systems and operates eight locations throughout the region. Its specialties include endocrinology gasteroenterology/hepatology/nutrition genetics hematology and oncology infectious disease neurology nephrology orthopedics and rheumatology.

In 2015 the company opened the new Youth Pride Clinic within the Adolescent Health Center at the Sheikh Zayed Campus for Advanced Pediatric Medicine.

EXECUTIVES

EVP; Physician In Chief and Chief Academic Officer Director ChildrenÂ's Research Institute, Mark Batshaw
EVP; Chief Medical Officer Ambulatory and Community Health Services, Denice Cora-Bramble

SVP Center for Heart Lung and Kidney Disease;
  Co-Director Children's National Heart Institute;
  Acting SVP Center for Cancer and Blood
  Disorders, Gerard R. Martin
President and CEO, Kurt D. Newman
SVP Center for Neuroscience and Behavioral
  Health, Roger J. Packer
EVP and Chief Legal Officer, Raymond S. Sczudlo
EVP and CFO, Douglas T. Myers
EVP; Chief Development Officer Children's
  Hospital Foundation, Pam King Sams
EVP and Chief People Officer, Darryl Varnado
SVP Child Health Advocacy Institute; Professor
  and Vice Chair Department of Pediatrics, Joseph
  Wright
EVP; Chief Medical Officer Hospital and Specialty
  Services, David Wessel
Chief Research Officer ChildrenÂ's Research
  Institute, Mendel Tuchman
VP Nursing; Chief Nursing Officer, Linda Talley
EVP; COO Patient Care Services, Kathleen E.
  Chavanu Gorman
EVP and Chief Strategy Officer, Elizabeth Flury
VP and CIO; Chief Medical Information Officer
  Bear Institute, Brian Jacobs
Vice Chairman Medical Education, Mary Ottolini
SVP Joseph E. Robert Jr. Center for Surgical
  Care; Chief of Pediatric Surgery, Anthony Sandler
Medical Director, Joshua (Josh) Attridge
Director Of Nursing, Colleen Whitmore
Vice President Communications Public Relations
  And Marketing, Lauren Fisher
Vice President Operations, Christine Heath

LOCATIONS

HQ: CHILDREN' S NATIONAL MEDICAL CENTER
  111 MICHIGAN AVE NW, WASHINGTON, DC
  200102916
Phone: 202 476-5000
Web: WWW.CHILDRENSNATIONAL.ORG

PRODUCTS/OPERATIONS

Selected Departments and Programs
Back/spine surgery
Bone marrow transplant
Cancer
Cardiac surgery
Fetal medicine
Genetics and metabolism
Imaging/radiology
Neurosurgery
Obesity
Pediatric anesthesiology
Pediatric cardiology
Pediatric surgery
Weight loss surgery

COMPETITORS

Adventist HealthCare
Ascension Health
Children' s Healthcare
  of Atlanta
Children' s Hospital
  Boston
Children' s Hospital of
  Philadelphia
Children' s Hospital of
  Pittsburgh
Children' s Hospital of
  Richmond
Children' s Hospital of
  The King' s Daughters
Children' s Medical
  Center of Dallas
Cincinnati Children' s
  Hospital
Dell Children' s
  Medical Center

Georgetown University
  Hospital
HSC Pediatric Center
IU Health
Inova
Johns Hopkins Medicine
Kennedy Krieger
  Institute
MedStar Health
Providence Hospital
  (Washington DC)
Seattle Children' s
  Hospital
Shriners Hospitals For
  Children
St. Jude Children' s
  Research Hospital
Washington Hospital
  Center

HISTORICAL FINANCIALS
Company Type: Private

Income Statement — FYE: June 30

	REVENUE ($ mil.)	NET INCOME ($ mil.)	NET PROFIT MARGIN	EMPLOYEES
06/09	516	16	3.2%	6,000
06/07	694	76	11.0%	—
Annual Growth	(13.8%)	(53.6%)	—	—

2009 Year-End Financials
Return on assets: 16.9%   Cash ($ mil.): 65
Return on equity: 3.2%
Current ratio: 0.80

CHILDRENS HOSPITAL MEDICAL CENTER OF AKRON

What started as a nursery more than 100 years ago but has since turned into the largest pediatric health care system in northeast Ohio? If you guessed Akron Children's Hospital you'd be right on the money. The health system operates through more than 80 locations scattered around the state including its flagship 253-bed hospital in Akron. Among Children's specialized services are cardiology orthopedics rehabilitation and home care. It also has a second 50-bed inpatient hospital called the Akron Children's Beeghly Campus. The main hospital's emergency department treats nearly 70000 patients each year. Its regional burn center sees about 3700 visits per year.

Operations
Each year Akron Children's Hospital sees some 800000 outpatients performs more than 15000 surgeries and admits more than 10000 inpatients.

Geographic Reach
Akron Children's Hospital is a major teaching facility affiliated with Northeastern Ohio Medical University and offering nearly a dozen subspecialty fellowship training programs. Children's also runs one of the state's largest pediatric primary care networks with 15 offices in seven counties including Cuyahoga Medina Wayne Tuscawaras and Portage.

Sales and Marketing
In 2014 Medicaid payments accounted for 52% of gross patient service revenue while commercial payments accounted for 44%.

Financial Performance
The hospital's net revenue was about $701000 in fiscal 2014 with about 90% of that coming from patient services revenues.

Strategy
The system has expanded its campuses and opened new facilities to broaden its care offerings. In 2014 it opened its first location in Columbiana County opened a pediatric specialty care office in Mansfield and expanded its sports rehabilitation hours and services at LifeCenter Plus in Hudson.

EXECUTIVES

President and CEO, William H. (Bill) Considine
VP Medical Services; Clinical Leader Ohio
  Children's Hospitals Solutions for Patient
  Safety, Michael Bird
VP Managed Care, Karen Richter
VP Operations and COO, Grace Wakulchik

EVP, Shawn Lyden
VP Akron Children's Hospital Foundation, John
  Zoilo
Noah Miller Chair Department of Pediatrics,
  Norman C. Christopher
VP Akron Children's Mahoning Valley, Sharon
  Hrina
CFO, Michael Trainer
VP Patient Services and Chief Nursing Officer,
  Lisa Aurilio
CIO, Tom Ogg
VP Department of Pediatrics, Cindy Dormo
Chief Medical Information Officer, Amy Maneker
VP Surgical Subspecialty Practices, Craig McGhee
Chief Medical Officer, Robert McGregor
Director Of Home Healthcare Srv, Sally L Hartline
Director Of Pharmacy, John Lepto
Vice President Human Resources, Walt Schwoeble
Pharm D, Martha Blackford
Medical Director of the Locust Pediatric Care
  Group, Cooper White
Director of Pharmacy, Todd Grisez
Vice President Surgical Services, Meridith Slosberg
Director Of Nursing, Les Sherman
Vice President and General Counsel, Mary Link
Vice President Information Technology, Chris
  McLean
Executive Vice President, Dean Wright
Vice President Administration, Sharin Hrina
Vice President Medical Services, Mike Bird
Secretary To Beth Smith, Jill Oleksy
Board Member, J Attebery
Auditors: ERNST & YOUNG LLP AKRON OH

LOCATIONS

HQ: CHILDRENS HOSPITAL MEDICAL CENTER OF
  AKRON
  1 PERKINS SQ, AKRON, OH 443081063
Phone: 330 543-1000
Web: WWW.AKRONCHILDRENS.ORG

COMPETITORS

Akron General Medical
  Center
Aultman Health
  Foundation
Lake Health
Mercy Medical Center
  (NY)
MetroHealth System
Nationwide Children' s
  Hospital

OhioHealth
Parma Community
  General Hospital
Robinson Memorial
  Hospital
Summa Health System
The Cleveland Clinic
University Hospitals
  Health System

HISTORICAL FINANCIALS
Company Type: Private

Income Statement — FYE: December 31

	REVENUE ($ mil.)	NET INCOME ($ mil.)	NET PROFIT MARGIN	EMPLOYEES
12/13	623	80	13.0%	4,763
12/12	579	46	8.1%	—
12/09	438	46	10.5%	—
12/08	387	0	—	—
Annual Growth	10.0%	—	—	—

2013 Year-End Financials
Return on assets: 2.2%   Cash ($ mil.): 37
Return on equity: 13.0%
Current ratio: 1.30

CHILTON HOSPITAL

Chilton Medical Center (formerly Chilton Memorial Hospital) serves the residents of northern New Jersey's Morris and Passaic counties. The acute-care facility has some 260 beds and provides emergency diagnostic inpatient surgical and outpatient care. The hospital operates with a staff of about 650 physicians who practice in 60 fields of health care. Chilton Medical Center offers such specialties as a cancer center surgical weight-loss programs occupational health orthopedics stroke care pediatrics and dialysis. Chilton Medical Center merged with Atlantic Health System in 2014.

Change in Company Type

To gain resources associated with being part of a broader health network Chilton Medical Center merged with Atlantic Health System in 2014. Atlantic Health operates a handful of hospitals in New Jersey and the merger will help providers lower costs share best practices and provide broader patient access to care.

Geographic Reach

Chilton Medical Center's main medical campus including the Collins Pavilion for outpatient care cancer treatment and surgery is located in Pompton Plains New Jersey. The hospital also operates medical laboratories physical and occupational therapy clinics and family health centers in Pompton Plains Butler Haskell Hewitt and Wayne New Jersey. All told it serves patients in more than 33 communities.

Operations

Chilton Medical Center's orthopedic center is recognized as a top US facility for joint replacement surgeries. Other specialty centers on the medical campus include the cardiovascular interventional lab the breast center an interventional radiology lab and a pediatric emergency department.

Strategy

The Center is upgrading and expanding its facilities and services to keep up with demand.

In 2013 the hospital's cancer center underwent a $4.4 million renovation and the breast center introduced 3-D mammography.

In 2012 Chilton Medical Center completed most of a $24 million modernization project which included the cardiovascular interventional lab the breast center total joint center cancer center and surgical services facilities.The Center has also launched the Chilton Health Network offering health care services and care providers in communities throughout Northwestern New Jersey. Services offered include blood draw sites physical therapy and occupational health as well as partnerships with physician practices in the specialties of obstetrics/gynecology primary care colorectal surgery cardiology and orthopedics.

Company Background

The hospital was originally founded in 1954 as a 50-bed facility.

EXECUTIVES

Director Of Health Information Direct, Patricia Ledford
Vice President Of Sales And Marketing, Richard Andraws
Executive Vice President Of Information Technology, Mary Abed

LOCATIONS

HQ: CHILTON HOSPITAL
97 W PARKWAY, POMPTON PLAINS, NJ 074441647
Phone: 973 831-5000
Web: WWW.CHILTONHEALTH.ORG

PRODUCTS/OPERATIONS

Selected Services
Bariatric Services
Breast Center
Breast Surgery
Cardiac Rehabilitation and Conditioning
Cancer Center
Cardiovascular Interventional Lab
Classes and Events

Diabetes Education
Emergency Care
Heart and Vascular Care
Hyperbaric Oxygen Therapy
Imaging
Intensity-Modulated Radiation Therapy
Interventional Radiology
Laboratory
Lactation Support Services
Mental Health Hotline
Mother Baby Center
Occupational Health
Occupational Therapy
Orthopedics (Total Joint Center)
Pain Management
Parent and Childbirth Education
Pediatrics
Pediatric Emergency Department
Positron Emission Tomography (PET/CT) Scan
Physical Therapy
Robot-Assisted Surgery
Sleep Health Institute
Speech Language Pathology
Stroke Care
Support Groups
Travel Medicine Program
Weight Loss Surgery
Wound Care

COMPETITORS

Barnabas Health
Catholic Health Initiatives
JFK Health System
Raritan Bay Medical Center
Robert Wood Johnson University Hospital at Rahway
Somerset Medical Center
St. Joseph's Healthcare System
The Valley Hospital

HISTORICAL FINANCIALS

Company Type: Private

Income Statement — FYE: December 31

	REVENUE ($ mil.)	NET INCOME ($ mil.)	NET PROFIT MARGIN	EMPLOYEES
12/12	165	9	5.9%	1,188
12/08	0	0	—	—
12/05	128	2	1.9%	—
12/04	129	0	—	—
Annual Growth	3.1%	—	—	—

2012 Year-End Financials

Return on assets: 3.1%   Cash ($ mil.): 16
Return on equity: 5.9%
Current ratio: 1.10

CHRISTIAN BROTHERS INVESTMENT SERVICES INC.

LOCATIONS

HQ: CHRISTIAN BROTHERS INVESTMENT SERVICES INC.
20 N WACKER DR STE 2000, CHICAGO, IL 606063002
Phone: 312 526-3343
Web: WWW.CBISONLINE.COM

Income Statement — FYE: December 30

	ASSETS ($ mil.)	NET INCOME ($ mil.)	INCOME AS % OF ASSETS	EMPLOYEES
12/11	2,079	100	4.8%	45
12/10	2,167	68	3.1%	—
12/09	1,863	0	—	—
12/05	2,191	0	—	—
Annual Growth	(0.9%)	—	—	—

CHRISTIAN HOSPITAL NORTHEAST - NORTHWEST

Christian or heathen if you're in the St. Louis area and need medical care Christian Hospital wants to help. The not-for-profit hospital which has some 485 beds is part of BJC HealthCare. Established in 1903 it specializes in a range of treatment areas including diabetes and cancer care and cardiothoracic surgery. Its more than 430 physicians also offer services in 40 other specialties from primary care to pulmonology. Christian Hospital offers a comprehensive mental health and substance abuse program that includes an inpatient option as well as specialization in geriatric mental wellness. The hospital is headed by president Ron McMullen a long-time health care administrator.

Christian Hospital prides itself on being the first in the area to offer pioneering procedures. For example it was the first community hospital in the region to offer Video Assisted Thoracoscopic Surgery (VATS) lobectomy an advanced resectioning procedure to remove tumors in lung cancer patients.

Shortly before that Christian Hospital broke new ground by becoming the first community hospital in St. Louis to provide the Gliasite procedure. Gliasite is a brachytherapy (internal radiation therapy) procedure that treats patients with newly diagnosed metastatic or recurrent brain tumors.

EXECUTIVES

President, Ronald B. (Ron) McMullen
VP and Chief Medical Officer, Melanie Mueth
VP Human Resources, Bryan Hartwick
VP Finance, John Katsianis
Manager Public Relations and Internal Communications, Bret Berigan

LOCATIONS

HQ: CHRISTIAN HOSPITAL NORTHEAST - NORTHWEST
11133 DUNN RD, SAINT LOUIS, MO 631366119
Phone: 314 355-2300
Web: WWW.CHRISTIANHOSPITAL.ORG

COMPETITORS

Ascension Health
Barnes-Jewish Hospital
HCA
Memorial Hospital (Illinois)
Mercy Health
Mercy Hospital St. Louis
RehabCare
SSM Health Care
St. Anthony's Medical Center
Tenet Healthcare

HISTORICAL FINANCIALS

Company Type: Private

Income Statement

FYE: December 31

	REVENUE ($ mil.)	NET INCOME ($ mil.)	NET PROFIT MARGIN	EMPLOYEES
12/08	213	(24)	—	2,493
12/00	207	(20)	—	—
12/97	206	5	2.6%	—
Annual Growth	0.3%	—	—	—

CHRISTIANA CARE HEALTH SERVICES INC.

LOCATIONS

HQ: CHRISTIANA CARE HEALTH SERVICES INC.
501 W 14TH ST, WILMINGTON, DE 198011013
Phone: 302 733-1000

HISTORICAL FINANCIALS

Company Type: Private

Income Statement

FYE: June 30

	REVENUE ($ mil.)	NET INCOME ($ mil.)	NET PROFIT MARGIN	EMPLOYEES
06/09	1,097	(55)	—	8,800
06/07	1,102	122	11.1%	—
06/05	0	0	—	—
06/04	847	0	—	—
Annual Growth	5.3%	—	—	—

2009 Year-End Financials

Return on assets: 4.5%
Return on equity: (-5.1%)
Current ratio: 1.60
Cash ($ mil.): 237

CHRISTUS HEALTH

In CHRISTUS there is no east or west but plenty of care nonetheless. The not-for-profit Catholic health care system operates about 350 medical facilities from its more than 60 hospitals including general hospitals and long-term acute care facilities to clinics and outpatient centers. It operates mostly in Louisiana and Texas where its hospitals are but also has facilities in Arkansas Georgia Iowa Missouri and New Mexico and in six states in Mexico and one in Chile. In addition to its acute care facilities CHRISTUS runs medical groups home health and hospice agencies and senior living facilities. Specialized services include oncology pediatrics rehabilitation and women's and children's health care.

Operations

In addition to its more than 30 hospitals CHRISTUS also operates about 20 long-term care facilities 175 clinics and outpatient centers and dozens of other "health ministries" including mobile clinics fitness centers and daycare centers for adults and children.

Geographic Reach

CHRISTUS has a dozen hospitals in Texas and Louisiana one in Puebla Mexico and one in Santiago Chile. Its clinics outpatient centers long-term care facilities (under the Dubois and Advanced Care names) are found in Texas Louisiana Iowa Georgia Missouri and New Mexico in the US and in the Mexican states of Chihuahua Coahuila Nuevo León Puebla San Luis Potosíacute; and Tamaulipas.

Financial Performance

In 2013 CHRISTUS reported a 3% increase in revenue from $3.6 billion to $3.7 billion based on increased net patient and premium revenues. Net income was $261 million against net loss in 2012 due to an increase in investment returns.

Strategy

CHRISTUS has been expanding its Continuing Care division which includes non-acute care operations like home care hospice palliative care residential facilities and fitness centers.

Another goal of CHRISTUS Health is to reduce overcrowding and such misuses as patients being seen for routine illnesses in its emergency rooms. To that end and to make primary care a bit more accessible the company has opened immediate care clinics in a number of Texas Wal-Mart stores. CHRISTUS Health has plans to expand the clinics into Wal-Marts in Louisiana.

CHRISTUS Health has taken other steps to try to offset some costs of indigent care including pushing for the establishment of hospital districts to pay for charity care costs in some of its markets. It has also sold some of it facilities.

The organization has been focused on growing its operations in Mexico where it operates about a dozen clinics in six states. CHRISTUS Health's Mexico operations are a majority-owned partnership with Monterrey-based Muguerza. The organization's main Monterrey facility became the first Mexican hospital to win accreditation from the Joint Commission International a unit of the organization that certifies US hospitals.

Because Mexican citizens overwhelmingly rely on public hospitals run by the national health care system CHRISTUS Muguerza markets itself as a "medical tourism" destination where Americans can go for cheaper and lower-hassle medical care. Services include acute and primary care dental care urgent care and post-surgical rehabilitation.

Company Background

CHRISTUS Health was formed through the 1999 merger of Incarnate Word Health System and Sisters of Charity Health System. Both systems have their roots in the religious order Sisters of Charity of the Incarnate Word founded when three French nuns arrived in Texas in 1866 to care for the poor and sick.

EXECUTIVES

EVP and Chief Clinical Officer, John A. Gillean
CEO, Ernie W. Sadau
EVP and Chief Administrative Officer, Linda McClung
SVP and CIO, George S. Conklin
President and COO, Eugene A. Woods
EVP Strategic Alliances and Group Operations, Jeffrey M. (Jeff) Puckett
EVP and CFO, Randolph W. Safady
Clinic Supervisor, Luisa Santiago
Vice President Of Engineering, William Allen
Vice President Performance Effectiveness, Sherry Tichenor
Vice President Mission Integration, Jim Pomeroy
Vice President And Administrator, Jerry Rodriguez
Director Of Radiology And Compliance Officer, Raymond Ramos
Vice President Management, Inez Kernick
Chief Development Officer Christus Physician Group Vice President System Service Line Development, Jessica Arguijo
Medical Director, Scott Spencer
Director Of Pharmacy, Dale Smith
Medical Director, Iqtidar Khan
Vice President Of Mission Integration, Mike Sullivan
Vice President Philanthropy Christus S, Karen Bonner
Medical Director, Paul James
Vice President Managed Care, Shannon Stansbury
Admissions Director, Donna Henning
Radiology Director And Compliance Officer, Jv Cabral
Chairman, Richard L. (Dick) Clarke
Auditors: ERNST & YOUNG LLP HOUSTON TX

LOCATIONS

HQ: CHRISTUS HEALTH
919 HIDDEN RDG, IRVING, TX 750383813
Phone: 469 282-2000

PRODUCTS/OPERATIONS

2013 Payor Mix

	% of total
Managed care organizations	43
Medicare	23
Self-pay	17
Medicaid	10
Commercial insurance	7
Total	**100**

2013 Revenues

	$ mil.	% of total
Patient services	3,224	87
Premium revenue	182	5
Other revenue	182	5
Equity in income of unconsolidated organizations	111	3
Total	**3,701**	**100**

Selected Facilities in Texas

CHRISTUS HomeCare - Corpus Christi
CHRISTUS HomeCare - Texarkana
CHRISTUS Hospital - St. Elizabeth
CHRISTUS Hospital - St. Mary
CHRISTUS Jasper Memorial Hospital
CHRISTUS Santa Rosa Alamo Heights Imaging Center
CHRISTUS Santa Rosa Ambulatory Surgery Center
CHRISTUS Santa Rosa Cancer Center
CHRISTUS Santa Rosa Children's Hospital
CHRISTUS Santa Rosa Hospital - City Centre
CHRISTUS Santa Rosa Hospital - Medical Center
CHRISTUS Santa Rosa Hospital - New Braunfels
CHRISTUS Santa Rosa Hospital - Westover Hills
CHRISTUS Santa Rosa Imaging Center
CHRISTUS Santa Rosa Outpatient Rehabilitation Center
CHRISTUS Santa Rosa Rehabilitation Hospital
CHRISTUS Santa Rosa Rehabilitation Services - Downtown
CHRISTUS Santa Rosa Rehabilitation Services - Medical Center
CHRISTUS Santa Rosa Wound Care and Hyperbaric Center - Downtown
CHRISTUS Santa Rosa Wound Care and Hyperbaric Center - Medical Center
CHRISTUS Spohn Family Center Northside
CHRISTUS Spohn Family Health Center
CHRISTUS Spohn Family Health Center Falfurrias
CHRISTUS Spohn Family Health Center Padre Island
CHRISTUS Spohn Family Health Center Robstown
CHRISTUS Spohn Family Health Center San Diego
CHRISTUS Spohn Family Health Center Westside
CHRISTUS Spohn Health System
CHRISTUS Spohn Hospital Alice
CHRISTUS Spohn Hospital Beeville
CHRISTUS Spohn Hospital Corpus Christi - Memorial
CHRISTUS Spohn Hospital Corpus Christi - Shoreline
CHRISTUS Spohn Hospital Corpus Christi - South
CHRISTUS Spohn Hospital Kleberg
CHRISTUS Spohn Medical Group - Obstetrics and Gynecology Associates
CHRISTUS St. Catherine Hospital
CHRISTUS St. John Hospital
CHRISTUS St. Michael Health System
CHRISTUS St. Michael Rehabilitation Hospital
CHRISTUS Transplant Institute
CHRISTUS Visiting Nurse Association - Houston
CHRISTUS Visiting Nurse Association - Nassau Bay
CHRISTUS Visiting Nurse Association - San Antonio
David Christopher Goldsbury Center for Children and Families
Dubuis Hospital of Beaumont

Dubuis Hospital of Bryan Texas
Dubuis Hospital of Corpus Christi
Dubuis Hospital of Houston Texas (long-term acute care)
Dubuis Hospital of Paris
Dubuis Hospital of Port Arthur Texas (long-term acute care)
Dubuis Hospital of Texarkana

Selected Other US Facilities

Advance Care Hospital of Fort Smith (Arkansas)
Advance Care Hospital of Hot Springs (Arkansas)
CHRISTUS Coushatta Health Care Center (Coushatta Louisiana)
CHRISTUS HomeCare - Jennings (Louisiana)
CHRISTUS HomeCare - Lake Charles (Louisiana)
CHRISTUS HomeCare - Shreveport (Louisiana)
CHRISTUS Hospice and Palliative Care - Alexandria (Louisiana)
CHRISTUS Schumpert Health System (Shreveport Louisiana)
CHRISTUS Schumpert Highland (Shreveport Louisiana)
CHRISTUS Schumpert St. Mary Place (Shreveport Louisiana)
CHRISTUS St. Frances Cabrini Hospital (Alexandria Louisiana)
CHRISTUS St. Patrick Hospital (Lake Charles Louisiana)
CHRISTUS St. Vincent (Santa Fe New Mexico)
Dubuis Hospital of Alexandria (Louisiana)
Dubuis Hospital of Lake Charles (Louisiana)
Dubuis Hospital of Shreveport (Louisiana)
Dubuis Hospital of St. Louis (Chesterfield Missouri)
Natchitoches Parish Hospital (Louisiana)
Southern Crescent Hospital for Specialty Care (Riverdale Georgia)

Selected Facilities in Mexico

CHRISTUS MUGUERZA Hospital Alta Especialidad (Monterrey Nuevo Leon)
CHRISTUS MUGUERZA Hospital Conchita (Monterrey Nuevo Leon)
CHRISTUS MUGUERZA Hospital Del Parque (Chihuahua)
CHRISTUS MUGUERZA Hospital Reynosa (Tamaulipas¸ C.P.)
CHRISTUS MUGUERZA Hospital Saltillo (Coahuila)
CHRISTUS MUGUERZA Hospital Sur (Monterrey Nuevo Leon)
CHRISTUS MUGUERZA Hospital UPAEP (Puebla)

COMPETITORS

Ascension Health	Memorial Hermann
Catholic Health	Healthcare
Initiatives	Mercy Health
Community Health	Methodist Hospital
Systems	System
HCA	St. Luke' s Episcopal
Iasis Healthcare	Hospital
Intermountain Health	Tenet Healthcare
Care	Texas Children' s
LifePoint Health	Hospital
MD Anderson Cancer	Universal Health
Center	Services
Memorial Health	University of Utah
Services	Hospitals & Clinics

HISTORICAL FINANCIALS

Company Type: Private

Income Statement

	REVENUE ($ mil.)	NET INCOME ($ mil.)	NET PROFIT MARGIN	EMPLOYEES
06/13	646	124	19.3%	25,000
06/10	3,653	55	1.5%	—
06/09	3,466	(411)	—	—
Annual Growth	(34.3%)	—	—	—

2013 Year-End Financials

Return on assets: 33.8%   Cash ($ mil.): 13
Return on equity: 19.2%
Current ratio: —

CHRISTUS HEALTH CENTRAL LOUISIANA

CHRISTUS St. Frances Cabrini Hospital provides a wide range of medical services to the denizens of Alexandria Louisiana. If you're ailing down south there's not much the hospital can't do to help especially in the area of cancer. Founded in 1950 the 240-bed St. Frances Cabrini Hospital has a staff of more than 320 physicians providing services that include emergency care women's health surgery and cardiology. For the insomniacs among us the hospital provides specialized care through its sleep center. St. Francis Cabrini's parent company is one of the nation's major hospital operators —with about 50 facilities located around the country.

Auditors: ERNST & YOUNG US LLP HOUSTON

LOCATIONS

HQ: CHRISTUS HEALTH CENTRAL LOUISIANA
3330 MASONIC DR, ALEXANDRIA, LA 713013841
Phone: 318 487-1122
Web: WWW.CHRISTUSHEALTH.ORG

COMPETITORS

General Health System	Our Lady of the Lake
Lafayette General	RMC
Medical Center	River Parishes
Lane Regional Medical	Hospital
Center	Woman' s Hospital
Our Lady of Lourdes	

HISTORICAL FINANCIALS

Company Type: Private

Income Statement

	REVENUE ($ mil.)	NET INCOME ($ mil.)	NET PROFIT MARGIN	EMPLOYEES
06/13	222	5	2.3%	1,287
06/10	219	(0)	—	—
06/09	217	1	0.7%	—
06/08	1,027	0	—	—
Annual Growth	—	—	—	—

2013 Year-End Financials

Return on assets: 5.7%   Cash ($ mil.): 62
Return on equity: 2.3%
Current ratio: 6.70

CHRISTUS SANTA ROSA HEALTH CARE CORPORATION

Auditors: ERNST & YOUNG US LLP HOUSTON

LOCATIONS

HQ: CHRISTUS SANTA ROSA HEALTH CARE CORPORATION
333 N SANTA ROSA ST, SAN ANTONIO, TX 782073108
Phone: 210 704-2011
Web: WWW.CHRISTUSSANTAROSA.ORG

HISTORICAL FINANCIALS

Company Type: Private

Income Statement

	REVENUE ($ mil.)	NET INCOME ($ mil.)	NET PROFIT MARGIN	EMPLOYEES
06/13	612	2	0.4%	3,700
06/10	577	(19)	—	—
06/09	501	14	2.9%	—
06/05	1,150	0	—	—
Annual Growth	—	—	—	—

2013 Year-End Financials

Return on assets: 7.9%   Cash ($ mil.): 53
Return on equity: 0.4%
Current ratio: 2.40

CHUGACH ALASKA CORPORATION

At the heart of Chugach Alaska Corporation is a vision of indigenous people running their own businesses on their own land. Chugach Alaska was formed following the activation of the Alaska Native Claims Settlement Act (which was passed by the US Congress in 1971) to provide land management services for the 928000-acre Chugach region of Alaska. The company derives the bulk of its sales from oil and gas production mining commercial timber and tourist activities that occur in the region and from its engagement in military base construction projects at more than 30 locations in Alaska the US Pacific Northwest and the Western Pacific. Chugach Alaska's shareholders consist of Aleut Eskimo and Indian natives.

Geographic Reach

With operations in Alaska the Pacific Northwest and the Western Pacific the company has major offices in Alabama Alaska Hawaii and Nevada.

Operations

In 2011 the company's Chugach World Services unit secured a $32 million contract (with the option for an additional $33 million) for housing and maintenance operations at Naval Base Guam and Andersen Air Force Base Guam.

In late 2010 the Chugach Alaska Services unit won a renewal of its existing oil spill prevention and response contract with Alyeska Pipeline Service Company. The new contract to service the Alaska Pipeline runs from 2011 to 2016.

Financial Performance

To raise cash in 2013 Chugach Alaska sold its three-story former headquarters building in downtown Anchorage.

Strategy

Developing and sustaining multiple revenues streams has been a key to the company's growth. Chugach Alaska is looking to continue to grow its Alaskan gas natural gas projects while diversifying into markets that are not traditional for the company such as the niche market of environmentally responsible guided tourism.

Expanding its global engineering footprint in 2012 the company acquired bankrupt Hawaii-based engineering firm Heide & Cook LLC.

Company Background

Chugach Alaska was founded in 1972 as an Alaska Native Claims Settlement Act Corporation. A nine-person board of directors elected from the corporation's more than 2300 shareholders oversees Chugach Alaska's management and operations. The company has gone from filing bankruptcy protection in 1990 (in the wake of the Exxon Valdez oil spill and a major cannery fire) to generating about $1 billion in annual revenues.

EXECUTIVES

Vice President Finance, Angela Astle

LOCATIONS

HQ: CHUGACH ALASKA CORPORATION
3800 CENTERPOINT DR # 700, ANCHORAGE, AK 995035825
Phone: 907 563-8866
Web: WWW.CHUGACH-AK.COM

PRODUCTS/OPERATIONS

Selected Services
Base Operating Services
Construction Services
Educational Services
Engineering Services
IT/Telecommunications
Manufacturing Services
Oil and Gas Services

Selected Subsidiaries
Chugach Alaska Services Inc. (CASI)
Chugach Education Services Inc. (CESI)
Chugach Federal Solutions Inc. (CFSI)
Chugach Government Services Inc. (CGSI)
Chugach Industries Inc. (CII)
Chugach Information Technology Inc. (CITI)
Chugach Management Services Inc. (CMSI)
Chugach McKinley Inc. (CMI)
Chugach Support Services Inc. (CSSI)
Chugach Systems Integration Llc (CSI)
Chugach World Services Inc. (CWSI)
Heide & Cook LLC. (H&C)
Wolf Creek Federal Services Inc. (WCFS)

COMPETITORS

ConocoPhillips Alaska	Freegold Ventures
Doyon	Jacobs Engineering
Fluor	Sealaska

HISTORICAL FINANCIALS

Company Type: Private

Income Statement

FYE: December 31

	REVENUE ($ mil.)	NET INCOME ($ mil.)	NET PROFIT MARGIN	EMPLOYEES
12/13	608	19	3.2%	4,822
12/12	708	20	2.9%	—
12/11	765	24	3.1%	—
12/10	936	0	—	—
Annual Growth	(13.4%)	—	—	—

2013 Year-End Financials

Return on assets: 4.4%   Cash ($ mil.): 57
Return on equity: 3.2%
Current ratio: 2.50

CIC GROUP INC.

CIC Group can see clearly that its future (like its present) is in heavy manufacturing and construction. Its group of commercial and industrial subsidiaries specialize in the manufacture maintenance and repair of equipment for the crude oil natural gas coal and other energy industries. Its largest subsidiary is Nooter/Eriksen which supplies heat recovery steam generators for combustion gas turbines worldwide. CIC's Nooter Construction is a construction contractor serving the refining petrochemical pulp and paper and power industries

among others. The employee-owned holding company was formed in 2002.

Operations
CIC through its 20 subsidiaries is engaged in the heavy industrial construction of refineries and petrochemical and power plants. It also designs and builds heat recovery systems for power plants.

Sales and Marketing
Some of the company's largest customers include Ameren Calpine Chevron ConocoPhillips Exxon Mobil Florida Power & Light and Royal Dutch Shell.

Strategy
The company is taking advantage of the low price and abundance of natural gas in the US which has encouraged companies to shift the manufacture of petrochemical plants to the US from the Middle East and Asia.However CIC is also strengthening its position in the growth markets of Eastern Europe and Asia. In 2012 the company announced plans to work on photovoltaic projects for Chinese solar manufacturer LDK Solar and to act as a distributor for the company.

Financial Performance Although privately held the company reported 2012 revenue of $1.2 billion up 30% from 2011. CIC anticipates revenue of $2 billion by 2017 or 2018.

EXECUTIVES

Vice President Of Marketing, Francesco Lagutaine
V Pres Finance-treas, Derek Falb

LOCATIONS

HQ: CIC GROUP INC.
530 MARYVILLE CENTRE DR, SAINT LOUIS, MO 631415825
Phone: 314 682-2900
Web: WWW.CICGROUP.COM

PRODUCTS/OPERATIONS

Selected Subsidiaries
ArcMelt
Delta Nooter
Megamet Sold Metals Co.
Nooter Construction
Nooter/Eriksen s.r.l.
Pressline Services
RMF Nooter
Schoeller Bleckmann Nooter GmbH
St. Louis Metallizing
Superior Corporate Travel
Wyatt Field Service Co.
Wyatt Virgin Islands

COMPETITORS

BWX Technologies	Mitsubishi Heavy
Clarkson Construction	Industries
Fluor	Phillips-Medisize
Fred Weber	U.S. Pipe
Jacobs Engineering	

HISTORICAL FINANCIALS

Company Type: Private

Income Statement

FYE: November 30

	REVENUE ($ mil.)	NET INCOME ($ mil.)	NET PROFIT MARGIN	EMPLOYEES
11/12	1,149	0	—	1,500
11/11	838	0	—	—
11/10	758	0	—	—
11/08	1,120	0	—	—
Annual Growth	0.6%	—	—	—

2012 Year-End Financials

Return on assets: 8.5%   Cash ($ mil.): 123
Return on equity: —
Current ratio: 1.30

CIMA ENERGY LTD.

Auditors: DELOITTE & TOUCHE LLP HOUSTON

LOCATIONS

HQ: CIMA ENERGY LTD.
100 WAUGH DR STE 500, HOUSTON, TX 770074600
Phone: 713 209-1112
Web: WWW.CIMA-ENERGY.COM

HISTORICAL FINANCIALS

Company Type: Private

Income Statement

FYE: December 31

	REVENUE ($ mil.)	NET INCOME ($ mil.)	NET PROFIT MARGIN	EMPLOYEES
12/07	1,195	8	0.7%	65
12/06	902	11	1.3%	—
12/05	872	0	—	—
12/04	569	0	—	—
Annual Growth	28.0%	—	—	—

2007 Year-End Financials

Return on assets: —   Cash ($ mil.): 16
Return on equity: 0.7%
Current ratio: 0.80

CITATION OIL & GAS CORP.

Citation Oil & Gas is writing its own ticket to prosperity in the petroleum industry. The oil and gas development and production company has interests in about 15000 wells (in more than 480 separately designated fields) and reported 210 million barrels of proved oil equivalent reserves (91% oil) in 2012. Its oil fields are in the Mid-Continent Illinois Basin Permian Basin and Rocky Mountain regions. Citation seeks out properties with high levels of crude oil declining production with long reserve life and low risk. The company uses a variety of techniques to recover oil and gas including waterflood and infill drilling. Subsidiary Citation Crude Marketing sells the company's products to refiners.

Geographic Reach
Citation explores for oil and gas in more than 480 fields in 13 states in the central third of the US with major holdings in the Illinois Basin Mid-Continent Permian Basin and Rocky Mountain regions. It has offices in Midland Texas; Gillette Wyoming; and Oklahoma City.

Operations
Citation operates in 13 states and manages its field operations on a decentralized basis through four of its regional operating areas including Central region Rocky mountain region Southern Oklahoma region and West Texas region.The Central region based operation has about 3900 active wells with a capacity of producing 7330 barrels of oil per day of oil and 2.9 million cu. ft. per day of gas. The Central Region team is focused on developing assets in the Illinois Basin specifically the properties it acquired in the Noble acquisition along with continuing exploitation of its legacy Salem Unit

In its Rocky mountain region Citation has drilled 18 horizontal wells in Bowes since 2007 and has three additional wells planned for 2013-14. This region has a net capacity of producing 5135 barrels of oil per day and 10.9 million cu. ft. per day of gas.In Southern Oklahoma region in its Wildcat Jim field Citation drilled 20 infill wells in 2012 and planned for 10 more in 2013. Citation is also actively drilling Hunton/Viola wells in Carter and Stephens County Oklahoma in the Shoveltum Hunton trend with 13 planned for 2013. This region's capacity is 11840 barrels of oil per day of oil and 12.6 million cu. ft. per day of gas; and operates about 6500 active wells.In West Texas region the company intends to expand its production base in West Texas and New Mexico making it one of the more mature of all of Citation's regions. Its net capacity is 4510 barrels of oil per day of oil and 5.9 million cu. ft. per day of gas.

Sales and Marketing

In addition to its upstream activities Citation is also engaged in crude oil marketing activities through its Citation Crude Marketing unit.

Strategy

Citation has pursued a focused business strategy of acquiring and operating mature onshore oil (and some gas) properties in the US. It has invested $1.7 billion in more than 80 oil and gas reserve acquisitions since 1985. As a result of these acquisitions and subsequent property development Citation has a net production of 28800 barrels of oil and 32 million cubic feet of gas per day. Going forward Citation continues to pursue growth strategy which is focused on two fronts; the acquisition of long-lived domestic onshore oil production; and the exploitation and enhancement of its producing properties through the application of primary secondary and tertiary recovery techniques.Advances in drilling and completion technologies along with improved commodity prices have contributed to an increase in Citation's infill drilling activity and waterflood expansion opportunities. Infill drilling projects (including vertical and horizontal wells) aim to increase production volumes and recoverable reserves through down spacing or pattern optimization.

In the Rockies Citation is focusing on horizontal drilling in several fields. In Southern Oklahoma it is developing properties it acquired from Noble Energy and is also drilling deeper wells in the Shoveltum Hunton trend. West Texas activities are focused on developing the North Robertson and Jordan fields.

Mergers and Acquisitions

In 2012 Citation acquired 100 additional leases and units in Kansas from Noble Energy near Citation's existing Fairport and Bemis-Schutts fields for $140 million. This acquisition significantly expanded Citation's operations in Kansas boosting its production in that state by almost 300%.

Company Background

The company was formed in 1981 by Forrest E. Harrell Sr.

EXECUTIVES

Vice President, Craig Townsend
Senior Vice President Secretary And Ge, Wayne Wiesen
Auditors: PRICEWATERHOUSECOOPERS LLP H

LOCATIONS

HQ: CITATION OIL & GAS CORP.
14077 CUTTEN RD, HOUSTON, TX 770692212
Phone: 281 891-1000
Web: WWW.COGC.COM

COMPETITORS

Adams Resources	EOG
Anadarko Petroleum	Exxon Mobil
Apache	Hunt Consolidated
BP	Jones Energy
Cabot Oil & Gas	Key Energy
Chesapeake Energy	National Fuel Gas
Chevron	Noble Energy
Cimarex	Pioneer Natural
ConocoPhillips	Resources
Devon Energy	Royal Dutch Shell

HISTORICAL FINANCIALS
Company Type: Private

Income Statement
FYE: December 31

	REVENUE ($ mil.)	NET INCOME ($ mil.)	NET PROFIT MARGIN	EMPLOYEES
12/13	462	248	53.6%	507
12/12	424	224	53.0%	—
12/11	449	251	56.0%	—
12/09	233	0	—	—
Annual Growth 18.7%	—	—	—	—

2013 Year-End Financials
Return on assets: —
Return on equity: 53.6%
Current ratio: 0.50
Cash ($ mil.): 15

CITIZENS ENERGY GROUP

Hoosiers are happy to have their homes provided with gas and water services by Public Utilities of the City of Indianapolis (dba Citizens Energy and CWA Authority public charitable trusts). Its Citizens Water unit provides water and wastewater services to 300000 customers in Indianapolis; Citizens Gas serves more than 266000 gas customers. Citizens Energy also provides steam heating and chilled water cooling services to about 250 customers through Citizens Thermal Energy. The regional utility also has a small oil production unit (Citizens Oil Division). Its Citizens Resources unit has joint venture stakes in some companies not regulated by the Indiana Utility Regulatory Commission such as ProLiance Energy.OperationsCitizens Energy operates six business segments: Citizens Gas Water Steam Chilled Water Oil and Citizens Resources Steam and Chilled Water. Citizen Resources holds affiliate joint venture interests including ProLiance Energy and a number of subsidiaries including Westfield Gas a regulated natural gas distribution utility. Citizens Oil has produced more than 6 million barrels of oil since 1969 from Greene County Indiana. CWA Authority provides wastewater services.Financial Performance

The company's revenues increased by 50% in 2012 due to an increase in water and wastewater revenues. (The water and wastewater segments which were acquired in August 2011). This growth was offset by a decrease in Westfield Gas and Citizens Gas revenues due to lower usage driven by a warmer winter lower gas cost recovery revenues.

Strategy

In 2012 Citizens Energy filed a plan with the Indiana Utility Regulatory Commission to create a multistate transportation and industrial fueling business Using liquefied natural gas (LNG) the new Citizens Energy subsidiary will market and sell LNG as a competitive alternative to diesel fuel for use by heavy-duty vehicles and by drilling rigs marine vessels and railway locomotives.

Mergers and Acquisitions

Expanding its water and wastewater coverage in 2013 Citizens Energy (with the cooperation of The Indiana Office of Utility Consumer Counselor and the City of Westfield agreed to transfer Westfield Utilities to Citizens Energy for $91 million.

Responding to the company's efficient operation of its gas utility in 2011 the Indianapolis City/County Council sold its debt-laden water and wastewater utility (CWA Authority) to Citizens Energy in a $1.9 billion deal. The transaction reshaped the utility's business organization and transformed Citizens Energy into a multiutility.

Company Background

The company was first organized as a public charitable trust in 1887. In a 2008 rebranding Citizens Gas & Coke Utility changed its operating name to Citizens Energy Group to reflect the company's closing of its old smokestack industry (coke manufacturing operations for steelmakers and smelter) and its new strategic emphasis on energy conservation.

EXECUTIVES

Vice President Information Technology, John Lucas
Vice President Controller, Blaire Dougherty
Vice President Call Center, Gregory Sawyers
Vice President Corporate Development, Aaron Johnson
Auditors: DELOITTE & TOUCHE LLP INDIANA

LOCATIONS

HQ: CITIZENS ENERGY GROUP
2020 N MERIDIAN ST, INDIANAPOLIS, IN 462021306
Phone: 317 924-3341
Web: WWW.CITIZENSENERGYGROUP.COM

PRODUCTS/OPERATIONS

2012 Sales

	$ mil.	% of total
Utility	650	93
Non-utility	45	7
Total	**696**	**100**

2012 Sales

	% of total
Citizens Gas	37
Water	24
Wastewater	22
Steam	9
Chilled Water	6
Oil	1
Resources	1
Total	**100**

COMPETITORS

American States Water	NIPSCO
Duke Energy	Vectren
Indiana Municipal Power Agency	Veolia Environnement

HISTORICAL FINANCIALS
Company Type: Private

Income Statement
FYE: September 30

	REVENUE ($ mil.)	NET INCOME ($ mil.)	NET PROFIT MARGIN	EMPLOYEES
09/13	711	(81)	—	1,100
09/12	696	(11)	—	—
09/11	463	32	7.0%	—
09/10	440	0	—	—
Annual Growth 17.3%	—	—	—	—

2013 Year-End Financials
Return on assets: —
Return on equity: (-11.4%)
Current ratio: 0.70
Cash ($ mil.): 194

CITRUS VALLEY HEALTH PARTNERS INC.

Citrus Valley Health Partners is a 660-bed hospital system that serves the residents of California's San Gabriel Valley region located between Los Angeles and San Bernardino. It operates through four health care facilities: Citrus Valley Medical Center (CVMC) Queen of the Valley Campus CVMC Inter-Community Campus Foothill Presbyterian Hospital and Citrus Valley Hospice. Citrus Valley Health Partners also operates a home health care provider that offers nursing and rehabilitation care. The hospital system boasts several areas of specialty including diabetes care cancer treatment palliative care wound care and cardiac therapy.

Geographic Reach

Citrus Valley Health Partners serves about 1 million residents from Covina Glendora and other California communities located in the San Gabriel Valley region.

Operations

Representing the largest slice of the Citrus Valley Health Partners system the CVMC Queen of the Valley Campus manages 325 beds and handles more than 54000 emergency room visits each year. The campus includes the Geleris Family Cancer Center; it is also known for birthing services that include a Level III Newborn Intensive Care Unit and it boasts robotic surgery systems and rehabilitation programs such as speech occupational and physical therapy for both children and adults.

With 220 beds the CVMC Inter-Community Campus specializes in cancer treatment electrophysiology cardiac care and wound care. The health system's Foothill Presbyterian Hospital boasts 105 beds and focuses on general acute care and such specialty services as an outpatient diabetes education program and rehabilitation. The Citrus Valley Hospice is a 10-bed inpatient facility that is the first freestanding hospice of its kind in California. Citrus Valley Home Health provides nursing and rehabilitation care.

Altogether the system employs some 1000 physicians at its facilities.

Strategy

As part of a renovation and modernization program in 2013 the organization launched a construction program at its CVMC Inter-Community Campus to increase emergency operating and diagnostic capabilities. Once completed (in 2015) the new emergency department will nearly double the capacity of the campus' current 12-bed department. New patient treatment stations will enable medical nursing and support professionals to provide improved urgent care and other diagnostic care and treatment to more than 40000 patients each year.

In 2013 the Speech Pathology Outpatient Program expanded to include a Voice Clinic at Citrus Valley Medical Center —Queen of the Valley Campus in West Covina.

To reduce operational expenses that year Citrus Valley Health Partners signed a five-year $4.5 million managed print services agreement with Auxilio. Through the deal Auxilio will help the network improve process efficiencies supply chain management volume reduction and other initiatives.

Company Background

Inter-Community Campus began as a seven-bed hospital founded in 1922 by sisters Melisse and Mary Wittler a nurse and a schoolteacher.

EXECUTIVES

Clinical Director, Bruce Sindel

Vice President Medical Affairs, Richard Gisi
Auditors: ERNST & YOUNG LLP LOS ANGELES

LOCATIONS

HQ: CITRUS VALLEY HEALTH PARTNERS INC.
210 W SAN BERNARDINO RD, COVINA, CA
917231515
Phone: 626 331-7331
Web: WWW.CVHP.ORG

PRODUCTS/OPERATIONS

Selected Services
Cancer services
Diabetes care unit
Diabetes education program
Emergency room services
Home health
Hospice
Maternity services
Newborn intensive care
Palliative care
Pediatric services
Rehabilitation
Robotic surgery

COMPETITORS

Anaheim Regional Medical Center
City of Hope
Glendale Adventist Medical Center
Good Samaritan Hospital (Los Angeles)
Memorial Health Services
Methodist Hospital of Southern California
Newhall Memorial Hospital
Pasadena Hospital Association
St. Joseph Health System
St. Jude Medical Center
UC Irvine Medical Center
Western Medical Center - Santa Ana

HISTORICAL FINANCIALS
Company Type: Private

Income Statement
FYE: December 31

	REVENUE ($ mil.)	NET INCOME ($ mil.)	NET PROFIT MARGIN	EMPLOYEES
12/13	467	34	7.4%	2,800
12/03	280	(2)	—	—
12/02	278	(9)	—	—
12/01	256	0	—	—
Annual Growth	5.1%	—	—	—

2013 Year-End Financials
Return on assets: —
Return on equity: 7.4%
Current ratio: 0.90
Cash ($ mil.): 18

CITRUS VALLEY MEDICAL CENTER INC.

Auditors: HBLA CERTIFIED PUBLIC ACCOUNTA

LOCATIONS

HQ: CITRUS VALLEY MEDICAL CENTER INC.
1115 S SUNSET AVE, WEST COVINA, CA 917903940
Phone: 626 962-4011
Web: WWW.CVHP.ORG

HISTORICAL FINANCIALS
Company Type: Private

Income Statement
FYE: December 31

	REVENUE ($ mil.)	NET INCOME ($ mil.)	NET PROFIT MARGIN	EMPLOYEES
12/12	384	22	5.8%	3,500
12/09	311	(2)	—	—
12/08	293	(12)	—	—
12/04	303	0	—	—
Annual Growth	3.0%	—	—	—

2012 Year-End Financials
Return on assets: 13.4%
Return on equity: 5.8%
Current ratio: 0.60
Cash ($ mil.): 17

CITY OF HOPE NATIONAL MEDICAL CENTER

LOCATIONS

HQ: CITY OF HOPE NATIONAL MEDICAL CENTER
1500 DUARTE RD, DUARTE, CA 910103012
Phone: 626 256-4673
Web: WWW.CITYOFHOPE.ORG

HISTORICAL FINANCIALS
Company Type: Private

Income Statement
FYE: September 30

	REVENUE ($ mil.)	NET INCOME ($ mil.)	NET PROFIT MARGIN	EMPLOYEES
09/13	696	59	8.5%	1,900
09/12	663	76	11.5%	—
09/09	580	86	14.8%	—
09/08	695	0	—	—
Annual Growth	0.0%	—	—	—

2013 Year-End Financials
Return on assets: 7.4%
Return on equity: 8.5%
Current ratio: 1.40
Cash ($ mil.): 31

CITY OF HUNTSVILLE ELECTRIC SYSTEMS

LOCATIONS

HQ: CITY OF HUNTSVILLE ELECTRIC SYSTEMS
112 SPRAGINS ST NW, HUNTSVILLE, AL 358014902
Phone: 256 535-1200
Web: WWW.HSVUTIL.ORG

Income Statement
FYE: September 30

	REVENUE ($ mil.)	NET INCOME ($ mil.)	NET PROFIT MARGIN	EMPLOYEES
09/12	470	9	2.0%	634
09/11	493	10	2.1%	—
09/10	456	5	1.3%	—
09/09	451	0	—	—
Annual Growth	1.4%	—	—	—

2012 Year-End Financials

Return on assets: 7.7%   Cash ($ mil.): 18
Return on equity: 2.0%
Current ratio: 1.40

CITY PUBLIC SERVICES OF SAN ANTONIO

And the award for being the energy distributor for the seventh-largest city in the US goes to City Public Service of San Antonio (also known as CPS Energy). Serving 728000 electricity customers and 328000 natural gas customers the utility operates in a 1514-sq.-mi. service territory. CPS Energy also has a generating capacity of more than 6570 MW from its 16 fossil-fueled power plants and its ownership interests in STP's South Texas Nuclear Project and wind power and solar power projects. As a municipally owned utility CPS Energy is exempt from retail competition in Texas.

Geographic Reach

CPS Energy serves customers in Bexar County and portions of Atascosa Bandera Comal Guadalupe Kendall Medina and Wilson counties.

Financial Performance

In fiscal year 2014 CPS Energy's revenues increased by 9% due to a growth in electric sales and higher fuel recovery revenues. The company also benefited from higher regulatory and energy efficiency and conservation cost recoveries and an increase in sales volumes. Gas revenues were also up by $28.4 million thanks to an increase in sales volumes and a higher unit cost of fuel. CPS Energy's net income increased by 145% in fiscal year 2014 due to higher revenues and lower STP (nuclear power plant) and operating and maintenance expenses partially offset by an increase in depreciation expenses unrealized losses from the change in fair value of investments higher interest expenses and an increase in payments to the City.

Strategy

Pushing renewables to reduce green house gas emissions to meet state and federal standards CPS Energy is now leading in wind-energy capacity among municipally owned utilities across the US with almost 860 MW of wind energy under contract in 2012 and more planned to come on line that year. The company has a goal of getting 20% of its power from renewable sources by 2020 including 100 MW from solar power. It also plans to cut its customers' demand for electricity by 771 MW by that year. In a major acceleration of its green energy/conservation commitments in fiscal year 2012 CPS Energy announced plans to deactivate its J.T. Deely Units 1 and 2 coal-fired power plants in fiscal year 2018 instead of the projected dates of fiscal year 2032 and fiscal year 2033.

Looking to reduce both power use and its carbon footprint CPS Energy is retrofitting more than 1 million electric and gas meters in order to bring them into a smart technology grid to help customers save money and conserve power. It is also encouraging customers to switch to compact fluorescent lights and has a goal of reducing power demand by 771 MW by 2020.

Company Background

A venerable company CPS Energy traces its roots to the 1860s when its predecessor opened a manufactured gas plant on Houston Street.

EXECUTIVES

Vice President, Milton B Lee
Vice President of Customer Service and Solutions, Maria Koudouris
Senior Vice President of Energy Supply, Richard (Dick) Pena
EVP and General Counsel, Carolyn E. Shellman
President and CEO, Doyle N. Beneby, age 55
Executive Vice President and Chief Strategy and Technology Officer, Cris Eugster
VP Finance, Justin Locke
Vice President Media Relations, Lisa Lewis
Vice President External Relations, Rudy Garza
Vice President Revenue Management, Keith Albers
Vice President Information Technology, Martha Mitchell
Vice President, Patsy Velez
Senior Vice President Power Generation, Tammy Preiss
Vice President, Eugene Montreuil
Vice President, Jesse Orta
Vice President Marketing, Donald Murray
Vice President Customer Technology Services, Ralph Alonzo
Vice President Of Sales And Marketing, Eduardo Flores
National Account Manager, Mark Leineweber
Acting Chief Info Office Chief Adm Office Vice President And Chief Administrative, Jelynne Leblaburley
Vice President, Matt Haecker
Senior Vice President, Judy Palmieri
Senior Vice President Partner Solutions, Deborah Gunn
Vice President, Hubert Smith
Senior Vice President of Energy Delivery Services, Fred James
Board Member, Paul Escamilla
Board Member, Elbert Hargesheimer
Auditors: GARZA PREIS & CO LLC/BAKER

LOCATIONS

HQ: CITY PUBLIC SERVICES OF SAN ANTONIO
145 NAVARRO ST, SAN ANTONIO, TX 782052986
Phone: 210 353-2222
Web: WWW.CPSENERGY.COM

PRODUCTS/OPERATIONS

2014 Sales

	% of total
Electric	90
Gas	9
Other	1
Total	**100**

COMPETITORS

AEP	Energy Future
AES	NextEra Energy
Duke Energy	ONEOK

Income Statement
FYE: January 31

	REVENUE ($ mil.)	NET INCOME ($ mil.)	NET PROFIT MARGIN	EMPLOYEES
01/13	2,213	2	0.1%	3,743
01/12	2,258	21	0.9%	—
01/11	2,068	78	3.8%	—
01/10	1,930	0	—	—
Annual Growth	4.7%	—	—	—

2013 Year-End Financials

Return on assets: —   Cash ($ mil.): 271
Return on equity: 0.1%
Current ratio: 0.90

CITY UTILITIES OF SPRINGFIELD MO

City Utilities of Springfield Missouri springs to action with multiple services and products. The multi-utility supplies electricity natural gas and water for residents and businesses in the southwestern Missouri town. It has about 1870 miles of power lines and 1260 miles of natural gas mains serves about 110000 electric customers 82000 natural gas customers and 81000 water customers. It also operates the municipal bus system which has 25 regular street buses and five demand/response buses and serves about 790 broadband contracts through SpringNet Telecommunications. City Utilities of Springfield has a service region of 320 sq. ml. and serves a base population of 229000.

Geographic Reach

The multi-utility's service territory covers Springfield Missouri portions of Greene county and a part of northern Christian county.

Financial Performance

In 2012 City Utilities of Springfield's revenues declined by 4% primarily due to milder-than-usual weather crimping demand (heating degree days were 21% below normal). This drop was partially offset by an increase in revenues from its Transportation Telco/Broadband and Water segments. In 2012 revenues from electric retail sales increased 5% thanks to rate increases. However off-system sales volumes decreased 38%.

Natural gas sales decreased 15% as a direct result of lower volumes due to a mild winter and lower natural gas prices.

Water retail sales increased in 2012 to $36.4 million as compared to $32.8 million in 2011 thanks in part to lower-than-usual rainfall.

Telco/Broadband had 25 new SpringNet customers billed in 2012 and saw its revenues rise by 6%.

Strategy

With coal-fired plants accounting for 62% of its power generation capacity City Utilities of Springfield is looking to boost its green power options. The utility offers its customers the option of using renewable wind-generated electricity imported to Springfield from a Kansas wind farm (the 50 MW Smoky Hills Wind Farm in Salina).

In 2013 City Utilities of Springfield was working on a deal to buy solar power from Missouri's largest solar energy farm – a 5 MW plant on a 40 acre site in eastern Greene County near to the multi-utility's McCartney natural gas turbine between Springfield and Strafford.

Company Background

The utility traces its origins to the gas works of Springfield Gas Lighting Company which opened in 1874. In 1945 Springfield Gas and Electric was bought by the City of Springfield resulting in the creation of City Utilities of Springfield.

EXECUTIVES

Associate General Manager Operations, Wade Stinson
Associate General Manager Electric Supply, Scott Miller
Associate General Manager and General Counsel, John Black
Manager - Communications, Joel Alexander
Associate General Manager of Development, Dean Thompson
Associate General Manager - Finance, Mike Finch
Auditors: BKD LLP SPRINGFIELD MO

LOCATIONS

HQ: CITY UTILITIES OF SPRINGFIELD MO
301 E CENTRAL ST, SPRINGFIELD, MO 658023858
Phone: 417 863-9000
Web: WWW.CITYUTIL.COM

HISTORICAL FINANCIALS

Company Type: Private

Income Statement

FYE: September 30

	ASSETS ($ mil.)	NET INCOME ($ mil.)	INCOME AS % OF ASSETS	EMPLOYEES
09/13	1,760	14	0.8%	980
09/12	1,765	16	0.9%	—
09/11	1,776	18	1.0%	—
09/10	1,790	0	—	—
Annual Growth	(0.6%)	—	—	—

2013 Year-End Financials

Return on assets: 3.4%   Sales ($ mil.) 394
Return on equity: 3.6%

CITYSERVICEVALCON LLC

You don't have to live in the city to get the services of CityServiceValcon which markets and distributes petroleum products throughout the Inland Northwest and Rocky Mountain regions of the US as well as in the adjacent Plains states. Its products include gasoline diesel aviation fuels lubricants propane and heating oil. The company has diesel gasoline and heating oils for delivery through its network of bulk plants. CityServiceValcon also operates cardlock fueling facilities under the Pacific Pride brand name. Regional independent petroleum marketers City Service and Valcon merged their operations in 2003 to form CityServiceValcon.

Automotive gasoline brands represented by CityServiceValcon include Exxon Mobil Chevron and ConocoPhillips. The company also delivers aviation fuels (including Phillips 66 Aviation Fuels to Fixed Base Operators (FBOs) across the region.

Valcon Distributing has its roots in Kalispell Montana dating to the 1930s. City Service was co-founded by secretary and treasurer Dick Dasen in 1969.

EXECUTIVES

Information Technology Director and Vice President Finance, Kurt Tonjum
Vice President Marketing, Ed Croymans

LOCATIONS

HQ: CITYSERVICEVALCON LLC
640 W MONTANA ST, KALISPELL, MT 599013834
Phone: 406 755-4321
Web: WWW.CITYSERVICEVALCON.COM

COMPETITORS

Farstad Oil	SPF Energy
Redwood Coast Petroleum	Wilson Oil

HISTORICAL FINANCIALS

Company Type: Private

Income Statement

FYE: September 30

	REVENUE ($ mil.)	NET INCOME ($ mil.)	NET PROFIT MARGIN	EMPLOYEES
09/08	625	4	0.6%	150
09/07	490	3	0.6%	—
09/06	459	4	1.0%	—
Annual Growth	16.6%	(8.0%)	—	—

2008 Year-End Financials

Return on assets: 1.9%   Cash ($ mil.): 1
Return on equity: 0.6%
Current ratio: 1.20

CLAPP S NURSING CENTER INC.

LOCATIONS

HQ: CLAPP S NURSING CENTER INC.
5229 APPOMATTOX RD, PLEASANT GARDEN, NC 273138202
Phone: 336 674-2252

HISTORICAL FINANCIALS

Company Type: Private

Income Statement

FYE: September 30

	REVENUE ($ mil.)	NET INCOME ($ mil.)	NET PROFIT MARGIN	EMPLOYEES
09/09	830	(44)	—	55
09/03	2	0	4.7%	—
09/02	2	0	19.2%	—
09/01	2	0	—	—
Annual Growth	109.0%	—	—	—

2009 Year-End Financials

Return on assets: —   Cash ($ mil.): —
Return on equity: (-5.4%)
Current ratio: 2.70

CLARE ROSE INC.

Clare Rose has risen to the top with help from The King of Beers. The company a top beer wholesaler in the US primarily markets Anheuser-Busch products including Budweiser Michelob Bacardi and Busch branded products. Clare Rose domi-

nates distribution of the US beer maker's brands on New York's Long Island and Staten Island. The firm also carries other products including those of Heineken Redhook Ale and Widmer Brothers (both owned by Craft Brewers Alliance) Kona Brewing China's Harbin and Japan's Kirin. Founded in 1936 by Clare Rose the company is still owned and operated by the Rose family.

A longtime resident of Patchogue the company pulled up stakes in fall 2010 and moved into a new 265000 sq.-ft. facility in Yaphank New York. Clare Rose has proposed bulldozing its old Patchogue facility and replacing it with a 200-unit condo project worth $80 million as part of the town's efforts to revitalize the downtown area and add centrally located housing.

Founder Clare Rose died in 2010 at the age of 98.

EXECUTIVES

Vice President Information Technology, Gary Neumen
Vice President of Sales and Marketing, Matt Holthaus
Secretary Treasurer and Director of Sales, George Macdonald
Auditors: RIZZI SCHWARZ & TARASKAS LLP

LOCATIONS

HQ: CLARE ROSE INC.
100 ROSE EXECUTIVE BLVD, SHIRLEY, NY 119671524
Phone: 631 475-2337
Web: WWW.CLAREROSE.COM

COMPETITORS

Empire Merchants	Phoenix Beverages
Manhattan Beer Distributors	Yuengling & Son

HISTORICAL FINANCIALS

Company Type: Private

Income Statement

FYE: December 31

	REVENUE ($ mil.)	NET INCOME ($ mil.)	NET PROFIT MARGIN	EMPLOYEES
12/13	201	6	3.3%	267
12/12	209	9	4.5%	—
12/11	199	8	4.2%	—
12/10	200	0	—	—
Annual Growth	0.2%	—	—	—

2013 Year-End Financials

Return on assets: 1.1%   Cash ($ mil.): 8
Return on equity: 3.3%
Current ratio: 1.00

CLAREMONT HEALTH SYSTEM INC

Auditors: REZNICK GROUP BALTIMORE MD

LOCATIONS

HQ: CLAREMONT HEALTH SYSTEM INC
1515 HULSE RD, POINT PLEASANT BORO, NJ 087424527
Phone: 732 295-9300
Web: WWW.ADSNAC.ORG

HISTORICAL FINANCIALS

Company Type: Private

Income Statement
FYE: June 30

	REVENUE ($ mil.)	NET INCOME ($ mil.)	NET PROFIT MARGIN	EMPLOYEES
06/09	937	(51)	—	115
06/04	9	0	2.8%	—
Annual Growth	150.8%	—	—	—

2009 Year-End Financials

Return on assets: 0.1%   Cash ($ mil.): —
Return on equity: (-5.5%)
Current ratio: 1.30

CLASSIC STAR GROUP LP

LOCATIONS

HQ: CLASSIC STAR GROUP LP
6324 EDEN DR, HALTOM CITY, TX 761176129
Phone: 817 834-2868
Web: WWW.CLASSICSTARGROUP.COM

HISTORICAL FINANCIALS

Company Type: Private

Income Statement
FYE: December 31

	REVENUE ($ mil.)	NET INCOME ($ mil.)	NET PROFIT MARGIN	EMPLOYEES
12/13	639	3	0.5%	17
12/12	555	2	0.4%	—
12/11*	530	1	0.3%	—
10/10	339	0	—	—
Annual Growth	23.5%	—	—	—

*Fiscal year change

2013 Year-End Financials

Return on assets: 1.9%   Cash ($ mil.): —
Return on equity: 0.5%
Current ratio: 0.70

CLAY ELECTRIC COOPERATIVE INC.

Clay Electric Cooperative covers a lot of ground in Florida. The utility distributes electricity to 14 counties in the northeastern part of the state including the suburbs of Jacksonville and Gainesville. It delivers power to about 165000 residential commercial and industrial members over more than 12900 miles of distribution and transmission lines. The consumer-owned utility offers electronic funds transfer average billing and a seniors' payment plan to residential customers and backup diesel power generation and special rate plans to businesses. The consumer-owned utility has a stake in Seminole Electric Cooperative which provides generation services to Clay Electric and nine other cooperatives.

Geographic Reach

The cooperative serves customers in the Florida counties of Alachua Baker Bradford Clay Columbia Flagler Gilchrist Lake Levy Marion Putnam Suwannee Union and Volusia. It has six district offices (Gainesville Keystone Heights Lake City Orange Park Palatka and Salt Springs).

Strategy

To encourage conservation and green energy use the coop also supports customers' installation of small photovoltaic solar displays on their own homes through an arrangement whereby Seminole Electric purchases electricity generated and delivered to Clay Electric from any of its members' qualifying solar power systems.

Like other non-profit cooperatives Clay Electric refunds any annual profits to its members as credit refunds. In 2012 the company made $5.25 million in refunds available to its members or about $19 a customer.

That year Clay Electric announced that it would further cut its members' bills due to weak natural gas prices lowering the costs of power production from its gas-fired plants.

Ownership

Clay Electric is a cooperative owned by it member/users.

Company Background

The company was founded in 1937 as part of a national rural electrification drive.

EXECUTIVES

General Manager and CEO, Bill Phillips
Director Member and Public Relations, Henry Barrow
Director of Engineering, Herman Dyal
Director of Finance and Administration, Mark Maxwell
Director of Information and Communication Technology, Bruce McHollan
Manager Energy Services, Sherman Phillips
Manager Communications, Larry E. Horne
Editor, Wayne Mattox
Video Services Coordinator, Tom Whitney
Director of Operations, Howard Mott
District Manager, Tommy Tomlinson
CEO and General Manager, Richard K. (Ricky) Davis
Director District Operations, Bill Thompson
District Manager, Kerry Page
District Manager, Jim Beeler
Communications Specialist, Amanda Hernandez
Manager Safety and Training, Lee Hicks
Safety and Training Coordinator, Mark Mosley
Director Human Resources, Chip Gray
Auditors: JACKSON THORNTON & CO PC MON

LOCATIONS

HQ: CLAY ELECTRIC COOPERATIVE INC.
225 W WALKER DR, KEYSTONE HEIGHTS, FL 326567617
Phone: 352 473-4917
Web: WWW.CLAYELECTRIC.COM

COMPETITORS

Florida Power & Light	Gainesville Regional
Florida Public	Utilities
Utilities	JEA

HISTORICAL FINANCIALS

Company Type: Private

Income Statement
FYE: December 31

	REVENUE ($ mil.)	NET INCOME ($ mil.)	NET PROFIT MARGIN	EMPLOYEES
12/13	339	11	3.4%	444
12/12	337	8	2.4%	—
12/11	356	20	5.7%	—
12/10	376	0	—	—
Annual Growth	(3.4%)	—	—	—

2013 Year-End Financials

Return on assets: 0.8%   Cash ($ mil.): 6
Return on equity: 3.4%
Current ratio: 0.50

CLAYCO INC.

Clayco is a top US general building contractor that offers real estate architecture design engineering and construction services. The privately owned company serves a range of industries with a focus on industrial corporate government residential institutional and financial facilities. Projects include distribution and logistics centers industrial facilities and food and beverage industry warehouses and plants. Clayco also has constructed headquarters and operation centers call and data centers sports and education facilities and retail centers. Its Clayco Realty Group provides land development site selection and project financing.

Geographic Reach

Missouri-based Clayco has offices in Chicago and St. Louis. The firm which is seeking to grow its global presence has major projects in 43 US states and three other countries.

Operations

Clayco operates through several businesses: Clayco Realty Group Forum Studio and Concrete Strategies.

Clayco Realty Group is a full-service real estate development firm that has been involved in the design-build development of 4000-plus acres of land and more than 19 million sq. ft. of commercial industrial residential mixed-use and hospitality space that altogether exceeds a value of $1.5 billion. Having partnered with Optimus Development on many projects Clayco in 2013 merged the Optimus business into its Clayco Realty Group.

Its other subsidiary Forum Studio is an architecture/planning/interior design firm. It serves both national and international clients.

Concrete Strategies a general contracting firm that specializes in concrete design provides US customers with architectural site cast concrete structural concrete flatwork site utilities and other concrete construction for commercial projects.

Financial Performance

Clayco's revenues exceeded $912 million in 2013 up from $872 million in 2012.

Sales and Marketing

It has designed facilities for the Dow Chemical Company Amazon Caterpillar Procter and Gamble 3M and Chevron.

Strategy

Clayco has vaulted to the top ranks of US general building contractors by developing its own building technique of tilt-up a process of concrete building construction. The group specializes in building distribution/warehouse facilities and sports headquarters and training facilities. To support its growth the firm in 2014 moved its corporate headquarters to Chicago where it plans to double the number of employees there during the next several years. Clayco plans to hire new architects designers and project managers and expand its concrete and infrastructure business in Illinois.

Clayco which weathered the downturn in the construction business by relying on its diverse service offerings in a variety of geographic markets and taking on government-funded projects is seeking new projects in new markets. In 2014 the company completed an addition to and renovation of the Houston Police Federal Credit Union main office (near downtown Houston) nearly doubling its size to accommodate the growing number of members.

In 2013 Clayco launched a new business unit focusing on energy and transportation projects in North America.

That year it built a 450000-sq.-ft. distribution center for Caterpillar Inc. in Mexico that features a full-service kitchen for employees soccer field and outdoor grill.

Company Background

Clayco was founded in 1984 by CEO Robert Clark.

EXECUTIVES

Chairman and CEO, Robert G. (Bob) Clark
Chief Operating Officer & Partner, Steven R. (Steve) Sieckhaus
Principal Clayco Real Estate Services and Partner, Tom Schroyer
President Forum Studio, Chris Cedergreen
SVP and Partner, Kevin McKenna
SVP and Partner, P. Kirk Warden
President, Russ Burns
SVP and Partner, Tom Sieckhaus
Chief Financial Officer, Tony Schofield
President Concrete Strategies, Joe Vitale
EVP and Partner, Dave Moses
President Clayco Realty Group, Chris McKee
Vice President Preconstruction Services, Kurt Jaeger
Senior Vice President, Sandra Marks
Auditors: DGLF CPAS & BUSINESS ADVISORS

LOCATIONS

HQ: CLAYCO INC.
35 E WACKER DR STE 1300, CHICAGO, IL 606012110
Phone: 312 658-0747
Web: WWW.CLAYCORP.COM

PRODUCTS/OPERATIONS

Selected Projects
308 Green Street
Air Products
BJC Administrative Office Building
Express Scripts 6
First Community - Richmond Heights
Gateway Plaza
Houston Police Federal Credit Union
Mercy Chesterfield Health Campus
Missouri Baptist Hospital Medical Office Building
Reinsurance Group of America
Stifel Nicolaus
University of Chicago Medical Center West Center for Care and Discovery Parking Garage
Washington University School of Medicine Scott McKinley Research Building
Zenithridge at Southpointe
Zurich North American Headquarters

Selected Subsidiaries
Clayco Realty Group
Concrete Strategies
Forum Studio Inc.

COMPETITORS

AECOM	KHS&S
Alberici	Kinsley Construction
Alter Group	Korte
Amusement Leisure	M. A. Mortenson
Baker Concrete	McCarthy Building
Barton Malow	Populous Inc.
Bechtel	Skanska USA Building
H and M Construction	The Austin Company
Hensel Phelps Construction	Turner Corporation
	Whiting-Turner
Hunt Construction	
James G. Davis Construction	

HISTORICAL FINANCIALS
Company Type: Private

Income Statement
FYE: December 31

	REVENUE ($ mil.)	NET INCOME ($ mil.)	NET PROFIT MARGIN	EMPLOYEES
12/13	466	5	1.3%	500
12/12	391	2	0.6%	—
12/11	511	2	0.5%	—
12/10	443	0	—	—
Annual Growth	1.7%	—	—	—

2013 Year-End Financials
Return on assets: 5.0%
Return on equity: 1.3%
Current ratio: 0.20
Cash ($ mil.): 24

CLEVELAND CONSTRUCTION INC.

Cleveland Construction Inc. (CCI) has ventured beyond Cleveland to offer its services nationwide. Beyond general contractor work CCI provides design build construction management and interior trades services for commercial and institutional projects. Also a top interior contractor in the US the contractor installs finishes such as drywall acoustic wall panels and specialty ceilings. Its projects have included hospitals universities correctional facilities hotels convention centers sports complexes retail outlets (including Wal-Mart stores) and public projects such as the Ohio State Stadium and the George Bush Intercontinental Airport in Houston. Founded in 1980 the company remains family-owned.

Geographic ReachCCI is licensed to build in 43 US states (as of early 2016) and operates six regional offices including three in Ohio (Cleveland Cincinnati and Columbus) and the rest in Naples Florida; Charlotte North Carolina; and Jessup Maryland.Sales and MarketingCCI's projects have included auto dealerships corporate offices multifamily and student housing industrial facilities hospitals universities correctional facilities hotels (including Candlewood Suites) convention centers sports complexes retail outlets (including Wal-Mart superstores in Florida) and government buildings such as the Ohio State Stadium the George Bush Intercontinental Airport in Houston.The company's insurance partner (as of early 2016) is Chubb Group of Insurance Companies.Strategy-Cleveland Construction continued in 2016 to manage 50 projects at a time on average with a large bonding capacity at $100 million per single project and $350 million in aggregate.

Some of its recent projects include the 22-story 300-room hotel tower built atop the EpiCentre in Charlotte North Carolina (started in November 2015 and scheduled to be finished in late 2017); the managed construction project on the 56000 sq. ft. 14-screen Xscape Theatre in Riverview Florida (awarded in December 2015); and the world's largest Candlewood Suites Hotel —complete with 310 rooms spanning a total of nearly 154000 sq. ft. —at the Fort Sam Houston military base in San Antonio (completed in October 2014).

The firm celebrated the historic completion of its 50 millionth square foot of retail space after it completed a Walmart Supercenter in Economy Pennsylvania in February 2014.

EXECUTIVES

Vice President Estimating Interiors, Neal Keller
Vice President, Keith Ziegler
CEO, Richard G. Small
CFO and VP Project Management, Mark T. Small
Sales and Marketing, Matthew Young
President, Dan Wireman
Vice President Of Construction, David Sawicki
Vice President BD, Edward (Ed) Paradise
Vice President, James (Jamie) Small
Vice President, Rhett Stayer
Vice President, George Gaharan
Auditors: SKODA MINOTI MAYFIELD VILLAGE

LOCATIONS

HQ: CLEVELAND CONSTRUCTION INC.
8620 TYLER BLVD, MENTOR, OH 440604348
Phone: 513 398-8900
Web: WWW.CLEVELANDCONSTRUCTION.COM

PRODUCTS/OPERATIONS

Selected Services
Construction Management
Construction Services
Design-Build
General Contracting
Interior Contracting
Preconstruction

COMPETITORS

Albert M. Higley	The Haskell Company
The Austin Company	

HISTORICAL FINANCIALS
Company Type: Private

Income Statement
FYE: December 31

	REVENUE ($ mil.)	NET INCOME ($ mil.)	NET PROFIT MARGIN	EMPLOYEES
12/09	217	25	11.9%	800
12/08	186	24	12.9%	—
12/07	2,003	0	—	—
Annual Growth	—191622.6%			

2009 Year-End Financials
Return on assets: 14.9%
Return on equity: 11.9%
Current ratio: 1.00
Cash ($ mil.): 15

CLIFTONLARSONALLEN LLP

CliftonLarsonAllen (CLA) is all about the numbers. The major accounting firm serves privately-owned firms and their principals along with not-for-profits and government agencies. It is organized as a holding company with three main segments: public accounting wealth management and outsourcing services. With more than $3 billion in client assets under management and 500 partners CLA is a top 10 US accounting firm. It primarily serves clients in the agribusiness financial employee benefit plan healthcare and manufacturing industries along with various levels of government.

Geographic Reach

Minnesota-based CLA boasts more than 90 offices in about 20 states and the District of Columbia.

Operations

The company's service areas include audit accounting tax consulting outsourcing and wealth advisory. Its investment advisory services are conducted through CliftonLarsonAllen Wealth Advisors LLC. CLA serves clients outside the US through its affiliations with Nexia International and HLB International.

Sales and Marketing

CLA which counts more than 150000 clients serves privately-held businesses individuals not-for-profits and governmental entities. Its major client groups include agribusiness and cooperatives dealerships employee benefit plans federal government financial institutions healthcare manufacturing and distribution companies as well as state and local governments.

Financial Performance

CLA logged $550 million in revenue in 2012.

Strategy

The firm's growth strategy focuses on partnerships and acquisitions. Mergers and Acquisitions

Looking to take advantage of the implementation of healthcare reform in the US CLA in 2013 acquired Idaho-based national healthcare consulting firm Beck Advisory Group. It also bought accounting firm Monaghan Group boosting its outsourcing practice and services in the Charlotte North Carolina area as well as Indiana-based Nonprofit Financial Solutions a firm focused on providing nonprofits with CFO consulting and outsourcing services.

In 2014 the company acquired Illinois Agricultural Auditing Association an accounting and consulting organization that allows CLA to expand its presence in Illinois to more than a dozen locations with the addition of IAAA's Bloomington/Normal and Springfield locations.CLA followed up the purchase by buying Massachusetts consulting firm Bankers Advisory Inc.; Maryland-based OneSource Professional Services Group a consulting technology accounting and tax services firm; and Sullivan Rogers & Company a Massachusetts CPA and consulting firm dedicated to the state and local government market.

Company Background

CLA was formed in 2011 by the merger of Clifton Gunderson and LarsonAllen. Prior to the pairing both companies had been active in expanding across the country by purchasing smaller firms and parts of other firms.

EXECUTIVES

COO, David E. Bailey
CFO, Sharon Ten Clay
CIO, Steve Noble
CEO CliftonLarsonAllen Wealth Advisors LLC, Tony Hallada
CEO and Chief Business Officer, Denny Schleper

LOCATIONS

HQ: CLIFTONLARSONALLEN LLP
220 S 6TH ST STE 300, MINNEAPOLIS, MN 554021418
Phone: 612 376-4500
Web: WWW.CLIFTONLARSONALLEN.COM

Selected Locations
Arizona
California
Colorado
Florida
Idaho
Illinois
Indiana
Iowa
Maryland
Massachusetts
Michigan
Minnesota
Mississippi
Missouri
New Jersey

New Mexico
New York
North Carolina
Ohio
Pennsylvania
Texas
Virginia
Washington
Wisconsin

PRODUCTS/OPERATIONS

Selected Services
Audit and assurance
Consulting
　Employee benefit plans
　Executive search
　Forensic
　Information security
　Litigation support
　Risk management
　Technology
　Transaction support
　Valuation
International
Outsourcing
Private client tax and wealth advisory
Tax
Tax education for CPAs

COMPETITORS

BDO
BKD LLP
Baker Tilly Virchow
　Krause
CBIZ Accounting Tax &
　Advisory Services
Crowe Horwath
Deloitte & Touche
Eide Bailly

Ernst & Young LLP
Grant Thornton
KPMG L.L.P.
Moore Stephens
　International
PricewaterhouseCoopers
UK
RSM US
SVA

HISTORICAL FINANCIALS

Company Type: Private

Income Statement

FYE: December 31

	REVENUE ($ mil.)	NET INCOME ($ mil.)	NET PROFIT MARGIN	EMPLOYEES
12/13	563	154	27.5%	3,600
12/12	569	204	36.0%	—
Annual Growth	(1.1%)	(24.4%)	—	—

2013 Year-End Financials

Return on assets: 0.6%　　Cash ($ mil.): 6
Return on equity: 27.5%
Current ratio: 2.30

CLUNE CONSTRUCTION COMPANY L.P.

Auditors: KPMG

LOCATIONS

HQ: CLUNE CONSTRUCTION COMPANY L.P.
10 S RIVERSIDE PLZ # 2200, CHICAGO, IL 606063728
Phone: 312 726-6103
Web: WWW.CLUNEGC.COM

HISTORICAL FINANCIALS

Company Type: Private

Income Statement

FYE: December 31

	REVENUE ($ mil.)	NET INCOME ($ mil.)	NET PROFIT MARGIN	EMPLOYEES
12/12	421	6	1.4%	250
12/11	285	5	1.9%	—
12/10	206	2	1.0%	—
Annual Growth	42.9%	71.0%	—	—

2012 Year-End Financials

Return on assets: 25.4%　　Cash ($ mil.): 1
Return on equity: 1.4%
Current ratio: 1.10

COAST CITRUS DISTRIBUTORS

Coast Citrus Distributors is a leading wholesale distributor of fresh fruits and vegetables in Mexico and the US. The company supplies a variety of produce including bananas lettuce limes and potatoes to retail grocers and other food customers. It distributes under the names Coast Citrus Coast Tropical Olympic Fruit and Vegetable and Importadora y Exportadora. Coast Citrus Distributors operates half a dozen distribution facilities in California Texas and Florida. It also has about five locations in Mexico. The late Roberto Alvarez founded the family-owned business in 1950.

In early 2010 Chiquita Brands International sold its 49% equity investment in Coast Citrus Distributors. The sale netted Chiquita $18 million in cash and helped to improve its liquidity.

EXECUTIVES

Vice President Purchasing, Stanley Alvarez
Auditors: PKF SAN DIEGO CA

LOCATIONS

HQ: COAST CITRUS DISTRIBUTORS
7597 BRISTOW CT, SAN DIEGO, CA 921547419
Phone: 619 661-7950
Web: WWW.COASTCITRUS.COM

COMPETITORS

A. Duda & Sons
Albert's Organics
American Fruit &
　Produce
Borg Produce
Chiquita Brands

Fresh Del Monte
　Produce
FreshPoint
General Produce
Interfresh
The Oppenheimer Group

HISTORICAL FINANCIALS

Company Type: Private

Income Statement

FYE: December 29

	REVENUE ($ mil.)	NET INCOME ($ mil.)	NET PROFIT MARGIN	EMPLOYEES
12/12	281	2	1.0%	389
12/11*	297	3	1.0%	—
01/11	294	4	1.4%	—
06/10	293	0	—	—
Annual Growth	(1.4%)	—	—	—

*Fiscal year change

2012 Year-End Financials

Return on assets: 6.0%　　Cash ($ mil.): 13
Return on equity: 1.0%
Current ratio: 1.60

COAST ELECTRIC POWER ASSOCIATION

There's no coasting for the Coast Electric Power Association when it comes to providing residents in three southern Mississippi counties with electricity. The utility uses a 6400-mile distribution network to serve its more than 76000 members (the great majority or which are residential customers) in Hancock Pearl River and Harrison counties. Coast offers electronic fund transfer and average monthly payment plans and rebates on energy efficient home improvements. The utility's power is generated by South Mississippi Electric Power an association of Coast and 10 other cooperatives. It partners with Touchstone Energy Cooperatives.

The member-owned electric cooperative started serving the Gulf Coast in 1937 with 25 miles of power lines and 50 members.

EXECUTIVES

Senior System Engineer Vice President Of Engineering, Scott Brown
Vice President Of Pearl River County O, Louis Lee
Auditors: JACKSON THORNTON & CO PC MO

LOCATIONS

HQ: COAST ELECTRIC POWER ASSOCIATION
18020 HIGHWAY 603, KILN, MS 395568487
Phone: 228 363 7000
Web: WWW.COASTEPA.COM

COMPETITORS

Entergy Mississippi   Southern Pine EPA
Mississippi Power

HISTORICAL FINANCIALS

Company Type: Private

Income Statement   FYE: December 31

	REVENUE ($ mil.)	NET INCOME ($ mil.)	NET PROFIT MARGIN	EMPLOYEES
12/13	187	12	6.8%	238
12/12	184	13	7.2%	—
12/11	185	13	7.3%	—
12/10	196	0	—	—
Annual Growth	(1.6%)	—	—	—

2013 Year-End Financials

Return on assets: —   Cash ($ mil.): 1
Return on equity: 6.8%
Current ratio: 0.30

COASTAL FEDERAL CREDIT UNION

LOCATIONS

HQ: COASTAL FEDERAL CREDIT UNION
1000 SAINT ALBANS DR, RALEIGH, NC 276097347
Phone: 919 420-8000
Web: WWW.COASTAL24.COM

HISTORICAL FINANCIALS

Company Type: Private

Income Statement   FYE: December 31

	ASSETS ($ mil.)	NET INCOME ($ mil.)	INCOME AS % OF ASSETS	EMPLOYEES
12/08	2,087	2	0.1%	400
12/07	1,881	13	0.7%	—
12/06	46	16	34.9%	—
Annual Growth	566.5%	(63.2%)	—	—

2008 Year-End Financials

Return on assets: —   Sales ($ mil): 140
Return on equity: 1.6%

COASTAL PACIFIC FOOD DISTRIBUTORS INC.

Coastal Pacific Food Distributors (CPF) fuels the military forces from facility to fork. The company is one of the top wholesale food distributors that primarily serves the US armed forces across the Western US and in the Far East. As part of its business CPF provides a full line of groceries to military bases run by the US Army Navy Air Force and Marines. It delivers a variety of products from distribution centers located in California Washington and Hawaii. CPF also offers information system programming services for its customers to track sales and shipping as well as procurement and logistics through partnerships in Iraq Kuwait and Saudi Arabia. The company was founded in 1986.

Geographic Reach

California-based CPF caters to the Western US as well as Alaska Hawaii Guam Japan Okinawa Korea Singapore Kwajalein Diego Garcia and the Philippines. Its business extends to the Middle East through partnerships for procurement and logistics with other companies. These additional areas include Iraq Kuwait and Saudi Arabia.

Operations

CPF has grown to become the second-largest worldwide military distributor of food and related products.

As part of its business CPF operates distribution centers in California Washington Hawaii and Canada. In California its largest Stockton facility spans more than 500000 sq. ft. while its Ontario center boasts 429000 sq. ft. Its distribution center in Fife Washington is 153000 sq. ft. A 45000-sq.-ft. facility in Hawaii delivers food to four military commissaries.

Strategy

The company works to support its existing markets. In 2013 CPF opened a new prime vendor platform in Calamba Luguna Philippines as it looks to serve future growth there. The platform supports Naval ships with dry chill and frozen items.

Sales and Marketing

Industry partners that keep CPF busy include the Defense Logistics Agency the Defense Commissary Agency Air Force NAF Purchasing Office Navy Exchange (NEXCOM) Army and Air Force Exchange Service (AAFES) and the American Logistics Association to name a few.

The company counts on food manufacturers to keep its customers happy. They include Kraft Foods Tyson Foods Procter & Gamble General Mills Nestle ConAgra Unilever Frito-Lay Campbell J.M. Smucker Global Military Marketing Mars S&K Sales Del Monte Corp. Georgia-Pacific Johnson & Johnson and Alder Foods.

EXECUTIVES

General Manager, Brian Murdoch
Vice President of Finance, Monika Bertke
CEO President, Frank Pecoraro
VP Business Development, Jeffrey King
Corporate Director of Merchandising, Bill Faucette
Business Manager, Debbie May
Senior Business Manager, Frank Costa
General Manager of Division, Marlin Vleet
Chief Financial Officer, Bill Ungerman
Chief Operating Officer, Terry F. Wood
Vice President of Distribution, Tim Tveitnes
Auditors: DIXON HUGHES GOODMAN LLP NORF

LOCATIONS

HQ: COASTAL PACIFIC FOOD DISTRIBUTORS INC.
1015 PERFORMANCE DR, STOCKTON, CA 952064925
Phone: 909 947-2066
Web: WWW.CPFD.COM

PRODUCTS/OPERATIONS

Selected Products
Bakery
Candy
Deli
Fresh & frozen meats
Frozen foods
Pet foods
Refrigerated items
Sushi

Selected Brokers
Acosta Sales & Marketing
Alder Foods Inc.
Bisek & Co. Inc.
Dixon Marketing Inc.
Dunham & Smith Agencies
Elite Brands
Finnegan International Sales
First Wave Sales
Gateway Military LLC
Global Office Building
HI-PAC Ltd
Mid Valley
Overseas Service Corporation
Otis McAllister
Parra Sales Inc
Reese Group
S&K
S. Schwartz Sales Inc.
Turnkey Management
WEBCO General Partnership

COMPETITORS

AdvancePierre   Richmond Wholesale
JTM Provisions   Meat

HISTORICAL FINANCIALS

Company Type: Private

Income Statement   FYE: December 28

	REVENUE ($ mil.)	NET INCOME ($ mil.)	NET PROFIT MARGIN	EMPLOYEES
12/13	1,260	17	1.4%	459
12/12	1,212	15	1.2%	—
12/11*	1,162	25	2.2%	—
01/11	1,113	0	—	—
Annual Growth	4.2%	—	—	—

*Fiscal year change

2013 Year-End Financials

Return on assets: 4.9%   Cash ($ mil.): 5
Return on equity: 1.4%
Current ratio: 1.30

COBB ELECTRIC MEMBERSHIP CORPORATION

Cobb Electric Membership Corporation (Cobb EMC) makes sure that Cobb County Georgia residents can cook corn on the cob (and anything else) using either electric power or natural gas. The utility distributes electricity to more than 200000 meters (more than 177000 residential commercial and industrial members) in Cobb County and four other north metro Atlanta counties. Cobb EMC operates about 10000 miles of power lines. The company's Gas South unit markets natural gas to customers who receive their service on Atlanta Gas & Light's natural gas distribution pipelines in Georgia.

Geographic Reach

One of the largest of Georgia's 41 EMCs Cobb EMC's distribution system covers approximately 1434 square miles (Cobb Bartow Cherokee Fulton and Paulding counties in the north metro Atlanta area and Randolph Calhoun Quitman and Clay counties in Southwest Georgia).

Operations

Its Cobb Energy Management provides administrative and labor support to Cobb EMC and offers phone and Internet services to Cobb EMC's customers primarily through subsidiaries. Cobb Energy Management provides call center training tree trimming and billing software services and other ancillary support to EMC's core activities.

Financial Performance

In 2012 the company reported a 46% increase in revenues thanks to a 10% rise in natural gas sales which outpaced a 2% decline in electric revenues. Net income grew by 194% in 2012 as a result of higher net sales and lower operating costs.

Strategy

Cobb EMC is a partner in Power4Georgians a consortium of six Georgia EMCs that collectively is developing a comprehensive strategy to provide reliable and affordable energy to the EMC members.

In 2013 as part of its ongoing transition out of non-energy businesses Cobb EMC announced today plans to cut its workforce by up to 20% percent through a company-wide offer of voluntary separation packages.

In 2012 Smart Energy Capital LLC and Jacoby Development Inc. signed a power purchase deal with Cobb EMC to provide power from the Azalea Solar Facility the largest solar power plant (10MW) in Georgia and one of the largest in the Southeast.

Company Background

The cooperative has been embroiled in litigation in recent years and in 2011 a Cobb County grand jury indicted Cobb EMC Dwight Brown on 31 counts of theft and racketeering. Brown was replaced as CEO by W.T. "Chip" Nelson.

The gas and support companies were merged into EMC as wholly owned units in 2009 as a way to streamline EMC's overall operations. The company has also sold a number of former assets to raise cash including Cooperative Business Ventures in 2009 for $2 million and the health and welfare brokerage business of Cooperative Benefits and Financial Services for a gain of $470000 in 2010.

Formed in 1938 Cobb EMC began life as an electric utility with 489 residential members and 14 commercial customers.

EXECUTIVES

Vice President Of Operations, Jay Kenyon
Assoc Vice President Of Engineer, Wanda Lee
Vice President Operations, Alan (Al) Freeman
Vice President Human Resources, Angie Jones
Vice President Of Finance, Frank Myers
Associate Vice President of Marketmg, Kevan Espy
Vice Chairman Of The Board Of Directors, Bryan Boyd
Board member, Edward (Ed) Crowell

LOCATIONS

HQ: COBB ELECTRIC MEMBERSHIP CORPORATION
1000 EMC PKWY NE, MARIETTA, GA 300607908
Phone: 770 429-2222
Web: WWW.COBBEMC.COM

HISTORICAL FINANCIALS

Company Type: Private

Income Statement

FYE: December 31

	REVENUE ($ mil.)	NET INCOME ($ mil.)	NET PROFIT MARGIN	EMPLOYEES
12/13*	416	(8)	—	548
04/09	641	3	0.6%	—
12/08	381	(0)	—	—
12/07	367	0	—	—
Annual Growth	2.1%	—	—	—

*Fiscal year change

2013 Year-End Financials

Return on assets: 10.6%   Cash ($ mil.): 16
Return on equity: (-1.9%)
Current ratio: 1.30

COBORN'S INCORPORATED

Coborn's hopes you'll shop at your convenience. The company operates 52 stores across Minnesota North Dakota South Dakota Iowa Illinois and Wisconsin under the Coborn's Cash Wise Foods and Save-A-Lot banners. To support its more than 100 retail locations Coborn's operates its own central bakery dry cleaning facility and grocery distribution center. It supplies its stores with baked goods deli items and meat from its own central bakery and manufacturing plant. Along with its grocery stores the firm owns and operates pharmacies and convenience liquor and video stores.

Geographic Reach

Based in Minnesota Coborn's operates across the Upper Midwest in Minnesota the Dakotas Iowa Illinois and Wisconsin.

Operations

As part of its business Coborn's operates under several banner names including Cash Wise Foods Save-A-Lot Economart Food Pride Mike's Super Value and namesake Coborn's. These supermarkets are supported by their own central bakery dry cleaning facility and grocery distribution center. The company also runs more than 65 standalone convenience liquor video and pharmacy locations.

Strategy

Independently-owned Corborn's is building a sizable empire in the Upper Midwest through acquisitions and organic growth. In 2015 it purchased Marketplace Foods which owns four grocery/liquor stores in Western Wisconsin. The four Marketplace Foods stores are located in Hayward Menomonie Rice Lake and St. Croix Falls and will continue to operate as Marketplace Foods.

In fall 2013 it acquired four Captain Jack's liquor stores in Bismarck North Dakota as well as a single Bill's Liquor store in Mandan. (North Dakota's economy is growing rapidly thanks to the oil boom.)

Company Background

Founded in 1921 when Chester Coborn started a single produce market the company opened its first Cash Wise Foods store in 1979 and its first convenience store in 1986.

EXECUTIVES

V Pres Of It, Dale D Monson

LOCATIONS

HQ: COBORN' S INCORPORATED
1445 HIGHWAY 23 E BLDG A, SAINT CLOUD, MN 563040952
Phone: 763 389-1350
Web: WWW.COBORNS.LIFEPICS.COM

PRODUCTS/OPERATIONS

Selected Store Formats
Convenience stores (Little Dukes Holiday)
Hardware stores (Ace)
Liquor stores
Pharmacies
Restaurants (Subway)
Supermarkets (Coborn' s Cash Wise Foods JK Markets Save-A-Lot)
Video stores

COMPETITORS

7-Eleven	Kroger
ALDI	Lunds
Couche-Tard	Target Corporation
Cub Foods	Wal-Mart
Kowalski' s Markets	

HISTORICAL FINANCIALS

Company Type: Private

Income Statement

FYE: December 28

	REVENUE ($ mil.)	NET INCOME ($ mil.)	NET PROFIT MARGIN	EMPLOYEES
12/13	1,246	30	2.5%	7,000
12/12	1,220	32	2.7%	—
12/11	1,191	29	2.4%	—
12/10	1,103	0	—	—
Annual Growth	4.1%	—	—	—

2013 Year-End Financials

Return on assets: 4.1%   Cash ($ mil.): 21
Return on equity: 2.5%
Current ratio: 0.30

COC PROPERTIES INC.

Auditors: BATCHELOR TILLERY & ROBERTS

LOCATIONS

HQ: COC PROPERTIES INC.
110 MACKENAN DR STE 300, CARY, NC 275117901
Phone: 919 462-1100
Web: WWW.CARYOIL.COM

HISTORICAL FINANCIALS
Company Type: Private

Income Statement			FYE: December 31	
	ASSETS ($ mil.)	NET INCOME ($ mil.)	INCOME AS % OF ASSETS	EMPLOYEES
12/13	77	3	4.4%	100
12/12	76	2	3.6%	—
12/11	76	2	2.7%	—
12/09	67	0	—	—
Annual Growth	3.6%	—	—	—

2013 Year-End Financials

Return on assets: —
Return on equity: 0.2%
Sales ($ mil.): 1,829

COLLEGE ENTRANCE EXAMINATION BOARD

There are three letters every high school student must learn: S A and T. Who is responsible for making those letters so infamous? Why The College Board of course. The not-for-profit association owns and administers the Scholastic Assessment Test (SAT) College-Level Examination Program (CLEP) and the Advanced Placement Program (AP) at high schools nationwide. It also offers guidance counseling financial aid student assessment standardized testing and professional development courses. The College Board was founded in 1900; its members include nearly 6000 schools colleges universities and other educational institutions.

Operations

The College Board's services reach more than 7 million students at 23000 high schools and 3800 colleges in the US and abroad. It also serves some 130000 AP teachers and administers 3.2 million AP exams annually. Some of the College Board's tests such as the SAT are administered at schools with support from third parties such as Educational Testing Services.

Geographic Reach

The College Board has main offices in New York City and Reston Virginia. It also has six regional offices scattered across the US; these offices handle administrative duties for testing administrations in their respective regions. The organization's member institutions include schools in more than 60 countries; College Board exams are administered in more than 180 countries and territories worldwide.

Strategy

In 2015 the Board released free personalized online practice for the redesigned SAT at KhanAcademy.org. This was part of the organization's efforts to increase student success. (The redesign of the SAT also served to meet that purpose.)

Company Background

The College Board was created by a group of colleges as a way to expand access to higher education. The SAT (originally called the College Boards) was formed to help colleges and universities identify "deserving" students through shared entrance exams.

EXECUTIVES

Vice President, Arthur (Art) Doyle
COO, Jeremy Singer
SVP and CIO, Terri Shaw
President CEO and Trustee, David Coleman
Vice President Engineering, Cindy Bailey
Senior Vice President, Ranjit Sidhu
Vp Of Access To Rigor Campaign, Veronica Conforme
Vice President And Secretary, Dorothy Sexton
Vice President Government Relations, Jimmy R Wynn
Senior Vice President Relationship Development, Ivette Castro
Vice President Chief Accounting Officer, Gary Meyer
Vice President Membership, Marycarroll Scott
Senior Vice President Finance And Chie, Tom Higgins
Vice President Of Information Technology, Peter Propf
Vice Chair, Shirley A. Ort
Chairman, Maghan Keita
Assistant Treasurer, Thomas (Thom) McNamara
Board Member, Vivian Lee
Auditors: PRICEWATERHOUSECOOPERS LLP N

LOCATIONS

HQ: COLLEGE ENTRANCE EXAMINATION BOARD
45 COLUMBUS AVE, NEW YORK, NY 100236917
Phone: 212 713-8000
Web: WWW.COLLEGEBOARD.ORG

PRODUCTS/OPERATIONS

Selected services
Advanced Placement (college readiness)
Big Future (college planning)
CLEP (College-Level Examination Program)
CollegeEd (college planning career guidance)
College Search (college readiness)
CSS/Financial Aid PROFILE (financial aid application service)
EXCELerator (school district consultation services college readiness)
PSAT/NMSQT (practice for SAT National Merit Scholarship Qualifying Test)
ReadiStep (middle school assessment high school readiness)
SAT SAT Subject Tests and SAT Readiness Tools
Scholarship Search (scholarship aid)
SpringBoard (pre-AP college readiness)
Student Search Service (sends student testing information to colleges and scholarship programs)

COMPETITORS

ACT Inc.	Educate
Bridges Transitions	Kaplan
College Coach	McGraw Hill Financial
ETS	Questar Assessment
Edmentum	The Princeton Review

HISTORICAL FINANCIALS
Company Type: Private

Income Statement			FYE: June 30	
	REVENUE ($ mil.)	NET INCOME ($ mil.)	NET PROFIT MARGIN	EMPLOYEES
06/13	779	93	12.0%	1,259
06/12	746	26	3.6%	—
06/11	705	102	14.5%	—
06/10	668	0	—	—
Annual Growth	5.3%	—	—	—

2013 Year-End Financials

Return on assets: —
Return on equity: 12.0%
Current ratio: 3.00
Cash ($ mil.): 147

COLLEGE OF THE HOLY CROSS

College of The Holy Cross has some real Crusaders. The Jesuit-founded college with sports teams nicknamed the Crusaders is a liberal arts undergraduate institution in central Massachusetts with more than 2900 students. Some of the school's more popular areas of study include liberal arts' favorites such as English history and political science but also multidisciplinary concentrations and specialty programs including biochemistry Latin American studies and women's studies. The co-educational school has more than 300 full- and part-time faculty with a 10:1 student-to-faculty ratio. Holy Cross is the oldest Catholic college in New England.

Geographic Reach

College of The Holy Cross is located on a 170-acre campus in Worcester Massachusetts. Its students come from throughout the US and about 16 countries. In 2014 some 63% of its full-time students came for outside of Massachusetts.

Operations

Student tuition was $46550 per year for the fiscal year 2015-16. The school also offered $46 million for financial aid for the year.

Financial Performance

College of the Holy Cross reported a 2% revenue increase in 2014 due to higher income from student tuition and fees auxiliary enterprises including living and dining services and external contributions. Tuition —about $46500 per student per year — is the school's largest revenue contributor. The school's net income increased by 65% in 2014 due to higher non-operating contributions and investment returns. It reported operating cash outflow of $2 million in 2014 due to higher cash used in net realized and unrealized gains on investments and contributions for long-term investment and facilities.

Company Background

The colleges as founded in 1843 by the second bishop of Boston Benedict Joseph Fenwick of the Society of Jesus.

EXECUTIVES

Senior Vice President, Frank Vellaccio
VP Student Affairs and Dean of Students, Jacqueline D. Peterson
VP Administration and Finance, Michael J. Lochhead
Director Information Technology Services, Ellen J. Keohane
President, Philip L. Boroughs
Chief Investment Officer, Timothy M. Jarry
Dean of the College, Margaret N. Freije
Director of Admissions, Ann McDermott
Vice President for Development and Alumni Relations, Tracy Barlok
Medical Director, Christine Purington
Chairman, P. Kevin Condron
Secretary Treasurer, Charles Baker
Auditors: KPMG LLP BOSTON MA

LOCATIONS

HQ: COLLEGE OF THE HOLY CROSS
1 COLLEGE ST, WORCESTER, MA 016102395
Phone: 508 793-2011
Web: WWW.HOLYCROSS.EDU

PRODUCTS/OPERATIONS

2014 Sales

	% of total
Net student fees	45

Long-term investment income used in operations	37
Others	18
Total	**100**

Selected Programs

Anthropology
Art History
Biology
Chemistry
Chinese
Classics
Computer Science
Economics
Economics and Accounting
Education
English
French
German
History
Italian
Mathematics
Modern Languages & Literatures
Music
Philosophy
Physics
Political Science
Psychology
Religious Studies
Russian
Sociology
Spanish
Studies in World Literature
Studio Art
Theatre
Career Programs
  Business
  Engineering
  Health Professions
  Law
  Teacher Education Program
Multidisciplinary and Specialty Programs
  Africana Studies
  Asian Studies
  Biochemistry
  Biological Psychology
  Education
  Environmental Studies
  Latin American and Latino Studies
  Naval Science
  Peace and Conflict Studies
  Women' s and Gender Studies

COMPETITORS

Boston College
Fairfield University
Fordham University
Molloy College

HISTORICAL FINANCIALS

Company Type: Private

Income Statement

FYE: June 30

	REVENUE ($ mil.)	NET INCOME ($ mil.)	NET PROFIT MARGIN	EMPLOYEES
06/14	163	112	68.4%	949
06/13	160	67	42.2%	—
06/12	154	(16)	—	—
06/11	151	0	—	—
Annual Growth	2.6%	—	—	—

2014 Year-End Financials

Return on assets: 13.9%
Return on equity: 68.4%
Current ratio: —

Cash ($ mil.): 37

COLONIAL SAVINGS F.A.

LOCATIONS

HQ: COLONIAL SAVINGS F.A.
  2600 WEST FWY, FORT WORTH, TX 761027109
Phone: 817 390-2000
Web: WWW.COLONIALSAVINGS.COM

HISTORICAL FINANCIALS

Company Type: Private

Income Statement

FYE: September 30

	ASSETS ($ mil.)	NET INCOME ($ mil.)	INCOME AS % OF ASSETS	EMPLOYEES
09/13	1,074	72	6.8%	650
09/12	1,103	47	4.3%	—
09/11	927	38	4.2%	—
09/10	1,037	0	—	—
Annual Growth	1.2%	—	—	—

2013 Year-End Financials

Return on assets: —
Return on equity: 33.2%

Sales ($ mil): 219

COLORADO SEMINARY

Want a mile-high education? Colorado Seminary which does business as University of Denver (DU) offers graduate and undergraduate degrees in more than 100 fields of study including law government humanities education engineering and psychology. About 12000 undergraduate and graduate students from across the US and more than 90 countries are enrolled at the school. Former Secretary of State Condoleezza Rice former Interior Secretary Gale Norton and former Coors Brewing CEO Peter Coors attended DU. Founded in 1864 the university has a staff of some 650 faculty members; its student-to-faculty ratio is 10:1. DU is located on a 125-acre campus.

Strategy

DU has added about 20 buildings since 1997 to enhance its academic administrative athletic and residential capacities. Projects have included a soccer stadium and a center for international security and diplomacy within the School of International Studies. In 2011 DU built a new Academic Commons building which houses the school's Penrose Library.

EXECUTIVES

Executive Vice President, Curtis Burch
Director of Admissions and Recruiting, Julie Schellman
Clinical Director, Margaret Riddle
Secretary at the Burns School, Debra Ortlip

LOCATIONS

HQ: COLORADO SEMINARY
  2199 S UNIVERSITY BLVD, DENVER, CO 802104711
Phone: 303 871-2000
Web: WWW.DU.EDU

PRODUCTS/OPERATIONS

Selected Schools and Programs

Undergraduate Schools and Colleges
  Daniels College of Business
  Division of Natural Sciences & Mathematics
  Division of Arts Humanities and Social Sciences
  Josef Korbel School of International Studies
  Morgridge College of Education

School of Engineering and Computer Science
University College
  Women' s College
Graduate and Professional Programs
Daniels College of Business
Divisions of Arts Humanities and Social Sciences
Divisions of Natural Sciences and Mathematics
Graduate School of Professional Psychology (GSPP)
Graduate School of Social Work (GSSW)
Graduate Tax Program
Interdisciplinary Degree Programs
Josef Korbel School of International Studies
Morgridge College of Education (MCE)
School of Engineering and Computer Science
The Sturm College of Law
University College

HISTORICAL FINANCIALS

Company Type: Private

Income Statement

FYE: June 30

	REVENUE ($ mil.)	NET INCOME ($ mil.)	NET PROFIT MARGIN	EMPLOYEES
06/14	396	122	31.0%	2,770
06/12	367	56	15.5%	—
06/11	398	96	24.2%	—
06/10	469	0	—	—
Annual Growth	(4.2%)	—	—	—

2014 Year-End Financials

Return on assets: 17.0%
Return on equity: 31.0%
Current ratio: —

Cash ($ mil.): 58

COLSA CORPORATION

COLSA doesn't mind being called a little defensive. The company provides advanced technology systems and services to US government agencies such as the Missile Defense Agency and NASA. COLSA which specializes in radar and guidance system technology offers services including engineering and testing developing war games simulations analyzing radar technology and virtual prototyping. Its information systems services include integration maintenance and administration for large computer centers. COLSA also offers a software system for nuclear power plants and a gateway for sending simulation data to remote systems. COLSA was founded in 1980.

Geographic Reach

COLSA has offices in Alabama Arizona California Colorado Florida and Washington DC. About a third of COLSA's employees work directly at Redstone Arsenal home to the U.S. Army Aviation and Missile Command the Space and Missile Defense Command and components of the Defense Intelligence Agency and the Missile Defense Agency.

Sales and Marketing

Primarily working with defense agencies COLSA has sought to diversify its client base by adding other government bodies such as the Department of Justice. COLSA also plans to pursue international clients.

EXECUTIVES

Vice President MDA Programs, Jim Hunter
Vice President Advanced Research Center, John (Jack) Welt
Vice President, Penny Chilton

LOCATIONS

HQ: COLSA CORPORATION
6728 ODYSSEY DR NW, HUNTSVILLE, AL 358063305
Phone: 256 964-5555
Web: WWW.COLSA.COM

PRODUCTS/OPERATIONS

Selected Services
Information services
  Computer center design and engineering
  Computer center operation and maintenance
  Information assurance/security
Programmatic support
  Acquisition management
  Independent assessment
  Test support
System engineering
  Configuration management
  Modeling and simulation
  Software engineering
  Test engineering
  Testbed design development and operation
System integration
  Command control communications computers and
  intel (C4I) systems
  Hardware/software systems
  Security systems

COMPETITORS

CACI International	Northrop Grumman
Computer Sciences	Raytheon
Corp.	SM&A
HP Enterprise Services	UNICOM Government

HISTORICAL FINANCIALS

Company Type: Private

Income Statement
FYE: December 31

	REVENUE ($ mil.)	NET INCOME ($ mil.)	NET PROFIT MARGIN	EMPLOYEES
12/13	201	15	7.9%	890
12/12	186	11	5.9%	—
12/11	152	11	7.8%	—
12/10	155	0	—	—
Annual Growth	8.9%	—	—	—

2013 Year-End Financials

Return on assets: 10.2%   Cash ($ mil.): 14
Return on equity: 7.9%
Current ratio: 1.70

COLUMBIA COLLEGE CHICAGO

Columbia College Chicago revels in its creative reputation. Specializing in arts and media the private not-for-profit school offers undergraduate and graduate degrees in the visual performing media and communication arts. The college offers more than 120 academic programs including architecture and interior design photography dance television theater film music composition journalism and marketing communications. Comedian Andy Richter and Wheel of Fortune host Pat Sajak are among the school's notable alumni. Founded in 1890 as the Columbia School of Oratory the college is located in several buildings in downtown Chicago and has about 12000 students. Average teacher to student ratio is 20:1.

Geographic Reach

Internationally-recognized Columbia College Chicago's student enrollment consists of students from all 50 states and more than 40 foreign nations. Its urban campus is located in Chicago's South Loop.

Operations

Columbia College Chicago welcomed a newly-constructed academic building in 2010. The Media Production Center includes a pair of sound stages a motion-capture studio an animation lab and classrooms. The college added the center to meet the demands of its more popular fields of study. Indeed its most popular majors include Film & Video Art & Design and Arts Entertainment & Media Management in that order.

Many of the college's students live on campus. About 2200 students live in four residence centers helping to make Columbia the second-largest college for out-of-state students in Illinois. The college pays the Education Advancement Fund (EAF) a corporation owned by Columbia College Chicago and two other Chicago educational institutions to develop operate and own the University Center of Chicago (UCC) about $11.5 million (including $3 million for its share of the residential life and meal plan expenses) toward its maximum rental liability in connection with its lease of 824 beds in fiscal year 2013. The UCC is managed by an international real estate management firm with the firm's chairman and CEO serving as a college board member.

Financial Performance

Rising tuition and fees (net of tuition allowances) and student housing (net of room allowances) as well as government grants and contracts all contributed to Columbia College Chicago's 2% revenue rise in fiscal 2012 as compared to 2011. Net income during the same reporting period dropped some 47% due to disappointing investment returns capital gifts for facilities and collections and expenses related to recognition of change in pension-funded status. StrategyThe school is wrapping up a $100 million campaign that consisted of three parts: student scholarships support of building projects and endowment-building. Its top priority has been student scholarships. While the school focused on maintaining manageable costs its tuition still remains relatively high.

EXECUTIVES

Vice Chair And Senior Vice President, Warren K Chapman
Assistant Vice President For Budget Management Academic Affairs, David (Dave) Valadez
Associate Vice President Of Business Affairs, Timothy Bauhs
Assistant To The Provost Provost Senior Vice President, Theodore Harwood
Vice President Of Human Resources, Ellen Ryan
Vice President, Joy Jones
Associate Vice President Of Business Affairs and Contr, Matt Jaehrling
Secretary Fiction Writing, Nicole Chakalis
Secretary, Rayna McKinley

LOCATIONS

HQ: COLUMBIA COLLEGE CHICAGO
600 S MICHIGAN AVE FL 5, CHICAGO, IL 606051996
Phone: 312 663-1600
Web: WWW.COLUM.EDU

PRODUCTS/OPERATIONS

Selected Schools
School of Fine & Performing Arts
School of Liberal Arts & Sciences
School of Media Arts

HISTORICAL FINANCIALS

Company Type: Private

Income Statement
FYE: August 31

	REVENUE ($ mil.)	NET INCOME ($ mil.)	NET PROFIT MARGIN	EMPLOYEES
08/10	244	18	7.6%	1,000
08/09	246	23	9.7%	—
08/08	0	0	—	—
Annual Growth	—	3259.5%	—	—

2010 Year-End Financials

Return on assets: 2.9%   Cash ($ mil.): 32
Return on equity: 7.6%
Current ratio: —

COLUMBIA PROPERTY TRUST INC.

Real estate investment trusts nsk

EXECUTIVES

Pres-ceo, E N Mills
Vice President Controller, Elka Wilson
Auditors: DELOITTE & TOUCHE LLP ATLANTA

LOCATIONS

HQ: COLUMBIA PROPERTY TRUST INC.
1 GLENLAKE PKWY STE 1200, ATLANTA, GA 303287267
Phone: 770 449-7800
Web: WWW.COLUMBIAPROPERTYTRUST.COM

HISTORICAL FINANCIALS

Company Type: Private

Income Statement
FYE: December 31

	REVENUE ($ mil.)	NET INCOME ($ mil.)	NET PROFIT MARGIN	EMPLOYEES
12/14	540	92	17.1%	2
12/13	526	15	3.0%	—
Annual Growth	2.7%	489.3%	—	—

2014 Year-End Financials

Return on assets: 19.7%   Cash ($ mil.): 149
Return on equity: 17.1%
Current ratio: —

COLUMBIA ST MARYS HOSPITAL MILWAUKEE

Auditors: DELOITTE TAX LLP MILWAUKEE W

LOCATIONS

HQ: COLUMBIA ST MARYS HOSPITAL MILWAUKEE
4425 N PORT WASHINGTON RD, GLENDALE, WI
532121082
Phone: 414 326-2230

HISTORICAL FINANCIALS

Company Type: Private

Income Statement				FYE: June 30
	REVENUE ($ mil.)	NET INCOME ($ mil.)	NET PROFIT MARGIN	EMPLOYEES
06/13	440	4	1.0%	—
06/11	493	(29)	—	—
06/10	548	(0)	—	—
Annual Growth	(7.0%)	—	—	—

2013 Year-End Financials

Return on assets: 5.5%   Cash ($ mil.): —
Return on equity: 1.0%
Current ratio: 2.70

COMMAND TRANSPORTATION LLC

LOCATIONS

HQ: COMMAND TRANSPORTATION LLC
7500 FRONTAGE RD, SKOKIE, IL 600773213
Phone: 847 213-2200
Web: WWW.COMMANDTRANSPORTATION.COM

HISTORICAL FINANCIALS

Company Type: Private

Income Statement				FYE: December 31
	REVENUE ($ mil.)	NET INCOME ($ mil.)	NET PROFIT MARGIN	EMPLOYEES
12/13	405	11	2.9%	550
12/12	329	13	4.1%	—
12/08	157	6	3.9%	—
12/07	101	0	—	—
Annual Growth	26.0%	—	—	—

2013 Year-End Financials

Return on assets: —   Cash ($ mil.): 5
Return on equity: 2.9%
Current ratio: 6.80

COMMUNITY ASPHALT CORP.

Community Asphalt provides paving services for the road more traveled. The company's services include grading and paving pavement milling surveying excavation on- and off-road hauling drainage utilities base finishing and highway sweeping. It also provides engineering contracting and design/build services; projects include parking lots industrial and retail complexes auto race tracks and airport runways. Formed in 1980 Community Asphalt has three asphalt plants in southeastern Florida. It also operates a limestone quarry and a fleet of dump trucks. In 2006 Community Asphalt

and Spain's Obrasc n Huarte Lain (OHL) made a stock purchase agreement which gave OHL a controlling interest in the company.

EXECUTIVES

Vice President General Manager West Palm Beach, John (Jack) Morris
Vice President Operations, Victor Marimon
Vice President and General Manager Vero, Brian Beetle
Vice President, Vivian Marimon
Auditors: DELOITTE & TOUCHE LLP BOCA RA

LOCATIONS

HQ: COMMUNITY ASPHALT CORP.
9675 NW 117TH AVE STE 108, MEDLEY, FL
331781244
Phone: 305 884-9444
Web: WWW.CACORP.NET

COMPETITORS

Angelo Iafrate
Baker Concrete
Boh Bros Construction
C.W. Matthews
Cherry Hill Construction
Megatran
Oldcastle Materials
The Middlesex Corporation

HISTORICAL FINANCIALS

Company Type: Private

Income Statement				FYE: December 31
	REVENUE ($ mil.)	NET INCOME ($ mil.)	NET PROFIT MARGIN	EMPLOYEES
12/13	208	(4)	—	640
12/12	243	2	1.0%	—
12/11	260	3	1.2%	—
12/10	330	0	—	—
Annual Growth	(14.2%)	—	—	—

2013 Year-End Financials

Return on assets: —   Cash ($ mil.): 39
Return on equity: (-2.1%)
Current ratio: 0.60

COMMUNITY CARE INC.

Auditors: MCGLADREY LLP MADISON WI

LOCATIONS

HQ: COMMUNITY CARE INC.
1555 S LAYTON BLVD, MILWAUKEE, WI 532151924
Phone: 414 902-2526
Web: WWW.COMMUNITYCAREINC.ORG

HISTORICAL FINANCIALS

Company Type: Private

Income Statement				FYE: December 31
	REVENUE ($ mil.)	NET INCOME ($ mil.)	NET PROFIT MARGIN	EMPLOYEES
12/13	351	4	1.4%	700
12/12	333	11	3.3%	—
12/11	322	11	3.4%	—
12/10	341	0	—	—
Annual Growth	0.9%	—	—	—

2013 Year-End Financials

Return on assets: 2.7%   Cash ($ mil.): 52
Return on equity: 1.4%
Current ratio: 5.10

COMMUNITY HEALTH CHOICE INC

Auditors: DELOITTE TAX LLP HOUSTON TX

LOCATIONS

HQ: COMMUNITY HEALTH CHOICE INC
2636 S LOOP W STE 700, HOUSTON, TX 770545630
Phone: 713 295-2200
Web: WWW.CHCHEALTH.ORG

HISTORICAL FINANCIALS

Company Type: Private

Income Statement				FYE: December 31
	REVENUE ($ mil.)	NET INCOME ($ mil.)	NET PROFIT MARGIN	EMPLOYEES
12/12	637	(17)	—	85
12/09	425	9	2.2%	—
Annual Growth	14.5%	—	—	—

2012 Year-End Financials

Return on assets: —   Cash ($ mil.): 125
Return on equity: (-2.7%)
Current ratio: 1.70

COMMUNITY HEALTH NETWORK INC.

Community Hospitals of Indiana (aka Community Health Network) has Indianapolis surrounded. The health care system includes about a half a dozen acute-care hospitals all operating under the Community Hospital moniker. One Community Hospital Anderson is located outside the state capital. It also runs the Community Heart and Vascular Hospital. Community Health Network whose origin reaches back to the 1950s has a total of about 1080 staffed beds and 1400-plus physicians. The network also includes more than 100 community care sites including physician practices community clinics surgery centers occupational health facilities a rehabilitation center and home health practices.

Operations

Together with its clinics health pavilions surgery centers and physician affiliations Community Health Network's service area covers an eight-county area in central Indiana. Various specialty centers treat digestive and joint ailments wounds spinal problems and gastrointestinal disease and also provide imaging services. Community's Med-Check clinics offer routine checkups and screenings in stand-alone locations while its MedCheck Express locations inside area Wal-Mart stores serve customers where they shop. Four Wellspring pharmacies all but one of which are located inside hospitals cover prescriptions patient education and wellness programs.

Among the system's notable features the Community Heart and Vascular Hospital (formerly Indiana Heart Hospital) which opened its doors in 2003 is an all-digital facility with digital equipment and wireless communications systems linking all its operations. Additionally the 42-bed neonatal intensive care room at Community Hospital North is one of the nation's largest labor delivery recovery and postpartum units and Westview Hospital is the state's only such facility offering osteopathic services.

Strategy

The health network is expanding in and around Indianapolis. In 2012 Community Healthcare Network (CHN) partnered with Johnson Memorial Hospital to build a $14 million70000-square-foot three-story medical facility Stones Crossing Health Pavilion which will house many outpatient services. The pavilion will also offer primary and specialty care physicians rehab and sports medicine services (including adult and pediatric rehabilitation) and lab services. The facility is scheduled to open in the summer of 2013. In 2011 CHN partnered with Centerre Healthcare of Nashville Tennessee to build a $23 million inpatient rehabilitation hospital in northeast Indianapolis. The new 63000-square-foot 60-bed facility is designed to serve the medical rehabilitation needs of neurological stroke and traumatic injury patients. Community's inpatient rehabilitation program Hook Rehabilitation will move its services and staff to the new rehabilitation hospital closing the unit located within Community Hospital East. The move will allow Community East to streamline operations and focus on its core services: emergency care cardiovascular and stroke care surgical services and the Center for Joint Health. The hospital is expected to open by mid-2013.

EXECUTIVES

President and CEO Community Health Network, William E. (Bill) Corley, age 72

President and CEO Community Hospital Anderson, William C. (Bill) VanNess

President CEO of the network, Bryan A. Mills

President Community Hospital North, Barbara (Barb) Summers

CEO, Timothy L. Hobbs

CEO The Indiana Heart Hospital, Thomas A. Malasto

CEO Community Home Health Services, Jessie Westlund

President Community Hospital East, Robin Ledyard

President Community Hospital South, Anthony Lennen

President and CEO, Beth Tharp

Chief Information Officer, Ron Strachan

CFO, Joe Kessler

COO, Tony Javorka

Vice President Information Technology, Cindy Reese

Vice President of Medical Affairs, James (Jamie) Williams

Executive Vice President Of Behavioral Health, Suzanne Clifford

Vice President Revenue Cycle Management, Charles Meadows

Regional Vice President, Myron Lewis

Regional President, Jason Fahrlander

Vice President Heart And Vascular Services, Pam London

Director Of Nursing, Michael Kuhn

Medical Director Critical Care, Robert (Bob) Joseph

Senior Vice President and Head Human Resources, Jeffrey (Jeff) Purkey

Clinical Director, Rhea Oliver

Medical Director, Eric Vonderohe

Pharmacy Residency Program Director Pharmd Bcps, Tracy Sprunger

Clinical Director, Elsie Broda

Medical Director, Brian Foley

Vice President, Anne Murphy

Vice President Clinical Development Oncology, William (Bill) Fisher

Medical Director Department Of Radiology, Todd Harris

Network Vice President Ambulatory Development, Jon Fohrer

Network Vice President Legal Services General Counsel, Karen Ann Lloyd

Director of Nursing, Marsa Clendenen

Clinical Director, James (Jamie) Kluzinski

Clinical Director Behavioral Health, Karla Kirby

Clinical Director Adult Behavioral Care Services, Barbara (Barb) Selvey

Network Vice President Quality Resources Risk Management, Jean Putnam

Vice President Patient Services and CNE, Pamela (Pam) Hunt

Vice President of Nursing, Paige Dooley

Vice President, Susan (Sue) Sandberg

Vice President Integrated Support Services for Community, Sherry Sidwell

Board Member, Karen Waninger

Secretary Treasurer, Sachin Dave

LOCATIONS

HQ: COMMUNITY HEALTH NETWORK INC.
7330 SHADELAND STA # 200, INDIANAPOLIS, IN 462563957
Phone: 317 621-1085
Web: WWW.ECOMMUNITY.COM

PRODUCTS/OPERATIONS

Selected Facilities and Affiliates
Community Health Pavilions
Community Heart and Vascular Hospital
Community Hospital Anderson
Community Hospital East
Community Hospital North
Community Hospital South
Community Imaging Centers
Community Physicians of Indiana network
Community Spine Center
Community Westview Hospital
Hook Rehabilitation Center
Indiana Surgery Centers
Indianapolis Endoscopy Center
MedCheck walk-in clinics
MedCheck Express clinics
Wellspring Pharmacy chain

COMPETITORS

Ball Memorial Hospital	Riverview Hospital
Henry County Memorial Hospital	St. Elizabeth Regional Health
IU Health	St. Vincent Health
IU Health Bloomington Hospital	Wabash County Hospital
Memorial Hospital (Logansport)	

HISTORICAL FINANCIALS

Company Type: Private

Income Statement

FYE: December 31

	REVENUE ($ mil.)	NET INCOME ($ mil.)	NET PROFIT MARGIN	EMPLOYEES
12/13	1,763	179	10.2%	5,000
12/12	384	44	11.7%	—
12/09	679	35	5.2%	—
12/08	337	0	—	—
Annual Growth	39.2%	—	—	—

2013 Year-End Financials

Return on assets: 4.1%
Return on equity: 10.2%
Current ratio: 1.30

Cash ($ mil.): 253

COMMUNITY HEALTH SYSTEM

Munroe Regional Health System operates the Munroe Regional Medical Center and affiliated facilities serving residents of north central Florida's Marion County and surrounding areas. Munroe Regional Medical Center is a 500-bed acute care hospital that offers comprehensive medical surgical and emergency care along with programs devoted to cardiovascular care stroke prevention and care orthopedics and women's health. The hospital is operated under a lease agreement with the Marion County Hospital District. Munroe Regional Health System also provides home health services and operates outpatient clinics providing primary care diagnostic and rehabilitation therapy services.

Operations

Munroe Regional Medical Center employs some 500 physicians. Its staff members handle more than 22000 inpatient admissions each year as well as 107000 emergency room visits and 55000 outpatient care visits.

Geographic Reach

Munroe Regional Health System serves those who reside in the north central Florida county of Marion as well as its surrounding areas.

Financial Performance

The system reported a 5% increase in revenue due to higher surgical procedures outpatient visits and emergency room visits. Higher operating expenses and a drop in investment returns lead to a small loss.

Strategy

Munroe Regional Health System has expanded its services by partnering with other health care providers and by forming strategic joint ventures. Such partners include Clinical Lab Solutions Heart of Florida Health Center Medical Imaging Center Munroe HealthCare TimberRidge Imaging Center TimberRidge Nursing and Rehabilitation and Women's Imaging Center.

For access to four additional operating rooms a pair of procedure rooms and a 6% market share Munroe Regional Health System in 2013 acquired a 20% stake in Surgery Center of Ocala. The surgery center which performs some 4200 procedures each year benefits as well from the health system's greater purchasing power for its supplies and medicine.

In mid-2013 hospital operator Health Management Associates (HMA) announced that it entered a letter of intent to lease and operate the Munroe Regional organization. If successful the agreement would bring Munroe Regional under HMA's clinical affiliation with the University of Florida Shands Hospital. Munroe Regional would continue to operate under the guidance of a local board of trustees.

EXECUTIVES

SVP and COO, Paul Clark

Interim President & CEO, Richard D. (Rich) Mutarelli

VP and CIO, Carl Candullo Jr.

President and CEO, Stephen A. (Steve) Purves, age 58

Vice President Human Resources, Dan O'Connor

VP Strategic Planning and Marketing, Mike G. Robertson

VP and Chief Nursing Officer, Pam Michell

Senior Vice President Physician Services, Marc J. Miller

SVP Medical Affairs and Chief Quality Officer, Lon McPherson

Vice President Human Resources, Dan OConnor
Vice President Finance, Rhonda Kautz
Chairman, Ron Ewers
Vice Chairman, Charles Dassance
Senior Vice President of Medical Affairs & Chief Quality Officer, Lon H. McPherson

LOCATIONS

HQ: COMMUNITY HEALTH SYSTEM
1500 SW 1ST AVE, OCALA, FL 344716504
Phone: 352 351-7200
Web: WWW.MUNROEREGIONAL.COM

PRODUCTS/OPERATIONS

Selected Specialties
Bariatrics
Critical Care
Emergency Care including Children' s Express
Intermediate Care
Invasive Cardiology
LifeTime Center
Maternal Child Health
Midwifery Services
Neurology
Orthopedics
Surgical Services
Telemetry
Urology

COMPETITORS

Adventist Health System Sunbelt Healthcare
Baptist Health South Florida
Baptist Health System
Bay Medical Center
Florida Hospital Heartland
HCA
Jackson County Hospital of Florida
Kindred Healthcare
Mount Sinai Medical Center of Florida
Orlando Health
Tallahassee Memorial HealthCare
UF&Shands

HISTORICAL FINANCIALS

Company Type: Private

Income Statement

FYE: September 30

	REVENUE ($ mil.)	NET INCOME ($ mil.)	NET PROFIT MARGIN	EMPLOYEES
09/09	313	(7)	—	2,179
09/08	312	(3)	—	—
09/06	263	4	1.5%	—
09/05	267	0	—	—
Annual Growth	4.0%	—	—	—

2009 Year-End Financials

Return on assets: —   Cash ($ mil.): 52
Return on equity: (-2.4%)
Current ratio: 0.60

COMMUNITY HOSPITAL OF THE MONTEREY PENINSULA

Community Hospital of the Monterey Peninsula has a sunny disposition when it comes to medical care. The not-for-profit health care facility provides general medical and surgical services to residents of Monterey California. It has about 235 acute care and skilled nursing beds and offers specialty services including cardiac and cancer care obstetrics orthopedics and rehabilitation. In addition to its main facility the hospital operates several ancillary centers including a mental health clinic an inpatient hospice medical laboratory branches and several outpatient centers offering diagnostic imaging diabetes care and other services.

Geographic Reach

The company has facilities in Carmel Marina Monterey and Seaside counties in California.

Operations

Community Hospital offers a broad range of healthcare services at 15 locations including the main hospital outpatient facilities satellite laboratories a mental health clinic a short-term skilled nursing facility Hospice of the Central Coast and business offices.

In 2012 the hospital systems served 12130 inpatients in 2012. It also had 49565 emergency visits 283181 outpatient visits and assisted in 1193 births.

Financial Performance

Medicare accounted for 53% of Community Hospital of the Monterey Peninsula's revenues in 2012; commercial insurance 23% and Medi-Cal 10%.

Strategy

To improve care in its service territory the hospital is working to increase best-practice sharing among physicians. It is also supporting information sharing by coordinating electronic health records (EHRs).

In 2014 the hospital received a $200000 contribution from the Auxiliary of Community Hospital of the Monterey Peninsula completing a five-year $1 million pledge by the service organization to support the hospital.

Company Background

As health care costs skyrocket in the US Community Hospital of the Monterey Peninsula has worked to lower its expenses. Between 2008 and 2011 the organization lowered annual costs by about $44 million.

Community Hospital of the Monterey Peninsula was founded in 1934.

EXECUTIVES

Vice President Nursing, Terril Lowe

LOCATIONS

HQ: COMMUNITY HOSPITAL OF THE MONTEREY PENINSULA
23625 HOLMAN HWY, MONTEREY, CA 939405902
Phone: 831 624-5311
Web: WWW.CHOMP.ORG

PRODUCTS/OPERATIONS

Selected Community Hospital Service Locations
Community Hospital of the Monterey Peninsula: Monterey
Carol Hatton Breast Care Center: Monterey
Development/Patient Business Services: Monterey
Hartnell Professional Center: Monterey Peninsula
Primary Care/Satellite Laboratory: Carmel
Peninsula Wellness Center: Marina
Ryan Ranch Outpatient Campus: Monterey
Seaside Satellite Laboratory: Seaside
Westland House: Monterey

Selected Services
Bariatric Surgery
Behavioral Health Services
Carol Hatton Breast Care Center
Comprehensive Cancer Center
Diabetes
Diagnostic and Interventional Radiology
Emergency
Family Birth Center
Hospice of the Central Coast
Intermediate Intensive Care Nursery
Laboratory Services
Nutrition Therapy Program
Orthopedics
Outpatient Immunology Services
Outpatient Surgery Center
Pulmonary Wellness Services
Radiation Oncology
Rehabilitation Services
Sleep disorders
Social Services
Stroke Program
Tyler Heart Institute (Cardiac Care)
Westland House Skilled Nursing Facility
Wound Care and Hyperbaric Healing

COMPETITORS

Dignity Health
John Muir Health
Queen of the Valley Medical Center
Salinas Valley Memorial
Sequoia Healthcare District
Stanford Hospital and Clinics
Sutter Health
The Palo Alto Medical Foundation
UCSF Medical

HISTORICAL FINANCIALS

Company Type: Private

Income Statement

FYE: December 31

	REVENUE ($ mil.)	NET INCOME ($ mil.)	NET PROFIT MARGIN	EMPLOYEES
12/12	442	81	18.4%	1,947
12/09	475	26	5.6%	—
12/08	406	32	8.0%	—
12/06	373	0	—	—
Annual Growth	2.9%	—	—	—

2012 Year-End Financials

Return on assets: 2.8%   Cash ($ mil.): 70
Return on equity: 18.4%
Current ratio: 1.70

COMMUNITY MEMORIAL HEALTH SYSTEM

Auditors: ERNST & YOUNG US LLP SAN DIEG

LOCATIONS

HQ: COMMUNITY MEMORIAL HEALTH SYSTEM
147 N BRENT ST, VENTURA, CA 930032809
Phone: 805 652-5011
Web: WWW.CMHSHEALTH.ORG

HISTORICAL FINANCIALS

Company Type: Private

Income Statement

FYE: December 31

	REVENUE ($ mil.)	NET INCOME ($ mil.)	NET PROFIT MARGIN	EMPLOYEES
12/13	320	24	7.7%	2,200
12/09	279	9	3.4%	—
12/04	167	4	2.9%	—
12/02	51	0	—	—
Annual Growth	18.0%	—	—	—

2013 Year-End Financials

Return on assets: 15.7%   Cash ($ mil.): 12
Return on equity: 7.7%
Current ratio: 0.20

COMPASSION INTERNATIONAL INC

Auditors: CAPIN CROUSE LLP GREENWOOD I

LOCATIONS

HQ: COMPASSION INTERNATIONAL INC
12290 VOYAGER PKWY, COLORADO SPRINGS, CO
809213694
Phone: 719 487-7000
Web: WWW.COMPASSION.COM

HISTORICAL FINANCIALS

Company Type: Private

Income Statement
FYE: June 30

	REVENUE ($ mil.)	NET INCOME ($ mil.)	NET PROFIT MARGIN	EMPLOYEES
06/14	719	8	1.2%	1,000
06/13	659	15	2.3%	—
06/12	598	13	2.3%	—
06/11	551	0	—	—
Annual Growth	9.2%	—	—	—

2014 Year-End Financials

Return on assets: 2.6%   Cash ($ mil.): 96
Return on equity: 1.2%
Current ratio: 1.50

CONCORD HOSPITAL INC.

Concord Hospital is agreeably an acute care regional hospital serving central New Hampshire. The hospital has some 300 licensed beds and provides general inpatient and outpatient medical care as well as specialist centers for cardiology orthopedics cancer care urology and women's health. Concord Hospital operates other medical facilities either on its main campus or nearby including surgery imaging diagnostic hospice and rehabilitation facilities as well as physician practice locations. With roots reaching back to 1884 Concord Hospital is part of the Capital Region Health Care system which also offers mental health and home health care services.

Operations

With a staff of some 350 doctors Concord Hospital sees about 18000 patients (including some 9000 rehabilitation patients) performs more than 9600 surgeries and handles about 65000 emergency room visits and 1200 births each year. The hospital provides services in about 40 specialty medical fields.

As part of Capital Region Health Care Concord Hospital shares education purchasing and outpatient service functions (and expenses) with its network sister entities which include the Concord Regional Visiting Nurse Association and the Riverbend Community Mental Health center. Through Capital Regional Health Care Concord Hospital also has affiliations with area organizations including Dartmouth-Hitchcock Medical Center Concord Ambulatory Center and Concord Imaging Center.

Concord Hospital is also part of a collaborative network the Granite Healthcare Network with four regional New Hampshire health care providers: Elliot Health System (which operates the Elliot Hospital) LRGHealthcare (consisting of Lakes Region General Hospital and Franklin Regional Hospital) Southern New Hampshire Health System (operating the Southern New Hampshire Medical Center) and Wentworth-Douglass Hospital. Hospitals in the network remain independently managed and owned and have the option to participate or not participate in each of the group efforts.

Geographic Reach

Concord Hospital is located on a 110-acre campus in Concord New Hampshire. It provides services in area communities including Allenstown Andover Barnstead Boscawen Bow Bradford Canterbury Chichester Deering Dunbarton Epsom Henniker Hillsboro Hopkinton Loudon Northwood Pembroke Pittsfield Salsibury Warner Washington Weare Webster and Windsor.

Sales and Marketing

Medicare and Medicaid accounted for some 27% and 3% of net patient revenues respectively in 2014.

Financial Performance

Annual operating revenues increased 3% to some $440 million due to higher net patient revenues in 2014. However net income fell 72% to $18 million due to factors including loss from pension adjustments and declines in net unrealized gains. Cash flow from operations rose 14% to $32 million as less cash was used in accounts receivable and towards supplies and other assets.

Strategy

To help control the spiraling costs of medical care in the US as well as to meet health reform mandates Concord and its affiliated facilities are launching programs to share technology and administrative resources such as claims management software data storage linen service liability insurance pooling and Medicare patient management. Concord Hospital has also launched independent initiatives to improve quality and patient safety programs including putting infection reduction protocols in place consolidating electronic health record (EHR) consolidation efforts and enacting medication management practices.

EXECUTIVES

Vice President Community Affairs, Pamela (Pam) Puleo
Vice President Physician Services, Marjo Mitchell
Director of Pharmacy; Director of Pharmacy Services; Marketing Director, David (Dave) Depiero
Vice President Acute Care Nursing, Jean Tenhaken
Vice President finance, Scott Sloane
Director Of Health Information Medical Records Director, Jodi Panzino
Vice President Acute Care Nursing, Jean T Haken
Respiratory Therapy Director, Doug Hall
Vice President of Medical Records, Mark Carwell
Vice President Operations Cno, Diane Allen
Secretary And Treasurer Medical Staff, Lisa Atkinson
Treasurer, Michael Schuman
Auditors: BAKER NEWMAN NOYES MANCHESTER

LOCATIONS

HQ: CONCORD HOSPITAL INC.
250 PLEASANT ST, CONCORD, NH 033012598
Phone: 603 227-7000
Web: WWW.CONCORDHOSPITAL.ORG

PRODUCTS/OPERATIONS

2014 Sales

	% of total
Net patient service revenue	93
Other revenue	6
Disproportionate share revenue	1
Net assets released from restrictions for operations	-
Total	**100**

Selected Services

Ambulatory Care Center
Behavioral Health
Breast Care Center
Cancer
Cardiac
Center for Health Promotion
Child Life
Clinical Decision Unit
Day Surgery Center
Diabetes Self-Management Education
Concord Hospital Medical Group
Emergency Services
End Of Life
Family Health Centers
Infectious Disease
Intensive Care
Laboratory Services
Maternity
Neurology
Occupational Health
Orthopedics
Pediatrics
Primary Care
Radiology
Rehabilitation
Sleep Center
Surgery
Urology
Walk-in Urgent Care
Women's Health
Wound Care

COMPETITORS

Cambridge Health Alliance	Frisbie Memorial Hospital
Catholic Medical Center	HCA Partners HealthCare
Elliot Health System	Southern New Hampshire Medical Center
Exeter Health Resources	Steward Health Care

HISTORICAL FINANCIALS

Company Type: Private

Income Statement
FYE: September 30

	REVENUE ($ mil.)	NET INCOME ($ mil.)	NET PROFIT MARGIN	EMPLOYEES
09/13	371	11	3.0%	2,000
09/10	369	18	5.1%	—
09/09	349	0	—	—
09/08	1,823	0	—	—
Annual Growth	—	—	—	—

2013 Year-End Financials

Return on assets: 5.5%   Cash ($ mil.): 24
Return on equity: 3.0%
Current ratio: 1.00

CONCORDIA UNIVERSITY

Auditors: MOSS ADAMS LLP PORTLAND OREG

LOCATIONS

HQ: CONCORDIA UNIVERSITY
2811 NE HOLMAN ST, PORTLAND, OR 972116099
Phone: 503 288-9371
Web: WWW.CU-PORTLAND.EDU

HISTORICAL FINANCIALS
Company Type: Private

Income Statement
FYE: April 30

	REVENUE ($ mil.)	NET INCOME ($ mil.)	NET PROFIT MARGIN	EMPLOYEES
04/13*	512	(44)	—	180
06/12	44	2	4.5%	—
06/11	40	3	8.8%	—
06/10	39	0	—	—
Annual Growth	135.9%	—	—	—

*Fiscal year change

2013 Year-End Financials
Return on assets: —
Return on equity: (-8.6%)
Current ratio: 0.10
Cash ($ mil.): —

CONNECTICUT CHILDREN'S MEDICAL CENTER

When their tiny tykes need some TLC Nutmeg Staters turn to Connecticut Children's Medical Center (CCMC). The 190-bed children's hospital is located on two campuses and provides a variety of pediatric services including surgery behavioral care and emergency medicine. Its facilities house pediatric trauma and intensive care units that receives referral patients from hospitals throughout the region. The medical center also conducts clinical research and provides pediatric training to health professionals. In addition CCMC operates outpatient facilities throughout Connecticut and a school for children with physical and behavioral challenges.

Operations

At its main campus CCMC employs 1100 medical professionals practicing in more than 30 specialty care fields. The hospital handles about 6500 inpatient admissions more than 55000 emergency department visits and 10000 surgeries. The medical center also operates the Faculty Practice Plan an integrated full-service multi-specialty pediatric practice providing care to children and their families. The practice employs about 170 physicians and mid-level practitioners.

Founded in 1996 CCMC is the only academic medical center dedicated exclusively to pediatric care in western New England making it a popular destination for medical training and research program participants. As the primary teaching facility for the University of Connecticut School of Medicine's Department of Pediatrics the hospital is home to a number of clinical research and physician training programs including several two-year fellowships in pediatric subspecialties and a three-year fellowship in pediatric emergency medicine. Other hospital divisions conduct clinical trials in fields including oncology hematology endocrinology gastroenterology and infectious disease.

Geographic Reach

CCMC operates about 20 locations across Connecticut and portions of Massachusetts. Its main hospital campus is in Hartford while its secondary acute care center is in Waterbury (on the campus of Saint Mary's Hospital). Other locations include ambulatory surgery specialty care and general pediatric care offices.

Strategy

CCMC grows by expanding its facilities and its range of patient services. It also strives to expand its services into new territories in southern New England including through partnerships with other area health care providers. In addition the medical center is working to increase its participation in basic and clinical research programs.

It expanded facilities by opening a new 18000-square-foot day surgery center with state of the art facilities. Plans are underway for a new Cardiovascular Care Center for children.

EXECUTIVES
Executive Vice President And Chief Operating Officer, Theresa Hendricksen
Director Of Nursing, Gail Karas
Auditors: ERNST & YOUNG LLP HARTFORD C

LOCATIONS
HQ: CONNECTICUT CHILDREN' S MEDICAL CENTER
282 WASHINGTON ST, HARTFORD, CT 061063322
Phone: 860 545-9000
Web:
WWW.CONNECTICUTCHILDRENSFOUNDATION.ORG

PRODUCTS/OPERATIONS
Selected Programs & Services
Acute Inpatient Rehabilitation
Adolescent Health
Asthma Center
Audiology
Bereavement
Cardiology
Cardiovascular Surgery
CCMC School
Center for Motion Analysis
Child and Family Support
Child Health Data Center
Child Protection
Childhood Injury Prevention
Childhood Obesity Awareness and Prevention
Clinical Nutrition
Craniofacial
Critical Care/Pediatric Intensive Care
Cyto-Genetics and Genetic Testing
Day Surgery
Dentistry
Developmental and Behavioral Pediatrics
Diagnostic Cardiology
Digestive Diseases Hepatology and Nutrition
Ear Nose and Throat
Echocardiography
EKG
Emergency Medicine
Emergency Psychiatry
Endocrinology and Diabetes
Feeding
Food Allergy
Genetics
General Surgery
Gynecology
Hand Surgery
Hematology and Oncology
High Risk Infant Follow Up
HIV
Infectious Diseases
Inpatient Medicine
Lead Prevention
Neonatology
Nephrology
Neurogenetics
Neurology
Neurophysiology Lab (EEG)
Neurophysiology - Video Telemetry
Neurosurgery
Occupational Therapy
Ophthalmology
Oral and Maxillofacial Surgery
Organ Transplantation Care
Orthopaedics
Orthotics and Prosthetics
Otolaryngology
Pain Medicine
Pediatric Medicine

Pediatric Pathology
Physical Therapy
Plastic Surgery
Primary Care
Pro-Kids: Primary Care for substance abuse exposed infants
Psychiatry/Psychology
Pulmonary Medicine
Pulmonary Function and Exercise Lab
Radiology
Rehabilitation Medicine
Research
Respiratory Care
Rheumatology
Sleep Diagnostic Laboratory
Special Kids Support Center
Speech-Language Pathology
Sports Medicine
Sports Physical Therapy
TEAM Club: weight management
Trauma Program - Video Telemetry
Urology

COMPETITORS
Backus
Baystate Health
Baystate Medical Center
Bridgeport Hospital
Bristol Hospital
Day Kimball Hospital
Griffin Health
Harrington Memorial Hospital
Hartford Health Care
Lawrence & Memorial Hospital
MidState Medical Center
New Milford Hospital
Saint Francis Hospital and Medical Center
St. Vincent' s Health Services
Yale-New Haven Hospital
Yale-New Haven Hospital Saint Raphael Campus

HISTORICAL FINANCIALS
Company Type: Private

Income Statement
FYE: September 30

	REVENUE ($ mil.)	NET INCOME ($ mil.)	NET PROFIT MARGIN	EMPLOYEES
09/13	264	(2)	—	1,117
09/10	210	10	4.8%	—
09/09	192	6	3.6%	—
09/08	1,415	0	—	—
Annual Growth	—	—	—	—

2013 Year-End Financials
Return on assets: 20.0%
Return on equity: (-1.1%)
Current ratio: 0.20
Cash ($ mil.): 1

CONNECTICUT STATE UNIVERSITY SYSTEM

The Connecticut State University System (CSUS) is the largest public university system in Connecticut and consists of four universities –Central Connecticut State University Eastern Connecticut State University Southern Connecticut State University and Western Connecticut State University. CSUS has an enrollment of more than 36000 students and its schools offer undergraduate and graduate degrees in some 180 subjects. Programs include courses in liberal arts sciences (including meteorology) business nursing education and technology. CSUS traces its roots to 1849 when Central Connecticut State University was founded. It is part of the broader Connecticut State Colleges & Universities (ConnSCU) system.

Geographic Reach

CSUS has university locations in Danbury New Britain New Haven and Willimantic Connecticut.

Operations

Tuition and fees account for 60% of the CSUS' revenues; the rest come from auxiliary activities grants and other sources.

Altogether the ConnSCU organization includes the four universities of CSUS and some 12 community colleges as well as the Charter Oak State College. ConnSCU entities offer more than 1200 degrees and certificates and enroll some 92000 students.

Financial Performance

Revenue was relatively flat in fiscal 2012 falling less than 1% to some $425.5 million as CSUS saw a decrease in revenue from tuition fees grants contracts and auxiliary activity. Net assets decreased 31% to $38.5 million on lower state appropriations.

Strategy

Originally overseen by a board of trustees in 2011 oversight of CSUS was placed under the Connecticut Board of Regents for Higher Education. The Board of Regents also governs the state's community and technical college system and the state's Charter Oak online college. As part of the coordinated system CSUS has raised its minimum standards for admissions and is collaborating with local school districts to improve high school students' readiness for college. The effort has reduced the number of students requiring remedial classes in core academic areas.

To meet the needs of a changing student population the ConnSCU entities are increasing their online course offerings.

EXECUTIVES

Vice President Facilities Infrastructure, ELAINE CLARK

Vice President For Community Colleges, David Levinson

Vice President For Human Resources, Steve Weinberger

Interim Vice President for Human Resources, Laurie Dunn

Auditors: PRICEWATERHOUSECOOPERS LLP HA

LOCATIONS

HQ: CONNECTICUT STATE UNIVERSITY SYSTEM
39 WOODLAND ST, HARTFORD, CT 061052337
Phone: 860 493-0000
Web: WWW.CT.EDU

HISTORICAL FINANCIALS

Company Type: Private

Income Statement
FYE: June 30

	REVENUE ($ mil.)	NET INCOME ($ mil.)	NET PROFIT MARGIN	EMPLOYEES
06/11	428	55	13.0%	2,800
06/10	413	22	5.5%	—
Annual Growth	3.6%	143.9%	—	—

2011 Year-End Financials
Return on assets: 2.2%
Return on equity: 13.0%
Current ratio: 1.20
Cash ($ mil.): 176

CONNEXUS ENERGY

Connexus Energy connects more Minnesotans to electricity than any other cooperative. The member-owned organization distributes power to more than 127000 customers in the northern suburbs of Minneapolis-St. Paul. Connexus buys its power from generation and transmission cooperative Great River Energy and distributes it through more than 8880 miles of overhead and underground power lines. It also operates 47 electrical substations. Residential customers account for the bulk of sales. The cooperative is governed by a board of directors elected by its members.

Geographic Reach

Connexus Energy's service territory in Minnesota covers parts of Anoka Chisago Hennepin Isanti Ramsey Sherburne and Washington counties.

Financial Performance

Connexus Energy's revenues increased by 6% in 2012 and its net margin by 23%.

Strategy

The member-owned entity is focused on keeping rates affordable. The company also works directly with its members to help them to find better ways to control energy use. In 2012 its programs for residential and commercial members reduced Connexus Energy's wholesale power costs by $1.7 million. The company also gave returned to its members $5.9 million through its Cash Back program.

Company Background

Connexus Energy formerly Anoka Electric Cooperative was founded in 1937 as part of the Franklin D. Roosevelt government's national rural electrification drive.

EXECUTIVES

Executive Vice President Tech corporate, Ken Fiereck

Vice President, John (Jack) Gasal

Auditors: EIDE BAILLY LLP SIOUX FALLS

LOCATIONS

HQ: CONNEXUS ENERGY
14601 RAMSEY BLVD NW, RAMSEY, MN 553036775
Phone: 763 323-2600
Web: WWW.CONNEXUSENERGY.COM

COMPETITORS

ALLETE	Otter Tail
Dakota Electric	

HISTORICAL FINANCIALS

Company Type: Private

Income Statement
FYE: December 31

	REVENUE ($ mil.)	NET INCOME ($ mil.)	NET PROFIT MARGIN	EMPLOYEES
12/13	258	0	—	250
12/10	211	8	4.1%	—
12/09	213	11	5.4%	—
12/08	1,544	0	—	—
Annual Growth	(30.1%)	—	—	—

2013 Year-End Financials
Return on assets: 6.5%
Return on equity: —
Current ratio: 1.90
Cash ($ mil.): —

CONSIGLI CONSTRUCTION CO INC.

LOCATIONS

HQ: CONSIGLI CONSTRUCTION CO INC.
72 SUMNER ST, MILFORD, MA 017571663
Phone: 508 473-2580
Web: WWW.CONSIGLI.COM

HISTORICAL FINANCIALS

Company Type: Private

Income Statement
FYE: December 31

	REVENUE ($ mil.)	NET INCOME ($ mil.)	NET PROFIT MARGIN	EMPLOYEES
12/12	616	34	5.6%	390
12/11	297	12	4.3%	—
12/10	0	0	—	—
12/09	297	0	—	—
Annual Growth	27.5%	—	—	—

2012 Year-End Financials
Return on assets: 15.8%
Return on equity: 5.6%
Current ratio: 0.20
Cash ($ mil.): 29

CONSOLIDATED GRAIN & BARGE COMPANY

Auditors: KPMG LLP NEW ORLEANS LA

LOCATIONS

HQ: CONSOLIDATED GRAIN & BARGE COMPANY
WASHINGTON & WATER ST, WAYNE CITY, IL 62895
Phone: 618 895-2181
Web: WWW.CGB.COM

HISTORICAL FINANCIALS

Company Type: Private

Income Statement
FYE: May 31

	REVENUE ($ mil.)	NET INCOME ($ mil.)	NET PROFIT MARGIN	EMPLOYEES
05/14	7,093	44	0.6%	650
05/12	5,996	50	0.8%	—
05/08	4,386	31	0.7%	—
05/07	2,849	0	—	—
Annual Growth	13.9%	—	—	—

2014 Year-End Financials
Return on assets: 3.2%
Return on equity: 0.6%
Current ratio: 0.40
Cash ($ mil.): 5

CONSUMER PRODUCT DISTRIBUTORS INC.

Consumer Product Distributors helps convenience stores provide convenient services to their customers. The company which operates as J. Polep Distribution Services is a leading wholesale supplier serving more than 4000 convenience retailers in New York Pennsylvania and the New England states. J. Polep distributes a variety of products including cigarettes and other tobacco items candy dairy products frozen foods snack items and general merchandise as well as alcohol and other beverages. As part of its business J. Polep provides merchandising sales and marketing and technology services. The family-owned company was founded as Polep Tobacco in 1898 by Charles Polep.

Geographic Reach

The distribution company serves chain and independent retailers in six New England states as well as New York and Pennsylvania. Its distribution centers are located in Massachusetts Rhode Island and Connecticut.

Operations

Consumer Product Distributors ranks as one of the nation's top 12 convenience store distributors. To support its operations the company supplies customers with products through distribution centers located in Massachusetts (in Chicopee and Woburn) in Rhode Island (in Providence) and in Connecticut (in West Haven).

Mergers and Acquisitions

Company subsidiary Rachael's Food Corporation based in Chicopee Massachusetts entered the meat manufacturing business in late 2012 when the company acquired 122-year-old family-owned Grote and Weigel a hot dog and meat processor based in Bloomfield Connecticut. Soon after Rachael's Food Corporation also purchased family-owned meat processor Mucke's and transferred its operations to the Grote and Weigel unit. The 2012 purchases followed the company's acquisition of Springfield Smoked Fish. The food corporation's facilities are USDA-inspected and HACCP-certified.

EXECUTIVES

President, Jeffrey M. (Jeff) Polep
VP and Manager Information Systems and Technology, Paul Marusek
Vice President Chief Financial Officer, Bill Fitzsimmons
VP Human Resources, Stephen (Steve) Martin
Auditors: MEYERS BROTHERS KALICKA PC

LOCATIONS

HQ: CONSUMER PRODUCT DISTRIBUTORS INC.
705 MEADOW ST, CHICOPEE, MA 010134820
Phone: 413 592-4141
Web: WWW.JPOLEP.COM

PRODUCTS/OPERATIONS

Selected Products
Alcohol
  Spirits
  Wine
Automotive
  Branded Motor Oils
  Mag 1
  Additives
  Cleaning Supplies
Bakery/Pastry
  Rachael's Gourmet
  Mrs. Freshley's
  Dolly Madison

  Bon Appetite
  Bellow's House
  Diana's
  Table Talk
Beverages
  Poland Springs (Nestle Waters)
  Adirondack Soda
  Arizona
  Florida's Natural
  Simply Juices
  Sweet Leaf Tea
  Trade Winds
  Daily Juice

Selected Services
Credit & Return Policy
Management Information Systems
Merchandising Support
Sales and Marketing Support

COMPETITORS

Atlantic Dominion	Harold Levinson
C&S Wholesale	McLane
Core-Mark	SUPERVALU
Eby-Brown	Tripifoods
H. T. Hackney	

HISTORICAL FINANCIALS
Company Type: Private

Income Statement
FYE: September 27

	REVENUE ($ mil.)	NET INCOME ($ mil.)	NET PROFIT MARGIN	EMPLOYEES
09/14	898	2	0.3%	400
09/13	855	2	0.3%	—
09/12*	804	3	0.4%	—
10/11	778	0	—	—
Annual Growth	4.9%	—	—	—

*Fiscal year change

2014 Year-End Financials
Return on assets: 3.7%
Return on equity: 0.3%
Current ratio: 1.60
Cash ($ mil.): —

CONSUMERS UNION OF UNITED STATES INC

Consumers Union of United States (CU) inspires both trust and fear. Best known for publishing Consumer Reports magazine the independent not-for-profit organization also serves as a consumer watchdog through other print publications and the Web (ConsumerReports.org). Its subscription site rates products ranging from candy bars to cars. CU tests and rates thousands of products annually through its National Testing and Research Center. CU accepts no advertising and derives income from the sale of Consumer Reports and other services and from non-commercial contributions grants and fees. CU traces its roots to 1926 when engineer Frederick Schlink organized a "consumer club" to rate products.

Geographic Reach

CU's magazines websites and newsletters have a combined subscription base of more than 8 million.

At its headquarters in Yonkers New York CU houses the Testing and Research Center which consists of 50 labs and offices. The organization also has an Auto Test Center in Connecticut; and three advocacy offices in Washington DC; Austin Texas; and San Francisco California.

Operations

CU testifies before legislative and regulatory entities and files lawsuits on behalf of consumers. The organization is governed by an 18-member board. Board members are elected by CU members and meet three times a year.

Sales and Marketing

The company's major industry markets include energy health care media and safety.

Strategy

To preserve its independence CU does not permit its ratings or comments to be used commercially.

In addition to its Consumer Reports publication CU publishes ShopSmart a magazine aimed at women who want a quick read on consumer items such as food beauty products and home and yard products. CU also covers health information through its ConsumerReportsHealth.org website and the Consumer Reports Health Ratings Center. It has a presence in the blogging world with Consumerist.com which provides snarky coverage of retail markups and shopper complaints. Rounding out its portfolio of offerings the organization delivers ratings of product categories to smart phones via its Consumer Reports Mobile service.

HISTORY

In 1926 engineer Frederick Schlink organized a "consumer club" (in White Plains New York) which distributed lists of recommended and non-recommended products. The lists led to the founding of Consumers' Research and a magazine devoted to testing products.

Schlink moved the group to Washington New Jersey in 1933. In 1935 three employees formed a union. Schlink fired them. Faced with another strike that year Schlink accused the strikers of being "Red" and responded with strikebreakers and armed detectives. The next year the strikers set up their own organization the Consumers Union of United States (CU).

CU's first magazine Consumers Union Reports came out three months later and rated products that the fledgling organization could afford to test such as soap and breakfast cereals. Subsequent issues focused on food and drug regulation and working conditions for women in textile mills.

The organization drew the wrath of both Reader's Digest and Good Housekeeping (which accused it in 1939 of prolonging the Depression). The next year the House Un-American Activities Committee put CU on its list of suspect organizations. CU cut staff and dropped "Union" from its magazine title but circulation remained low until after WWII.

By 1950 however Americans began consuming again helping to boost circulation to almost 400000. During the 1950s CU published a series of reports on the health hazards of smoking.

In 1960 CU helped found the International Organization of Consumers Unions (now Consumers International) to foster the consumer movement worldwide. Rhoda Karpatkin was hired as publisher in 1974. During the 1970s CU established consumer advocacy offices in California Texas and Washington DC.

Recession and an increase in not-for-profit mailing rates caused the organization to lose money in the early 1980s. CU looked to its readers who donated more than $3 million. The organization was hit by a 13-week strike in 1984 by union members calling for more say in management.

In 1996 CU slapped "not acceptable" ratings on the Isuzu Trooper and the Acura SLX. The next year the National Highway Traffic Safety Administration declared that CU's testing procedure of the Trooper was flawed but CU stood by its tests of the vehicle.

CU hit another bump in 1998 when it was compelled to retract a story on the nutritional value of Iams and Eukanuba pet food. Admitting its test results were incorrect CU's retraction of the story was something of a rarity —its last retraction had occurred almost 20 years earlier when the organization retracted a story on condoms.

A legal dispute broke out in 1999 between CU and automakers Isuzu and Suzuki which claimed negative reviews by Consumer Reports constituted defamation. The following year a jury found CU guilty of falsely reporting on the Isuzu but declined to impose fines on the publisher. (Suzuki eventually settled its case out of court in 2004.)

Karpatkin announced she would step down as president in 2001 and was replaced by chairman James Guest. That same year CU agreed to license its content to Internet portal Yahoo! Retailer Sharper Image (later TSIC) sued CU over an article unflattering to the company's popular air purifier device but a judge threw out the suit in late 2004.

In 2006 CU launched ShopSmart a shopping magazine geared at women aged 30 to 45. The next year it launched ConsumerReportsHealth.org and the Consumer Reports Health Ratings Center. In 2009 the company entered the blogging world with Consumerist.com which it purchased from Gawker Media.

The following year it introduced its Consumer Reports Mobile service which delivers product ratings to cell phones. Feats for CU in 2010 include discoveries of a potential safety hazard of Toyota's Lexus GX460 and a signal-loss problem with Apple's phone 4 which resulted in a recall from Toyota and Apple's announcement of a free remedy.

EXECUTIVES

Executive Vice President, Joel Gurin
Vice President and General Manager Magazines and Newsletter Products, Brent Diamond
Vice President Human Resources, Lisa Cribari
Auditors: KPMG LLP NEW YORK NY

LOCATIONS

HQ: CONSUMERS UNION OF UNITED STATES INC
101 TRUMAN AVE, YONKERS, NY 107031057
Phone: 914 378-2000
Web: WWW.CONSUMERSUNION.ORG

PRODUCTS/OPERATIONS

2014 Sales

	$ mil.	% of total
Subscriptions newsstand & other sales	234	90
Contributions	20	8
Net assets released from restrictions	3	1
Other	0	1
Total	**259**	**100**

Content Areas
Autos
Food
Health Care
Money
Phones and Media
Product Safety

Selected Offerings

Magazines and newsletters
  Consumer Reports Magazine
  Consumer Reports Money Advisor (newsletter)
  Consumer Reports on Health (newsletter)
  ShopSmart
Websites
  ConsumerReports.org
  ConsumerReportsHealth.org
  Consumerist.com

COMPETITORS

Better Business Bureaus	National Technical Systems
Hearst Magazines	RELX Group

International Data Group
J.D. Power
Kelley Blue Book
Shopping.com
Trusted Media Brands
Underwriters Labs
Yelp

HISTORICAL FINANCIALS
Company Type: Private

Income Statement
FYE: May 31

	REVENUE ($ mil.)	NET INCOME ($ mil.)	NET PROFIT MARGIN	EMPLOYEES
05/13	259	3	1.4%	480
05/11	252	32	12.9%	—
05/10	242	9	3.7%	—
05/09	1,700	0	—	—
Annual Growth	**(37.5%)**	—	—	—

2013 Year-End Financials

Return on assets: 7.5%   Cash ($ mil.): 21
Return on equity: 1.4%
Current ratio: 0.10

CONTI ENTERPRISES INC.

Conti Enterprises is continuing its tour of duty as a civil and heavy construction firm. Active primarily in the Northeast the company provides construction management general contracting and design/build services for a range of projects including commercial and industrial buildings power plants environmental remediation physical security upgrades and infrastructure such as dams roads bridges and rail systems. The company often participates in public-private partnerships. Clients have included the Army Corps of Engineers the EPA the FAA the Department of Energy Con Edison and Dominion Resources.

Conti Enterprises has entered the renewable energy market in a significant way. In recent years it has formed new firms —Alternity Power Alternity Wind Power and SunDurance Energy —to help customers implement green technologies to develop large-scale wind projects and to develop solar power respectively.

Conti Enterprises traces its roots to a company formed in 1906 by the great-grandfather of current CEO Kurt Conti. The company has offices in Massachusetts New Jersey Pennsylvania and Louisiana as well as in Israel.

EXECUTIVES

President and CEO, Kurt G. Conti
VP Operations, William Picken
EVP Business Development, Jay Price
Auditors: COHN REZNICK LLP EATONTOWN N

LOCATIONS

HQ: CONTI ENTERPRISES INC.
2045 LINCOLN HWY, EDISON, NJ 088173334
Phone: 908 561-9025
Web: WWW.CONTICORP.COM

PRODUCTS/OPERATIONS

Selected Affiliates

Alternity Wind Power (on-site clean energy generation)
Conti Federal Services (federal government contracting)
Conti Power & Industrial (power industry construction services)
Conti of New York LLC
Conti of Pennsylvania
Conti Services LLC (private sector design/build)

Lehigh Fabrication & Precast LLC (precast concrete and metal fabrication)
SunDurance Energy LLC (solar power solutions)

COMPETITORS

Andrew Velez Construction	Burns and Roe
BBL Construction Services	Colas Inc.
Barr & Barr	E.W. Howell
	Judlau Contracting

HISTORICAL FINANCIALS
Company Type: Private

Income Statement
FYE: December 31

	REVENUE ($ mil.)	NET INCOME ($ mil.)	NET PROFIT MARGIN	EMPLOYEES
12/09	198	0	—	250
12/08	198	0	—	—
12/05	123	0	—	—
12/04	115	0	—	—
Annual Growth	**11.4%**	—	—	—

2009 Year-End Financials

Return on assets: 4.1%   Cash ($ mil.): 11
Return on equity: —
Current ratio: 1.50

CONTINUUM ENERGY SERVICES L.L.C.

Auditors: GRANT THORNTON LLP TULSA OK

LOCATIONS

HQ: CONTINUUM ENERGY SERVICES L.L.C.
1323 E 71ST ST STE 300, TULSA, OK 741365068
Phone: 918 492-2840
Web: WWW.SEMINOLEENERGY.COM

HISTORICAL FINANCIALS
Company Type: Private

Income Statement
FYE: December 31

	REVENUE ($ mil.)	NET INCOME ($ mil.)	NET PROFIT MARGIN	EMPLOYEES
12/13	2,092	5	0.2%	159
12/12	1,558	16	1.0%	—
12/11	2,021	26	1.3%	—
12/10	2,009	0	—	—
Annual Growth	**1.4%**	—	—	—

2013 Year-End Financials

Return on assets: —   Cash ($ mil.): 11
Return on equity: 0.2%
Current ratio: 1.00

CONTRACK INTERNATIONAL INC.

LOCATIONS
HQ: CONTRACK INTERNATIONAL INC.
6862 ELM ST STE 500, MC LEAN, VA 221013838
Phone: 703 358-8800
Web: WWW.CONTRACK.COM

HISTORICAL FINANCIALS
Company Type: Private

Income Statement
FYE: December 31

	REVENUE ($ mil.)	NET INCOME ($ mil.)	NET PROFIT MARGIN	EMPLOYEES
12/13	372	(26)	—	6,200
12/09	181	15	8.8%	—
12/08	166	18	10.9%	—
12/07	0	0	—	—
Annual Growth	—	—	—	—

2013 Year-End Financials
Return on assets: 9.9%
Return on equity: (-7.2%)
Current ratio: 0.60
Cash ($ mil.): 27

CONTRACTORS STEEL COMPANY

Steel service center operator Contractors Steel provides products such as bars (cold-rolled and hot-rolled) pipe plate sheet structural members (angles beams and channels) and tubing. The company's fabricating and processing services include burning grinding plasma cutting sawing and shearing. Contractors Steel operates from facilities in Michigan and Ohio. The company maintains its own fleet of delivery trucks. Chairman president and CEO Donald Simon founded Contractors Steel in 1960.

EXECUTIVES
Chairman President CEO and Treasurer, Donald R. (Don) Simon
V Pres-sec, Esther Simon, age 81
Auditors: ROBINSON PIETRAS KALISKY & C

LOCATIONS
HQ: CONTRACTORS STEEL COMPANY
36555 AMRHEIN RD, LIVONIA, MI 481501182
Phone: 734 464-4000
Web: WWW.CONTRACTORSSTEEL.COM

COMPETITORS
Alro
Mill Steel
Peerless Steel

HISTORICAL FINANCIALS
Company Type: Private

Income Statement
FYE: October 31

	REVENUE ($ mil.)	NET INCOME ($ mil.)	NET PROFIT MARGIN	EMPLOYEES
10/10	184	6	3.5%	250
10/09	153	(24)	—	—
10/08	632	0	0.0%	—
Annual Growth	(46.0%)	1889.7%		

2010 Year-End Financials
Return on assets: 5.8%
Return on equity: 3.5%
Current ratio: 3.70
Cash ($ mil.): 15

CONWAY HOSPITAL INC.

Conway Medical Center (CMC) finds a way to provide a wide range of health care services to residents of eastern South Carolina. The private not-for-profit 210-bed hospital (served by a medical staff of 200) provides services including primary diagnostic emergency surgical maternal and pediatric and rehabilitative care. CMC specializes in heart health hospice care and occupational health. Additionally CMC operates the Kingston Nursing Center an about 90-bed long-term nursing and rehabilitative care facility and the Conway Physicians Group which is home to about 10 physician practices offering a range of specialties.

Geographic Reach
The hospital system serves patients in eastern South Carolina.

Financial Analysis
CMC receives financial support in part through donations to the Conway Medical Center Foundation which was founded in 1988 to provide financial and voluntary staffing support to the hospital.

Company Background
The center expanded its operations in 2009 with the completion of a new patient tower with about 65 patient beds new nurses stations for streamlined patient care and updated technology.

EXECUTIVES
Chief Executive Officer, Philip A. (Phil) Clayton
Executive Vice President Fiscal Services, Bret Barr
VP Human Resources, Craig Hyman
Administrator Kingston Nursing Center/Medstar, Laura Fowler
VP Ancillary Services, Dwight Gentry
Executive Director Foundation, Berns Massey
VP Facility Management, Kevin Lovett
Vice-President Nursing Services, Tony Minshew
Vice-President Physician Services, Warren Ratley
Vice-President Medical Affairs, Preston Strosnider
Director IT, Mickey Waters
Auditors: GRANT THORNTON LLP COLUMBIA

LOCATIONS
HQ: CONWAY HOSPITAL INC.
300 SINGLETON RIDGE RD, CONWAY, SC 295269142
Phone: 843 347-7111
Web: WWW.CONWAYMEDICALCENTER.COM

PRODUCTS/OPERATIONS

Selected Departments and Services
Center for Wound Healing
Critical Care Services
Diabetes Management
Diagnostic
Endoscopy

Heart Center
Hospice
Joint Replacement Center
Laboratory Services
Long Term Care
Mammography
Medical Services Center
Palliative Care
Pediatric Center
Pulmonary Rehabilitation
Rehabilitation
Senior Privileges Club
Sleep Disorders Center
Subacute
Surgical Services
The Birthplace
Weight Loss Surgery
Wellness & Fitness Center

COMPETITORS
Carolinas Hospital System
Georgetown Hospital System
Grand Strand Regional Medical Center
McLeod Health
Medical University of South Carolina
New Hanover Regional Medical Center
Roper St. Francis Healthcare

HISTORICAL FINANCIALS
Company Type: Private

Income Statement
FYE: September 30

	REVENUE ($ mil.)	NET INCOME ($ mil.)	NET PROFIT MARGIN	EMPLOYEES
09/14	179	28	15.8%	1,200
09/13	162	21	13.3%	—
09/12	158	16	10.2%	—
09/11	149	0	—	—
Annual Growth	6.2%	—	—	—

2014 Year-End Financials
Return on assets: 3.2%
Return on equity: 15.8%
Current ratio: 1.30
Cash ($ mil.): 13

COOK CHILDREN'S MEDICAL CENTER

Auditors: BKD LLP HOUSTON TX

LOCATIONS
HQ: COOK CHILDREN' S MEDICAL CENTER
801 7TH AVE, FORT WORTH, TX 761042796
Phone: 682 885-4000
Web: WWW.COOKCHILDRENS.ORG

HISTORICAL FINANCIALS
Company Type: Private

Income Statement
FYE: September 30

	REVENUE ($ mil.)	NET INCOME ($ mil.)	NET PROFIT MARGIN	EMPLOYEES
09/13	828	160	19.4%	2,000
09/09	563	99	17.7%	—
09/08	157	4	2.8%	—
09/05	347	0	—	—
Annual Growth	11.5%	—	—	—

2013 Year-End Financials
Return on assets: 7.7%
Return on equity: 19.4%
Current ratio: 1.00
Cash ($ mil.): 269

COOPERATIVE ELEVATOR CO.

Cooperative Elevator represents and serves northern Michigan bean and grain farmers. The agricultural cooperative is made up of approximately 900 member/owners. It operates storage facilities and processing plants offers crop marketing and agronomy services and provides farm supplies to its members including seed feed fertilizer herbicides fuel and agricultural chemicals. The co-op's bean farmers grow black red pinto and navy beans which are distributed in bulk throughout the US as well as in Africa and the Caribbean. Cooperative Elevator's grain farmers produce wheat soy corn barley and oats and the co-op provides storage and market services such as price updates for these commodities.

EXECUTIVES

Vice President, Mike Janowicz
Auditors: CLIFTONLARSONALLEN LLP MIDDL

LOCATIONS

HQ: COOPERATIVE ELEVATOR CO.
7211 E MICHIGAN AVE, PIGEON, MI 48755
Phone: 989 453-4500
Web: WWW.COOPELEV.COM

COMPETITORS

ADM
CHS
Cargill
Chippewa Valley Bean
Della Natura
  Commodities

Kelley Bean
Organic Bean & Grain
Star of the West
United Producers
Zeeland Farm

HISTORICAL FINANCIALS

Company Type: Private

Income Statement

	REVENUE ($ mil.)	NET INCOME ($ mil.)	NET PROFIT MARGIN	EMPLOYEES
01/14	277	9	3.6%	136
01/13	293	12	4.4%	—
01/12	242	13	5.4%	—
01/11	166	0	—	—
Annual Growth	18.4%	—	—	—

2014 Year-End Financials

Return on assets: 15.4%   Cash ($ mil.): —
Return on equity: 3.6%
Current ratio: —

COOPERATIVE FOR ASSISTANCE AND RELIEF EVERYWHERE INC.

The Cooperative for Assistance and Relief Everywhere (CARE) strives to be the beginning of the end of poverty. The organization works to reduce poverty in about 85 countries by helping communities in areas such as health education economic development emergency relief and agriculture. CARE supports more than 1100 projects to combat poverty. It also operates a small economic activity development (SEAD) unit that supports moneymaking activities. Through SEAD CARE provides technical training and savings and loans programs to help people —particularly women — open or expand small businesses. CARE was founded in 1945 to give aid to WWII survivors.

Geographic Reach

From its headquarters in Atlanta CARE serves poor communities in nearly 85 countries. It does not provide assistance in the US.

Operations

In addition to its home office in Georgia CARE maintains field offices in about 10 US cities including Boston Chicago Miami New York and Washington DC. The group's international field offices are located in more than 55 countries.

CARE's 1100 projects reach 122 million people more than half of which are women. About 90% of the funds that CARE receives go toward its aid efforts. The organization helps people in the poorest communities of developing nations. (It does not provide assistance in the US.)

Strategy

CARE is supported by donations from thousands of individuals and dozens of corporations foundations and other charitable organizations in the US. Some of the participating organizations include World Wildlife Fund Covance Merck Meredith Corporation and the Wal-Mart Foundation. The group also receives funding and supplies from government agencies including the United Nations and European Union. As a result of the economic downturn CARE has been working to raise contribution levels as governments businesses and individuals cut back their spending including charitable donations.

Financial Performance

CARE's revenue increased a modest 1% to $590 million in fiscal 2011 as compared to 2010. While it logged a drop in revenues from the US government the organization saw a boost in private contributions —totaling $310 million —from CARE international members.

EXECUTIVES

Senior Vice President Global Support Services, Patrick (Paddy) Solomon
Associate Vice President Resource Development Services, Joanne Delgiorno Bowers
Vice Chair, Doris Meissner
Board Member, Gilles Concordel
Auditors: ERNST & YOUNG LLP ATLANTA G

LOCATIONS

HQ: COOPERATIVE FOR ASSISTANCE AND RELIEF EVERYWHERE INC.
151 ELLIS ST NE FL 1, ATLANTA, GA 303032437
Phone: 404 681-2552
Web: WWW.CARE.ORG

PRODUCTS/OPERATIONS

Selected International Partner Organizations
Covance Inc.
Merck Foundation
Meredith Corporation
The Wal-mart Foundation
WWF

HISTORICAL FINANCIALS

Company Type: Private

Income Statement

FYE: June 30

	REVENUE ($ mil.)	NET INCOME ($ mil.)	NET PROFIT MARGIN	EMPLOYEES
06/13	492	(18)	—	10,000
06/11	589	10	1.7%	—
06/08	713	40	5.6%	—
06/05	1,545	0	—	—
Annual Growth	—	—	—	—

2013 Year-End Financials

Return on assets: 11.8%   Cash ($ mil.): 67
Return on equity: (-3.8%)
Current ratio: 0.70

COOPERATIVE PRODUCERS INC.

Auditors: PAWLING FINN & TORRELL CPAS

LOCATIONS

HQ: COOPERATIVE PRODUCERS INC.
205 N SHOWBOAT BLVD, HASTINGS, NE 689017002
Phone: 402 463-5148
Web: WWW.CPICOOP.COM

HISTORICAL FINANCIALS

Company Type: Private

Income Statement

FYE: November 30

	REVENUE ($ mil.)	NET INCOME ($ mil.)	NET PROFIT MARGIN	EMPLOYEES
11/07	395	8	2.2%	550
11/06	233	2	0.9%	—
11/05	236	1	0.5%	—
11/04	178	0	—	—
Annual Growth	30.3%	—	—	—

2007 Year-End Financials

Return on assets: 17.6%   Cash ($ mil.): —
Return on equity: 2.2%
Current ratio: 0.10

COOPERATIVE REGIONS OF ORGANIC PRODUCER POOLS

Cooperative Regions of Organic Producers Pool (CROPP) is the largest organic farming cooperative in North America. The group's 1840-plus farmer/members produce the co-op's Organic Valley Family of Farms and Organic Prairie brands of fluid and shelf-stable milk along with cheese butter and soy milk. Beyond the dairy barn the cooperative also offers organic citrus juices produce eggs meats and poultry. Its Organic Valley products are sold by food retailers and its ingredients are marketed to other organic food processors. Wisconsin-headquartered CROPP's farmer/members are located throughout North America and Australia. The co-op was founded in 1988.

Geographic Reach

The Wisconsin-based cooperative's farmer members are located in 35 US states including California and Florida and three Canadian provinces. It also has members in Australia.

Financial Performance

The co-op's sales grew 8% in 2013 versus 2012 to $928 million after increasing by 20% in the previous annual comparison. Sales have risen sharply along with increasing demand for organic milk and other dairy foods. CROPP added 10 new members in 2013. The co-op struggled in 2013 as a result of a fire that burned down part of its headquarters building. The blaze occurred about a year after the co-op completed a $6.7 million addition to the structure.

Strategy

CROPP seeks to quench consumers' growing thirst for organic milk with new products including the 2012 launch of Organic Valley Grassmilk an organic specialty milk produced from cows that are 100% grass fed. Organic Valley Grassmilk attained nationwide distribution in mid-2013.

The co-op operates under a regional business model by which milk is produced bottled and distributed in the region where it's farmed to ensure fewer miles from farm to table and to support local economies. About 75% of the co-ops 1800-plus farmers are located in the "Heartland" region of the US which includes Iowa Illinois Kansas Minnesota North Dakota Nebraska South Dakota Wisconsin Indiana Ohio and Michigan.

EXECUTIVES

Vice President Sales, Eric Newman
CEO, George Siemon
COO, Louise Hemstead
CFO, Mike Bedessem
Auditors: HENNEN & ASSOCIATES PLC S

LOCATIONS

HQ: COOPERATIVE REGIONS OF ORGANIC PRODUCER POOLS
1 ORGANIC WAY, LA FARGE, WI 546396604
Phone: 608 625-2602
Web: WWW.ORGANICVALLEY.COOP

PRODUCTS/OPERATIONS

Selected Products
Butter
Cheese
Cottage cheese
Cream
Cream cheese
Eggs
Healthy snacks
Juice
Meat
Milk
Sour cream
Soy
Yogurt

COMPETITORS

Albert's Organics	Land O' Lakes
Aurora Organic Dairy	Laura's Lean Beef Co.
Berkeley Farms	Lifeway Foods
Chiquita Brands	Niman Ranch
Crowley Foods	Oberweis Dairy
Dairy Crest	Odwalla
Dairy Farmers of America	Organically Grown Company
Dakota Beef	Rachel's Organic Dairy
Dannon	Rockview Dairies
Dean Foods	Sargento
Dole Food	Springfield Creamery
Egg Innovations	Stonyfield Farm
Foster Dairy Farms	Straus Family Creamery
Fresh Del Monte Produce	Stremicks Heritage Foods

Friendship Dairies
Galaxy Nutritional Foods
Garelick Farms
Great Lakes Cheese
Jonathan Sprouts
Keller's Creamery
Turkey Hill Dairy
Tyson Foods
Tyson Fresh Meats
United Natural
Willow Wind Organic Farms

HISTORICAL FINANCIALS
Company Type: Private

Income Statement
FYE: December 31

	REVENUE ($ mil.)	NET INCOME ($ mil.)	NET PROFIT MARGIN	EMPLOYEES
12/10	619	12	2.0%	764
12/08	527	3	0.7%	—
12/07	1,171	0	0.0%	—
Annual Growth	(19.1%)	4341.1%	—	—

2010 Year-End Financials
Return on assets: 8.3%
Return on equity: 2.0%
Current ratio: 1.30
Cash ($ mil.): 29

COPLEY HEALTH CARE PARTNERSHIP

LOCATIONS

HQ: COPLEY HEALTH CARE PARTNERSHIP
380 SUMNER ST, STOUGHTON, MA 020723470
Phone: 781 341-2300
Web: WWW.COPLEY-NH.COM

HISTORICAL FINANCIALS
Company Type: Private

Income Statement
FYE: September 30

	REVENUE ($ mil.)	NET INCOME ($ mil.)	NET PROFIT MARGIN	EMPLOYEES
09/09*	1,039	76	7.4%	150
12/97	7	0	—	—
12/96	7	0	8.3%	—
12/95	7	0	—	—
Annual Growth	41.8%	—	—	—

*Fiscal year change

2009 Year-End Financials
Return on assets: —
Return on equity: 7.4%
Current ratio: 2.60
Cash ($ mil.): 1

CORE CONSTRUCTION GROUP LTD.

LOCATIONS

HQ: CORE CONSTRUCTION GROUP LTD.
866 N MAIN ST, MORTON, IL 615501602
Phone: 309 263-0808

HISTORICAL FINANCIALS
Company Type: Private

Income Statement
FYE: December 31

	REVENUE ($ mil.)	NET INCOME ($ mil.)	NET PROFIT MARGIN	EMPLOYEES
12/13	636	0	—	6
12/12	624	0	—	—
12/06	620	0	—	—
12/05	0	0	—	—
Annual Growth	—	—	—	—

2013 Year-End Financials
Return on assets: 12.9%
Return on equity: —
Current ratio: 0.20
Cash ($ mil.): 32

CORE CONSTRUCTION INC.

CORE Construction fits into the core clique of contractors in the southwestern US. The company formerly Targent General is one of the top contractors in the region; it also has offices in Florida and Illinois. CORE offers construction management general contracting and design/build services for municipal educational health care office residential retail sports institutional and industrial projects. It has worked on projects as diverse as Phoenix's Chase Field Ballpark Dodge Theatre and Lower Buckeye Jail. German immigrant Otto Baum founded the company in 1937.

CORE Construction is the seventh largest builder of schools in the US. The company is focusing its efforts on commercial developments affordable housing and senior care facilities.

CORE Construction has regional offices in Arizona Florida Illinois Nevada and Texas

ARIG (Al Rajhi Investment Group) owns a majority stake in the company.

EXECUTIVES

Vice President Finance, Dennis Barber
Vice President Director of Preconstruction Services, Clint Heinold
Vice President, Fred Knapp
Executive Vice President, Brad Roberts
Treas, John (Jack) Verhoff

LOCATIONS

HQ: CORE CONSTRUCTION INC.
3036 E GREENWAY RD, PHOENIX, AZ 850324414
Phone: 602 494-0800
Web: WWW.CORECONSTRUCT.COM

COMPETITORS

DPR Construction	Summit Builders
Jaynes Companies	Sundt
Kitchell	Tutor Perini
McCarthy Building	

Income Statement   FYE: December 31

	REVENUE ($ mil.)	NET INCOME ($ mil.)	NET PROFIT MARGIN	EMPLOYEES
12/13	219	0	—	60
12/12	162	0	—	—
12/11	206	0	—	—
12/10	244	0	—	—
Annual Growth	(3.5%)	—	—	—

2013 Year-End Financials

Return on assets: 10.7%   Cash ($ mil.): 3
Return on equity: —
Current ratio: 0.10

CORPORATE TRAVEL CONSULTANTS INC

Corporate Travel Consultants (CorpTrav) brings order to the chaos of globetrotting go-getters and far-flung meetings on foreign soil. The company offers Internet-based booking reporting compliance and management tools through CorpTrav On-line as well as meeting and incentive travel arrangements. Its online tools allow customers to check health advisories travel alerts and strike updates for planned destinations. CorpTrav has offices in Chicago Dallas New York and San Francisco. The agency partners with GlobalStar to provide global support and service to travelers. CEO Bonnie Lorefice founded CorpTrav in 1976.

EXECUTIVES

Vp, Barb Lea-Maijala
Managing Director, Gina Maylath
Senior Vice President, Lisa Donavanberry

LOCATIONS

HQ: CORPORATE TRAVEL CONSULTANTS INC
450 E 22ND ST STE 100, LOMBARD, IL 601486175
Phone: 630 691-9100
Web: WWW.CORPTRAV.COM

COMPETITORS

Adelman Travel	BCD Travel
Advantage Performance Network	Carlson Wagonlit
American Express	USTravel

HISTORICAL FINANCIALS
Company Type: Private

Income Statement   FYE: December 31

	REVENUE ($ mil.)	NET INCOME ($ mil.)	NET PROFIT MARGIN	EMPLOYEES
12/14	222	1	0.7%	120
12/12	209	1	0.9%	—
12/10	135	0	0.4%	—
12/09	116	0	—	—
Annual Growth	13.7%	—	—	—

2014 Year-End Financials

Return on assets: 0.3%   Cash ($ mil.): 4
Return on equity: 0.7%
Current ratio: 3.00

CORPORATION FOR PUBLIC BROADCASTING

This organization is made possible by a grant from the federal government and by support from viewers like you. The Corporation for Public Broadcasting (CPB) is a private not-for-profit corporation created by the federal government that receives appropriations from Congress to help fund programming for more than 1000 locally-owned public TV and radio stations. CPB-funded programs are distributed by the Public Broadcasting Service (PBS) National Public Radio (NPR) and Public Radio International (PRI). Funds are also used for research on media and education. CPB was created by Congress in 1967.

Funding for CPB has often been a political hot potato and a target for critics opposed to using government money for educational and cultural programming. Supporters however have been just as quick to promote the benefits of publicly funded news and informational programming that addresses groups and issues often ignored by commercial broadcasters.

HISTORY

As commercial radio began to fill the radio dial the FCC in 1945 reserved 20 channels from 88 FM to 92 FM for noncommercial educational broadcasts. The first public television station started broadcasting in 1953 and by 1965 there were 124 public TV stations across the country. To help allocate government funds to these public TV and radio stations Congress created the Corporation for Public Broadcasting (CPB) in 1967. CPB created the Public Broadcasting Service (PBS) in 1969 and National Public Radio (NPR) in 1970.

CPB has always been politically controversial; critics have often charged it with elitism cultural bias and liberalism. When Republicans gained control of Congress in 1994 their laundry list of grievances included government cultural spending. They were foiled in their effort to eliminate funding for CPB however in part because of public support for public television. Congress still cut funding by $100 million forcing CPB to reduce its staff by almost 25% and introduce performance criteria for stations seeking grant money including listenership and community financial support minimums.

Robert Coonrod was promoted to CEO in 1997. The following year Congress approved additional funding to help public television's transition from analog to digital broadcasting. Frank Cruz was appointed chairman of CPB in 1999. At about the same time increased funding for 2003 (funding is approved two years in advance) was threatened when it was discovered that some PBS stations were giving their mailing lists to the Democratic party for fundraising purposes. Nevertheless funding for CPB was increased in the 2001 budget.

In late 2001 businesswoman Katherine Milner Anderson was voted in as chairman taking over for Cruz (who remained on the board). After serving two consecutive terms as chairman Anderson was replaced by veteran journalist Kenneth Tomlinson in 2003.

CPB's funding was approved at $350 million for 2002 and $365 million for 2003. Coonrod left the company the following year. Former COO Kathleen Cox and CPB agreed to a one-year contract for her to serve as president and CEO. However she left the post after nine months.

Chairman Tomlinson resigned in 2005 amid allegations that he violated CPB policies by using his position to get funding for programs with a conservative political view. That same year former Republican National Committee co-chairwoman Patricia Harrison was named the new CEO of the CPB.

EXECUTIVES

EVP and COO, Steven J. Altman
Senior Vice President Radio, Greg Schnirring
Senior Vice President Education and Childrens Content Operations, Debra Sanchez
Senior Vice President Television Digital Video Content, Jennifer (Jen) Lawson
Senior Vice President General Counsel, Westwood Smithers
Vice President Business Affairs, Jackie Livesay
Vice President And Controller, Richard Loutsch
Vice President Diversity and Innovation, Sylvia Bugg
Senior Vice President System Development And Media Strategy, Ted Krichels

LOCATIONS

HQ: CORPORATION FOR PUBLIC BROADCASTING
401 9TH ST NW STE 200, WASHINGTON, DC
200042129
Phone: 202 879-9600
Web: WWW.CPB.ORG

HISTORICAL FINANCIALS
Company Type: Private

Income Statement   FYE: September 30

	REVENUE ($ mil.)	NET INCOME ($ mil.)	NET PROFIT MARGIN	EMPLOYEES
09/13	446	(18)	—	99
09/09	482	0	—	—
Annual Growth	(1.9%)	—	—	—

2013 Year-End Financials

Return on assets: 1.5%   Cash ($ mil.): 127
Return on equity: (-4.2%)
Current ratio: 1.30

COUNTRYMARK COOPERATIVE HOLDING CORPORATION

LOCATIONS

HQ: COUNTRYMARK COOPERATIVE HOLDING CORPORATION
225 S EAST ST STE 144, INDIANAPOLIS, IN
462024059
Phone: 800 808-3170
Web: WWW.COUNTRYMARK.COM

HISTORICAL FINANCIALS
Company Type: Private

Income Statement   FYE: December 31

	REVENUE ($ mil.)	NET INCOME ($ mil.)	NET PROFIT MARGIN	EMPLOYEES
12/08	1,325	26	2.0%	425
12/07	964	56	5.9%	—
Annual Growth	37.5%	(52.4%)	—	—

COUNTY OF MARICOPA

LOCATIONS

HQ: COUNTY OF MARICOPA
9801 W VAN BUREN ST, TOLLESON, AZ 853532833
Phone: 623 478-4000
Web: WWW.TUHSD.ORG

HISTORICAL FINANCIALS

Company Type: Private

Income Statement

FYE: June 30

	REVENUE ($ mil.)	NET INCOME ($ mil.)	NET PROFIT MARGIN	EMPLOYEES
06/14	1,750	(119)	—	919
06/13	1,797	(66)	—	
06/12	1,820	(58)	—	
06/99	25	0	—	
Annual Growth	32.7%	—	—	—

2014 Year-End Financials

Return on assets: 4.3%
Return on equity: (-6.8%)
Current ratio: —

Cash ($ mil.): 32

COUNTY OF TARRANT

Auditors: KPMG LLP DALLAS TX

LOCATIONS

HQ: COUNTY OF TARRANT
100 E WEATHERFORD ST, FORT WORTH, TX
761022100
Phone: 817 884-1291
Web: WWW.TARRANT-TX.TAMU.EDU

HISTORICAL FINANCIALS

Company Type: Private

Income Statement

FYE: September 30

	REVENUE ($ mil.)	NET INCOME ($ mil.)	NET PROFIT MARGIN	EMPLOYEES
09/13	537	20	3.8%	139
09/12	518	(27)	—	
09/11	515	(87)	—	
Annual Growth	2.2%	—	—	—

2013 Year-End Financials

Return on assets: 15.7%
Return on equity: 3.8%
Current ratio: 3.20

Cash ($ mil.): 537

COVENANT HEALTH SYSTEM

Covenant Health System ties West Texas and Eastern New Mexico together with quality health care. The health services provider offers some 1100 beds in its five primary acute-care and specialty hospitals; it also manages about a dozen affiliated community hospitals. Covenant Health System part of the St. Joseph Health System also maintains a network of family health care and medical clinics. Covenant Health System's major facilities are Covenant Medical Center Covenant Specialty Hospital and Covenant Women's and Children's Hospital. The health system also includes some 20 clinics and 50 physician practices and its extensive outreach programs target isolated rural communities with mobile services.

Operations

The system's five hospitals include Covenant Medical Center Covenant Medical Center-Lakeside Covenant Specialty Hospital and Covenant Children's Hospital. It also operates three schools for healthcare careers in nursing radiography and surgical technology respectively.

Strategy

The Christian-based system which calls itself a ministry focuses on providing benefits to the community. Its key priorities include mental health dentistry diabetes home health management and childhood obesity.

Background

Covenant Health System was founded when two Lubbock hospitals St. Mary of the Plains Hospital (now known as Covenant Medical Center-Lakeside) and the Lubbock Methodist Hospital System (including the flagship Methodist Hospital which is now known as Covenant Medical Center) merged in 1998.

EXECUTIVES

Vice President Corporate Wellness Program, Lindy Lauderdale
Pharmacy Manager, Shanna Hamilton
Senior Vice President Regional Services, Steve Beck
Director Of Pharmacy Director Of Pharmacy Services, Bill Welch
Vice President, Sharon Prather
Vp Mission Integration, Clarke Cochran
Vice President Assistant Chief Medical Officer, Paul Walter
Auditors: ERNST & YOUNG US LLP FORT WOR

LOCATIONS

HQ: COVENANT HEALTH SYSTEM
3615 19TH ST, LUBBOCK, TX 794101209
Phone: 806 725-1011
Web: WWW.COVENANTHEALTH.ORG

PRODUCTS/OPERATIONS

Selected Facilities
Covenant Heart and Vascular Institute
Covenant Hospital Levelland
Covenant Hosptial Plainview
Covenant Medical Center
Covenant NeuroScience Institute
Covenant Specialty Hospital
Covenant Women's and Children's Hospital (formerly Covenant Medical Center-Lakeside)
Joe Arrington Cancer Research and Treatment Center
Owens-White Outpatient Rehabilitation Center

Selected Schools
School of Nursing
School of Radiography
School of Surgical Technology

COMPETITORS

Baptist St. Anthony's Health System	Tenet Healthcare
Del Sol Medical Center	Texas Health Resources
HealthSouth	The Methodist Health System
Hunt Memorial	University Medical
NW Texas Healthcare	Center of El Paso
Parkland Health & Hospital System	

HISTORICAL FINANCIALS

Company Type: Private

Income Statement

FYE: June 30

	REVENUE ($ mil.)	NET INCOME ($ mil.)	NET PROFIT MARGIN	EMPLOYEES
06/13	552	35	6.5%	5,700
06/09	1,185	(38)	—	—
06/08	572	8	1.5%	—
Annual Growth	(0.7%)	33.8%	—	—

2013 Year-End Financials

Return on assets: 7.4%
Return on equity: 6.5%
Current ratio: 3.20

Cash ($ mil.): 64

COVENANT MEDICAL CENTER INC

Covenant Medical Center (operating as Covenant HealthCare) has made a pact with Wolverine Staters to try to keep them in good health. The not-for-profit health care provider operates more than 20 inpatient and outpatient care facilities including its two main Covenant Medical Center campuses. It serves residents in a 20-county area of east-central Michigan with additional facilities in Bay City Frankenmuth and Midland. Specialized care services include cardiovascular health cancer treatment and obstetrics. The regional health care system has more about 650 beds.

Operations

Covenant HealthCare programs and services range from high-risk obstetrics and neonatal/pediatric intensive care to acute care. Its assets include cardiology oncology orthopedics robotic surgery and Level II Adult and Pediatric Trauma Center.

The health system has more than 20 inpatient and outpatient facilities and a trauma/emergency department that provides 85000 visits per year. The system employs more than 500 physicians from 52 medical specialties.

Sales and Marketing

Covenant HealthCare markets its services via social media.

Financial Performance

In 2014 the company's revenue increased 4% to $528 million as patient service revenue rose; this gain was partially offset by a decline in realized gain and other revenues. An increase in salaries and wages as well as higher supplies expenses led to a 12% decline in net income (to $57 million).

Cash flow from operations also fell slipping 20% to $48 million as accounts receivable increased.

Strategy

Expanding its infrastructure to keep up with demand in 2014 Covenant HealthCare added 11456 sq. ft. to its Emergency Department. The addition allows for more efficient triage enhanced patient waiting areas and additional space for current technology. It added 18 treatment bays to the existing 47 and also brought a dedicated CT scanner and mini-laboratory within the department.Also that year it opened the assisted living community of Covenant Glen in Frankenmuth. The 35000 sq. ft. structure has 45 rooms (15 dedicated to memory care and 30 with assisted living beds).

Company Background

Covenant HealthCare was formed in 1998 through the merger of Saginaw General and St. Luke's Hospitals.

EXECUTIVES

Operating Room Director, John Germain
Medical Director, Louis Constan
Vice President Of Patient Care, Carol Stoll
Director of Pharmacy, Terry Wernette
Auditors: ERNST & YOUNG US LLP ATLANTA

LOCATIONS

HQ: COVENANT MEDICAL CENTER INC
1447 N HARRISON ST, SAGINAW, MI 486024727
Phone: 989 583-0000
Web: WWW.COVENANTHEALTHCARE.COM

PRODUCTS/OPERATIONS

2014 Revenues

	% of total
Net patient service revenues	95
Other revenues	5
Total	**100**

Selected services

Bariatrics
Birth Center
Cancer Care
Cardiology - Center for the Heart
Childbirth Classes
da Vinci Robotic Surgery
Diabetes Self-Management Program
Emergency Care Center
Imaging and Diagnostics
Neonatal Intensive Care
Neurology
Osteoporosis
Orthopaedics
Pediatrics
Physical Medicine and Rehab.
Pulmonary/Respiratory Care
Sleep Center
Surgical Services
Trauma
Urologic Surgery
Women's Health
Wound Healing Center

COMPETITORS

Genesys Health System	McLaren Health Care
Genesys Regional	Munson Healthcare
Medical Center	Sparrow Health System
Hurley Medical Center	University of Michigan
McLaren Bay	Health System

HISTORICAL FINANCIALS

Company Type: Private

Income Statement
FYE: June 30

	REVENUE ($ mil.)	NET INCOME ($ mil.)	NET PROFIT MARGIN	EMPLOYEES
06/13	513	31	6.2%	3,900
06/10	508	28	5.5%	—
06/09	467	(14)	—	—
06/08	1,608	0	—	—
Annual Growth	**—**	**—**	**—**	**—**

2013 Year-End Financials
Return on assets: 11.7%　　Cash ($ mil.): 42
Return on equity: 6.2%
Current ratio: 0.50

COVERALL NORTH AMERICA INC.

Coverall North America operating as Coverall Health-Based Cleaning System has commercial cleaning covered. Through more than 90 support centers and 9000 franchisees worldwide (including branches in Asia Australia the Middle East and the Americas) the company offers franchises that provides janitorial services to retail locations office buildings health care facilities manufacturing plants government facilities schools and airports. Services include routine cleaning decontamination cleaning carpet cleaning restroom sanitation and floor restoration. Prominent customers have included Fed Ex the United States Postal Service Orkin and Schenker. The company was founded in 1985.

The company continues to expand its franchise offerings domestically and internationally as facilities around the world need their floors scrubbed and their windows cleaned. The Coverall Health-Based Cleaning System is specifically intended to reduce the spread of germs in public places and commercial environments. Organizations will always seek ways to eliminate lost productivity and reduce costs associated with illness and the Coverall Health-Based Cleaning System claims to reduce public health risks.

EXECUTIVES

Vice President Of Marketing, Diane Emo
Regional Vice President Western Division Sales, Valerie (Val) Dennis
Vice President, Joe Smid
Reg Vp Sales, Tyler Dickinson
Managing Director Of Sales (Medical Commercial Cleaning), Adam Cruts
Regional Vice President Central Division Sales, Mike Gumiela
Vice President Of Sales, Patrick (Paddy) Demarinis
Auditors: MCGLADREY & PULLEN LLP WEST

LOCATIONS

HQ: COVERALL NORTH AMERICA INC.
350 SW 12TH AVE, DEERFIELD BEACH, FL 334423106
Phone: 561 922-2500
Web: WWW.COVERALL.COM

COMPETITORS

ABM Industries	ISS A/S
ARAMARK	Jani-King
CleanNet USA	ServiceMaster

HISTORICAL FINANCIALS

Company Type: Private

Income Statement
FYE: December 31

	REVENUE ($ mil.)	NET INCOME ($ mil.)	NET PROFIT MARGIN	EMPLOYEES
12/07	225	13	5.9%	476
12/06	205	6	3.2%	—
12/05	103	0	0.0%	—
Annual Growth	**47.6%**	**13164.3%**	**—**	**—**

2007 Year-End Financials
Return on assets: 6.1%　　Cash ($ mil.): 3
Return on equity: 5.9%
Current ratio: 0.50

CREATIVE MANAGEMENT INC

LOCATIONS

HQ: CREATIVE MANAGEMENT INC
935 ROUTE 34 STE 3A, MATAWAN, NJ 077473282
Phone: 732 696-2201

HISTORICAL FINANCIALS

Company Type: Private

Income Statement
FYE: December 31

	REVENUE ($ mil.)	NET INCOME ($ mil.)	NET PROFIT MARGIN	EMPLOYEES
12/11	532	1	0.3%	50
12/98	4	0	2.4%	
Annual Growth	**44.6%**	**23.4%**	**—**	**—**

2011 Year-End Financials
Return on assets: 2.4%　　Cash ($ mil.): 3
Return on equity: 0.3%
Current ratio: 0.80

CREIGHTON UNIVERSITY

Consistently ranked among the top universities in the Midwest Creighton University is a Jesuit Catholic university with an enrollment of approximately 8000 undergraduate graduate and professional students. With a student-to-faculty ratio of 11:1 it offers more than 70 majors through nine schools and colleges including institutions focused on arts and sciences business law medicine dentistry pharmacy and nursing. Its 130-acre campus is adjacent to the downtown business district of Omaha Nebraska. Creighton University was founded in 1878 and named after Omaha businessman Edward Creighton.

Geographic Reach

In addition to teaching international students from about 40 countries at its Omaha campus Creighton University offers hands-on service and learning programs in the Dominican Republic and the Middle East. It also has international affiliate or exchange programs with institutions in about 55 countries.

Operations

In addition to core curriculum the university has a long history of providing medical education. Many of its on-site medical training programs are provided at the facilities of medical care provider Alegent Creighton Health (formerly Alegent Health). Creighton University also has a partnership with the St. Joseph's Hospital and Medical Center in Phoenix Arizona. In addition the university conducts research programs in various scientific fields.

Following student tuition and fees which account for about 53% of annual revenue health services bring in about 18% of sales.

Financial Performance

Revenue fell 11.5% to $371 million in 2014 from lower health services revenue and grant and contract revenues which was partly offset by increased tuition and fee income. Net income increased 9%.

Strategy

To expand its services for students Creighton University looks to launch new degree programs enhance facilities and increase partnerships with other educational medical and research institutions. In 2012 the university launched its first 100% online degree program (for a Bachelor of Science in Integrated Leadership) and in 2013 it opened the Creighton Business Institute to improve its business leadership development offerings.

In 2014 Creighton University and Alegent Creighton Health made plans for a new medical complex next to the campus in downtown Omaha. The 90000-sqquare-foot building will serve area residents with outpatient emergency and diagnostic services.

Creighton previously sold its 26% stake in the 400-bed Creighton University Medical Center (CUMC) in Omaha to Alegent. Tenet Healthcare owned a majority stake in the hospital which was also acquired by Alegent. The transaction also made Alegent's network of care centers the primary teaching sites for Creighton University's School of Medicine and other health-related schools. Creighton University already partnered with Alegent on a number of health-related professional education and research programs prior to the deal and the university believes that its students will benefit from the expanded relationship.

EXECUTIVES

Assistant Vice President Student Servi, Tanya Winegard
Associate Vice President for, John E (Jack) Pierce
Director of Admissions And Scholarships, SARAH RICHARDSON
Vice President For Finance, Jan Madsen
Assistant Vice President Alumni Relations, Anna Nubel
Assistant Vice President Development, Matthew (Matt) Gerard
Associate Vice President, Colette O'Meara-mckinney
Assistant Vice President Principal Gif, Diane Crowley
Vice President For Finance, Alex Kubicek
Assoc Vice President for Information Technology, Bob Rauscher
Department Head Learning Resources Center, Diana Boone
Vice President University Ministry, Andrew F (Andy) Alexander
Vice President For Student Services, Tami Thibodeau
Associate Vice President for Health Sciences, Sade Kosoko-Lasaki
Vice President Of, Kate Steier
Vice President, Mike Nichols
Assistant Vice President Of Information Technology, Mary Herrington
Vice President for Health Sciences, Stephanie Reed
Department Chair, Michael Makoid
Associate Vice President for Residence Life, Richard (Dick) Rossi
Assistant Vice President Information Technology, Mark Mongar
Medical Director, Stephen (Steve) Lanspa
Vice President, Melissa (Mel) Uhl
Senior Vice President Operations, Daniel E (Dan) Burkey
Vice President of Administration, Katie Kelsey
Vice President for Programming, Mattie Smyth
Vice President, Laura Simic
Board Member, Andrew Hoh
Treasurer, Samantha Russell
Vice Chair, Richard Goering
Auditors: KPMG LLP LINCOLN NE

LOCATIONS

HQ: CREIGHTON UNIVERSITY
2500 CALIFORNIA PLZ, OMAHA, NE 681780002
Phone: 402 280-2900
Web: WWW.CREIGHTON.EDU

PRODUCTS/OPERATIONS

2013 Revenue

	$ mil.	% of total
Student tuition & fees	190	46
Health care services	115	28
Auxiliary enterprises	31	8
Grants & contracts	27	7
Investment income	14	4
Contributions	11	3
Released assets	11	3
Other	5	1
Total	**407**	**100**

HISTORICAL FINANCIALS
Company Type: Private

Income Statement
FYE: June 30

	REVENUE ($ mil.)	NET INCOME ($ mil.)	NET PROFIT MARGIN	EMPLOYEES
06/13	407	84	20.7%	5,000
06/12	419	(28)	—	—
06/11	414	79	19.2%	—
06/10	405	0	—	—
Annual Growth	**0.2%**	—	—	—

2013 Year-End Financials
Return on assets: —
Return on equity: 20.7%
Current ratio: —
Cash ($ mil.): 58

CREST INDUSTRIES LLC (DE)

Auditors: LESTER MILLER & WELLS ALEXAN

LOCATIONS

HQ: CREST INDUSTRIES LLC (DE)
4725 HIGHWAY 28 E, PINEVILLE, LA 713604730
Phone: 318 448-8287
Web: WWW.CRESTOPERATIONS.COM

HISTORICAL FINANCIALS
Company Type: Private

Income Statement
FYE: December 31

	ASSETS ($ mil.)	NET INCOME ($ mil.)	INCOME AS % OF ASSETS	EMPLOYEES
12/13	249	32	13.1%	415
12/12	202	28	14.0%	—
12/11	170	15	8.9%	—
12/10	163	0	—	—
Annual Growth	**15.2%**	—	—	—

2013 Year-End Financials
Return on assets: 3.3%
Return on equity: 10.0%
Sales ($ mil): 328

CREST OPERATIONS LLC

Crest Operations part of Crest Industries distributes and installs electrical substations and transmission products for electric power generation and utility customers worldwide through its DIS-TRAN and Beta Engineering subsidiaries. Other subsidiaries grow pine and hardwood trees in Louisiana and Texas (Crest Natural Resources) and make wooden utility poles and cross arms. Crest's Mid-State Supply Company subsidiary is a Louisiana-based distributor of electrical products that has showrooms for appliances and lighting. Crest Operations was founded in 1958.

EXECUTIVES

Vice President, Patrick (Paddy) Smith
Vice President Human Resources, Jane Walker
Executive Vice President, R Grassi
Auditors: LESTER MILLER & WELLS ALEXAN

LOCATIONS

HQ: CREST OPERATIONS LLC
4725 HIGHWAY 28 E, PINEVILLE, LA 713604730
Phone: 318 448-0274
Web: WWW.CRESTOPERATIONS.COM

COMPETITORS

Consolidated Electrical
Graybar Electric
WESCO International

HISTORICAL FINANCIALS
Company Type: Private

Income Statement
FYE: December 31

	REVENUE ($ mil.)	NET INCOME ($ mil.)	NET PROFIT MARGIN	EMPLOYEES
12/13	326	34	10.7%	300
12/12	240	28	12.1%	—
12/11	196	16	8.2%	—
12/08	178	0	—	—
Annual Growth	**12.9%**	—	—	—

2013 Year-End Financials
Return on assets: 3.3%
Return on equity: 10.7%
Current ratio: 0.20
Cash ($ mil.): 21

CROSSLAND CONSTRUCTION COMPANY INC.

Crossland Construction has crossed the prairie transitioning from a local player in Columbus Kansas to a firm with a strong regional presence. The company designs builds and manages construction of government education healthcare retail and other buildings from a handful of offices in Kansas Missouri Arkansas Oklahoma Colorado and Texas. Customers have included Harley-Davidson SAM'S CLUB McCune Brooks Hospital Embassy Suites and a variety of school districts and municipalities. Crossland builds everything from office buildings and warehouses to veteran's memorials and airports. The company which often works in partnership with PBA Architects was founded by Ivan Crossland Sr. in 1978.

Sales and Marketing

Crossland Construction serves a variety of customer types such as Embassy Suites Harley-Davidson school districts and municipalities. In 2013 it's working with Pittsburgh State University to build a new Center for the Arts among other projects.

The construction firm's services include pre-construction construction management general construction services design build and self-performance capabilities.

Geographic Reach

With the capacity to perform work in more than 40 states Kansas-based Crossland Construction has offices in Kansas Texas Arkansas Oklahoma Colorado and Missouri.

Awards and Recognition

One of the top builders in the US Crossland Construction is ranked 95th among 400 Top US contractors by ENR Magazine.

Strategy

In recent years Crossland Construction has expanded its business to Colorado by establishing an office in Denver in 2012. To serve clients in the Oklahoma City and Edmond Oklahoma metropolitan area Crossland Construction opened a division office in Oklahoma City that is leveraging existing relationships with the lucrative and growing oil and gas industries in that market.

It also works to promote construction as a career path. Crossland Construction works to maintain a solid workforce by investing in education at two levels. The company's Crossland Academy offers current employees the chance to earn certificates in concrete welding heavy equipment operation and storm water protection in addition to a complete curriculum laid out by the National Center for Construction Education and Research (NCCER). Its Crossland Connection program helps elementary through high school students learn about careers in construction. High school students are offered the same NCCER curriculum as employees to prepare for a trade apprenticeship or to enter a college construction trades program.

EXECUTIVES

Vice President, Brad Wilson
Vice President, Brad Delmont
Vice President Midwest Region, Danny Langerot
Vice President Business Development And Real Estate, Ashley Thompson
Vice President of Marketing and Business Devolopment, Christopher (Chris) Crossland
Auditors: MAYER HOFFMAN MCCANN PC TOPE

LOCATIONS

HQ: CROSSLAND CONSTRUCTION COMPANY INC.
833 S EAST AVE, COLUMBUS, KS 667252307
Phone: 479 464-7077
Web: WWW.CROSSLANDCONSTRUCTION.COM

PRODUCTS/OPERATIONS

Selected Services
Pre-Construction
Construction Management
General Construction Services
Design Build
Self-Performance Capabilities

Selected Areas of Work
Distribution Centers
Educational
Healthcare
Heavy/civil
Hospitality
Manufacturing Plants
Meeting Spaces
Municipal
Office
Retail
Sporting Facilities

COMPETITORS

Austin Commercial	Harvey Builders
Austin Industries	KBR
Baldwin & Shell	Spawglass Holding
C.F. Jordan	Structure Tone
CDI Contractors	Southwest
Cadence McShane	Tellepsen Builders
Dean Word	Turner Construction
Fluor	W.S. Bellows
Gilbane Building Company	

HISTORICAL FINANCIALS

Company Type: Private

Income Statement

FYE: July 31

	REVENUE ($ mil.)	NET INCOME ($ mil.)	NET PROFIT MARGIN	EMPLOYEES
07/08	434	10	2.4%	715
07/07	336	11	3.4%	—
07/04	1,315	0	—	—
Annual Growth	—	2209.5%	—	—

2008 Year-End Financials

Return on assets: —
Return on equity: 2.4%
Current ratio: 0.20
Cash ($ mil.): 21

CROWDER CONSTRUCTION COMPANY INC

Two may be company but a firm located in the Southeast US specializing in bridge and highway civil environmental and industrial construction is a Crowd(er) as in Crowder Construction. The company's projects include parking decks highway and bridge water and sewer treatment plant construction. Projects completed by its Crowder Electrical unit range from power substations to light rail facilities. The now employee-owned company was founded in Charlotte North Carolina in 1947 by Bill and O. P. Crowder; it continues to be led by the Crowder family.

EXECUTIVES

Chairman President and CEO, Otis A. Crowder
Vice President Sales, Edward Tart
Upper Management Vice President, Rachel Waller
Vice President Of People Development, Claudia Dodgen

LOCATIONS

HQ: CROWDER CONSTRUCTION COMPANY INC
6425 BROOKSHIRE BLVD, CHARLOTTE, NC 282160301
Phone: 704 372-3541
Web: WWW.CROWDERCC.COM

COMPETITORS

Alberici	Oldcastle Materials
English Construction Company	S. T. Wooten
Hubbard Group	Skanska USA Civil

HISTORICAL FINANCIALS

Company Type: Private

Income Statement

FYE: March 31

	REVENUE ($ mil.)	NET INCOME ($ mil.)	NET PROFIT MARGIN	EMPLOYEES
03/14	233	0	—	900
03/13	233	0	—	—
03/12	222	0	—	—
03/11	186	0	—	—
Annual Growth	7.8%	—	—	—

2014 Year-End Financials

Return on assets: 6.5%
Return on equity: —
Current ratio: 0.50
Cash ($ mil.): 16

CROWN BATTERY MANUFACTURING COMPANY

Crown Battery Manufacturing doesn't let its power go to its head. The company manufactures and sells industrial batteries and chargers automotive batteries and commercial battery products to clients across North America. Products serve clients in the marine railroad mining and automotive industries; the company also offers products with deep-cycle and other heavy-duty applications. Other products include battery chargers and battery cleaners for industrial applications. The company was founded in 1926 by German immigrant William J. Koenig.

Geographic Reach

Crown Battery has 12 sales and distribution offices located throughout North America. It has distributors and dealers in the Americas Europe Africa Asian-Pacific Australia and New Zealand.

Operations

The company's batteries are used in everything from cars trucks material handling equipment and locomotives to electric lift trucks traffic and floor management equipment and renewable energy systems.

EXECUTIVES

Vice President Human Resources, Scott Macina
Vice President Of Human Resources, Scott Messina
Auditors: MCGLADREY LLP CLEVELAND OHIO

LOCATIONS

HQ: CROWN BATTERY MANUFACTURING COMPANY
1445 MAJESTIC DR, FREMONT, OH 434209190
Phone: 419 332-0563
Web: WWW.C-LINEBATTERY.COM

PRODUCTS/OPERATIONS

Selected Products
Batteries and Battery parts
Battery Chargers
Commercial
Deep Cycle
Marine
Sealed Lead Acid
Utility Starting
Industrial
  Lift Truck
  Rail Road
  Mining
Other

Powerhouse Chargers
Powerhouse Cleaners

COMPETITORS

C&D Technologies	GS Yuasa
Eagle-Picher	Interstate Batteries
East Penn	Johnson Controls Power
Manufacturing	Solutions
EnerSys	Ritar Power
Exide	Valence Technology

HISTORICAL FINANCIALS
Company Type: Private

Income Statement
FYE: September 30

	REVENUE ($ mil.)	NET INCOME ($ mil.)	NET PROFIT MARGIN	EMPLOYEES
09/14	214	12	5.6%	550
09/13	196	10	5.5%	—
09/12	191	6	3.2%	—
09/11	215	0	—	—
Annual Growth	(0.2%)	—	—	—

2014 Year-End Financials
Return on assets: 8.4%   Cash ($ mil.): 2
Return on equity: 5.6%
Current ratio: 1.10

CROZER-KEYSTONE HEALTH SYSTEM

Crozer-Keystone Health System provides a full range of health care in the Philadelphia metropolitan area. The health system's facilities include five acute care hospitals four outpatient care centers and a sports science and technology center. Combined its not-for-profit member hospitals have about 840 beds. The hospitals' specialty units include trauma cardiac cancer orthopedic wound healing obesity sleep disorder and women's and children's health centers. The system also operates family occupational and diagnostic health clinics as well as home health and hospice agencies. In early the company agreed to be acquired by for-profit hospital operator Prospect Medical Holdings.

Operations

The Crozer-Keystone Health System's five hospitals include Community Hospital Crozer-Chester Medical Center Delaware County Memorial Hospital Springfield Hospital and Taylor Hospital. The health system's medical staff —consisting of about 1100 physicians and 4000 nurses —provides wellness and preventative care acute and long-term care and rehabilitative and restorative care. Altogether its hospitals handle some 140000 emergency room visits per year.

The system's subsidiary hospitals educate future physicians through residencies in family practice internal medicine women's health pediatrics and a variety of osteopathic and allied health training programs. Most residency training takes place at the 460-bed Crozer-Chester Medical Center through the system's affiliation with the Temple University Medical School. Crozer-Keystone residents are able to use the system's facilities as well as those of its educational affiliates as they train.

Geographic Reach

Crozer-Keystone Health System serves residents of Delaware County Pennsylvania and portions of northern Delaware and western New Jersey.

Strategy

The health system began what is known as a "medical home" model in 2011 in an effort to develop strong patient relationships. The model engages primary care practices to serve as central sources for all of a patient's health care needs by coordinating with specialists maintaining electronic medical records and prompting follow-up visits.Responding to the fact that one-third of its total visitors looked at its website before coming to Crozer-Keystone hospitals the company launched a redesigned mobile-responsive website in 2015 allowing users to easily find providers and practices and set up appointments through smart phones desktops and tablets. It also updated its web-based patient portal MyCKHealth to a mobile-friendly format so potential patients could more easily get access to its services.

Crozer-Keystone also partners with other area providers and charitable organizations to conduct community outreach and medical research programs.

After struggling financially Crozer-Keystone began looking for ways to find more stable footing. In 2016 it reached an agreement to be acquired by California-based hospital operator Prospect Medical Holdings which plans to invest at least $200 million in Crozer-Keystone over the next five years. With the additional funding the system will be able to improve its facilities enabling it to better provide health care in its market.

Company Background

Crozer-Keystone was created in 1990 through the partnership of Delaware County Memorial Hospital Springfield Hospital and Crozer-Chester Medical Center. Later Sacred Heart Hospital joined the system and was renamed Community Hospital. Then came Springfield Hospital and the system's newest member Taylor Hospital which joined the system in 1997.

EXECUTIVES

Vice President Managed Care, Linda Hart
Director Of Home Healthcare Svs, Jane Hanahan
Vice President Finance, Maryanne Spallucci
Director Of Infection Control, Jane Sheeran
Secretary Specialist, Elaine Fidorowicz
Auditors: WITHUMSMITHBROWN PC MORRISTOW

LOCATIONS

HQ: CROZER-KEYSTONE HEALTH SYSTEM
100 W SPROUL RD, SPRINGFIELD, PA 190642033
Phone: 610 338-8200

PRODUCTS/OPERATIONS

Selected Facilities in Pennsylvania
Hospitals
Community Hospital (Chester)
Crozer-Chester Medical Center (Upland)
Delaware County Memorial Hospital (Drexel Hill)
Springfield Hospital (Springfield)
Taylor Hospital (Ridley Park)
Outpatient Centers
Crozer Brinton Lake (Glen Mills)
Crozer Health Pavilion at Brinton Lake
Crozer Medical Plaza at Brinton Lake
Crozer-Keystone Cancer Center at Brinton Lake
Delaware County Memorial Hospital (DCMH) Health Pavilion (Drexel Hill)
Media Medical Plaza (Media)
Philadelphia CyberKnife
Sports Club
The Healthplex Sports Club (Springfield)
Other Facilities
Centers for Occupational Health
Community Health and Wellness Services
Crozer-Keystone Health Network of Physicians

COMPETITORS

Abington Memorial Hospital
Albert Einstein Healthcare Network
AtlantiCare
Children' s Hospital of Philadelphia

Christiana Care
Doylestown Hospital
Inspira Health Network
Jefferson Health System
Johns Hopkins Health System
Lancaster General
Lehigh Valley Health Network
Memorial Hospital (PA)
Mercy Health System
North Philadelphia Health System
Shore Memorial Hospital
TUHS
University of Maryland Medical System
University of Pennsylvania Health System
Virtua Health

HISTORICAL FINANCIALS
Company Type: Private

Income Statement
FYE: June 30

	REVENUE ($ mil.)	NET INCOME ($ mil.)	NET PROFIT MARGIN	EMPLOYEES
06/13	807	102	12.7%	7,100
06/10	50	0	1.6%	—
06/09	49	(1)	—	—
06/08	170	0	—	—
Annual Growth	—	—	—	—

2013 Year-End Financials
Return on assets: 14.0%   Cash ($ mil.): 60
Return on equity: 12.7%
Current ratio: 1.10

CSAA INSURANCE GROUP

LOCATIONS

HQ: CSAA INSURANCE GROUP
3055 OAK RD, WALNUT CREEK, CA 945972098
Phone: 925 279-2300

HISTORICAL FINANCIALS
Company Type: Private

Income Statement
FYE: December 31

	REVENUE ($ mil.)	NET INCOME ($ mil.)	NET PROFIT MARGIN	EMPLOYEES
12/08	438	10	2.3%	6,500
12/07	599	0	0.1%	—
12/06	1,301	0	—	—
Annual Growth	(42.0%)	62356.1%	—	—

2008 Year-End Financials
Return on assets: —   Cash ($ mil.): 82
Return on equity: 2.3%
Current ratio: 0.40

CSC SUGAR LLC

Auditors: GRANT THORNTON LLP MINNEAPOLI

LOCATIONS

HQ: CSC SUGAR LLC
36 GROVE ST STE 2, NEW CANAAN, CT 068405329
Phone: 203 846-5610
Web: WWW.CSCSUGAR.COM

HISTORICAL FINANCIALS

Company Type: Private

Income Statement

FYE: December 31

	REVENUE ($ mil.)	NET INCOME ($ mil.)	NET PROFIT MARGIN	EMPLOYEES
12/09	574	18	3.2%	40
12/08	790	5	0.7%	—
12/07	77	0	—	—
Annual Growth	—161578.7%			

2009 Year-End Financials

Return on assets: 2.1%
Return on equity: 3.2%
Current ratio: 0.20

Cash ($ mil.): 4

CSI LEASING INC.

CSI Leasing provides computer products leasing for customers in the Americas Europe and Asia. The company targets businesses looking to lower operational costs by avoiding expenses related to ownership and upkeep of computer and communications network gear. It provides off-lease services through its EPC subsidiary which remarkets recycles and disposes of information technology equipment —and securely wipes and/or destroys the data on the equipment when it is returned. CSI serves clients in such industries as software financial services government and education. Majority-owned by employees and led by cofounder and chairman Ken Steinback the company was founded in 1972 as Computer Sales International.

Geographic Reach

CSI Leasing is based in Saint Louis Missouri with offices in the US and around the world from Australia and Austria to Singapore Spain and the UK.

Financial Performance

Privately held CSI reports annual revenue of around $13 million the amount for 2014. The company reported $14 million revenue for 2013 and $14 million for 2012. It maintains about $1.6 billion in assets according its report.

Strategy

In 2015 CSI agreed to sell 35% of its common stock to Century Tokyo Leasing Corporation one of the largest leasing companies in Japan. Century Tokyo offers IT and automobile leasing as well as highly specialized financing for real estate shipping aircraft healthcare and environmental energy. The companies have done business with each other since 2003 and have had a joint marketing agreement for three years.

EXECUTIVES

President and COO, Stephen G. (Steve) Hamilton, age 60
Vice Chairman and CEO, E. William (Bill) Gillula, age 70
EVP and General Counsel, Lorraine Cherrick
President EPC Inc., Dan Fuller
President International Division, Arnaldo Rodriguez
EVP and National Sales Manager, Craig Ault
EVP and Chief Pricing Officer, Phil Cagney
EVP and CFO, Fred OÃNeal
EVP and Chief Credit Officer, Don Pratt
Vice President, Tom Brown
Vice President Lease Management, Kathie Haberstroh-nelke
Senior Vice President Sales, Chip Deson

Assistant Vice President Of Finance, Matt Kersting
Vice President Accounting, Janine Todd
Legal Secretary, Shannon Hulahan
Assistant Vice President Of Applications Development, Bill Elmore
Assistant Vice President, Joe Finnagan
Assistant Vice President Corporate Tax, Kirk Kasicki
Vice President, Tony Ruggeri
Vice President, Dan Toscano
Senior Vice President Marketing, Rick Guilander
Vice President, Michelle Thompson
Vice President, Nikki Douglas
Marketing Vice President, Mark Crain
Vice President, Karyn Voorhees
Vice President Marketing, Tim Tucker
Vice President, Jason Brock
Senior Vice President, Chris Schmidt
Vice President, Steve Schokmiller
Exective Vice President Syndications, Carlos Milian
Vice President and Assistant General Counsel (2000), Jeffrey L (Jeff) Rousseau
Vice President Finance, Donald (Don) Pratt
Senior Vice President, Mike Nichter
Executive Vice President And Co Chief Financial Officer, Frederick (Fred) Neal
Senior Vice President, Eric Ausubel
Chairman, Kenneth B. (Ken) Steinback, age 73

LOCATIONS

HQ: CSI LEASING INC.
9990 OLD OLIVE STREET RD # 101, SAINT LOUIS, MO 631415930
Phone: 314 997-4934
Web: WWW.CSILEASING.COM

PRODUCTS/OPERATIONS

Lifecycle Services
Leasing consultation
Financing options
Consolidation of leased assets from multiple manufacturers
Online tracking of leased assets
Disposal of equipment and sanitizing of hard drives

COMPETITORS

Blackwell Consulting	Pacific Rim Capital
CalFirst	Pitney Bowes
Dell	Pomeroy IT
HP Financial Services	Syscap
IBM Global Financing	ePlus
Ingram Micro	

HISTORICAL FINANCIALS

Company Type: Private

Income Statement

FYE: June 30

	REVENUE ($ mil.)	NET INCOME ($ mil.)	NET PROFIT MARGIN	EMPLOYEES
06/09	362	16	4.5%	540
06/03	531	14	2.7%	—
06/02	502	13	2.7%	—
06/01	576	0	—	—
Annual Growth	(5.6%)	—	—	—

2009 Year-End Financials

Return on assets: 8.0%
Return on equity: 4.5%
Current ratio: —

Cash ($ mil.): 21

CTSC LLC

CTSC (Chenega Technology Services Corporation) is a certified Alaska Native Corporation (ANC) that provides support services to federal agencies.

Its core competencies include base operations and facilities management engineering information technology intelligence support logistics and training. Partnering with prime government contractors and sub-contractors CTSC offers information systems development system integration support to military operations network engineering and technical analysis. As an ANC the company enjoys no-bid contracts with the government. CTSC is a subsidiary of Chenega Corporation.

CTSC oversees four additional subsidiaries –Chenega Advanced Solutions and Engineering Chenega Integrated Systems Chenega Management and Chenega Operations Services.

EXECUTIVES

President & CEO Chenega Corporation, Charles W. Totemoff
President, Ken Ogden
Director Human Resources, Melissa Boone
Auditors: MCGLADREY LLP FREDERICK MARY

LOCATIONS

HQ: CTSC LLC
10505 FURNACE RD STE 205, LORTON, VA 220792636
Phone: 703 493-9880
Web: WWW.CHENEGA.JOBS

COMPETITORS

Arctic Slope Regional Corporation	Sealaska
	chugach alaska

HISTORICAL FINANCIALS

Company Type: Private

Income Statement

FYE: September 30

	REVENUE ($ mil.)	NET INCOME ($ mil.)	NET PROFIT MARGIN	EMPLOYEES
09/09	181	15	8.8%	620
09/08	582	14	2.4%	—
09/07	0	0	—	—
Annual Growth	—	—	—	—

2009 Year-End Financials

Return on assets: 9.3%
Return on equity: 8.8%
Current ratio: 1.60

Cash ($ mil.): —

CUMBERLAND COUNTY HOSPITAL SYSTEM INC.

Don't fear for a lack of medical services at Cumberland County Hospital System (doing business as Cape Fear Valley Health System). The medical provider comprises five acute-care and specialty hospitals with about 765 total beds and more than a dozen primary-care physician practices scattered throughout the region in North Carolina. The hospital system serves residents of coastal North Carolina providing general and specialized medical services such as cancer treatment open-heart surgery psychiatric care and rehabilitation. It also operates the HealthPlex fitness and wellness facility and provides home health and hospice services.

Operations

Cumberland County Hospital System is the ninth-largest health systems in North Carolina with more than 935000 patient visits annually. It is also Cumberland County's largest non-government employer.The system's 490-bed county hospital Cape Fear Valley Medical Center specializes in heart care cancer treatment and surgical services. Cumberland's other health centers include: the 66-bed acute care Highsmith-Rainey Specialty Hospital; the 78-bed Cape Fear Valley Rehabilitation Center; Bladen County Hospital; and the 41-bed acute care Hoke Hospital.Additionally the system's Cape Fear Valley Behavioral Health Care boasts a 32-bed psychiatric facility a full-service Risk Labor and Delivery department a Level-III Neonatal Intensive Care Unit (UNIT) for newborns and a pediatric Intensive Care Unit (PICU).

Geographic Reach

Cumberland County Hospital System's facilities are located throughout the six-county Cape Fear region near the city of Wilmington in the Southeastern part of North Carolina.Financial PerformanceCumberland's revenue fell by 2% to $646 million in 2014 primarily due declines in patient revenue. Despite declining revenue the system's excess of revenue over expenses grew by 13% to $36.5 million mostly thanks to lower salary expenses but also thanks to lower medical supply costs and fewer other expenses. Cumberland's cash generated from operations rose by 15% to $51 million mostly because the system spent less cash on its employee and vendor payments.

EXECUTIVES

Respiratory Therapy Director, Christopher (Chris) Meredith
Senior Vice President For Human Resources, William Pryor
Vice President, Lynda Clark
Pharmd, Amy Jones
Treasurer, James Shearer
Board Member, Teresa Jackson
Secretary Supply Chain Services, Michelle (Mitch) Hewitt
Auditors: DELOITTE TAX LLP RALEIGH NC

LOCATIONS

HQ: CUMBERLAND COUNTY HOSPITAL SYSTEM INC.
1638 OWEN DR, FAYETTEVILLE, NC 283043424
Phone: 910 609-4000
Web: WWW.CAPEFEARVALLEY.COM

PRODUCTS/OPERATIONS

2014 Sales

	% of total
Net patient service revenue	96
Other revenue	4
Total	**100**

Selected Services

Birth center
Healthplex
Heart and vascular
Imaging/diagnostics
Minority health
Neuroscience
Orthopedics
Outpatient services
Pediatrics
Physician practice
Rehabilitation
Scancer treatment
Surgical services
Weight loss surgery

COMPETITORS

Alamance Regional Medical Center
Annie Penn Hospital
Carolinas HealthCare System
Cone Health
Danville Regional Medical Center
Duke University Health System
High Point Regional Health System
Morehead Memorial Hospital
Rex Healthcare
Rowan Regional Medical Center
UNC Hospitals
Vidant Health

Wake Forest University Baptist Medical Center
WakeMed

HISTORICAL FINANCIALS
Company Type: Private

Income Statement
FYE: September 30

	REVENUE ($ mil.)	NET INCOME ($ mil.)	NET PROFIT MARGIN	EMPLOYEES
09/07	504	23	4.6%	5,000
09/06	492	29	6.0%	—
09/05	1,753	0	0.0%	—
Annual Growth	(46.4%)	28202.0%	—	—

2007 Year-End Financials
Return on assets: 4.7%   Cash ($ mil.): 11
Return on equity: 4.6%
Current ratio: 1.30

CUMBERLAND COUNTY SCHOOLS

Auditors: HAIGH BYRD & LAMBERT LLP FA

LOCATIONS

HQ: CUMBERLAND COUNTY SCHOOLS
2465 GILLESPIE ST, FAYETTEVILLE, NC 283063053
Phone: 910 678-2300
Web: WWW.CCS.K12.NC.US

HISTORICAL FINANCIALS
Company Type: Private

Income Statement
FYE: June 30

	REVENUE ($ mil.)	NET INCOME ($ mil.)	NET PROFIT MARGIN	EMPLOYEES
06/11	444	3	0.8%	6,210
06/09	454	0	0.1%	—
06/06	0	0	—	—
06/05	0	0	—	—
Annual Growth	—	—	—	—

2011 Year-End Financials
Return on assets: —   Cash ($ mil.): 69
Return on equity: 0.8%
Current ratio: —

CYCLE LINK (U.S.A.) INC.

LOCATIONS

HQ: CYCLE LINK (U.S.A.) INC.
1330 VALLEY VISTA DR, DIAMOND BAR, CA 917653910
Phone: 909 861-5888
Web: WWW.CYCLELINK.COM

HISTORICAL FINANCIALS
Company Type: Private

Income Statement
FYE: December 31

	REVENUE ($ mil.)	NET INCOME ($ mil.)	NET PROFIT MARGIN	EMPLOYEES
12/14	435	2	0.5%	41
12/12	406	0	0.1%	—
Annual Growth	3.6%	145.1%	—	—

2014 Year-End Financials
Return on assets: 4.6%   Cash ($ mil.): 1
Return on equity: 0.5%
Current ratio: 0.80

CYSTIC FIBROSIS FOUNDATION

The Cystic Fibrosis Foundation funds cystic fibrosis (CF) research and medical programs. Founded in 1955 the organization supports clinical trials and specialized health-care centers provides grants for independent research operates university research centers encourages drug development through matching funds and offers CF-related information and educational materials. Its Cystic Fibrosis Foundation Therapeutics (CFFT) subsidiary partners with pharmaceutical companies and research facilities to develop CF drugs. The foundation provides funding training and accreditation for about 110 treatment centers in the US. It has about 75 chapters and branch offices nationwide.

EXECUTIVES

Vice President Of Communications, Marybeth McMahon
Vice President For Government Affairs, Mary Dwight
Board Member, Gary Eisenberger
Auditors: PRICEWATERHOUSECOOPERS LLP M

LOCATIONS

HQ: CYSTIC FIBROSIS FOUNDATION
6931 ARLINGTON RD STE 200, BETHESDA, MD 208145269
Phone: 301 951-4422
Web: WWW.CFF.ORG

PRODUCTS/OPERATIONS

2010 Revenue Sources

	$ mil.	% of total
Pharmacy	137	44
Special events	81	26
Royalties	53	17
General contributions	37	11
Interest	.6	1
Other	2	1
Total	**313**	**100**

HISTORICAL FINANCIALS
Company Type: Private

Income Statement
FYE: December 31

	REVENUE ($ mil.)	NET INCOME ($ mil.)	NET PROFIT MARGIN	EMPLOYEES
12/13	405	247	60.9%	550
12/12	297	175	58.8%	—
12/08	138	(2)	—	—
12/07	246	0	—	—
Annual Growth	8.6%	—	—	—

2013 Year-End Financials
Return on assets: 5.6% Cash ($ mil.): 57
Return on equity: 60.9%
Current ratio: 0.70

D REYNOLDS COMPANY LLC

LOCATIONS
HQ: D REYNOLDS COMPANY LLC
2680 SYLVANIA CROSS DR, FORT WORTH, TX
761375023
Phone: 214 630-9000
Web: WWW.REYNCO.COM

HISTORICAL FINANCIALS
Company Type: Private

Income Statement
FYE: December 31

	REVENUE ($ mil.)	NET INCOME ($ mil.)	NET PROFIT MARGIN	EMPLOYEES
12/13	559	40	7.3%	360
12/12	562	46	8.3%	—
12/06	378	23	6.3%	—
12/05	0	0	—	—
Annual Growth	—	—	—	—

2013 Year-End Financials
Return on assets: 6.8% Cash ($ mil.): —
Return on equity: 7.3%
Current ratio: 1.00

D W W CO. INC.

First Orange County then the world —or at least as far as Arizona and Mexico. Megadealer David Wilson Automotive Group has its roots in Orange County California with 16 branches that stretch to east to Scottsdale and now south to Puerto Vallarta Mexico. David Wilson's Automotive locations sell new and used Acura Ford Honda and Mazda cars as well as Toyota and Lexus brand vehicles. The group's dealerships also operate parts and service departments; some offer fleet services. Dealership Web sites allow customers to search inventory schedule service appointments and request quotes. David Wilson owns the company that bears his name

The company's growth strategy includes promoting form within. The owner hires sales managers only and promotes them to general managers over time as openings emerge. He also offers higher pay and benefits that many of his peers but demands that sales target are achieved.

Wilson graduated with from college in 1970 with a degree in religion and philosophy but found that his true calling was to the people on the highways not the ones in the pews. In 1985 Wilson bought Toyota of Orange and planted the seeds of his empire.

EXECUTIVES
Chairman and CEO, David Wilson

LOCATIONS
HQ: D W W CO. INC.
1400 N TUSTIN ST, ORANGE, CA 928673902
Phone: 714 639-6750
Web: WWW.TOYOTAOFORANGE.COM

COMPETITORS

AutoNation	Penske Motor Group
Holman Enterprises	Tuttle-Click
Marty Franich	piercey automotive

HISTORICAL FINANCIALS
Company Type: Private

Income Statement
FYE: December 31

	REVENUE ($ mil.)	NET INCOME ($ mil.)	NET PROFIT MARGIN	EMPLOYEES
12/08	162	7	4.6%	135
12/07	199	7	3.8%	—
12/06	229	12	5.2%	—
12/05	214	0	—	—
Annual Growth	(8.8%)	—	—	—

2008 Year-End Financials
Return on assets: 0.6% Cash ($ mil.): 23
Return on equity: 4.6%
Current ratio: 0.20

D/L COOPERATIVE INC.

Yes the farmer takes a wife then hi-ho the dairy-o the farmer takes membership in milk-marketing organizations such as Dairylea Cooperative. Owned by some 2000 dairy farmers in the northeastern US Dairylea processes and markets 6.3 billion pounds of milk for its farmers annually to dairy-product customers including food manufacturers. Its Agri-Services holding company provides members with a full range of financial and farm-management services as well as insurance. Its Empire Livestock Marketing unit operates regional livestock auction locations. Dairylea which was established in 1907 by New York dairy farmers merged with the US's largest milk marketing coop Dairy Farmers of America in 2014.

Ownership

Dairylea joined Kansas City Missouri-based Dairy Farmers of America (DFA) in April 2014 to expand its geographic coverage. Prior to joining DFA Dairylea has had a joint marketing venture (Dairy Marketing Services or DMS) with the national coop. DFA has 13000 members in 48 states. The Dairylea name became a brand of DFA and maintained a field office and staff in Syracuse.

Geographic Reach

Dairylea sells 6 billion pounds of raw milk annually through a milk-marketing network that stretches from Maine to Ohio to Maryland.

Services provided by holding company Agri-Services LLC include insurance coverage information management livestock marketing loan programs milk price risk management services business planning and consulting services purchasing programs and investment and retirement planning advice.

Operations

Through its DMS partnership with Dairy Farmers of America Dairylea sells and distributes raw milk. DMS serves both organizations as well as independent producers and cooperatives that produce 16 billion pounds of milk each year.

Financial Performance

Dairylea has annual sales of about $1 billion.

EXECUTIVES
CFO, Gregory I. (Greg) Wickham
President Chairman, William Beeman
Treasurer and Director, David R. Chamberlain
Assistant Treasurer and Director, Calvin Wood
Public Relations, Jennifer Huson
Media Contact, Karen Cartier
Executive Assistant, Krista Piper
Vice President, David White
Second VP Board of Directors and Secretary, William Beeman
Treasurer and Director, David R. Chamberlain
First VP Board of Directors, Raymond J. Diebold
Assistant Treasurer and Director, Calvin Wood
Director, Todd Hathorn
Director, G. Douglas Young
Director, James Madigan
Director, Sanford Stauffer
Director, Glen Gasstrom
Director, Lawrence Woodruff Jr.
Director, Edgar A. King
Director, Dale Van Erden
Director, Arnold Dueppengiesser
Director, Donald Risser
Director, Richard Baldwin
Auditors: HERBEIN COMPANY INC READING

LOCATIONS
HQ: D/L COOPERATIVE INC.
5001 BRITTONFIELD PKWY, EAST SYRACUSE, NY
130579201
Phone: 315 233-1000
Web: WWW.DAIRYLEA.COM

PRODUCTS/OPERATIONS

Selected Affiliates & Subsidiaries
Agri-Edge Development
Agri-Max Financial Services
Agri-Services Agency
Dairy Risk Management Services
Eagle Dairy Direct
Empire Livestock Marketing Services

COMPETITORS

Agri-Mark	Keller' s Creamery
Associated Milk Producers	Land O' Lakes
Dean Foods	Maryland & Virginia Milk Producers
Foremost Farms	Quality Chekd
Garelick Farms	

HISTORICAL FINANCIALS
Company Type: Private

Income Statement
FYE: March 31

	REVENUE ($ mil.)	NET INCOME ($ mil.)	NET PROFIT MARGIN	EMPLOYEES
03/11	1,333	1	0.1%	107
03/10	1,066	1	0.1%	—
Annual Growth	25.1%	7.6%	—	—

2011 Year-End Financials
Return on assets: 9.2% Cash ($ mil.): 14
Return on equity: 0.1%
Current ratio: 0.60

DAIRYAMERICA INC.

Auditors: DELOITTE & TOUCHE LLP FRESNO

LOCATIONS

HQ: DAIRYAMERICA INC.
7815 N PALM AVE STE 250, FRESNO, CA 937115531
Phone: 559 251-1078
Web: WWW.CALIFORNIADAIRIES.COM

HISTORICAL FINANCIALS

Company Type: Private

Income Statement

	REVENUE ($ mil.)	NET INCOME ($ mil.)	NET PROFIT MARGIN	EMPLOYEES
12/13	1,617	18	1.1%	51
12/12	1,222	21	1.8%	—
12/11	1,319	19	1.5%	—
12/10	1,514	0	—	—
Annual Growth	2.2%			

2013 Year-End Financials

Return on assets: —
Return on equity: 1.1%
Current ratio: 1.60
Cash ($ mil.): —

DAKOTA ELECTRIC ASSOCIATION

The Dakota Electric Association delivers electricity to residents of southeastern Minnesota the Gopher State so they don't have to burrow underground to outlast those long cold winters. The member-owned utility serves more than 103000 customers in portions of Dakota Goodhue Rice and Scott counties south of Minneapolis-St. Paul. The co-op gets its power wholesale from transmission cooperative Great River Energy and distributes it more than 4010 miles of power lines nearly two-thirds of which are buried. Dakota Electric is pushing energy efficiency programs and products to help save its customers money.

Geographic Reach

The company serves parts of Dakota Goodhue Scott and Rice counties in southern Minnesota.

Operations

Dakota Electric purchases power from Great River Energy and distributes electricity to commercial residential farming street lighting and irrigation customers. It has 2792 miles of underground power lines and 1220 miles of overhead lines.

Financial Performance

In 2013 the company's revenue increased by 2%. Dakota Electric's commercial members accounted for 41% of revenues; residential and farming 58%; and street lighting and irrigation 1%.Its net income grew by 5% in 2013 thanks to higher revenues and the absence of a loss from discontinued operations.Dakota Electric's operating cash inflow increased to $13.13 million in fiscal 2013 (from $5.61 million in 2012) due to higher net income and a change in the working capital.

Strategy

The co-op seeks to maintain and upgrade its power infrastructure and service to its members while keep power costs low.

As part of this strategy Dakota Electric operates a for-profit subsidiary Midwest Energy Services. That unit's subsidiaries provides complementary services to Dakota Electric's main power delivery business. They offer standby power generator and solar panel installation and leasing services (Energy Alternatives) and substation engineering services (Consulting Engineers Group).

Company Background

Dakota Electric was formed in 1937 as part of the Roosevelt Administration's national rural electrification drive.

EXECUTIVES

Vice President, Dirk Rotty
Vice President Regulatory, Stan McNeil
Secretary, Bill Holton
Secretary, Paul Trapp
Board Of Directors, David Jones

LOCATIONS

HQ: DAKOTA ELECTRIC ASSOCIATION
4300 220TH ST W, FARMINGTON, MN 550249583
Phone: 651 463-6212
Web: WWW.DAKOTAELECTRIC.COM

COMPETITORS

ALLETE	WEC Energy
Connexus Energy	Xcel Energy
Otter Tail	

HISTORICAL FINANCIALS

Company Type: Private

Income Statement

	REVENUE ($ mil.)	NET INCOME ($ mil.)	NET PROFIT MARGIN	EMPLOYEES
12/13	205	8	4.2%	100,000
12/09	178	7	3.9%	—
12/08	185	6	3.8%	—
12/06	132	0	—	—
Annual Growth	6.4%			

2013 Year-End Financials

Return on assets: 18.7%
Return on equity: 4.2%
Current ratio: 0.50
Cash ($ mil.): —

DAKOTA SUPPLY GROUP INC.

Dakota Supply Group (DSG) distributes electrical communications and mechanical equipment to customers through more than a dozen branch locations in Minnesota North Dakota and South Dakota. The company stocks approximately 25000 products. DSG carries products from 3Com 3M A. O. Smith Buckingham Manufacturing Corning Emerson Electric Ferraz Shawmut General Electric Honeywell Hubbell Moen Schneider Electric and Zurn Industries among other manufacturers. The company was founded in 1898. An employee stock ownership plan holds nearly all of Dakota Supply.

EXECUTIVES

Territory Manager Northern Minnesota, Mike McNabb
Auditors: EIDEBAILLY LLP FARGO NORTH D

LOCATIONS

HQ: DAKOTA SUPPLY GROUP INC.
2601 3RD AVE N, FARGO, ND 581024016
Phone: 701 237-9440
Web: WWW.DAKOTASUPPLYGROUP.COM

COMPETITORS

Border States Electric	Viking Electric
J. H. Larson	

HISTORICAL FINANCIALS

Company Type: Private

Income Statement

	REVENUE ($ mil.)	NET INCOME ($ mil.)	NET PROFIT MARGIN	EMPLOYEES
12/13	369	16	4.5%	620
12/12	297	15	5.3%	—
12/11	211	13	6.6%	—
12/09	162	0	—	—
Annual Growth	22.9%			

2013 Year-End Financials

Return on assets: 4.2%
Return on equity: 4.5%
Current ratio: 1.30
Cash ($ mil.): 2

DANA-FARBER CANCER INSTITUTE INC.

The Dana-Farber Cancer Institute fights cancer on two fronts: It provides treatment to cancer patients young and old and researches new cancer diagnostics treatments and preventions. The organization's scientists also research AIDS treatments and cures for a host of other deadly diseases. Patients receive treatment from Dana-Farber through its cancer centers operated in conjunction with Brigham and Women's Hospital Children's Hospital Boston and Massachusetts General Hospital. The institute is also a principal teaching affiliate of Harvard Medical School. Dana-Farber is funded by the National Cancer Institute the National Institute of Allergy and Infectious Diseases and private contributions.

Geographic Reach

The institute primarily serves patients in New England. Dana-Farber's main campus is in Boston's Longwood Medical Area and it also has facilities in Brighton Milford South Weymouth and Pittsfield (all in Massachussets); Londonderry New Hampshire; and Waterford Connecticut. Dana-Farber Community Cancer Care physician practices are in seven communities throughout eastern Massachusetts.

Operations

Dana-Farber reports more than 38300 patient visits a year and is involved in some 700 clinical trials.

Dana-Farber provides care to children and adults with cancer while advancing the understanding diagnosis treatment cure and prevention of cancer and related diseases. As an affiliate of Harvard Medical School and a Comprehensive Cancer Center designated by the National Cancer Institute the Institute also provides training for new generations of physicians and scientists designs programs that promote public health particularly among high-risk and underserved populations and disseminates innovative patient therapies and scientific discoveries to target community across the US and around the world. In 2014 the hospital has a community benefit of $6.75 million.

Financial Performance

The institute reported a 7% rise in revenues in 2014 thanks to an increase in patient service revenues unrestricted contributions and bequests and other operating revenues. Revenues from the Medicare and Medicaid programs accounted for approximately 25% and 5% respectively of Dana-Farber's net patient service revenue in 2014Net income decreased by 11% due to an increase in temporarily restricted net assets and contributions.

Strategy

When it comes to patient care Dana-Farber emphasizes the importance of forming research and treatment partnerships with other health care organizations. To that end the institute has opened a handful of treatment clinics on other medical campuses including one at Faulkner Hospital in southwest Boston and another at Milford Regional Medical Center in Massachusetts.

Along with expanding on other campuses Dana-Farber built a new cancer care center on its main campus in Boston.

Although Dana-Farber directs its research efforts toward saving lives from deadly diseases some of its discoveries also bring in a tidy income as the company and its research partners occasionally license out their drug discoveries to pharmaceutical companies. In 2015 new research by Dana-Farber scientists raised the prospect of cancer therapy that works by converting a tumor's best friends in the immune system into its gravest enemies. In a study published in the journal Science an international collaboration of investigators from Dana-Farber Harvard Medical School Boston Children's Hospital and the University of Strasbourg uncovered a mechanism that allows key immune system cells to keep a steady rein on their more belligerent brother cells thereby protecting normal healthy tissue from assault. The discovery has powerful implications for cancer. By blocking the mechanism with a drug it may be possible to turn the attack-suppressing cells into tumor-attacking cells.

Company Background

In 2013 the institute and Lawrence + Memorial Cancer Center opened a $34.5 million 47000 sq.-ft. cancer facility in Waterford Connecticut.

The Yawkey Center for Cancer Care named in honor of long-time contributor The Yawkey Foundation opened in 2011 to serve a growing number of patients. The 275000-sq.-ft center's 14-stories house most of Dana-Farber's adult outpatient care. The building has more than 100 exam rooms about 140 infusion chairs and a number of consultation rooms for family and patients. It also connected Dana-Farber to other campus buildings and to its clinical partners Brigham and Women's Hospital and Children's Hospital Boston.

Dana-Farber Cancer Institute was founded as a children's cancer research foundation in 1947 by Dr. Sidney Farber. The institute later expanded its services to provide programs for adults as well as children.

EXECUTIVES

EVP and COO, Dorothy E. Puhy, age 63
President and CEO, Edward J. Benz
Chair Department of Radiation Oncology, Jay R. Harris
Chair Department of Medical Oncology, James D. Griffin
Chair Department of Pediatric Oncology, Stuart H. Orkin
Chief Scientific Officer, Barrett J. Rollins
CFO, Michael L. Reney
Chief Department of Imaging, Annick D. Van den Abbeele
Chief Surgical Officer, Scott J. Swanson

Chair Department of Psychosocial Oncology and Palliative Care, Susan D. Block
Chief Medical Officer, Craig A. Bunnell
Chief Clinical Research Officer, Bruce E. Johnson
Director Of Pharmacy, Sylvia Bartel
Vice President Nsg Clinical Services, Lori Buswell
Director Of Infection Control, Susan O'Rourke
Senior Vice President Human Resources, Deborah (Deb) Hicks
Medical Director for Clinical Trials Operations, Jeffrey (Jeff) Clark
Senior Vice President Communications, Steven Singer
Assistant Vice President Individual Giving, Berenice Ronthal
Vice President Research Administration and Finance, Mark Daniel
Assistant Vice President Development Marketing and Donor Relations, Jan Lawlor
Vice President Of Finance, John Stewart
Vice President Clinical Bussiness Development, Elizabeth Liebow
Medical Director, Lisa Manera
Director of Nursing and Clinical Services, Janet Bagley RN
Assistant Secretary, Kathleen Harkey

LOCATIONS

HQ: DANA-FARBER CANCER INSTITUTE INC.
450 BROOKLINE AVE, BOSTON, MA 022155450
Phone: 617 632-3000
Web: WWW.DANA-FARBER.ORG

PRODUCTS/OPERATIONS

2014 Sales

	% of total
Patients Services	62
Research	30
Unrestricted Contributions and Bequests	6
Other revenue	2
Total	**100**

Selected Clinical Affiliations

Dana-Farber/Brigham and Women's Cancer Center (outpatient services for adult cancer patients provided by Dana-Farber; and inpatient care provided by Brigham and Women's Hospital)
Dana-Farber/Children's Hospital Cancer Center (Dana-Farber Cancer Institute and Children's Hospital Boston outpatient care for children provided at Dana-Farber's Jimmy Fund Clinic)
Dana-Farber/Harvard Cancer Center (Beth Israel Deaconess Medical Center Brigham and Women's Hospital Children's Hospital Boston and Massachusetts General Hospital collaborate on research cancer prevention and treatments and therapies for cancer patients)
Dana-Farber/Lawrence + Memorial Cancer Center (cancer facility Waterford Connecticut).
Dana-Farber/Partners Cancer Care (consolidated adult oncology programs and clinical research of Dana-Farber Cancer Institute Brigham and Women's Hospital and Massachusetts General Hospital)

Selected Satellite Centers

Dana-Farber/Brigham and Women's Cancer Center at Faulkner Hospital in Jamaica Plain (southwest Boston area)
Dana-Farber/Brigham and Women's Cancer Center at Milford Regional Medical Center (Massachusetts)
Dana-Farber/Brigham and Women's Cancer Center in clinical affiliation with South Shore Hospital (South Weymouth Massachusetts)
Dana-Farber/New Hampshire Oncology-Hematology (Londonderry)
Adult Treatment Centers and Clinical Services
Blood Cancers
Breast Cancer
Cancer Genetics and Prevention
Cutaneous (Skin) Cancer
Gastrointestinal Cancer
Genitourinary Cancer
Gynecologic Cancer
Head and Neck Cancer
Hematology

Melanoma
Neuro-Oncology
Sarcoma
Thoracic (Lung) Cancer
Pediatric Treatment Centers and Clinical Services
Blood Disorders Center
Brain Tumor Center
Hematologic Malignancies Center
Solid Tumors Center
Stem Cell Transplant Center

COMPETITORS

Baystate Health
Beth Israel Deaconess Medical Center
Boston Medical Center
Brigham and Women's Hospital
Care New England
CareGroup
Children's National Medical Center
Emory Healthcare
Fox Chase Cancer Center
Johns Hopkins Medicine
MD Anderson Cancer Center
Mayo Clinic
Memorial Sloan-Kettering
Partners HealthCare
Roswell Park Cancer Institute
St. Elizabeth's Medical Center
St. Jude Children's Research Hospital

HISTORICAL FINANCIALS

Company Type: Private

Income Statement

FYE: September 30

	REVENUE ($ mil.)	NET INCOME ($ mil.)	NET PROFIT MARGIN	EMPLOYEES
09/13	635	56	8.8%	3,000
09/10	894	16	1.9%	—
09/09	816	28	3.5%	—
Annual Growth	**(6.1%)**	**18.4%**	**—**	**—**

2013 Year-End Financials

Return on assets: 11.0%   Cash ($ mil.): 84
Return on equity: 8.8%
Current ratio: 1.00

DANBURY HOSPITAL DEVELOPMENT FUND INC

Auditors: ERNST & YOUNG LLP HARTFORD C

LOCATIONS

HQ: DANBURY HOSPITAL DEVELOPMENT FUND INC
24 HOSPITAL AVE FL 6, DANBURY, CT 068106077
Phone: 203 797-7000

HISTORICAL FINANCIALS

Company Type: Private

Income Statement

FYE: September 30

	REVENUE ($ mil.)	NET INCOME ($ mil.)	NET PROFIT MARGIN	EMPLOYEES
09/12	502	53	10.6%	6
09/09	5	(2)	—	—
09/08	12	5	47.0%	—
09/01	0	0	—	—
Annual Growth	**—**	**—**	**—**	**—**

2012 Year-End Financials

Return on assets: 5.1%   Cash ($ mil.): 54
Return on equity: 10.6%
Current ratio: 1.80

DANIS BUILDING CONSTRUCTION COMPANY

Danis Building Construction can reach from the Buckeye state to the Sunshine state. The company provides commercial and industrial construction services in Ohio Indiana Kentucky Tennessee North Carolina Georgia and Florida. The third-generation family-owned company offers construction management design/build general construction and build-to-suit lease-back services. It specializes in public and private building and industrial projects such as offices health care facilities retail complexes hotels cultural facilities schools and industrial plants. Its projects have included the Cincinnati Children's Hospital and a federal courthouse in Kentucky. B.G. Danis established the company in 1916. Danis Building Construction was once part of real estate and construction group The Danis Companies which built such notable Ohio landmarks as the Orville Wright home Kettering Tower and the University of Dayton Arena. In 1997 it became incorporated as an independent entity from The Danis Companies. Danis operates four offices in Cincinnati Columbus and Dayton Ohio and Jacksonville Florida.

EXECUTIVES

Vice President, Marty Mulhall
Vice President Of Operation, Robert (Bob) Fernandez
Vice President of Business Development, Troy Erbes
Vice President, Brian Didiano
Auditors: BARNES DENNIG & CO LTD CI

LOCATIONS

HQ: DANIS BUILDING CONSTRUCTION COMPANY
3233 NEWMARK DR, MIAMISBURG, OH 453425422
Phone: 937 228-1225
Web: WWW.DANIS.COM

COMPETITORS

Albert M. Higley
Corna Kokosing
 Construction Company
Envoy Inc.

Gilbane Building
 Company
Messer Construction
Ruscilli Construction

HISTORICAL FINANCIALS

Company Type: Private

Income Statement

FYE: December 31

	REVENUE ($ mil.)	NET INCOME ($ mil.)	NET PROFIT MARGIN	EMPLOYEES
12/08	217	0	—	475
12/07	208	0	—	—
12/06	0	0	—	—
12/04	0	0	—	—
Annual Growth	—	—	—	—

2008 Year-End Financials

Return on assets: 15.2%
Return on equity: —
Current ratio: 0.40
Cash ($ mil.): 21

DARTMOUTH-HITCHCOCK CLINIC

The New England Alliance for Health (NEAH) brings together health care facilities and professionals looking to improve health in the New England region. Members of the alliance include about 20 community hospitals home health care agencies and mental health centers in New Hampshire Vermont and Massachusetts. While the members collaborate on wellness quality and communication initiatives each member of the alliance is an independently owned and operated not-for-profit organization with its own board of directors. Collaborative services provided by NEAH include procurement staff training information technology quality control and finance as well as the coordination of facility policies and planning.

Geographic Reach

New Hampshire holds the largest number of NEAH members (10) while the organization has six participants in Vermont and one in Massachusetts.

Operations

NEAH's core services are provided to and funded by all of its member organizations. In addition the alliance provides some voluntary services (such as licensing and insurance services) that are funded only by the participating members.

An affiliated organization the New England Pharmacy Collaborative (NEPC) handles drug purchases for the health care members.

Ownership

NEAH is a limited liability corporation owned and managed by one of its members the Mary Hitchcock Memorial Hospital (part of the Dartmouth-Hitchcock Medical Center) in Lebanon New Hampshire. However its services are funded by all of its member facilities.

Company Background

NEAH was formerly known as Dartmouth-Hitchcock Alliance; it changed its name in 2009.

EXECUTIVES

Medical Director Information Systems, Peter J Molberg
COO, Stephen LeBlanc
Medical Director Vascular Lab, Robert (Bob) Zwolak
Medical Director, Sanders Burstein
Director Of Health Information Management, Sharene Evans
Vice Presidenthuman Resources, John (Jack) Malanowski
Vice President Clinical Services, Karen Buttrey
Vice President, Christine Schon
Medical Director, Timothy (Tim) Lukovits
Vice President Assistant Administrator Marketing and Planning, Deanna Howard
Vice President Revenue Management, Mary Boudewyns
Treasurer, Ellen Flaherty
Secretary To The Director, Michele Foley
Vice Chairman Department of Orthopaedics, Sohail Mirza
Auditors: PRICEWATEHOUSECOOPERS LLP BO

LOCATIONS

HQ: DARTMOUTH-HITCHCOCK CLINIC
1 MEDICAL CENTER DR, LEBANON, NH 037560001
Phone: 603 650-5000
Web: WWW.PATIENTS.DARTMOUTH-HITCHCOCK.ORG

PRODUCTS/OPERATIONS

Selected Services
Core Services

Financial Planning and Benchmarking
Information Services
Materials Management and Pharmacy Services
Professional Staff Education and Development
Program Administration
Quality Improvement/Loss Prevention
Other Services
Licenses
Property and Casualty Insurance Program

Selected Alliance Members
Massachusetts
 Cooley Dickinson Health Care (Northampton)
New Hampshire
 Alice Peck Day Memorial Hospital (Lebanon)
 Cheshire Medical Center (Keene)
 Cottage Hospital (Woodsville)
 Dartmouth-Hitchcock Medical Center (Lebanon includes Mary Hitchcock Memorial Hospital)
 Monadnock Community Hospital
 New London Hospital
 Upper Connecticut Valley Hospital (Colebrook)
 Valley Regional Hospital (Claremont)
 Weeks Medical Center (Lancaster)
 West Central Behavioral Health (Lebanon)
Vermont
 Brattleboro Memorial Hospital
 Grace Cottage Hospital (Townshend)
 Mt. Ascutney Hospital (Windsor)
 Northeastern Vermont Regional Hospital (St. Johnsbury)
 Southwestern Vermont Medical Center (Bennington)
 Springfield Hospital
 VNA and Hospice of VT and NH

COMPETITORS

AMN Healthcare
HealthTrust
MedAssets
Novation

Premier Inc.
Vizient Inc.
Winchester Healthcare

HISTORICAL FINANCIALS

Company Type: Private

Income Statement

FYE: June 30

	REVENUE ($ mil.)	NET INCOME ($ mil.)	NET PROFIT MARGIN	EMPLOYEES
06/13*	406	18	4.6%	9,300
09/08	5	0	—	—
09/06	0	0	0.1%	—
Annual Growth	138.9%	307.7%	—	—

*Fiscal year change

DATS TRUCKING INC.

DATS Trucking specializes in less-than-truckload (LTL) freight transportation in the western US but that's not all there is to the company's operations. In addition to its LTL operations in which freight from multiple shippers is combined into a single trailer DATS Trucking provides truckload transportation. The company's tanker division Overland Petroleum transports gasoline diesel fuel and other petroleum products. Overall DATS Trucking operates a fleet of about 500 tractors and 2500 trailers. It offers LTL service outside its home territory via The Reliance Network a group of regional carriers that covers the US and Canada. President and CEO Don Ipson founded DATS Trucking in 1988.

The company operates from a network of about 40 terminals to serve destinations in Arizona California Colorado Idaho Nevada New Mexico Utah Texas and Wyoming. It has been gradually adding facilities in order to enhance its service offerings. Outside its core territory DATS Trucking serves portions of the Pacific Northwest and the southern US through partnerships with other carriers.

Along with its transportation operations DATS Trucking provides warehousing and distribution services.

EXECUTIVES

Vice President Of Operations, David Ipson

LOCATIONS

HQ: DATS TRUCKING INC.
321 N OLD HIGHWAY 91, HURRICANE, UT
847373194
Phone: 435 673-1886
Web: WWW.DATSTRUCKING.COM

COMPETITORS

Bulkmatic	Schneider National
Central Freight Lines	Swift Transportation
FedEx Freight	UPS Freight
J.B. Hunt	Werner Enterprises
Kenan Advantage Group	YRC Worldwide
Penn Tank Lines	

HISTORICAL FINANCIALS

Company Type: Private

Income Statement

FYE: December 31

	REVENUE ($ mil.)	NET INCOME ($ mil.)	NET PROFIT MARGIN	EMPLOYEES
12/07	717	1	0.3%	475
12/06	658	7	1.2%	—
12/05	600	1	0.2%	—
12/04	391	0	—	—
Annual Growth 22.3%	—	—	—	—

DAVIDSON'S INC.

Auditors: EIDE BAILLY LLP PHOENIX ARIZ

LOCATIONS

HQ: DAVIDSON' S INC.
6100 WILKINSON DR, PRESCOTT, AZ 863016162
Phone: 928 776-8055
Web: WWW.GALLERYOFGUNS.COM

HISTORICAL FINANCIALS

Company Type: Private

Income Statement

FYE: November 30

	REVENUE ($ mil.)	NET INCOME ($ mil.)	NET PROFIT MARGIN	EMPLOYEES
11/14	322	15	4.7%	89
11/13	395	20	5.1%	—
11/12	265	11	4.4%	—
11/11	182	0	—	—
Annual Growth 21.0%	—	—	—	—

2014 Year-End Financials

Return on assets: 6.1%　　　Cash ($ mil.): 1
Return on equity: 4.7%
Current ratio: 0.80

DBSI INC

LOCATIONS

HQ: DBSI INC
12426 W EXPLORER DR, BOISE, ID 837131572
Phone: 208 955-9800
Web: WWW.DBSI.COM

HISTORICAL FINANCIALS

Company Type: Private

Income Statement

FYE: December 31

	ASSETS ($ mil.)	NET INCOME ($ mil.)	INCOME AS % OF ASSETS	EMPLOYEES
12/07	244	15	6.4%	70
12/06	168	2	1.6%	—
12/05	150	25	17.0%	—
12/04	70	0	—	—
Annual Growth 51.2%	—	—	—	—

2007 Year-End Financials

Return on assets: 4.9%　　　Sales ($ mil): 625
Return on equity: 2.5%

DCR SYSTEM HOUSE INC.

LOCATIONS

HQ: DCR SYSTEM HOUSE INC.
660 LINTON BLVD STE 218C, DELRAY BEACH, FL
334448187
Phone: 561 998-3737

HISTORICAL FINANCIALS

Company Type: Private

Income Statement

FYE: December 31

	REVENUE ($ mil.)	NET INCOME ($ mil.)	NET PROFIT MARGIN	EMPLOYEES
12/14	484	2	0.5%	40
12/13	438	2	0.5%	—
Annual Growth 10.5%	8.2%	—	—	—

2014 Year-End Financials

Return on assets: 0.5%　　　Cash ($ mil.): 3
Return on equity: 0.5%
Current ratio: 4.90

DCR WORKFORCE INC.

LOCATIONS

HQ: DCR WORKFORCE INC.
7815 NW BACON SQ BLVD 224, BOCA RATON, FL
334871345
Phone: 561 998-3737
Web: WWW.DCRWORKFORCE.COM

HISTORICAL FINANCIALS

Company Type: Private

Income Statement

FYE: December 31

	REVENUE ($ mil.)	NET INCOME ($ mil.)	NET PROFIT MARGIN	EMPLOYEES
12/13	702	2	0.3%	82
12/12	548	2	0.5%	—
12/11	464	2	0.6%	—
12/01	12	0	—	—
Annual Growth 39.9%	—	—	—	—

2013 Year-End Financials

Return on assets: 0.7%　　　Cash ($ mil.): 3
Return on equity: 0.3%
Current ratio: 3.00

DE PAUL UNIVERSITY

In the land of da Bulls and da Bears there's DePaul. One of the largest private not-for-profit universities in the US DePaul has a total of about 24000 students attending classes at its five Chicago-area campuses. Also one of the country's largest Catholic institutions of higher learning the university offers more than 300 undergraduate and graduate programs through 10 colleges and schools including the Kellstadt Graduate School of Business and the College of Communication. It has a student teacher ratio of 17 to 1. DePaul was founded in 1898 by the Vincentian religious community and is named after 17th century French priest St. Vincent de Paul.

Geographic Reach

DePaul's five Chicago-area campuses are located in Lincoln Park the Loop Naperville Oak Forest and the O'Hare area. Although 67% of its students come from Illinois DePaul's student body represents the 50 US states and about 100 countries.

Financial Performance

DePaul has annual budget of about $550 million and its endowment is about $447 million. Undergraduate tuition for the 2014-2015 academic year was $34390.

EXECUTIVES

EVP Financial Affairs, Robert L. (Bob) Kozoman
VP Facilities, Robert (Bob) Janis
President, Dennis H. Holtschneider, age 53
Dean College of Commerce and Kellstadt Graduate School of Business, Ray Whittington
Dean School for New Learning, Marisa Alicea
Dean Theatre School, John Culbert
Dean College of Computing and Digital Media, David Miller
VP Information Services, Bob McCormick
Dean College of Communication, Salma Ghanem
Provost, Marten denBoer
VP Planning and Presidential Administration, Jay Braatz
SVP Enrollment Management, David Kalsbeek
Dean College of Science and Health, Gerald P. Koocher
Athletic Director, Jean Lenti-Ponsetto
Interim Dean College of Liberal Arts and Social Sciences, Lucy Rinehart
Dean College of Law, Jennifer Rosato Perea
Dean School of Education, Paul Zionts
Executive Vice President For Operations Loop, Susan (Sue) Carolan
Clinical Director, Alexander Brown

Vice President Enrollment Management, Glenna Ousley

Vice President of Finance Operating Loop Campus, Rebecca Awells

Associate Vice President of Academic Affairs, Charles (Chas) Strain

Director Of Admissions, Dennis Shea

Associate Vice President Advancement Services And Campaign Director, Erin Moran

Assistant Vice President Planned Giving, Joel Schaeffer

Associate Vice President Advocacy And Community Affairs, Cynthia Summers

Assistant Vice President for Marketing Communications, Gwyn Friend

Vice President Finance, Patricia (Pat) Butterfield

Assistant Vice President, Peter Harris

Associate Vice President Of Advancement, Abena Apea

Vice President Student Affairs, Eugene Zdziarski

Executive Vice President Academic Affairs, John Kozak

Vice President Teaching Learning Resources, Edward (Ed) Udovic

Associate Vice President Financial Aid, Paula Luff

Vice President Student Affairs, James Doyle

Assistant Vice President University Ministry Lpc, Guillermo Acampuzano

Assistant Vice President GEMS Loop Campus, Suzanne Adepeder

Associate Vice President Of Compensation, Ben Parma

Assistant Vice President Academic Affairs LOOP, Jane Gerard (Ginny) Csj

Vice President Student Affairs Lincoln Park Campus, Kathryn Ao'brien

Board Member, Finn Horvath

Secretary Treasurer, Leah Bryant

Board Member, R Ostrander

Auditors: KPMG LLP CHICAGO IL

LOCATIONS

HQ: DE PAUL UNIVERSITY
1 E JACKSON BLVD, CHICAGO, IL 606042287
Phone: 312 362-6714
Web: WWW.ITUNES.DEPAUL.EDU

HISTORICAL FINANCIALS

Company Type: Private

Income Statement

FYE: June 30

	REVENUE ($ mil.)	NET INCOME ($ mil.)	NET PROFIT MARGIN	EMPLOYEES
06/14	564	59	10.5%	3,895
06/13	558	76	13.6%	—
06/12	546	39	7.2%	—
06/11	535	0	—	—
Annual Growth	1.8%	—	—	—

2014 Year-End Financials

Return on assets: 7.9%
Return on equity: 10.5%
Current ratio: —
Cash ($ mil.): 50

DEACONESS HEALTH SYSTEM INC.

While it primarily presides over numerous health care facilities in the southwestern corner of Indiana Deaconess Health System also serves residents in parts of southeastern Illinois and western Kentucky. The system consists of two general

acute-care hospitals as well as specialty hospitals for women's health mental health and medical rehabilitation. Its flagship Deaconess Hospital boasts 365 beds and serves as a regional referral center. Deaconess Health also operates a standalone cancer treatment center medical group practice Deaconess Clinic and about 20 outpatient and urgent care clinics. Its Deaconess Health Plans unit is a PPO network that contracts with various health insurers.

Geographic Reach

Deaconess Health System primarily serves those who reside in 26 counties in Southern Indiana Southeast Illinois and West Kentucky.

Operations

As part of its operations the health system comprises half a dozen facilities including Deaconess Hospital (365 beds) Deaconness Gateway Hospital (120 beds) The Women's Hospital (50 beds) Deaconess Cross Pointe (60 beds) HealthSouth Deaconess Rehabilitation Hospital (80 beds) and The Heart Hospital of Deaconess Gateway (24 beds). It also operates primary care locations such as Deaconess Clinic Deaconess Primary Care for Seniors and Deaconess Urgent Care.

The hospital treats 18000 inpatients 350000 outpatients 65000 emergency patients and 7500 surgical patients each year. Financial Performance In 2014 net sales increased by 13% due to higher revenues from net patient service.Deaconess Health System's net patient service revenue increased due to increased contractual adjustments. Medicare and Medicaid together accounted 57% of total net sales in 2014. Commercial and managed care and Self pay and other accounted for 36% and 7% respectivelyIn 2014 net income increased by 40% compared to 2013. The primary reason was due to increased sales partially offset by decreased benefit related changes other than net periodic benefit cost.Deaconess Health System's net cash provided by the operating activities increased by 28%.

Strategy

Deaconess Health System has been focused on improving information technology systems including the implementation of an electronic health record (EHR) system. It has increased efficiencies through IT initiatives by installing new automated medication dispensing and prescription management programs.

MyChart is available at Deaconess Hospital Main Deaconess Gateway Deaconess Riley Hospital for Children The Heart Hospital Cross Point all Deaconess Clinic locations Deaconess Critical Care Deaconess Family Practice and Residency and Deaconess Primary Care for Seniors physician offices. MyChart is a secure online health management tool that connects MyChart patients to their personalized health information. MyChart contains inpatient and outpatient test results and information.In 2015 the company finalized a letter of intent to partner directly with Methodist Hospital on a not-for-profit joint venture to bring additional and enhanced healthcare services to Henderson. The joint venture will improve access to care providers and quality of care in Henderson. Deaconess Health System purchased 10-plus acres of land off Barret Boulevard near Walmart in Henderson in 2014.

Company Background

Founded in 1892 Deaconess Hospital is a teaching facility that offers residency and clinical education programs in addition to providing general and specialty inpatient care. It also conducts medical research programs.

EXECUTIVES

Pharmd, Meredith L Petty
Medical Director, Rodney Beeler
Medical Director, Thomas Davidson

Nursing Director, Jill Buttry
Vice President, Bruce Etneier
Operating Room Director, Leticia Bahr
Medical Director, Doug Hatler
Medical Director, Holly Schutz
Infection Control Director, Mellodee Montgomery
Vice President For Student, Evelyn Levino
Vice President Patient Care Services, Cherona J Hajewski
Director of Respiratory Therapy, Duane Hudson
Auditors: BLUE & CO LLC INDIANAPOLIS

LOCATIONS

HQ: DEACONESS HEALTH SYSTEM INC.
600 MARY ST, EVANSVILLE, IN 477101658
Phone: 812 450-5000
Web: WWW.DEACONESS.COM

PRODUCTS/OPERATIONS

Selected Services

Back & Spine
Behavioral Health
Cancer
Children' s Health
Clinical Research
Diabetes
Emergency Care
Joint Replacement
Orthopedic
Pain Management
Physical Medicine
Radiology
Respiratory
Senior Health
Weight Loss
Women' s Health
Wound Care

COMPETITORS

Ball Memorial Hospital
Baptist Health Madisonville
Commonwealth Health Corporation
Community Health Network
Daviess Community Hospital
Good Samaritan Hospital (IN)
Henry County Memorial Hospital
Kosciusko Community Hospital
Memorial Hospital (Logansport)
St. Mary' s Medical Center of Evansville

HISTORICAL FINANCIALS

Company Type: Private

Income Statement

FYE: September 30

	REVENUE ($ mil.)	NET INCOME ($ mil.)	NET PROFIT MARGIN	EMPLOYEES
09/13	695	83	12.0%	6,086
09/12	3	(18)	—	—
09/11	3	(19)	—	—
09/10	619	0	—	—
Annual Growth	3.9%	—	—	—

2013 Year-End Financials

Return on assets: —
Return on equity: 12.0%
Current ratio: 1.60
Cash ($ mil.): 52

DEACONESS HOSPITAL INC

Deaconess Hospital provides benevolent medical assistance to residents of southern Indiana western Kentucky and southeastern Illinois. The not-for-profit hospital is a 365-bed acute care medical facility that is the flagship hospital of the Deaconess Health System. Specialized services include cardiovascular surgery cancer treatment orthopedics neurological and trauma care. The hospital also offers home health care hospice services and medical equipment rental and it operates outpatient family practice surgery wellness and community outreach centers. Founded in 1892 Deaconess Hospital is a teaching and research facility affiliated with the Indiana University School of Medicine.

Geographic Reach

Deaconess Hospital is located in Evansville Indiana and provides services to about 26 surrounding counties.

Operations

Deaconess handles about 18000 inpatient visits per year. It also sees about 350000 outpatients and 65000 emergency room visitors and it handles about 7500 annual surgery procedures.

Strategy

To improve services to area residents Deaconess Hospital is expanding its outpatient care facilities and enhancing its IT resources. For instance in 2013 it moved its urgent care center to a larger more efficient facility. The hospital is also pursuing recognition for specialist programs such as its stroke center which was certified as a level one facility in 2013.

EXECUTIVES

Vice President Support Services, Bruce Epmeier
Auditors: BLUE & CO LLC INDLIANAPOLIS

LOCATIONS

HQ: DEACONESS HOSPITAL INC
 600 MARY ST, EVANSVILLE, IN 477101674
Phone: 812 450-5000
Web: WWW.DEACONESS.COM

Selected Services

24-hour Emergency Center
Cancer Services
Corporate Wellness
Family Medicine Clinic
Heart Services
Home Medical Equipment
Home-based Medical Care
Hospice Care
Inpatient and Outpatient Surgery
Mental Health Services
Neuro Services
Orthopedics
Pediatrics
Physician Referral Service
Radiology Services
Residency Program
Support Groups and Programs
Women's Hospital

COMPETITORS

Ball Memorial Hospital
Baptist Health
Baptist Health
 Madisonville
Commonwealth Health
 Corporation
Community Health
 Network
Daviess Community
 Hospital
Good Samaritan
 Hospital (IN)

Henry County Memorial
 Hospital
Jewish Hospital & St.
 Mary's HealthCare
Kosciusko Community
 Hospital
Memorial Hospital
 (Logansport)
Norton Healthcare
St. Mary's Medical
 Center of Evansville

Income Statement FYE: September 30

	REVENUE ($ mil.)	NET INCOME ($ mil.)	NET PROFIT MARGIN	EMPLOYEES
09/13	544	17	3.3%	4,357
09/12	577	58	10.1%	—
09/11	550	49	9.0%	—
09/10	524	0	—	—
Annual Growth	1.3%	—	—	—

2013 Year-End Financials

Return on assets: 4.6%   Cash ($ mil.): 43
Return on equity: 3.3%
Current ratio: 1.60

DECATUR MEMORIAL HOSPITAL

Not-for-profit Decatur Memorial Hospital (DMH) serves residents of Macon and neighboring counties in central Illinois. The 300-bed regional medical facility has a staff of 300 physicians who provide acute and tertiary care. DMH operates about a dozen Centers of Excellence in areas including cancer heart and lung women's health birthing allergy orthopedic and stroke care. Other health care services include preventive care through its DMH Wellness Center; home health and hospice programs and local urgent care and primary care through centers in the surrounding area.

Geographic Reach

DMH operates about 30 satellite facilities in addition to the main hospital facility in Decatur Illinois. It serves Central Illinois residents in all of Macon County and parts of Dewitt and Moultrie counties.OperationsIn addition to general and specialty care services DMH conducts education and clinical research programs partly through affiliations with the University of Illinois College of Medicine (basic and clinical medicine programs) and with Southern Illinois University School of Medicine (family practice residency). The hospital also conducts nurse training programs in partnership with area schools.

In 2013 DMH reported 10941 inpatient admissions; 264301 outpatient visits; 49505 emergency room visits; and more than 1000 births.The hospital contributed $43 million in community benefits that year.

Strategy

DMH is expanding its services and facilities to better serve patients.

In 2013 it introduced a new surgical table (the hana table) for use in minimally invasive hip replacement surgery and trauma procedures. It also installed the GE Discovery 750w 3.0T MRI system—the first GE trimodality CT/PET/MR imaging system installed in the US.

In addition DMH opened a new breast feeding clinic staffed by certified lactation counselors and a board certified lactation consultant.

In 2012 the hospital introduced the O-arm Multidimensional Imaging Systemm manufactured and distributed by the Navigation division of Medtronic and opened Decatur Memorial Hospital Varicose Vein Center at its main hospital facility.Company Background

DMH has established several express care clinics at select Wal-Mart locations and in 2011 it introduced online e-visits to help patients receive treatment for non-critical conditions. Patients submit information on symptoms and a DMH provider then addresses treatment of such conditions as colds and coughs stomach ailments minor infections allergies and rashes.

DMH' use of technology has also brought it recognition by being chosen as the winner of Modern Healthcare's 2011 IT Case Study Contest. DMH improved procedures for managing inpatient diabetes care through adoption of new IT tools including electronic nursing documentation computerized physician order entry and glucose monitoring systems.

The system has been recognized three consecutive years as a Top 50 Cardiovascular Hospital by Truven Health Analytics.

Thomson Reuters recognized DMH as one of the nation's 100 Top Hospitals in 2011. It has also been recognized by other analytical firms for its cardiovascular care services.

DMH was established in 1916.

EXECUTIVES

Occupational Therapy Director, Jeff Brown
Vice President, Kim Stone

LOCATIONS

HQ: DECATUR MEMORIAL HOSPITAL
 2300 N EDWARD ST, DECATUR, IL 625264192
Phone: 217 877-8121
Web: WWW.DECATURMEMORIALHOSPITAL.ORG

PRODUCTS/OPERATIONS

Selected Services

Arthur Medical Center
Births at DMH
Bone and Joint Center
Brain & Stroke Center
Breast Center
Cafeteria
Cancer Care Institute
Center for Advanced Molecular Medicine
Center for Minimally Invasive Surgery
Center for Sight
Central Illinois Orthopaedic Center
Central Illinois Surgery Center of DMH
Chaplaincy Services
Coffee Shop
Corporate Health
Customer Service
Dialysis Inpatient Services
Emergency Care Center
ENTA Allergy Head & Neck Institute
e-visits
Express Care
Family Birth Center
Family Lodge
Forsyth Imaging Center
Forsyth Physical Therapy
Forsyth Professional Center
Foundation
Gift Shop
Heart & Lung Institute
Home Health Services
Hospice
Institutional Review Board (IRB)
Kenwood Medical Center
Medical Equipment
Medical Home
Millennium Pain Center
Nurse Anesthesia Program
Occupational Medicine
Parish Nursing Program
Pastoral Services
Pharmacy
 Physical T
Physical Therapy - East Gate
Physician Plaza Pharmacy
PrimeTime Services
Psychological Services
Radiation Oncology
Radiology
Radiology Interventional
Rehabilitation Services

Physical Occupational & Speech Therapy
Senior Health and Wellness Center
SHORE
Sleep Center
South Shores Imaging Center
South Shores Medical Center
Sports Enhancement Center/Physical Therapy
Sports Medicine
  Sports Med
Sullivan Medical Center
Thrift Shop
Thyroid Surgical Institute
Vascular Center
Volunteer Services
Wellness Center
Women' s Health & Breast Center
Wound Clinic

COMPETITORS

Advocate BroMenn	Memorial Medical
Carle Hospital	Center
Hospital Sisters	Sarah Bush Lincoln
Health System	Health Center

HISTORICAL FINANCIALS
Company Type: Private

Income Statement

FYE: September 30

	REVENUE ($ mil.)	NET INCOME ($ mil.)	NET PROFIT MARGIN	EMPLOYEES
09/13	249	(8)	—	1,311
09/12	272	10	3.8%	
/ 0	0	—	—	
Annual Growth	—	—	—	

2013 Year-End Financials
Return on assets: 1.2%
Return on equity: (-3.6%)
Current ratio: 1.40
Cash ($ mil.): 23

DEKALB COUNTY BOARD OF EDUCATION

Auditors: RUSSELL W HINTON CPA CGFM

LOCATIONS

HQ: DEKALB COUNTY BOARD OF EDUCATION
  1701 MOUNTAIN INDUS BLVD, STONE MOUNTAIN,
  GA 300831027
Phone: 678 676-1200
Web: WWW.FSC.FERNBANK.EDU

HISTORICAL FINANCIALS
Company Type: Private

Income Statement

FYE: June 30

	REVENUE ($ mil.)	NET INCOME ($ mil.)	NET PROFIT MARGIN	EMPLOYEES
06/07	1,128	350	31.1%	16,000
06/06	1,055	10	0.9%	—
Annual Growth	7.0%	3405.8%		

2007 Year-End Financials
Return on assets: 4.9%
Return on equity: 31.1%
Current ratio: 1.40
Cash ($ mil.): 116

DEKALB COUNTY PUBLIC LIBRARY

Auditors: KPMG LLP ATLANTA GA

LOCATIONS

HQ: DEKALB COUNTY PUBLIC LIBRARY
  215 SYCAMORE ST FL 4, DECATUR, GA 300303413
Phone: 404 370-3070
Web: WWW.DEKALBLIBRARY.ORG

HISTORICAL FINANCIALS
Company Type: Private

Income Statement

FYE: December 31

	REVENUE ($ mil.)	NET INCOME ($ mil.)	NET PROFIT MARGIN	EMPLOYEES
12/07	622	(124)	—	228
12/06	622	186	30.0%	—
12/05	564	56	10.0%	—
Annual Growth	5.1%	—	—	—

2007 Year-End Financials
Return on assets: 9.0%
Return on equity: (-20.0%)
Current ratio: —
Cash ($ mil.): 536

DEKALB MEDICAL CENTER INC.

As far as DeKalb is concerned da healthier da better! Beginning as a rural hospital DeKalb Regional Health System now serves all of the Atlanta metropolitan area. The health system operating as DeKalb Medical is home to two acute care hospitals - DeKalb Medical at North Decatur and DeKalb Medical at Hillandale (with a combined total of about 550 beds). It also operates a 75-bed long-term rehabilitation hospital —DeKalb Medical at Downtown Decatur. Specialty hospital services include oncology cardiology orthopedics and diabetes care. The health system which was founded in 1961 also operates primary specialty and mobile health care clinics partly through the DeKalb Medical Physicians Group.

Operations

The health network of three hospitals staffs more than 800 physicians who represent about 55 medical specialties including neurosurgery interventional radiology sports medicine endovascular surgery gynecology emergency medicine and infectious disease. Altogether DeKalb Medical's facilities had some 27000 inpatient visits 123000 outpatient encounters 120000 emergency department visits and delivered some 5000 babies during 2014.

In addition to medical services DeKalb Medical offers educational residency programs in subjects including pharmacy nursing and podiatry. It also operates a school for radiology technicians.

Geographic Reach

In addition to its main facilities in Decatur and Hillandale the company has operations in Lilburn Lithonia Snellville Stone Mountain and Tucker Georgia.

Strategy

DeKalb Medical is a self-supporting not-for-profit community hospital that does not receive tax dol-

lars as part of its funding. The hospital system's operating budget comes solely from patient fees; DeKalb Medical reinvests any excess income into expanding or updating its services and facilities to meet Atlanta's growing population. The DeKalb Medical Foundation was established in 1991 and since then has funded improvements in facilities technology and community outreach programs.

EXECUTIVES

Rph, Rebecca White
Vice President Patient Care Services, Susan (Sue) Breslin
Medical Director, Leslie Pope
Nursing Director, Barbara (Barb) Kleynen
Vice President, Margie Maxey
Medical Director Of Emergency Services, Pascal Crosley
Vice President Strategic Services and Managed Care, Jim Forstner
Vpma, Duane Barclay
Secretary Admin For Cancer Center, Dorothy Carter
Board Member, Beverly Hutchinson
Auditors: WARREN AVERETT LLC BIRMINGHAM

LOCATIONS

HQ: DEKALB MEDICAL CENTER INC.
  2701 N DECATUR RD, DECATUR, GA 300335918
Phone: 404 501-1000
Web: WWW.DEKALBMEDICAL.ORG

PRODUCTS/OPERATIONS

Selected Specialties
Cancer Center
Community Programs
Corporate Health Services
Emergency Department
Heart and Vascular Services
Orthopedic Services
Podiatry
Radiology and Medical Imaging
Rehabilitation Services
Senior Services
Sleep Center
Surgical Weight Loss
Volunteers
Wellness Center
Women' s Services
Workswell Services
Wound Care

COMPETITORS

Children' s Healthcare	HCA
of Atlanta	Northside Hospital
Emory Healthcare	Piedmont Healthcare
Grady Health System	St. Mary' s Health Care
Gwinnett Health System	WellStar Health System

HISTORICAL FINANCIALS
Company Type: Private

Income Statement

FYE: June 30

	REVENUE ($ mil.)	NET INCOME ($ mil.)	NET PROFIT MARGIN	EMPLOYEES
06/11	422	0	0.2%	2,700
06/10	397	(15)	—	—
06/09	390	0	—	—
06/08	370	0	—	—
Annual Growth	4.5%	—	—	—

2011 Year-End Financials
Return on assets: —
Return on equity: 0.2%
Current ratio: 0.30
Cash ($ mil.): 21

DELI MANAGEMENT INC.

This company knows a good sandwich when serves one. Deli Management operates Jason's Deli a chain of sandwich shops with more than 240 company-owned and franchised locations. The quick casual eateries specialize in deli-style sandwiches including such signature varieties as Bird to the Wise The New York Yankee and Rueben THE Great. The chain also serves panini and po'boy sandwiches pasta dishes soups and salads. Many Jason's outposts provide delivery and catering services as well as online ordering. President Joe Tortorice and partner Rusty Coco started the company in 1976.

Geographic Reach

The company has units in about 30 states throughout the US. Most of the restaurants are found in Texas and other parts of the South.

Strategy

Like other chains in the quick casual segment Jason's Deli aims to provide fast service while maintaining a higher quality of food. The company promotes its use of organic ingredients and removed high fructose corn syrup (HFCS) from all of the food items on its menu.

Within the quick casual segment Jason's Deli faces competition from leaders such as Panera Bread and Chipotle Mexican Grill. The quick-service sandwich market is dominated by leading brands Subway and Quiznos.

EXECUTIVES

Director Franchise Sales and Development, Gene Barber
Customer Relations Department Atlanta, Jeffrey Bigger
Human Resources Northern Region Florida and Alabama, Joe Loyd
Human Resources Southeast Region, Alex Cone
VP Operations, Peter J. (Pete) Verde
Auditors: WATHEN DESHONG & JUNCKER CPA

LOCATIONS

HQ: DELI MANAGEMENT INC.
  2400 BROADWAY ST, BEAUMONT, TX 777021904
Phone: 409 838-1976
Web: WWW.JASONSDELI.COM

COMPETITORS

Burger King	Panera Bread
CKE Restaurants	Popeyes
Chick-fil-A	Potbelly Sandwich Shop
Chipotle	Quiznos
Church's Chicken	Schlotzsky's
Einstein Noah	Sonic Corp.
Restaurant Group	Souper Salad
Jack in the Box	Subway
Jimmy John's	Thundercloud Inc.
Kahala	Wendy's
McAlister's	Whataburger
McDonald's	YUM!
Panda Restaurant Group	

HISTORICAL FINANCIALS
Company Type: Private

Income Statement				FYE: December 31
	REVENUE ($ mil.)	NET INCOME ($ mil.)	NET PROFIT MARGIN	EMPLOYEES
12/08	344	5	1.7%	6,000
12/06	344	5	1.7%	—
12/05	1,402	0	0.0%	—
Annual Growth	(37.4%)	3425.2%	—	—

2008 Year-End Financials
Return on assets: 2.3%   Cash ($ mil.): 1
Return on equity: 1.7%
Current ratio: 0.40

DELTA DENTAL OF TENNESSEE

Auditors: PLANTE MORAN PLLC EAST LANSI

LOCATIONS

HQ: DELTA DENTAL OF TENNESSEE
  240 VENTURE CIR, NASHVILLE, TN 372281604
Phone: 615 255-3175
Web: WWW.DELTADENTALTN.COM

HISTORICAL FINANCIALS
Company Type: Private

Income Statement				FYE: December 31
	ASSETS ($ mil.)	NET INCOME ($ mil.)	INCOME AS % OF ASSETS	EMPLOYEES
12/12	70	6	9.8%	92
12/10	62	3	5.1%	—
12/09	46	1	4.1%	—
12/03	23	0	—	—
Annual Growth	12.8%	—	—	—

2012 Year-End Financials
Return on assets: 0.6%   Sales ($ mil.): 456
Return on equity: 1.5%

DENNIS K BURKE INC

Auditors: TONNESON & COMPANY INC WAKE

LOCATIONS

HQ: DENNIS K BURKE INC
  284 EASTERN AVE, CHELSEA, MA 021503318
Phone: 617 884-7800
Web: WWW.BURKEOIL.COM

HISTORICAL FINANCIALS
Company Type: Private

Income Statement				FYE: April 30
	REVENUE ($ mil.)	NET INCOME ($ mil.)	NET PROFIT MARGIN	EMPLOYEES
04/13	858	7	0.8%	110
04/12	929	3	0.3%	—
04/11	807	0	0.1%	—
04/10	596	0	—	—
Annual Growth	12.9%	—	—	—

2013 Year-End Financials
Return on assets: 1.8%   Cash ($ mil.): —
Return on equity: 0.8%
Current ratio: 0.90

DEPAUW UNIVERSITY

DePauw University is a private co-educational liberal arts university with an approximate enrollment of 2300 students. Its campus boasts some 36 major buildings across nearly 700 acres including a 520-acre nature preserve located 45 miles west of Indianapolis. The university offers undergraduate degrees from more than 30 academic departments and programs as well as fellowships in media management and science. Prominent alumni include former US Vice President Dan Quayle former US Rep. Lee Hamilton and best-selling author Barbara Kinsolver. DePauw was founded in 1837 by the Methodist Church. The university's School of Music founded in 1884 is one of the oldest in the US.

Geographic Reach

From its campus in Greencastle Indiana DePauw University spans some 700 acres at its main campus and a large nature preserve. The educational institution also offers students experiential learning opportunities off campus and abroad.

Operations

DePauw University with a student/faculty ratio of 10:1 maintains more than 200 faculty members. In general university tuition and fees run nearly $38300. Including room and board fees can reach $48950. The university is supported by a $513 million endowment.

EXECUTIVES

Vice President for Facilities Management
  Facilities Management, Richard (Dick) Vance
Vice President Finance Administration, Bradley Kelsheimer
Vice President Academic Affairs, John Stimpert
Associate Vice President for Development, Randy Rogers
Secretary Data Entry Admission, Teresa Y Roberts
Secretary, Pamela Woodall
Secretary, Linda Wrede
Secretary Sociology and amp Anthropology Political Science, Krista Dahlstrom
Secretary of Student Academic Support Services, Sheree L Custis
Secretary Data Entry admissions, Debra J Sands
Auditors: CROWE HORWATH LLP CHICAGO IL

LOCATIONS

HQ: DEPAUW UNIVERSITY
  313 S LOCUST ST, GREENCASTLE, IN 461351736
Phone: 765 658-4800
Web: WWW.DEPAUW.EDU

PRODUCTS/OPERATIONS

Selected Academic Centers
Bartlett Reflection Center
Center for Student Engagement
Center for Teaching & Learning
Geographic Information Systems Lab
The Compton Center for Peace and Justice
The Compton Center for Peace and Justice
The Green Center for the Performing Arts
The Janet Prindle Institute for Ethics
The McDermond Center for Management and Entreprenuership
The Peeler Art Center
The Pulliam Center for Contemporary Media

HISTORICAL FINANCIALS

Company Type: Private

Income Statement

FYE: June 30

	REVENUE ($ mil.)	NET INCOME ($ mil.)	NET PROFIT MARGIN	EMPLOYEES
06/13	246	94	38.4%	652
06/12	154	5	3.7%	—
06/11	147	2	1.7%	—
06/10	121	0	—	—
Annual Growth	26.4%	—	—	—

2013 Year-End Financials

Return on assets: 4.7%
Return on equity: 38.4%
Current ratio: 0.20
Cash ($ mil.): 29

DESERET GENERATION AND TRANSMISSION CO-OPERATIVE

Its service area may be dry but it is not a power desert thanks to Deseret Generation and Transmission Cooperative (aka Deseret Power) which supplies wholesale electricity to its members (six retail distribution cooperatives) and other bulk energy customers in Arizona Colorado Nevada Utah and Wyoming. The member-owned utility operates 223 miles of transmission lines and it has interests in two power generation facilities in Utah that give it 550 MW of capacity. Deseret Power also operates its own coal mine which fuels its main power plant through subsidiary Blue Mountain Energy; other operations include the transportation of coal by railroad and the development of a limestone extraction facility.

The retail distribution cooperatives served by Deseret Power supply electricity to more than 45000 customers in their service areas. Deseret Power's Bonanza (500 MW) power plant in Utah has been ranked as one of the cleanest-burning coal-fired plants in the US.

The non-profit cooperative's key strategy revolves around its ownership operation and vertical integration of its primary assets and services — the coal mine where coal is extracted to fuel its power plants the power generation facilities as well the power lines used to transmit the electricity it produces. This integration and self-reliance allows it to manage costs and reinvest profits.

Deseret Power was formed in 1978 by six regional rural electric cooperatives.

EXECUTIVES

Vice President Marketing, Curt Winterfeld
Auditors: DELOITTE & TOUCHE LLP SALT L

LOCATIONS

HQ: DESERET GENERATION AND TRANSMISSION CO-OPERATIVE
10714 S JORDAN GTWY # 300, SOUTH JORDAN, UT 840953922
Phone: 435 781-5737
Web: WWW.WYOMINGREA.ORG

PRODUCTS/OPERATIONS

Member Distribution Cooperatives
Bridger Valley Electric Association
Dixie Escalante Rural Electric Association
Flowell Electric Association
Garkane Energy Association
Moon Lake Electric Association
Mt. Wheeler Power

COMPETITORS

Arch Coal
Bonneville Power
IPA
PacifiCorp
Peabody Energy
Utah Associated Municipal Power Systems

HISTORICAL FINANCIALS

Company Type: Private

Income Statement

FYE: December 31

	REVENUE ($ mil.)	NET INCOME ($ mil.)	NET PROFIT MARGIN	EMPLOYEES
12/07	242	(9)	—	250
12/06	218	10	5.0%	—
12/05	1,732	0	0.0%	—
Annual Growth	(62.6%)	—	—	—

2007 Year-End Financials

Return on assets: 5.7%
Return on equity: (-4.0%)
Current ratio: 1.10
Cash ($ mil.): 12

DEVCON CONSTRUCTION INCORPORATED

Devcon Construction has built a sturdy business from building in the Bay Area. One of the area's top general building contractors Devcon has constructed more than 30 million sq. ft. of office industrial and commercial space. Its focus is on Northern California mainly in the San Francisco Bay Area and Silicon Valley. The company provides engineering design/build and interior design services. It specializes in high-tech projects including data centers and industrial research and development facilities. In addition to building company facilities and offices Devcon works on such projects as hotels restaurants parking structures retail stores sports facilities and schools.

Geographic Reach
Based in Milpitas California Devcon maintains several satellite offices in California in Petaluma Stockton and Santa Cruz as well as an office in Reno Nevada.

Strategy
Although most of Devcon's work is in California the company also has completed projects in Nevada Oregon Idaho Texas Massachusetts and Florida. Recent projects in the San Francisco Forty Niners Stadium in Santa Clara San Jose Sharks Ice Center in Pleasanton and the Stanford Research Computing Facility.

The company partnered with US-based Central Concrete in 2012 to supply its high-performing low-CO2 concrete for the new San Francisco 49er Stadium. The move showcases Devcon's focus on sustainability as part of its projects.

EXECUTIVES

Vice President Of Construction, Daisy Pereira
Auditors: JOHANSON & YAU ACCOUNTANCY COR

LOCATIONS

HQ: DEVCON CONSTRUCTION INCORPORATED
690 GIBRALTAR DR, MILPITAS, CA 950356317
Phone: 408 942-8200
Web: WWW.DEVCON-CONST.COM

PRODUCTS/OPERATIONS

Selected Projects

1880 Mission Street San Francisco

3333 Scott Blvd. Buildings A B & C Santa Clara
Anderson Collection At Stanford University Stanford
Barnes & Nobles Palo Alto
Cisco Parking Structure 1 San Jose
Cisco Parking Structure 2 San Jose
Downtown Sunnyvale Town Center Sunnyvale
El Camino Family Housing South San Francisco
Fresno Hyatt Place Hotel Fresno
Friedenrich Center For Translational Research At 800 Welch Road
Lawson Lane East - Buildings A & B Santa Clara
Oakland Air Traffic Control Tower (ATCT) Oakland
San Francisco 49ers Stadium Santa Clara
San Jose Earthquakes - MLS Soccer Stadium San Jose
SanDisk Milpitas
Santa Clara University Admissions & Enrollment Services Building Santa Clara
Sharks Ice Center Pleasanton
Stanford Research Computing Facility Stanford
The Plaza At Triton Park Foster City
University Plaza Palo Alto
Villa Siena Nursing Care Units Mountain View

COMPETITORS

Charles Pankow Builders	KPRS Construction
DPR Construction	Obayashi
Hathaway Dinwiddie Construction	Rudolph & Sletten
Hensel Phelps Construction	Structure Tone
	Swinerton
	Turner Corporation
	Webcor Builders

HISTORICAL FINANCIALS

Company Type: Private

Income Statement

FYE: December 31

	REVENUE ($ mil.)	NET INCOME ($ mil.)	NET PROFIT MARGIN	EMPLOYEES
12/13	1,012	12	1.2%	350
12/12	779	3	0.5%	—
12/11	434	1	0.3%	—
12/10	469	0	—	—
Annual Growth	29.2%	—	—	—

2013 Year-End Financials

Return on assets: 18.2%
Return on equity: 1.2%
Current ratio: 0.90
Cash ($ mil.): 14

DEVEREUX FOUNDATION

Devereux Foundation endeavors to make a difference in the lives of people with behavioral psychological intellectual or neurological problems. A not-for-profit organization Devereux serves children adolescents and adults and their families through about 15 centers in about a dozen states. Its offerings include hospitalization group homes respite care family counseling and vocational training. Devereux also conducts behavioral health research and provides consulting services for other organizations with similar concerns. The group's work began in 1912 when Philadelphia educator Helena Devereux began working with three special education students in her parents' home.

Operations

The foundation's Institute of Clinical and Professional Training and Research (ICPTR) operates the Center for Effective Schools the Center for Resilient Children and Direct Care Training Resources to provide training for psychology psychiatry social work and special education professionals.

Geographic Reach

Devereux Foundation maintains facilities in Arizona California Colorado Connecticut Florida Georgia Massachusetts New Jersey New York Pennsylvania and Texas.

Devereux's revenue decreased by about 1% in 2013 to $391 million due to a decline in client revenue. Its net income increased 55% as salaries and benefits declined while other income (investments and donations) increased. That year the foundation provided $18.2 million in charity care.

Financial Performance

In 2014 revenue rose 2% to $400 million due to an increase in net client revenue. This was partially offset by a decrease in investment earnings and unrestricted contributions.

Strategy

The foundation's strategy for growth includes expanding its clinical expertise investing in new technologies to facilitate knowledge improving collaborations and communications with families and meeting its quality goals.

Devereux is examining its centers and corporate departments while it continues to place the highest value on building relationships with the people and public agencies that use its services. Key elements to its strategic plan include quality management national branding and maintaining fiscal responsibility to ensure a strong balance sheet. The foundation is also looking to expand opportunities for its intellectual properties and services through partnerships with school systems and universities and through expanded services for people with autism and added community-based adult services. It is rolling out an electronic health record system and upgrading its accounting and billing systems.

In 2015 the foundation opened the Autism Assessment Center in Pennsylvania. The year before that it added Tannerhill a child-serving agency in Rhode Island to its network. It was renamed Devereux Rhode Island.

Mergers and Acquisitions

Devereux acquired the Threshold Center for Autism in 2015. The 36-bed program includes a residential center three group homes a dental clinic a specialty school serving individuals with intellectual and developmental disabilities and an adult day treatment program.

Company Background

The organization's Institute of Clinical Training and Research was founded in 1938. It provides professional training in psychology psychiatry social work and special education.

EXECUTIVES

Vice President Human Resources, Timothy (Tim) Dillon
Vice President Operations and Organizational Development, Sarah Lenahan
Treasurer, Steven H Mansh, age 60
Auditors: ERNST & YOUNG LLP PHILADELPH

LOCATIONS

HQ: DEVEREUX FOUNDATION
444 DEVEREUX DR, VILLANOVA, PA 190851932
Phone: 610 520-3000
Web: WWW.DEVEREUX.ORG

Selected Centers
Arizona
California
Colorado

Connecticut
Florida
Georgia
Massachusetts
New Jersey
New York
Pennsylvania
Texas

PRODUCTS/OPERATIONS

2014 Revenue

	$ mil.	% of total
Client revenue	375	94
Investment income	7	2
Unrestricted contributions	5	1
Other revenue	11	3
Total	**400**	**100**

Selected Services

After care programs
Community-based group homes
Family counseling and therapy
Foster care homes
Hospital inpatient and outpatient settings
Partial hospitalization
Preventive and post-discharge services
Residential and day treatment programs
Respite care programs
Special education day schools
Supervised apartments
Transitional living arrangements
Vocational and pre-vocational training

COMPETITORS

CIGNA Behavioral Health
CRC Health
Diakon Lutheran Social Ministries
Hazelden Betty Ford
HealthSouth
Magellan Health
Mental Health Network
Northwestern Human Services
Physiotherapy Associates
Providence Service
Select Medical
UBH
Universal Health Services
Watson Institute
YAI National Institute for People with Disabilitie

HISTORICAL FINANCIALS
Company Type: Private

Income Statement
FYE: June 30

	REVENUE ($ mil.)	NET INCOME ($ mil.)	NET PROFIT MARGIN	EMPLOYEES
06/13	391	3	0.9%	6,000
06/12	395	(5)	—	—
06/11	395	17	4.5%	—
06/08	384	0	—	—
Annual Growth	**0.3%**	**—**	**—**	**—**

2013 Year-End Financials
Return on assets: —
Return on equity: 0.9%
Current ratio: 0.90
Cash ($ mil.): 3

DFB PHARMACEUTICALS INC.

DFB Pharmaceuticals contributes to drug development and manufacturing processes by providing essential ingredients. The company produces various pharmaceutical ingredients for its own use and for other drug makers through its Phyton Biotech operating subsidiary. Phyton Biotech uses its plant cell culture technology to make APIs (active pharmaceutical ingredients). Phyton Biotech is a global provider of chemotherapeutic agents including paclitaxel and docetaxel APIs and taxane intermediates. Affiliate Phyton LTD. operates Phyton Biotech LLC and Phyton Biotech GmbH.

Geographic Reach

DFB Pharmaceuticals is based in Texas. Phyton Biotech has development and manufacturing facilities near Hamburg Germany and in Vancouver Canada.

Operations

Phyton Biotech which has produced taxanes for products such as anti-cancer drug Taxol (marketed by Bristol-Myers Squibb) focuses on producing plant-cell-culture-based ingredients used in chemotherapy drugs. Phyton Biotech provides taxane plant-cell fermentation and protein development services to help drugmakers formulate new APIs; it also offers rapid scale-up manufacturing services of ingredients as products are developed and commercialized.

The total production capacity of the taxanes train runs up to 880000 liters per year. Phyton also offers development services to its customers via plant cell fermentation chemical semi-synthesis and purification for taxanes secondary metabolites recombinant proteins and other active ingredients.

Sales and Marketing

The company focuses on patient payor and provider needs in the wound care and surgical markets Phyton Biotech markets its products to companies in the Biopharmaceuticals Cosmeceuticals Nutraceuticals and Pharmaceuticals sectors.

Financial Performance

The company gets about half of its revenues from marketed compounds or services as a result of acquisitions or partnerships.

Strategy

DFB is growing its core businesses and expand its portfolio of products and technologies through dedicated research and development efforts and through strategic business partnerships. The company's services and solutions are focused primarily on semi-solid and liquid dosage forms. Phyton Biotech is focusing on bringing a new generation of PCF-produced small molecules and protein therapeutics to the market.

To generate cash and refocus its business DFB sold a majority stake in its contract manufacturing unit DPT Laboratories to Renaissance Acquisition Holdings in 2012. Through the DPT transaction DFB retained an interest in the DPT business and gained a seat on Renaissance's board.

DFB also sold its Healthpoint subsidiary a maker of prescription drugs to prevent or treat disorders associated with skin and soft tissue to Smith & Nephew for some $782 million. The unit had been facing a federal investigation into questionable marketing activities.

EXECUTIVES

President and COO DPT Laboratories, Paul H. Johnson
President and COO Healthpoint, Travis E. Baugh, age 59
Chairman and CEO, H. Paul Dorman
Chief Medical Officer Healthpoint, Bert Slade
Auditors: ERNST & YOUNG LLP SAN ANTONIO

LOCATIONS

HQ: DFB PHARMACEUTICALS INC.
3909 HULEN ST, FORT WORTH, TX 761077253
Phone: 817 900-4050
Web: WWW.DFB.COM

COMPETITORS

Ash Stevens
Covance
Perrigo
Pharmaceutical Product

Formatech
Jubilant Life Sciences
Lonza

Development
Ranbaxy Laboratories

HISTORICAL FINANCIALS
Company Type: Private

Income Statement

FYE: December 31

	REVENUE ($ mil.)	NET INCOME ($ mil.)	NET PROFIT MARGIN	EMPLOYEES
12/10	322	0	—	700
12/08	318	0	—	—
12/07	1,916	0	0.0%	—
Annual Growth	(44.8%)	—	—	—

2010 Year-End Financials
Return on assets: 4.7% Cash ($ mil.): 8
Return on equity: —
Current ratio: 0.90

DIALYSIS CLINIC INC.

Dialysis Clinic Inc. or DCI is dedicated to caring for patients with end-stage renal disease (ESRD). The not-for-profit company which operates a network of more than 210 dialysis centers serving more than 14000 patients in 27 states also provides kidney transplant assistance services. Affiliate DCI Donor Services is an organ and tissue procurement agency. DCI also funds kidney-related research and educational programs and is affiliated with various universities and teaching hospitals throughout the US including Tufts University the University of Arizona and Tulane University.

Geographic ReachThe company has its locations in Alabama Arizona Arkansas California Colorado Connecticut Florida Georgia Indiana Iowa Kentucky Louisiana Maine Massachusetts Missouri Montana Nebraska Nevada New Jersey New Mexico New York North Carolina Ohio Pennsylvania South Carolina Tennessee and Texas.

Strategy

DCI grows its network of facilities by forming partnerships with health care providers and other organizations. The company provides funding for construction and operation of the facility and it provides clinic support services including supply procurement and central laboratory services (through its DCI Lab subsidiary).

In 2012 the company opened a dialysis clinic in Albuquerque its first dialysis clinic in the South Valley region of New Mexico.

Company Background

DCI was established in 1971 by nephrologist Keith Johnson.

EXECUTIVES

Top Computer Executive CIO Vice President Or, Teresa Yates
Medical Director, Christos Argyropoulos
Secretary Data Entry, Dawna Babyak
Secretary, Gloria Gabriel
Auditors: DELOITTE & TOUCHE LLP NASHVIL

LOCATIONS

HQ: DIALYSIS CLINIC INC.
1633 CHURCH ST STE 500, NASHVILLE, TN 372032948
Phone: 615 327-3061
Web: WWW.DCIINC.ORG

COMPETITORS

DaVita
FMCNA
Fresenius

Renal Advantage
U.S. Renal Care

HISTORICAL FINANCIALS
Company Type: Private

Income Statement

FYE: September 30

	REVENUE ($ mil.)	NET INCOME ($ mil.)	NET PROFIT MARGIN	EMPLOYEES
09/14	663	35	5.4%	5,000
09/13	650	50	7.8%	—
09/12	664	45	6.8%	—
09/11	642	0	—	—
Annual Growth	1.1%	—	—	—

2014 Year-End Financials
Return on assets: 2.5% Cash ($ mil.): 230
Return on equity: 5.4%
Current ratio: 4.20

DICKINSON COLLEGE

Located in Carlisle Pennsylvania Dickinson College is a private liberal arts college with a penchant for international study. The small but selective college has an annual enrollment of some 2400 students half of which study abroad in programs that span 24 countries on six continents. The college offers more than 40 programs in arts and humanities (including a significant foreign language program) social sciences and natural sciences. It also offers minors in fields including astronomy creative writing and film studies. Dickinson College traces its roots back to 1773; it is named for John Dickinson who signed the US Constitution and was known as "The Penman of the [American] Revolution."

EXECUTIVES

Department Head, Julie Vastine
Department Chair, Lars English
Auditors: KPMG LLP HARRISBURG PA

LOCATIONS

HQ: DICKINSON COLLEGE
COLLEGE & LOUTHER ST, CARLISLE, PA 17013
Phone: 717 245-1010
Web: WWW.DICKINSONATHLETICS.COM

HISTORICAL FINANCIALS
Company Type: Private

Income Statement

FYE: June 30

	REVENUE ($ mil.)	NET INCOME ($ mil.)	NET PROFIT MARGIN	EMPLOYEES
06/14	173	51	29.4%	632
06/13	159	37	23.5%	—
06/12	115	(0)	—	—
06/11	159	0	—	—
Annual Growth	2.8%	—	—	—

2014 Year-End Financials
Return on assets: 6.9% Cash ($ mil.): 14
Return on equity: 29.4%
Current ratio: —

DIMENSIONS HEALTH CORPORATION

Dimensions Healthcare System takes care of the many many facets of a human's dimensions. Dimensions Healthcare System operates a handful of medical facilities serving the residents in Prince George's County Maryland and the surrounding area. Acute care centers include Prince George's Hospital Center and Laurel Regional Hospital. Specialty services include rehabilitation behavioral health cardiology emergency medicine senior care pediatrics and a sleep disorders center. The not-for-profit health care system was established in 1982.

Geographic Reach

Prince George's Hospital is located in Cheverly Maryland (in Prince George's County) while the Laurel Regional Hospital is located in Laurel Maryland. Major outpatient centers are located in Bowie and Lanham.

OperationsDimensions holds a strong market share in its region caring for about 180000 patients per year. Each of its hospitals offers a range of different specialty care including 24-hour emergency care at Laurel Regional Hospital and Prince George's Hospital Center. It also provide round-the-clock urgent care at the Bowie Health Campus which includes an outpatient building and a surgery center. Other major facilities include the Glenridge Medical Center another outpatient clinic for internal medicine and other specialties and the Pemberton Senior Health Center.The system's Prince George Hospital is a safety-net hospital which means at least half of its patients are uninsured or covered by government programs that pay at lower reimbursement rates than commercial insurers. The facility is also a teaching hospital and a regional referral center. Prince George's Hospital was among the first in Maryland to be designated a Cardiac Intervention Center for heart attack victims making it is a referral location for such patients as well. The not-for-profit network leases some of its facilities from Prince George's County.StrategyTo improve care and attract more patients and specialists to its facilities Dimensions has been expanding its hospitals in recent years. Laurel Regional Hospital for instance has recently enhanced its birthing center vascular catheterization laboratory and wound care centers and it has added new sleep wellness and specialty care units.

LOCATIONS

HQ: DIMENSIONS HEALTH CORPORATION
7582 ANNAPOLIS RD, HYATTSVILLE, MD 207841744
Phone: 301 322-2326
Web: WWW.PRINCEGEORGESCOUNTYMD.GOV

PRODUCTS/OPERATIONS

Selected Maryland Locations
Bowie Health Campus (Bowie)
 Bowie Health Center
 Dimensions Surgery Center
 Larkin Chase Care and Rehabilitation Center
 Mullikin Medical Center
Glenridge Medical Center (Lanham)
Laurel Regional Hospital (Laurel)
Prince George' s Hospital Center (Cheverly)
Rachel H. Pemberton Senior Health Center (Brentwood)

COMPETITORS

Adventist HealthCare
Anne Arundel Medical Center
Bon Secours Health
Calvert Memorial Hospital

Civista Health
Franklin Square Hospital Center
GBMC
Johns Hopkins Health System

HISTORICAL FINANCIALS

Company Type: Private

Income Statement

FYE: June 30

	REVENUE ($ mil.)	NET INCOME ($ mil.)	NET PROFIT MARGIN	EMPLOYEES
06/13	365	(1)	—	2,800
06/06	367	17	4.8%	—
06/05	338	3	1.2%	—
06/04	345	0	—	—
Annual Growth	0.6%	—	—	—

2013 Year-End Financials

Return on assets: 14.3% Cash ($ mil.): 39
Return on equity: (-0.3%)
Current ratio: 0.80

DIMEO CONSTRUCTION COMPANY

Dimeo Construction has built a reputation in New England. The company provides general contracting design/build and construction management services ranging from pre-planning to post-construction commissioning. It focuses on commercial education health care residential and public projects such as schools hospitals corporate headquarters research and development facilities and shopping centers. It also has worked on renovation projects such as The Mark Twain House & Museum and the Ocean House. The family-owned company was established in 1930 by Joseph Dimeo. Current CEO Brad Dimeo represents the third generation to lead the firm.

Dimeo Construction has offices in Boston; New Haven Connecticut; and Providence Rhode Island. The company has completed work for several of the region's Fortune 500 companies including CIGNA Hasbro and United Technologies Corporation. Its green side has emerged as well as it has completed eco-friendly projects for the likes of IKEA CVS Health and Yale University.

EXECUTIVES

President, Bradford S. Dimeo
executive Vice President at Dimeo Construction, Stephen F. Rutledge
CFO, Steven B. Avery
Auditors: STOWE & DEGON LLC WESTBOROUGH

LOCATIONS

HQ: DIMEO CONSTRUCTION COMPANY
75 CHAPMAN ST, PROVIDENCE, RI 029055496
Phone: 401 781-9800
Web: WWW.DIMEO.COM

COMPETITORS

Gilbane Building Company
Heery
Imperial Construction Group
Konover Properties
Skanska USA Building
Turner Construction
Walsh Brothers

HISTORICAL FINANCIALS

Company Type: Private

Income Statement

FYE: June 30

	REVENUE ($ mil.)	NET INCOME ($ mil.)	NET PROFIT MARGIN	EMPLOYEES
06/12	373	6	1.7%	300
06/11	300	9	3.1%	—
06/10	356	9	2.7%	—
06/09	567	0	—	—
Annual Growth	(13.0%)	—	—	—

2012 Year-End Financials

Return on assets: — Cash ($ mil.): 78
Return on equity: 1.7%
Current ratio: 1.20

DIRECT RELIEF

Direct Relief International wants to relieve the health problems of people around the world. The not-for-profit organization is dedicated to providing health care support and emergency relief to people in developing countries as well as victims of disasters and war. Active in 50 US states and 70 countries it gives medicine supplies and equipment through partnerships with local groups that make specific requests and coordinates distribution. The group also has partnered with nonprofit clinics and community health centers to provide medical care and medicine for homeless and low-income people in California. Direct Relief was founded in 1948 by Estonian immigrant William Zimdin.

The organization also has applied its experience with domestic relief efforts to help victims of hurricanes along the Gulf Coast.

Looking to maintain its funding during the economic downturn Direct Relief sought to appeal to Money magazine readers by being part of its November 2009 cover story "What to do with $1000 $10000 or $50000 Now." As part of the article Direct Relief cited that $10000 would purchase medical supplies for 800 victims of the next Gulf Coast hurricane.

EXECUTIVES

EVP and CFO, Bhupindarpal (Bhupi) Singh, age 55
President and CEO, Thomas Tighe
Director Operations, Rick Snekvik
VP Philanthropic Investment, Anthoula Randopoulos
Director Direct Relief USA, Damon Taugher
Director International Program Operations, Genevieve Bitter
Director Emergency Preparedness and Response, Brett Williams
COO, Annie Maxwell
Manager Logistics and Distribution, James Howard
Director Human Resources Administration and Compliance, Judy Gerrard Partch
Director Information Technology, Ross Comstock
Director Research and Analysis, Andrew Schroeder
Controller, Julie Aguiniga
Manager Media Relations, Jim Prosser
Manager Communications, Andrew Fletcher
VP Marketing and Development, Kerri Murray
System Administrator, George Linker
Manager SAP Applications, Saravanan Selvaraj

LOCATIONS

HQ: DIRECT RELIEF
27 S LA PATERA LN, GOLETA, CA 931173214
Phone: 805 964-4767
Web: WWW.DIRECTRELIEF.ORG

HISTORICAL FINANCIALS

Company Type: Private

Income Statement

FYE: June 30

	REVENUE ($ mil.)	NET INCOME ($ mil.)	NET PROFIT MARGIN	EMPLOYEES
06/13	388	(0)	—	2
06/12	299	(17)	—	—
06/11	405	95	23.6%	—
06/09	164	0	—	—
Annual Growth	23.9%	—	—	—

2013 Year-End Financials

Return on assets: — Cash ($ mil.): 1
Return on equity: (-0.1%)
Current ratio: —

DOCTOR'S ASSOCIATES INC.

You're more likely to catch a sub than a train at these Subway stations. Doctor's Associates owns the Subway chain of sandwich shops the world's largest quick-service restaurant chain by number of locations having surpassed burger giant McDonald's. It boasts about 41500 locations in more than 100 countries. Virtually all Subway restaurants are franchised and offer such fare as hot and cold sub sandwiches turkey wraps and salads. The eateries are located in freestanding buildings as well as in airports convenience stores sports facilities and other locations.

Geographic Reach

The company's network of eateries stretching from Afghanistan to Zambia is a testament to how effectively the franchising model can be used to expand a dining concept. Part of the reason for Subway's success is the portability and adaptability of the dining concept. The sandwich restaurants can be found in a vast array of locations including shopping center food courts suburban strip malls and even military bases. The company is particularly focused on expanding its international presence in Asia and Central Europe.

Operations

With the ability to fit one of its restaurants almost anywhere Subway can offer franchisees lower startup costs as compared to other concepts that require large areas for food preparation or dining space. Many of Subway's franchisees operate just a single location but a few oversee a large estate.

Local operators who own the individual restaurants use the Subway name in exchange for royalties and other fees. This allows Doctor's Associates to expand its sandwich business without the cost of construction and operation. (Domiciled in Florida the company operates its franchising business largely through Connecticut-based affiliate World Franchise Headquarters.)

Sales and Marketing

Like its fast-food brethren Subway relies heavily on continuous television advertising and sponsorships to promote itself. It has marketing partnerships with dozens of companies and celebrity spokespeople.

Strategy

The Subway chain has tapped into the health food and weight loss zeitgeist in the US prominently featuring in its advertising Jared Fogle a man who famously lost nearly 250 lbs. by switching to a Subway sandwich diet. The chain continues to tout the health benefits of its sandwiches over traditional burgers and fries by introducing new low-fat menu items.

Subway has been developing an upscale concept called Subway Café. The new format conceived for office buildings and other high-end locations is larger than the average Subway restaurant and features coffee espresso lattes and hot chocolate along with an expanded breakfast menu.

Ownership

Doctor's Associates is owned by co-founders Fred DeLuca and Peter Buck.

Company Background

Co-founders DeLuca and Buck opened the first Subway in 1965.

HISTORY

In 1965 17-year-old Fred DeLuca dreamed of becoming a doctor while working as a stock boy in a Bridgeport Connecticut hardware store to earn college tuition. It wasn't enough so he cornered family friend Peter Buck at a backyard barbecue and asked for advice. Buck a nuclear physicist suggested DeLuca open a submarine sandwich shop and put up $1000 to get him started.

As the summer of 1965 was coming to an end DeLuca rented a small location in a remote area of Bridgeport opened Pete's Super Submarines and there he sold foot-long sandwiches. On the first day the sandwiches were so popular that DeLuca hired his own customers to work behind the counter; by the end of the day he had sold out of all his supplies. The sandwiches continued to be popular for a while but within a few months the shop started losing money and DeLuca and Buck found that selling submarine sandwiches was a seasonal business. They decided they could create an illusion of success by opening a second location and then a third. The third store was finally successful partly because of its more visible location and increased marketing and partly because of a new name —Subway.

DeLuca and Buck had set a goal of 32 shops opened by 1975 but they had only 16 by 1974. They realized that the only way they could reach their goal in one year was to license the Subway name. The first franchise opened that year in Wallingford Connecticut and they opened 32 by the end of 1975. The partners hit 100 by 1978 then 200 by 1983 and DeLuca set a new goal: 5000 Subway shops by 1994. The first international Subway opened in Bahrain in 1984 and DeLuca achieved his goal of 5000 shops by 1990.

During the 1990s DeLuca experimented with several other franchise concepts including We Care Hair (budget styling salons) Cajun Joe's (spicy fried chicken) and Q Burgers. But none of these ventures fared as well as his sandwich empire. As Subway grew however controversy surrounding its treatment of franchisees began to surface. A Federal Trade Commission investigation of the company was dropped in 1993 but Subway continued to battle franchisees complaining about broken contracts market over-saturation (and therefore too much competition and self-cannibalization) and what the franchisees viewed as unreasonably high royalty fees.

In spite of its franchising troubles Subway kept growing. It expanded into Russia and China in the mid-1990s and opened its 11000th restaurant in 1995. In 1997 Subway inked deals with the Army Navy and Air Force exchange services to bring Subway units to military bases. Two years later the

company opened its 14000th restaurant in Mount Gambier Australia an event that coincided with Subway's renewed push to expand internationally.

The company got some unexpected publicity in 1999 when 22-year-old Jared Fogle claimed that he dropped 245 pounds from his 425-pound frame by subsisting on a diet of Subway turkey sandwiches. Subway helped Fogle extend his 15 minutes of fame by featuring him and his oversized pants in a TV commercial. (The company has since built an entire campaign around Fogle that features other weight watchers attributing their success to Jared and Subway.) Subway introduced its largest menu initiative ever in 2000 when it unveiled its Subway Selects Gourmet Sandwiches adding 13 items to the menu. In April 2001 the company opened its 15000th store.

Also that year Buck retired as chairman but stayed on as a member of the board of directors. Becoming one of the fastest-growing franchises in the world Subway expanded from 16000 locations in 2002 to more than 22000 stores by the end of 2004.

All US Subway outlets switched from Pepsi to Coke products in 2005. Two years later the chain surpassed 21000 locations in the US.

EXECUTIVES

Vice President Subway Purchasing, Joe Leahey

LOCATIONS

HQ: DOCTOR'S ASSOCIATES INC.
325 BIC DR, MILFORD, CT 064613072
Phone: 203 877-4281
Web: WWW.SUBWAY.COM

COMPETITORS

Burger King	Panera Bread
CKE Restaurants	Papa John's
Chick-fil-A	Popeyes
Chipotle	Potbelly Sandwich Shop
Church's Chicken	Quiznos
Dairy Queen	Sonic Corp.
Domino's	Starbucks
Jack in the Box	Tim Hortons
McDonald's	Wendy's
Panda Restaurant Group	YUM!

HISTORICAL FINANCIALS

Company Type: Private

Income Statement

FYE: December 31

	ASSETS ($ mil.)	NET INCOME ($ mil.)	INCOME AS % OF ASSETS	EMPLOYEES
12/10	114	7	6.5%	650
12/08	95	6	6.6%	—
Annual Growth	9.3%	8.4%	—	—

2010 Year-End Financials

Return on assets: —
Return on equity: 0.7%
Sales ($ mil): 1,049

hospital which has some 600 doctors on staff also includes a women's health center a sleep therapy division and the Joslin Diabetes Center. Established in 1975 Doctors Community Hospital provides community health services such as educational programs and support groups for specific medical conditions.

EXECUTIVES

Vice President Finance, Dennis Scanlon
Auditors: COHEN RUTHERFORD & KNIGHT PC

LOCATIONS

HQ: DOCTORS' HOSPITAL INC.
8118 GOOD LUCK RD, LANHAM, MD 207063574
Phone: 301 552-8118
Web: WWW.DCHWEB.ORG

PRODUCTS/OPERATIONS

Selected Services

Bariatric services
Breast health
Cancer services
Cardiac services
Diabetes services
Diagnostic service
Emergency services
Neurosciences
Orthopedic services
Robotic surgery
Sleep center
Surgical services
Sears/nose/throat
Support groups
Therapy services
Wound care

COMPETITORS

Adventist HealthCare	Johns Hopkins Medicine
Bon Secours Health	MedStar Health
Calvert Memorial Hospital	Providence Hospital (Washington DC)
Civista Health	Suburban Hospital
Dimensions Healthcare	

HISTORICAL FINANCIALS

Company Type: Private

Income Statement

FYE: June 30

	REVENUE ($ mil.)	NET INCOME ($ mil.)	NET PROFIT MARGIN	EMPLOYEES
06/13	181	1	0.7%	1,200
06/11	211	16	7.9%	—
06/10	198	(1)	—	—
06/09	0	0	—	—
Annual Growth	—	—	—	—

2013 Year-End Financials

Return on assets: 24.5%
Return on equity: 0.7%
Current ratio: 0.20
Cash ($ mil.): 22

DON FORD SANDERSON INC

LOCATIONS

HQ: DON FORD SANDERSON INC
6400 N 51ST AVE, GLENDALE, AZ 853014600
Phone: 623 842-8600
Web: WWW.SANDERSONFORD.COM

DOCTORS' HOSPITAL INC.

Doctors Community Hospital is an acute care and surgical hospital serving the Washington DC area. The not-for-profit medical center admits 12000 patients each year and has some 220 beds and offers standard and specialty services such as diagnostics emergency and cardiac care diagnostics rehabilitation wound care and neurology. The

HISTORICAL FINANCIALS
Company Type: Private

Income Statement
FYE: December 31

	REVENUE ($ mil.)	NET INCOME ($ mil.)	NET PROFIT MARGIN	EMPLOYEES
12/13	692	5	0.8%	416
12/12	590	3	0.6%	—
12/11	510	3	0.7%	—
12/09	301	0	—	—
Annual Growth 23.1%	—	—	—	—

2013 Year-End Financials
Return on assets: 0.7%
Return on equity: 0.8%
Current ratio: 0.30
Cash ($ mil.): 6

DOOLEY'S PETROLEUM INC.

Auditors: CONWAY DEUTH & ASSOCIATES PL

LOCATIONS
HQ: DOOLEY'S PETROLEUM INC.
304 MAIN AVE, MURDOCK, MN 562718033
Phone: 320 875-2641
Web: WWW.DOOLEYPETRO.COM

HISTORICAL FINANCIALS
Company Type: Private

Income Statement
FYE: December 31

	REVENUE ($ mil.)	NET INCOME ($ mil.)	NET PROFIT MARGIN	EMPLOYEES
12/12	334	2	0.8%	110
12/11	359	2	0.6%	—
12/10	250	1	0.7%	—
12/09	205	0	—	—
Annual Growth 17.6%	—	—	—	—

2012 Year-End Financials
Return on assets: 2.2%
Return on equity: 0.8%
Current ratio: 0.60
Cash ($ mil.): 2

DORCHESTER FARMERS COOPERATIVE

Auditors: GARDINER THOMSEN LINCOLN NE

LOCATIONS
HQ: DORCHESTER FARMERS COOPERATIVE
208 W DEPOT ST, DORCHESTER, NE 683432375
Phone: 402 946-4631
Web: WWW.FARMERSCO-OPERATIVE.COM

HISTORICAL FINANCIALS
Company Type: Private

Income Statement
FYE: August 31

	REVENUE ($ mil.)	NET INCOME ($ mil.)	NET PROFIT MARGIN	EMPLOYEES
08/13	833	24	3.0%	270
08/12	918	22	2.5%	—
08/11	695	21	3.1%	—
08/10	576	0	—	—
Annual Growth 13.1%	—	—	—	—

2013 Year-End Financials
Return on assets: 1.1%
Return on equity: 3.0%
Current ratio: 0.80
Cash ($ mil.): 41

DOYLESTOWN HOSPITAL HEALTH AND WELLNESS CENTER INC.

It takes a village to own a hospital and Doylestown Hospital is owned by the local women's civic organization Village Improvement Association (VIA Health). Founded in 1923 the hospital serves southeastern Pennsylvania and neighboring areas of New Jersey. With some 240 beds Doylestown Hospital provides a variety of acute and tertiary medical services. Specialties include cardiac surgery cancer care (as part of the University of Pennsylvania Cancer Network) and orthopedics. Affiliated with the hospital are two Pine Run nursing and assisted-living centers. Doylestown Hospital the flagship facility of the Doylestown Health system.

Operations

The hospital employs some 420 doctors across 50 specialties including radiology gastroenterology urology and pulmonology. Doylestown is also a certified chest pain center (via The Woodall Chest Pain Center) and a joint commission-certified primary stroke center. Additional hospital departments cover emergency critical care birthing rehabilitation and robotic surgery services.

In addition to the main medical center Doylestown Hospital operates three outpatient locations: The Health and Wellness Center in Warrington an Open MRI center in Hartsville and The Pavilion outpatient building located adjacent to the hospital. The parent organization VIA Health runs the Pine Run retirement centers as well as community health facilities.

Geographic Reach

Doylestown Hospital serves Bucks and Montgomery counties in Pennsylvania (including northern suburbs of Philadelphia) and Hunterdon and Mercer counties in neighboring New Jersey.

EXECUTIVES
Medical Director, Joseph Auteri
Director Of Radiology, Ronald Costanzo
Director Of Admissions, Kathy Murphy
Vice President and Chief Medical Officer, Scott S Levy
Director of Radiology, William (Bill) Corse
Board Of Directors, Gregory Gallant
Member Of The Board, Richard Lambert
Auditors: GRANT THORNTON LLP PHILADELPH

LOCATIONS
HQ: DOYLESTOWN HOSPITAL HEALTH AND WELLNESS CENTER INC.
595 W STATE ST, DOYLESTOWN, PA 189012597
Phone: 215 345-2200
Web: WWW.DOYLESTOWN-HOSPITAL.NET

PRODUCTS/OPERATIONS

Selected Services
Hospice
Medical Imaging/Radiology
Outpatient Testing
Rehab/Therapy
Surgical Services
Visiting Nurse/Home Care
Women's Services
Cardiac-Neuro Services
Diabetes Management
GI/Endoscopy
Fibromyalgia
Lab Services
Medical Library
Mammography
Nutrition Counseling - Healthy Directions

COMPETITORS
Abington Memorial Hospital
Children's Hospital of Philadelphia
Jefferson Health System
Lehigh Valley Health Network
North Philadelphia Health System
Pennsylvania Hospital
Shore Memorial Hospital
St. Luke's University Health Network
Tenet Healthcare
University of Pennsylvania Health System

HISTORICAL FINANCIALS
Company Type: Private

Income Statement
FYE: June 30

	REVENUE ($ mil.)	NET INCOME ($ mil.)	NET PROFIT MARGIN	EMPLOYEES
06/13	265	16	6.0%	2,853
06/10	234	3	1.5%	—
06/09	202	6	3.1%	—
06/08	467	0	—	—
Annual Growth	—	—	—	—

2013 Year-End Financials
Return on assets: 21.3%
Return on equity: 6.0%
Current ratio: 0.20
Cash ($ mil.): 11

DPR CONSTRUCTION INC.

From bio labs to wafer fabs DPR Construction runs the gamut for its high-tech and health care clients. The employee-owned firm provides general contracting and construction management services for the advanced technology/mission-critical life sciences health care higher education and corporate office markets. The construction firm specializes in developing retail stores hospitals data centers clean rooms laboratories manufacturing facilities and green buildings. Altogether DPR Construction boasts about 20 regional offices nationwide. Company head Doug Woods former CEO Peter Nosler and secretary/treasurer Ron Davidowski (the D P and R in DPR Construction) founded the firm in 1990.

Operations

Since its founding the company has completed some 8500 projects. DPR Construction has expertise in collaborative virtual building and Building Information Modeling (BIM) sustainability pre-construction and other niche areas.

Geographic Reach

To maintain a presence near customers DPR boasts nearly 20 regional offices. Its operations span 10 states including Arizona California Colorado North Carolina Florida Georgia Maryland Texas Virginia and Washington DC.

Sales and Marketing

DPR serves several core markets including advanced technology corporate offices healthcare higher education and life sciences. Customers have includes CHRISTUS Health Clif Bar & Company Intuit Facebook and Kaiser Permanente.

Strategy

The company is looking to leverage its expanded East Coast operations especially in the growing mid-Atlanticmarket. Its three offices in Maryland Virginia and the District of Columbia also serve customers in West Virginia Delaware Pennsylvania and New Jersey.

DPR has been focusing on eco-friendly construction. More than 40% of its projects incorporate green building techniques or products and approximately one in four of its employees are Leadership in Energy and Environmental Design (LEED) certified.

EXECUTIVES

Management Committee, Jim Dolen
Management Committee, Peter A. Salvati
President, Douglas E. (Doug) Woods
Management Committee, Eric Lamb
Regional Manager Raleigh-Durham NC Office, Mark Whitson
Regional Manager Tampa FL Office, Page W. McKee
Regional Manager Redwood City, Jody Quinton
Regional Manager Baltimore and Washington DC, Greg Haldeman
Management Committee, George Pfeffer
Management Committee, Mike Ford
Regional Manager West Palm Beach, Deborah Beetson
Regional Manager Austin and Houston TX Offices, Gary Nauert
Regional Manager Phoenix, David Elrod
Regional Manager San Diego, Jay Leopold
Regional Manager Sacramento, Mark Cirksena
Regional Manager San Jose, Scott Greubel
CFO, Michele Leiva
Regional Manager San Francisco, Mike Humphrey
Regional Manager Richmond VA, Lisa Lingerfelt
Regional Manager Atlanta, Russ Brockelbank
Regional Manager Denver Office, Michael Devens
Regional Manager Newport Beach and Pasadena CA Offices, Dave Seastrom
Regional Manager Orlando FL Office, Scott Lyons
Vice President Information Technology, Joe Yau
Vice President Engineering, Dustin Rothwell
Vice Chairman, Daniel Valentine
Auditors: PRICEWATERHOUSECOOPERS LLP LO

LOCATIONS

HQ: DPR CONSTRUCTION INC.
1450 VETERANS BLVD OFC, REDWOOD CITY, CA 940632618
Phone: 650 474-1450
Web: WWW.DPR.COM

Selected Offices
Atlanta
Austin TX
Baltimore
Denver
Houston
Newport Beach CA
Orlando Florida

Pasadena CA
Phoenix
Raleigh-Durham NC
Redwood City CA
Richmond VA
Sacramento CA
San Diego CA
San Francisco CA
San Jose CA
Tampa Florida
Washington DC
West Palm Beach FL

COMPETITORS

Austin Industries	Jacobs Engineering
Bechtel	M. A. Mortenson
Devcon Construction	PC Construction
Fluor	Skanska USA Building
Hensel Phelps	Swinerton
Construction	Turner Corporation
Hoffman Corporation	Whiting-Turner

HISTORICAL FINANCIALS

Company Type: Private

Income Statement FYE: December 31

	REVENUE ($ mil.)	NET INCOME ($ mil.)	NET PROFIT MARGIN	EMPLOYEES
12/08	1,836	68	3.7%	2,300
12/00	1,958	25	1.3%	—
Annual Growth	(0.8%)	13.0%	—	—

2008 Year-End Financials

Return on assets: —
Return on equity: 3.7%
Current ratio: 0.50

Cash ($ mil.): 162

DRAKE UNIVERSITY

You won't find duck duck goose as part of the curriculum at Drake University. The Des Moines Iowa school provides undergraduate and graduate education programs for some 5500 students through its six colleges and schools: arts and sciences business and public administration education journalism and mass communications law and pharmacy and health sciences. It has a 15:1 student-to-faculty ratio. A private school Drake University was founded in 1881 with seed money from General Francis Marion Drake a Civil War general and former Iowa governor banker railroad builder and attorney. Drake University also hosts the Drake Relays one of the largest track and field events in the US.

Geographic Reach

Drake is located on a 150-acre campus in Des Moines Iowa. Its students hail from across the US and about 50 international countries.

Operations

The university offers more than 70 undergraduate programs as well as 20 graduate degrees. Drake employs 280 full-time faculty members. In addition to its main colleges and schools the university operates centers and institutes in fields including agricultural law finance humanities professional studies public policy scientific research and entrepreneurship.

Tuition and fees at the university runs at about $29000 each year and account for two-thirds of revenue.

Strategy

Expansion efforts at Drake include the opening of several new learning and laboratory facilities at the College of Pharmacy and Health Sciences in

2013. The university is also working to streamline administrative functions to control expenses.

EXECUTIVES

Vice President, John (Jack) Smith
Auditors: DENMAN & COMPANY LLP WEST DES

LOCATIONS

HQ: DRAKE UNIVERSITY
2507 UNIVERSITY AVE, DES MOINES, IA 503114505
Phone: 515 271-2011
Web: WWW.ARTSCI.DRAKE.EDU

PRODUCTS/OPERATIONS

Selected Services
College of Arts and Sciences
College of Business and Public Administration
College of Pharmacy and Health Sciences
Law School
School of Education
School of Journalism and Mass Communication

HISTORICAL FINANCIALS

Company Type: Private

Income Statement FYE: June 30

	REVENUE ($ mil.)	NET INCOME ($ mil.)	NET PROFIT MARGIN	EMPLOYEES
06/14*	196	8	4.5%	830
05/13	184	4	2.5%	—
05/12	180	5	2.9%	—
05/10	123	0	—	—
Annual Growth	12.4%	—	—	—

*Fiscal year change

2014 Year-End Financials

Return on assets: 12.2%
Return on equity: 4.5%
Current ratio: 0.50

Cash ($ mil.): 38

DREXEL UNIVERSITY

Drexel doesn't want to train its dragons but to educate them in a wide range of disciplines. Drexel University (home of the Drexel Dragons) is a private coeducational institution of higher learning with an enrollment of more than 26000 undergraduate and graduate students and a student-teacher ratio of about 17:1. It operates more than a dozen schools and colleges in the US; the Drexel University College of Medicine is the one of the country's largest private medical schools. Drexel runs a mandatory co-operative education program that helps students gain real-world experience while supplying local employers with trained workers. Philadelphia financier and philanthropist Anthony Drexel founded the university in 1891.

Operations

One of the 15 largest private universities in the US Drexel offers more than 200 degree programs in 15 colleges and schools. Drexel Online was one of the first Internet-based distance education programs. It offers more than 100 degree programs. In research the university garners about $110 million in funding with about $88 million from federal sources.

Geographic Reach

Besides its three campuses in Philadelphia Drexel has educational operations in Malvern Pennsylvania and Sacramento California and it has research partnerships in China and Israel.

Financial Performance

For Drexel's fiscal 2013 (ends June) revenue increased nearly to $965 million and expenses came in a just under $900 million. Its assets grew to $1.1 billion in 2013 up from $946 million the previous year.

Strategy

Drexel is working with Amtrak and Brandywine Realty Trust to develop a mixed-use project on 75 acres around Philadelphia's 30th Street Station. Next door to that site Drexel is developing its Innovation Neighborhood project on 12 acres of its campus. That project is designed to attract and start high-tech businesses.

Drexel in 2014 opened a 23000-square-foot facility in Philadelphia's Center City that includes space for clinical services and research for its College of Nursing and Health Professions.

Mergers and Acquisitions

In September 2012 Drexel acquired the Academy of Natural Sciences of Philadelphia (ANS) establishing it as a not-for-profit subsidiary of the university.

EXECUTIVES

Associate Vice President For Planning An, Nancy Trainer

Vice President And General Counsel, Michael (Mel) Exler

Vice President Univ Facilities, Robert (Bob) Francis

President and CEO Academy of Natural Sciences of Drexel University, George W. Gephart

Dean College of Arts and Sciences, Donna Murasko

Dean College of Nursing and Health Professions, Gloria F. Donnelly

Interim VP and CIO Information Resources and Technology, Kenneth S. Blackney

Dean Westphal College of Media Arts and Design, Allen Sabinson

Dean Thomas R. Kline School of Law, Roger J. Dennis

Athletic Director, Eric Zillmer

Dean University Libraries, Danuta Nitecki

EVP Treasurer and COO, Helen Y. Bowman

Dean College of Engineering, Joseph Hughes

President, John A. Fry

Executive Vice Provost and Dean of the Graduate College, James Herbert

SVP Online Learning and President Drexel Online, Susan C. Aldridge

Dean and SVP Medical Affairs College of Medicine, Daniel V. Schidlow

Provost and EVP, M. Brian Blake

Director School of Biomedical Engineering Science and Health Systems, Kenneth A. Barbee

Dean Pennoni Honors College, Paula Marantz Cohen

Dean Close School of Entrepreneurship, Donna De Carolis

Director Center for Hospitality and Sport Management, Jonathan Deutsch

VP Finance CFO and Associate Treasurer, Jeff Eberly

VP and Dean Admissions, Chris Ferguson

Dean LeBow College of Business, Frank Linnehan

Interim Dean College of Computing and Informatics, Spiros Mancoridis

Director A.J. Drexel Autism Institute, Craig Newschaffer

Dean Dornside School of Public Health, Ana Diez Roux

Dean School of Education, Nancy Butler Songer

Dean Graduate School of Biomedical Sciences and Professional Studies College of Medicine, Elisabeth Van Bockstaele

Senior Assoc Vice President Public Safety, DOMENIC CECCANECCHIO

Senior Vice President Of Communications, Lori Doyle

Associate Vice President Financial Plann, Amy Bosio

Vice President Of Finance, Jimmy Wong

Associate Vice President Internal Audit, Louis Siegel

MDSA Vice President, Kerry Diblasio

Senior Vice President, Keith Orris

Department Head, Kirk Heilbrun

Vice President Information Technology And Operations, Chris Shull

Associate Vice President and Director of Investments, Catherine (Cathy) Ulozas

Senior Vice President Of Enrollment, Joan McDonald

Senior Vice President, Anthony Caneris

Assistant Vice President, David (Dave) Toll

Assistant Vice President For Recruitment, Casey Turner

Senior Vice President, Phyllis Lewis

Assistant Vice President Internal Audit And Management Consulting, Billy Shea

Vice President, Barbara Ryan

Senior Vice President, James Tucker

Associate Vice President College Of Engi, John Dolan

Assistant Vice President Core Enterprise Systems, Michael McCabe

Senior Vice President Institution Advancement, Barbara (Barb) Spiro

Vice President, Pete Frisko

Senior Vice President, Carl Oxholm

Assistant Vice President, Pe Ungaro

Chairman Board of Trustees, Richard A. Greenawalt

Secretary Iiia, Sandra Narinesingh

Secretary, Stephanie Weekly

Board Member, Matt Rowe

Secretary Treasurer, Bruce Eisenstein

Treasurer, Samson Shepherd

Board Member, Kathleen Miller

Auditors: DELOITTE & TOUCHE LLP PHILADE

LOCATIONS

HQ: DREXEL UNIVERSITY
3141 CHESTNUT ST, PHILADELPHIA, PA 191042875
Phone: 215 895-2000
Web: WWW.DREXEL.EDU

PRODUCTS/OPERATIONS

Selected Schools and Colleges

Antoinette Westphal College of Media Arts & Design
Bennett S. Lebow College of Business
College of Arts and Sciences
College of Engineering
The College of Information Science and Technology
College of Law
College of Nursing and Health Professions
Drexel University College of Medicine
Earle Mack School of Law
Pennoni Honors College
Richard C. Goodwin College of Professional Studies
School of Biomedical Engineering Science and Health Systems
School of Education
School of Public Health

HISTORICAL FINANCIALS

Company Type: Private

Income Statement

FYE: June 30

	REVENUE ($ mil.)	NET INCOME ($ mil.)	NET PROFIT MARGIN	EMPLOYEES
06/13	965	107	11.1%	2,868
06/12	910	34	3.8%	—
06/11*	896	166	18.6%	—
12/08	0	0	—	—
Annual Growth	—	—	—	—

*Fiscal year change

2013 Year-End Financials

Return on assets: 6.2%
Return on equity: 11.1%
Current ratio: —

Cash ($ mil.): 87

DRISCOLL CHILDREN'S HOSPITAL

Auditors: BKD LLP HOUSTON TX

LOCATIONS

HQ: DRISCOLL CHILDREN' S HOSPITAL
3533 S ALAMEDA ST, CORPUS CHRISTI, TX 784111721
Phone: 361 694-5000
Web: WWW.DCHCC.ORG

HISTORICAL FINANCIALS

Company Type: Private

Income Statement

FYE: April 30

	REVENUE ($ mil.)	NET INCOME ($ mil.)	NET PROFIT MARGIN	EMPLOYEES
04/13	525	102	19.4%	1,500
04/12	248	54	22.1%	—
04/11	232	46	19.9%	—
04/10	215	0	—	—
Annual Growth	34.6%			

2013 Year-End Financials

Return on assets: 1.1%
Return on equity: 19.4%
Current ratio: 2.00

Cash ($ mil.): 110

DTJ HOLDINGS INC.

Roberts & Dybdahl can't sell you a house but it can sell you some important pieces. The company is a wholesale distributor of lumber lumber products and building materials to customers in Illinois Indiana Iowa Kansas Nebraska and Wisconsin. Products include treated lumber boards shingles siding studs trusses joists and engineered wood products. Roberts & Dybdahl operates about 10 distribution centers and some half a dozen on-site truss manufacturing facilities able to custom build roof and floor trusses to customer specifications. The company was founded as Carroll Wholesale in 1955 by Howard Roberts and Hub Dybdahl.

EXECUTIVES

Director Purchasing, Cyndee Johnson

Manager Regional Trading Lumber Kansas, Brandon Alles

Regional Trading Manager Lumber Iowa, Alan Shearer

Regional Sales Manager Lumber Wisconsin, William (Bill) Johnson

Regional Trading Manager Lumber Illinois, Jim Jones

Assistant Regional Trading Manager Lumber Illinois, John Rich

Regional Trading Manager Lumber Illinois, Kerry Russell

Auditors: MCGLADREY LLP DES MOINES IO

LOCATIONS

HQ: DTJ HOLDINGS INC.
5034 GRAND RIDGE DR, WEST DES MOINES, IA 502655754
Phone: 515 262-6600
Web: WWW.ROBERTSDYBDAHL.COM

2009 Locations

	No.
Iowa	3
Illinois	2
Indiana	1
Kansas	1
Nebraska	1
Wisconsin	1
Total	**9**

COMPETITORS

84 Lumber	Huttig Building
Babcock Lumber	Products
Builders FirstSource	International Paper
Edward Hines Lumber	Weekes Forest Products
HD Supply	

HISTORICAL FINANCIALS

Company Type: Private

Income Statement

FYE: December 31

	REVENUE ($ mil.)	NET INCOME ($ mil.)	NET PROFIT MARGIN	EMPLOYEES
12/12	220	1	0.7%	238
12/11	181	0	0.5%	—
12/10	187	1	0.8%	—
12/09	160	0	—	—
Annual Growth	**11.2%**	—	—	—

2012 Year-End Financials

Return on assets: 1.2%   Cash ($ mil.): 2
Return on equity: 0.7%
Current ratio: 2.20

DUCON TECHNOLOGIES INC.

Auditors: SALBORO AND ASSOCIATES NEW YO

LOCATIONS

HQ: DUCON TECHNOLOGIES INC.
5 PENN PLZ STE 2403, NEW YORK, NY 100011848
Phone: 631 694-1700
Web: WWW.DUCON.COM

HISTORICAL FINANCIALS

Company Type: Private

Income Statement

FYE: December 31

	REVENUE ($ mil.)	NET INCOME ($ mil.)	NET PROFIT MARGIN	EMPLOYEES
12/12	479	4	0.9%	471
12/10	403	8	2.0%	—
12/09	412	7	1.7%	—
12/05	328	0	—	—
Annual Growth	**5.5%**	—	—	—

2012 Year-End Financials

Return on assets: 1.8%   Cash ($ mil.): 5
Return on equity: 0.9%
Current ratio: 2.70

DUPONT HOSPITAL FOR CHILDREN

Auditors: KPMG LLP JACKSONVILLE FL

LOCATIONS

HQ: DUPONT HOSPITAL FOR CHILDREN
1600 ROCKLAND RD, WILMINGTON, DE 198033607
Phone: 302 651-4000
Web: WWW.NEMOURS.ORG

HISTORICAL FINANCIALS

Company Type: Private

Income Statement

FYE: December 31

	REVENUE ($ mil.)	NET INCOME ($ mil.)	NET PROFIT MARGIN	EMPLOYEES
12/09	706	150	21.4%	3,068
12/08	420	12	3.0%	—
Annual Growth	**68.0%**	**1104.3%**	—	—

2009 Year-End Financials

Return on assets: —   Cash ($ mil.): 171
Return on equity: 21.4%
Current ratio: 1.50

DUQUESNE UNIVERSITY OF THE HOLY SPIRIT

Duquesne University of The Holy Ghost keeps a keen eye on the spiritual as well as the academic. The school offers more than 100 undergraduate degree programs about 65 graduate and professional degree programs and more than 20 doctoral programs at schools of business education law liberal arts nursing pharmacy health sciences natural and environmental sciences music and leadership and professional advancement. Duquesne was founded in 1878 as the Pittsburgh Catholic College of the Holy Ghost. It has an annual enrollment of more than 10000 undergraduate graduate and law students.

EXECUTIVES

Chancellor, John E. Murray, age 82
President, Charles J. Dougherty, age 66
VP Academics and Provost, Ralph L. Pearson
VP Business and Management, Stephen Schillo
Executive Vice President for, Sean M. Hogan
Dean School of Nursing, Eileen Zungolo
Dean Rangos School of Health Sciences, Gregory Frazer
Dean School of Natural and Environmental Science, David Seybert
Dean School of Music, Edward Kocher
Director Animal Care, J. Douglas Bricker
Managing Director Tamburitzans, Paul Stafura
Executive Director CTS, John Ziegler
Acting Dean College of Liberal Arts, Albert Labriola
Dean School of Law, Donald Guter
Dean Palumbo Donahue School of Business, Alan Miciak
Dean School of Education, Olga Welch
Dean School of Leadership and Professional Advancement, Dorothy Bassett

---

Associate Vice President Academic Affa, Alexandra Gregory
Provost Vice President Academic Affairs, Timothy (Tim) Austin
Vice President Of Membership Beta Alpha Psi, Emily Stephen
Chairman, P. David Pappert
Vice Chair, Marie M. Jones
Treasurer, Antony Davies
Auditors: DELOITTE & TOUCHE LLP PITTSBU

LOCATIONS

HQ: DUQUESNE UNIVERSITY OF THE HOLY SPIRIT
600 FORBES AVE, PITTSBURGH, PA 152193016
Phone: 412 396-6000
Web: WWW.DUQ.EDU

HISTORICAL FINANCIALS

Company Type: Private

Income Statement

FYE: June 30

	REVENUE ($ mil.)	NET INCOME ($ mil.)	NET PROFIT MARGIN	EMPLOYEES
06/13	357	20	5.7%	3,601
06/12	262	7	2.8%	—
06/11	333	21	6.6%	—
06/10	290	0	—	—
Annual Growth	**7.2%**	—	—	—

2013 Year-End Financials

Return on assets: 10.4%   Cash ($ mil.): 40
Return on equity: 5.7%
Current ratio: 0.20

DURHAM PUBLIC SCHOOLS

Auditors: RIVES & ASSOCIATES LLP RALEI

LOCATIONS

HQ: DURHAM PUBLIC SCHOOLS
511 CLEVELAND ST, DURHAM, NC 277013334
Phone: 919 560-2000
Web: WWW.DPSNC.NET

HISTORICAL FINANCIALS

Company Type: Private

Income Statement

FYE: June 30

	REVENUE ($ mil.)	NET INCOME ($ mil.)	NET PROFIT MARGIN	EMPLOYEES
06/11	398	20	5.2%	4,500
06/10	331	7	2.3%	—
06/09	0	0	—	—
Annual Growth	—	**60857.7%**	—	—

2011 Year-End Financials

Return on assets: —   Cash ($ mil.): 51
Return on equity: 5.2%
Current ratio: 1.60

DUVAL COUNTY PUBLIC SCHOOLS

Auditors: CHERRY BEKAERT & HOLLAND LL

LOCATIONS

HQ: DUVAL COUNTY PUBLIC SCHOOLS
1701 PRUDENTIAL DR, JACKSONVILLE, FL
322078152
Phone: 904 390-2000
Web: WWW.DUVALSCHOOLS.ORG

HISTORICAL FINANCIALS
Company Type: Private

Income Statement
FYE: June 30

	REVENUE ($ mil.)	NET INCOME ($ mil.)	NET PROFIT MARGIN	EMPLOYEES
06/13	1,077	(10)	—	13,000
06/07	1,189	27	2.3%	
06/06	1,063	(22)	—	
Annual Growth	0.2%	—	—	—

2013 Year-End Financials
Return on assets: 2.3%   Cash ($ mil.): 79
Return on equity: (-1.0%)
Current ratio: —

DYNASTY FARMS INC.

Auditors: BIANCHI KASAVAN & POPE LLP

LOCATIONS

HQ: DYNASTY FARMS INC.
740 AIRPORT BLVD, SALINAS, CA 939014510
Phone: 831 755-1398
Web: WWW.PIM4U.COM

HISTORICAL FINANCIALS
Company Type: Private

Income Statement
FYE: December 31

	REVENUE ($ mil.)	NET INCOME ($ mil.)	NET PROFIT MARGIN	EMPLOYEES
12/13	324	(1)	—	100
12/12	270	4	1.5%	—
12/11	282	0	0.0%	—
12/10	257	0	—	—
Annual Growth	7.9%	—	—	—

2013 Year-End Financials
Return on assets: 0.8%   Cash ($ mil.): —
Return on equity: (-0.5%)
Current ratio: 0.90

E-Z MART STORES INC.

E-Z Mart Stores aims to make filling gas tanks and stomachs EZR for small-town America. The regional convenience store chain operates about 295 stores across four neighboring states including Arkansas Louisiana Oklahoma and Texas. Rather than build its own stores the company usu-

ally expands through acquisitions. In addition to the standard hot dogs sodas coffee and cigarettes most E-Z Mart locations also offer Shell Conoco Phillips 66 or CITGO gasoline. E-Z Mart was founded in 1970 by Jim Yates in Nashville Arkansas. Yates died in 1998 when the plane he was piloting crashed leaving his daughter Sonja Hubbard at the company's helm as CEO.

Geographic Reach
Ranked #35 on Convenience Store News' "Top 100 Convenience Stores Report" E-Z Mart is a regional c-store chain that primarily serves Texas and Arkansas as well as Oklahoma and Louisiana.

Sales and Marketing
Aiming to offer the chain's customers access to updated fuel prices a list of locations and in-store promotions among other items E-Z Mart partnered with OpenStore by GasBuddy to roll out a new E-Z Mart website and mobile app. The fully integrated mobile app enables consumers to send feedback from their mobile phones and receive time-sensitive electronic mobile coupons.

Strategy
While E-Z Mart has trimmed its store count during the past decade or so including exiting markets such as Missouri it continues to make strategic acquisitions. Like other convenience store operators seeking to boost in-store sales E-Z Mart is expanding its food and beverage offering adding fresh-brewed iced tea to all of its stores and installing freezers. Outside the company has a deal with Redbox to place its movie rental kiosks outside of E-Z Mart stores.

EXECUTIVES

Vice President Maintenance, Dale Sides
Vice President Operations Division II, Harold Hicks
Vice President, Lanny Mcalester
Auditors: BKD LLP FORT SMITH AR

LOCATIONS

HQ: E-Z MART STORES INC.
602 FALVEY AVE, TEXARKANA, TX 755016677
Phone: 903 832-6502

2014 Stores

	No.
Texas	96
Arkansas	95
Oklahoma	80
Louisiana	18
Total	**289**

COMPETITORS

7-Eleven	Love's Country Stores
Allsup's	QuikTrip
Brookshire Grocery	Racetrac Petroleum
Chevron	Susser Holdings
Exxon Mobil	Valero Energy
Krause Gentle	

HISTORICAL FINANCIALS
Company Type: Private

Income Statement
FYE: December 31

	REVENUE ($ mil.)	NET INCOME ($ mil.)	NET PROFIT MARGIN	EMPLOYEES
12/13	1,003	15	1.5%	2,100
12/12	1,018	33	3.3%	—
12/11	961	13	1.4%	—
12/10	793	0	—	—
Annual Growth	8.2%	—	—	—

2013 Year-End Financials
Return on assets: 2.5%   Cash ($ mil.): 5
Return on equity: 1.5%
Current ratio: 0.30

E. C. BARTON & COMPANY

E. C. Barton & Company sells a variety of home-building tools and goods under a handful of banner names. A member of industry cooperative Do It Best the company sells lumber and building materials through more than 120 locations throughout Texas as well as 14 other states in the Southeast and the Northeast. It operates several divisions including Barton's Builders Material Company E.C.B. Brokerage and Surplus Purchasing Surplus Warehouse and Grossman's Bargain Outlet. E. C. Barton also manages an e-commerce site. Professional builders and remodelers generate most of the company's revenue. Founded in 1885 the company is employee-owned.

Geographic Reach
E. C. Barton operates its 120-plus stores in 15 states including Alabama Arkansas Florida Louisiana Massachusetts Missouri Mississippi New York North Carolina Ohio Pennsylvania Rhode Island South Carolina Tennessee and Texas. More than half of its stores are located in four states: Arkansas New York Texas and Massachusetts.

Sales and Marketing
The retailer serves both professional builders and remodelers and is part of cooperative Do It Best.

Operations
The company has organized its business into a handful of divisions: Barton's Grossman's Bargain Outlet Builders Material Company E.C.B. Brokerage and Surplus Purchasing and Surplus Warehouse.

EXECUTIVES

President and CEO, Niel Crowson
Secretary and Treasurer, Tom Rainwater
Manager Builders Material Company, Steve Gage
Vice President Of Operations, Kevin Pierce
Vice President Distribution, Ron Bellas
Vice President Of Store Operations Bargain Outlet Division, Bill Ringelstein
Auditors: JONES & COMPANY LTD JONESBO

LOCATIONS

HQ: E. C. BARTON & COMPANY
2929 BROWNS LN, JONESBORO, AR 724017208
Phone: 870 932-6673
Web: WWW.ECBARTON.COM

PRODUCTS/OPERATIONS

Selected Products
Bath
Ceiling fans and light kits
Ceilings
Composite decking
Doors
Driveway sealer
Electrical
Flooring
Kitchens
Lighting
Moulding
Outdoor living
Paint
Paint sundries
Pine / oak / vinyl boards
Roofing
Screws & nails
Tools & hardware
Wall planking plywood & shims
Water heaters
Windows

Selected Divisions
Barton's

Builders Material Company
E.C.B. Brokerage and Surplus Purchasing
Grossman' s Bargain Outlet
Surplus Warehouse

COMPETITORS

84 Lumber
Ace Hardware
Builders FirstSource Southeast Group
Diamond Hill Plywood
Guardian Building Products Distribution
Home Depot
Lowe' s
Northern Tool
Snavely Forest Products
Stock Building Supply
True Value
WinWholesale

HISTORICAL FINANCIALS

Company Type: Private

Income Statement

FYE: October 30

	REVENUE ($ mil.)	NET INCOME ($ mil.)	NET PROFIT MARGIN	EMPLOYEES
10/14	247	0	0.4%	700
10/13	241	(1)	—	—
10/12	265	(2)	—	—
10/11	263	0	—	—
Annual Growth	(2.1%)	—	—	—

2014 Year-End Financials

Return on assets: 3.4%   Cash ($ mil.): 3
Return on equity: 0.4%
Current ratio: 0.40

EAST BATON ROUGE PARISH SCHOOL DISTRICT

LOCATIONS

HQ: EAST BATON ROUGE PARISH SCHOOL DISTRICT
1050 S FOSTER DR, BATON ROUGE, LA 708067221
Phone: 225 922-5400
Web: WWW.EBRSCHOOLS.ORG

HISTORICAL FINANCIALS

Company Type: Private

Income Statement

FYE: June 30

	REVENUE ($ mil.)	NET INCOME ($ mil.)	NET PROFIT MARGIN	EMPLOYEES
06/07	427	393	92.0%	6,800
06/05	427	34	8.0%	—
06/03	1,120	0	—	—
Annual Growth	—	4594.1%		

2007 Year-End Financials

Return on assets: 2.0%   Cash ($ mil.): 219
Return on equity: 92.0%
Current ratio: 6.60

EAST JEFFERSON GENERAL HOSPITAL

LOCATIONS

HQ: EAST JEFFERSON GENERAL HOSPITAL
4200 HOUMA BLVD, METAIRIE, LA 700062996
Phone: 504 454-4000
Web: WWW.EJGH.ORG

HISTORICAL FINANCIALS

Company Type: Private

Income Statement

FYE: December 31

	REVENUE ($ mil.)	NET INCOME ($ mil.)	NET PROFIT MARGIN	EMPLOYEES
12/12*	346	(25)	—	3,436
05/10	0	(0)	—	—
05/09	0	0	21.8%	—
Annual Growth	549.2%			

*Fiscal year change

2012 Year-End Financials

Return on assets: 15.7%   Cash ($ mil.): 7
Return on equity: (-7.5%)
Current ratio: 0.60

EAST TENNESSEE CHILDREN'S HOSPITAL ASSOCIATION INC.

ETCH has made a permanent mark on the lives of countless children over the years. Knoxville-based East Tennessee Children's Hospital (ETCH) with more than 150 beds provides a full range of health care services to children from eastern Tennessee and portions of surrounding states. Among its 30 specialized services are cardiology neonatal care orthopedics and psychiatry as well as cystic fibrosis and hearing impairment services. The hospital also offers support such as for families of children stricken by cancer. The hospital's roots are in the foundation of Knox County Crippled Children's Hospital in 1937 with less than 50 beds.

Geographic Reach

The medical center primarily serves 16 counties in eastern Tennessee: Anderson Blount Campbell Claiborne Cocke Grainger Hamblen Jefferson Knox Loudon Monroe Morgan Roane Scott Sevier and Union. It also provides services in other Tennessee counties and nearby portions of Kentucky North Carolina and Virginia.

Operations

With a total of about 450 physicians ETCH handles some 6000 inpatient visits per year while its emergency department treats some 70000 patients each year. The hospital is designated as a comprehensive regional pediatric center by the state of Tennessee. As such it operates a level III neonatal intensive care unit (ICU) and a level I trauma center and partners with smaller area hospitals in an effort to provide pediatric training support and patient transfer services. ETCH also partners with larger acute care hospitals including the University of Tennessee Medical Center to provide collaborative care services.

The medical center provides medical training services as well such as student internships nursing scholarships clinical rotations and residency programs. Some programs are offered through partnerships with area universities and colleges including the University of Tennessee and Lincoln Memorial University's DeBusk College of Osteopathic Medicine.

EXECUTIVES

Nursing Director, Danni Varlan
Vice President for Development and Community Services, Carlton M Long
Vice President Patient Care, Laura Barnes
Nursing Director Critical Care Services, Sheri S Smith
Vice President, Joe Childs
Secretary Treasurer, Leanne Gibbs
Auditors: PERSHING YOAKLEY & ASSOCIATES

LOCATIONS

HQ: EAST TENNESSEE CHILDREN' S HOSPITAL ASSOCIATION INC.
2018 W CLINCH AVE, KNOXVILLE, TN 379162301
Phone: 865 541-8000
Web: WWW.ETCH.COM

PRODUCTS/OPERATIONS

Selected Services
Cancer
Cardiac
Emergency department
Hematology
Home health
Inpatient services
Intensive care unit (pediatric and neonatal)
Laboratory services
Mental health
Nutrition
Obesity
Orthopedics
Outpatient services
Radiology
Rehabilitation
Respiratory care
Sleep medicine
Surgical services
Sedation services
Transport service
Trauma

COMPETITORS

Akron Children' s Hospital
All Children' s Hospital
Children' s Hopsital of Chicago
Children' s Hospital Boston
Children' s Hospital Colorado
Children' s Hospital and Health System
Children' s Hospital of Philadelphia
Children' s Hospital of Richmond
Children' s Mercy Hospital
Cincinnati Children' s Hospital
Covenant Health
Dell Children' s Medical Center
Nationwide Children' s Hospital
Shriners Hospitals For Children
Tennova Healthcare
University Health System Inc.

HISTORICAL FINANCIALS
Company Type: Private

Income Statement
FYE: June 30

	REVENUE ($ mil.)	NET INCOME ($ mil.)	NET PROFIT MARGIN	EMPLOYEES
06/14	210	23	11.3%	1,500
06/13	216	37	17.4%	—
06/12	209	29	14.2%	—
06/11	183	0	—	—
Annual Growth	4.7%	—	—	—

2014 Year-End Financials
Return on assets: 6.7%
Return on equity: 11.3%
Current ratio: 1.70
Cash ($ mil.): 20

EAST TENNESSEE STATE UNIVERSITY

East Tennessee State University (ETSU) is a public coeducational member of the Tennessee Board of Regents' network of 45 postsecondary educational institutions. The university has 11 colleges and schools representing arts and sciences business and technology clinical and rehabilitative health sciences education medicine nursing pharmacy public health honors as well as continuing and graduate studies. It offers approximately 125 undergraduate programs 95 master's programs and a dozen doctoral programs as well as graduate certificates teacher licensure and specialist programs. Founded as East Tennessee State Normal School in 1911 ETSU has an enrollment of more than 15000 students.

ETSU's main campus is located in Johnson City. It also operates a branch campus in Kingsport two sites for the College of Medicine and College of Pharmacy at Mountain Home Veteran's campus and a location in Elizabethton. The university also offers online courses worldwide and programs at many locations throughout its service region.

From its Appalachian vantage ETSU offers studies of the region including an undergraduate program entitled "Bluegrass Old-Time and Country Music." The school claims to offer the world's only master's degree in reading with a storytelling concentration.

Strategic planning through 2015 encompasses a broad range of objectives. These include: elevating and supporting accessibility to its educational programs; enabling student success through counsel mentorships support and more; expanding and enhancing research community service and scholarly activities; supporting diversity; refining stewardship to realize marginal cost revenue and achieve efficiencies; increasing arts on display on campus and building support for a new visual and performing arts facility. ETSU is also aiming to gain a silver rating in the Sustainability Tracking Assessment and Rating System (STARS).

EXECUTIVES

Vice President University Advancement, Richard (Dick) Manahan
Assoc Vice President Univ Alumni, ROBERT (Bob) PLUMMER
Assistant Vice President Of University Center, TONY WARNER
Vice President, Hanah Stribling
Vice President, Danielle Jocelyn
Vice President For Academic Affairs, Sherry Armitage
Vice President, Michael Wells
Vice President of Membership, Emily Murr
Vice President, Joni Watson
Vice President of Internal Communication, Kelli Carter
Executive Vice President, Kayla Morgan
Vice President Of Finance, Whitney Martin
Vice President, William Miller
Assistant Vice President Performance Fund Eval, Cynthia Sue Burnley
Vice President of External Communication, Cassie Johnson
Associate Vice President Student Services Admin, Sally Lee
Office Manager Vice President Business And Finance, Bonnie Chandley
Vice President Finance and Administration, David D (Dave) Collins
Associate Vice President Facilities Planning Management and Construction, Bill Rasnick
Medical Director, Salah Shurbaji
Vice President of Communications, Frank Rivera
Secretary, Andrea McKinney
Secretary 3 Finance Aid Stdt Aff Com, Wendy Williams
Treasurer, Isaac Boven
Treasurer, Rachael Loven
Secretary, Halie Dyer
Secretary, Tessa Johnson
Secretary, Sandy Greene
Treasurer, Lisa Booher
Secretary, Megan Jamerson
Secretary 3 Child Study Center, Barbara (Barb) Wolff
Secretary 3 Student Services COM, Sheba Keaton
Secretary 3 Internal Medicine, Dolores Moore
Secretary 2 Student Housing, Susan (Sue) Lilly
Secretary 3 Internal Medicine, Yvette Font
Secretary 3 Maintenance Of Plant admin, Julie Robinette
Secretary 3 Assoc Dean Academic Affairs, Heather Love
Secretary 3 Academic Support JC, Ruby DeMoss
Secretary 2 Educ Leadership Policy Analysis, Joanna Wicker
Secretary 1 CAPS Administration, Paulette Davis
Secretary 3 University Advisement, Ian Steidle
Secretary 3 Academic Support Kingsport, Jessica Strom

LOCATIONS

HQ: EAST TENNESSEE STATE UNIVERSITY
807 UNIVERSITY PKWY, JOHNSON CITY, TN 376146500
Phone: 423 439-1000
Web: WWW.ETSU.EDU

PRODUCTS/OPERATIONS

Selected Colleges and Schools
Bill Gatton College of Pharmacy
Claudius G. Clemmer College of Education
College of Arts and Sciences
College of Business and Technology
College of Clinical and Rehabilitative Health Sciences
College of Nursing
College of Public Health
Honors College
James H. Quillen College of Medicine
School of Continuing Studies
School of Graduate Studies

Selected Facilities
Center for Academic Achievement
Charles C. Sherrod Library
ETSU and General Shale Brick Natural History Museum and Visitor Center
Governors and Centennial residence halls
Scott M. Niswonger Digital Media Center
Warren-Greene Golf Center
Wayne G. Basler Center for Physical Activity

HISTORICAL FINANCIALS
Company Type: Private

Income Statement
FYE: June 30

	REVENUE ($ mil.)	NET INCOME ($ mil.)	NET PROFIT MARGIN	EMPLOYEES
06/13	179	6	3.6%	2,400
06/08	14	7	51.7%	—
06/06	16	8	53.9%	—
06/05	995	0	—	—
Annual Growth	(19.3%)	—	—	—

2013 Year-End Financials
Return on assets: 1.5%
Return on equity: 3.6%
Current ratio: 1.00
Cash ($ mil.): 20

EAST TEXAS MEDICAL CENTER REGIONAL HEALTHCARE SYST

East Texas Medical Center (ETMC) Regional Healthcare System works to meet the health care needs of residents of the Piney Woods. The not-for-profit health system operates more than a dozen hospitals across eastern Texas along with behavioral rehabilitation and home health care businesses. Its flagship 450-bed Tyler location serves as the hub and referral center for satellite medical centers located in more rural locations. The system also runs numerous primary care and outpatient clinics throughout the region. Serving more than 300000 patients each year ETMC operates an emergency ambulance service subsidiary and a clinical laboratory which provide services to the ETMC Regional Healthcare System.

Geographic Reach
ETMC serves the more than 1 million people who reside in East Texas communities. It caters to nearly 20 Texas counties including Anderson Camp Cherokee Ellis Franklin Freestone Henderson Hopkins Houston Panola Red River Rusk Shelby Smith Trinity Upshur Van Zandt and Wood. These communities range in size from fewer than 500 residents to more than 50000.

Operations
The flagship ETMC Tyler facility offers specialized care for cancer and cardiovascular and neurological conditions. It is a Level I regional trauma center and provides diagnostic and outpatient surgery services.

The system is organized so that primary care is provided in the rural health clinics. Secondary care is also provided locally in the ETMC affiliate hospitals. High-level secondary and tertiary care is provided at ETMC Tyler.

Strategy
To keep up with the needs of its residents the ETMC Regional Healthcare System works to expand its operations.

In 2013 ETMC Pittsburg broke ground on a 5000-sq.-ft. expansion of the hospital's surgery department. Its East Texas Medical Center Regional Healthcare System also added a pair of emergency transport helicopters valued at more than $9 million.

In 2012 the company completed $30-million expansion and renovation project at East Texas Medical Center Henderson including a new emergency department grand lobby and clinic space. It also wrapped up the second phase of an expansion project at ETMC Fairfield that involved adding a new entrance lobby clinic space cardiopulmonary rehabilitation facility and administrative suite.

Its 100-bed Henderson Memorial Hospital joined the network in 2009 as ETMC Henderson. Soon after becoming part of the network ETMC assisted its new affiliate with facility upgrades that included building new emergency department facilities renovating old rooms and installing new electrical and HVAC systems all completed in 2011. ETMC also expanded its Trinity facility with a 15-bed patient wing at the cost of $7.4 million and expanded its mammography services at ETMC Cedar Creek Lake. A $35 million ETMC Quitman facility is expected to be completed in 2013.

ETMC also concentrates on upgrading its information systems. The healthcare system's data exchange organization FirstNet Exchange received a grant from the state of Texas in 2011 to develop and operate a secure health information network to support hospitals and clinicians.

Sales and Marketing

The Medicare program accounted for 50% of net patient revenues in 2012; Medicaid contributed 12% of the same. Some 16% of total net patient service revenue came from commercial insurance carriers and preferred provider organizations.

Financial Performance

Due to an increase in patient service revenue ETMC's revenue rose by 6% to $942 million in 2012 from $888 million in 2011. Net income for the same reporting period dropped some 92% to $1.1 million from $16 million due to rising salaries and wages and employee benefits expenses as well as from an increase in loss from defined benefit pension adjustment.

EXECUTIVES

Clinic Supervisor, Dawn Lambright
Vice President Of Engineering, Larry Davis
Director Of Infection Control, Amber Sims
Director Of Him, Christa Wyatt
Nursing Director, Maria Kulma
Senior Vice President, Jerry Massey

LOCATIONS

HQ: EAST TEXAS MEDICAL CENTER REGIONAL
HEALTHCARE SYST
1000 S BECKHAM AVE, TYLER, TX 757011908
Phone: 903 597-0351
Web: WWW.ETMC.ORG

PRODUCTS/OPERATIONS

Selected Health and Medical Services
Bariatric Surgery Center
Behavioral Health Center
Cancer Institute
Cardiovascular Institute
Digestive Disease Center
Emergency Services
Fitness Centers
Home Health
Neurological Institute
Orthopedic Institute
Plastic Surgery
Podiatry Care
Radiology and Imaging
Rehabilitation Center
Sleep Disorders Center
Specialty Hospital
Transplant Center
Urology Institute
Women's Health
Wound Healing Center

Selected East Texas Medical Center Hospitals
ETMC Athens
ETMC Carthage
ETMC Clarksville
ETMC Crockett

ETMC Fairfield
ETMC Gilmer
ETMC Henderson
ETMC Jacksonville
ETMC Lake Palestine
ETMC Mount Vernon
ETMC Pittsburg
ETMC Quitman
ETMC Rehabilitation Hospital (Tyler)
ETMC Specialty Hospital (Tyler)
ETMC Trinity
ETMC Tyler

COMPETITORS

Community Health Systems
Good Shepherd Health System
HCA
Hunt Memorial Memorial Health System of East Texas
Tenet Healthcare
Trinity Mother Frances Hospital and Clinics
Wadley Regional Medical Center
Woodland Heights Medical Center

HISTORICAL FINANCIALS

Company Type: Private

Income Statement

FYE: October 31

	REVENUE ($ mil.)	NET INCOME ($ mil.)	NET PROFIT MARGIN	EMPLOYEES
10/08	876	30	3.4%	7,600
10/07	827	40	4.8%	
10/06	837	0	—	—
10/05	837	0	—	—
Annual Growth	1.5%	—	—	—

2008 Year-End Financials

Return on assets: —
Return on equity: 3.4%
Current ratio: 2.90
Cash ($ mil.): 175

EASTERN BAG AND PAPER COMPANY INCORPORATED

Eastern Bag and Paper Co. (dba EBP Supply) is a leading distributor of paper products in the northeastern US. In addition to disposable tableware and packaging the company offers foodservice products (including china and glassware) restaurant equipment (can openers refrigerators) personal care items (bath mats roll towels) and cleansers and maintenance supplies (air fresheners vacuums). Its name-brand products are used by the industrial healthcare foodservice and janitorial industries. Founded in 1918 by Samuel Baum the company is owned and run by CEO Meredith Baum Reuben.

Geographic Reach

The company operates three distribution centers in Connecticut Massachusetts and New Jersey and maintains a fleet of more than 70 trucks and trailers. EBP Supply's distribution area spans a dozen states from Maine to northern Virginia.

Sales and Marketing

EBP Supply serves several sectors such as commercial building and facility healthcare foodservice institutional (including both government and education) and hospitality and recreation.

Operations

EBP Supply has earned longtime relationships with affiliates such as the US Green Building Coun-

cil International Sanity Supply Association Women's Business Enterprise National Council Government Services Agency Building Owners and Managers Association National Association of College Food Service Mass Restaurant Association and the New England Sanitary Supply Association. The company boasts national distribution thanks to its alliance with Network Distribution Services.

Strategy

In fall 2012 the company rebranded adopted a new logo and launched a new website EBPsupply.com to better convey its expanded product line. The rebranding was designed to focus on the company's customer-centric approach. In addition to the cleaning and restaurant supplies EBP Supply offers delivery consulting training and equipment repair services.

EXECUTIVES

Vice President, Joseph Lopresti
Vice President And Sales Manager Healthcare Services, Dan Colcord
Vice President Of Marketing, Ken Rosenberg
Senior Vice President Marketing Product Strategy, Michael (Mel) Kaplan
Vice President, Alan (Al) Schachter
Vice President Business Development Manager, Neil Armbruster
Vice President, Brian Reddy
Vice President I Connecticut Sales, Walt Ancker
Vice President Operations, Don Burton
Vice President Strategic Accounts, Alan Schachter
Auditors: BLUM SHAPIRO & COMPANY PC W

LOCATIONS

HQ: EASTERN BAG AND PAPER COMPANY INCORPORATED
200 RESEARCH DR, MILFORD, CT 064602880
Phone: 203 878-1814
Web: WWW.EASTERNBAG.COM

PRODUCTS/OPERATIONS

Selected Cleaning Brands
3M
Andersen Mat
Bay West
Berry Plastics Corporation
Certo
Clarke
Clorox
Diversey
Georgia-Pacific Professional
Glit
Gojo
Hospeco
Kimberly-Clark Professional
Procter & Gamble Professional
Rubbermaid Commercial Products
SCA Tork
Starco
Taski
Unger
US Chemical
Wausau Paper
Wilen

Selected Foodservice Brands
3M
Anchor Packaging
Bagcraft Papercon
Bay West
Cambro
Candle Lamp
Certo
Chicopee
Chinet
Crown Poly
D&W Fine Pack
Dart/Solo
Dixie
Dopaco
Duro Bags
ECO Products
Elkay Plastics

Fabri-Kal
Fold-Pak
FoodHandler
Genpak
Gordon Paper
Greenweave
Hoffmaster
Huhtamaki
Inline Pastics
McNairn Packaging
Morcon
National Checking Company
NCCO
Oneida
Pactiv
Royal Paper Products
Rubbermaid Commercial Products
Sabert
Safety Zone
San Jamar
SCA Tork
Scotch-Brite
Vollrath
Yoshi

Selected Products
Cleaning supplies & equipment
Foodservice packaging
Paper goods
Smallwares

COMPETITORS

AFFLINK	Perkins Paper
MAINES	RDA Advantage
Penn Jersey	Sysco

HISTORICAL FINANCIALS
Company Type: Private

Income Statement
FYE: December 31

	REVENUE ($ mil.)	NET INCOME ($ mil.)	NET PROFIT MARGIN	EMPLOYEES
12/13	182	2	1.1%	285
12/12	177	1	0.6%	—
12/11	174	0	—	—
12/08	0	0	—	—
Annual Growth	—	—	—	—

2013 Year-End Financials
Return on assets: 3.7%
Return on equity: 1.1%
Current ratio: 1.70
Cash ($ mil.): —

EASTERN MICHIGAN UNIVERSITY

Eastern Michigan University (known affectionately as just plain Eastern) has long been an affordable place to study your way into a better career. The university began as a teachers' college in 1849 and it still graduates one out of every four teachers in Michigan. Eastern has an enrollment of more than 23000 students (90% are Michigan residents) who participate in undergraduate and graduate degree programs on its campus in the southeastern part of the state. Its 200 majors minors and concentrations are offered through colleges of arts and sciences business education technology and health and human services.

Geographic Reach
In addition to its 800-acre main campus in Ypsilanti Michigan which includes more than 120 buildings the university operates continuing education campuses in Brighton Detroit Flint Jackson Livonia Monroe and Traverse City. Students at-

tending Eastern hail from across the US and some 85 international countries.

Operations
Eastern employs 700 full-time faculty members and has a student-to-teacher ratio of 19:1. In addition to its five academic colleges and an honors college the school has 14 research centers and institutes that conduct studies into fields including community development business development education textiles and product development. The university also gives students the opportunity to participate in more than 20 division I NCAA varsity sports teams. Annual tuition for state residents runs at about $9000 per year.

Sales and Marketing
To attract nontraditional students Eastern has created accelerated Continuing Education programs with classes held on weekends and evenings. It is also steadily adding online coursework and seeks to attract military personnel. Its Return to Learn program is specifically geared to serve displaced workers who need additional education to rejoin the workforce.

Financial Performance
The university reported operating revenue of $227 million in fiscal 2013 a slight increase (1%) from 2012 results on higher student tuition and fee revenue (prompted by a rate increased approved by the state board of regents in 2012).

Strategy
To meet its goal of expanding international student opportunities Eastern strengthened its partnerships with Wuhan University (China) and Korea National University of Education in 2012. It also has a collaboration with Tianjin University in China to provide joint business degrees. In addition the university has partnered with several Michigan community colleges to provide joint degree programs and it is expanding its online course offerings.

EXECUTIVES

Interim Assistant Vice President For A, David (Dave) Woike
Vice President, David (Dave) Carroll
Associate Vice President Marketing, Theodore Coutilish
Auditors: PLANTE & MORAN PLLC PORTAGE

LOCATIONS

HQ: EASTERN MICHIGAN UNIVERSITY
202 WELCH HALL, YPSILANTI, MI 481972214
Phone: 734 487-2031
Web: WWW.EMICH.EDU

PRODUCTS/OPERATIONS

Selected Colleges Schools and Departments
College of Arts and Sciences
  African American Studies
  Art
  Biology
  Chemistry
  Communications and Theatre Arts
  Computer Science
  Economics
  English Language and Literature
  Foreign Languages and Bilingual Studies
  Geography and Geology
  History and Philosphy
  Mathematics
  Music and Dance
  Physic and Astronomy
  Political Science
  Psychology
  Sociology Anthropology and Criminology
College of Business
  Accounting and Finance
  Computer Information Systems
  Management
  Marketing
College of Education
  Leadership and Counseling

Special Education
Teacher Education
College of Health and Human Services
  School of Health Promotion and Human Performance
  School of Health Sciences
  School of Nursing
  School of Social Work
College of Technology
  Military Science and Leadership
  School of Engineering Technology
  School of Technology Studies

HISTORICAL FINANCIALS
Company Type: Private

Income Statement
FYE: June 30

	REVENUE ($ mil.)	NET INCOME ($ mil.)	NET PROFIT MARGIN	EMPLOYEES
06/13	227	(3)	—	2,000
06/11	221	24	11.2%	—
06/10	217	(1)	—	—
06/09	211	0	—	—
Annual Growth	1.8%	—	—	—

2013 Year-End Financials
Return on assets: —
Return on equity: (-1.5%)
Current ratio: 0.60
Cash ($ mil.): 11

EASTERN SHIPBUILDING GROUP INC.

Auditors: CARR RIGGS & INGRAM LLC RIDG

LOCATIONS

HQ: EASTERN SHIPBUILDING GROUP INC.
2200 NELSON AVE, PANAMA CITY, FL 324014969
Phone: 850 763-1900
Web: WWW.EASTERNSHIPBUILDING.COM

HISTORICAL FINANCIALS
Company Type: Private

Income Statement
FYE: December 31

	REVENUE ($ mil.)	NET INCOME ($ mil.)	NET PROFIT MARGIN	EMPLOYEES
12/13	398	50	12.7%	975
12/12	304	44	14.6%	—
12/11	183	20	11.4%	—
12/08	170	0	—	—
Annual Growth	18.5%	—	—	—

2013 Year-End Financials
Return on assets: 8.5%
Return on equity: 12.7%
Current ratio: 0.80
Cash ($ mil.): 47

EASTERN VIRGINIA MEDICAL SCHOOL

Eastern Virginia Medical School (EVMS) sends graduated physicians down the Hampton Roads. The school offers medical and doctoral degrees residencies and specialty programs such as reproductive medicine. The community-oriented school does not have a teaching hospital but rather partners with about a dozen regional hospitals. Its main campus is part of the Eastern Virginia Medical Center which is also home to Sentara Norfolk General Hospital and Children's Hospital of The King's Daughters located in the Hampton Roads region of southeastern Virginia. The south campus hosts pediatric and diabetes research programs. EVMS also has research programs devoted to cancer infectious diseases and heart disease.

Operations

Established in 1973 EVMS operates under a state charter and operates as a public institution. Its governing board is comprised of representatives from surrounding communities as well as appointees from the EVMS Foundation which conducts fundraising activities for the school.

The school enrolls some 350 students in its residency internship and fellowship programs which cover about 40 fields. It also provides professional education programs for about 450 students. EVMS has about 450 faculty members many of which are engaged in its extensive research programs. The school is the largest biomedical research organization in southeastern Virginia.

Financial Performance

EVPS reported a 5% decrease in operating revenue to $227 million in 2012 from lower state funding private gifts and interest income. Net income also fell 69% to $11.4 million as a result of lower revenue and increased expenses from instruction management and patient care costs.

Strategy

In 2012 EVMS entered discussions with the College of William & Mary over a possible merger or affiliation agreement. Under proposed terms of the deal which must be approved by Virginia's governing entities EVMS would join the College of William & Mary organization becoming known as the William & Mary School of Medicine. The two schools have worked together on projects in the past including conducting research collaborations. As they worked towards a merger the schools increased collaborative research programs in 2013.

In addition EVMS has been working to improve its facilities so that it can increase its enrollment numbers in both the physician assistant and medical doctorate programs. A new medical education and research building that meets this need was opened in mid-2011. The school also adds new programs such as a new biotechnology graduate program launched in 2012.

EXECUTIVES

Vice President, Nell M Reece
Treasurer, Brian S Dipace
Secretary, Ashley Womack
Auditors: KPMG LLP NORFOLK VA

LOCATIONS

HQ: EASTERN VIRGINIA MEDICAL SCHOOL
714 WOODIS AVE, NORFOLK, VA 235101026
Phone: 757 446-6052
Web: WWW.EVMS.EDU

HISTORICAL FINANCIALS
Company Type: Private

Income Statement
FYE: June 30

	REVENUE ($ mil.)	NET INCOME ($ mil.)	NET PROFIT MARGIN	EMPLOYEES
06/14	234	16	7.1%	1,500
06/13	229	21	9.4%	—
06/12	226	17	7.5%	—
06/11	238	0	—	—
Annual Growth	(0.6%)	—	—	—

2014 Year-End Financials
Return on assets: 4.0% Cash ($ mil.): 23
Return on equity: 7.1%
Current ratio: 1.30

ED STAUB & SONS PETROLEUM INC.

Auditors: ISLER GROUP LLC KLAMATH FALL

LOCATIONS

HQ: ED STAUB & SONS PETROLEUM INC.
19828 STATELINE RD, TULELAKE, CA 961348404
Phone: 530 667-2227
Web: WWW.EDSTAUB.COM

HISTORICAL FINANCIALS
Company Type: Private

Income Statement
FYE: March 31

	REVENUE ($ mil.)	NET INCOME ($ mil.)	NET PROFIT MARGIN	EMPLOYEES
03/14	344	1	0.3%	170
03/13	331	0	0.3%	—
Annual Growth	3.8%	19.3%	—	—

2014 Year-End Financials
Return on assets: 2.0% Cash ($ mil.): 1
Return on equity: 0.3%
Current ratio: 0.80

EDUCATIONAL CREDIT MANAGEMENT CORPORATION

Auditors: BAKER TILLY VIRCHOW KRAUSE LLP

LOCATIONS

HQ: EDUCATIONAL CREDIT MANAGEMENT CORPORATION
1 IMATION PL, SAINT PAUL, MN 551283422
Phone: 651 221-0566
Web: WWW.ECMCFOUNDATION.ORG

HISTORICAL FINANCIALS
Company Type: Private

Income Statement
FYE: December 31

	ASSETS ($ mil.)	NET INCOME ($ mil.)	INCOME AS % OF ASSETS	EMPLOYEES
12/11	802	87	10.9%	634
12/10	951	(15)	—	—
12/08	65	49	74.7%	—
12/04	193	0	—	—
Annual Growth	22.6%	—	—	—

2011 Year-End Financials
Return on assets: — Sales ($ mil): 383
Return on equity: 22.9%

EDWARD HOSPITAL

LOCATIONS

HQ: EDWARD HOSPITAL
801 S WASHINGTON ST, NAPERVILLE, IL 605407499
Phone: 630 355-0450
Web: WWW.EDWARD.ORG

HISTORICAL FINANCIALS
Company Type: Private

Income Statement
FYE: June 30

	REVENUE ($ mil.)	NET INCOME ($ mil.)	NET PROFIT MARGIN	EMPLOYEES
06/13	517	52	10.1%	4,700
06/12	530	30	5.7%	—
06/10	481	24	5.2%	—
06/09	450	0	—	—
Annual Growth	3.5%			

EFFINGHAM EQUITY

Auditors: BLUE & COMPANY LLC SEYMOUR

LOCATIONS

HQ: EFFINGHAM EQUITY
201 W ROADWAY AVE, EFFINGHAM, IL 624012101
Phone: 217 342-4101
Web: WWW.EFFINGHAMEQUITY.COM

HISTORICAL FINANCIALS
Company Type: Private

Income Statement
FYE: December 31

	REVENUE ($ mil.)	NET INCOME ($ mil.)	NET PROFIT MARGIN	EMPLOYEES
12/13	333	9	2.7%	348
12/10	51	12	23.8%	—
12/09	230	8	3.7%	—
12/08	1,692	0	—	—
Annual Growth	—	—	—	—

2013 Year-End Financials
Return on assets: 4.6% Cash ($ mil.): 11
Return on equity: 2.7%
Current ratio: 0.10

EIDE BAILLY LLP

Eide Bailly is how the West was audited. The company which was founded in 1917 provides clients with audit accounting tax and consulting services from more than 20 offices in nearly a dozen western and central US states. Eide Bailly's target industries include construction agricultural processing oil and gas real estate renewable energy government financial services manufacturing health care and not-for-profit organizations. Additional services are provided by subsidiaries and affiliates including Eide Bailly Technology Consulting. International services are provided through Eide Bailly's affiliation with HLB International. The accounting firm serves some 44000 clients annually.

Geographic Reach

Fargo North Dakota-based Eide Bailly has offices in Arizona Colorado Idaho Iowa Minnesota Montana Oklahoma Utah Washington and the Dakotas.

Financial Performance

Edie Bailly's net fees amounted to $192 million in fiscal 2014 (ended April) up from $171 million in the prior year. The firm's tax services audit and assurance and consulting/other businesses accounted for 40% 37% and 21% of the total respectively.

Strategy

Edie Bailly is growing its business through the acquisition of regional accounting firms to better compete with larger national firms.

Mergers and Acquisitions

In August 2014 the accounting firm acquired Fort Collins-based Sample & Bailey CPAs expanding its Colorado presence to Fort Collins. Previously Eide Bailly expanded into Utah in 2012 with the purchase of Schmitt Griffiths Smith & Co. adding about $6 million to its total revenue. More significantly Edie Bailly announced plans to merge with fellow accountancy Milwaukee-based Wipfli in 2012. However the deal was called off later that year when the two firms could not reach an agreement on key terms.

Other recent purchases include Williston North Dakota-based CPA firm Voller Lee Seuss & Associates. The purchase which closed in December 2012 expanded Edie Bailly's resources and services to clients in the rapidly-growing Bakken Oil Region in western North Dakota. Also in late 2012 the firm acquired Clark & Srsich LLC a boutique tax firm in Littleton Colorado.

EXECUTIVES

Managing Partner, Denise Juliana
Vice Chair, Kevin Doyle

LOCATIONS

HQ: EIDE BAILLY LLP
4310 17TH AVE S, FARGO, ND 581033339
Phone: 701 239-8500
Web: WWW.EIDEBAILLY.COM

PRODUCTS/OPERATIONS

2013 Services by Category

	% of total
Tax Services	40
Audit & Assurance	38
Affiliates	2
Consulting and other	20
Total	**100**

Selected Services

Accounting
Audit & assurance
Employee benefits
Enterprise risk management
Financial services
Forensic & valuation
International services
Tax
Technology consulting
Transaction services
Wealth management

COMPETITORS

BDO Seidman	Ernst & Young LLP
BKD LLP	Grant Thornton
CliftonLarsonAllen	KPMG L.L.P.
Crowe Horwath	PricewaterhouseCoopers
Deloitte & Touche	US

HISTORICAL FINANCIALS
Company Type: Private

Income Statement

FYE: April 30

	REVENUE ($ mil.)	NET INCOME ($ mil.)	NET PROFIT MARGIN	EMPLOYEES
04/14	192	65	33.8%	1,282
04/13	167	56	33.9%	
04/12	148	51	34.5%	
04/11	142	0	—	
Annual Growth	**10.6%**	—	—	—

2014 Year-End Financials

Return on assets: 1.1%
Return on equity: 33.8%
Current ratio: 1.00

Cash ($ mil.): 6

EISENHOWER MEDICAL CENTER

The Eisenhower Medical Center is perhaps better known for the name of a first lady than the 34th US president: The not-for-profit medical campus is the home of the Betty Ford Center. In addition to the renowned alcohol and drug rehabilitation center Eisenhower Medical Center comprises the more than 540-bed Eisenhower Memorial Hospital the Barbara Sinatra Children's Center and the Annenberg Center for Health Sciences. In addition to medical surgical and emergency services the hospital offers cancer care neurology orthopedics cardiology and rehabilitation. An accredited teaching hospital it also conducts training and research programs and operates outpatient clinics in surrounding areas.

Geographic Reach

The Eisenhower Medical Center's main facilities are located on its 130-acre campus in Rancho Mirage California. Outpatient facilities are located in Rancho Mirage and area communities including Cathedral City La Quinta and Palm Springs.

Operations

Eisenhower Medical Center maintains the leading market share in its service location representing nearly 50% of the area.

In addition to patient services Eisenhower Medical Center provides residency programs for aspiring students through affiliations with the Keck School of Medicine (University of Southern California) and the Linda Loma University's School of Medicine. The physician training programs are offered through the newly established School of Graduate Medical Education and Research and include family medicine internal medicine and preliminary (one-year) residency programs.

Strategy

Eisenhower Medical Center's residency programs were launched in the summer of 2013 after the hospital received national accreditation. The hospital worked for several years to add medical training services to help meet the growing shortage of primary care physicians in the Coachella Valley. The establishment of the graduate school required capital improvements to the hospital's facilities causing it to launch a $32 million fundraising campaign that year.

The medical center has also been working to maintain its market share by launching a number of facility expansion campaigns in recent years. For instance in 2010 it completed construction of a $213 million addition to its main hospital that included 160 patient beds a cafeteria information systems and other departments. The addition was named the Eisenhower Walter and Leonore Annenberg Pavilion.

The medical center is expanding its outpatient care centers to provide greater services to surrounding communities and reduce the patient burden on hospital emergency rooms. For instance Eisenhower Medical Center opened a new primary and specialty outpatient care center in Palm Springs in 2013.

Eisenhower Medical Center faces some financial challenges due to a high volume of elderly Medicare patients. As a result it has made efforts to attract more self-pay patients to its facilities. In addition the hospital has incurred substantial debt due to its construction efforts; however it aims to recoup through increased revenues from the added facilities and through its successful fundraising efforts.

Company Background

Eisenhower Medical Center was dedicated in 1971 to honor former president Dwight Eisenhower who spent part of his retirement in the Coachella Valley. The late entertainer Bob Hope and his wife were the hospital's biggest benefactors having donated the original land for the hospital and continuing to help fundraising efforts until his death in 2003.

EXECUTIVES

Director Of Him, Khalil Ismail
Director of Patient Relations Public Relations Manager, Connie Norton
Vice President Support Services, Ali Tourkaman
Vice President Healthcare Services, Ann Mostofi
Clinical Director, Janet Sullivan
Vice President, Laura Fritz
Vice President Patient Care Services And Chief Nursing Officer, Louise White
Radiology Medical Director, Brian Herman
Center Vice President, Barbara (Barb) Sinatra
Vice President and Chief Medical Officer, Alan (Al) Williamson
Vice President Finance, Sharon Henderson
Medical Librarian, Nancy Waite-O'Brien
Section Chief of Internal Medicine and Secretary Treasurer of Medical Staff, Robert (Bob) Waterbor
Secretary, Linda Lewis
Auditors: ERNST AND YOUNG LLP IRVINE C

LOCATIONS

HQ: EISENHOWER MEDICAL CENTER
39000 BOB HOPE DR, RANCHO MIRAGE, CA 922703221
Phone: 760 340-3911
Web: WWW.EMC.ORG

PRODUCTS/OPERATIONS

Selected Facilities

Eisenhower Medical Center (Rancho Mirage)
  Annenberg Center for Health Sciences (continuing education for health professionals)
  Barbara Sinatra Children' s Center (pediatrics)
  Betty Ford Center (alcohol and substance abuse)
  School of Graduate Medical Education and Research
Eisenhower George and Julia Argyros Health Center (La Quinta)
Eisenhower Health Centers at Plaza del Sol (Palm Springs)
Eisenhower Health Centers at Rimrock (Palm Springs)
Eisenhower Health Centers at Sunrock (Palm Springs)
Eisenhower Occupational Health (Cathedral City)
Eisenhower Physical and Occupational Health (La Quinta)
Rancho Mirage Medical Center (Rancho Mirage)

Selected Services

Adult Day Care
Bariatric Center
Center for Geropsychiatry
Cancer

Cardiovascular
Clinical Trials
Diabetes
Eisenhower Health Centers
Eisenhower Wellness Institute
Emergency Department
Imaging
Labtechniques
Neuroscience
Nutrition
Occupational Health
Orthopedics
Parkinson' s Center
Rehabilitation Services
Robotics Institute
Urgent Care
Wound Care Center

COMPETITORS

Anaheim Regional	HCA
Medical Center	HealthSouth
Arrowhead Medical	Memorial Health
Center	Services
Cedars-Sinai Medical	Palomar Health
Center	Providence Health &
Citrus Valley Health	Services
Partners	Scripps health
Community Hospital of	Southwest Healthcare
San Bernardino	Tenet Healthcare
Dignity Health	UCSD Medical
Grossmont Hospital	

HISTORICAL FINANCIALS

Company Type: Private

Income Statement

FYE: June 30

	REVENUE ($ mil.)	NET INCOME ($ mil.)	NET PROFIT MARGIN	EMPLOYEES
06/13	501	(27)		2,200
06/10	411	6	1.7%	—
06/09	394	25	6.4%	—
Annual Growth	6.1%	—	—	—

2013 Year-End Financials

Return on assets: 15.8%   Cash ($ mil.): 88
Return on equity: (-5.5%)
Current ratio: 0.30

EISNERAMPER LLP

EisnerAmper provides accounting and consulting services for middle-market businesses and Fortune 500 companies. It specializes in industries and sectors including health sciences sports and entertainment not-for-profit financial services and technology. EisnerAmper provides auditing and accounting services tax planning legal support bankruptcy consulting corporate finance employee benefits plan services and IT consulting. Services outside the US are provided through EisnerAmper's Cayman Islands office as well as through its affiliation with PKF International. Founded in 1963 the firm operates out of US offices on the East and West coast.

Operations

As part of its services EisnerAmper specializes in structuring organizing and managing its clients' businesses as well as heading up their reporting requirements. It enlists the help of cross-border specialists who support the needs of multinational companies with a US presence.

The company also provides wealth management asset protection planning and tax advisory services to high net worth individuals. Other primary service lines include human capital advisory employee benefit plan audits fund services litigation support

and forensic accounting bankruptcy and insolvency and royalty audits.

The company provides full audit services to clients with off-shore needs through its PKF Cayman unit.

Geographic Reach

The company serves clients worldwide through nearly 10 offices in the cities of San Francisco; Iselin New Jersey; New York City and Syosset New York; Philadelphia and Jenkintown Pennsylvania; and the Cayman Islands.

Sales and Marketing

The company targets a broad range of clients from many industries working with high net worth individuals family offices closely-held businesses start-ups middle market and Fortune 500 companies. EisnerAmper's client base includes more than 1200 hedge funds 175 private equity funds and 150-plus insurance companies as well as banks and credit unions.

Strategy

To better serve its clients and grow EisenAmper has expanded its service offerings in recent years. In late 2014 the company launched its new affiliate David Wiener and Company LLC to provide accounting and related consulting and advisory services to marketing communications and professional services industries. Also in 2014 EisnerAmper introduced its Compliance and Regulatory Services (CARS). It's a full-service consultancy that provides outsourced compliance programs to US and offshore investment advisors. CARS aims to serve the needs of clients who manage all asset classes such as alternative and nonalternative investment vehicles including wealth managers managed account platforms mutual funds broker-dealers and family offices. EisenAmper has also made strategic cuts to be able to spend more on its partners and staff. In late 2014 for example the firm consolidated its Philadelphia-area offices into one central office in the region to increase efficiency and free up more capital for new hires and promotion opportunities.The firm has been looking to expand its reach over the past few years as well. In 2013 EisnerAmper opened a new Metropark location to provide nearly 400 partners and employees —who stretch across its Edison Bridgewater Hackensack and Wall offices — with a new facility. In 2012 the firm launched a mobile website www.eisneramper.com to help its clients gain easy access to the company's resources including blogs events and service and industry expertise.

Company Background

EisnerAmper was created in 2010 through the combination of Eisner and Amper Politziner & Mattia similar accounting firms based in New Jersey. Now under one umbrella the company enjoys enhanced service capabilities and geographic reach.

EXECUTIVES

Managing Partner, Charles (Charly) Weinstein
CIO, Amir Segev
CFO, Jeffrey Melnick
Chairman, Howard Cohen

LOCATIONS

HQ: EISNERAMPER LLP
750 3RD AVE FL 16, NEW YORK, NY 100172716
Phone: 212 949-8700
Web: WWW.EISNERAMPER.COM

PRODUCTS/OPERATIONS

Selected Areas of Specialization
Automotive
Financial services
Health care
Law firms
Not-for-profit organizations

Real estate
Sports & entertainment
Technology companies
Services
Audit & Assurance
Bankruptcy & Restructuring
Compliance & Regulatory Services
Consulting Services
Corporate Finance
Employee Benefit Plans
Federal Government Contracting
International Services
Litigation Services
Outsourced Finance and Accounting
Personal Wealth Advisors
Private Business Accounting & Advisory
Public Companies
Tax Services

COMPETITORS

Anchin Block & Anchin	Heffler Radetich &
Citrin Cooperman	Saitta
Crowe Horwath	KPMG L.L.P.
Deloitte & Touche	PricewaterhouseCoopers
Ernst & Young Global	US
Grant Thornton	

HISTORICAL FINANCIALS

Company Type: Private

Income Statement

FYE: January 31

	REVENUE ($ mil.)	NET INCOME ($ mil.)	NET PROFIT MARGIN	EMPLOYEES
01/14	425	58	13.7%	1,895
01/13	247	55	22.5%	—
01/12	230	59	25.9%	—
01/11	173	0	—	—
Annual Growth	34.8%	—	—	—

2014 Year-End Financials

Return on assets: 0.5%   Cash ($ mil.): 34
Return on equity: 13.7%
Current ratio: 3.50

EL DORADO FURNITURE CORP

The road to El Dorado Furniture is covered in sand. The company sells home furnishings in South Florida through about a dozen retail showrooms and a pair of outlets located in Broward Miami-Dade Palm Beach and Lee counties. El Dorado Furniture stores offer wood upholstered and leather furniture for every room in the house as well as mattresses bedding and decorative accessories. Its stores are designed to look like small towns with building façades situated along a boulevard; some locations also feature cafés. Founded in 1967 and run by the Capó family El Dorado Furniture has become the nation's largest Hispanic-owned retail enterprises.

Geographic Reach

The retailer's showrooms and outlets are located in Florida's Palm Beach Broward Miami-Dade and Lee counties.

Sales and Marketing

El Dorado has grown to offer the largest selection of furniture and mattresses in South Florida.

Unique to the furniture retailer its stores feature what it calls a Boulevard showroom which includes more than 20 individually themed storefronts open into specialized furniture shops. The marketing strategy remains one of the company's biggest draws for customers.

As part of the company's bricks-and-mortar business it produces and maintains an online catalog that's searchable by category product name or SKU.

Strategy

Besides its specialized showrooms El Dorado Furniture offers customers free home decorating advice from its design experts.

As Florida's real estate market rebounds post-recession El Dorado Furniture has worked to expand its business within the state by purchasing a shopping center on Florida's Gulf Coast in 2012. The Lee County purchase included a 179000-sq.-ft. shopping center to house a 70000-sq.-ft. El Dorado showroom. It's banking on a store of this caliber to bring in at least $10 million.

Awards and Recognition

El Dorado Furniture is ranked among the top 50 furniture retailers in the country.

LOCATIONS

HQ: EL DORADO FURNITURE CORP
4200 NW 167TH ST, MIAMI GARDENS, FL 330546112
Phone: 305 624-9700
Web: WWW.ELDORADOFURNITURE.COM

2014 Stores

	No.
Miami-Dade	7
Broward	3
Palm Beach	2
Lee	1
Total	**13**

PRODUCTS/OPERATIONS

Selected Products
Beds & Bedrooms
Furniture
Home office
Home decor & accents
Mattresses
Outdoor furniture

COMPETITORS

Baer's Furniture	Leader's Casual
City Furniture	Furniture
Havertys	Rooms To Go
La-Z-Boy	W.S. Badcock

HISTORICAL FINANCIALS
Company Type: Private

Income Statement
FYE: December 31

	REVENUE ($ mil.)	NET INCOME ($ mil.)	NET PROFIT MARGIN	EMPLOYEES
12/13	165	29	18.0%	705
12/12	153	25	16.9%	—
12/11	152	23	15.5%	—
12/10	131	0	—	—
Annual Growth	**8.0%**	—	—	—

2013 Year-End Financials
Return on assets: 5.8%   Cash ($ mil.): 31
Return on equity: 18.0%
Current ratio: 2.00

ELECTRIC POWER BOARD OF THE METROPOLITAN GOVERNMENT OF NASHVILLE

The Electric Power Board of the Metropolitan Government of Nashville and Davidson County is a mouthful. Its operating name Nashville Electric Service (NES) sounds much better. And talking of sound the legendary "Nashville Sound" would be hard to hear without the resources of this power distributor which serves more than 360000 customers in central Tennessee. NES is one of the largest government-owned utilities in the US. The company is required to purchase all its power from another government-owned operator the Tennessee Valley Authority (TVA).

NES operates about 91000 distribution transformers more than 230 substations 5700 miles of power lines and more than 200000 utility poles.

It serves customers in the City of Nashville and Davidson County.

In 2011 the company posted a 13% jump in revenues thanks to a rate increase and stronger demand brought on by a warmer-than-usual summer. The higher revenues outpaced higher distribution costs and (coupled with lower administrative and general expenses) allowed NES to post a 35% spike in operating income for the year.

Anticipating deregulation both NES and TVA are expecting changes in their relationship. NES is ready to rock 'n' roll after the expected divorce. The company wants to cut its obligations to TVA and pursue other power sources including open-market purchasing and self-generation.

NES is also investing in educating its customers to reduce energy use as a way to cut carbon emissions and lower costs —through public education programs on conservation strategies and the use of renewables and green technology. Walking the talk in 2011 NES installed energy-efficient light bulbs and took other measures at its headquarters building to reduce electrical use by 11% and water use by 18%. It also recycles and reuses the oil in its transformer network.

EXECUTIVES

General Counsel, Eugene W. Ward
President and CEO, Decosta E. Jenkins
VP Information Systems and CIO, Victor L. (Vic) Hatridge
VP Operations Engineering, Paul H. Allen
Chairman, Robert A. (Rob) McCabe Jr., age 62
VP and Chief Customer Care Officer, Teresa Corlew
EVP and COO, Allen Bradley
VP Human Resources, Herb Deberry
VP Corporate Affairs, Laura S. Tidwell
VP and CFO, Teresa Broyles-Aplin
VP Operations Transmission and Distribution, Dennis Boehms
VP Operations, Eddie Andrews
Vice Chairman, Samuel Howard
Director, Robert A. (Rob) McCabe Jr., age 62
Vice Chair, Mary Jo Price
Director, Richard Courtney
Vice Chairman, Samuel Howard
Auditors: CROSSLIN & ASSOCIATES PC N

LOCATIONS

HQ: ELECTRIC POWER BOARD OF THE METROPOLITAN GOVERNMENT OF NASHVILLE
1214 CHURCH ST, NASHVILLE, TN 372460001
Phone: 615 747-3831
Web: WWW.NESPOWER.COM

COMPETITORS

AEP	Piedmont Natural Gas
AGL Resources	Public Service
Constellation Energy Group	Enterprise Group
MLGW	SCANA
	Southern Company

HISTORICAL FINANCIALS
Company Type: Private

Income Statement
FYE: June 30

	REVENUE ($ mil.)	NET INCOME ($ mil.)	NET PROFIT MARGIN	EMPLOYEES
06/09	1,146	16	1.4%	990
06/08	1,030	33	3.2%	—
06/07	962	44	4.6%	—
06/06	903	0	—	—
Annual Growth	**8.3%**	—	—	—

2009 Year-End Financials
Return on assets: 9.4%   Cash ($ mil.): 91
Return on equity: 1.4%
Current ratio: 1.30

ELECTRIC POWER RESEARCH INSTITUTE INC.

The Electric Power Research Institute (EPRI) knows there's more to electricity than putting a plug in a socket. From its headquarters in Palo Alto California the institute works to bring together investor-owned and government-owned utility companies as well as other industry representatives. EPRI operates as a not-for-profit research consortium that organizes and funds collaborative research. The organization identifies and works on issues related to electricity generation delivery and use including questions related to environmental protection. More than 10% of the organization's members are located outside the US. EPRI was founded in 1973.

Geographic Reach

EPRI serves more than 30 countries. Its members provide some 90% of the electricity generated and delivered in the US. To support its operations EPRI maintains offices in Madrid and Tokyo as well as in half a dozen locations in the US. It has offices and laboratories in Palo Alto California; Charlotte North Carolina; Dallas Texas; Lenox Massachusetts; Knoxville Tennessee; and Washington DC.

Operations

The institute's research portfolio includes Environment & Renewable Energy Generation Nuclear and Power Delivery and Utilization. EPRI works to make electricity production and its use sustainable for current and future generations. It also focused on advanced generation technologies and emissions controls as well as environmentally-responsible technologies that enable the long-term operation of existing nuclear plants and the deployment of advanced nuclear power plants. It's also interested in developing technologies and approaches to facilitate improved grid reliability energy use efficiency and grid transformation.

Strategy

EPRI's technology strategy encompasses long-term and broad societal visions and goals through its Electricity Technology Roadmap. One such goal is the role of the electric sector and electricity-based technologies in reducing greenhouse gas emissions by 2030.

Through collaboration with other research institutes EPRI is able to tackle more research topics. In 2013 EPRI collaborated with the Japan Nuclear Safety Institute (JANSI) and began participating in a number of EPRI's nuclear research programs. Previously EPRI entered a three-year collaboration with the International Atomic Energy Agency (IAEA) to promote public benefit research into nuclear power plant development operation decommissioning and waste disposal. The collaboration which extends through 2015 offers technical engagement on issues regarding nuclear plant development in countries initiating commercial nuclear power programs.

EXECUTIVES

Vice President Marketing, Dennis Murphy
Senior Vice President Chief Financial Officer and Treasurer, Pamela (Pam) Keefe
Vice President of Sales and Marketing, Henry A (Hal) Courtright
CIO Chief Technology Officer Vice President Information Technology, Clark Gellings
Vp Nuclear, Neil Wilmshurst
Vice President, Mark F McGranaghan
Vice President Legal, Salvador Casente
Vice President Environment And Renewables, Marsha Grossman
Vice President Nuclear Power, Christian Larsen
Vice President Generation, C Thomas Alley
Advisory Board Member, Karen Johnson

LOCATIONS

HQ: ELECTRIC POWER RESEARCH INSTITUTE INC.
   3420 HILLVIEW AVE, PALO ALTO, CA 943041382
Phone: 650 855-2000
Web: WWW.EPRI.COM

PRODUCTS/OPERATIONS

Selected Research Topics
Cable aging management
Concrete aging management
Controls and monitoring modernization
Extended fuel storage for spent nuclear fuel
Flexible operation of fossil assets
Irradiation effects on nuclear components
Transmission system life extension through inspection technologies

HISTORICAL FINANCIALS

Company Type: Private

Income Statement

FYE: December 31

	REVENUE ($ mil.)	NET INCOME ($ mil.)	NET PROFIT MARGIN	EMPLOYEES
12/13	383	26	6.9%	891
12/06	285	16	5.9%	—
12/05	276	265	96.0%	—
12/04	504	0	—	—
Annual Growth	—	—	—	—

2013 Year-End Financials

Return on assets: 17.2%   Cash ($ mil.): 139
Return on equity: 6.9%
Current ratio: 0.90

ELECTRIC RELIABILITY COUNCIL OF TEXAS INC.

ERCOT works to ensure that Texas power grid errors are caught before triggering a massive blackout. The Electric Reliability Council of Texas (ERCOT) is responsible for the reliable operation of 550 generation units (74000 MW capacity) and a 40500-mile power transmission system carrying about 85% of the state's electric load and serving 23 million customers. A member of the North American Electric Reliability Council ERCOT functions as the independent system operator for the region. It also administers financial settlement for the competitive wholesale bulk-power market and oversees customer switching for 6.7 million Texans who live in areas where they have a competitive choice of power supplier.

Geographic Reach

ERCOT's territory covers about 75% of Texas' land area; it excludes most of the northern panhandle region and parts of West Texas (around El Paso) and East Texas (around Texarkana and Beaumont).

Operations

The council monitors and schedules the flow of wholesale energy on the grid balancing supply with demand and enabling fair competitive access. ERCOT maintains records on grid activities and market participants and schedules power on the electric grid connecting transmission lines and generation units.

Financial Performance

ERCOT reported a 1% to decline in revenues in 2012. It generates revenues from System administration fees; Nodal implementation surcharge; Reliability organization pass-through; and Membership fees and other. In 2012 System administration fees and Nodal implementation surcharge accounted for 93% of ERCOT's total revenues.

Strategy

In 2012 the council released a report pointing out that the combination of a fast-growing population and the closing of older coal-powered plants meant that power demand in Texas would begin to outstrip its power capacity and that new cleaner burning power plants would need to be built along with the use of renewable energy sources and the adoption of serious conservation measures in order to avoid future power interruptions.

To meet state and federal green energy requirements the organization is working on integrating wind power sources into its operating grid. Texas boasts 10000 MW of wind power generation the most in the country. In July 2012 ERCOT reported a record output of 8370 MW of wind energy or about 18% of its total load.

Texas state government has kept ERCOT physically isolated from other grid systems (primarily to avoid federal regulation and charges). However this policy came under scrutiny in early 2011 when a cold snap led to the loss of 50 generating units forcing rolling outages across Texas in order to lower demand and prompting ERCOT to access power from Mexico for a short time.

Ownership

ERCOT is a membership-based 501(c)(4) non-profit corporation.

Company Background

The entity is governed by a board of directors and subject to oversight by the Public Utility Commission of Texas and the Texas State Legislature. The Legislature restructured the Texas electric market in 1999.

EXECUTIVES

SVP and COO, Cheryl Mele
President and CEO, Bill Magness
Chief of Staff, Jeyant Tamby
Treasurer, Leslie Wiley

LOCATIONS

HQ: ELECTRIC RELIABILITY COUNCIL OF TEXAS INC.
   7620 METRO CENTER DR, AUSTIN, TX 787441613
Phone: 512 225-7000
Web: WWW.ERCOT.COM

PRODUCTS/OPERATIONS

2012 Sales

	% of total
System administration fees	49
Nodal implementation surcharge	44
Reliability organization pass-through	5
Membership fees & other	2
Total	**100**

HISTORICAL FINANCIALS

Company Type: Private

Income Statement

FYE: December 31

	REVENUE ($ mil.)	NET INCOME ($ mil.)	NET PROFIT MARGIN	EMPLOYEES
12/11	279	(1)	—	625
12/10	272	19	7.0%	—
12/09	206	28	13.9%	—
12/08	186	0	—	—
Annual Growth	14.4%	—	—	—

2011 Year-End Financials

Return on assets: —   Cash ($ mil.): 660
Return on equity: (-0.7%)
Current ratio: 1.30

ELLIOT HOSPITAL OF THE CITY OF MANCHESTER

Elliot Health System provides medical care to southern New Hampshire. The health care organization operates Elliot Hospital an acute care hospital with nearly 300 beds that is home to a regional cancer center a designated regional trauma center and a level III neonatal intensive care unit (NICU). In addition to general and surgical care the hospital offers rehabilitation behavioral health obstetrics cardiology and lab services. The system also operates the Elliot Physician Network which operates primary care centers specialty clinics and surgery centers in various regional communities. Elliot Hospital was founded in 1890.

Operations

Elliot Hospital is Manchester's designated Regional Trauma Center. Additional facilities include the Elliot Breast Health Center Elliot Urgent Care Elliot Senior Health Center and New Hampshire's Hospital for Children.

Strategy

Elliot Health System has expanded throughout the region by constructing new outpatient care centers in nearby towns. Most recently Elliot Health completed construction of satellite facilities including an ambulatory care center and a senior health center. In 2015 it partnered with Northeast

Rehabilitation Hospital to create a new rehabilitation floor within its Elliot Hospital.

EXECUTIVES

Director Of Home Healthcare Srv, Carla Braveman
Vice President Of Human Resources, Catherine Bardier
Managing Director, Lisa Williams
Auditors: WILLIAM STEELE & ASSOCIATES PC

LOCATIONS

HQ: ELLIOT HOSPITAL OF THE CITY OF MANCHESTER
1 ELLIOT WAY, MANCHESTER, NH 031033502
Phone: 603 669-5300
Web: WWW.ELLIOTHOSPITAL.ORG

PRODUCTS/OPERATIONS

Selected Centers and Services
Aeronautics Medicine
Adult Day Programs
Bariatric Surgery
Behavioral Health
Breast Health Center
Cardiology Services
Center for Sleep Evaluation
Center for Wound Care & Hyberbaric Medicine
Childbirth And Family Education
Community Health and Wellness
Critical Care at The Elliot
Diabetes and Outpatient Nutrition Services
Diagnostic Imaging
Elliot 1-Day Surgery Center
The Elliot at Hooksett
Elliot Behavioral Health Services
Elliot Endocrinology Associates
Elliot Gastroenterology
Elliot General Surgical Specialists
Elliot Maternal Fetal Medicine
Elliot Medical Center at Londonderry
Elliot Neurology Associates
Elliot Obstetrics and Gynecology
Elliot Orthopaedic Surgical Specialists
Elliot Physician Network
Elliot Regional Cancer Center
Elliot Sports Medicine
Elliot Trauma Center
Elliot Wellness Center
Endoscopy Center
Health Education Library
Home Medical Equipment
Hospitalist Program
Infection Control Department
Inpatient Care/Nursing Units
Laboratory Services
Max K. Willscher Urology Center
Neurophysiology
New England EMS Institute
New Hampshire Arthritis Center
Nursing Units/Inpatient Care
Nutrition Services
Occupational Health & Wellness
Oral Maxillofacial Surgery Center
Oxygen Therapy
Pain Management Center
Pediatric Surgery
Pharmacy Services
Pulmonary Medicine
Pulmonary Rehabilitation
Physical Therapy
Rehabilitation
Respiratory Care
Senior Health Center
Sports Medicine
Surgery
Speech Therapy
  Urgent Car
  Urgent Car
Visiting Nurse Association of Manchester & So. NH Inc.
Weight Management
Wellness Center
Women' s & Children' s Services
Wound Center

COMPETITORS

Caritas Holy Family Hospital	Frisbie Memorial Hospital

Catholic Medical Center
Concord Hospital
Exeter Health Resources
HCA
Lahey Health System
Southern New Hampshire Medical Center

HISTORICAL FINANCIALS
Company Type: Private

Income Statement
FYE: June 30

	REVENUE ($ mil.)	NET INCOME ($ mil.)	NET PROFIT MARGIN	EMPLOYEES
06/10	324	7	2.4%	2,000
06/09	288	0	—	—
06/08	502	0	0.0%	—
Annual Growth	(19.6%)	2074.8%	—	—

2010 Year-End Financials
Return on assets: —
Return on equity: 2.4%
Current ratio: 0.20
Cash ($ mil.): 28

ELLIS HOSPITAL

Schenectady-based Ellis Hospital (dba Ellis Medicine) serves the residents of New York's capital area as part of Ellis Medicine a 438-bed community and teaching health care system. The hospital provides emergency inpatient medical/surgical and psychiatric care including diagnostic primary and rehabilitative care. The hospital is also home to centers of excellence in the treatment of and care for heart and cardiovascular ailments cancer women's health issues stroke-related problems and behavioral health concerns. It also operates the Ellis Center the Bellvue Woman's Center the satellite outpatient clinic Ellis Health Center and recently-constructed Medical Center of Clifton Park.

Operations
Ellis Hospital is part of Ellis Medicine a 438-bed community and teaching health care system serving the Albany New York area. Ellis Medicine has four campuses - Ellis Hospital Ellis Health Center Bellevue Woman's Center and Medical Center of Clifton Park - five additional service locations and more than 700 affiliated physicians.

The hospital's specialty services include a nationally recognized Heart Center a New York State designated Stroke Center and advanced surgery programs such as cardiothoracic orthopedic neurological and vascular among others. The facility features diagnostic imaging and a modern 36-bed intensive care unit.

The McClellan Street Health Center offers outpatient services primary care short-stay rehabilitation and nursing home services. Ellis Medicine Bariatric Care Centers offers a surgical weight loss program.Ellis Hospital also operates academic programs to prepare students for careers in health care and nursing.

Geographic Reach
The hospital serves patients in the Albany Saratoga Schenectady Fulton and Montgomery counties of upstate New York.Sales and MarketingMedicare and Medicaid payments accounted for 53% of net patient service revenues in fiscal 2014.Financial PerformanceEllis Hospital reported a 2% increase in revenue to $388 million in 2014 due to an increase in net patient service revenues. However it reported a net loss of $5.5 million due to losses on extinguishment of debt and changes in net unrealized gains on investments. Affiliate pension and post-retirement-related changes other than net periodic benefit costs also contributed to

the loss.Cash flow from operations rose 54% to $28 million in 2014 as accounts payable and accrued expenses declined.

Strategy
All of the Schenectady facilities are undergoing expansion or improvement efforts to increase service offerings. In 2013 a $61-million project to expand emergency care and parking at Ellis Hospital was begun; it was completed in early 2015. The project expanded treatment stations to 60 (from 47) and added a new two-story 212-space parking garage. Other capital improvements include a $17-million expansion and modernization of Bellevue Women's Center. Recently completed improvements include the relocation of Ellis' 82-bed nursing home and short-stay rehabilitation center and the creation of the Medical Center of Clifton Park.

EXECUTIVES

Admissions Director, Terry Stearns
Pharmacy Manager, Mary Durma
Pharmacy Manager, Erin Buckley
Director Of Pharmacy, Martin Killian
Vice President Legal Affairs and Genral Counsel, Anoush Scott
Vice President of Operations, Patti Hammond
Vice President of Nursing, Cece Lynch
Medical Director of Informatics, Igor Kraeve
Vice President Financial Services Chief Financial Officer, G E Hoffman
Vice Chair, Stephen Pagano
Treasurer, Robert (Bob) Murray
Auditors: KPMG LLP ALBANY NY

LOCATIONS

HQ: ELLIS HOSPITAL
1101 NOTT ST, SCHENECTADY, NY 123082489
Phone: 518 243-4000
Web: WWW.ELLISMEDICINE.ORG

PRODUCTS/OPERATIONS

2014 Sales

	% of total
Net patient service revenue	98
Other operating revenue	2
Net assets released from restrictions used for operations	-
Total	**100**

Selected Services
Emergency
Cancer/Oncology
Neuroscience
Orthopedics
Primary care
Weight Loss
Women' s Health

Selected Facilities
Bariatric Care Center
Bellevue Woman' s Center
Ellis Health Center
Ellis Hospital
Medical Center Clifton Park
Primary Care
Clifton Park
Glenville
Latham
Schenectady (Nott St.)
Schenectady (McClellan St.)
School of Nursing

COMPETITORS
Albany Medical Center
Lifetime Health
Oneida Healthcare Center
SUNY Upstate Medical University
St. Joseph' s Hospital Health Center
St. Peter' s Health Partners
United Health Services Hospitals
Upstate University Hospital at Community General

Income Statement FYE: December 31

	REVENUE ($ mil.)	NET INCOME ($ mil.)	NET PROFIT MARGIN	EMPLOYEES
12/13	380	38	10.1%	2,000
12/12	379	10	2.8%	—
12/09	373	14	4.0%	—
12/08	3	0	—	—
Annual Growth	156.1%	—	—	—

2013 Year-End Financials

Return on assets: 5.8%   Cash ($ mil.): 17
Return on equity: 10.1%
Current ratio: 0.80

ELMHURST MEMORIAL HOSPITAL INC

Elmhurst Memorial Healthcare operates Elmhurst Memorial Hospital an acute care facility located in DuPage County Illinois in the western suburbs of Chicago. Founded in 1926 the hospital provides a comprehensive range of medical services –from emergency care to specialty cancer and orthopedics care to behavioral health services. In addition to the 310-bed main hospital Elmhurst Memorial Healthcare operates several facilities such as doctors' offices outpatient centers occupational health programs and other ancillary health care operations. Elmhurst Memorial Healthcare is part of Edward-Elmhurst Healthcare after it merged with Edward Hospital & Health Services and Linden Oaks.

Change in Company Type

Elmhurst Memorial Healthcare Edward Hospital & Health Services and Linden Oaks merged in 2013 to create a larger integrated health system. Combined the system operates three hospitals and more than 50 outpatient facilities. It has some $1 billion in annual revenues.

Operations

Aside from its Elmhurst Memorial Hospital Main Campus Elmhurst Memorial Healthcare operates several other facilities such as the Berteau Campus Center for Health Lombard Health Center Addison Health Center Elmhurst Memorial Sleep Center Occupational Health Services Wood Dale and an outpatient surgery center clinic primary care associates medical associates and hematology oncology associates offices under the Elmhurst banner.

The newer acute care hospital known as the Elmhurst Memorial Hospital Main Campus features about 260 private inpatient rooms as well as a high-tech emergency department and surgical and diagnostic imaging facilities. It includes the Elmhurst Memorial Center for Health which boasts outpatient clinics and a medical office building for general practice and specialty physicians.

Each year Elmhurst Memorial Hospital has some 48000 emergency department visits and performs some 3400 inpatient and 5500 outpatient surgeries.

Geographic Reach

Elmhurst Memorial Healthcare and its hospital serve the western suburbs of Chicago specifically the county residents of DuPage.

Strategy

To provide its communities with quality cancer care Elmhurst Memorial Healthcare constructed a new cancer care facility that boasts medical oncologist offices an infusion center Cyberknife robotic radiosurgery system and radiation oncology services.

In 2015 Elmhurst Memorial Hospital opened a bariatrics and weight management center that provides surgical and non-surgical services.

The system has been expanding by opening new facilities. In 2014 it opened its second walk-in clinic which provides treatment for minor illnesses. The following year Elmhurst broke ground on a new three-story health center in Hinsdale.

There are also plans for the old Elmhurst Memorial Hospital campus known as the Berteau Campus. While the Berteau Campus' inpatient and emergency care operations were transferred to the new Main Campus the Berteau Campus' emergency room became an outpatient urgent care center. The campus also includes inpatient behavioral health and recovery facilities as well as outpatient cancer care physical therapy and occupational health clinics. For the long term Elmhurst Memorial Healthcare plans to transform the Berteau Campus into a senior health and housing center by closing or moving the existing operations to other or new locations.

EXECUTIVES

Director Of Pharmacy, Dennis Ludwig
Associate Vice President Strategy and Planning, Cheryl Eck

LOCATIONS

HQ: ELMHURST MEMORIAL HOSPITAL INC
155 E BRUSH HILL RD, ELMHURST, IL 601265658
Phone: 331 221-1000
Web: WWW.EMHC.ORG

PRODUCTS/OPERATIONS

Selected Services
Breast Health Center
Cardiovascular Services
EMH Laboratory
Family Birthing Center
Home Health and Hospice
Immediate Care Centers
Occupational Health
Orthopedics
Radiology
Surgery
Cancer Center
Emergency Department

COMPETITORS

Adventist Health System Sunbelt Healthcare
Advocate Health Care
Alexian Brothers Health System
Central DuPage Hospital
Covenant Ministries
Gottleib Memorial Hospital
Loyola University Health System
Northwest Community Healthcare
Rush System for Health
University of Chicago Medical Center
Wheaton Franciscan Services

HISTORICAL FINANCIALS
Company Type: Private

Income Statement FYE: June 30

	REVENUE ($ mil.)	NET INCOME ($ mil.)	NET PROFIT MARGIN	EMPLOYEES
06/09	305	20	6.6%	2,444
06/08	345	(22)	—	—
06/07	341	43	12.7%	—
06/05	327	0	—	—
Annual Growth	(1.7%)	—	—	—

ELWYN

Elwyn isn't a character out of Harry Potter or Lord of the Rings. It's a not-for-profit organization that serves more than 13000 disabled and disadvantaged people of all ages at multiple sites through education rehabilitation and vocational counseling. The organization also operates residential communities including more than 80 group homes and apartments and provides a variety of health care services for persons with developmental physical and emotional disabilities. The group also publishes training materials and hosts conferences and seminars for human services professionals. Founded in 1852 as a school for children with mental retardation Elwyn is one of the oldest organizations of its kind in the US.

Geographic Reach

Elwyn's main campus is in Philadelphia with satellite locations in California New Jersey and Delaware.

Operations

Elwyn operates two for-profit subsidiaries. Its PEMS unit an applied technology service provides a variety of enhanced management services. The organization's Grace Pharmacy Inc. is a full-service pharmacy operation that specializes in long-term care clients.

Elwyn Commercial Laundry specializes in laundry services for hospitals nursing homes surgical centers and other health care related organizations.

Company Background

At a time when most people with mental disabilities were left to live on the streets or thrown in prison Dr. Alfred Elwyn proposed a special school to help "feeble-minded children." The school attracted the best minds of the time and grew quickly adding residential services and custodial care of adults in 1877.

EXECUTIVES

Vice President Information Technology, Richard S (Dick) Smith
Vice President, Scott Campbell
Vice Chairman, J Leaman
Auditors: KREISCHER MILLER HORSHAM PA

LOCATIONS

HQ: ELWYN
111 ELWYN RD, MEDIA, PA 190634622
Phone: 610 891-2000
Web: WWW.CAELWYN.ORG

PRODUCTS/OPERATIONS

Selected Services
Behavioral health services
Deaf services
Early childhood services
Education services
Research and health services
Supports for living
Work and adult day services

COMPETITORS

Res-Care

HISTORICAL FINANCIALS

Company Type: Private

Income Statement

FYE: June 30

	REVENUE ($ mil.)	NET INCOME ($ mil.)	NET PROFIT MARGIN	EMPLOYEES
06/12	211	1	0.7%	2,500
06/11	264	14	5.5%	—
06/10	254	6	2.4%	—
06/09	192	0	—	—
Annual Growth	3.1%	—	—	—

2012 Year-End Financials

Return on assets: —
Return on equity: 0.7%
Current ratio: —

Cash ($ mil.): 12

EMBRY-RIDDLE AERONAUTICAL UNIVERSITY INC.

Embry-Riddle Aeronautical University (ERAU) helps students solve the mysteries of space and flying. The not-for-profit corporation teaches aviation aerospace and engineering to about 30000 students a year (and a student-teacher ratio of about 13:1). ERAU which offers hands-on training through a fleet of 90 instructional aircraft has residential campuses in Daytona Beach Florida and Prescott Arizona. Its Embry-Riddle Worldwide program provides learning through more than 150 teaching centers and online training in the US Canada Europe and Middle East. It offers bachelor's master's and doctoral degrees in 35 areas.

Operations

The school has been adding non-degree programs to its curriculum in recent years in order to reach a broader range of students (such as working adults). Its worldwide campus houses the Center for Professional Education (CPE) which provides professional certification experience and training to corporate and professional adult learners. Many CPE programs are administered online; the school also offers a variety of seminars and workshops. ERAU's non-degree programs include English language training and aviation safety and security short courses.

Its fleet of more than 90 instructional aircraft includes American Champion Decathlon Cessna 150 Cessna 162 Cessna 172 G1000 Cessna 172R Cessna 172S Cessna 172S Nav III Cessna 182RG Diamond DA42 Diamond DA42NG Piper PA28R and Piper PA44. Embry-Riddle also has roughly 40 simulators at both campuses.

ERAU students enroll from 50 states and 120 nations with 14% of international students at the Daytona Beach campus and 4% at the Prescott campus.

Geographic Reach

ERAU's campuses provide instruction through more than 150 locations in Asia Canada Europe and the US through online learning. Its students come from all 50 US states and 98 countries.

Financial Performance

The annual operating budget of ERAU is about $340 million. From 2012 to 2013 (ended June) it had a 3% increase in operating revenue due to a 5% increase in tuition and fees. Operating income increased 5.7% to $314 million due to a spike in expenses related to student services flight instructions and auxiliary enterprises expenses. The decline was also due to a decrease in non-operating activities. Including non-operating revenue ERAU's net income increased to $27 million in 2013 from $24 million the previous year.

Strategy

ERAU's growth strategy involves adding additional degree programs to its curriculum in order to increase the amount of tuitions. In 2013 it launched three new degree programs: astronomy; cyber intelligence; and security software engineering.

The university maintains relationships with airlines for training which helps graduates get jobs. On the research side ERAU opened a new observatory equipped with a 40-inch telescope the largest university based telescope in Florida.

Also benefiting from additional offices ERAU opened a new location in the Fort Worth Alliance Airport in Texas in 2012.

Company Background

ERAU was founded to train pilots in 1925 by barnstormer John Paul Riddle and entrepreneur T. Higbee Embry.

EXECUTIVES

Senior Vice President And Provost, Richard H (Dick) Heist
Senior Vice President, Randy Howard
Vice President For Administration, Rodney (Rod) Cruise
Executive Vice President, Marty Smith
Department Chair, Garret Messner
Auditors: BDO USA LLP MIAMI FLORIDA

LOCATIONS

HQ: EMBRY-RIDDLE AERONAUTICAL UNIVERSITY INC.
600 S CLYDE MORRIS BLVD, DAYTONA BEACH, FL 321143966
Phone: 386 226-6000
Web: WWW.ERAU.EDU

HISTORICAL FINANCIALS

Company Type: Private

Income Statement

FYE: June 30

	REVENUE ($ mil.)	NET INCOME ($ mil.)	NET PROFIT MARGIN	EMPLOYEES
06/14	340	34	10.1%	4,719
06/13	384	26	7.0%	—
06/12	318	24	7.6%	—
06/11	359	0	—	—
Annual Growth	(1.7%)	—	—	—

2014 Year-End Financials

Return on assets: 13.4%
Return on equity: 10.1%
Current ratio: 1.80

Cash ($ mil.): 120

EMERSON HOSPITAL

Ralph Waldo Emerson said "the first wealth is health" and Emerson Hospital would agree. The hospital tends to the well-being of patients in and around historic Concord Massachusetts. The 179-bed community hospital is staffed by more than 300 doctors and specialists. Emerson partners with Massachusetts General on several specialty programs including pain management neonatology and radiation oncology which is housed within its Bethke Cancer Center. It also operates outpatient clinics serving residents in nearby communities such as Groton Sudbury and Westford. All told Emerson provides advanced medical services to more than 300000 people.

Geographic Reach

Emerson provides medical services to people in 25 communities in Massachusetts including Concord Groton Sudbury and Westford.

Operations

Emerson offers services at its main campus in Concord and at health centers in Westford Groton and Sudbury. It also offer services at the Center for Specialty Care on Baker Avenue in Concord the Center for Sports Rehabilitation in Concord and Westford and the Breast Health Center in Concord and Westford. Emerson's Integrative Health & Wellness Center in Concord provides a place where the community can participate in classes aimed at keeping them healthy.

The company's main hospital has more than 37500 emergency department visits per year. Emerson is well known for its outstanding nursing care and patient-centered facilities including the Bethke Cancer Center and the Birthing Center which has the area's only Special Care Level 2 Nursery for moderately ill newborns.

Strategy

To extend its coverage and skill base Emerson also partners with larger and/or specialist hospitals and medical facilities in the region including Boston IVF Brigham and Women's Hospital Children's Hospital Boston Hospice of the North Shore and Greater Boston and Massachusetts General.

In 2015 Emerson and Massachusetts General Hospital teamed up to bring all cancer services under one umbrella to form the Mass General Cancer Center at Emerson Hospital–Bethke. Emerson Hospital also partners with several leading Massachusetts hospitals. In 2015 it also opened new rehabilitation center at Concord Woods Office Park and also opened the Dr. Robert C. Cantu Concussion Center.

Company Background

The hospital founded in 1911 is named for Charles Emerson a nephew of Ralph Waldo Emerson.

EXECUTIVES

President Medical Staff, Raj Devarajan
Director Of Radiology, Pat Sousa
Physical Therapy Director, Terry Enis
Vice President, Karl Kussin
Vice President of Operations, Eric Stastney

LOCATIONS

HQ: EMERSON HOSPITAL
133 ORNAC, CONCORD, MA 017424169
Phone: 978 369-1400
Web: WWW.EMERSONHOSPITAL.ORG

PRODUCTS/OPERATIONS

Selected Facilities

Breast Health Center (Concord)
Center for Specialty Care (Concord)
Center for Sports Rehabilitation and Specialty Services (Concord)
Emerson Main Campus (Concord)
Emerson Medical at Bedford (Bedford)
Emerson Medical at Sudbury (Sudbury)
Groton Health Center (Groton)
Integrative Health and Wellness Center (Concord)
Laboratory Services (Concord)
Westford Health Center (Westford)

COMPETITORS

Lahey Health System	Steward Health Care
Newton-Wellesley Hospital	Winchester Healthcare

HISTORICAL FINANCIALS
Company Type: Private

Income Statement
FYE: September 30

	REVENUE ($ mil.)	NET INCOME ($ mil.)	NET PROFIT MARGIN	EMPLOYEES
09/13	183	2	1.6%	1,450
09/12	180	3	1.9%	—
09/09	0	0	—	—
09/06	146	0	—	—
Annual Growth	3.2%	—	—	—

2013 Year-End Financials
Return on assets: 9.6%
Return on equity: 1.6%
Current ratio: 1.50

Cash ($ mil.): 27

EMILY DICKINSON MUSEUM

LOCATIONS

HQ: EMILY DICKINSON MUSEUM
280 MAIN ST, AMHERST, MA 010022349
Phone: 413 542-8161
Web: WWW.EMILYDICKINSONMUSEUM.ORG

HISTORICAL FINANCIALS
Company Type: Private

Income Statement
FYE: June 30

	REVENUE ($ mil.)	NET INCOME ($ mil.)	NET PROFIT MARGIN	EMPLOYEES
06/14	511	333	65.2%	4
06/13	404	214	52.9%	—
Annual Growth	26.6%	55.9%	—	—

2014 Year-End Financials
Return on assets: 1.9%
Return on equity: 65.2%
Current ratio: 0.40

Cash ($ mil.): 42

EMJ CORPORATION

EMJ does it all for the mall. Founded in 1968 by namesake Edgar M. Jolley the company specializes in building and renovating retail outlets and shopping centers throughout the US. It is also known for other building projects such as offices warehouses churches hotels multifamily residences hospitals and wind farms. Working from five offices nationwide EMJ provides general construction and construction management. The company's pre-construction services include creating detailed budgets and construction schedules and coordinating permitting utility companies and municipal requirements. To track a project's progress and monitor costs EMJ offers quality control and safety and warranty management.

Geographic Reach

From its base in Chattanooga Tennessee EMJ serves clients through a handful of US offices in Massachusetts Tennessee Texas and California.

Operations

EMJ owns several operating divisions including Signal Energy which engineers and builds renewable energy projects such as wind farms and solar and biomass energy projects. Another division Accent Construction Management provides site selection budgeting scheduling and other services. Its RedStone Construction Services builds commercial retail hospitality healthcare government facilities and others. It is focused on fostering economic growth in Native American communities.

Sales and Marketing

EMJ has built more than 500 million sq. ft. of construction projects. Its client roster includes Academy Barnes & Noble Bed Bath & Beyond Blue Cross and Blue Shield Home Depot PetSmart and Winn-Dixie.

The company serves several sectors such as airports education entertainment government and civic grocery healthcare hospitality industrial and warehouse and Native American tribal communities office buildings parking lifestyle and mixed use development retail renewable energy renovations and worship centers.

Strategy

The company is working on projects for Whole Foods Market TownPlace Suites Silverdale Baptist student center and Dick's Sporting Goods. Inked in 2013 EMJ's $250-million deal with Native American Chris Samples operating under the name RedStone Construction Services is building a 500-room hotel and expanding a casino in Tulsa Oklahoma.

EXECUTIVES

Senior Vice President Operations, Clint Dean
Vice President, Christopher Hall
Vice President, Ray Catlin
Vice President of Estimating, James T (Jamie) Tyson
Vice President, Ken Colgate
Vice President, Alfonso Leon
Vice President, Lance Gopffarth
Vice President Estimating, Earl Carstens
Senior Vice President, Philip Augustino
Senior Vice President, Drew Smith
Vice President, Wes Jones
Vice President Southwest Office, Drew Halsey

LOCATIONS

HQ: EMJ CORPORATION
2034 HAMILTON PLACE BLVD # 400,
CHATTANOOGA, TN 374216061
Phone: 423 855-1550
Web: WWW.EMJCORP.COM

PRODUCTS/OPERATIONS

Selected Projects
Airports
Education
Entertainment
Government/civic
Grocery
Healthcare
Hospitality
Industrial/warehouse
Lifestyle/mixed use development and retail
Native American tribal communities
Office buildings
Parking
Renewable energy
Renovations
Worship centers

Selected Services
Construction
Construction management
General contracting
Pre-construction services
Quality control
Safety consultation
Site evaluation
Warranty

COMPETITORS

Case Contracting	Hoar Construction
Embree Construction	JESCO
Fisher Development	Rodgers Builders
Graycor	S.D. Deacon
Hardaway Construction	Skanska USA Building
Hardin Construction	Weis Builders
Hayward Baker	Workman Commercial

HISTORICAL FINANCIALS
Company Type: Private

Income Statement
FYE: December 31

	REVENUE ($ mil.)	NET INCOME ($ mil.)	NET PROFIT MARGIN	EMPLOYEES
12/12	428	1	0.5%	210
12/11	437	0	0.1%	—
12/08	821	7	1.0%	—
12/07	959	0	—	—
Annual Growth	(14.9%)	—	—	—

2012 Year-End Financials
Return on assets: 0.1%
Return on equity: 0.5%
Current ratio: 1.10

Cash ($ mil.): 31

EMPIRE SOUTHWEST LLC

With CAT-like tread Empire Southwest has created a heavy equipment sales rental and leasing empire in the US Southwest. One of the largest Caterpillar dealerships in the US Empire Southwest operates through five divisions: hydraulic service machinery power systems precision machining and transport. The company's equipment includes backhoes compactors dozers front shovels loaders pipelayers telehandlers and tractors. It also handles equipment used for mining and forestry projects. Empire Southwest also sells ARCO agricultural equipment carries batteries power generators engines and tools and has a service department.

Geographic Reach

Since moving to the Southwest Empire has carved out a territory that includes more than 30 communities in Arizona southeastern California and portions of northern Mexico.

Operations

Empire Southwest consists of five operating divisions. Empire Machinery sells rents and provides product support for Caterpillar equipment and other brands. Empire Power Systems sells rents and provides product support for the Caterpillar engines used to provide power for electricity generation water pumping and other industrial applications.

Empire Transport hauls heavy equipment and other oversize loads for customers and other Empire divisions while Empire Precision Machining is a large machining shop that can handle massive components. Empire Hydraulic Service specializes in repairing and refurbishing all brands of heavy equipment hydraulic systems.

Sales and Marketing

The company targets the agriculture mining demo and scrap oil and gas forestry on-highway truck general construction heavy construction railway power marine and waste management industries.

Company Background

The company was founded in 1950 when Jack Whiteman acquired Empire Machinery (which held the Caterpillar and John Deere dealerships in eastern Oregon). In 1959 he relocated to Arizona and took over a Caterpillar dealership there.

EXECUTIVES

President and CEO, Jeffrey S. (Jeff) Whiteman
Executive Vice President, Chris Zaharis

LOCATIONS

HQ: EMPIRE SOUTHWEST LLC
  1725 S COUNTRY CLUB DR, MESA, AZ 852106099
Phone: 480 633-4000
Web: WWW.EMPIRE-CAT.COM

PRODUCTS/OPERATIONS

Selected Industries Served
Agriculture
Demo and Scrap
Forestry
General Construction
Governmental
Heavy Construction
Landscaping
Marine
Mining
Oil and Gas
On-Highway Truck
Paving
Pipeline
Quarry and Aggregates
Waste

COMPETITORS

Arnold Machinery   Multiquip
Cashman Equipment   NES Rentals
Cummins   Sunbelt Rentals
Komatsu   United Rentals
Komatsu America

HISTORICAL FINANCIALS

Company Type: Private

Income Statement				FYE: October 31
	REVENUE ($ mil.)	NET INCOME ($ mil.)	NET PROFIT MARGIN	EMPLOYEES
10/12	881	53	6.1%	1,450
10/11	683	38	5.6%	—
10/10	528	22	4.3%	—
10/09	448	0	—	—
Annual Growth	25.3%	—	—	—

EMPLOYERS RESOURCE MANAGEMENT COMPANY

Auditors: EIDE BAILLY LLP BOISE IDAHO

LOCATIONS

HQ: EMPLOYERS RESOURCE MANAGEMENT COMPANY
  1301 S VISTA AVE STE 200, BOISE, ID 837052576
Phone: 208 376-3000
Web: WWW.EMPLOYERSRESOURCE.COM

Income Statement				FYE: June 30
	REVENUE ($ mil.)	NET INCOME ($ mil.)	NET PROFIT MARGIN	EMPLOYEES
06/11	357	0	0.1%	95
06/08	425	1	0.3%	—
06/07	612	0	—	—
Annual Growth	(12.6%)	2100.7%	—	—

2011 Year-End Financials

Return on assets: 0.1%   Cash ($ mil.): 5
Return on equity: 0.1%
Current ratio: 0.30

ENERGYUNITED ELECTRIC MEMBERSHIP CORPORATION

Electrical energy and propane energy come together under the auspices of EnergyUnited Electric Membership. One of North Carolina's largest power utilities EnergyUnited distributes electricity to more than 120000 residential and business customers in 19 counties. The member-owned not-for-profit cooperative also provides propane to 23000 customers in 74 counties in North and South Carolina and it also offers home security bill management and facility monitoring services. The third largest supplier of residential electricity in the state its service territory includes three of the largest cities in North Carolina - Charlotte Greensboro and Winston-Salem.

The company's strategy aims at delivering reliable energy services at affordable prices. In 2010 EnergyUnited made upgrades to its distribution system (installing fiber optic cable and improving communication through Radio Frequency devices) and expanded its renewable energy portfolio (including buying solar power from a newly opened solar farm in Taylorville).

These improvements including the installation of Smart Meters for all members (completed in 2011) enabled the company to cut rates twice in 2010. As a result the company reported lower revenues and net margins for the year.

EnergyUnited was formed through the 1998 merger of Crescent Electric Membership and Davidson Electric Membership.

EXECUTIVES

Vice President Sales And Economic Development, Tim Holder
Vice President of Human Resources, Eric McIntire

LOCATIONS

HQ: ENERGYUNITED ELECTRIC MEMBERSHIP CORPORATION
  567 MOCKSVILLE HWY, STATESVILLE, NC 286258269
Phone: 704 873-5241
Web: WWW.ENERGYUNITED.COM

COMPETITORS

Crestwood Equity   SCANA
Duke Energy

HISTORICAL FINANCIALS

Company Type: Private

Income Statement				FYE: December 31
	REVENUE ($ mil.)	NET INCOME ($ mil.)	NET PROFIT MARGIN	EMPLOYEES
12/14	274	9	3.5%	175
12/13	258	7	2.8%	—
12/12	245	13	5.5%	—
12/11	215	0	—	—
Annual Growth	8.4%	—	—	—

2014 Year-End Financials

Return on assets: 8.1%   Cash ($ mil.): 8
Return on equity: 3.5%
Current ratio: 0.80

EP ENERGY LLC

Auditors: ERNST & YOUNG LLP HOUSTON TE

LOCATIONS

HQ: EP ENERGY LLC
  1001 LOUISIANA ST, HOUSTON, TX 770025089
Phone: 713 420-2600
Web: WWW.EPENERGYCONSULTING.COM

HISTORICAL FINANCIALS

Company Type: Private

Income Statement				FYE: December 31
	REVENUE ($ mil.)	NET INCOME ($ mil.)	NET PROFIT MARGIN	EMPLOYEES
12/14	3,084	148	4.8%	1,000
12/13	1,640	549	33.5%	—
Annual Growth	88.0%	(73.0%)	—	—

2014 Year-End Financials

Return on assets: 4.6%   Cash ($ mil.): 21
Return on equity: 4.8%
Current ratio: 0.30

EPIC AVIATION LLC

Auditors: PRICEWATERHOUSECOOPERS LLP PO

LOCATIONS

HQ: EPIC AVIATION LLC
  3841 FAIRVIEW INDUST 15, SALEM, OR 973021179
Phone: 503 362-3633
Web: WWW.EPICAVIATION.COM

HISTORICAL FINANCIALS

Company Type: Private

Income Statement				FYE: December 31
	REVENUE ($ mil.)	NET INCOME ($ mil.)	NET PROFIT MARGIN	EMPLOYEES
12/13	1,439	0	—	144
12/12	1,439	0	—	—
12/11	1,439	0	—	—
12/10	1,439	0	—	—
Annual Growth	(0.0%)	—	—	—

2013 Year-End Financials

Return on assets: 3.1%   Cash ($ mil.): 1
Return on equity: —
Current ratio: 0.60

ERIE COUNTY MEDICAL CENTER CORP.

LOCATIONS

HQ: ERIE COUNTY MEDICAL CENTER CORP.
462 GRIDER ST, BUFFALO, NY 142153098
Phone: 716 898-3000
Web: WWW.ECMC.EDU

HISTORICAL FINANCIALS

Company Type: Private

Income Statement

	REVENUE ($ mil.)	NET INCOME ($ mil.)	NET PROFIT MARGIN	EMPLOYEES
				FYE: December 31
12/13	467	9	2.0%	3,300
12/12	425	13	3.1%	—
Annual Growth	10.1%	(31.1%)	—	—

2013 Year-End Financials

Return on assets: 8.0%   Cash ($ mil.): 8
Return on equity: 2.0%
Current ratio: 0.50

ERM-NA HOLDINGS CORP.

Auditors: KPMG LLP PHILADELPHIA PA

LOCATIONS

HQ: ERM-NA HOLDINGS CORP.
75 VALLEY STREAM PKWY, MALVERN, PA 193551406
Phone: 484 913-0300
Web: WWW.ERM.COM

HISTORICAL FINANCIALS

Company Type: Private

Income Statement

	REVENUE ($ mil.)	NET INCOME ($ mil.)	NET PROFIT MARGIN	EMPLOYEES
				FYE: March 31
03/14	353	34	9.8%	1,573
03/13	335	26	8.0%	—
03/12	376	25	6.8%	—
03/11	334	0	—	—
Annual Growth	1.8%	—	—	—

2014 Year-End Financials

Return on assets: 3.4%   Cash ($ mil.): 11
Return on equity: 9.8%
Current ratio: 0.80

ERP OPERATING LIMITED PARTNERSHIP

Real estate investment trusts nsk
Auditors: ERNST & YOUNG LLP CHICAGO IL

LOCATIONS

HQ: ERP OPERATING LIMITED PARTNERSHIP
2 N RIVERSIDE PLZ STE 400, CHICAGO, IL
606062624
Phone: 312 474-1300

HISTORICAL FINANCIALS

Company Type: Private

Income Statement

	ASSETS ($ mil.)	NET INCOME ($ mil.)	INCOME AS % OF ASSETS	EMPLOYEES
				FYE: December 31
12/14	22,950	658	2.9%	3,600
12/13	22,834	1,905	8.3%	—
12/12	17,201	881	5.1%	—
Annual Growth	15.5%	(13.5%)	—	—

2014 Year-End Financials

Return on assets: 5.9%   Sales ($ mil.): 2,614
Return on equity: 25.2%

ESTES EXPRESS LINES INC.

Estes Express makes a business out of beating expectations. Founded during the Depression with a Chevy truck the company has grown into a multiregional less-than-truckload (LTL) freight hauler. Its fleet of some 6600 tractors and 24600 trailers operates via a network of 210 terminals dotting the US. Service in Canada is provided by TST Overland Express an ExpressLINK partner and in Mexico through affiliate Almex. Estes Express works with designated carriers to offer door-to-door delivery in the Caribbean and in Mexico. Subsidiary Estes Forwarding Worldwide services ocean/air freight forwarding. The company is owned and run by the family of founder W.W. Estes.

Geographic Reach

Estes Express offers regional service to all 50 US states. It also offers direct service to Canada Mexico and the Caribbean.

Operations

The company operates through several divisions and companies. Divisions include Estes Time-Critical (offering four levels of shipping) Level2 Logistics (business-to-business and business-to-consumer shipping) Estes Specialized Truckload and Delivery Services and Estes SureMove (customers load shipments themselves and Estes provides transportation). Companies include Estes Forwarding Worldwide Estes Brokerage Estes Leasing and Big E Transportation.

Strategy

Estes Express has continued to build out its LTL business by offering expedited delivery volume truckload transportation supply chain management nationwide brokerage services warehousing services and equipment leasing. The latter has provided such rental services as laundry trucks for the Department of Veterans Affairs. Its slate of services are supported by an upgraded wireless on-board pickup and delivery system featuring real-time data enabling terminals and drivers to process freight more efficiently. It has also formed a Mexico third-party logistics subsidiary Estes Logistica for managing freight consolidation and transportation to points south of the US border.

The company purchased about $180 million in equipment in 2014 with another $220 million planned for 2015. It is also upgrading its network to create new hubs breakbulks and bypass terminals to reduce rehandling stops.

Estes Express over the years has opened new offices in San Francisco Los Angeles Dallas Chicago Miami and New York. In 2014 it opened a 34-door terminal in North Chicago to support the continuing market growth in the Midwest. It also opened a new terminal in Oswego Illinois to accommodate increased demand for the company's services in the Chicagoland area.

Company Background

The company was formed in 1931.

EXECUTIVES

Vice President Human Resources, Tom Donahue
President and CEO, Rob W. Estes, age 63
President and CEO Estes Forwarding Worldwide, Scott Fisher
COO, Billy Hupp
VP and Chief Information Officer, Bob Fowler
Vice President Customer Service, Mike Campese
Vice President Of Operations, Al Bucher
Vice President Sales, Patricia Robinson
Vice President Marketing, Jeff Paseaur
Vice President Operations, John Son
Regional Vice President Midwest, Ron Giordon
Regional Vice President Southwest, Steve Adkins
Vice President Safety, Curtis Carr
Vice President Sales, John Rogers
Vice President Pricing, Paul Dugent

LOCATIONS

HQ: ESTES EXPRESS LINES INC.
3901 W BROAD ST, RICHMOND, VA 232303962
Phone: 804 353-1900
Web: WWW.ESTES-EXPRESS.COM

PRODUCTS/OPERATIONS

Selected Services

Global (airfreight ocean international consolidation/deconsolidation customs brokerage international freight forwarding)
Less-than-truckload (regional national international/offshore)
Time critical (expedited guaranteed time/date definite)
Volume & truckload (LTL full loads backhaul services truckload brokerage dedicated truckload)

COMPETITORS

AAA Cooper Transportation	R+L Carriers
ArcBest	Ryder System
Averitt Express	Saia
FedEx Freight	UPS Freight
Old Dominion Freight	Vitran
Penske Truck Leasing	YRC Worldwide

HISTORICAL FINANCIALS

Company Type: Private

Income Statement

	REVENUE ($ mil.)	NET INCOME ($ mil.)	NET PROFIT MARGIN	EMPLOYEES
				FYE: December 31
12/13	1,958	71	3.6%	14,000
12/12	1,864	63	3.4%	—
12/11	1,738	52	3.0%	—
12/10	1,506	0	—	—
Annual Growth	9.1%	—	—	—

EVANGELICAL COMMUNITY HOSPITAL

Evangelical Community Hospital brings the good news of community health to residents in central Pennsylvania. The hospital provides a wide range of medical services to communities in the Susquehanna Valley. Among its specialized services are home health care and hospice maternity oncology rehabilitation and pediatrics. The hospital delivers more than 1000 babies annually and treats more than 30000 patients in its emergency department each year. Its outreach network includes family practice offices and other medical services. Despite its name the hospital has no affiliation with any religious organization.

OperationsThe hospital has 132 patient beds and 18 bassinets about 200 physicians on medical staff and about 900 clinical employees including lab technicians nurses therapists and radiology technicians.Affiliated organizations include Evangelical Medical Services Organization Evangelical Community Hospital Pharmacy and Home Care Products and Evangelical Ambulatory Surgical Center.

Geographic Reach

Evangelical Community Hospital serves patients in Northumberland Snyder and Union counties in Pennsylvania.Sales and MarketingIn 2014 Blue Cross and Blue Shield payments accounted for 29% of net patient revenue while Medicare accounted for 26%. Other third-party payers represented a combined 31%.Financial PerformanceRevenue increased 13% to $182.7 million in 2014 as net patient service earnings rose and due to gains on the sale and disposal of property and equipment. Net income rose 40% to $17 million an increase that was driven by the higher income and investment earnings as well as an increase in contributions and grants.Cash flow from operations more than doubled rising 103% to $29 million in 2014.StrategyThe hospital's $32 million expansion project includes the addition of eight new advanced operating rooms two new catheterization labs and seven new patient rooms.In 2014 the hospital signed dbtech (a tech vendor it has used since 2010) to implement dbtech's eFolders solution which collects automates and distributes content in order to streamline workflows.Company Background

Evangelical Community Hospital was established in 1926.

EXECUTIVES

Director of Medical Records, Joyce Telatovich
Associate Vice President Of Primary And Specialty Care, Andrew (Andy) Gibbons
Vice President of Nursing Administration, Paul Tarves
Vice President of Operations, Kendra Aucker
Director of Surgery, Baird RN
Vice President Medical Affairs, J Ginsburg
Board Member, Carol Graybeal
Secretary, Sheryl Vrabel
Secretary, Jamie Vadella
Board Member, James (Jamie) Patterson
Auditors: PARENTEBEARD LLC WILLIAMSPOR

LOCATIONS

HQ: EVANGELICAL COMMUNITY HOSPITAL
1 HOSPITAL DR, LEWISBURG, PA 178379350
Phone: 570 522-2000
Web: WWW.EVANHOSPITAL.COM

PRODUCTS/OPERATIONS

2014 Sales

	% of total
Net patient service revenues less provision for bad debt	96
Other revenues	4
Net assets released from restrictions	-
Total	**100**

Selected Services

Bariatric Services
Cardiopulmonary Services
Cardiovascular Services
Diabetes Clinic
Digestive Services
Emergency Services
Evangelical Ambulatory Surgical Center
Hospice
Imaging Services
Joint Replacement Program
Laboratory Services
Lifeline
Nutrition Counseling Services
Obstetrics and Gynecology
Occupational Medicine
Oncology Services
Orthopaedic Services
Outpatient Clinics
Pastoral Services
Pediatrics
Physical Rehabilitation
Pre Hospital Services
Sleep Disorder Center
Stomal Therapy Clinic
Surgical Services
The Family Place
The Infusion Center
Thyra M. Humphreys Center for Breast Health
Vascular Center

COMPETITORS

Geisinger Health System
Lewistown Hospital
Mercy Health Partners Toledo
PinnacleHealth System

HISTORICAL FINANCIALS

Company Type: Private

Income Statement

FYE: June 30

	REVENUE ($ mil.)	NET INCOME ($ mil.)	NET PROFIT MARGIN	EMPLOYEES
06/13	162	12	7.7%	1,360
06/12	154	9	6.2%	—
06/11	142	18	12.6%	—
06/10	122	0	—	—
Annual Growth	9.7%	—	—	—

2013 Year-End Financials

EWING IRRIGATION PRODUCTS INC.

You can thank Ewing Irrigation Products for that lush verdant golf course you occasionally call home. The company wholesales more than 13000 types of irrigation products for water management/conservation and erosion control for commercial and residential yards golf courses landscaping hardscape and turf maintenance. Ewing serves customers in the aquaculture food processing industrial process piping plumbing pool/spa construction and water treatment sectors. The family owned company also supplies water features landscape lighting and pumps.

Geographic Reach

Ewing operates more than 190 locations in 22 US states.

OperationsEwing is the largest family-owned supplier of landscape and water management products in the US and a leading authority on the latest water management products trends and best practices. The company offers commercial and residential irrigation supplies water management services landscape and turf products hardscape landscape lighting water features and erosion control. It also offers industry-leading informational seminars.

Sales and Marketing

The company serves various industries like sports turf golf agricultural and industrial industries. It sells its products through its branch locations and online website.

Ewing maintains open warehouses where landscape contractors and other Green Industry professionals can select their own parts. Its advanced online ordering and resource facility at www.ewing1.com allows customers to track jobs order materials manage their account online and more. Ewing Education Services (www.ewingeducationservices.com) provides quality hands-on training programs to more than 3000 landscape and irrigation professionals every year.

Strategy

Ewing has expanded in recent years opening new branch offices in Arkansas Alabama and South Carolina as well as by reorganizing its executive board to align with regional growth opportunities.

In 2013 Ewing restructured its operations to provide itwith added flexibility and focus in achieving sales goals and growth objectives. This included the appointment of three new vice presidents to oversee Ewing's Western Central and Eastern Divisions.

Company Background

Ewing was founded in 1922 as Atlas Lawn Sprinkler in San Francisco. King W. Ewing acquired and renamed the company in 1948. His family still owns and operates Ewing Irrigation Products.

EXECUTIVES

Vice President of Marketing, Raul Gonzales
Sr V Pres-credit, Rilus Graham
Vice President, Mark Creighton
Executive Vice President, Richard (Dick) Ayork
Vice President of Industry Relations, Raul Gonzalez
Auditors: CLIFTONLARSONALLEN LLP PHOEN

LOCATIONS

HQ: EWING IRRIGATION PRODUCTS INC.
3441 E HARBOUR DR, PHOENIX, AZ 850340908
Phone: 602 437-9530
Web: WWW.EWING1.COM

PRODUCTS/OPERATIONS

Selected Products

Erosion Control/Hydroseeding
Golf
Hardscape
Industrial Plastics
Landscape Lighting
Pumps
Residential and Commercial
Sports Fields
Turf Products

Water Features
Water Management/Conservation

COMPETITORS

Home Depot	Sears
Horizon Distributors	Toro Company
Lowe's	Wal-Mart
Orbit Irrigation	
Products	

HISTORICAL FINANCIALS

Company Type: Private

Income Statement
FYE: June 29

	REVENUE ($ mil.)	NET INCOME ($ mil.)	NET PROFIT MARGIN	EMPLOYEES
06/12	315	10	3.2%	850
06/10	260	0	—	—
06/09	278	11	4.0%	—
06/08	306	0	—	—
Annual Growth	**0.7%**	**—**	**—**	**—**

2012 Year-End Financials

Return on assets: 8.6%
Return on equity: 3.2%
Current ratio: 0.40
Cash ($ mil.): —

EXCELITAS TECHNOLOGIES CORP.

Auditors: PRICEWATERHOUSECOOPERS LLP BO

LOCATIONS

HQ: EXCELITAS TECHNOLOGIES CORP.
200 WEST ST FL 1, WALTHAM, MA 024511195
Phone: 978 745-3200
Web: WWW.EXCELITAS.COM

HISTORICAL FINANCIALS

Company Type: Private

Income Statement
FYE: January 1

	REVENUE ($ mil.)	NET INCOME ($ mil.)	NET PROFIT MARGIN	EMPLOYEES
01/12*	322	0	—	3,200
12/12	324	0	—	—
Annual Growth	**0.7%**	**—**	**—**	**—**

*Fiscal year change

FAIRFIELD MEDICAL CENTER

Fairfield Medical Center is a more than 220-bed acute care hospital serving residents in southeastern and central Ohio. In addition to providing comprehensive medical and surgical care Fairfield Medical Center offers specialty services including cancer cardiovascular women's and children's health and rehabilitation services. The not-for-profit hospital also operates offsite facilities for physician practices as well as specialty diagnostic and laboratory services. The Center employs more than 250 physicians and is served by a number of volunteer organizations which help to support and operate it.

Geographic Reach
The hospital serves the Ohio counties of Fairfield Perry Hocking and Athens.

Operations
Fairfield Medical Center handles some 10000 inpatient admissions each year. It also sees about 250000 outpatients and handles 2500 surgeries and 1000 birthing procedures.

Strategy
Fairfield Medical Center has launched a $38 million facility expansion program called Project BRIGHT (Build Revitalize and Innoate for Greater Health care Tomorrow). Through the project the medical center is adding a new hospital wing with 30 private patient rooms a surgery center and clinical support areas.

To further expand services and reach more patients the hospital is also forming collaborations and making acquisitions.

In 2013 Fairfield Medical Center partnered with New Vision to provide a medical stabilization service for individuals who are undergoing detoxification from drugs and/or alcohol. That year the Center opened Fairfield Healthcare Professionals Bremen to offer occupational health and primary care services. It also opened the Cancer Resource Center.In 2012 Fairfield Medical Center expanded its services with the opening of the Emery and Evelyn Williams Graduate Medical Education Resource Center and the Fairfield Medical Heartburn Center.

Mergers and Acquisitions
In 2013 Fairfield Medical Center bought River View Imaging Center and renamed it Fairfield Medical Diagnostic Services at River View.

Company Background
The hospital entered into the convenient clinic market by pairing with Wal-Mart to open a seven-day walk-in clinic called the Clinic at Walmart in Canal Winchester Ohio in 2011. Two more Wal-Mart locations were added in Lancaster and Logan. The clinics offer school physicals immunizations treatment for common illnesses and other minor medical treatments.

On the acquisitions side Fairfield bought River View Surgery Center from a group of physician owners (70%) and Mount Carmel Health System (30%) for $8.5 million also in 2011. The hospital also paid about $1 million that year to buy out what had been a joint venture and gain full ownership of Fairfield Diagnostic Imaging.

Fairfield Medical Center's original hospital dates back to 1916.

EXECUTIVES

Medical Records Director, Cheryl Henney
Secretary, Carol Marx
Vice Chair, Laura Tussing
Secretary, Terese Haungs
Secretary And Materials Management, Joy Harden

LOCATIONS

HQ: FAIRFIELD MEDICAL CENTER
401 N EWING ST, LANCASTER, OH 431303371
Phone: 740 687-8000
Web: WWW.FMCHEALTH.ORG

PRODUCTS/OPERATIONS

Selected Centers and Services
Bariatrics
Cancer Care
Emergency Care
Ewing Square Infusion Clinic
Fairfield Healthcare Professionals
Fairfield Medical Diagnostic Services
Heartburn Center
Internal Medicine Clinic
Maternity Care

Orthopedic Care
Outpatient
Physical Therapy & Rehabilitative Services
River View Surgery Services
Snider Cardiovascular Institute
Southeast Ohio Sleep Disorder Center
Surgery
The Pavilion (Surgery and Medical Office)
Womens Health
Wound Clinic

COMPETITORS

Genesis HealthCare System (Ohio)	Mount Carmel Health Nationwide Children's
Licking Memorial Health Systems	Hospital OhioHealth

HISTORICAL FINANCIALS

Company Type: Private

Income Statement
FYE: December 31

	REVENUE ($ mil.)	NET INCOME ($ mil.)	NET PROFIT MARGIN	EMPLOYEES
12/09	197	7	3.8%	2,200
12/08	187	(11)	—	—
12/07	744	0	—	—
Annual Growth	**—15655.9%**	**—**	**—**	**—**

2009 Year-End Financials

Return on assets: 5.8%
Return on equity: 3.8%
Current ratio: 1.30
Cash ($ mil.): 13

FAIRFIELD UNIVERSITY

Fairfield University welcomes students to the fair fields of Connecticut and prepares them for a life of service. The university is a private Jesuit school with an enrollment of more than 5000 undergraduate and graduate students. It offers about 40 undergraduate majors as well as 40 graduate degree programs through six schools and colleges: College of Arts and Sciences; School of Nursing; School of Engineering; Dolan School of Business; Graduate School of Education and Allied Professions; and University College. With a faculty of about 550 professionals Fairfield University has one campus in Fairfield Connecticut and offers about 60 study abroad programs.

Geographic Reach
Fairfield University has a 200-acre campus on the Connecticut coast and offers a variety of study abroad programs including courses in Italy Ireland Australia Brazil and Nicaragua. It also engages about 200 international students on its Connecticut campus.

Operations
The university has a student to faculty ratio of 11:1.

Financial Performance
Most of the institution's earnings come from student tuition and fees. Fairfield University reported a less than 0.5% rise in revenues in 2014 due to higher net tuition and fees partially offset by a drop in contributions and investment returns.

Net income increased by 42% in 2014 due to a growth in non-operating income from investment returns and contributions.Operating cash flow increased by 52% as the result of higher net income and an increase in cash generated from accounts payable other accrued liabilities and deferred revenues.

Strategy
Fairfield University aims to prepare students to take on leadership and service roles developing

creativity and intelligence while fostering social responsibility and ethical and religious values.

In 2015 the university launched a new master of science degree in business analytics which focuses on developing new insights and understanding of business performance based on data and statistical methods attributes increasingly in demand in a variety of industries.In 2014 the School of Engineering opened a materials characterization laboratory to help prepare students to work in the aerospace biomedical and materials industries among a number of other science and engineering fields.

Company Background

As part of its mission to create new opportunities for its students in 2011 Fairfield University added a new study abroad program in Brazil. In addition in 2012 it formed a partnership with Bridgeport Hospital to transition hospital RNs into the School of Nursing's Bachelor of Science degree program.

The university was established by the Society of Jesus in 1942.

EXECUTIVES

President, Jeffrey P. von Arx, age 68
SVP Administration and Chief of Staff, Mark C. Reed
EVP and COO, Kevin Lawlor
CIO, Paige Francis
Dean Dolan School of Business, Donald E. Gibson
Dean College of Arts and Sciences, Robbin Crabtree
Dean Graduate School of Education and Allied Professions, Faith-Anne Dohm
Dean School of Engineering, Bruce Berdanier
Dean School of Nursing, Lynn Babington
VP Finance Treasurer and CFO, Michael Trafecante
Vice President Of University Advancement, George Diffley
Vice President University Advancement, Wally Halas
Academic Vice President, Orin Grossman
Associate Vice President for Marketing and Communications, Jennifer (Jen) Anderson
Associate Vice President for Development, Geri Derbyshire
Vice President For Student Affairs, Thomas (Thom) Pellegrino
First Vice President, Len Roberto
Operations Assistant Academic Vice President, Alexa Mullady
Vice President Of Business And Finance, Elizabeth (Beth) Hastings
Department Chair, Glenn Sauer
Assistant Vice President, James Fitzpatrick
Secretary dean of Freshmen, Brigida Salvioli
Secretary Residence Life, Maria Curesky
Secretary Advancement, Doreen Obanner
Secretary University College, Deborah (Deb) Mcguire
Secretary, Tracey Robert
Treasurer, Philip Lane
Secretary Annual Giving Development, Bonnie Gleason
Secretary Graduate School Of Education And Allied, Cathy Tuttle
Secretary, Susan Rakowitz
Auditors: PRICEWATERHOUSECOOPERSLLP NEW

LOCATIONS

HQ: FAIRFIELD UNIVERSITY
1073 N BENSON RD, FAIRFIELD, CT 068245195
Phone: 203 254-4000
Web: WWW.FAIRFIELD.EDU

PRODUCTS/OPERATIONS

2014 Sales

	$ mil.	% of total
Net tuition and fees	129	67
Auxiliary services	37	20
Investment return	10	6
Contributions	6	3
Government grants and financial aid	3	2
Department and other revenues	3	2
Total	**192**	**100**

Selected Products

Accounting
American Studies
Applied Ethics
Art History
Asian Studies
Biology
Black Studies
Catholic Studies
Chemistry and Biochemistry
Classical Studies
Communication
Computer Engineering
Economics
Education
Electrical Engineering
English
Environmental Studies
Film Television and Media Arts
Finance
French
German
History
Individually Designed Major
Information Systems
International Business
International Studies
Italian
Irish Studies
Italian Studies
Judaic Studies
Latin American and Caribbean Studies
Liberal Studies
Management
Marketing
Mathematics
Mechanical Engineering
Modern Languages and Literatures
Music
Nursing
Peace and Justice Studies
Philosophy
Physics
Politics
Psychology
Religious Studies
Russian East European and Central Asian Studies
Sociology and Anthropology
Software Engineering
Spanish
Studio Art
Theatre
Visual and Performing Arts

HISTORICAL FINANCIALS

Company Type: Private

Income Statement

	REVENUE ($ mil.)	NET INCOME ($ mil.)	NET PROFIT MARGIN	EMPLOYEES
06/14	192	56	29.4%	883
06/13	191	39	20.7%	—
06/12	187	(0)	—	—
06/11	176	0	—	—
Annual Growth	**2.9%**	**—**	**—**	**—**

FYE: June 30

2014 Year-End Financials

Return on assets: 9.2%   Cash ($ mil.): 51
Return on equity: 29.4%
Current ratio: —

FAIRLEIGH DICKINSON UNIVERSITY

It's fair to say that Fairleigh Dickinson University (FDU) is the largest private university in New Jersey. It has an enrollment of approximately 12000 students and 260 full-time faculty members. It has a student-teacher ratio of 14:1 and offers more than 100 undergraduate and graduate degree programs as well as doctoral programs in clinical psychology and school psychology. In addition to its main Metropolitan Campus in Teaneck New Jersey; the university also offers degree programs at the College at Florham in Madison New Jersey; at FDU-Vancouver in Canada; and at Wroxton College in Oxfordshire England. Fairleigh Dickinson was founded in 1942.

Geographic Reach

The university operates a main Metropolitan Campus located in Teaneck New Jersey. It also has a campus in Vancouver Canada and offers degree programs to students through partnerships with other institutions such as the College at Florham in Madison Wisconsin and at Oxfordshire England's Wroxton College. FDU is the first American university to own and operate an overseas campus.

Operations

Some of the school's many disciplines include business education engineering hotel and restaurant management liberal arts (including communication criminal justice film and animation psychology and theater) nursing and allied health and the sciences.

Of its more than 260 full-time faculty members 85% hold a Ph.D. or terminal degree in their field.

Strategy

The school offers students combined degree programs that allow them to earn a master's or professional degree at an accelerated pace in more than a dozen disciplines.

Entering agreements with universities worldwide has also given FDU the opportunity to exchange faculty conduct joint research projects and collaborate on educational initiatives. FDU is the first comprehensive university in the world to require its undergraduates to undergo distance learning. Such global partnerships include Galen University in Belize; Reims Management School in France; and Ross University Medical School in Dominica.

EXECUTIVES

Assistant Vice President for Administration Administration Vice President Office, Robert (Bob) Valenti
Auditors: PRICEWATERHOUSECOOPERS LLP

LOCATIONS

HQ: FAIRLEIGH DICKINSON UNIVERSITY
1000 RIVER RD, TEANECK, NJ 076661914
Phone: 201 692-2000
Web: WWW.VIEW.FDU.EDU

Selected Global Partnerships

Belize
  Galen University
Brazil
  Centro Universitario (UNA)
  Faculdades Integradas de Vitoria (FDV)
China
  Northeastern University - Shenyang China
Shenyang U
  Capital University of Economics and Business (Beijing)
Colombia
  Universidad Autonoma de Bucaramanga
Cyprus

Intercolle
Dominica
  Ross University Medical School
Dominican Republic
  Pontificia Universidad Catolica Madre y Maestra
Ecuador
  Universidad Catolica de Santiago de Guayaquil
  (Guayaquil)
France
  IECS - Strasbourg Graduate School of Management
  Reims Management School
Germany
  Fachhochsc
Hong Kong
  Chinese University of Hong Kong
  University of Hong Kong
  Lignan University
Hungary
  Central European University
India
  Alliance Business School
Israel
  Ben-Gurion University of the Negev (Beer-Sheva)
Korea
  Kyungnam University
  Sungkyungkwan University
  Woosuk University
Lebanon
  University
Malaysia
  University College Sedaya International
Mexico
  Universidad Autónoma de Guadalajara School of
  Medicine
Monaco
  International University of Monaco
Philippines
  University of the East
Poland
  Karola Marcinkowski Medical School
Singapore
  Republic Polytechnic- Singapore
  Temasek Po
Spain
  International University Study Center - Barcelona
  Spain
  Universidad Alfonso X el Sabio - Madrid Spain
  University of Cordoba

PRODUCTS/OPERATIONS

Selected Colleges
Becton College
Petrocelli College
Silberman College
University College

HISTORICAL FINANCIALS
Company Type: Private

Income Statement
FYE: June 30

	REVENUE ($ mil.)	NET INCOME ($ mil.)	NET PROFIT MARGIN	EMPLOYEES
06/13	211	21	10.3%	1,505
06/12	204	7	3.9%	—
06/11	202	22	11.3%	—
06/10	191	0	—	—
Annual Growth	3.3%	—	—	—

2013 Year-End Financials
Return on assets: —   Cash ($ mil.): 58
Return on equity: 10.3%
Current ratio: —

FAIRVIEW HEALTH SERVICES

It's fair to say that when it comes to health care Fairview Health Services takes the long view. The not-for-profit system serves Minnesota's Twin Cities and nearby communities. Fairview Health is affiliated with the medical school of the University of Minnesota and counts among its 10 hospitals the University of Minnesota Medical Center. The hospitals house more than 2500 beds and provide comprehensive medical and surgical services. The system also operates primary and specialty care clinics that provide preventive and wellness care. Additionally it operates retail pharmacies and nursing homes and provides home health care and rehabilitation. Fairview plans to merge with University of Minnesota Physicians.

Operations

Fairview operates more than 40 primary care clinics seven urgent care clinics more than 55 specialty service centers some 50 senior housing locations and 30-plus retail pharmacies scattered across the state. It employs more than 2300 physicians. The health system was one of the first in the nation to initiate a pay scheme for clinic doctors that rewards them for the manner in which they treat patients favorable satisfaction surveys and their ability to keep patients healthy and out of the hospital rather than simply for the number of tests run.

Fairview provides a host of senior care options through its Ebenezer unit that include assisted and independent living adult day care and health services designed specifically for the elderly and administered by specialists that include geriatricians.

The company's affiliated physician organizations include Behavioral Healthcare Providers University of Minnesota Physicians and Fairview Physician Associates.

Sales and Marketing

Negotiated contracts and commercial channels account for about two-thirds of the company's revenues while Medicare accounts for about a quarter of revenues. Medicaid and self-pay channels round out the sales.

Financial PerformanceFairview's revenues grew by 5% to $3.4 billion in 2013 due to an increase in revenues from net patient services and other operating revenues; this was slightly offset by a decrease in revenue from net assets released from restriction. Net income grew 51% that year to $244.3 million led by the increase in revenues and investment returns. Also contributing to the improvement was the absence of disaffiliation loss of subsidiaries which had occurred the prior year.Cash flow from operations grew by $8 million to $79.3 million in 2013; the rise in net income and changes in current liabilities and other assets led to the inflow.StrategyFairview has grown through organic initiatives and via acquisitions. It has recently made several improvements to its new specialty center including adding a physical therapy gym refurbishing its pediatric floor renovating the neonatal intensive care unit and adding a larger laboratory.

In 2013 the University of Minnesota proposed taking over Fairview which would have then been combined with South Dakota's Sanford Health. That deal ultimately fell through but in 2015 Fairview announced plans to instead merge with the school's private physician network University of Minnesota Physicians. The combined company is to be named University of Minnesota Health. (That brand was launched in early 2014 prior to organizations' announced intention to combine forces.)

Company Background
Fairview was founded in 1906.

EXECUTIVES
Vice President, Leann Born

LOCATIONS
HQ: FAIRVIEW HEALTH SERVICES
  2450 RIVERSIDE AVE, MINNEAPOLIS, MN 554541450
Phone: 612 672-6300
Web: WWW.UMPHYSICIANS.OIT.UMN.EDU

PRODUCTS/OPERATIONS

2013 Sales

	% of total
Net patient service revenues	86
Other	14
Total	**100**

Selected Facilities
Bloomington Lake Clinic
Fairview Lakes Medical Center (Wyoming)
Fairview Maple Grove Medical Center
Fairview Northland Medical Center (Princeton)
Fairview Red Wing Medical Center
Fairview Ridges Hospital (Burnsville)
Fairview Southdale Hospital (Edina)
Fairview University Medical Center-Mesabi (Hibbing)
Maple Grove Hospital
University of Minnesota Amplatz Children' s Hospital
  (Minneapolis)
University of Minnesota Medical Center (Minneapolis)

Selected Services
Acupuncture
Allergies asthma & immunology
Artery & vein care
Athletic training
Audiology & hearing aid services
Behavioral health
Births
Bleeding & clotting disorders
Blood & marrow transplant
Breast care
Cancer care
Chiropractic services
Cosmetic services
Critical care
Dermatology
Ear nose & throat care
Emergency care
Endocrinology
Eye care
Family medicine
Gastroenterology
Genetic counseling
Hand therapy
Heart care
Home care & hospice
Home infusion
Infectious disease
Internal medicine
International travel medicine
Interpreter & translation services
Kidney care
Laboratories
Lactation services
Lung care
Maternal/fetal medicine
Neonatal intensive care
Neurosciences
Nutrition
Obstetrics & gynecology
Occupational medicine
Orthopedics
Orthotics & prosthetics
Pain management
Palliative care
Pharmacy
Physical therapy
Plastic & reconstructive surgery
Podiatry
Preventive care
Primary care
Radiology & imaging

Rehabilitation
Rheumatology
Senior services
Sleep medicine
Spine care
Sports medicine
Stroke care
Surgery
Trauma
Urgent care
Urology
Vascular care
Weight loss
Wound care

COMPETITORS

Abbott Northwestern
  Hospital
Allina Hospitals
Bethesda Hospital
Catholic Health
  Initiatives
CentraCare Health
HealthEast Care System

Mayo Clinic
North Memorial Health
  Care
Park Nicollet Health
  Services
Regions Hospital
St. John's Hospital
  (Minnesota)

HISTORICAL FINANCIALS

Company Type: Private

Income Statement

FYE: December 31

	REVENUE ($ mil.)	NET INCOME ($ mil.)	NET PROFIT MARGIN	EMPLOYEES
12/13	3,370	249	7.4%	18,000
12/12	3,218	168	5.2%	—
12/11	2,575	4	0.2%	—
12/09	2,744	0	—	—
Annual Growth	5.3%	—	—	—

2013 Year-End Financials

Return on assets: 4.9%
Return on equity: 7.4%
Current ratio: 0.90
Cash ($ mil.): 34

FAITH TECHNOLOGIES INC.

Keeping the faith in technology is a basic commitment of Faith Technologies one of the largest privately held electrical and specialty systems contractors in the US. The company's specialties include electrical contracting and service automated controls lighting security technology and preconstruction. It primarily serves clients in the commercial government industrial institutional health care manufacturing power residential retail transportation and data center sectors. The company has worked on a range of projects such as airports bridges correctional facilities government agencies hospitals restaurants and shopping centers.Established in 1972 employee-owned Faith Technologies has around 15 locations in Georgia Kansas Minnesota Missouri Oklahoma and Wisconsin and is licensed to do business in some 45 states. In 2009 its Faith Technologies Tulsa division in Oklahoma merged with Alpha Electrical Services. Also that year the company completed the final phase of a nationwide transition by converting all 10 of its Town & Country Electric locations in Wisconsin under the Faith Technologies banner.Faith Technologies opened its 15th location in Minneapolis in 2010.

EXECUTIVES

Executive Vice President, Darryl Betro

Executive Vice President Operations Neenah, Jim Totzke
Executive Vice President of Risk, Bob Dakovich
Vice President Of Safety Lenexa, Rocky Rowlett
Auditors: GRANT THORNTON LLP MILWAUKEE

LOCATIONS

HQ: FAITH TECHNOLOGIES INC.
  225 MAIN ST, MENASHA, WI 549523186
Phone: 920 225-6500
Web: WWW.FAITHTECHNOLOGIES.COM

COMPETITORS

Aldridge Electric
EEI
EMCOR

Guarantee Electrical
Sachs Electric

HISTORICAL FINANCIALS

Company Type: Private

Income Statement

FYE: December 31

	REVENUE ($ mil.)	NET INCOME ($ mil.)	NET PROFIT MARGIN	EMPLOYEES
12/12	260	9	3.8%	1,820
12/11	248	4	1.9%	—
12/10	228	2	1.0%	—
12/09	219	0	—	—
Annual Growth	5.9%	—	—	—

2012 Year-End Financials

Return on assets: 5.9%
Return on equity: 3.8%
Current ratio: —
Cash ($ mil.): —

FAMILY EXPRESS CORPORATION

Convenience is all in the family at this Indiana chain. Family Express operates about 50 convenience store/gasoline stations in north central and northwestern Indiana (split almost evenly between city and rural locations). The chain's Cravin's Market in-house foodservice features fresh sandwiches fruits vegetables salads and a selection of floral items. Family Express also has launched its own proprietary brands including Java Wave gourmet coffees Squeeze Freeze carbonated beverages natural spring water and bread and milk products. In addition Family Express operates a small fleet of delivery trucks that say "moo." The company was founded in 1975.

EXECUTIVES

Vice President Marketing, Bill Nolan
Auditors: MCMAHON & ASSOCIATES CPAS PC

LOCATIONS

HQ: FAMILY EXPRESS CORPORATION
  213 S STATE ROAD 49, VALPARAISO, IN 463837976
Phone: 219 531-6490
Web: WWW.FAMILYEXPRESS.COM

COMPETITORS

7-Eleven
Casey's General Stores
Chevron

Exxon Mobil
Speedway

HISTORICAL FINANCIALS

Company Type: Private

Income Statement

FYE: December 31

	REVENUE ($ mil.)	NET INCOME ($ mil.)	NET PROFIT MARGIN	EMPLOYEES
12/12	379	5	1.4%	500
12/10	277	4	1.6%	—
12/09	244	2	1.2%	—
12/07	275	0	—	—
Annual Growth	6.6%	—	—	—

2012 Year-End Financials

Return on assets: 2.4%
Return on equity: 1.4%
Current ratio: 0.60
Cash ($ mil.): 6

FAMILY HEALTH INTERNATIONAL INC

Known as FHI 360 Family Health International believes that health is wealth. From a handful of offices located in the US Asia-Pacific and South Africa FHI 360 funds and manages public health programs research education and other resources in more than 60 countries. Founded in 1971 as the International Fertility Research Program of the University of North Carolina at Chapel Hill FHI 360 primarily focuses on and supports HIV/AIDS prevention research reproductive health services and maternal and neonatal health programs. The organization works with governments private agencies and non-governmental organizations to develop the most appropriate programs for different areas.

EXECUTIVES

Vice President International Program Management, Laura Kayser

LOCATIONS

HQ: FAMILY HEALTH INTERNATIONAL INC
  359 BLACKWELL ST STE 200, DURHAM, NC 277012477
Phone: 919 544-7040
Web: WWW.FHI360.ORG

PRODUCTS/OPERATIONS

Selected Services
Behavior-change communication
Capacity-building
Clinical trials services
Creative services
Data analysis
Quality assurance
Research services
Social marketing
Training and technical assistance

HISTORICAL FINANCIALS

Company Type: Private

Income Statement

FYE: September 30

	REVENUE ($ mil.)	NET INCOME ($ mil.)	NET PROFIT MARGIN	EMPLOYEES
09/13	664	10	1.5%	4,000
09/09	327	2	0.9%	—
09/08	369	3	0.9%	—
09/07	154	0	—	—
Annual Growth	—	—	—	—

2013 Year-End Financials
Return on assets: 10.4%   Cash ($ mil.): 120
Return on equity: 1.5%
Current ratio: 1.40

FARM CREDIT SERVICES ILLINOIS ACA

Auditors: PRICEWATERHOUSECOOPERS LLP MI

LOCATIONS

HQ: FARM CREDIT SERVICES ILLINOIS ACA
1100 FARM CREDIT DR, MAHOMET, IL 618538532
Phone: 217 590-2200
Web: WWW.FCSILLINOIS.COM

HISTORICAL FINANCIALS

Company Type: Private

Income Statement

FYE: December 31

	ASSETS ($ mil.)	NET INCOME ($ mil.)	INCOME AS % OF ASSETS	EMPLOYEES
12/13	3,338	63	1.9%	165
12/12	3,304	63	1.9%	—
12/11	2,843	56	2.0%	—
12/10	2,607	0	—	—
Annual Growth	8.6%	—	—	—

FARM CREDIT SERVICES OF AMERICA PCA/FLCA

LOCATIONS

HQ: FARM CREDIT SERVICES OF AMERICA PCA/FLCA
5015 S 118TH ST, OMAHA, NE 681372210
Phone: 402 348-3554
Web: WWW.FCSAMERICA.COM

HISTORICAL FINANCIALS

Company Type: Private

Income Statement

FYE: December 31

	ASSETS ($ mil.)	NET INCOME ($ mil.)	INCOME AS % OF ASSETS	EMPLOYEES
12/13	21,274	0	—	10,000
12/04	8,475	294	3.5%	—
12/03	7,633	114	1.5%	—
12/02	6,976	0	—	—
Annual Growth	10.7%	—	—	—

2013 Year-End Financials

Return on assets: —   Sales ($ mil): 514
Return on equity: —

FARM CREDIT WEST

LOCATIONS

HQ: FARM CREDIT WEST
1478 STONE POINT DR # 450, ROSEVILLE, CA 956612869
Phone: 916 724-4800

HISTORICAL FINANCIALS

Company Type: Private

Income Statement

FYE: December 31

	ASSETS ($ mil.)	NET INCOME ($ mil.)	INCOME AS % OF ASSETS	EMPLOYEES
12/13	6,925	156	2.3%	165
12/12	6,668	151	2.3%	—
12/11	6,282	176	2.8%	—
12/10	6,129	0	—	—
Annual Growth	4.2%	—	—	—

FARMERS CO-OPERATIVE ELEVATOR COMPANY

Auditors: CARLSON HIGHLAND NEW ULM MIN

LOCATIONS

HQ: FARMERS CO-OPERATIVE ELEVATOR COMPANY
1972 510TH ST, HANLEY FALLS, MN 562453082
Phone: 507 768-3448
Web: WWW.FARMERSCOOPELEVATOR.COM

HISTORICAL FINANCIALS

Company Type: Private

Income Statement

FYE: December 31

	REVENUE ($ mil.)	NET INCOME ($ mil.)	NET PROFIT MARGIN	EMPLOYEES
12/13	311	4	1.3%	56
12/12	371	4	1.1%	—
12/11	354	2	0.8%	—
12/10	243	0	—	—
Annual Growth	8.5%	—	—	—

2013 Year-End Financials

Return on assets: 2.4%   Cash ($ mil.): 4
Return on equity: 1.3%
Current ratio: 0.10

FARMERS COOPERATIVE COMPANY

The importance of cooperation –it's one of life's most important lessons. Dating back to the early 1900s the Farmers Cooperative Company (FCC) learned that lesson early on. The 5500-member-plus co-op offers agronomy and grain marketing services to its members who oversee some 3 mil-lion acres of farmland in central and north central Iowa. The largest of its kind in Iowa FCC operates 40 grain elevators and provides soil testing and mapping services. It sells supplies including seed feed and fertilizer to its members. The acquisitive coop was itself acquired by another Iowa coop NEW Cooperative in 2014.

Ownership

NEW Cooperative merged with Farmers Cooperative Company (FCC) in September 2014. Under the terms of the merger agreement all current employees of FCC will remain and become employees of NEW Cooperative.

Operations

Farmers Cooperative (FCC) operates four departments: Agronomy Feed Grain and Seed. Agronomy serves customers at some 40 locations across central Iowa and is one of the largest agronomy divisions in the the state. The Feed department has six manufacturing locations across central north central and northwest Iowa. FCC's feed mills produce more than 900000 tons of complete feed annually. FCC has 40 grain elevators across its membership area. More than 118 million bushels of grain are handled annually. FCC also has grain storage capacity of 75 million bushels. The cooperative's Seed department works closely with the Agronomy division since both serve the same customers.

EXECUTIVES

CEO, Roger Koppen
SVP Grain Marketing and Logistics, Jon Setterdahl
SVP and CFO, Mark Miner
COO, Chris Pearson
Seed Manager, Tom Hall
VP Agronomy Sales, Pat Zmolek
VP Feed Sales, John Malin
Business Development Manager, Lonnie Hansen
Marketing Manager, Dave Lemke
Sr. Vice President - Operations, Devin Mogler
Controller, Justin Nepper
Operations Manager, Justin Sollmann
Sr. Vice President of Grain Operations, Marvin Hodgson
Controller Manager, Molly Blanchfield
Business Development Manager serves our trade area, Ned Lenh
Marketing Manager, Ron Simmons
Sr. Vice President - Feed, Ron Hollenbeck
Operations Manager, Todd Scheer
Marketing Manager, Kirk Johnson
Chief Executive Officer, Jim Chism
Auditors: MERIWETHER WILSON & COMPANY

LOCATIONS

HQ: FARMERS COOPERATIVE COMPANY
105 GARFIELD AVE, FARNHAMVILLE, IA 505386712
Phone: 515 544-3213
Web: WWW.FCCOOP.COM

PRODUCTS/OPERATIONS

Selected Departments

Agronomy
Feed
Grain
Seed

COMPETITORS

ADM	Five Star Co-op
Ag Processing Inc.	Gold-Eagle Cooperative
CHS	Heartland Co-op
Cargill	Ingredion
DeBruce Grain	Scoular
Farm Service Cooperative	Swiss Valley Farms
Farmers Cooperative Society	West Central Co-op

HISTORICAL FINANCIALS
Company Type: Private

Income Statement
FYE: August 31

	REVENUE ($ mil.)	NET INCOME ($ mil.)	NET PROFIT MARGIN	EMPLOYEES
08/10	779	10	1.3%	450
08/09	894	13	1.5%	—
Annual Growth	(12.8%)	(19.9%)		

2010 Year-End Financials
Return on assets: 5.6%
Return on equity: 1.3%
Current ratio: —
Cash ($ mil.): —

FARMERS COOPERATIVE SOCIETY

When farmers cooperate society benefits. Through its seven centers in northwest Iowa Farmers Cooperative Society offers its member/farmers a full range of agricultural growing and marketing products and services including crop-storage facilities and business consulting. Its feedlot with room for some 5500 head of cattle helps members buy and care for feeder cattle and provides discounts on grain for members. The co-op also operates a member-only How-To Building Store in Sioux Center Iowa that sells hardware lawn-care products lumber and paint as well as brand-name home appliances. Farmers Cooperative Society has roots dating back to 1907.

To provide the right product for its members the co-op's How-To Building store uses over 40 suppliers such as Andersen CertainTeed Toro and Weber-Stephen Products. The co-op also sells pork producers with products through suppliers like AP Valco and Chore-time. The co-op also supplies pork producers through suppliers such as AP Valco and Chore-time.

EXECUTIVES

Manager Feed Division, Brad De Vries
Manager Feed Mill, Kevin Hulstein
Manager Lumber Division, Ron Boon
Location Manager Little Rock (IA), Ed Mayland
Location Manager Melvin (IA), Brad Knock
Manager Agronomy Department, Stan Feekes
President, Marvin Wynia
Operations Manager, Todd Kludt
Operations Manager, Tom Olsen
Operations Manager, Jason Hoekstra
Division Sales Manager, Kris Norgaard
Quality Control Manager, Scott Berg

LOCATIONS

HQ: FARMERS COOPERATIVE SOCIETY
317 3RD ST NW, SIOUX CENTER, IA 512501897
Phone: 712 722-2671
Web: WWW.FARMERSCOOPSOCIETY.COM

COMPETITORS

AGRI Industries	Miles Enterprises
Five Star Co-op	Premier AG Co-Op Inc.
Gold-Eagle Cooperative	Sears
Heartland Co-op	True Value
Home Depot	Wal-Mart
Lowe's	West Central Co-op

HISTORICAL FINANCIALS
Company Type: Private

Income Statement
FYE: July 31

	REVENUE ($ mil.)	NET INCOME ($ mil.)	NET PROFIT MARGIN	EMPLOYEES
07/14	418	3	0.9%	160
07/13	496	4	1.0%	—
07/12*	434	8	1.9%	—
12/11	0	0		—
Annual Growth	—	—	—	

*Fiscal year change

2014 Year-End Financials
Return on assets: 2.8%
Return on equity: 0.9%
Current ratio: —
Cash ($ mil.): 2

FARMERS GRAIN TERMINAL INC.

Auditors: HUDSON CISNE & CO LLP LITTLE

LOCATIONS

HQ: FARMERS GRAIN TERMINAL INC.
1977 HARBOR FRONT RD, GREENVILLE, MS 387019588
Phone: 662 332-0987
Web: WWW.FGTCOOP.COM

HISTORICAL FINANCIALS
Company Type: Private

Income Statement
FYE: July 31

	REVENUE ($ mil.)	NET INCOME ($ mil.)	NET PROFIT MARGIN	EMPLOYEES
07/14	878	23	2.7%	82
07/13	929	19	2.1%	—
07/12	615	12	2.1%	—
07/11	471	0	—	—
Annual Growth	23.1%	—	—	

2014 Year-End Financials
Return on assets: 2.5%
Return on equity: 2.7%
Current ratio: 2.10
Cash ($ mil.): 80

FARMERS' SUPPLY COMPANY INC.

LOCATIONS

HQ: FARMERS' SUPPLY COMPANY INC.
1320 N LOCUST AVE, LAWRENCEBURG, TN 384642298
Phone: 931 762-3568

HISTORICAL FINANCIALS
Company Type: Private

Income Statement
FYE: August 31

	REVENUE ($ mil.)	NET INCOME ($ mil.)	NET PROFIT MARGIN	EMPLOYEES
08/14	326	3	1.2%	11
08/13	3	0	2.8%	—
08/12	3	0	1.2%	—
08/11	2	0	—	—
Annual Growth	396.7%	—	—	

2014 Year-End Financials
Return on assets: —
Return on equity: 1.2%
Current ratio: 1.20
Cash ($ mil.): 29

FATHER FLANAGAN'S BOY'S HOME INC

LOCATIONS

HQ: FATHER FLANAGAN'S BOY'S HOME INC
14086 MOTHER THERESA LN, BOYS TOWN, NE 680107552
Phone: 402 498-1111
Web: WWW.BOYSTOWN.ORG

HISTORICAL FINANCIALS
Company Type: Private

Income Statement
FYE: December 31

	REVENUE ($ mil.)	NET INCOME ($ mil.)	NET PROFIT MARGIN	EMPLOYEES
12/10	393	61	15.7%	2,700
12/09	398	93	23.4%	—
12/08	298	108	36.4%	—
12/07	298	0	—	—
Annual Growth	9.6%	—	—	

2010 Year-End Financials
Return on assets: 2.8%
Return on equity: 15.7%
Current ratio: 0.20
Cash ($ mil.): 9

FATHER MURRAY NURSING CENTER

Auditors: DELOITTE TAX LLP DETROIT MI

LOCATIONS

HQ: FATHER MURRAY NURSING CENTER
8444 ENGLEMAN, CENTER LINE, MI 480151567
Phone: 586 755-2400
Web: WWW.FATHERMURRAYHCC.COM

HISTORICAL FINANCIALS

Company Type: Private

Income Statement

	REVENUE ($ mil.)	NET INCOME ($ mil.)	NET PROFIT MARGIN	EMPLOYEES
06/09	1,562	(1)	—	317
06/08	15	(0)	—	—
Annual Growth	9831.8%	—	—	—

FYE: June 30

2009 Year-End Financials

Return on assets: —
Return on equity: (-0.1%)
Current ratio: 2.20
Cash ($ mil.): —

FAYETTE COMMUNITY HOSPITAL INC.

If you do too much boogying at the Fayetteville Bluegrass Blast or slip in the sleet at the Christmas in Fayetteville festival Piedmont Fayette Hospital (PFH) is there to help. The acute care hospital is home to centers in cardiovascular medicine diabetes treatment sleep disorder therapy women's health fitness and rehabilitative care. With more than 500 physicians on staff the former Fayette Community Hospital has the ability to treat just about whatever comes through its doors –from ear nose throat problems to pediatric dentistry. The about 155-bed hospital opened in 1997 and is part of the not-for-profit Piedmont Healthcare network.

EXECUTIVES

CFO and Compliance Officer, John Miles

LOCATIONS

HQ: FAYETTE COMMUNITY HOSPITAL INC.
1255 HIGHWAY 54 W, FAYETTEVILLE, GA 302144526
Phone: 770 719-7000
Web: WWW.PIEDMONT.ORG

PRODUCTS/OPERATIONS

Selected Specialties

Anesthesiology
Cardiopulmonary services
Colon and rectal surgery
Dermatology
Emergency medicine
ENT (ear nose and throat)
Family practice
Gastroenterology
General surgery
Hematology
Internal medicine
Nephrology
Neurology
OB/GYN
Oncology
Ophthalmology
Orthopedic surgery
Pathology
Pediatric anesthesiology
Pediatric dentistry
Pediatric neurosurgery
Pediatrics
Plastic surgery
Pulmonology
Radiation oncology

Radiology
Urology
Vascular surgery

Selected Facilities

24-hour Emergency Department
Minor Emergency Care
Outpatient Diagnostic Center
Rehabilitation and Fitness Center
Sleep Order Laboratory
Women's Imaging Center

COMPETITORS

Adventist Health System Sunbelt Healthcare
DeKalb Medical
Emory Healthcare
Grady Health System
Gwinnett Health System
Northside Hospital
Upson Regional Medical Center
WellStar Kennestone Hospital
West Georgia Health System

HISTORICAL FINANCIALS

Company Type: Private

Income Statement

	REVENUE ($ mil.)	NET INCOME ($ mil.)	NET PROFIT MARGIN	EMPLOYEES
06/13	283	23	8.4%	1,045
06/09	165	18	11.0%	—
06/08	163	12	7.7%	—
06/05	1,449	0	—	—
Annual Growth				

FYE: June 30

2013 Year-End Financials

Return on assets: 5.9%
Return on equity: 8.4%
Current ratio: 2.70
Cash ($ mil.): 1

FCTG HOLDINGS INC.

LOCATIONS

HQ: FCTG HOLDINGS INC.
10250 SW GREENBURG RD # 300, PORTLAND, OR 972235443
Phone: 503 246-8500
Web: WWW.FCTG.COM

HISTORICAL FINANCIALS

Company Type: Private

Income Statement

	REVENUE ($ mil.)	NET INCOME ($ mil.)	NET PROFIT MARGIN	EMPLOYEES
01/09	1,535	2	0.2%	410
01/08	2,055	1	0.1%	—
Annual Growth	(25.3%)	50.3%	—	—

FYE: January 31

2009 Year-End Financials

Return on assets: 2.7%
Return on equity: 0.2%
Current ratio: 0.90
Cash ($ mil.): 3

FEED THE CHILDREN INC.

Tuppence a bag might feed some birds but it takes more to feed growing children. Feed The Children (FTC) is a not-for-profit Christian charity that distributes food medicine clothing and other necessities. In the US FTC accepts bulk contributions of surplus food from businesses packages it in various ways at six main facilities nationwide and distributes it to food banks homeless shelters churches and other organizations that help feed the hungry. In more than 120 countries overseas FTC works with organizations such as schools orphanages and churches to provide food medical supplies clothing and educational support to the needy. Larry and Frances Jones founded FTC in 1979.

Gifts-in-kind and contributions combined for around 97% of revenues in 2010. FTC distributed over 133 million pounds of food and other essentials to children and their families in all 50 states and internationally in 2010. Of the 133 million pounds of food distributed worldwide about 105 million pounds were distributed in the US.

While FTC has focused its efforts on feeding children the organization also concentrates on supplying them with support through outreach programs. FTC launched an educational initiative named H.E.L.P. (or Homeless Education and Literacy Program) which works with outreach coordinators in elementary and middle schools to provide homeless students with school supplies books and personal-care items in addition to food.

The organization's FTC Transportation subsidiary picks up in-kind donations from corporate warehouses and distributes them to one of the charity's six regional distribution centers.

EXECUTIVES

Vice President Of Corporate Services, Gary Young
V Chb, Vic Diffee
Auditors: MCGLADREY & PULLEN LLP MELBOU

LOCATIONS

HQ: FEED THE CHILDREN INC.
333 N MERIDIAN AVE, OKLAHOMA CITY, OK 731076507
Phone: 405 942-0228
Web: WWW.FEEDTHECHILDREN.ORG

HISTORICAL FINANCIALS

Company Type: Private

Income Statement

	REVENUE ($ mil.)	NET INCOME ($ mil.)	NET PROFIT MARGIN	EMPLOYEES
06/13	453	42	9.3%	160
06/11	436	10	2.4%	—
06/10	520	(367)	—	—
06/09	1,189	0	—	—
Annual Growth	(21.4%)	—	—	—

FYE: June 30

2013 Year-End Financials

Return on assets: 1.3%
Return on equity: 9.3%
Current ratio: 0.70
Cash ($ mil.): 3

FERMI RESEARCH ALLIANCE LLC

LOCATIONS

HQ: FERMI RESEARCH ALLIANCE LLC
KIRK ROAD AND PINE ST, BATAVIA, IL 60510
Phone: 630 406-7901
Web: WWW.FRA-HQ.ORG

HISTORICAL FINANCIALS

Company Type: Private

Income Statement

FYE: September 30

	REVENUE ($ mil.)	NET INCOME ($ mil.)	NET PROFIT MARGIN	EMPLOYEES
09/10	424	1	0.4%	5
09/08	339	1	0.4%	—
Annual Growth	11.8%	22.8%	—	—

2010 Year-End Financials

Return on assets: —
Return on equity: 0.4%
Current ratio: 1.70
Cash ($ mil.): 2

FERRIS STATE UNIVERSITY

Going to college is no carnival but Ferris State University still hopes the experience is enjoyable. The career-oriented public university offers more than 180 degree programs including associate's bachelor's master's and doctoral degrees through the colleges of Allied Health Sciences Arts and Sciences Business Education and Human Services Optometry Pharmacy Technology and Kendall College of Art and Design. The school has some 14500 students on 21 campuses located across Michigan. Ferris State was founded in 1884 by Michigan educator and statesman Woodbridge N. Ferris.

EXECUTIVES

Vice President For Univ Advancement, John (Jack) Willey
Assistant Vice President For Physical Plant, Mike Hughes
Senior Vice President, Ted Halm
Associate Vice President for Development, Carla Miller
Interim Vice President University Adva, Shelly Armstong
Department Chairman, Jim Woolen
Assistant Vice President For Academic Affairs, Roxanne Cullen
Interim Vice President for Student Affairs, Donald (Don) Flickinger
Assoc Provost Assoc Vice President for Research, Kisten Salomanson
Senior Vice President, Richard Duffett
Associate Vice President For Student Affairs, Michael (Mel) Cairns
Vice Chanc Vice President Kendall, Sand Davison-wilson
Associate Vice President For Advancement, David Lepper
Vice President For Academic Affairs, Thomas (Thom) Oldfield
Vice President of Marketing, Ruth Ridderman
Vice President Of Programming, Ronny Latimore
Vice President For Academic Affairs, Michael Harris
Vice President, Geri Johnson
Assistant Vice President, Michael (Mel) Hughes
Assoc Vice President Comm Marketing, Shelly Armstrong
Associate Vice President For Academic Affairs, Roberta (Bobbi) Teahen
Secretary Level III, Shannon Yost
Secretary, Lisa Knudson
Secretary Deans Office, Andrea Ruggles
Secretary Level II, Darlene Waring
Secretary Level II, Lori Armstrong
Secretary, Sarah Rogers
Secretary Level II, Carri Griffis
Secretary, Alison Divanni
Secretary, Carrie Curtis
Secretary, Ella Shaw
Board Member, Linda Kuk
Secretary, Jean Bennett
Secretary Treasurer, Janna Baxter
Treasurer For The Spe Student Chapter, Russell (Russ) Ankenbrandt
Secretary, Kelly Hicks
Secretary, Sarah Sargent
Secretary, Rosie Jorgensen
Secretary Pharmaceutical Sciences, Melissa (Mel) Saunders
Auditors: ANDREWS HOOPER PAVLIK PLC GRA

LOCATIONS

HQ: FERRIS STATE UNIVERSITY
1201 S STATE ST, BIG RAPIDS, MI 493072714
Phone: 231 591-2000
Web: WWW.OSPREY.FERRIS.EDU

HISTORICAL FINANCIALS

Company Type: Private

Income Statement

FYE: June 30

	REVENUE ($ mil.)	NET INCOME ($ mil)	NET PROFIT MARGIN	EMPLOYEES
06/14	162	20	12.6%	1,200
06/13	164	15	9.3%	—
06/12	158	10	6.5%	—
06/11	153	0	—	—
Annual Growth	1.9%	—	—	—

2014 Year-End Financials

Return on assets: 11.8%
Return on equity: 12.6%
Current ratio: 2.20
Cash ($ mil.): 56

FERROUS PROCESSING AND TRADING COMPANY

Auditors: PRICEWATERHOUSECOOPERS LLP DE

LOCATIONS

HQ: FERROUS PROCESSING AND TRADING COMPANY
3400 E LAFAYETTE ST, DETROIT, MI 482074962
Phone: 313 582-2910
Web: WWW.FPT1.COM

HISTORICAL FINANCIALS

Company Type: Private

Income Statement

FYE: May 31

	REVENUE ($ mil.)	NET INCOME ($ mil.)	NET PROFIT MARGIN	EMPLOYEES
05/14	1,154	14	1.2%	425
05/11	1,272	41	3.3%	—
05/10	915	23	2.6%	—
Annual Growth	6.0%	(11.9%)	—	—

2014 Year-End Financials

Return on assets: 7.7%
Return on equity: 1.2%
Current ratio: 2.00
Cash ($ mil.): 6

FINANCIAL INDUSTRY REGULATORY AUTHORITY INC.

FINRA is one of the long arms of the law for the securities industry. A non-governmental regulatory authority FINRA regulates all securities firms (roughly 4250) that conduct business in the US. Its activities include writing and enforcing rules; enforcing federal securities laws; licensing and registering brokerages and private equity firms; and providing educational information and arbitration services to investors. The regulator works with the SEC and the Fed and possesses the authority to issue fines and bar violators among other punitive actions. FINRA was formed in 2007 from the consolidation of the National Association of Securities Dealers and certain regulatory and enforcement elements of the NYSE.

Geographic Reach

FINRA operates from Washington DC and New York with 20 regional offices around the US. It also has more than 160000 branch offices and some 635000 registered securities representatives.

Operations

Under the oversight of the SEC FINRA brought 1541 disciplinary actions against registered people and firms in 2012 (an increase of 53 from 2011) levied fines totally more than $69 million and ordered payback in the amount of $34 million to investors (a record amount) that were harmed throughout the year.

Financial Performance

FINRA obviously benefits when lawmakers and regulators crack down on fraud and the breaking of securities laws that led up to the Great Recession. As such the bulk of its revenues (about 80%) come from the collection of regulatory user and contract service fees.

FINRA suffered a net loss of $84 million for 2011 mostly as a result of non-recurring costs related to the development of new data center facilities in New York and Maryland. The net loss was also due to increased integration expenses used to extend FINRA's cross market surveillance capabilities.

EXECUTIVES

V Pres, Rob Renner
Executive Vice President Corporate Communications Government Relat, Gregory Ahern
Legal Secretary, Delcina Allen

Associate Vice President And Associate General Counsel, Gary Lipkin

Vice President And Director of Nextgeneration Exam Program And Risk Management, George Walz

Vice President, Angela Goelzer

Associate Vice President And Associate General Counsel, Kosha Dalal

Associate Vice President and Associate General Counsel, Joel Fickett

Vice President, Joe Savage

Executive Vice President And Chief Of Enforcement, Brad Bennett

Executive Vice President, John Malitzis

Executive Vice President Investment Companies Corporate Financing, Thomas (Thom) Selman

Associate Vice President and Chief Counsel, James (Jamie) Day

Vice President Of Regulatory Development And Services, Krisoula Dailey

Vice President Of Government Relations, Julie Bauer

Vice President, Scott Brown

Senior Vice President of Amex Enforcement, David (Dave) Rosenstein

Vice President Of Member Relations, Chip Jones

Senior Vice President Of Market Regulation, Cameron Funkhouser

Associate Vice President and Associate General Counsel, Jim Wrona

Managing Director In The Member Regulation Division, William (Bill) Jannace

Vice President Internal Audit, Michael Hourigan

Vice President of Management and Administration and Enforcement, Susan (Sue) Murdoch

Vice President of Business Area Audit and Internal Audit, Timothy (Tim) Pupo

Vice President of Corporate Financing, Joseph (Jo) Price

Senior Vice President, Timothy Thompson

Senior Vice President, Joe Ierace

Senior Vice President Operational Regulation, William Wollman

Associate Vice President And Associate General Counsel Specializing In Litigation, Terri Reicher

Senior Vice President Technology Finance, Raymond Gregory

Senior Vice President Of Regulatory Services, Angela (Angie) Posillico

Senior Vice President Operational Regulation, William (Bill) Wollman

Vice President, Geraldine Walsh

Senior Vice President, Timothy (Tim) Thompson

Legal Secretary, Natalie Reed

Vice President and Assoc Gc, Gary Ford

Assistant Secretary, Jennifer (Jen) Piorko

Auditors: ERNST & YOUNG LLP MCLEAN VIR

LOCATIONS

HQ: FINANCIAL INDUSTRY REGULATORY AUTHORITY INC.
1735 K ST NW, WASHINGTON, DC 200061506
Phone: 301 590-6500
Web: WWW.FINRA.ORG

PRODUCTS/OPERATIONS

2012 Sales

	% of total
Regulatory revenue	46
User revenue	19
Contract services revenue	15
Transparency services revenue	6
Dispute resolution revenue	5
Other revenue	1
Total	**100**

Income Statement
FYE: December 31

	REVENUE ($ mil.)	NET INCOME ($ mil.)	NET PROFIT MARGIN	EMPLOYEES
12/13	900	1	0.2%	3,400
12/12	878	10	1.2%	—
12/11	880	(84)	—	—
12/10	849	0	—	—
Annual Growth	**2.0%**	—	—	—

2013 Year-End Financials

Return on assets: 3.5%
Return on equity: 0.2%
Current ratio: 0.60

Cash ($ mil.): 376

FIRELANDS REGIONAL HEALTH SYSTEM

Firelands Regional Health System primarily operates through its Firelands Regional Medical Center (FRMC). The center serves eight counties in northern Ohio. It operates two hospital campuses with a total of 400 beds a medical office building and outpatient clinics throughout the region. FRMC's medical staff of 225 represents more than 35 specialties. The center's broad range of services include cardiovascular care home health care mental health services palliative care dialysis oncology care and chemical dependency programs. It also has hospital network and teaching affiliations with several area hospitals medical schools and community colleges. The medical center is supported by a non-profit foundation.

FRMC is the only breast imaging Center of Excellence in its service region. It is also an accredited chest pain center and a certified primary stroke center.

In 2012 Firelands Regional Health System expanded through the acquisition of the imaging center women's imaging center urgent care and occupational health center service lines that Northern Ohio Medical Specialists had previously operated. Firelands Physician Group now operates the urgent care service line with FRMC managing the other lines.

FRMC was ranked #1 in Ohio in 2011 and in the top 5% nationally for vascular surgery and overall orthopedic surgery. It also received other distinctions for patient safety (in the top 5% in the US) acute inpatient rehabilitation (in the top 10% in the country) and cardiovascular services (a Thomson Top 100 Hospital) that year.

The center achieved operating revenues of $3 million in 2010. FRMC's uncompensated care or charity care totaled more than $26 million most of which related to costs of services not covered by Medicare or Medicaid.

Improving the quality and breadth of its services as well as expanding accessibility to its services are cornerstones of Firelands Regional Medical Center's strategy for growth. Its commitment to these goals is evidenced by its standing among its peers in the region.

EXECUTIVES

Director of Radiology Do Radiology Director Nuclear Medicine Director Radiol Diagnostic Imaging, Michael (Mel) Vickery

LOCATIONS

HQ: FIRELANDS REGIONAL HEALTH SYSTEM
1111 HAYES AVE, SANDUSKY, OH 448703323
Phone: 419 557-7400
Web: WWW.FIRELANDS.COM

Selected Counties Served

Firelands Counseling and Recovery Services
Erie
Huron
Lorain
Ottawa
Sandusky
Seneca
Wyandot
Firelands Home Health Services
Erie
Huron
Lorain
Ottawa
Richland
Sandusky
Seneca
Wood
Firelands Regional Medical Center
Erie
Huron
Ottawa
Sandusky

PRODUCTS/OPERATIONS

Selected Services and Facilities

Behavioral health
Cancer Center
Clinics
Corporate health
Endocrine and diabetes
Dialysis Center
Digestive Health Center
Emergency room
Firelands 55+ Club
Healthy Lifestyles
Heart and Vascular Institute
Home health services
Imaging services
Infusion Center
Laboratory services
Maternity/Pediatrics
Pain relief
Pharmacy services
Rehabilitation
Respiratory services
Sleep disorders
Spine Center & Neurosciences
Surgical services
Women's health
Wound care programs

Selected Affiliations

Hospital Networks
Community Care Five (five local independent hospitals collaborating within the region)
University Hospitals Rainbow Babies & Children's Hospital (collaboration and pediatric hospitalist physician staffing agreement)
University Hospitals Seidman Cancer Center (collaboration and physician staffing agreement
Teaching and Clinical
BGSU Firelands
Bowling Green State University
Erie Huron Ottawa Vocational Education
Lorain County Community College
Lourdes College (Sylvania Ohio)
Medical University of Ohio - Toledo
Midwestern University College of Osteopathic Medicine (Glendale Arizona)
Ohio University Heritage College of Osteopathic Medicine (Athens Ohio)
University of Health Sciences College of Osteopathic Medicine (Kansas City Missouri)
University of Osteopathic Medicine Health Sciences (Des Moines Iowa)
Sandusky Career Center
Terra Community College

COMPETITORS

Fairfield Medical Center	ProMedica
Kindred Healthcare	Robinson Memorial Hospital
Lake Health	Samaritan Regional Health System
Mercy Health Partners Toledo	The Cleveland Clinic
Mount Carmel Health	Toledo Hospital
Nationwide Children's Hospital	University Hospitals Health System
Oakwood Healthcare	University of Toledo Medical Center
OhioHealth	

HISTORICAL FINANCIALS
Company Type: Private

Income Statement
FYE: December 31

	REVENUE ($ mil.)	NET INCOME ($ mil.)	NET PROFIT MARGIN	EMPLOYEES
12/12	200	36	18.1%	1,635
12/11	230	11	5.0%	—
12/10	0	(0)	—	—
12/09	0	0	—	—
Annual Growth	—	—	—	—

2012 Year-End Financials
Return on assets: 4.0%
Return on equity: 18.1%
Current ratio: 1.10
Cash ($ mil.): 10

FIRST COOPERATIVE ASSOCIATION

LOCATIONS
HQ: FIRST COOPERATIVE ASSOCIATION
960 RIVERVIEW DR, CHEROKEE, IA 510121492
Phone: 712 225-5400
Web: WWW.FIRSTCOOP.COM

HISTORICAL FINANCIALS
Company Type: Private

Income Statement
FYE: August 31

	REVENUE ($ mil.)	NET INCOME ($ mil.)	NET PROFIT MARGIN	EMPLOYEES
08/14	390	9	2.5%	130
08/03	121	(2)	—	—
08/02	111	1	1.0%	—
08/00	0	0	—	—
Annual Growth	—	—	—	—

2014 Year-End Financials
Return on assets: 2.0%
Return on equity: 2.5%
Current ratio: 0.20
Cash ($ mil.): —

FIRST ELECTRIC CO-OPERATIVE CORPORATION

First Electric Cooperative wasn't the first electric cooperative ever formed but it was the first such entity created in its home state. The member-owned utility distributes power to more than 85000 customers in 17 central and southeastern Arkansas counties. It also offers its members a range of energy products and value-added services including energy efficient Marathon water heaters surge and lightning protection equipment and compact fluorescent light bulbs. Some 72% of the cooperative's revenues come from residential customers; commercial and industrial customers account for another 20% and the rest comes from such sources as irrigation and street lighting.

Maintaining and upgrading infrastructure is a major strategy of First Electric Cooperative which has more than 9460 miles of distribution lines and 42 electrical substations. In 2008 it added about 100 miles of power lines and completed a new substation near Romance in White County.

First Electric Cooperative was formed in 1937 (with 150 member-owners) as part of President Franklin Roosevelt's nationwide push to bring affordable electricity to rural areas across the country.

EXECUTIVES
Vice President Ofoperations, Larry Harp
Vice President of Engineering, Jon Joyce
Executive Vice President, Brad Ford
Auditors: BOLINGER SEGARS GILBERT & MOSS

LOCATIONS
HQ: FIRST ELECTRIC CO-OPERATIVE CORPORATION
1000 S JP WRIGHT LOOP RD, JACKSONVILLE, AR 720765264
Phone: 501 982-4545
Web: WWW.FIRSTELECTRIC.COOP

COMPETITORS
Arkansas Electric	Entergy Arkansas
Coast Electric Power	

HISTORICAL FINANCIALS
Company Type: Private

Income Statement
FYE: December 31

	REVENUE ($ mil.)	NET INCOME ($ mil.)	NET PROFIT MARGIN	EMPLOYEES
12/13	184	0	—	237
12/07	154	20	13.3%	—
12/06	0	0	—	—
12/05	1,151	0	—	—
Annual Growth	(20.5%)	—	—	—

2013 Year-End Financials
Return on assets: 1.9%
Return on equity: —
Current ratio: 6.90
Cash ($ mil.): 11

FIRSTFLEET INC.

FirstFleet helps its customers move their freight —not just by the truckload but by providing fleets of trucks. The company offers dedicated contract carriage in which it supplies its customers with tractors and trailers and the drivers to operate them. In addition FirstFleet provides related fleet management logistics and maintenance services. The company operates a fleet of about 1450 trucks and tractors from facilities in some 30 states in the US and it provides transportation services throughout the 48 contiguous states and in Canada and Mexico. FirstFleet began operations in 1986.

EXECUTIVES
President, Gary Wilson
VP and CFO, David Beeny
VP Operations, Daniel Piper

LOCATIONS
HQ: FIRSTFLEET INC.
202 HERITAGE PARK DR, MURFREESBORO, TN 371291556
Phone: 615 890-9229
Web: WWW.FIRSTFLEETINC.COM

COMPETITORS
AAA Cooper Transportation	Penske Truck Leasing
CRST International	Ruan Transportation Management Systems
Cardinal Logistics Management	Ryder System
Covenant Transportation	Schneider National
J.B. Hunt	U.S. Xpress
	Werner Enterprises

HISTORICAL FINANCIALS
Company Type: Private

Income Statement
FYE: March 31

	REVENUE ($ mil.)	NET INCOME ($ mil.)	NET PROFIT MARGIN	EMPLOYEES
03/12	288	2	1.0%	2,000
03/10	259	0	0.2%	—
03/09	274	0	0.1%	—
03/08	288	0	—	—
Annual Growth	0.1%	—	—	—

2012 Year-End Financials
Return on assets: 2.2%
Return on equity: 1.0%
Current ratio: 1.10
Cash ($ mil.): —

FIVE STAR COOPERATIVE

If Old MacDonald actually had a farm he'd want to be a member of the Five Star Cooperative. Operating in north-central and northeast Iowa Five Star has operations in more than 15 small to mid-sized towns in the Hawkeye State. The cooperative is divided into five divisions according to the products and services offered —agronomy petroleum (diesel fuel and home heating oil) feed (for beef cattle and swine) grain and hardware —it operates a True Value hardware store in New Hampton that offers all the usual hardware products and services. Established in 1916 Five Star Cooperative provides a full complement for its member/farmers.

EXECUTIVES

Vice Chairman, Leon Zeien
Auditors: GARDINER THOMSEN PC CHARLE

LOCATIONS

HQ: FIVE STAR COOPERATIVE
1949 N LINN AVE, NEW HAMPTON, IA 506599406
Phone: 641 394-3052
Web: WWW.FIVESTAR.COOP

PRODUCTS/OPERATIONS

Selected Office Locations
Burchinal
Dougherty
Hanlontown
Ionia
Joice
Klemme
Lake Mills
Lawler
Mason City
Nashua
New Hampton
North Washington
Rockwell
Ventura

COMPETITORS

ADM Alliance Nutrition
DeBruce Grain
Farmers Cooperative
 Society
GROWMARK

Heartland Co-op
Orscheln Farm and Home
Rabo AgriFinance
West Central Co-op

HISTORICAL FINANCIALS

Company Type: Private

Income Statement

FYE: June 30

	REVENUE ($ mil.)	NET INCOME ($ mil.)	NET PROFIT MARGIN	EMPLOYEES
06/14	364	7	2.0%	140
06/13	427	8	1.9%	—
06/12	479	9	2.0%	—
06/11	376	0	—	—
Annual Growth	(1.1%)	—	—	—

2014 Year-End Financials

Return on assets: 1.4%   Cash ($ mil.): —
Return on equity: 2.0%
Current ratio: 0.30

FLEMING GANNETT INC

Engineering firm Gannett Fleming has waded through water waste and sludge for nearly a century. Gannett Fleming operates through more than a dozen subsidiaries that offer a variety of services that range from design/build construction management ground testing and soil strengthening site remediation structural rehabilitation electrical and mechanical installation geophysical mapping and surveying and 3D visualization. Founded in 1915 Gannett Fleming serves the transportation water and wastewater facilities energy and environmental industries working on projects around the world from more than 60 offices across North America and Middle East.

Operations

While the firm is heavily involved in traffic and transportation projects its water and wastewater infrastructure work is perhaps its hallmark. Gannett Fleming has worked on hundreds of treatment plants and pumping stations in addition to thousands of miles of water and sewer systems. Over the past decade Gannett Fleming has designed more than 200 new and renovated dams and has offered its construction management and inspection services for projects with a total construction cost of more than $4 billion.

The company's long list of services has helped it endure dips in the economy. Its 25 lines of business include information technology transportation environmental resources facilities dams and hydraulics site development and construction management services.

Gannett Fleming's design practice GeoDecisions develops master plans for highways railroads bridges and airports. It also designs new dams and modifications on those needing repair.Geographic Reach

Gannett Fleming has more than 60 offices has offices in the US Canada Mexico Qatar and the United Arab Emirates. It has been involved in infrastructure and community improvement work in more than 65 countries.Sales and Marketing

Gannett Fleming serves both the private and public sectors on projects throughout the US and abroad. Some of its clients have included JEA Washington Suburban Sanitary Commission the City of Baltimore New Jersey Department of Transportation Michigan Department of Environmental Quality the U.S. Army Corps of Engineers and Chevron.StrategyGannett Flemming has made a series of office relocations to be closer to its clients and project work in recent years. In 2014 the company relocated its office in Milwaukee Wisconsin as part of its partnership with Chicago-based MPR Engineering Corp which specializes in water wastewater and water reclamation and reuse services with the goal of supporting the growing water-related business and research happening in the Midwestern region. That year it also moved its Michigan operations in Detroit to Ann Arbor and moved its San Francisco Bay operations in California from Mill Valley to San Bruno.The company has also enriched its service offerings and broadened its geographic reach over the past few years through strategic acquisitions. In late 2014 Gannett Fleming bought Pennsylvania-based contractor Innovative Engineering which expanded its electrical engineering procurement and turnkey-construction service offerings. In early 2013 the firm purchased Griffin Engineering and Technical Services to extend its reach into a key research region of North Carolina broaden its HVAC system solution offerings and move it more into the biotech pharma and healthcare markets.

Mergers and Acquisitions

In August 2014 Gannett Fleming acquired electrical design-build contractor Innovative Engineering (doing business as IETC) to expand its electrical engineering procurement and turnkey-construction service offerings. In January 2013 Gannett Fleming acquired Griffin Engineering and Technical Services which was added to its mechanical and electrical practices group. The purchase expands Gannett Fleming's presence in the Research Triangle region of North Carolina and its testing adjusting and balancing of HVAC systems which increases its reach into the biotech pharmaceutical and healthcare fields.

EXECUTIVES

Senior Vice President, John (Jack) Kenny
Sr V Pres, John (Jack) Derr
Vice President, George Campanella
Vice President, Naldo Gonzalez
Vice President, Martha Averso
Vice President, Thomas Leech
Vice President, Michael May
Vice President, Chen Yen
Co Chair (Speakers And Treasurer), Cari Beenenga

Vice Chairman President and Chief Operating Officer, Robert (Bob) Scaer
Auditors: STAMBAUGH NESS PC HANOVER P

LOCATIONS

HQ: FLEMING GANNETT INC
207 SENATE AVE, CAMP HILL, PA 170112316
Phone: 717 763-7211
Web: WWW.GFNET.COM

PRODUCTS/OPERATIONS

Selected Services
Construction Management
 Bridges
 Commissioning Services
 Dams
 Facilities
 Roads and Highways
 Transit and Rail
 Water/Wastewater
Dams & Hydraulics
 Dam Investigations/Inspections
 Design
 Emergency Response Planning
 Hydrologic and Hydraulic Modeling
 Permitting
Environmental Resources
 Environmental Management
 Industrial Waste Management
 Oil and Gas Services
 Site Investigation and Remediation
 Solid Waste Management
 Water/Wastewater
Facilities
 Architectural
 Electrical
 Elevators and Escalators
 Facilities Management
 Healthcare Regulatory Compliance
 Industrial Process
 Information and Controls
 Mechanical
 Security Services
 Structural
GeoDecisions
 Application Design and Development
 Geographic Information Systems Mapping Analysis and Engineering Support
 Transportation Operations/ITS/Traffic
 Web Services
Geotechnical/Earth Sciences
 Earth Structures
 Foundations
 Geophysics
 Geotechnical Laboratory Services
 Ground Modification
 Groundwater and Hydrogeology
 Site Evaluation
Information Technology
 3D Building Information Modeling (BIM)
 3D Visualization and CADD
 Certified Training
 Digital Printing
 Graphics and Multimedia Design
 IT Services
 Reprographics
Planning
 Community
 Environmental
 Municipal Waste and Recycling
 Transportation
Site Development
 Bid/Construction Phase Services
 Drainage/Stormwater Management
 Environmental/Subsurface Investigations
 Green Design
 Land Development/Subdivision Plans
 Landscape Architecture
 Permitting/Agency Coordination
 Planning
 Traffic/Parking Studies
 Site/Roadway Designs
 Surveys
 Water and Sewer Systems
Sustainability
 Energy
 Facilities
 Industrial/Private

Military
Public/Government Agencies
Technology
Transportation
Water Supply
Transportation
Airports
Bridges
Highways
Transit/Rail
Transportation Operations/ITS/Traffic

Selected Subsidiaries & Affiliates
GANCOM (reprographics digital printing and graphic design)
Ganflec Architects & Engineers Inc. (general architectural and engineering design)
Gannett Fleming Pharmaceutical & Biotechnology Services (design and construction services on pharmaceutical and biotechnology facilities)
Gannett Fleming Project Development Corp. (design and construction management on commercial and industrial facilities)
Gannett Fleming Transit & Rail Systems (design and construction management on railway and rail transit systems)
Gannett Fleming Valuation and Rate Division (consulting to public utilities and railroads)
Gannett Fleming Williams Geotechnical Group (geotechnical engineering quality control testing construction inspection)
GeoDecisions (computerized mapping and database management services)
IT Services Division (computer consulting)
L.G. Hetager Drilling (exploratory drilling and testing services)
TerraSure (real estate remediation)
Vertical Transportation Excellence (consulting on elevator escalator moving walks material handling design and other specialty services)

COMPETITORS

AECOM	K&M Engineering and
Bechtel	Consulting
Black & Veatch Ltd.	Louis Berger
CH2M HILL	MWH Global
Jacobs Engineering	Parsons Brinckerhoff

HISTORICAL FINANCIALS
Company Type: Private

Income Statement
FYE: December 31

	REVENUE ($ mil.)	NET INCOME ($ mil.)	NET PROFIT MARGIN	EMPLOYEES
12/13	309	7	2.3%	1,743
12/11	286	4	1.6%	—
12/10	287	2	0.8%	—
12/09	283	0	—	—
Annual Growth	2.2%	—	—	—

2013 Year-End Financials
Return on assets: 5.3%   Cash ($ mil.): 7
Return on equity: 2.3%
Current ratio: 1.90

FLETCHER ALLEN HEALTH CARE INC.

The University Of Vermont Medical Center (formerly Fletcher Allen Health Care) provides medical care in the Green Mountain State. The company operates an academic medical center in alliance with the University of Vermont. The not-for-profit health system serves residents of Vermont and northern New York through three primary hospital campuses and more than 130 outpatient clinics patient care sites and outreach programs. Its acute care medical centers have a combined 560-bed capacity and a medical staff of some 800 health care providers representing medical specializations including emergency/trauma care pediatrics and women's health. The health care system is a subsidiary of Fletcher Allen Partners.

Geographic Reach
The University Of Vermont Medical Center serves 160000 people who live in Vermont's Chittenden and Grand Isle counties.

Operations
The health system receives some 60000 emergency visits each year and its hospitals handle more than 50000 inpatient and outpatient visits per year as well as 2000 births.

Working with the University of Vermont's College of Medicine and College of Nursing and Health Sciences The University Of Vermont Medical Center helps connect bedside experience with medical research to improve overall quality of care. It also provides hands-on educational services for medical and nursing students as well as professionals undergoing specialty training.

Financial Performance
The company's revenues accounted for 68% of Fletcher Allen Partners' total revenues in 2014.

Strategy
In order to provide a cohesive health network in the region the health system is working to create an integrated care network in its service territory. It is also working to build out its IT and data management capabilities

The University of Vermont Medical Center also has affiliations with other area providers to increase referrals and cooperative care including Alice Hyde Medical Center Canton-Potsdam Hospital Moses Ludington Hospital Central Vermont Medical Center Champlain Valley Physicians Hospital and the Elizabethtown Community Hospital. It seeks to form new partnerships with additional facilities.

In 2015 the company changed its name from Fletcher Allen Health Care to The University of Vermont Medical Center as part of a branding strategy approved by the Fletcher Allen Partners and University of Vermont boards.

Company Background
The hospital system was created through the 1995 merger of the Fanny Allen Hospital (which opened in 1894) the Medical Center Hospital of Vermont (or Mary Fletcher Hospital founded in 1876) and the University Health Center (formed in 1971). The hospitals are now known as Fanny Allen Campus Medical Center Campus and UHC Campus.

Fletcher Allen Health Care completed the implementation of an electronic health records (EHR) system that connects patient records at all of its facilities in 2010.

EXECUTIVES
Vice President Hospital Services, Dawn LeBaron
Vice President Jeffords Institute For Quality And Operational Effectiveness, Anna Noonan
SVP and CIO, Charles (Chuck) Podesta
President and CEO, John R. Brumsted
SVP and CFO, Roger Deshaies
President and CEO University of Vermont Medical Group, Paul Taheri
VP Marketing and Communications, Teresa Murphy
SVP COO and Chief Nursing Officer, Sandra L. Felis
Chief Medical Officer, Stephen Leffler
Interim President UVM Medical Group Fletcher Allen, Howard Schapiro
Chief Medical Information Officer, Adam P. Buckley
CEO Inter-Lakes Health, Chip Holmes
Medical Director, Scott Yeager
Vice President Washington Dc Operations, Betsy Sussman
Medical Director, Kennith Sartorelli
Pharmacy Manager, Robert Emery
Pharmacy Manager, William R Rogers
Pharmacy Manager;Manager, Mark Diparlo
Svp Accountable Care And Revenue Strategy, Todd Moore
Respiratory Therapy Director, Isabelle Sargeant
Vice President, Thomas Kristiansen
Vice President Finance and Operations, Ricky Padgett
Medical Director Of Case Management, Norman (Norm) Ward
Vice President Human Resources Operations, Laurie Gunn
Vice President Supply Chain, Charles (Chas) Miceli
Senior Vice President and General Counsel, Spencer Knapp
Health Care Vice President, Mitch Norotsky
Vice Chair, Michel Benoit
Chairman, John Powell
Treasurer, Lou Fletcher
Secretary, Maureen Estus
Board Member, Russell Tracy

LOCATIONS
HQ: FLETCHER ALLEN HEALTH CARE INC.
111 COLCHESTER AVE # 75911, BURLINGTON, VT
054011416
Phone: 802 847-0000
Web: WWW.FLETCHERALLEN.ORG

PRODUCTS/OPERATIONS

Selected Services
Cancer Care
Heart & Vascular
Orthopedics
Primary Care
Urgent Care
Women's Health

COMPETITORS
Albany Medical Center
Ellis Hospital
New England Alliance for Health
NewYork-Presbyterian Healthcare
North Shore-Long Island Jewish Health System
Rutland Regional Medical Center
Southwestern Vermont Health Care
Springfield Hospital
St. Peter's Health Partners

HISTORICAL FINANCIALS
Company Type: Private

Income Statement
FYE: September 30

	REVENUE ($ mil.)	NET INCOME ($ mil.)	NET PROFIT MARGIN	EMPLOYEES
09/14	1,065	69	6.5%	6,000
09/13	1,043	88	8.4%	—
09/12	900	46	5.2%	—
09/09	0	0	—	—
Annual Growth	—	—	—	—

2014 Year-End Financials
Return on assets: 1.9%   Cash ($ mil.): 212
Return on equity: 6.5%
Current ratio: 1.90

FLINT ELECTRIC MEMBERSHIP CORPORATION

The Native American inhabitants of Georgia may have used flint to spark the fires that brought light to their dwellings. Central Georgians today rely on the Flint Electric Membership Corporation which does business as Flint Energies to light their homes. Flint Energies serves 250000 residential commercial and industrial customers (through 82500 meters) in 17 counties Fort Benning and the city of Warner Robins. The customer-owned cooperative operates more than 6250 miles of distribution line and about 50 substations. Flint Energies first flicked the switch in 1937.

As part of its commitment to green energy practices in 2009 Flint Energies teamed up with the EPA's ENERGY STAR program to promote energy conserving appliances and strategies to its customers.

Georgia has 42 electric membership cooperatives; Flint Energies ranks as the seventh largest. It is also the 34th largest of the 990 electric cooperatives in the US.

EXECUTIVES

Chairman, William L. Brown
SVP Member and Community Services, Jimmy Autry
Vice Chairman, Neal L. Talton
Manager Public Relations, Marian Douglas
Director, Jeff S. Pierce Jr.
Vice Chairman, Neal L. Talton
Director, David H. Cleveland
Director, Arthur Head
Director, Sam M. Wellborn III
Director, Paul E. Hibbitts
Director, Jane W. Perfect
Director, Jackie Robinson
Director, Jeff Wainwright
Auditors: MCNAIR MCLEMORE MIDDLEBROOKS

LOCATIONS

HQ: FLINT ELECTRIC MEMBERSHIP CORPORATION
3 S MACON ST, REYNOLDS, GA 310763104
Phone: 478 847-3415
Web: WWW.FLINTENERGIES.COM

COMPETITORS

Georgia Power	Southeastern Power
MEAG Power	Administration

HISTORICAL FINANCIALS
Company Type: Private

Income Statement
FYE: December 31

	REVENUE ($ mil.)	NET INCOME ($ mil.)	NET PROFIT MARGIN	EMPLOYEES
12/13	188	0	—	227
12/12	174	0	—	—
12/08	180	7	4.1%	—
12/07	148	0	—	—
Annual Growth	4.0%	—	—	—

2013 Year-End Financials
Return on assets: 9.9%   Cash ($ mil.): 36
Return on equity: —
Current ratio: 0.30

FLORIDA CLINICAL PRACTICE ASSOCIATION INC.

LOCATIONS

HQ: FLORIDA CLINICAL PRACTICE ASSOCIATION INC.
1329 SW 16TH ST STE 4250, GAINESVILLE, FL 326081128
Phone: 352 265-8017

HISTORICAL FINANCIALS
Company Type: Private

Income Statement
FYE: June 30

	REVENUE ($ mil.)	NET INCOME ($ mil.)	NET PROFIT MARGIN	EMPLOYEES
06/14	483	9	2.0%	2
06/13	419	2	0.5%	—
06/12	360	(11)	—	—
06/11	379	0	—	—
Annual Growth	8.4%	—	—	—

2014 Year-End Financials
Return on assets: 4.3%   Cash ($ mil.): 37
Return on equity: 2.0%
Current ratio: 3.60

FLORIDA HOSPITAL MEDICAL GROUP INC.

LOCATIONS

HQ: FLORIDA HOSPITAL MEDICAL GROUP INC.
900 WINDERLEY PL STE 1400, MAITLAND, FL 327517229
Phone: 407 200-2355
Web: WWW.FHMEDICALGROUP.COM

HISTORICAL FINANCIALS
Company Type: Private

Income Statement
FYE: December 31

	REVENUE ($ mil.)	NET INCOME ($ mil.)	NET PROFIT MARGIN	EMPLOYEES
12/12	314	(8)	—	350
12/08	177	0	—	—
Annual Growth	15.3%	—	—	—

2012 Year-End Financials
Return on assets: 7.7%   Cash ($ mil.): —
Return on equity: (-2.9%)
Current ratio: 1.30

FLORIDA HOSPITAL WATERMAN INC

Florida Hospital Waterman is a 270-bed community hospital serving the residents of Lake County Florida just north of Orlando. The hospital provides a full range of acute care services including cardiac and cancer care emergency services obstetrics pediatrics and rehabilitation. It also offers outpatient surgery diagnostic imaging laboratory and home health services. As part of its portfolio of services Florida Hospital Waterman operates a primary care clinic. Established in 1938 and named after the philanthropic leader of the Waterman Fountain Pen Company Florida Hospital Waterman has been part of the Adventist Health System since 1992.

Strategy

The Lake County area hospital has been focused on adding more beds to its facility after being at or above 80% occupancy for the past few years. In late 2012 it built out its sixth floor to expand its bed count by 60. The move was necessary to accommodate the growing influx of the area's winter residents. Florida Hospital Waterman is also expanding technologies and services to increase its offerings for area residents. In 2012 it improved orthopedic capabilities when it began using the newly developed MAKO Surgical RIO robotic surgery system and the Stryker Triathlon custom fit implant system.

As it works to continue to enhance quality safety and affordability for its patient community in 2012 Florida Hospital Waterman joined the Centers for Medicare & Medicaid Services Partnership for Patients program which is coordinated by group purchasing organization Premier. The alliance of medical companies is focused on health care performance improvements.

EXECUTIVES

Director Of Operating Room, Heather Wood
Director Of Nursing, Patricia Dolan
Ambulatory Services Director, Jennifer (Jen) Cooper
Nursing Director, Dennis Holm
Vice President Chief Medical Officer, Vinay Mehindru
Director Of Him, Karen Mathias

LOCATIONS

HQ: FLORIDA HOSPITAL WATERMAN INC
1000 WATERMAN WAY, TAVARES, FL 327785266
Phone: 352 253-3333

PRODUCTS/OPERATIONS

Selected Services
Cancer Institute
Child Care Center
Community Clinic
Diagnostic Imaging
Emergency Department
Foundation
Heart Center
Home Care
Laboratory
Joint Replacement Center
Nutrition
Partial knee resurfacing (MAKOplasty)
Pediatrics
Rehabilitation Institute
Respiratory Therapy
Stroke Center
Surgical Services
Support Groups
Vascular Center of Excellence
Women's Health
Precious Beginnings

HISTORICAL FINANCIALS

Company Type: Private

Income Statement

FYE: December 31

	REVENUE ($ mil.)	NET INCOME ($ mil.)	NET PROFIT MARGIN	EMPLOYEES
12/13	204	16	7.9%	1,200
12/12	217	19	8.7%	—
12/09	211	18	8.9%	—
12/08	174	0	—	—
Annual Growth	3.2%	—	—	—

2013 Year-End Financials

Return on assets: 6.2%
Return on equity: 7.9%
Current ratio: 1.70
Cash ($ mil.): 187

FLOYD HEALTHCARE MANAGEMENT INC.

If you need heart help in the Heart of Dixie Floyd Healthcare Management is there for you. Its main hospital Floyd Medical Center has more than 300 beds and serves northwestern Georgia and northeastern Alabama with more than 40 medical specialties. In addition to medical surgical and emergency care (including a Level II trauma center and Level III neonatal intensive care unit) the hospital offers rehabilitation programs hospice and home health care. It also operates a 25-bed community hospital (Polk Medical Center) and the 53-bed Floyd Behavioral Health Center. Floyd Healthcare also operates outpatient centers including primary care surgery and urgent care locations. The organization was founded in 1942.

Operations

Floyd Healthcare Management's main hospital facility Floyd Medical Center employs 300 physicians and handles 102500 emergency visits each year. It also manages some 249000 outpatient visits and 2200 births and it specialized in fields including orthopedic surgery stroke care bariatric surgery and breast care. The system also operates about 40 primary care practices and urgent care facilities in surrounding areas.

In partnership with the Floyd County Commission Floyd County Department of Family and Children Services (DFCS) and physicians in the community Floyd sponsors the Floyd County Clinic where low-income uninsured residents of Floyd County can receive free primary medical care services through the faculty and resident medical students enrolled in the Floyd Family Medicine Residency program.

Floyd Medical Center also provides community outreach programs through its mobile mammography vans and a range of other services aimed at improving access to health care throughout the service area.

Geographic Reach

Floyd Healthcare Management serves Rome Rockmart and other communities in Polk and Floyd counties.

Sales and Marketing

Third-party payers contributed some 40% of Floyd Healthcare's net patient service revenue in 2014 followed by Medicare (which contributed 33%).

Financial Performance

Sales increased 2% to $334.8 million in fiscal 2014 for Floyd Healthcare Management due to higher patient service revenue and other earnings. A majority of the company's sales come from patient revenue with more than 30% of that sourced to Medicare reimbursements. Despite the rise in revenue net income fell 34% to $14.9 million that year however due to lower actuarial gains and higher expenses.

Cash flow from operations rose 82% to $34.5 million on inflows from accounts payable.

Strategy

The organization invests in improving care for its service territory. In 2014 community hospital Polk Medical Center opened a new 65000-sq.-ft. medical complex featuring 12 emergency rooms a new surgical program with modern operating rooms improved diagnostic and imaging services and a medical office building. Also in 2014 Floyd Medical Center renovated its sixth floor adding more private beds for patients.

The network launched a technology initiative in 2013 to implement a physician order entry system; the tool will help to reduce medical errors and improve patient care.

EXECUTIVES

President CEO, Kurt Stuenkel
Chief Medical Affairs, Dee B. Russell
SVP and COO, Warren A. (Sonny) Rigas
Vice President Chief Financial Officer, Rick Sheerin
VP, Alison Land
VP, Greg Polley
VP Market Development, Dan Sweitzer
VP and Chief Nursing Officer, Shelia Bennett
General Counsel, Wade Monk
Chief Medical Officer, Joe Biuso
Corporate Compliance Officer, Julie Rogers

LOCATIONS

HQ: FLOYD HEALTHCARE MANAGEMENT INC.
304 TURNER MCCALL BLVD SW, ROME, GA
301655621
Phone: 706 509-5000
Web: WWW.FLOYD.ORG

PRODUCTS/OPERATIONS

Selected Services

Adult Psychiatric Services
Alcohol and Chemical Dependency
Bariatric Medicine Surgery and Aftercare
Breast Health
Behavioral Health
Cancer Care
Cardiac Catheterization
Cardiology
Cardiac Rehabilitation
Childbirth and Aftercare
Corporate Health
Dementia and Alzheimer' s
Diabetes Care
Echocardiography
Emergency Care
Family Medicine
Family Medicine Residency Program
Gynecology
Hospice
Hospitalist Care
Hyperbarics and Wound Care
Infusion Therapy
Intensive Care
Interventional Cardiology

IV Therapy
Joint Replacement
Laboratory
Level III Neonatal Intensive Care Unit
Level II Trauma Care
Maternity
Neurology
Neuropsychology
Neurosurgery
Occupational Medicine
Oncology
Orthopedics
Pediatrics
Pediatric Intermediate Care
Pharmacy Inpatient and Outpatient
Primary Care
Pulmonary Rehabilitation
Radiology
Inpatient Rehabilitation
Outpatient Rehabilitation
Sleep Disorders
Spine Center
Sports Medicine Services
Stroke
Surgery Inpatient and Outpatient
Urgent Care
Vascular Surgery
Wound Care and Hyperbarics

HISTORICAL FINANCIALS

Company Type: Private

Income Statement

FYE: June 30

	REVENUE ($ mil.)	NET INCOME ($ mil.)	NET PROFIT MARGIN	EMPLOYEES
06/11	332	11	3.4%	2,400
06/10	288	8	3.0%	—
06/08	237	11	4.8%	—
06/06	215	0	—	—
Annual Growth	9.0%	—	—	—

2011 Year-End Financials

Return on assets: —
Return on equity: 3.4%
Current ratio: 0.40
Cash ($ mil.): 10

FOOD FOR THE POOR INC.

Food For The Poor feeds spiritual and physical hunger. The Christian charity provides health social economic and religious services for impoverished people in 17 countries in Latin America and the Caribbean. Food For The Poor believes its organization serves God by helping those most in need distributing requested goods through local churches and charities. The group works through Caritas the American-Nicaraguan Foundation and others to provide vocational training clinic and school construction educational materials feeding programs and medical supplies. Food For The Poor has distributed more than $3 billion in goods since its 1982 inception; the group uses 96% of its funds on programs.

Since its founding Food For The Poor has distributed more than 43900 tractor-trailer loads of aid to the poor built 50000 housing units and completed 568 water projects to provide clean water and sanitation for hundreds of thousands of villagers.

In 2008 to help hurricane battered residents in the Caribbean Food For The Poor sent more than 160 shipping containers of relief supplies including food water medical supplies personal care items and building materials. More than $7 million worth of aid was sent to storm-ravaged areas in Haiti Jamaica the Dominican Republic.

EXECUTIVES

Vice President Of International Operations, Rachmani Domersant
Secretary and General Counsel, David (Dave) Price
Auditors: CAPIL CROUSE LLP LAWRENCEVILL

LOCATIONS

HQ: FOOD FOR THE POOR INC.
6401 LYONS RD, COCONUT CREEK, FL 330733602
Phone: 954 427-2222
Web: WWW.FOODFORTHEPOOR.ORG

HISTORICAL FINANCIALS

Company Type: Private

Income Statement

	REVENUE ($ mil.)	NET INCOME ($ mil.)	NET PROFIT MARGIN	EMPLOYEES
12/13	1,030	1	0.2%	335
12/12	900	4	0.4%	—
Annual Growth	14.4%	(57.1%)	—	—

2013 Year-End Financials

Return on assets: 0.5%
Return on equity: 0.2%
Current ratio: 2.30
Cash ($ mil.): 12

FORCE 3 INC.

In the world of federal IT contractors Force 3 aims to be a force to be reckoned with. The company provides integrated computer network systems for government agencies and to a smaller extent private industry customers. Force 3's services include consulting network design system integration training and support. The company also provides network security assessment services as well as business continuity and disaster recovery. The company specializes in military hospital network systems and has done work for more than 150 military medical facilities. Force 3 was founded in 1991 by Chairman Rocky Cintron.

Geographic Reach

Force 3 has offices in Crofton Maryland and Herndon Virginia.

Sales and Marketing

To provide its services Force 3 partners with notable technology companies like Apple Cisco Systems Citrix EMC NetApp and VMware.

The company has worked on IT contracts with the Department of Defense National Institutes of Health and the General Services Administration. In 2013 it won bids as a subcontractor on a $6.9 billion contract with the Navy and a $267 million contract with the GSA.

Mergers and Acquisitions

In 2012 Force 3 bought medical imaging technology provider secureRAD expanding its expertise to commercial and veterinary health care clients. The company sees the deal as an important one as it estimates the medical image storage and management market to be valued at around $6.6 billion.

EXECUTIVES

V Pres, Jim Bird, age 68
CEO, Les Trachtman
CTO, Sudhir Verma
Chief Revenue Officer, Michael (Mike) Greaney
CTO, Chris Knotts
CFO, Steve Scribner
Chairman, Rocky D. Cintron
Vice Chairman, James B. (Jim) Bird

LOCATIONS

HQ: FORCE 3 INC.
2151 PRIEST BRIDGE DR # 7, CROFTON, MD 211142466
Phone: 301 261-0204
Web: WWW.FORCE3.COM

PRODUCTS/OPERATIONS

Selected Technology Partners
Apple
Cisco Systems
Citrix
EMC
NetApp
VMware

Selected Products and Services
Borderless Networks
Cisco Certified Training
Communications and Collaboration
Customer Innovation Center
Cyber Security
Data Center
DISA Network STIG Assessment
DISA Wireless Network STIG Assessment
IM/IT Support Services
Implementation Services
Medical Image Management
Virtualized Desktop Infrastructure
VMware Ready Telework Solution

COMPETITORS

Accenture
CACI International
Computer Sciences Corp.
General Dynamics Information Technology
HP Enterprise Services
Infosys
NTT DATA
Raytheon
Tata Consultancy
Unisys
Xerox

HISTORICAL FINANCIALS

Company Type: Private

Income Statement

	REVENUE ($ mil.)	NET INCOME ($ mil.)	NET PROFIT MARGIN	EMPLOYEES
12/09	257	7	2.7%	300
12/08	325	5	1.8%	—
12/07	1,934	0	—	—
Annual Growth	(63.5%)	28133.2%	—	—

2009 Year-End Financials

Return on assets: 2.3%
Return on equity: 2.7%
Current ratio: 1.20
Cash ($ mil.): 9

FORDHAM UNIVERSITY

A private Catholic university Fordham offers its 15100 students —hailing from 48 US states and some 65 other countries — degree programs through 10 graduate and undergraduate schools.

Called the Jesuit University of New York Fordham has four locations including the original Rose Hill campus in the Bronx (often the scene of location shooting for movies TV shows and commercials) the Westchester campus the Lincoln Center campus in Manhattan as well as a biological field station in Armonk New York and international centers in China and the UK.

Geographic Reach

The Rose Hill campus is located on 85 acres in the Bronx and offers studies in business liberal arts science and religion. The Lincoln Center campus provides education business administration social services and legal training while the Westchester campus provides graduate programs in a variety of subjects. The Armonk field station is the headquarters for a number of university research programs.

Operations

The university offers more than 50 majors in liberal arts sciences and business. It has a student/faculty ratio of 14:1. It has almost 750 full-time instructors (including 24 Jesuits). Some 93% of its faculty holds a Ph.D. or other terminal degree.

Financial Performance

In 2014 Fordham had $542.4 million in operating revenues and $726 million in endowments and other investments. Undergraduate tuition in 2014-15 was $44450 per student.

Company Background

The school opened in 1841 as St. John's College. It officially changed its name to Fordham University in 1907.

EXECUTIVES

Vice President, Jeffrey (Jeff) Gray
Vice President Government Relations, Thomas (Thom) Dunne
President, Joseph M. McShane
Provost, Stephen Freedman
VP Finance, Frank Simio
VP Technology and CIO, Frank Sirianni
Dean Fordham College at Lincoln Center, Robert R. Grimes
Interim Dean Fordham College at Rose Hill, John Harrington
Dean Gabelli School of Business, Donna Rapaccioli
Dean Fordham School of Professional and Continuing Studies, Isabelle Frank
Dean Graduate School of Arts and Sciences, Eva Badowska
Dean Graduate School of Education, James J. Hennessy
Dean Graduate School of Religion and Religious Education, C. Colt Anderson
Dean Graduate School of Social Service, Debra M. McPhee
Dean School of Law, Michael M. Martin
Associate Vice President For Development, Michael (Mel) Boyd
Vice President, Deborah Russelli
Assistant Vice President University Marketing Communications, Kate Spencer
Vice President of Public Relations, Grace Zhang
Vice President, Dan Smith
Vice President Of Finance Of Fordham Women, Jenny Han
Associate Vice President and Chief of Staff, Beverly Musgrave
Vice President, Joseph (Jo) Quinn
Vice President Facilities, Peter (Pete) Bundock
Director of Admissions, John (Jack) Buckley
Chairman Board of Trustees, Robert D. (Bob) Daleo, age 66
Vice Chairman Board of Trustees, Edward M. Stroz
Board Of Directors, Herb Jones
Auditors: KPMG LLP NEW YORK NY

LOCATIONS

HQ: FORDHAM UNIVERSITY
441 E FORDHAM RD, BRONX, NY 104589993
Phone: 718 817-1000
Web: WWW.BNET.FORDHAM.EDU

PRODUCTS/OPERATIONS

Selected Colleges
Graduate and Professional
Graduate School of Arts and Sciences
Graduate School of Business Administration
Graduate School of Education
Graduate School of Religion and Religious Education
Graduate School of Social Services
School of Law
Undergraduate
Fordham College at Lincoln Center
Fordham College at Rose Hill
Fordham College of Liberal Studies
Gabelli School of Business

HISTORICAL FINANCIALS

Company Type: Private

Income Statement

FYE: June 30

	REVENUE ($ mil.)	NET INCOME ($ mil.)	NET PROFIT MARGIN	EMPLOYEES
06/14	566	100	17.7%	4,070
06/12	518	60	11.6%	—
06/11	494	283	57.4%	—
06/10	568	0	—	—
Annual Growth	(0.1%)	—	—	—

2014 Year-End Financials

Return on assets: 11.2%   Cash ($ mil.): 1
Return on equity: 17.7%
Current ratio: —

FOREX CAPITAL MARKETS L.L.C.

Auditors: ERNST & YOUNG LLP NEW YORK

LOCATIONS

HQ: FOREX CAPITAL MARKETS L.L.C.
55 WATER ST FL 50, NEW YORK, NY 100413203
Phone: 212 897-7660
Web: WWW.FXCMPRO.COM

HISTORICAL FINANCIALS

Company Type: Private

Income Statement

FYE: December 31

	ASSETS ($ mil.)	NET INCOME ($ mil.)	INCOME AS % OF ASSETS	EMPLOYEES
12/08	341	104	30.5%	400
12/07	365	4	1.3%	—
12/06	0	0	—	—
Annual Growth	256020.1%	—	—	—

2008 Year-End Financials

Return on assets: —   Sales ($ mil): 302
Return on equity: 34.4%

FORGE INDUSTRIES INC.

Forge Industries connects a diverse group of businesses. Operating via several subsidiaries the family-owned private holding company distributes thousands of products from industrial gears and bearings to asphalt and concrete construction equipment. Businesses include construction/landscape equipment maker Miller Spreader and sister companies Akron Gear & Engineering and Bearing Distributors (BDI) Forge's global product and service distributor. Forge's lineup includes curb builders and hand tools as well as rebuild and repair gearboxes redesign customer equipment customize gear reducers and machining services. Customers work in the automotive package handling food processing and landscape industries.

Auditors: KPMG LLP

LOCATIONS

HQ: FORGE INDUSTRIES INC.
4450 MARKET ST, YOUNGSTOWN, OH 445121512
Phone: 330 782-8301

COMPETITORS

Applied Industrial Technologies	NTN Bearing Corp. of America
Bosch Rexroth	WESCO International
DXP Enterprises	

HISTORICAL FINANCIALS

Company Type: Private

Income Statement

FYE: December 31

	REVENUE ($ mil.)	NET INCOME ($ mil.)	NET PROFIT MARGIN	EMPLOYEES
12/08	537	6	1.2%	2,000
12/07	605	0	—	—
12/06	0	0	—	—
12/05	404	0	—	—
Annual Growth	9.9%	—	—	—

2008 Year-End Financials

Return on assets: 7.7%   Cash ($ mil.): 9
Return on equity: 1.2%
Current ratio: 0.90

FOX HEAD INC.

Got a need for speed and big jumps? Fox Racing makes and distributes motocross and other extreme sport apparel accessories and protective gear such as racewear pants jerseys gloves boots and helmets emblazoned with its fox head graphic logo. The company also offers bicycle motocross (BMX) and mountain bike apparel T-shirts hats jeans hoodies and pullovers and jackets. Line extensions include eyewear footwear and surf and wakeboard wear. Fox Racing sells its apparel through retail sporting goods and cycle and surf shops nationwide. International offices are located in Canada and the UK. Founded in 1974 by Geoff Fox the company is family-owned and run by its second generation.

Geographic Reach

Based in Irvine California Fox Racing sells its products through specialty shops in the US Canada and the UK. The company with its Fox Head logo is an international leader in youth lifestyle clothing. It also operates additional offices in California and Spain.

Strategy

The company which sells apparel and accessories for motocross BMX surfing mountain biking and wakeboarding has been working to roll out more lifestyle-type products aside from its hardcore motocross offerings. To this end Fox Racing offers a line of casual wear and high-performance sunglasses and goggles for sports spectators. Its eyewear is made under an exclusive worldwide licensing agreement with sports accessories maker Oakley which is owned by behemoth Luxottica.

Particularly because more than 35% of the company's fans are under the age of 18 Fox Racing has made its website available to smartphone users asserting that customers can buy products in fewer than 60 seconds.

As one of the best-selling brands of motocross apparel globally Fox Racing has worked with motocross riders including Ricky Carmichael James Stewart Damon Bradshaw Rick Johnson Mark Barnett Doug Henry Jeremy McGrath and Steve Lamson as part of its research and development efforts to provide them with maximum protection and performance as well as freedom of movement.

Fox Racing is looking at expanding its business across Europe. An alliance it inked in 2013 with Cofton Maryland's Creative Logistics Solutions (CLS) is helping the company with its goal. Fox Racing is leveraging CLS's InfoShip which communicates with Fox Racing's centralized InfoShip server located in California to process shipping transactions at its Netherlands site (in Eersel) with remote support by CLS.

Sales and Marketing

Fox Racing sells its products worldwide through distributors and partners in more than 50 countries including Australia Brazil Canada Colombia Japan New Zealand South Africa the UK and the United Arab Emirates.

To reinforce its presence in the motocross industry and spur young athletes to join the sports it supports Fox Racing keeps its brand in front of new and existing customers by sponsoring many professional riders.

EXECUTIVES

VP Sales, Greg Fox
President and CEO, Peter Fox

LOCATIONS

HQ: FOX HEAD INC.
18400 SUTTER BLVD, MORGAN HILL, CA 950372819
Phone: 408 776-8633
Web: WWW.FOXHEAD.COM

PRODUCTS/OPERATIONS

Selected Sports Supported
Motocross (motorsport racing)
BMX (bicycle motocross)
MTB (mountain/trail motocross)
Surfing
Wakeboarding

COMPETITORS

Alliance Sports Group	Pacific Sunwear
American Recreation Products	Patagonia Inc.
Billabong	Quiksilver
Columbia Sportswear	Vans
Oakley	Volcom

HISTORICAL FINANCIALS
Company Type: Private

Income Statement
FYE: December 31

	REVENUE ($ mil.)	NET INCOME ($ mil.)	NET PROFIT MARGIN	EMPLOYEES
12/09	216	20	9.4%	462
12/08	244	24	10.0%	—
12/07	444	0	—	—
Annual Growth	—	3430.2%	—	—

2009 Year-End Financials
Return on assets: 3.2% Cash ($ mil.): 34
Return on equity: 9.4%
Current ratio: 4.60

FOXWORTH GALBRAITH LUMBER COMPANY

Foxworth-Galbraith Lumber Company is helping to build out the Southwest. The company sells hardware lumber paint plumbing equipment tools and other building supplies through more than 20 locations across Texas New Mexico Arizona and Colorado (versus about 70 stores in 2006). Foxworth-Galbraith's main customers are residential and commercial builders; other clients include do-it-yourselfers specialty contractors and federal and state agencies. Foxworth-Galbraith is still owned and operated by the families of W.L. Foxworth and H.W. Galbraith who founded the company in Dalhart Texas in 1901 to take advantage of railroad construction.

Geographic Reach

Texas-based Foxworth-Galbraith covers the Southest in Arizona Colorado New Mexico and Texas.

Financial Performance

The company logged $198 million in gross sales in 2012.

Sales and Marketing

Foxworth-Galbraith serves several sectors providing services to sub-contractors repair and maintenance professionals landscapers and Realtors.

Operations

The company's commercial division supplies materials manufactured components engineered wood and specialty and environmental products for certain special projects that have included government light commercial and Native American projects. Completed building projects include Cheddar's (Independence Missouri) Jack In The Box (Broken Arrow Oklahoma) McDonald's (Englewood Colorado) and Well Fargo bank (Waco Texas).

Foxworth-Galbraith also provides other services such as project support (cabinet design custom paint matching and special-order products) and truss services (manufacturers and engineers trusses and wall panels) for residential and commercial projects. The firm also provides installation and delivery services.

Strategy

The decline in new home construction due to the economic downturn in the US led Foxworth-Galbraith to slash its store count by about 70% compared to its operations in the mid-2000s. The company also sold its headquarters building in 2011. The building supplies retailer's store count has held steady at about 20 locations (primarily in Texas and New Mexico) in recent years.

EXECUTIVES
Regional Vice President, Ken Frank
Vice President Unit 5504, George Tennison
Auditors: JOHNSON & SHELDON PC AMARI

LOCATIONS
HQ: FOXWORTH GALBRAITH LUMBER COMPANY
4965 PRESTON PARK BLVD # 400, PLANO, TX 750935180
Phone: 972 665-2400
Web: WWW.FOXGAL.COM

2013 Stores
	No.
Texas	10
New Mexico	6
Arizona	3
Colorado	2
Total	**21**

PRODUCTS/OPERATIONS

Selected Product Categories
Building materials
Cabinets
Electrical
Hardware
Lawn and garden
Lumber
Paint
Plumbing
Tools

COMPETITORS
84 Lumber	Home Depot
A.C. Houston Lumber	Lowe's
Ace Hardware	McCoy Corp.
BMC	Sears
Bison Building	Sherwin-Williams
Materials	Stock Building Supply
Builders FirstSource	Sutherland Lumber
Do it Best	True Value

HISTORICAL FINANCIALS
Company Type: Private

Income Statement
FYE: December 31

	REVENUE ($ mil.)	NET INCOME ($ mil.)	NET PROFIT MARGIN	EMPLOYEES
12/13	228	1	0.7%	2,500
12/12	197	0	0.4%	—
12/11	164	(3)	—	—
12/10	154	0	—	—
Annual Growth	13.9%	—	—	—

2013 Year-End Financials
Return on assets: 3.9% Cash ($ mil.): —
Return on equity: 0.7%
Current ratio: —

FRANCIS SAINT MEDICAL CENTER

It may be guided by Catholic principles but you don't have to be a saint to get medical care at Saint Francis Medical Center. The hospital serves a five-state region from Missouri (its home base) to Arkansas with about 285 beds. Services include emergency medicine orthopedics cancer rehabilitation and women's health care. It also offers heart and neurosciences institutes as well as diabetes education and wound healing centers. The health care provider which was established in 1875 partners with Poplar Bluff Medical Partners to provide outpatient care at Poplar Bluff Medical Complex. Services include family practice OB-GYN and pain management.

Operations

Saint Francis Medical Center also partners with Landmark Holdings of Missouri to provide long-term acute care services through the 30-bed Landmark Hospital. The only facility of its kind between St. Louis and Memphis the hospital provides long-term care for patients who need complex medical care from catastrophic accidents or chronic diseases.

The hospital partners with the doctor-owned Physicians Alliance Surgery Center to provide outpatient surgery services in the region. Specialties provided at the center include gynecology ophthalmology orthopedic retinal and ENT (ear nose and throat) surgeries as well as general procedures.

Geographic Reach

Saint Francis Medical Center serves about 650000 people in Arkansas Kentucky Missouri Illinois and Tennessee.

Strategy

Saint Francis Medical Center has been expanding its facilities to offer more specialized services. Recent additions include its heart hospital and cancer institute. In 2015 it opened a new five-story patient tower including new and renovated space. It is also working on an orthopedic and neuroscience center and new surgery women's and children's health facilities.

EXECUTIVES
Medical Director, Emma Grote
Co Medical Director, Wen-yu Lee
Infection Control Director, Gayla Tripp
Operating Room Director, Marlene Lyon
Auditors: KERBER ECK & BRAECKEL LLP CAR

LOCATIONS
HQ: FRANCIS SAINT MEDICAL CENTER
211 SAINT FRANCIS DR, CAPE GIRARDEAU, MO 637035049
Phone: 573 331-3000
Web: WWW.SFMC.NET

PRODUCTS/OPERATIONS

Selected Services
Cancer institute
Emergency trauma & urgent care services
Gastroenterology services
Heart hospital
Neurosciences institute
Orthopedic institute
Primary care
Services to business
Women & children's services

COMPETITORS
Barnes-Jewish Hospital	St. Anthony's Medical
Memorial Hospital	Center
(Illinois)	St. John's Hospital
Southeast Missouri	(Illinois)
State University	
Southern Illinois	
Healthcare	

HISTORICAL FINANCIALS
Company Type: Private

Income Statement
FYE: June 30

	REVENUE ($ mil.)	NET INCOME ($ mil.)	NET PROFIT MARGIN	EMPLOYEES
06/11	423	48	11.4%	1,500
06/10	369	34	9.3%	—
06/09	743	0	0.0%	—
Annual Growth	(24.5%)	39185.7%	—	—

2011 Year-End Financials
Return on assets: —   Cash ($ mil.): 40
Return on equity: 11.4%
Current ratio: 0.40

FRANCISCAN ALLIANCE INC.

The Franciscan Alliance keeps watch over a family of hospitals. The not-for-profit organization operates more than a dozen hospitals in Indiana and south suburban Chicago. The hospitals house about 3500 beds and include specialist centers for cancer care heart and vascular care weight loss pediatrics and women's health. In addition to inpatient acute care services they operate numerous outpatient facilities and medical practices within their local service areas. Other subsidiaries and affiliates perform clinical laboratory tests offer home health services and provide support services to the system. Franciscan Alliance was founded and is sponsored by the Sisters of St. Francis of Perpetual Adoration.

Operations

Franciscan Alliance's hospitals handle about 100000 inpatient visits annually. The organization also handles about 3 million outpatient visits each year at its hospitals clinics and practice offices. Its physician practice organization includes about 700 doctors.

Along with providing a wide range of health care services Franciscan Alliance educates future health care providers through affiliations with area universities. The schools offer a variety of degree programs in fields including nursing medical technician and pharmacy residency.

Geographic Reach

Franciscan Alliance's hospitals are located in about ten communities in Indiana as well as in southern Chicago suburbs. The facilities serve patients in parts of Michigan as well. The organization also operates hundreds of outpatient clinics and physician offices in the area as well as a data center in Beech Grove Indiana.

Strategy

In 2011 the Sisters of St. Francis of Perpetual Adoration decided to change the name of the health system from Sisters of St. Francis Health Services to Franciscan Alliance to spread brand awareness and illustrate cohesiveness among the system's various facilities. The name change came after several months of consumer research and took about a year to be fully implemented across the entire system.

Franciscan Alliance also expanded through new construction in 2011 with the completion of the first phase of its Indianapolis Campus Expansion project. The health system moved a number of services into the new patient tower there including emergency services surgical suites and a wound care institute. In 2012 the company closed its Beech Grove hospital and consolidated services to the expanded Indianapolis center. It also opened a new short-stay hospital in Carmel that year.

In 2013 however the company announced that it would explore options to sell all or part of its two Franciscan St. James Health hospitals. The organization sought a partner to invest in capital improvements at the facilities. No buyer stepped forward but economic conditions improved enough by 2014 that the alliance said it was no longer searching for a buyer or investor. It also broke ground on a Hospice facility opened a specialized wound-care center and started a $10.2 million renovation at its St. Margaret facility.

Mergers and Acquisitions

In 2011 Franciscan Alliance grew its outpatient facilities by acquiring Surgical Hospital of Munster which serves as an outpatient surgery center of Franciscan Physicians Hospital.

EXECUTIVES

Senior Vice President Administrative Services, Joel Hoff
Director Of Pharmacy, Alan Alfrey
Vice President Marketing and Business Development, Lisa Decker
Vice President Human Resources, Tom Creevey
Vice President Medical Services and Quality Initiatives, Donald (Don) Edelen
Vice President Material Resources, Matt Mayer
Clinical Director Nursing Practice, Jody Mathew
Auditors: PRICEWATERHOUSECOOPERS LLP PH

LOCATIONS

HQ: FRANCISCAN ALLIANCE INC.
1515 W DRAGOON TRL, MISHAWAKA, IN 465444710
Phone: 574 256-3935
Web: WWW.FRANCISCANALLIANCE.ORG

PRODUCTS/OPERATIONS

Selected Operations
St. Anthony Health (Crown Point and Michigan City Indiana)
St. Elizabeth Health (Crawfordsville Lafayette Central Lafayette East Indiana)
St. Francis Health (Carmel Indianapolis and Mooresville Indiana)
St. James Health (Chicago Heights and Olympia Fields Illinois)
St. Margaret Health (Hammond and Dyer Indiana)
Franciscan Healthcare Munster (formerly Physicians Hospital; Munster Indiana)

Selected Services
Anticoagulation Clinics
Behavioral Health
Cancer Care
Colon and Rectal Surgery
Diabetes Care
Ear Nose and Throat
Emergency Medicine
Heart & Vascular
Home Health Care
Hospice
Imaging
Joint & Spine Care
Laboratory Services
Neurology
Neurosurgery
Occupational Health
Ophthalmology
Pain Management
Palliative Medicine
Pediatrics
Plastic Surgery
Primary Care Physicians
Pulmonary Medicine
Registered Dietitians
Rehabilitation Services
Robotic Surgery
Senior Services
Sleep Disorders
Sports Medicine
Surgical Services
Urgent Care
Weight Loss/Bariatrics
Women's Health/OBGYN
Wound Care

Selected Hospitals
Franciscan St. Anthony - Crown Point
Franciscan St. Anthony - Michigan City
Franciscan St. Elizabeth - Lafayette Central
Franciscan St. Elizabeth - Lafayette East
Franciscan St. Elizabeth - Crawfordsville
Franciscan St. Francis - Carmel
Franciscan St. Francis - Indianapolis
Franciscan St. Francis - Mooresville
Franciscan St. James - Chicago Heights
Franciscan St. James - Olympia Fields
Franciscan St. Margaret - Dyer
Franciscan St. Margaret - Hammond
Franciscan Healthcare - Munster

COMPETITORS

Advocate Health Care
Ascension Health
Community Health Network
Covenant Ministries
IU Health
Memorial Hospital & Health System
NorthShore University HealthSystem
Northwestern Memorial HealthCare
Porter Health Care System
Riverview Hospital
Rush System for Health
Sinai Health System
St. Bernard Hospital and Health Care Center
Union Hospital (Indiana)
University of Chicago Medical Center

HISTORICAL FINANCIALS

Company Type: Private

Income Statement

FYE: December 31

	REVENUE ($ mil.)	NET INCOME ($ mil.)	NET PROFIT MARGIN	EMPLOYEES
12/12	2,625	136	5.2%	9,000
12/07	2,065	204	9.9%	—
12/06	1,983	186	9.4%	—
Annual Growth	4.8%	(5.1%)	—	—

2012 Year-End Financials

Return on assets: 5.8%   Cash ($ mil.): 176
Return on equity: 5.2%
Current ratio: 0.40

FRANKLIN AND MARSHALL COLLEGE

Franklin & Marshall College named after Benjamin Franklin and John Marshall is a private liberal arts institution serving about 2400 students. It offers academic and research programs in about 60 fields including biology chemistry English history mathematics political science art sociology and environmental studies. It offers programs in 11 languages including Arabic and Greek. Franklin & Marshall College was created in 1853 through the merger of Franklin College (founded in 1787 with a contribution from Ben Franklin) and Marshall College (opened in 1836 and named after Chief Justice John Marshall).

Geographic Reach

Franklin & Marshall's students hail from more than 40 states and 40 foreign countries. The college's main campus is located in Lancaster Pennsylvania. It also maintains a 100-acre wildlife refuge (Millport Conservancy) in nearby Warwick Township through a partnership with the Wohlsen family; students conduct environmental studies at the refuge.

Franklin & Marshall also conducts study abroad and field study programs at 200 locations in nations including Australia China Costa Rica Denmark France India the UK. About half of the college's students participate in study abroad programs or travel courses.

Operations

Franklin & Marshall has a student-to-teacher ratio of 10:1 and its average class size is about 19 students. The school's tuition and fees run at around $44000 per year plus some $12000 in room and board fees. In addition to its core academic programs about two-thirds of students participate in research programs. The college also participates in the NCAA Division III athletic conference.

Financial Performance

Franklin & Marshall reported a 6% increase in revenues to $121 million in 2012 due to higher earnings from student tuition and fees private contributions auxiliary activities and dividend and interest income. Net income fell in 2012 however to a loss of $10 million due to increased operating expenses and a decline in non-operating activities (net losses on investments) as well as benefit costs and other expense and loss factors.

Strategy

Franklin & Marshall's mission includes strengthening academics through rigorous liberal arts and knowledge discovery programs; enhancing student growth and development; and developing a long-term business model to generate new revenues while controlling costs and increasing value. Programs under these three broad goals include the creation of a 10-year alumni support program global impact projects and alumni and parent engagement efforts.

EXECUTIVES

Vice President For College Advancement, Matthew Eynon
Vice President, Joel Eigen
Vice President Alumni Relations, Javier Novell
Associate Vice President For College Advancement, Patrick (Paddy) Burke
Associate Vice President for Information Systems and Library Services, Kathleen Spencer
Associate Vice President For Finance, James (Jamie) Pitz
Associate Vice President for Finance, Wendy Starner
Vice President, Michael Murray
Secretary And Vice President For External Affairs, Keith Orris
Associate Vice President of Student and Post graduate Development, Beth Throne
Vice President: Business Club, Jennifer (Jen) Geyman
Associate Vice President For Administation, Barry Bosley
Treasurer, Brett Caesar
Secretary Counseling Services, Janice M Sexton
Auditors: KPMG LLP PHILADELPHIA PA

LOCATIONS

HQ: FRANKLIN AND MARSHALL COLLEGE
415 HARRISBURG AVE, LANCASTER, PA 176032827
Phone: 717 291-3911
Web: WWW.FANDM.EDU

PRODUCTS/OPERATIONS

Selected Services
Africana Studies
American Studies
Animal Behavior
Anthropology
Arabic
Art History
Astronomy
Astrophysics
Biochemistry and Molecular Biology
Bioinformatics
Biology
Business Organizations and Society
Chemistry
Chinese
Classical Archaeology and Ancient History
Comparative Literary Studies
Computer Science
Creative Writing

Dance
Economics
Engineering
English Literature
Environmental Management (3-2 Program)
Environmental Science
Environmental Studies
Film and Media Studies
French
Geosciences
German and German Studies
Government
Greek
Hebrew
History
International Studies
Italian
Japanese
Judaic Studies
Latin
Linguistics
Materials Studies
Mathematics
Music
Neuroscience
Philosophy
Physics
Pre-Law (Legal Professions Advising)
Pre-Med (Health Professions Advising)
Psychology
Public Health
Public Policy
Religious Studies
Russian and Russian Studies
Science Technology and Society
Scientific and Philosophical Studies of Mind
Sociology
Spanish
Studio Art
Theatre

HISTORICAL FINANCIALS

Company Type: Private

Income Statement			FYE: June 30
	REVENUE ($ mil.)	NET INCOME ($ mil.)	NET PROFIT MARGIN	EMPLOYEES
06/13	165	9	5.6%	722
06/11	114	46	40.7%	—
06/10	141	10	7.3%	—
06/08	110	0	—	—
Annual Growth	8.4%	—	—	—

2013 Year-End Financials
Return on assets: 2.9%   Cash ($ mil.): 1
Return on equity: 5.6%
Current ratio: 0.10

FRANKLIN HOSPITAL

Franklin Hospital is part of the North Shore-Long Island Jewish Health System. The medical center has more than 300 beds and provides emergency and specialty care services. Franklin Hospital includes the 120-bed Orzac Center a long-term care rehabilitation unit as well as a 21-bed psychiatric unit and an adult day care center. Franklin Hospital also provides outpatient care —including pediatrics and women's health —and home health services. Established in 1963 as a small community hospital Franklin offers services and programs to the residents of Nassau and southeastern Queens Counties.

EXECUTIVES

VP Public Relations, Terry Lynam
President Medical Staff, Leonard Timpone
Human Resources Business Partner, Stacie Caplin

Director Rehabilitation Services, Alex Hellinger
Director Nutrition, Edward G. Cox
Director Radiology, Thomas Knichel
Chief Orthopedics, Norman Sveilich
Chief Executive Officer, Hervey Davis
Executive Director, Catherine Hottendorf
Acting Medical Director, Anthony Shallash
President Medical Staff, Gautam Reddy
CIO, John Bosco

LOCATIONS

HQ: FRANKLIN HOSPITAL
900 FRANKLIN AVE, VALLEY STREAM, NY 115802190
Phone: 516 256-6000
Web: WWW.CONCORDHOSPITAL.ORG

COMPETITORS

Catholic Health Services of Long Island
Catholic Healthcare System
Continuum Health Partners
MediSys Health Network
New York City Health and Hospitals
New York Health Care
New York Hospital Queens

HISTORICAL FINANCIALS

Company Type: Private

Income Statement			FYE: December 31
	REVENUE ($ mil.)	NET INCOME ($ mil.)	NET PROFIT MARGIN	EMPLOYEES
12/12	175	5	3.2%	1,300
12/08*	169	(3)	—	—
04/05	0	(0)	—	—
12/01	103	0	—	—
Annual Growth	5.0%	—	—	—

*Fiscal year change

2012 Year-End Financials
Return on assets: 5.7%   Cash ($ mil.): —
Return on equity: 3.2%
Current ratio: 0.30

FRAZIER INDUSTRIAL COMPANY (INC)

This company's racket is structural steel storage systems. Frazier Industrial Co. is a leading manufacturer of structural as opposed to roll-formed steel storage racks at nearly a dozen production centers located across the US Canada and Mexico. These facilities can adapt production to demand and receive just-in-time delivery of raw materials. Customers use Frazier Industrial's storage racks in warehouses factories farms and other industrial and commercial facilities. Among the company's storage products is the Glide 'N Pick pallet cart that automatically rolls out for greater ease in retrieving items. Frazier Industrial is owned by CEO William Mascharka.

Geographic Reach

The manufacturing company operates throughout North America.

Operations

Frazier Industrial has manufacturing locations in Idaho New Jersey New York Pennsylvania South Carolina and Wisconsin. Outside the US it has plants in Mexicali and Monterrey Mexico and in Ontario Canada.

The company boasts sales offices nationwide in Canada and in 10 US states including New Jersey

Georgia Massachusetts Texas Ohio Illinois California Washington and New York.

Sales and Marketing

Relying on a network of about a dozen fabrication facilities located throughout the US Mexico and Canada Frazier Industrial is able to meet tight construction deadlines while also guaranteeing manufacturing flexibility.

Customers include some of the world's top suppliers including Procter & Gamble Unilever and Nestle.

Strategy

Frazier Industrial is taking a stand for environmentally sound business practices as green initiatives become a focal point for customers. To this end Frazier sources all of its steel sections from North American mini-mills which only use recycled scrap material. Fittingly all of Frazier Industrial's scrap raw material is fully recyclable. Because the company receives preformed structural sections energy output is minimal; these structural parts require only cutting punching and welding. The location of Frazier Industrial's production centers helps to keep travel time and fuel expenses to a minimum. They are all within 400 miles of the company's raw material suppliers and within 500 miles of major North American population centers.

In 2013 the company launched a semi-automated high-density pallet mole system across North America. The pallet mole system a specific material handling technology maximizes available floor space enabling customers to store pallets up to 6-high and 50 positions deep while measurably increasing warehouse productivity.

Company Background

Frazier Industrial was founded in 1949.

EXECUTIVES

CEO, William L. Mascharka
President, Carlos Oliver
VP Manufacturing, Lon McAllister
VP Operations, John Goffredo
VP Purchasing, Dana Ansel
Vice President Asrs Sales, Roger Mefford
Vice President, Chris Deibel
National Account Manager, Tom Schenkenberger
Auditors: EISNERAMPER LLP ISELIN NJ

LOCATIONS

HQ: FRAZIER INDUSTRIAL COMPANY (INC)
91 FAIRVIEW AVE, LONG VALLEY, NJ 078533381
Phone: 908 876-3001
Web: WWW.FRAZIER.COM

PRODUCTS/OPERATIONS

Selected Products
Drive-In/Drive-Thru Storage
Frazier Design-Build
Glide-In Push-Back Storage
Glide N' Pick Order Picking Cart
Klamp-Fast Cantilever Rack
Pick-to-Belt Systems
Rack Supported Buildings
Safety Accessories
SelecDeck Carton Flow System
Sentinel Selective Pallet Rack
The Pallet Mole

COMPETITORS

Actionrack	Lyon Workspace
Edsal Manufacturing	Products
Interlake Mecalux	Steel of West Virginia

HISTORICAL FINANCIALS

Company Type: Private

Income Statement

FYE: December 31

	REVENUE ($ mil.)	NET INCOME ($ mil.)	NET PROFIT MARGIN	EMPLOYEES
12/13	230	3	1.4%	750
12/12	183	2	1.6%	—
12/11	178	4	2.7%	—
12/10	133	0	—	—
Annual Growth 19.8%	—	—	—	—

2013 Year-End Financials

Return on assets: 5.8%
Return on equity: 1.4%
Current ratio: 0.70

Cash ($ mil.): 3

FREDERICK MEMORIAL HOSPITAL INC.

Frederick Memorial Healthcare System cares for the sick and unhealthy across The Old Line State. The system operates Frederick Memorial Hospital an acute care facility with some 240 beds and 20 satellite facilities in and around Frederick Maryland. Specialty services include cardiology oncology pediatrics and psychiatry. Other facilities in the system include FMH Immediate Care at Oak Street FMH Crestwood FMH Medical Fitness FMH Rose Hill FMH Wellness FMH Urbana Mt. Airy Health Services and the FMH Regional Cancer Therapy Center. The hospital traces its historical roots all the way back to 1902.

Sales and Marketing

Medicare and Medicaid payments together represent about 45% of Frederick Memorial Healthcare System's net patient revenues. HMOs and PPOs account for about 20% while Blue Cross makes up another 15%.

Financial Performance

Revenue declined 1% in 2014 as net patient services and other operating earnings decreased. Net income fell 67% to $8.6 million that year. That decline was due to realized and unrealized losses on interest rate swaps as well as pension adjustments.

Cash flow from operations rose 24% to $25 million on changes in accounts payable and accrued expenses.

Strategy

The system expands by opening new outpatient facilities expanding into new service areas and adopting new technologies. In 2014 it selected Tableau and FTI Catalyst for its business analytics. Tableau will provide data analysis on admissions discharges surgical outcomes emergency services and other sources while FTI Catalyst will provide data modeling and management services.

EXECUTIVES

Medical Director Of Utilization, James (Jamie) Trumble
Director Of Home Healthcare Srv, Heidi Brown
Vice President Ambulatory Services, Don Schilling
Admissions Director, Bridget Puryear
Respiratory Therapy Director, Jane Casadonte
Director Of Patient Relations, Nan Principe-crockett
Auditors: ERNST & YOUNG LLP BALTIMORE

LOCATIONS

HQ: FREDERICK MEMORIAL HOSPITAL INC.
400 W 7TH ST, FREDERICK, MD 217014593
Phone: 240 566-3300
Web: WWW.FMH.ORG

PRODUCTS/OPERATIONS

Selected Centers
FMH Crestwood
FMH Immediate Care at Oak Street
FMH Medical Fitness
FMH Regional Cancer Therapy Center
FMH Rose Hill
FMH Urbana
FMH Wellness
Frederick Memorial Hospital
Mt. Airy Health Services

Selected Medical Services
Behavioral Health
Cancer Care
Cardiac Rehabilitation
Cardiology Services
Diabetes Center
Emergency Services
Home Health Services
Hospice/Home Care Information
Hospitalist Care
Imaging Vascular Services
Laboratory Wellness Center
Medical Fitness Women and Children
Occupational Health
Orthopedic Services
Pain and Palliative Care
Pharmacy
Pulmonary Function Lab
Pulmonary Rehab Program
Rehabilitation
Robotics
Sleep Disorders
Smoking Cessation Program
Stroke Center
Surgical Services
Wound Care and Hyperbaric Medicine

COMPETITORS

Adventist HealthCare	Johns Hopkins Medicine
Children's National	Loudoun Healthcare
Medical Center	Meritus Health

HISTORICAL FINANCIALS

Company Type: Private

Income Statement

FYE: June 30

	REVENUE ($ mil.)	NET INCOME ($ mil.)	NET PROFIT MARGIN	EMPLOYEES
06/13	344	4	1.3%	2,600
06/12	355	(13)	—	—
06/11	348	15	4.6%	—
06/10	307	0	—	—
Annual Growth 3.9%	—	—	—	—

2013 Year-End Financials

Return on assets: 10.8%
Return on equity: 1.3%
Current ratio: 0.40

Cash ($ mil.): 28

FREEMAN HEALTH SYSTEM

Freeman Health System (FHS) offers comprehensive health and behavioral health services to the residents of Arkansas Kansas Missouri and Oklahoma through three hospitals with a total of more than 500 beds. Specialty facilities include a full-service cardiothoracic and vascular program at the Freeman Heart Institute and behavioral health services through its Ozark Health Center. Community-owned not-for-profit FHS also operates two urgent care centers a separate sleep center several doctors' office buildings and serves as a teaching hospital with three residency programs (ear nose and throat; emergency medicine; and internal medicine). FHS employs more than 300 physicians in 60 specialties.

Operations

FHS operates three Missouri hospitals - Freeman Hospital West and Freeman Hospital East in Joplin and Freeman Neosho in Neosho. Its Ozark Center provides behavioral health services to patients from Missouri Arkansas Oklahoma and Kansas.

Strategy

Like most health care providers FHS has been working to update it facilities and expand it offerings. To that end in 2013 it opened a transitional living and life skills assistance center for homeless teens and teamed with an autism support group to design an autism treatment program for its Ozark Center. The prior year it christened Will's Place behavioral health center for children and opened a $2 million sports and rehabilitation center.

Company Background

Located in Joplin Missouri — the site of the deadly E5 tornado that killed 161 people in May 2011—Freeman Health System was the only fully functional hospital in the aftermath of the disaster. Rival St. John's Regional Medical Center just two miles away was destroyed. However Ozark Health Center FHS's behavioral health division lost nine buildings in the disaster.

EXECUTIVES

Vice President For Retail And Clinical Operations, Debbie Koelkebeck
Secretary, Larry McIntire
Auditors: BKD LLP SPRINGFIELD MO

LOCATIONS

HQ: FREEMAN HEALTH SYSTEM
 1102 W 32ND ST, JOPLIN, MO 648043503
Phone: 417 623-2801
Web: WWW.FREEMANHEALTH.COM

PRODUCTS/OPERATIONS

Selected Services
Autism Services
Behavioral/mental health
Bladder care
Cancer care
Children' s Miracle Network Hospitals
Clinical trials
Cosmetic/reconstructive surgery
Critical Care (ICU)
Diabetes education
Digestive care
Emergency medicine
Family care
Family counseling
Geriatric medicine
Health screenings
Hearing services
Home care
Internal medicine
Internet Addiction Services
Kidney Care
Lung care
Maternity
Neonatal intensive care
Nephrology & dialysis
Neurology & neurosurgery
Occupational medicine
Orthopedics
Pain management
Palliative care
QuickMeds Pharmacy™
Radiology

Rehabilitation
Senior Services
Skilled nursing
Sleep disorders
Sports medicine
Substance abuse services
Surgery
Tobacco cessation
Transitional Care Unit (TCU)
Urgent care
Women' s Services
Wound care

Selected Facilities
Freeman Hospital West - Joplin MO
Freeman Hospital East - Joplin MO
Freeman Neosho Hospital - Neosho MO
Freeman Business Center - Joplin MO
Ozark Center - Joplin Missouri

COMPETITORS

Catholic Health Initiatives	Heartland Regional Medical
Children' s Mercy Hospital	Mercy Health

HISTORICAL FINANCIALS
Company Type: Private

Income Statement
FYE: March 31

	REVENUE ($ mil.)	NET INCOME ($ mil.)	NET PROFIT MARGIN	EMPLOYEES
03/11	452	7	1.7%	3,887
03/10	474	30	6.5%	—
03/09	619	0	0.0%	—
Annual Growth	(14.5%)	13560.1%	—	—

2011 Year-End Financials
Return on assets: 3.0%   Cash ($ mil.): 25
Return on equity: 1.7%
Current ratio: 1.10

FREMAR L.L.C.

Auditors: GARDINER THOMSEN PC SIOUX

LOCATIONS

HQ: FREMAR L.L.C.
 300 N BROADWAY AVE, MARION, SD 570432000
Phone: 605 648-3941
Web: WWW.CENFARMCOOP.COM

HISTORICAL FINANCIALS
Company Type: Private

Income Statement
FYE: July 31

	REVENUE ($ mil.)	NET INCOME ($ mil.)	NET PROFIT MARGIN	EMPLOYEES
07/12	301	7	2.5%	60
07/11	280	8	2.9%	—
07/10	225	8	3.6%	—
07/09	269	0	—	—
Annual Growth	3.8%	—	—	—

2012 Year-End Financials
Return on assets: 0.3%   Cash ($ mil.): 9
Return on equity: 2.5%
Current ratio: 0.30

FRESH MARK INC.

This company continues to make its mark in the processed meat market. Fresh Mark is a leading producer of smoked and processed meat products for the domestic and international retail and food-service industries. From its three plants in Ohio the company makes and markets such products as deli meats hot dogs lunch meats hams and bacon sold under the names Superior's Brand and Sugardale. The company also produces private-label processed meat products for others and supplies the foodservice industry through its Sugardale Food Service business. Founded in 1920 Fresh Mark is owned and operated by the Genshaft family.

Geographic Reach

Ohio-based Fresh Mark sells its products nationwide. It operates processing facilities in the Ohio cities of Canton Massillon and Salem.

Operations

Doing business as Superior's Brand Meats Fresh Mark makes and supplies smoked and processed meats for the US retail and foodservice industries. Products include bacon ham wieners dry sausages specialty meat items and deli and luncheon meats.

Some of its brands include Superior's Brand and Sugardale.

Sales and Marketing

The company's customers include major grocery chains and restaurant and foodservice operators across the US. It also distributes its products internationally and offers private-label services to customers.

Fresh Mark supports its brands through a variety of efforts such as marketing advertising public relations sports and event sponsorship merchandising and point-of-sale.

Strategy

One of the largest privately owned companies in its industry Fresh Mark has grown from a regional supplier of smoked and processed meats to a leading supplier nationwide. It's ranked among the top 40 of the nation's leading 150 meat and poultry companies as measured by National Provisioner magazine.

EXECUTIVES

Vice President Supply Chain, Rick Hawley
National Accounts Manager, Randy Donaldson
National Sales Manager, Bryan Newton
Auditors: ERNST & YOUNG LLP AKRON OH

LOCATIONS

HQ: FRESH MARK INC.
 1888 SOUTHWAY ST SE, MASSILLON, OH 44648
Phone: 330 834-3669
Web: WWW.FRESHMARK.COM

PRODUCTS/OPERATIONS

Selected Products
Bacon
Deli meats
Dry sausage
Ham
Luncheon meats
Specialty meat items
Weiners

COMPETITORS

Birchwood Meat & Provision	Hormel
Boar' s Head	Indiana Packers
Cargill Meat Solutions	JBS USA
Carl Buddig	Johnsonville Sausage
Coleman Natural Foods	Kraft Foods Group Inc.
ConAgra	Smithfield Foods
Farmland Foods	Tyson Foods

HISTORICAL FINANCIALS

Company Type: Private

Income Statement

FYE: January 1

	REVENUE ($ mil.)	NET INCOME ($ mil.)	NET PROFIT MARGIN	EMPLOYEES
01/11*	795	59	7.5%	2,300
12/07	534	31	5.8%	—
12/06	481	21	4.5%	—
12/05	481	0	—	—
Annual Growth	10.6%	—	—	—

*Fiscal year change

2011 Year-End Financials

Return on assets: 3.9%
Return on equity: 7.5%
Current ratio: 0.90

Cash ($ mil.): 4

FRESNO COMMUNITY HOSPITAL AND MEDICAL CENTER

Auditors: MOSS ADAMS LLP STOCKTON CA

LOCATIONS

HQ: FRESNO COMMUNITY HOSPITAL AND MEDICAL CENTER
2823 FRESNO ST, FRESNO, CA 937211324
Phone: 559 228-5312
Web: WWW.COMMUNITYMEDICAL.ORG

HISTORICAL FINANCIALS

Company Type: Private

Income Statement

FYE: August 31

	REVENUE ($ mil.)	NET INCOME ($ mil.)	NET PROFIT MARGIN	EMPLOYEES
08/10	1,027	9	0.9%	5,045
08/09	1,010	65	6.5%	—
Annual Growth	1.7%	(85.9%)	—	—

2010 Year-End Financials

Return on assets: —
Return on equity: 0.9%
Current ratio: 0.30

Cash ($ mil.): 74

FROEDTERT MEMORIAL LUTHERAN HOSPITAL INC

Patients in southeastern Wisconsin count on Froedtert Memorial Lutheran Hospital for a full range of health services including trauma transplant sports medicine and senior care. The 500-bed hospital also known as Froedtert & The Medical College of Wisconsin is part of the Froedtert (pronounced "fray-dert") Health system. Specialty units include cancer dermatology neuroscience birthing fertility urology and vein clinics. The hospital also serves as a teaching facility for the Medical College of Wisconsin and it partners with the Children's Hospital of Wisconsin to provide pediatric services. Froedtert Hospital which was founded in 1980 operates the only adult Level I trauma center in the region.

Operations

Froedtert Health offers medical practice care in roughly 25 specialties and sub-specialties. Beyond the hospital's walls it operates four diagnostic imaging centers as well as rehabilitation facilities and a handful of primary care clinics in the community. The Froedtert Health system also includes Community Memorial Hospital in Menomonee Falls Wisconsin; St. Joseph's Hospital in West Bend Wisconsin; and Froedtert Health Medical Group.

Altogether the system's hospitals have 781 beds and see nearly 40000 admissions annually. They also manage more than 900000 outpatient visits each year. In 2014 Froedtert Hospital alone had about 65000 emergency department visits more than 736000 outpatient visits and delivered more than 2000 babies.

Strategy

To help advance the health of its service communities Froedtert Health is investing some $12 million to establish a new 22000-sq.-ft. health clinic in Milwaukee. It is partnering with clinic operator Sixteenth Street Community Health Centers on the project which is intended to address the needs of medically underserved neighborhoods. The facility will provide specialty care cancer prevention and access to cancer clinical trials.

EXECUTIVES

Vp Perioperative Services, Gary Colpaert
Vice President Patient Care nursing, Kathleen Bechtel
Director Of Clinical Services, Karl Schultz
Senior Vice President Medical Affair, Andrew J (Andy) Norton
Vice President and General Counsel, Catherine (Cathy) Eastham
Vice President Data Processing, Mike Jones
Executive Vice President, Peter (Pete) Pruessing
Vice President Marketing, Kathleen Perlewitz
Vice President Chief diversity Officer, Joseph (Jo) Hill
Medical Director, Lois Connolly
Nursing Director Transplant Nephrology Nursing, Rose GaskellBsnRn
Vice President Information Systems, Rod Dykehouse
Executive Vice President, Rodney C (Rod) Dykehouse
Treas, Roger Pierce
Auditors: KPMG LLP COLUMBUS OH

LOCATIONS

HQ: FROEDTERT MEMORIAL LUTHERAN HOSPITAL INC
9200 W WISCONSIN AVE, MILWAUKEE, WI 532263522
Phone: 414 805-3000
Web: WWW.FROEDTERT.COM

PRODUCTS/OPERATIONS

Selected Departments Centers and Programs
Clinical Cancer Center
  Blood and Lymph Node Cancer Program
  Blood and Marrow Transplant Program
  Bone and Connective Tissue Cancer Program
  Brain and Spine Tumor Program
  Breast Cancer Program
  Cancer Genetics Screening Program
  Colorectal Cancer Program
  Endocrine Cancer Program
  Eye/Orbital Cancer Program
  Geriatric Oncology
  Gynecologic Cancer Program
  Head and Neck Cancer Program
  Liver Pancreas and Bile Duct Cancer Program
  Neuro-oncology Cognitive Clinic
  Palliative Care Program
  Plastic Surgery Center
  Prostate and Urologic Cancer Program
  Skin Cancer Center
  Thoracic Cancer Program (Lung and Esophageal Cancers)
Heart and Vascular Center
  Adult Congenital Heart Disease
  Advanced Heart Failure and Cardiac Transplantation
  Aortic Disease
  Arrhythmia and Atrial Fibrillation
  Coronary Artery Disease (CAD)
  Hereditary Hemorrhagic Telangiectasia (HHT)
  Hypertrophic Cardiomyopathy (HCM)
  Preventive Cardiology and Lipid Therapy
  Peripheral Arterial Disease (PAD)
  Pulmonary Hypertension
  Valvular Disease
  Venous Thrombotic Disease
  Venous and Vein Disease
  Women and Heart Disease
Neurosciences Center
  Brain Injury Program
  Brain and Spine Tumor Program
  Comprehensive Epilepsy Program
  Comprehensive Spasticity Management Program
  Memory Disorders Program
  Neuro-Oncology Cognitive Clinic
  Normal Pressure Hydrocephalus
  Parkinson's and Movement Disorders Program
  Sleep Disorders Program
  SpineCare Program
  Spinal Cord Injury Center
  Stroke and Neurovascular Program

COMPETITORS

Children's Hospital and Health System
Columbia St. Mary's Ministry Health Care
ProHealth Care
Rockford Health System
Waukesha Memorial
Wheaton Franciscan Services

HISTORICAL FINANCIALS

Company Type: Private

Income Statement

FYE: June 30

	REVENUE ($ mil.)	NET INCOME ($ mil.)	NET PROFIT MARGIN	EMPLOYEES
06/12	1,057	101	9.6%	3,459
06/11	980	79	8.1%	—
06/10	894	59	6.7%	—
06/09	810	0	—	—
Annual Growth	9.3%	—	—	—

2012 Year-End Financials

Return on assets: —
Return on equity: 9.6%
Current ratio: 3.70

Cash ($ mil.): 39

FRUIT GROWERS SUPPLY COMPANY INC

Shipping cartons are the real fruit of labor for Fruit Growers Supply (FSG). The non-profit cooperative association supplies affiliate Sunkist Growers and other agricultural businesses with packing materials fertilizer and related implements. Offerings include a range of equipment used to grow pick package and transport many commodity cash crops. FSG also provides packing services and custom design and installation of irrigation systems. It owns and operates some 335000 acres of timberland along the West coast (a source of box material and income) a carton manufacturing and supply plant and seven retail operations centers. FGS is owned by 6000-plus citrus growers and shippers in the US.

Geographic Reach

To serve the agricultural community FGS operates six operation centers which feature central buying and warehousing capabilities specialized ordering and custom design irrigation departments in California and Arizona. It also operates the Ontario Carton Plant in California. Its Northern Operations own and manage 277863 acres of forestland owned in fee in Siskiyou Shasta and Lassen Counties in northern California; 21410 acres in Jackson Douglas Lane Linn and Klamath Counties in south western Oregon; and 28663 acres in Clallam Grays Harbor Jefferson Lewis Pacific and Skamania Counties in Western Washington.

Operations In addition to cartons FGS operates a pallet-manufacturing subsidiary United Wholesale Lumber which is supplied by its timberland resources. The association is one of the largest landowners in California; its timberland (which also spans Oregon and Washington) is overseen by a forestry-trained staff that manages timber sales logging and reforestation. Although the association branched out to corrugated cardboard cartons it maintains timberland as a renewable resource to help reduce overhead expenses. This investment allows FGS to operate without additional capital investment from its members.

Most FSG products and services support members' Sunkist's marketing organization. To this end in a typical year its plant will produce 80 million citrus containers. FGS sells to non-member vineyards and ranch owners too enabling it to defray plant operating costs. Its operations centers provide over-the-counter sales customer service and support for irrigation systems as well as wind machines used to protect fruit crops from cold damage.

Strategy

Growing its milling operations in 2013 FGS announced plans to build a small log mill in Yreka California to process small diameter logs into lumber for use in the making of pallets as well as for other agricultural and non-agricultural purposes.

Company Background

The company was founded in 1907.

HISTORY

The company was formed in 1907 by the members of California Fruit Growers Exchange (now Sunkist Growers) and has grown with the expansion of citrus production in California.

EXECUTIVES

Vice President Northern Operations and Strategic Planning Timberlands, Charles (Chas) Brown
Vice President Finance, Mitch Lewellen

LOCATIONS

HQ: FRUIT GROWERS SUPPLY COMPANY INC
14130 RIVERSIDE DR, SHERMAN OAKS, CA
914232313
Phone: 805 933-2723
Web: WWW.FRUITGROWERS.COM

PRODUCTS/OPERATIONS

Selected Products and Services
Agricultural Equipment
Cartons
Fertilizers and Pesticides
Grower Supplies
Harvesting Supplies
Irrigation Design and Installation
Lawn and Garden Supplies
Packaging
Packinghouse Supplies
Packing Services
Pallets

Powered Equipment
Small Engine Repair

COMPETITORS

Caraustar	Pro-Fac
Gibraltar Packaging	WestRock
Green Bay Packaging	

HISTORICAL FINANCIALS

Company Type: Private

Income Statement

FYE: December 31

	REVENUE ($ mil.)	NET INCOME ($ mil.)	NET PROFIT MARGIN	EMPLOYEES
12/13	203	5	2.8%	240
12/12	179	6	3.8%	—
12/11	177	6	3.9%	—
12/10	151	0	—	—
Annual Growth	10.4%	—	—	—

2013 Year-End Financials

Return on assets: 6.3% Cash ($ mil.): —
Return on equity: 2.8%
Current ratio: 0.60

GAINESVILLE REGIONAL UTILITIES (INC)

Multi-service utility Gainesville Regional Utilities (GRU) started out small more than a century ago but has been gaining ground ever since. The company (now the fifth largest municipal electric utility in Florida) is the sole utilities provider in Gainesville and surrounding areas in Alachua County. The municipal utility distributes electric water wastewater natural gas and telecommunications services to approximately 93000 retail and wholesale customers. GRU has interests in power generation facilities that give it more than 600 MW of capacity. It also offers internet and other communications services. GRU gets the bulk of its revenues from its electric utility operations.

Operations

GRU operates electric water wastewater natural gas and telecommunications utilities. Its five utility power plants are Deerhaven Generating Station John R. Kelly Generating Station Kanapaha Water Reclamation Facility Main Street Water Reclamation Facility and Murphree Water Treatment Plant. In 2012 GRU also operated 752 miles of natural gas main lines and had 33200 natural gas customers.

Financial Performance

In 2012 GRU's operating sales and service revenues decreased 7% AS the result of lower consumption offset by higher rate increases implemented in October 2011 along with a decrease in fuel costs of $16 million. (Fuel costs are passed directly through to icustomers as part of a fuel adjustment charge which is reported as revenues).

The company's net income decreased by 46% in 2012.

GRU contributed more than $36 million to the City of Gainesville's General Fund in 2012.

Strategy

The multi-utility is pushing conservation and green energy as a way to increase operational efficiency reduce carbon emissions and help its customers save money. In order to help meet the state's clean energy requirements GRU installs photovoltaic panels on selected buildings and provides a solar water heating rebate program for its

customers. It even offers customers a supply of woodchips (a by-product of the routine trimming done by GRU's Vegetation Management Department to reduce the number of tree-related electrical outages).

As part of its ongoing green energy push in 2011 GRU began offering its customers a 6% annual interest loan for pre-approved items including certified (ENERGY STAR) refrigerators efficient central air conditioning systems and solar photovoltaic systems.

Ownership

GRU is the City of Gainesville's combined municipal utility system.

Company Background

The company was founded in 1912.

EXECUTIVES

CFO, Justin M. Locke
General Manager Utilities, Edward Bielarski
CIO, Walter Banks
Acting COO, Thomas R. Brown
Vice President, Lewis Walton
Vice President, Patricia Kafle
Auditors: EARNST & YOUNG LLP ORLANDO F

LOCATIONS

HQ: GAINESVILLE REGIONAL UTILITIES (INC)
301 SE 4TH AVE STE A105, GAINESVILLE, FL
326016857
Phone: 352 334-3400
Web: WWW.CITYOFGAINESVILLE.ORG

HISTORICAL FINANCIALS

Company Type: Private

Income Statement

FYE: September 30

	REVENUE ($ mil.)	NET INCOME ($ mil.)	NET PROFIT MARGIN	EMPLOYEES
09/09	369	33	9.1%	750
09/08	349	18	5.2%	—
Annual Growth	5.7%	83.0%	—	—

2009 Year-End Financials

Return on assets: — Cash ($ mil.): 9
Return on equity: 9.1%
Current ratio: 2.00

GALLAUDET UNIVERSITY

Gallaudet University (GU) gives deaf and hard-of-hearing students the chance to be in the majority. Designed to accommodate hearing-impaired students GU offers undergraduate and graduate degrees in more than 40 majors to about 2000 students annually. The bilingual university which uses both American Sign Language (ASL) and English admits a small number of hearing ASL-proficient students to each incoming freshman class. Through its Laurent Clerc National Deaf Education Center GU provides training and support for teachers and parents of hearing impaired children and operates demonstration schools. Founded in 1864 GU was named for Thomas Hopkins Gallaudet a pioneer in education for the deaf.

Operations

For the purposes of budgeting and operating its educational institution GU is divided into two major component programs: its university and the Laurent Clerc National Deaf Education Center. The center's primary focus as part of a federal mandate is to develop and disseminate innovative curriculum materials and teaching strategies to schools and programs nationwide. The center includes the

Model Secondary School for the Deaf (MSSD) and the Kendall Demonstration Elementary School (KDES). MSSD serves students in grades nine through 12 while KDES serves infants and their parents continuing service through the eighth grade.

Also part of its operations the Gallaudet Research Institute studies the demographics and assessment of deaf and hard of hearing people in the educational system as well as language and learning processes. For its research the institute involves students in its studies.

Open to all students whether they're deaf hard of hearing or hearing GU's graduate programs include master of arts or master of science degrees specialist degrees certificates and doctoral degrees across several fields involving professional services to deaf and hard of hearing people.

Undergraduate tuition for GU runs about $13424 for US students.

Geographic Reach

From its 99-acre campus in Washington DC GU is a federally chartered university that caters to students nationwide as well as students in developing and non-developing countries (about 30 in total).

Strategy

GU is working through a five-year five-pronged strategic plan that runs through 2015. It includes a handful of lofty goals. GU is working to grow its enrollment of full-time undergraduates full- and part-time graduate students and continuing education students to 3000 by 2015. (In the fall of 2013 the university's enrollment was 1872.) GU's also focused on boosting its six-year undergraduate graduation rate to 50% refining a core set of undergraduate and graduate programs aimed at career success and positioning the university as the epicenter of research development and outreach. GU as its final and more far-reaching goal is concentrating on securing a sustainable revenue base by expanding and diversifying its funding partnerships while also increasing its operating efficiency. The university raised more than it goal of $3.2 million in new gifts and pledges for 2013.

EXECUTIVES

President, Roberta J. (Bobbi) Cordano
Mobile Vice President, Kevin Myers
Vice President, Shondra Mitchell
Vice President of Gallaudet University, Kendall Hall
Vice President For Laurent Clerc National Deaf Education Center, Ed Bosso
Vice President, Jordan Ramser
Vice President Administration, Gaynelle Hayes
Vice President, Michael (Mel) Janger
Secretary, Greg Farber
Treasurer, Michael (Mel) Awbrey
Auditors: GRANT THORNTON LLP NEW YORK

LOCATIONS

HQ: GALLAUDET UNIVERSITY
  800 FLORIDA AVE NE, WASHINGTON, DC 200023600
Phone: 202 651-5000
Web: WWW.GALLAUDET.EDU

PRODUCTS/OPERATIONS

Selected Programs
Gallaudet Research Institute
Gallaudet University
Laurent Clerc National Deaf Education Center
Kendall Demonstration Elementary School
Model Secondary School for the Deaf

HISTORICAL FINANCIALS

Company Type: Private

Income Statement

FYE: September 30

	REVENUE ($ mil.)	NET INCOME ($ mil.)	NET PROFIT MARGIN	EMPLOYEES
09/13	171	(0)	—	1,200
09/12	190	17	9.2%	—
09/11	177	4	2.7%	—
09/10	179	0	—	—
Annual Growth	(1.4%)	—	—	—

2013 Year-End Financials

Return on assets: 10.2%   Cash ($ mil.): 16
Return on equity: —
Current ratio: 0.40

GALLUP INC.

More than a pollster Gallup draws from its research and behavioral studies to offer consulting services related to performance management. Other specialties include branding marketing and recruiting. The company delivers its services on the Web through its Gallup University campuses and through about 40 global offices. It draws customers from a variety of industries including automotive business services health care hospitality manufacturing and retail. Despite its diversified business offerings the company is still most famous for its Gallup Poll surveys. It is owned by its employees.

Geographic Reach

Gallup's nearly 40 offices are spread around the Americas Asia Pacific Europe the Middle East and Africa.

Operations

Gallup has a staff of more than 2000 professionals. Gallup News reports on the world's 7 billion citizens based on Gallup's continuous polling in 160 countries.

Strategy

In addition to its famous polls and research surveys the company's Gallup Consulting division provides expertise in measuring employee satisfaction and engagement and in teaching managers and workers how to develop their strengths in order to be the best at their jobs. Gallup consultants help private and public sector organizations boost organic growth through measurement tools strategic advice and education.

Ownership

Gallup is an employee-owned company.

Company Background

The company was founded in 1935 by Dr. George Gallup a pioneer in the science of polling.

EXECUTIVES

CIO, Phil Ruhlman
Vice Chairman; Dean Gallup University, Connie Rath
Chief Operating Officer, Jane E. Miller, age 50
Chief Marketing Officer; Executive Publisher Gallup Press, Lawrence M. (Larry) Emond
Chairman and CEO, Jim Clifton
CFO, James (Jim) Krieger
Editor-in-Chief Gallup, Frank M. Newport
Regional Director Former Soviet Union Countries, Neli Esipova
Regional Director Latin America, Johanna Godoy
Regional Director Latin America, Jesus Rios
Regional Director Asia, Rajesh Srinivasan
Regional Director Sub-Saharan Africa, Robert D. Tortora
Global Practice Leader Brand and Customer Engagement, Ed O'Boyle
Auditors: KPMG OMAHA NE

LOCATIONS

HQ: GALLUP INC.
  901 F ST NW STE 400, WASHINGTON, DC 200041419
Phone: 202 715-3030
Web: WWW.GALLUP.COM

PRODUCTS/OPERATIONS

Selected Consulting Practice Areas
Customer relationship management
Employee development and training
Employee performance measurement
Employee relationship management
Executive coaching
Performance strategy analysis
Sales force training
Succession planning
Talent-based hiring

Selected Gallup Poll Topics
Business
Economics
Education
Government and public affairs
Healthcare
Lifestyle issues
Politics and elections
Religion and values
Other Products and Services
Books
Gallup University (management education)
Subscription publications

COMPETITORS

Abt Associates	IBOPE Zogby
Bain & Company	International
Booz Allen	International
Boston Consulting	Demographics
Development Dimensions	J.D. Power
International	Kantar Group
Edison Media Research	Maritz
Harris Interactive	McKinsey & Company
Hay Group	ORC International

HISTORICAL FINANCIALS

Company Type: Private

Income Statement

FYE: December 31

	REVENUE ($ mil.)	NET INCOME ($ mil.)	NET PROFIT MARGIN	EMPLOYEES
12/13	249	13	5.4%	2,000
12/12	275	23	8.4%	—
12/11	303	34	11.2%	—
12/09	264	0	—	—
Annual Growth	(1.4%)	—	—	—

2013 Year-End Financials

Return on assets: 4.4%   Cash ($ mil.): 30
Return on equity: 5.4%
Current ratio: 0.70

GARDEN PALS INC.

LOCATIONS

HQ: GARDEN PALS INC.
  3768 MILLIKEN AVE STE A, MIRA LOMA, CA 917521037
Phone: 909 605-0200
Web: WWW.GARDENPALS.COM

HISTORICAL FINANCIALS

Company Type: Private

Income Statement
FYE: December 31

	REVENUE ($ mil.)	NET INCOME ($ mil.)	NET PROFIT MARGIN	EMPLOYEES
12/12	668	7	1.2%	20
12/11	6	0	0.3%	—
12/10	7	0	0.1%	—
Annual Growth	854.7%	3871.3%	—	—

2012 Year-End Financials

Return on assets: 14.6%   Cash ($ mil.): 4
Return on equity: 1.2%
Current ratio: 0.50

GARFF ENTERPRISES INC.

Auditors: MAYER HOFFMAN MC CANN PC SAL

LOCATIONS

HQ: GARFF ENTERPRISES INC.
405 S MAIN ST STE 1200, SALT LAKE CITY, UT 841113412
Phone: 801 257-3400
Web: WWW.KENGARFF.COM

HISTORICAL FINANCIALS

Company Type: Private

Income Statement
FYE: December 31

	REVENUE ($ mil.)	NET INCOME ($ mil.)	NET PROFIT MARGIN	EMPLOYEES
12/13	576	14	2.5%	855
12/03	481	10	2.1%	—
12/02	270	4	1.5%	—
12/01	189	0	—	—
Annual Growth	9.7%	—	—	—

2013 Year-End Financials

Return on assets: 1.4%   Cash ($ mil.): 26
Return on equity: 2.5%
Current ratio: 0.20

GAVI FUND

Auditors: KPMG LLP MCLEAN VA

LOCATIONS

HQ: GAVI FUND
1776 I ST NW STE 600, WASHINGTON, DC 200063765
Phone: 202 478-1050
Web: WWW.GAVIALLIANCE.ORG

HISTORICAL FINANCIALS

Company Type: Private

Income Statement
FYE: December 31

	REVENUE ($ mil.)	NET INCOME ($ mil.)	NET PROFIT MARGIN	EMPLOYEES
12/08	306	(625)	—	100
12/06*	388	1,953	503.1%	—
06/01	18,546	16	0.1%	—
Annual Growth	(40.1%)	—	—	—

*Fiscal year change

2008 Year-End Financials

Return on assets: —   Cash ($ mil.): 536
Return on equity: (-203.7%)
Current ratio: —

GEHAN HOMES LTD.

They say everything is bigger in Texas and for Gehan Homes that hopefully applies to the number of homes sold. Gehan Homes builds single-family houses in about 60 communities in and around Austin Dallas Fort Worth Houston and San Antonio. Its houses range in price from the low $100000s to the low $300000s. Gehan Homes owns the land it builds on and provides mortgage brokerage through majority-owned Suburban Mortgage. Through cutting costs and slowing down production the homebuilder is working to stay afloat in a market that has caused several competitors to file for bankruptcy or shut down operations. John Gehan founded the family-owned company in the 1960s.

EXECUTIVES

Vice President Sales And Marketing, Shannon Powers
Vice President Construction, Lee Battle
Auditors: GRANT THORNTON LLP DALLAS TE

LOCATIONS

HQ: GEHAN HOMES LTD.
15725 DALLAS PKWY STE 300, ADDISON, TX 750013850
Phone: 972 663-9100
Web: WWW.GEHANHOMES.COM

COMPETITORS

Beazer Homes	KB Home
CalAtlantic	Lennar
D.R. Horton	Main Street Homes
David Weekley Homes	McGuyer Homebuilders
Highland Homes	Meritage Homes
Holiday Builders	PulteGroup
Hovnanian Enterprises	

HISTORICAL FINANCIALS

Company Type: Private

Income Statement
FYE: December 31

	REVENUE ($ mil.)	NET INCOME ($ mil.)	NET PROFIT MARGIN	EMPLOYEES
12/07*	214	4	1.9%	175
11/02	150	13	9.1%	—
Annual Growth	7.4%	(21.8%)	—	—

*Fiscal year change

2007 Year-End Financials

Return on assets: 2.0%   Cash ($ mil.): 6
Return on equity: 1.9%
Current ratio: 0.10

GELBER GROUP LLC

Gelber Group develops proprietary technology-based trading models for dealing in equities cash currencies commodities sovereign debt futures and related options markets. The company no longer has outside clients or investors; all of its trading activity is undertaken for its own account. Gelber Group which previously provided electronic trading services to individual professional traders was co-founded in 1982 by Brian Gelber (company chairman and president) and Frank Gelber (CFO). In addition to its Chicago Apparel Center headquarters the company also boasts offices in Connecticut New Jersey and New York as well as the UK.

Geographic Reach

With a 42000-sq.-ft. home office in Chicago and offices in the US (in the states of New York New Jersey California and Massachusetts) and in London Gelber Group trades across all major asset classes in the Americas Europe and Asia.

Strategy

Focusing on technology management and service as a leader in algorithmic trading Gelber Group works to expand its business globally to liquid electronic markets. The company looks to tap new trading opportunities across the world's financial and commodity markets.

Sales and Marketing

The investment firm serves individual professional traders trading groups or institutions.

EXECUTIVES

Chairman President CEO, Brian Gelber
Chief Technology Officer, Patrick Coffey
Auditors: MCGLADREY & PULLEN LLP CHICA

LOCATIONS

HQ: GELBER GROUP LLC
350 N ORLEANS ST FL 7, CHICAGO, IL 606541601
Phone: 312 253-0005
Web: WWW.GELBERGROUP.COM

PRODUCTS/OPERATIONS

Selected Markets
Cash
Commodities
Currencies
Equities
Futures
Sovereign debt

COMPETITORS

ADM Investor Services	R.J. O' Brien
Interactive Brokers	Rosenthal Collins
Investment Technology	TradeStation
Newedge	

HISTORICAL FINANCIALS

Company Type: Private

Income Statement
FYE: December 31

	ASSETS ($ mil.)	NET INCOME ($ mil.)	INCOME AS % OF ASSETS	EMPLOYEES
12/07	338	112	33.3%	300
12/04	106	70	65.8%	—
12/03	0	0	—	—
Annual Growth	—	811.0%	—	—

2007 Year-End Financials

Return on assets: 1.8%   Sales ($ mil): 224
Return on equity: 50.3%

GENESIS HEALTH SYSTEM

Genesis Health System operates three acute care hospitals in Iowa and Illinois that have more than 660 beds total and employ some 700 doctors. Genesis Medical Center in Davenport Iowa with more than 500 beds is the system's flagship facility; the hospital offers a range of general surgical and specialist health services. The system's Illini Campus in Silvis Illinois features an assisted-living center. The Genesis Medical Center Dewitt Campus serves that Iowa town and the surrounding area with its 13-bed hospital nursing home and related care facilities. Genesis Health System also operates physician practices outpatient centers and a home health agency.

Operations

Altogether Genesis Health System has more than 100 locations including hospitals convenient care locations Genesis Health Group sites physical rehabilitation clinics and outpatient service centers.

Strategy

In 2014 the system invested $15 million in the new Genesis HealthPlex in Bettendorf.

The following year Genesis Health System entered into a partnership with technology vendor Cerner Corporation to improve its patient care enterprise management systems.

Company Background

Genesis Health System had its genesis in 1869 with the establishment of Mercy Hospital (one of the first hospitals west of the Mississippi) and in the 1895 founding of St. Luke's Hospital. The two hospitals merged in 1994 to form the health system.

EXECUTIVES

Vice President Corporate Communications and Business Development, Kenneth (Ken) Croken
Vice President Clinical Services, Rob Nelson
Vice President Medical Staff Affairs, Peter Metcalf
Director Of Pharmacy, Kevin Cahill
Medical Librarian, Deborah Rhue
Vice President Human Resources, Edwin Maxwell
Vice President Outpatient Services, Kevin Youmans
Senior Vice President Human Resources Diversity Officer, Sarah Blessing
Director Of Nursing, Sheri Williams
Medical Records Director, Betsy Tibbitts
Clinic Supervisor, Kathryn Ellsworth
Pharmacy Manager, Bill Schmidt
Vice President Of Human Resources, Heidi McMahon
Vice President Special Projects, Beth Fox
Vice President Of Nursing, Palmer Steward
Medical Director Of Physical Medicine And Rehabilitation Services, Chin Conway
Vice President Of Finance The Americas, Sarah Goodwin
Vice President Legal Affairs, Judith (Judi) Mondello
Vice President Support Services, Mike Sharp
Vice Chair, Fritz Swearingen
Board Member, Deborah Stafford
Board Member, Deborah (Deb) Stafford
Auditors: MCGLADREY & PULLEN LLP DAVENP

LOCATIONS

HQ: GENESIS HEALTH SYSTEM
 1227 E RUSHOLME ST, DAVENPORT, IA 528032459
Phone: 563 421-1000
Web: WWW.GENESISHEALTH.COM

PRODUCTS/OPERATIONS

Selected Services
Bariatric Surgery
Behavioral Health
Birthing Services
Cancer
Cardiology
Home Health/Hospice
Neuroscience
Nursing Homes
Physical Medicine & Rehab
Senior Services

COMPETITORS

Blessing Hospital
Catholic Health Initiatives
McDonough District Hospital
Mercy Health Network
ORHC
OSF Healthcare System
UnityPoint Health
University of Iowa Hospitals and Clinics

HISTORICAL FINANCIALS

Company Type: Private

Income Statement

FYE: June 30

	REVENUE ($ mil.)	NET INCOME ($ mil.)	NET PROFIT MARGIN	EMPLOYEES
06/10	461	16	3.5%	5,000
06/09	993	0	—	—
06/08	1,643	0	0.0%	—
Annual Growth	(47.0%)	3045.0%	—	—

2010 Year-End Financials

Return on assets: —
Return on equity: 3.5%
Current ratio: 0.80
Cash ($ mil.): 43

GENESIS HEALTHCARE SYSTEM

Genesis HealthCare System takes care of the beginning (and the middle and the end) of a patient's medical experience. The not-for-profit system health care system consists of two acute care hospitals (Genesis-Bethesda and Genesis-Good Samaritan Hospital) in Zanesville Ohio. In addition to general medical emergency and surgical care the hospitals' specialty areas include oncology trauma cardiovascular health orthopedics neurology and women's health. Genesis HealthCare also operates facilities for pharmacy child development and home health and hospice services as well as family practice and specialist offices.

Geographic Reach

Genesis HealthCare serves residents of six counties in southeastern Ohio including the counties of Coshocton Guernsey Morgan Muskingum Noble and Perry. The Health System has 45 locations across Ohio.Operations

The health system's services include open-heart surgery trauma care a Level II neonatal intermediate care unit neurosurgery and comprehensive cancer services.

Genesis HealthCare's outpatient facilities include the offices of some 300 physicians. Its Genesis HealthPlex provides a number of specialist services. The health system also operates the Community Ambulance Service as a joint venture between Genesis HealthCare and Community EMS. The service operates throughout Zanesville and is equipped with a computer-aided dispatch system that automatically monitors and records incoming calls and response times.

Financial Performance

The system's revenues increased by 11% to $422 million in 2013 due to a growth in net patient revenues and pharmacy sales and others. About 51% of its net patient revenues came from Medicare and Medicaid.Genesis HealthCare reported net income of $17 million in 2013 compared to a net loss in 2012 due to the absence of loss on refunding of debt unrealized gains on trading securities and a change in fair value of interest rate swap agreement.

Strategy

In 2013 the company began building a new state-of-the-art medical center with 260 beds on the grounds of the Bethesda Hospital. The $125 million project includes complete renovation of the existing hospital with a new patient tower an outpatient cancer center and a medical office building. Completion is expected in 2015.

As part of its other expansion efforts in 2013 Genesis Rehabilitation Services opened a new rehab facility for its pediatric patients. In 2012 it added a breast care center at the outpatient center (HealthPlex) and a heart and vascular clinic at the Good Samaritan campus during 2012. To expand its network and help a smaller facility to remain independent the organization agreed to provide management services to the Coshocton County Memorial Hospital that year. It also partnered with other area organizations to build a recreational center in the community of Muskingum.

To further enhance its services Genesis HealthCare became a Level III Trauma Center in 2012. The designation means that patients with serious trauma-related injuries are able to get specialized trauma care at the system's facilities.

In addition Genesis HealthCare is implementing an electronic health record (EHR) system that connects Genesis HealthCare hospitals and physician offices throughout the region. The total cost of the multi-year installation is roughly $50 million. In 2012 about 60 physicians at 20 practice locations were connected to the organization's EHR system (made by Epic Systems) and Genesis HealthCare boasted about 5400 active health professionals in the medical records (MyChart) feature of the Epic EHR. It also launched an Epic revenue cycle management program that year to improve registration scheduling and billing processes.

Company Background

Genesis HealthCare was formed in 1997 when the Bethesda and Good Samaritan hospitals merged.

EXECUTIVES

Medical Director, Daniel Scheerer
Director of Surgery Services Medical Director For Cardiovascular Surgical Services, Gregory Keagy
Director Of Him, Darrel Moore
Vice President, Clare McKeever
Director of Radiology, Charles (Chas) Muchnok
Director of Radiology, Shane Backus
Medical Director, Larry Cook
Medical Director, Firas Eladoumikdachi
Home Health Care Director, Lori Junk
Director of Pharmacy, Pete Hamilton
Vice Chairman, Walter E Offinger
Auditors: PLANTE & MORAN PLLC COLUMBUS

LOCATIONS

HQ: GENESIS HEALTHCARE SYSTEM
 800 FOREST AVE, ZANESVILLE, OH 437012821
Phone: 740 454-5000
Web: WWW.GENESISHCS.ORG

PRODUCTS/OPERATIONS

Selected Services
Cancer
Emergency and trauma
Heart and vascular
Neurosciences
Orthopedic care
Women' s health

Selected Facilities
Genesis-Bethesda Hospital
Genesis-Good Samaritan Hospital
Genesis CareGivers
Genesis Children' s Center
Genesis HomeCare
Genesis Lifestyle & Fitness Center
Northside Home Infusion
Northside Oxygen & Medical Equipment
Northside Pharmacy
Quality Care Partners

COMPETITORS

Catholic Health
 Initiatives
Fairfield Medical
 Center
Licking Memorial
 Health Systems

Mercy Health (OH)
Mount Carmel Health
Nationwide Children' s
 Hospital
OhioHealth
Select Medical

HISTORICAL FINANCIALS

Company Type: Private

Income Statement
FYE: December 31

	REVENUE ($ mil.)	NET INCOME ($ mil.)	NET PROFIT MARGIN	EMPLOYEES
12/10	369	15	4.2%	3,500
12/09	353	23	6.7%	—
12/07	95	0	—	—
Annual Growth	—	3881.1%	—	—

2010 Year-End Financials
Return on assets: 4.7%
Return on equity: 4.2%
Current ratio: 1.20
Cash ($ mil.): 18

GENESIS HEALTHCARE SYSTEM

LOCATIONS

HQ: GENESIS HEALTHCARE SYSTEM
 2951 MAPLE AVE, ZANESVILLE, OH 437011406
Phone: 740 454-4000
Web: WWW.GENESISHCS.ORG

HISTORICAL FINANCIALS

Company Type: Private

Income Statement
FYE: December 31

	REVENUE ($ mil.)	NET INCOME ($ mil.)	NET PROFIT MARGIN	EMPLOYEES
12/08	317	(49)	—	2,500
12/06	0	0	3.3%	—
Annual Growth	3359.7%	—	—	—

2008 Year-End Financials
Return on assets: 3.8%
Return on equity: (-15.6%)
Current ratio: 1.20
Cash ($ mil.): 12

GENICA CORPORATION

Think of Genica as computerdom's bargain basement. The company sells computer components peripherals and accessories —mainly overstocks and closeouts —over the Internet. It operates through two business units: Computer Geeks (which targets consumers through its geeks.com website) and Evertek Computer (which markets to small businesses and FORTUNE 500 firms via evertek.com). The company which offers more than 3000 brand-name products was formed by the merger of online seller Computer Geeks with computer importer/distributor Evertek Computer and its Hong Kong-based sister firm Evertek Trading. Chairman and CEO Frank Segler owns a majority stake in Genica.

Geographic Reach

Temecula California-based Genica operates a 190000-sq.-ft. commercial property in Oceanside California —90% of which is dedicated to warehousing and fulfillment services. The company also has offices in Taiwan and Hong Kong.

Operations

Genica's wholesale unit Evertek Computer contributes about two-thirds of its sales while the consumer division Computer Geeks accounts for the rest.

Sales and Marketing

The company is able to buy higher quantities of products allowing it to receive larger price discounts. It boasts a dedicated sales team and dynamic e-commerce web sites. Genica also uses targeted marketing programs to reach its customers.

EXECUTIVES

Vice President Marketing and Procurement, Chris
 Herzog
Auditors: SWENSON ADVISORS LLP SAN DIE

LOCATIONS

HQ: GENICA CORPORATION
43195 BUSINESS PARK DR, TEMECULA, CA
925903629
Phone: 855 433-5747
Web: WWW.GENICA.COM

PRODUCTS/OPERATIONS

Selected Operations
Evertek.com
Geeks.com

COMPETITORS

Amazon.com
CDW
CompUSA
CompuCom
Enable Holdings
Insight Enterprises

Newegg
PC Connection
PC Mall
Systemax
Zones
eBay

HISTORICAL FINANCIALS

Company Type: Private

Income Statement
FYE: December 31

	REVENUE ($ mil.)	NET INCOME ($ mil.)	NET PROFIT MARGIN	EMPLOYEES
12/09	172	5	3.2%	334
12/08	164	3	2.2%	—
12/07	672	0	—	—
Annual Growth	(49.4%)	53932.2%	—	—

2009 Year-End Financials
Return on assets: 1.9%
Return on equity: 3.2%
Current ratio: 0.20
Cash ($ mil.): —

GENPACT LIMITED

LOCATIONS

HQ: GENPACT LIMITED
 105 MADISON AVE FL 2, NEW YORK, NY 100160297
Phone: 646 624-5900
Web: WWW.GENPACT.COM

HISTORICAL FINANCIALS

Company Type: Private

Income Statement
FYE: December 31

	REVENUE ($ mil.)	NET INCOME ($ mil.)	NET PROFIT MARGIN	EMPLOYEES
12/11	1,600	191	11.9%	325
12/10	1,258	149	11.8%	—
12/09	1,120	134	12.0%	—
Annual Growth	19.5%	19.0%	—	—

2011 Year-End Financials
Return on assets: 1.3%
Return on equity: 11.9%
Current ratio: 1.20
Cash ($ mil.): 408

GEORGIA REGENTS UNIVERSITY

LOCATIONS

HQ: GEORGIA REGENTS UNIVERSITY
 1120 15TH ST, AUGUSTA, GA 309120004
Phone: 800 869-1113
Web: WWW.MCG.ORG

HISTORICAL FINANCIALS

Company Type: Private

Income Statement
FYE: June 30

	REVENUE ($ mil.)	NET INCOME ($ mil.)	NET PROFIT MARGIN	EMPLOYEES
06/13	522	19	3.6%	7,500
06/09	423	5	1.3%	—
06/08	418	9	2.2%	—
Annual Growth	4.6%	15.6%	—	—

2013 Year-End Financials
Return on assets: 11.4%
Return on equity: 3.6%
Current ratio: 0.60
Cash ($ mil.): 21

GEORGIA SOUTHERN UNIVERSITY

Georgia Southern University shows students that higher education can be just peachy. Georgia Southern offers its student body more than 125 bachelor master and doctoral programs from eight colleges; academic fields include business education science and public health. One of 35 colleges and universities in the University System of Georgia it enrolls more than 20500 students most of which hail from Georgia. The average class size of lower division courses is about 43 upper division 23 and graduate level 11. The student to faculty ratio is 22:1.

Geographic Reach

Georgia Southern has a main campus Statesboro and graduate centers in Augusta Brunswick Dublin and Savannah; it also offers distance learning programs.

Operations

The university has some 3260 full time employees including faculty. Some 47% of its faculty are female 21% are minorities and 76% have doctorate level degrees. About 48% of the faculty are tenured while 24% are on tenure track.

Financial Performance

Georgia Southern saw an 8% increase in revenues in fiscal 2013 as the result of higher tuition and fees state appropriation grants contracts and other sources. It also reflected the impact of the acquisition of the Herty Advanced Material Center (transferred to Georgia Southern by the state legislature in 2012). Tuition and fees contributed about 50% of fiscal year 2013 revenues.

Strategy

Expanding its facilities in 2013 Georgia Southern opened a $41.4 million 158000 sq. ft. Biological Sciences Building (housing five active-learning classrooms 10 teaching labs and 15 research labs) for use by more than 1300 undergraduate and graduate biology students.

Company Background

Founded as a district agricultural school in 1906 the institution became a university in 1990.

EXECUTIVES

President, Bruce Grube
VP Business and Finance, Ronald J. Core
Controller, Kim Thompson
VP Academic Affairs and Provost, Linda M. Bleicken
VP Student Affairs and Enrollment Management, Teresa E. Thompson
VP University Advancement, William I. Griffis
Associate VP Center for International Studies, Nancy W. Shumaker
Director Administrative Office of Alumni Relations, Frank Hook III
Director Business and Finance, Keith Roughton
Director Student Affairs Office of Career Services, Warren Riles
Director Office of Financial Accounting, William C. Bird
Director Administrative Department of Procurement and Contract Services, George A. Horn
Registrar, Thomas M. Deal
Director Student Affairs and Enrollment Management Technical Services, Theodore E. Williams
Director Advancement Services, Jodi R. Collins
Director Admissions, Susan Braxton Davies
Controller, Georj L. Lewis
Director Student Affiars Office of Financial Aid, Connie Griggs Murphey
Associate Director Human Resources, Melanee Jo Morales
VP Information Technology Services, Steve Burrell
Associate Dean Library, Ann H. Hamilton
Director Administrative Office of Marketing and Communications, Christian H. Flathman
Dean College of Business Administration, Ronald E. Shiffler
Dean College of Education, Lucindia Chance
Dean College of Graduate Studies, Timothy P. Mack
Dean College of Health and Human Services, Frederick K. Whitt
Dean Jiann-Ping Hsu College of Public Health, Charles J. Hardy

Dean College of Liberal Arts and Social Sciences, Sue M. Moore
Dean College Science and Technology, Bret S. Danilowicz
Auditors: GREG S GRIFFIN ATLANTA GEOR

LOCATIONS

HQ: GEORGIA SOUTHERN UNIVERSITY
1582 SOUTHERN DR, STATESBORO, GA 30458
Phone: 912 681-5224
Web: WWW.GSUSTORE.COM

HISTORICAL FINANCIALS
Company Type: Private

Income Statement

	REVENUE ($ mil.)	NET INCOME ($ mil.)	NET PROFIT MARGIN	EMPLOYEES
06/13	206	32	15.9%	1,700
06/12	185	0	0.5%	—
06/11	177	10	5.8%	—
06/10	151	0	—	—
Annual Growth	10.8%	—	—	—

FYE: June 30

2013 Year-End Financials
Return on assets: 3.0%
Return on equity: 15.9%
Current ratio: 1.70
Cash ($ mil.): 42

GEORGIA TECH FOUNDATION INC.

Auditors: KPMG LLP ATLANTA GA

LOCATIONS

HQ: GEORGIA TECH FOUNDATION INC.
760 SPRING ST NW STE 400, ATLANTA, GA 303081028
Phone: 404 894-8345
Web: WWW.GTF.GATECH.EDU

HISTORICAL FINANCIALS
Company Type: Private

Income Statement

	REVENUE ($ mil.)	NET INCOME ($ mil.)	NET PROFIT MARGIN	EMPLOYEES
06/14	309	207	67.1%	30
06/13	198	67	34.1%	—
06/12	74	(41)	—	—
06/11	266	0	—	—
Annual Growth	5.1%	—	—	—

FYE: June 30

2014 Year-End Financials
Return on assets: 1.7%
Return on equity: 67.1%
Current ratio: —
Cash ($ mil.): 3

GEORGIA TRANSMISSION CORPORATION

With Georgia on its mind Georgia Transmission provides electric transmission services to power producers and distribution utilities. The company primarily transports power for its 39 member distribution cooperatives (out of Georgia's total of 42 coops) and their electricity supplier Oglethorpe Power. Georgia Transmission owns 3060 miles of transmission lines asn more that 640 substations. It jointly owns and plans the state's entire 17500 miles of transmission lines through the Integrated Transmission System in collaboration with Georgia Power MEAG Power and Dalton Utilities.The economic downturn in 2008 and 2009 and unusually mild summers in 2009 and 2010 resulted in a slowing of the growth of the power load. Nevertheless Georgia Transmission is committed to upgrading its infrastructure to keep up with a growing population and to maintain regulatory compliance. It expects to add 1.2 million residnetial customers by 2020. In 2010 Georgia Transmission built more than 190 projects including six new electrical substations and 45 miles of power line.The entity collects revenues for network services from its Member Systems and Oglethorpe Power pursuant to long-term transmission agreements. In 2010 it reported an increase in revenues thanks to increased interest depreciation and other factors. Net margin was flat for the year.Georgia Transmission was formed in 1974 as the transmission arm of Oglethorpe. In 1997 Georgia Transmission became a stand-alone power transmission cooperative.

EXECUTIVES

Vice President System Planning, Russ Schussler

LOCATIONS

HQ: GEORGIA TRANSMISSION CORPORATION
2100 E EXCHANGE PL, TUCKER, GA 300845342
Phone: 770 270-7400
Web: WWW.GATRANS.COM

HISTORICAL FINANCIALS
Company Type: Private

Income Statement

	REVENUE ($ mil.)	NET INCOME ($ mil.)	NET PROFIT MARGIN	EMPLOYEES
12/13	263	0	—	160
12/09	229	14	6.3%	—
12/08	225	13	6.0%	—
Annual Growth	3.2%	—	—	—

FYE: December 31

2013 Year-End Financials
Return on assets: 99.3%
Return on equity: —
Current ratio: 0.20
Cash ($ mil.): 39

GERBER CHILDRENSWEAR LLC

Gerber Childrenswear may be one of the first companies to make kids brand-conscious. The company makes infant and toddler clothing sold under the licensed Gerber and Curity labels as well as its own Onesies brand. Products include sleepwear underwear playwear cloth diapers footwear and bibs. Through a licensing deal with Jockey International Gerber Childrenswear also offers Jockey-branded underwear sleepwear and thermal items for children. The company sells its products primarily through national retailers (such as Wal-Mart Kmart and Toys "R" Us) department stores and specialty shops. Gerber Childrenswear is a unit of Childrenswear LLC a portfolio company of investment firm Sun Capital Partners.

Stung by rising freight costs the company shuttered its distribution center in Evergreen Alabama in 2009 and outsourced the duties to a logistics contractor based near Charleston South Carolina. The move saved Gerber Childrenswear the additional expense of transporting its imported garments from East Coast ports to Alabama. About 80 workers were laid off as a result of the decision.

EXECUTIVES

Senior Vice President Business Development Marketing, Jeanne Dullea
Vice President Of Human Resources, David Hammer
Vice President Sourcing, Tom McRae
Vice President Of Operations, Samuel Beason
Auditors: PRICEWATERHOUSECOOPERS LLP SP

LOCATIONS

HQ: GERBER CHILDRENSWEAR LLC
 7005 PELHAM RD, GREENVILLE, SC 296155782
Phone: 864 987-5200
Web: WWW.GERBERCHILDRENSWEAR.COM

PRODUCTS/OPERATIONS

Selected Products
Bedding
Bibs and burp cloths
Cloth diapers and liners
Gift sets
Layettes
Playwear
Towels
Training pants
Sleepwear
Socks and booties
Underwear
Washcloths

COMPETITORS

Carter's	Garan
Children's Place	Gymboree
Crown Crafts	Old Navy
Disney	Springs Global US
Fruit of the Loom	The Gap

HISTORICAL FINANCIALS
Company Type: Private

Income Statement				FYE: January 29
	REVENUE ($ mil.)	NET INCOME ($ mil.)	NET PROFIT MARGIN	EMPLOYEES
01/11	160	5	3.2%	120
01/09	193	6	3.4%	—
Annual Growth	(9.1%)	(12.0%)	—	—

2011 Year-End Financials
Return on assets: 9.8%   Cash ($ mil.): —
Return on equity: 3.2%
Current ratio: 0.40

GERRITY'S SUPER MARKET INC.

Gerrity's Super Market is not yet part of a matriarchal society but does boast that it's where Mom is "always in charge!" The regional grocery chain operates about 10 supermarkets under the Gerrity's Supermarket banner in Lackawanna and Luzerne counties in northeastern Pennsylvania. The regional chain also operates an online grocery order and home delivery service. Founded in 1895 by William Gerrity the family-owned company is run by mother and son team Joyce ("Mom") and Joseph Fasula. Gerrity's Supermarkets is a member of the Shursave Supermarkets Co-op.

EXECUTIVES

President and Co-owner, Joyce A. Fasula
VP and Co-owner, Joseph (Joe) Fasula
Auditors: MCGRAIL MERKEL QUINN SCRANTON

LOCATIONS

HQ: GERRITY' S SUPER MARKET INC.
 950 N SOUTH RD STE 5, SCRANTON, PA 185041430
Phone: 570 342-4144
Web: WWW.GERRITYS.COM

COMPETITORS

ALDI	Wal-Mart
Golub	Wegmans
Redner' s Markets	Weis Markets
Wakefern Food	

HISTORICAL FINANCIALS
Company Type: Private

Income Statement				FYE: December 29
	REVENUE ($ mil.)	NET INCOME ($ mil.)	NET PROFIT MARGIN	EMPLOYEES
12/13*	158	4	2.6%	900
01/06	114	1	1.2%	—
01/05	116	28	24.1%	—
12/03	425	0	—	—
Annual Growth	(9.4%)	—	—	—

*Fiscal year change

2013 Year-End Financials
Return on assets: 2.6%   Cash ($ mil.): 2
Return on equity: 2.6%
Current ratio: 0.70

GILLETTE CHILDREN'S SPECIALTY HEALTHCARE

Caring for the Twin Cities' tiniest tykes and most truculent teens Gillette Children's Specialty Healthcare provides diagnostic therapeutic and support services to children adolescents and young adults. Gillette Children's consists of a main campus in St. Paul Minnesota and eight clinics in the immediate and outlying areas of the city. The health system also provides adult services at its St. Paul-Phalen clinic. The main campus hospital (with about 345 beds) operates Centers of Excellence for cerebral palsy craniofacial services and pediatric neurosciences among others. The not-for-profit hospital also provides outreach services through its mobile health care unit.

Geographic Reach

Gillette Children's Twin Cities Hospital and clinic locations include the St. Paul Campus (hospital and clinic); Burnsville Clinic (on the Fairview Ridges Hospital Campus 20 miles south of the St. Paul Campus); Maple Grove Clinic 30 miles northwest of the St. Paul Campus; Minnetonka Clinic (in the Children's West complex in Minnetonka); Minnetonka Therapies (rehabilitation services for families in the western Twin Cities); Gillette Lifetime Specialty Healthcare St. Paul - Phalen Clinic (outpatient services for teen and adult patients)The medical network's Greater Minnesota outpatient clinics include Brainerd Lakes Clinic (serving families in central and northern Minnesota); Duluth Clinic (specialty services for families in northeastern Minnesota); Willmar Clinic (serving families in central and western Minnesota).

In 2012 Gillette Children's served more than 25000 patients from the US and abroad.

Financial Performance

Gillette Children's revenues grew by 16% in 2012 due to higher net patient service revenues as a result of an increase in revenues from government payors other third-party payors and self-pay and an increase in unrestricted net assets available for operational use.

In 2012 government payors accounted for 22% of the company's revenues; other third-party payors accounted 76%.The medical network's net income grew from $1.5 million in 2011 to $23 million in 2012 thanks to higher revenues an investment return (versus a loss in 2011) and absence of a loss on disposal of assets.

Strategy

In 2014 Gillette Children's announced that it exceeded its $10 million Capital Campaign fundraising goal raising a total of $11.1 million in support of its St. Paul hospital expansion project. In 2013 the network completed its expansion project which began in 2010 and which included a new outpatient care building and enclosed skybridge expanded Pediatric Intensive Care Unit a state-of-the-art surgical suite a surgical simulation center and an outdoor healing garden. It also enhanced its world-renowned Center for Gait and Motion Analysis and its Neurosciences and Orthopedics/Surgical inpatient units.

Company Background

Gillette Children's was founded in 1897.

EXECUTIVES

Chief Executive Officer President, Margaret E. Perryman
Medical Director and Board Member, Steven Koop
Vice President of Development, Jon Galloway
Vice President Chief Financial Officer, James Haddican
Vice President of Strategic Planning and Support Services, Kathryn J. Wardrop
Vice President of Human Resources, Elizabeth (Betty) Rivard
Vice Chair, James Rechtiene
Secretary and Director, Kevin Walker
Treasurer and Director, David Glaser
Vice President of Patient Services, Karen Brill
President CEO and Director, Margaret E. Perryman
Medical Director and Board Member, Steven Koop
Secretary and Director, Kevin Walker
Treasurer and Director, David Glaser
Director, Todd Fisher
Director, Braxton Haulcy

Director, James Hynes
Director, Scott Ward
Director, Beverly Wical
Auditors: DELOITTE TAX LLP MINNEAPOLIS

LOCATIONS

HQ: GILLETTE CHILDREN' S SPECIALTY
HEALTHCARE
200 UNIVERSITY AVE E, SAINT PAUL, MN 551012507
Phone: 651 291-2848
Web: WWW.GILLETTECHILDRENS.ORG

PRODUCTS/OPERATIONS

Selected Services
Center for Cerebral Palsy
Center for Craniofacial Services
Center for Gait and Motion Analysis
Center for Pediatric Neurosciences
Center for Pediatric Orthopedics
Centers for Pediatric Rehabilitation
Center for Pediatric Subspecialty Care

COMPETITORS

Abbott Northwestern Hospital
Allina Hospitals
Bethesda Hospital
Fairview Health
HealthEast Care System
Kennedy Krieger Institute
Methodist Hospital System
North Memorial Health Care
Park Nicollet Health Services
St. John' s Hospital (Minnesota)
University of Minnesota Medical Center

HISTORICAL FINANCIALS

Company Type: Private

Income Statement

	REVENUE ($ mil.)	NET INCOME ($ mil.)	NET PROFIT MARGIN	EMPLOYEES
12/13	208	17	8.4%	623
12/09	139	7	5.5%	—
12/08	133	0	—	—
12/02	70	0	—	—
Annual Growth	10.4%	—	—	—

FYE: December 31

2013 Year-End Financials

Return on assets: 2.6%   Cash ($ mil.): 12
Return on equity: 8.4%
Current ratio: 2.00

GLASS MTN. PUMICE INC

LOCATIONS

HQ: GLASS MTN. PUMICE INC
3400 KAUAI CT STE 206, RENO, NV 895094828
Phone: 775 826-3399

HISTORICAL FINANCIALS

Company Type: Private

Income Statement

	REVENUE ($ mil.)	NET INCOME ($ mil.)	NET PROFIT MARGIN	EMPLOYEES
01/10*	350	0	—	15
03/03	2	(0)	—	—
03/02	2	0	4.0%	—
Annual Growth	86.9%	—	—	—

FYE: January 31

*Fiscal year change

2010 Year-End Financials

Return on assets: 14.2%   Cash ($ mil.): 1
Return on equity: —
Current ratio: 0.40

GLENDALE ADVENTIST MEDICAL CENTER INC

Treating ladies from Pasadena and other patients throughout the suburbs of sunny Southern California Glendale Adventist Medical Center (GAMC) is a stalwart community member. The hospital is part of Adventist Health a not-for-profit group of about 20 hospitals and health care organizations in four western states. GAMC provides a range of specialty services including cancer treatment cardiology emergency medicine neuroscience home care psychiatry rehabilitation and women's healthcare. It also provides medical training and residency programs. The 515-bed hospital was founded in 1905 by the Seventh-Day Adventist Church.

Operations
GAMC employs more than 800 physicians and provides services to about 20000 inpatients each year. It also handles 46000 emergency department visits 20000 home health visits 280000 outpatient appointments and 2500 births each year. Its physicians perform around 3400 inpatient and 3900 outpatient surgeries annually.

Geographic Reach
GAMC is located in Glendale California and serves surrounding communities in Southern California.

Strategy
GAMC is expanding its hospital facilities technologies and programs to enhance patient care. The hospital has also implemented its electronic health record (EHR) system including computerized order entry and bar code medication systems for improved patient safety. In addition GAMC introduced a new extended internship program for medical students studying clinical care fields.

EXECUTIVES

Director Of Pharmacy, Romic Eskandarian
Svp Clinical Services, Gwen Matthews
Vice President Ancillary Services, Rob Marchuk
Vice President Of Information Technology, Michael Cann
Director of Radiology Services, Tom Paw
Vice President Nursing Pt Care, Gwen Mathews

LOCATIONS

HQ: GLENDALE ADVENTIST MEDICAL CENTER INC
1509 WILSON TER, GLENDALE, CA 912064007
Phone: 818 409-8000
Web: WWW.GLENDALEADVENTIST.COM

PRODUCTS/OPERATIONS

Selected Operations
Advanced Surgical Program
Cancer Services
Heart & Vascular Institute
Neuroscience Institute
Orthopedic Services
Physical Medicine & Rehabilitation
Spine Institute
Women' s Services

COMPETITORS

Anaheim Regional   Long Beach Memorial
Medical Center   Los Angeles County

Brotman Medical Center   Health Department
Cedars-Sinai Medical   Methodist Hospital of
Center   Southern California
Childrens Hospital Los   Pasadena Hospital
Angeles   Association
City of Hope   Tenet Healthcare
Dignity Health   Western Medical Center
Glendale Memorial   - Santa Ana
Hospital   White Memorial Medical
Hollywood Presbyterian   Center
Medical Center

HISTORICAL FINANCIALS

Company Type: Private

Income Statement

	REVENUE ($ mil.)	NET INCOME ($ mil.)	NET PROFIT MARGIN	EMPLOYEES
12/12	387	5	1.4%	2,600
12/09	307	12	4.1%	—
12/07*	273	0	0.1%	—
06/05	985	0	—	—
Annual Growth	(11.0%)	—	—	—

FYE: December 31

*Fiscal year change

2012 Year-End Financials

Return on assets: 2.9%   Cash ($ mil.): 39
Return on equity: 1.4%
Current ratio: 3.10

GLOBAL HEALTH SOLUTIONS INC

LOCATIONS

HQ: GLOBAL HEALTH SOLUTIONS INC
325 SWANTON WAY, DECATUR, GA 300303001
Phone: 404 592-1430

HISTORICAL FINANCIALS

Company Type: Private

Income Statement

	REVENUE ($ mil.)	NET INCOME ($ mil.)	NET PROFIT MARGIN	EMPLOYEES
08/13	1,574	0	—	2
08/10	1,120	0	0.0%	—
08/09	980	0	—	—
Annual Growth	12.6%	—	—	—

FYE: August 31

GLOBAL TRADING ENTERPRISES LLC

Auditors: HERBEIN & COMPANY INC READI

LOCATIONS

HQ: GLOBAL TRADING ENTERPRISES LLC
504 SHARPTOWN RD, SWEDESBORO, NJ 080853161
Phone: 856 223-9966
Web: WWW.RASTELLIFOODSGROUP.COM

HISTORICAL FINANCIALS
Company Type: Private

Income Statement
FYE: December 26

	REVENUE ($ mil.)	NET INCOME ($ mil.)	NET PROFIT MARGIN	EMPLOYEES
12/09	319	8	2.7%	150
12/08	253	5	2.3%	—
12/07	683	0	—	—
Annual Growth	—65896.6%	—	—	—

2009 Year-End Financials

Return on assets: 3.5% Cash ($ mil.): —
Return on equity: 2.7%
Current ratio: 1.10

GOLD-EAGLE COOPERATIVE

For Gold-Eagle Cooperative service to its member/farmers is the golden rule. The firm is a member-owned agricultural co-op located in north central Iowa. It offers its members grain drying custom crop spraying feed seed fertilizer and other bulk and packaged farm chemicals storage and warehousing as well as feed milling and marketing. The co-op runs a transportation fleet of grain-hoppers feed-bottle trucks and specialty trailers that take members' crops to and from its facilities. Gold-Eagle operates nine grain elevator/service center locations.

EXECUTIVES

Vice President Brand Marketing, Mike Profetto
Vice President, Paul Rasmussen

LOCATIONS

HQ: GOLD-EAGLE COOPERATIVE
415 LOCUST ST, GOLDFIELD, IA 505425092
Phone: 515 825-3161
Web: WWW.GOLDEAGLECOOP.COM

COMPETITORS

ADM	GROWMARK
Ag Processing Inc.	Heartland Co-op
Bunge Limited	JR Simplot
CHS	NEW Cooperative
Cargill	West Central Co-op
DeBruce Grain	Wilbur-Ellis
Farmers Cooperative Society	

HISTORICAL FINANCIALS
Company Type: Private

Income Statement
FYE: September 30

	REVENUE ($ mil.)	NET INCOME ($ mil.)	NET PROFIT MARGIN	EMPLOYEES
09/09	302	10	3.3%	170
09/08	304	9	3.2%	—
09/07	216	5	2.5%	—
09/06	131	0	—	—
Annual Growth	31.9%	—	—	—

2009 Year-End Financials

Return on assets: 1.3% Cash ($ mil.): 6
Return on equity: 3.3%
Current ratio: 0.60

GOLDEN GRAIN ENERGY LLC

The fruited plains with their golden grains have yielded Golden Grain Energy an ethanol production company with a plant in Iowa that converts corn into ethanol which is most commonly used as an additive to unleaded gasoline. Other uses include high octane fuel enhancer and a non-petroleum fuel substitute. Golden Grain Energy's plant has a production capacity of 110 million gallons of ethanol and 120000 tons of distillers grains per year. The distillers grains are used to produce animal feed. In 2009 with raw material costs rising and selling prices falling the company cut back production at the plant.

EXECUTIVES

Board Member, Jim Boeding
Board Member, Earl Brandt
Board Member, Jim Ludeking
Auditors: MCGLADREY LLP DES MOINES IOW

LOCATIONS

HQ: GOLDEN GRAIN ENERGY LLC
1822 43RD ST SW, MASON CITY, IA 504017071
Phone: 641 423-8525
Web: WWW.GOLDENGRAINENERGY.COM

PRODUCTS/OPERATIONS

2006 Sales

	% of total
Ethanol	91
Distillers grains	9
Total	**100**

2007 Sales

	% of total
Ethanol	89
Distillers grains	11
Total	**100**

2008 Sales

	% of total
Ethanol	84
Distillers grains	16
Total	**100**

COMPETITORS

ADM	Hawkeye Energy Holdings
Aventine	
GreenField Ethanol	POET

HISTORICAL FINANCIALS
Company Type: Private

Income Statement
FYE: October 31

	REVENUE ($ mil.)	NET INCOME ($ mil.)	NET PROFIT MARGIN	EMPLOYEES
10/14	289	79	27.4%	47
10/13	350	14	4.0%	—
10/12	327	6	2.0%	—
10/11	324	0	—	—
Annual Growth	(3.8%)	—	—	—

2014 Year-End Financials

Return on assets: 1.9% Cash ($ mil.): 47
Return on equity: 27.4%
Current ratio: 7.10

GOOD SAMARITAN HOSPITAL

LOCATIONS

HQ: GOOD SAMARITAN HOSPITAL
401 15TH AVE SE, PUYALLUP, WA 983723795
Phone: 253 697-1885
Web: WWW.MULTICARE.ORG

HISTORICAL FINANCIALS
Company Type: Private

Income Statement
FYE: December 31

	REVENUE ($ mil.)	NET INCOME ($ mil.)	NET PROFIT MARGIN	EMPLOYEES
12/12	418	27	6.5%	1,510
12/09	313	74	23.9%	—
Annual Growth	10.2%	(28.7%)	—	—

GOOD SAMARITAN HOSPITAL CORVALLIS

LOCATIONS

HQ: GOOD SAMARITAN HOSPITAL CORVALLIS
3600 NW SAMARITAN DR, CORVALLIS, OR 973303700
Phone: 541 757-5111
Web: WWW.SAMHEALTH.ORG

HISTORICAL FINANCIALS
Company Type: Private

Income Statement
FYE: December 31

	REVENUE ($ mil.)	NET INCOME ($ mil.)	NET PROFIT MARGIN	EMPLOYEES
12/12	312	(3)	—	900
12/08	231	5	2.3%	—
12/04	65	(1)	—	—
12/02	1,478	0	—	—
Annual Growth	(14.4%)	—	—	—

2012 Year-End Financials

Return on assets: 3.4% Cash ($ mil.): —
Return on equity: (-1.0%)
Current ratio: 1.10

GOOD360

Gifts in Kind International helps companies find ways to be kind. The not-for-profit organization accepts gifts of products and services from corporate clients and distributes these donations to more than 150000 community charities in the US and globally that directly help communities and people in need. About half of the FORTUNE 100 makes contributions through Gifts in Kind International which has certified more than 200000 charities as potential recipients. Gifts in Kind International began operating in 1983 when 3M donated $12 million in new office equipment. The organization is known for its cost-efficiency as more than 99% of its donations go directly to communities.

Gifts In Kind appointed Cindy Hallberlin formerly chief ethics diversity and accountability officer for U.S. Foodservice as its president and CEO in June 2009. Hallberlin succeeded Barry Anderson who had served as interim president and CEO since September 2008 when Richard Wong stepped down after his three-year contract.

The group publishes catalogs of software toys and retailers so non-profits can shop for what they need. Companies who wish to participate sign up and non-profits are directed to locations in their area.

Gifts have come from companies such as Adobe Systems Dell General Motors Marvel Entertainment and Sara Lee and have gone to organizations such as Boys & Girls Clubs of America Habitat for Humanity Newborns in Need Sister Cities International and Youth Service America.

EXECUTIVES

V Pres, Melissa (Mel) Trumpower
Auditors: BDO USA LLP BETHESDA MD

LOCATIONS

HQ: GOOD360
1330 BRADDOCK PL STE 600, ALEXANDRIA, VA 223149702
Phone: 703 836-2121
Web: WWW.GIFTSINKIND.ORG

HISTORICAL FINANCIALS

Company Type: Private

Income Statement

	REVENUE ($ mil.)	NET INCOME ($ mil.)	NET PROFIT MARGIN	EMPLOYEES
12/08	426	0	—	36
12/07	388	32	8.3%	
12/06	995	0	—	
Annual Growth	—	—	—	—

FYE: December 31

2008 Year-End Financials

Return on assets: 0.3%
Return on equity: —
Current ratio: 0.20
Cash ($ mil.): —

GOODFELLOW BROS. INC.

The good men at Goodfellow Bros. build everything from golf courses to runways to dams and residences. The family-owned company specializes in heavy construction infrastructure transportation systems and housing and recreation facilities in the western continental US and Hawaii. Goodfellow Bros. also offers earth moving and paving services. Its Blasting Technologies subsidiary blasts drills and demolishes rock and other structures. The company was founded in 1921 by brothers Jack Bert and Jim Sr. Their early business included the first excavation work on the Grand Coulee Dam in 1933. Now the company has a number of planned communities public facilities and other projects under its belt.

EXECUTIVES

V Pres, Daniel Goodfellow, age 60
Vice President Finance, Ronald Lester
Vice President, Dan Goodfellow
Vice President, Chad Goodfellow

LOCATIONS

HQ: GOODFELLOW BROS. INC.
1407 WALLA WALLA AVE, WENATCHEE, WA 988011530
Phone: 509 667-9095
Web: WWW.GOODFELLOWBROS.COM

PRODUCTS/OPERATIONS

Projects and Services

Airports
Blasting
Crushing paving and grading
Environmental and emergency responses
Golf Courses
Harbors and marinas
Heavy mechanical and infrastructure
Highways
Landfills
Public and private facilities
Private developments and planned communities
Reservoirs and dams
Wind farms

COMPETITORS

Bechtel	Macro-Z-Technology Co.
C.C. Myers	PCL Construction
GLY Construction	Enterprises
Granite Construction	Parsons Corporation
Harnish Group	S.D. Deacon
J.F. Shea	

HISTORICAL FINANCIALS

Company Type: Private

Income Statement

	REVENUE ($ mil.)	NET INCOME ($ mil.)	NET PROFIT MARGIN	EMPLOYEES
12/13	203	7	3.6%	1,050
12/09	240	19	8.2%	—
12/08	0	0	—	
12/07	519	0	—	
Annual Growth	(14.5%)	—	—	—

FYE: December 31

2013 Year-End Financials

Return on assets: —
Return on equity: 3.6%
Current ratio: 0.90
Cash ($ mil.): 32

GOODWILL INDUSTRIES OF SOUTHEASTERN WISCONSIN INC.

LOCATIONS

HQ: GOODWILL INDUSTRIES OF SOUTHEASTERN WISCONSIN INC.
5300 N 118TH CT, MILWAUKEE, WI 532253084
Phone: 414 847-4159
Web: WWW.GOODWILLSEW.COM

HISTORICAL FINANCIALS

Company Type: Private

Income Statement

	REVENUE ($ mil.)	NET INCOME ($ mil.)	NET PROFIT MARGIN	EMPLOYEES
12/13	347	13	3.9%	3,391
12/12	255	13	5.4%	—
12/11	293	11	3.9%	—
12/10	277	0	—	—
Annual Growth	7.7%	—	—	—

FYE: December 31

2013 Year-End Financials

Return on assets: 3.1%
Return on equity: 3.9%
Current ratio: 1.20
Cash ($ mil.): 21

GPM INVESTMENTS LLC

GPM Investments is where it's at for convenience store operators Fas Mart and Shore Stop. The investment firm operates more than 465 company-owned stores and some 145 independent convenience stores in 10 states mainly on the East Coast. The company has a high concentration of Fas Mart and Shore Stop stores in Virginia; others are located in nine states from Connecticut to Tennessee. The stores sell BP Exxon Marathon and Valero brand gas. (GPM's petroleum wholesaling business delivers petro to independent dealers.) In addition to the usual beer smokes and snacks the stores sell hot foods for breakfast lunch and dinner including the company's own brand of fried Fas Chicken at cafe sites.

Geographic Reach

Richmond Virginia-based GPM operates more than 600 convenience stores in Virginia North Carolina Delaware Maryland Pennsylvania New Jersey Connecticut Rhode Island South Carolina and Tennessee.

Operations

In addition to convenience stores GPM also operates 15 Subway franchises one Taco Bell franchise and 50 restaurants that serve Southern fried chicken.

Strategy

To help fund investments in new capital improvement projects and in acquisitions GPM entered into a $35 million credit facility with PNC Bank N.A. in 2012. Maturing in November 2016 the credit facility allows GPM to open new stores and improve existing locations. To this end the convenience store operator has offered to buy a 50% stake in EZ Energy Ltd. based in Ramat Gan Israel for $15 million. The company typically uses funding received through credit facilities to improve its locations with brighter interior and exterior lighting wider aisles and cleaner stores. It is also increasing its marketing efforts through social media to target younger shoppers.

Fast-growing GPM Investments in growing through acquisitions. Indeed in 2013 the company made its largest acquisition to date propelling its store count to more than 600 locations in 10 states.

Mergers and Acquisitions

In August 2013 GPM acquired the Southeastern division of VPS Convenience Store Group from Sun Capital Partners. The regional division operates more than 260 stores and 33 dealer sites and was cobbled together from acquisitions that included the Scotchman Young's Li'l Cricket Everyday Shop and Cigarette City banners. Most of the newly-acquired stores are in the Carolinas where GPM's retail presence is thin. Earlier in August GPM purchased five stores operating under the Get & Zip banner in Virginia. Most of the

EXECUTIVES

Vice President Petroleum and Facilities Management, Chris Giacobone
Vice President Facilities Management, Peter Meyer
Vice President Financial Planning, Kevin Perlowski
Senior Vice President Marketing, Bill Reilly
Executive Vice President, Eyal Nuchamovitz
Auditors: GRANT THORNTON LLP RALEIGH

LOCATIONS

HQ: GPM INVESTMENTS LLC
8565 MAGELLAN PKWY # 400, RICHMOND, VA 232271167
Phone: 804 266-1363
Web: WWW.FASMART.COM

Selected Locations
Connecticut
Delaware
Maryland
New Jersey
North Carolina
Pennsylvania
Rhode Island
South Carolina
Tennessee
Virginia

COMPETITORS

7-Eleven	Racetrac Petroleum
Cumberland Farms	Sheetz
Exxon Mobil	The Pantry
Gate Petroleum	Wawa Inc.

HISTORICAL FINANCIALS

Company Type: Private

Income Statement

FYE: December 31

	REVENUE ($ mil.)	NET INCOME ($ mil.)	NET PROFIT MARGIN	EMPLOYEES
12/08	1,249	(1)	—	1,300
12/07	891	3	0.4%	—
Annual Growth	40.2%	—	—	—

2008 Year-End Financials

Return on assets: 1.7%
Return on equity: (-0.1%)
Current ratio: 0.40
Cash ($ mil.): 12

GRACE HEIGHTS HEALTH AND REHABILITATION CENTRE

LOCATIONS

HQ: GRACE HEIGHTS HEALTH AND REHABILITATION CENTRE
109 FOOTHILLS DR, MORGANTON, NC 286555152
Phone: 828 580-7000
Web: WWW.BLUERIDGEHEALTH.ORG

HISTORICAL FINANCIALS

Company Type: Private

Income Statement

FYE: September 30

	REVENUE ($ mil.)	NET INCOME ($ mil.)	NET PROFIT MARGIN	EMPLOYEES
09/09*	788	(20)	—	140
12/04	6	0	8.8%	—
12/02	5	(0)	—	—
Annual Growth	101.2%	—	—	—

*Fiscal year change

2009 Year-End Financials

Return on assets: 0.1%
Return on equity: (-2.6%)
Current ratio: 1.30
Cash ($ mil.): —

GRAEBEL COMPANIES INC.

Graebel can move your table ... and just about anything else you need relocated. Offering both domestic and international household and commercial relocation services most of the company's business comes from firms transferring employees but it also provides individual household moving services and storage as well as freight forwarding. Graebel operates from service centers throughout the US and from international forwarding offices at major ports. It provides transportation services in Asia Europe the Middle East and Africa through hubs in Prague and Singapore and elsewhere in the world via a network of partners. Dave Graebel founded the family-run company in 1950.

Geographic Reach
Graebel has operations in Colorado and other locations throughout the US; it provides moving services in 165 countries and maintains an international presence in the Czech Republic Prague Singapore and Shanghai.

Operations
In addition to providing its moving services the company offers storage services freight forwarding and move management. Because the company insists on tight background checks and security measures Graebel serves specialized industries as well as high-end customers.

Additionally Graebel handles relocations for libraries hotels health care facilities and the entertainment industry. To serve its customers better the company offers its Graebel Relocation app (application) which gives clients their relocation facts and status of their transfers via an iPhone or iPad tablet computer; its services can also be accessed through an Android app.

EXECUTIVES

Senior Vice President of Human Resources, Mary Dymond
COO; President Graebel Movers International, William (Bill) Graebel
CFO, Brad Siler
SVP Marketing and Public Relations, Carolyn White
President Global Services and Move Management Inc, Jim Petzel
COO, Ron Dunlap
President Relocation Services, Debbie Maupin
Vice President, Pam Capecci
Regional Vice President And General Manager, Tom Thersen

Senior Vice President, Cameron Blakely
Vice President Global Client Development, Craig Chapman
Vice President, Jeff Bulinski
Vice President Commercial Planning and Implementation, Paige Wagner
Chairman, David (Dave) Graebel
Auditors: WIPFLI LLP WAUSAU WISCONSIN

LOCATIONS

HQ: GRAEBEL COMPANIES INC.
16346 AIRPORT CIR, AURORA, CO 800111558
Phone: 303 214-6683
Web: WWW.GRAEBELMOVING.COM

PRODUCTS/OPERATIONS

Selected Services
Bar-coded inventory and asset management
Corporate headquarters office and one-time office relocation
Healthcare industry relocation project services
High density filing systems storage solutions
Hospitality industry furniture fixtures and equipment (FF&E) services
Just-In-Time deliveries
MAC management
Project management
Records storage and disposal
Relocation services
Single-source logistic services and management
Sub-contractor data telephony electrical coordination
Systems furniture transport delivery installation and reconfiguration
Warehouse and distribution services
Worldwide air ocean transportation including less-than-truckload truckload / padded van services

COMPETITORS

A-1 Freeman Moving & Storage	National Van Lines
ALTAIR Global Relocation	Paxton Van Lines
Ace Relocation Systems	Prudential
Arpin Van Lines	SIRVA
Atlas World Group	Seino Transportation Co
Bekins	Suddath
Brookfield Global Relocation	TheMIGroup
Business Relocation Services	UniGroup
Move Solutions	Weichert Relocation Resources
	Wheaton Van Lines

HISTORICAL FINANCIALS

Company Type: Private

Income Statement

FYE: December 31

	REVENUE ($ mil.)	NET INCOME ($ mil.)	NET PROFIT MARGIN	EMPLOYEES
12/12	341	4	1.3%	1,771
12/11	322	3	0.9%	—
12/09	260	(3)	—	—
12/06	334	0	—	—
Annual Growth	0.4%	—	—	—

2012 Year-End Financials

Return on assets: 11.9%
Return on equity: 1.3%
Current ratio: 1.00
Cash ($ mil.): 3

GRAHAM ENTERPRISE INC.

LOCATIONS

HQ: GRAHAM ENTERPRISE INC.
446 MORRIS AVE, MUNDELEIN, IL 600601919
Phone: 847 393-7724
Web: WWW.GRAHAMEI.COM

HISTORICAL FINANCIALS

Company Type: Private

Income Statement

	REVENUE ($ mil.)	NET INCOME ($ mil.)	NET PROFIT MARGIN	EMPLOYEES
				FYE: December 31
12/13	849	4	0.5%	350
12/12	794	7	1.0%	—
12/11	765	7	1.0%	—
12/10	566	0	—	—
Annual Growth	14.4%	—	—	—

2013 Year-End Financials

Return on assets: 0.4%
Return on equity: 0.5%
Current ratio: 0.30
Cash ($ mil.): —

GRAND STRAND REGIONAL MEDICAL CENTER LLC

Grand Strand Regional Medical Center (GSRMC) is an acute care hospital serving Myrtle Beach South Carolina and surrounding Georgetown and Horry counties. The 220-bed hospital a designated trauma center is home to the only cardiac surgery program in those counties. GSRMC has a staff of more than 250 physicians representing a range of specializations including oncology wound treatment and emergency care women's health pediatrics rehabilitation behavioral health and treatment for sleeping disorders. Grand Strand Regional Medical Center includes the medical center and other satellite diagnostic ambulatory care and senior care facilities throughout the area.

LOCATIONS

HQ: GRAND STRAND REGIONAL MEDICAL CENTER LLC
809 82ND PKWY, MYRTLE BEACH, SC 295724607
Phone: 843 449-4411
Web: WWW.GRANDSTRANDMED.COM

COMPETITORS

Carolinas HealthCare System	Laurens County Hospital
Carolinas Hospital System	McLeod Health
Conway Medical Center	Medical University of South Carolina
Georgetown Hospital System	Palmetto Health
Greenville Hospital System	Roper St. Francis Healthcare
	Soliant Health

GRAND VIEW HOSPITAL

Grand View Health (GVH) formerly Grand View Hospital hopes to give patients a glimpse of great health care. The hospital provide emergency inpatient surgery and specialty services including cardiology orthopedics sleep diagnostic rehabilitation women's and children's care and other medical services to the Bucks County region of Pennsylvania. GVH's oncology program is affiliated with the Fox Chase Cancer Center in Philadelphia. The medical center also operates primary care and outpatient clinics in the region and it provides home health hospice fitness and community outreach programs. The hospital has about 200 beds.

Geographic Reach

The company has offices in 25 locations. In addition to its main hospital in Sellersville Pennsylvania GVH operates outpatient centers in Sellersville Harleysville and Pennsburg as well as a cancer center in Chalfont and a health center in Quakertown.

Operations

More than 33000 patients visited the hospital's emergency room in 2014 and GVH had more than 171000 outpatient visits. Its 355 physicians performed 9388 inpatient and about 7000 outpatient surgeries that year.

Sales and Marketing

The hospital markets its services through print billboard and television campaigns.

Strategy

GVH has grown in recent years by expanding its medical facilities and services

In 2015 the hospital system introduced dropless cataract surgery as a new convenient option for the surgical removal of a cataract.It also opened a Lung Care Center in Sellersville.

Company Background

In 2010 it opened a new labor and delivery unit and in 2012 it began offering neonatology services through a partnership with the Children's Hospital of Philadelphia.

GVH was founded in 1913.

EXECUTIVES

Vice President Of Medical Affairs, Jane Ferrymd
Secretary, William S Aichele, age 65
Auditors: PARENTEBEARD LLC PHILADELPHIA

LOCATIONS

HQ: GRAND VIEW HOSPITAL
700 LAWN AVE, SELLERSVILLE, PA 189601548
Phone: 215 453-4000
Web: WWW.GVH.ORG

Selected Locations

Grand View Medical Company
Harleysville Outpatient Center

HISTORICAL FINANCIALS

Company Type: Private

Income Statement

	REVENUE ($ mil.)	NET INCOME ($ mil.)	NET PROFIT MARGIN	EMPLOYEES
				FYE: April 30
04/13	265	65	24.6%	1,000
04/09	0	0	38.0%	—
Annual Growth	641.9%	565.8%	—	—

2013 Year-End Financials

Return on assets: 2.5%
Return on equity: 24.6%
Current ratio: 2.50
Cash ($ mil.): —

Health Center at Quakertown
High Point Professional Building
Pennsburg Outpatient Center
Physician Suites at Dublin
Sellersville Outpatient Center

PRODUCTS/OPERATIONS

Selected Services and Centers

Acute Rehabilitation Unit
Ambulance/Transport Services
Case Management
Child Immunization Clinic
  Children's
Clinical Research
Diabetes Education
Emergency Department
Grand View Information Line
Health Promotion and Wellness
Healthy Beginnings Plus
Home Health Care Services
Industrial Medicine
Laboratory (Blood Work) Services at Grand View Hospital
Lifestyle Fitness Center
Medical Equipment and Supplies
Men's Health
Nutritional Counseling Services
Pediatric Weight Management (Grand New Youth)
Physical Medicine & Rehabilitation
Pulmonary Rehabilitation
Radiology Services (X-ray) Senior Services
Stoneridge Sleep Center
Sports Medicine
Support Groups & Consultations
Weight Management (Grand New You)
Wound Care Center

COMPETITORS

Abington Memorial Hospital
Children's Hospital of Philadelphia
Doylestown Hospital
Jefferson Health System
Lehigh Valley Health Network
North Philadelphia Health System
St. Luke's University Health Network
Tenet Healthcare
University of Pennsylvania Health System

HISTORICAL FINANCIALS

Company Type: Private

Income Statement

	REVENUE ($ mil.)	NET INCOME ($ mil.)	NET PROFIT MARGIN	EMPLOYEES
				FYE: June 30
06/13	168	31	18.7%	1,600
06/12	169	(26)	—	—
06/11	177	10	5.7%	—
06/10	182	0	—	—
Annual Growth	(2.7%)	—	—	—

2013 Year-End Financials

Return on assets: —
Return on equity: 18.7%
Current ratio: 1.80
Cash ($ mil.): 25

GRANDVIEW HEALTH HOME

LOCATIONS

HQ: GRANDVIEW HEALTH HOME
49 WOODBINE LN, DANVILLE, PA 178218022
Phone: 570 275-2129
Web: WWW.GRANDVIEWHH.COM

HISTORICAL FINANCIALS

Company Type: Private

Income Statement
FYE: June 30

	REVENUE ($ mil.)	NET INCOME ($ mil.)	NET PROFIT MARGIN	EMPLOYEES
06/09	1,262	4	0.4%	240
06/99	2	2	89.8%	—
06/98	63,307	1	0.0%	—
Annual Growth	(29.9%)	11.3%	—	—

2009 Year-End Financials

Return on assets: 0.1%   Cash ($ mil.): —
Return on equity: 0.4%
Current ratio: 1.30

GRANITE SCHOOL DISTRICT

Auditors: SQUIRE & COMPANY PC OREM UT

LOCATIONS

HQ: GRANITE SCHOOL DISTRICT
2500 S STATE ST, SALT LAKE CITY, UT 841153110
Phone: 385 646-5000
Web: WWW.GRANITESCHOOLS.ORG

HISTORICAL FINANCIALS

Company Type: Private

Income Statement
FYE: June 30

	REVENUE ($ mil.)	NET INCOME ($ mil.)	NET PROFIT MARGIN	EMPLOYEES
06/09	528	14	2.7%	8,000
06/08	510	18	3.6%	—
06/07	0	0	—	—
Annual Growth	—	2849.6%	—	—

GRANITE TELECOMMUNICATIONS LLC

Granite Telecommunications is looking for rock solid growth as a reseller of telecommunications services to commercial clients in the US and Canada. The company is a wholesaler of local and long distance telephone service as well as broadband Internet connections over 1.3 million lines provided by network operators. It serves corporate clients many of whom run offices in multiple states offering them no account transfer charges and no term or volume contracts on telephone service. Granite also designs and installs network cabling and security systems and provides loss prevention and risk management services.

Geographic Reach

Granite serves clients across Canada and the US from offices in Florida Massachusetts Georgia New York and Rhode Island.

Operations

The company serves more than 4840 corporate clients in more than a half a million locations. Its customers include most of the US Fortune 100 companies and its customer retention rate is more than five times higher than the industry average. It has about 1.4 million phone lines; about 1.3 billion lines are business lines and 100000 are data lines. The company uses copper wiring found in traditional telecommunication networks which provide reliable and cost-effective service. Granite's subsidiary Granite Guard is a leading provider of loss prevention and risk management services solely for businesses.

Financial Performance

The company reported in September 2014 that is annual revenue was more than $1 billion. Granite said it has grown at a 20% annual rate.

Strategy

The company is on a fast expansion track. In 2014 it opened a 10000-square-foot office in New York City to meet an expected increase in business. It reached an agreement with AT&T in which AT&T will continue to supply telephone and data service to Granite customers through 2017. Granite also partnered with Global Capacity to use Global Capacity's infrastructure for broadband connections in the US and Canada.

EXECUTIVES

SVP and COO, Rand Currier
Founder and CEO, Robert T. (Rob) Hale
CFO, Richard Wurman
National Account Manager, Jim Coffey
National Account Manager, Larry Sylvain
National Account Manager, Michael (Mel) Perrone
National Account Manager, Robert (Bob) Meegan
National Account Manager, William Drago
National Account Manager, Austin Edwards
National Account Manager, Erhan Dilek
National Accounts Manager, Drew Mullert
Vice President, Sam Kline
National Account Manager, Matt Olem
National Sales Manager, Dan Pratt
National Sales Manager, Rick Steinbauer

LOCATIONS

HQ: GRANITE TELECOMMUNICATIONS LLC
100 NEWPORT AVENUE EXT # 1, QUINCY, MA 021712126
Phone: 617 933-5500
Web: WWW.GRANITENET.COM

PRODUCTS/OPERATIONS

Products and Services
Broadband
Data Services (Business Security Structured Cabling)
Telephone Service

COMPETITORS

5LINX	Rogers Communications
ACN Inc.	Sprint Communications
AT&T	Verizon
BCE	World Communications
EarthLink	

HISTORICAL FINANCIALS

Company Type: Private

Income Statement
FYE: December 31

	REVENUE ($ mil.)	NET INCOME ($ mil.)	NET PROFIT MARGIN	EMPLOYEES
12/13	865	228	26.4%	650
12/12	736	187	25.5%	—
12/11	609	143	23.5%	—
12/10	517	0	—	—
Annual Growth	18.7%	—	—	—

2013 Year-End Financials

Return on assets: 4.2%   Cash ($ mil.): 46
Return on equity: 26.4%
Current ratio: 0.70

GREAT NORTHERN CORPORATION

Auditors: GRANT THORNTON LLP MILWAUKEE

LOCATIONS

HQ: GREAT NORTHERN CORPORATION
395 STROEBE RD, APPLETON, WI 549148782
Phone: 920 739-3671
Web: WWW.GREATNORTHERNCORP.COM

HISTORICAL FINANCIALS

Company Type: Private

Income Statement
FYE: December 31

	REVENUE ($ mil.)	NET INCOME ($ mil.)	NET PROFIT MARGIN	EMPLOYEES
12/13	392	31	8.0%	1,032
12/07	231	16	7.2%	—
12/05	196	12	6.3%	—
12/04	1,389	0	—	—
Annual Growth	(13.1%)	—	—	—

2013 Year-End Financials

Return on assets: 5.1%   Cash ($ mil.): —
Return on equity: 8.0%
Current ratio: 1.00

GREENSTONE FARM CREDIT SERVICES ACA

One of the largest associations in the Farm Credit System GreenStone offers FARM CREDIT SERVICES (FCS) provides short intermediate and long-term loans; equipment and building leases; appraisal services; and life and crop insurance to farmers in Michigan and Wisconsin. It serves about 15000 members and has nearly 40 locations. Through an alliance with AgriSolutions a farm software and consulting company Greenstone provides income tax planning and preparation services farm business consulting and educational seminars. FCS Mortgage provides residential loans for rural properties as well as loans for home improvement construction and refinancing.

Dairy and cash crop loans each account for nearly a quarter of GreenStone FCS' loan portfolio which is rounded out by rural residential real estate and greenhouses hogs and other commodities.

EXECUTIVES

Exec V Pres, Melissa (Mel) Stolicker
Exec V Pres, Peter Lemmer
Vice President Human Resources, Bethany Barker
Regional Vice President, Erin Dubois
Vice President Commercial Lending, Tyson Lemon
Regional Vice President, David Ballman
Regional Vice President, Tim McTigue
Senior Vice President Sales, Brad Henion

Vice President Credit, Kevin Emison
Senior Vice President Chief Credit Off, Paul
 Anderson
Senior Vice President Capital Markets, Al Compton
Vice President of Marketing and Public Relations,
 Melissa (Mel) Rogers
Vice President Financial Services, Leo Pasch
Vice President Commercial, Dana Kirk
Senior Vice President Commercial Lending, John
 Jones
Vice President Commercial Credit, Gayle Olson
Vice President Credit, Steve Kluemper
Vice President Commercial Lending, Larry Urban
Vice President Credit, Thomas (Thom) Urban
Vice President of Sales and Customer Relations,
 Ben Mahlich
Second Vice President, Shane Kenner
Regional Vice President Northeast Region, Carl
 Treml
Vice President Commercial Lending, Thomas
 (Thom) Wilson
Senior Vice President Chief Human Resources,
 Sphr B Barker
Auditors: PRICEWATERHOUSECOOPERS LLP MI

LOCATIONS

HQ: GREENSTONE FARM CREDIT SERVICES ACA
 3515 WEST RD, EAST LANSING, MI 488237312
Phone: 517 324-0213
Web: WWW.GREENSTONEFCS.COM

COMPETITORS

COUNTRY Financial   Rabobank Group
FB BanCorp

HISTORICAL FINANCIALS

Company Type: Private

Income Statement — FYE: December 31

	ASSETS ($ mil.)	NET INCOME ($ mil.)	INCOME AS % OF ASSETS	EMPLOYEES
12/07	4,317	69	1.6%	380
12/06	3,691	63	1.7%	
Annual Growth	17.0%	8.9%	—	—

GREENWICH HOSPITAL ASSOCIATION INC

Auditors: YALE NEW HAVEN HEALTH SVC NEW

LOCATIONS

HQ: GREENWICH HOSPITAL ASSOCIATION INC
 5 PERRYRIDGE RD, GREENWICH, CT 068304697
Phone: 203 863-3000
Web: WWW.GREENHOSP.ORG

HISTORICAL FINANCIALS

Company Type: Private

Income Statement — FYE: September 30

	REVENUE ($ mil.)	NET INCOME ($ mil.)	NET PROFIT MARGIN	EMPLOYEES
09/13	312	27	8.9%	1,600
09/09	307	22	7.3%	
09/05	1	0	—	
09/03	188	0	—	
Annual Growth	5.2%	—	—	—

2013 Year-End Financials
Return on assets: 1.9%   Cash ($ mil.): 25
Return on equity: 8.9%
Current ratio: 1.20

GROSSMONT HOSPITAL CORPORATION

Residents of the eastern San Diego community of La Mesa California depend on Grossmont for medical care. Grossmont Hospital is a 540-bed not-for-profit health care facility. The hospital which opened in 1955 has a staff of about 700 physicians. The full-service acute care facility provides specialty services in the areas of cardiology oncology mental health orthopedics pediatrics physical therapy sleep therapy hospice and women's health care. The Grossmont Hospital Corporation is a subsidiary of Sharp HealthCare; it operates the Grossmont Hospital through a lease agreement with state-owned Grossmont Hospital District.

Strategy

Grossmont Hospital is undergoing expansion and improvement efforts. Current projects include renovation efforts (including energy and utility upgrades) on the existing hospital and the construction of new hospital wings and buildings on the surrounding grounds. In 2012 the company began work on a new $60 million heart and vascular center that will include diagnostic laboratory and surgery space.

An earlier $80 million stage of the hospital's expansion project was completed in 2009 and included construction of a five-story critical care and emergency center tower (adding 90 beds) as well as other renovations and utility upgrades. The improvement efforts are funded by public general obligation bonds approved in 2006 and overseen by a citizens' board and the Grossmont Hospital District which will fund a total of up to $247 million in construction efforts by 2016.

Company Background

The property and buildings of Grossmont Hospital are owned by the Grossmont Hospital District which was formed in 1952. The Grossmont Hospital Corporation was created in 1991 as a subsidiary of Sharp HealthCare exclusively to run a 30-year lease (expiring in 2021) of state-owned Grossmont Hospital District.

EXECUTIVES

R.N. Board Secretary, Gloria A. Chadwick
Chief Executive Officer, Barry Jantz
Chairman, Robert Klaiber
Board Vice President, Gloria A. Chadwick
Director, Deborah McElravy
Director, Michael Emerson
Director, Michael T. Long
CEO and Director, Barry Jantz
Auditors: ERNST & YOUNG US LLP SAN DIEG

LOCATIONS

HQ: GROSSMONT HOSPITAL CORPORATION
 5555 GROSSMONT CENTER DR, LA MESA, CA
 919423077
Phone: 619 740-6000
Web: WWW.SHARP.COM

COMPETITORS

Adventist Health
Eisenhower Medical
 Center
Scripps health
Tenet Healthcare
Tri-City Healthcare
Palomar Health   District
Paradise Valley   UCSD Medical
 Hospital
Rady Children's
 Hospital

HISTORICAL FINANCIALS

Company Type: Private

Income Statement — FYE: September 30

	REVENUE ($ mil.)	NET INCOME ($ mil.)	NET PROFIT MARGIN	EMPLOYEES
09/13	621	69	11.1%	2,697
09/09	500	41	8.3%	—
09/08	452	37	8.3%	—
09/04	327	0	—	—
Annual Growth	7.4%	—	—	—

2013 Year-End Financials
Return on assets: 2.2%   Cash ($ mil.): 6
Return on equity: 11.1%
Current ratio: 1.10

GROUP O INC.

The "O" in Group O stands for optimization. It also stands for Ontiveros the family that leads this company. Founded by chairman Robert Ontiveros Group O is one of the largest Hispanic-owned companies in the US. It helps big businesses improve their operations through three divisions: marketing packaging and supply chain. It offers everything from direct mail creation to shrink wrap procurement to warehousing and distribution and business intelligence. It has served clients from various industries including food and beverage (Kerry) consumer goods (P&G) manufacturing (Johnson Controls) pharmaceutical (Bristol-Myers Squibb) and telecommunications (AT&T).

Geographic Reach

Group O maintains a national network of more than 20 facilities mostly concentrated in the Midwest (Illinois Iowa and Minnesota) and Texas. Other sales offices and warehouses are located in California Nevada Pennsylvania and various southern states. It also works with more than 7000 suppliers in more than 30 countries.

Operations

Group O is a diversified business process outsourcing provider specializing in marketing supply chain packaging and business analytics products.

The company's supply chain division mainly serves heavy equipment and high technology OEMs while its packaging division targets manufacturers and distributors in need of streamlining their packaging processes. It procures and distributes bags stretch films tapes and other materials and also repairs calibrates and upgrades equipment to optimize performance.

Its SMART Audit reporting tool provides realtime reports that monitor production and spending across a plant network so that companies can take appropriate cost reduction actions. Meanwhile its marketing division offers a range of service offerings including marketing analytics customer rewards programs direct mail and e-mail marketing outsourced printing and a customer call center.

The company's Business Analytics unit has experts that can guide companies that seek to make sense out of unstructured and structured data — providing strategists and decision-makers with new insights into customer behavior while maximizing both new and existing channels. The team guides the creation implementation and management of tools in the latest applications and platforms across a comprehensive spectrum of existing systems.

Sales and Marketing

The company serves FORTUNE 500 clients across a broad range of industries including food and beverage telecommunications manufacturing consumer packaged goods retail financial services pharmaceutical healthcare technology energy and the public sector.

Strategy

In 2014 Group O launched a new website for its O-vations service offering which is aimed at helping companies optimize the design and operation of enterprise-scale reward programs. Key services range from program design and management technology integration operations and communications value-added services and reporting and analytics. That year the company also opened its Business Analytics unit in Hyderabad India. The team helps generate customer acquisition and loyalty marketing insights that clients can then use to make better business decisions.

Company Background

Ontiveros established Group O in 1974 as Bi-State Packaging which sold packaging materials and equipment to manufacturers. Today it is one of the top 15 Hispanic-owned businesses in the nation.

EXECUTIVES

CEO, Gregg Ontiveros
CFO, Bob Marriott
VP and CIO, Mike Huntley
SVP Business Development, Mike De La Cruz
Executive Director of Program Management, Kimberly Davis
President Marketing Solutions, Charles Wetzel
VP Operations Supply Chain Solutions, Tony Lopez
Vice President Humn Rsrcs, Kim Fox
Vice President Corporate Accounts, Matt Ontiveros
Senior Vice President And Chief Diversity Officer, Debbie Storey
Vice President Operations, Dorothy Tubbs
Vice President Enterprise Architect, Kevin Maione
Senior Vice President Business Operations, Joe Harper
Vice President O2 Client Relationship Executive And Business Development, Mark Beasley
Vice President Enterprise Architect, Kevin Mainoe
Chairman, Robert (Bob) Ontiveros

LOCATIONS

HQ: GROUP O INC.
4905 77TH AVE E, MILAN, IL 612643250
Phone: 309 736-8100
Web: WWW.GROUPO.COM

PRODUCTS/OPERATIONS

Selected Services
Marketing
 Analytics
 Consumer and trade fulfillment
 Customer call center and workforce management
 Direct mail and e-mail optimization
 Print management outsourcing
 Rewards and loyalty programs
Packaging
 Equipment supply and repair (bagging case handling labeling shrinking and stretch wrapping systems)
 Materials supply (labels poly bags protective packaging sanitation products shrink and stretch films and tape)
 Stretch film equipment auditing
Supply chain
 Business process outsourcing
 Distribution
 Global sourcing
 Inventory management
 Order management
 Supplier management
 Warehousing

Selected Industries Served
Food and Beverage
Telecommunications
Manufacturing
Consumer Packaged Goods
Financial Services
Pharmaceutical
Health care
Technology

COMPETITORS

Brightstar Corp.
CEVA Logistics U.S.
GENCO Distribution System
Jay Group
Kenco Logistics Services
Ozburn-Hessey Logistics
The Bernd Group
UPS Supply Chain Solutions
Weber Logistics

HISTORICAL FINANCIALS
Company Type: Private

Income Statement
FYE: December 31

	REVENUE ($ mil.)	NET INCOME ($ mil.)	NET PROFIT MARGIN	EMPLOYEES
12/13	569	5	1.0%	1,520
12/05	240	5	2.2%	—
Annual Growth	11.4%	0.9%	—	—

2013 Year-End Financials
Return on assets: 87.9%
Return on equity: 1.0%
Current ratio: 0.90
Cash ($ mil.): 7

GROVE SERVICES INC.

Auditors: MCGLADREY & PULLEN LLP BURLI

LOCATIONS

HQ: GROVE SERVICES INC.
100 WILLIAM ST STE 210, WELLESLEY, MA 024813702
Phone: 781 772-1187
Web: WWW.GROVESERVICES.ORG

HISTORICAL FINANCIALS
Company Type: Private

Income Statement
FYE: December 31

	REVENUE ($ mil.)	NET INCOME ($ mil.)	NET PROFIT MARGIN	EMPLOYEES
12/08	307	7	2.5%	14
12/07	257	2	1.2%	
12/06	882	0	—	
Annual Growth	—	2083.2%	—	—

2008 Year-End Financials
Return on assets: 3.0%
Return on equity: 2.5%
Current ratio: 1.80
Cash ($ mil.): 11

GROWMARK INC.

Retail farm-supply and grain-marketing cooperative GROWMARK can mark its growth by the grain. A member-owed agricultural co-op GROWMARK has more than 100000 members. Under the FAST STOP name the co-op runs more than 250 fuel stations and convenience stores in the Midwest. Its Seedway subsidiary sells commercial vegetable seed and farm seed for turf and grains including alfalfa corn wheat and soybeans. GROWMARK also offers fertilizer seeds ethanol biodiesel and farm financing. Its MID-CO COMMODITIES subsidiary trades grain and offers advice regarding futures and options.

Geographic Reach

GROWMARK is headquartered in Bloomington Illinois and serves customers in more than 40 states and Ontario Canada. SEEDWAY maintains eight office and warehouse locations in Vermont New York Pennsylvania and Florida.

Strategy

Cooperation is important within and among agricultural cooperatives. A strong believer in the latter part of this principle GROWMARK has marketing agreements and alliances with among others fertilizer maker and distributor CF Industries pet-food producer PRO-PET agribusiness company Syngenta and rural financial services provider CoBank.

Mergers and Acquisitions

GROWMARK acquires fertilizer storage terminals and transportation infrastructure on a regular basis.

EXECUTIVES

Vice President, Jim Spradlin
Vice Chairman, John Reifsteck
CEO, Jeff Solberg
Vice President General Counsel, Brent Bostrom
VP Eastern Retail Operations, Steve Buckalew
VP and CFO, Marshall Bohbrink
VP Energy, Kevin Carroll
VP Midwest Retail and Acquisitions, Shelly Kruse
VP Grain, Brent Ericson
Vice President Human Resources & Compliance, Gary Swango
VP Agronomy, Mark Orr
VP Financial and Risk Management, Mike Woods
VP Member Services, Denny Worth
Vice President Information Technology, George Key
Vice President Information Systems, Marvin Weisert
National Account Manager, Norman Frank
Vice President Information Technology, George Mueller
Vice President Of Information Technology, Rick Norton
Vice President Member Services, Dennis Farmer
Vice President, Paul Eckhart
Vice President Finance, Jeffrey (Jeff) Solberg
Vice Chairman, Rick Nelson
Vice Chairman, Chet Esther
Assistant Treasurer, John Fruin
Auditors: ERNST & YOUNG LLP CHICAGO IL

LOCATIONS

HQ: GROWMARK INC.
1701 TOWANDA AVE, BLOOMINGTON, IL 617012057
Phone: 309 557-6000
Web: WWW.GROWMARK.COM

PRODUCTS/OPERATIONS

Selected Retail Products and Operations
COMFORT PRO (propane heating oil)
FAST STOP (fuel facilities)
FS (farm supplies)
Green Yard (turf seed fertilizer)
Seedway (farm turf and vegetable seed)

Selected Member Cooperatives and Subsidiaries
AgVantage FS Inc.
AgView Grain LLC
Evergreen FS Inc.
GROWMARK FS LLC
MID-CO COMMODITIES
Northern Grain Marketing LLC
Seedway LLC

Total Grain Marketing LLC
Western Grain Marketing LLC

COMPETITORS

ADM	Marathon Oil
AGRI Industries	NC Hybrids
Ag Processing Inc.	Orscheln Farm and Home
BP	Pfister Hybrid Corn
Barkley Seed	Pioneer Hi-Bred
Bayer CropScience	Rabo AgriFinance
CHS	Sakata Seed
Cargill	Seed Enterprises
Chevron	Southern States
Costco Wholesale	Terra Nitrogen
DeBruce Grain	Wal-Mart
Exxon Mobil	Wilbur-Ellis

HISTORICAL FINANCIALS
Company Type: Private

Income Statement
FYE: August 31

	REVENUE ($ mil.)	NET INCOME ($ mil.)	NET PROFIT MARGIN	EMPLOYEES
08/14	10,372	166	1.6%	1,036
08/13	10,171	189	1.9%	—
08/12	10,057	249	2.5%	—
08/11	8,597	0	—	—
Annual Growth	6.5%	—	—	—

2014 Year-End Financials
Return on assets: 3.9%
Return on equity: 1.6%
Current ratio: 0.80
Cash ($ mil.): 83

GRUNLEY CONSTRUCTION CO. INC.

Grunley gets it done from the monumental to the mundane. Founded in 1955 Grunley Construction Company provides general contracting engineering architectural and construction management services and specializes in the renovation restoration and modernization of historic buildings in the Washington DC area. Its projects range from prestigious undertakings —the Smithsonian Institution the Washington Monument and the US Treasury building —to more pedestrian endeavors such as office buildings apartment buildings schools and power plants. The company also has lent its services to the construction of embassies airports and military facilities.

EXECUTIVES

Chairman, Martin Grunley
President, Kenneth (Ken) Grunley
Chief Estimator, Andrew Phillips
Strategic Planning Business Development and New Technology, Joel Zingeser
Communications Manager, Donna Duncan
HR Generalist, Gloria Nokes
Project Manager, Rodney Nichols
Project Manager, Daniel L. Patete
Superintendent, Robert Dalton
Estimating Assistant, Michael Ann Balloch
President He, Greg Druga
VP Special Projects Group, John Greenwell
Director Preconstruction Services, Walker Tom
Project Executive, Chip Scott
Vice President of Pre-Construction Services, Tom Walker
Auditors: BAKER TILLY VIRCHOW KRAUSE LL

LOCATIONS

HQ: GRUNLEY CONSTRUCTION CO. INC.
15020 SHADY STE 500, ROCKVILLE, MD 20850
Phone: 240 399-2000
Web: WWW.GRUNLEY.COM

COMPETITORS

Hega Construction Company	Parsons Transportation
	S. W. Rodgers

HISTORICAL FINANCIALS
Company Type: Private

Income Statement
FYE: December 31

	REVENUE ($ mil.)	NET INCOME ($ mil.)	NET PROFIT MARGIN	EMPLOYEES
12/11	323	0	—	320
12/10	310	0	—	—
12/09	1,129	0	0.0%	—
Annual Growth	(46.5%)			

2011 Year-End Financials
Return on assets: 0.6%
Return on equity: —
Current ratio: 0.90
Cash ($ mil.): 17

GUARANTEE ELECTRICAL COMPANY

Guarantee Electrical has been a power in St. Louis since it "guaranteed" to light up the 1904 World's Fair. (It delivered on the guarantee). Now a major US electrical contractor the company offers commercial institutional and industrial services including construction design/build communications/data and maintenance. Guarantee Electrical operates throughout the country and has worked on such varied projects as the MGM Grand in Las Vegas and several post office and prison facilities. Its GECO Systems division installs and services intercom closed-circuit television and other audio-visual systems. The Oertli family owns and operates the firm.Geographic ReachGuarantee Electrical is headquartered in St. Louis with offices in Granite City Illinois; Denver; and Benicia California. As a member of Federated Electrical Contractors the firm has more than 30 joint venture partners operating in 60 cities across North America the UK and Japan. StrategyThe company serves the education data center health care heavy industrial hospitality/gaming and high rise markets. The firm is currently at work on the electrification and process control instrumentation installation for a new waste water treatment plant in Cape Girardeau Missouri its eighth water treatment project in the state and 11th nationally.OwnershipThe company is nearing completion of a multiyear ownership transition program designed to convert the previously 100% family-owned firm to an employee stock ownership plan (ESOP).

EXECUTIVES

Chairman and Chief Executive Officer, Frederick J. (Rick) Oertli
Executive Vice President Missouri Operations, Roger Oertli
President, Douglas (Doug) Mertzlufft
Senior Vice President Colorado Operations, Steve Juan
Senior Vice President of National Operations, David M. Gralike

Chief Financial Officer, Josh Voegtli, age 38
Senior Vice President, Nazeeh Kiblawi
Vice President Of Operations, Dave Gralike
Vice President of Project, Dipak Kapadia
Vice President Of Marketing, Steve Briesacher
Vice President of Preconstruction Services, Jason Wiegand
Vice President, Mike Minor
Secretary, Nancy Martinez
Assistant Treasurer, ED Rode
Auditors: UHY LLP ST LOUIS MISSOURI

LOCATIONS

HQ: GUARANTEE ELECTRICAL COMPANY
3405 BENT AVE, SAINT LOUIS, MO 631162601
Phone: 314 772-5400
Web: WWW.GECO.COM

PRODUCTS/OPERATIONS

Selected Projects
Alton Memorial Hospital expansion
Southern Illinois Office of Guarantee Electrical
SunCoke Energy Inc. coke oven plant
Saint Louis Art Museum expansion
Emerson Data Center
River City Casino
Express Scripts Technology & Innovation Center

COMPETITORS

Conti Electric	MDU Construction
Dycom	Services
EMCOR	Quanta Services
Integrated Electrical Services	

HISTORICAL FINANCIALS
Company Type: Private

Income Statement
FYE: September 30

	REVENUE ($ mil.)	NET INCOME ($ mil.)	NET PROFIT MARGIN	EMPLOYEES
09/14	168	0	—	700
09/13	169	0	—	—
09/12	135	0	—	—
09/11	119	0	—	—
Annual Growth	12.1%	—	—	—

2014 Year-End Financials
Return on assets: 7.5%
Return on equity: —
Current ratio: 1.40
Cash ($ mil.): 3

GUEST SERVICES INC.

Guest Services satisfies hungry and sleepy patrons. The company provides contract food services and hospitality-management services nationwide. It operates cafeterias and onsite restaurants and offers catering to businesses hotels hospitals conference centers and government operations including the US Supreme Court the US House of Representatives and the National Park Service. For leisure and resort facilities Guest Services also provides special-event catering and offers management services such as marketing human resources procurement quality-assurance and information technology services. Guest Services was founded in 1917 as a private company to serve governmental agencies.
Operations
Guest Services serves some 250 facilities across the US and more than 25 million guests each year. The company also owns Lancaster Foods one of

the largest wholesale produce companies in the mid-Atlantic region.

Additional offerings include corporate accounting systems and food safety and health support.

Geographic Reach

Based in Fairfax Virginia Guest Services serves a variety of customers nationwide.

Sales and Marketing

Guest Services serves several clients including government and business dining facilities museums hotels resorts conference centers luxury condominiums senior living centers health care systems state and national park recreation school and university dining facilities specialty retail stores and full-service restaurants.

Customers have included Washington DC's National Mall and Memorial Park. Guest Services also manages food lodging and recreation services at state parks in West Virginia New York and California.

Strategy

Guest Services has been expanding its portfolio of premium properties. For example it owns and manages the DoubleTree Suites by Hilton Naples. In 2013 Guest Services acquired The Lodge and Spa at Breckenridge which overlooks Colorado's Breckenridge Village. With 45 rooms the property is a popular destination for weddings and corporate events. It's adding food and beverage service in-house catering and event planning to the property's services.

EXECUTIVES

CEO, Gerard T. Gabrys
President and COO, Jeffrey A. Marquis
President Lancaster Foods, John Gates
VP Hotel Division South, Barry G. Trice
VP Sales and Marketing, Jerry Chadwich
VP and CFO, Nico Foris
Assistant Vice President of Operations Division, Rick Wayland
Auditors: PRICEWATERHOUSECOOPERS LLP M

LOCATIONS

HQ: GUEST SERVICES INC.
3055 PROSPERITY AVE, FAIRFAX, VA 220312290
Phone: 703 849-9300
Web: WWW.GUESTSERVICES.COM

PRODUCTS/OPERATIONS

Selected Services
Audits
Corporate Support Services
Financial Accounting Systems
Food Safety and Health
Human Resources
IT
Maintenance Support
Management Information Systems
Marketing
Onsite Test Kitchen
PeopleSoft Processing
Procurement
Quality Assurance
Safety
Security
Test Kitchen
Training

COMPETITORS

ARAMARK	Delaware North
Centerplate	Sodexo USA
Compass Group USA	Valley Services

HISTORICAL FINANCIALS

Company Type: Private

Income Statement

FYE: December 31

	REVENUE ($ mil.)	NET INCOME ($ mil.)	NET PROFIT MARGIN	EMPLOYEES
12/13	387	2	0.6%	3,500
12/12	377	2	0.7%	—
12/11	369	0	0.0%	—
12/10	346	0	—	—
Annual Growth	3.8%	—	—	—

2013 Year-End Financials

Return on assets: 2.9%
Return on equity: 0.6%
Current ratio: 0.90
Cash ($ mil.): 2

GUILDNET INC.

Auditors: LOEB & TROPER LLP NEW YORK N

LOCATIONS

HQ: GUILDNET INC.
15 W 65TH ST, NEW YORK, NY 100236601
Phone: 212 769-6200
Web: WWW.GUILDNETNY.ORG

HISTORICAL FINANCIALS

Company Type: Private

Income Statement

FYE: December 31

	REVENUE ($ mil.)	NET INCOME ($ mil.)	NET PROFIT MARGIN	EMPLOYEES
12/13	672	45	6.8%	377
12/12	433	42	9.8%	—
12/07	225	(13)	—	—
12/06	168	0	—	—
Annual Growth	21.8%	—	—	—

2013 Year-End Financials

Return on assets: 0.3%
Return on equity: 6.8%
Current ratio: 0.20
Cash ($ mil.): 13

GUILFORD COUNTY SCHOOL SYSTEM

Auditors: DIXON HUGHES GOODMAN LLP WINS

LOCATIONS

HQ: GUILFORD COUNTY SCHOOL SYSTEM
712 N EUGENE ST, GREENSBORO, NC 274011622
Phone: 336 370-8100
Web: WWW.GCSNC.COM

HISTORICAL FINANCIALS

Company Type: Private

Income Statement

FYE: June 30

	REVENUE ($ mil.)	NET INCOME ($ mil.)	NET PROFIT MARGIN	EMPLOYEES
06/11	692	(0)	—	8,000
06/09	0	(0)	—	—
06/03	0	0	—	—
06/02	546	0	—	—
Annual Growth	2.7%	—	—	—

2011 Year-End Financials

Return on assets: 1.9%
Return on equity: (-0.1%)
Current ratio: 0.70
Cash ($ mil.): 28

GWINNETT HOSPITAL SYSTEM INC.

Auditors: KPMG LLP ATLANTA GA

LOCATIONS

HQ: GWINNETT HOSPITAL SYSTEM INC.
1000 MEDICAL CENTER BLVD, LAWRENCEVILLE, GA 300467694
Phone: 678 343-3428
Web: WWW.GWINNETTMEDICALCENTER.ORG

HISTORICAL FINANCIALS

Company Type: Private

Income Statement

FYE: June 30

	REVENUE ($ mil.)	NET INCOME ($ mil.)	NET PROFIT MARGIN	EMPLOYEES
06/14	642	34	5.4%	2,050
06/13	587	53	9.2%	—
06/11	592	56	9.5%	—
06/10	579	0	—	—
Annual Growth	2.6%	—	—	—

2014 Year-End Financials

Return on assets: 4.0%
Return on equity: 5.4%
Current ratio: 2.50
Cash ($ mil.): 24

H. J. RUSSELL & COMPANY

H.J. Russell & Company one of the nation's largest minority-owned enterprises helps shape southeastern cities. It's a general contractor construction manager property manager and developer that specializes in affordable multifamily housing and mixed-use communities. It also has expertise in building airports hospitals office towers retail stores and schools. Its development arm Russell New Urban Development offers such services as feasibility analysis land development and asset management; it has more than $500 million in development underway. H.J. Russell also manages more than 6000 apartment and public housing units. The family-owned company was founded by chairman Herman J. Russell in 1952.

Geographic Reach

Firmly rooted in Atlanta H.J. Russell conducts much of its business in Georgia. The company has increasingly looked outside of the state to diversify its projects. Beyond Atlanta Russell has offices in Chicago Dallas Florida New York North Carolina Ohio and Phoenix.

Operations

H.J. Russell & Company is active on many fronts. Its menu of interconnected services includes: Real Estate Development; Program Management (established 1976); Construction (est. 1962); and Property Management. More than half of the firm's employees work in its development division Russell New Urban Development which is closely intertwined with the construction side of the family business. It is a formula that the firm relies on for growth.

Strategy

The downturn in the construction market during the recession left H.J. Russell depending on its various service offerings and geographic diversity to weather the storm. Facing lagging revenues the company cut costs and reduced staff as it waited for the economy to rebound.

H.J. Russell also looked for more non-residential work. The company keeps its non-residential client and project roster diverse serving the commercial institutional and public sectors. Some of the company's key projects include the $1.9 billion Dallas/Fort Worth International Airport Atlanta's $6.2 billion Hartsfield-Jackson Development the $1.6 billion Maynard H. Jackson Jr. International Terminal the US headquarters of The Coca-Cola Company Howard University and the Birmingham Civil Rights Institute. It also regularly builds stores for retail giants Target and The Home Depot.

Company Background

After leading the group for more than 50 years Herman Russell stepped down as CEO and handed the reins of the company to his children in 2004.

EXECUTIVES

Vice President Commercial Construction, Barry Compton
Vice President Sales and Operations, Sonia Booker
Senior Vice President, Valerie (Val) Calloway
Vice President Legal Affairs, Eric Hilton
Vice President, Bruce Harris
Vice President Multifamily Residential Construction, Greg Dixon
Vice President Joint Ventures, James (Jamie) Wille

LOCATIONS

HQ: H. J. RUSSELL & COMPANY
504 FAIR ST SW, ATLANTA, GA 303131206
Phone: 404 330-1000
Web: WWW.HJRUSSELL.COM

PRODUCTS/OPERATIONS

Selected Projects
Airport
Commercial
Government
Healthcare
Higher Education
Industrial
Interiors
K-12
Manufacturing
Parking Structures
Public Assembly
Residential
Retail
Transportation

Selected Services
Construction
Program management

Property management
Real estate development

COMPETITORS

Barton Malow	Cousins Properties
Batson-Cook	Hardin Construction
Brasfield & Gorrie	Shelco
Brice Building	Weitz
Choate Construction	Winter Construction
Comstock Holding	

HISTORICAL FINANCIALS
Company Type: Private

Income Statement   FYE: December 31

	REVENUE ($ mil.)	NET INCOME ($ mil.)	NET PROFIT MARGIN	EMPLOYEES
12/09	170	2	1.2%	733
12/08	222	3	1.8%	—
12/07	321	0	—	—
Annual Growth	—64434.9%		—	—

2009 Year-End Financials

Return on assets: 13.4%   Cash ($ mil.): 17
Return on equity: 1.2%
Current ratio: 1.30

H. LEE MOFFITT CANCER CENTER & RESEARCH INSTITUTE HOSPITAL INC.

The H. Lee Moffitt Cancer Center and Research Institute founded in 1986 is a National Cancer Institute-designated Comprehensive Cancer Center located on the Tampa campus of the University of South Florida. The institute carries it out its stated mission of "contributing to the prevention and cure of cancer" through patient care research and education. It operates a 210-bed medical and surgical facility as well as outpatient treatment programs and a blood and marrow transplant program. Its research programs include study in the areas of molecular oncology immunology risk assessment health outcomes and experimental therapeutics.

Operations

The Moffitt Cancer Center sees more than 9000 cancer inpatients each year; it also handles some 328000 outpatient visits annually. In addition to its 40-bed blood and marrow transplant center which performs 400 annual transplants the hospital includes more than a dozen operating rooms and extensive diagnostic radiology and radiation therapy labs. The Cancer Screening and Prevention Center offers genetic testing for certain kinds of hereditary cancers (breast ovarian colon and melanoma).

The Moffitt Research Institute conducts a wide range of cancer studies and some of its drug discovery research programs are managed through partnerships with pharmaceutical companies and other research laboratories. The research institute also relies on funding grants from organizations such as the National Institutes of Health. It has received more than $80 million in grant funding and participated in some 300 clinical trials.

The Moffitt Cancer Center likewise has educational and health care alliances with a number of Florida hospitals and colleges including a three-

way cancer care and research partnership with Shands HealthCare and the University of Florida. Through its affiliated network program (the Moffitt Oncology Network) Moffitt works with community doctors and centers across Florida to provide enhanced cancer services throughout the state. It also operates a number of outpatient clinics in surrounding areas.

Geographic Reach

Through its main campus and numerous outpatient sites Moffitt Cancer Center primarily serves residents of seven Florida counties: Hernando Hillsborough Manatee Pasco Pinellas Polk and Sarasota. It also serves patients from other areas of Florida and neighboring states.

Sales and Marketing

HMO and PPO plans account for about 65% of patient service revenues while reimbursements from Medicare and Medicaid plans account for another 32% of sales.

Financial Performance

Revenue at Moffitt Cancer Center and Research Institute increased 1% to $779 million in 2013 from $772 the previous year due to higher patient service revenues. After a net loss in 2012 the institute reported net income of $26 million due to an increase in net assets and non-operating gains. Cash from operations also grew by $77 million due to the net income increase and cash generated from an estimated third-party settlement.

Strategy

Moffitt Cancer Center conducts expansion and facility improvement projects to enhance services for its cancer patients. For instance it launched construction of a new $74 million outpatient facility at the current McKinley office site in 2013; the location is near the main campus and will provide surgery infusion imaging research and other services. It also formed a partnership with Space Coast Cancer Center Boca Raton Regional Hospital Advinus Therapeutics and Lehigh Valley Health Network to improve cancer care for all the organizations.

EXECUTIVES

VP and CIO, Mark Hulse
President and CEO, Alan List
executive Vice President of clinical affairs, Douglas Letson
Auditors: ERNST & YOUNG LLP TAMPA FL

LOCATIONS

HQ: H. LEE MOFFITT CANCER CENTER & RESEARCH INSTITUTE HOSPITAL INC.
12902 USF MAGNOLIA DR, TAMPA, FL 336129416
Phone: 813 745-4673
Web: WWW.MOFFITT.ORG

PRODUCTS/OPERATIONS

Selected Services
Chemotherapy
Diagnosis
Emotional Support
Integrative Medicine
Labwork Scans and Biopsy
Other Patient Services
Pain Management
Radiation
Screening and Genetics
Spiritual Support
Surgical Care
Well-Being

Selected Research Fields
Basic Science Division
    Cancer Imaging and Metabolism
    Drug Discovery
    Immunology
    Integrated Mathematical Oncology
    Molecular Oncology
    Tumor Biology
Population Science Division

Biostatistics and Bioinformatics
Cancer Epidemiology
Health Outcomes & Behavior

COMPETITORS

All Children's Hospital	Mayo Clinic Jacksonville
Baptist Hospital of Miami	Memorial Sloan-Kettering
Bay Medical Center	Oak Hill Hospital
Boca Raton Regional Hospital	Roswell Park Cancer Institute
Dana-Farber	Sacred Heart Health System
Fox Chase Cancer Center	South Georgia Medical Center
Jackson County Hospital of Florida	St. Vincent's Health System
MD Anderson Cancer Center	
Manatee Memorial Hospital	

HISTORICAL FINANCIALS

Company Type: Private

Income Statement

FYE: June 30

	REVENUE ($ mil.)	NET INCOME ($ mil.)	NET PROFIT MARGIN	EMPLOYEES
06/14	855	50	5.9%	4,200
06/13	779	26	3.4%	—
06/12	771	(7)	—	—
06/11	744	0	—	—
Annual Growth	4.7%	—	—	—

2014 Year-End Financials

Return on assets: 6.8%
Return on equity: 5.9%
Current ratio: 1.50

Cash ($ mil.): 96

HABITAT FOR HUMANITY INTERNATIONAL INC.

Thanks to Habitat for Humanity more than 5 million people worldwide know there's no place like home. The mission of the not-for-profit ecumenical Christian organization is to provide adequate and affordable shelter. It has built or remodeled more than 800000 houses at cost for families who demonstrate a need and are willing to invest "sweat equity" during construction. Homeowners make payments on no-interest mortgages; Habitat for Humanity funnels the funds back into the construction of homes for others. The group operates in all 50 states the District of Columbia Guam and Puerto Rico in addition to affiliates in nearly 80 countries. It was founded in 1976 by Linda Fuller and her late husband Millard.

Operations

Habitat for Humanity works to offer access to decent and affordable shelter. It supports funding models that give families that have limited resources the ability to make needed improvements to their homes. The organization has more than 1400 local affiliates nationwide and more than 70 national organizations globally.

In addition to its home-building and rehabbing operations Habitat for Humanity supports recovery efforts following natural disasters. In late 2012 it launched its first fleet of mobile response units to assist victims of superstorm Sandy. The vans

carried tools and equipment to assist families with critical home repairs. While the quick-response vans address the short-term needs of storm victims the organization provides long-term assistance as well. Previously the organization responded to the 2010 7.0-magnitude earthquake that hit Haiti. Habitat for Humanity's support included providing starter kits for making immediate home repairs and preparing emergency shelter cleaning up debris and identifying salvageable materials and rebuilding with improved construction methods.

Geographic Reach

Georgia-based Habitat for Humanity International operates throughout North America as well as in Africa and the Middle East the Asia-Pacific Region Europe and Central Asia Latin America and the Caribbean. The organization works in about 80 nations worldwide.

Sales and Marketing

The company's corporate partners include: DOW Bank of America JCPenny MARS and P&G.

Financial Performance

Habitat for Humanity's fiscal 2014 (ends June) revenue fell some 11% as compared to the previous year to nearly $278 million. It attributes the decrease to a dip in US government grants. Most of the organization's government grant revenue — $44.8 million —originated from the Neighborhood Stabilization Program grant received from the US Department of Housing and Urban Development.

Strategy

Habitat for Humanity's nascent turnaround is credited to changes made at the beginning of the recession. Faced with a depressed housing market in many US states Habitat for Humanity shifted gears to get the most for its money. It refocused its efforts on rehabing homes rather than building new as renovating is less costly than building from the ground up. Also the organization began to repurpose a growing number of foreclosed and empty homes by buying and renovating them then selling them to low-income families at reduced prices. It also pared down its operations. As a result the housing group has slashed expenses and shed staff in hopes of being able to reach out to more of those in need with less overhead.

As part of Habitat for Humanity's new 2014-18 Strategic Plan the organization partners with local microfinance lenders to serve more families. In 2013 Habitat for Humanity Thailand launched a home improvement microsavings program via an agreement with the Bank for Agriculture and Agricultural Cooperatives to support families in the Maha Sarakham province. In 2014 Nissan Motor Co. formed a $1 million global partnership with Habitat for Humanity to launch joint projects in India Indonesia the Philippines Thailand and Vietnam. The new partnership facilitates home building and the construction of evacuation shelters for use during natural disasters in the five Asian countries. It also involves donating vehicles that help to support construction efforts.

EXECUTIVES

EVP International, Michael (Mike) Carscaddon
SVP Communications, Chris Clarke
President and CEO, Jonathan T. M. Reckford
VP Asia and the Pacific, Richard (Rick) Hathaway
SVP U.S. and Canada, Larry Gluth
VP Latin America and the Caribbean, Torre Nelson
SVP Administration and CFO, Ed Quibell
VP Europe Middle East and Africa, Gregory Foster
VP Information Technology and CIO, Gail Hyde
President and CEO Canada, Mark Rodgers
Director Media Relations, Donald Bonin
Vice President Internal Audit, Juan Montalvo
Executive Vice President Habitat for Humanity International, Mike Carscaddon
Vice Chairman, Henry G. Cisneros
Vice Chairman, Alex Silva

Chairman, Renee Glover
Auditors: ERNST & YOUNG US LLP GREENVIL

LOCATIONS

HQ: HABITAT FOR HUMANITY INTERNATIONAL INC.
121 HABITAT ST, AMERICUS, GA 317093498
Phone: 800 422-4828
Web: WWW.HABITAT.ORG

PRODUCTS/OPERATIONS

2014 Revenue

	$ mil.	% of total
Contributions	161	58
Donations-in-kind	60	22
Government grants	22	12
Other	33	8
Total	**277**	**100**

HISTORICAL FINANCIALS

Company Type: Private

Income Statement

FYE: June 30

	REVENUE ($ mil.)	NET INCOME ($ mil.)	NET PROFIT MARGIN	EMPLOYEES
06/13	296	(29)	—	1,500
06/12	292	(31)	—	—
06/11	1	0	7.0%	—
Annual Growth	1418.9%			

2013 Year-End Financials

Return on assets: —
Return on equity: (-10.0%)
Current ratio: 0.40

Cash ($ mil.): 27

HACKENSACK UNIVERSITY MEDICAL CENTER

Hackensack University Medical Center (HUMC) is an acute care teaching and research hospital that serves the residents of northern New Jersey and parts of New York. The hospital has about 775 beds and staffs more than 2200 medical professionals. HUMC administers general medical surgical emergency and diagnostic care. The medical center also includes specialized treatment centers including a children's hospital a women's hospital a cancer center and a heart and vascular hospital. HUMC is part of the Hackensack University Health Network which also includes a physician practice group and a joint venture that operates two community hospitals. Hackensack University Health Network is merging with Meridian Health.

Operations

HUMC helps train future dentists and doctors through its affiliation with the University of Medicine and Dentistry of New Jersey. It expanded its education programs in 2012 by partnering with the Stevens Institute of Technology to offer joint biomedical training programs.

The hospital also performs research through the David Joseph Jurist Research Center for Tomorrow's Children. The center has roughly 475 research programs in operation at any given time.

Financial Performance

Medicare accounts for 29.5% of HUMC's funding; HMOs 28%; and Blue Cross 28%.

Strategy

The company grows organically and through acquisitions partnerships and affiliations.

To expand its services HUMC broke ground on a $35 million project to expand and renovate its trauma and emergency facilities in 2012 (scheduled to open in 2015).

Hackensack University Health Network is increasing its partnerships and affiliations with other regional care providers following the trend of US hospitals seeking to improve and lower the cost of health care through shared services and resources. The network partnered up with Texas-based LPH Hospital Group in 2012 to reenovate the Pascack Valley Hospital (now HackensackUMC Pascack) in Westwood New Jersey. Hackensack took over the bankrupt facility's ER back in 2007 and in 2012 the joint venture launched a $90 million project to revamp the rest of the 130-bed acute-care community hospital. It reopened in 2013.

Hackensack University Health Network also formed a joint venture with an area physician group to open two ambulatory surgery centers in 2012 and it entered a collaboration with CVS Health's MinuteClinic to open new urgent care centers.

That year HUMC formed a joint venture partnership with community physicians and United Surgical Partners International to buy and operate ambulatory surgery centers in Bergen County: Hackensack Endoscopy Center and the Endoscopy Center of Bergen County.

Mergers and Acquisitions

In 2015 the Hackensack University Health Network agreed to merge with fellow New Jersey care provider Meridian Health. The combined system to be named Hackensack Meridian Health will have 11 hospitals and two children's hospitals. The deal which is one of a number of consolidation efforts by hospitals in the state is pending regulatory approval.

Company Background

To simplify its operations HUMC sold its hospice operations to Amedisys in 2011. The health provider previously sold its home health agency to Amedisys in 2009 to generate revenue and control costs after struggling with financial losses throughout the year due to declining admissions.

HUMC completed construction of its new John Theurer Cancer Center in late 2010 giving it one of the largest comprehensive cancer centers in the US. The center includes diagnostic and treatment units that focus on specific types of cancers.

HUMC was founded as a hospital in 1888 with 12 beds.

EXECUTIVES

Chairman Department of Ophthamology, Michael Rosenberg
Executive Vice President And Chief Financial Officer, Robert L (Bob) Glenning
Vice President Patient Financial Services, Anne Pritcheta
Vice President Supply Chain, Jackie Trobiano
Director of Nursing, Julianna Brickner
Vice President, Brittany Chiusolo
Admissions Director, William Hunt
Vice President Patient Financial Services, Anne Pritchett
Vice President Nursing, Laura Cima
Vice President Information Services, Roderick Clemente
Senior Vice President Chief Medical Officer and Governor, Peter (Pete) Gross
Executive Vice President and Chief Medical Officer, Ihor S Sawczuk
Vice President Network Development, Kathy Stumf

LOCATIONS

HQ: HACKENSACK UNIVERSITY MEDICAL CENTER
30 PROSPECT AVE STE 1, HACKENSACK, NJ
076011912
Phone: 201 996-2000
Web: WWW.HACKENSACKUMC.ORG

PRODUCTS/OPERATIONS

Selected Facilities
Donna A. Sanzari Women's Hospital
Hackensack University Medical Center Mountainside
Hackensack University Medical Center Pascack
Heart & Vascular Hospital
John Theurer Cancer Center
Joseph M. Sanzari Children's Hospital
    Tomorrows Children's Institute for Cancer and Blood Disorders

COMPETITORS

Bergen Regional Medical	Lenox Hill Hospital
Bronx-Lebanon Hospital	Montefiore Medical
Continuum Health	NewYork-Presbyterian
Partners	Healthcare
Englewood Hospital and	Newark Beth Israel
Medical Center	Medical Center
Hospital for Special	St. Joseph's
Surgery	Healthcare System
	Valley Health System

HISTORICAL FINANCIALS
Company Type: Private

Income Statement
FYE: December 31

	REVENUE ($ mil.)	NET INCOME ($ mil.)	NET PROFIT MARGIN	EMPLOYEES
12/08	1,037	(86)	—	7,175
12/07	1,183	48	4.1%	—
12/05	1,004	26	2.6%	—
12/04	873	0	—	—
Annual Growth	4.4%	—	—	—

2008 Year-End Financials
Return on assets: 11.3%   Cash ($ mil.): 275
Return on equity: (-8.3%)
Current ratio: 1.50

HACKLEY HOSPITAL

Medical professionals at Hackley Hospital aim to heal. Operating as as Mercy Health Partners Hackley Campus the hospital is a 210-bed acute care facility that serves patients living in Muskegon opposite the thumb on Michigan's shoreline. The teaching hospital offers such services as behavioral health care a sleep analysis lab a bariatric treatment center a cancer center stroke care emergency medicine and rehabilitation therapies. Mercy Health Partners Hackley Campus is part Mercy Health Partners Muskegon.

Operations

Mercy Health Muskegon is a Trinity Health division that operates three additional Michigan hospitals as well as outpatient care centers. Together the Mercy Health Muskegon division employs about 375 doctors and serves 21000 inpatients each year; it also handles some 137000 emergency and urgent care patients.

Strategy

To improve quality of care and process efficiencies Mercy Health Muskegon implemented an electronic health record (EHR) system during 2011. The network also expands by adding new facilities specialty services and affiliations in the region.

Company Background

The medical center opened in 1904. In 2008 Hackley Hospital's former parent (Hackley Health System) merged with Mercy General Health Partners to form Mercy Health Partners Muskegon.

EXECUTIVES

Regional President & CEO - Trinity Health West Michigan, Roger W. Spoelman, age 61
CFO, Gary Allore
Interim VP Human Resources, Greg Loomis
Chief Medical Officer, F. Remington Sprague
President & CEO Lakeshore Campus, Jay Bryan
Chief Nursing Officer & VP Patient Care Services, Kimberly A Maguire
Interim President & COO, Gregory A Loomis

LOCATIONS

HQ: HACKLEY HOSPITAL
    1700 CLINTON ST, MUSKEGON, MI 494425591
Phone: 231 728-4950
Web: WWW.MERCYHEALTHMUSKEGON.COM

PRODUCTS/OPERATIONS

Selected Centers and Services
Aesthetics
Athletic Performance Center
Bariatric Surgery
Behavioral Health
Birth Center
Bladder Control Clinic
Diabetes Management Clinic and Education
Emergency and Urgent Care
Healthcare Equipment
Imaging Center of Excellence
Johnson Family Cancer Center
Laboratories
Life Counseling
Lymphedema Therapy
Memory Clinic
Muskegon Community Health Project
Neurosurgery
Orthopedics
Orthotics and Prosthetics
Pain Clinic
Pharmacies
Primary Care
Rehabilitation and Sports Medicine
Safe Kids West Michigan
Sleep Disorders Center
Spine Services
The Dan and Mavis Thill Heart and Vascular Institute
Weight Management
Women's Health
Workplace Health

COMPETITORS

Borgess Health	Sheridan Community
Borgess Medical Center	Hospital
Bronson Battle Creek	Shriners Hospitals For
Bronson Health Care	Children
Children's Hospital of	Sparrow Health System
Michigan	Spectrum Health
Covenant HealthCare	University of Michigan
Gerber Memorial	Health System
Holland Hospital	Zeeland Community
McLaren Bay	Hospital

HISTORICAL FINANCIALS
Company Type: Private

Income Statement
FYE: June 30

	REVENUE ($ mil.)	NET INCOME ($ mil.)	NET PROFIT MARGIN	EMPLOYEES
06/13	177	5	3.2%	1,500
06/10	151	(42)	—	—
06/09	144	(6)	—	—
06/08	1,673	0	—	—
Annual Growth	(36.1%)	—	—	—

HAGGEN INC.

Haggen showers shoppers in the Pacific Northwest with salmon coffee and other essentials. One of the area's largest independent grocers Haggen operates some 130 supermarkets in Washington and Oregon as well as California Nevada and Arizona. Most of the stores were acquired from Albertsons in late 2014. After the purchase Haggen sued Albertsons for attempted monopolization and unfair competition. In late 2015 Haggen filed for Chapter 11 bankruptcy protection. The chain was founded in 1933 in Bellingham Washington.

Change in Company Type

Florida-based Comvest Partners purchased control of the company from brothers and co-chairmen Don and Rick Haggen who retained minority ownership and their seats on the grocery chain's board. Comvest said it targeted Haggen for its first-rate customer service and product selection noting that the supermarket chain is expected to continue operating as an independent entity.

Operations

Haggen runs its retail business under two banner names: Haggen Food & Pharmacy and TOP Food & Drug.

Geographic Reach

Haggen serves customers primarily in Washington but also in Oregon.

Strategy

In late 2014 the company announced it would purchase 146 Vons Pavilions Albertsons and Safeway stores being sold as part of the pending merger of Albertsons and Safeway. More than 80 of the new stores are located in California.

Aiming to boost its business and strengthen its competitive position the grocery operator whittled down its stores portfolio in 2013 to about 20 locations from 30 by shuttering underperforming stores. It's also rebranding many of its TOP Food & Drug stores as Northwest Fresh. The Northwest Fresh theme emphasizes local products new service departments and departments named after local geographic references. The supermarket chain is rebannering all of its TOP stores under the Haggen name and new theme to reinforce its local roots and differentiate itself from its national competition.

Having been a customer since 2007 Haggen also extended a supply partnership with Unified Grocers through 2018.

Focused on brick-and-mortar efforts Haggen had set aside its e-commerce initiative. To keep up with the Joneses of supermarket fortune Haggen partnered with ShopEaze.com (an e-commerce service provider) which failed leaving Haggen without an online store.

Awards and Recognition

Industry publication Supermarket News ranks Haggen one of the 75 largest grocery chains in the US. It's also the Northwest's largest independent grocer.

Company Background

Haggen traces its roots back to 1933 when Ben Haggen alongside his wife Dorothy and brother-in-law Doug Clark launched the Economy Food Store in Bellingham Washington with a combined investment of $1100. They later moved and changed the name to White House Market before moving to yet another location in 1957 and adopting the name Haggen's Thriftway.

EXECUTIVES

Vice President, Mike Lobaugh
Vice President Pharmacy, Gaetano Dipasqua
Vice President Information Technology Mis, Fred Byrum
Vice President Center Store, Michael (Mel) Tyson
Senior Vice President Marketing, Chris Linskey
Vice President Center Store, Jaime Praeger
Vice President Center Store, Michael Tyson
Senior Vice President Operations, Wendy Oliver
Senior Vice President Operations, John (Jack) Turley
Auditors: MOSS ADAMS LLP

LOCATIONS

HQ: HAGGEN INC.
2211 RIMLAND DR STE 300, BELLINGHAM, WA 982265699
Phone: 360 733-8720
Web: WWW.HAGGEN.COM

2014 Stores

Washington	15
Oregon	2
Total	**0** **17**

COMPETITORS

Costco Wholesale	Smart & Final
Fred Meyer Stores	Target Corporation
Grocery Outlet	Trader Joe' s
Quality Food	Wal-Mart
SUPERVALU	Walgreen
Safeway	WinCo Foods

HISTORICAL FINANCIALS
Company Type: Private

Income Statement   FYE: December 31

	REVENUE ($ mil.)	NET INCOME ($ mil.)	NET PROFIT MARGIN	EMPLOYEES
12/07	787	8	1.1%	3,900
12/06	758	6	0.9%	—
12/05	164	0	—	—
Annual Growth	—20237.1%	—	—	—

2007 Year-End Financials
Return on assets: 4.9%   Cash ($ mil.): 6
Return on equity: 1.1%
Current ratio: 0.30

HAMPTON WOODS HEALTH & REHABILITATION CENTER

LOCATIONS

HQ: HAMPTON WOODS HEALTH & REHABILITATION CENTER
200 HMPTON WODS CMPLX RD, JACKSON, NC 278459503
Phone: 252 534-0131

HISTORICAL FINANCIALS
Company Type: Private

Income Statement   FYE: September 30

	REVENUE ($ mil.)	NET INCOME ($ mil.)	NET PROFIT MARGIN	EMPLOYEES
09/09	435	(4)	—	90
09/00	2	(0)	—	—
Annual Growth	76.0%	—	—	—

2009 Year-End Financials
Return on assets: —   Cash ($ mil.): —
Return on equity: (-1.1%)
Current ratio: 2.00

HARFORD COUNTY BOARD OF EDUCATION (INC)

Auditors: SB & COMPANY LLC HUNT VALLEY

LOCATIONS

HQ: HARFORD COUNTY BOARD OF EDUCATION (INC)
102 S HICKORY AVE, BEL AIR, MD 210143731
Phone: 410 838-7300
Web: WWW.HCPS.ORG

HISTORICAL FINANCIALS
Company Type: Private

Income Statement   FYE: June 30

	REVENUE ($ mil.)	NET INCOME ($ mil.)	NET PROFIT MARGIN	EMPLOYEES
06/14	522	(5)	—	5,400
06/13	535	(4)	—	—
06/12	536	1	0.3%	—
06/08	572	0	—	—
Annual Growth	(1.5%)	—	—	—

2014 Year-End Financials
Return on assets: 1.7%   Cash ($ mil.): 7
Return on equity: (-1.0%)
Current ratio: —

HARLAND M. BRAUN & CO. INC.

Hide (the raw material) and seek (find a buyer) are all in a day's work for Harland M. Braun & Co. Operating through its subsidiary Braun Export the company supplies raw hide goods primarily cattle hides and skins and to a lesser extent pigskin and kipskins to tanners. A slate of services is provided for leather (wet blue and crust) hide and skin manufacturing as well as brokering exporting and importing. Dotting the US Braun & Co.'s processing facilities tie in with several suppliers of Holstein steer hides. Partnerships are sealed with such meat packers as JBS Packerland Group Central Valley Meat Creekstone Farms Premium Beef Manning Beef Nebraska Beef and American Beef Packers.

Established more than 45 years ago Harland M. Braun is a frequent recipient of the "Good Corporate Citizens" award given by the Sanitation Districts of Los Angeles County. The "Atta Boy!" recognizes businesses that meet the County's environmental wastewater discharge requirements.

EXECUTIVES

President, Mike Hamilton
VP Sales, Dick Veale
Office Manager Finance, Karen Thareererg
Controller, Brian Jung
Documentation Assistant, Christine Cho
Production Supervisor Manufacturing, Sergio Novo
Logistics Manager, Brenda A. Ho
General Manager, Roland Sebastian
Quality Control Operator, Gene Beenders
Sales Manager, Rene Buchhammer
Sales Assistant, Chad Robertson
Documentation Supervisor, Ryan Tang
Founder, Harland Braun

LOCATIONS

HQ: HARLAND M. BRAUN & CO. INC.
4010 WHITESIDE ST, LOS ANGELES, CA 900631617
Phone: 323 263-9275
Web: WWW.BRAUNEXP.COM

COMPETITORS

Danier Leather
Pittards
S. B. Foot Tanning

HISTORICAL FINANCIALS

Company Type: Private

Income Statement				FYE: October 31
	REVENUE ($ mil.)	NET INCOME ($ mil.)	NET PROFIT MARGIN	EMPLOYEES
10/13	307	0	0.0%	30
10/12	277	0	0.2%	—
10/11	290	0	0.0%	—
10/10	212	0		
Annual Growth	13.1%	—	—	—

2013 Year-End Financials

Return on assets: 3.8%
Return on equity: —
Current ratio: 0.70
Cash ($ mil.): 1

HARLEE MANOR INC.

LOCATIONS

HQ: HARLEE MANOR INC.
463 W SPROUL RD, SPRINGFIELD, PA 190642120
Phone: 610 544-2200
Web: WWW.HARLEEMANOR.COM

HISTORICAL FINANCIALS

Company Type: Private

Income Statement				FYE: June 30
	REVENUE ($ mil.)	NET INCOME ($ mil.)	NET PROFIT MARGIN	EMPLOYEES
06/09	1,164	62	5.4%	151
06/98	8	0	6.3%	—
Annual Growth	55.9%	53.6%	—	—

2009 Year-End Financials

Return on assets: —
Return on equity: 5.4%
Current ratio: 1.80
Cash ($ mil.): —

HARRISON MEDICAL CENTER

Auditors: MOSS ADAMS LLP EVERETT WASHI

LOCATIONS

HQ: HARRISON MEDICAL CENTER
2520 CHERRY AVE, BREMERTON, WA 983104229
Phone: 360 744-6510
Web: WWW.HARRISONMEDICAL.ORG

HISTORICAL FINANCIALS

Company Type: Private

Income Statement				FYE: April 30
	REVENUE ($ mil.)	NET INCOME ($ mil.)	NET PROFIT MARGIN	EMPLOYEES
04/13	351	17	5.1%	2,400
04/12	345	(22)		—
04/11	363	15	4.2%	—
04/10	343	0	—	—
Annual Growth	0.7%	—	—	—

2013 Year-End Financials

Return on assets: 4.1%
Return on equity: 5.1%
Current ratio: 1.20
Cash ($ mil.): 17

HARTFORD HOSPITAL

Auditors: ERNST & YOUNG LLP HARTFORD

LOCATIONS

HQ: HARTFORD HOSPITAL
80 SEYMOUR ST, HARTFORD, CT 061028000
Phone: 860 545-5555
Web: WWW.HARTFORDPHO.COM

HISTORICAL FINANCIALS

Company Type: Private

Income Statement				FYE: September 30
	REVENUE ($ mil.)	NET INCOME ($ mil.)	NET PROFIT MARGIN	EMPLOYEES
09/13	903	37	4.1%	7,500
09/09	828	(23)	—	—
09/08	1,771	(21)	—	—
Annual Growth	(12.6%)	—	—	—

2013 Year-End Financials

Return on assets: 2.5%
Return on equity: 4.1%
Current ratio: 1.90
Cash ($ mil.): 20

HATCH MOTT MACDONALD GROUP INC.

Hatch Mott MacDonald (HMM) is the consulting engineering subsidiary of Mott MacDonald and offers planning project development analysis design construction management facility maintenance and facility management for all types of infrastructure projects to public and private clients across North America. It specializes in tunnels wastewater systems pipelines rail and transit systems buildings and utilities. Customers are both private companies and municipalities. HMM strategically acquires specialized engineering firms in new regions to expand its service offerings and geographic market reach. Formed in 1996 HHM now boasts a staff of 25000 and has more than 75 offices in the US and Canada.

Geographic Reach

New Jersey-based Hatch Mott MacDonald has offices in about two dozen US states including California Florida Massachusetts New York and Texas as well as in Alberta British Columbia New Brunswick Newfoundland and Labrador Nova Scotia and Ontario Canada.

Strategy

Hatch Mott MacDonald (HMM) continued in 2016 to work on infrastructure and other large projects for public (including municipalities and airports) and private sector clients across North America. Some of its recent projects have included Sacramento's Bradshaw Interceptor Pipeline work for the District of Columbia Water and Sewer Authority the Nipigon River Bridge the Halton Booster Pumping Station the JFK Airport Deicing Facility the Genesee Street ITS Corridor and the New York Harbor Water Siphon Replacement project. The engineering firm has historically grown by acquiring smaller engineering firms across a variety of specialty practices and regions to expand its service offerings and bolster its expertise. Mergers and AcquisitionsIn 2014 HMM purchased Coast & Harbor Engineering which focuses on protecting and restoring coastlines and developing port and harbor infrastructure. The deal also adds the smaller company's offices in New Orleans (a top market for HMM) San Francisco Austin Delray Beach and Edmonds Washington.

Company Background

In May 2012 the company acquired Canadian consulting specialist Engineering Northwest. The Thunder Bay Ontario-based firm focused on highway municipal water and wastewater engineering and project and construction management services. Also in 2012 HMM extended its reach to New Orleans with the purchase of Lambert Engineers an engineering and architectural firm there. With its extensive infrastructure needs New Orleans was a fertile market for HMM's services and complemented the firm's other Gulf Coast offices from Florida to Texas.

In 2011 HMM acquired Richard P. Arber Associates a professional consulting engineering firm in Lakewood Colorado to expand its water and wastewater practice in the western US. Also that year it purchased North Carolina-based transportation firm Gibson Engineers.

EXECUTIVES

Principal, John Davenport
Owner, Mott MacDonald
CEO President, Nicholas DeNichilo

Vice President Information Strategy, James (Jamie) Forster
Vice President, Russell Johnson
Vice President Information and Communication Technologies, Ron Sattan
Auditors: BDO USA LLP WOODBRIDGE NJ

LOCATIONS

HQ: HATCH MOTT MACDONALD GROUP INC.
111 WOOD AVE S STE 5, ISELIN, NJ 088302700
Phone: 973 379-3400
Web: WWW.HATCHMOTT.COM

PRODUCTS/OPERATIONS

Selected Services
Asset management
Aviation
Environment
Highways & bridges
Information management
Life-safety & security
Model-based Design/BIM
Pipelines
Ports
Project delivery
Rail & transit
Site development
Sustainability
Transportation planning
Tunnels
Wastewater
Water

COMPETITORS

3i Infrastructure	E M C Engineers
AREVA NP	Fagen Inc.
Bechtel	Fluor
Black & Veatch Ltd.	Lauren Engineers
Burns and Roe	Sargent & Lundy
CDI Engineering Solutions	

HISTORICAL FINANCIALS
Company Type: Private

Income Statement
FYE: December 31

	REVENUE ($ mil.)	NET INCOME ($ mil.)	NET PROFIT MARGIN	EMPLOYEES
12/13	507	34	6.8%	2,500
12/12	477	27	5.7%	—
12/11	440	25	5.8%	—
12/10	374	0	—	—
Annual Growth	10.7%	—	—	—

2013 Year-End Financials
Return on assets: 4.3%
Return on equity: 6.8%
Current ratio: 1.50
Cash ($ mil.): 54

HATTIESBURG CLINIC PROFESSIONAL ASSOCIATION

LOCATIONS

HQ: HATTIESBURG CLINIC PROFESSIONAL ASSOCIATION
415 S 28TH AVE, HATTIESBURG, MS 394017283
Phone: 601 579-5444
Web: WWW.HATTIESBURGCLINIC.COM

HISTORICAL FINANCIALS
Company Type: Private

Income Statement
FYE: December 31

	REVENUE ($ mil.)	NET INCOME ($ mil.)	NET PROFIT MARGIN	EMPLOYEES
12/09	303	1	0.6%	1,693
12/08	280	0	0.3%	—
12/07	266	0	0.1%	—
12/06	245	0	—	—
Annual Growth	7.3%	—	—	—

2009 Year-End Financials
Return on assets: 1.9%
Return on equity: 0.6%
Current ratio: 0.80
Cash ($ mil.): —

HAWKINS CONSTRUCTION COMPANY

Hawkins Construction provides both commercial building and heavy/highway contracting services. The diversified contractor has a project portfolio that includes regional banks warehouses schools churches and prisons. It also works on highways bridges site developments and parking structures and is one of the Midwest's largest road builders. Clients include the University of Nebraska Mutual of Omaha and Hewlett-Packard. The family-owned company began with a successful contract bid in 1922 by Kenneth Hawkins and his brother Earl for what is now Lincoln Nebraska's Memorial Stadium; the firm was incorporated in 1960 by Kenneth and his son Fred.

EXECUTIVES

Vice President, David (Dave) Langenberg
Vice President, Tom Crockett
Vice President, Chris Harnly
V Pres, Kurt Peyton

LOCATIONS

HQ: HAWKINS CONSTRUCTION COMPANY
2516 DEER PARK BLVD, OMAHA, NE 681053771
Phone: 402 342-4455
Web: WWW.HAWKINS1.COM

COMPETITORS

Oldcastle Materials	Turner Corporation
Pepper Construction	Walsh Group
Peter Kiewit Sons'	

HISTORICAL FINANCIALS
Company Type: Private

Income Statement
FYE: December 31

	REVENUE ($ mil.)	NET INCOME ($ mil.)	NET PROFIT MARGIN	EMPLOYEES
12/13	160	9	5.6%	400
12/12	0	0	50.1%	—
12/08	238	16	6.7%	—
12/07	223	0	—	—
Annual Growth	(5.3%)	—	—	—

2013 Year-End Financials
Return on assets: 12.3%
Return on equity: 5.6%
Current ratio: 1.20
Cash ($ mil.): 23

HAWTHORNE MACHINERY CO.

Leader of the track Hawthorne Machinery a Caterpillar dealership sells and rents more than 300 CAT equipment models including tractors trucks loaders compactors harvesters graders excavators and power systems. It also provides more than 73000 parts and repair services for industrial and construction contractors and other public and private customers around San Diego County. Hawthorne Machinery offers new and used equipment and rentals of brand-name equipment by such blue chip OEMs as Kubota Spartan and Sullair. The company was founded in 1956 by Tom Hawthorne.

Geographic Reach

Outside of San Diego Hawthorne has 20 locations in Hawaii Guam American Samoa and Saipan.

Sales and Marketing

Hawthorne sells rents and provides parts and services to various industries including general building construction landscaping marine paving and power generation. One of its main customers is BAE Systems.

EXECUTIVES

Vice President and General Counsel, Stephen E (Steve) Wittman

LOCATIONS

HQ: HAWTHORNE MACHINERY CO.
16945 CAMINO SAN BERNARDO, SAN DIEGO, CA 921272499
Phone: 858 674-7000
Web: WWW.HAWTHORNECAT.COM

PRODUCTS/OPERATIONS

Selected Products
Farrow systems
Machinery
  Articulated trucks
  Backhoe loaders
  Cold planers
  Compact track & multi terrain loaders
  Compactors
  Feller bunchers
  Forest machines
  Forwarders
  Harvesters
  Hydraulic excavators
  Industrial loaders
  Knuckleboom loaders
  Material handlers
  Motor graders
  Off-highway trucks
  Paving equipment
  Pipelayers
  Road reclaimers
  Skid steer loaders
  Skidders
  Telehandlers
  Track loaders
  Track-type tractors
  Underground mining
  Wheel dozers
  Wheel excavators
  Wheel loaders
  Wheel tractor-scrapers
Power systems
  Air compressors
  Electric power (generator sets)
  Marine (commercial & pleasure craft engines auxiliary generator sets)
Work tool attachments
  Augers
  Backhoes
  Blades
  Brooms

Brushcutters
Buckets
Backhoe front/rear
Compact wheel loader
Excavator
Loader
Skid steer loader
Telehandlers
Cold Planers
Compactors
Couplers
Backhoe rear
Excavator
Loader
Felling heads
Forks
Backhoe loader
Compact wheel loader
Loader
Skid steer loader
Telehandlers
Grapples
Hammers
Harvester heads
Lift groups
Material handling arms
Mulchers
Multi-processors
Rakes
Rippers
Saws
Scarifiers
Shears
Snow blowers
Snow plows & snow wings
Stump grinders
Thumbs
Tillers
Trenchers
Truss booms

COMPETITORS

AMECO	Small Parts
Johnson Machinery	Manufacturing
Pacific Rim Capital	Sunbelt Rentals
Peterson Power	United Rentals

HISTORICAL FINANCIALS
Company Type: Private

Income Statement
FYE: December 31

	REVENUE ($ mil.)	NET INCOME ($ mil.)	NET PROFIT MARGIN	EMPLOYEES
12/07	338	0	0.1%	1,000
12/06	377	7	2.0%	—
12/03	170	44	26.2%	—
12/02	176	0	—	—
Annual Growth	13.9%	—	—	—

2007 Year-End Financials
Return on assets: 13.2% Cash ($ mil.): 10
Return on equity: 0.1%
Current ratio: 0.30

HAYS MEDICAL CENTER INC.

Hays Medical Center brings big city health care to rural Kansas. The not-for-profit hospital which has about 210 beds provides both acute and tertiary medical care to the Midwestern plains serving more than 13000 emergency patients each year. In addition to medical surgical and pediatric care Hays Medical Center offers home care hospice skilled nursing rehabilitation and behavioral health services. It operates centers for cardiac care (the DeBakey Heart Institute) fitness and rehabilitation (Center for Health Improvement) orthopedics (Hays Orthopedic Institute) and cancer treatment (the Dreiling/Schmidt Cancer Center). The organization also operates specialty and rural health clinics.

Operations

Hays Medical Center has a partnership with Pawnee Valley Community Hospital a critical-access hospital in Larned.

The hospital sees some 6700 admissions and performs some 173000 outpatient procedures annually. Its specialty and rural health clinics typically have about 146000 office visits.

Sales and Marketing

Hays Medical Center maintains a local market share of nearly 90% with total primary/secondary/tertiary service at 25%.

Strategy

The medical center has grown its business through selective acquisitions and hospital expansion projects. In 2013 completed the $3.8 million expansion and renovation of the Dreiling/Schmidt Cancer Institute and Breast Care Center which began construction in 2012. That expansion provided four more treatment rooms expanded exam rooms and a consultation center.

Hays Medical Center has also added reconstructive surgery services with the addition of a cosmetic surgeon and expanded its surgical capabilities by agreeing to assist with operations at nearby St. Joseph Memorial Hospital.

Company Background

The medical center was formed in 1991 through the merger of a pair of religiously affiliated facilities.

EXECUTIVES

Vice President Operations, Karen Wagner
Vice President Of Information Technology, Steve Balthazor
INFECTION Control Director, Richard (Dick) Matzke
Nursing Director OB Peds, Celeste Gray
Nursing Director, Richard Webb
Auditors: WENDLING NOE NELSON & JOHNSON

LOCATIONS

HQ: HAYS MEDICAL CENTER INC.
2220 CANTERBURY DR, HAYS, KS 676012370
Phone: 785 623-5000
Web: WWW.HAYSMED.COM

PRODUCTS/OPERATIONS

Selected Departments
Billing/Financial
Dietary
Education
Emergency Department
Fitness Center
Hospice
Hospitalists
Imaging
Lifeline
Occupational Therapy
Palliative Care
Pharmacy
Rehabilitation
  In-Patient
  Out Patient
Respiratory Therapy
Senior Focused Care
Sexual Assault Response Team
Sleep and Neurodiagnostic
Special Nursing Services
Sports Medicine
Volunteer Services
Wound Healing and Hyperbaric Center
Weight Loss Surgery
WorkSMART

COMPETITORS
Adventist Health System Sunbelt Healthcare
Sisters of Charity of Leavenworth
Stormont-Vail HealthCare
University of Kansas Medical Center
Via Christi Health System

HISTORICAL FINANCIALS
Company Type: Private

Income Statement
FYE: June 30

	REVENUE ($ mil.)	NET INCOME ($ mil.)	NET PROFIT MARGIN	EMPLOYEES
06/13	199	17	8.5%	1,178
06/12	209	17	8.1%	—
06/11	189	9	4.8%	—
06/10	184	0	—	—
Annual Growth	2.6%	—	—	—

2013 Year-End Financials
Return on assets: 3.3% Cash ($ mil.): 7
Return on equity: 8.5%
Current ratio: 1.90

HDR ENGINEERING INC.

Auditors: ERNST & YOUNG LLP OMAHA NE

LOCATIONS

HQ: HDR ENGINEERING INC.
8404 INDIAN HILLS DR, OMAHA, NE 681144098
Phone: 402 399-1000
Web: WWW.HDRINC.COM

HISTORICAL FINANCIALS
Company Type: Private

Income Statement
FYE: December 28

	REVENUE ($ mil.)	NET INCOME ($ mil.)	NET PROFIT MARGIN	EMPLOYEES
12/13	1,416	62	4.4%	6,111
12/12	1,257	73	5.9%	—
12/11	1,185	38	3.3%	—
12/10	865	0	—	—
Annual Growth	17.8%	—	—	—

2013 Year-End Financials
Return on assets: 4.4% Cash ($ mil.): 13
Return on equity: 4.4%
Current ratio: 0.10

HEALTH FIRST INC.

Health First works to keep Florida's Space Coast denizens in tip-top shape. The not-for-profit health system operates four hospitals in Brevard County. Health First's biggest hospital is Holmes Regional Medical Center in Melbourne with more than 500 beds. Its Cape Canaveral Hospital and Palm Bay Community Hospital have 150 and 60 beds respectively. Its Viera Hospital is a 100-bed acute-care hospital. The system also runs outpatient clinics a home health service and a physicians group. Its for-profit subsidiary Health First Health Plans is the county's largest insurer with about 60000 commercial members and 23000 Medicare members.

Geographic Reach

Health First operates four hospitals and a health insurance company in Brevard County Florida.

Operations

The company operates four hospitals (Holmes Regional Medical Center Palm Bay Hospital Cape Canaveral Hospital and Viera Hospital) and offers a wide variety of health insurance plan options for patients in Brevard and Indian River Counties. Health First is the largest multi-specialty physician group on Florida's Space Coast. It also operates to Brevard County's only trauma center and a number of outpatient and wellness services including four pro-health and fitness centers.

Strategy

To expand its capacity Health First makes complementary acquisitions and pursues organic growth.

In 2103 Health First opened of a new center for fracture care at Health First Holmes Regional Medical Center and the center for joint replacement at Health First Viera Hospital. That year it formed a new Small Group Preferred Provider Organization (PPO) Plan offering increased flexibility when it comes to out-of-network coverage and fulfilling the needs of employer groups in its service area.

Mergers and Acquisitions

In 2012 the company acquired Melbourne Internal Medicine Associates (250 physician providers based in Melbourne) to increase patient quality safety and the patient experience. The entity was renamed the Health First Medical Group in 2013.

Company Background

In 2011 Health First partnered with Nemours to expand pediatric care in Brevard County. That year Health First Health Plans opened a new Vero Beach office to serve residents of Indian River County and launch its Medicare Advantage plans to the rest of Indian River County.

Despite an ongoing lawsuit with Wuesthoff Health System (which claims that Health First has an unfair monopoly of hospital services in Brevard County) the company forged ahead with construction of its fourth hospital in the county the Viera hospital campus. The Medical Plaza at Viera Health Park which will includes offices for multi-specialty physicians and a diagnostic/imaging center opened in 2010. And the park's centerpiece Viera Hospital a 100-bed acute-care hospital opened in 2011.

Health First was founded in 1995 through a merger of regional hospitals. The Brevard Hospital (now Holmes Regional Medical Center) first opened in 1937.

EXECUTIVES

Vice President And Corporate Counsel, David (Dave) Mathias
Vice President MD, Joseph L (Jo) Collins
Executive Vice President Chief Strategy Officer, Drew Rector
Medical Director, Miguel Fernandez
Vice President Of Medical Staff, David Norris
Vice President Clinical Informatics, Judy Smith
Vice President Of Nursing, Nicki Andersen
Vice President Of Growth And Development, Bridget Mace
Vice President And Medical Director Of Clinical Services Health First Health Plans, Jennifer (Jen) Brady
Board Member, Timothy (Tim) Laird
Auditors: ERNST & YOUNG LLP ORLANDO FL

LOCATIONS

HQ: HEALTH FIRST INC.
6450 US HIGHWAY 1, ROCKLEDGE, FL 329555747
Phone: 321 434-4300
Web: WWW.HEALTH-FIRST.ORG

Selected facilities
Cape Canaveral Hospital (Cocoa Beach)
Holmes Regional Medical Center (Melbourne)

Palm Bay Community Hospital (Palm Bay)
Viera Hospital (Viera)

COMPETITORS

Adventist Health System Sunbelt Healthcare
Aetna
CIGNA
Florida Blue
HCA
Orlando Health
Osceola Regional Medical Center
Tenet Healthcare
Wuesthoff Health System

HISTORICAL FINANCIALS

Company Type: Private

Income Statement
FYE: September 30

	REVENUE ($ mil.)	NET INCOME ($ mil.)	NET PROFIT MARGIN	EMPLOYEES
09/14	1,136	90	7.9%	6,900
09/13	1,059	51	4.8%	
09/11	129	(0)	—	
09/08	104	0	—	
Annual Growth	48.8%	—	—	—

2014 Year-End Financials

Return on assets: 12.2%   Cash ($ mil.): 132
Return on equity: 7.9%
Current ratio: 1.50

HEALTH PARTNERS PLANS INC.

Health Partners wants to partner up with Pennsylvanians in need of health care. The company is a not-for-profit health plan that provides health benefits to some 210000 Medicaid recipients in the Philadelphia area. Its HealthChoices plans for Medicaid participants cover medical dental prescription and vision costs. Its KidzPartners program is provided in partnership with the state of Pennsylvania's Children's Health Insurance Program (CHIP). Its provider network includes about 6000 primary and specialty care doctors and 30 hospitals in the region. The company also provides community outreach and wellness programs. Health Partners was founded in 1985 by a group of hospitals in the Philadelphia area.

Geographic Reach

Health Partners' plans cover members in Philadelphia and in Chester Delaware Bucks and Montgomery counties outside the city.

Strategy

Health Partners signed a provider contract with the University of Pennsylvania Health System that will increase access to care in Philadelphia for Health Partners Medicare members. The agreement increases Health Partners' network to include more than 1300 additional physicians from the Health System's network of practices and four hospitals.

Health Partners has been working to enhance its community health programs in recent years. It launched its Computer Health Care Management Education program to provide free monthly computer lessons combined with tutorials about healthy lifestyle programs.

It also teamed up with the Norcom Community Center to offer HealthChoices and KidzPartners members fitness benefits at the facility; the company has a total of more than 20 fitness centers in

its expanding provider network. The KidzPartners program provides free or affordable insurance coverage to children and teens who don't qualify for Medicaid.

Company Background

The area hospitals that own Health Partners are Albert Einstein Medical Center Aria Health Temple University Hospital Episcopal Hospital and two Tenet Healthcare facilities (Hahnemann University Hospital and St. Christopher's Hospital for Children).

EXECUTIVES

Vice President of Provider Affairs, Rebecca Kohl
Vice President of Marketing, Caroline Russell
Vice President Of Production Development And Sales, Lovell Harmon
Vice President Government Relations And Compliance, Kearline Mckellar-Jones
Vice President, Johnna Baker
Senior Vice President Resources Management And Compliance, Vickie Sessoms
Vice President Sales, John (Jack) Sehi
Vice President Utilization Management, Andrea D'Angelo
Senior Vice President CIO, Joe Brand
Auditors: KPMG LLP PHILADELPHIA PA

LOCATIONS

HQ: HEALTH PARTNERS PLANS INC.
901 MARKET ST STE 500, PHILADELPHIA, PA 191074496
Phone: 215 849-9606
Web: WWW.HEALTHPART.COM

COMPETITORS

Aetna	Highmark
CIGNA	Independence Blue
Coventry Health Care	Cross
Gateway Health Plan	Keystone Mercy
Health Net	UnitedHealth Group

HISTORICAL FINANCIALS

Company Type: Private

Income Statement
FYE: December 31

	REVENUE ($ mil.)	NET INCOME ($ mil.)	NET PROFIT MARGIN	EMPLOYEES
12/13	1,000	(0)	—	620
12/12	1,034	(1)	—	
12/09	805	2	0.4%	
12/08	702	0	—	
Annual Growth	7.3%	—	—	—

2013 Year-End Financials

Return on assets: —   Cash ($ mil.): 95
Return on equity: —
Current ratio: 0.50

HEALTH QUEST SYSTEMS INC.

Auditors: PRICEWATERHOUSECOOPERS LLP NE

LOCATIONS

HQ: HEALTH QUEST SYSTEMS INC.
1351 ROUTE 55 STE 200, LAGRANGEVILLE, NY 125405144
Phone: 845 475-9500
Web: WWW.HEALTH-QUEST.ORG

HISTORICAL FINANCIALS
Company Type: Private

Income Statement
FYE: December 31

	REVENUE ($ mil.)	NET INCOME ($ mil.)	NET PROFIT MARGIN	EMPLOYEES
12/13	706	103	14.6%	2,000
12/12	692	8	1.2%	—
12/11	699	(4)	—	—
12/09	64	0	—	—
Annual Growth 82.1%	—	—	—	—

2013 Year-End Financials
Return on assets: —
Return on equity: 14.6%
Current ratio: 1.00

Cash ($ mil.): 62

HEALTH RESEARCH INC.

Health Research Inc. (HRI) knows where the money is. The group is a not-for-profit organization that helps the New York State Department of Health and its affiliated Roswell Park Cancer Institute solicit evaluate and administer financial support. Sources of that support come from federal and state government sources other non-profits and businesses. HRI's Technology Transfer office also assists the Department of Health in sharing its research findings with other public and private institutions and finding ways to create biomedical technologies through private sector development. HRI was founded in 1953 and has administered $7 billion over its lifetime.

HRI's Technology Transfer office has aided several research organizations in recent years such as ones studying prostate specific antigen (or the PSA test) photodynamic therapy and pox virus vectors among others.

EXECUTIVES
Executive Director, Michael Nazarko
Associate Director Technology Transfer, Robert (Bob) Gallo
Auditors: KPMG LLP ALBANY NY

LOCATIONS
HQ: HEALTH RESEARCH INC.
150 BROADWAY STE 560, MENANDS, NY 122042736
Phone: 518 431-1200
Web: WWW.HEALTHRESEARCH.ORG

HISTORICAL FINANCIALS
Company Type: Private

Income Statement
FYE: March 31

	REVENUE ($ mil.)	NET INCOME ($ mil.)	NET PROFIT MARGIN	EMPLOYEES
03/14	703	13	1.9%	1,400
03/13	665	25	3.9%	—
03/12	661	(10)	—	—
03/11	665	0	—	—
Annual Growth 1.9%	—	—	—	—

2014 Year-End Financials
Return on assets: 4.3%
Return on equity: 1.9%
Current ratio: 0.30

Cash ($ mil.): 137

HEALTHEAST CARE SYSTEM

LOCATIONS
HQ: HEALTHEAST CARE SYSTEM
1700 UNIVERSITY AVE W # 5, SAINT PAUL, MN 551043727
Phone: 651 232-5353
Web: WWW.HEALTHEAST.ORG

HISTORICAL FINANCIALS
Company Type: Private

Income Statement
FYE: August 31

	REVENUE ($ mil.)	NET INCOME ($ mil.)	NET PROFIT MARGIN	EMPLOYEES
08/14	943	8	0.9%	5,500
08/13	946	33	3.5%	—
08/12*	928	25	2.7%	—
11/11	226	0	—	—
Annual Growth 60.9%	—	—	—	—

*Fiscal year change

HEARTLAND HEALTH

Heartland Health provides medical care in the heart of the Midwest. The integrated health care system serves residents of northwest Missouri as well as bordering areas of Kansas and Nebraska. Its flagship facility is Heartland Regional Medical Center a 350-bed acute-care hospital that features an emergency room and Level II trauma center as well as specialty care programs in heart disease cancer and obstetrics. Heartland Health also provides primary care through a multi-specialty medical practice (Heartland Clinic) and it offers home health hospice and long-term care services from the primary medical center facility. The company's Community Health Improvement Solutions unit is an HMO health insurer.

StrategyIn 2012 Heartland Health joined the Mayo Clinic Care Network which will enable to it to tap the knowledge and expertise of Mayo Clinic physicians to better serve its patients.

Company BackgroundHeartland Health was formed in 1984 through the merger of two St. Joseph Missouri hospital: Methodist Medical Center and St. Joseph's Hospital. The two facilities trace their roots back to 1924 and 1861 respectively.

EXECUTIVES
Clinic Manager, Bobbi Wheeler
Vice President Human Resources, Michael (Mel) Pulido
Vice President Of Information Technology, James Direnna
Vice President, Charles Mullican
Vice Chairman, Carol Roever
Board Of Directors, Nancy Donahue
Auditors: BKD LLP KANSAS CITY MO

LOCATIONS
HQ: HEARTLAND HEALTH
5325 FARAON ST, SAINT JOSEPH, MO 645063488
Phone: 816 271-6000
Web: WWW.MYMOSAICLIFECARE.ORG

PRODUCTS/OPERATIONS
Selected Affiliates
Atchison Hospital (Atchison KS)
Community Hospital (Fairfax MO)
Community Medical Center (Falls City NE)
Dental Clinic (St. Joseph MO)
Laser Cosmedic Center (Platte City MO)
North Kansas City Hospital (North Kansas City MO)
The Surgery Center (St. Joseph MO)

COMPETITORS
Ascension Health
BJC HealthCare
Blue Cross and Blue Shield of Kansas City
Catholic Health Initiatives
Children's Mercy Hospital
CoxHealth
HCA
Mercy Health
Mercy Hospital Springfield
Saint Luke's Health System
Shawnee Mission Medical Center
Sisters of Charity of Leavenworth
Truman Medical Centers
University of Kansas Medical Center

HISTORICAL FINANCIALS
Company Type: Private

Income Statement
FYE: June 30

	REVENUE ($ mil.)	NET INCOME ($ mil.)	NET PROFIT MARGIN	EMPLOYEES
06/14	560	64	11.4%	32,000
06/13	572	76	13.4%	—
06/12	584	10	1.8%	—
06/11	528	0	—	—
Annual Growth 2.0%	—	—	—	—

2014 Year-End Financials
Return on assets: 2.5%
Return on equity: 11.4%
Current ratio: 1.50

Cash ($ mil.): 27

HEARTLAND REGIONAL MEDICAL CENTER

Heartland Regional Medical Center strives for healthy hearts minds and bodies in the US heartland. The acute care hospital a subsidiary of Heartland Health provides medical services to residents of St. Joseph Missouri and some 20 surrounding counties in northwest Missouri southeast Nebraska and northeast Kansas. Heartland Regional Medical Center encompasses specialty centers for trauma and long-term care acute rehabilitation cancer heart disease and birthing. As part of the services provided by the medical center Heartland Regional Medical Center offers services such as arthritis pain and wound treatments as well as home health and hospice care.

Geographic Reach

Operating in Missouri Heartland Regional Medical Center serves the residents and visitors of its home state as well as those in Nebraska and Kansas. Altogether the medical center caters to a more than 20-county area.

Strategy

As part of its operations Heartland Regional Medical Center partners with several managed care organizations such as Aetna CCN Managed Care Coventry Healthcare and Blue Cross Blue Shield of Kansas City to give its patients payment options for its health services. In 2012 Heartland Regional Medical Center developed an accountable care organization. It's a participant in the Medicare Shared Savings Program and enters into other similar shared savings arrangements with commercial self-insured or other third-party payors.

In recent years the medical facility has been investing in growing its footprint. Heartland Regional Medical Center is funding a $55-million expansion project that includes adding a handful of new operating rooms and renovating 10 more.

Financial Performance

In fiscal 2012 as compared to 2011 Heartland Regional Medical Center's revenue rose some 8% and its net income saw a 31% boost.

Company Ownership

Heartland Regional Medical Center is a subsidiary of Heartland Health.

EXECUTIVES

Vice Chairman, Carol Roever

LOCATIONS

HQ: HEARTLAND REGIONAL MEDICAL CENTER
5325 FARAON ST, SAINT JOSEPH, MO 645063488
Phone: 816 271-7211

PRODUCTS/OPERATIONS

Selected Services
Appendectomy
Cholecystectomy
Colon Resection
Hernia Repair
Nephrectomy
Assisted Vaginal Hysterectomy
Peritoneal Dialysis Catheter Placement
Pyloromyotomy
Tubal Ligation
Abdominal Perineal Resection
Adrenalectomy
Colostomy
Gastric Banding
Gastric Bypass
Gastric Sleeve
Gastrostomy Tube Placement
Laser Lysis of Adhesions/Endometriosis
Nissan Fundoplication
Salpingo-Oophorectomy
Prostatectomy

COMPETITORS

Ascension Health
BJC HealthCare
Catholic Health
 Initiatives
Children' s Mercy
 Hospital
CoxHealth
Mercy Health
Saint Luke' s Health
 System

Shawnee Mission
 Medical Center
Sisters of Charity of
 Leavenworth
Truman Medical Centers
University of Kansas
 Medical Center

HISTORICAL FINANCIALS

Company Type: Private

Income Statement

	REVENUE ($ mil.)	NET INCOME ($ mil.)	NET PROFIT MARGIN	EMPLOYEES
06/13	604	44	7.4%	2,600
06/12	564	11	2.0%	—
06/11	514	72	14.0%	—
06/10	483	0	—	—
Annual Growth	7.7%	—	—	—

FYE: June 30

2013 Year-End Financials
Return on assets: 14.9%
Return on equity: 7.4%
Current ratio: 0.30

Cash ($ mil.): 12

HENDRICK MEDICAL CENTER

Auditors: CONDLEY AND COMPANY LLP A

LOCATIONS

HQ: HENDRICK MEDICAL CENTER
 1900 PINE ST, ABILENE, TX 796012432
Phone: 325 670-2000
Web: WWW.EHENDRICK.ORG

HISTORICAL FINANCIALS

Company Type: Private

Income Statement

	REVENUE ($ mil.)	NET INCOME ($ mil.)	NET PROFIT MARGIN	EMPLOYEES
08/13	305	46	15.3%	2,400
08/08	280	18	6.7%	—
08/07	233	22	9.6%	—
08/06	349	0	—	—
Annual Growth	(1.9%)	—	—	—

FYE: August 31

2013 Year-End Financials
Return on assets: 6.5%
Return on equity: 15.3%
Current ratio: 1.10

Cash ($ mil.): —

HENRY FORD HEALTH SYSTEM

Built around a hospital founded by Detroit's favorite son the not-for-profit Henry Ford Health System (HFHS) is a hospital network that is also involved in medical research and education. The system's half-dozen hospitals –including the flagship Henry Ford Hospital as well as Henry Ford Wyandotte Hospital and mental health facility Kingswood Hospital –are home to roughly 2200 beds. HFHS also operates a 1200-doctor-strong medical group (with more than 40 specialties) as well as nursing homes hospice and a home health care network. The system's Health Alliance Plan of Michigan provides managed care and health insurance to more than half a million members.

Operations

Along with its hospitals large and small the system also operates more than 30 medical centers and maintains partnerships with community health services. About 20% of ambulatory care and 10% of acute care services in the region are provided by HFHS. In 2013 its hospitals took in more than 89000 patients and delivered more than 7900 babies. It also had 3.2 million outpatient visits and performed more than 88000 surgical procedures. HFHS conducts more than 285000 home health care visits annually.

For patients who need more than an ambulance to get them to the hospital the Henry Ford Hospital provides air ambulance transportation. The flagship hospital provides transport for critically ill and trauma patients within a 150-mile radius of Detroit (in Michigan Ohio and Ontario) via its Air Med 1 aeromedical helicopter.

Affiliated with Wayne State University's School of Medicine the health system is a leading education and research center with ongoing research in areas such as stroke heart disease cancer and diabetes. Wayne State and HFHS have agreed to expand their affiliation by increasing the number of medical students who train at Henry Ford working together on research projects and opening a new research center. HFHS trains more than 1500 future physicians every year. Henry Ford Hospital is responsible for many of those providing about 45 accredited programs to medical students.

Flagship facility Henry Ford Hospital is an 877-bed tertiary care hospital education and research complex. Kingswood Hospital is a 100-bed hospital offering inpatient care for individuals with acute episodes of mental illness. Henry Ford Macomb Hospital has 349 beds while Henry Ford West Bloomfield Hospital has 191 beds. Henry Ford Wyandotte Hospital is 401-bed acute care facility.

Geographic Reach

HFHS serves patients in Detroit and southeastern Michigan.

Sales and Marketing

Medicare accounted for 45% of payors in 2014 followed by Blue Cross (23%) Medicaid (17%) and self-pay and other (15%).

Financial Performance

Revenue increased 4% to $4.7 billion in 2014 as net patient services and health care premiums rose. However the system reported a net loss of $54.6 million that year as it used cash in pension and other post-retirement net adjustments and lost money on investments.

Cash flow from operations more than doubled to $142 million due to a decline in pension and health care premium receivables and changes in trading securities and accounts payable.

StrategyHFHS grows organically and through partnerships. In 2012 it teamed up with Presbyterian Villages of Michigan forming a joint venture to operate the Center for Senior Independence. The Center is now a separate not-for-profit organization expected to increase the number of seniors it serves from 230 to nearly 1000 by 2016.

HFHS has increased its physician base by launching a subsidiary the Henry Ford Physician Network which is composed of private practice and hospital-employed physicians as well as the existing Henry Ford Medical Group.

In 2014 the system launched a clinical trial to investigate a new drug to treat tinnitus a chronic ringing of the head or ears.

Company Background

Automaker Henry Ford founded Henry Ford Hospital in 1915.

EXECUTIVES

Exec V Pres, Mark Kelly
Executive Vice President; Chief Executive Officer Henry Ford Medical Group, William A (Bill) Conway
Director of Radiology, Zachary S (Zach) Delproposto
Vice President, Linda Esquina
Senior Vice President of Marketing and, Rose Glenn
Director of Radiology, Xia Wang
Senior Vice President, Joseph (Jo) Schmitt
Director of Radiology, Joseph M (Jo) Silva
Director of Radiology, John W (Jack) Bonnett
Vice President Supply Chain Management, James (Jamie) O'Connor
Vice President, Tom Nantais
Vice President Chief Human Resources O, Kathy Oswald
Vice President Corporate Strategic Planning, Joel Keiper
Vice President Reimbursement And Contracting, Mary Whitbread
Vice President Business Effectiveness, Vimal Chowdhry
Vice President Clinical Transformation And Information Technology Integration, Matt Walsh

Vice President, Mike Ellis
Director of Radiology, Eric Spickler
Vice President Information Technology, Veeresh Nama
Vice President Risk Finance, John (Jack) Mucha
Executive Vice President; President and Chief Executive Officer Health Alliance Plan, James (Jamie) Connelly
Radiology Director, Michael (Mel) Davis
Vice President, Greg Solecki
Secretary, Jasmine Parks

LOCATIONS

HQ: HENRY FORD HEALTH SYSTEM
1 FORD PL, DETROIT, MI 482023450
Phone: 313 916-2600
Web: WWW.HENRYFORD.COM

PRODUCTS/OPERATIONS

2014 Payer Distribution

	% of total
Medicare	45
Blue Cross	23
Medicaid HMO/Medicaid	17
Self-pay & other	15
Total	**100**

2014 Sales

	$ in mil
% of total	
Healthcare premium	48
Net patient service	46
Investment income	2
Other income	4
Total	**100**

Selected Operations

Hospitals
Henry Ford Hospital
Henry Ford Macomb Hospitals
Henry Ford West Bloomfield Hospital
Henry Ford Wyandotte Hospital
Kingswood Hospital (mental health care)
Other
Greenfield Health Systems (dialysis provider)
Health Alliance Plan of Michigan (health plan)
Henry Ford Continuing Care (nursing homes)
Henry Ford Health Products (medical supply retailer)
Henry Ford Home Health Care (home health)
Henry Ford Medical Centers and Urgent Care (urgent care)
Henry Ford Medical Group (physician's group)
Henry Ford OptimEyes (eye care services)
Hospices of Henry Ford (hospice)

COMPETITORS

Ascension Health	Mount Clemens Regional
Beaumont Health System	Medical Center
Blue Cross Blue Shield	Oakwood Healthcare
of Michigan	OmniCare Health Plan
Crittenton Hospital	St. John Health
Detroit Medical Center	Total Health Care
Garden City Hospital	Trinity Health (Novi)
Harper-Hutzel Hospital	University of Michigan
McLaren Health Care	Health System

HISTORICAL FINANCIALS

Company Type: Private

Income Statement — FYE: December 31

	REVENUE ($ mil.)	NET INCOME ($ mil.)	NET PROFIT MARGIN	EMPLOYEES
12/13	4,517	135	3.0%	23,000
12/09	2,118	26	1.3%	—
12/08	1,083	(122)	—	—
12/07	1,820	0	—	—
Annual Growth	**16.4%**	—	—	—

2013 Year-End Financials

Return on assets: 3.5%   Cash ($ mil.): 471
Return on equity: 3.0%
Current ratio: 1.00

HENRY MAYO NEWHALL MEMORIAL HOSPITAL

Had a bit too much mayo? Arteries feeling a bit clogged? Henry Mayo Newhall Memorial Hospital exists for just this reason (among others). The hospital serves the healthcare needs of the Santa Clarita Valley in northern Los Angeles County. The not-for-profit community hospital houses more than 220 beds and provides general medical and surgical care as well as trauma services (it is a Level II trauma center) outpatient services psychiatric care and emergency services among other specialties. In operation since 1975 the hospital was built to serve the needs of the at-the-time unincorporated City of Santa Clara on land donated by The Newhall Land and Farming Company.

Henry Mayo Memorial's physicians offer patients more than 70 different medical specialties that range from a widely hailed cancer program to an advanced primary stroke center spine and joint program an acute rehab unit growing cardiology services outpatient wound care services and physical and occupational therapies. The hospital also offers extensive maternity programs that include lactation support and childbirth education programs.

The hospital is undergoing a number of expansions including the addition of more intensive care unit (ICU) beds a larger emergency room expanded surgery department the construction of two helipads to receive patients via helicopter and the development of a new Neonatal Intensive Care Unit (NICU). All of the construction is part of Henry Mayo Memorial's 15-year master plan to expand and upgrade to accommodate a growing patient population. Henry Mayo Hospital is also building an inpatient hospital to house up to another 120 hospital beds. The hospital addition will operate 24 hours a day seven days a week and its development will provide Santa Clarita residents with close to 360 total patient beds. Opening is anticipated for 2016. To sum up the 15 year development plan includes the inpatient building up to three medical office buildings a new central plant and up to four parking structures. Other campus modifications include additional acute care beds in the pavilion one helipad on a parking structure and one on the new inpatient building. The plan also includes the new ICU NICU expanded imaging services new operating rooms and centers of excellence. The entire project is expected to cost $300 million and is being funded through operations bonds philanthropy and private investments.

EXECUTIVES

Senior Vice President Chief Operating Officer, John Schleif
Nursing Director, Vivian Rebel
Vice President Procurement, Fredy Shen
Senior Vice President and Director Business Development, Terry Stone
Director Of Nursing, Sue Galvin
Nursing Director Medical Surgical Service.., Susan (Sue) Romero
Director Of Him, Kelly Torrance
Vice President of Sales and Marketing, Bob Yerby

LOCATIONS

HQ: HENRY MAYO NEWHALL MEMORIAL HOSPITAL
23845 MCBEAN PKWY, SANTA CLARITA, CA 913552001
Phone: 661 253-8000
Web: WWW.HENRYMAYO.COM

COMPETITORS

Aptium Oncology
Brotman Medical Center
Cedars-Sinai Medical Center
Childrens Hospital Los Angeles
Glendale Adventist Medical Center
Good Samaritan Hospital (Los Angeles)
HCA
Hoag Memorial Hospital
Hollywood Presbyterian Medical Center
Los Angeles County Health Department
Marin General Hospital
Methodist Hospital of Southern California
Providence Saint Joseph Medical Center
Tenet Healthcare
United Surgical Partners

HISTORICAL FINANCIALS

Company Type: Private

Income Statement — FYE: September 30

	REVENUE ($ mil.)	NET INCOME ($ mil.)	NET PROFIT MARGIN	EMPLOYEES
09/09	205	11	5.8%	1,000
09/06	145	10	6.9%	—
09/05	1,525	0	0.0%	—
Annual Growth	**(39.4%)**	**1040.7%**		

2009 Year-End Financials

Return on assets: —   Cash ($ mil.): 41
Return on equity: 5.8%
Current ratio: 0.50

HENRY MODELL & COMPANY INC.

A model corporate citizen retailer Henry Modell & Company sells sporting goods fitness equipment apparel and brand-name athletic footwear as America's oldest family-owned and -operated sporting goods retailer. Established in 1889 the business also ensures it has local team apparel on hand. Through more than 155 stores that operate under the Modell's Sporting Goods banner the company serves some 10 East Coast states and the District of Columbia. Known for its reasonably priced branded products Modell's locates its stores in malls regional shopping centers and busy urban areas. It also boasts an online presence at Modells.com.

Geographic Reach
New York (home to 69 stores) and New Jersey (with 36 stores) are the sporting goods chain's major markets. The retailer also has stores in Connecticut Pennsylvania Rhode Island Maryland Massachusetts New Hampshire Delaware Virginia and the District of Columbia.

Sales and Marketing
Modell's markets and sells its products through its stores and online.

Strategy
To ensure it has all its bases covered Henry Modell & Company offers licensed products from nearly 30 sports leagues. Also during recent years Henry Modell & Company has focused on designing more appealing and accessible stores. To this end most Modell's locations have been renovated to provide improved accommodations for shoppers. Also the retailer has opened three stores in New York City including its redesigned 20000-sq.-ft. flagship store in Times Square.

To improve wireless performance in all of its stores in 2014 the company partnered with DecisionPoint Systems integrating DecisionPoint's mobile computing and wireless infrastructure system into its operations.

Company Background

Hungarian immigrant Morris Modell first sold menswear from a Lower East Side pushcart in New York City before he founded Henry Modell & Company in 1889. Led by CEO Mitchell Modell the company is operated by the fourth generation of the Modell family.

EXECUTIVES

CEO, Mitchell B. (Mitch) Modell, age 61
Executive Vice President Finance, Lawrence Brustein
VP Information Technology, Hans Kantor
Assistant Vice President Service Delivery and Support, Fred Marinelli
Vice President Of Planning, Justin Miller
Vice President Operations Production Manufacturing, James (Jamie) Buoni
Vice President Marketing and Advertising, Tami Mohney
Assistant Vice President Network and Data Center Operations, Diane Huff
Executive Vice President, Cary Deleo
Vice President Of Sales, Jim Mcdonald
Vice President, Willy Kaplan
Executive Vice President, Doug Epstein
Auditors: BDO USA LLP NEW YORK NY

LOCATIONS

HQ: HENRY MODELL & COMPANY INC.
498 7TH AVE FL 20, NEW YORK, NY 100186704
Phone: 212 822-1000
Web: WWW.MODELLS.COM

2013 Locations

	No.
New York	67
New Jersey	35
Pennsylvania	19
Maryland	10
Connecticut	7
Massachusetts	7
Virginia	6
District of Columbia	2
New Hampshire	2
Delaware	1
Rhode Island	1
Total	**157**

PRODUCTS/OPERATIONS

Selected Product Categories

Accessories
Apparel
Baseball
Basketball
Boxing/martial arts
Camping/hiking
Cycling
Electronics/optics
Fan shop-pro/college
Field hockey
Fishing
Fitness
Football
Footwear
Games
Golf
Ice/roller hockey
In-Line/roller skating
Lacrosse
Optics/telescopes
Outdoor recreation
Paintball
Pilates
Racquetball/squash
Roller hockey
Rugby
Running
Scooters
Skateboarding
Snow sports
Soccer
Softball
Tennis
Water recreation
Winter recreation
Wrestling
Yoga

COMPETITORS

Athleta	Hat World
Dick's Sporting Goods	Olympia Sports
Dunham's	Sears
Eastern Mountain Sports	Sports Authority
Foot Locker	Target Corporation
	Wal-Mart

HISTORICAL FINANCIALS

Company Type: Private

Income Statement

FYE: February 1

	REVENUE ($ mil.)	NET INCOME ($ mil.)	NET PROFIT MARGIN	EMPLOYEES
02/14	604	(4)	—	5,430
02/13*	607	0	0.1%	
01/12	570	(3)	—	
01/11	558	0	—	
Annual Growth	**2.7%**			

*Fiscal year change

2014 Year-End Financials

Return on assets: 8.1% Cash ($ mil.): 5
Return on equity: (-0.8%)
Current ratio: 0.10

HENSEL PHELPS CONSTRUCTION CO.

Hensel Phelps Construction builds it all from the courthouse to the big house. The employee-owned general contractor provides a full range of development pre-construction construction and renovation services for commercial institutional and government projects throughout the US and abroad. Its project portfolio includes prisons airports arenas laboratories government complexes offices and more. Major public and private clients have included the US Army Corps of Engineers IBM United Airlines The University of Texas Kodak and Whole Foods. Hensel Phelps founded the eponymous company as a homebuilder in 1937.

Geographic Reach

Colorado-based Hensel Phelps Construction has seven regional offices throughout the continental US including two in California. The company operates internationally most often for US federal projects but also for foreign governments and private enterprises. Its Honolulu branch oversees operations in Hawaii Guam the Marshall Islands and Asia.

Sales and Marketing

Sectors served include aviation commercial education government health care hospitality industrial and justice.

Financial Performance

One of America's largest private companies Hensel Phelps reported $2 billion in revenue in 2014.

Strategy

Hensel Phelps ranks in the top three (by Engineering News Record) among general contractors and construction managers in the US in the aero-

space government and "green" government office sectors. The company self-performs (as opposed to subcontracting) most of the work tied to a specific project. That ability helps keep costs and schedules in check. Its construction services include concrete work quality control safety management waste management among others.

In 2016 the company was awarded a contract to build a new 285000-sq.-ft. office tower in Denver. Other notable projects include a new central library in Austin Texas.

EXECUTIVES

President Phelps Development, Eric L. Wilson
CFO, Stephen J. (Steve) Carrico
EVP, Wayne S. Lindholm
EVP, Jon W. Ball
President and CEO, Jeffrey K. (Jeff) Wenaas
EVP, Michael J. Choutka
EVP, Richard G. Tucker
President Hensel Phelps Services, Edwin (Glen) Miller
V Pres, Steve M Grauer
Vice President Of Technology Systems, Jose Vasquez
Vice President Of Information Systems, Rashad Friday
Vice President Of Information Systems, Daniel Sherard
Senior Management (Senior Vice President General Manager Director), Laird Heikens
Vice President Of Information Technology, Quincy Yaw
Vice President Of Information Systems, Jason Spencer
Auditors: KPMG LLP DENVER CO

LOCATIONS

HQ: HENSEL PHELPS CONSTRUCTION CO.
420 6TH AVE, GREELEY, CO 806312332
Phone: 970 352-6565
Web: WWW.HENSELPHELPS.COM

PRODUCTS/OPERATIONS

Selected Projects

Hilton Hok
Aegis Asho
Regional O
Guam NAVFAC Bachelor Enlisted Quarters (BEQ)
Mamizu Utilities and Site Improvements Phase I
Samaritan MOB and Parking Structure
Santa Clara Valley Medical Center Receiving and Support Center
Santa Clara Family Justice Center
Santa Clara Valley Medical Center Receiving and Support Center
Rotary PlayGarden
Norman Y. Mineta San José International Airport Terminal Area Improvement Program (TAIP)
Vantage Data Center V2
Vantage Data Center V1

Selected Services

Construction
  Change management
  Construction waste management
  LEED project registration
  Quality control
  Safety management
  Scheduling
  Self-performing concrete
  Status reporting
  Subcontractor management
  Sustainability audits
  Quality control
Development
  Feasibility studies
  Financing
  Green building planning/education
  Land acquisition
  Leasing
  Pro forma review
Post-construction
  As-built documentation

Building operations
Certificate of occupancy
Commissioning and warranty programs
LEED project certification
Moving services
Preconstruction
Bid packaging
Budgeting/cost modeling
Design management
Estimating
Green building and planning/education
Phasing plans
Regulatory investigation
Scheduling
Status reporting
Subcontractor prequalification
Value engineering

Selected Markets

Commercial
Education
High technology
Industrial
International
Justice
Leisure
Medical
Multiresidence
Public
Transportation

COMPETITORS

Balfour Beatty	M. A. Mortenson
Construction	McCarthy Building
C.F. Jordan	PCL Employees Holdings
CH2M HILL	Rooney Holdings
Clark Construction	Skanska USA Building
Group	Turner Corporation
Fluor	Tutor Perini
Gilbane	Walbridge Aldinger
Hunt Construction	Walsh Group
Jacobs Engineering	Whiting-Turner
KBR	

HISTORICAL FINANCIALS

Company Type: Private

Income Statement				FYE: December 31
	REVENUE ($ mil.)	NET INCOME ($ mil.)	NET PROFIT MARGIN	EMPLOYEES
12/13	2,248	57	2.6%	2,000
12/12*	1,220	35	2.9%	—
05/12	2,178	54	2.5%	—
05/11	2,494	0	—	—
Annual Growth	(3.4%)	—	—	—

*Fiscal year change

2013 Year-End Financials

Return on assets: 9.5%
Return on equity: 2.6%
Current ratio: 0.90

Cash ($ mil.): 213

HERSHEY ENTERTAINMENT & RESORTS COMPANY

Life is sweet for Hershey Entertainment & Resorts. The company owns the many chocolate-related entertainment destinations in Hershey Pennsylvania. Its holdings include Hersheypark one of the nation's top amusement parks with more than 65 rides and attractions; ZooAmerica wildlife park; the Hotel Hershey; and the Hershey Lodge. Hershey Entertainment also owns four golf courses and the Giant Center arena in Hershey. Hershey Entertainment & Resorts is fully owned by the Hershey Trust Company which controls a majority stake in candymaker The Hershey Company. The Hershey Trust Co. also acts as trustee for the Milton Hershey School.

Geographic Reach

Hershey Entertainment & Resorts targets visitors who live within a day's drive (such as Nassau and Suffolk counties on Long Island New York as well as Philadelphia and Washington DC) of its facilities and resorts.

Operations

The company comprises Hershey Entertainment Group and the Resorts Group. The entertainment group includes Hersheypark Hershey Theatre Hershey Nursery Hershey Laundry & Dry Cleaning Giant Center Hersheypark Stadium The Star Pavilion Hershey Bears Hersheypark Arena and ZooAmerica North American Wildlife Park. Resorts include The Hershey Hotel Hershey Lodge The Spa at the Hotel Hershey Hershey Country Club and Hersheypark Camping Resort.

Hershey Entertainment & Resorts partners with the likes of AXME Paper & Supply Co. Amtrak Capital BLUE Chevrolet Dietz & Watson Entenmann's Gelco and Giant Groups among others.

Hersheypark consists of a dozen roller coaster rides and more than 65 rides and attractions 20 of which are kiddie rides. Among its attractions are nearly 15 unique water attractions in The Boardwalk at Hersheypark.

Sales and Marketing

The company markets its facilities as lower cost alternatives to more expensive destinations such as Walt Disney Parks and Resorts which advertise nationally.

Strategy

Hershey Entertainment & Resorts's strategy is to remain focused on its core hotels restaurants spas and entertainment offerings. Plans call for adding updates and growing the company's existing businesses to keep things fresh for visitors.

Company Background

Hersheypark opened in 1907 by Milton Hershey as a picnic grounds for his employees. The privately held Hershey Entertainment & Resorts company was founded in 1927 when Milton separated his chocolate manufacturing operations from his other businesses.

EXECUTIVES

Vice President Of Operations, John Lawn
Treasurer, Wendy McClintock

LOCATIONS

HQ: HERSHEY ENTERTAINMENT & RESORTS COMPANY
100 HOTEL RD, HERSHEY, PA 170339507
Phone: 717 534-3131
Web: WWW.THEHOTELHERSHEY.COM

PRODUCTS/OPERATIONS

Selected Operations

Amusement parks
Hersheypark
ZooAmerica
Hotels
Hershey Lodge
The Hotel Hershey
The Spa at the Hotel Hershey
Other
Giant Center
Hershey Golf Collection
Hershey Highmeadow Campground
Hersheypark Stadium

COMPETITORS

Adventureland	Kennywood
Cedar Fair	LEGO
Disney Parks & Resorts	SeaWorld

Great Wolf	Six Flags
Herschend	Universal Parks
Entertainment	

HISTORICAL FINANCIALS

Company Type: Private

Income Statement				FYE: December 31
	REVENUE ($ mil.)	NET INCOME ($ mil.)	NET PROFIT MARGIN	EMPLOYEES
12/09	270	6	2.6%	7,100
12/08	273	13	5.1%	—
12/07	1,333	0	0.0%	—
Annual Growth	(54.9%)	16391.2%	—	—

2009 Year-End Financials

Return on assets: 3.0%
Return on equity: 2.6%
Current ratio: 0.20

Cash ($ mil.): 2

HF MANAGEMENT SERVICES LLC

Auditors: ERNST & YOUNG LLP NEW YORK

LOCATIONS

HQ: HF MANAGEMENT SERVICES LLC
100 CHURCH ST FL 17, NEW YORK, NY 100072607
Phone: 212 801-6000

HISTORICAL FINANCIALS

Company Type: Private

Income Statement				FYE: December 31
	REVENUE ($ mil.)	NET INCOME ($ mil.)	NET PROFIT MARGIN	EMPLOYEES
12/12	815	83	10.2%	1,850
12/08	267	50	18.8%	—
12/07	222	7	3.3%	—
12/06	178	0	—	—
Annual Growth	28.8%	—	—	—

2012 Year-End Financials

Return on assets: 1.3%
Return on equity: 10.2%
Current ratio: 1.90

Cash ($ mil.): 207

HICKMAN WILLIAMS & COMPANY

Hickman Williams makes carbon products (anthracite coal metallurgical coke and reactive char coke) and metals and alloys (chromium manganese and silicon) used by metals producers. The company also manufactures service injection systems and cored wire feeding units for metal production facilities. Hickman Williams operates about 50 warehouse facilities throughout the nation. Founded by Richard Hickman and Harry Williams in 1891 the company is now owned by its employees.

EXECUTIVES

Executive Vice President, Pam Evans
Auditors: ERNST & YOUNG LLP CINCINNATI

LOCATIONS

HQ: HICKMAN WILLIAMS & COMPANY
250 E 5TH ST STE 300, CINCINNATI, OH 452024198
Phone: 513 621-1946
Web: WWW.HICWILCO.COM

COMPETITORS

Berlin Metals   Reliance Steel
Eagle Steel Products

HISTORICAL FINANCIALS

Company Type: Private

Income Statement
FYE: March 31

	REVENUE ($ mil.)	NET INCOME ($ mil.)	NET PROFIT MARGIN	EMPLOYEES
03/14	245	0	—	93
03/13	287	5	2.0%	—
03/12	0	0	—	—
03/11	299	0	—	—
Annual Growth	(6.4%)	—	—	—

2014 Year-End Financials
Return on assets: 6.3%   Cash ($ mil.): 22
Return on equity: —
Current ratio: 2.30

HIGH INDUSTRIES INC.

High Industries has ascended to the top of the steel and construction business. Doing business as High Companies its subsidiaries are active in heavy construction and materials mostly along the East Coast. Its High Steel Structures is one of North America's largest steel bridge fabricators. Other group companies include High Steel Service Center (metal processing) High Concrete Group (precast concrete) High Transit (specialty hauler) and High Structural Erectors (field erection services). Affiliates of High Companies such as High Hotels are active in real estate. Tracing its roots to a welding shop founded by Sanford H. High in 1931 the family-owned company is controlled by the High Family Council.

OperationsHigh Industries operates through its five affiliates: High Steel Structures High Steel Service Center High Concrete Group High Transit and High Structural Erectors.

High Steel Structures is the largest steel bridge girder manufacturer in the US serving as a fabricator and erector of more than 6000 bridges since 1980. Bridge projects include the Arthur Ravenel Jr. Bridge in South Carolina and the Frederick Douglass - Susan B. Anthony Memorial Bridge in New York. Its biggest project was the $85-million high-occupancy lanes on the I045 Virginia Capital Beltway.High Transit is a specialty hauler that serves all affiliated companies of High Industries. When High Transit isn't busy hauling for its parent it offers specialty services for companies in the civil construction manufacturing transportation building construction Marcellus Shale and heavy equipment industries.

High Structural Erectors (formed in 2013) provides erection services to the infrastructure commercial institutional and industrial markets.Geographic ReachHeadquartered in Lancaster Pennsylvania High Industries caters mostly to clients across the US's East Coast. The vast ma-

jority of its offices are in Pennsylvania but High also operates in Florida South Carolina North Carolina Maryland New Jersey Pennsylvania New York Ohio and Illinois. Sales and MarketingHigh Industries serves a diverse group of customers throughout the Eastern and Midwestern US including businesses in the infrastructure commercial institutional and industrial markets.StrategyHigh Industries regularly adds to its service offerings by opening new lines of business. In 2013 it formed High Structural Erectors LLC —which specializes in constructing structural steel and precast concrete architectural precast and cladding —to complement its service offerings with the abilities and expertise of its other two subsidiary companies High Steel Structures and High Concrete Group.

EXECUTIVES

Vice President Of Marketing, Brian Reichert
Vice President Wholesale Marketing Men, Lisa Fulginiti
Vice President, Brian Urban
Senior Vice President, Brad Mowbray
Board Member, Steve Gaul
Treasurer, James Tritch
Board Member, Michael F (Mel) Shirk
Auditors: KPMG LLP HARRISBURG PA

LOCATIONS

HQ: HIGH INDUSTRIES INC.
1853 WILLIAM PENN WAY, LANCASTER, PA
176016713
Phone: 717 293-4444
Web: WWW.HIGHINDUSTRIES.ORG

PRODUCTS/OPERATIONS

Selected Affiliates
High Industries Inc.
  High Concrete Group LLC
  High Steel Service Center Inc.
  High Steel Structures Inc.
  High Structural Erectors LLC
  High Transit LLC
High Real Estate Group LLC
  Greenfield Architects Ltd.
  High Associates Ltd.
  High Construction Company
  High Environmental Health & Safety Consulting Ltd.
  High Hotels Ltd.
  High Investors Ltd.

COMPETITORS

AK Steel Holding   Nucor
  Corporation   Peter Kiewit Sons'
American Bridge   Schuff
  Company   Skanska USA Civil
Dukane Precast   United States Steel
Flatiron Construction   Walsh Group
New Era Builders   Williams Industries

HISTORICAL FINANCIALS

Company Type: Private

Income Statement
FYE: December 31

	ASSETS ($ mil.)	NET INCOME ($ mil.)	INCOME AS % OF ASSETS	EMPLOYEES
12/09	230	0	—	2,107
12/08	272	31	11.7%	—
12/07	266	23	8.7%	—
12/06	297	0	—	—
Annual Growth	(8.2%)	—	—	—

2009 Year-End Financials
Return on assets: 8.9%   Sales ($ mil): 319
Return on equity: —

HIGH POINT REGIONAL HEALTH SYSTEM

Hospital stays are usually not the high point of one's life but High Point Regional Health System aims to make patients comfortable. Its main facility is High Point Regional Hospital a medical/surgical facility with about 380 beds serving the Piedmont Triad region of North Carolina. The private not-for-profit health care system also operates the Carolina Regional Heart Center Neuroscience Center Piedmont Joint Replacement Center Emergency Center Culp Women's Center and Hayworth Cancer Center. Other operations include primary care physician practices mental health wound care and home health care services. The hospital was founded in 1904. It became part of the UNC Health Care System in 2013.

Change in Company Type

The hospital became part of the UNC Health Care System (also known as University of North Carolina Hospitals) in 2013 through a merger transaction. Through the deal UNC Health will invest $150 million in capital improvements at High Point Regional as well as $50 million in community health initiatives. High Point Regional remains a not-for-profit entity with its own supporting foundation.

Geographic Reach

High Point Regional Hospital is located in High Point North Carolina and serves the Piedmont Triad region.

Operations

High Point Regional Hospital has a medical staff of about 2300 workers (including 400 physicians) and serves 120000 patients annually. It handles some 63000 emergency room visits 185000 outpatient care visits and 1500 births each year. The hospital also provides more than $40 million in community care programs including charity medical programs.

Other services offered through the Health System include diabetes treatment mental health bariatrics fitness wound care imaging and rehabilitation. It also operates Regional Physicians Multispecialty Group (a physicians practice organization) High Point Surgery Center and the Millis Regional Health Education Center.

Sales and Marketing

High Point Regional Hospital uses television commercials and social media to promote its services in the region.

Financial Performance

High Point reported a modest 6% revenue gain due to higher patient payments. Net income rose sharply due to a change in investment reporting while cash flow held steady.

Strategy

The organization began looking for a strategic partner in 2012 with the goal of leveraging its position in the changing US health care landscape. It formed an agreement with UNC Health Care later that year and the merger was completed in April 2013.

Prior to that High Point had signed an agreement with Duke Medicine to expand services for oncology and cardiovascular patients.

EXECUTIVES

Vice President Services, Katherine (Kate) Burns
Medical Director, Gregory Mieden
Vice President of Finance Chief Financial Officer, Kimberly Crews
Auditors: DIXON HUGHES GOODLMAN LLP CHA

LOCATIONS

HQ: HIGH POINT REGIONAL HEALTH SYSTEM
601 N ELM ST, HIGH POINT, NC 272624398
Phone: 336 878-6000
Web: WWW.HIGHPOINTREGIONAL.COM

PRODUCTS/OPERATIONS

Selected Centers and Services
Primary Centers
  The Carolina Regional Heart Center
  Culp Women's Center
  The Emergency Center
  Hayworth Cancer Center
  The Neuroscience Center
  The Piedmont Joint Replacement Center
Other Centers
  Adult Health
  Behavioral Health
  Diabetes Self-Care Management Center
  The Fitness Center at High Point Regional
  The Fitness Center at Kernersville
  Heart Strides
  Millis Regional Health Education Center
  MRI and Open MRI
  Online Nursery
  PET Imaging
  Premier Imaging
  Regional Center for Bariatric Surgery
  Regional Physicians
  Regional Wound Center
  Rehab Services
  Robotic Surgery
  The Stroke Center
  Vascular Services

COMPETITORS

Alamance Regional Medical Center
Carolinas HealthCare System
Cone Health
Tenet Healthcare
Wake Forest University Baptist Medical Center

HISTORICAL FINANCIALS

Company Type: Private

Income Statement   FYE: September 30

	REVENUE ($ mil.)	NET INCOME ($ mil.)	NET PROFIT MARGIN	EMPLOYEES
09/13	209	(21)	—	2,338
09/12	274	1	0.7%	—
09/11	276	(13)	—	—
09/10	296	0	—	—
Annual Growth	(10.9%)	—	—	—

2013 Year-End Financials
Return on assets: 14.9%   Cash ($ mil.): 7
Return on equity: (-10.3%)
Current ratio: 0.50

HIGH POINT SOLUTIONS INC.

High Point Solutions can solve your networking needs. The company supplies network hardware —routers switches and access servers —to telecommunications companies and other large enterprises. High Point's procurement specialists provide equipment from leading manufactures such as Cisco Systems and Nortel Networks. The company also provides services in repair network design and installation. Owners Mike and Tom Mendiburu maintain a lean-and-mean corporate philosophy: a small staff dedicated to procurement and focused on speed and service for a short list of large clients. The brothers founded High Point in 1996.

EXECUTIVES

Vice President Sales, Mike Liebson

LOCATIONS

HQ: HIGH POINT SOLUTIONS INC.
5 GAIL CT, SPARTA, NJ 078713438
Phone: 973 940-0040
Web: WWW.HIGHPOINT.COM

PRODUCTS/OPERATIONS

Selected Suppliers
ADTRAN
Cisco Systems
Extreme Networks
Foundry Networks
Juniper Networks
Lucent Technologies
Nortel Networks
Riverstone Networks

COMPETITORS

Avaya	Tech Data
CompuCom	Telmar Network
Ingram Micro	Technology
MTM Technologies	Verizon
Nortel Networks	Westcon
Pomeroy IT	

HISTORICAL FINANCIALS

Company Type: Private

Income Statement   FYE: December 31

	REVENUE ($ mil.)	NET INCOME ($ mil.)	NET PROFIT MARGIN	EMPLOYEES
12/13	197	7	4.0%	75
12/12	107	0	—	—
12/09	9	0	—	—
12/08	0	0	—	—
Annual Growth	—	—	—	—

2013 Year-End Financials
Return on assets: 10.2%   Cash ($ mil.): —
Return on equity: 4.0%
Current ratio: 1.10

HIGH STEEL STRUCTURES LLC

Steel fabricator High Steel Structures helps to build bridges —literally. The company manufactures structural steel beams and girders used to build bridges and elevated roads in the US. High Steel also makes steel structures for buildings such as manufacturing plants power plants and sports arenas and offers erection services and emergency repair services. Working with contractors such as Balfour Beatty Skanska and Middlesex High Steel has fabricated steel for thousands of bridges mainly along the East Coast. The company has four fabrication plants in Pennsylvania and is a part of High Industries. High Steel traces its roots back to 1931 when it was founded as High Welding Company.

High Steel was challenged in the past few years when the construction industry declined and the price of steel rose. But the company is working on projects with stimulus dollars as state departments of transportation begin awarding contracts for new roads and bridges.

EXECUTIVES

President, Jeffery L. Sterner
Auditors: KPMG LLP HARRISBURG PA

LOCATIONS

HQ: HIGH STEEL STRUCTURES LLC
1915 OLD PHLADELPHIA PIKE, LANCASTER, PA 176023410
Phone: 717 299-5211
Web: WWW.HIGHSTEEL.COM

COMPETITORS

American Bridge	L. B. Foster
Company	Schuff
Commercial Metals	Stupp Bros.
Hirschfeld Steel	Williams Industries

HISTORICAL FINANCIALS

Company Type: Private

Income Statement   FYE: December 31

	REVENUE ($ mil.)	NET INCOME ($ mil.)	NET PROFIT MARGIN	EMPLOYEES
12/09	180	0	—	600
12/08	131	7	5.4%	—
12/07	135	5	4.4%	—
Annual Growth	15.4%	—	—	—

2009 Year-End Financials
Return on assets: 7.6%   Cash ($ mil.): —
Return on equity: —
Current ratio: 0.80

HILAND DAIRY FOODS COMPANY. LLC

Reflecting the herd mentality of its industry Hiland Dairy Foods is a joint venture between Prairie Farms Dairy and Dairy Farmers of America. Hiland's cows produce the raw ingredient for churning out butter ice cream fluid milk cheese yogurt and other dairy products free of artificial growth hormones. The milk is distributed through 25 sites dotting the southwest US. Beyond dairy Hiland supplies juices bottled milk and coffee (cravélatté) as well as green tea water and other to-go drinks. It features limited-run specialty items such as peanut butter s'mores ice cream. Founded in 1938 the farmer-owned venture operates manufacturing plants in the Midwest.

Geographic Reach

Hiland Dairy Foods serves customers in several states including Arkansas Colorado Kansas Iowa Missouri Nebraska Oklahoma and Texas. To support its operations the cooperative boasts nearly a dozen plants in Arkansas Kansas Missouri Nebraska and Oklahoma.

Operations

It is a full-service dairy with a bulging products portfolio that includes the ubiquitous milk cartons as well as ice cream yogurt cheese sour cream dairy-based dips half and half whipping cream butter cheese and orange juice. The company's products are free of antibiotics and artificial growth hormones.

In line with the company's focus on sustainable initiatives the farmer-owned dairies that provide raw materials to Hiland Dairy Foods work to preserve and protect resources. To this end the dairy cooperative recycles and saves water batteries oil cardboard office paper plastic aluminum. In all it has saved more than 19000 barrels of oil and a total of 6.6 million KWh of electricity.

Strategy

In 2013 Hiland Dairy Foods undertook the effort of marketing the milk and dairy products of two of the nation's leading family-owned and -operated dairy farms. Coleman Dairy Foods which has been a division of Hiland Dairy Foods since 2006 began marketing its own dairy items under the Hiland Dairy Foods label. The benefit to both companies is that retail demand is higher for dairy products that are sold under one brand name and one UPC across multiple states and markets.

Company Ownership

Hiland Dairy Foods operates as a joint venture between Prairie Farms Dairy and Dairy Farmers of America.

EXECUTIVES

Vice President Sales And Marketing, Ted Barlows
Auditors: BKD LLP SPRINGFIELD MO

LOCATIONS

HQ: HILAND DAIRY FOODS COMPANY. LLC
1133 E KEARNEY ST, SPRINGFIELD, MO 658033435
Phone: 417 862-9311
Web: WWW.HILANDDAIRY.COM

Selected Plant Locations
Chandler Oklahoma
Fayetteville Arkansas
Fort Smith Arkansas
Kansas City Missouri
Little Rock Arkansas
Norfolk Nebraska
Norman Oklahoma
Omaha Nebraska
Springfield Missouri
Wichita Kansas

PRODUCTS/OPERATIONS

Selected Products
Butter
Cheese
Cottage cheese
Cravélatté (milk and coffee)
Creams/Half-and-Half
Dips
Egg nog
Egg substitute
Fruit-flavored drinks
Ice cream
Juice
Lactose-free milk
Lemonade
Milk
Sour cream
Tea
To-go drinks
Water
Yogurt

COMPETITORS

Agri-Mark	Land O' Lakes
Associated Milk	MMPA
Producers	Nestl©
Blue Bell	Oberweis Dairy
ConAgra	Organic Valley
Dairylea	Roberts Dairy
Dean Foods	Saputo
Dreyer' s	Sargento
Fonterra	Smith Dairy
Great Lakes Cheese	Snapple
Hornell Brewing	Wells' Dairy
Kemps LLC	

HISTORICAL FINANCIALS
Company Type: Private

Income Statement
FYE: September 30

	REVENUE ($ mil.)	NET INCOME ($ mil.)	NET PROFIT MARGIN	EMPLOYEES
09/11	958	8	0.9%	1,350
09/10	588	24	4.2%	—
09/09	2,110	0	—	—
Annual Growth	(32.6%)	35387.7%	—	—

2011 Year-End Financials
Return on assets: 2.6%
Return on equity: 0.9%
Current ratio: 0.90
Cash ($ mil.): 19

HILL PHYSICIANS MEDICAL GROUP INC.

Hill Physicians Medical Group is the doctors' answer to HMOs. The company is an independent practice association (IPA) serving some 300000 health plan members in northern California. The company contracts with managed care organizations throughout the region —including HMOs belonging to Aetna CIGNA and Health Net —to provide care to health plan members through its provider affiliates. Its network includes about 3800 primary care and specialty physicians 38 hospitals and 24 urgent care centers. The company also provides administrative services for doctors and patients. PriMed a management services organization created Hill Physicians Medical Group in 1984 and still runs the company.

Geographic Reach

Hill Physicians Medical Group's member facilities are located in Alameda Contra Costa El Dorado Placer Sacramento San Francisco San Joaquin San Mateo Solano and Yolo counties in northern California.

Financial Performance

Hill Physicians Medical Group reported a 3% increase in 2013 to about $455 million due to higher health plan revenues and investment income. Net income grew by 15% to some $13.6 million that year due to higher revenues and cost savings programs.

Strategy

Hill Physicians Medical Group has been working to enhance its technology systems to improve coordination of care including installing electronic prescription and referral management systems. It is also forming partnerships with area insurers and hospitals to improve communication among regional providers as well as to control overall health care costs. For instance the company teamed up with Dignity Health and Blue Shield of California to form an accountable care organization (ACO).

EXECUTIVES

Vice President Legal Services And Chief, Wendy Chow
Vice President for Performance Strategy, Terry Hill

LOCATIONS

HQ: HILL PHYSICIANS MEDICAL GROUP INC.
2409 CAMINO RAMON, SAN RAMON, CA 945834285
Phone: 925 820-3536
Web: WWW.HILLPHYSICIANS.COM

PRODUCTS/OPERATIONS

Selected Health Plan Partners
Aetna of California
Alliance CompleteCare
Anthem/Blue Cross of California
Blue Shield of California
Blue Shield 65 Plus
CIGNA Healthcare of California
Health Net of California
Health Net Medicare
United Healthcare West (formerly Pacificare)
SCAN
Secure Horizons by United Healthcare
Western Healthcare Advantage

COMPETITORS

Alta Bates Summit Medical Center	Orion HealthCorp
Beaver Medical Group	Prospect Medical
HealthCare Partners	The Palo Alto Medical Foundation

HISTORICAL FINANCIALS
Company Type: Private

Income Statement
FYE: December 31

	REVENUE ($ mil.)	NET INCOME ($ mil.)	NET PROFIT MARGIN	EMPLOYEES
12/10	427	5	1.2%	488
12/06	427	5	1.2%	—
12/05	1,401	0	—	—
Annual Growth	(21.1%)	1018.5%	—	—

2010 Year-End Financials
Return on assets: —
Return on equity: 1.2%
Current ratio: 0.80
Cash ($ mil.): 42

HILL/AHERN FIRE PROTECTION LLC

LOCATIONS

HQ: HILL/AHERN FIRE PROTECTION LLC
11045 GAGE AVE, FRANKLIN PARK, IL 601311437
Phone: 847 288-5100
Web: WWW.HILLAHERN.COM

HISTORICAL FINANCIALS
Company Type: Private

Income Statement
FYE: December 31

	REVENUE ($ mil.)	NET INCOME ($ mil.)	NET PROFIT MARGIN	EMPLOYEES
12/11	5,669	185	3.3%	40
12/10	2,568	80	3.1%	—
Annual Growth	120.7%	130.7%	—	—

2011 Year-End Financials
Return on assets: 4.4%
Return on equity: 3.3%
Current ratio: 2.30
Cash ($ mil.): 480

HILLCO LTD.

LOCATIONS

HQ: HILLCO LTD.
    1435 HWY 258 N, KINSTON, NC 285047208
Phone: 252 523-9094
Web: WWW.HILL-CO.COM

HISTORICAL FINANCIALS

Company Type: Private

Income Statement   FYE: December 31

	REVENUE ($ mil.)	NET INCOME ($ mil.)	NET PROFIT MARGIN	EMPLOYEES
12/08*	481	18	3.8%	7,000
09/07	481	18	3.8%	—
09/99	1	2	203.9%	—
12/98	1	0	—	—
Annual Growth	79.7%	—	—	—

*Fiscal year change

HINES INTERESTS LIMITED PARTNERSHIP

Hines has many interests but none of them involve ketchup. The real estate firm invests in develops renovates manages and finances commercial real estate including high-rise office buildings industrial parks medical facilities mixed-use developments and master-planned residential communities. Its portfolio boasts more than 1280 properties completed under development managed or invested. They span 100-plus cities worldwide and 516 million sq. ft. Hines has collaborated with such world-renowned architects as I. M. Pei Philip Johnson and Frank Gehry. Management services include marketing tenant relations and contract negotiations. Chairman Gerald Hines founded the family-controlled firm in 1957.

Geographic Reach

Houston-based Hines has offices in more than 110 US cities and some 18 countries worldwide including Australia Brazil Canada China Germany India Mexico and the UK. It maintains regional offices in Atlanta Chicago Houston New York San Francisco and London as well as in 65 other cities.

Sales and Marketing

Besides large master-planned communities and land developments Hines provides services to office residential mixed-use industrial hotel medical and sports facilities.

Operations

Hines manages 378 properties totaling nearly 152 million sq. ft. which includes 84.3 million sq. ft. for third parties.

Since 1991 Hines has employed a range of investment strategies to pursue acquisition and development opportunities through 42 investment vehicles (40 privately-offered and two publicly-offered) with more than $22 billion in equity. Additionally $5.3 billion of partner capital has been committed to one-off investments.

Publicly-offered Hines Real Estate Investment Trust (Hines REIT) targets office properties throughout the US but also has investments in retail and industrial properties. The firm's public non-traded real estate investment trust Hines Global REIT has raised more than $155 million to invest in commercial real estate properties and other real estate investment in the US and overseas. Hines is especially interested in making investments in China by developing housing and high-end shopping malls. The firm also closed out its first Brazilian development fund in 2011.

Hines' investor partners and clients include major public and private pension funds government investment authorities insurance companies financial institutions endowments and individual investors. Sometimes the company which invests in real estate through several funds teams up with investors on special projects. Hines formed a joint venture with the California Public Employees' Retirement System to develop sustainable office buildings. Hines entered a similar joint venture with New York State Common Retirement Fund to invest more than $1 billion in office and medical office projects in the US.

Financial Performance

One of the world's largest real estate organizations Hines controls assets valued at more than $25 billion.

Strategy

Hines has purchased more than $20 billion in prime real estate since 1993.

In the US Hines is working to become more diversified and chasing down acquisition opportunities where they exist. In 2012 Hines and a subsidiary of a real estate fund managed by Oaktree Capital Management acquired Irvine Corporate Center a two-story 126622-sq.-ft. office building within the Irvine Business Complex. In 2013 the pair also acquired the eight-acre Maxis office building.

Farther afield Hines Global REIT purchased a two-building logistics facility in the Upper Silesia region of Poland for $25.8 million. Other acquisitions include office properties in London and Brisbane Australia.

The company has a particular interest in sustainable development. Its Hines Green Office unit has handled nearly 200 Leadership in Energy and Environmental Design-certified and LEED registered projects.

In 2011 the firm created a new contracting company that works for its multifamily division which has been experiencing a surge in demand.

EXECUTIVES

EVP; CEO Europe/Middle East Region, Michael J. G. Topham
EVP; CEO West Region, James C. (Jim) Buie
Senior Managing Director, Kenneth W. (Ken) Hubbard
EVP; CEO Midwest and Southeast Regions, C. Kevin Shannahan
Vice Chairman and Chief Investment Officer, C. Hastings (Hasty) Johnson
CFO, Charles M. Baughn
EVP Conceptual Construction, Jerrold P. Lea
EVP; CEO Southwest Region, Mark Cover
SVP and CIO, Jesse Carrillo
CEO Investment Management, Colin Shepherd
CEO Capital Markets and East Region, Christopher D. Hughes
Senior Managing Director and Chief Risk Officer Investments, Tom Owens
Senior Vice President Risk Management, Rick Vance
Senior Vice President, Doug Munro
Senior Vice President Human Resources, Stephanie Fore
Senior Vice President Operations, Ilene Allen
Vice President, Richard (Dick) Vance
Vice President, Bill Olson
Vice President, TY Bennion
Vice President Controller, Craig McKenzie
Senior Vice President, John (Jack) Mooz
Vice President, Mary Mccarthy
Vice President Finance, Agnes Olejniczak
Senior Vice President, Scott Murray
Vice President Controller, Brian Siebert
Executive Vice President, Jim Buie
Senior Vice President, Thomas (Thom) D'Arcy
Vice President, Jay Wyper
Senior Vice President Corporate Communications, George Lancaster
Senior Vice President, Thomas (Thom) Owens
Vice President Controller, Mark Cummings
Vice President, Michael (Mel) Desguin
Vice President, Michael (Mel) Allen
Vice President, Kevin Shannahan
Vice President, Thor Headley
Senior Vice President and Controller, Keith Montgomery
Senior Vice President, Leo Chen
Senior Vice President, Thomas (Thom) Kruggel
Vice President of Engineering Services Hines Interests Ltd, Andrew (Andy) Kitchens
Vice President, David (Dave) Robinson
Vice President Construction, Michael (Mel) Greene
Vice President, Greg McGrath
Vice President, Travis Overall
Vice President, Louis Sklar
Senior Vice President Corporate Engineer, Clayton Ulrich
Vice President, Douglas (Doug) Donovan
Vice President Mep Construction, Marty Olhava
Senior Vice President, Andy Trowbridge
Vice President Construction, John (Jack) Frank
Vice President Engineering, Johnathon Reynolds
Senior Vice President East, Tommy Craig
Vice President Construction, Jerry L Brown
Vice President Of Property Management, Lee Wallis
Vice President, Lawrence Peterson
Senior Vice President of Research, Joshua (Josh) Scoville
Vice President, Adil Noorani
Vice President Construction, Larry J Mccarty
Vice President, Wally Peterson
Vice President construction, Rocky Brown
Vice President Controller, Mimi Ribeiro
Vice President Construction, Jim Gutmann
Vice President Construction, Frank Garigliano
Vice President Construction, Gregory Spivey
Vice President, Kurt Hartman
Senior Vice President, Kay Forbes
Vice President, Rob Witte
Vice President, Bill Neeson
Senior Vice President and Fund Manager, David (Dave) Congdon
Chairman, Gerald D. Hines
Auditors: ERNST & YOUNG LLP HOUSTON TX

LOCATIONS

HQ: HINES INTERESTS LIMITED PARTNERSHIP
2800 POST OAK BLVD # 4800, HOUSTON, TX
770566118
Phone: 713 621-8000
Web: WWW.HINES.COM

PRODUCTS/OPERATIONS

Selected Services
Acquisition & Disposition Services
    Building pro forma
    Cash flow pro forma
    Closing
    Financing
    Investor pro forma
    Market evaluation
    Property evaluation
    Risk analysis
    Strategic planning
Asset & Property Management Services
    Acquisition & sales coordination
    Budgeting accounting & control
    Construction management
    Energy management
    Facility management
    Marketing & leasing

Parking management
Preventative maintenance programs
Project development & redevelopment
Project financing
Property management
Public relations
Real estate & market assessments
Risk management
Security
Strategic planning project positioning & repositioning
Tax analysis & administration
Tenant relations
Vendor contract negotiations
Development Services
Accounting control & reporting
Architectural & engineering contract negotiations
Budget development & administration
Conceptual construction
Construction buyout
Construction management
Design coordination
Environmental evaluation
Feasibility & market analysis
Governmental approval coordination
Marketing & public relations
Operations & maintenance planning
Pro forma development
Scheduling
Site evaluation
Tenant construction management
Marketing & Leasing Services
Broker relations
Investment market assessment
Lease negotiations
Market assessment
Marketing plan development
National Tenant Program coordination
Project assessment
Public relations
Repositioning strategy
Tenant prospecting

COMPETITORS

Brookfield Office	Lincoln Property
Properties	Mack-Cali
CBRE Group	Shorenstein
Captec	Tishman Speyer
Cencor Realty	Transwestern
Equity Office	Commercial Services
Jones Lang LaSalle	

HISTORICAL FINANCIALS

Company Type: Private

Income Statement

FYE: December 31

	REVENUE ($ mil.)	NET INCOME ($ mil.)	NET PROFIT MARGIN	EMPLOYEES
12/10	234	0	—	3,200
12/09	200	0	—	
12/08	1,216	0	—	
Annual Growth	—	—	—	—

2010 Year-End Financials

Return on assets: —
Return on equity: —
Current ratio: 2.60

Cash ($ mil.): 229

HINSHAW & CULBERTSON LLP

Hinshaw & Culbertson's 500 lawyers offer a wide range of legal services though the firm specializes in commercial and defense litigation and corporate environmental employment and construction law. It represents professionals dealing with corporate health care taxation malpractice white collar crime insurance coverage immigra-

tion intellectual property securities and real estate liability and risk management issues. The firm also offers legal advisement services to architects engineers and people residing in the financial services sector. Hinshaw & Culbertson has about 25 offices throughout 12 states in the US. The firm was founded in 1934.

Geographic Reach

Hinshaw & Culbertson has offices in Arizona California Florida Illinois Indiana Massachusetts Minnesota Missouri New York Oregon Rhode Island and Wisconsin.

Sales and Marketing

The firm represents clients in investigations by state and federal agencies such as the US Department of Justice and the US Securities and Exchange Commission.

Strategy

The firm's lawyers include several former federal and state prosecutors with extensive experience concerning white collar crime. In 2012 Hinshaw & Culbertson launched its White Collar Crime & Internal Investigations Blog. The blog addresses legal issues events and other news involving internal investigations white collar crime fraud and abuse.

Also in 2012 Hinshaw & Culbertson relocated its Miami office to a larger facility representing an approximately 50% increase the amount of space it occupies. The firm made the move as part of its continued expansion strategy in south Florida.

EXECUTIVES

Managing Partner, J. William Roberts
Executive Managing Director, Paul R. Boken
CFO, Robert P. Johnson
Vice President Moderates, Theresa Concepcion
Vice President, Jennifer Friedman
Legal Secretary, Jamie Schwab
Legal Secretary, Kris Bailey
Chairman, Kevin Joseph Burke
Secretary, Deb Bammann
Secretary, Arlene Banas
Secretary, Mary Velazquez
Board Member, Peter E (Pete) Pederson

LOCATIONS

HQ: HINSHAW & CULBERTSON LLP
222 N LASALLE ST STE 300, CHICAGO, IL 60601
Phone: 312 704-3000
Web: WWW.HINSHAWLAW.COM

PRODUCTS/OPERATIONS

Selected Practices
Construction law
Corporate and business Law
Environmental law
Government
Health care
Insurance services
Labor and employment
Litigation
Professional liability
School law

Selected Industries Served
Construction
Financial services
Health care
Insurance
Legal
Manufacturing
Real estate
Retail
Transportation

COMPETITORS

Baker & McKenzie	Schiff Hardin
Chapman and Cutler LLP	Seyfarth Shaw
Jenner & Block	Sidley Austin
Kirkland & Ellis	

HISTORICAL FINANCIALS

Company Type: Private

Income Statement

FYE: December 31

	REVENUE ($ mil.)	NET INCOME ($ mil.)	NET PROFIT MARGIN	EMPLOYEES
12/10	202	98	48.5%	1,010
12/03	124	53	43.1%	—
12/02	116	50	43.2%	—
12/01	108	0	—	—
Annual Growth	7.2%	—	—	—

2010 Year-End Financials

Return on assets: —
Return on equity: 48.5%
Current ratio: 3.00

Cash ($ mil.): 9

HOAG MEMORIAL HOSPITAL PRESBYTERIAN

Serving California's Orange County population Hoag Memorial Hospital Presbyterian boasts several hospitals and even more clinics to cater to area residents. The not-for-profit health care system is home to two acute care hospitals seven health centers five urgent care centers and a network of more than 1500 physicians. Its hospitals include Hoag Hospital Irvine and Hoag Hospital Newport Beach in Southern California. Combined the two hospitals have 617 beds and provide a comprehensive range of medical and surgical services with specialized expertise in a number of areas such as oncology cardiovascular disease neuroscience and orthopedics. Hoag is an affiliate of St. Joseph Health.

Operations

As part of its operations Hoag operates a pair of hospitals —Hoag Hospital Irvine and Hoag Hospital Newport Beach —as well as more than half a dozen health centers located in Aliso Viejo Costa Mesa Fountain Valley Huntington Beach Irvine and Newport Beach.

Hoag offers a comprehensive blend of health care services that includes five institutes providing specialized services in the following areas: cancer heart and vascular neurosciences women's health and orthopedics through Hoag's affiliate Hoag Orthopedic Institute.

Strategy

In 2014 Hoag and Newport Bay Surgery Center (a leading West coast ophthalmology surgery center) invested in the surgery center creating a partnership between the physician-owners and Hoag that paves the way for further cooperation around eye care.

Company Background

In 2013 Hoag formed an affiliation with St. Joseph Health a Catholic-sponsored health network with operations in three states. The two Hoag hospitals were combined into a new regional network known as Covenant Health Network which also includes five nearby St. Joseph facilities. The Hoag and St. Joseph facilities retain their independent identities and religious affiliations.

Hoag was Founded in 1952.

EXECUTIVES

Vice President Facilities and Operations, Jim Rice
Vice President Human Resources, Janet Blue

Senior Vice President Chief Information Officer, Timothy (Tim) Moore
Medical Director, Winnie Brown
Medical Director, Richard Doering
Senior Vice President and Interim Chief Financial Officer, Andrew (Andy) Guarni
Vice President Centers of Excellence, Trish Bartel
Vice President, John Baker
Vice President Performance Improvement, Bruce Davidson
Managing Director, Amer Jabara
Vice President of Sales and Marketing, Debra Legan
Senior Vice President Real Estate and Facilities, Sanford Smith
Vice President Marketing and Corporate Communications, Nina B Robinson
Senior Vice President Clinical Operations and Chief Nursing Officer, Richard (Dick) Martin
Vice President Operations, Holnagel Dori

LOCATIONS

HQ: HOAG MEMORIAL HOSPITAL PRESBYTERIAN
1 HOAG DR, NEWPORT BEACH, CA 926634162
Phone: 949 764-5689
Web: WWW.HOAG.ORG

Selected Operations
Hospitals
  Hoag Hospital Irvine
  Hoag Hospital Newport Beach
  Hoag Orthopedic Institute
Health Centers
  Hoag Health Center-Aliso Viejo
  Hoag Health Center-Costa Mesa
  Hoag Health Center-Fountain Valley
  Hoag Health Center-Huntington Beach
  Hoag Health Center-Irvine (Woodbridge)
  Hoag Health Center-Irvine (Woodbury)
  Hoag Health Center-Newport Beach

PRODUCTS/OPERATIONS

Selected Services
Cancer
Heart and Vascular
Neuroscience
Orthopedic
Women' s Health

COMPETITORS

Adventist Health	St. Joseph Health
Anaheim Regional	System
Medical Center	St. Joseph Hospital of
Children' s Hospital of	Orange
Orange County	St. Jude Medical
Citrus Valley Health	Center
Partners	Tenet Healthcare
Dignity Health	Torrance Memorial
Long Beach Memorial	Medical Center
Memorial Health	Trinity Health (Novi)
Services	UC Irvine Medical
Pasadena Hospital	Center
Association	Western Medical Center
Saddleback Memorial	- Santa Ana
Medical Center	

HISTORICAL FINANCIALS
Company Type: Private

Income Statement
FYE: September 30

	REVENUE ($ mil.)	NET INCOME ($ mil.)	NET PROFIT MARGIN	EMPLOYEES
09/13	784	155	19.8%	3,800
09/12	757	136	18.0%	—
Annual Growth	3.6%	14.3%	—	—

2013 Year-End Financials
Return on assets: 3.4%   Cash ($ mil.): 91
Return on equity: 19.8%
Current ratio: 0.60

HOLIDAY BUILDERS INC.

Holiday Builders is out to make buying a new home a vacation-like experience. The company a 100% employee-owned enterprise since 1999 builds single-family detached homes throughout Florida and in Alabama South Carolina and Texas. Since its inception the company has built more than 30000 homes sold primarily to first-time and value-conscious buyers. The company offers full homebuying services to its clients through HBI Title Company Holiday Builders Real Estate HB Designs and a partnership with Shelter Mortgage. Holiday Builders was founded in 1983.

EXECUTIVES

Division President, Jeremiah Gore
Vice President Business Development, Michelle Smallwood
Vice President Of Commercial, Bob Graves
Auditors: BERMAN HOPKINS WRIGHT & LAHAM

LOCATIONS

HQ: HOLIDAY BUILDERS INC.
2293 W EAU GALLIE BLVD, MELBOURNE, FL 329353184
Phone: 321 610-5156
Web: WWW.HOLIDAYBUILDERS.COM

COMPETITORS

Adams Homes	Lennar
David Weekley Homes	PulteGroup
Gehan Homes	

HISTORICAL FINANCIALS
Company Type: Private

Income Statement
FYE: December 31

	REVENUE ($ mil.)	NET INCOME ($ mil.)	NET PROFIT MARGIN	EMPLOYEES
12/07	234	(26)	—	101
12/06	699	40	5.8%	—
12/05	1,030	0	—	—
Annual Growth	—	—	—	—

2007 Year-End Financials
Return on assets: 0.8%   Cash ($ mil.): 57
Return on equity: (-11.2%)
Current ratio: 1.00

HOLLAND COMMUNITY HOSPITAL INC

Holland Hospital (formerly Holland Community Hospital) provides a comprehensive range of health services to residents of western Michigan's Lakeshore region. The 190-bed not-for-profit hospital provides a variety of medical care and health services including primary emergency diagnostic surgical rehabilitative and inpatient behavioral health care. Holland Hospital is home to centers of excellence in the treatment of sleep disorders cancer women's health issues and cardiovascular ailments. The hospital provides community health and wellness education programs and operates a regional community health clinic. Founded in 1917 Holland Hospital employs some 330 physicians across 14 medical specialties.
Operations

Holland Hospital had about 29000 urgent care visits and more than 41000 emergency department visits in 2013. It also reported some 16000 surgeries 1700 births 42000 outpatient discharges and 41000 home health visits.
Sales and Marketing
Medicare accounted for some 40% of the hospital's net patient revenues in 2014 followed by Blue Cross (22%) and Medicaid (11%).
Financial Performance
Holland Hospital reported revenue of $217 million and net income of $7 million in 2014.
Strategy
Expanding its menu of health care services in 2013 Holland Hospital opened a new in-patient Spine & Orthopedics unit to meet growing demand. The 23400-sq. ft. facility has 24 private rooms and a dedicated rehabilitation area to speed recovery. In May 2014 the hospital completed construction of a new office building that houses cardiology and vascular specialists.
Also in 2014 the hospital partnered with Spectrum Health member West Michigan Heart to open local offices on its main campus. Holland Hospital and Spectrum Health have a history of collaborations that includes the establishment of the Lakeshore Area Radiation Oncology Center and the Holland Community Health Center.

EXECUTIVES

Vice President Human Resources, Michael (Mel) Matthews
Information Technology Vice President, Eric Scott
Vice President of Nursing and Chief Nursing Officer, Patti Vandort
Vice President Human Resources, Chuck Kolruss
Vice President Quality, Mark Pawlak
Medical Librarian, Mary Wyels
Medical Director, Daniel (Dan) Decook
Auditors: PLANTE & MORAN PLLC PORTAGE

LOCATIONS

HQ: HOLLAND COMMUNITY HOSPITAL INC
602 MICHIGAN AVE, HOLLAND, MI 494234999
Phone: 616 748-9346
Web: WWW.HOLLANDHOSPITAL.ORG

Selected Locations
Holland Hospital Main Campus (Holland Michigan)
Holland Hospital Medical Building (Zeeland Michigan)
Lakeshore Medical Campus (Holland Michigan)
Holland Hospital Laboratory & Rehabilitation Services (Douglas Michigan)
854 South Washington Medical Offices (Holland Michigan)
844 South Washington Medical Offices (Holland Michigan)
Holland Hospital Center for Good Health (Holland Michigan)
Surgery Center of Western Michigan (Holland Michigan)
Lakeshore Area Radiation Oncology Center (Holland Michigan)
Community Health Center (Holland Michigan)

PRODUCTS/OPERATIONS

Selected Services
Alcohol & Drug Abuse Treatment
Allergies
Ambulatory Treatment Unit
Arthritis
Asthma
Back Pain
Behavioral Health
Bladder Health
Bone & Joint Center
Bone Health
Boven Birth Center
Cancer
Cardiopulmonary
Cardiovascular Services
Center for Good Health
Colonoscopy
Comprehensive Breast Services

CT Scan
da Vinci Robotic Assisted Surgery
Depression
Diabetes
Diagnostic Imaging
Ears Nose & Throat
Edema
Email Broadcasts
Emergency Services
Endoscopy Center
Family Medicine
Fibromyalgia
Gastroenterology
Gynecology
Heart
Hip
Home Health Services
Hospitalists
Hysterectomy
Intensive Care Unit/ICU
Interventional Radiology
Joint Replacement Center
Kidney
Knee
Laboratory Services
Lactation Services (Breastfeeding)
Lakeshore Health Partners
Leukemia
Locations
Lymphedema
Mammography
Medical Services
Menopause
Men' s Health
Mental Health Services: Inpatient
Mental Health Services: Outpatient
MRI
Nephrology (Kidney)
Neurology
Neurosurgery
Non-Hodgkin' s Lymphoma
Nutrition Services
OB/GYN
Osteoporosis
Pain Management
Pediatrics
Pelvic Health
Physical Therapy
Podiatry
Postpartum Depression
Press Room
Prevention & Wellness
Providers
Psychiatry
Pulmonary Services
Quality
Radiology
Radiology Oncology
Rehabilitation Services
Respiratory Services
School Nursing
Shoulder
Skin Care
Sleep Center
Special Care Nursery
Spine & Orthopedics
Spine Neck & Back
Sports Medicine
Stroke
Substance Abuse Treatment
Surgical Services
Telemetry
Ultrasound
Urgent Care
Urology Services
Walk-In-Care
Women' s Midlife
Women' s Services
Wound Care
X-ray
Zeeland Medical Offices

COMPETITORS

Mercy Health Hackley
Spectrum Health
Zeeland Community Hospital

HISTORICAL FINANCIALS
Company Type: Private

Income Statement
FYE: March 31

	REVENUE ($ mil.)	NET INCOME ($ mil.)	NET PROFIT MARGIN	EMPLOYEES
03/10*	170	10	6.2%	1,500
12/08	0	0	—	—
03/07	938	0	0.0%	—
Annual Growth	(43.4%)	3607.9%		

*Fiscal year change

2010 Year-End Financials
Return on assets: —
Return on equity: 6.2%
Current ratio: —
Cash ($ mil.): 23

HOLLINGSWORTH OIL CO. INC.

The Hollingsworth Companies meets companies' industrial-strength needs. The company develops and builds industrial parks and facilities in the southeastern US. It provides build-to-suit and finish-to-suit structures primarily on its SouthPoint Business Park pad-ready sites located in Alabama North Carolina Tennessee and Virginia. Developments typically range from 50000 sq. ft. to 500000 sq. ft. Hollingsworth also provides facility expansion and funding services. All of the company's SouthPoint properties are located in areas convenient to interstate highways and airport services. CEO and owner Joe Hollingsworth Jr. founded The Hollingsworth Companies in 1986.

Both contractor and developer The Hollingsworth Companies is able to complete custom-built facilities in as little as three months.

Joe Hollingsworth's book The Southern Advantage published in 2003 establishes the South as an increasingly desirable region for industrial manufacturing due to lower tax burdens rapidly growing population and Right-to-Work protections.

EXECUTIVES

CEO The Hollingsworth Companies, Joe A. Hollingsworth Jr.
SVP Architecture and Business Development, Tom Wortham
Director Industrial Real Estate, Warren Green
Director Industrial Real EstateNorth Carolina, Chip Sisk
Director Industrial Real Estate Alabama, Tommy Marr
Internal Operations Manager, Amanda Hensley
CFO, Timothy Lennon
Auditors: ROBINSON HUGHES & CHRISTOPHER

LOCATIONS

HQ: HOLLINGSWORTH OIL CO. INC.
1503 MEMORIAL BLVD STE B, SPRINGFIELD, TN 371723269
Phone: 615 242-8466
Web: WWW.HOCLUBES.COM

COMPETITORS

American Buildings
Belz
Childress Klein
Crescent Resources
Gladstone Commercial
Highwoods Properties
Varco Pruden Buildings

HISTORICAL FINANCIALS
Company Type: Private

Income Statement
FYE: December 31

	REVENUE ($ mil.)	NET INCOME ($ mil.)	NET PROFIT MARGIN	EMPLOYEES
12/13	564	0	0.1%	300
12/12	584	0	0.0%	—
12/11	593	0	0.1%	—
12/10	501	0	—	—
Annual Growth	4.0%	—	—	—

2013 Year-End Financials
Return on assets: 3.5%
Return on equity: 0.1%
Current ratio: 0.30
Cash ($ mil.): —

HOLMES REGIONAL MEDICAL CENTER INC.

If you're a Great Space Coaster you might depend on Holmes Regional Medical Center in times of medical need. The general acute-care hospital which houses about 515 beds and provides comprehensive medical and surgical care serves residents of Brevard County on Florida's Space Coast. A member of not-for-profit health care system Health First Holmes Regional Medical Center offers specialty care in a number of areas including trauma oncology cardiology orthopedics pediatrics and women's health. It also operates an air ambulance service a stroke care center a full-service endoscopy unit and an outpatient diagnostic facility as well as advanced robotic surgery and joint replacement centers.

EXECUTIVES

Vice President, James S (Jamie) Mitchell

LOCATIONS

HQ: HOLMES REGIONAL MEDICAL CENTER INC.
1350 HICKORY ST, MELBOURNE, FL 329013224
Phone: 321 434-7000
Web: WWW.HOLMESREGIONALMEDICALCENTER.ORG

PRODUCTS/OPERATIONS

Selected Centers and Services
The Birth Suites
Cancer care
da Vinci robotics surgery
Diabetes
Emergency room
First Flight aeromedical helicopter
Family library
The Heart Center (cardiac care and rehabilitation services)
Holmes Trauma Center
Interventional neuroradiology (stroke care)
Interventional radiology/Y-90
Outpatient services
Orthopedics
QuickCare walk-in clinic
VitalWatch (eICU)

COMPETITORS

Adventist Health System Sunbelt Healthcare
HCA
Nemours Foundation
Orlando Health
UF&Shands
Wuesthoff Health System

HISTORICAL FINANCIALS
Company Type: Private

Income Statement
FYE: September 30

	REVENUE ($ mil.)	NET INCOME ($ mil.)	NET PROFIT MARGIN	EMPLOYEES
09/13	391	0	0.2%	2,778
09/12	411	63	15.3%	—
09/06	0	0	0.3%	—
09/05	0	0	—	—
Annual Growth	210.7%	—	—	—

2013 Year-End Financials
Return on assets: 0.9%
Return on equity: 0.2%
Current ratio: 2.50
Cash ($ mil.): 140

HOLTEC INTERNATIONAL CORPORATION

Auditors: ERNST & YOUNG LLP PHILADELPH

LOCATIONS

HQ: HOLTEC INTERNATIONAL CORPORATION
1 HOLTEC DR STE 1, MARLTON, NJ 080533438
Phone: 856 797-0900
Web: WWW.HOLTECINTERNATIONAL.COM

HISTORICAL FINANCIALS
Company Type: Private

Income Statement
FYE: December 31

	REVENUE ($ mil.)	NET INCOME ($ mil.)	NET PROFIT MARGIN	EMPLOYEES
12/13	305	101	33.4%	700
12/11	256	86	33.7%	—
12/10	266	77	29.2%	—
12/09	1,952	0	—	—
Annual Growth	(37.1%)	—	—	—

2013 Year-End Financials
Return on assets: 5.0%
Return on equity: 33.4%
Current ratio: 0.70
Cash ($ mil.): 30

HOLY CROSS HEALTH INC.

Auditors: DELOITTE & TOUCHE LLP PHILADE

LOCATIONS

HQ: HOLY CROSS HEALTH INC.
1500 FOREST GLEN RD, SILVER SPRING, MD
209101460
Phone: 301 754-7000
Web: WWW.HOLYCROSSHEALTH.ORG

HISTORICAL FINANCIALS
Company Type: Private

Income Statement
FYE: June 30

	REVENUE ($ mil.)	NET INCOME ($ mil.)	NET PROFIT MARGIN	EMPLOYEES
06/13	404	40	10.0%	3,270
06/12	414	22	5.4%	—
06/11	416	33	8.1%	—
06/10	394	0	—	—
Annual Growth	0.8%	—	—	—

2013 Year-End Financials
Return on assets: 10.9%
Return on equity: 10.0%
Current ratio: 0.80
Cash ($ mil.): 21

HOLY CROSS HOSPITAL INC.

Holy Cross Hospital's patients have more than just doctors on their side. Holy Cross is a Catholic community hospital serving the Ft. Lauderdale Florida area. The hospital has about 560 beds and offers inpatient and outpatient medical services along with a cancer treatment center heart and vascular center women's health center orthopedic unit and home health division as well as outpatient imaging centers. It also operates family health and specialist clinics in the region. Sponsored by the Sisters of Mercy Holy Cross Hospital is a part of Trinity Health.

Geographic Reach

The hospital operates in South Florida's Broward and Palm Beach counties. In addition to its main campus n Fort Lauderdale the hospital has satellite locations across Broward and Palm Beach counties including Holy Cross Urgent Care and Imaging Centers in Fort Lauderdale and east Boca Raton Holy Cross Medical Group offices and Holy Cross HealthPlex.

Operations

Holy Cross Hospital employs some 600 physicians including specialists in about 40 medical fields. The organization's Holy Cross Medical Group physician practice group has more than 150 doctors working at about 30 clinics. The hospital also operates the Holy Cross HealthPlex which includes an orthopedic institute a women's health center a wound healing center diagnostic imaging and laboratory facilities and an outpatient surgery center.

Strategy

To enhance service offerings and bring in more area residents Holy Cross Hospital is working to enhance its facilities and improve its technologies.

In 2015 Holy Cross Hospital and Massachusetts General Hospital Cancer Center in Boston entered into a five-year affiliation agreement that expands the collaboration first begun in 2010.

On the innovation front that year the hospital offered its patients the MyCareLink Patient Monitor––a simplified remote monitoring system with global cellular technology that transmits patients' cardiac device diagnostic data to their clinicians from any location where a cellular signal is available.

To align itself with the goals of US federal health reform measures in 2014 Holy Cross Hospital joined the accountable care organization (ACO) facilitated by CIGNA. In 2013 it also joined the ACO facilitated by Blue Cross and Blue Shield of Florida. The ACOs aim to coordinate care for area Medicare residents in order to improve care quality and lower medical costs in the region.

Company Background

Holy Cross Hospital was part of Catholic Health East's (CHE) Southeast division. CHE merged with Michigan-based Trinity Health in 2013.

In 2012 it added a new surgery device for aneurysm embolization treatment procedures. In addition the medical center opened a new meditation chapel and healing garden. The following year Holy Cross Hospital built a new urgent care and diagnostic imaging center in Fort Lauderdale's Rio Vista community to improve patient access to outpatient services.

The hospital was established in 1953 and opened in 1995.

EXECUTIVES

Respiratory Therapy Director, Boez Ilderice
Medical Records Director, Jay Schatz
Vice President Mission Effectiveness Sponsorship, Rita Levasseur

LOCATIONS

HQ: HOLY CROSS HOSPITAL INC.
4725 N FEDERAL HWY, FORT LAUDERDALE, FL 333084668
Phone: 954 771-8000
Web: WWW.HOLY-CROSS.COM

PRODUCTS/OPERATIONS

Selected Services
Back Pain Management
Bariatrics
Cancer
Center for Optimal Health
Comprehensive Stroke Center
Diagnostic Imaging
Emergency
Epilepsy Monitoring Unit
Heart and Vascular
Heart Research
Home Health
International Services
Maternal/Child Health
Medical Group
Neurology and Spine
Orthopedics
Outpatient Services
Rehabilitation Institute
Robotics
Sleep Disorder Lab
Spine Center
Wellness Pavilion
Women's Center
Wound Healing and Hyperbarics

COMPETITORS

Adventist Health System Sunbelt Healthcare
Ascension Health
Baptist Health South Florida
Broward Health
Florida Hospital Heartland
HCA
Mount Sinai Medical Center of Florida
Northwest Medical Center
South Broward Hospital District
Tenet Healthcare

HISTORICAL FINANCIALS

Company Type: Private

Income Statement

FYE: December 31

	REVENUE ($ mil.)	NET INCOME ($ mil.)	NET PROFIT MARGIN	EMPLOYEES
12/12	426	21	5.0%	2,300
12/09	420	7	1.7%	—
12/08*	373	(25)	—	—
04/05	0	0	—	—
Annual Growth	141.0%	—	—	—

*Fiscal year change

2012 Year-End Financials

Return on assets: —
Return on equity: 5.0%
Current ratio: 1.00

Cash ($ mil.): 17

HOLY SPIRIT HOSPITAL OF THE SISTERS OF CHRISTIAN CHARITY

Holy Spirit Health tends to the health of the incarnate. The Holy Spirit Health System (HSHS) provides cardiology women's health care pediatric care and other acute and emergency medical services to the residents of greater Harrisburg in south-central Pennsylvania. The flagship Holy Spirit Hospital has some 310 beds as well as a level III neonatal intensive care unit. The hospital also operates an adjoining cardiac treatment facility and it has a network of affiliated family practice urgent care surgical and specialty health clinics. HSHS was established in 1963 and is an affiliate of Geisinger Health System.

Change in Company Type

As part of a national trend of hospital consolidation HSHS became an affiliate of Geisinger Health System in 2014. The system continues to be sponsored by the Sisters of Christian Charity.

Operations

The Holy Spirit Hospital employs more than 500 physicians and operates specialty care centers include an endoscopy clinic a hyperbaric wound healing unit and women's post-surgical recovery unit. Outpatient facilities include cardiology clinics family medicine centers surgery clinics and pediatric and women's health centers. Altogether HSHS annually handles some 16000 inpatient admissions 250000 outpatient visits 52000 emergency room visits and 1200 births.

HSHS employs a number of hospitalists who follow the patient's progress from admission to discharge and ensure follow-up care. The hospital also provides community health seminars to educate the public on common health concerns and the benefits of preventative care.

Geographic Reach

HSHS operates in a five-county service territory surrounding Harrisburg in south-central Pennsylvania. It has facilities in Camp Hill Carlisle Chambersburg Dillsburg Duncannon Harrisburg Lemoyne Marysville Mechanicsburg New Cumberland New Kingstown and Shippensburg.

Strategy

HSHS has undergone a number of expansions in recent years opening numerous outpatient centers to deliver care closer to home in the communities in which it serves. Also many hospitals are growing their outpatient services because they tend to bring in more income and help compensate for downward pricing on inpatient hospital stays from private and public health care payers. The system is focused on adding new locations to its network welcoming more family medicine offices (and their existing patients).

The organization expanded clinical services in areas including cryoablation cardiac rehabilitation sleep diagnostics and urgent care during 2012 and 2013. It also opened a new data center increase and improve use of electronic health record (EHR) systems.

EXECUTIVES

Director Of Infection Control, Joanne Adkins
Auditors: PARENTEBEARD LLC WILLIAMSPORT

LOCATIONS

HQ: HOLY SPIRIT HOSPITAL OF THE SISTERS OF CHRISTIAN CHARITY
503 N 21ST ST, CAMP HILL, PA 170112288
Phone: 717 763-2100
Web: WWW.HSH.ORG

PRODUCTS/OPERATIONS

Selected Centers and Services
Atrial Fibrillation Center
Behavioral Health
Broad Street Family Health Center
Cancer Care
Capital Cardiovascular Associates
Cardiac Rehab
Carlisle Family Health Center
Centers fo
Devonshire Family Health Center
Diabetes Services
Diagnostic
Dillsburg Family Health Center
Duncannon Family Health Center
Emergency Services
Gastrointestinal Services
Green Hill Family Health Center
Heart Care
Holy Spirit Endocrinology Center
Home Health Care
Hospitalist Program
Imaging Services
Internal Medicine of Mechanicsburg
Kunkel Group's LAP-BAND Program
Kunkel Surgical Group
Laboratory Services
Lewin & Nadar Cardiology Associates
Magill Family Health Center
Maternal Assistance Program
Maternity
Medical Outreach
Nutrition Services
Occupational Health
Orthopedics
Palliative Care
Pharmacy Services
Physical Therapy
Preparing for Your Appointment
Research & Clinical Trials
Ryder Barnes and Associates (pediatrics)
Silver Creek Family Health Center
Sleep Studies
Snoke Family Health Center
Speech Therapy
Spirit Urgent Care
Surgical Services
Travel Health Services
Vascular Associates
Women's Services
Wound Healing & Hyperbarics

COMPETITORS

Hershey Medical Center
PinnacleHealth System
Pocono Health System
Saint Vincent Health System
Sharon Regional Health System
University of Pennsylvania Health System
WellSpan Health

HISTORICAL FINANCIALS

Company Type: Private

Income Statement

FYE: June 30

	REVENUE ($ mil.)	NET INCOME ($ mil.)	NET PROFIT MARGIN	EMPLOYEES
06/10	271	11	4.2%	2,698
06/09	5	0	—	—
06/08	1,650	0	0.0%	—
Annual Growth	(59.4%)	2533.5%	—	—

2010 Year-End Financials

Return on assets: —
Return on equity: 4.2%
Current ratio: —

Cash ($ mil.): 8

HOMELAND ENERGY SOLUTIONS LLC

Auditors: MCGLADREY LLP DES MOINES IOW

LOCATIONS

HQ: HOMELAND ENERGY SOLUTIONS LLC
2779 HIGHWAY 24, LAWLER, IA 52154
Phone: 563 238-5555
Web: WWW.HOMELANDENERGYSOLUTIONS.COM

HISTORICAL FINANCIALS

Company Type: Private

Income Statement

FYE: December 31

	REVENUE ($ mil.)	NET INCOME ($ mil.)	NET PROFIT MARGIN	EMPLOYEES
12/14	330	68	20.8%	42
12/13	400	28	7.1%	—
12/12	359	0	0.1%	—
12/11	419	0	—	—
Annual Growth	(7.6%)	—	—	—

2014 Year-End Financials

Return on assets: 2.7%
Return on equity: 20.8%
Current ratio: 0.80

Cash ($ mil.): 32

HOOSIER ENERGY RURAL ELECTRIC COOPERATIVE INC

Who's yer daddy? In terms of providing electricity for many Indianans (and some residents of Illinois) that would be Hoosier Energy Rural Electric Cooperative which provides wholesale electric power to 18 member distribution cooperatives in 59 central and southern Indiana counties and 11 counties in southeastern Illinois. These electric cooperatives serve 300000 consumers (650000 residents businesses industries and farms) in a 18000 sq. ml. service area. Hoosier Energy operates six power plants and a 1720-mile transmission system and maintains the Tuttle Creek Reservoir in Southwest Indiana. Hoosier Energy is part of the Touchstone Energy network of electric cooperatives.

Geographic Reach

The company delivers power to member distribution cooperatives in central and southern Indiana and southeastern Illinois.

Operations

Hoosier Energy operates coal- natural gas- and renewable energy-generation plants. It delivers electricity via a 1720-mile transmission network including 21 major substations and more than 350 delivery points.

Financial Performance

In 2013 the power coop's revenues increased by 3% due to higher member revenues and increased sales of electricity. Net income grew by 1% as the result of higher revenues and slight decrease in maintenance costs.

Strategy

To advance its push for more renewable sources Hoosier Energy is pursuing cost-effective generating projects and supply contracts including the Clark-Floyd Landfill Methane Generation plant which has four landfill/coal bed methane projects and which has purchased power agreements for wind and hydropower. These measures are expected to provide 7% of member energy sales annually.

Its recent capital projects include a $400 million multi-year upgrade of the Merom Station investing $18 million in power delivery projects to support growth and reliability and continuing progress toward renewable energy goals with the commercial operation of the Osprey Point coalbed methane plant and the Livingston landfill-methane plant.

Company Background

In 2011 the coop was operating a 2.5 MW landfill methane generation facility in addition to buying 25 MW of wind energy.

Expanding its geographic coverage in 2011 Hoosier Energy began to supply power to the Wayne-White Counties Electric Cooperative when that coop's contract with an independent power supplier ended. The distribution coop serves 13500 residential farm and business consumers in 11 counties in southeastern Illinois.

Hoosier Energy was formed in 1948 as part of the nationwide rural electrification drive initiated by the Roosevelt administration in the 1930s.

EXECUTIVES

Vice President Power Production, Robert (Bob) Hochstetler
Vice President Power Supply, David W (Dave) Sandefur
Vp Finance, Donna Snyder
Auditors: DELOITTE & TOUCH LLP INDIANAP

LOCATIONS

HQ: HOOSIER ENERGY RURAL ELECTRIC COOPERATIVE INC
7398 N STATE ROAD 37, BLOOMINGTON, IN 474049424
Phone: 812 356-4291
Web: WWW.HEPN.COM

PRODUCTS/OPERATIONS

2012 Sales

	$ mil.	% of total
Members	532	82
Nonmembers	115	18
Other	0	-
Total	**647**	**100**

Member Cooperatives
Bartholomew County REMC
Clark County REMC
Decatur County REMC
Daviess-Martin County REMC
Dubois REC Inc.
Harrison REMC

Henry County REMC
Jackson County REMC
Johnson County REMC
Orange County REMC
RushShelby Energy
South Central Indiana REMC
Southeastern Indiana REMC
Southern Indiana Power
Utilities District of Western Indiana REMC
Wayne-White Counties Electric Cooperative
WIN Energy REMC
Whitewater Valley REMC

COMPETITORS

IPALCO Enterprises
Indiana Michigan Power
Indiana Municipal Power Agency

HISTORICAL FINANCIALS
Company Type: Private

Income Statement
FYE: December 31

	REVENUE ($ mil.)	NET INCOME ($ mil.)	NET PROFIT MARGIN	EMPLOYEES
12/13	667	28	4.2%	450
12/12	647	27	4.3%	—
12/11	649	30	4.7%	—
12/09	575	0	—	—
Annual Growth	**3.8%**	—	—	—

2013 Year-End Financials
Return on assets: 8.2%
Return on equity: 4.2%
Current ratio: 0.60
Cash ($ mil.): 91

HORIZON RESOURCES

Auditors: JUNKERMIER CLARK CAMPANELLA

LOCATIONS

HQ: HORIZON RESOURCES
317 2ND ST W, WILLISTON, ND 588015903
Phone: 701 572-2171
Web: WWW.HORIZONRESOURCES.COOP

HISTORICAL FINANCIALS
Company Type: Private

Income Statement
FYE: December 31

	REVENUE ($ mil.)	NET INCOME ($ mil.)	NET PROFIT MARGIN	EMPLOYEES
12/12	470	25	5.3%	150
12/11	379	15	4.1%	—
12/10	238	15	6.4%	—
12/09	161	0	—	—
Annual Growth	**42.8%**	—	—	—

2012 Year-End Financials
Return on assets: 2.4%
Return on equity: 5.3%
Current ratio: 0.90
Cash ($ mil.): 15

HORRY TELEPHONE COOPERATIVE INC.

Horry Telephone Cooperative (HTC) is the incumbent local exchange carrier (ILEC) serving rural Horry County in South Carolina (population:

about 270000). HTC offers local and long-distance voice service Internet access cable TV home security service and mobile phone service (through AT&T Mobility). It also offers business services such as remote recovery LAN and WAN design and firewall and network security and provides bundled telecommunications services to residential and business customers via its Bluewave fiber-to-the-home business. Membership in the cooperative is open to any customer who receives at least one of HTC's primary services.

Geographic Reach

HTC maintains nine offices throughout Horry County in Myrtle Beach Conway Longs Loris and Murrells Inlet.

Company Background   The company first brought phone service to the coastal area in the early 1950s with help from the Horry Electric Cooperative and the Rural Electrification Administration.

EXECUTIVES

Secretary, Carol Chasteen

LOCATIONS

HQ: HORRY TELEPHONE COOPERATIVE INC.
3480 HIGHWAY 701 N, CONWAY, SC 295265702
Phone: 843 365-2151
Web: WWW.HTCINC.NET

COMPETITORS

AT&T
Comcast
Comporium Communications
DIRECTV
DISH Network
Hargray
Sprint Communications
T-Mobile USA
Time Warner Cable
U.S. Cellular
Verizon

HISTORICAL FINANCIALS
Company Type: Private

Income Statement
FYE: December 31

	REVENUE ($ mil.)	NET INCOME ($ mil.)	NET PROFIT MARGIN	EMPLOYEES
12/13	177	21	12.2%	690
12/09	172	4	2.5%	—
12/08	162	3	2.2%	—
12/07	1,361	0	—	—
Annual Growth	—	—	—	—

2013 Year-End Financials
Return on assets: 17.8%
Return on equity: 12.2%
Current ratio: 0.90
Cash ($ mil.): 18

HOSPITAL OF CENTRAL CONNECTICUT

The Hospital of Central Connecticut an acute care facility serves the communities of central Connecticut from two campuses. With approximately 415 beds and more than 400 physicians the hospital offers a full range of diagnostic and treatment services as well as education and prevention programs. Its diabetes treatment program is an affiliate of the Boston-based Joslin Diabetes Center; the hospital is also affiliated with the University of Connecticut School of Medicine and other universities. Central Connecticut Health Alliance (CCHA) is the parent company of The Hospital of Central Connecticut and is part of the Hartford Health Care network.

Operations

In addition to its 415 acute-care beds the two Hospital of Central Connecticut campuses have about 30 bassinets. Through its university affiliations the hospital facilities provide residency and training programs in fields including critical care internal medicine gastroenterology general surgery and pulmonary medicine. It also conducts medical research including clinical trials in fields such as diabetes mental health and cancer treatment.

Affiliates that are part of the CCHA organization include Alliance Occupational Health Central Connecticut Senior Health Services Central Connecticut Physical Medicine and Central Connecticut VNA. CCHA affiliates provide a wide range of whole-life services throughout the region.

Geographic Reach

The Hospital of Central Connecticut's two Connecticut locations are the Bradley Memorial Campus in Southington and the New Britain General Campus in New Britain.

Strategy

In 2015 the hospital system opened a 75000-sq. ft. cancer center at the Hartford HealthCare Cancer Institute. Services include prevention and detection; treatments including chemotherapy radiation therapy and radiosurgery; ongoing support; and clinical trials.

Hospital of Central Connecticut also recently opened a Family Health Center including a primary care medical office outpatient lab radiology center and wound care center. The center which opened in 2013 also offers hyperbaric services such as hyperbaric oxygen therapy.

Company Background

The Hospital of Central Connecticut was formed through the merger of New Britain General Hospital and Bradley Memorial Hospital.

EXECUTIVES

Medical Director, Greg Fauteux
Director Of Radiology, Kevin Dickey
Director Of Nursing, Karen McAvoy
Vice President, Alex Misura
Clinical Director Department of Psychiatry and Outpatient Behavioral Health, Gustavo Nava
Nursing Director of Quality Strategy and Outcomes, Kathy Walsh
Legal Secretary, Kimberly Paulakos
Senior Vice President Medical Affairs and Chief Medical Officer, Steven (Steve) Hanks
Board Member, Lisa King
Executive Board Member, Annette Salina
Board Member, Jillian Wanik
Auditors: SASLOW LUFKIN & BUGGY LLP AV

LOCATIONS

HQ: HOSPITAL OF CENTRAL CONNECTICUT
100 GRAND ST, NEW BRITAIN, CT 060522016
Phone: 860 224-5011
Web: WWW.THOCC.ORG

PRODUCTS/OPERATIONS

Selected Centers and Services
Bariatric surgery
Breast care
Cancer Center
Cardiovascular
Clinical research
Diabetes care
Emergency services
Endocrine and bone health
Family Enrichment Center
Healthy Aging Center
Joint and Spine Center
Laboratory
Lifeline
Maternity
Medical services
Nursing

Occupational health
Occupational therapy
Outpatient services
Pain management
Palliative care
Pediatrics
Physical medicine
Primary care and specialty practices
Psychiatry
Radiology
Sleep disorders
Speech therapy
Stroke Center
Surgical services
Vascular Center
Weigh Your Options
Wellness programs
Wound care

COMPETITORS

Bristol Hospital
Lawrence & Memorial Hospital
Saint Francis Hospital and Medical Center
Waterbury Hospital
Western Connecticut Health Network
Yale New Haven Health System

HISTORICAL FINANCIALS

Company Type: Private

Income Statement

FYE: September 30

	REVENUE ($ mil.)	NET INCOME ($ mil.)	NET PROFIT MARGIN	EMPLOYEES
09/09	401	(71)	—	2,500
09/08	358	8	2.5%	—
09/06	83	0	0.0%	—
Annual Growth 69.1%		—	—	—

2009 Year-End Financials

Return on assets: —
Return on equity: (-17.8%)
Current ratio: 0.80
Cash ($ mil.): 22

HOSPITAL THE DANBURY INC

Auditors: ERNST & YOUNG LLP HARTFORD

LOCATIONS

HQ: HOSPITAL THE DANBURY INC
24 HOSPITAL AVE, DANBURY, CT 068106077
Phone: 203 739-7000
Web: WWW.DANBURYHOSPITAL.ORG

HISTORICAL FINANCIALS

Company Type: Private

Income Statement

FYE: September 30

	REVENUE ($ mil.)	NET INCOME ($ mil.)	NET PROFIT MARGIN	EMPLOYEES
09/13	501	4	0.9%	3,000
09/12	529	56	10.6%	—
09/11	1,133	23	2.1%	—
09/10	485	0	—	—
Annual Growth 1.1%		—	—	—

2013 Year-End Financials

Return on assets: 6.7%
Return on equity: 0.9%
Current ratio: 1.50
Cash ($ mil.): 59

HOUSING AUTHORITY OF THE CITY OF TAMPA

LOCATIONS

HQ: HOUSING AUTHORITY OF THE CITY OF TAMPA
5301 W CYPREFL ST STE 100, TAMPA, FL 33607
Phone: 813 341-9101
Web: WWW.THAFL.COM

HISTORICAL FINANCIALS

Company Type: Private

Income Statement

FYE: March 31

	REVENUE ($ mil.)	NET INCOME ($ mil.)	NET PROFIT MARGIN	EMPLOYEES
03/14	417	(0)	—	233
03/03	74	9	13.2%	—
03/02	49	10	21.6%	—
03/99	3	0	—	—
Annual Growth 37.3%		—	—	—

2014 Year-End Financials

Return on assets: 0.1%
Return on equity: (-0.1%)
Current ratio: 3.00
Cash ($ mil.): 24

HOUSTON SAM STATE UNIVERSITY

Part of the Texas State University System Sam Houston University has an enrollment of nearly 18500 students. It consists of six schools: Business Administration Criminal Justice Education Fine Arts and Mass Communications Humanities and Social Sciences and Sciences. The university offers some 130 undergraduate and master programs as well as doctoral programs in counselor education criminal justice educational leadership reading and clinical psychology. It offers more than 20 undergraduate and graduate degrees entirely online. Sam Houston State was founded as Sam Houston Normal Institute in 1879 and is named after Texas hero General Sam Houston.

Geographic Reach

From its campus in Huntsville Texas Sam Houston State serves a diverse student body that represents about 60 countries. It also offers degrees for both undergraduates and graduates through its online educational system.

Operations

With a student/faculty ratio of 19:1 and an average class size of about 30 students Sam Houston State boasts a modest full-time undergraduate tuition and fees rate of approximately $2700. About 72% of the university's faculty members hold doctoral or terminal degrees.

Sales and Marketing

Sam Houston State sources its student population globally. Across its undergraduates and graduates the university's students hail from some 60 countries. The educational institution is also working to expand its online student system which it has developed in recent years to support the needs of students unable to attend classes on campus.

EXECUTIVES

Department Chair, Christopher Wilson
Vice President University Advancement, Frank Holmes
Senior Vice President, Edwina Reece
Vice President (Membership Development), Melva Gomez
Vice President, William Robinson
Vice President Head Of Group Information Technology, Seth Lecompte
Senior Vice President, David McKinney
Vice President, Frank James
Membership Vice President, Shirin Edwin
Vice President for Finance and Operations, Alvin Hooten
Secretary =, Theresa Garvin
Secretary, Janie Joyce
Secretary, Bradley Wesner

LOCATIONS

HQ: HOUSTON SAM STATE UNIVERSITY
1806 AVE J, HUNTSVILLE, TX 77340
Phone: 936 294-1111
Web: WWW.SHSU.EDU

PRODUCTS/OPERATIONS

Selected Colleges
College of Business Administration (COBA)
College of Criminal Justice (CJ)
College of Education (COE)
College of Fine Arts and Mass Communication (COFAMC)
College of Humanities & Social Sciences (CHSS)
College of Sciences (COS)

HISTORICAL FINANCIALS

Company Type: Private

Income Statement — FYE: August 31

	REVENUE ($ mil.)	NET INCOME ($ mil.)	NET PROFIT MARGIN	EMPLOYEES
08/13	183	16	9.1%	2,200
08/08	136	63	46.5%	—
08/07	128	14	11.6%	—
08/06	0	0	—	—
Annual Growth	—	—	—	—

2013 Year-End Financials

Return on assets: 6.2%   Cash ($ mil.): 113
Return on equity: 9.1%
Current ratio: 1.20

HOVENSA LLC

HOVENSA brings together US and Latin American know-how and operations to handle oil products in the US Virgin Islands. HOVENSA is a joint venture of Hess and Venezuelan oil giant PDVSA (its major crude oil supplier). Once the largest private employer in the US Virgin Islands the company operated a 500000-barrels-per-day crude oil refinery on St. Croix along with two specialized oil processing complexes a 150000-barrels-per-day fluid catalytic cracking unit and a 58000-barrels-per-day delayed coker unit. However the St. Croix refinery had run up losses for years; it was shut down in 2012 and was put up for sale in 2013.

Strategy

Citing high operating and maintenance costs (the refinery was fueled by oil not the cheaper natural gas) and the growth of lower-cost refineries in emerging markets HOVENSA has posted $1.3 billion in losses since 2009. As a result the company decided to cut its losses by converting the re-

finery into an oil storage terminal which can take advantage of St. Croix's strategic location. Its 55-ft. deep harbor enables it to receive crude oil tanker deliveries from Venezuela and around the world. The storage terminal employs about 100 workers. The shutdown of the refinery resulted in more than 2000 employes being laid off.

Company Background

In 2009 the global economic downturn depressed demand for oil caused a dip in production and prompted the company to lay off 270 employees (about 21% of its total contract workers).

Crude thoughput has declined steadily at HOVENSA due to weaker refining margins and planned and unplanned maintenance from 402000 barrels per day (bpd) in 2009 to 390000 bpd in 2010 to 284000 bpd in 2011.

EXECUTIVES

President and COO, Lawrence J. (Larry) Kupfer
EVP, Alexander A. (Alex) Moorehead
VP and Deputy COO, Marco Crovesi
VP Environmental Health and Safety, Richard (Dick) Smullen
VP Refinery Operations, Peter (Pete) Barba
Finance Manager, Mike Fennessey
Purchasing Manager, Gary Miller
President Chief Operating Officer of HOVENSA, Brian K. Lever
Auditors: ERNST & YOUNG LLP NEW YORK N

LOCATIONS

HQ: HOVENSA LLC
1 ESTATE HOPE, CHRISTIANSTED, VI 00820
Phone: 340 692-3000
Web: WWW.HOVENSALLC.COM

COMPETITORS

Chevron
ConocoPhillips
Exxon Mohil
Marathon Oil
Royal Dutch Shell
Sunoco
Valero Energy

HISTORICAL FINANCIALS

Company Type: Private

Income Statement — FYE: December 31

	REVENUE ($ mil.)	NET INCOME ($ mil.)	NET PROFIT MARGIN	EMPLOYEES
12/09	10,048	(451)	—	1,300
12/08	17,479	94	0.5%	—
Annual Growth	(42.5%)	—	—	—

2009 Year-End Financials

Return on assets: 3.2%   Cash ($ mil.): 77
Return on equity: (-4.5%)
Current ratio: 0.20

HPS LLC

Auditors: MEYAARD TOLMAN & VENLET PC C

LOCATIONS

HQ: HPS LLC
3275 N M 37 HWY, MIDDLEVILLE, MI 493339126
Phone: 269 795-3308
Web: WWW.HPSNET.NET

HISTORICAL FINANCIALS

Company Type: Private

Income Statement — FYE: June 30

	REVENUE ($ mil.)	NET INCOME ($ mil.)	NET PROFIT MARGIN	EMPLOYEES
06/14	862	0	0.1%	38
06/13	898	0	0.1%	—
06/12	705	0	0.0%	—
06/11	755	0	—	—
Annual Growth	4.5%	—	—	—

2014 Year-End Financials

Return on assets: —   Cash ($ mil.): 4
Return on equity: 0.1%
Current ratio: 1.50

HUGHES SATELLITE SYSTEMS CORPORATION

Auditors: KPMG LLP DENVER COLORADO

LOCATIONS

HQ: HUGHES SATELLITE SYSTEMS CORPORATION
100 INVERNESS TER E, ENGLEWOOD, CO 801125308
Phone: 303 706-4000

HISTORICAL FINANCIALS

Company Type: Private

Income Statement — FYE: December 31

	REVENUE ($ mil.)	NET INCOME ($ mil.)	NET PROFIT MARGIN	EMPLOYEES
12/14	1,807	102	5.7%	2
12/13	1,542	(34)	—	—
12/12	1,432	(12)	—	—
Annual Growth	12.3%	—	—	—

2014 Year-End Financials

Return on assets: 5.2%   Cash ($ mil.): 225
Return on equity: 5.7%
Current ratio: 1.20

HUMAX USA INC.

Humax USA prefers to connect with its customers through its products. The company develops and manufactures flat-panel TV sets and digital set-top boxes for satellite cable and terrestrial connections. Humax USA is the US-based subsidiary of Korean consumer electronics manufacturing firm Humax Co. which was founded in 1989. The brand has become one of the most popular worldwide among set-top boxes. Humax's products are available in more than 90 countries as well as in the US. The company primarily serves customers in Asia and Europe.

To expand its presence in the US market Humax USA has partnered with the likes of DIRECTV and TiVo to offer products integrated with their technology.

EXECUTIVES

Chairman and CEO, Dae Gyu Byun

President Humax USA, T.H. Kim
SVP Sales and Marketing Humax USA, Christopher
C. Cudina

LOCATIONS

HQ: HUMAX USA INC.
  17501 VON KARMAN AVE, IRVINE, CA 926146207
Phone: 949 251-5200
Web: WWW.HUMAXDIGITAL.COM

COMPETITORS

DIRECTV   Sony USA
SANYO   TiVo
Samsung Electronics

HISTORICAL FINANCIALS

Company Type: Private

Income Statement
FYE: December 31

	REVENUE ($ mil.)	NET INCOME ($ mil.)	NET PROFIT MARGIN	EMPLOYEES
12/14	448	0	0.1%	26
12/13	317	0	0.1%	—
12/12	290	0	0.2%	—
12/11	347	0	—	—
Annual Growth	8.9%	—	—	—

2014 Year-End Financials

Return on assets: 23.0%   Cash ($ mil.): 1
Return on equity: 0.1%
Current ratio: 0.40

HUNTER ROBERTS CONSTRUCTION GROUP LLC

Auditors: GRASSI & CO CPAS PC JERI

LOCATIONS

HQ: HUNTER ROBERTS CONSTRUCTION GROUP LLC
  225 LIBERTY ST FL 6, NEW YORK, NY 102812602
Phone: 212 321-6800
Web: WWW.HUNTERROBERTSCG.COM

HISTORICAL FINANCIALS

Company Type: Private

Income Statement
FYE: December 31

	REVENUE ($ mil.)	NET INCOME ($ mil.)	NET PROFIT MARGIN	EMPLOYEES
12/13	762	3	0.4%	260
12/12	706	1	0.2%	—
12/10	458	7	1.7%	—
Annual Growth	18.4%	(26.8%)	—	—

2013 Year-End Financials

Return on assets: —   Cash ($ mil.): 61
Return on equity: 0.4%
Current ratio: 0.40

HUNTINGTON CABELL HOSPITAL INC

LOCATIONS

HQ: HUNTINGTON CABELL HOSPITAL INC
  1340 HAL GREER BLVD, HUNTINGTON, WV
  257010195
Phone: 304 526-2000
Web: WWW.CABELLHUNTINGTON.ORG

HISTORICAL FINANCIALS

Company Type: Private

Income Statement
FYE: September 30

	REVENUE ($ mil.)	NET INCOME ($ mil.)	NET PROFIT MARGIN	EMPLOYEES
09/13	391	13	3.4%	2,500
09/08	313	(3)	—	—
09/07	302	(8)	—	—
09/06	261	0	—	—
Annual Growth	5.9%	—	—	—

2013 Year-End Financials

Return on assets: 4.8%   Cash ($ mil.): 71
Return on equity: 3.4%
Current ratio: 2.20

HURLEY MEDICAL CENTER INC.

A community hospital owned by the City of Flint Hurley Medical Center is a teaching hospital serving Genesee Lapeer and Shiawassee counties in eastern Michigan. The 440-bed acute care facility is affiliated with the medical schools of Michigan State University and The University of Michigan. It provides care in areas such as cancer mental health rehabilitation surgery and women's health and it is a regional center for pediatrics. Hurley Medical Center also offers advanced specialty care such as trauma care neonatal intensive care kidney transplantation burn medicine and bariatric (weight loss) surgery. The center was founded in 1908 and is owned by the state of Michigan.

Operations

Hurley Medical Center has a physician health organization (PHO) partnership with the Professional Medical Corporation. The Hurley PHO of Mid-Michigan is a multi-specialty physician group that contracts with managed care organizations to provide care.

The hospital has an affiliation partnership with the Henry Ford Health System; the two health care providers offer a joint kidney transplantation program. Hurley Medical Center also operates the Genesys Hurley Cancer Institute in partnership with the Genesys Regional Medical Center.

Financial Performance

Hurley's revenue increased 3% in 2013 as it took in more patient payments. It reported a net loss of $2.3 million due to increased expenses including salaries unrealized losses on investments.

Strategy

The medical center works to update and expand its services on a regular basis. In 2012 it doubled in size with the opening of the Paul F. Reinhart Emergency Trauma Center.

EXECUTIVES

Director Of Pharmacy, Amy Benko
Vice President of Service Line Development,
 Michael (Mel) Burnett
Vice President, Karen Lopez
Interim Vice President for, Beth Brophy
Radiology Director, Dawn Hiller
Physical Therapy Director, Dean Frick
Respiratory Therapy Director, Veena Erinjeri
Vice President Of Human Resources, Jay Kitson
Medical Records Director, Jodie Brady
Vice President of Operations, Melanie Gavulic
Director of Admissions, Linda Hills
Radiology Director, Dawn Sturk
Secretary, Pamela (Pam) Glenn
Board Member, Michael (Mel) Marulli

LOCATIONS

HQ: HURLEY MEDICAL CENTER INC.
  1 HURLEY PLZ, FLINT, MI 485035902
Phone: 810 257-9000
Web: WWW.HURLEYMC.COM

COMPETITORS

Covenant HealthCare   McLaren Health Care
Crittenton Hospital   Munson Healthcare
Detroit Medical Center   Sparrow Health System
Genesys Regional   St. John Health
 Medical Center   Trinity Health (Novi)
Henry Ford Health
 System

HISTORICAL FINANCIALS

Company Type: Private

Income Statement
FYE: June 30

	REVENUE ($ mil.)	NET INCOME ($ mil.)	NET PROFIT MARGIN	EMPLOYEES
06/08*	350	3	1.1%	2,884
03/08	250	0	0.1%	—
Annual Growth	**********%	**********%	—	—

*Fiscal year change

2008 Year-End Financials

Return on assets: 4.8%   Cash ($ mil.): 24
Return on equity: 1.1%
Current ratio: 1.10

HURON HEALTH CARE CENTER INC

LOCATIONS

HQ: HURON HEALTH CARE CENTER INC
  1920 CLEVELAND RD W, HURON, OH 448391211
Phone: 419 433-4990
Web: WWW.PROVIDER-SERVICES.NET

HISTORICAL FINANCIALS

Company Type: Private

Income Statement
FYE: December 31

	REVENUE ($ mil.)	NET INCOME ($ mil.)	NET PROFIT MARGIN	EMPLOYEES
12/09	584	58	10.0%	125
12/98	3	0	—	—
12/97	3	3	97.8%	—
12/96	3	0	—	—
Annual Growth	48.0%	—	—	—

2009 Year-End Financials
Return on assets: —   Cash ($ mil.): —
Return on equity: 10.0%
Current ratio: 2.00

HY-VEE INC.

Give Hy-Vee a high five for being one of the largest privately owned US supermarket chains despite serving some modestly sized towns in the Midwest. The company runs some 235 stores in eight Midwestern states. About half of its supermarkets are in Iowa as are most of its 20-plus Hy-Vee drugstores. It distributes products to its stores through several subsidiaries including Lomar Distributing (specialty foods) and Perishable Distributors of Iowa (fresh foods). Other activities include construction and specialty pharmacies. Charles Hyde and David Vredenburg founded the employee-owned firm in 1930. It takes its name from a combination of its founders' names.

Geographic Reach

Hy-Vee's stores are located in Illinois Iowa Kansas Minnesota Missouri Nebraska South Dakota and Wisconsin. The company supplies its stores from distribution centers in Chariton and Cherokee Iowa.

Operations

In addition to its food and drug retail operations Hy-Vee offers customers financial products. Adding to its menu of financial services Hy-Vee subsidiary Midwest Heritage Bank in 2011 acquired Iowa-based L&K Insurance a full-line insurance agency. L&K changed its name to Midwest Heritage Insurance Services post sale.

Financial Performance

Hy-Vee's 235 stores ring up more than $8 billion in annual sales.

Strategy

Hy-Vee is gradually expanding in several key markets in the Midwest including Chicago Minneapolis-St. Paul and Madison Wisconsin. To that end the regional grocery chain in 2014 announced plans to enter the Twin Cities market. In 2013 the chain opened its second supermarket in Madison after entering the Madison market in 2009. To cater to local tastes the company says the 80000-sq.-ft. Madison store has the largest cheese selection of any Hy-Vee supermarket. Hy-Vee is also testing a smaller-format store (about 20000-25000 sq. ft. with no pharmacies) in select locations. It's also adding stores in its core Iowa market with a supermarket slated to open in Winterset in 2014.

Going beyond traditional grocery fare Hy-Vee in 2013 acquired its joint venture partner's stake in Hy-Vee Weitz Company a construction firm based in Des Moines. The grocery store operator renamed the company Hy-Vee Construction and plans to expand the in-house construction management group. The company also teamed up with specialty pharmacy operator Amber Pharmacy to form a new company (called Hy-Vee Pharmacy Solutions) to provide services for patients with complex and chronic health problems including Crohn's disease hemophilia psoriasis and other chronic ailments. The grocery chain has also been focusing on adding Hy-Vee Gas convenience units (some 80 locations include these) wine and spirits stores pharmacies and Hy-Vee HealthMarket departments.

Ric Jurgens in 2012 retired as chairman and CEO after 43-years with Hy-Vee. He was succeeded by president and COO Randy Edeker.

EXECUTIVES

EVP and Chief Merchandising Officer, Jon S. Wendel, age 52
Chairman President and CEO, Randy Edeker, age 53
EVP and Chief Customer Officer, Sheila Laing
EVP CFO and Treasurer, Mike Skokan
Vice Chairman EVP and Chief Administrative Officer, Andy McCann
EVP Western Region, Brett Bremser
EVP and COO, Jay Marshall
EVP Eastern Region, Darren Baty
Rph, Helen Eddy
Vice President Retail Information Technology, Julie Proffitt
Assistant Vice President Sec, Angie Rosenberger
Assistant Vice President Of Operations, Rob Eslick
Assistant Vice President Bakery Operations, Tony Byington
Senior Vice President Of Purchasing, Ken Waller
Assistant Vice President Construction, Mark Brauer
Assistant Vice President Engineering and Construction, Dave Kozak
Assistant Vice President Meat Operations, Kenan Judge
Director of Pharmacy Technology, Michael (Mel) Wilson
Assistant Vice President Marketing Communications, Donna Tweeten
Assistant Vice President Operations NorthEast, Dan Wampler
Vice President Sales, Katie Graham
Assistant Vice President, Tony Kaska
Assistant Vice President Audit Services, Juli Egeland
Assistant Vice President Store, Mark Millsap
Vice President Distribution, Tod Hockenson
Vice President, Karl Kruse
Assistant Vice President risk Management, Janet Crocker
Vice President Human Resources, Leigh Walters
Assistant Vice President Retail Systems, Christy Myers
Assistant Vice President Human Resources, Kate Wolfe
Assistant Vice President Operations Bakery, Don Wilkens
Assistant Vice President Brand Image, Wendy Hiatt
Senior Vice President Secretary and General Counsel, Steve Meyer
Vice President Store Development, Jeff Markey
Assistant Vice President Distribution, Rob Douglas
Assisant Treasurer, Jeff Pierce
Secretary to Greg Frampton, Stacey Groff

LOCATIONS

HQ: HY-VEE INC.
5820 WESTOWN PKWY, WEST DES MOINES, IA 502668223
Phone: 515 267-2800
Web: WWW.HY-VEE.COM

PRODUCTS/OPERATIONS

2012 Stores

	No.
Supermarkets	212
Drugstores	22
Total	**234**

Selected Subsidiaries

D & D Foods Inc. (salads dips and meats)
Florist Distributing Inc. (flowers plants and florist supplies)
Hy-Vee Construction L.C. (construction)
Hy-Vee Pharmacy Solutions (specialty pharmacy services)
Hy-Vee Weitz Construction L.C. (construction)
Lomar Distributing Inc. (specialty foods)
Midwest Heritage Bank FSB (banking)
Perishable Distributors of Iowa Ltd. (meat fish seafood and ice cream)

COMPETITORS

ALDI	Niemann Foods
Associated Wholesale Grocers	Rite Aid
	Roundy' s
Ball' s Food	SUPERVALU
CVS	Save-A-Lot Food Stores
Casey' s General Stores	Target Corporation
Fareway Stores	Wal-Mart
Kmart	Walgreen
Kroger	

HISTORICAL FINANCIALS

Company Type: Private

Income Statement

FYE: September 28

	REVENUE ($ mil.)	NET INCOME ($ mil.)	NET PROFIT MARGIN	EMPLOYEES
09/14	8,014	0	—	62,000
09/13	8,014	0	—	—
09/12*	7,682	0	—	—
10/11	0	0	—	—
Annual Growth	—	—	—	—

*Fiscal year change

2014 Year-End Financials

Return on assets: 6.8%   Cash ($ mil.): 7
Return on equity: —
Current ratio: 0.20

HYDROCARBON EXCHANGE CORP.

Auditors: BDO USA LLP DALLAS TEXAS

LOCATIONS

HQ: HYDROCARBON EXCHANGE CORP.
5910 N CNTRL EXPY # 1380, DALLAS, TX 752065125
Phone: 214 987-0257
Web: WWW.HYDROCARBONEXCHANGE.COM

HISTORICAL FINANCIALS

Company Type: Private

Income Statement

FYE: June 30

	REVENUE ($ mil.)	NET INCOME ($ mil.)	NET PROFIT MARGIN	EMPLOYEES
06/13	340	1	0.3%	8
06/12	263	0	0.3%	—
06/11	354	1	0.3%	—
06/10	325	0	—	—
Annual Growth	1.4%	—	—	—

2013 Year-End Financials

Return on assets: —   Cash ($ mil.): 6
Return on equity: 0.3%
Current ratio: 1.20

ILLINOIS INSTITUTE OF TECHNOLOGY

Chicago has some cool architecture due in part to the Illinois Institute of Technology (IIT). The school offers more than 100 undergraduate and graduate degree programs in engineering science psychology architecture business law humanities and design. In addition to three campuses in Chicago IIT also has locations in Summit-Argo (Moffet campus) and Wheaton (Daniel F. and Ada L. Rice campus). The institute has an enrollment of some 8000 undergraduate graduate business school and law school students with a student-to-faculty ratio of 8:1.

Operations

IIT's heritage includes the innovative Bauhaus tradition that set up shop at the university in the 1930's. These days its innovation is expressed in the form of interdisciplinary research on such themes as Energy and Sustainability Improving the Quality of Life and Perfect Power. IIT maintains about 30 research institutes with major centers focused on the study of transportation infrastructure sustainable energy electricity innovation biomedical science and engineering and food safety and health.

Financial Performance

IIT reported $265 million in revenues in fiscal 2014 and 2013. In fiscal 2014 IIT generated 55% of its revenues from tuition and fees; 22% from grants and contracts; 4% from its endowment; and the balance from other sources. Higher tuition charges lifted tuition and fees' contribution to the total by 2% in fiscal 2014.

Strategy

IIT regularly evaluates its offerings and adds new degree programs to meet the needs of a changing society. In 2012 it introduced a Master's degree program for cyber forensics and security majors.

In 2013 IIT received a $10 million grant to help build a state-of-the-art innovation center (which is scheduled to break ground in 2016). Named the Ed Kaplan Family Institute for Innovation and Tech Entrepreneurship it will promote innovation guide ideas along the path to becoming products and serve as a hub for various entrepreneurship initiatives. The school is also forming two new colleges: the College of Science and Lewis College of Human Sciences which includes programs in humanities social sciences and psychology. It also formed a new college Food Science and Nutrition in the School of Applied Technology which includes its Institute for Food Safety and Health.

Company Background

IIT was created in 1940 by the merger of Armour Institute (founded in 1893) with Lewis Institute (established in 1895).

EXECUTIVES

Vice President Community Affairs And Outrch Extern, Leroy Kennedy
Provost Senior Vice President Acad Affairs, ALAN W (Al) CRAMB
Vice President Marketing and Communications, Jeanne Hartig
Vice President Technology, Sidney Guralnick
Vice President of Facilities and Public Safety, Bruce Watts
Vice President of Research Graduate College, Ali Cinar
Associate Vice President of Finance and Controller, Brian Laffey
Associate Vice President International Aff International Affairs, Mary Dawson
Assistant Vice President, Jeanne Arens
Vice President International Affairs, Darsh Wasan
Associate Vice President of Human Resources, Antoinette Murril
Vice President External Affairs, David (Dave) Baker
Vice President and General Counsel, Mary Anne Smith
Vice Chairman, David J (Dave) Vitale
Secretary and Vice President, Roopa Gir
Assistant SEC, Michael C (Mel) McGibbon
Auditors: KPMG LLP CHICAGO ILLINOIS

LOCATIONS

HQ: ILLINOIS INSTITUTE OF TECHNOLOGY
10 W 35TH ST, CHICAGO, IL 606163717
Phone: 312 567-3000
Web: WWW.IIT.EDU

PRODUCTS/OPERATIONS

Selected Schools and Colleges
Armour College of Engineering
Chicago-Kent College of Law
College of Architecture
College of Psychology
College of Science and Letters
Institute of Design
School of Applied Technology (SAT)
Stuart School of Business

HISTORICAL FINANCIALS

Company Type: Private

Income Statement

FYE: May 31

	REVENUE ($ mil.)	NET INCOME ($ mil.)	NET PROFIT MARGIN	EMPLOYEES
05/13	259	37	14.5%	1,662
05/12	249	(6)	—	—
05/11	305	8	2.9%	—
05/10	333	0	—	—
Annual Growth	(8.0%)	—	—	—

2013 Year-End Financials

Return on assets: 6.7%   Cash ($ mil.): 11
Return on equity: 14.5%
Current ratio: —

ILLINOIS MUNICIPAL ELECTRIC AGENCY

Auditors: BAKER TILLY VIRCHOW KRAUSE LL

LOCATIONS

HQ: ILLINOIS MUNICIPAL ELECTRIC AGENCY
3400 CONIFER DR, SPRINGFIELD, IL 627118301
Phone: 217 789-4632
Web: WWW.IMEA.ORG

HISTORICAL FINANCIALS

Company Type: Private

Income Statement

FYE: April 30

	REVENUE ($ mil.)	NET INCOME ($ mil.)	NET PROFIT MARGIN	EMPLOYEES
04/14	327	17	5.4%	28
04/13	304	15	5.1%	—
04/12	280	18	6.4%	—
04/11	176	0	—	—
Annual Growth	22.8%	—	—	—

2014 Year-End Financials

Return on assets: 5.0%   Cash ($ mil.): 57
Return on equity: 5.4%
Current ratio: 1.20

IMMACULATE MARY HOME

LOCATIONS

HQ: IMMACULATE MARY HOME
2990 HOLME AVE, PHILADELPHIA, PA 191361830
Phone: 215 335-2100
Web: WWW.IMMACULATEMARYHOME.ORG

HISTORICAL FINANCIALS

Company Type: Private

Income Statement

FYE: June 30

	REVENUE ($ mil.)	NET INCOME ($ mil.)	NET PROFIT MARGIN	EMPLOYEES
06/09	2,568	185	7.2%	350
06/98	15	4	29.6%	—
Annual Growth	59.0%	39.9%	—	—

2009 Year-End Financials

Return on assets: —   Cash ($ mil.): —
Return on equity: 7.2%
Current ratio: 1.60

IMMIXGROUP INC.

immixGroup offers a blend of information technology (IT) business development and consulting services to help tech firms do business with federal state and local government agencies. Through its technology sales division the company is a hardware and software reseller for such manufacturers as IBM Oracle and Hewlett-Packard. It also offers customized public sector channel development programs outsourced government contract management and IT consulting and execution. Other services include market intelligence sales training and recruiting. immixGroup serves more than 250 tech manufacturers and its government partner network includes more than 600 resellers systems integrators and other providers. Arrow Electronics acquired immixGroup in 2015.

Change in Company Type

Arrow Electronics completed the acquisition of immixGroup in March 2015. The purchase enables Arrow to expand its growing IT services business to the government sector. For immixGroup the deal puts it in the mix of resources deploye by a company that sits in the Fortune 150.

Operations

The company operates two subsidiaries: EC America Inc. and immixTechnology Inc.

Sales and Marketing

immixGroup sells its services with software providers as partners including Appian Apica Aruba A10 Networks and Adaptive. Its customers include federal agencies state governments and agencies and municipalities. Recent customers are the Texas Department of Information Resources NASA and the US Army.

Financial Performance

immixGroup has been the recipient of more than 950 federal contracts and subcontracts from October 2014 through May 2015. The value of the contracts was more than $90 million.

EXECUTIVES

Vice President Marketing, Allan Rubin
Vp Government Channels Division, Skip Liesegang
Vice President Operations, William (Bill) Bottoms
Executive Vice President, Steve Charles
Auditors: DIXON HUGHES GOODMAN LLP TYS

LOCATIONS

HQ: IMMIXGROUP INC.
8444 WESTPARK DR STE 200, MC LEAN, VA 221025112
Phone: 703 752-0610
Web: WWW.IMMIXGROUP.COM

PRODUCTS/OPERATIONS

Business Services	Channel Development
Contract Management	
Install Base Practice	
Lead Generation	
Leasing	
Market Intelligence	
Marketing	
SLED Program	
Training	
Event Center Usage	
IT Solutions	Cloud Services
Software Solutions	
Information Management	
Project Management & PMO	

COMPETITORS

Accenture
BAE Systems Technology Solutions
Booz Allen
CACI International
Computer Sciences Corp.
DLT Solutions
HP Enterprise Services
Honeywell Technology Solutions
IBM Global Services
Leidos
Lockheed Martin Information Systems
ManTech
McKinsey & Company
Northrop Grumman Info Systems
Raytheon Intelligence Information and Services
Unisys

HISTORICAL FINANCIALS
Company Type: Private

Income Statement
FYE: May 31

	REVENUE ($ mil.)	NET INCOME ($ mil.)	NET PROFIT MARGIN	EMPLOYEES
05/13	505	12	2.4%	201
05/12	502	13	2.6%	—
05/11	43	16	37.9%	—
05/10	563	0	—	—
Annual Growth	(3.5%)	—	—	—

2013 Year-End Financials
Return on assets: 25.1%
Return on equity: 2.4%
Current ratio: 1.00
Cash ($ mil.): 31

IMMIXTECHNOLOGY INC.

LOCATIONS

HQ: IMMIXTECHNOLOGY INC.
8444 WESTPARK DR STE 200, MC LEAN, VA 221025112
Phone: 703 752-0610
Web: WWW.IMMIXGROUP.COM

HISTORICAL FINANCIALS
Company Type: Private

Income Statement
FYE: May 31

	REVENUE ($ mil.)	NET INCOME ($ mil.)	NET PROFIT MARGIN	EMPLOYEES
05/10	536	11	2.2%	201
05/09	403	6	1.7%	—
05/05	717	0	—	—
Annual Growth	—	1715.2%	—	—

2010 Year-End Financials
Return on assets: 16.0%
Return on equity: 2.2%
Current ratio: 1.00
Cash ($ mil.): 10

IMPERIAL IRRIGATION DISTRICT

Imperial Irrigation District (IID) keeps the lights on and the water flowing. A public agency IID is the six largest public power utility in the state of California providing generation transmission and distribution services to more than 145000 residential commercial and industrial customers. It is also the largest irrigation district in the US with more than 3000 miles of canals and drains delivering water to active farmland and providing wholesale water to local municipalities primarily in the Southern California desert corridors of Imperial Valley and Coachella Valley. The district is governed by a five-member board of directors elected by district residents.

Strategy

In the area of renewable energy IID is part of a statewide effort to significantly increase solar energy development and production by the year 2017. In 2011 it announced a public-private partnership with renewable energy generators. The partnership involves the signing of interconnection and transmission service agreements among IID CalEnergy Generation 8minuteenergy Ormat Technologies and the Los Angeles Department of Water and Power. It's the first step in a renewable energy transmission expansion plan to increase capacity enough to support more than a dozen renewable energy construction projects.

In addition IID offers a variety of programs to assist its customers in reducing their personal energy consumption including rebates for buying select energy efficient products online home energy audits and funding for residential projects that involve installing solar technologies such as photovoltaic (PV) systems.

Financial Performance

IID saw its revenues increase 6% from $530 million in 2011 to $562 million in 2012. The growth was driven by a 12% surge in water revenue; this was due to a rise in water transfer rates and a volume increase in water transferred to the San Diego County Water Authority and the Coachella Valley Water District of about $5 million. Power revenues also climbed 4% in 2012 due to a spike in energy sales mainly from residential customers.

Company Background

Founded in 1911 IID acquired properties from the financially struggling California Development Company and its Mexican subsidiary. By 1922 it had purchased 13 mutual water companies each of which had developed and operated distribution canals in the Imperial Valley. Principal water customers today include farm operators and municipalities that treat the water and resell it to their residential and business customers. The district entered the power business in 1936 to utilize the hydroelectric generation of the All-American Canal. Since that time IID has added geothermal natural gas coal and solar to its energy generation portfolio. Its electric services account for majority of IID's annual revenues.

EXECUTIVES

President, Norma Sierra Galindo
Vice President, Alfonso Juarez
Secretary Admin, Georgine Armstrong
Board Member, Ronnie Jones

LOCATIONS

HQ: IMPERIAL IRRIGATION DISTRICT
333 E BARIONI BLVD, IMPERIAL, CA 922511773
Phone: 800 303-7756
Web: WWW.IID.COM

HISTORICAL FINANCIALS
Company Type: Private

Income Statement
FYE: December 31

	REVENUE ($ mil.)	NET INCOME ($ mil.)	NET PROFIT MARGIN	EMPLOYEES
12/07	524	151	29.0%	1,300
12/06	503	108	21.5%	—
12/05	408	62	15.3%	—
12/04	367	0	—	—
Annual Growth	12.6%	—	—	—

2007 Year-End Financials
Return on assets: 8.7%
Return on equity: 29.0%
Current ratio: 1.00
Cash ($ mil.): 165

INDEPENDENT PHARMACY COOPERATIVE

Auditors: GRANT THORNTON LLP MILWAUKEE

LOCATIONS

HQ: INDEPENDENT PHARMACY COOPERATIVE
1550 COLUMBUS ST, SUN PRAIRIE, WI 535903901
Phone: 608 825-9556
Web: WWW.IPCRX.COM

HISTORICAL FINANCIALS
Company Type: Private

Income Statement
FYE: December 31

	REVENUE ($ mil.)	NET INCOME ($ mil.)	NET PROFIT MARGIN	EMPLOYEES
12/13	1,058	2	0.2%	65
12/11	806	1	0.2%	—
12/10	869	1	0.2%	—
12/09	642	0	—	—
Annual Growth 13.3%		—	—	—

2013 Year-End Financials
Return on assets: 5.7%
Return on equity: 0.2%
Current ratio: 0.60
Cash ($ mil.): 17

INDEPENDENT SCHOOL DISTRICT 1 OF TULSA COUNTY

LOCATIONS

HQ: INDEPENDENT SCHOOL DISTRICT 1 OF TULSA COUNTY
3027 S NEW HAVEN AVE, TULSA, OK 741146131
Phone: 918 746-6800
Web: WWW.TULSASCHOOLS.ORG

HISTORICAL FINANCIALS
Company Type: Private

Income Statement
FYE: June 30

	REVENUE ($ mil.)	NET INCOME ($ mil.)	NET PROFIT MARGIN	EMPLOYEES
06/11	403	(10)	—	6,115
06/08	388	9	2.4%	—
06/07	373	(17)	—	—
06/06	0	0	—	—
Annual Growth	—	—	—	—

2011 Year-End Financials
Return on assets: —
Return on equity: (-2.6%)
Current ratio: 1.60
Cash ($ mil.): 167

INDIANA UNIVERSITY FOUNDATION INC.

Hoosier favorite fund-raiser? If you're a fan of Indiana University then it might well be the Indiana University Foundation (IUF). The not-for-profit foundation raises more than $100 million annually in donations from individuals corporations and institutional organizations; alumni gifts account for about half of IUF's funds. It manages an endowment of about $1 billion and provides administrative services for gift accounts and scholarship and fellowship accounts. The organization has offices in Bloomington and Indianapolis. IUF was established in 1936.

EXECUTIVES

Vice Chairman, August M. (Gus) Watanabe, age 73
President CEO and Director, Curtis R. Simic
SVP and CFO, James P. (Jim) Perin
Executive Director Finance and Controller, Gina Reel
SVP Development, Kent Dove
Chairman, Adam W. Hebert Jr.
VP Indianapolis, William G. Heller
VP Regional Campuses, James E. Smith
VP and Chief Investment Officer, Gary A. Stratten
Secretary, Karen J. Pieper
SVP Development, Marti Heil
Vice Chairman, August M. (Gus) Watanabe, age 73
Director, David I. Klapper, age 65
Director, David C. Evans
Director, William G. Mays, age 68
Director, Stephen A. Stitle, age 65
Director, Alecia A. DeCoudreaux, age 59
President CEO and Director, Curtis R. Simic
Director, Jay B. Hunt, age 75
Director, Stephen L. (Steve) Ferguson
Director, Randall C. Morgan Jr.
Director, Patrick A. Shoulders
Director, Kathryn Ryan Booth
Director, Bill C. Brown
Director, William P. Carmichael
Director, Gayle C. Cook
Director, Clarence H. Doninger
Director, David G. Elmore
Director, Richard E. Ford
Director, Ezra H. (Zeke) Friedlander
Director, Jack M. Gill
Director, Moses W. Gray
Director, Ann L. Harrison
Director, V. William Hunt
Director, Needham S. Hurst
Director, Robert W. Lanum
Director, Dale Ellen Leff
Director, Jane Halagiere Martin
Director, Joseph T. Morrow
Director, John D. Peterson
Director, N. E. (Ned) Pfau
Director, Thomas D. Rush
Director, Scott C. Schurz
Director, Richard C. Searles
Director, Julie Inskeep Simpson
Director, James G. Sinclair
Director, Cynthia Simon (Cindy) Skjodt
Director, Fred G. Steingraber
Director, Milton R. (Milt) Stewart
Director, Gregg T. Summerville
Director, W. Michael (Mike) Wells
Director, Desmond C. Wong, age 63
Director, Richard E. Woosnam
Auditors: DELOITTE & TOUCHE LLP INDIANA

LOCATIONS

HQ: INDIANA UNIVERSITY FOUNDATION INC.
1500 N STATE ROAD 46 BYP, BLOOMINGTON, IN 47408
Phone: 812 855-8311
Web: WWW.IUFOUNDATION.IU.EDU

HISTORICAL FINANCIALS
Company Type: Private

Income Statement
FYE: June 30

	ASSETS ($ mil.)	NET INCOME ($ mil.)	INCOME AS % OF ASSETS	EMPLOYEES
06/13	2,277	107	4.7%	220
06/12	2,105	(11)	—	—
06/11	2,054	255	12.4%	—
06/10	1,767	0	—	—
Annual Growth 8.8%		—	—	—

2013 Year-End Financials
Return on assets: 15.1%
Return on equity: 40.8%
Sales ($ mil): 262

INDIANA UNIVERSITY HEALTH BLOOMINGTON INC.

Indiana University Health Bloomington wants to put a bloom back in patients' cheeks. The facility operating as IU Health Bloomington provides care in a ten-county region in south central Indiana. The not-for-profit hospital —which includes a 350-bed main campus in Bloomington and a 25-bed rural hospital in Paoli —provides care in a number of medical specialties including cardiovascular disease cancer orthopedics and neuroscience. It also runs home health and hospice urgent care lab and specialty care facilities as well as physician practices under the name Southern Indiana Physicians. IU Health Bloomington is part of the Indiana University Health (IU Health) system.

Geographic Reach
IU Health Bloomington has a customer base of about 415000 patients in a 10-county area in south central Indiana. The hospital serves as a regional referral center for other hospitals in the area.

Operations
The company's operations include Indiana University Health Paoli (Paoli) Indiana University Health Morgan Hospital (Morgan) and Indiana University Health White Memorial Hospital (White).

Strategy
Like most hospitals IU Health Bloomington enters partnerships to extend its patient reach. In 2012 IU Health Bloomington and a Monroe County YMCA collaborated to provide a new space in a new northwest YMCA dedicated to IU Health for physical therapy orthopedic services sports medicine and health and wellness services.

Company Background
After several years of negotiations IU Health Bloomington officially became an integrated part of the Clarian network at the start of 2010. Then at the beginning of 2011 Clarian changed its name to IU Health to clarify its relationship with Indiana University and to provide a unified brand to connect all of its facilities.

EXECUTIVES

EVP and Chief Nurse Executive, Linda Q. Everett
Medical Director, Lee McKinley
Director Of Nursing, Pam Adams
Clinical Director, Vicki Phelps
Medical Director, Mark Bauman
Secretary, Karen Tveten
Auditors: ERNST & YOUNG LLP INDIANAPOLI

LOCATIONS

HQ: INDIANA UNIVERSITY HEALTH BLOOMINGTON INC.
601 W 2ND ST, BLOOMINGTON, IN 474032317
Phone: 812 353-9830
Web: WWW.BLOOMINGTONHOSPITAL.ORG

PRODUCTS/OPERATIONS

Selected Services
Anticoagulation Center
Assisted Medical Transportation
Behavioral Health
Cancer
Cardiovascular
Children' s Therapy Center
Diabetes Center
Emergency
Home Care
Home Medical Equipment

Hospice
Laboratory
Neuroscience
Occupational
Orthopedics
Pain Center
Primary Care
Radiology
Rehabilitation
Sleep Lab
Surgical
Urgent Care Centers
Women and Children' s
Wound Center

COMPETITORS

Ascension Health	Memorial Hospital
Community Health	(Logansport)
Network	Riverview Hospital
Daviess Community	St. Vincent Health
Hospital	Union Hospital
Franciscan Alliance	(Indiana)
Henry County Memorial	Wabash County Hospital
Hospital	

HISTORICAL FINANCIALS
Company Type: Private

Income Statement
FYE: December 31

	REVENUE ($ mil.)	NET INCOME ($ mil.)	NET PROFIT MARGIN	EMPLOYEES
12/12	355	64	18.1%	3,200
12/11	391	22	5.7%	—
12/10	359	30	8.4%	—
12/09	346	0	—	—
Annual Growth	0.8%	—	—	—

2012 Year-End Financials

Return on assets: 4.1% Cash ($ mil.): 74
Return on equity: 18.1%
Current ratio: 2.50

INDIANA UNIVERSITY HEALTH INC.

Indiana University Health (IU Health) cares about health care for all in the state of Indiana. As one of the largest health systems in the state not-for-profit IU Health owns or is affiliated with more than 20 hospitals and health centers throughout the state including three major hospitals — Methodist Hospital Indiana University Hospital and Riley Hospital for Children —that serve the downtown Indianapolis area. The largest Methodist Hospital features the Methodist Research Institute which conducts research and clinical trials. The system's hospitals also serve as teaching facilities for Indiana University's medical school.

Operations
IU Health partners with Indiana University School of Medicine to give patients access to innovative therapies. The organization is composed of hospitals physicians and other care providers dedicated to offering quality care throughout Indiana and beyond.

The system has more than 3000 beds and more than 2100 physicians. In addition to hospitals the health system offers additional services through a network of primary and specialty care clinics and a home health care business. In 2013 Indiana University Health reported more than 135700 total patient admissions and more than 2.6 million outpatient visits.

IU Health is not only an educational establishment —it's considered a major research hub with total grant research funding of some $260 million. It has about 1500 residents and fellows conducting roughly 1500 research studies. Together Indiana University Health and Indiana University School of Medicine work together to train physicians using a blended curriculum of research and treatments on actual patients.

Geographic Reach
IU Health offers its services through 80 locations in the US.

Sales and Marketing
In fiscal 2013 managed care payments accounted for 54% of the company's patient revenues. Medicare and Medicaid accounted for 21% and 5% respectively while self-pay and other payors made up the balance.

Financial Performance
In 2013 IU Health reported a nearly 6% decrease to $5.2 billion in revenue due to a dip in patient revenue. Net income fell 16% to $562 million due to decreases in net patient service and other earnings.

Cash flow from operations also fell in 2013 sliding 61% to $232 million as a result of lower net income and an increase in cash used in patient accounts receivable.

Strategy
The system's growth strategy includes expanding into the city's growing (and affluent) suburbs with majority-owned for-profit facilities located in Avon and Carmel. The system (along with the Indiana University School of Medicine) is investing $100 million to increase its neuroscience services. As part of the investment plan the two built a Neuroscience Center of Excellence near the Methodist Hospital which opened in 2014.

Also that year IU Health announced plans to open a dozen urgent care clinics across central Indiana by the end of 2016.

While it continues to expand in 2013 the organization responded to the changing health care landscape in the US by announcing plans to cut about 800 hospital jobs and realign certain service offerings. The moves come as part of an effort to reduce expenses by about $1 billion over a five-year period during a time when large-scale health organizations across the US look to control medical costs.

Mergers and Acquisitions
In 2013 IU Health purchased Wipperman Occupational Health a South Bend clinic offering occupational health and wellness to area employers. The facility was rebranded IU Health Occupational Services Wipperman Clinic.

Company Background
IU Health was formed in 1997 as Clarian Health Partners.

EXECUTIVES

President and CEO, Daniel F. (Dan) Evans, age 66
President IU Health Methodist Hospital and IU Health University Hospital, Herbert C. Buchanan
President and CEO IU Health Bloomington Hospital, Mark E. Moore
CEO IU Health Arnett Hospital, Al W. Gatmaitan
President, Dennis M. Murphy
EVP and Chief Nurse Executive, Linda Q. Everett
President System Clinical Services, Ron Stiver
President and CEO IU Health Ball Memorial Hospital, Michael Haley
President IU Health Starke Hospital, Craig Felty
Interim EVP and Chief Medical Executive; SVP Quality; Chief Medical Executive IU Health Physicians, John C. Kohne
EVP and Chief Administrative Officer, Ryan C. Kitchell
President and CEO IU Health North Hospital and IU Health Saxony Hospital, Jonathan Goble

President and CEO Riley Hospital for Children at IU Health, Jeff Sperring
President and CEO IU Health west Hospital, Matt Bailey
President and CEO IU Health Tipton Hospital, Michael Harlowe
CEO IU Health Paoli Hospital, Larry Bailey
President and CEO IU Health La Porte Hospital, G. Thor Thordarson
President and CEO IU Health Goshen Hospital, Randy Christophel
President IU Health Blackford Hospital, Steven West
President and CEO IU Health Bedford Hospital, Bradford W. Dykes
Chief Mission and Values Officer, Kevin Armstrong
Executive Vice President Chief Operating Officer, Samuel (Sam) Odle
Vice President Clinical Operations, Heidi Jankowski
Director of Pharmacy Benefits, Nahid Jamzadeh
Director of Pharmacy Methodist Pharmacy, Tate N Trujillo
Clinical Director, Sheila Smith
Administrative Assistant Vice President, Elizabeth Thompson
Vice President System Quality, Jo Brooks
Vice President Operations, Lori Luther
Vice President, Michelle Altobella
Vice President of Goverment Affairs, Tory C Castor
Vice President Chief Nursing Officer, Linda Chase
Chairman, Anne Nobles, age 58
Vice Chairman, Thomas Chapman
Auditors: ERNST & YOUNG LLP INDIANAPOLI

LOCATIONS

HQ: INDIANA UNIVERSITY HEALTH INC.
1701 N SENATE BLVD, INDIANAPOLIS, IN 462021239
Phone: 317 962-2000
Web: WWW.IUHEALTH.ORG

PRODUCTS/OPERATIONS

Selected Facilities
INDIANAPOLIS-AREA HOSPITALS
Indiana University Hospital (dba IU Health University Hospital Indianapolis)
Methodist Hospital (dba IU Health Methodist Hospital Indianapolis)
Riley Hospital for Children (dba Riley Hospital for Children at IU Health Indianapolis)
IU Simon Cancer Center
Clarian North Medical Center (dba IU Health North Hospital Carmel)
Clarian West Medical Center (dba IU Health West Hospital Avon)
STATEWIDE PARTNERS
Clarian Arnett Health (dba IU Health Arnett Hospital Lafayette)
Ball Memorial Hospital (dba IU Health Ball Memorial Hospital Muncie)
Bedford Regional Medical Center (dba IU Health Bedford Hospital Bedford)
Blackford Community Hospital (dba IU Health Blackford Hospital Hartford City)
Bloomington Hospital (dba IU Health Bloomington Hospital Bloomington)
Bloomington Hospital of Orange County (dba IU Health Paoli Hospital Paoli)
Goshen Health System (dba IU Health Goshen Hospital Goshen)
LaPorte Regional Health System (dba IU Health LaPorte Hospital La Porte)
Midwest Proton Radiotherapy Institute (dba IU Health Proton Therapy Center Bloomington)
Starke Memorial Hospital (dba IU Health Starke Hospital Knox)
Tipton Hospital (dba IU Health Tipton Hospital Tipton)
METHODIST MEDICAL PLAZAS (outpatient centers)
Georgetown Medical Plaza
Methodist Medical Plaza Eagle Highlands
Methodist Medical Plaza East
Methodist Medical Plaza North
Methodist Medical Plaza South

COMPETITORS

Ascension Health	Henry County Memorial
Banner Health	Hospital
Catholic Health	MedStar Health
Initiatives	Riverview Hospital
Community Health	St. Elizabeth Regional
Network	Health
Community Hospital	St. Vincent Health
Anderson	Tenet Healthcare
Daviess Community	Union Hospital
Hospital	(Indiana)
Franciscan Alliance	
Good Samaritan	
Hospital (IN)	

HISTORICAL FINANCIALS
Company Type: Private

Income Statement
FYE: December 31

	REVENUE ($ mil.)	NET INCOME ($ mil.)	NET PROFIT MARGIN	EMPLOYEES
12/08	1,889	(23)	—	17,242
12/06	2,478	159	6.4%	—
Annual Growth	(12.7%)	—	—	—

2008 Year-End Financials
Return on assets: 16.3%   Cash ($ mil.): 237
Return on equity: (-1.3%)
Current ratio: 1.10

INDYNE INC.

InDyne offers out-of-this-world technology expertise. The company provides information technology science and engineering and technical and administrative services primarily to US government agencies including NASA. It develops custom software designs Web sites and builds computer networks. InDyne's science and engineering division designs aerospace systems provides space mission support and crew training and offers structural and fluid analysis. Its technical and administrative services unit handles imagery operations data management media services and operations support. InDyne's projects have included the development of custom database software for the CDC and the Department of Transportation.Geographic ReachThe company has offices across the US often on or near government facilities. Its locations include Alabama California Florida New Mexico Ohio Virginia and Washington DC.

EXECUTIVES

President CEO, C. Donald Bishop
Director Human Resources, Margaret James
CFO, Robert (Bob) Miller
VP Strategic Programs, Jeff Riemer
VP-Ops, Skip Olson
Auditors: ARGY WILTSE & ROBINSON PC M

LOCATIONS

HQ: INDYNE INC.
11800 SUNRISE VALLEY DR # 250, RESTON, VA
201915300
Phone: 703 903-6900
Web: WWW.INDYNEINC.COM

PRODUCTS/OPERATIONS

Selected Services
Range Services
Base Operations Maintenance
Security Systems
Communication Services
Information Technology
Multimedia Services

COMPETITORS

Alion	
CACI International	
Computer Sciences Corp.	
Dynamics Research	
General Dynamics Information Technology	
HP Enterprise Services	
IBM Global Services	
Leidos	
Lockheed Martin Information Systems	
ManTech	
Northrop Grumman Info Systems	
UNICOM Government	
Unisys	

HISTORICAL FINANCIALS
Company Type: Private

Income Statement
FYE: December 31

	REVENUE ($ mil.)	NET INCOME ($ mil.)	NET PROFIT MARGIN	EMPLOYEES
12/10	260	6	2.6%	1,700
12/09	255	7	3.0%	—
12/08	1,449	0	0.0%	—
Annual Growth	(57.6%)	1951.1%	—	—

2010 Year-End Financials
Return on assets: —   Cash ($ mil.): —
Return on equity: 2.6%
Current ratio: —

INFINITE ENERGY INC.

Infinite wisdom? No. Infinite energy? Yes. Infinite Energy does not provide its customers with the natural high of endorphins or with the latest health diet but with the more prosaic commodity of natural gas. The company supplies natural gas to clients in Florida Georgia and New York. Wholesale customers include municipalities institutions and utilities; Infinite Energy also sells to large and small commercial establishments (including restaurants) and to residential customers.

Former utility energy buyers Darin Cook and Rich Blaser established Infinite Energy in 1994. It started up operations that year in Florida and in Georgia in 1998.

In 2004 the company launched operations in New York.

In 2007 in a innovative marketing move it offered residential customers in New York and New Jersey two month of free gas supply in a bid to attract new customers.

EXECUTIVES

Vice President And General Counsel, Becky Patrick
Vice President Sales and Marketing, Peter (Pete) Page
Vice President Marketing, Bill Kinneary

LOCATIONS

HQ: INFINITE ENERGY INC.
7001 SW 24TH AVE, GAINESVILLE, FL 326073704
Phone: 352 331-1654
Web: WWW.INFINITEENERGY.COM

COMPETITORS

Eversource Energy	New Jersey Natural Gas
Florida Gas	Piedmont Natural Gas
Transmission	SCANA
National Grid USA	

HISTORICAL FINANCIALS
Company Type: Private

Income Statement
FYE: December 31

	REVENUE ($ mil.)	NET INCOME ($ mil.)	NET PROFIT MARGIN	EMPLOYEES
12/09	477	13	2.7%	250
12/05	583	4	0.8%	—
12/04	474	8	1.8%	—
12/03	335	0	—	—
Annual Growth	6.0%	—	—	—

2009 Year-End Financials
Return on assets: —   Cash ($ mil.): 12
Return on equity: 2.7%
Current ratio: 0.70

INLAND COUNTIES REGIONAL CENTER INC.

LOCATIONS

HQ: INLAND COUNTIES REGIONAL CENTER INC.
1365 S WATERMAN AVE, SAN BERNARDINO, CA
924082804
Phone: 909 890-3000
Web: WWW.INLANDRC.ORG

HISTORICAL FINANCIALS
Company Type: Private

Income Statement
FYE: June 30

	REVENUE ($ mil.)	NET INCOME ($ mil.)	NET PROFIT MARGIN	EMPLOYEES
06/13	314	(2)	—	550
06/10	267	(3)	—	—
06/09	271	0	—	—
06/08	590	0	—	—
Annual Growth	—	—	—	—

2013 Year-End Financials
Return on assets: 8.6%   Cash ($ mil.): 6
Return on equity: (-0.7%)
Current ratio: 1.20

INNOVATIVE AG SERVICES CO.

Auditors: MERIWETHER WILSON AND COMPANY

LOCATIONS

HQ: INNOVATIVE AG SERVICES CO.
2010 S MAIN ST, MONTICELLO, IA 523107707
Phone: 319 465-3501
Web: WWW.INNOVATIVEAG.COM

HISTORICAL FINANCIALS
Company Type: Private

Income Statement
FYE: August 31

	REVENUE ($ mil.)	NET INCOME ($ mil.)	NET PROFIT MARGIN	EMPLOYEES
08/14	855	23	2.8%	500
08/13	1,165	12	1.1%	—
08/12	1,420	22	1.6%	—
08/11	1,011	0	—	—
Annual Growth	(5.4%)	—	—	—

2014 Year-End Financials
Return on assets: 1.2%
Return on equity: 2.8%
Current ratio: 1.00
Cash ($ mil.): 57

INOVA HEALTH CARE SERVICES

LOCATIONS
HQ: INOVA HEALTH CARE SERVICES
8110 GATEHOUSE RD 200E, FALLS CHURCH, VA
220421217
Phone: 703 289-2000
Web: WWW.INOVA.ORG

HISTORICAL FINANCIALS
Company Type: Private

Income Statement
FYE: December 31

	REVENUE ($ mil.)	NET INCOME ($ mil.)	NET PROFIT MARGIN	EMPLOYEES
12/09	1,663	200	12.0%	13,000
12/03	1,012	46	4.6%	—
12/02	1	(0)	—	—
12/01	0	0	—	—
Annual Growth	—	—	—	—

2009 Year-End Financials
Return on assets: —
Return on equity: 12.0%
Current ratio: 0.20
Cash ($ mil.): 170

INSTITUTE FOR DEFENSE ANALYSES INC

The Institute for Defense Analyses founded in 1947 to provide technical analyses of weapons is a federally funded organization that works for the US government's defense agencies as well as for other government entities. The institute's focus areas include war and defense systems evaluations materials and information technology assessments resource cost and readiness analyses and force and strategy assessments. The Institute for Defense Analyses' Science and Technology Policy Institute analyzes global science and tech trends to help the US government formula policy.

EXECUTIVES
President and CEO, David S.C. Chu
Vice President: of Technology, Dale Lichtblau

Vice Presidents Secretary, Betty Schultz
Chair, Suzanne H. (Sue) Woolsey, age 74
Board Member, Rod Williams
Auditors: PRICEWATERHOUSECOOPERS LLP MC

LOCATIONS
HQ: INSTITUTE FOR DEFENSE ANALYSES INC
4850 MARK CENTER DR, ALEXANDRIA, VA
223111882
Phone: 703 845-2000
Web: WWW.IDA.ORG

COMPETITORS
Charles Stark Draper Laboratory
Lawrence Livermore Lab
QinetiQ
Quantum Research
Sandia National Laboratories

HISTORICAL FINANCIALS
Company Type: Private

Income Statement
FYE: September 27

	REVENUE ($ mil.)	NET INCOME ($ mil.)	NET PROFIT MARGIN	EMPLOYEES
09/13	219	18	8.5%	1,500
09/12	221	23	10.5%	—
09/11	226	0	0.0%	—
09/10	227	0	—	—
Annual Growth	(1.2%)	—	—	—

2013 Year-End Financials
Return on assets: —
Return on equity: 8.5%
Current ratio: 0.50
Cash ($ mil.): 13

INSTITUTE OF INTERNATIONAL EDUCATION INC.

Auditors: PRICEWATERHOUSECOOPERS LLP NE

LOCATIONS
HQ: INSTITUTE OF INTERNATIONAL EDUCATION INC.
809 UNITED NATIONS PLZ, NEW YORK, NY
100173503
Phone: 212 883-8200
Web: WWW.IIE.ORG

HISTORICAL FINANCIALS
Company Type: Private

Income Statement
FYE: September 30

	REVENUE ($ mil.)	NET INCOME ($ mil.)	NET PROFIT MARGIN	EMPLOYEES
09/13	435	4	1.1%	450
09/12	384	(2)	—	—
09/11	366	(4)	—	—
09/10	331	0	—	—
Annual Growth	9.5%	—	—	—

2013 Year-End Financials
Return on assets: —
Return on equity: 1.1%
Current ratio: 0.80
Cash ($ mil.): 95

INTELLIGENT SOFTWARE SOLUTIONS INC.

Intelligent Software Solutions is no dummy when it comes to software development and IT systems analysis. The privately-held company develops and integrates custom software used for such applications as data visualization and analysis pattern detection and mission planning for the aerospace defense and maritime industries. It also provides on-site product and development support and training. As a government contractor it serves a range of public sector agencies within the US Department of Defense US Department of Homeland Security and US Air Force. Intelligent Software Solutions corporate clients have included Lockheed Martin Northrop Grumman and Leidos.

With expertise in counter-terrorism homeland security intelligence and special operations the company has about 100 projects under dozens of contracts. In 2012 Intelligent Software Solutions won $120 million in new contracts with the Air Force Research Labs to support several US government clients with data integration and analysis and reporting software used for situational awareness.

The company is expanding its geographic footprint to better serve key clients outside of its home state of Colorado. It opened a new office in New York state the previous year and an office in Florida in 2010 adding to other satellite locations in Massachusetts Virginia and Washington DC. The Rome New York office was established to better support its client there the Air Force Research Labs while its Tampa Florida facility houses part of the company's combat systems division that support the US Central Command (CENTCOM).

Intelligent Software Solutions also does some business overseas. In 2011 the company was awarded a contract with awarded a contract from the UK's Ministry of Defence to develop predictive reasoning and pattern-analysis software for improving the British military's situational awareness in theaters around the world. In late 2012 it acquired the assets of New Jersey-based Xpect Software which offers a complementary product suite (Dfuze) and expands Intelligent Software Solutions into new international markets.

Intelligent Software Solutions was established in 1997 by four former engineers from GTE Government Systems (which was acquired by General Dynamics in 1999).

EXECUTIVES
Vice President Global Enterprise Solutions, Kevin Moffatt
Vice President Xpect Solutions, Laine Napier
Vice President, Marcus Featherston
Vice President Of National Systems, Rob Rogers
Auditors: EKS & H LLLP DENVER COLORADO

LOCATIONS
HQ: INTELLIGENT SOFTWARE SOLUTIONS INC.
5450 TECH CENTER DR # 400, COLORADO SPRINGS, CO 809192339
Phone: 719 452-7000
Web: WWW.ISSINC.COM

COMPETITORS
BAE SYSTEMS
Booz Allen
CACI International
CIBER
Camber Corp.
ComGlobal Systems
Computer Sciences Corp.

Computer Technology Associates
General Dynamics Information Technology
Jacobs Engineering
L-3 Communications
Leidos
ManTech
MetroStar Systems
Northrop Grumman
QinetiQ
Raytheon
UNICOM Government

HISTORICAL FINANCIALS

Company Type: Private

Income Statement

FYE: December 31

	REVENUE ($ mil.)	NET INCOME ($ mil.)	NET PROFIT MARGIN	EMPLOYEES
12/11	167	12	7.5%	650
12/10	121	7	6.2%	—
12/09	86	0	0.0%	—
Annual Growth	39.1%	30647.7%	—	—

2011 Year-End Financials

Return on assets: 4.3%   Cash ($ mil.): —
Return on equity: 7.5%
Current ratio: —

INTERBOND CORPORATION OF AMERICA

Interbond Corporation of America (doing business as BrandsMart USA) boasts more than 500 brand names across its nearly 50000 electronics and entertainment products. It sells them in the US and internationally. It offers low-priced appliances computers TVs car stereos mobile phones personal care gadgets movie music games and more. The retailer runs about 10 electronics stores under the BrandsMart USA banner in the South Florida and Atlanta metropolitan areas. Each stocks more than $8 million in merchandise. BrandsMart USA also sells products online providing shipping for orders placed throughout the US Latin America and the Caribbean. Chairman Robert Perlman founded the company in 1977.

Geographic Reach

Aside from its home office and warehouse facilities in Hollywood Florida BrandsMart USA operates stores in South Florida and in Georgia providing some 2600 jobs. Its clearance center is located in Florida's South Broward County.

Operations

BrandsMart USA is one of the nation's largest volume-per-store retailers. With help from its low-price strategy the retailer has performed relatively well in the consumer electronics niche which once included bankrupt rivals such as Circuit City.

The company operates in Latin America and the Caribbean through a marketing agreement with shopping facilitator Punto Mio. Using Punto Mio's integration technology international customers accessing BrandsMart USA's website can browse products listed in their local currencies (purchase prices include applicable delivery fees and taxes).

Sales and Marketing

BrandsMart USA stores are known for their brightly lit interiors and neon price tags as well as

their noisy bustling atmospheres. The simple presentation scheme helps to keep price tags low and to move crowds of customers. The retailer faces competition from the likes of Best Buy hhgregg and Wal-Mart.

To promote an eco-friendly message Brands-Mart USA runs a Go Green Trade In Program a take-back initiative in partnership with the Consumer Electronics Exchange. The program issues BrandsMart USA gift cards to shoppers who trade in their unwanted electronics (including gaming consoles MP3 players and mobile phones) which are then recycled by the Consumer Electronics Exchange.

EXECUTIVES

Vice President Sales, Neil Anello
Auditors: KAUFMAN ROSSIN & CO PA MIAM

LOCATIONS

HQ: INTERBOND CORPORATION OF AMERICA
3200 SW 42ND ST, FORT LAUDERDALE, FL
333126813
Phone: 954 797-4000
Web: WWW.PROD.BRANDSMARTUSA.COM

2013 Stores

	No.
Florida	5
Georgia	4
Total	9

PRODUCTS/OPERATIONS

Selected Products

Appliances
Blu-rays & DVDs
Headphones
Home audio
Car audio & GPS
Computers
Fitness
Games
Home security
Mobile phones
Office products
Personal care
Tablets
Toys
TVs
Wellness

Selected Brands

Bose
Dell
Electrolux
Epson
Frigidaire
iRobot
LG
Logitech
Samsung
Sharp
Sony

COMPETITORS

Best Buy	RadioShack
Costco Wholesale	Sears
Fry's Electronics	Wal-Mart
Home Depot	hhgregg

HISTORICAL FINANCIALS

Company Type: Private

Income Statement

FYE: September 24

	REVENUE ($ mil.)	NET INCOME ($ mil.)	NET PROFIT MARGIN	EMPLOYEES
09/11	743	3	0.5%	2,400
09/10	800	7	0.9%	—
09/08	320	0	0.0%	—
Annual Growth	32.3%	2377.1%	—	—

2011 Year-End Financials

Return on assets: 5.0%   Cash ($ mil.): 1
Return on equity: 0.5%
Current ratio: —

INTERBOND HOLDING CORP.

Auditors: KAUFMAN ROSSIN AND CO

LOCATIONS

HQ: INTERBOND HOLDING CORP.
3200 SW 42ND ST, FORT LAUDERDALE, FL
333126813
Phone: 954 797-4000
Web: WWW.BRANDSMARTUSA.COM

HISTORICAL FINANCIALS

Company Type: Private

Income Statement

FYE: September 25

	REVENUE ($ mil.)	NET INCOME ($ mil.)	NET PROFIT MARGIN	EMPLOYEES
09/10	800	7	0.9%	2,100
09/09	826	8	1.0%	—
Annual Growth	(3.2%)	(12.4%)	—	—

2010 Year-End Financials

Return on assets: 6.3%   Cash ($ mil.): 2
Return on equity: 0.9%
Current ratio: 0.10

INTERMOUNTAIN HEALTH CARE INC

If you whoosh down the side of one of Idaho's majestic mountains and take a nasty spill Intermountain Health Care (dba Intermountain Healthcare) will pick you up and put you back together. From air ambulance services to urgent care clinics and general hospitals Intermountain has all the tools to mend skiers (and non-skiers alike) in Utah and southern Idaho. With about 1100 physicians the not-for-profit health system operates 22 hospitals and 185 urgent care clinics as well as home health care agencies and rehabilitation centers. Its hospitals have a combined total of about 2700 licensed beds.

Operations

Its hospitals range from general surgical to specialty care including orthopedic and pediatric facilities. Along with the full spectrum of physical health care services Intermountain also offers comprehensive mental health and substance abuse programs for patients of all ages. The organization's spectrum of care includes acute inpatient residential treatment day treatment chemical dependency inpatient/detoxification and intensive outpatient programs. To serve the region's uninsured and low-income residents Intermountain owns or supports 15 community and school primary care clinics.

The organization conducts cancer research through its partnership with Huntsman Cancer Institute at the University of Utah. The two share data best practices funding and co-conduct clinical trials. They also operate a number of cancer-specific treatment centers including multi-disciplinary tumor-specific clinics designed to provide one-stop service for cancer patients to meet with different cancer specialists on the same day for a more comprehensive treatment plan. Other areas of research include cardiovascular intensive medicine surgical care and behavioral health.

On the physician side the Intermountain Medical Group administers multi-specialty health care services in clinics located throughout the region. The group also operates urgent care clinics under the ExpressCare InstaCare and KidsCare banners.

Entering itself into the "what doesn't Intermountain do?" category the health system also provides health and dental insurance plans through its SelectHealth division. SelectHealth provides coverage for large and small employer groups runs the state Children's Health Insurance Program and administers a high-risk insurance pool for the state of Utah.

In 2013 Intermountain reported 474450 emergency room visits; 133973 acute patient admissions; 39552 inpatient surgeries; and 30972 births. Insurance provider SelectHealth had 660000 members.

Geographic Reach

Intermountain serves the health care needs of Utah and Idaho residents.

Sales and Marketing

Commercial insurance accounted for about 60% of the system's net patient revenues in 2013; payments received under the Medicare and Medicaid programs accounted for 26% and 12% respectively while self-pay accounted for 5%.

Financial Performance

In 2013 revenues grew 7% to $5 billion due to an increase in premiums and admission fees (but partially offset by an increase in provision for bad debts). Net income more than doubled that year growing 183% to $1.5 billion. Factors leading to the rise included increases in investment returns and unrecognized changes in funded status of post-retirement benefit plans.

Cash flow from operations fell 5% to $671 million in 2013 due to increases in salaries benefits supplies and other operating expenses.

Strategy

Intermountain uses its dedicated supply chain organization to continuously improve system efficiency. In addition to delivering medical supplies the unit also oversees hospital vehicles and recently switched them all to natural gas.

In 2013 it teamed up with several leading IT companies (including Xi3 Intel Dell and NetApp) to form Intermountain's Healthcare Transformation Lab on the campus of its flagship hospital Intermountain Medical Center in Murray Utah. The lab researches develops and measures new ideas to improve patient care. The same year it worked with GE to established a research center to reduce radiation during tomography procedures.

Intermountain has also joined peers Mayo Clinic Cleveland Clinic and others in the High Value Healthcare Collaborative to share information to improve health care manage and save costs and extend best practices out to physicians clinics and hospitals throughout the US. In 2015 the company announced a partnership with hospital Uintah Basin Medical Center to bring the Intermountain Life Flight program to Roosevelt bringing trauma and specialty care to residents of all of eastern Utah. This marked the company's first partnership with a non-Intermountain facility.

The company is also collaborating with the Centers for Medicare & Medicaid Services and other health systems to examine ways to improve health care safety and reduce costs by preventing patient injuries and complications.

In 2014 Intermountain introduced its mobile application Health Hub. One of its features is GermWatch which tells users which diseases are active in Utah communities.

Company Background

Intermountain was formed in 1975 when the Church of Jesus Christ of Latter Day Saints donated 15 hospitals to local communities.

EXECUTIVES

Vice President Community Benefit, Mikelle Moore
CEO Intermountain Medical Group, Linda C. Leckman
President and CEO SelectHealth, Patricia R. Richards
EVP and CFO, Bert R. Zimmerli
EVP and COO, Laura S. Kaiser
VP and CIO, Marc Probst
Chief Development Officer, David L. Flood
President and CEO, Charles W. Sorenson
VP Supply Chain and Support Services; Chief Purchasing Officer, Brent Johnson
VP Clinical Operations and Chief Nursing Officer, Kim Henrichsen
Chief Medical Officer, Brent E. Wallace
CEO Primary ChildrenÂ's Medical Center, Katherine A. (Katy) Welkie
President Weber State University, Ann Millner
Director Patient Care Nursing, Paul Blad
Vice President Revenue Cycle Organization, Todd Craghead
Medical Director, David (Dave) Pombo
Medical Director, Terry Clemmer
Medical Director, Keith Robbins
Pharmacy Manager, Robert Dengg
Assistant Vice President Communications, Tom Vitelli
Assistant Vice President, Kathleen Konishi
Vice President Of Engineering, Craig Bedford
Assistant Vice President Compensation and Benefits, David (Dave) Adams
Pharmacy Manager, Brenda Winger
Vice President Management, Jim Darrington
Vice President Marketing and Communication, Todd Frehse
Medical Director Utah County Region, Gordon Harkness
Pharmacy Manager, Tom Shelley
Medical Director, Gregory Gochnour
Medical Director, Scott Hansen
Vice President Marketing, Jerry Edgington
Medical Director, James Orme
Director Of Admissions, Louise Green
Director Of Pharmacy, Scott Yardley
Medical Director, Justin Abbott
Director Media Relations, Daron Cowley
Director Media Relations, Jess Gomez
Vice President Information Technology, Matt Weed
Medical Librarian, Don McFall
Clinic Manager, Rebecca Beck
Pharmacy Manager, Beth Johnson
Medical Director, Scott Whittle
Clinic Manager, Summer Patterson
Clinic Manager, Teri Roberts
Clinic Manager, Amy Tippets
Clinic Manager, Laurie Clayton
Pharmacy Manager, Elizabeth Burnham
Clinic Manager, Brock Place
Clinic Manager, Maribel Olmos
Medical Director US Synthetic Clinic, Spencer Scoville
Medical Director Epilepsy Program, Tawnya Constantino
Medical Director Adult Service, Craig Shane
Medical Director, Wayne Cannon
Director Of Radiology, Susan Raymond
Medical Director of The Anticoagulation, Kory Anderson
Medical Director, Eugene Worth
Medical Director, Kristian Kemp

Clinic Manager, Gay Tregaskis
Medical Director Intermountain Medical Group And Kidscare, Mark Briesacher
Medical Director Hospitals Urban Central Region, William Hamilton
Vice President, Eric Cannon
Vice President Business Ethics and Compliance, Suzie Draper
Vice President Human Resources, Dan Zuhlke
Vice President Information Technology, Karl West
Vice President And General Counsel, Doug Hammer
Assistant Vice President Financial, Craig Jacobsen
Vice President Strategic Planning, Gregory Pou Poulsen
Assistant Vice President Clinical Inform, Tammy Madsen
Medical Director, Donald (Don) Lappe
RPH, Rob Tadje
Vice Chairman, Bruce T. Reese
Chairman, A. Scott Anderson
Secretary, Nicole Houghton
Secretary, Jeri Lay
Secretary, Sheri Jones
Secretary, Elise Reeves
Secretary, Candyce Penman
Secretary, Rene Warner
Secretary, Maxine Buhler
Secretary, Terri Bowen
Treasurer, Kent Johnson
Board Member, Cody Thornock
Secretary, Kenna Thiriot
Secretary, Leah Church
Secretary, Lisa Mjos
Auditors: KPMG LLP SALT LAKE CITY UTAH

LOCATIONS

HQ: INTERMOUNTAIN HEALTH CARE INC
36 S STATE ST STE 1600, SALT LAKE CITY, UT 841111441
Phone: 801 442-2000
Web: WWW.INTERMOUNTAINHEALTHCARE.ORG

PRODUCTS/OPERATIONS

Selected Hospitals
Alta View Hospital (Sandy UT)
American Fork Hospital (Utah)
Bear River Valley Hospital (Tremonton UT)
Cassia Regional Medical Center (Burley ID)
Delta Community Medical Center (Utah)
Dixie Regional Medical Center (St. George UT)
Fillmore Community Medical Center (Utah)
Garfield Memorial Hospital (Panguitch UT)
Heber Valley Medical Center (Heber City UT)
Intermountain Medical Center (Murray UT)
LDS Hospital (Salt Lake City)
Logan Regional Hospital (Orem UT)
McKay-Dee Hospital Center (Ogden UT)
McKay-Dee Behavioral Health Institute
Orem Community Hospital (Utah)
Park City Medical Center (Park City UT)
Primary Children' s Medical Center (Salt Lake City)
Riverton Hospital (Riverton UT)
Sanpete Valley Hospital (Mt. Pleasant UT)
Sevier Valley Hospital (Richfield UT)
TOSH - The Orthopedic Specialty Hospital (Murray UT)
Utah Valley Regional Medical Center (Provo UT)
Valley View Medical Center (Cedar City UT)

Selected Other Facilities
Northern Idaho and Utah
 Clinics
 Bear River Clinic
 Budge Clinic
 Canyon View Orthopedics & Associates
 Isom Plastic Surgery
 Logan Clinic
 South Cache Valley Clinic
 Summit Clinic
Home Health Hospice and Home Medical Equipment
Cassia
Logan
Tremonton
InstaCare and KidsCare

Logan InstaCare
WorkMed
Burley
Logan
Tremonton
Davis - Weber
Clinics
Bountiful Clinic
Calton/Harrison Orthopedic Clinic
Endocrine Diabetes
Herefordshire Clinic
Layton Clinic
McKay-Dee Cardiology Clinic
McKay-Dee Dermatology & Plastic Surgery
McKay-Dee ENT Clinic
McKay-Dee Foot and Ankle Clinic
McKay-Dee Internal Medicine Clinic
McKay-Dee Rheumatology Clinic
McKay-Dee Urogynecology Clinic
North Ogden Clinic
Northern Utah Pediatrics
Northern Utah Surgeons
Ogden Cardiovascular Associates
South Ogden Clinic
Sports Medicine Specialists - Bountiful
Summit Orthopedics
Syracuse Clinic
Wasatch OB/GYN
Home Health Hospice and Home Medical Equipment
Ogden
InstaCare and KidsCare
Bountiful InstaCare
Bountiful KidsCare
Herefordshire InstaCare
Layton InstaCare
Layton KidsCare
North Ogden InstaCare
North Ogden KidsCare
South Ogden InstaCare
Syracuse InstaCare
ExpressCare
Smith' s Food & Drug - Farmington
WorkMed
Layton
Ogden
Greater Salt Lake Valley
Clinics
Alta View Specialty Clinic
Avenues Specialty Clinic
Bryner Clinic
Central Valley ENT Head & Neck Surgery
Central Valley Thyroid & Parathyroid Clinic
Cottonwood Endocrine & Diabetes Center
Cottonwood Family Practice
Cottonwood Internal Medicine
Gorang Family Practice
Heart and Lung Surgical Associates
Hillcrest Pediatrics
Holladay Clinic
Holladay Pediatrics
Holladay Pediatrics - North
Internal Medicine Associates
Medical Tower Family Practice
Memorial Clinic
Mountain View Pediatrics
Noyes Surgical Oncology
Obstetrics & Gynecology Specialists
Orthopedic Specialty Group Clinics
Park City Specialty Clinic
Plastic Surgery Center
Pulmonology Clinic
Salt Lake Clinic
Sandy Clinic
Sandy OB/GYN
South Jordan Clinic
South Sandy Clinic
Southridge Clinic
Southridge OB/GYN
Southridge Pediatrics
Surgical Specialists
Taylorsville Clinic
Utah Heart Clinic
Urological Institute Clinics
West Jordan Clinic
Home Health Hospice and Home Medical Equipment
Salt Lake City
InstaCare and KidsCare
Holladay InstaCare
Memorial InstaCare
Memorial KidsCare
Mountain View Pediatrics KidsCare

Murray InstaCare
Sandy InstaCare
Southridge InstaCare
Southridge KidsCare
Taylorsville InstaCare
Taylorsville KidsCare
West Jordan InstaCare
West Jordan KidsCare
ExpressCare
Smith' s Food & Drug - Draper
Smith' s Food & Drug - Salt Lake City
WorkMed
Murray
Salt Lake City
Greater Utah Valley
Clinics
American Fork Internal Medicine & Dermatology
American Fork Pulmonary Clinic
American Fork Surgical Associates
Central Orem Clinic
Heber Valley Clinic
Highland Clinic
Legacy OB/GYN Clinic
North Canyon Family Practice
North Orem Clinic
North Valley Pediatrics
Physical Medicine & Rehabilitation
Provo Neurological Clinic
Saratoga Springs Clinic
Springville Clinic
Utah Valley Ear Nose & Throat
Utah Valley Heart & Lung Surgical Associates
Utah Valley Internal Medicine Clinic
Utah Valley Orthopaedics & Sports Medicine
Utah Valley Pediatric Specialists
Utah Valley Pulmonary Clinic
Utah Valley Vein Clinic
Home Health Hospice and Home Medical Equipment
Heber City
Orem
Urgent Care
Highland InstaCare
North Orem InstaCare
Provo InstaCare
Saratoga Springs InstaCare
Springville InstaCare
WorkMed
Orem
Springville
Central Utah
Clinics
Ephraim Clinic
Fillmore Clinic
Manti Family Clinic
Moroni Clinic
Mt. Pleasant Clinic
North Sevier Medical Clinic
Richfield Family Practice
Sevier Valley Family Practice
Home Health Hospice and Home Medical Equipment
Delta
Fillmore
Mt. Pleasant
Richfield
WorkMed
Moroni
Mt. Pleasant
Southern Utah
Clinics
Canyon View Family Practice
Cardiovascular & Thoracic Surgery - St. George
Cedar City Clinic
Dixie Plastic & Reconstructive Surgery
Hurricane Valley Clinic
Pulmonary Medicine Clinic - St. George
Redrock Pediatrics
Rim Rock Orthopaedics & Sports Medicine
River Road Family Practice
River Road Internal Medicine
Southern Utah Behavioral Health
Southern Utah Surgical Associates
Southwest Cardiology - St. George
Southwest Neurology Associates
Southwest Regional Cancer Clinic
Southwest Rheumatology Associates
Southwest Spine & Pain Center
Sunset Clinic
Valley View Heart Clinic
Women' s Health Specialists
Zion Orthopaedics & Sports Medicine
Home Health Hospice and Home Medical Equipment

Cedar City
St. George
InstaCare and KidsCare
Cedar City InstaCare
Hurricane Valley InstaCare
River Road InstaCare
Sunset InstaCare
WorkMed
Cedar City
St. George

COMPETITORS

CHRISTUS Health	Regence BlueCross
HCA	BlueShield of Utah
HealthSouth	St. Mark' s
Iasis Healthcare	University of Utah
LifePoint Health	Hospitals & Clinics
Ogden Regional Medical	
Center	

HISTORICAL FINANCIALS

Company Type: Private

Income Statement

FYE: December 31

	REVENUE ($ mil.)	NET INCOME ($ mil.)	NET PROFIT MARGIN	EMPLOYEES
12/13	5,041	1,546	30.7%	23,000
12/12	4,700	546	11.6%	—
12/11	4,049	6	0.2%	—
12/10	4,381	0	—	—
Annual Growth	4.8%	—	—	—

2013 Year-End Financials

Return on assets: —
Return on equity: 30.7%
Current ratio: 0.80

Cash ($ mil.): 607

INTERNATIONAL BROTHERHOOD OF TEAMSTERS

One of the largest and best-known labor unions in the US the International Brotherhood of Teamsters has 1.4 million members. The Teamsters represents workers in some 20 industry sectors including airlines freight parcel delivery industrial trades and public service. More than 200000 of the union's members are employees of package delivery giant United Parcel Service. Besides negotiating labor contracts with employers on behalf of its members the union oversees pension funds and serves as an advocate in legislative and regulatory arenas. The union and its affiliates have about 1900 local chapters in the US and Canada including about 475 Teamsters locals. The Teamsters union was founded in 1903.

Teamsters chief James P. Hoffa (son of assumed-dead union leader Jimmy Hoffa) is working to improve the union's image after implementing ethics policies aimed at rooting out internal corruption and ties to organized crime. Hoffa first elected in 1998 wants the Teamsters to police themselves and to put an end to the government supervision under which the union has operated since 1989.

The Teamsters have packed up and moved out from under the AFL-CIO umbrella and joined fellow unions Unite Here (textile hotel and restaurant workers) Service Employees International (SEIU) United Food and Commercial Workers and others in the rival Change to Win Coalition. The group hopes to reverse the decline of labor jobs and union membership in the US by focusing its time and money on recruiting rather than on participating in political campaigns. Other key issues for Change to Win include health care immigration and retirement security.

HISTORY

Two rival team-driver unions the Drivers International Union and the Teamsters National Union merged to form the International Brotherhood of Teamsters in 1903. Led by Cornelius Shea the Teamsters established headquarters in Indianapolis. Daniel Tobin (president for 45 years starting in 1907) demanded that union locals obtain executive approval before striking. Membership expanded from the team-driver base prompting the union to add Chauffeurs Stablemen and Helpers to its name (1909).

Following the first transcontinental delivery by motor truck (1912) the Teamster deliverymen traded their horses for trucks. The union then recruited food processing brewery and farm workers among others to augment Teamster effectiveness during strikes. It joined the American Federation of Labor in 1920.

Until the Depression the Teamsters was still a small union of predominantly urban deliverymen. Then Farrell Dobbs a Trotskyite Teamster from Minneapolis organized the famous Minneapolis strikes in 1934 to protest local management's refusal to allow the workers to unionize. Workers clashed with police and National Guard units for 11 days before management acceded to the workers' demands. The strikes demonstrated the potential strength of unions and Teamsters membership swelled. Although union power ebbed during WWII the union continued to grow. It moved its headquarters to Washington DC in 1953.

The AFL-CIO expelled the Teamsters in 1957 when Teamster ties to the mob became public during a US Senate investigation. New Teamsters boss Jimmy Hoffa eluded indictment and took advantage of America's growing dependence on trucking to negotiate the powerful National Master Freight Agreement (1964). Hoffa also organized industrial workers. He used a union pension fund to make mob-connected loans and was later convicted of jury tampering and sent to prison. In 1975 four years after his release Hoffa vanished without a trace and is believed to have been the victim of a Mafia hit.

The Teamsters rejoined the AFL-CIO in 1987 and the following year settled a racketeering lawsuit filed by the US Justice Department by allowing government appointees to discipline corrupt union leaders help run the union and oversee its elections. The election of self-styled reformer Ronald Carey in 1991 (he received 49% of the vote) seemed to portend real changes for the union; each of his six predecessors had been accused of or imprisoned for criminal activities. However membership dropped by 40000 in both 1991 and 1992.

Carey won re-election as union president in 1996 over rival and son of former boss Jimmy Hoffa James P. Hoffa (whom Carey accused of having ties to organized crime). A 15-day strike by the Teamsters' UPS employees in 1997 led to the delivery company's agreement to combine part-time jobs into 10000 new full-time positions. That year Carey's re-election was overturned amid a campaign finance investigation that netted guilty pleas from three Carey associates and the Teamsters leader was disqualified from running for re-election in 1998. Carey was officially expelled from the Teamsters by the federal government and Hoffa won the 1998 election over Tom Leedham (who was backed by the union's reform wing).

Promising to fight corruption Hoffa hired former federal prosecutor Edwin Stier and several former FBI agents to help him operate Project RISE (respect integrity strength and ethics) a new in-house anti-corruption program. In 2002 the union began lobbying against plans to allow Mexican trucking companies to transport goods across the US.

In 2005 the Teamsters joined four other unions representing more than 5 million workers to call for sweeping reform in the AFL-CIO. They released a proposal to revitalize the labor movement by focusing on growth and empowerment. When AFL-CIO president John Sweeney failed to heed their calls the Teamsters joined the Service Employees International Union in boycotting the umbrella group's annual convention and joining the Change to Win Coalition.

EXECUTIVES

Vice President, John Murphy
General President, James P. (Jim) Hoffa, age 74
General Secretary-Treasurer, Ken Hall
Corporate Vice President Human Resources, Joena Berrios
Vice President Information Technology, Myron Sharp
Vice President Local 697, David Yoders
International Vice President, Donald (Don) Siegel
Sec Treas, Dennis Raymond
General Secretary and Treasurer, C Thomas Keegel
Auditors: NOVAK FRANCELLA LLC NEW YORK

LOCATIONS

HQ: INTERNATIONAL BROTHERHOOD OF TEAMSTERS
25 LOUISIANA AVE NW, WASHINGTON, DC 200012130
Phone: 202 624-6800
Web: WWW.TEAMSTER.ORG

PRODUCTS/OPERATIONS

Trade Divisions
Airline
Bakery and Laundry
Brewery and Soft Drink
Building Material and Construction
Carhaul
Dairy
Food Processing
Freight
Graphic Communications
Industrial Trades
Motion Picture and Theatrical Trade
Newspaper Magazine and Electronic Media
Parcel and Small Package
Port
Public Services
Rail
Solid Waste
Tankhaul
Trade Show and Convention Centers
Warehouse

HISTORICAL FINANCIALS

Company Type: Private

Income Statement

FYE: December 31

	REVENUE ($ mil.)	NET INCOME ($ mil.)	NET PROFIT MARGIN	EMPLOYEES
12/09	172	12	7.2%	649
12/08	155	(22)	—	—
12/07	91	0	—	—
Annual Growth	—353635.6%	—	—	—

2009 Year-End Financials

Return on assets: 17.7%   Cash ($ mil.): 50
Return on equity: 7.2%
Current ratio: 0.80

INTERNATIONAL RELIEF AND DEVELOPMENT INC.

LOCATIONS

HQ: INTERNATIONAL RELIEF AND DEVELOPMENT INC.
1621 N KENT ST STE 400, ARLINGTON, VA 222092119
Phone: 703 247-3068
Web: WWW.IRD.ORG

HISTORICAL FINANCIALS

Company Type: Private

Income Statement

FYE: December 31

	REVENUE ($ mil.)	NET INCOME ($ mil.)	NET PROFIT MARGIN	EMPLOYEES
12/09	510	2	0.4%	313
12/08	539	0	0.1%	—
12/07	0	0		—
Annual Growth	—34858.0%			

2009 Year-End Financials

Return on assets: 7.6%   Cash ($ mil.): 29
Return on equity: 0.4%
Current ratio: 0.60

INTERNET CORPORATION FOR ASSIGNED NAMES AND NUMBERS

Can anyone manage the Internet? This group says "ICANN." The Internet Corporation for Assigned Names and Numbers (ICANN) is a not-for-profit organization responsible for the management of the Internet's domain name system (DNS) allocation of Internet protocol (IP) addresses and assignment of protocol parameters. The DNS allows people to type in an address like "www.hoovers.com" rather than the string of numbers that represents the underlying IP address. Internet users register some 20 domain names ending in .com .org .info and .net among others through ICANN-accredited DNS registrars. The group is also managing the application process for a slew of new generic top-level domains (gTLDs).

ICANN's staff overseen by an international group of directors called the Governmental Advisory Committee works with governments and corporations (such as Microsoft) on several continents to manage the technical elements that allow the Internet to function predictably worldwide. At the end of 2011 some 310 top-level domains were included in the DNS root zone. These include country code top-level domains (called ccTLDs) such as .de for Germany and .cn for China. Although ICANN's work is global in scope the group operates under a contract with the US Department of Commerce. The company publishes an online magazine giving subscribers the latest developments with ICANN.

In mid-2011 ICANN approved a plan that allows people to apply for new generic top-level domains (gTLDs) beyond the typical .com .org and .net. The group began the process of accepting these gTLD applications in January 2012; technology giants Apple Samsung Google and Amazon have been the first to jump at the chance. It was reported that Google applied for more than 100 gTLDs — such as .dad and .book —at a cost of nearly $20 million. Applicants had sought to own some 2000 domains by midyear. At a cost of $185000 per application ICAAN has generated about $350 million as part of the gTLD process alone. Of the $185000 application fee about $60000 is dogeared for what the organization has deemed the "risk contingency fund."

One issue that the organization grapples with is so-called "domain name tasting" which has resulted in a dramatic rise in registrations and cancellations. This "tasting" is when someone buys a domain name and places per-click ads on the site to see whether the site will make a profit. If it does not look likely the domain name will be dropped within a five-day "grace period" offered by ICANN.

EXECUTIVES

Vice President. Russia Computer Information Systems And Eastern Europe, Veni Markovski
Vice President of Government Affairs Americas, Jamie Hedlund
Vice President For Industry Engagement, Cyrus Namazi
Vice President Chief Security Officer, Jeffrey Moss
Vice Chairman, Bruce Tonkin
Auditors: ERNST & YOUNG US LLP SAN DIEG

LOCATIONS

HQ: INTERNET CORPORATION FOR ASSIGNED NAMES AND NUMBERS
12025 WATERFRONT DR # 300, LOS ANGELES, CA 900942536
Phone: 310 823-9358
Web: WWW.ICANN.ORG

PRODUCTS/OPERATIONS

Selected Generic Top-level Domains
.aero
.asia
.biz
.cat
.com
.coop
.edu
.gov
.info
.int
.jobs
.mil
.mobi
.museum
.name
.net
.org
.pro
.tel
.travel
.xxx

HISTORICAL FINANCIALS

Company Type: Private

Income Statement   FYE: June 30

	REVENUE ($ mil.)	NET INCOME ($ mil.)	NET PROFIT MARGIN	EMPLOYEES
06/13	236	85	36.3%	160
06/10	68	9	13.7%	—
06/09	59	0	—	—
06/08	1,841	0	—	—
Annual Growth	(33.7%)	—	—	—

2013 Year-End Financials
Return on assets: 10.5%   Cash ($ mil.): 64
Return on equity: 36.3%
Current ratio: 0.40

INVACARE CORPORATION (TW)

LOCATIONS

HQ: INVACARE CORPORATION (TW)
39400 TAYLOR PKWY, NORTH RIDGEVILLE, OH 440356270
Phone: 440 329-6000

HISTORICAL FINANCIALS

Company Type: Private

Income Statement   FYE: December 31

	REVENUE ($ mil.)	NET INCOME ($ mil.)	NET PROFIT MARGIN	EMPLOYEES
12/11	1,801	(4)	—	45
12/10	1,722	25	1.5%	—
12/09	1,693	41	2.4%	—
Annual Growth	3.1%	—	—	—

2011 Year-End Financials
Return on assets: 8.3%   Cash ($ mil.): 34
Return on equity: (-0.2%)
Current ratio: 1.00

IOWA HEALTH SYSTEM

The land where the tall corn grows is also the land of Iowa Health System (IHS) which does business as UnityPoint. The integrated health care system operates some 15 acute care hospitals that serve large communities throughout Iowa as well as parts of western Illinois and Madison Wisconsin. UnityPoint also supports about a dozen rural hospitals and it manages about 300 physician clinics located in rural and suburban areas. The system's hospitals provide general medical-surgical care as well as care in a number of medical specialties such as cardiovascular disease and home health services. Founded in 1993 UnityPoint has about 3700 licensed beds.

Operations
In 2014 the system had about 155000 patient admissions facilitated 20000 births and saw a total of some 4.5 million patients.

Geographic Reach
UnityPoint Health includes a dozen hospitals in 10 Iowa cities four in Illinois and another in Wisconsin. Its largest geographic markets served are Anamosa Cedar Rapids Des Moines Dubuque Fort Dodge Sioux City and Waterloo Iowa; the Quad Cities/Muscatine region in Iowa and Illinois; Peoria Illinois; and Madison Wisconsin.

Strategy
In early 2013 Iowa Health System rebranded itself UnityPoint to showcase its mission to be a point of unity for patient care. It probably also helped that the company was expanding and including health care facilities in other states. That same year it picked up new affiliates in Illinois expanded its broadband Internet access program

across Iowa and added Meriter Health Services of Madison Wisconsin. The health system operates many of its member hospitals through similar affiliation agreements where it provides administration contracting billing legal recruitment information technology and other central services. In 2015 the system built a new primary care facility in Cedar Falls Iowa.

The system is also expanding in areas beyond its physical locations. In 2015 it partnered with MDLive to begin offering telehealth services in Iowa and it added a plane to its air ambulance fleet. UnityPoint also plans to launch a new insurance firm with not-for-profit organization HealthPartners.

EXECUTIVES

President and CEO UnityPoint Health -Des Moines, Eric Crowell
CEO, Bill Leaver
VP and CIO, Joy M. Grosser
SVP and Chief Clinical Officer; President and CEO UnityPoint Clinic, Alan S. Kaplan
President and Chief Strategy Officer, Kevin Vermeer
SVP and CFO, Mark Johnson
President and CEO Meriter-UnityPoint Health - Madison, Arthur Nizza
CEO UnityPoint Health -Fort Dodge, Sue Thompson
VP Marketing and Communications, Susan Haider
VP Payor Innovation; CEO UnityPoint at Work, Brian Jones
CEO UnityPoint Health -St. Luke's -Sioux City, Lynn Wold
CEO Jones Regional Medical Center Anamosa, Eric Briesemeister
President and CEO UnityPoint Health -Dubuque, David Brandon
President and CEO UnityPoint Health -Peoria, Debbie Simon
President and CEO UnityPoint Health -Trinity (Quad Cities Muscatine), Rick Seidler
President and CEO UnityPoint Health -Waterloo, Pam Delagardelle
President and CEO St. Luke's -Cedar Rapids, Ted Townsend
Vice President Business Development And Marketing, Sid Ramsey
Vice President Of Human Resources, Joyce McDanel
Vice President Of Medical Affairs, Mark Purtle
Vice President Finance Chief Financial Officer Methodist, Rob Quin
Vice President Of Practice Operations, Matt Behrens
Chairman, Mike Williams
Vice Chair, Mike Stone
Auditors: BKD LLP KANSAS CITY MISSOURI

LOCATIONS

HQ: IOWA HEALTH SYSTEM
1776 WEST LAKES PKWY # 400, WEST DES MOINES, IA 502668239
Phone: 515 241-6161
Web: WWW.UNITYPOINT.ORG

PRODUCTS/OPERATIONS

Selected Facilities
Metropolitan Hospitals
    Allen Memorial Hospital Corporation (Waterloo Iowa)
    Iowa Lutheran Hospital (Des Moines Iowa)
    Iowa Methodist Medical Center (Des Moines Iowa)
    Blank Children' s Hospital (Des Moines Iowa)
    Methodist Medical Center of Illinois (Peoria Illinois)
    Methodist West Hospital (West Des Moines Iowa)
    St. Luke' s Hospital (Cedar Rapids Iowa)
    St. Luke' s Regional Medical Center (Sioux City Iowa)
    Jones Regional Medical Center (Anamosa Iowa)
    The Finley Hospital (Dubuque Iowa)
    Trinity Bettendorf (Bettendorf Iowa)

Trinity Moline (Moline Illinois)
Trinity Muscatine (Muscatine Iowa)
Trinity Regional Medical Center (Fort Dodge Iowa)
Trinity Rock Island (Rock Island Illinois)
Rural Hospitals
Buena Vista Regional Medical Center (Storm Lake Iowa)
Clarke County Hospital (Osceola Iowa)
Community Memorial Hospital (Sumner Iowa)
Greater Regional Medical Center (Creston Iowa)
Greene County Medical Center (Jefferson Iowa)
Grundy County Memorial Hospital (Grundy Center Iowa)
Guthrie County Hospital (Guthrie Center Iowa)
Guttenberg Municipal Hospital (Guttenberg Iowa)
Humboldt County Memorial Hospital (Humboldt Iowa)
Loring Hospital (Sac City Iowa)
Pocahontas Community Hospital (Pocahantas Iowa)

COMPETITORS

Avera Health
Blessing Hospital
CHI Health
Genesis Health System
McDonough District Hospital
Mercy Health Network
Methodist Health System
ORHC
OSF Healthcare System
University of Iowa Hospitals and Clinics

HISTORICAL FINANCIALS

Company Type: Private

Income Statement

FYE: December 31

	REVENUE ($ mil.)	NET INCOME ($ mil.)	NET PROFIT MARGIN	EMPLOYEES
12/13	2,841	369	13.0%	18,923
12/12	2,732	220	8.1%	—
12/11	2,380	159	6.7%	—
12/09	109	0	—	—
Annual Growth	125.7%	—	—	—

2013 Year-End Financials

Return on assets: 4.8%
Return on equity: 13.0%
Current ratio: 1.20
Cash ($ mil.): 197

ISO NEW ENGLAND INC.

The transmission lines in the Northeast power grid keep humming because of ISO New England. The not-for-profit corporation is responsible for electricity generation and transmission throughout Connecticut Maine Massachusetts New Hampshire Rhode Island and Vermont. The independent systems operator (ISO) runs the 31000 MW generating capacity grid that is owned by utilities of the New England Power Pool and manages the wholesale electric market. The power grid is made up of hundreds of generating units (about 350 under direct ISO New England control) connected by some 8500 miles of high-voltage transmission lines. It provides power to more than 6.5 million households and businesses.

Geographic Reach

ISO New England serves end users in Connecticut Maine Massachusetts New Hampshire Rhode Island and Vermont. The power grid has 13 interconnections to power systems in New York State and Canada.

Operations

ISO New England's three primary responsibilities are: the reliable operation of New England's bulk electric power system; the development oversight and equitable administration of the region's wholesale electricity marketplace; and the management of the bulk electric power system and the wholesale markets' planning processes.

Sales and Marketing

Its customers include power generators publicly owned entities suppliers transmission owners and demand‑response and alternative resources providers.

Financial Performance

In 2013 the company traded $9.2 billion in wholesale electricity markets ($8 billion in energy markets and $1.2 billion in capacity and ancillary services markets).

In 2013 natural gas pipeline constraints and higher demand caused by a very hot summer an a very cold winter drove up natural gas and wholesale electricity prices over 2012's record low prices. Higher gas prices pushed wholesale electricity prices in New England up by 55% in 2013. The higher energy price pushed the total value of the region's wholesale energy market up 54% that year. The region also spent 54% more in the energy markets.

Strategy

The company has invested $5.6 billion in transmission upgrades since 2002 (more than 14000 MW of new power plant projects) and has committed at least another $5 billion over the next decade. In addition to meet federal and state regulations on lowering carbon emissions ISO New England has set 2020 goals of attaining at least 30% of its power supply from renewable sources (primarily wind power) in its participating states in New England. Since 2003 the company has reduced air emissions from the power generation in its service area by 60%.

Under the company's management the region has attracted $11 billion in private transmission investment through 2017.

In 2013 ISO New England launched the Distributed Generation Forecast Working Group a regional forum for interested parties to provide input to the ISO on a new long-term distributed generation forecast.

Company Background

ISO New England was formed as a response to the Great Northeast Blackout of 1965 as a way to ensure the reliability of the region's electric power industry. In 2005 Federal regulators upgraded the company to a regional transmission organization (RTO) a move that strengthened the corporation's authority to manage the grid.

EXECUTIVES

Vice President System Operations, Peter (Pete) Brandien
President CEO and Director, Gordon van Welie
VP Information Services, Jamshid A. Afnan
VP and CFO, Robert C. Ludlow
EVP and COO, Vamsi Chadalavada
VP Market Operations, Kevin A. Kirby
VP Market Development, Robert Ethier
Vice President Information Technology, Stephen Rourke
Vice President, Chris Harden
Vice President Market Monitoring, Jeff McDonald
Vice President Human Resources, Janice S Dickstein
Chairman, Kathryn J. (Kate) Jackson
Secretary, Jane Carpenter
Auditors: KPMG LLP BOSTON MA

LOCATIONS

HQ: ISO NEW ENGLAND INC.
   1 SULLIVAN RD, HOLYOKE, MA 010402841
Phone: 413 535-4000
Web: WWW.ISONEWENGLAND.COM

COMPETITORS

New York ISO
PJM Interconnection
Trans-Elect

HISTORICAL FINANCIALS

Company Type: Private

Income Statement

FYE: December 31

	REVENUE ($ mil.)	NET INCOME ($ mil.)	NET PROFIT MARGIN	EMPLOYEES
12/13	157	0	—	560
12/10	128	0	—	—
12/09	123	0	—	—
12/08	1,008	0	—	—
Annual Growth	—	—	—	—

2013 Year-End Financials

Return on assets: —
Return on equity: —
Current ratio: 0.10
Cash ($ mil.): 84

ITA GROUP INC

ITA Group (doing business as ITAGroup) bets it can make your company better. Specializing in performance marketing ITAGroup (standing for "Ideas to Action") builds and manages programs that help clients increase sales and customer satisfaction through incentives and training. The company's services include research and program design administration fulfillment and measurement for employee recognition and rewards programs business-to-business loyalty programs and sales incentive programs. ITAGroup also provides business meeting and event planning services.

Geographic Reach

ITAGroup is based in West Des Moines Iowa with a dozen sales offices located across the US in Boca Raton Chicago Dallas Detroit Indianapolis Los Angeles Minneapolis Philadelphia San Francisco and the greater New York City area.

Strategy

ITAGroup's Emerging Markets Division consults with companies on corporate recognition and incentive programs. The unit is focused specifically on helping middle market businesses effectively use incentive and recognition programs to create loyalty among employees and customers.

Sales and Marketing

ITAGroup offers a specially designed app for companies using Salesforce CRM.

Company Background

The company was originally founded in 1963.

EXECUTIVES

President and CEO, Thomas J. (Tom) Mahoney
SVP and CFO, Brent VanderWaal
VP and CIO, John Rose
SVP Event Management, Mary Z. Bussone
Vice President Sales, John (Jack) Mccabe
Vice President Information Technology, Dave Dueland
Vice President Marketing Manager, Julie Sherman
Regional Vice President Of Sales, John (Jack) Auer
Assistant Treasurer, Ronna Rivas
Auditors: MCGLADREY LLP DES MOINES IA

LOCATIONS

HQ: ITA GROUP INC
   4600 WESTOWN PKWY STE 100, WEST DES MOINES, IA 502661042
Phone: 515 326-3400
Web: WWW.ITAGROUP.COM

HISTORICAL FINANCIALS

Company Type: Private

Income Statement

FYE: August 31

	REVENUE ($ mil.)	NET INCOME ($ mil.)	NET PROFIT MARGIN	EMPLOYEES
08/13	288	0	—	550
08/12	288	0	—	—
08/11	233	0	—	—
08/10	0	0	—	—
Annual Growth	—	—	—	—

2013 Year-End Financials

Return on assets: 6.1%
Return on equity: —
Current ratio: 0.90
Cash ($ mil.): 44

J & H OIL COMPANY

Auditors: UHY LLP STERLING HEIGHTS MIC

LOCATIONS

HQ: J & H OIL COMPANY
2696 CHICAGO DR SW, GRAND RAPIDS, MI
495191628
Phone: 616 534-2181
Web: WWW.JHOIL.COM

HISTORICAL FINANCIALS

Company Type: Private

Income Statement

FYE: June 30

	REVENUE ($ mil.)	NET INCOME ($ mil.)	NET PROFIT MARGIN	EMPLOYEES
06/13	373	2	0.5%	70
06/12	349	2	0.6%	—
06/11	291	0	0.2%	—
06/10	221	0	—	—
Annual Growth	19.1%	—	—	—

2013 Year-End Financials

Return on assets: 2.2%
Return on equity: 0.5%
Current ratio: 1.60
Cash ($ mil.): 6

J M SMITH CORPORATION

J M Smith Corporation has gone from corner drugstore to supplying drugstores and more. The family owned holding company's primary subsidiary is Smith Drug which provides purchasing and distribution services for more than 1000 independent pharmacies in more than 20 US states. It also operates through QS/1 Data Systems and Integral Solutions both of which offer data management software and services for pharmacies care providers and government agencies. Smith Premier provides prescription benefit management while other divisions offer automated dispensing systems for pharmacies and marketing services for drugmakers. Other units include Norgenix and RxMedic Systems.

Geographic Reach

Smith Drug serves customers in 21 states primarily in the southern US as well as Washington DC and the Virgin Islands.

Operations

The company operates through six business units: Smith Drug Company QS/1 Smith Premier Services Integral Solutions Group Norgenix and RxMedic Systems.

In addition to being its oldest subsidiary J M Smith's core Smith Drug unit is one of the top private wholesale drug distributors in the US. The company's Smith Premier unit also has a nationwide presence providing prescription management services through some 57000 contracted pharmacies.

Meanwhile the growing QS/1 division has installed more than 12000 health care and pharmacy automation systems and has more than 20 service offices across the US. The Integral Solutions unit which has about 15 offices scattered across the nation offers communication networking systems for universities banks and manufacturers in addition to health care customers.

J M Smith newest subsidiary Norgenix is a specialty pharmaceutical medical device and biotech company that engages in the development commercialization and sales of pharmaceutical products that serve the unmet needs within women's health. It acquires or licenses rights for select pharmaceuticals which it then markets through its direct sales force in North America. Norgenix is focused on the women's health markets and began marketing its first hormone replacement therapy in 2009.

RxMedic Systems provides leading-edge dispensing technology to pharmacies.

Sales and Marketing

The company supplies products services and technologies to pharmacies institutions local government agencies and businesses across the US.

Strategy

J M Smith's cornerstone Smith Drug subsidiary continues to be a key growth component doubling the number of states in which it operates over the last decade. However the company is also extolling its energies towards developing and introducing innovative data management and technology solutions through other subsidiaries to meet the rising demand for such solutions in the health care market.

Smith Premier is working to help customers go paperless by offering electronic prescription processing while RxMedic's dispensing systems allow pharmacies to increase productivity with its robotic counting and dispensing equipment.

The company's QS/1 subsidiary has experienced rapid growth in recent years as pharmacies and care providers increasingly look to automate processes and the Integral Solutions unit also benefits from recent trends in the health care market to improve electronic communication systems.

Partnerships are also key to J M Smith's growth. In 2014 Norgenix partnered with CrossBay Medical for the co-promotion of the SonoSure a device for use to access the uterine cavity for saline infusion sonohysterography and to obtain an endometrial biopsy if needed using the same device.

In 2013 QS/1 and RxTran formed a partnership that will allow QS/1 to offer its pharmacies prescription translation software through RxTran following to the commitment to provide its pharmacy customers with the tools they need to offer the best patient care possible. RxTran provides translation services in 17 different languages for QS/1 allowing its pharmacy customers to request medical instructions in patients' native languages including in Arabic Bengali French German Greek Haitian Creole Hindi Italian Korean Polish Portuguese Russian Simplified Chinese Spanish Tagalog Traditional Chinese and Vietnamese.That year J M Smith formed a partnership with iMedicare (an iPad application) to help pharmacies efficiently serve the growing number of Medicare patients across the country. iMedicare can quickly present Medicare plan options that best fit the needs of each Medicare patient.In 2012 it teamed up with A/R Allegiance Group LLC to integrate with COLLECTPlus™within SystemOne. Partnering with A/R Allegiance and the COLLECTPlus program allows JM Smith to offer its customers the only billing and collection solution that is fully integrated.Company Background

In 2010 Smith expanded by acquiring health equipment manufacturing firm RxMedic. Through the purchase the company entered the automated dispensing system market.

J M Smith was founded in 1943 by drugstore proprietor James Smith and is run by the Smith family.

EXECUTIVES

Chairman and CEO, William (Bill) Cobb
CFO, James C. Wilson
Senior Vice President Business Development, Rick Simerly
Vice President, Linda Campbell
Secretary, Russell Weber

LOCATIONS

HQ: J M SMITH CORPORATION
101 W SAINT JOHN ST # 305, SPARTANBURG, SC
293065179
Phone: 864 542-9419
Web: WWW.QS1.COM

Selected Office Locations

Altamonte Springs FL
Brandon MS
Columbia SC
Dallas TX
Fairmont WV
Gray ME
Hermitage PA
Houston TX
Indianapolis IN
Lexington KY
Mechanicsburg PA
Miami FL
Morrisville GA
Paragould AR
Perry GA
Pleasant Hill MO
Richmond VA
Seattle WA
Spartanburg SC
St. Paul MN
Sturbridge MA
Valdosta GA
Valencia CA
Wake Forest NC

PRODUCTS/OPERATIONS

Selected Divisions

Integral Solutions Group
Norgenix Pharmaceuticals
QS/1
RxMedic
Smith Drug Company
Smith Premier Services

COMPETITORS

AmerisourceBergen
CVS
Cardinal Health
Express Scripts
HP Enterprise Services
Kinray
McKesson
PharMerica

Fiserv
H. D. Smith Wholesale
Drug

HISTORICAL FINANCIALS
Company Type: Private

Income Statement

FYE: February 28

	REVENUE ($ mil.)	NET INCOME ($ mil.)	NET PROFIT MARGIN	EMPLOYEES
02/14	2,370	38	1.6%	1,050
02/13	2,362	26	1.1%	—
02/12	2,479	25	1.0%	—
02/11	2,437	0	—	—
Annual Growth	(0.9%)	—	—	—

2014 Year-End Financials
Return on assets: 10.0%   Cash ($ mil.): 153
Return on equity: 1.6%
Current ratio: 1.20

J. D. STREETT & COMPANY INC.

Word on the street is that J. D. Streett tries to stay streets ahead of its rivals as it supplies its customers with a wide range of fuels oxygenates lubricants transmission fluids and antifreezes. The company operates more than 20 retail locations (convenience stores and gas stations) under its own ZX label and/or BP brand in Missouri and Illinois. J. D. Streett also serves more than 10 international markets. In addition the company offers terminalling services for distillate ethanol and oil products and owns and operates a chain of discount cigarette shops (most that also sell beer) across Missouri.

Its seven-acre petroleum terminal complex in St. Louis has a total capacity or more than of 485000 barrels and is capable of handling more than 25000 barrels a day. It also has a 252000 barrel terminal in Lemay Missouri. The terminals are centrally located and easily accessible by highway river rail and pipeline enabling the company to control costs.

J. D. Streett has a long track record of keeping the wheels of vehicles turning. It was formed in 1884 to make grease for wagon wheels.

EXECUTIVES
Sales Manager, Chuck Whelehon
Sales Manager Unbranded Fuel Sales Rep, Tom Irwin
Operations General Manager, William Starbuck
Auditors: BKD LLP ST LOUIS MISSOURI

LOCATIONS
HQ: J. D. STREETT & COMPANY INC.
  144 WELDON PKWY, MARYLAND HEIGHTS, MO 630433100
Phone: 314 432-6600
Web: WWW.JDSTREETT.COM

COMPETITORS
BP Lubricants USA	PetroLiance
Fuchs Lubricants	U.S. Venture
Lubrizol	Vesco Oil

HISTORICAL FINANCIALS
Company Type: Private

Income Statement

FYE: December 31

	REVENUE ($ mil.)	NET INCOME ($ mil.)	NET PROFIT MARGIN	EMPLOYEES
12/13	316	5	1.8%	240
12/12	342	(11)	—	—
12/11	366	3	0.8%	—
12/10	313	0	—	—
Annual Growth	0.3%	—	—	—

2013 Year-End Financials
Return on assets: 2.4%   Cash ($ mil.): 1
Return on equity: 1.8%
Current ratio: 0.80

J. H. FINDORFF & SON INC.

J.H. Findorff & Son has been building its resume since the 19th century. The company constructs commercial and institutional projects in the US Midwest. It provides general contracting design/build and construction management services. Projects include schools government buildings health care centers hotels condos offices and shopping complexes. Findorff also self-performs trade work including carpentry concrete masonry drywall and steel erection. Among its projects is Madison Wisconsin's Children's Museum and the Overture Center for the Arts. It also built the Wisconsin Institutes for Discovery at The University of Wisconsin-Madison. John Findorff founded the company as J.H. Findorff in 1890.

Geographic Reach
The firm has offices in Madison and Milwaukee Wisconsin.

Financial Performance
Findorff which completes more than $300 million in construction annually rings up between $250 million and $300 million in sales per year.

Ownership
The construction firm is owned by the directors and employees.

EXECUTIVES
Vice President Of Operations, Mike Dillis
Vice President Business Development, Jeff Tubbs

LOCATIONS
HQ: J. H. FINDORFF & SON INC.
  300 S BEDFORD ST, MADISON, WI 537033622
Phone: 608 257-5321
Web: WWW.FINDORFF.COM

PRODUCTS/OPERATIONS

Selected Services
Preconstruction
Construction management
General contracting
Design/Build
Self-performed trades
Special projects
Building information modeling

COMPETITORS
Boldt	Market & Johnson
C. G. Schmidt	Miron Construction
C.D. Smith	Walsh Group
Hunt Construction	Weis Builders
Hunzinger Construction	

HISTORICAL FINANCIALS
Company Type: Private

Income Statement

FYE: September 30

	REVENUE ($ mil.)	NET INCOME ($ mil.)	NET PROFIT MARGIN	EMPLOYEES
09/12	320	4	1.3%	500
09/11	209	0	0.1%	—
09/08	322	3	1.2%	—
09/06	248	0	—	—
Annual Growth	4.4%	—	—	—

2012 Year-End Financials
Return on assets: 2.9%   Cash ($ mil.): 74
Return on equity: 1.3%
Current ratio: 1.20

J. P. CULLEN & SONS INC.

Auditors: BAKER TILLY VIRCHOW KRAUSE LL

LOCATIONS
HQ: J. P. CULLEN & SONS INC.
  330 E DELAVAN DR, JANESVILLE, WI 535462711
Phone: 608 754-6601
Web: WWW.JPCULLEN.COM

HISTORICAL FINANCIALS
Company Type: Private

Income Statement

FYE: March 31

	REVENUE ($ mil.)	NET INCOME ($ mil.)	NET PROFIT MARGIN	EMPLOYEES
03/14	407	0	—	600
03/13	376	0	—	—
03/12	302	0	—	—
03/11	243	0	—	—
Annual Growth	18.7%	—	—	—

2014 Year-End Financials
Return on assets: 3.6%   Cash ($ mil.): 24
Return on equity: —
Current ratio: 0.90

J.D. ABRAMS L.P.

J.D. Abrams builds the infrastructure that helps travelers drive across Texas. While highway and bridge construction projects from the Texas Department of Transportation make up the bulk of its construction work the civil engineering and construction firm also works on flood control dams reservoirs waterways railroad test track airport taxiways and other infrastructure projects in Texas and elsewhere in the Sun Belt. J.D. Abrams also operates two subsidiaries Transmountain Equipment and Austin Prestress which runs a concrete casting plant. Founded in 1966 the company operates from four Texas-based offices in Austin Dallas El Paso and Houston.

Geographic ReachJ.D. Abrams operated four offices in Texas as of early 2016 in the cities of Austin Dallas El Paso and Houston. Its two subsidiary operations Austin PreStress and Transmountain Equipment are both located in Austin Texas. Austin PreStress also has manufacturing facilities in Austin and El Paso.StrategyWhile highway and bridge construction projects from the Texas Department of Transportation continued in early 2016 to make up the bulk of its construction work J.D. Abrams has also worked on design and build projects in Texas and Louisiana the High Speed - Strict Tolerance Rocket Sled Test Track at Holloman AFB in New Mexico flood control dams in Sanderson Texas the Segmental Bridge near Pascagoula Mississippi waterway and channel work in El Paso and military housing infrastructure in Fort Bliss (El Paso Texas) among other projects. It's also helped provide emergency response repair and clean up services.Company BackgroundFounded in El Paso in 1966 the company is owned and managed by members of the Abrams family.

EXECUTIVES

Chairman President and CEO, Jon F. Abrams
VP Operations, Brad Everett
CFO, Kelly Gallagher
SVP; Area Manager Dallas, C. P. (Pat) Worrell
President Austin Prestress, Jim Abrams
Area Manager Houston, William G. (Bill) Duguay
Manager El Paso, Alfonso (Al) Fernandez
Senior Vice President Area Manager Dallas, C Worrell
Board Member, Joe Hernandez
Auditors: SCHMI BROADDUS NUGENT GANO PC

LOCATIONS

HQ: J.D. ABRAMS L.P.
111 CONGRESS AVE STE 2400, AUSTIN, TX 787014298
Phone: 512 243-3317
Web: WWW.JDABRAMS.COM

COMPETITORS

C.F. Jordan	Sterling Construction
Holloman	Zack Burkett

HISTORICAL FINANCIALS

Company Type: Private

Income Statement

FYE: December 31

	REVENUE ($ mil.)	NET INCOME ($ mil.)	NET PROFIT MARGIN	EMPLOYEES
12/13	155	(2)	—	750
12/12	176	(2)	—	—
12/09	307	15	4.9%	—
12/08	42	0	—	—
Annual Growth 29.3%	—	—	—	—

2013 Year-End Financials

Return on assets: 7.5%   Cash ($ mil.): 34
Return on equity: (-1.7%)
Current ratio: 1.70

J.H. WILLIAMS OIL COMPANY INC.

Auditors: DOWELL & PEREZ PA TAMPA F

LOCATIONS

HQ: J.H. WILLIAMS OIL COMPANY INC.
1237 E TWIGGS ST, TAMPA, FL 336023139
Phone: 813 228-7776
Web: WWW.JHWOIL.COM

HISTORICAL FINANCIALS

Company Type: Private

Income Statement

FYE: December 31

	REVENUE ($ mil.)	NET INCOME ($ mil.)	NET PROFIT MARGIN	EMPLOYEES
12/13	395	0	0.1%	35
12/12	382	(0)	—	
12/11	355	(0)	—	
12/10	278	0	—	
Annual Growth 12.4%		—		

2013 Year-End Financials

Return on assets: 2.6%   Cash ($ mil.): —
Return on equity: 0.1%
Current ratio: 0.50

JACKSON ELECTRIC MEMBERSHIP CORPORATION

Jackson EMC distributes electricity to more than 197800 individual customers (more than 210200 meters) in 10 counties around Atlanta and in northeastern Georgia. The majority of customers are residential with commercial and industrial customers accounting for 42% of fiscal year 2013 revenues. One of the largest nonprofit power cooperatives in the US and the largest electric cooperative in Georgia Jackson EMC is owned by its members. The cooperative's generation and transmission partners include Oglethorpe Power Corp. Georgia Systems Operation and Georgia Transmission Corp.

Operations

Jackson EMC operates 86 substations and more than 13550 miles of power line.

Financial Performance

In fiscal 2013 the coop reported a revenue increased of 1%. Net income declined slightly by 0.3%. That year the non-profit coop returned $5.5 million in margin refunds to nearly 201000 members.

Strategy

Among other initiatives Jackson EMC is promoting conservation and green energy options as a way to slow energy growth and reduce greenhouse gas emissions. Initiatives include advocating the use of more efficient light bulbs and the widespread use of solar panels for power generation.

Ownership

The cooperative is owned by its members.

Company Background

Although the county of Jackson is named after a Georgia statesman from the Revolutionary War era Jackson Electric Membership Corporation (Jackson EMC) can trace its roots more directly to US president Franklin Roosevelt whose frequent trips to Warm Springs alerted him to the shortage of affordable electric power outside of major cities. Jackson EMC was founded in 1938 as part of the Roosevelt government's national rural electrification drive.

EXECUTIVES

Secretary Treasurer And Director, Rodney Chandler

LOCATIONS

HQ: JACKSON ELECTRIC MEMBERSHIP CORPORATION
850 COMMERCE RD, JEFFERSON, GA 305493329
Phone: 706 367-5281
Web: WWW.JACKSONEMC.COM

HISTORICAL FINANCIALS

Company Type: Private

Income Statement

FYE: December 31

	REVENUE ($ mil.)	NET INCOME ($ mil.)	NET PROFIT MARGIN	EMPLOYEES
12/13*	472	0	—	445
05/13	475	21	4.6%	—
05/12	472	21	4.6%	—
05/11	462	0	—	—
Annual Growth 0.7%		—		

*Fiscal year change

2013 Year-End Financials

Return on assets: 13.9%   Cash ($ mil.): 57
Return on equity: —
Current ratio: 1.30

JACKSON ENERGY AUTHORITY

Jackson Energy Authority has the power and the authority to provide for all of Jackson Tennessee's energy needs. The municipal utility distributes electricity natural gas and water and provides wastewater services to about 40000 residential commercial and industrial customers in Jackson and surrounding areas. Jackson Energy also sells propane and offers broadband telecommunications services (cable Internet and telephone). Other services provided by Jackson Energy Authority include the sale of outdoor security lights surge protection systems gas grills and decorative lights.

As part of its strategy to reduce carbon emission conserve energy and help its customers cut costs Jackson Energy Authority's Wise Energy program provides practical energy saving advice to gas power and water users.

The company was formed by the City of Jackson in 1959 to combine its three separate utilities (natural gas electricity and water/wastewater) under one utility operation. A five-member Board of Directors appointed by the Mayor and City Council of Jackson governs Jackson Energy Authority.

EXECUTIVES

Vice Chairman Of The Board, Martha Lanahan
Auditors: ALEXANDER THOMPSON ARNOLD PLLC

LOCATIONS

HQ: JACKSON ENERGY AUTHORITY
119 E COLLEGE ST, JACKSON, TN 383016201
Phone: 731 422-7500
Web: WWW.JAXENERGY.COM

HISTORICAL FINANCIALS

Company Type: Private

Income Statement

FYE: June 30

	REVENUE ($ mil.)	NET INCOME ($ mil.)	NET PROFIT MARGIN	EMPLOYEES
06/14	250	24	9.8%	425
06/13*	243	22	9.3%	—
12/11	243	22	9.4%	—
06/10	218	0	—	—
Annual Growth	3.4%	—	—	—

*Fiscal year change

2014 Year-End Financials

Return on assets: 11.7%   Cash ($ mil.): 64
Return on equity: 9.8%
Current ratio: 2.10

JACO OIL COMPANY

Jaco Oil Company is jockeying for its piece of the convenience store pie. The company's Fastrip Food Stores subsidiary operates more than 50 convenience stores and gas stations primarily in and around Bakersfield California but also in Arizona. Besides offering customers traditional convenience-store fare which includes coffee milk beer snacks tobacco and the like the Fastrip chain stocks a full range of grocery items and provides in-store financial service centers. Financial services include check cashing payday loans wire transfer services via The Western Union Company refund anticipation loans and other services at many locations. Jaco Oil Company was founded in 1970.

Geographic Reach

Jaco Oil owns and operates gasoline service stations and convenience stores in the Western US.

Operations

The company operates nearly 50 stores in Bakersfield and Kern counties as well as in Fresno Sacramento and the Chico area. It also has four stores in Arizona located in Bullhead Casa Grande and Nogales. As part of its business Jaco Oil offers food beverages and financial services such as payday loans wire transfer services and tax preparation services.

Strategy

Fastrip works to distinguish itself from other convenience store chains by stocking a complete assortment of grocery items including such staples as sugar flour salt cake mix and even green beans. The chain bills itself as a Mini Grocery Store a strategy that other retailers including Dollar General and drugstore-giant Walgreen have adopted. It's also always open (24/7/365).

Auditors: MOSS ADAMS LLP LOS ANGELES C

LOCATIONS

HQ: JACO OIL COMPANY
3101 STATE RD, BAKERSFIELD, CA 933084931
Phone: 661 393-7000
Web: WWW.JACO.COM

2013 Stores

	No.
California	49
Arizona	4
Total	**53**

PRODUCTS/OPERATIONS

Selected Services

Check cashing
EBT
Ice
Liquior
Lottery
Money orders
Money transfers
Phone cards
Quick serve restaurant
Restrooms
WIC

Selected Products

Alcoholic beverages
Beverages
Coffee
Dairy
Food
Fountain drinks
Groceries
Snacks
Tobacco products

COMPETITORS

7-Eleven	Ralphs Grocery
Chevron	Stater Bros.
Couche-Tard	Vons
Dollar General	Walgreen
Exxon Mobil	

HISTORICAL FINANCIALS

Company Type: Private

Income Statement

FYE: December 31

	REVENUE ($ mil.)	NET INCOME ($ mil.)	NET PROFIT MARGIN	EMPLOYEES
12/12	829	28	3.5%	350
12/11	794	20	2.6%	—
12/10	644	10	1.6%	—
12/08	517	0	—	—
Annual Growth	12.5%	—	—	—

2012 Year-End Financials

Return on assets: 2.7%   Cash ($ mil.): 52
Return on equity: 3.5%
Current ratio: 2.10

JAMES M D HOFFMAN

LOCATIONS

HQ: JAMES M D HOFFMAN
40 HART ST BLDG D, NEW BRITAIN, CT 060521743
Phone: 860 826-1101

HISTORICAL FINANCIALS

Company Type: Private

Income Statement

FYE: September 30

	REVENUE ($ mil.)	NET INCOME ($ mil.)	NET PROFIT MARGIN	EMPLOYEES
09/09	401	(71)	—	3
09/07	350	(1)	—	—
Annual Growth	7.0%	—	—	—

2009 Year-End Financials

Return on assets: —   Cash ($ mil.): 22
Return on equity: (-17.8%)
Current ratio: 0.80

JAMES MADISON UNIVERSITY INC.

James Madison is known as the Father of the Constitution and America's fourth president but he also has a public institution of higher education named after him. James Madison University (JMU) offers some 70 undergraduate and 40 graduate degrees through more than a half-dozen colleges including arts and letters business education visual and performing arts and science and mathematics. The university enrolls about 20000 students mostly undergrads with a faculty of 1200 teachers and a student-to-faculty ratio of 16:1. JMU also has extensive men's and women's athletic programs. JMU was established in 1908 in Harrisonburg Virginia.

Geographic Reach

James Madison University is located on on a 470-acre campus in Harrisonburg located in the Shenandoah Valley of Virginia. Altogether the university operates more than 112 building on 720 acres. More than 70% of its students are residents of Virginia while the rest pay out-of-state tuition fees.

Strategy

In 2012 James Madison University increased the number of colleges from seven to eight (including the graduate school) when it broke up its College of Integrated Science and Technology into two new schools. The new College of Health and Behavioral Studies includes the psychology health sciences nursing social work and communication disorders programs while the College of Integrated Science and Engineering includes computer science integrated science and technology engineering programs. The move helps the university meet the growing need for education programs for health and human behavior professionals.

EXECUTIVES

Provost Vice President Academic Affairs, Douglas T (Doug) Brown

Assistant Vice President Budget Management, Diane Stamp

Medical Director, Stephen Rodgers

Assoc Vice President Information Services, KIMBERLY A DONOHOE

Senior Vice President University Advancement, Cassie Henry

Associate Vice President Assessment, Dary Erwin

Associate Vice President Advancement Information Services Interim, Christopher (Chris) Pipkins

Assistant Vice President Executive Director International Pgms, Lee Sternberger

Associate Vice President for Development, Weston W Hatfield

Assistant Vice President, Jeff Gilligan

Vice President, Carol Hurney

Department Head, Harold Teer

Vice President, Kathy Floyd

Vice President Of Human Resources, Kendall Capps

Department Head, Eric Maslen

Assoc Vice President Business Services, Towana Moore

Managing Director Of Chicago Il Market, Sharon Radibush

Senior Vice President for Administration and Finance, Nicholas Langridge

Department Head, R Myers

Senior Vice President University Advancement, Joanne Carr

Department Head, Allen (Al) Lewis

LOCATIONS

HQ: JAMES MADISON UNIVERSITY INC.
  800 S MAIN ST, HARRISONBURG, VA 228070002
Phone: 540 568-6211
Web: WWW.JMU.EDU

PRODUCTS/OPERATIONS

Selected Schools
College of Arts and Letters
College of Business
College of Education
College of Health and Behavioral Studies
College of Integrated Science and Engineering
College of Science and Mathematics
College of Visual and Performing Arts
The Graduate School

Selected Degrees
Bachelor of Arts (BA)
Bachelor of Science (BS)
Bachelor of Music Education (BMEd)
Bachelor of Business Administration (BBA)
Bachelor of General Studies (BGS)
Bachelor of Music (BM)
Bachelor of Social Work (BSW)
Bachelor of Science in Nursing (BSN)
Doctor of Psychology (PsyD)
Master of Arts (MA)
Master of Fine Arts (MFA)
Master of Science (MS)
Master of Business Administration (MBA)
Master of Science in Education (MSEd)
Master of Arts in Teaching (MAT)
Master of Education (MEd)
Master of Music (MM)
Master of Public Administration (MPA)
Educational Specialist (EdS)
Doctor of Audiology (AUD)
Doctor of Philosophy (PhD)
Doctor of Musical Arts (DMA)
Master o Science in Nursing (MSN)
Master of Occupational Therapy (MOT)
Master of Physician Assistant Studies (MPAS)

HISTORICAL FINANCIALS

Company Type: Private

Income Statement

	REVENUE ($ mil.)	NET INCOME ($ mil.)	NET PROFIT MARGIN	EMPLOYEES
06/14	377	62	16.5%	1,700
06/13	365	71	19.7%	—
06/11	323	56	17.5%	—
06/08	270	0	—	—
Annual Growth	5.7%	—	—	—

2014 Year-End Financials

Return on assets: 12.1%   Cash ($ mil.): 146
Return on equity: 16.5%
Current ratio: 1.70

JAMESON MEMORIAL HOSPITAL

LOCATIONS

HQ: JAMESON MEMORIAL HOSPITAL
  1211 WILMINGTON AVE, NEW CASTLE, PA
161052595
Phone: 724 658-9001
Web: WWW.JAMESONHEALTH.ORG

HISTORICAL FINANCIALS

Company Type: Private

Income Statement

FYE: June 30

	REVENUE ($ mil.)	NET INCOME ($ mil.)	NET PROFIT MARGIN	EMPLOYEES
06/13	303	4	1.4%	1,063
06/12	270	3	1.1%	—
06/11	109	4	4.1%	—
06/10	111	0	—	—
Annual Growth	39.4%	—	—	—

2013 Year-End Financials

Return on assets: —   Cash ($ mil.): 1
Return on equity: 1.4%
Current ratio: —

JEFFERSON HOMEBUILDERS INC.

Culpeper Wood Preservers may sound like the name of an environmental non-profit but this Virginia-based building materials supplier has more commercial interests in mind. The company manufactures and distributes pressure-treated lumber from plants located in the midwestern and northeastern US (pressure treating protects wood from damage by moisture and insects). Products include standard dimensional lumber decking boards plywood and timbers. The company also makes such specialty products as deck accessories lattice fencing moulded products and landscaping items.

In response to increased demand the company has locations in Virginia Indiana Maryland and South Carolina. Culpeper sells about 500 million board feet of lumber annually.

Culpeper established in 1972 is owned and operated by brothers Joe and Ronald Daniel who serve respectively as president and vice president of the company.

EXECUTIVES

CEO, Joseph R. (Joe) Daniel
Treasurer, Doris Batiste
President, Joseph R. (Josh) Daniel

LOCATIONS

HQ: JEFFERSON HOMEBUILDERS INC.
  501 N MAIN ST, CULPEPER, VA 227012607
Phone: 540 825-5898
Web: WWW.CULPEPERWOOD.COM

COMPETITORS

Georgia-Pacific   Weyerhaeuser
Louisiana-Pacific

HISTORICAL FINANCIALS

Company Type: Private

Income Statement

FYE: September 30

	REVENUE ($ mil.)	NET INCOME ($ mil.)	NET PROFIT MARGIN	EMPLOYEES
09/07	157	3	2.0%	177
09/06	165	5	3.1%	—
09/05	912	0	0.0%	—
Annual Growth	(58.5%)	19522.0%		

JEFFERSON HOSPITAL ASSOCIATION INC.

Jefferson Regional Medical Center (JRMC) provides acute care and other health services to residents of Pine Bluff and an 11-county area of southern Arkansas. The not-for-profit community-owned hospital has about 470 acute care beds and offers general medical and surgical care as well as services in a range of specialties including urology orthopedics cardiology and oncology. It also has a 25-bed skilled nursing unit that cares for patients transitioning to long-term care or home care. A network of clinics offers outpatient surgery diagnostic imaging wound care and other ambulatory health services. Additionally the health system operates a nursing school and home health and hospice agencies.

To bring its operations up to speed with modern technology requirements in the health care industry JRMC has implemented an electronic health record (EHR) system and is employing that system to comply with meaningful use guidelines from the US government. In fact JRMC was a frontrunner in the movement to bring medical records online first moving to install EHR systems in 2003.

The hospital also expanded its services for the southern Arkansas region by becoming certified as a Level II trauma center in 2010. JRMC has also expanded and upgraded its wellness centers to serve the exercise needs of the community.

EXECUTIVES

Vice President Of Information Technology, Claudia Carberry
Director of Health Information Management, Elijah Blackburn
Director Of Home Healthcare, Barbara Barr
Nurse Manager Of Psych Unit, Diane Boyd
Infection Control Director, Nikki Wallace
Executive Vice President, Tom Harbuck
Auditors: CLIFTONLARSONALLEN LLP ST LOU

LOCATIONS

HQ: JEFFERSON HOSPITAL ASSOCIATION INC.
  1600 W 40TH AVE, PINE BLUFF, AR 716036301
Phone: 870 541-7100
Web: WWW.DAVISLIFECARE.ORG

COMPETITORS

Arkansas Heart Hospital	St. Vincent Health System
Baptist Health (Arkansas)	University of Arkansas Weirton Medical Center
Conway Regional Health System	White County Medical Center
Sparks Health System	

HISTORICAL FINANCIALS
Company Type: Private

Income Statement
FYE: June 30

	REVENUE ($ mil.)	NET INCOME ($ mil.)	NET PROFIT MARGIN	EMPLOYEES
06/13	180	0	0.2%	1,700
06/10	198	11	5.6%	—
06/09	5	(4)	—	—
06/07	941	0	—	—
Annual Growth	—	—	—	—

2013 Year-End Financials
Return on assets: 19.9% Cash ($ mil.): 10
Return on equity: 0.2%
Current ratio: 0.50

JEFFERSON UNIVERSITY PHYSICIANS

Auditors: PRICEWATERHOUSECOOPERS LLP PH

LOCATIONS
HQ: JEFFERSON UNIVERSITY PHYSICIANS
1020 WALNUT ST, PHILADELPHIA, PA 191075543
Phone: 215 955-6000

HISTORICAL FINANCIALS
Company Type: Private

Income Statement
FYE: June 30

	REVENUE ($ mil.)	NET INCOME ($ mil.)	NET PROFIT MARGIN	EMPLOYEES
06/11	337	(2)	—	4
06/10	300	8	2.7%	—
06/09	259	24	9.3%	—
Annual Growth 13.9%				

2011 Year-End Financials
Return on assets: — Cash ($ mil.): 65
Return on equity: (-0.8%)
Current ratio: 1.10

JERSEY CITY MEDICAL CENTER INC

With roots extending back to 1882 Jersey City Medical Center (JCMC) may have history but it's not stuck in the past. The 350-bed acute-care hospital serves residents of New Jersey's Hudson County area. Operated by Liberty Healthcare the hospital includes a trauma center a perinatal center and a heart institute. JCMC also offers pediatric women's health rehabilitation and ambulatory care and it is a teaching affiliate for the Mount Sinai School of Medicine. JCMC's modern incarnation came about in the Great Depression when it was constructed by a political ally of Franklin Roosevelt.

Geographic Reach

The 15-acre JCMC campus which overlooks the New York Harbor and the Liberty State Park is also home to the Wilzig Hospital and the Provident Bank Ambulatory Center. JCMC offers a Mobile Health Screening Unit that will travel to underserved areas throughout Hudson County. The hospital is the primary medical facility serving New York's Hudson Essex and Union counties.

OperationsJCMC operates as a regional referral center meaning that it takes on complicated cases from smaller community hospitals in the area. As an area teaching hospital the hospital offers medical residency programs in internal medicine and nursing. It also offers continuing education courses to keep its medical residents up on the latest medical developments.JCMC's mobile outreach program provides health and wellness screenings dispense care and offer health education. It is funded through a grant provided by The New Jersey Department of Health and Senior Services. Among other things the van will provide diabetes HIV and mental health screenings as well as perform blood pressure checks offer preventive care and educate people on the streets of Hudson County and Jersey City. The van travels to health fairs and regularly scheduled outreach events such as at schools and senior centers. StrategyIn mid-2013 JCMC announced that it has entered an agreement to become part of the Barnabas Health system. The merger was expected to close by the end of 2013 following regulatory approval.JCMC focuses on expanding and improving services for area residents. The hospital opened a hand and upper extremity unit in 2013 to address the needs of patients with pain and functional difficulties related to arthritis carpal tunnel syndrome injuries and other conditions. It also added about 200 new physicians during 2012 to enhance patient access to general and specialty care. It opened a new gastrointestinal disorder center on the main campus in 2012 and it expanded its cardiac care services with the opening of a new electrophysiology lab.In 2012 it announced plans to renovate and re-open the former Greenville Hospital campus in Jersey City as an outpatient facility to meet the rising needs for ambulatory care in the area.

EXECUTIVES
Radiology Medical Director, Anthony Tramontana
Medical Director, Chalapathy Narisety
Vice President of Patient Care Services, Brenda Hall
Director Of Radiology, Linda Saguil
Director Of Nursing, Irene Ondieki

LOCATIONS
HQ: JERSEY CITY MEDICAL CENTER INC
355 GRAND ST, JERSEY CITY, NJ 073024321
Phone: 201 915-2000
Web: WWW.LIBERTYHEALTH.ORG

PRODUCTS/OPERATIONS

Selected Locations
Emergency Services at JCMC
Family Regional Perinatal Center
Fannie E. Rippel Foundation Heart Institute
General Pediatrics at JCMC
Nursing at JCMC
Provident Bank Ambulatory Center
Port Authority Heroes of Sept 11 Trauma Center
The Rehabilitation Services Department
Volunteer Services at JCMC
Wilzig Hospital

COMPETITORS
Bergen Regional Medical
Bronx-Lebanon Hospital
Continuum Health Partners
Englewood Hospital and Medical Center
Hackensack University Medical Center
Hospital for Special Surgery
Lenox Hill Hospital
Montefiore Medical
Newark Beth Israel Medical Center
Robert Wood Johnson University Hospital at Rahway
St. Joseph's Healthcare System
The Valley Hospital
Valley Health System

HISTORICAL FINANCIALS
Company Type: Private

Income Statement
FYE: December 31

	REVENUE ($ mil.)	NET INCOME ($ mil.)	NET PROFIT MARGIN	EMPLOYEES
12/13	367	30	8.2%	1,942
12/08	249	8	3.3%	—
12/02	202	0	0.2%	—
12/01	1,173	0	—	—
Annual Growth	(9.2%)	—	—	—

2013 Year-End Financials
Return on assets: 9.0% Cash ($ mil.): 39
Return on equity: 8.2%
Current ratio: 1.20

JET PEP INC.

LOCATIONS
HQ: JET PEP INC.
9481 HIGHWAY 278 W, HOLLY POND, AL 35083
Phone: 256 796-2237

HISTORICAL FINANCIALS
Company Type: Private

Income Statement
FYE: December 31

	REVENUE ($ mil.)	NET INCOME ($ mil.)	NET PROFIT MARGIN	EMPLOYEES
12/13	349	6	2.0%	80
12/12	341	2	0.7%	—
12/11	350	1	0.5%	—
12/10	316	0	—	—
Annual Growth 3.4%		—	—	—

2013 Year-End Financials
Return on assets: 2.4% Cash ($ mil.): 9
Return on equity: 2.0%
Current ratio: 0.70

JET SPECIALTY INC.

Auditors: WEAVER AND TIDWELL LLP SAN A

LOCATIONS
HQ: JET SPECIALTY INC.
211 MARKET AVE, BOERNE, TX 780063050
Phone: 830 331-9457
Web: WWW.JETSPECIALTY.COM

HISTORICAL FINANCIALS
Company Type: Private

Income Statement
FYE: December 31

	REVENUE ($ mil.)	NET INCOME ($ mil.)	NET PROFIT MARGIN	EMPLOYEES
12/13	323	38	11.9%	171
12/12	266	39	14.8%	—
12/11	169	17	10.1%	—
12/10	98	0	—	—
Annual Growth	48.6%	—	—	—

JEWISH COMMUNAL FUND

Auditors: EISNERAMPER LLP NEW YORK NY

LOCATIONS
HQ: JEWISH COMMUNAL FUND
575 MADISON AVE STE 703, NEW YORK, NY 100228591
Phone: 212 752-8277

HISTORICAL FINANCIALS
Company Type: Private

Income Statement
FYE: June 30

	ASSETS ($ mil.)	NET INCOME ($ mil.)	INCOME AS % OF ASSETS	EMPLOYEES
06/13	1,179	110	9.3%	14
06/12	1,012	(57)	—	—
06/11	1,086	42	3.9%	—
06/10	971	0	—	—
Annual Growth	6.7%	—	—	—

2013 Year-End Financials
Return on assets: —
Return on equity: 28.3%
Sales ($ mil): 390

JFK HEALTH SYSTEM INC.

JFK Health System provides medical services in a tri-county area in central New Jersey through flagship facility JFK Medical Center. The hospital has about 500 acute care beds and is one of the Garden State's major health care facilities. Included in the medical center complex are JFK Johnson Rehabilitation Institute JFK New Jersey Neuroscience Institute and a number of outpatient care and imaging centers. A separate site Muhlenberg Campus consists of a satellite emergency room and outpatient care facilities as well as schools of nursing and medicine. Other JFK Health System facilities provide primary and specialty services as well as senior living home health and hospice care.

Geographic Reach
JFK Health System serves patients in the central New Jersey counties of Middlesex Union and Somerset.

Operations

JFK Health System's Muhlenberg Campus educational programs offer degrees in nursing radiography radiation therapy nuclear medicine and diagnostic medical sonography. Students have access to JFK's equipment and clinical facilities.

Another set of the system's facilities the JFK Hartwyck Nursing Convalescent and Rehabilitation Centers are located at three other separate sites. Combined they house more than 500 beds for nursing home subacute rehabilitation and respite-care patients. One of the units is the only center in the state and one of very few in the country offering specialty care for Huntington's disease patients.

Strategy
JFK Health System regularly expands and upgrades its facilities and its medical equipment to keep pace with modern health care needs. For instance in 2011 JFK Medical Center began construction of a three-story ER pavilion on top of its existing emergency department.

Company Background
Formerly Solaris Health the not-for-profit system took the JFK Health System name in 2011 to align with its flagship facility. It previously took on the Solaris name in 1997 when JFK Medical Center (founded in 1967) and Muhlenberg Regional Medical Center (founded in 1894) merged. The Muhlenberg inpatient operations were discontinued in 2008 victim of an economically declining population base.

EXECUTIVES
COO JFK Medical Center, J. Scott Gebhard
President and CEO, Raymond F. Fredericks
Medical Director, Andrew Larson
Vice President Of Human Resources, Shir Higginsbouers
Chair, Michael Kleiman
Auditors: PARENTEBEARD LLC CLARK NEW J

LOCATIONS
HQ: JFK HEALTH SYSTEM INC.
65 JAMES ST, EDISON, NJ 088203947
Phone: 732 321-7000

Selected Facilities
JFK At Home
JFK Hartwyck Nursing and Rehabilitation Centers
JFK Johnson Rehabilitation Institute
JFK Medical Center
JFK MediPlex Surgery Center
JFK Muhlenberg Campus
JFK Muhlenberg Harold B. & Dorothy A. Snyder Schools
JFK New Jersey Neuroscience Institute
Whispering Knoll Assisted Living

COMPETITORS
Atlantic Health	Robert Wood Johnson
Barnabas Health	University Hospital
CentraState Healthcare System	Saint Peter's University Hospital
Continuum Health Partners	Somerset Medical Center
East Orange General Hospital	St. Joseph's Healthcare System
NewYork-Presbyterian Healthcare	Staten Island University Hospital
Newark Beth Israel Medical Center	Trinitas Regional Medical Center
Raritan Bay Medical Center	

HISTORICAL FINANCIALS
Company Type: Private

Income Statement
FYE: December 31

	REVENUE ($ mil.)	NET INCOME ($ mil.)	NET PROFIT MARGIN	EMPLOYEES
12/12	481	9	2.1%	6,735
12/11	509	11	2.2%	—
12/10	500	(12)	—	—
12/09	488	0	—	—
Annual Growth	(0.5%)	—	—	—

2012 Year-End Financials
Return on assets: 6.2%
Return on equity: 2.1%
Current ratio: 1.40
Cash ($ mil.): 48

JOERIS GENERAL CONTRACTORS LTD.

Auditors: PADGETT STRATERMANN & CO SAN

LOCATIONS
HQ: JOERIS GENERAL CONTRACTORS LTD.
1390 E BITTERS RD, SAN ANTONIO, TX 782162914
Phone: 210 286-8696
Web: WWW.JOERIS.COM

HISTORICAL FINANCIALS
Company Type: Private

Income Statement
FYE: October 31

	REVENUE ($ mil.)	NET INCOME ($ mil.)	NET PROFIT MARGIN	EMPLOYEES
10/13	351	3	1.1%	200
10/12	188	0	—	—
10/10	188	0	—	—
10/09	0	0	—	—
Annual Growth	—	—	—	—

2013 Year-End Financials
Return on assets: 9.6%
Return on equity: 1.1%
Current ratio: 0.90
Cash ($ mil.): 32

JOHN C. LINCOLN HEALTH NETWORK

John C. Lincoln Health Network takes care of the health of John Q. Public in Arizona. The not-for-profit health care network serves the northern Phoenix area and is home to two hospitals: John C. Lincoln Deer Valley Hospital with more than 200 beds and John C. Lincoln North Mountain Hospital with roughly 260 beds (the Valley's first Magnet nursing hospital an accredited Chest Pain Center and the host of a Level 1 Trauma Center). The system also features a children's care facility various physician and dental clinics a food bank and assisted living facilities for the elderly all operating under the Desert Mission moniker. John C. Lincoln Health Network is part of the Scottsdale

Lincoln Health Network along with Scottsdale Healthcare.

Operations

John C. Lincoln Health Network has a staff of about 1100 physicians.

In addition to its hospital locations the network includes physician practices for primary and specialty care as well as medical imaging and research centers. John C. Lincoln's facilities serve about 750000 patients each year and provide specialty services in fields including cardiology pulmonary care neuroscience and women's health. The Deer Valley Hospital is also home to Mendy's Place the North Valley's only 24-hour hospital emergency center exclusively for children and an accredited Chest Pain Center.

In 2012 John C. Lincoln Health Network had 748019 patient visits to its hospitals and physicians and specialty practices; 26868 exams at the breast health and research center; and 8719 adult day health care visits.

Its specialized medical services includes heart care pulmonary care neurosciences emergency care and a Breast Health and Research Center. Community services include Desert Mission Food Bank a dental clinic for uninsured children a resource center for families in crisis and a child care center. The John C. Lincoln Health Foundation conducts philanthropic efforts.

The health system's Desert Mission Food Bank distributed roughly 41000 emergency food boxes to members of its community in 2012. Other locations providing community outreach services include the Community Health Center Children's Dental Clinic Lincoln Learning Center Adult Day Health Care and Neighborhood Renewal. The Marley House Behavioral Health Clinic provides mental health and related services for children and adults on a sliding scale basis in English and Spanish.

Strategy

In 2013 John C. Lincoln expanded its infrastructure opening the John C. Lincoln Sonoran Health and Emergency Center a new emergency center and outpatient clinic in Phoenix. The $18 million project includes an emergency department medical practice and diagnostic imaging facilities.

Upgrading its technology in 2012 John C. Lincoln Deer Valley Hospital added the da Vinci Si Robotic Surgical System. To help it improve its medical record keeping that year the health system's primary care offices launched JCL Connect electronic health records software.

Mergers and Acquisitions

To strengthen its footing in the Arizona marketplace in 2014 John C. Lincoln formed an affiliation with Scottsdale Healthcare. The combined networks operating under the moniker Scottsdale Lincoln Health Network include five hospitals with some 3700 affiliated physicians and an extensive outpatient services network.

Company Background

The hospital gained its first real funding in 1933 from millionaire entrepreneur John C. Lincoln the founder of Lincoln Electric.

EXECUTIVES

Vice President clinical Support Services, David (Dave) Price
Occupational Therapy Director, Susan Hoffmeister
Infection Control Director, Betty Rogers
Respiratory Therapy Director, Jeanette Kieffer
Vice President of Revenue Operations, Brian Smit
Vice President Human Resources, Frank Cummins
Medical Librarian, Patrick King
Senior Vice President, Ma Anspach
Medical Director for John C. Lincoln Trauma Services, Alicia Mangram
Treasurer, Charez Norris

LOCATIONS

HQ: JOHN C. LINCOLN HEALTH NETWORK
2500 E DUNLAP AVE, PHOENIX, AZ 85020
Phone: 602 870-6060
Web: WWW.JCL.COM

Hospitals

Deer Valley Hospital: Phoenix Arizona
North Mountain Hospital: Phoenix Arizona

PRODUCTS/OPERATIONS

Selected Centers and Services

Breast Health and Research Center
Cancer Treatment
Cardiac Care
Deep Vein Thrombosis Program
Emergency Care
Heartburn Program
Level I Trauma Center
Medical Imaging
Neurosciences
Orthopedics
Outpatient Surgery Centers
Pediatrics
Pulmonary Program
Reconstructive Plastic Surgery
Scarless Surgery
Uterine Fibroid Treatment
Varicose Vein Treatment

COMPETITORS

Banner Health
Community Health Systems
Dignity Health
Flagstaff Medical Center
Iasis Healthcare
Northern Arizona Healthcare
Phoenix Children's Hospital
Scottsdale Healthcare
Universal Health Services
University of Arizona Health Network
Yuma Regional Medical Center

HISTORICAL FINANCIALS

Company Type: Private

Income Statement
FYE: December 31

	REVENUE ($ mil.)	NET INCOME ($ mil.)	NET PROFIT MARGIN	EMPLOYEES
12/13	584	44	7.6%	3,500
12/12	509	32	6.4%	—
12/11	486	17	3.6%	—
12/10	551	0	—	—
Annual Growth	2.0%	—	—	—

2013 Year-End Financials

Return on assets: 4.7%
Return on equity: 7.6%
Current ratio: 1.30

Cash ($ mil.): 40

JOHN D ARCHBOLD MEMORIAL HOSPITAL

LOCATIONS

HQ: JOHN D ARCHBOLD MEMORIAL HOSPITAL
915 GORDON AVE, THOMASVILLE, GA 317926699
Phone: 229 228-2000
Web: WWW.ARCHBOLD.ORG

HISTORICAL FINANCIALS

Company Type: Private

Income Statement
FYE: September 30

	REVENUE ($ mil.)	NET INCOME ($ mil.)	NET PROFIT MARGIN	EMPLOYEES
09/13	301	24	8.0%	2,700
09/12	230	26	11.3%	—
09/09	342	33	9.9%	—
09/06	296	0	—	—
Annual Growth	0.2%	—	—	—

2013 Year-End Financials

Return on assets: 12.1%
Return on equity: 8.0%
Current ratio: 0.30

Cash ($ mil.): 8

JOHN F KENNEDY CENTER FOR THE PERFORMING ARTS

The John F. Kennedy Center for the Performing Arts also known as The Kennedy Center traces its roots to 1958 when president Dwight Eisenhower signed the National Cultural Center Act calling for a privately funded venture featuring a variety of classic and contemporary programming with an educational focus. The center was a pet project and fund raiser beneficiary of president Kennedy; it was named as a living memorial to him after his death. Located on 17 acres overlooking the Potomac River in Washington D.C. the center opened in 1971 and presents some 2000 events a year including musicals dance performances and jazz and orchestral concerts. It also produces TV programming workshops and lectures.

EXECUTIVES

Vice President Marketing, David (Dave) Kitto
Vice President of Production, Mickey Berra
Vice President Institutional Affairs, Kathy Kruse
Vice President, John Dow
Assistant Secretary, Ann Stock
Assistant Treasurer Opera House Family Theater Terrace Gallery Explore The Arts, Tony Terronez
Second Assistant Treasurer, Thaddeus (Thad) Bailey

LOCATIONS

HQ: JOHN F KENNEDY CENTER FOR THE PERFORMING ARTS
2700 F ST NW, WASHINGTON, DC 205660002
Phone: 202 416-8000
Web: WWW.KENNEDY-CENTER.ORG

COMPETITORS

Nederlander Producing Company
Smithsonian
The National Gallery

HISTORICAL FINANCIALS
Company Type: Private

Income Statement
FYE: September 30

	REVENUE ($ mil.)	NET INCOME ($ mil.)	NET PROFIT MARGIN	EMPLOYEES
09/13	211	10	5.0%	1,144
09/10	182	21	11.9%	—
09/09	156	(7)	—	—
09/08	186	0	—	—
Annual Growth	2.6%	—	—	—

2013 Year-End Financials
Return on assets: 6.5%
Return on equity: 5.0%
Current ratio: 0.30
Cash ($ mil.): 16

JOHN SNOW INCORPORATED

LOCATIONS
HQ: JOHN SNOW INCORPORATED
44 FARNSWORTH ST FL 7, BOSTON, MA 022101223
Phone: 617 482-9485
Web: WWW.JSI.COM

HISTORICAL FINANCIALS
Company Type: Private

Income Statement
FYE: December 31

	REVENUE ($ mil.)	NET INCOME ($ mil.)	NET PROFIT MARGIN	EMPLOYEES
12/13	426	6	1.5%	297
12/10	321	4	1.5%	—
12/09	220	5	2.3%	—
12/08	1,827	0	—	—
Annual Growth	—	—	—	—

2013 Year-End Financials
Return on assets: 3.6%
Return on equity: 1.5%
Current ratio: 2.70
Cash ($ mil.): 38

JOHN T. MATHER MEMORIAL HOSPITAL OF PORT JEFFERSON NEW YORK INC.

Shipbuilder John T. Mather envisioned a legacy that would keep his community of Port Jefferson in good health and John T. Mather Memorial Hospital came to fruition in 1929 one year after it's namesake's death. The not-for-profit hospital has some 250 beds and provides a variety of health care services to the residents of Port Jefferson New York and surrounding areas of Suffolk County. Services include emergency care occupational therapy psychiatry and radiology. Mather Hospital is a member of Long Island Health Network an asso-

ciation of about a dozen affiliated hospitals all serving Long Island. It is also Magnet® recognized hospital by the American Nurses Credentialing Center.

Operations

Mather Hospital has some 600 physicians both full-time employees and affiliates who serve some 12000 inpatient customers annually. The emergency room handles about 44000 visits per year. It provides than 18000 diagnostic breast health screenings annually. The hospital's specialty service units include the Fortunato Breast Health Center which provides outpatient diagnostics as well as centers for sleep disorder treatment bariatrics wound care and stroke management.

In addition to its membership in the Long Island Health Alliance Mather Hospital has formed a partnership with nearby St. Charles Hospital and Rehabilitation Center to provide tandem services in some areas including cancer and pediatric care.

Financial Performance

The hospital reported a 6% increase in revenues in 2012 thanks to higher patient services revenue and other non-patient care services. It saw net loss of $2 million year (compared to net income in 2011) due to an increase in expenses (salaries benefits supplies and other) and depreciation.

Strategy

The company grows through organic initiatives. In 2013 Mather Hospital broke ground on a new patient care pavilion. The expansion the first at the hospital in more than ten years will house a 35-single-bedded patient care unit; offices and teaching facilities for a Graduate Medical Education Program with residencies in Internal Medicine Family Practice Medicine Psychiatry and Transitional Year; and a conference center. The new facility which adds more than 28400 sq. ft. of space to the existing hospital will be known as the Arthur & Linda Calace Family Pavilion.In 2012 the hospital began using an electronic health records system to improve patient safety and care. Other 2012 initiatives included a cardiac computed tomography angiography program which uses digital imaging to diagnose heart disease. Mather also launched a Palliative Medicine program for patients with a serious or chronic illness.

Looking to green resources to cut its carbon emissions and costs Mather Hospital is using lower cost hydropower to reduce its energy costs by $2.5 million over seven years through the ReCharge NY award from the New York Power Authority. It also has a solar power unit.Company BackgroundIn 2011 Mather Hospital became the first Long Island hospital to use solar power via a federally funded state energy grant. It built a 50 KW photovoltaic ground-mounted solar panel bank on its campus.

The hospital was founded in 1929 as the first not-for-profit community hospital in the Town of Brookhaven.

EXECUTIVES
V Pres, Frank T Lettera, age 69
Ambulatory Services Director, Karen Tuzzolo
Assistant Vice President Of Nursing, Theresa Grimes
Vice President Chief Information Officer Informati, Steven (Steve) Heiman
Associate Vice President Patient Care Nursing, Loretta Wagner
Vice President Of Information Technology, Mark Borek
Vice President Operations, Tamara Weiss
Infection Control Director, Raymond Luttinger
Senior Vice President Administration, Kevin Murray
Assistant Vice President Of Finance, Frank Sini
Respiratory Therapy Director, Ted Nilsson
Vice Chairman, Harold Tranchon

LOCATIONS
HQ: JOHN T. MATHER MEMORIAL HOSPITAL OF PORT JEFFERSON NEW YORK INC.
75 N COUNTRY RD, PORT JEFFERSON, NY 117772119
Phone: 631 476-2738
Web: WWW.MATHERHOSPITAL.ORG

PRODUCTS/OPERATIONS

Selected Centers and Services
Bariatric Surgery Center of Excellence
Behavioral Health Services
Breast Health Center
Critical Care
Emergency Department
Hospitalists
Hyperbaric Oxygen Therapy Unit
Imaging Services/Radiology
Infusion Center
Intensivists
Joint Replacement Program
Laboratory
Lithotripsy
Lymphedema Program
Pain Management Program
Palliative Medicine
Physical Therapy
Prostate Health Program
Respiratory Therapy
Transitional Care Unit
Sleep Disorders Center
Surgical Services
Wound Treatment Center

COMPETITORS
CSH
Catholic Health Services of Long Island
Catholic Healthcare System
Long Island College Hospital
New York City Health and Hospitals
NewYork-Presbyterian Healthcare
North Shore-Long Island Jewish Health System

HISTORICAL FINANCIALS
Company Type: Private

Income Statement
FYE: December 31

	REVENUE ($ mil.)	NET INCOME ($ mil.)	NET PROFIT MARGIN	EMPLOYEES
12/13	276	6	2.2%	1,700
12/12	238	(0)	—	—
12/08	192	2	1.3%	—
12/06	181	0	—	—
Annual Growth	6.2%	—	—	—

2013 Year-End Financials
Return on assets: 5.1%
Return on equity: 2.2%
Current ratio: 1.20
Cash ($ mil.): 10

JOHNSON & JOHNSON PATIENT ASSISTANCE FOUNDATION INC

LOCATIONS

HQ: JOHNSON & JOHNSON PATIENT ASSISTANCE
FOUNDATION INC
1 JOHNSON AND JOHNSON PLZ, NEW BRUNSWICK,
NJ 089330001
Phone: 732 524-1394

HISTORICAL FINANCIALS

Company Type: Private

Income Statement

FYE: December 31

	REVENUE ($ mil.)	NET INCOME ($ mil.)	NET PROFIT MARGIN	EMPLOYEES
12/13	741	13	1.8%	2
12/10	425	(6)	—	—
12/09	355	(2)	—	—
Annual Growth 20.2%				

2013 Year-End Financials

Return on assets: —
Return on equity: 1.8%
Current ratio: —

Cash ($ mil.): 46

JOHNSON & WALES UNIVERSITY INC

Things are a little upside-down at Johnson & Wales University and that's just the way they like it. The private not-for-profit accredited institution provides what it calls an upside-down curriculum allowing students to take courses in their major during the first year so they learn right away if their career choice is right for them. At the end of two years of study students earn an associate's degree and the opportunity to go on to earn a bachelor's degree. Founded in 1914 the school enrolls more than 17000 students across its four campuses in Colorado Florida North Carolina and Rhode Island. It offers degrees in business education food-service hospitality culinary arts and technology.

Geographic Reach

The university's campuses as located in (Providence) Rhode Island (North Miami) Florida (Denver) Colorado and (Charlotte) North Carolina.

Operations

Undergraduate tuition at Johnson & Wales University runs more than $26000.

Financial Performance

Johnson & Wales University in 2012 logged revenue increases of 3% as compared to 2011 due to net student fees. The educational institution points to increases in tuition and fees residence and dining and scholarships for the gains. Net income meanwhile dropped by 94% for the same reporting period thanks to rising operating expenses and declining non-operating activities attributable to weak investment returns.

Sales and Marketing

The university sources its student body from nearly 100 countries. Its top 10 international populations (among its more than 1800 international students) hail from China South Korea Taiwan Saudi Arabia India Morocco Turkey the Bahamas the Netherlands and Malaysia.

EXECUTIVES

Chancellor, John J. Bowen
Provost and Vice Chancellor, Thomas L. G. Dwyer
President Denver Campus, Robin Krakowsky
President and COO Providence Campus, Mim L. Runey
Treasurer and CFO, Joseph J. Greene
President Charlotte Campus, Robert C. Mock, age 49
CIO, Marianne Doran-Collins
President North Miami Campus, Larry Rice
Vice President Engineering Research and Development, Veera S Gaul
Vice President Of Academic Affairs, Jeffrey Senese
Vice President Of Communications, Douglas Whiting
Vice President Student Affairs and Dean Students, Ron Martel
Vice President Human Resources, Diane D'Ambra
Department Chairman, Gill Stansfield
Vice President, Johannes Busch
Vice President of Alumni Board, Taylor Anthony
Department Chair Beverage, Edward (Ed) Korry
Department Chairperson, Che Sabitoni
Senior Vice President Student Services, Marie Bernardo-sousa
Vice President of Career Development and Alumni Relations, Donna Yena
Senior Vice President General Counsel, Wayne Kezirian
Senior Vice President Institutional Advancement, Patricia (Pat) McLaughlin
Department Chair Culinary Nutrition, Marleen Swanson
Chairman, Guy B. Snowden
Auditors: MCGLADREY LLP BOSTON MASSACH

LOCATIONS

HQ: JOHNSON & WALES UNIVERSITY INC
8 ABBOTT PARK PL, PROVIDENCE, RI 029033775
Phone: 401 598-1000
Web: WWW.JWU.EDU

PRODUCTS/OPERATIONS

Selected Colleges and Schools

The Alan Shawn Feinstein Graduate School
College of Business
College of Culinary Arts
The Hospitality College
School of Technology

Selected Operations

CAFE LLC
Griffin Realty Enterprises Inc.
Griffin Realty of Rhode Island-Florida Inc.
Harborside Enterprises Inc.
J.W.C. Corporation
J&W Corporation
Johnson & Wales Alumni Services Corporation
Johnson & Wales University
Johnson & Wales University Club

HISTORICAL FINANCIALS

Company Type: Private

Income Statement

FYE: June 30

	REVENUE ($ mil.)	NET INCOME ($ mil.)	NET PROFIT MARGIN	EMPLOYEES
06/13	349	37	10.6%	1,400
06/12	353	4	1.2%	—
06/11	343	75	22.0%	—
06/10	427	0	—	—
Annual Growth (6.6%)				

2013 Year-End Financials

Return on assets: —
Return on equity: 10.6%
Current ratio: —

Cash ($ mil.): 4

JOHNSTON ENTERPRISES INC.

Johnston Enterprises serves the harvesters of America's amber waves of grain. The company offers farmers in Oklahoma and other Midwestern states grain-processing and storage facilities and inland water transportation services through its Johnston Grain and Johnston Port Terminals divisions. Its Johnston Seed subsidiary sells wildflower and turf wild forage and native grass seed and wildlife feed. The company was founded in 1893 by W. B. Johnston and is owned and operated by the founder's descendants president Lew Meibergen and COO Butch Meibergen.

EXECUTIVES

Vice President, Steve Taylor
Vice President, Joey Meibergen

LOCATIONS

HQ: JOHNSTON ENTERPRISES INC.
411 W CHESTNUT AVE, ENID, OK 737012057
Phone: 580 233-5800
Web: WWW.JEINC.COM

COMPETITORS

ADM	Cargill
Ag Processing Inc.	DeBruce Grain
Andersons	Owensboro Grain
Bartlett and Company	Scoular
CGC	Stewart Grain
CHS	

HISTORICAL FINANCIALS

Company Type: Private

Income Statement

FYE: April 30

	REVENUE ($ mil.)	NET INCOME ($ mil.)	NET PROFIT MARGIN	EMPLOYEES
04/13	334	1	0.5%	280
04/12	297	1	0.5%	—
04/11	289	1	0.5%	—
04/10	140	0	—	—
Annual Growth 33.6%				

2013 Year-End Financials

Return on assets: 2.1%
Return on equity: 0.5%
Current ratio: 0.10

Cash ($ mil.): 2

JORDAN CF INVESTMENTS LLP

A high-flier in construction services C.F. Jordan is a top building contractor that offers preconstruction design/build development and project management services. The company has traditionally built hotels and resorts but has diversified into military residential highway and school construction. Its contracts include projects for the Immigration and Naturalization Service for border patrol stations health care centers and detention centers. Other works have included Sea World in San Antonio the Insights Science Museum in El Paso and the Pearl Harbor Commissary and Exchange in Hawaii. Chairman Charles "Paco" Jordan started the Texas-based firm in 1988.

C.F. Jordan has worked throughout Texas as well as 30 other states and in Mexico. Its civil construction division works extensively on Texas Department of Transportation projects in West Texas and builds other highway and road construction projects in New Mexico. Its concrete division pours slabs and builds concrete garages in Texas and southern New Mexico.

EXECUTIVES

Executive Vice President, Paul Bauer
Auditors: SCHMID BROADDUS NUGENT GANO PC

LOCATIONS

HQ: JORDAN CF INVESTMENTS LLP
7700 CF JORDAN DR, EL PASO, TX 799128808
Phone: 915 877-3333

COMPETITORS

D.R. Horton	Manhattan Construction
Harvey Builders	Structure Tone
Hensel Phelps	Southwest
Construction	Summit Builders
Hunt Companies	Turner Corporation
Hunt Construction	Tutor Perini
J.D. Abrams	

HISTORICAL FINANCIALS
Company Type: Private

Income Statement
FYE: December 31

	REVENUE ($ mil.)	NET INCOME ($ mil.)	NET PROFIT MARGIN	EMPLOYEES
12/09	337	3	1.1%	500
12/08	337	3	1.1%	—
12/05	1,911	0	—	—
Annual Growth	(35.2%)	1686.3%	—	—

2009 Year-End Financials
Return on assets: 6.1%   Cash ($ mil.): 19
Return on equity: 1.1%
Current ratio: 0.40

JUPITER MEDICAL CENTER INC.

Nope this hospital is not on the fifth planet from the Sun but by Jupiter it delivers great health care to a number of Floridians. Located just north of West Palm Beach Jupiter Medical Center provides specialty services that include cancer treatment cardiologyorthopedics emergency medicine wound care birthingand pain management. Not-for-profit Jupiter Medical Center consists of more than 205 private acute-care beds and 120 long-term rehab and hospice beds. The hospital is affiliated with the University of Miami's Miller School of Medicine.

OperationsThe not-for-profit 327-bed regional medical center has 207 private acute-care hospital beds and 120 long-term care sub-acute rehabilitation and Hospice beds. Jupiter Medical Center provides a broad range of services with specialty concentrations in cardiology oncology imaging orthopedics & spine digestive health

emergency services lung a thoracic women's health weight management and men's health. In 2014 the hospital reported 9925 admission; 6870 surgeries; 1154 births and 31076 ER visits.

Jupiter Medical Center's Community Benefit contributed $10.1 million in 2014. Financial Performance

In 2014 the company's revenues increased by 3% due to increase in investment income contribution and net patient's revenues. Revenues from Medicare and Medicaid accounted for 48% and 2% of total net patient's revenues. Jupiter Medical Center's net income increased by 111%in 2014 due to higher revenues and an increase in restricted and unrestricted assets. Strategy As a not-for-profit organization the company invests all of its financial resources into the Medical Center to enhance its capacity to deliver the most advanced medicine and to ensure access to quality health care for all. In a climate of industry reformation Jupiter Medical Center is stretching out to make a transformational change beyond acute care strengthening its position by focusing on improving its services outcomes and costs.

Company Background

The company launched NuVista Living in 2011 to become a partner in NuVista's Institute for Healthy Living Life Science and Research project under development. The $70 million facility which opened in 2013 expanded the northern Palm Beach County community's access to a full spectrum of rehabilitative and long-term care while adding about 150 new jobs in the area.

Established in 1956 as the convalescence center for a retirement village the Medical Center was transformed into a full-service acute-care hospital in 1979.

EXECUTIVES

Occupational Therapy Director, Ray Beane
Medical Director, Jefferson R Vaughan
Operating Room Director, Beth Suriano
Director Of Infection Control, Linda Wilson
Vice President Human Resources, Peter (Pete) Gloggner
Vice President Of It, Steve Meyers
Vice President General Counsel, Kelly Sullivan
Medical Records Director, Susan Denny
Director Of Admissions, Peggy Sawyer
Vice President Physician Services, Paula Zalucki
Auditors: ERNEST AND YOUNG LLP BOCA RAT

LOCATIONS

HQ: JUPITER MEDICAL CENTER INC.
1210 S OLD DIXIE HWY, JUPITER, FL 334587205
Phone: 561 747-2234
Web: WWW.JUPITERMED.COM

PRODUCTS/OPERATIONS

2014 Sales

	% of total
Net Patients revenue	91
Investment income	2
Contribution	1
Change in net realized gains	1
Other revenue	5
Total	**100**

Selected Medical Services
Cancer Services
Cardiology
Clinical Research
Children' s and Women' s / OB
Comprehensive Breast Care
Diabetes Education
Digestive Health
Emergency Services
Health and Rehabilitation
Hospice Care
Imaging
Laboratory Services

Men' s Health
Occupational Health
Orthopedic and Spine
Outpatient Medical Nutrition Therapy
Pain Management
The Pavilion
Sleep Center
Stroke Program
Surgical Services
Robotic Surgery
Thoracic Surgery
Travel Immunizations
Urgent Care
Weight Loss (Bariatrics)
Wound Care / Hyperbarics

COMPETITORS

Boca Raton Regional Hospital	Northwest Medical Center
Broward Health	Palms West Hospital
Columbia Hospital	Raulerson Hospital
HCA	South Broward Hospital
Heart & Family Health Institute	District
Lawnwood Medical Center	St. Lucie Medical
	Tenet Healthcare

HISTORICAL FINANCIALS
Company Type: Private

Income Statement
FYE: September 30

	REVENUE ($ mil.)	NET INCOME ($ mil.)	NET PROFIT MARGIN	EMPLOYEES
09/13	179	6	3.7%	1,500
09/12	174	6	3.8%	—
09/11	185	4	2.5%	—
09/10	176	0	—	—
Annual Growth	0.5%	—	—	—

2013 Year-End Financials
Return on assets: 9.4%   Cash ($ mil.): 23
Return on equity: 3.7%
Current ratio: 1.50

K & M TIRE INC.

Auditors: HELLMAN NOMINA CPA DELPHOS O

LOCATIONS

HQ: K & M TIRE INC.
965 SPENCERVILLE RD, DELPHOS, OH 458332351
Phone: 419 695-1061
Web: WWW.KMTIRE.COM

HISTORICAL FINANCIALS
Company Type: Private

Income Statement
FYE: September 30

	REVENUE ($ mil.)	NET INCOME ($ mil.)	NET PROFIT MARGIN	EMPLOYEES
09/14	308	8	2.7%	350
09/13	293	8	2.9%	—
09/12	258	7	3.0%	—
09/11	220	0	—	—
Annual Growth	11.8%	—	—	—

2014 Year-End Financials
Return on assets: 5.2%   Cash ($ mil.): —
Return on equity: 2.7%
Current ratio: 0.60

KADLEC REGIONAL MEDICAL CENTER

Kadlec Regional Medical Center is an acute care hospital facility serving southeastern Washington and northeastern Oregon. In addition to providing comprehensive medical surgical and emergency services the hospital provides neonatal intensive care cardiopulmonary rehabilitation interventional cardiology neurology cancer care and other specialist services. Not-for-profit Kadlec Regional has some 270 inpatient beds including pediatric intensive intermediate and critical care capacity. It also operates outpatient physician offices and clinics in surrounding areas.

Geographic Reach

Kadlec Regional has hospital and clinic locations in Hermiston Kennewick Pasco Pendleton Prosser and Richland.

Operations

Kadlec Regional's cardiovascular programs include open heart surgery and interventional cardiology. The hospital also operates an all-digital outpatient imaging center and the region's only level III neonatal intensive care unit (NICU). Kadlec was is also designated as a Level 1 Cardiac Center and a Level 2 Stroke Center. Area specialist practices include centers for dermatology colorectal surgery nephrology pediatrics women's health ENT (ear nose and throat) and foot and ankle practices. Kadlec Regional also operates satellite urgent care and family practice clinics.

The Kadlec Neuroscience Center offers a wide range of services to treat and diagnose conditions related to the brain spine spinal cord & peripheral nervous system.In 2013 the hospital reported more than 2700 births 66000 emergency department visits and about 15000 admissions.

That year Kadlec Regional provided $27 million in charity care.

Financial Performance

The hospital reported revenue of $312 million in 2012 consisting of $305 million in net patient service earnings and other revenue of some $7.5 million. Kadlec Regional brought in profits of some $29 million.

Strategy

The hospital has undergone aggressive expansion efforts adding a new patient tower with diagnostic outpatient and intermediate care and surgery rooms. Kadlec Regional is enhancing its specialty service units in fields to attract specialists and increase revenue.The organization launched a $10 million project to expand its NICU unit in 2013. It will add 27 private and semi-private rooms and new observation gathering and lactation areas.

It is also expanding outpatient service facilities such as a new $19 million three-story specialty physician practice office that opened in Richland in 2013. The new building increases collaboration between various surgical and medical specialists in the Kadlec Regional clinic network.

The year the company also expanded its emergency room offerings through the opening of the Kadlec ER in Kennewick. The new 15-bed ER is the first in the region to operate as a freestanding facility like traditional hospital-based ERs.

Mergers and Acquisitions

Kadlec Regional also absorbs other area providers. In 2013 Inland Cardiology Associates become part of the Kadlec Regional health system. The region's largest independent group of experienced cardiologists Inland provides comprehensive invasive noninvasive and interventional services throughout southeast Washington and northeast Oregon.

Company Background

In 2011 it partnered with the nearby PMH Medical Center to increase collaboration and specialist referrals between the two hospitals. The partnership extends the reach of Kadlec Regional's medical specialists to additional communities and brings PMH online with Kadlec Regional's electronic health record system. Both hospitals remained independently run.

The hospital system was founded in 1944.

EXECUTIVES

Vp/finance Cfo, Julie Meek
Vice President of Medical Affairs, Dale Hoekema
Technical Vice President, Nathan Sheeran
Auditors: MOSS ADAMS LLP YAKIMA WASHIN

LOCATIONS

HQ: KADLEC REGIONAL MEDICAL CENTER
888 SWIFT BLVD, RICHLAND, WA 993523514
Phone: 509 946-4611
Web: WWW.KADLECMED.ORG

PRODUCTS/OPERATIONS

Selected Services
The Birth Center
Bloodless Medicine and Surgery
Cancer Care
Cardiac Care
Cardiac Catheterization
CardioPulmonary Rehabilitation
Cardiovascular and Thoracic Surgery
CaringBridge
Clinical Decision Unit
Coumadin Clinic
Diabetes Learning Center
Diagnostic Imaging
Don and Lori Watts Pediatric Center
Emergency Department
Emergency Room-Kennewick
Home Health Care
Imaging
Inpatient Rehabilitation and Therapy
Intensive Care Unit
Joint Care Center
Kadlec Academy
Kadlec Healthy Ages
Kadlec Medical Associates
Neonatal Intensive Care Unit
Occupational Medicine
Occupational Therapy
Ostomy Support Group
Outpatient Imaging Center
Outpatient Procedures
Physical Therapy
Planetree
Rehabilitation and Therapy Services
Speech Therapy
Urgent Care
Water Therapy
Wound Healing Center

COMPETITORS

Adventist Health
Asante Health System
Legacy Health System
PeaceHealth
Providence Health & Services
Sacred Heart Medical Center
Salem Hospital
Wenatchee Valley Medical Center
Yakima Valley Memorial

HISTORICAL FINANCIALS
Company Type: Private

Income Statement
FYE: December 31

	REVENUE ($ mil.)	NET INCOME ($ mil.)	NET PROFIT MARGIN	EMPLOYEES
12/13	375	25	6.7%	2,668
12/12	312	16	5.2%	—
12/10	277	3	1.3%	—
12/09	255	0	—	—
Annual Growth 10.1%	—	—	—	—

2013 Year-End Financials

Return on assets: —
Return on equity: 6.7%
Current ratio: 1.70
Cash ($ mil.): 29

KAISER FOUNDATION HOSPITALS INC

Kaiser Foundation Hospitals is on a roll. The hospital group operates 38 acute care hospitals and almost 630 medical offices in eight states (California Colorado Georgia Hawaii Maryland Oregon Virginia and Washington) and Washington D.C. The company's largest presence is in California where the majority of its hospitals are located. Hawaii and Oregon are home to one hospital each. Specialty facilities include three behavioral health and chemical dependency clinics the Denver area and more than a dozen dental clinics in Oregon and Washington.

Operations

Its doctors group is controlled by Permanente Medical Groups and its HMO is offered through Kaiser Foundation Health Plan. Altogether about 9.6 million members are enrolled in its HMO. The company has more than 17425 doctors.

Sales and Marketing

Kaiser Foundation Hospitals and Kaiser Foundation Health Plan's Capital spending in 2014 was $2.8 billion compared to $3.3 billion in 2013.

Company Background

The company was founded in 1945.

EXECUTIVES

Executive Vice President, Arthur (Art) Southam
EVP Kaiser Foundation Hospitals and Health Plan; Group President Kaiser Permanente Northern California and Mid-Atlantic States; President Kaiser Permanente Northern California, Gregory A. Adams
EVP Kaiser Foundation Hospitals and Health Plan; Group president Kaiser Permanente Southern California and Hawaii; President Kaiser Permanente Southern California, Benjamin K. Chu
Chairman Southern California Permanente Medical Group and Executive Medical Director, Edward Ellison
Medical Director Hospitalists, Scott Ediger
OperationSenior Vice President, Terri Pagelow
Vice President Business Information Officer (CIO) Middle Atlantic Region Kaiser Permanente, Harry Fox
Associate Medical Director clinical Process Improvement colorado Permanente Medical Group, Bill Marsh
Vice President Of Engineering, Anne Dench
Vice President It, Susannah Patton
Vice President, Yvonne Webb
National Vice President, Elisa Mendel

Vice President Of Health Insurance Exchanges, Bill Wehrle

Senior Vice President, Barry A Wolfman

Medical Director of Radiology, Chris Jensen

Vice President Business Information Officer Health Plan, Diane Comer

Vice President Business Development, Vicky Choi

Vice President Outpatient Pharmacy Services, Joseph (Jo) Douglas

Senior Vice President Of Financial Operations, Michael (Mel) McAnder

Vice President Strategic Planning, Vivian Tan

Vice President Engineering, Jeffrey Stiger

Vice President For Operations, Rame Hemstreet

Regional President, Barbara West

Vice President of Information Technology, Kathy Scheirman

Director of Nursing Services, Glenda Totten

Managing Director public Equity, Robert (Bob) Blagden

Vice President Learning And Organizational Development, Robert Sachs

Vice President Nursing Pt Care, Anita Zuniga

Vice President Finance, William Glitsch

Exec V Pres, Patrick (Paddy) Courneya

Medical Director, Andrew Lum

Vice President of Sales and Broker Relations, Tom Carter

Vice President Sales and Account Management Labor and Trust, Chris Blass

Medical Director, Gregory Shay

Vice President Quality And Service, Ellie Godfrey

Vice President Compensation, Debora Catsavas

Vice President Financial Services Operations, Marlene Foster

Clinical Director, Jessica Mantoani

Vice President Communications, Nancy Cartwright

Vice President Financial Systems, Lynette Seid

Senior Vice President Area Manager, Gerald (Jerry) Mccall

Vice President, Richard Frias

Vice President Supplier Service Management, June Burgett

Vice President, Robb Munson

Vice President Finance, Janice Murphy

Senior Vice President Chief Strategic Planning Officer, Paul Swenson

Vice President Of Internal Audit, Cindy Overmyer

Vice President Chief Financial Officer National Medicare and Medicaid Finance, Shawn Freeman

Vice President Marketing Sales and Business Development, Chris Hause

Vice President, Jill Rivers

Senior Vice President, Christopher (Chris) Boyd

Senior Vice President, Larry Wilson

Senior Vice President, Jed Weissberg

Vice President Enterprise Architecture, Simon Nazarian

Vice President Workplace Safety and Environmental Stewardship Officer, Kathy Gerwig

Radiology Director, Michael (Mel) Bruse

Supervisor of Medical Records, Sharon Merrill

Senior Management Senior Vice President General Manager Director, Anne Mcnealis

Vice President Direct Sales Individual and Family Plans, Evelyn Shaffer

Vice President Information Technology Finance Portfolio, Steve Stock

Vice President Information Technology, Julie Miller-phipps

Clinic Supervisor, Jacquie McCurdy

Vice President Risk Adjustment and Information Management, Hovannes Daniels

Physical Therapy, Leah Nelson

Vice President Account Management and Sales, Tina Bartelmay

Pharmd, Mena Shaker

Pharmd, Eric Cohen

Vice President Shared Application Services, Ken Goltara

Ambulatory Services Director, Janet Lundberg

Vice President Pharmacy Operations and Services, Suzanne Shea

Vice President of Primary Care and Medical Specialties, Ginny McLain

Assistant Treasurer and Director Cash Management, Robert (Bob) Venema

LOCATIONS

HQ: KAISER FOUNDATION HOSPITALS INC
1 KAISER PLZ STE 2600, OAKLAND, CA 946123673
Phone: 510 271-5800
Web: WWW.HEALTHY.KAISERPERMANENTE.ORG

PRODUCTS/OPERATIONS

Selected Hospitals
Antioch Medical Center
Fremont Medical Center
Fresno Medical Center
Hayward Medical Center
Manteca Medical Center
Modesto Medical Center
Oakland Medical Center
Redwood City Medical Center
Richmond Medical Center
Roseville Women and Children' s Center
San Jose Medical Center
Santa Clara Medical Center
Sacramento Medical Center
South San Francisco Medical Center
South Sacramento Trauma Center
Santa Rosa Medical Center
San Francisco Medical Center
San Rafael Medical Center
Vacaville Medical Center
Vallejo Medical Center
Walnut Creek Medical Center
Baldwin Park Medical Center
Downey Medical Center
Fontana Medical Center
Los Angeles Medical Center
Moreno Valley Community Hospital
Orange County - Anaheim Medical Center
Orange County - Irvine Medical Center
Panorama City Medical Center
Riverside Medical Center
San Diego Medical Center
Harbor City (South Bay Medical Center)
Woodlands Hills Medical Center
West Los Angeles Medical Center
Sunnyside Medical Center (Portland Oregon area)
Moanalua Medical Center (Hawaii)

COMPETITORS

Adventist Health	HCA
Ascension Health	LifePoint Health
Banner Health	Mercy Health (OH)
CHRISTUS Health	Sutter Health
Catholic Health Initiatives	Tenet Healthcare
Community Health Systems	The Cleveland Clinic
Dignity Health	Universal Health Services

HISTORICAL FINANCIALS
Company Type: Private

Income Statement
FYE: December 31

	REVENUE ($ mil.)	NET INCOME ($ mil.)	NET PROFIT MARGIN	EMPLOYEES
12/09	14,795	429	2.9%	175,668
12/08	0	0	99.0%	—
12/05	9,852	774	7.9%	—
Annual Growth	10.7%	(13.7%)	—	—

2009 Year-End Financials
Return on assets: —
Return on equity: 2.9%
Current ratio: —
Cash ($ mil.): 57

KALEIDA HEALTH

Kaleida Health provides a kaleidoscope of services to residents of western New York. The health system operates five acute care hospitals including Buffalo General Hospital and Gates Vascular Institute (combined with about 550 beds) The Women & Children's Hospital of Buffalo (200) DeGraff Memorial Hospital (70) and Millard Fillmore Suburban Hospital (260). Community health needs are met through a network of some 80 medical clinics. Kaleida Health also operates skilled nursing care facilities and provides home health care through its Visiting Nursing Association. To help train future medical professionals Buffalo General Hospital is a teaching affiliate of the State University of New York.

Operations

Kaleida Health is also home to the Deaconess Center and Waterfront long-term care facilities. Along with primary care the system's network of outpatient centers offers medical and surgical subspecialty care dental and oral surgery services and behavioral health and outpatient alcohol treatment services. Kaleida Health also operates the Pediatric Trauma Center and Pediatric HIV/AIDS Center for the Western New York (WNY).

In 2012 the health system had 55125 inpatient discharges 158902 emergency department visits and 2.3 million clinic and lab visits.

Financial Performance

The company's revenues grew by 3% to $1.2 billion in 2012 thanks to higher net patient service revenues and other revenues (including increases from a medical resident tax refund and HITECH incentive funds). It reported that 37% of net patient service revenues came from Medicare; 21% from New York State Medicaid; and 38% from commercial insurance plans.Kaleida Health saw net income of $52 million in 2012 (compared to a net loss in 2011) as the result of higher revenues and an increase in investment returns (including a gain from a net change in unrealized gains and losses on investments).

Strategy

In an effort to draw in more patients to the eight communities in which it already operates in the US Kaleida Health has become one of a handful of US medical providers to market itself to patients north of the border in Canada. The organization launched a marketing campaign in Ontario over the years that included a website aimed at pulling in Canadian patients seeking bariatric care for obesity gastrointestinal services (such as colonoscopies) joint replacement or spinal surgery pediatric care and radiology services. Overall Kaleida is focused on attracting Canadian patients who can either pay out-of-pocket or patients seeking non-emergency services covered in the US by the Ontario Health Insurance Program.

Growing its operations in 2013 The Kaleida Health Laboratories (which performs more than 4 million tests a year) opened four new patient service centers in New York (Tonawanda Lancaster Buffalo and Cheektowaga).

Teaming up with Olean General Hospital (OGH) in 2013 Kaleida Health and OGH opened their new interventional cardiac catheterization lab joint-venture in the Southern Tier of New York.

Kaleida Health and The University at Buffalo opened a new 10-story vascular institute and research building in 2012. The $291 million Gates Vascular Institute and the University at Buffalo's Clinical and Translational Research Center integrates Kaleida Health's physicians and UB researchers in a collaborative effort to deliver clinical care investigate the causes of a wide range of human diseases and spin-off new biotechnology businesses and jobs.

In 2012 Kaleida Health's Visiting Nursing Association of Western New York received regulatory approval to expand into four additional counties.

To raise cash in 2013 Kaleida Health sold the former Millard Fillmore Gates Circle Hospital to TM Montante Development for commercial development.

Mergers and Acquisitions

In 2013 The Visiting Nursing Association of Western New York was selected as the provider of choice to buy the Livingston County Certified Home Health Agency. In 2012 it was selected as the provider of choice to purchase the Wyoming Certified Home Health Agency.

Company Background

Along with trying to grab a share of the Canadian market Kaleida is working to renovate and refurbish its current locations to draw in more patients. In late 2011 the system completed renovations of its maternity services at Women & Children's Hospital of Buffalo. The new Mother-Baby Unit offers 14 additional single rooms with private showers and enhanced amenities. The health system underwent another complete renovation that serves as an additional Mother-Baby Unit as well as inpatient beds for the Perinatal Center gynecology and other women's services.

EXECUTIVES

Vice President of Human Resources, Daniel (Dan) Farberman
Director Of Radiology, John (Jack) Mycek
Vice President Of Human Resources, Daniel Farberman
Executive Vice President and Chief Human Resources Officer, Toni L Booker

LOCATIONS

HQ: KALEIDA HEALTH
726 EXCHANGE ST, BUFFALO, NY 142101484
Phone: 716 859-8000
Web: WWW.KALEIDAHEALTH.ORG

PRODUCTS/OPERATIONS

Selected Facilities
Buffalo General Hospital (Buffalo)
Deaconess Center (Buffalo)
DeGraff Memorial Hospital (North Tonawanda)
Gates Vascular Institute (Buffalo)
Millard Fillmore Suburban Hospital (Williamsville)
VNA Home Care Services (Allegany County Chautauqua County Erie County Genesee County Niagara County)
Women and Children's Hospital of Buffalo (Buffalo)

Selected Services
Admissions
Adult Day Services
Allergy & Immunology Clinic
Anesthesia
Bariatric Program
Bereavement Services
Blood Draw Labs
Breast Reconstruction Surgery Information
Buffalo Niagara MRI Center
Cardiac Program
Center for Asthma & Environmental Exposure
Center for Wound Care
Chest Pain Center
Colorectal Surgery
Community Health Department
DeGraff Skilled Nursing Facility
Diabetes-Endocrinology Center of Western New York
Dialysis Treatments
Diversity & Inclusion
Ear Nose and Throat Center/Otolaryngology
Easy Referrals
Emergency Department
Epilepsy Family Planning Center
Gastroenterology
Geriatric Center of Western New York
Hernia Center

Imaging Services
Immunology Laboratory
Laboratory and Pathology
Maternity Services
Minimally Invasive Surgery
Minor Surgery
Multiple Sclerosis
Neonatology
Neuropsychology
Neurosciences
Neurosurgery and Procedures
Obstetrics and Gynecology
Occupational Therapy
Orthopedics
Parkinson's Disease Comprehensive Movement Disorder Center
Pastoral Care
Personal Care Services
Personal Response System (Lifeline)
Pharmacy - High Street
Pharmacy Pharmacy - Suburban Family Pharmacy
Pharmacy Residency Program
Physical Therapy Prenatal Testing
Primary Care
Rehabilitation Medicine - Acute Medical
Rehabilitation Rehabilitation Services
Retinal
Surgical Services
Robotic Surgery
School Based Health Centers
Security
Speech Therapy - Outpatient
Spirit of Women
Stroke Program
Subacute Rehabilitation
Surgical Services
Telehealth Home Monitoring
The Greater Buffalo
United Accountable Healthcare
Urology Services
Vascular Lab
Vascular Services
Visiting Nursing Association of WNY
VNA Diabetes Program
Women's Services
Wound Care

COMPETITORS

Catholic Health System
Ellis Hospital
Hamot Medical Center
Kane Community Hospital
Lifetime Health
Oneida Healthcare Center
SUNY Upstate Medical University
St. Joseph's Hospital Health Center
St. Peter's Health Partners
St. Vincent Health System
Titusville
United Health Services Hospitals
Upstate University Hospital at Community General

HISTORICAL FINANCIALS
Company Type: Private

Income Statement
FYE: December 31

	REVENUE ($ mil.)	NET INCOME ($ mil.)	NET PROFIT MARGIN	EMPLOYEES
12/09	1,155	75	6.5%	9,000
12/08	1,102	(208)	—	—
12/07	1,059	81	7.7%	—
12/06	997	0	—	—
Annual Growth	5.0%	—	—	—

2009 Year-End Financials
Return on assets: —
Return on equity: 6.5%
Current ratio: 0.70
Cash ($ mil.): 118

KAMO ELECTRIC COOPERATIVE INC.

Auditors: BKD LLP OKLAHOMA CITY OK

LOCATIONS

HQ: KAMO ELECTRIC COOPERATIVE INC.
500 S KAMO DR, VINITA, OK 743014613
Phone: 918 256-5551
Web: WWW.KAMOPOWER.COM

HISTORICAL FINANCIALS
Company Type: Private

Income Statement
FYE: December 31

	REVENUE ($ mil.)	NET INCOME ($ mil.)	NET PROFIT MARGIN	EMPLOYEES
12/13	372	24	6.6%	154
12/12	354	21	6.2%	—
12/11	361	19	5.3%	—
12/10	332	0	—	—
Annual Growth	3.9%	—	—	—

2013 Year-End Financials
Return on assets: 10.8%
Return on equity: 6.6%
Current ratio: 0.30
Cash ($ mil.): 5

KANSAS STATE UNIVERSITY

K-State is a big deal in the Little Apple. Located in Manhattan Kansas (aka the Little Apple) Kansas State University (K-State) is a land grant institution that has an enrollment of some 24000 students. It offers more than 250 undergraduate majors 65 master's degrees 45 doctoral degrees and more than 20 graduate certificate programs. Major fields of study include agriculture technology and veterinary medicine. Notable alumni include former White House press secretary Marlin Fitzwater and actor Gordon Jump. Along with the University of Kansas and other universities technical schools and community colleges in the state K-State is governed by The Kansas Board of Regents.

Geographic Reach

K-State has its main campus on 670-acres in Manhattan Kansas. It also has satellite campuses in Salina and Olathe. It also has agricultural and research centers at five Kansas locations. The university's students come from all 50 US states and more than 90 countries.

Operations

With a student-to-faculty ratio of 20:1 K-State ranks among top US colleges and has one of the highest levels of prestigious scholarship winners (including Rhodes Marshall and Truman scholars) in the US. The university also has several notable research organizations in fields including agriculture and genetic science.

K-State is also big on sports and is part of the Big 12 Conference of collegiate athletics.

Financial Performance

K-State increased revenues by 9% to $541 million in 2012 due to higher income from student fees; government and non-government grants and contracts (for research and athletic activities); and auxiliary enterprises. Net income decreased 24% to $47 million due to higher operating expenses and lower non-operating revenues which was attributed to lower state appropriation levels and higher interest expenses.

Strategy

K-State is expanding its facilities and programs to meet the needs of its students. It completed the first $22 million phase of its National Bio and Agro-Defense Facility in 2012 as well as work on a new student recreational housing classroom and athletics facilities. In 2011 it added a new bachelor's degree program in social work. It also expanded its partnership with the Chinese scholarship council to allow additional students from China to study at K-State.

Company Background

K-State was established in 1858 as Bluemont Central College; five years later it was one of the first colleges in the US to be designated a land-grant school.

EXECUTIVES

ASA Vice President, Tatiana Nzinkeu
Medical Director, Becky Taylor
Senior Vice President Development Cdo, Shane Giese

LOCATIONS

HQ: KANSAS STATE UNIVERSITY
ANDERSON HALL 110, MANHATTAN, KS 66506
Phone: 785 532-6210
Web: WWW.KSU.EDU

PRODUCTS/OPERATIONS

Selected Colleges and Departments
College of Agriculture
  Agricultural Economics
  Agronomy
  Animal Sciences and Industry
  Entomology
  Food Science Institute
  Grain Science and Industry
  Plant Pathology
College of Architecture Planning and Design
  Architecture
  Interior Architecture and Product Design
  Landscape Architecture/Regional and Community
    Planning
College of Arts and Sciences
  Aerospace Studies
  American Ethnic Studies
  Art
  Biochemistry
  Chemistry
  Economics
  English
  Geography
  Geology
  History
  International and Area Studies
  Journalism and Mass Communications
  Kinesiology
  Mathematics
  Military Science
  Modern Languages
  Music
  Philosophy
  Physics
  Political Science
  Psychology
  Statistics
  Women's Studies
College of Business Administration
  Accounting
  Finance
  Management
  Marketing
College of Education
  Educational Leadership
  Elementary Education
  Secondary Education
  Special Education Counseling and Student Affairs
College of Engineering
  Architectural Engineering and Construction Science

Biological and Agricultural Engineering
Chemical Engineering
Computing and Information Science
Electrical and Computer Engineering
Mechanical and Nuclear Engineering
College of Human Ecology
  Apparel Textiles and Interior Design
  Gerontology
  Human Nutrition
College of Technology and Aviation
  Arts Sciences and Business
  Aviation Technology
College of Veterinary Medicine
  Anatomy and Physiology
  Clinical Sciences

COMPETITORS

Baylor University	University of Colorado
Iowa State University	University of Missouri
Oklahoma State	University of Nebraska
Texas A&M	University of Oklahoma
Texas Tech	University of Texas
The University of	Wichita State
Kansas	University

HISTORICAL FINANCIALS
Company Type: Private

Income Statement
FYE: June 30

	REVENUE ($ mil.)	NET INCOME ($ mil.)	NET PROFIT MARGIN	EMPLOYEES
06/13	558	60	10.8%	5,168
06/10	459	50	11.0%	—
06/09	420	10	2.6%	—
06/08	1,988	0	—	—
Annual Growth	(22.4%)	—	—	—

2013 Year-End Financials
Return on assets: —
Return on equity: 10.8%
Current ratio: 2.60
Cash ($ mil.): 226

KBS REAL ESTATE INVESTMENT TRUST III INC.

Auditors: ERNST & YOUNG LLP IRVINE CAL

LOCATIONS

HQ: KBS REAL ESTATE INVESTMENT TRUST III INC.
620 NEWPORT CENTER DR, NEWPORT BEACH, CA
926606420
Phone: 949 417-6500
Web: WWW.KBSCAPITALADVISORS.COM

HISTORICAL FINANCIALS
Company Type: Private

Income Statement
FYE: December 31

	ASSETS ($ mil.)	NET INCOME ($ mil.)	INCOME AS % OF ASSETS	EMPLOYEES
12/14	2,386	(12)	—	2
12/13	1,311	(21)	—	—
12/12	349	(7)	—	—
12/11	130	0	—	—
Annual Growth	163.2%	—	—	—

2014 Year-End Financials
Return on assets: 18.6%
Return on equity: (-6.5%)
Sales ($ mil): 188

KBS STRATEGIC OPPORTUNITY REIT INC.

LOCATIONS

HQ: KBS STRATEGIC OPPORTUNITY REIT INC.
620 NEWPORT CENTER DR, NEWPORT BEACH, CA
926606420
Phone: 949 417-6500
Web: WWW.KBS-CMG.COM

HISTORICAL FINANCIALS
Company Type: Private

Income Statement
FYE: December 31

	ASSETS ($ mil.)	NET INCOME ($ mil.)	INCOME AS % OF ASSETS	EMPLOYEES
12/14	1,022	(23)	—	2
12/13	776	11	1.5%	—
12/12	537	(10)	—	—
12/11	258	0	—	—
Annual Growth	58.2%	—	—	—

2014 Year-End Financials
Return on assets: 17.5%
Return on equity: (-22.4%)
Sales ($ mil): 106

KELLSTROM AEROSPACE LLC

Does the spell-check at aircraft parts inventory service Kellstrom Aerospace correct "enginuity"? Using its ingenuity to specialize in engines made by CFM International General Electric Pratt & Whitney and Rolls-Royce the company supplies new and overhauled products for military and commercial aircraft. Kellstrom doing business as Kellstrom Industries also provides maintenance for military and commercial aircraft components. Customers include commercial airlines US and foreign military forces and maintenance repair and overhaul facilities. Kellstrom Aerospace was established in 1990 and has been privately owned since 2002.

Geographic Reach

Kellstrom has offices in Austria Denmark Finland Germany Greenland Iceland Ireland Norway Sweden Switzerland Israel Cyprus Greece Turkey the UK and the US.

Operations

The company operates through three business segments: High Tech Avionics Aerospace Distribution and Kellstrom Power Group. High Tech Avionics operates as a repair station specializing in component and maintenance for commercial and military aircraft. Aerospace Distribution supplies aircraft parts as well as provides logistics and material management support to customers that have included Delta Air Lines Eagle Services-Asia and Beaver Aerospace.

Kellstrom Power Group is an industrial turbine aftermarket supplier and maintains a comprehensive inventory of more than 10000 line items for LM6000 LM2500 and LM5000 gas turbines and the associated packages and BOP equipment.

Strategy

Kellstrom strengthened its market presence in mid-2013 through the purchase of AirLiance Materials a supplier of high-quality surplus parts to the global air transport and MRO industry. The deal fortified Kellstrom's Commercial Aerospace segment and augmented its customer base to more than 1000 customers.

Ownership

Investment firm Inverness Management owns a controlling stake in Kellstrom. It led a group that bought the assets in 2002 of Kellstrom Industries which had filed for Chapter 11 bankruptcy earlier that year.

EXECUTIVES

President and CEO, Dennis A. Zalupski

LOCATIONS

HQ: KELLSTROM AEROSPACE LLC
3701 S FLAMINGO RD, MIRAMAR, FL 330272934
Phone: 954 538-2000
Web: WWW.AEROSONIC.COM

PRODUCTS/OPERATIONS

Selected Products and Services
Aerospace Distribution - Aftermarket Parts
Commercial Aerospace
  Commercial airframes
  Commercial engines
  Inventory management & support
  Purchasing management
  Repair management & support
Defense Aerospace
  Engines
  C-130
  P-3
  F-16
  T-56
  Military aircraft and parts
  Repair
Kellstrom Power Group - Aeroderivative gas turbines
Repair & Repair Management - High Tech Avionics and
  Accessories
  Air data computers
  Auto pilots
  FAA approved repair and overhaul
  Flight control systems
  Flight management computers
  Mode control panels
  TCAS computers

COMPETITORS

AAR Corp.	Triumph Group
First Aviation	Willis Lease
Thales Communications	

HISTORICAL FINANCIALS

Company Type: Private

Income Statement

	REVENUE ($ mil.)	NET INCOME ($ mil.)	NET PROFIT MARGIN	EMPLOYEES
				FYE: December 31
12/12	180	6	3.5%	262
12/11	155	0	0.6%	—
12/10	149	2	1.8%	—
12/09	163	0	—	—
Annual Growth	3.4%	—	—	—

KENERGY CORP.

Kenergy kens energy as the Scots might say. Electric distribution cooperative Kenergy serves about 55000 customers in 14 counties (Breckinridge Caldwell Crittenden Daviess Hancock Henderson Hopkins Livingston Lyon McLean Muh-

lenberg Ohio Union and Webster) in Western Kentucky. Kenergy serves its customer base of households commercial enterprises and industries via more than 6700 miles of power lines. The customer-owned company is part of Touchstone Energy Cooperatives a national alliance of more than 600 local consumer-owned electric utility cooperatives.

EXECUTIVES

Vice President Finance And Accounting, Steve Thompson

LOCATIONS

HQ: KENERGY CORP.
6402 OLD CORYDON RD, HENDERSON, KY 424209392
Phone: 270 926-4141
Web: WWW.KENERGYCORP.COM

COMPETITORS

Duke Energy Kentucky	Warren RECC
Kentucky Utilities	

HISTORICAL FINANCIALS

Company Type: Private

Income Statement

	REVENUE ($ mil.)	NET INCOME ($ mil.)	NET PROFIT MARGIN	EMPLOYEES
				FYE: December 31
12/13	506	0	0.0%	155
12/12	495	0	0.0%	—
12/11	426	0	0.0%	—
12/10	402	0	—	—
Annual Growth	8.0%	—	—	—

2013 Year-End Financials

Return on assets: 10.4%   Cash ($ mil.): 2
Return on equity: —
Current ratio: 1.00

KENNEDY HEALTH SYSTEM INC.

Like its namesake The Kennedy Health System is all about service to the public. The system operates three acute care hospitals with more than 600 beds in southern interior New Jersey. Its operations include several outpatient centers and wellness programs cancer care dialysis centers primary care facilities and a nursing home. Its outpatient services are vast and varied ranging from behavioral and occupational health centers to balance centers (to treat dizziness and balance problems) and sleep centers. Affiliated with the Rowan University School of Osteopathic Medicine Kennedy Health System was founded in 1965 as John F. Kennedy Hospital. It plans to merge with Thomas Jefferson University Hospitals.

Operations

Kennedy Health employs more than 4000 health care professionals and associates including 900 physicians. Its Kennedy University Hospital in Washington Township has specialist centers for wound care diagnostics stroke and neonatal care some of which are nationally recognized.

Through its affiliation with Rowan University the organization provides one of the largest physician training programs in New Jersey. Its former affiliation with the University of Medicine and Dentistry of New Jersey ended when the state of New Jersey dissolved the university and reassigned the

affiliation to Rowan which is part of the Penn Cancer Network.

In addition to the hospital's 600 acute care beds the system's Kennedy Health Care Center is a 130-bed skilled nursing and rehabilitation home for seniors and a separate 60-bed sub-acute wing.

Geographic Reach

Kennedy Health serves residents in the New Jersey counties of Burlington Camden and Gloucester. Its southern New Jersey hospitals are located in Cherry Hill Stratford and Washington Township.

Financial Performance

The health system reported revenues of $495 million in 2012.

Strategy

The system announced plans to join together with Philadelphia-based Thomas Jefferson University Hospitals. The merger will follow a "hub-and-hub" model through which Kennedy Health will get equal representation on the organization's governing board. If approved the deal will also mark the third such transaction for Jefferson in the past year.

In 2013 Kennedy Health expanded the Kennedy Cancer Center by adding a TrueBeam linear accelerator which allows doctors to perform more precise cancer treatment procedures. The system also expanded its outpatient wound care program by partnering with Accelecare to operate an advanced wound care and hyperbaric oxygen therapy center on the Kennedy University Hospital campus. Other expanded services include behavioral health family clinic services and home health and added dialysis.

The company partnered with RadNet in 2014 to acquire two imaging facilities in southern New Jersey. The joint venture dubbed Garden State Radiology Network intends to also develop new facilities in the region.

EXECUTIVES

President and CEO, Joseph W. Devine
VP Information Systems and Technology and CIO, Thomas J. Balcavage
Chief Physician Executive, Carman A. Ciervo
Chief Nurse Executive and VP Clinical Services, Helene Burns
Chief Medical Officer, H. Timothy Dombrowski
VP Information Systems and Technology and CIO, Tammy Curren
Vice Chairman, Bruce J. Paparone
Vice Chairman, Albert E. Smith

LOCATIONS

HQ: KENNEDY HEALTH SYSTEM INC.
1099 WHITE HORSE RD, VOORHEES, NJ 080434405
Phone: 856 488-6500
Web: WWW.KENNEDYHEALTH.ORG

PRODUCTS/OPERATIONS

Selected Services and Units
Ambulatory Services
Balance Center
Bariatric Surgery
Behavioral Health
Cancer Center
Diabetes Control Center
Kennedy Health Alliance
Kennedy Foundation
Kennedy Neuroscience Center
Laboratory Services
Medical Imaging
Robotic Surgery
Sleep Center
STAT Medical Transport
Women's and Children's Services

COMPETITORS

Albert Einstein Healthcare Network
Capital Health System

Children's Hospital of Philadelphia
Crozer-Keystone Health System
Fox Chase Cancer Center
Inspira Health Network
Lourdes Health
Our Lady of Lourdes Medical Center
Princeton HealthCare
Shore Memorial Hospital
Tenet Healthcare
The Cooper Health System
University of Pennsylvania Health System
Virtua Health

HISTORICAL FINANCIALS
Company Type: Private

Income Statement
FYE: September 30

	REVENUE ($ mil.)	NET INCOME ($ mil.)	NET PROFIT MARGIN	EMPLOYEES
09/09*	355	10	3.1%	3,030
12/08	455	(15)	—	—
12/07	16	0	—	—
Annual Growth	—23787.8%	—	—	—

*Fiscal year change

2009 Year-End Financials
Return on assets: 3.1%   Cash ($ mil.): 23
Return on equity: 3.1%
Current ratio: 0.70

KENNEDY KRIEGER INSTITUTE INC.

Kennedy Krieger Institute is dedicated to the research education and treatment of children with brain disorders spinal cord injuries and developmental disabilities. It operates more than 55 outpatient clinics that provide services in behavioral psychology family support occupational and physical therapies and speech pathology among others. Altogether the institute serves more than 20000 individuals each year. Its 70-bed inpatient pediatric hospital caters to children who suffer from feeding problems and severe behaviors such as self-injury and aggression. Kennedy Krieger also runs a school for special-education students ages 3 to 21 to help prepare them for integration into their communities.

Geographic Reach
Kennedy Krieger has 11 locations in Baltimore; it also has campuses in Columbia and Rockville Maryland.

Operations
The institute's primary operating segments include healthcare research and special education. The Healthcare segment includes a 45-bed inpatient unit admitting more than 325 patients per year more than 55 specialty outpatient clinics (150000 annual visits). It also trains more that 400 healthcare professionals each year. Healthcare activities accounted for 57% of net patient revenues in 2012.

As part of its operations Kennedy Krieger's Hugo W. Moser Research Institute delves into a variety of scientific areas involving brain and spinal cord problems in children. Its focus ranges from those caused by genetics to those developed by injury. Kennedy Krieger Institute specializes in more than 45 diverse brain spinal cord and musculoskeletal disorders including autism cerebral palsy brain injury Down syndrome feeding disorders

muscular dystrophy spina bifida and spinal cord injury.

The institute's Special Education program operates non-public special education schools for students from kindergarten to grade eight high school a specialized autism program and partnership programs to public schools.

Financial Performance
The institute's revenues dropped by 5% in 2012 due to a decline in tuition revenue grant and contract revenues and the absence of revenues from medical equipment sales. Medicaid contributed more than 40% of Kennedy Krieger's revenues in 2012; Blue Cross 23%; commercial 17% and management care 11%. Kennedy Krieger reported a net loss of $14 million in 2012 as the result of lower revenues an increase in loss on interest rate swaps and unrealized gains/losses on investments.

Strategy
To further its mission Kennedy Krieger partners with other institutions such as NYU Langone Medical Center to establish an environment for data-sharing. In late 2012 Kennedy Krieger kicked off a collaboration with the medical center for autism research. The two groups lead the Autism Brain Imaging Data Exchange (ABIDE) a global database of brain scans shared by more than 15 leading international research institutions and academic medical centers. The institute's academic partnership will allow for progress in understanding brain structure and function in autism and in turn help Kennedy Krieger better care for the communities its serves.

Company Background
Kennedy Krieger was founded in 1937 as the Children's Rehabilitation Institute. It was renamed the Kennedy Institute in 1968 and became the Kennedy Krieger Institute in 1992.

EXECUTIVES

Vp Human Resources, Michael Loughran
Cota, Gina Covi
Director Of Physical Therapy, Christopher Joseph
Vice President, Larry Triplett
Senior Vice President, Lainey Sachs
Vice President Finance, Ellen Milles
Infection Control Director, Lori Cuomo
Secretary, Linda Baynes
Board Of Directors, Gove Allen
Secretary, Karla Salley
Secretary, Ann Snitcher
Auditors: PRICEWATERHOUSECOOPERS LLP B

LOCATIONS

HQ: KENNEDY KRIEGER INSTITUTE INC.
707 N BROADWAY, BALTIMORE, MD 212051888
Phone: 443 923-9200
Web: WWW.KENNEDYKRIEGER.ORG

PRODUCTS/OPERATIONS

Selected Spec2014 Sales

	$ mil.	% of total
Net patient service revenues	130	60
Tuition revenues	43	20
Grant & contract revenues	31	15
Net assets released for operating activities	8	4
Fundraising contributions	1	-
Other	1	1
Total	**217**	**100**

ializations
Autism spectrum disorders
Behavioral disorders
Bone disorders
Brain injury
Cerebral palsy
Developmental disorders
Down syndrome
Feeding disorders
Learning disorders
Muscular dystrophy
Rehabilitation

Sleep disorders
Spina bifida
Spinal cord injury and paralysis
Sturge-Weber syndrome
Outpatient Programs
Albright Clinic
Aquatic Therapy Program
Assistive Technology Clinic
Audiology Program
Barth Syndrome Clinic
Behavior Management Clinic
Behavioral Psychology Outpatient
Bone Disorders Program
Botulinum Toxin Treatment Program
Brachial Plexus Clinic
Brain Injury Early Assessment
Brain Injury Outpatient Clinics
Brain Injury Responsiveness Program
Center for Autism and Related
Center for Development and Learning
Center for Genetic Muscle Disorders
Child and Family Therapy Clinic
Constraint Induced and Bimanual
Cranial Cervical Clinic
Day Feeding Program
Deafness-Related Evaluations
Developmental Cognitive Neurology
Down Syndrome Clinic and Research
Fairmount Rehabilitation Programs
Family Center
Family Center Outpatient Mental
Feeding Disorders Clinic
Focused Interdisciplinary Therapy
Fragile X Clinic
Genetic Counseling
Healthy Lifestyles Therapy Program
Holoprosencephaly and Related
Hunter Nelson Sturge-Weber Center
Interdisciplinary Brain Injury
International Adoption Clinic
International Center for Spinal
Intrathecal Baclofen Program (ITBP)
Limb Differences Clinic
Military Behavioral Health Services
Movement Disorders Program (MDP)
Neonatal Intensive Care Unit (NICU)
Neurobehavioral Outpatient Clinic
Neurology and Neurodevelopmental
Neurology and Neurogenetics Clinic
Neuropsychology Department
Neurorehabilitation Concussion
Nutrition Outpatient Program
Occupational Therapy Clinic
Orthopedic Outpatient Clinic
Osteogenesis Imperfecta Clinic
Outpatient Psychiatry Clinic
Pediatric Developmental Disorders
Pediatric Pain Rehabilitation
Pediatric Psychology Clinic
Phelps Center for Cerebral Palsy
Philip A. Keelty Center for Spina
Physical Therapy Clinic
Post-Orthopedic Surgery Program
Seating Clinic
Sickle Cell Neurodevelopmental
Sleep Disorders Clinic and Lab
Social Work Outpatient Mental
Specialized Transition Program
Speech and Language Outpatient
Tuberous Sclerosis Clinic
Weight Management Program
Laboratories
Clinical Neurophysiology Laboratory
Genetics Laboratories at Kennedy
Inpatient Programs
Brain Injury Responsiveness Program
Pediatric Feeding Disorders
Pediatric Pain Rehabilitation
Pediatric Rehabilitation Unit
Neurobehavioral Unit (NBU)
Continuums
Neurobehavioral Continuum
Pediatric Feeding Disorders
Pediatric Rehabilitation Continuum
Community Programs
Child and Family Support Program
Family Center Community Programs
PACT: Helping Children
Specialized Health Needs
Community Rehabilitation Program

COMPETITORS

Children's National
  Medical Center
Children's Specialized
  Hospital
Gillette Children's

Johns Hopkins Medicine
Shriners Hospitals For
  Children
Watson Institute

HISTORICAL FINANCIALS

Company Type: Private

Income Statement

FYE: June 30

	REVENUE ($ mil.)	NET INCOME ($ mil.)	NET PROFIT MARGIN	EMPLOYEES
06/13	213	13	6.5%	2,200
06/09	200	(23)	—	—
Annual Growth	1.6%	—	—	—

2013 Year-End Financials

Return on assets: 2.0%
Return on equity: 6.5%
Current ratio: 0.90
Cash ($ mil.): 10

KENNEDY MEMORIAL HOSPITAL UNIVERSITY MEDICAL CENTER INC

LOCATIONS

HQ: KENNEDY MEMORIAL HOSPITAL UNIVERSITY
MEDICAL CENTER INC
1099 WHITE HORSE RD FL 3, VOORHEES, NJ
080434405
Phone: 856 566-2000
Web: WWW.KENNEDYHEALTH.ORG

HISTORICAL FINANCIALS

Company Type: Private

Income Statement

FYE: December 31

	REVENUE ($ mil.)	NET INCOME ($ mil.)	NET PROFIT MARGIN	EMPLOYEES
12/09*	455	17	3.8%	2
09/09	339	9	2.8%	—
12/08	426	(14)	—	—
12/07	372	0	—	—
Annual Growth	10.5%	—	—	—

*Fiscal year change

2009 Year-End Financials

Return on assets: 4.3%
Return on equity: 3.8%
Current ratio: 0.50
Cash ($ mil.): 9

KENNESTONE HOSPITAL INC

Auditors: PRICEWATERHOUSECOOPERS LLP PH

LOCATIONS

HQ: KENNESTONE HOSPITAL INC
805 SANDY PLAINS RD, MARIETTA, GA 300666340
Phone: 770 792-5023
Web: WWW.WELLSTAR.ORG

HISTORICAL FINANCIALS

Company Type: Private

Income Statement

FYE: June 30

	REVENUE ($ mil.)	NET INCOME ($ mil.)	NET PROFIT MARGIN	EMPLOYEES
06/13	791	123	15.6%	—
06/10	800	123	15.5%	—
Annual Growth	(0.4%)	(0.2%)	—	—

2013 Year-End Financials

Return on assets: 4.1%
Return on equity: 15.6%
Current ratio: 4.60
Cash ($ mil.): —

KENT COUNTY MEMORIAL HOSPITAL

As one of Rhode Island's largest hospitals Kent County Memorial Hospital offers Ocean Staters a sea of medical care options. The healthcare facility provides inpatient acute care as well as outpatient services (such as diagnostic imaging) and primary care. It also offers a range of specialties including cardiology orthopedics oncology surgery pediatrics and women's health. A member of the Care New England Health System Kent Hospital opened in 1951 with 90 beds; today the hospital has about 360 beds and a staff of some 600 doctors.

Geographic Reach

Kent Hospital is located on a 60-acre campus in Warwick Rhode Island (11 miles south of Providence); it also operates satellite primary care and diagnostic centers in the area. The hospital provides care to about 300000 residents across central Rhode Island in communities including Coventry Cranston Exeter Greenwich North Kingstown and Warwick.

Operations

As a member of Care New England Kent Hospital is affiliated with the University of New England College of Osteopathic Medicine (UNECOM) for medical education. IT also has relationships with the University of Rhode Island Rhode Island College Northeastern University and medical training and research other organizations.

The Kent Hospital staff works in more than 30 specialty areas. The hospital's care team includes more than 2300 nurses technical professionals and support staff. Kent Hospital's ER is the second busiest in the state with some 67000 annual visits. Overall the hospital handles 15000 inpatient admissions each year including 1000 births and conducts about 15000 inpatient and outpatient surgeries annually.

Financial Performance

The hospital brought in $315.3 million in revenue during fiscal 2011. Kent Hospital's net revenue was some $3.2 million as operating expenses totaled $312.1 million.

During fiscal 2011 Kent Hospital provided $13.9 million in community and charity health care services.

Strategy

Kent Hospital opened its newly constructed ambulatory surgery center in 2013. The center includes eight surgery suites including specialist facilities for endoscopic and interventional spine procedures. Other facility expansions have included the opening of a $2 million emergency cardiac angioplasty center in 2009. In addition Kent Hospital has expanded its outpatient care and clinical research programs in recent years.

EXECUTIVES

Director of Nursing, John (Jack) Audett
Vice President Human Resources, Dave Campbell
Vice President, Zygmunt Maksymowicz
Vice President And Genl Cnsl, Joseph Dipietro
Director Of Nursing, Mary Glynn
Senior Vice President Human Resources, Patricia Recupero
Medical Director, Michael (Mel) Dacey

LOCATIONS

HQ: KENT COUNTY MEMORIAL HOSPITAL
455 TOLL GATE RD, WARWICK, RI 028862770
Phone: 401 737-7000
Web: WWW.KENTRI.ORG

PRODUCTS/OPERATIONS

Selected Centers and Services

Behavioral Health Unit
Breast Health
Cancer Care
Cardiology
Colonoscopy
Continuing Medical Education Program
Cosmetic Surgery
CT Scan (CAT Scan or Computerized Axial Tomography)
Dentistry
Diagnostic Imaging Services
Dialysis
Education
Emergency Medicine
Endocrinology
Endoscopy
Expresscare Service
Eye Care
Family Practice
Food and Nutrition Services
Gastroenterology
Gift Shop
Hearing Assessment/Newborns
Home Medical Equipment (HME)
Hypertension
INNOVATION CENTER
Intensive Care Unit
Internal Medicine
Interventional Radiology (Special Procedures Suite)
Kent Hospitalists
Kids Choose to be Healthy
Laboratory Services
Library
Magnetic Resonance Imaging (MRI)
Multiple Sclerosis Center
  Neonatal I
Nephrology
Neurology/Neurosurgery
Nuclear Medicine
Occupational Therapy
Orthopedics
Outpatient Rehabilitation Services
Outpatient Surgery
Palliative Care
Parkinson's Information and Referral Center
Pastoral Care
Pediatric Emergency Services
Pediatrics
Physical Therapy
Physician Relations
Podiatry
Prolotherapy
Psychiatry
Pulmonary Medicine
Radiology
Rehabilitation Center
Rheumatology
Sleep Lab
Social Services

Speech-Language Pathology
Stroke Center
Support Groups
Thoracic Surgery
Ultrasound
Urology
Videostroboscopy
Women's Diagnostic Imaging Center
Wound Recovery and Hyperbaric Medicine Center

COMPETITORS

Baystate Health	Southcoast Health
Day Kimball Hospital	Southcoast Hospitals
Memorial Hospital of	Group
Rhode Island	Sturdy Memorial
Partners HealthCare	Yale New Haven Health
Roger Williams Medical	System
Center	

HISTORICAL FINANCIALS
Company Type: Private

Income Statement
FYE: September 30

	REVENUE ($ mil.)	NET INCOME ($ mil.)	NET PROFIT MARGIN	EMPLOYEES
09/13*	339	(0)	—	1,850
12/09	0	(0)	—	—
12/05	0	0	4.8%	—
09/04	200	0	—	—
Annual Growth	**6.0%**	—	—	—

*Fiscal year change

KENT GENERAL HOSPITAL INC

LOCATIONS

HQ: KENT GENERAL HOSPITAL INC
640 S STATE ST, DOVER, DE 199013599
Phone: 302 674-4700
Web: WWW.BAYHEALTH.ORG

HISTORICAL FINANCIALS
Company Type: Private

Income Statement
FYE: June 30

	REVENUE ($ mil.)	NET INCOME ($ mil.)	NET PROFIT MARGIN	EMPLOYEES
06/08	362	33	9.2%	2,600
06/07	362	33	9.2%	—
06/06	1,121	0	—	—
Annual Growth	**—34012.7%**	—	—	—

2008 Year-End Financials
Return on assets: —
Return on equity: 9.2%
Current ratio: 1.20
Cash ($ mil.): 11

KENTUCKY MEDICAL SERVICES FOUNDATION INC.

Does the mailbox at your old Kentucky home contain doctors' bills? They might be from Kentucky Medical Services Foundation. The physician's practice group provides billing and other administrative services for the more than 600 physicians and other health care providers affiliated with the University of Kentucky's health system UK HealthCare. The network provides more than 80 specialty services offers educational programs and operates acute medical centers including Chandler Hospital Good Samaritan Hospital and Kentucky Children's Hospital.

EXECUTIVES

Executive Director, Darrell Griffith
IT Manager, Jamie Tillett
Associate Director Business Operations, Peggy Halcomb
Human Resources Manager, Garland Strang
Auditors: DEAN DORTON ALLEN FORD PLLC L

LOCATIONS

HQ: KENTUCKY MEDICAL SERVICES FOUNDATION INC.
2333 ALUMNI PARK PLZ # 200, LEXINGTON, KY 405174022
Phone: 859 257-7910
Web: WWW.KMSF.ORG

COMPETITORS

Appalachian Regional Healthcare	Jewish Hospital & St. Mary's HealthCare
Baptist Health	Norton Healthcare
Catholic Health Initiatives	

HISTORICAL FINANCIALS
Company Type: Private

Income Statement
FYE: June 30

	REVENUE ($ mil.)	NET INCOME ($ mil.)	NET PROFIT MARGIN	EMPLOYEES
06/13	225	(0)	—	150
06/10	196	(4)	—	—
06/09	189	2	1.4%	—
06/08	1,523	0	—	—
Annual Growth	**(31.8%)**	—	—	—

2013 Year-End Financials
Return on assets: 1.2%
Return on equity: (-0.2%)
Current ratio: 24.70
Cash ($ mil.): 41

KETTERING MEDICAL CENTER

Kettering Health Network keeps Ohio in a healthy state. The network named for famed inventor Charles F. Kettering is an Ohio-based healthcare system that comprises about 75 outpatient facilities including seven acute care hospitals: Kettering Medical Center Grandview Medical Center Sycamore Medical Center Southview Medical Center Fort Hamilton Hospital Greene Memorial Hospital and Soin Medical Center. Other facilities include a mental health hospital (Kettering Behavioral Hospital) and multiple outpatient diagnostic senior care and urgent care clinics. Among its specialized services are heart care rehabilitation orthopedics women's health and emergency medicine.

Geographic Reach

Kettering Health's facilities are located in Dayton Ohio and the surrounding towns of Beavercreek Hamilton Kettering Miamisburg and Xenia.

Operations

Several times in recent years Kettering Health has been named by Thomson Reuters as one of the Top 10 US Healthcare Systems.

As part of its healthcare system it operates nine radiology centers 10 pharmacies eight outpatient rehab centers seven sleep centers 13 sports medicine centers and five wound centers.

As a not-for-profit entity Kettering Health provides some $120 million in community care benefits each year including health screenings education programs charity care for uninsured patients and covering Medicare/Medicaid shortfalls for under-insured patients).

Strategy

Kettering makes capital investments in its medical centers to better serve its communities. In 2012 it opened a new hospital the Soin Medical Center to serve the Dayton-area community of Beavercreek. The $135 million construction project created a five-story 95-bed medical center featuring emergency maternity orthopedic and surgery units.

Kettering works to improve specialty units and equipment at its existing inpatient hospitals as well as technologically advanced hospitals tend to attract better physicians and therefore patients. The company launched a $5 million improvement project in 2012 to enhance emergency room services at the Fort Hamilton Hospital including physician recruitment efforts and new service provisions. A 5000-sq.-ft. facility addition has also increased the department's capacity from 36000 patients to 52000 patients per year.

The health network is also intent on expanding its outpatient facility network. For instance in 2011 it added a new emergency department to the Huber Health Center an outpatient care center in Huber Height to enhance care for area residents. The $9 million expansion effort added 40 new health professionals to the facility. In addition the company added a new primary care office in Liberty Township in 2012.

It's expanding in Ohio as well through a 2014 collaboration with Health Innovations of Ohio. Kettering is adding new freestanding emergency room facilities in 2015 in Franklin and in Eaton at the tune of $19 million.

To keep its database up to date Kettering in 2014 enlisted the help of ProVation Order Sets to oversee its clinical content management system.

Mergers and Acquisitions

Kettering Health added another hospital in 2010 when the 175-bed Fort Hamilton Hospital joined its ranks. Fort Hamilton had exited its former affiliation with UC Health (previously named The Health Alliance) and joined the Kettering network to gain the benefits of belonging to a larger organization such as group purchasing and pooled administrative functions.

EXECUTIVES

CEO, Fred Manchur
President, Roy Chew
CFO, Russ Wetherell
SVP Soin Medical Center and Greene Memorial Hospita, Terry Burns
President Fort Hamilton Hospital, Mark Smith

SVP Southview Medical Center, Rebecca Lewis
SVP Sycamore Medical Center, Wally Sackett
EVP and President Kettering Medical Center,
Jarrod McNaughton
EVP Finance and Clinical Integration Strategy,
Todd Anderson
President Soin Medical Center and Greene
Memorial Hospital, Rick Dodds
Vice President Of Human Resources, Beverly
Morris
Corporate Integrity And Ethics Vice President,
Robert Patterson
Vice President Of Finance Svs, Brett Spenst
Vice President of Patient Financial Services, Larry
Zumstein
Vice President for Patient Care and Clinical
Services, Belinda Mallett
Director of Rehab Medicine Svs; Occupational
Therapy Director, Diane Ryckman
Medical Director Sycamore Pain Management,
Nirmala Abraham
Vice President of Clinical Quality and Patient
Safety, Chris Turner
Medical Director, Benjamin (Ben) Schuster
Medical Director of Informatics, Charlie Watson
Auditors: CLARK SCHAEFER HACKETT & CO D

LOCATIONS

HQ: KETTERING MEDICAL CENTER
3535 SOUTHERN BLVD, KETTERING, OH 454291298
Phone: 937 298-4331
Web: WWW.KETTERINGHEALTH.ORG

PRODUCTS/OPERATIONS

Selected Ohio Facilities

Acute Care Hospitals
Fort Hamilton Hospital (Hamilton)
Grandview Medical Center (Dayton)
Greene Memorial Hospital (Xenia)
Kettering Medical Center (Kettering)
Soin Medical Center (Beavercreek)
Southview Medical Center (Dayton)
Sycamore Medical Center (Miamisburg)
Other
Adolescent Recovery Center of Hope
Beavercreek Health Center
Beavercreek Health Park
Charles H. Huber Health Center
Corwin M. Nixon Health Center
Englewood Community Medical Center
Kettering Behavioral Hospital (Dayton)
Sugarcreek Health Center
Sycamore Glen Health Center
Sycamore Glen Retirement Center
Sycamore Primary Care Center
Urgent Care Centers (regional)

Selected Services

Assisted Living
Back Pain
Bariatric
Behavioral Health
Bladder Confidence
Breast Health
Cancer Care
Cardiovascular
Corporate Wellness
Community Outreach
Counseling
Diabetes
Emergency
Epilepsy
Executive Health
Fertility
Gamma Knife
Heart Care
Home Care
Hyperbaric Medicine
Imaging
Independent Living
Mammography
Maternity
Mental Health
Minimally Invasive Surgery
Neonatal Care

Neuroscience
NeuroRehab
Nutrition Counseling
Obstetrics
Oncology
Orthopedics
Pain Management
Palliative Care
Pastoral Care
Pelvic Control
Physical Therapy
Pulmonary Rehab
Radiology
Rehab Therapy
Reproductive
Robotic Surgery
Senior Living
Short-term Rehab
Skilled Nursing
Sleep
Spine
Spiritual Services
Sports Medicine
Stroke
Surgery
Urgent Care
Weight Loss
Wound Care

COMPETITORS

AdCare	Mount Carmel Health
Adena Health System	OhioHealth
Cincinnati Children's	Premier Health
Hospital	Partners
Fairfield Medical	Regency Hospital
Center	Select Medical
Licking Memorial	TriHealth
Health Systems	UC Health
Mercy Health (OH)	University Hospitals
MetroHealth System	Health System

HISTORICAL FINANCIALS

Company Type: Private

Income Statement

FYE: December 31

	REVENUE ($ mil.)	NET INCOME ($ mil.)	NET PROFIT MARGIN	EMPLOYEES
12/09	531	40	7.6%	3,100
12/04	628	40	6.4%	—
12/03	568	561	98.6%	—
12/02	496	0	—	—
Annual Growth	1.0%	—	—	—

2009 Year-End Financials

Return on assets: —
Return on equity: 7.6%
Current ratio: 0.20
Cash ($ mil.): 13

KEY COOPERATIVE

Auditors: GARDINER THOMSEN PC DES MOI

LOCATIONS

HQ: KEY COOPERATIVE
13585 620TH AVE, ROLAND, IA 502368061
Phone: 515 388-4341
Web: WWW.KEYCOOP.COM

HISTORICAL FINANCIALS

Company Type: Private

Income Statement

FYE: September 30

	REVENUE ($ mil.)	NET INCOME ($ mil.)	NET PROFIT MARGIN	EMPLOYEES
09/14	371	4	1.1%	180
09/13	531	10	2.0%	—
09/12	541	8	1.5%	—
09/11	451	0	—	—
Annual Growth	(6.3%)	—	—	—

2014 Year-End Financials

Return on assets: 8.7%
Return on equity: 1.1%
Current ratio: 0.80
Cash ($ mil.): 5

KEY FOOD STORES CO-OPERATIVE INC.

Key Food Stores Co-Operative is a friend to independent New York area grocers. The co-op provides retail support and other services to 150 independently owned food retailers in the New York City area. Key Food's member-owners run stores mainly in Brooklyn and Queens but also in the other boroughs and surrounding counties. It operates stores primarily under the Key Food banner but it also has Key Food Marketplace locations that feature expanded meat deli and produce departments. In addition the co-op supplies Key Foods-branded products to member stores. Among its members are Pick Quick Foods Dan's Supreme Super Markets Gemstone Supermarkets and Queens Supermarkets. Key Foods was founded in 1937.

Geographic Reach

Staten Island-based Key Food Stores Co-Operative operates supermarkets across the five boroughs and on Long Island in upstate New York and in New Jersey and Pennsylvania.

Financial Performance

Key Foods Stores has annual sales of about $1.5 billion.

Strategy

Key Food has been expanding in Queens and Brooklyn and on Long Island after scaling back in Manhattan —where many of its stores were converted to Duane Reade drugstores as the pharmacy chain expanded and took over individual locations. To that end in late 2013 the regional grocer launched a new banner called Urban Market in Brooklyn. The 16000-square foot store in Williamsburg was the co-op's 150th location. The cooperative is expanding aggressively adding more than 30 locations under the Key Food Key Fresh & Natural and Food Dynasty banners including stores in Harlem and the Bronx. It also recently reopened a store in Coney Island that was destroyed by Hurricane Sandy in 2012.

EXECUTIVES

Vice President Strategic Planning, George
Knobloch
Auditors: ANCHIN BLOCK & ANCHIN LLP NE

LOCATIONS

HQ: KEY FOOD STORES CO-OPERATIVE INC.
1200 SOUTH AVE, STATEN ISLAND, NY 103143413
Phone: 718 370-4200
Web: WWW.KEYFOODS.COM

PRODUCTS/OPERATIONS

Selected Banners
Food Dynasty
Food World
Holiday Farms
Key Food
Key Food Marketplace
Key Fresh & Natural
Locust Valley
Milford Farms
Urban Market
Vitelio's Marketplace

COMPETITORS

A&P	Fresh Direct
D'Agostino	Gristede's Foods
Supermarkets	King Kullen Grocery
Food Emporium	Walgreen

HISTORICAL FINANCIALS
Company Type: Private

Income Statement
FYE: April 26

	REVENUE ($ mil.)	NET INCOME ($ mil.)	NET PROFIT MARGIN	EMPLOYEES
04/14	753	0	0.0%	66
04/11	537	(0)	—	—
04/10	0	0	—	—
Annual Growth	—	—	—	—

2014 Year-End Financials
Return on assets: 5.3%   Cash ($ mil.): 6
Return on equity: —
Current ratio: 0.90

KEYSTOPS LLC

Auditors: BKD LLP BOWLING GREE KENTUC

LOCATIONS

HQ: KEYSTOPS LLC
376 REASONOVER AVE, FRANKLIN, KY 421344003
Phone: 270 586-8283
Web: WWW.KEYSTOPS.COM

HISTORICAL FINANCIALS
Company Type: Private

Income Statement
FYE: September 30

	REVENUE ($ mil.)	NET INCOME ($ mil.)	NET PROFIT MARGIN	EMPLOYEES
09/14	900	3	0.3%	200
09/13	903	2	0.3%	—
09/12	860	1	0.2%	—
09/11	810	0	—	—
Annual Growth	3.5%	—	—	—

2014 Year-End Financials
Return on assets: 3.3%   Cash ($ mil.): 2
Return on equity: 0.3%
Current ratio: 0.80

KGBO HOLDINGS INC

Total Quality Logistics sets a high standard for moving merchandise. The third-party logistics (non-asset based) provider specializes in arranging freight transportation using reefers (refrigerated trucks) vans and flatbeds —moving in excess of 500000 loads each year. The trucking brokerage company serves more than 7000 clients across the US Canada and Mexico ranging from small businesses to Fortune 500 organizations. Founded in 1997 by company president Ken Oaks Total Quality Logistics (TQL) has contracts with carriers that include single owner operators and large fleets. Customers have included Kroger Dole Food and Laura's Lean Beef.

Geographic Reach
TQL largely caters to customers in the Greater Cincinnati Area where it has nearly five offices. It has about 25 satellite locations located in Chicago; Cleveland; Charlotte North Carolina; Charleston South Carolina; Detroit; Indianapolis; Denver; Columbus Ohio; Houston; Lexington Kentucky; Louisville; Nashville Tennessee; Orlando Florida; Dayton Ohio; Erlanger Kentucky; Pittsburgh; Tampa; and Austin Texas.

Operations
The company began as a produce shipper —not a popular item for most brokers because it is perishable —and expanded into flatbed shipments and other dry freight. As a non-asset-based business TQL does not own trucks or warehouses nor does it employ drivers. Rather it arranges for independent carrier companies and owner/operators to transport its customers' freight; TQL manages the shipment while it is on the road. Additionally the company has no expensive overhead and is not limited by fleet size equipment or shipping routes allowing more flexibility for its customers.

Sales and Marketing
The company serves more than 10000 customers and 50000 carriers across North America to move more than 800000 loads each year. Customers include Dole Food Wholesalers and Kroger.

Financial Performance
TOL posted $1.6 billion in annual sales for 2013 up from the $1.4 billion it posted the previous year. With no expense overhead to bog down its balance sheet the company has enjoyed three straight years of sizable growth.

Strategy
TQL grows its business by gradually launching additional locations and sales offices in key cities across the country. In 2013 it expanded its sales office in Charlotte North Carolina and moved its operations in Lexington Kentucky to a larger space. Also that year TQL launched a new sales office in Orlando Florida. In 2012 the company opened new offices in the key metropolitan areas of Cleveland Detroit and Pittsburgh. In 2014 it announced plans to launch a new office in Nashville Tennessee.

EXECUTIVES

President, Kenneth Oaks
EVP, Kerry Byrne
Auditors: BARNES DENNIG & CO LTD CI

LOCATIONS

HQ: KGBO HOLDINGS INC
4289 IVY POINTE BLVD, CINCINNATI, OH 452450002
Phone: 513 831-2600
Web: WWW.TQL.COM

COMPETITORS

Alliance Shippers
C.H. Robinson Worldwide
Echo Global
MIQ Logistics
Menlo Worldwide
Roadrunner Transportation Systems
Ryder System
Schneider Logistics
Transplace
UPS Supply Chain Solutions

HISTORICAL FINANCIALS
Company Type: Private

Income Statement
FYE: December 30

	REVENUE ($ mil.)	NET INCOME ($ mil.)	NET PROFIT MARGIN	EMPLOYEES
12/12	1,387	0	—	2,150
12/11	1,046	0	—	—
12/10	762	0	—	—
Annual Growth	34.9%	—	—	—

KIMBALL HILL INC

LOCATIONS

HQ: KIMBALL HILL INC
5999 NEW WILKE RD STE 306, ROLLING MEADOWS, IL 600084503
Phone: 847 364-7300
Web: WWW.KHHCORP.COM

HISTORICAL FINANCIALS
Company Type: Private

Income Statement
FYE: September 30

	REVENUE ($ mil.)	NET INCOME ($ mil.)	NET PROFIT MARGIN	EMPLOYEES
09/07	900	(220)	—	900
09/05	1,146	86	7.6%	—
09/04	927	55	6.0%	—
09/03	786	0	—	—
Annual Growth	3.4%	—	—	—

2007 Year-End Financials
Return on assets: 10.8%   Cash ($ mil.): 31
Return on equity: (-24.5%)
Current ratio: —

KING COUNTY PUBLIC HOSPITAL DISTRICT NO 2

Auditors: KPMG LLP SEATTLE WA

LOCATIONS

HQ: KING COUNTY PUBLIC HOSPITAL DISTRICT NO 2
12040 NE 128TH ST, KIRKLAND, WA 980343013
Phone: 425 899-1000

HISTORICAL FINANCIALS
Company Type: Private

Income Statement
FYE: December 31

	REVENUE ($ mil.)	NET INCOME ($ mil.)	NET PROFIT MARGIN	EMPLOYEES
12/07	301	6	2.3%	2,800
12/04	229	(7)	—	—
Annual Growth	9.5%	—	—	—

Return on assets: 5.5% Cash ($ mil.): 6
Return on equity: 2.3%
Current ratio: 0.80

KINGSBROOK JEWISH MEDICAL CENTER INC

Kingsbrook Jewish Medical Center (KJMC) cares for the health needs of all Brooklyn residents. Founded in 1925 to serve the area's Jewish community the campus includes an acute care hospital with about 320 inpatient beds and an adult and pediatric long-term care facility with 540 beds. KJMC provides emergency surgical cardiology gastroenterology pulmonary wound care and diagnostic imaging services as well as skilled nursing services. The hospital also serves as a training facility for medical dental and pharmacy residents. It also operates a primary and specialty care outpatient center and a rehabilitation institute.

Geographic Reach

KJMC is located in the East Flatbush neighborhood of Brooklyn. The hospital also operates the Pierre Toussaint Family Health Center in Brooklyn.

Operations

KJMC's specialty inpatient units include its Traumatic Brain Injury and Coma Recovery Unit (part of the Kingsbrook Rehabilitation Institute). Other centers of excellence include a geriatric inpatient psychiatry program to serve the borough's mentally challenged elderly residents as well as centers for radiology wound healing orthopedic surgery women's health and pharmacy services. The outpatient center provides family practice services and specialist care in about 20 medical fields.

KJMC's skilled nursing facility known as Rutland Nursing Home provides skilled nursing care physical rehabilitation comprehensive wound care a specialty unit for ventilator-dependent residents and a range of sub-acute services. Rutland Nursing Home also has a dedicated pediatric long-term care unit for children with severe developmental and metabolic disorders. Because it is located on the KJMC campus all of the medical center's resources are available to the residents.

Financial Performance

In 2012 revenue dipped less than 1% as patient and resident services income dropped. But compensation and supply costs rose so KJMC ended with a $5 million net loss. Cash flow held steady.

Strategy

KJMC is making investments in its facilities to better serve the growing needs of its community. To that end in 2011 the center broke ground on a new emergency department increasing its capacity to handle about 6000 additional ER visits per year. It is also renovating its ambulatory care facilities and expanding community programs (such as its adult day health services program). Both projects are expected to be complete in 2014. In addition in 2012 the hospital opened a new outpatient specialty care facility; the project took two years to complete and incorporates new processes for the efficient coordination of care for patients with multiple medical conditions.

The hospital is also upgrading its data systems to improve efficiencies. In 2013 it selected the ClearDATA health cloud platform to host its offsite backup system. Shifting its IT infrastructure to the platform will help KJMC reduce capital expenses and minimize risk.

Other efforts at KJMC include initiatives to reduce patient readmissions and hospital-acquired conditions.

EXECUTIVES

President CEO, Linda Brady
Director Marketing and Public Affairs, Enid Dillard
CIO, Nympha Meindel
VP Operations and COO, Kevin Molloy

LOCATIONS

HQ: KINGSBROOK JEWISH MEDICAL CENTER INC
585 SCHENECTADY AVE STE 2, BROOKLYN, NY 112031809
Phone: 718 604-5000
Web: WWW.KINGSBROOK.ORG

PRODUCTS/OPERATIONS

Selected Centers of Excellence
Comprehensive Wound Healing and Hyperbaric Center
Department of Physical Medicine and Rehabilitation
Geriatric Psychiatry
Gynecological Services / Minimally Invasive
  Laparoscopic Surgery
Non-Invasive Vascular Laboratory
Ophthalmology and Neuro-ophthalmology
Orthopedics and Joint Replacement
Pharmacy
Radiology
Rutland Adult Day Health Care Center
Rutland Nursing Home
Traumatic Brain Injury and Coma Recovery Unit
Vascular Center of Excellence

Selected Clinical Services
Cardiovascular
  Cardiac Cath Lab
Emergency Services
  Emergency Department
Neurosciences
  Electroencephalography (EEG)
Oncology
  Chemotherapy
Orthopedics
  Arthroscopy
Radiology Nuclear Medicine and Imaging
  Computed Tomography (CT)
  Magnetic Resonance Imaging (MRI)
  Single Photon Emission Computerized Tomography
  (SPECT)
Rehabilitation
  Physical Therapy
Special Care
  Coronary Intensive Care (CCU)
  Intensive Care Unit (ICU)
Subprovider Units
  Psychiatric
  Rehabilitation
  Skilled Nursing (SNF)
Wound Care
  Hyperbaric Oxygen
  Wound care

COMPETITORS

Brooklyn Hospital Center
Lutheran HealthCare
Maimonides Medical Center
MediSys Health Network
Montefiore Medical
New York City Health and Hospitals
New York Methodist Hospital
NewYork-Presbyterian Healthcare
North Shore-Long Island Jewish Health System
SUNY Downstate

HISTORICAL FINANCIALS
Company Type: Private

Income Statement
FYE: December 31

	REVENUE ($ mil.)	NET INCOME ($ mil.)	NET PROFIT MARGIN	EMPLOYEES
12/08	241	(3)	—	2,100
12/05	227	(14)	—	—
12/02	0	0	—	—
Annual Growth	—	—	—	—

2008 Year-End Financials
Return on assets: 11.2% Cash ($ mil.): 6
Return on equity: (-1.6%)
Current ratio: 0.80

KIRBY - SMITH MACHINERY INC.

Auditors: STEAKLEY & GILBERT PC OKLA

LOCATIONS

HQ: KIRBY - SMITH MACHINERY INC.
6715 W RENO AVE, OKLAHOMA CITY, OK 731276590
Phone: 817 378-0600
Web: WWW.KIRBY-SMITH.COM

HISTORICAL FINANCIALS
Company Type: Private

Income Statement
FYE: December 31

	REVENUE ($ mil.)	NET INCOME ($ mil.)	NET PROFIT MARGIN	EMPLOYEES
12/13	337	30	9.0%	385
12/12	290	31	10.7%	—
12/11	214	17	8.1%	—
12/10	149	0	—	—
Annual Growth	31.2%	—	—	—

2013 Year-End Financials
Return on assets: 3.5% Cash ($ mil.): —
Return on equity: 9.0%
Current ratio: 1.60

KIRBY RISK CORPORATION

Kirby Risk sees nothing risky about helping harness a little electrical energy. The company named after one of its co-founders supplies electrical products (process automation products drives and motors lighting fuses wire and cable) and services to the Midwestern US. The company operates through four business units comprising Electrical Supply Service Center Mechanical Solutions and Service and Precision Machining. The Electrical Supply distribution unit handles more than 20000 products from some 500 manufacturers including GE Thomas & Betts and Rockwell Automation. Other operations include ARCO Electric Products (phase converters). CEO James Risk III owns the company that was founded in 1926.

Operations

The company's Electrical Supply division stocks lighting and power instruments while the Kirby Risk Service Center makes custom wiring harnesses control panels subassemblies and kits for industrial customers. Mechanical Solutions and Service is the repair end of the business it also sells motors power transmissions and generators.

Kirby Risk Precision Machining offers precision machining using CNC (computer numerical control) technology. ARCO manufactures roto-phase converters which are rotary-type generators (different from static phase converters) as well as power factor correction capacitors.

Sales and Marketing

The company has roughly 35 customer service locations throughout Illinois Indiana and Ohio.

Company Background

Otto Keiffer and J. Kirby Risk founded the company as the Keiffer-Risk Battery Company in 1926 in an abandoned blacksmith shop in Lafayette Indiana.

EXECUTIVES

CEO, James K. (JIm) Risk
VP and CFO, Jason Bricker
President Kirby Risk Electrical Supply, John Burke
President and COO Manufacturing Group, Douglas A. Mansfield
Vice President Of Human Resources, Doug Gutridge
Auditors: BKD LLP INDIANAPOLIS IN

LOCATIONS

HQ: KIRBY RISK CORPORATION
1815 SAGAMORE PKWY N, LAFAYETTE, IN 479041765
Phone: 765 448-4567
Web: WWW.KIRBYRISK.COM

PRODUCTS/OPERATIONS

Selected Divisions
Arco Electric Products
Electrical supply
Mechanical solutions and service
Precision machining
Service center

COMPETITORS

Anixter International	Premier Farnell
Consolidated	Rexel Inc.
Electrical	SUMMIT Electric Supply
Graybar Electric	Skyworks
Hagemeyer North	W.W. Grainger
America	WESCO International

HISTORICAL FINANCIALS

Company Type: Private

Income Statement

FYE: December 31

	REVENUE ($ mil.)	NET INCOME ($ mil.)	NET PROFIT MARGIN	EMPLOYEES
12/13	401	0	—	950
12/12	398	0	—	—
12/11	377	0	—	—
12/10	399	0	—	—
Annual Growth	0.1%	—	—	—

2013 Year-End Financials

Return on assets: 6.3%   Cash ($ mil.): 38
Return on equity: —
Current ratio: 2.40

KISATCHIE CORPORATION

LOCATIONS

HQ: KISATCHIE CORPORATION
9258 HIGHWAY 84, WINNFIELD, LA 714837560
Phone: 318 628-4116

HISTORICAL FINANCIALS

Company Type: Private

Income Statement

FYE: March 31

	REVENUE ($ mil.)	NET INCOME ($ mil.)	NET PROFIT MARGIN	EMPLOYEES
03/09	398	50	12.6%	1,100
03/06	1	0	44.3%	—
03/04	1	1	77.2%	—
03/03	48	0	—	—
Annual Growth	41.8%	—	—	—

2009 Year-End Financials

Return on assets: —   Cash ($ mil.): 1
Return on equity: 12.6%
Current ratio: 5.40

KITCHELL CORPORATION

From the first structure design sketch to the last brick laid Kitchell builds the whole kit and caboodle. The employee-owned company which operates through half a dozen subsidiaries offers general contracting project and construction management engineering and architectural services and environmental services. Its projects run the gamut of public- and private-sector work and include bioscience labs casinos student housing hotels jails custom homes and performing arts centers. Kitchell is also active in facility and project management and real estate development as well as fleet management and air conditioning equipment wholesale supply. While the western US is its primary area of focus Kitchell boasts projects in about two dozen US states.

Operations

As part of its business Kitchell operates specialized divisions and subsidiaries to support its initiatives and its clients. Separate divisions include American Refrigeration Supplies Environmental Services Facilities Development Custom Homes Healthcare and Native American.Kitchell is focused on its "One Kitchell" initiative which emphasizes the benefits (to the company and its customers) of collaboration between Kitchell and its subsidiaries. Kitchell's corporate services group provides support services (including human resources legal and information technology) across all operating units. In addition the operating units work together on a host of projects to better serve customers.The company's Facilities Development Inc. subsidiary provides a complete program of Clinical Technology Planning purchasing and installation and occupancy/transition planning services to healthcare-related organizations.

Through its CGL/Kitchell joint venture the company provides facilities management to both public and private owners in the Western US.

Geographic Reach

Arizona-based Kitchell operates out of 9 offices in Arizona Southern and Northern California Tennessee Texas and Iowa. The company works on projects throughout some 30 US states.

Sales and Marketing

The company serves several sectors such as corrections healthcare utility alternative energy hospitality retail Native American performing arts and academic communities. It markets itself as the Engineering Procurement and Construction (EPC) provider of choice for municipalities and private clients nationwide.

Customers have included Wild Horse Pass Hotel and Casino John C. Lincoln Health Network Banner Health UC San Diego Jacobs Medical Center The University of Arizona Medical Center American Campus Communities Phoenix Children's Hospital and Rough Rock Community School.

Strategy

Kitchell is known for having the capacity to construct 500-bed hospitals arts and cultural sites and casinos as well as for expanding high-end retail centers. Recent projects have included the $14.7 million Phoenix Children's Southwest Valley Center in Avondale (completed in 2013) and a 1000-seat bingo hall at Casino Arizona in Scottsdale (completed in 2012).

Kitchell touts its reputation as a culturally sensitive company so much so that it devoted an entire division to Native American construction projects namely hotels and casinos. It offers cultural sensitivity training for employees gearing up to work on a reservation. Kitchell relies largely on customer word of mouth for new and repeat business in this market. Projects include the Black Oak Casino in California and schools and a wellness and conference center for the Hopi Tribe in Northern Arizona.

Another focus for Kitchell is alternative energy. It targets large solar farms of between 5 and 280 megawatts and commercial and urban solar solutions including photovoltaic installations on the rooftops of existing buildings.

EXECUTIVES

Vice President Information Technology, James B Hoyne, age 65
President Kitchell Development Co., Jeff Allen
President Kitchell Capital Expenditure Managers Inc., Russell Fox
President and CEO, James T (Jim) Swanson
President Kitchell Contractors Inc., Dan Pierce
President hardison/downey construction inc., Nick Crisci
President American Refrigeration Supplies Inc., Steve Martin
Treasurer, Dick Crowley
Auditors: MAYER HOFFMAN MCCANN PC PH

LOCATIONS

HQ: KITCHELL CORPORATION
1707 E HIGHLAND AVE # 100, PHOENIX, AZ 850164668
Phone: 602 264-4411
Web: WWW.KITCHELL.COM

PRODUCTS/OPERATIONS

Selected Services
Construction services
  Custom homes
  Engineering & architectural services
  Environmental services
  Facilities development
  General contracting
  Program/project/construction management
Fleet services
Property management
Real estate development
Refrigeration supplies

Selected Subsidiaries

American Refrigeration Supplies
FDI Planning Consultants
hardison/downey
Kitchell Capital Expenditure Managers
Kitchell Contractors
Kitchell Development Company

COMPETITORS

Balfour Beatty	Summit Builders
CORE Construction	Sundt
Flintco	Swinerton
Gilbane	Turner Corporation
Jacobs Engineering	Tutor Perini
McCarthy Building	

HISTORICAL FINANCIALS
Company Type: Private

Income Statement
FYE: December 31

	REVENUE ($ mil.)	NET INCOME ($ mil.)	NET PROFIT MARGIN	EMPLOYEES
12/10	480	0	—	946
12/09	677	0	—	—
12/08	1,027	0	0.0%	—
Annual Growth	(31.6%)	—	—	—

2010 Year-End Financials
Return on assets: 12.7%
Return on equity: —
Current ratio: 1.10
Cash ($ mil.): 65

KLAMATH FALLS INTERCOMMUNITY HOSPITAL AUTHORITY

LOCATIONS

HQ: KLAMATH FALLS INTERCOMMUNITY HOSPITAL AUTHORITY
2865 DAGGETT AVE, KLAMATH FALLS, OR 976011106
Phone: 541 883-6150
Web: WWW.SKYLAKES.ORG

HISTORICAL FINANCIALS
Company Type: Private

Income Statement
FYE: September 30

	ASSETS ($ mil.)	NET INCOME ($ mil.)	INCOME AS % OF ASSETS	EMPLOYEES
09/13	216	15	7.0%	9
09/09	143	0	—	—
09/92	10	0	0.5%	—
Annual Growth	15.5%	31.0%	—	—

2013 Year-End Financials
Return on assets: 1.4%
Return on equity: 3.4%
Sales ($ mil): 447

KMM TELECOMMUNICATIONS

LOCATIONS

HQ: KMM TELECOMMUNICATIONS
9 LAW DR STE 13, FAIRFIELD, NJ 070043233
Phone: 973 244-1380
Web: WWW.KMMTEL.COM

HISTORICAL FINANCIALS
Company Type: Private

Income Statement
FYE: December 31

	REVENUE ($ mil.)	NET INCOME ($ mil.)	NET PROFIT MARGIN	EMPLOYEES
12/13	892	10	1.2%	125
12/08	868	13	1.5%	—
12/07	789	17	2.2%	—
12/06	483	0	—	—
Annual Growth	9.1%	—	—	—

2013 Year-End Financials
Return on assets: 8.5%
Return on equity: 1.2%
Current ratio: 0.60
Cash ($ mil.): 1

KNIGHTS OF COLUMBUS

Good Knight! The Knights of Columbus is a formidable volunteer group boasting 15000 councils made up of 1.9 million Roman Catholic male members in the US Canada Mexico Cuba the Philippines Poland and several other countries. The fraternal organization is also a force to be reckoned with in the insurance world providing life insurance annuities and long-term care insurance to its members and their families. In addition the group manages the Knights of Columbus Museum in New Haven Connecticut featuring exhibits of religious art and history.

Geographic Reach

The Knights of Columbus comprises more than 14900 local councils throughout the US Canada Mexico Puerto Rico Guam and the U.S. Virgin Islands. It also has councils in the Bahamas Cuba the Dominican Republic Guatemala Panama the Philippines Poland and Saipan.

Operations

The Knights of Columbus was formed to render financial aid to members and their families. Mutual aid and assistance are offered to sick disabled and needy members and their families. Social and intellectual fellowship is promoted among members and their families through educational charitable religious social welfare war relief and public relief works. is also engaged in religious education the support of public policy issues (including immigration reform marriage protection opposing abortion) and charitable activities such as disaster relief.The entity is a Catholic family fraternal service organization. This theme permeates the entire Service Program: all Church community council family culture of life and youth activities. The Service Program is designed to establish each council as an influential and important force within the community elevate the status of the programming personnel provide more meaningful and relevant programs of action establish direct areas of re-

sponsibility build leadership and ensure the success of council programs.

Strategy

In 2015 The Knights of Columbus created a new class of mutual funds that will invest based on Catholic values and will be marketed to faith-based institutions such as orders of nuns dioceses or Catholic universities. The New Haven-based Knights also created a new investment adviser firm Knights of Columbus Asset Advisors.

Expanding internationally in 2014 the Knights of Columbus opened a new branch in South Korea to support that country's growing Catholic population. (It also established a presence in Ukraine and Lithuania in 2013).In 2014 The Knights of Columbus funded the purchase of an ultrasound machine for a Baltimore area pregnancy center making it the 500th such gift by the Knights to a pregnancy center dedicated to helping women keep and care for their unborn babies. It also expanded its successful Coats for Kids program by teaming up with the New Haven Police Department providing officers with coats to distribute as they encounter children and families in need. The Knights of Columbus has established a new scholarship program to help fund the education of seminarians preparing to become Catholic chaplains in the US Armed Forces. The program will distribute $1 million in scholarship money to the Archdiocese for the Military Services USA over a period of five years at a rate of $200000 per year.

During 2014 the organization launched its new Long-Term Care Plus product across 40 states Canada (excluding Quebec) and Puerto Rico.

Company Background

The Knights of Columbus was founded in New Haven by Father Michael J. McGivney in 1882 and has been selling insurance since its founding

EXECUTIVES

Supreme Knight, Carl A. Anderson
Deputy Supreme Knight, Logan T. Ludwig
Supreme Treasurer, Michael J. O'Connor
Supreme Chaplain, William E. Lori
Assistant Vice President Of Application Development, Niki Kratzert
Vice President For Communications, Patrick Korten
Vice President Certified and Support Services, Lynn Hussey
Vice President, Anthony Minopoli

LOCATIONS

HQ: KNIGHTS OF COLUMBUS
1 COLUMBUS PLZ STE 1700, NEW HAVEN, CT 065103326
Phone: 203 752-4000
Web: WWW.EASTONKOFC.ORG

PRODUCTS/OPERATIONS

2013 Charitable Contributions

State & local affiliates	79
Supreme Council	21

Total	0	100

HISTORICAL FINANCIALS
Company Type: Private

Income Statement
FYE: December 31

	ASSETS ($ mil.)	NET INCOME ($ mil.)	INCOME AS % OF ASSETS	EMPLOYEES
12/13	20,534	113	0.6%	2,300
12/12	19,401	127	0.7%	—
12/11	18,026	81	0.4%	—
12/10	16,861	0	—	—
Annual Growth	6.8%	—	—	—

KNOUSE FOODS COOPERATIVE INC.

Is there a Knouse in the house? Might be. With retail brand names such as Apple Time Lucky Leaf Musselman's Lincoln and Speas Farm Knouse Foods Cooperative's apple products are in many a pantry. The company is a growers' co-op made up of some 150 Appalachian Mountain and Midwestern grower/members. It processes its members' apples for sale as canned and bottled applesauce juice cider vinegar apple butter pie fillings and snack packs all of which are available nationwide. In addition to stocking supermarket shelves Knouse founded in 1949 supplies foodservice operators and industrial-ingredient companies with bulk apple and other fruit products. It also offers private-label and co-packing services.

Geographic Reach

The company operates half a dozen processing plants in Pennsylvannia —covering nearly 2.4 million sq. ft. on about 300000 acres —and a single plant in Paw Paw Michigan.

Operations

The company's business segments include: retail; foodservice which supplies restaurants cafeterias healthcare facilities and other institutional customers; an industrial/ingredient division that provides customized products for industrial clients; and co-packing.

Knouse gets an A for all things Apple but also makes the grade with foodservice cheese sauces dessert toppings and fillings and puddings. And along with apple its pie fillings include apricot blackberry blueberry cherry lemon peach pineapple raisin raspberry and strawberry.

Strategy

In recent years companies like Knouse have been focused on packaging to make its products more portable. To this end Knouse in 2014 introduced Musselman's Squeezables single-serve apple sauce.

EXECUTIVES

Treas, Craig M Hinkle, age 46

LOCATIONS

HQ: KNOUSE FOODS COOPERATIVE INC.
800 PACH GLEN IDAVILLE RD, PEACH GLEN, PA 173750001
Phone: 717 677-8181
Web: WWW.KNOUSEFOODSERVICE.COM

PRODUCTS/OPERATIONS

Selected Products
Apple butter
Apple juice & cider
Apple sauce
Pie filling
Specialty fruit (cherries sliced apples)

COMPETITORS

BakeMark
Big Heart Pet Brands
Birds Eye
Chelan Fruit Company
Chiquita Brands
Dole Food
Eagle Family Foods

Odwalla
Old Orchard
Seneca Foods
Shamrock Foods
Smucker
Snapple
Sun-Rype

H. J. Heinz Limited
Monster Beverage
Mott's
Naked Juice
Ocean Spray

Tree Top
TreeHouse
Tropicana
Wet Planet Beverages

HISTORICAL FINANCIALS
Company Type: Private

Income Statement
FYE: June 30

	REVENUE ($ mil.)	NET INCOME ($ mil.)	NET PROFIT MARGIN	EMPLOYEES
06/08	270	7	2.8%	1,200
06/07	259	2	0.8%	—
06/06	248	2	1.0%	—
06/05	239	0	—	—
Annual Growth	4.2%	—	—	—

2008 Year-End Financials
Return on assets: 6.4%
Return on equity: 2.8%
Current ratio: 0.40
Cash ($ mil.): —

KNOX COUNTY HOSPITAL

Good Samaritan Hospital provides a full slate of healthcare services to both southwest Indiana and southeast Illinois. Its services include cardiology emergency care orthopedics women's health and pediatrics among others. The 230-bed hospital is located a few blocks from the Wabash River which forms the border between the Hoosier and Prairies states. Good Samaritan operates specialty units as well including same-day surgery breast care behavioral health radiology sleep cancer care and rehabilitation centers. It also provides home health and hospice services. Established in 1908 with 25 beds Good Samaritan was Indiana's first county hospital.

Geographic Reach

Located in Vincennes Indiana Good Samaritan serves residents along the neighboring southern borders of both Indiana and Illinois.

Operations

Busy regional hospital Good Samaritan logs more than 458000 outpatient visits each year as well as an additional 35950 visits to its emergency room. It boasts an Imaging Center Dayson Heart Center and Cancer Pavilion with a 25000-sq.-ft. comprehensive oncology care center.

Good Samaritan is a member of the Voluntary Hospital Association Indiana Hospital Association and Genesis Health.

Sales and Marketing

The hospital uses TV advertising to market its services.

Strategy

While Good Samaritan is focused on serving patients as an outpatient facility the regional hospital is nearing completion of a new inpatient tower. It's building a 200000-sq.-ft. five-story 120-bed inpatient tower at the cost of $109 million. As part of this BEACON project Good Samaritan is redesigning key healthcare service areas and upgrading its critical engineering systems. Project completion dates span 2014 to late 2016 for the BEACON project.

To make information more readily available to its patients Good Samaritan in 2012 rolled out an Indiana Health Information Exchange clinical messaging service called DOCS4DOCS. The service

provides a portal for accessing lab results radiology reports transcripts pathology and hospital admissions reports and discharge and transfer reports. Good Samaritan is one of several thousand participating hospitals along with physician practices labs and radiology centers.

EXECUTIVES

Vice President Of Medical Affairs, Charles (Chas) Hedde
Vice President Of Human Resources, Emily Heineke
Occupational Therapy Director, Tammy Klein
Vice President Nursing, Carol Olson
Medical Director, Victor Kirchoff
Vice President Professional Support Services, Scott Kaminski
Secretary, Linda Bezy
Auditors: BKD LLP INDIANAPOLIS INDIANA

LOCATIONS

HQ: KNOX COUNTY HOSPITAL
520 S 7TH ST, VINCENNES, IN 475911038
Phone: 812 882-5220
Web: WWW.GSHVIN.ORG

PRODUCTS/OPERATIONS

Selected Centers
Dayson Heart Center
Cancer Pavilion
Imaging Center

COMPETITORS

Daviess Community Hospital
Deaconess Health System
IU Health
Southern Illinois Healthcare

St. John's Hospital (Illinois)
St. Mary's Medical Center of Evansville
Wabash County Hospital

HISTORICAL FINANCIALS
Company Type: Private

Income Statement
FYE: December 31

	REVENUE ($ mil.)	NET INCOME ($ mil.)	NET PROFIT MARGIN	EMPLOYEES
12/13	198	4	2.1%	1,850
12/12	191	12	6.6%	—
12/11	175	8	4.8%	—
12/10	156	0	—	—
Annual Growth	8.2%	—	—	—

2013 Year-End Financials
Return on assets: 6.3%
Return on equity: 2.1%
Current ratio: 1.80
Cash ($ mil.): 29

KOOTENAI HOSPITAL DISTRICT

LOCATIONS

HQ: KOOTENAI HOSPITAL DISTRICT
2003 KOOTENAI HEALTH WAY, COEUR D ALENE, ID 838146051
Phone: 208 625-4000

HISTORICAL FINANCIALS

Company Type: Private

Income Statement

FYE: December 31

	REVENUE ($ mil.)	NET INCOME ($ mil.)	NET PROFIT MARGIN	EMPLOYEES
12/12	310	26	8.4%	1,892
12/07	211	23	11.2%	—
12/06	192	188	98.0%	—
12/05	0	0		—
Annual Growth	—	—	—	—

2012 Year-End Financials

Return on assets: 4.8%   Cash ($ mil.): 46
Return on equity: 8.4%
Current ratio: 2.00

KPH HEALTHCARE SERVICES INC.

Founded by Burt Orrin Kinney who opened the company's first drugstore in 1903 Kinney Drugs has grown to number about 100 stores in central and northern New York and Vermont. Most of the company's stores are free-standing units with pharmacies one-hour photo developing services and a growing selection of convenience foods. The 100%-employee-owned company maintains its own distribution warehouse and offers about 800 different products including Kinney-branded over-the-counter medicines. Pharmacy accounts for 75% of sales. Besides retail stores the firm operates ProAct prescription benefit management firm HealthDirect institutional pharmacy services and HealthDirect mail order pharmacy services.

Geographic ReachUpstate New York-based Kinney Drugs operates more than 75 stores in New York and about two dozen locations in Vermont as well as a distribution warehouse.

Financial Performance

The employee-owned company rings up more than $800 million in annual sales. Prescription drugs sales account for about three-quarters of Kinney Drugs' total sales.

Strategy

To distinguish itself from its national competitors including Walgreen CVS and Wal-Mart the regional retailer strives to maintain a hometown feel. To that end it launched the KinneyCare Discount Prescription Plan for its insured and uninsured pharmacy customers. Under the plan more than 350 generic prescriptions are available for $12 for a 90-day supply. The plans costs $10 a year to enroll. The chain's ReadyScripts automated refill program sends messages to remind patients to pick up their prescriptions and offers free delivery to the mobility-impaired customers. Taking a page from

its large rivals Kinney is moving to provide health care services in addition to filling prescriptions. In 2014 Kinney teamed with a local health care organization to open a Healthy You Wellness Center to treat lung problems at a store in Syracuse New York. The wellness center is staffed by specialists from Pulmonary Health Physicians PC and will focus on disease management and immediate care of certain health concerns. Kinney Drugs national rivals Walgreen and CVS both operate a growing number of in-store clinics. The regional drugstore chain hopes to open more Health You Wellness Centers in the near future.

With the worst of the recession –and concurrent decrease in spending on health care and prescription drugs –behind it Kinney acquired four independent pharmacies in central New York and Vermont in mid-2012 and has since added about a half a dozen more bringing its store count to about 100 locations.

EXECUTIVES

Vice President Professional Services, Owen Halloran
Pharmacy Manager, Harold Lehman
Vice President Senior Vice President finance Direc, Michael (Mel) Burgess
Director of Pharmacy Operations, Mike Duteau
Board Of Directors, Rebecca Horn
Auditors: DANNIBLE & MCKEE LLP SYRACUS

LOCATIONS

HQ: KPH HEALTHCARE SERVICES INC.
520 E MAIN ST, GOUVERNEUR, NY 136421561
Phone: 315 287-1500
Web: WWW.KINNEYDRUGS.COM

2013 Stores

New York	77
Vermont	23
Total	0 100

COMPETITORS

BJ' s Wholesale Club	Stop & Shop
CVS	Target Corporation
Costco Wholesale	Wal-Mart
Kmart	Walgreen
Rite Aid	

HISTORICAL FINANCIALS

Company Type: Private

Income Statement

FYE: December 31

	REVENUE ($ mil.)	NET INCOME ($ mil.)	NET PROFIT MARGIN	EMPLOYEES
12/08	711	10	1.5%	3,000
12/07	666	11	1.8%	—
12/06	606	9	1.6%	—
12/05	525	0		—
Annual Growth	10.6%	—	—	—

2008 Year-End Financials

Return on assets: 5.5%   Cash ($ mil.): 3
Return on equity: 1.5%
Current ratio: 0.40

KRAMM HEALTHCARE CENTER INC

LOCATIONS

HQ: KRAMM HEALTHCARE CENTER INC
743 MAHONING ST, MILTON, PA 178472232
Phone: 570 742-2681

HISTORICAL FINANCIALS

Company Type: Private

Income Statement

FYE: June 30

	REVENUE ($ mil.)	NET INCOME ($ mil.)	NET PROFIT MARGIN	EMPLOYEES
06/09	925	98	10.7%	330
06/00	5	0	3.8%	—
06/98	1	0		—
06/97	4	0		—
Annual Growth	56.0%	—	—	—

2009 Year-End Financials

Return on assets: —   Cash ($ mil.): —
Return on equity: 10.7%
Current ratio: 1.00

KRUEGER INTERNATIONAL INC.

Krueger International can be found in cubicles classrooms cafeterias and college dorms. The company which does business as KI makes ergonomic seating cabinets and other furniture used by businesses healthcare organizations government agencies and educational institutions. The company offers everything from benches and beds to desks and tables not to mention shelving filing systems movable walls and trash bins. KI markets its products through sales representatives furniture dealers architects and interior designers worldwide. Founded in 1941 KI was purchased in the 1980s by its managers who later allowed employees to buy stock. Today KI is 100% employee owned.

Operations

Boasting $700 million in sales and the title of sixth-largest contract furniture manufacturer in the industry KI operates a variety of subsidiaries including KI UK Ltd. KI East Asia Sdn. Bhd KI Nova Scotia KI Canada KI-Sebel and KI India.

KI also owns three subsidiaries: AWP Wood Products Pallas Textiles and Spacesaver. Quebec-based AWP Wood Products makes architectural wood doors for the office partition industry. Pallas Textiles which operates out of Wisconsin creates textile products for contract upholstery panel systems and wall-coverings healthcare environments and casements. Spacesaver Corporation also located in Wisconsin makes high-density mobile storage systems for office institutional and industrial applications and is a major supplier of steel shelving systems rotary storage systems and storage accessories.

The company maintains nine manufacturing sites around the globe. Besides its four locations in Wisconsin (in Bonduel Fort Atkinson Green Bay and Manitowoc) KI operates production facilities in High Point North Carolina; Penmroke Ontario

Canada; and Tupelo Mississippi. In 2012 KI expanded its Green Bay Wisconsin plant (at the tune of $3.3 million) by more than 100000 sq. ft. for additional elbow room devoted to manufacturing shipping receiving and warehousing.

Geographic Reach

Based in Wisconsin KI sells its products worldwide and operates manufacturing facilities and sales offices in the US Canada China and India as well as throughout Europe Latin America and Asia. It has subsidiaries based in the UK Canada India and Malaysia. Its showrooms are in several metropolitan areas across the US Toronto and London.

Sales and Marketing

KI sells its products globally through furniture dealers sales representatives architects and interior designers. It primarily serves the educational university healthcare business and government markets. The company staffs direct sales offices around the world and also boasts showrooms in metropolitan areas to display its products to potential business and individual customers.

Strategy

KI is well-regarded in the classroom furniture market and is a leading supplier for both K-12 schools and universities. The company has outfitted classrooms lecture halls administrative offices computer labs media centers residence halls and student unions. KI has been a government vendor for more than six decades providing furnishings for an assortment of federal agencies including all branches of the military. KI's corporate products are ergonomically designed to help individuals work more comfortably and efficiently. In addition to these core customer groups KI has also installed its furnishings in outdoor public spaces sports arenas conference centers and airports.

It regularly rolls out new products. In 2013 KI launched the Grazie Seating Collection through a collaboration between renowned designer Giancarlo Piretti and in 2012 introduced the elegant and sophisticated Affina Collection an expansive seating and table line designed by Paul James and Dan Cramer. KI also expanded its existing product licensing agreement with UK seating industry leader Boss Design in 2013 to give Boss Design an extended reach into the US market and KI a broader portfolio of lounge task seating and occasional table items.Company BackgroundThe company has expanded its network of showrooms in the US and abroad over the years. KI added a showroom in Houston in 2010 to boost its US presence which includes about 10 locations in half a dozen states. To better serve its Asian and European customers the company operates through a showroom in Shanghai China. KI has international showrooms in London Malaysia Mexico Puerto Rico and Toronto. To support its growth KI completed a $3.3-million 100000-sq.-ft. plant expansion in 2012 to reduce costs and streamline its business. The move boosts its manufacturing shipping receiving and warehousing space.

As its showroom presence grew KI also formed new sales partnerships. The company tapped Heartland Furniture Group a contract furniture representative in 2011 to take care of existing customer accounts and broker sales in Kansas Missouri and southern Illinois.It's also looked to acquisitions to extend the reach of its business. In 2011 KI purchased Sebel Furniture Limited from GWA Group Ltd. a top supplier of building fixtures in Australia. The $24 million deal has given KI a foothold in the commercial furniture business in Australia New Zealand the UK and Hong Kong.

EXECUTIVES

Chairman and CEO, Richard J. (Dick) Resch
President, Brian Krenke
Vice President, Dennis Mickeleit
Vice President, Norman (Norm) Nance
Asst Sec, Michael (Mel) Pum
Asst Sec, Michael Novitski
Auditors: BAKER TILLY VIRCHOW KRAUSE LL

LOCATIONS

HQ: KRUEGER INTERNATIONAL INC.
1330 BELLEVUE ST, GREEN BAY, WI 543022197
Phone: 920 468-8100
Web: WWW.KI.COM

PRODUCTS/OPERATIONS

Selected Products
Auditorium seating
Beds
Benches
Bookcases
Carrels
Chairs
Desks
File cabinets
Lecterns
Movable walls
Planters
Power and data connections
Receptacles
Recliners
Residence hall furniture
Sleepers
Special events seating
Stools
Tables

COMPETITORS

ABCO Office Furniture	Kewaunee Scientific
Allsteel	Kimball International
Bretford	Knoll Inc.
CFGroup	La-Z-Boy
Columbia Manufacturing	Norstar Office
Edsal Manufacturing	Products
Global Group	Sagus
HNI	Steelcase
Haworth Inc.	Trendway
Herman Miller	Virco Mfg.
Inscape corp	

HISTORICAL FINANCIALS
Company Type: Private

Income Statement
FYE: December 31

	REVENUE ($ mil.)	NET INCOME ($ mil.)	NET PROFIT MARGIN	EMPLOYEES
12/11	649	56	8.8%	2,300
12/10	615	59	9.6%	—
12/08	1,377	0	0.0%	—
Annual Growth	(22.2%)	4991.3%	—	—

2011 Year-End Financials
Return on assets: 5.1%
Return on equity: 8.8%
Current ratio: 0.80
Cash ($ mil.): 3

KUTZTOWN MANOR INC

LOCATIONS

HQ: KUTZTOWN MANOR INC
120 TREXLER AVE, KUTZTOWN, PA 195309725
Phone: 610 683-6220

HISTORICAL FINANCIALS
Company Type: Private

Income Statement
FYE: June 30

	REVENUE ($ mil.)	NET INCOME ($ mil.)	NET PROFIT MARGIN	EMPLOYEES
06/09	1,125	153	13.7%	154
06/01	7	0	3.2%	—
06/00	86,376	0	0.0%	—
Annual Growth	(38.3%)	84.1%	—	—

2009 Year-End Financials
Return on assets: —
Return on equity: 13.7%
Current ratio: 6.20
Cash ($ mil.): 2

KWIK TRIP INC.

Midwesterners who need to make a quick trip to get gas or groceries cigarettes or donuts race on over to Kwik Trip stores. Kwik Trip owns and operates about 500 Kwik Trip Kwik Star Hearty Platter and Tobacco Outlet Plus convenience stores in Iowa Minnesota and Wisconsin. The company also runs about a dozen Hearty Platter restaurants and cafes some 40 Tobacco Outlet Plus (TOP) cigar stores and car washes at some Kwik Trip store locations. All Kwik Trip stores built since 1990 are owned by Convenience Store Investments a separate firm which leases the land and stores to Kwik Trip. Kwik Trip which opened its first store in 1965 in Eau Claire Wisconsin is owned by the family of CEO Don Zietlow.

Geographic Reach

The company operates in Iowa Minnesota and Wisconsin.

Operations

To supply its stores with baked goods and other foods Kwik Trip operates a 60000-square-foot commissary and research facility at its headquarters in southwestern Wisconsin. The bakery produces the Kwickery Bake Shoppe line of bagels buns cookies donuts muffins and more and its dairy packages the Nature's Touch brand of fresh milk ice cream orange juice and water. The company has opened a new 65000-square-foot dairy facility in its hometown of La Crosse to supply its own stores (and those owned by others) with ice cream yogurt and other dairy products. Longer term the company hopes to develop its own plastic bottle manufacturing plant. Food service currently accounts for about a third of the company's annual profit ahead of fuel.

Kwik Trip vertically integrates by processing its own gasoline and producing and packaging products to be sold in its convenience stores.

Subsidiary Convenience Transportation LLC provides transportation to the company. Since 2006 Kwik Trip has also partnered with Marshfield Food Safety LLC a full-service microbiological laboratory that provides third-party on-site food safety laboratory services.

Strategy

Kwik Trip is growing quickly. In 2014 it opened 34 convenience stores in the Twin Ports market of Duluth Minnesota and Superior Wisconsin. That year the company added compressed natural gas (CNG) to three more convenience store and fueling station bringing its total to 28 sites in Wisconsin that sell CNG.

Kwik Trip is testing a new 5000-square-foot store format designed to appeal to soccer moms and other female customers. The new more upscale look includes wood fixtures and subdued florescent lighting combined with accent lighting. To supply its larger store base the company is building a new 65000-square-foot dairy facility in its hometown of La Crosse.

To compensate for shrinking fuel and tobacco margins the regional convenience store chain has been expanding its food offerings — adding soup and chili to its menu of pizza tacos salads and other hot and fresh items -and plans to enter the take-home meals market with entrees such as lasagna chicken beef pork fish and meat loaf. Indeed over the past several years the company has greatly expanded its food production activities and has begun selling food on a wholesale basis to other retailers including noncompeting retailers and school districts. The company estimates that by 2030 the wholesale business could account for as much as half of the food that Kwik Trip produces.

Company Background

The John Hansen family founded Kwik Trip in Eau Claire Wisconsin in 1965. In 2000 the Hansens sold their interest in Kwik Trip to the Zietlow family for $120 million. The two families had jointly owned Kwik Trip since 1972.

EXECUTIVES

President and CEO, Donald P. (Don) Zietlow, age 80
VP and Director Petroleum Operations, Steve Zietlow
Vice President, Scott Frost
Vice President, Ginny Skogen
Vice President, David Woodruff
Vice President Of Operations Support, Steve Loehr
Auditors: MCGLADREY & PULLEN LLP MINNE

LOCATIONS

HQ: KWIK TRIP INC.
1626 OAK ST, LA CROSSE, WI 546032308
Phone: 608 793-6331
Web: WWW.KWIKTRIP.COM

PRODUCTS/OPERATIONS

Selected Banners
Hearty Platter
Kwik Star
Kwik Trip
Tobacco Outlet Plus

COMPETITORS

7-Eleven	Denny' s
Brinker	Exxon Mobil
Carlson Restaurants	Hy-Vee
Casey' s General Stores	Krause Gentle
Chevron	Northern Tier Energy
Couche-Tard	Roundy' s
Cub Foods	

HISTORICAL FINANCIALS

Company Type: Private

Income Statement   FYE: September 27

	REVENUE ($ mil.)	NET INCOME ($ mil.)	NET PROFIT MARGIN	EMPLOYEES
09/08	3,640	23	0.7%	10,500
09/04	1,887	24	1.3%	—
Annual Growth	17.9%	(0.8%)	—	—

2008 Year-End Financials

Return on assets: 3.1%   Cash ($ mil.): 1
Return on equity: 0.7%
Current ratio: 0.40

KYUNGSHIN-LEAR SALES AND ENGINEERING LLC

Auditors: ERNST & YOUNG LLP CIUDAD JUA

LOCATIONS

HQ: KYUNGSHIN-LEAR SALES AND ENGINEERING LLC
100 SMOTHERS RD, MONTGOMERY, AL 361175505
Phone: 334 523-9512

HISTORICAL FINANCIALS

Company Type: Private

Income Statement   FYE: December 31

	REVENUE ($ mil.)	NET INCOME ($ mil.)	NET PROFIT MARGIN	EMPLOYEES
12/13	342	2	0.7%	105
12/12	319	3	1.0%	—
12/11	256	(0)	—	—
12/09	84	0	—	—
Annual Growth	41.8%	—	—	—

2013 Year-End Financials

Return on assets: 5.4%   Cash ($ mil.): 8
Return on equity: 0.7%
Current ratio: 0.50

LAFAYETTE GENERAL MEDICAL CENTER INC

Serving the people of Acadiana (southern Louisiana) Lafayette General Medical Center (LGMC) provides general inpatient medical and surgical care as well as specialized trauma care and neonatal intensive care. The not-for-profit hospital which has more than 365 beds also offers home health services outpatient care occupational medicine and mental health care. As part of umbrella group Lafayette Health LGMC is affiliated with Lafayette General Surgical Hospital St. Martin Hospital Acadia General Hospital University Hospital and Clinics and Abrom Kaplan Memorial Hospital. It's also a teaching hospital for LSU. Non-profit foundation Lafayette General Foundation supports and governs Lafayette Health.

Operations

LGMC has evolved from a six-bed sanitarium that opened in 1911 to become the region's only community-owned and managed hospital. The 10-floor hospital now has larger rooms bathrooms and showers. It has also updated the Louisiana Extended Care Hospital its long-term acute care unit as well as its adult emergency department. New pediatric treatment and waiting areas were added to the emergency department and a new in-patient rehab unit was created. In 2013 LGMC became a teaching hospital for nearby Louisiana State University (LSU).

A strong community member LGMC not only makes financial contributions to further medical education and research it also coordinates events and provides free screenings to the public it serves.

Strategy

Like many health care providers facing reforms in the industry the hospital is developing a new patient-centered model of care delivery using evidenced-based practices and collaboration between patients their families and clinical ancillary and support staff members to improve outcomes and gain efficiencies. LGMC has been the first hospital in the area to bring in new technology like the DaVinci robotic surgical system to offer wifi access hospital-wide and to continuously upgrade and expand its facilities.

EXECUTIVES

Vice President / Chief Nursing Officer, Rebecca (Becki) Benoit
CEO / VP University Hospital & Clinics, Jared Stark
Executive Vice President / CEO Lafayette General Medical Center, Patrick W. Gandy Jr.
Senior Vice President / Chief Financial Officer, Roger Mattke
Vice President Information Systems / Chief Information Officer, Edwina Mallery
President and CEO, David L. Callecod
Vice President Marketing Business Development, Carolyn Huval
Vice President of Cancer Services, Craig Ortego
Vice Chairman, Edward J. Krampe
General Counsel and Chief Compliance Officer, Gordon Rountree
Assistant Vice President Network Development, Paul Molbert
Chairman, Clay M. Allen
Chief Medical Officer, Ziad Ashkar
CEO / VP St. Martin Hospital, Katie Hebert

LOCATIONS

HQ: LAFAYETTE GENERAL MEDICAL CENTER INC
1214 COOLIDGE BLVD, LAFAYETTE, LA 705032621
Phone: 337 289-7991
Web: WWW.LAFAYETTEGENERAL.COM

PRODUCTS/OPERATIONS

Selected Affiliates
Abrom-Kaplan Hospital
Acadia General Hospital
Cancer Center of Acadiana
Cardiovascular Institute of the South
CyberKnife Louisiana
Family Health Plaza (Minor Emergency Clinic) - River Ranch
Family Health Plaza South - Sugar Mill Pond Youngsville
Lafayette Behavioral Health
Lafayette General Endoscopy
Lafayette General Imaging
Lafayette General Surgical Hospital
Lafayette General Telemedicine Clinic
Neuroscience Center
Opelousas General Health System
Savoy Medi
St. Martin Hospital
University Hospital & Clinics
Urgent Care Clinics

COMPETITORS

Baton Rouge General	LifePoint Health
CHRISTUS St. Frances	Our Lady of Lourdes
Cabrini Hospital	Women & Children' s
HCA	Hospital

HISTORICAL FINANCIALS
Company Type: Private

Income Statement
FYE: September 30

	REVENUE ($ mil.)	NET INCOME ($ mil.)	NET PROFIT MARGIN	EMPLOYEES
09/13	342	44	12.9%	1,626
09/12	268	25	9.6%	—
09/09	181	1	1.1%	—
09/08	177	0	—	—
Annual Growth	14.1%	—	—	—

2013 Year-End Financials
Return on assets: 7.9%   Cash ($ mil.): 54
Return on equity: 12.9%
Current ratio: 1.20

LAFAYETTE PARISH SCHOOL BOARD

Auditors: KOLDER CHAMPAGNE SLAVEN & CO

LOCATIONS
HQ: LAFAYETTE PARISH SCHOOL BOARD
113 CHAPLIN DR, LAFAYETTE, LA 705082101
Phone: 337 521-7000
Web: WWW.LPSSONLINE.COM

HISTORICAL FINANCIALS
Company Type: Private

Income Statement
FYE: June 30

	REVENUE ($ mil.)	NET INCOME ($ mil.)	NET PROFIT MARGIN	EMPLOYEES
06/13	339	45	13.5%	3,400
06/10	322	8	2.7%	—
06/09	326	15	4.9%	—
06/08	0	0	—	—
Annual Growth				

2013 Year-End Financials
Return on assets: —   Cash ($ mil.): 126
Return on equity: 13.5%
Current ratio: —

LAHEY CLINIC HOSPITAL INC.

LOCATIONS
HQ: LAHEY CLINIC HOSPITAL INC.
41 MALL RD, BURLINGTON, MA 018050002
Phone: 781 273-5100
Web: WWW.LAHEY.ORG

HISTORICAL FINANCIALS
Company Type: Private

Income Statement
FYE: September 30

	REVENUE ($ mil.)	NET INCOME ($ mil.)	NET PROFIT MARGIN	EMPLOYEES
09/13	774	228	29.5%	5,000
09/12	796	192	24.1%	—
Annual Growth	(2.7%)	19.0%		

2013 Year-End Financials
Return on assets: 3.2%   Cash ($ mil.): 253
Return on equity: 29.5%
Current ratio: 7.50

LAKE COUNTY SCHOOLS

Auditors: PURVIS GRAY & COMPANY LLP O

LOCATIONS
HQ: LAKE COUNTY SCHOOLS
201 W BURLEIGH BLVD, TAVARES, FL 327782407
Phone: 352 253-6500
Web: WWW.LAKE.K12.FL.US

HISTORICAL FINANCIALS
Company Type: Private

Income Statement
FYE: June 30

	REVENUE ($ mil.)	NET INCOME ($ mil.)	NET PROFIT MARGIN	EMPLOYEES
06/13	342	(26)	—	—
06/12	337	(24)	—	—
Annual Growth	1.5%	—	—	—

2013 Year-End Financials
Return on assets: 1.6%   Cash ($ mil.): 102
Return on equity: (-7.8%)
Current ratio: —

LAKE HOSPITAL SYSTEM INC.

The aptly named Lake Hospital System (doing business as Lake Health) serves several northeast Ohio communities located along Lake Erie and throughout Lake County. The not-for-profit health system comprises two main hospital campuses (TriPoint Medical Center and West) which together house more than 350 beds as well as a dozen ancillary facilities offering rehabilitative care outpatient surgery urgent care services primary care and specialist doctors' offices and diagnostic imaging. The system's Lake Health Physician Group includes physicians ranging from family practitioners to vascular surgeons.

Geographic Reach

Lake Health has 16 facilities throughout Lake Geauga Ashtabula and Cuyahoga counties in Ohio.

Operations

The health network has 600 physicians 2700 health care professionals and almost 1000 volunteers.

In 2012 Lake Health saw 74233 emergency room visits and had a total of 18794 admissions.

Its physicians performed 4121 inpatient and 6861 outpatient surgeries. In 2012 the system provided $12 million for community benefit.

Company Background

In 2011 Lake Health opened Willoughby Physical Therapy located within the Willoughby Fit-Works. Lake Health also completed a new emergency room at the Madison Campus and opened a clinic located in the Madison Walmart Supercenter increasing the number of its facilities to 16.

In 2010 Lake Health acquired three Spectrum Diagnostic Imaging sites located in Mentor Willoughby Hills and Lyndhurst and opened a clinic in the Middlefield Walmart Supercenter. Lake Health also opened a comprehensive Balance Center and expanded its Sleep Center services.

Lake Health opened the TriPoint Medical Center in 2009. The $155 million medical center replaced the aging 100-year-old LakeEast Medical Center. The modern four-story TriPoint hospital features 119 private patient rooms as well as digital technology and integrative medicine therapies like healing touch and music therapy.

Lake Health was founded in 1902 by the Daughters of the American Revolution.

EXECUTIVES
Infection Control Director, Pat Cassella
Director Of Operating Room Materials, Mary Gallik
Managing Director, Ferole Parmelee
Vice President of Administrative Services, Steve Karns
Vice President Perioperative Services, Andrea Wasdovich
Senior Vice President, Mary Ogrinc
Director Of Health Information, Kimberly Krueger
Emergency Tech And Secretary, Young Gallo
Secretary Scheduler, Melissa (Mel) Zimmerman

LOCATIONS
HQ: LAKE HOSPITAL SYSTEM INC.
7590 AUBURN RD, PAINESVILLE, OH 440779176
Phone: 440 354-2400
Web: WWW.LAKEHEALTH.ORG

Selected Facilities
Lyndhurst Diagnostics
Madison Campus
Madison Emergency Room
Mentor Campus
Mentor Diagnostics
Mentor Physical Therapy
Painesville Quick Care Center
The Clinic At Madison
The Clinic At Middlefield
Tyler Urgent Care Center
TriPoint Medical Center
West Medical Center
Willoughby Hills Diagnostics
Willoughby Physical Therapy
Chardon Campus
Willowick Campus

PRODUCTS/OPERATIONS

Selected Services
Anti-Coagulation Clinic
Cancer Services
Cardiac Services
Chronic Kidney Disease Clinic
Congestive Heart Failure Clinic
Diabetes Care Center
Emergency Services
Family Birthing Center
Geriatric Psychiatry
Home Health
Imaging Services
Integrated Medicine
Men' s Health
Occupational Health
Orthopedics/Sports Medicine
Pain Management
Senior Services
Sleep Center
Surgical Services

Women' s Services
Wound Care Center

COMPETITORS

Akron Children' s Hospital	Robinson Memorial Hospital
Akron General Health System	Summa Health System
	The Cleveland Clinic
Akron General Medical Center	University Hospitals Health System
MetroHealth System	
Parma Community General Hospital	

HISTORICAL FINANCIALS

Company Type: Private

Income Statement

FYE: December 31

	REVENUE ($ mil.)	NET INCOME ($ mil.)	NET PROFIT MARGIN	EMPLOYEES
12/12	315	5	1.7%	2,200
12/11	360	23	6.5%	—
12/08	278	(31)	—	—
12/02	184	0	—	—
Annual Growth	5.5%	—	—	—

2012 Year-End Financials

Return on assets: 6.0% Cash ($ mil.): 10
Return on equity: 1.7%
Current ratio: 1.30

LAKELAND REGIONAL HEALTH SYSTEM

Auditors: PLANTE & MORAN PLLC ST JOSE

LOCATIONS

HQ: LAKELAND REGIONAL HEALTH SYSTEM
1234 NAPIER AVE, SAINT JOSEPH, MI 490852112
Phone: 269 983-8300
Web: WWW.LAKELANDHEALTH.ORG

HISTORICAL FINANCIALS

Company Type: Private

Income Statement

FYE: September 30

	REVENUE ($ mil.)	NET INCOME ($ mil.)	NET PROFIT MARGIN	EMPLOYEES
09/09	359	25	7.2%	2,430
09/08	353	(15)	—	—
09/07	329	44	13.4%	—
09/06	249	0	—	—
Annual Growth	12.9%	—	—	—

2009 Year-End Financials

Return on assets: 3.1% Cash ($ mil.): 31
Return on equity: 7.2%
Current ratio: 1.10

LAKELAND REGIONAL HEALTH SYSTEMS INC.

Auditors: PERSHING YOAKLEY & ASSOCIATES

LOCATIONS

HQ: LAKELAND REGIONAL HEALTH SYSTEMS INC.
1324 LAKELAND HILLS BLVD, LAKELAND, FL
338054543
Phone: 863 687-1100
Web: WWW.LRMC.COM

HISTORICAL FINANCIALS

Company Type: Private

Income Statement

FYE: September 30

	REVENUE ($ mil.)	NET INCOME ($ mil.)	NET PROFIT MARGIN	EMPLOYEES
09/14	685	67	9.9%	3,124
09/13	24	(13)	—	—
09/12	582	67	11.6%	—
09/11	541	0	—	—
Annual Growth	8.2%	—	—	—

2014 Year-End Financials

Return on assets: 9.4% Cash ($ mil.): 22
Return on equity: 9.9%
Current ratio: 1.00

LAKELAND REGIONAL MEDICAL CENTER INC.

In the land o' lakes Lakeland Regional Medical Center (LRMC) cares for residents' physical ailments. LRMC serves Florida's Polk County (roughly between Kissimmee and Tampa) through an acute care hospital with approximately 850 beds. Among its specialty services are cardiac care cancer treatment senior care urology emergency medicine orthopedics women's and children's health care and surgery. LRMC also operates general care and specialty outpatient clinics. Additionally the hospital provides medical training programs for radiology specialists. Its LRMC Foundation offers financial support for indigent patients facing ongoing treatment.

Operations

LRMC is part of Lakeland Regional Health System a not-for-profit organization that also includes Lakeland Regional Cancer Center Lakeland Regional Family Health Center and Lakeland Regional Health Medical Group.

Annually LRMC has more than 41000 admissions and performs more than 15000 surgeries. Its emergency department treats more than 200000 patients each year.

Financial Performance

Revenue in 2014 totaled $633 million (representing 92% of Lakeland Regional Health System's revenue) while net income totaled $67 million.

LRMC funds its activities through charges to patients for inpatient and outpatient services as well as from non-hospital activities such as its cafeteria gift and uniform shops and physicians' answering service. Although the hospital also receives payment from federal agencies such as Medicaid and Medicare they along with other managed care entities have cut their reimbursement levels causing LRMC's charity care levels to increase.

Strategy

The hospital has been undergoing facility and data systems improvement efforts to enhance care and increase efficiencies. It recently expanded its intensive care department and upgraded technology in areas including radiology orthopedics and chemotherapy.

In 2014 Lakeland Regional Health System announced plans to build an eight-story women and children pavilion at LRMC. The $250 million addition will include 300000 sq. ft. of space including 32 private rooms for mothers and newborns a 30-bed neonatal intensive care unit 64 private rooms for women's surgical and medical care three surgical suites and 12 private suites for labor delivery and recovery. It will also have an education and conference center. The pavilion is expected to open in 2017.

EXECUTIVES

President and Chief Medical Officer, Mack Reavis
Rph Staff Pharmacist, Susan (Sue) Wright
Vice President Human Resources and Total Rewards, Amy Barry
Vice President Legal and Risk Management, Mary Pater
Vice President Human Resources, Jeff Gilray
Radiology Director, Gregg Jacob
Operating Room Director, Margie Voyles
Vice President, Teresa Horn
Associate Vice President of Finance, Jon Boyette
Secretary, Christine Johnston
Auditors: KPMG LLP TAMPA FL

LOCATIONS

HQ: LAKELAND REGIONAL MEDICAL CENTER INC.
1324 LAKELAND HILLS BLVD, LAKELAND, FL
338054500
Phone: 863 687-1100
Web: WWW.LRMC.COM

PRODUCTS/OPERATIONS

Selected Facilities

Lakeland Regional Cancer Center
Lakeland Regional Medical Center (LRMC) Foundation
Lakeland Regional Orthopedics Associates
Lakeland Regional Rehabilitation and Sports Medicine Clinic

Selected Services and Centers

Emergency
Family health center
Gastroenterology
Heart center
Mental health & addictions
Neurosurgery
Nursing
Oncology care
Orthopedic care
Palliative care
Pharmacy
Rehabilitation and sports medicine clinic
Robotic surgery
School of radiologic technology
Stroke center
Surgery
Trauma services
Women and children
Wound center

COMPETITORS

Adventist Health System Sunbelt Healthcare
All Children' s Hospital
Baptist Health South Florida
BayCare Health System
Bayfront Health
DeSoto Memorial
Florida Hospital Tampa Bay Division
HCA
Iasis Healthcare
Manatee Memorial Hospital
Sarasota Memorial Hospital
Tampa General Hospital
Winter Haven Hospital

HISTORICAL FINANCIALS
Company Type: Private

Income Statement
FYE: September 30

	REVENUE ($ mil.)	NET INCOME ($ mil.)	NET PROFIT MARGIN	EMPLOYEES
09/13	584	55	9.4%	3,100
09/11	0	0	1.0%	—
09/10	612	21	3.5%	—
09/09	567	0	—	—
Annual Growth	0.7%	—	—	—

2013 Year-End Financials
Return on assets: —
Return on equity: 9.4%
Current ratio: 0.90
Cash ($ mil.): —

LAKESIDE INDUSTRIES INC.

Lakeside Industries is one of the largest highway contractors in the Pacific Northwest. A leading asphalt paving contractor and manufacturer the company works on municipal commercial and industrial sites as well as residential projects. It also sells hot-mix and cold asphalt to other paving contractors. It has about a dozen offices in western Washington northwestern Oregon and central Idaho. Owned by the founding Lee family Lakeside Industries was established when the family combined their mining sand and gravel asphalt and trucking businesses in 1972.

EXECUTIVES
SEC Treas, Hank Waggoner

LOCATIONS
HQ: LAKESIDE INDUSTRIES INC.
6505 226TH PL SE STE 200, ISSAQUAH, WA 980278905
Phone: 425 313-2600
Web: WWW.LAKESIDEIND.COM

Selected Locations
Aberdeen WA
Anacortes WA
Bellevue ID
Centralia WA
Kent WA
Lacey WA
Longview WA
Monroe WA
Port Angeles WA
Portland OR
Seattle
Vancouver WA

COMPETITORS
Balfour Beatty Infrastructure
Koch Industries Inc.
Peter Kiewit Sons'
The Cruz Corporation

HISTORICAL FINANCIALS
Company Type: Private

Income Statement
FYE: November 30

	REVENUE ($ mil.)	NET INCOME ($ mil.)	NET PROFIT MARGIN	EMPLOYEES
11/07	205	0	—	750
11/05	147	5	4.0%	—
11/04	0	0	—	—
11/03	136	0	—	—
Annual Growth	10.9%	—	—	—

2007 Year-End Financials
Return on assets: 4.2%
Return on equity: —
Current ratio: 1.90
Cash ($ mil.): 21

LANE INDUSTRIES INCORPORATED

Auditors: PRICEWATERHOUSECOOPER LLP HA

LOCATIONS
HQ: LANE INDUSTRIES INCORPORATED
90 FIELDSTONE CT, CHESHIRE, CT 064101212
Phone: 203 235-3351
Web: WWW.LANECONSTRUCT.COM

HISTORICAL FINANCIALS
Company Type: Private

Income Statement
FYE: December 31

	REVENUE ($ mil.)	NET INCOME ($ mil.)	NET PROFIT MARGIN	EMPLOYEES
12/13	1,140	(23)	—	4,500
12/11	1,002	18	1.8%	—
12/10	914	16	1.8%	—
12/09	848	0	—	—
Annual Growth	7.7%	—	—	—

2013 Year-End Financials
Return on assets: 6.9%
Return on equity: (-2.1%)
Current ratio: 0.80
Cash ($ mil.): 25

LANSING BOARD OF WATER AND LIGHT

Letting off a little steam is a good thing for Lansing Board of Water and Light which provides electricity to 95000 residential commercial and industrial customers and water to about 55000 customers in Lansing Michigan. The city-owned utility also produces and distributes steam to 162 customers along 14 miles of steam line. Lansing Board of Water and Light can chill out too. Its chilled water system delivers up to 10000 tons of chilled water capacity to 16 customers to cool the interior of buildings in the downtown area. Lansing Board of Water and Light is the largest municipally owned utility in the state. It is also a major employer in the Lansing area.
Operations

In addition to its power generation and distribution assets Lansing Board of Water and Light owns and operates water wells a raw water transmission system water conditioning facilities and an extensive water distribution system serving potable water to customers in the Greater Lansing area.
Financial Performance

In 2013 the company's revenues increased by 5% due to higher wholesale sales. Net income declined by 85% as the result of higher operating costs due to higher fuel cost associated with electric and steam generation and costs associated with a major ice storm.
Strategy

To meet Clean Air Act compliance standards in 2014 Lansing Board of Water and Light began using an activated carbon injection system to reduce mercury emissions at its Erickson power plant by 90%.
Company Background

In 2007 Lansing Board of Water and Light became the first utility in Michigan to adopt a Renewable Portfolio Standard - setting specific goals for acquiring renewable energy. By law all Michigan utilities must get 10% of their energy from renewable sources by 2015. In 2008 the utility broke ground on the largest largest solar cell array in Michigan in downtown Lansing.

Lansing Board of Water and Light was founded in 1885 when the citizens of Lansing approved a $100000 bond issue to establish a water system to provide the town with drinking water and fire protection. The utility added electricity to its services in 1892 and steam heat in 1919.

EXECUTIVES
Vice Chairman, Sandra Zerkle
Corporate Secretary, Rhonda Jones
CFO, Susan Devon
Executive Director Water Operations and Special Projects, Dick Peffley
Executive Director Strategic Planning and Development, George Stojic
Executive Director Electric Operations, Doug Wood
Director Governmental and Public Relations, Calvin Jones
Director Internal Audit, Susan Pifer
General Manager, J. Peter Lark
Manager Electric System Integrity, Alan Carroll
Director Human Resources, Terri L. Singleton
Energy Efficiency Specialist, Aileen Gow
General Counsel, Brandie Ekren
Manager Finance and Planning, William (Bill) Aldrich
Director Communications, Mark Nixon
Chairman, Frank B. Lain
Marketing Manager, Sue Warren
Vice Chairman, Sandra Zerkle
Director, Julee M. Rodocker
Director, Robert W. Cochran
Director, Peter W. Kramer
Director, Tony DeLuca
Auditors: PLANTE & MORAN PLLC EAST LANS

LOCATIONS
HQ: LANSING BOARD OF WATER AND LIGHT
1201 S WASHINGTON AVE, LANSING, MI 489101650
Phone: 517 702-6000
Web: WWW.LBWL.COM

HISTORICAL FINANCIALS
Company Type: Private

Income Statement
FYE: June 30

	REVENUE ($ mil.)	NET INCOME ($ mil.)	NET PROFIT MARGIN	EMPLOYEES
06/11	306	7	2.5%	740
06/10	18	17	97.3%	—
Annual Growth	1567.1%	(57.2%)	—	—

2011 Year-End Financials
Return on assets: 6.5% Cash ($ mil.): 47
Return on equity: 2.5%
Current ratio: 1.50

LATEX CONSTRUCTION COMPANY INC

Auditors: BIRDSONG & ASSOCIATES LLC SU

LOCATIONS
HQ: LATEX CONSTRUCTION COMPANY INC
1353 FARMER RD NW, CONYERS, GA 300123488
Phone: 770 760-0820
Web: WWW.LATEXCONSTRUCTION.COM

HISTORICAL FINANCIALS
Company Type: Private

Income Statement
FYE: December 31

	REVENUE ($ mil.)	NET INCOME ($ mil.)	NET PROFIT MARGIN	EMPLOYEES
12/08	431	50	11.8%	400
12/07	272	40	14.7%	—
12/06	1,870	0	—	—
Annual Growth	—	5471.5%	—	—

2008 Year-End Financials
Return on assets: 4.7% Cash ($ mil.): 74
Return on equity: 11.8%
Current ratio: 2.00

LAUREN ENGINEERS & CONSTRUCTORS INC.

Lauren Engineers & Constructors is a contractor that targets the power chemical special metals and oil refining industries. In addition to its core engineering procurement and construction capabilities the company offers fabrication project management and mechanical and electrical maintenance services. With offices in Georgia Tennessee and Texas Lauren Engineers & Constructors serves about 25 states. It also operates in Canada with a presence in Calgary. Some of its power and chemical customers include Flying J Florida Power & Light General Electric Company and Procter & Gamble. The company was originally established in 1984 as a subsidiary of Comstock Mechanical.

Geographic Reach

Lauren Engineers & Constructors which is licensed in some 25 states maintains offices in the US in Georgia Tennessee and Texas as well as in Canada through subsidiary Kamtech Services Inc. (KSI). It operates a joint venture in India.

Operations

Boasting more than 1000 employees company-wide the contractor operates its business through three entities.

Lauren Concise an EPC contractor serves Canada's oil and gas sector. Leveraging its parent's strengths Lauren Concise offers turnkey engineering procurement and construction services in the country.

Another subsidiary Kamtech Services Inc. (KSI) is based in Canada and caters to the industrial sector with its building trades expertise in mechanical construction services.

Lauren CCL Engineers Private Limited a leader in Concentrated Solar Power (CSP) provides India with engineering procurement management and construction services for the country's thermal solar power facilities. Headquartered in Navi Mumbai Lauren CCL is a joint venture of CCL Optoelectronics Pvt. Ltd. and Lauren Engineers & Constructors.

Strategy

Lauren Engineers & Constructors' projects range from $500000 shutdowns to $500 million EPC power plants.

Completed projects include the modernization of a chemical plant for BAE Solution in Kingsport Tennessee; plants in Florida Nevada North Carolina and Virginia; and the Godawari Green Energy Limited project in Rajasthan India. The company was awarded a contract in 2013 from Holly Frontier El Dorado Refining for the Naphtha Fractionation and Splitting Project in Kansas.

Sales and Marketing

Lauren Engineers & Constructors serves a variety of customers. Typical clients –large and small –include Florida Power & Light Bosque Power General Electric Calpine Siemens Westinghouse Eastman Chemical DAK Americas Buhler Flying J Murphy Oil and Alon among others.

The company serves several sectors such as power chemical polymers and petrochemical and refining.

EXECUTIVES
EVP, Ron Johnson
Chairman and CEO, C. Cleve Whitener
EVP, John Hyland
EVP, Clint Rosenbaum
EVP, Jack Shoemate
CFO, Tom Modisett

LOCATIONS
HQ: LAUREN ENGINEERS & CONSTRUCTORS INC.
901 S 1ST ST, ABILENE, TX 796021502
Phone: 325 670-9660
Web: WWW.LAURENEC.COM

PRODUCTS/OPERATIONS

Selected Services
Construction
Engineering
EPC
Fabrication
Field Services
Modularization
Procurement
Project Management
Safety

Selected Markets
Chemical
Polymers
Power
Pulp & Paper
Refining
Solar Power
Special Metals

COMPETITORS
Bechtel	Gemma Power Systems
CH2M HILL	Jacobs Engineering
Fluor	KBR Building Group
ForeRunner Corporation	MYR Group

HISTORICAL FINANCIALS
Company Type: Private

Income Statement
FYE: December 31

	REVENUE ($ mil.)	NET INCOME ($ mil.)	NET PROFIT MARGIN	EMPLOYEES
12/13	163	(3)	—	1,000
12/12	129	(13)	—	—
12/11	249	(0)	—	—
12/10	162	0	—	—
Annual Growth	0.1%	—	—	—

2013 Year-End Financials
Return on assets: 6.3% Cash ($ mil.): 7
Return on equity: (-2.1%)
Current ratio: 0.80

LAWRENCE & MEMORIAL HOSPITAL INC.

Lawrence & Memorial Hospital (L&M) connects residents of Connecticut with health care whether they're near the Rhode Island border or enjoying the Connecticut River. The not-for-profit hospital founded in 1912 provides services to a 10-town region on the Connecticut shoreline and neighboring areas in the Northeast. L&M has roughly 280 beds and provides general acute care including medical surgical rehabilitative pediatric psychiatric and obstetrical services. The hospital also runs about a dozen community physician practices and specialty clinics.

Operations

Each year L&M sees some 87000 patients in its emergency room. It also admits about 13000 inpatients and conducts some 9000 surgeries annually. The hospital's specialty facilities include a cardiac catheterization lab a cancer center a sleep disorder unit and a the region's only neonatal ICU.

Affiliates of the L&M system include Joslin Diabetes Center L&M Physicians the Visiting Nurse Association of Southeastern Connecticut and Hospice Southeastern Connecticut.

Geographic Reach

L&M serves patients in eastern Connecticut as well as Washington County in Rhode Island and the Fishers Island region of New York State.

Strategy

The changing economy and health care landscape in the US has prompted many independent hospitals to seek affiliations with other medical providers as a means of controlling spending and enhancing care and L&M is no exception. Additionally the system provides patients with e-Connect a mobile-friendly portal where they can access hospital information and health records.

EXECUTIVES
Vice President Development And Community Relations, William Stanley
Vice President of Sales and Marketing, Wanda Carlson
Director Of Pharmacy, Warren Rogers
Director Of Operating Room, Karen Buck

Vice President Patient Care Services CNO, Lauren Williams
Vice President Chief Human Resources Officer, Donna Epps
Treasurer, Chester Kitchings
Auditors: PRICEWATERHOUSECOOPERS LLP HA

LOCATIONS

HQ: LAWRENCE & MEMORIAL HOSPITAL INC.
365 MONTAUK AVE, NEW LONDON, CT 063204769
Phone: 860 442-0711
Web: WWW.LMHOSPITAL.ORG

PRODUCTS/OPERATIONS

Selected Services
Core Services
  Cardiac Care
  Maternity Care
  Cancer Care
  Surgery
  Occupational Health Care
Other Services
  Behavioral Medicine
  Chronic Pain
  Diagnostic Imaging
  Emergency Services
  Gastroenterology
  Hand Center
  Infectious Diseases
  Joint Replacement Center
  Joslin Diabetes Center
  Laboratory
  Neurosurgery
  Pulmonary Disorders
  Pulmonary Rehabilitation
  Rehabilitation - Acute Inpatient
  Rehabilitation - Signature Outpatient
  Sleep Center
  Social Work
  Women' s and Infants Services
  Wound and Hyperbaric Center

COMPETITORS

Backus
Care New England
Connecticut Children' s Medical Center
Day Kimball Hospital
Harrington Memorial Hospital
Hartford Health Care
Hospital of Central Connecticut
Kent Hospital
Roger Williams Medical Center
Saint Francis Hospital and Medical Center
Sturdy Memorial
University of Connecticut Health Center
Waterbury Hospital
Yale New Haven Health System

HISTORICAL FINANCIALS
Company Type: Private

Income Statement   FYE: September 30

	REVENUE ($ mil.)	NET INCOME ($ mil.)	NET PROFIT MARGIN	EMPLOYEES
09/13	315	10	3.4%	2,200
09/10	324	8	2.6%	—
09/09	293	(11)	—	—
09/08	1,125	0	—	—
Annual Growth	(22.5%)	—	—	—

2013 Year-End Financials
Return on assets: 7.6%   Cash ($ mil.): —
Return on equity: 3.4%
Current ratio: 0.70

LEE COUNTY ELECTRIC COOPERATIVE INC.

If you are a Floridian who is a really early riser or a night owl Lee County Electric Cooperative (LCEC) may help light your way. The electric cooperative provides power to more than 198880 residential and commercial customers across five counties in southwestern Florida (Lee County and parts of Collier Hendry Charlotte and Broward counties. The member-owned non-profit electric utility operates more than 8000 miles of transmission and distribution lines and more than 20 substations. Tampa-based Seminole Electric Cooperative serves as LCEC's wholesale power supplier.

Geographic Reach

The company's service territory includes Cape Coral North Fort Myers Marco Island Sanibel and Captiva Islands Pine Island Everglades City Immokalee and parts of Lehigh Acres.

Financial Performance

In 2012 LCEC's revenues declined by 0.3% as the result of abnormally mild weather and conservation efforts by customers coupled with ongoing economic uncertainty all of which trimmed demand. Net income decreased by 11% in 2012 as the drop in net sales outpaced only slightly lower operating costs for the year.

As part of its non-profit charter LCEC returns surplus equity to its current and former members. In 2012 its Board of Trustees approved $12.9 million in equity distribution.

Strategy

The cooperative is working on a number of strategic initiatives in order to keep up with the demands of the growing population in its service area: maintain power quality enhance disaster recovery competency keep up with regulatory compliance requirements implement mobile workforce technology and keep employees engaged.

To better support its customers that year LCEC upgraded its website with improved navigation and additional energy management tips and tools.

Company Background

Under the leadership of Homer Welch (and as part of a nationwide rural electrification drive) LCEC began operations with 15 miles of distribution line and 158 members or about 1% of Lee County's 1940 population of 17500.
Auditors: PURVIS GRAY & COMPANY SARASOT

LOCATIONS

HQ: LEE COUNTY ELECTRIC COOPERATIVE INC.
4980 BAYLINE DR, FORT MYERS, FL 339173998
Phone: 800 599-2356
Web: WWW.LCEC.NET

HISTORICAL FINANCIALS
Company Type: Private

Income Statement   FYE: December 31

	REVENUE ($ mil.)	NET INCOME ($ mil.)	NET PROFIT MARGIN	EMPLOYEES
12/13	405	2	0.5%	400
12/12	404	2	0.6%	—
Annual Growth	0.3%	(12.7%)	—	—

2013 Year-End Financials
Return on assets: 9.9%   Cash ($ mil.): 2
Return on equity: 0.5%
Current ratio: 1.00

LEE LEWIS CONSTRUCTION INC.

General builder Lee Lewis Construction has waltzed across Texas and beyond to keep in step with the top US contractors. The company provides construction-related services and construction management for commercial institutional and industrial projects. Among its projects is the Garland ISD Special Events Center in Garland Texas; it also worked on the Grand Floridian Resort at Walt Disney World. The company earns much of its revenue from projects for Texas school systems. Projects for hometown neighbor Texas Tech University have generated a significant portion of the company's business. CEO Lee Lewis founded the company in 1976.

EXECUTIVES

Senior Vice President, Bob Fullington
Auditors: M WEISS AND ASSOCIATES INC

LOCATIONS

HQ: LEE LEWIS CONSTRUCTION INC.
7810 ORLANDO AVE, LUBBOCK, TX 794231942
Phone: 806 797-8400
Web: WWW.LEELEWIS.COM

COMPETITORS

Austin Industries	Hunt Construction
Beck Group	Manhattan Construction
Flintco	Skanska USA Building
Hensel Phelps Construction	Turner Construction

HISTORICAL FINANCIALS
Company Type: Private

Income Statement   FYE: June 30

	REVENUE ($ mil.)	NET INCOME ($ mil.)	NET PROFIT MARGIN	EMPLOYEES
06/09	229	6	2.8%	200
06/06	245	4	1.8%	—
06/05	176	2	1.3%	—
06/04	138	0	—	—
Annual Growth	10.6%	—	—	—

2009 Year-End Financials
Return on assets: 13.8%   Cash ($ mil.): 25
Return on equity: 2.8%
Current ratio: 1.50

LEE MEMORIAL HOSPITAL

LOCATIONS

HQ: LEE MEMORIAL HOSPITAL
2776 CLEVELAND AVE, FORT MYERS, FL 339015855
Phone: 239 343-2000
Web: WWW.LEEMEMORIAL.ORG

HISTORICAL FINANCIALS

Company Type: Private

Income Statement

FYE: September 30

	REVENUE ($ mil.)	NET INCOME ($ mil.)	NET PROFIT MARGIN	EMPLOYEES
09/13	632	135	21.4%	1,159
09/12	613	105	17.3%	—
Annual Growth	3.2%	27.5%	—	—

2013 Year-End Financials

Return on assets: 7.3%
Return on equity: 21.4%
Current ratio: 1.10

Cash ($ mil.): 23

LEGACY EMANUEL HOSPITAL & HEALTH CENTER

Legacy Emanuel Hospital and Health Center part of the Legacy Health System provides acute and specialized health care to residents of Portland Oregon and surrounding communities. The 420-bed teaching hospital's operations include centers devoted to trauma treatment burn care oncology birthing neurosurgery orthopedics and cardiology. It also houses a pediatric hospital and operates the region's Life Flight Network service which is owned by a consortium of local hospitals. Legacy Emanuel's emergency department handles more than 15600 visits every year.

Operations

Legacy Emanuel's trauma and burn centers are level I designated facilities meaning they receive severe trauma and burn cases from other area hospitals. The hospital's burn center is the only one of its kind in an area stretching from Seattle to Sacramento and Salt Lake City. Other specialist facilities at Legacy Emanuel include its maternity center and its diagnostic imaging and screening units.

The medical center sees more than 18000 inpatients each year. Its staff includes about 140 full-time doctors and dentists as well as 700 full-time registered nurses. The Randall Children's Hospital located within Legacy Emanuel has about 600 affiliated pediatricians and specialists on its staff and handles about 100000 patient encounters each year including 20000 emergency room visits.

Strategy

The hospital has undergone massive expansion efforts. The hospital has completed construction of the new Randall Children's Hospital facilities making it one of the largest pediatric facilities in the state. The new pediatric center is four times as large as the past facilities. Other expansion efforts in recent years include new acute and intensive care capacity.

Company Background

To expand its medical transportation services Legacy Emanuel and other owners of LFN teamed up to purchase 15 new helicopters in 2012.

Legacy Emanuel Hospital was established in 1912 by the Lutheran Church.

EXECUTIVES

SVP and Chief Medical Officer, George A. (Jack) Cioffi, age 53

SVP and CIO, Richard (Dick) Gibson, age 59
Chief Administrative Officer, Lori Morgan
VP-Community Rels & Mktg, Wayne Clark
Auditors: KPMG LLP PORTLAND OR

LOCATIONS

HQ: LEGACY EMANUEL HOSPITAL & HEALTH CENTER
2801 N GANTENBEIN AVE, PORTLAND, OR 972271623
Phone: 503 413-2200
Web: WWW.LEGACYHEALTH.ORG

PRODUCTS/OPERATIONS

Selected Centers and Services

Burn care
Cancer care
Children's care
Diabetes and nutrition
Emergency services
Family birth center
Gardens
High-risk obstetrics
Imaging
Injury prevention
Intensive care
Interventional and diagnostic cardiology
Level I trauma center
Life flight network
Maternal-fetal medicine
Neurology and neurosurgery including spine surgery
Orthopedics
Pediatrics
Rehabilitation (inpatient and outpatient)
Radiation oncology
Stroke
Surgery (including minimally invasive surgery)
Vascular clinic
Wound and ostomy clinic
Wound care and outpatient burn clinic

COMPETITORS

Adventist Health	PeaceHealth Southwest
Asante Health System	Medical Center
Dignity Health	Providence Health &
Kadlec Regional	Services
Medical Center	Salem Hospital
PeaceHealth	

HISTORICAL FINANCIALS

Company Type: Private

Income Statement

FYE: March 31

	REVENUE ($ mil.)	NET INCOME ($ mil.)	NET PROFIT MARGIN	EMPLOYEES
03/14	649	30	4.8%	3,619
03/13	566	6	1.1%	—
03/12	571	(6)	—	—
03/10	573	0	—	—
Annual Growth	3.2%	—	—	—

2014 Year-End Financials

Return on assets: 1.6%
Return on equity: 4.8%
Current ratio: 1.60

Cash ($ mil.): —

LEGACY HEALTH

Legacy Health System strives to create a legacy of positive health in the Portland/Vancouver metropolitan area. A not-for-profit provider of health care services in Oregon and Washington the health system operates half a dozen hospitals including Legacy Emanuel Hospital and Legacy Good Samaritan Hospital all founded by a variety of secular organizations. Legacy Health has more than 1100 total beds and its facilities provide such services as acute and critical care behavioral health and outpatient and health education programs. It also operates home health hospice and research facilities; emergency transportation helicopters; and a number of regional clinics and labs.

Operations

The company's hospitals include: Legacy Emanuel Hospital Randall Children's Hospital Legacy Good Samaritan Medical Center Legacy Meridian Park Medical Center Legacy Mount Hood Medical Center and Legacy Salmon Creek Medical Center in Washington.

Legacy Health System provides inpatient care to about 55000 visitors each year. Its Legacy Medical Group includes 300 affiliated physicians operating about 20 primary care clinics in the region as well as a number of specialty care centers in fields such as obstetrics pediatrics cardiology neurology and orthopedics.

In addition to providing medical care Legacy Health System partners with government and commercial entities to conduct medical research studies.

Geographic Reach

Legacy Health System operates six hospitals more than 50 outpatient clinics and a number of hospice research and diagnostic facilities in the Portland/Vancouver metropolitan area. It has three hospitals located in Portland as well as one each in Gresham Oregon; Tualatin Oregon; and Vancouver Washington.

Financial Performance

Legacy Health System reported a 9% increase in revenues to some $1.5 billion in 2014 marking several straight years of rising revenues due to organic growth.

The system reported a 7% increase in net income to some $95 million in 2014 due to increase in revenues partially offset by increased operating expenses.

Strategy

The company is focused on improving its existing hospitals. To conveniently bring fresh food directly to clinic patients suffering from chronic diseases in 2014 it opened the My Street Grocery at its Legacy Good Samaritan location in Legacy Emanuel Hospital with a larger more comprehensive storefront expanded days and times. It also opened a new cardiac care center at its Legacy Meridian Park Medical Center in 2013.

Legacy Health is also concentrating on opening new general care and specialty clinics partly through partnerships with area physicians. The addition of new clinics is designed not only to service the needs of small communities but also to ensure that referrals from area doctors help to sustain its nearby hospitals. In 2013 Legacy Health officially expanded its presence to the Westside of Portland with the opening of two new Legacy Medical Group clinics Legacy Medical Group — Cornell and Legacy Medical Group — Forest Heights. The new facilities allow Legacy to broaden its Portland-area offerings by providing pediatric orthopedic diagnostic and sports medicine services among others.

That year Legacy Devers Eye Institute also expanded its geographic presence by opening Legacy Devers Eye Institute – Emanuel. Legacy Health is also expanding primary care services for residents in Gresham and the surrounding East County communities and has started offering adult primary care services. In 2013 it broke ground on Legacy Laboratory Services' new expanded headquarters —a two-story 62000 sq. ft. structure adjacent to the lab's current facility which it shares with Legacy Research Institute.

In 2015 the system partnered with GoHealth Urgent Care to open urgent care centers in metropolitan Portland. That partnership began with GoHealth's five existing centers (formerly operating under the Northwest Urgent Care brand) and will add multiple new facilities which will operate under the Legacy-GoHealth moniker.

Company Background

The company was founded through the 1989 merger of HealthLink and Good Samaritan Hospital.

EXECUTIVES

Vice President Human Resources, Sonya Steves
SVP and Chief Nursing Officer, Carol Bradley
President and CEO, George J. Brown
Chief Administrative Officer Legacy Meridian Park Medical Center, Allyson Anderson
Chief Administrative Officer Legacy Salmon Creek Medical Center, Jonathan Avery
SVP and CIO, John Kenagy
Chief Administrative Officer Legacy Emanuel Medical Center, Lori Morgan
SVP and COO, Mike Newcomb
SVP and Chief Medical Officer, Lewis Low
Chief Administrative Officer Legacy Mount Hood Medical Center, Gretchen Nichols
Senior Vice President Chief Medical Officer, Jack Cioffi
Vice President Finance, Gordon Edwards
Vice President, Jim Sanger
Vp Finance, Scott Johnson
Senior Vice President Chief Development Officer, Maureen A Bradley
Clinical Vice President of Research, Tony Melaragno
Vice President Clinical, Juan Millan
Vice President Financial Services, Patricia (Pat) Gianelli
Vice President Legacy Laboratory Servi, Don Toussaint
Vice President, Will Mowe
Vice President Finance, Steven (Steve) Fhfma
Vice President Supply Chain Operations, Edwin Streeter
Board Of Directors, Randi Reiten
Auditors: KPMG LLP PORTLAND OR

LOCATIONS

HQ: LEGACY HEALTH
1919 NW LOVEJOY ST, PORTLAND, OR 972091503
Phone: 503 415-5600
Web: WWW.LEGACYHEALTH.ORG

PRODUCTS/OPERATIONS

Selected Facilities
Hospitals
Legacy Emanuel Hospital (Portland Oregon)
Legacy Good Samaritan Medical Center (Portland Oregon)
Legacy Meridian Park Medical Center (Tualatin Oregon)
Legacy Mount Hood Medical Center (Gresham Oregon)
Legacy Salmon Creek Medical Center (Vancouver Washington)
Randall Children' s Hospital At Legacy Emanuel (Portland Oregon)
Clinics
Legacy Medical Group - Battle Ground
Legacy Med
Legacy Med
Legacy Med
Legacy Med
Legacy Med
Legacy Medical Group - Fisher' s Landing
Legacy Medical Group - Forest Heights
Legacy Medical Group - Good Samaritan
Legacy Medical Group - Lake Oswego
Legacy Medical Group - Mount Hood
Legacy Med
Legacy Med
Legacy Med
Legacy Medical Group - West Linn
Legacy Med
Salmon Creek Family Medicine (Vancouver Washington)

Salmon Creek Internal Medicine (Vancouver Washington)
Urgent Care St. Helens (St. Helens Oregon)

COMPETITORS

Adventist Health
Asante Health System
Dignity Health
Kadlec Regional Medical Center
PeaceHealth
Providence Health & Services
Salem Hospital

HISTORICAL FINANCIALS

Company Type: Private

Income Statement

FYE: March 31

	REVENUE ($ mil.)	NET INCOME ($ mil.)	NET PROFIT MARGIN	EMPLOYEES
03/14	183	9	5.2%	8,000
03/12*	1,326	(0)	—	—
08/10	1,249	192	15.4%	—
03/10	1,249	0	—	—
Annual Growth	(38.1%)	—	—	—

*Fiscal year change

2014 Year-End Financials

Return on assets: 4.5%   Cash ($ mil.): 69
Return on equity: 5.2%
Current ratio: 1.30

LEHIGH UNIVERSITY

Lehigh University (LU) nestled in eastern Pennsylvania's Lehigh Valley offers about 90 undergraduate programs and majors at colleges of arts and sciences business and economics engineering and applied sciences and education. It also offers more than 40 masters and doctoral degree programs as well as certificate programs. Tuition is more than $40000 per year; more than half of students receive financial aid. LU has an enrollment of nearly 7000 undergraduate and graduate students. The university was founded in 1865 by entrepreneur and philanthropist Asa Packer.

Geographic Reach

One of the most selective schools in the nation it accepts about 3600 students per year out of the more than 12000 who apply; about a third of those accepted matriculate at LU.

Operations

The student to faculty ratio is 10:1 and the average class size is 27. The students are instructed by about 700 faculty memebrs.

EXECUTIVES

Vice President Internal Programming, Toni Isreal
Secretary, Tara Moughan
Auditors: KPMG LLP PHILADELPHIA PA

LOCATIONS

HQ: LEHIGH UNIVERSITY
27 MEMORIAL DR W UNIT 8, BETHLEHEM, PA 180153005
Phone: 610 758-3000
Web: WWW.LEHIGH.EDU

HISTORICAL FINANCIALS

Company Type: Private

Income Statement

FYE: June 30

	REVENUE ($ mil.)	NET INCOME ($ mil.)	NET PROFIT MARGIN	EMPLOYEES
06/14	367	156	42.6%	4,000
06/13	357	114	32.0%	—
06/12	423	23	5.5%	—
06/07	316	0	—	—
Annual Growth	2.2%	—	—	—

2014 Year-End Financials

Return on assets: 10.9%   Cash ($ mil.): 49
Return on equity: 42.6%
Current ratio: —

LEHIGH VALLEY HEALTH NETWORK INC.

Residents of the Lehigh Valley seeking medical care head uptown to facilities operated by the Lehigh Valley Health Network (LVHN). The not-for-profit health care provider operates through four full-service hospital campuses housing a total of about 1000 licensed beds. The medical center serves as a regional referral center for trauma and burn care and organ transplantation as well as specialty care in numerous areas such as cardiology women's health and pediatric surgery. LVHN also boasts a network of physician practices and community health centers as well as home health and hospice units.

Operations

The company's hospitals provide care in about 95 specialist fields including pediatric care burn treatment trauma care organ transplant cardiovascular care oncology and neurology. Its children's hospital includes inpatient emergency and specialist units. LVHN also conducts medical training programs and performs research in a range of different areas including cancer cardiovascular and infectious disease; a number of these programs are conducted through partnerships with entities including the H. Lee Moffitt Cancer Center and the University of South Florida's Morsani College of Medicine.

In addition to its core hospital operations the health organization has an alliance with the Sacred Heart Hospital of Allentown through which it provides Sacred Heart with certain services in the areas of cardiac care primary care telehealth services and mental health care. The two hospitals discussed but ultimately dismissed the possibility of a formal merger settling on being affiliated instead.

LVHN's 40 community clinics administer primary and specialty care for area residents including facilities for low-income patients. For patients (insured or not) who need care for minor ailments and routine tests LVHN operates a handful of retail health clinics under the Careworks brand. In addition the network includes a system of medical laboratories (Health Network Laboratories).

Geographic Reach

The LVHN system's main facilities are located in Allentown Bethlehem and Hazleton. With more than a dozen additional health centers the network provides services to residents of a five-county territory in Pennsylvania.

Financial Performance

Revenues increased 8% to $1.7 billion in 2014 on higher patient service and supporting operations revenues as well as higher investment earnings. Net income increased 59% to $95.5 million that year.

Strategy

LVHN opened the region's first pediatric emergency department at its Cedar Crest campus in 2011. The center houses about a dozen beds and is staffed by pediatric emergency physicians and nurses as well as a child life specialist. To further expand its emergency capabilities in 2013 the organization added emergency transportation services to its offerings.

In early 2014 LVHN merged with Greater Hazleton Health Alliance adding Hazleton General Hospital (now Lehigh Valley Hospital-Hazleton) to its network of facilities. The merger also added a physician group a hospital-based home health agency and a health and wellness center all in Hazleton

To promote care coordination and communication LVHN entered into a clinical affiliation with CVS Health in 2015. Through the partnership information on patient visits and prescriptions is accessible to care providers through secure electronic health record (EHR) systems.

EXECUTIVES

Senior Vice President Operations, James (Jamie) Geiger
SVP Patient Care Services and Chief Nursing Officer, Anne Panik
President and CEO, Brian Nester
COO, Terry Capuano
Chief medical officer, Thomas Whalen
SVP and CFO, Edward O'Dea
LVPG Clinical Educator Clinical Services, Rob Mangano
Vice President Government and Legislative Affairs, Mary Tirrell
Radiology Director, Robert (Bob) Kricun
Medical Director Education Technology, William (Bill) Bond
Vice President Of Customer Service, Dorothy Jacquez
Vice President Human Resources, Debby Patrick
Vice President, Lise Twiford
Cota L, Scott Racine
Vice President of Major Gifts, Paul Hurd
Director of Infection Control, Terry Burger
Vice Chairman Department Of Psychiatry, Susan (Sue) Wiley
Assistant Secretary, Glenn Guanowsky
Auditors: DELOITTE & TOUCHE LLP PHILADE

LOCATIONS

HQ: LEHIGH VALLEY HEALTH NETWORK INC.
1247 S CEDAR CREST BLVD, ALLENTOWN, PA
181036298
Phone: 610 402-8000
Web: WWW.LVHN.ORG

PRODUCTS/OPERATIONS

Selected Facilities
Community Health Centers
  Hamburg Community Health Center
  Lehigh Valley Health Center at Bath
  Lehigh Valley Health Center at Bethlehem Township
  Lehigh Valley Health Center at Hellertown
  Lehigh Valley Health Center at Kutztown
  Lehigh Valley Health Center at Saucon Valley
  Lehigh Valley Health Center at Trexlertown
  Upper Bucks Health & Diagnostic Center (in partnership with Grand View Hospital Quakertown)
Hospitals
  Lehigh Valley Hospital - 17th St. (short-stay hospital Salisbury Township in Allentown)
  Lehigh Valley Hospital - Cedar Crest (Allentown)
  Lehigh Valley Hospital - Muhlenberg (Bethlehem)

COMPETITORS

Abington Memorial Hospital
Ascension Health
Community Health Systems
Doylestown Hospital
Grand View
Jefferson Health System
Mercy Health System
Moses Taylor Hospital
North Philadelphia Health System
Pennsylvania Hospital
Reading Hospital and Medical Center
Sacred Heart Hospital of Allentown
Shore Memorial Hospital
St. Luke's University Health Network
Tenet Healthcare
University of Pennsylvania Health System
Wyoming Valley Health Care System

HISTORICAL FINANCIALS

Company Type: Private

Income Statement

FYE: June 30

	REVENUE ($ mil.)	NET INCOME ($ mil.)	NET PROFIT MARGIN	EMPLOYEES
06/14	1,694	224	13.3%	12,000
06/12	1,620	(63)	—	—
06/11	1,524	314	20.6%	—
06/10	1,399	0	—	—
Annual Growth	4.9%	—	—	—

2014 Year-End Financials

Return on assets: 4.2%   Cash ($ mil.): 44
Return on equity: 13.3%
Current ratio: 1.30

LEON COUNTY SCHOOL BOARD

Auditors: DAVID W MARTIN CPA TALLAHAS

LOCATIONS

HQ: LEON COUNTY SCHOOL BOARD
2757 W PENSACOLA ST, TALLAHASSEE, FL
323042907
Phone: 850 487-7100
Web: WWW.LEON.K12.FL.US

HISTORICAL FINANCIALS

Company Type: Private

Income Statement

FYE: June 30

	REVENUE ($ mil.)	NET INCOME ($ mil.)	NET PROFIT MARGIN	EMPLOYEES
06/11	340	56	16.5%	5,030
06/06	312	39	12.8%	—
06/05	21	0	0.3%	—
06/04	283	0	—	—
Annual Growth	2.6%	—	—	—

2011 Year-End Financials

Return on assets: 2.0%   Cash ($ mil.): 67
Return on equity: 16.5%
Current ratio: —

LESTER E. COX MEDICAL CENTERS

Where health care in the Ozarks is concerned Lester is more. Lester E. Cox Medical Centers (dba CoxHealth) provides a myriad of medical services to people in Missouri and Arkansas. CoxHealth's network includes five acute care hospitals (with more than 950 beds) and more than 80 physician clinics. Centers for cardiac care cancer treatment orthopedics mental health and women's health are among CoxHealth's specialized care options. Other operations include an ambulance service offering both ground and air transportation the Cox Health Systems HMO the Oxford HealthCare home health agency and educational programs. The organization was named after its primary fundraiser in the 1940s.

Operations

Each year CoxHealth handles about 500000 outpatient visits; 205000 emergency urgent care and trauma visits; 32000 ground ambulance transports; and nearly 4000 births. Its hospitals include Cox Medical Center South Cox Medical Center Branson Cox North Hospital Cox Monett Hospital and the Meyer Orthopedic and Rehabilitation Hospital. Its specialty clinics include centers for cancer orthopedics cardiovascular care women's and children's health outpatient surgery and diagnostic imaging.

Geographic Reach

CoxHealth serves about 25 communities in 25 counties in southwestern Missouri and northwestern Arkansas. Major facilities are located in Branson Monett and Springfield Missouri.

Sales and Marketing

The organization primarily receives income from commercial insurance reimbursements which account for about 60% of patient revenue. Other payer sources include Medicare and Medicaid plans and self-pay patients.

Strategy

Enduring through blizzards and tornadoes CoxHealth strives to improve its services and the health of its community.

Expanding its geographic coverage in 2013 CoxHealth completed a partnership deal with Skaggs Regional Medical Center which changed its name to Cox Medical Center Branson. CoxHealth plans to invest about $100 million into medical facilities in Branson.

The system also grows by adding or expanding facilities. It started construction of an expansion of its Cox Medical Center South facility in 2013. The organization has launched pediatric general surgery and urology programs as it looks to open the Dee Ann White Women's and Children's Hospital at the facility. In 2014 CoxHealth opened the first phase of its $30 million emergency department expansion at Cox Medical Center Branson. The following year the system opened the Springfield Center for Dyslexia and Learning. Other initiatives include upgrading clinical processes and information technology systems.

Company Background

CoxHealth was founded as Burge Deaconess Hospital in 1908. It became Lester E. Cox Medical Centers in 1968 following the death of Cox a St. Louis businessman who led a series of major fund raising campaigns in the 1940s critical to the survival and growth of the hospital.

EXECUTIVES

Vice President and Chief Medical Officer; and Medical Director Oxford Hospice, Dan Sontheimer

Senior Vice President Chief Hospital Officer, John Duff
Vice President and Chief Nursing Officer, Karen Kramer
SVP and CFO, Jacob McWay
Vice President and Chief Information Officer, Bruce Robison
President Cox HealthPlans, Jeffrey C. (Jeff) Bond
VP and Chief Clinical Officer, Ron Prenger
Vice President; President Cox Monett, Genny Maroc
Vice President; President Oxford Healthcare, Karen Thomas
Chairman Joint Operations Committee and Chief Integrated Physicians, Kenneth Powell
Vice President President Home Parenteral Services, H. Lynn Kelley
President and CEO; Director, Steven D. (Steve) Edwards
President CoxHealth Foundation, Lisa Alexander
President Cox College, Anne Liners Brett
Admissions Director, Cindy McKnelly
Vice President Administration, Debbie Cain
Medical Director, Kerry Randolph
Physical Therapy Director, Debbie Harris
Vice President Of Corporate Integrity, Betty Breshears
Vice President Clinical Services, Pete Leer
Secretary, Kathy Rigger

LOCATIONS

HQ: LESTER E. COX MEDICAL CENTERS
1423 N JEFFERSON AVE, SPRINGFIELD, MO 658021917
Phone: 417 269-3000
Web: WWW.COXHEALTH.COM

PRODUCTS/OPERATIONS

Selected Services
Air Care
Alzheimer's Disease
Behavioral Health
Brain and Spine Disorders
Breast Care
Cancer Services
Children's Health
Diabetes
Dialysis
Ear Nose and Throat (ENT)
Emergency Department
Fitness Centers
Food and Nutrition
Heart and Vascular
Home Health
Hyperbaric Medicine and Wound Care
Neuroscience
Occupational Medicine
Orthopedics
Parenting
Parkinson's Clinic
Pharmacy
Physical Medicine
Pregnancy
Radiology
Rehabilitation
Respiratory Care
Robotic Surgery
Sleep Disorders
Smoking Cessation
Specialty Services
Sports Medicine
Stroke
Trauma Services
Urgent Care
Weight Loss
Wellness Consultations
Women's Health
Workers' Compensation

COMPETITORS

Ascension Health	Shawnee Mission
BJC HealthCare	Medical Center
Catholic Health	Sisters of Charity of
Initiatives	Leavenworth

Children's Mercy Hospital
HCA
Mercy Health
Mercy Hospital Springfield
Saint Luke's Health System
St. Anthony's Medical Center
Tenet Healthcare
Truman Medical Centers
Universal Health Services
University of Kansas Medical Center

HISTORICAL FINANCIALS
Company Type: Private

Income Statement
FYE: September 30

	REVENUE ($ mil.)	NET INCOME ($ mil.)	NET PROFIT MARGIN	EMPLOYEES
09/13	858	105	12.3%	9,100
09/12	843	66	7.9%	—
09/09	876	29	3.4%	—
09/08	900	0	—	—
Annual Growth	(1.0%)	—	—	—

2013 Year-End Financials
Return on assets: 6.4%
Return on equity: 12.3%
Current ratio: 1.40
Cash ($ mil.): 39

LEWIS ENERGY GROUP L.P.

Auditors: BKD LLP SAN ANTONIO TEXAS

LOCATIONS

HQ: LEWIS ENERGY GROUP L.P.
10101 REUNION PL STE 1000, SAN ANTONIO, TX 782164157
Phone: 210 384-3200
Web: WWW.LEWISENERGY.COM

HISTORICAL FINANCIALS
Company Type: Private

Income Statement
FYE: December 31

	REVENUE ($ mil.)	NET INCOME ($ mil.)	NET PROFIT MARGIN	EMPLOYEES
12/13	769	107	14.0%	1,000
12/12	468	206	44.2%	—
Annual Growth	64.4%	(47.9%)	—	—

2013 Year-End Financials
Return on assets: —
Return on equity: 14.0%
Current ratio: 0.20
Cash ($ mil.): 75

LEXA INTERNATIONAL CORPORATION

Auditors: CITRIN COOPERMAN & COMPANY LL

LOCATIONS

HQ: LEXA INTERNATIONAL CORPORATION
1 LANDMARK SQ STE 407, STAMFORD, CT 069012601
Phone: 203 326-5200
Web: WWW.AXELJOHNSON.COM

HISTORICAL FINANCIALS
Company Type: Private

Income Statement
FYE: December 31

	ASSETS ($ mil.)	NET INCOME ($ mil.)	INCOME AS % OF ASSETS	EMPLOYEES
12/09	1,118	6	0.6%	1,204
12/08	1,241	4	0.4%	—
Annual Growth	(9.9%)	47.8%	—	—

2009 Year-End Financials
Return on assets: —
Return on equity: 0.2%
Sales ($ mil.): 2,598

LICKING MEMORIAL HEALTH SYSTEMS

Here to help Buckeye Staters lick disease is Licking Memorial Health Systems. The the not-for-profit health care provider operates the 230-bed Licking Memorial Hospital. Specialty services at the hospital include cancer care home health occupational health cardiology rehabilitation and obstetrics. Licking Memorial Hospital administers behavioral health care (including substance abuse treatments) through its Shepherd Hill department. The health system also includes area outpatient medical practices largely through the multi-specialty physician group Licking Memorial Health Professionals which has 100-plus physicians in various practices.

Geographic Reach
The company's medical offices are located throughout Licking County Ohio including Granville Hanover Heath Hebron Johnstown Newark and Pataskala.

Operations
In 2013 Licking Memorial Hospital handled about 9000 inpatient admissions as well as nearly 55000 emergency room visits 7500 surgeries and 1000 births. The hospital employs about 160 active staff members. The physicians' group operates through about 40 practices with 100 doctors.

The Licking Memorial Health Foundation is Licking Memorial Health Systems' fundraising and resource development organization.

Strategy
The opening of urgent care clinics helps health networks like Licking Memorial decrease the crowding and offset costs of hospital emergency room visits especially when it comes to caring for uninsured or under-insured patients.

In 2013 Licking Memorial Hospital opened an acute inpatient rehabilitation unit to provide rehabilitation services for patients with disabilities caused by illnesses surgery or injuries. The unit focuses on helping patients regain independence.

To expand its services in the field of outpatient emergency care Licking Memorial opened its second urgent care facility in 2012. The company also expanded its outpatient care capacity by acquiring an ambulatory care facility from the nearby Medical Center of Newark that year.

Looking to lower its carbon emissions in 2012 Licking Memorial Hospital installed a LiveRoof hybrid green roof system (the first such installation in Newark).

Financial Performance
In 2013 Licking Memorial Health Systems provided $50.4 million in uncompensated care of which $27.4 million was charity care.

Company Background

Licking Memorial Hospital has been named to Truven Health Analytics' national list of 100 Top Hospitals some 11 times.

Licking Memorial Health Systems was founded in 1898 by the Newark Hospital Association.

EXECUTIVES

Director Of Him, Sandy Mandich
Director Of Pharmacy, Jeff Smith
Vice President, Rhonda Maddern
Secretary, Vicki Parker
Auditors: MOUNTJOY CHILTON MEDLEY LLP C

LOCATIONS

HQ: LICKING MEMORIAL HEALTH SYSTEMS
1320 W MAIN ST, NEWARK, OH 430551822
Phone: 740 348-4000
Web: WWW.LMHEALTH.ORG

PRODUCTS/OPERATIONS

Selected Services
Behavioral Health Services
Cancer Care
Case Management
Child Wellness and Pediatric Care
Classes and Events
Clinics and Outpatient Services
Critical Care Units
Diabetes Care and Nutrition
Emergency Department
Endoscopy Services
Heart Care
Home Care Services
Infection Prevention
Laboratory Services
Medical Pediatric and Surgical Inpatient Units
Maternal Child
Pastoral Care
Radiology Services
Rehabilitation Services
Renal Dialysis
Respiratory Care
Sleep Laboratory
Surgical Services
Women's Health

COMPETITORS

Fairfield Medical Center
Genesis HealthCare System (Ohio)
Mount Carmel Health
Nationwide Children's Hospital
OhioHealth

HISTORICAL FINANCIALS

Company Type: Private

Income Statement — FYE: December 31

	REVENUE ($ mil.)	NET INCOME ($ mil.)	NET PROFIT MARGIN	EMPLOYEES
12/13	209	39	18.9%	1,700
12/11	184	(7)	—	—
12/10	198	4	2.2%	—
12/09	199	0	—	—
Annual Growth	1.2%	—	—	—

2013 Year-End Financials

Return on assets: —
Return on equity: 18.9%
Current ratio: 1.20
Cash ($ mil.): 6

LIFEBRIDGE HEALTH INC.

Like a bridge over troubled waters LifeBridge Health links ailing patients to care and healing. Serving the Baltimore region the not-for-profit company operates two general hospitals —Sinai Hospital of Baltimore and Northwest Hospital — with specialties including oncology neurology pediatrics and sports medicine. The LifeBridge Health network also provides long-term care at the Levindale Hebrew Geriatric Center and Hospital (nursing subacute and adult day care services) and the Courtland Gardens Nursing & Rehabilitation Center. Altogether the health system boasts some 1190 beds. LifeBridge's Health Wellness division includes a health and fitness program and community fitness center.

Operations

Sinai Hospital is a teaching hospital with residency programs for medical students training at Johns Hopkins University and University of Maryland. Levindale also serves as a teaching facility for medical dental nursing and social work students pursuing training to serve geriatric populations.

EXECUTIVES

EVP and President Sinai Hospital, Amy Perry
SVP; President Sinai Hospital of Baltimore, Neil M. Meltzer
SVP and CFO, Charles (Chuck) Orlando
President and CEO, Warren Green
SVP; President Northwest Hospital Center, Erik G. Wexler
VP and CIO, Karen Barker
VP Marketing and Community Relations, Rudy Miller
VP and CIO, Tressa Springmann
VP Human Resources, Taylor Foss
Vice President, Barbara Epke
Chairman, Benjamin S. Schapiro
VP Operations Engineering, Ev Amaral
Vice President Physician Services, Christine DeAngelis
SVP and CFO, David Krajewski
Vice President Government Relations and Advocacy, Martha Nathanson
Vice President and Legal Counsel, Joel Suldan
VP Capital Improvements and Campus Services, Peter Arn
Vice President Development, Julie Cox
VP Revenue Cycle, Tony Morris
SVP and President Northwest Hospital, Brian White
Chief Operating Officer, Jeff Watson
Vice President Chief Medical Officer, Daniel Silverman
Vice President Facilities, Lionel Weeks
Vice President Human Resources, Cheryl Boyer
SVP and President Levindale Hebrew Geriatric Center and Hospital and Courtland Gardens Nursing and Rehabilitation Center, Aric Spitulnik
Vice Chairman, Walter G. Amprey
Vice President Chief Nursing Officer, Diane Johnson
Auditors: KPMG LLP BALTIMORE MD

LOCATIONS

HQ: LIFEBRIDGE HEALTH INC.
2401 W BELVEDERE AVE, BALTIMORE, MD 212155216
Phone: 410 601-5653
Web: WWW.LIFEBRIDGEBLOGS.ORG

PRODUCTS/OPERATIONS

Selected Locations
Courtland Gardens Nursing & Rehabilitation Center
Levindale Hebrew Geriatric Center and Hospital
Northwest Hospital
Sinai Hospital

Selected Services
Bariatric and Minimally Invasive Surgery
Brain & Spine Institute
Cancer Institute
Hospitalist Program
Rubin Institute for Advanced Orthopedics
Vascular Institute

COMPETITORS

Anne Arundel Medical Center
Ascension Health
Bon Secours Health
Franklin Square Hospital Center
GBMC
Johns Hopkins Health System
MedStar Health
MedStar Union Memorial Hospital
University of Maryland Medical System

HISTORICAL FINANCIALS

Company Type: Private

Income Statement — FYE: June 30

	REVENUE ($ mil.)	NET INCOME ($ mil.)	NET PROFIT MARGIN	EMPLOYEES
06/13	1,033	53	5.2%	6,000
06/11	99	(3)	—	—
06/10	95	(2)	—	—
Annual Growth	121.0%	—	—	—

2013 Year-End Financials

Return on assets: 8.9%
Return on equity: 5.2%
Current ratio: 1.60
Cash ($ mil.): 181

LIFEWAY CHRISTIAN RESOURCES OF THE SOUTHERN BAPTIST CONVENTION

LifeWay Christian Resources of the Southern Baptist Convention helps to spread the teachings of Jesus. The company is a not-for-profit Christian publisher. It also sells Bibles CDs gifts software church furniture signs and other supplies. In addition to its roughly 200 LifeWay Christian Stores located in more than 25 states the retailer sells products online and through its catalog. LifeWay operates two of the nation's largest Christian conference facilities and summer camps. LifeWay Ridgecrest Conference Center in North Carolina and LifeWay Glorieta Conference Center in New Mexico together welcome some 2000 conference and overnight guests each year. LifeWay was founded in 1891 by Dr. J.M. Frost.

Geographic Reach

Based in Nashville LifeWay boasts offices and conference centers in three states: Tennessee New Mexico and North Carolina. In Nashville the company has more than 1.3 million sq. ft. of office retail parking conference and warehouse space that covers 14.6 acres. As part of its operations LifeWay has a 350000-sq.-ft. warehouse on 44 acres in Lebanon Tennessee that supports the LifeWay Christian Stores the company operates nationwide in more than 25 states and extends its reach globally through its website and catalogs.

Operations

The B&H Publishing Group produces Bibles books Sunday school teaching materials and audio and video products which are sold to bookstores and other retailers. Its Holman Christian Standard Bible is one of the best-selling versions in the US. As part of its digital outreach efforts Lifeway provides ministry services-related Digital Church which can be accessed through Lifeway's website and offers an array of resources for ministries including downloadable worship music and a video publishing utility.

Its Executive Communications and Relations division produces LifeWay's news and information services directs corporate events builds corporate relations and supports the office of the president. It works with state conventions and other evangelical organizations as well. The Technology division offers strategic retail enterprise and Internet services. The company's Research and Ministry Development division is where LifeWay conducts its research and explores new ministry ventures it calls "blue oceans." LifeWay's Finance and Business Services division which runs a conference center in Ridgecrest North Carolina oversees the company's financial policies and general accounting as well as directs business services such as legal investment purchasing real estate strategic planning corporate services and human resources.

EXECUTIVES

VP LifeWay Christian Stores, Tim Vineyard
VP Finance and Business Services; CFO, Jerry Rhyne
President and CEO, Thom S. Rainer
EVP, Brad Waggoner
VP B&H Publishing Group, Selma Wilson
VP Insights Division, Ed Stetzer
VP Church Resources Division, Eric Geiger
VP and CIO, Tim Hill
Senior Vice President Of Sales, Craig Featherstone
Vice President Of Cba Sales, Fred Evans
Vice President Of International Sales, Bob Vanfleteren
Auditors: ERNST & YOUNG LLP NASHVILLE

LOCATIONS

HQ: LIFEWAY CHRISTIAN RESOURCES OF THE SOUTHERN BAPTIST CONVENTION
1 LIFEWAY PLZ, NASHVILLE, TN 372341001
Phone: 615 251-2000
Web: WWW.LIFEWAY.COM

2013 Stores

	No.
Texas	26
Tennessee	21
North Carolina	14
Alabama	11
Georgia	11
Virginia	9
Florida	8
Kentucky	8
Arkansas	6
Mississippi	6
South Carolina	6
Louisiana	5
Minnesota	5
Missouri	5
Ohio	4
Pennsylvania	3
California	2
Illinois	2
Kansas	2
Maryland	2
Oklahoma	2
Washington	2
Colorado	1
Indiana	1
New Mexico	1
Oregon	1
Utah	1
Total	**165**

PRODUCTS/OPERATIONS

Selected Divisions
B&H Publishing Group
Church Resources
Executive Communications and Relations
Finance and Business Services
LifeWay Christian Stores
Research and Ministry Development
Technology

Selected Products
Apparel
Audio
Bibles
Books
Church supplies
Curriculum
eBooks
Events
Gifts
Magazines
Movies
Music
Video

COMPETITORS

Amazon.com	United Methodist
Baker Publishing	Publishing
Barnes & Noble	Wal-Mart
Deseret Management	
Family Christian	
Stores	

HISTORICAL FINANCIALS
Company Type: Private

Income Statement
FYE: September 30

	REVENUE ($ mil.)	NET INCOME ($ mil.)	NET PROFIT MARGIN	EMPLOYEES
09/14	500	(25)	—	2,477
09/13	481	79	16.5%	—
09/12	488	(35)	—	—
09/11	468	0	—	—
Annual Growth	2.2%	—	—	—

2014 Year-End Financials
Return on assets: 6.8%   Cash ($ mil.): 1
Return on equity: (-5.1%)
Current ratio: 0.60

LINCOLN GLEN MANOR

LOCATIONS
HQ: LINCOLN GLEN MANOR
2671 PLUMMER AVE STE A, SAN JOSE, CA 951254877
Phone: 408 267-1492
Web: WWW.LGMANOR.ORG

HISTORICAL FINANCIALS
Company Type: Private

Income Statement
FYE: September 30

	REVENUE ($ mil.)	NET INCOME ($ mil.)	NET PROFIT MARGIN	EMPLOYEES
09/09	477	22	4.6%	110
09/08	8	0	7.0%	—
/	0	0	—	—
Annual Growth	—	—	—	—

2009 Year-End Financials
Return on assets: —   Cash ($ mil.): 1
Return on equity: 4.6%
Current ratio: 1.70

LINCOLN PUBLIC SCHOOLS INC

Auditors: HSMC-ORIZON KANSAS CITY OMAH

LOCATIONS

HQ: LINCOLN PUBLIC SCHOOLS INC
5905 O ST, LINCOLN, NE 685102235
Phone: 402 436-1000
Web: WWW.LPS.ORG

HISTORICAL FINANCIALS
Company Type: Private

Income Statement
FYE: August 31

	REVENUE ($ mil.)	NET INCOME ($ mil.)	NET PROFIT MARGIN	EMPLOYEES
08/13	417	(19)	—	6,950
08/12	427	(39)	—	—
08/11	419	(38)	—	—
08/10	442	0	—	—
Annual Growth	(1.9%)	—	—	—

2013 Year-End Financials
Return on assets: —   Cash ($ mil.): —
Return on equity: (-4.6%)
Current ratio: —

LITTLE ROCK SCHOOL DISTRICT

Auditors: HUDSON CISNE & CO LLP LITTL

LOCATIONS

HQ: LITTLE ROCK SCHOOL DISTRICT
810 W MARKHAM ST, LITTLE ROCK, AR 722011306
Phone: 501 447-1000
Web: WWW.LRSD.ORG

HISTORICAL FINANCIALS
Company Type: Private

Income Statement
FYE: June 30

	REVENUE ($ mil.)	NET INCOME ($ mil.)	NET PROFIT MARGIN	EMPLOYEES
06/13	332	(3)	—	4,000
06/12	349	16	4.6%	—
06/11	337	(9)	—	—
06/10	314	0	—	—
Annual Growth	1.9%	—	—	—

2013 Year-End Financials
Return on assets: 5.4%   Cash ($ mil.): 62
Return on equity: (-1.1%)
Current ratio: —

LITTLE SIOUX CORN PROCESSORS LLC

Pursuing the corny American Heartland dream of profitable renewable energy Little Sioux Corn Processors operates an ethanol plant in northwest Iowa. (It actually owns a 60% interest in the limited partnership that owns the ethanol facility.) The company converts bushels of corn into ethanol distiller grains (used as feed for the dairy and beef industries) and corn oil. Ethanol is used as an additive to gasoline as well as a fuel enhancer for high-octane motors and it burns more cleanly than normal gasoline thereby reducing carbon monoxide emissions. Little Sioux's production capacity is about 90 million gallons of ethanol annually more than double its orginal capacity after successive expansions.

LOCATIONS

HQ: LITTLE SIOUX CORN PROCESSORS LLC
4808 F AVE, MARCUS, IA 510357070
Phone: 712 376-2800
Web: WWW.LITTLESIOUXCORNPROCESSORS.COM

COMPETITORS

ADM	GreenField Ethanol
Abengoa Bioenergy	Lake Area Corn
Badger State Ethanol	Processors
Cargill	POET

HISTORICAL FINANCIALS
Company Type: Private

Income Statement
FYE: September 30

	REVENUE ($ mil.)	NET INCOME ($ mil.)	NET PROFIT MARGIN	EMPLOYEES
09/13	346	4	1.3%	45
09/11	329	9	2.9%	—
/	0	0	—	—
Annual Growth	—	—	—	—

2013 Year-End Financials
Return on assets: 1.4%   Cash ($ mil.): —
Return on equity: 1.3%
Current ratio: 0.60

LLOG EXPLORATION COMPANY L.L.C.

Auditors: ERNST & YOUNG LLP NEW ORLEANS

LOCATIONS

HQ: LLOG EXPLORATION COMPANY L.L.C.
1001 OCHSNER BLVD STE 200, COVINGTON, LA
704338152
Phone: 504 833-7700
Web: WWW.LLOG.COM

HISTORICAL FINANCIALS
Company Type: Private

Income Statement
FYE: December 31

	REVENUE ($ mil.)	NET INCOME ($ mil.)	NET PROFIT MARGIN	EMPLOYEES
12/13	1,081	600	55.6%	75
12/12	650	207	32.0%	—
Annual Growth	66.3%	188.9%	—	—

2013 Year-End Financials
Return on assets: —   Cash ($ mil.): 161
Return on equity: 55.6%
Current ratio: 0.80

LODGING RLJ TRUST L P

Auditors: PRICEWATERHOUSECOOPERS LLP MC

LOCATIONS

HQ: LODGING RLJ TRUST L P
3 BETHESDA METRO CTR, BETHESDA, MD
208145330
Phone: 301 280-7777
Web: WWW.RLJLODGINGTRUST.COM

HISTORICAL FINANCIALS
Company Type: Private

Income Statement
FYE: December 31

	REVENUE ($ mil.)	NET INCOME ($ mil.)	NET PROFIT MARGIN	EMPLOYEES
12/14	1,109	136	12.3%	—
12/13	970	114	11.8%	—
12/12	854	41	4.8%	—
12/11	758	0	—	—
Annual Growth	13.5%	—	—	—

2014 Year-End Financials
Return on assets: 11.7%   Cash ($ mil.): 262
Return on equity: 12.3%
Current ratio: —

LONG BEACH MEMORIAL MEDICAL CENTER

Long Beach Memorial Medical Center (LBMMC) is an old-timer in the Long Beach health care market. A subsidiary of Memorial Health Services LBMMC provides a full range of health services to residents of the Long Beach California area. The medical center a 420-bed acute-care hospital was founded in 1907 and is one of the largest private hospitals on the West Coast. Services include primary emergency diagnostic surgical therapeutic and rehabilitative care. The hospital is home to centers for treatment of cancer heart stroke and women's and children's health concerns. It also provides home and hospice care programs as well as occupational health services.

Geographic Reach

Long Beach Memorial Medical Center (LBMMC) is one of the nation's largest private hospitals on the West Coast.

Operations

LBMMC comprises a breast center cancer institute center for women heart and vascular institute imaging center joint replacement center rehabilitation institute and stroke center. The medical center is a 420-bed acute-care hospital.

Strategy

LBMMC boasts an electronic medical record (EMR) system that connects the hospital and all of its affiliated physicians and pharmacies so that they can transfer patient information electronically between different care providers and locations. Hospitals that use an EMR are eligible for incentives and higher reimbursements from the federal government. Additionally EMRs help to reduce medical errors and increase patient safety by eliminating things like medication interactions and duplicate patient records.

LBMMC expanded its cancer services by building a new $31 million dedicated outpatient cancer facility. The MemorialCare Todd Cancer Institute at Long Beach Memorial which was completed in mid-2013 serves to supplement its current center which had reached capacity. With the new 65000-sq.-ft. MemorialCare Todd Cancer Institute pavilion LBMMC enhances its cancer care technology and capacity.

LBMMC has also expanded its robotics program beyond cardiology. The hospital recently established a new intensivist program in the Intensive Care Unit (ICU). The ICU program integrates teaching from the University of California Irvine residents and interns.

EXECUTIVES

CIO, Scott Joslyn
CFO, Wendy Dorchester
President and CEO, Barry Arbuckle
Vice President Human Resources, Jonathan S Berek
Nursing Director, Barbara (Barb) Lane
Vice President Loan Officer, Carol Nachreiner
Vice President Of Human Resources, Myra Gregorian
Director Of Nursing, Mary Jorgensen
Vice President Of Quality, Donna Hartman
Vice President of Technical Information Services, Kevin Torres
Vice President> Ambulatory Services, Pamela (Pam) Chevreaux
Director of Health and Safety, Ginger Alhadeff
Vice President Strategy Planning, Roshawn Blunt
Vice President Operations, Cheryl Jacob
Radiology Director, John Azaren
MHS Vice President General Counsel, Robert (Bob) Siemer
Vice President Material Resources, Gerald (Jerry) Olson
Secretary Executive, Donna Gorman
Secretary Department Medical, Maria Barajas
Secretary Executive, Donna Reyes
Secretary Department Medical, Linda Cox
Secretary Department Medical, Elvera Barycki
Board Member, Robert Freeman
Board Member, James Craig
Board Member, Peter Knudson
Board Member, John Dameron
Board Member, David Brown
Board Member, Kenneth Walker
Board Member, Sean Miller
Secretary, Dora Heller
Secretary Executive, Kathleen Webster
Secretary Executive, Martha Robertson
Secretary Executive, Barbara (Barb) Steinhauser
Secretary Executive, Kelly Ambrose
Secretary Department Medical, Heather Lawrence
Board Member, James Wells
Secretary Executive, Evelyn Satele
Secretary Department Medical, Natalie Strauss
Auditors: PRICEWATERHOUSECOOPERS LLP L

LOCATIONS

HQ: LONG BEACH MEMORIAL MEDICAL CENTER
2801 ATLANTIC AVE, LONG BEACH, CA 908061701
Phone: 562 933-2000
Web:
WWW.SUPPORTLONGBEACH.MEMORIALCARE.ORG

PRODUCTS/OPERATIONS

Selected Institutes & Centers
MemorialCare Breast Center at Long Beach Memorial
MemorialCare Cancer Institute
MemorialCare Center for Women
MemorialCare Heart & Vascular Institute
MemorialCare Imaging Center
MemorialCare Joint Replacement Center
MemorialCare Rehabilitation Institute
MemorialCare Stroke Center

COMPETITORS

Adventist Health
Aptium Oncology
Brotman Medical Center
Cedars-Sinai Medical Center
Childrens Hospital Los Angeles
Dignity Health
Glendale Adventist Medical Center
Good Samaritan Hospital (Los Angeles)
HCA
Hoag Memorial Hospital
Hollywood Presbyterian Medical Center
Los Angeles County Health Department
Methodist Hospital of Southern California
Newhall Memorial Hospital
Pasadena Hospital Association
Providence Health & Services
Providence Health System Southern California
Sutter Health
Tenet Healthcare
Torrance Memorial Medical Center
Trinity Health (Novi)
Western Medical Center - Santa Ana

HISTORICAL FINANCIALS

Company Type: Private

Income Statement

	REVENUE ($ mil.)	NET INCOME ($ mil.)	NET PROFIT MARGIN	EMPLOYEES
				FYE: June 30
06/11	1,083	63	5.9%	—
06/09	446	53	12.0%	—
Annual Growth	55.8%	8.8%	—	—

2011 Year-End Financials

Return on assets: —
Return on equity: 5.9%
Current ratio: 1.50
Cash ($ mil.): 4

LONG ISLAND UNIVERSITY

Long Island University (LIU) helps students see a long future in professional fields including medicine and business. LIU has an enrollment of more than 24000 students at multiple locations in New York State. The university employs more than 600 full-time faculty members and has a 12:1 student-to-teacher ratio. LIU offers 575 degree programs and certificates in fields including pharmacy nursing health sciences education liberal arts sciences business and information studies. The school traces its roots to 1886 when the Brooklyn College of Pharmacy was founded.

Geographic Reach

LIU has eight campuses in New York located in Brooklyn Brookville Brentwood Riverhead Rockland and Westchester). Internationally LIU Global offers study abroad programs in Asia Australia the Middle East and South America.

Strategy

LIU has expanded its offerings in recent years to meet current demands. It has added degree programs in fields such as digital game design computer information systems health sciences and human resource management.

EXECUTIVES

Assistant Vice President Sponsored Research, Kathryn Rockett
Vice President, Lucille Ambrosio
Assoc Vice President Development, Melodee Gandia
Vice President Academic Affairs, Jeffrey Kane
Assistant Dean Vpa, Benjamin Moore
Vice President Marketing Public Relations, Paola Kleinman
Vice President Long Island University, Jackie Nealon
Rph, Joseph Bova
Assistant Vice President Sponsored Research, Kitty Rockett
Assistant Treas, Judy Carbuto
Secretary, Arlene Weydig
Auditors: KPMG LLP NEW YORK NY

LOCATIONS

HQ: LONG ISLAND UNIVERSITY
700 NORTHERN BLVD, GREENVALE, NY 115481327
Phone: 516 299-2535
Web: WWW.LIU.EDU

HISTORICAL FINANCIALS

Company Type: Private

Income Statement

	REVENUE ($ mil.)	NET INCOME ($ mil.)	NET PROFIT MARGIN	EMPLOYEES
				FYE: August 31
08/12	484	4	0.9%	3,300
08/11	468	2	0.5%	—
08/10	370	(1)	—	—
08/09	363	0	—	—
Annual Growth	10.0%	—	—	—

2012 Year-End Financials

Return on assets: —
Return on equity: 0.9%
Current ratio: —
Cash ($ mil.): 89

LOOP LLC

LOOP (Louisiana Offshore Oil Port) offloads crude oil from tankers stores it and routes it to pipelines and refineries along the Gulf Coast and the Midwest. It is also the storage and terminalling facility for the MARS pipeline system and its supply of offshore Gulf of Mexico crude oil. Oil is stored in eight underground caverns leached out of a naturally occurring salt dome. These caverns are capable of storing about 50 million barrels of crude oil. The company is owned by Marathon Ashland Pipe Line Murphy Oil and Shell Oil. In addition to other services LOOP has an aboveground tank farm made up of six 600000 barrel tanks.

The company's port facility is located 18 miles south of Grand Isle Louisiana in 110 feet of water and is the only port in the US capable of offloading deep draft tankers. Although battered by Hurricane Katrina in 2005 LOOP's operations were only temporarily interrupted.

LOOP is connected to more than 50% of US refinery capacity and has offloaded more than 7 billion barrels of foreign crude oil in the past 27 years. LOOP was established in 1972 and converted to a limited liability company in 1996.

EXECUTIVES

Vice President of Engineering and Technology, Terrance R Coleman
Vice President Organizational Planning and Development, Happie Ledet

LOCATIONS

HQ: LOOP LLC
137 NORTHPARK BLVD, COVINGTON, LA 704335071
Phone: 985 632-6970
Web: WWW.LOOPLLC.COM

COMPETITORS

Chemoil
Martin Midstream Partners
Sunoco

HISTORICAL FINANCIALS

Company Type: Private

Income Statement

	REVENUE ($ mil.)	NET INCOME ($ mil.)	NET PROFIT MARGIN	EMPLOYEES
				FYE: December 31
12/09	243	87	35.8%	128
12/08	265	79	29.8%	—
12/06	235	104	44.2%	—
12/05	184	0	—	—
Annual Growth	7.3%	—	—	—

2009 Year-End Financials

Return on assets: —
Return on equity: 35.8%
Current ratio: —
Cash ($ mil.): —

LOS ANGELES COUNTY OFFICE OF EDUCATION

Auditors: VAVRINEK TRINE DAY & CO LL

LOCATIONS

HQ: LOS ANGELES COUNTY OFFICE OF EDUCATION
9300 IMPERIAL HWY, DOWNEY, CA 902422813
Phone: 562 922-6111
Web: WWW.LACOE.EDU

HISTORICAL FINANCIALS

Company Type: Private

Income Statement

	REVENUE ($ mil.)	NET INCOME ($ mil.)	NET PROFIT MARGIN	EMPLOYEES
				FYE: June 30
06/13	747	(9)	—	4,000
06/08	6	0	1.4%	—
Annual Growth	154.6%	—	—	—

LOS ANGELES DEPARTMENT OF WATER AND POWER

The Los Angeles Department of Water and Power (LADWP) keeps the movie cameras running and the swimming pools full. The largest municipally owned utility in the US LADWP provides electricity to 1.4 million residential and business customers and water to 666000 customers. The company has power plant interests that give it more than 7220 MW of generating capacity; it also buys and sells wholesale power. Most of the city's water supply is transported through two aqueduct systems from the Sierra Nevada Mountains; other water sources include wells and local groundwater basins. Because LADWP is city-owned its retail monopoly status has been unaffected by utility deregulation in California.

Financial PerformanceLADWP's operations are entirely financed by the sale of water and electric services. The multi-utility transfers about 7% of its annual electric revenues and 5% of its water revenues to the City of Los Angeles general fund.StrategyResidential customers form the largest client group of the utility's water service unit; commercial customers the largest customer class of the power segment. To enhance operating efficiencies and conserve energy the department has launched a 10-year $1 billion Smart Grid program to automate and upgrade the City's grid.It is also pushing to increase the amount of energy it generates from renewable sources (mainly wind and solar power) to meet state and federal clean air goals. LADWP got only 5% of it power from renewables in 2005 but has upped that amount to more than 20%. LADWP plans to sell its Navajo Generating Station in Arizona (by 2014) which will cut carbon emissions by a further 26%In 2013 LADWP signed a decade-long power purchase agreement to purchase renewable geothermal power (about 34 MW) from the Imperial Valley (enough to provide enough clean energy to serve 47600 Los Angeles homes).In addition as the Western US states battle a prolonged drought the utility is negotiating with water agencies across the region to ensure a reliable future supply for its citizens.OwnershipThe department is part of the City of Los Angeles.Company BackgroundLADWP was founded in 1902.

EXECUTIVES

Vice President, Robert K (Bob) Rozanski
Chief Administrative Officer, David H. Wiggs
Senior Assistant General Manager Power System, David H. (Dave) Wright
General Manager, Marcie L. Edwards
Senior Assistant General Manager Water System, Martin L. Adams
Chief Sustainability and Economic Development Officer, Nancy Sutley
CFO, Phil Leiber
Vice President Operations, James McDaniel
Vice President Operations, Kenneth Silver
Vice President, Dominick Rubalcava
Vice President, Ann Santilli
Vice President Information Technology, Dan Raftevold
Legal Secretary, Patricia Stanard
First Vice President, Demarlo Sims
Vice President, Desmond Johnson
President Board of Commissioners, Mel Levine

VP Board of Commissioners, William W. Funderburk
Secretary To Executive Vice President, Javier Romero
Secretary Legal, Lillian Catena
Board Secretary, John Burmahln
Secretary To The General Manager, Lourdes Zerrudo
Secretary, Lisa Solomon
Auditors: KPMG LLP LOS ANGELES CA

LOCATIONS

HQ: LOS ANGELES DEPARTMENT OF WATER AND POWER
111 N HOPE ST, LOS ANGELES, CA 900122607
Phone: 213 367-4211
Web: WWW.LADWP.COM

PRODUCTS/OPERATIONS

2012 Sales

	% of total
Electric	75
Water	25
Total	**100**

COMPETITORS

AES	Edison International
American States Water	PG&E Corporation
Avista	Sacramento Municipal
California Water	Utility
Service	Sempra Energy
Calpine	SouthWest Water
Duke Energy	

HISTORICAL FINANCIALS

Company Type: Private

Income Statement

FYE: June 30

	REVENUE ($ mil.)	NET INCOME ($ mil.)	NET PROFIT MARGIN	EMPLOYEES
06/11	3,125	57	1.8%	8,000
06/10	812	67	8.3%	—
Annual Growth	284.8%	(14.4%)	—	—

2011 Year-End Financials

Return on assets: —
Return on equity: 1.8%
Current ratio: 0.80
Cash ($ mil.): 630

LOUISIANA CHILDRENS MEDICAL CENTER INC

LOCATIONS

HQ: LOUISIANA CHILDRENS MEDICAL CENTER INC
200 HENRY CLAY AVE, NEW ORLEANS, LA 701185720
Phone: 504 896-9581
Web: WWW.CHNOLA.ORG

HISTORICAL FINANCIALS

Company Type: Private

Income Statement

FYE: December 31

	REVENUE ($ mil.)	NET INCOME ($ mil.)	NET PROFIT MARGIN	EMPLOYEES
12/13*	932	280	30.1%	3
03/13	500	10	2.1%	—
12/12	251	65	25.9%	—
12/11	478	0	—	—
Annual Growth	39.6%	—	—	—

*Fiscal year change

2013 Year-End Financials

Return on assets: 7.9%
Return on equity: 30.1%
Current ratio: 0.90
Cash ($ mil.): 332

LOUISIANA WHOLESALE DRUG COMPANY INC.

Auditors: JOHN S DOWLING & COMPANY OPE

LOCATIONS

HQ: LOUISIANA WHOLESALE DRUG COMPANY INC.
2085 I 49 S SERVICE RD, SUNSET, LA 70584
Phone: 337 662-1040

HISTORICAL FINANCIALS

Company Type: Private

Income Statement

FYE: August 2

	REVENUE ($ mil.)	NET INCOME ($ mil.)	NET PROFIT MARGIN	EMPLOYEES
08/13*	380	4	1.1%	52
07/12	386	4	1.1%	—
07/11	373	4	1.2%	—
07/10	372	0	—	—
Annual Growth	0.7%	—	—	—

*Fiscal year change

2013 Year-End Financials

Return on assets: 7.0%
Return on equity: 1.1%
Current ratio: 0.60
Cash ($ mil.): 24

LOYOLA MARYMOUNT UNIVERSITY INC

Loyola Marymount University (LMU) in Los Angeles is a Jesuit (Catholic) institution with an enrollment of more than 9500 students. It offers more than 115 graduate and undergraduate programs through four colleges: Bellarmine College of Liberal Arts College of Business Administration College of Communication and Fine Arts and Seaver College of Science and Engineering. There is also the School of Education and School of Film and Television. Other programs include the Graduate Division Continuing Education Program and Loyola Law School. LMU has an 11:1 student-to-faculty ratio. The university was formed in 1973 by the merger of Loyola College (founded in 1911) and Marymount Junior College.

Operations

The university offers about 60 majors and 55 minor study programs to its undergraduate students. LMU also offers more than 40 master's degrees two doctorates and a dozen certification programs. In total it employs about 2000 faculty and staff members.

LMU has partnerships with about a dozen public and private elementary and secondary schools in the Los Angeles area. Through the LMU Family of Schools model school demonstration program the university provides professional development and educational resources to the schools.

Geographic Reach

LMU is located on a 140-acre campus in Los Angeles.

Financial Performance

The university experienced a 3% increase in revenues from $320 million to $328 million due to higher net tuition and fee income auxiliary enterprise revenue and investment returns designated for operations. Tuition runs at some $40000 annually plus some $13000 in room and board. LMU reported net income of $63 million over a net loss in 2012 due to increased investment returns and gains on interest rate swaps. Cash from operations dropped by $6 million to $20 as the university used cash in account receivable and contributions for long-term investments.

Strategy

In 2013 LMU broke ground on a $110 million life sciences complex that will become Pereira Hall (for engineering) and Seaver Hall (for physics and math).

To increase student access to its programs LMU launched a new scholarship initiative in 2012. Through the program the university seeks to raise some $100 million for new scholarships through donations and endowment returns over a three-year period.

EXECUTIVES

Senior Vice President Administration, Lynne Scarboro
Senior Vice President University Relations, Dennis Slon
Vice President Vice President for Student Affairs, Lane Bove
Budget Analyst Enrollment Management Vice President Office, Gabriela De Anda
Executive Vice President and Provost, David (Dave) Burcham
Senior Vice President Administration, Evelynne Scarboro
Vice President Of Finance, John (Jack) Carvana
Board President, Kyle Studebaker
Treasurer, George Dasaro
Treasurer, Stephen Zaiss
Auditors: PRICEWATERHOUSECOOPERS LLP LO

LOCATIONS

HQ: LOYOLA MARYMOUNT UNIVERSITY INC
1 LMU DR STE 100, LOS ANGELES, CA 900452677
Phone: 310 338-3055
Web: WWW.LMU.EDU

PRODUCTS/OPERATIONS

Colleges and Schools
Bellarmine College of Liberal Arts
College of Business Administration
College of Communication and Fine Arts
Graduate Division
LMU Extension
Loyola Law School
School of Education
School of Film and Television
Seaver College of Science and Engineering

HISTORICAL FINANCIALS
Company Type: Private

Income Statement

	REVENUE ($ mil.)	NET INCOME ($ mil.)	NET PROFIT MARGIN	EMPLOYEES
05/13	328	62	19.1%	1,449
05/12	320	(16)	—	—
05/07	254	93	36.7%	—
05/06	234	0	—	—
Annual Growth	4.9%	—	—	—

FYE: May 31

2013 Year-End Financials
Return on assets: 11.0%   Cash ($ mil.): 27
Return on equity: 19.1%
Current ratio: —

LOYOLA UNIVERSITY MARYLAND INC.

Loyola University in Maryland is a Jesuit Catholic university that offers studies in liberal arts and sciences. In addition to its undergraduate programs Loyola has graduate degree programs in education speech pathology finance psychology modern studies pastoral counseling and engineering science. The university annually enrolls about 3500 undergraduate and some 2600 graduate students. The school has more than 300 full-time faculty and a student-teacher ratio of about 12:1. Loyola was founded in 1852 by Father John Early and eight other Jesuits.

EXECUTIVES

Vice President Advancement, David (Dave) Sears
Vp Academic Affairs, Timothy L Snyder
Division President, Sheilah Shaw Horton
Assistant Vice President Controller, Jare Allen
Vice President, Marc Camille
Vice President Technology, Evan Wagenfeld
Executive Vice President, Jordan Sowinski
Vice President Of Marketing, Filip Zigic
Vice President For Academic Affairs, Amy Wolfson
Corresponding Vice President, Taylor Reddan
Associate Vice President for Academic Affairs, Anne Young
Assistant Vice President Director of Athletics, Jim Paquette
Vice President Admin and Finance, John (Jack) Palmucci
Vice Presidents Academic Affairs, J Al Spoler
Secretary, Kathleen Cornell
Treasurer, Jillian Freeman
Secretary, Gary Gresh
Secretary, Lee Vasil
Auditors: KPMG LLP HARRISBURG PA

LOCATIONS

HQ: LOYOLA UNIVERSITY MARYLAND INC.
4501 N CHARLES ST, BALTIMORE, MD 212102601
Phone: 410 617-2000
Web: WWW.LOYOLA.EDU

HISTORICAL FINANCIALS
Company Type: Private

Income Statement

	REVENUE ($ mil.)	NET INCOME ($ mil.)	NET PROFIT MARGIN	EMPLOYEES
05/13	262	19	7.4%	2,066
05/12	185	(2)	—	—
05/11	238	11	5.0%	—
05/10	221	0	—	—
Annual Growth	5.8%	—	—	—

FYE: May 31

2013 Year-End Financials
Return on assets: 5.5%   Cash ($ mil.): 44
Return on equity: 7.4%
Current ratio: —

LOYOLA UNIVERSITY MEDICAL CENTER

Auditors: PRICEWATERHOUSECOOPERS LLP WA

LOCATIONS

HQ: LOYOLA UNIVERSITY MEDICAL CENTER
2160 S 1ST AVE, MAYWOOD, IL 601533328
Phone: 708 216-9000
Web: WWW.LOYOLAHEALTH.ORG

HISTORICAL FINANCIALS
Company Type: Private

Income Statement

	REVENUE ($ mil.)	NET INCOME ($ mil.)	NET PROFIT MARGIN	EMPLOYEES
06/11	938	14	1.6%	4
06/10	917	8	0.9%	—
Annual Growth	2.3%	75.7%	—	—

FYE: June 30

2011 Year-End Financials
Return on assets: —   Cash ($ mil.): 65
Return on equity: 1.6%
Current ratio: 0.30

LUCILE SALTER PACKARD CHILDREN'S HOSPITAL AT STANFORD

LOCATIONS

HQ: LUCILE SALTER PACKARD CHILDREN' S HOSPITAL AT STANFORD
725 WELCH RD, PALO ALTO, CA 943041601
Phone: 650 736-7398

HISTORICAL FINANCIALS
Company Type: Private

Income Statement

	REVENUE ($ mil.)	NET INCOME ($ mil.)	NET PROFIT MARGIN	EMPLOYEES
08/10	794	48	6.1%	1,100
08/09	772	76	9.9%	—
Annual Growth	2.8%	(36.4%)	—	—

FYE: August 31

2010 Year-End Financials
Return on assets: —   Cash ($ mil.): 192
Return on equity: 6.1%
Current ratio: 1.00

LUKOIL PAN AMERICAS LLC

Auditors: PRICEWATERHOUSECOOPERS LLP FL

LOCATIONS

HQ: LUKOIL PAN AMERICAS LLC
1095 AVE OF THE, NEW YORK, NY 10036
Phone: 212 221-4527

HISTORICAL FINANCIALS

Company Type: Private

Income Statement

FYE: December 31

	REVENUE ($ mil.)	NET INCOME ($ mil.)	NET PROFIT MARGIN	EMPLOYEES
12/08	4,745	5	0.1%	12
12/07	4,717	3	0.1%	—
12/06	3,021	23	0.8%	—
12/05	2,788	0	—	—
Annual Growth	**19.4%**	—	—	—

2008 Year-End Financials

Return on assets: —
Return on equity: 0.1%
Current ratio: 0.40
Cash ($ mil.): 1

LUMBER PRODUCTS AN OREGON CORPORATION

EXECUTIVES

President, Peter J. Hall
COO, Craig Hall
Branch Manager Tualatin, Tess Landis
Branch Manager Medford, Jerry Fitzpatrick
Branch Manager Eugene, Keith Lambright
Branch Manager Boise, Cal Emerson
Manager MaC, Ken Gloss
Branch Manager Denver, Tom Ludwig
Branch Manager Kent, Bill Plummer
Branch Manager Spokane, Randy McComas
Branch Manager Renton, Craig Edholm
Manager Sunrise Wood Products, Scott Richner
Branch Manager Bozeman, Brad Butterfield
Branch Manager Las Vegas, Robert Cleland
Branch Manager Albuquerque, Stan Kitts
Branch Manager Chandler, Mike Stump
Branch Manager Salt Lake City, Trace Cunningham
Branch Manager Sacramento, Keith Wambold
Manager Doors Division, John Myers
CFO, Bart Walker

LOCATIONS

HQ: LUMBER PRODUCTS AN OREGON CORPORATION
19855 SW 124TH AVE, TUALATIN, OR 970628007
Phone: 503 692-3322

COMPETITORS

ABC Supply
Arthur Lumber
Foxworth-Galbraith Lumber
Georgia-Pacific
Guardian Building Products Distribution
HD Supply
Huttig Building Products
Jewett-Cameron Trading
Pacific Coast Building Products
PrimeSource Building
Snavely Forest Products
Stock Building Supply
Weyerhaeuser

HISTORICAL FINANCIALS

Company Type: Private

Income Statement

FYE: December 31

	REVENUE ($ mil.)	NET INCOME ($ mil.)	NET PROFIT MARGIN	EMPLOYEES
12/07	437	2	0.6%	540
12/06	442	10	2.3%	—
12/05	398	13	3.5%	—
12/04	345	0	—	—
Annual Growth	**8.1%**	—	—	—

2007 Year-End Financials

Return on assets: 2.1%
Return on equity: 0.6%
Current ratio: 0.50
Cash ($ mil.): 1

M & H ENTERPRISES INC.

What M & H Enterprises builds in Vegas stays in Vegas. Also known as Martin-Harris Construction the company provides design/build general construction and construction management services to commercial institutional and industrial projects throughout the Southwest. In addition to its home state Martin-Harris also provides general contracting services in New Mexico Texas Colorado and Utah. Martin-Harris has completed office retail hospitality entertainment high-rise condominium and public works projects for clients such as Neiman Marcus Embassy Suites and US Air Force. The company was founded in 1976 by president and CEO Frank Martin. It has offices in Las Vegas and Phoenix.

EXECUTIVES

President and CEO, Frank Martin
President MHC Texas with a dedicated team of project managers, Kevin Zahm
VP Estimating, Frank (Guy) Martin
Auditors: FAIR ANDERSON & LANGERMAN LAS

LOCATIONS

HQ: M & H ENTERPRISES INC.
3030 S HIGHLAND DR, LAS VEGAS, NV 891091047
Phone: 702 385-5257
Web: WWW.MARTINHARRIS.COM

COMPETITORS

Balfour Beatty Construction
Turner Corporation

HISTORICAL FINANCIALS

Company Type: Private

Income Statement

FYE: December 31

	REVENUE ($ mil.)	NET INCOME ($ mil.)	NET PROFIT MARGIN	EMPLOYEES
12/13	191	1	0.9%	140
12/12*	179	1	0.9%	—
11/11	119	1	1.2%	—
12/10	168	0	—	—
Annual Growth	**4.3%**	—	—	—

*Fiscal year change

2013 Year-End Financials

Return on assets: —
Return on equity: 0.9%
Current ratio: 1.00
Cash ($ mil.): 9

M. M. FOWLER INC.

Auditors: NELSON & COMPANY PA CPA DUR

LOCATIONS

HQ: M. M. FOWLER INC.
4220 NEAL RD, DURHAM, NC 277052322
Phone: 919 309-2925
Web: WWW.FAMILYFARECONVENIENCESTORES.COM

HISTORICAL FINANCIALS

Company Type: Private

Income Statement

FYE: December 31

	REVENUE ($ mil.)	NET INCOME ($ mil.)	NET PROFIT MARGIN	EMPLOYEES
12/10	407	9	2.4%	28
12/09	332	6	2.1%	—
12/08	1,313	0	—	—
Annual Growth	**(44.3%)**	**40616.0%**	—	—

2010 Year-End Financials

Return on assets: —
Return on equity: 2.4%
Current ratio: 1.20
Cash ($ mil.): 21

M.G. OIL COMPANY

Auditors: KETEL THORSTENSON LLP RAPID

LOCATIONS

HQ: M.G. OIL COMPANY
1180 CREEK DR, RAPID CITY, SD 577034111
Phone: 605 342-0527
Web: WWW.MGOIL.OPENFOS.COM

HISTORICAL FINANCIALS

Company Type: Private

Income Statement

FYE: December 31

	REVENUE ($ mil.)	NET INCOME ($ mil.)	NET PROFIT MARGIN	EMPLOYEES
12/13	349	4	1.4%	450
12/12	338	5	1.7%	—
12/11	328	0	0.2%	—
12/10	253	0	—	—
Annual Growth	**11.3%**	—	—	—

2013 Year-End Financials

Return on assets: 3.3%
Return on equity: 1.4%
Current ratio: 0.50
Cash ($ mil.): 1

MACK-CALI REALTY L. P.

Auditors: PRICEWATERHOUSECOOPERS LLP NE

LOCATIONS

HQ: MACK-CALI REALTY L. P.
4 BECKER FARM RD STE 104, ROSELAND, NJ 070681734
Phone: 973 577-2472
Web: WWW.MACK-CALI.COM

HISTORICAL FINANCIALS
Company Type: Private

Income Statement
FYE: December 31

	ASSETS ($ mil.)	NET INCOME ($ mil.)	INCOME AS % OF ASSETS	EMPLOYEES
12/14	4,192	31	0.7%	2
12/13	4,515	(19)	—	—
12/12	4,526	46	1.0%	—
12/11	4,295	0	—	—
Annual Growth	(0.8%)	—	—	—

2014 Year-End Financials
Return on assets: 19.9%
Return on equity: 4.9%
Sales ($ mil): 636

MACOMB OAKLAND REGIONAL CENTER INC

Michigan's disabled citizens have more than a friend in MORC. The Macomb-Oakland Regional Center (MORC) advocates for adults and children with developmental physical or psychiatric disabilities hoping to improve the lives of its clients. In addition to finding homes and jobs and coordinating recreational activities for the disabled the not-for-profit organization helps connect customers with support services including psychology nursing and medical care. It also holds community education seminars and it provides home health visitation and rehabilitation therapy services through its MORC Home Care and MORC Rehab divisions. Founded in 1972 MORC serves over 4000 clients in the state.

EXECUTIVES
Medical Director, Robert Lechy
Vice President Beverly Thomas, John (Jack) Torrone

LOCATIONS
HQ: MACOMB OAKLAND REGIONAL CENTER INC
16200 19 MILE RD, CLINTON TOWNSHIP, MI 480381103
Phone: 586 263-8700
Web: WWW.THEAMORC.ORG

COMPETITORS
Gentiva	Magellan Health
HealthSouth	NHC

HISTORICAL FINANCIALS
Company Type: Private

Income Statement
FYE: September 30

	REVENUE ($ mil.)	NET INCOME ($ mil.)	NET PROFIT MARGIN	EMPLOYEES
09/13	198	(0)	—	300
09/12	193	0	0.1%	—
09/10	186	0	0.2%	—
09/09	181	0	—	—
Annual Growth	2.2%	—	—	—

2013 Year-End Financials
Return on assets: 8.0%
Return on equity: (-0.1%)
Current ratio: 0.60
Cash ($ mil.): 8

MAGNOLIA REHABILITATION & NURSING CENTER

LOCATIONS
HQ: MAGNOLIA REHABILITATION & NURSING CENTER
8133 MAGNOLIA AVE, RIVERSIDE, CA 925043409
Phone: 951 688-4321
Web: WWW.MAGNOLIA-REHAB.COM

HISTORICAL FINANCIALS
Company Type: Private

Income Statement
FYE: January 31

	REVENUE ($ mil.)	NET INCOME ($ mil.)	NET PROFIT MARGIN	EMPLOYEES
01/09	965	3	0.4%	140
01/98	3	(0)	—	—
Annual Growth	66.3%	—	—	—

2009 Year-End Financials
Return on assets: 0.1%
Return on equity: 0.4%
Current ratio: 1.20
Cash ($ mil.): —

MAIN LINE HOSPITALS INC.

Bryn Mawr Hospital a member of the Main Line Health network is an acute care facility providing a variety of inpatient and outpatient services in the western suburbs of Philadelphia. With some 320 beds Bryn Mawr Hospital is recognized nationally for its orthopedic program. Founded in 1893 by Dr. George Gerhard the teaching hospital also provides cancer cardiac surgical pediatric reproductive health diagnostic imaging psychiatric bariatric and wound care services. Bryn Mawr Hospital and the other Main Line Health facilities are part of community based not-for-profit network Jefferson Health System.OperationsBased in Bryn Mawr Pennsylvania Bryn Mawr Hospital boasts specialized departments such as a Comprehensive Breast Center; Wound Healing Center at Bryn Mawr Hospital; Outpatient Imaging Center; Center for Reproductive Medicine; Cancer Center; Main Line Health Heart Center; Center for Addictive Diseases; Level III Neonatal Intensive Care Unit; and Nemours Pediatric Partners at Bryn Mawr Hospital. The hospital also operates an outpatient health center in Newton Square Pennsylvania.Bryn Mawr Hospital admits some 18000 patients annually performing around 4800 inpatient and 6800 outpatient surgeries. It provides care to more than 2000 newborns and receives some 47000 emergency department visits each year. StrategyMain Line Health in 2015 announced plans to invest $200 million to modernize Bryn Mawr Hospital. The initiative is the most significant renovation ever for the hospital and it includes plans to build a five-story patient-care pavilion and convert all patient rooms to private rooms.Like many hospitals Bryn Mawr Hospital aims to expand its outpatient serv-

ices and connect to medical practices. The practice helps to boost the number of referrals to its facility and grow physician relations throughout the community.Bryn Mawr Hospital collaborates with Nemours/Alfred I. duPont Hospital for Children to provide 24/7 pediatric care for the pediatric inpatient unit and the pediatric emergency department with added board-certified emergency medicine physicians. In 2015 the hospital formed a partnership with Lifecycle WomanCare to provide specialized care to pregnant and postpartum families in the community.

EXECUTIVES
Medical Director of The Main Line Health Stroke Program, Gary Friday
Vice President Operations, Jim Paradis
Vice President Planning and Business Development, Joel Port
Vice President and Chief Medical Information Officer, Harm Scherpbier
Director Of Nursing, Michael (Mel) Buongiorno
Medical Director Bryn Mawr Rehab Hospital, John (Jack) Kraus

LOCATIONS
HQ: MAIN LINE HOSPITALS INC.
130 S BRYN MAWR AVE, BRYN MAWR, PA 190103121
Phone: 610 526-3000
Web: WWW.MAINLINEHEALTH.ORG

PRODUCTS/OPERATIONS

Selected Clinical Programs and Health Centers
American Day Treatment Center
Behavioral Health Inpatient Unit
Bryn Mawr Hospital/duPont Children's Health
Comprehensive Breast Center
Cancer Center/Radiation Oncology including IMRT
Cardiac/Pulmonary Rehabilitation
Center for Reproductive Medicine
Clinical Laboratory and Pathology
Community Services
Critical Care
Diabetes Management Program
Emergency Services
Enterostomal Therapy
Family Centered Maternity Unit
Family Practice
General Surgery and Subspecialties
Geriatric Services
Main Line Health Heart Center
Internal Medicine and Subspecialties
Interventional Radiology
Kidney Dialysis
Level III Neonatal Intensive Care Unit
Neurodiagnostic Center
Neurosciences
Nutritional Services
Occupational/Employee Health Services
Orthopedics/Joint Replacement Program
Pain Management Services
Pediatricians and Dedicated Pediatric Inpatient Unit
Perinatal Testing Center
Physical Medicine/Rehabilitation and Therapy
Pulmonary Diagnostic and Wellness Center
Sleep Medicine Services
Surgicenter
Travelers' Services
Wound Healing Center

COMPETITORS
Abington Memorial Hospital
Albert Einstein Healthcare Network
Christiana Care
Crozer-Keystone Health System
Doylestown Hospital
Memorial Hospital (PA)
Moses Taylor Hospital
North Philadelphia Health System
Tenet Healthcare
University of Pennsylvania Health System
Virtua Memorial

HISTORICAL FINANCIALS

Company Type: Private

Income Statement

FYE: June 30

	REVENUE ($ mil.)	NET INCOME ($ mil.)	NET PROFIT MARGIN	EMPLOYEES
06/10	953	114	12.0%	3,353
06/08	11	2	19.2%	—
Annual Growth	821.0%	627.4%	—	—

2010 Year-End Financials

Return on assets: 4.1%   Cash ($ mil.): 53
Return on equity: 12.0%
Current ratio: 1.50

MAINE MEDICAL CENTER

Maine Medical Center (MMC) makes healing happen for the residents of northern New England. Part of MaineHealth the not-for-profit medical center consists of a tertiary care community hospital The Barbara Bush Children's Hospital and outpatient clinics. Specialty services include cancer care geriatrics emergency medicine cardiovascular care rehabilitation neurology orthopedics and women's health. Through its partnership with the Tufts University School of Medicine the 640-bed teaching hospital provides a variety of medical education and training programs. MMC also conducts research through the Maine Medical Center Research Institute. The medical center was founded in 1874 with 40 beds.

Geographic Reach

Located in Portland the MMC serves the northern New England area.

Operations

MMC boasts a large ever-expanding outpatient segment that provides day surgery cardiac catheterization laboratory services and rehabilitation services. It also operates about three dozen outpatient clinics. MMC provides preventive and consultation services including the MMC Diabetes Center the AIDS Consultation Service and the Center for Lipids and Cardiovascular Health.

MMC is expanding the surgical facilities at its main campus. Due for completion in 2015 the medical center embarked on a $40-million expansion plan that will add five modern operating rooms including a cardiac hybrid operating room and 20 perioperative spaces for patient prep and recovery.

The medical center is one of the largest employers in its service territory with a workforce of some 6500. Its Maine Medical Partners physician organization maintains about 175 doctors who provide care at some 30 primary and specialty care centers. MMC also provides more than 20% of charity care for uninsured or underinsured patients in the state.

Strategy

In keeping with its reputation of being technologically forward the hospital operates a Telestroke Network that provides area residents with around-the-clock access to MMC's neurology and ER physicians. The Telestroke Network is a form of telemedicine an increasingly popular way of expanding access to care by allowing patients to "visit" physicians either telephonically or via streaming web and video. MMC is also one of a growing number of teaching hospitals to use high-tech simulation rooms to train medical students.

To improve the quality of care MMC is enacting evidence-based medicine programs. Through such programs hospitals seek to lower medical expenses and improve patient outcomes through data exchange systems that allow physicians to review best practices in specific medical fields. The hospital is also looking to expand its research programs by partnering with other area medical R&D firms.

EXECUTIVES

President and CEO, Richard W. (Rich) Petersen
Senior Vice President Chief Information Officer, Barry Blumenfeld
SVP Planning and Marketing Maine Medical Center and MaineHealth, Mark A. Harris
VP Medical and Academic Affairs; Chief Medical Officer and Academic Dean Tufts University School of Medicine Medical School Program, Peter W. Bates
EVP and COO, Jeffrey D. (Jeff) Sanders
President Medical Staff, M. Parker Roberts
President and a Principal of CBRE|Boulos Property Management, Morris Fisher
President MaineHealth, William L. Caron
Medical Director of Neurocritical Care, David (Dave) Seder
Director Of Pharmacy, Brian Marden
Pharmd, Marizela Savic
Medical Director for Tuberculosis Clinic, William (Bill) Williams
Medical Director of Family Medicine, Mark Bouchard
Nursing Director, Shannan Reid
Vice President Neurosciences Service Line, Kathryn Coolidge
Senior Vice President Clinical Services, Maureen Van Benthuysen
Director Of Nursing, Deborah Bachand
Vice President Revenue Cycle, Chausse Paul
Chairman, Christopher W. Emmons

LOCATIONS

HQ: MAINE MEDICAL CENTER
22 BRAMHALL ST, PORTLAND, ME 041023175
Phone: 207 662-0111
Web: WWW.MMC.ORG

PRODUCTS/OPERATIONS

Selected Specialty Centers
Cancer Institute
Cardiovascular Institute
Emergency Medicine
Family Birth Center
Joint Replacement Center
Neuroscience Institute
The Barbara Bush Children's Hospital

COMPETITORS

Eastern Maine Healthcare Systems	MaineGeneral Health
Franklin Community Health Network	Mercy Health System of Maine
Maine Coast Memorial Hospital	Parkview Hospital
	St. Joseph Healthcare

HISTORICAL FINANCIALS

Company Type: Private

Income Statement

FYE: September 30

	REVENUE ($ mil.)	NET INCOME ($ mil.)	NET PROFIT MARGIN	EMPLOYEES
09/13	908	118	13.0%	5,000
09/08	685	49	7.3%	—
Annual Growth	5.8%	18.9%	—	—

2013 Year-End Financials

Return on assets: 3.2%   Cash ($ mil.): 37
Return on equity: 13.0%
Current ratio: 0.80

MAINEGENERAL HEALTH

If you're aching or ailing within shouting distance of the Kennebec River in Maine then MaineGeneral Health is the place to head. The comprehensive health care organization features acute care hospitals outpatient clinics and physicians' practices long-term care centers and home health and hospice agencies. Its flagship facilities are the three main campuses (in state capital Augusta and Waterville farther north) of MaineGeneral Medical Center together featuring about 290 inpatient beds. MaineGeneral Health also runs nursing homes with some 270 beds in all as well as senior living apartments lab and imaging centers and inpatient rehabilitation and mental health facilities.OperationsMaineGeneral has a number of operations aimed at reaching underserved populations in rural parts of its service area. For instance the organization includes a small rural facility in northern Somerset County with an emergency room outpatient center and nursing home. And its HealthReach Network works with area hospitals and health care providers to ensure that some services (particularly home health care substance abuse treatment and mental health services) reach rural residents. Similarly the health care system hosts periodic specialty clinics that bring in doctors in medical specialties not represented on its own staff.StrategyIn 2009 MaineGeneral announced plans to build a new 225-bed medical center in north Augusta that would consolidate the inpatient operations of its hospital campuses. Two of the medical center campuses would close (Augusta Campus and Seton Campus) while the third (Thayer Campus) would become an outpatient/emergency care facility. Construction of the $322 million hospital began in 2011 with a completion date in late 2013.

EXECUTIVES

Vice President, Wendy Manter
Auditors: BAKER NEWMAN & NOYES PORTLAND

LOCATIONS

HQ: MAINEGENERAL HEALTH
35 MEDICAL CENTER PKWY, AUGUSTA, ME
043308160
Phone: 207 626-1000
Web: WWW.MAINEGENERAL.ORG

COMPETITORS

Eastern Maine Healthcare Systems	MaineHealth
Franklin Community Health Network	Mercy Health System of Maine
Maine Coast Memorial Hospital	Parkview Hospital
	St. Joseph Healthcare

HISTORICAL FINANCIALS
Company Type: Private

Income Statement
FYE: June 30

	REVENUE ($ mil.)	NET INCOME ($ mil.)	NET PROFIT MARGIN	EMPLOYEES
06/13	423	35	8.5%	3,800
06/12	440	(2)	—	—
06/11	421	46	10.9%	—
06/10	401	0	—	—
Annual Growth	1.8%	—	—	—

2013 Year-End Financials
Return on assets: 6.1%
Return on equity: 8.5%
Current ratio: 0.90
Cash ($ mil.): 18

MAINEGENERAL MEDICAL CENTER

Auditors: BAKER NEWMAN & NOYES PORTLAND

LOCATIONS

HQ: MAINEGENERAL MEDICAL CENTER
35 MEDICAL CENTER PKWY, AUGUSTA, ME
043308160
Phone: 207 626-1289
Web: WWW.MAINEGENERAL.ORG

HISTORICAL FINANCIALS
Company Type: Private

Income Statement
FYE: June 30

	REVENUE ($ mil.)	NET INCOME ($ mil.)	NET PROFIT MARGIN	EMPLOYEES
06/13	378	40	10.6%	2,200
06/11	372	39	10.7%	—
06/10	336	10	3.2%	—
06/09	990	0	—	—
Annual Growth	—	—	—	—

2013 Year-End Financials
Return on assets: 5.7%
Return on equity: 10.6%
Current ratio: 0.90
Cash ($ mil.): 10

MAINLINE INFORMATION SYSTEMS INC.

Auditors: KPMG LLP JACKSONVILLE FL

LOCATIONS

HQ: MAINLINE INFORMATION SYSTEMS INC.
1700 SUMMIT LAKE DR, TALLAHASSEE, FL
323177942
Phone: 850 219-5000
Web: WWW.MAINLINE.COM

HISTORICAL FINANCIALS
Company Type: Private

Income Statement
FYE: December 31

	REVENUE ($ mil.)	NET INCOME ($ mil.)	NET PROFIT MARGIN	EMPLOYEES
12/13	479	38	7.9%	568
12/12	520	35	6.8%	—
12/11	567	26	4.6%	—
12/10	576	0	—	—
Annual Growth	(5.9%)	—	—	—

2013 Year-End Financials
Return on assets: 4.9%
Return on equity: 7.9%
Current ratio: 1.50
Cash ($ mil.): 27

MAKE CORPORATION

Auditors: KUTCHINS ROBBINS & DIAMOND LT

LOCATIONS

HQ: MAKE CORPORATION
1 S 450 SMMIT AVE STE 165, OAKBROOK TERRACE, IL 60181
Phone: 630 376-0646
Web: WWW.MAKECOR.COM

HISTORICAL FINANCIALS
Company Type: Private

Income Statement
FYE: December 31

	REVENUE ($ mil.)	NET INCOME ($ mil.)	NET PROFIT MARGIN	EMPLOYEES
12/13	22,724	1,399	6.2%	192
12/12	20,101	851	4.2%	—
Annual Growth	13.1%	64.4%	—	—

MANAGEMENT AND TRAINING CORPORATION

Management & Training Corporation (MTC) prepares prison inmates for re-entry into society. It provides a variety of academic vocational and social-skills training in rehabilitation-oriented private prisons. Its holistic education model offers programs to help inmates avoid substance abuse as they also boost their engagement in community service find work and increase their cognitive skills. As part of its services MTC operates about two dozen correctional facilities in eight states through a contract with the Department of Labor. The company also operates Job Corps centers and provides health care related services to correctional facilities.

Geographic Reach

The company's main offices are located in Centerville Utah and it has satellite centers in Georgia Texas and Washington DC. MTC operates through almost 60 contracts in about 20 states including correctional facility contracts in Arizona California Florida Idaho Ohio New Mexico Mississippi and Texas.

MTC operates internationally providing governments NGOs ministries and private entities with customized training programs designed to help develop workforces. Its international unit has assisted clients in Africa Asia Australia the Middle East and North America.

Operations

MTC operates through four divisions: Correctional Job Corps MTC Medical and Economic & Social Development. Its correctional division operates facilities that house more than 31100 inmates and is one of the largest US correctional contractors for the Department of Labor. Its Job Corps division is the largest single operator of Job Corps centers in the US with more than 120 centers (serving 12000 students a year) across the US. Job Corps is a government funded job-training program for 16-to-24-year-old children and adults.

The company's MTC Medical unit provides subcontracted health care services to correctional facilities by employing a range of medical providers including dentists optometrists psychiatrists and psychologists and physicians. The Economic & Social Development division which offers research retraining and vocational training through contracts with organizations has provided vocational training to citizens in Iraq and research and retraining efforts in China Haiti Mongolia Southern Sudan Tunisia Pakistan Indonesia Jordan and Palestine.

The company trains its supervisors senior managers and executives through its MTC Corporate University while its MTC Institute performs research into forming best practices related to addressing issues facing those who work with Job Corps youth and prison inmates.

In 2013 MTC's Job Corps division had 22 contracts; Corrections 33; and Economic and Social Development 2.

Sales and Marketing

In addition to the Department of Labor the company has held contracts with the US Agency for International Development the African Development Bank UNICEF and other organizations. It also serves state agencies such as the Texas Department of Criminal Justice.

Financial Performance

MTC reported gross revenues of some $704 million in 2012.

Strategy

MTC expands by recruiting and retaining quality educators health professionals and international consultants. To maximize its employees' potential the company conducts leadership development programs for all of its employees. MTC also expands by adding new contracts with state correctional agencies.Working with MRC in 2014 the Wilkinson County Correctional Facility started a new program to help inmates deal with anger issues.

In 2013 the Texas Department of Criminal Justice awarded the company four-year ontract to operate the Bridgeport Pre-Parole Transfer Facility.That year MTC also secured contracts with Limestone County Texas and the Mississippi Department of Corrections.

Company Background

MRC was founded in 1981.

EXECUTIVES

Senior Vice President of Training Programs, John (Jack) Pedersen
President, R. Scott Marquardt
Vice President Corrections Marketing, Mike Murphy
Executive Vice President, Neil Adler
Senior Vice President Business Development And Administration, Sergio Molina

Vice President, Dean Hoffman
Vice President and General Counsel, Dawn Call
Vice President Job Corps Southeast Region,
 Lonnie Hall
Vice President Human Resources, Teresa Aramaki
**Vice President Information Systems and Chief
 Information Officer,** Richard (Dick) Skeen
Chairman, Robert Marquardt
Auditors: KPMG LLP SALT LAKE CITY UT

LOCATIONS

HQ: MANAGEMENT AND TRAINING CORPORATION
 500 N MARKET PLACE DR # 100, CENTERVILLE, UT
 840141708
Phone: 801 693-2600
Web: WWW.MTCTRAINS.COM

PRODUCTS/OPERATIONS

Selected Services
Communicate through formal and informal channels
Develop custom training for students clients & offenders
Manage facilities
Provide community connections
Provide data solutions

COMPETITORS

Avalon Correctional Services
Community Education Centers
Conmed Healthcare
Corizon
Corrections Corporation of America
G4S
GEO Group
MHM Services
Res-Care
Wexford Health

HISTORICAL FINANCIALS

Company Type: Private

Income Statement				FYE: December 31
	REVENUE ($ mil.)	NET INCOME ($ mil.)	NET PROFIT MARGIN	EMPLOYEES
12/13	735	50	6.9%	9,500
12/12	704	45	6.5%	—
12/11	687	30	4.4%	—
12/10	667	0	—	—
Annual Growth	3.3%	—	—	—

2013 Year-End Financials

Return on assets: 2.3%   Cash ($ mil.): 15
Return on equity: 6.9%
Current ratio: 0.20

MANAGEMENT SCIENCES FOR HEALTH INC.

Auditors: TONNESON & COMPANY CPAS PC WA

LOCATIONS

HQ: MANAGEMENT SCIENCES FOR HEALTH INC.
 200 RIVERS EDGE DR, MEDFORD, MA 021555479
Phone: 617 250-9500
Web: WWW.MSH.ORG

HISTORICAL FINANCIALS

Company Type: Private

Income Statement				FYE: June 30
	REVENUE ($ mil.)	NET INCOME ($ mil.)	NET PROFIT MARGIN	EMPLOYEES
06/13	321	2	0.7%	400
06/10	247	1	0.6%	—
06/08	134	1	0.9%	—
06/06	334	0	—	—
Annual Growth	—	—	—	—

2013 Year-End Financials

Return on assets: —   Cash ($ mil.): 29
Return on equity: 0.7%
Current ratio: 1.80

MAP INTERNATIONAL (INC.)

Auditors: CAPIN CROUSE LLP ATLANTA GEO

LOCATIONS

HQ: MAP INTERNATIONAL (INC.)
 4700 GLYNCO PKWY, BRUNSWICK, GA 315256901
Phone: 912 265-6010
Web: WWW.MAP.ORG

HISTORICAL FINANCIALS

Company Type: Private

Income Statement				FYE: September 30
	REVENUE ($ mil.)	NET INCOME ($ mil.)	NET PROFIT MARGIN	EMPLOYEES
09/14	320	15	4.9%	200
09/13	348	(3)	—	—
09/12	244	29	12.2%	—
09/11	140	0	—	—
Annual Growth	31.6%	—	—	—

2014 Year-End Financials

Return on assets: 0.1%   Cash ($ mil.): —
Return on equity: 4.9%
Current ratio: 0.40

MAR-JAC POULTRY INC.

From farm to table Mar-Jac Poultry's business is "poultry in motion." The company is one of the major processors of chicken sold to the domestic fast-food restaurant and foodservice market. Its operations include a hatchery to raise birds and a feed mill that churns 8500 tons of feed a week for some 200 farmers in Georgia who contract with the company to grow its chicks and broilers. Mar-Jac's plant processes about two million chickens a week which are vacuum-packed in its cold storage facility prior to shipment to mostly local distributors in the US and some international export customers. Mar-Jac was started by brothers Marvin and Jackson McKibbon in 1954 and later acquired by a group of poultry farmers.

Despite its humble origins the company has confronted a number of complex legal and regulatory issues. In 2011 the poultry farm appealed a fed-

eral court ruling that dismissed its claim for libel slander and product disparagement against CBS. A 60 Minutes program was covering a government investigation that implicated Mar-Jac in an alleged plot to launder money for terrorists using the chicken production industry as a cover. Mar-Jac also faced $380000 in OSHA fines for multiple willful safety and health violations in 2009.

EXECUTIVES

Vice President, Donald (Don) Bull
Vice President, Ron Weaver
Auditors: FROST PLLC LITTLE ROCK ARKA

LOCATIONS

HQ: MAR-JAC POULTRY INC.
 1020 AVIATION BLVD, GAINESVILLE, GA 305016839
Phone: 770 536-0561
Web: WWW.MARJACPOULTRY.COM

PRODUCTS/OPERATIONS

Selected Products
Boneless
 Butterflies
 Filets
 Tenders
 Thigh meat
Fast food
 6 piece
 8 piece
 9 piece
 Quarters
 Splits
Parts
 Cut Wings
 Drums
 Gizzards
 Leg quarters
 Livers
 Paws (export only)
 Split breasts
 Thighs
 Whole legs
 Whole wings
Whole birds
 With giblets
 Without giblets

COMPETITORS

Eberly Poultry	Plainville Farms
Foster Farms	Rose Acre Farms
Mountaire Farms	Sanderson Farms
Perdue Incorporated	Shelton' s
Petaluma Poultry	Tecumseh Poultry
Pilgrim' s Pride	Tyson Foods

HISTORICAL FINANCIALS

Company Type: Private

Income Statement				FYE: April 26
	REVENUE ($ mil.)	NET INCOME ($ mil.)	NET PROFIT MARGIN	EMPLOYEES
04/13	314	17	5.6%	1,200
04/12	283	8	2.9%	—
04/11	257	11	4.4%	—
04/10	262	0	—	—
Annual Growth	6.1%	—	—	—

2013 Year-End Financials

Return on assets: 2.5%   Cash ($ mil.): 33
Return on equity: 5.6%
Current ratio: 2.60

MARCH OF DIMES FOUNDATION

The March of Dimes Foundation has been lending a hand since 1938. Established by President Franklin Roosevelt to fight polio the organization has evolved into an advocate for the prevention of birth defects and infant mortality. Its focus areas include genetic birth defects premature birth parent education and expanding access to health care. The foundation provides information and support services for professionals and the public and supports research efforts. Most of the foundation's revenue comes from contributions to its signature March for Babies event and other fundraisers.

Financial Performance

In 2012 March of Dimes reported revenue of $219 million an increase of nearly 10% from 2011. A rise in investment gains was enough to offset a small decline in bequests and major gifts. The March for Babies raised just over $106 million nearly half of the organization's total revenue that year. In addition special events and direct response brought in a combined $90+ million while major gifts accounted for about $12 million.

Overall the foundation invested some $30 million in research to study premature birth defects and infant mortality in 2012. The research money is also used for medical treatments and prevention.

Company Background

The organization originally called The National Foundation for Infantile Paralysis owes its name to comedian Eddie Cantor. In an early fundraiser for the group Cantor appealed to radio listeners nationwide to send dimes to the White House. He called the campaign the March of Dimes after the popular newsreel feature The March of Time. The campaign was a success and The National Foundation for Infantile Paralysis formally became the March of Dimes in 1979.

EXECUTIVES

President and CEO, Jennifer L. Howse
EVP and COO, Jane E. Massey
SVP CFO and Assistant Treasurer, Richard E. Mulligan
Vice Chairman of the Maryland FBLA Board of Directors, Janice Icenhower
Vice President Direct Response Fundraising, Kimberly Haywood
Vice Chairman, David R. Smith
Trustee, Kenneth A. (Ken) May, age 54
Auditors: KPMG LLP NEW YORK NY

LOCATIONS

HQ: MARCH OF DIMES FOUNDATION
1275 MAMARONECK AVE, WHITE PLAINS, NY 106055298
Phone: 914 428-7100
Web: WWW.MARCHOFDIMES.COM

HISTORICAL FINANCIALS

Company Type: Private

Income Statement
FYE: December 31

	REVENUE ($ mil.)	NET INCOME ($ mil.)	NET PROFIT MARGIN	EMPLOYEES
12/13	202	(9)	—	1,200
12/09	214	35	16.4%	—
12/08	236	0	—	—
12/06	236	0	—	—
Annual Growth	(2.2%)	—	—	—

MARIETTA MEMORIAL HOSPITAL INC

LOCATIONS

HQ: MARIETTA MEMORIAL HOSPITAL INC
401 MATTHEW ST, MARIETTA, OH 457501699
Phone: 740 374-1400
Web: WWW.MMHOSPITAL.ORG

HISTORICAL FINANCIALS

Company Type: Private

Income Statement
FYE: September 30

	REVENUE ($ mil.)	NET INCOME ($ mil.)	NET PROFIT MARGIN	EMPLOYEES
09/13	303	(1)	—	1,100
09/09	119	(4)	—	—
09/08	119	2	2.4%	—
09/07	149	0	—	—
Annual Growth	12.5%	—	—	—

2013 Year-End Financials
Return on assets: 8.2%
Return on equity: (-0.4%)
Current ratio: 1.80
Cash ($ mil.): 35

2013 Year-End Financials
Return on assets: 5.4%
Return on equity: (-4.8%)
Current ratio: 0.50
Cash ($ mil.): 11

MARIST COLLEGE

Marist College is a gem among small private US colleges. The liberal arts college has a enrollment of more than 6300 students and a student-faculty ratio of 16-to-1. It offers more than 40 bachelor's and a dozen master's programs as well as some 20 certificate programs. It seven schools specialize in communication and the arts computer science and math continuing education liberal arts management science and social and behavioral sciences. In addition to its main 210-acre campus along the shores of the Hudson River the college has several off-campus extension sites that mainly cater to adult students. Marist was founded in 1929 to train new members in the Marist Brothers order of Catholic priests.

Operations

Marist College has recently been recognized by publications including Kiplinger's Private Finance magazine which named Marist as one of the best value private college in the US. It has also been on the Princeton Review's best colleges list with a special recognition for its extensive study abroad programs (including a branch campus in Florence Italy) as well as its business teaching criminal justice fashion and communication programs. Marist College also offers advanced IT resources to its students through a partnership with IBM which is also located in southeastern New York State.

Financial Performance

The college has an annual operating budget of $160 million.

In 2014 Marist College reported a 9% rise in revenues thanks to an increase in student tuition and fees as well as more grants and other income.

Company Background

Marist College was founded in 1929 as a training center for the brothers of the Roman Catholic Marist order.

EXECUTIVES

Associate Vice President for Academic Affairs, John T (Jack) Ritschdorff
Executive Vice President, Jeffrey Brackett
Executive Vice President, Geoffrey Brackett
Vice President, Sarah Wojtowicz
Associate Vice President for Human Resources, Deborah (Deb) Raikes-Colbert
Vice President, Allison Bolch
Vice President, Mary Abu
Vice President For College Advancement, Christopher Delgiorno
Vice President Sales, Margie Rowland
Student Body Executive Vice President, Timos Pietris
Vice President, Shawn Kaylor
Associate Vice President for Human Resources, Deborah (Deb) Raikes
Vice President Of Finance, Jeanie Plecenik
Vice President of Athletic Affairs, Briana Holmes
Vice President Class, Croix Laconsay
Vice President, Austin Christensen
Vice President, Nikki Rohan
Vice President of Enrollment Management, Debbie Dzielecki
Treasurer, Emma Gage
Vice Chairman, Ross A Mauri
Secretary, Tish Hicks
Treasurer, Sophia Todeasa
Treasurer, Alec Lee
Secretary Class, Courtney Cousineau
Secretary, Kailey Lyons
Secretary, Emily Lubrano
Auditors: GRANT THORNTON LLP NEW YORK

LOCATIONS

HQ: MARIST COLLEGE
3399 NORTH RD, POUGHKEEPSIE, NY 126011387
Phone: 845 575-3000
Web: WWW.CLUBS.MARIST.EDU

PRODUCTS/OPERATIONS

Majors
Accounting
American Studies
Applied Mathematics
Athletic Training
Biochemistry (B.A.)
Biochemistry (B.S.)
Biology
Biology Education
Biomedical Sciences
Business Administration
  Finance
  Human Resource Management
  International Business
  Marketing
Chemistry (B.A.)
Chemistry (B.S.)
Communication
  Advertising
  Communication Studies
  Journalism
  Public Relations
  Sports Communication
Computer Science
Computer Science/Game Design
Criminal Justice
Digital Media
Economics
Education
  Adolescence Education (Grades 7-12)
  Childhood/Special Education (Grades 1-6)
English
  Literature

Theatre
Writing
Environmental Science
  Policy
  Science
Fashion Design
Fashion Merchandising
Fine Arts
  Art History
  Studio Art
History
Information Technology and Systems
  Information Systems
  Information Technology
Mathematics
Media Studies and Production
Medical Technology
Modern Languages and Cultures
  French
  Italian
  Spanish
Philosophy
  Religious Studies
Political Science
  International Studies
  Public Affairs
Psychology
Psychology/Dual Certification/Special Education (1-6)
Social Work
Graduate Programs
Accounting MBA
MA in Communication
MA in Integrated Marketing Communication
MA in Mental Health Counseling
MA in Museum Studies
MA in School Psychology
Master of Arts in Educational Psychology
Master of Education (Initial Teaching Certification)
MBA- Master of Business Administration
MPA- Master of Public Administration
MS in Information Systems
MS in Software Development
Advanced Certificate in Information Systems

HISTORICAL FINANCIALS

Company Type: Private

Income Statement

FYE: June 30

	REVENUE ($ mil.)	NET INCOME ($ mil.)	NET PROFIT MARGIN	EMPLOYEES
06/13	228	33	14.7%	750
06/10	211	47	22.3%	—
06/09	159	0	—	—
06/08	0	0	—	—
Annual Growth	—	—	—	—

2013 Year-End Financials

Return on assets: 8.5%   Cash ($ mil.): 49
Return on equity: 14.7%
Current ratio: 0.40

MARITZ HOLDINGS INC.

Maritz may not send your employees on business trips but it will motivate them to go. The company's mission is to understand enable and motivate people to unleash their hidden potential enabling people to do things differently by developing their strengths knowledge and confidence. The Steve Maritz-owned company designs employee incentive and reward programs (including incentive travel rewards) and customer loyalty programs. It also plans corporate trade shows and events and offers traditional market research services such as the creation of product launch campaigns. Its programs are designed to help its clients improve workforce quality and customer satisfaction.

HISTORY

Edward Maritz an entrepreneur of Swiss-French descent founded the E. Maritz Jewelry Manufacturing Company in St. Louis in 1894. By 1900 the wholesaler and manufacturer of men's and women's jewelry was supplying retail jewelers across the South and West. By 1921 Maritz had become a major importer of Swiss watches which it sold to retail jewelers under the Merit Cymrex and Record brands. In the 1920s the company added diamond jewelry and silverware to its product mix. Edward Maritz died in 1929.

To drum up new business during the Depression Edward's son James began trying to sell watches and jewelry to large corporations for use as sales and service awards pioneering the incentive market. The first sale for a nationwide employee incentive campaign was to Caradine Hat a St. Louis hatmaker in 1930. In 1948 Maritz handled a $2 million incentive program for Chevrolet.

In 1950 the Maritz family split the business into two operations. Brother Lloyd handled the jewelry business (it died in 1955 when Lloyd died); James took over the incentive operations which flourished. In the 1950s James expanded his company's offerings to include merchandise awards and in 1958 travel incentive awards (arranged through the newly acquired Holiday House Travel Center of Detroit). The enterprise adopted the corporate name Maritz Inc. in 1961. During the 1960s and early 1970s Maritz made a series of acquisitions closely allied with its motivation endeavors including Lee Creative Research the nucleus of what would become its market research operations (1973). The organization expanded internationally with the opening of Maritz offices in the UK and Mexico in 1974.

In 1980 the company acquired the Wilding division of Bell & Howell which it merged with another unit to form Maritz Communications Co. James died in 1981. Maritz beefed up its travel operations in the 1980s acquiring corporate travel agency Traveler's Service (St. Louis 1981) Byfield Travel (Chicago 1984) Beverly Hills Travel (Los Angeles 1986) and Travel Counselors International (Virginia 1986).

These acquisitions led to record sales in 1989 but sliding results in the early 1990s prompted the company to streamline its operations by cutting overlapping units. After a family boardroom tussle in 1993 William Maritz expanded his control by buying out his sister's 50% stake in the company and putting his two sons on the board. His son Stephen Maritz subsequently took over as president.

As part of its international expansion strategy Maritz acquired The Research Business Group the UK's largest independently owned marketing research firm (1993) and BLC the largest performance-improvement company in France (1994). In 1997 the company established an office in Manila its first in Asia.

In 1998 William Maritz stepped down as CEO and retained the title of chairman; his son Stephen succeeded him. In 1998 and 1999 the company boosted its international presence with acquisitions in Canada (group travel firm Partners in Performance marketing research firm Thompson Lightstone & Co.) and the Netherlands (Maritz B.V.).

Facing heat from online incentive programs the company launched its own online service e-Maritz in 2000. It also started Heybridge an e-commerce subsidiary that helps small and midsized businesses sell over the Internet. In 2001 Maritz purchased Librix Learning an online learning company.

The following year it purchased travel and incentive business McGettigan (later to be renamed Mar-

tiz McGettigan) to add depth to its client offerings. Also that same year Peter and Philip Maritz (brothers of chairman and CEO Steve Maritz) sued the company purportedly seeking a greater role in managing the family business. In the summer of 2003 the brothers again filed suit against Steve alleging that the purchase of McGettigan cost $10 million more than what was originally presented to the board. Peter and Philip's suits are an attempt to cash out of the family business –which they feel lost value because of the McGettigan purchase –at a better price than they'd get now.

In early 2004 Maritz sold its data collection unit Delve to St. Louis-based Bush O'Donnell Capital Partners. The same year Maritz sold its TQ3 Travel Solutions division to Carlson Wagonlit Travel.

Steve Maritz became the sole owner of the company in 2006 after buying out his other family members' shares.

Maritz also expanded its product offerings and geographic reach in 2008 when it acquired Cascade Promotion Corporation a marketing and fulfillment business operating out of Boston Las Vegas and St. Louis. With Cascade catering to the gaming and technology industries the buyout gave Maritz access to growing niche markets.

Making ground into what it considers a high-growth market Maritz solidified its position in the prepaid card sector in 2010 when it acquired full ownership of American Express Incentive Services (AEIS). For more than a decade AEIS operated as a joint venture between Maritz and a subsidiary of American Express. AEIS is an independent issuer of prepaid products such as cards and American Express Travelers Cheques on the American Express network. The products are used for employee recognition consumer promotions and sales incentives.

EXECUTIVES

Chairman and CEO, W. Stephen (Steve) Maritz, age 58
President and COO, Dennis Hummel
CFO, Rick Ramos
President of Maritz Travel Company, David Peckinpaugh
Vice President Human Resources, David (Dave) Estes
Vice President Sales, Jack Stiehr
Division Vice President Maritz Research, Lisa Weaner
Vice President Finance, Frank Munsch
Vice President, Mike McClernon
Vice President of Sales and Marketing, Carrie Nolan
Division Vice President, Kari McGraw
Vice President Group Business Manager, Terry Erwin
Group Vice President, Tom Wilson
Vice President Of Business Development, Greg Bogue
Vice President Strategic Planning, Kathleen Bibbins
Vice President Sales, Tim O'Neill
Vice President of Finance and Assistant Treasurer, Matt Glazer
Vice President Pharma Sector, Dave Caldwell
Vice President Internal Audit, John (Jack) Farley
Vice President Corporate Development, John (Jack) Mcarthur
Director Finance Assistant Treasurer, Thomas (Thom) Sizemore
Auditors: KPMG LLP ST LOUIS MISSOURI

LOCATIONS

HQ: MARITZ HOLDINGS INC.
  1375 N HIGHWAY DR, FENTON, MO 630990001
Phone: 636 827-4000
Web: WWW.MARITZTRAVEL.COM

PRODUCTS/OPERATIONS

Selected Services

Marketing Research
  Custom marketing research
  Customer satisfaction and customer value analysis
  Data collection (focus groups telephone interviews)
  Maritz Polls and Maritz Research Reports
  Syndicated buyer research
  Telecommunications research
Performance Improvement
  Communications
  e-Learning
  Fulfillment
  Internet consulting
  Loyalty marketing
  Measurement and feedback
  Rewards and recognition
Travel
  Consulting services
  Corporate travel management
  Group travel services
  Travel award programs

COMPETITORS

Franklin Covey	J.D. Power
Gallup	JTB Corp.
GiftCertificates.com	Kantar Group
Harris Interactive	Motivcom
IMS Health	Nielsen
Information Resources Inc.	ORC International

HISTORICAL FINANCIALS

Company Type: Private

Income Statement

FYE: March 31

	REVENUE ($ mil.)	NET INCOME ($ mil.)	NET PROFIT MARGIN	EMPLOYEES
03/14	1,218	113	9.3%	2,955
03/13	1,256	42	3.3%	—
03/12	1,155	47	4.1%	—
03/11	1,158	0	—	—
Annual Growth	1.7%	—	—	—

2014 Year-End Financials

Return on assets: —
Return on equity: 9.3%
Current ratio: 0.80
Cash ($ mil.): 116

MARJAM SUPPLY CO. INC.

LOCATIONS

HQ: MARJAM SUPPLY CO. INC.
  885 CONKLIN ST, FARMINGDALE, NY 117352400
Phone: 631 249-4900
Web: WWW.MARJAM.COM

HISTORICAL FINANCIALS

Company Type: Private

Income Statement

FYE: December 31

	REVENUE ($ mil.)	NET INCOME ($ mil.)	NET PROFIT MARGIN	EMPLOYEES
12/13	341	15	4.4%	614
12/12	279	8	3.1%	—
12/11	258	2	1.2%	—
12/10	202	0	—	—
Annual Growth	19.0%	—	—	—

2013 Year-End Financials

Return on assets: 7.7%
Return on equity: 4.4%
Current ratio: 0.80
Cash ($ mil.): 1

MARKET AMERICA INC.

Calling itself a cross between Amazon and QVC Market America is an Internet marketer and broker of products and services from a variety of categories including apparel beauty and personal care electronics entertainment nutrition and sports. Market America sells more than 2500 of its own branded products (such as Isotonix Motives and Snap) and spotlights the offerings of more than 3000 other retailers (including Sears Staples and Wal-Mart) on its SHOP.COM web site (acquired in 2010). In addition the company manages UnFranchise a network marketing business with more than 180000 independent shopping consultants. The company was founded in 1992 by president and CEO James "JR" Ridinger.

Geographic Reach

Based in North Carolina the company has a presence in several global markets including the US Canada Australia Hong Kong Taiwan the UK and Mexico. It's expanding into Latin America. Through its website Market America provides access to its brands to consumers in 200-plus countries.

Operations

Market America's independent shopping consultants operate under the company's UnFranchise business model also referred to as "one-to-one marketing." The UnFranchise platform comes complete with a business plan customizable Web portal merchandising materials and management system. To develop community relations consultants can provide online assistance to shoppers in their areas and recruit potential UnFranchise consultants. Consultants earn commissions when shoppers purchase products and services through their Market America shopping portals. In 2010 Market America opened its UnFranchise business model to nonprofits. The company said individuals following its business model have netted more than $2 billion in commissions and retail profits since it was established.

Strategy

Operating in seven global markets Market America looks to expand into Spain Colombia Costa Rica Ecuador and the Dominican Republic. It's working to extend the reach of its UnFranchise business model to Latino entrepreneurs. The move marks the company's largest expansion in its history.

To bolster its position in Internet retailing Market America has been expanding its operations outside the US. The company has international branches in Canada Australia Hong Kong Taiwan and the Philippines. It plans to extend its reach to the UK Mexico Latin America and other markets where it does not yet have a presence.

Mergers and Acquisitions

Market America acquired e-tailer SHOP.COM in late 2010 to blend its marketing and brokering expertise with SHOP.COM's strength in technology and merchandising. The result creates a "social shopping" movement capable of challenging some of the Internet's leading shopping destinations. As part of the deal the two firms agreed to operate their websites separately.

Financial Performance

Market American rings up $500 million in sales annually. Since its founding the product brokerage and Internet marketing company boasts more than $5.3 billion in accumulated retail sales.

Ownership

Market America Inc. operates as a subsidiary of Market America Worldwide Inc.

EXECUTIVES

Vice President Operations, Brandi Quinn
Vice President of Information Technology Special Projects, Samantha Ritchie
Vice President Human Resources, Joe Bolyard
Vice President Of Human Resources, Kathleen Fairall
Senior Vice President and Director, Loren Ridinger
Executive Vice President, Dennis Franks

LOCATIONS

HQ: MARKET AMERICA INC.
  1302 PLEASANT RIDGE RD, GREENSBORO, NC 274099415
Phone: 336 605-0040
Web: WWW.MARKETAMERICA.COM

PRODUCTS/OPERATIONS

Selected Brands

Cellular Laboratories
Custom Cocktail
Fixx
Gene SNP DNA Analysis
Heart Health
Isotonix
MA Capital Resources
MA Webcenters
Matriskin
Motives
NutriClean
Pentaxyl
Pet Health
Prime
Royal Spa
Snap
Timeless Prescriptions
TLS Weight Loss Solution
Ultimate Aloe

Selected Product Categories

Anti-aging
Apparel jewelry and shoes
Automotive and tools
Baby products
Beauty products cosmetics
Books movies and video games
Cameras
Cell phones and communications
Computers
Consumer electronics
Crafts
Grocery
Health and nutrition
Home and Garden
Jewelry
Music
Party supplies
Pet supplies
Tickets
Toys

COMPETITORS

AMS Health Sciences	Overstock.com
Amazon.com	PriceGrabber.com
Amway	QVC
Astral Brands	Shaklee
Avon	Shopzilla
Buy.com	USANA Health Sciences
HSN	ViSalus
Mannatech	Yahoo!
Melaleuca	eBay
NexTag	

HISTORICAL FINANCIALS

Company Type: Private

Income Statement

FYE: December 31

	REVENUE ($ mil.)	NET INCOME ($ mil.)	NET PROFIT MARGIN	EMPLOYEES
12/09	224	15	7.0%	650
12/08	228	3	1.5%	—
12/07	218	0	0.0%	—
Annual Growth	1.5%	106006.5%	—	—

2009 Year-End Financials

Return on assets: 1.5%
Return on equity: 7.0%
Current ratio: 4.10

Cash ($ mil.): 55

MARQUETTE UNIVERSITY

A member of the Association of Jesuit Colleges and Universities Marquette University provides undergraduate graduate and professional courses and programs. It specializes in business engineering arts and sciences nursing law dentistry and other fields. The university offers undergraduates some 75 majors and 65 minors and post-graduate students about 50 doctoral and master's degree programs. With an enrollment of more than 11700 students Marquette University boasts a student/faculty ratio of 14:1. Its student population consists of students from all 50 US states and nearly 70 countries. Founded in 1881 the university is named after French missionary explorer Father Jacques Marquette.

Geographic Reach

Based in Milwaukee Wisconsin the Marquette University campus attracts students across the nation and from nearly 70 countries worldwide.

Operations

Marquette University an independent coeducational and not-for-profit institution of higher learning and research consists of a dozen separate colleges and schools.

Financial Performance

The educational institution logged a marginal 1% increase in revenue in fiscal 2012 as compared to 2011 due to rising tuition and fees contributions government and private grants and endowment income used in operations. Net income during the same reporting period dropped some 90% thanks to increases in operating expenses and declines in endowment gains in excess of the amount designated for current operations (net other).

Strategy

To boost its healthcare presence the Marquette University College of Nursing opened the Wheaton Franciscan Healthcare Center for Clinical Simulation in late 2012. The facility features a six-bed hospital suite with a pair of intensive care rooms two medical surgical rooms one pediatrics room and one labor and delivery suite.

EXECUTIVES

Vice President, Elizabeth Wescott
Vice President Of Administration, Betsy Philipose
Vice President, Kathy Scherbarth
Vice President Academic Affairs and PI, David (Dave) Buckholdt
Auditors: KPMG LLP MILWAUKEE WI

LOCATIONS

HQ: MARQUETTE UNIVERSITY
1250 W WISCONSIN AVE, MILWAUKEE, WI 532332225
Phone: 414 288-7223
Web: WWW.MARQUETTE.EDU

PRODUCTS/OPERATIONS

Selected Schools and Colleges

College of Business Administration
College of Education
College of Engineering
College of Health Sciences
College of Nursing
College of Professional Studies
Graduate School
Graduate School of Management
Helen Way Klingler College of Arts and Sciences
J. William and Mary Diederich College of Communications
Law School
School of Dentistry

HISTORICAL FINANCIALS

Company Type: Private

Income Statement

FYE: June 30

	REVENUE ($ mil.)	NET INCOME ($ mil.)	NET PROFIT MARGIN	EMPLOYEES
06/13	391	37	9.5%	3,000
06/12	385	9	2.4%	—
06/11	383	90	23.7%	—
06/10	449	0	—	—
Annual Growth	(4.5%)	—	—	—

2013 Year-End Financials

Return on assets: 2.5%
Return on equity: 9.5%
Current ratio: —

Cash ($ mil.): 41

MARS SUPER MARKETS INC

Whether men and women hail from Mars or Venus Mars Super Markets pays no mind: both sexes eat! The company is a chain of about 15 grocery stores in the Baltimore area. Founded by Joseph D'Anna in 1943 and still owned and run by the D'Anna family Mars Super Markets began in the middle of the Mars Estates military housing community. The regional supermarket chain supplies products to its store locations from its own 300000 sq. ft. distribution center in Baltimore offers a line of its own private label products and sells produce and seafood from local markets.

Rising competitive pressures in the regional grocery market have led to speculation that Mars may finally sell itself to a larger competitor. (Both SUPERVALU which owns local rival Shoppers Food & Pharmacy and Delhaize are rumored to be among potential suitors.) But Mars which is attractive because of its coveted store locations and distribution center has rejected buyout offers in the past.

EXECUTIVES

Executive Vice President Operations, Theodore D'Anna
Executive Vice President, Ted Anna
Secretary To Human Resources, Lisa Schautz

LOCATIONS

HQ: MARS SUPER MARKETS INC
9627 PHILADELPHIA RD, BALTIMORE, MD 212374154
Phone: 410 590-0500
Web: WWW.MARSFOOD.COM

COMPETITORS

7-Eleven	SUPERVALU
ALDI	Safeway
Acme Markets	Shoppers Food
Costco Wholesale	Warehouse
Food Lion	Wal-Mart
Giant Food	Weis Markets

HISTORICAL FINANCIALS

Company Type: Private

Income Statement

FYE: December 26

	REVENUE ($ mil.)	NET INCOME ($ mil.)	NET PROFIT MARGIN	EMPLOYEES
12/09	280	6	2.3%	1,700
12/06	300	11	3.8%	—
12/05	267	14	5.3%	—
12/04	0	0	—	—
Annual Growth	—	—	—	—

2009 Year-End Financials

Return on assets: 3.3%
Return on equity: 2.3%
Current ratio: 1.40

Cash ($ mil.): 25

MARSHALL NURSING SERVICES INC

Auditors: DOWNEAST ACCOUNTING BANGOR M

LOCATIONS

HQ: MARSHALL NURSING SERVICES INC
9 BEAL ST, MACHIAS, ME 04654
Phone: 207 255-3387

HISTORICAL FINANCIALS

Company Type: Private

Income Statement

FYE: September 30

	REVENUE ($ mil.)	NET INCOME ($ mil.)	NET PROFIT MARGIN	EMPLOYEES
09/09	362	(6)	—	110
09/02	3	0	1.0%	—
09/01	3	0	0.1%	—
Annual Growth	81.3%	—	—	—

2009 Year-End Financials

Return on assets: 0.1%
Return on equity: (-1.8%)
Current ratio: 0.40

Cash ($ mil.): —

MARSHALL UNIVERSITY

If "You Are Marshall" you know that Marshall University is a state-supported non-profit educational institution serving about 14000 students including 3500 graduate and medical students. The university offers about 55 baccalaureate and more than 50 graduate programs through more than a dozen colleges and schools. It also offers two Associate Programs two Ed.S four Doctoral Degree Programs and three First Professional programs. Marshall students attend classes either at the university's main campus in Huntington West Virginia; at its regional campuses; or online.

Geographic Reach

Marshall has locations in Huntington West Virginia (its main campus) as well as in South Charleston Campus Mid-Ohio Valley Center Teays Valley Center and Beckley Center. The university enrolls students from all counties in West Virginia 46 US states and the District of Columbia as well as from about 50 countries worldwide.

Operations

The university enrolls about 19% of the students from out of state. It has an undergraduate student/faculty ratio of 19:1 and the average class size is 23.

Financial Performance

Marshall reported flat revenues in fiscal year 2013 as an increase in revenues from students tuition and fees interest on loans receivables and sales and services of educational activities was partially offset by lower revenues from federal contracts and grants and from auxiliary enterprises.Net income increased by 38% in fiscal year 2013 due to a decline in operating expenses and higher investment income.

Strategy

In 2013 the university expanded its program portfolio with the introduction of master's degree in public administration and a bachelor of science degree in medical imaging with an emphasis in diagnostic medical sonography. That year Marshall continued building its $50 million new engineering complex on the Huntington campus as part of its strategy to upgrade facilities on its main campus.

Company Background

Named for former Chief Justice John Marshall the university was established in 1837. The 2006 movie "We Are Marshall" dramatizes the aftermath of the 1970 plane crash that killed most of Marshall's Thundering Herd football team.

EXECUTIVES

SVP Information Technology and CIO, Jan I. Fox
President, Jerome A. Gilbert
CEO Marshall University Foundation, Ronald Area
SVP Finance and CFO, Mary E. Heuton
SVP Operations, Brandi Jacobs-Jones
SVP Academic Affairs and Provost, Gayle Ormiston
SVP Communications and Marketing, Ginny Painter
Vice President For Research, John Maher
Vice President For Development, Scott Miller
Vice President Graduate Studies and Dean Graduate School of Education and Professional Development, Ronald (Ron) Childress
Vice President Communications And Marketing, Keith Spears
Assistant Vice President For Admin, Karen Kirtley
Chairman, Michael G. Sellards
Vice Chairman, Edward Howard
Board Member, Jeri Fogel
Secretary, Frances Mooney
Treasurer, Elaine Hardman

LOCATIONS

HQ: MARSHALL UNIVERSITY
1 JOHN MARSHALL DR, HUNTINGTON, WV
257550003
Phone: 304 696-2385
Web: WWW.MARSHALL.EDU

PRODUCTS/OPERATIONS

Selected Colleges and Schools
College of Business

College of Education and Human Services
College of Fine Arts
College of Health Professionals
College of Information Technology and Engineering
College of Liberal Arts
College of Science
Community and Technical College
Graduate College
School of Extended Education
School of Journalism and Mass Communications
School of Medicine
University College

HISTORICAL FINANCIALS

Company Type: Private

Income Statement

FYE: June 30

	REVENUE ($ mil.)	NET INCOME ($ mil.)	NET PROFIT MARGIN	EMPLOYEES
06/14	174	33	19.4%	1,632
06/13	175	26	14.9%	—
06/12	175	19	11.1%	—
06/08	172	0	—	—
Annual Growth	0.2%	—	—	—

2014 Year-End Financials

Return on assets: 5.6%   Cash ($ mil.): 87
Return on equity: 19.4%
Current ratio: 2.50

MARSHFIELD CLINIC INC.

Marshfield Clinic is a private group medical practice that operates more than 50 medical locations across Wisconsin. The network provides primary and tertiary care through its more than 700 physicians who represent about 80 medical specialties. Through two hospitals –the 25-bed Flambeau Hospital and the 40-bed Lakeview Medical Center — and dozens of clinics Marshfield annually serves roughly 380000 patients and handles 3.8 million patient encounters. Other parts of the network include Marshfield Laboratories and Security Health Plan of Wisconsin as well as medical education and research organizations.

Geographic Reach

Marshfield Clinic operates about 50 clinic locations and two hospitals in central western and northern Wisconsin. Its main hospital campuses are located in Park Falls and Rice Lake.

Operations

Marshfield Clinic's Security Health Plan of Wisconsin provides a variety of health insurance options to more than 200000 members in much of central northern and western Wisconsin. The Marshfield Clinic organization also includes Marshfield Labs one of the largest private practice full-service laboratory systems in the nation conducting more than 25 million tests annually.

Flambeau Hospital is a 25-bed Critical Access Hospital and provides 24-hour care for inpatient and outpatient services emergency ambulance services and home health & hospice service. Flambeau Hospital is jointly sponsored by Ministry Health Care and Marshfield Clinic.Lakeview Medical Center is a 40-bed nonprofit community hospital and provides 24-hour care for inpatient and outpatient services and emergency ambulance services. Lakeview Medical Center integrates modern design and technology with a calm healing environment.

Marshfield Clinic runs about 50 general and specialty medical clinics and dental offices in its service territory. It also has an outreach services program that collaborates with 1200 medical sites to provide care in surrounding regions.

The Marshfield Clinic Education Foundation programs for medical school graduates are internal medicine pediatrics dermatology and surgery. The company's research division Marshfield Clinic Research Foundation focuses on clinical research health and safety human genetics epidemiology and biomedical informatics.

Sales and Marketing

Features of the Security Health Plan include contacting members through reminder mailings and personal phone calls to aid with their health maintenance. Additionally affiliated home health nurses visit members at home or in the hospital to answer their questions about their medications or care and to provide needed resources for their recuperation.

Strategy

In 2015 CareCloud and Marshfield Clinic Information Services a healthcare IT company established from within the Marshfield Clinic announced a partnership to deliver a joint cloud-based solution to help improve the clinical financial and administrative outcomes of large ambulatory medical practices. The two parties have joined together MCIS' clinical solutions – including a physician-designed electronic health record (EHR) patient portal and population health management tool with CareCloud's practice management and medical billing software and services. The integrated solution which also includes unified customer implementation and support is optimized for the requirements of large practices across dozens of specialties. MCIS has collaborated with Marshfield Clinic to build a physician-designed cloud-based clinical solution that reflects our successful experiences supporting a renowned multi-specialty group of more than 700 physicians.Marshfield Clinic has a rich history in health information technology and software development. The Clinic has used a computer-based electronic health record for more than 20 years. Cattails Software Suite Marshfield Clinic's homegrown electronic health record was developed in conjunction with Clinic providers and the Information Systems Department. Cattails Software Suite played a significant role in the Clinic's success in the Centers for Medicare and Medicaid Services' Physician Group Practice project. Marshfield Clinic improved patient care while lowering health care costs during the five-year project – saving the Medicare program more than $118 million.In 2015 the company expanded outpatient services provided in the Ambulatory Surgery Center in Marshfield adding skilled nursing care in the East Wing of its Marshfield campus. Similar plans to lower the total cost of care have been designed for all of its mission-critical centers.The second phase of the plan includes construction of a new hospital of the future in Marshfield. A smaller more smartly-designed and more energy efficient high-tech facility will allow for highly-specialized care that requires a hospital setting.

The organization also advances its patient care through a collaboration with Cleveland Clinic. Together the organizations conduct research and development programs on new medical innovations.

Company Background

Marshfield Clinic announced the formation of a new subsidiary Marshfield Clinic Information Services in 2013. The unit will use the organizations health IT expertise to help other care providers implement electronic health record (EHR) systems and other population health management software programs and services.

The clinic was founded in 1916.

EXECUTIVES

Vice President Finance, Gary Mayeux
Pharmacy Manager, Stuart Guenther
Medical Director, Stephen C Zinsmeister
Managing Director, Rhonda Helmke
Medical Director, Adrienne Cruzd
Director of Pharmacy Security Health Plan, Twila Johnson
Vice President Rn, Michelle (Mitch) Brand
Medical Director, Guruprasad Naik
Medical Director, Vicki Vandezande
Vice President Of Implementation Services and Support, Melissa (Mel) Owens
Medical Director, Jacob Bingham
Medical Director, Laurence Friend
Medical Director of Informatics, John (Jack) Melski
Medical Director, J Douglas D Lee
Radiology Director, Shelly Stueber
Medical Director, Patrick (Paddy) Chen
Treasurer, Peter (Pete) Meyer
Secretary, Jan Kaiser
Secretary Transcriptionis, Phillips Dana

LOCATIONS

HQ: MARSHFIELD CLINIC INC.
1000 N OAK AVE, MARSHFIELD, WI 544495702
Phone: 715 387-5511
Web: WWW.MARSHFIELDCLINIC.ORG

PRODUCTS/OPERATIONS

Selected Services
Allergy and Asthma
Ambulatory Surgery
Anesthesia
Athletic Training
Audiology
Bariatric Surgery
Cancer Care
Cardiology (Heart Care)
Center for Community Outreach
Child Development Center
Dental Care
Dermatology
Diabetes Education
Ear Nose and Throat (ENT)
Emergency Medicine
Endocrinology (Diabetes and Metabolism)
Family Medicine
Gastroenterology (Digestive Care)
General Surgery
Genetic Services
Hospitalists (Hospital Care)
Infectious Diseases
Internal Medicine
Nephrology (Kidney Care)
Neurosciences (Neurology)
Nutrition Services
Obstetrics and Gynecology (OB/GYN)
Occupational Health
Oncology (Cancer Care)
Ophthalmology and Optometry (Eye Care)
Optical
Oral and Maxillofacial Surgery
Orthopedics
Orthotics and Prosthetics
Pain Management
Palliative Medicine
Pediatrics
Pharmacy
Physical and Occupational Therapy
Physical Medicine and Rehabilitation
Plastic and Cosmetic Surgery
Podiatry
Primary Care
Psychiatry and Psychology
Pulmonary Medicine (Lung Care)
Radiology
Rheumatology and Arthritis Care
Sports Medicine
TeleHealth
Urgent Care
Urology
Wound Healing

COMPETITORS

Blue Cross Blue Shield of Wisconsin
Compcare Health Services Insurance Corporation
Dean Health Systems Inc.
Group Health Cooperative
Gundersen Lutheran
Luther Midelfort
Meriter Health Services
Ministry Health Care
ThedaCare Inc.
University of Wisconsin Hospital and Clinics

HISTORICAL FINANCIALS

Company Type: Private

Income Statement

FYE: September 30

	REVENUE ($ mil.)	NET INCOME ($ mil.)	NET PROFIT MARGIN	EMPLOYEES
09/13	1,171	18	1.6%	6,900
09/09	1,062	78	7.4%	—
09/08	102	6	5.9%	—
Annual Growth	**62.8%**	**24.7%**	**—**	**—**

2013 Year-End Financials

Return on assets: 10.4%   Cash ($ mil.): 63
Return on equity: 1.6%
Current ratio: 0.50

MARTIN & BAYLEY INC.

Martin & Bayley (dba Huck's Food and Fuel) operates 115 Huck's convenience stores and a number travel centers in mostly in Illinois and Indiana but also in Missouri Kentucky and Tennessee. Half of its outlets are in Illinois. The company operates a commissary at its warehouse in Carmi Illinois to supply sandwiches chicken and other food items to its stores. Some stores sell Godfather's Pizza. Family-owned since its inception Martin & Bayley became a 100% employee-owned firm when the Martin and Bayley families sold their stakes in the company.

Geographic Reach
Martin & Bayley owns and operates convenience stores in Illinois Indiana Missouri Kentucky and Tennessee.

Sales and Marketing
The company's vendor includes Fritolay Jack Link's Kraft MillerCoors Nestle Pepsi Red Bull and Wonka.

The convenience store operator is growing in the south with new Hucks locations opening in Huntingdon Tennessee and Paducah and Hopkinson Kentucky.

Ownership
Martin & Bayley is owned by its employees.

Company Background
Founders Bob Martin and Frank Bayley formed a partnership in 1960. In 1974 they opened the first Huck's convenience store in Illinois. The Martins and the Bayleys sold the company to its employees in 2001.

EXECUTIVES

V Pres-human Resources, Audrey L Elwood
Vice President Marketing, Tim Tilford
Vice President Operations, Murat Tokad
Vice President Real Estate, Jim Whetstone
Vice President of Real Estate, Jim Whetsone
Marketing Vice President, Teresa Knasel
Vice President, John Long
Auditors: HARDING SHYMANSKI & COMPANY

LOCATIONS

HQ: MARTIN & BAYLEY INC.
1311A W MAIN ST, CARMI, IL 628211389
Phone: 618 382-2334
Web: WWW.MARTINANDBAYLEY.COM

PRODUCTS/OPERATIONS

2013 Stores

	No.
Illinois	55
Indiana	26
Kentucky	18
Missouri	14
Tennessee	2
Total	**115**

Selected Product Lines

Godfathers Pizza
5 Buck Huck
Bigg Swigg
Coffee
Deli Express
Fresh Brewed Ice Tea
Hot to Go at Huck's
Sweet Street

COMPETITORS

7-Eleven
Casey's General Stores
Chevron
Couche-Tard
Exxon Mobil
Krause Gentle
TravelCenters of America

HISTORICAL FINANCIALS

Company Type: Private

Income Statement

FYE: March 29

	REVENUE ($ mil.)	NET INCOME ($ mil.)	NET PROFIT MARGIN	EMPLOYEES
03/11	528	7	1.4%	1,500
03/10	466	5	1.1%	—
03/09	1,579	0	—	—
Annual Growth	**—12031.5%**		**—**	**—**

2011 Year-End Financials

Return on assets: 3.0%   Cash ($ mil.): 13
Return on equity: 1.4%
Current ratio: 0.50

MARTIN'S POINT HEALTH CARE INC.

Auditors: BAKER NEWMAN & NOYES PORTLAND

LOCATIONS

HQ: MARTIN'S POINT HEALTH CARE INC.
331 VERANDA ST STE 1, PORTLAND, ME 041035544
Phone: 207 828-2402
Web: WWW.MARTINSPOINT.ORG

HISTORICAL FINANCIALS

Company Type: Private

Income Statement

FYE: December 31

	REVENUE ($ mil.)	NET INCOME ($ mil.)	NET PROFIT MARGIN	EMPLOYEES
12/13	489	10	2.1%	729
12/09	267	30	11.3%	—
12/07	200	42	21.0%	—
12/06	168	0	—	—
Annual Growth	**16.4%**	**—**	**—**	**—**

Return on assets: —
Return on equity: 2.1%
Current ratio: 1.10

Cash ($ mil.): 68

MARYLAND AND VIRGINIA MILK PRODUCERS COOPERATIVE ASSOCIATION INC

Milk is "Mar-VA-lous" for the members of the Maryland & Virginia Milk Producers Cooperative Association. Known as Maryland & Virginia the co-op processes and sells milk for nearly 1500 member/farmers with dairy herds in the southeastern US and mid-Atlantic region. Maryland & Virginia produces fluid milk ice cream and cultured dairy products for retail sale under the Marva Maid Maola and Valley Milk brands. Its butter condensed milk and milk-powder products are sold primarily to food manufacturers. As a co-op it also offers agricultural supplies to its members. Maryland & Virginia operates three fluid-milk processing plants a manufacturing plant and an equipment-supply warehouse.

Geographic Reach

The co-op gets its milk from member farmers in Delaware Florida Georgia Kentucky Maryland North Carolina Ohio Pennsylvania South Carolina Tennessee Virginia and West Virginia. Its fluid processing plants are located in Newport News Virginia; Landover Maryland; and New Bern North Carolina. It has manufacturing facilities in Laurel Maryland and Strasburg Virginia and a warehouse in Frederick Maryland.

Operations

Maryland & Virginia operates three fluid processing plants a single manufacturing plant and a farm supply equipment division. It also owns a majority stake in Valley Milk LLC. The co-op transports more than 300 tanker truckloads of milk daily to nearly 30 different plants. Member farms range in size from fewer than 100 cows to more than 2000. Combined Maryland & Virginia members produce three billion pounds of milk annually.

Sales and Marketing

In addition to supermarkets the co-op counts customers such as Walgreens Starbucks Sheetz convenience stores and Dairy Queen among its customers.

Financial Performance

The co-op's revenue decreased by 5% to $1.3 billion in 2012 versus $1.4 billion in 2011 due to a decline in milk dairy and other products as well as sales of equipment and supplies partially offset by an increase in sales of its members' and non-members' raw milk. Despite the decline in sales the Maryland & Virginia reported a profit of $5.5 million in 2012 versus a loss of $2.8 million the prior year. Like other milk producers Maryland & Virginia has been contending with sluggish milk sales due to decreasing milk consumption beginning in the 1970s.

EXECUTIVES

Vice President Engineering And Technical support, Grant Gayman
Auditors: HERLIEM & COMPANY INC READI

LOCATIONS

HQ: MARYLAND AND VIRGINIA MILK PRODUCERS COOPERATIVE ASSOCIATION INC
1985 ISAAC NEWTON SQ W # 200, RESTON, VA 201905031
Phone: 703 742-6800
Web: WWW.MDVAMILK.COM

COMPETITORS

Associated Milk Producers	Dairylea
Dairy Farmers of America	Dean Foods
Dairy Manufacturers	Foremost Farms
	Land O' Lakes

HISTORICAL FINANCIALS

Company Type: Private

Income Statement
FYE: December 31

	REVENUE ($ mil.)	NET INCOME ($ mil.)	NET PROFIT MARGIN	EMPLOYEES
12/13	1,372	5	0.4%	550
12/12	1,296	5	0.4%	
12/11	1,362	(2)	—	—
12/10	1,219	0	—	—
Annual Growth	4.0%	—	—	—

2013 Year-End Financials

Return on assets: 2.6%
Return on equity: 0.4%
Current ratio: 0.90

Cash ($ mil.): —

MARYLAND SOUTHERN ELECTRIC COOPERATIVE INC

Historic Southern Maryland gets it power via the South Maryland Electric Cooperative (SMECO) which distributes electricity to about 154000 residential commercial and industrial customers in four counties via about 11360 miles of power line and 54 electric substations. One of the ten largest electric cooperatives in the US the member-owned enterprise gets its wholesale power supply through its membership in wholesale energy trading and risk management service company ACES Power Marketing. Overseen by a board of directors SMECO's single mission is to provide reliable competitively priced energy and related services to its members.

Geographic Reach

SMECO's 1150 sq. ml. service area includes all of Charles and St. Mary's counties and parts of of Calvert and Prince George's counties. Cities covered include Hughesville Leonardtown Prince Frederick and White Plains.

Financial Performance

In 2012 SMECO revenues decreased by 7% due to weaker residential power demand and lower costs paid for third-party purchased power. The coop's net income decreased by 15%.

Strategy

Like other coops SMECO is pushing conservation the use of green energy and smart technology to reduce power costs. It is also promoting the development of solar and wind energy and integrating it into the power supply it makes available to its members.

In addition SMECO is constructing the Southern Maryland Reliability Project which aims to upgrade SEMCOs existing 69000-volt transmission line to 230000 volts by 2015. The Project's expanded capacity will ensure a more reliable supply.

Ownership

SMECO is a customer-owned electric cooperative.

Company Background

In 1937 as part of the national rural electrification drive of the Roosevelt government a local committee in St. Mary's county and one representing Charles and Prince George's counties merged to form the Southern Maryland Tri-County Cooperative Association. The members converted this association into a non-profit membership cooperative in 1942 and changed its name to Southern Maryland Electric Cooperative.

In 2011 the coop's service areas felt the full brunt of Hurricane Irene which knocked out 11 transmission circuits and cut power 108000 customers and caused $7 million of damage to the coop's electric system.

EXECUTIVES

President and CEO, Austin J. Slater Jr.
SVP Information and Customer Services; CIO, Joseph Trentacosta
SVP Engineering and Operations; COO, Kenneth Capps
Chairman, Joseph V. (Joe) Stone Jr.
Secretary Treasurer and Director, Kenneth L. (Kenny) Dyson
Vice Chairman, Samuel J. (Jack) Hammett
SVP Financial Economic and Employee Services; CFO, Sonja M. Cox
Secretary Treasurer and Director, Kenneth L. (Kenny) Dyson

LOCATIONS

HQ: MARYLAND SOUTHERN ELECTRIC COOPERATIVE INC
15035 BURNT STORE RD, HUGHESVILLE, MD 206372699
Phone: 301 274-3111
Web: WWW.SMECO.COM

HISTORICAL FINANCIALS

Company Type: Private

Income Statement
FYE: December 31

	REVENUE ($ mil.)	NET INCOME ($ mil.)	NET PROFIT MARGIN	EMPLOYEES
12/10	492	17	3.5%	375
12/09	462	3	0.7%	—
12/08	2,121	0	0.0%	—
Annual Growth	(51.8%)	17166.9%	—	—

2010 Year-End Financials

Return on assets: 6.7%
Return on equity: 3.5%
Current ratio: 0.50

Cash ($ mil.): 9

MASONIC HOMES OF CALIFORNIA INC

Auditors: MOSS ADAMS LLP STOCKTON CA

LOCATIONS

HQ: MASONIC HOMES OF CALIFORNIA INC
1111 CALIFORNIA ST, SAN FRANCISCO, CA
941082252
Phone: 415 776-7000
Web: WWW.FREEMASON.ORG

HISTORICAL FINANCIALS

Company Type: Private

Income Statement

FYE: June 30

	REVENUE ($ mil.)	NET INCOME ($ mil.)	NET PROFIT MARGIN	EMPLOYEES
06/09	1,127	(6,855)	—	425
06/08	0	(94)	—	—
Annual Growth	1267173.0%	—	—	—

2009 Year-End Financials

Return on assets: 0.8%   Cash ($ mil.): 3
Return on equity: (-607.8%)
Current ratio: 0.20

MASSACHUSETTS HIGHER EDUCATION ASSISTANCE CORPORATION

Don't know how you're going to pay for college? You might want to consult ASA ASAP. The Massachusetts Higher Education Assistance Corporation which does business as American Student Assistance or ASA is a federal student loan guarantor one of the first in the country. The not-for-profit company provides Federal Family Education Loan Program (FFELP) guarantee origination fund delivery and default prevention services to students schools and lenders. ASA serves more than 1.6 million college loans borrowers across the US and manages a student loan portfolio worth more than $40 billion.OperationsIn addition to debt management services for borrowers ASA serves the US Department of Education with student loan default prevention and recovery services; college financial aid administrators with default prevention support training and regulatory guidance; andthe public as a whole with information about education loans financial literacy borrowing and financial planning for college.StrategyASA utilizes a "wellness" approach to borrowing which involves less emphasis on traditional loan collection and more on the "health" of each loan. With such practices the company keeps its default and delinquency rates below the national average.Company BackgroundThe company was established in 1956.

EXECUTIVES

President CEO, Paul Combe
EVP and, Michael Finn

Vice President For Financial Affairs, Mae St Julien
Medical Director, Victoria McEvoy
Vice President Human Resources, Lauren Rolfe

LOCATIONS

HQ: MASSACHUSETTS HIGHER EDUCATION
ASSISTANCE CORPORATION
100 CAMBRIDGE ST STE 1600, BOSTON, MA
021142518
Phone: 617 728-4507
Web: WWW.ASA.ORG

COMPETITORS

Access Group
Bank of America
Discover
First Marblehead
JPMorgan Chase
Nelnet
Pennsylvania Higher Education Assistance Agency
Sallie Mae

HISTORICAL FINANCIALS

Company Type: Private

Income Statement

FYE: June 30

	ASSETS ($ mil.)	NET INCOME ($ mil.)	INCOME AS % OF ASSETS	EMPLOYEES
06/13	375	48	12.9%	580
06/10	170	34	20.0%	—
06/09	148	0	—	—
06/08	19	0	—	—
Annual Growth	80.3%	—	—	—

2013 Year-End Financials

Return on assets: 10.2%   Sales ($ mil): 233
Return on equity: 20.8%

MASSACHUSETTS PORT AUTHORITY

Massachusetts Port Authority (Massport) operates three airports: Boston Logan International Hanscom Field and Worcester Regional. Logan is home to 50 airlines and is New England's largest airport and the first port of call for many international flights entering the US. (It accounts for the majority of Massport's revenues.) Hanscom Field operates as the region's main aviation airport and offers niche commercial services while Worcester Regional primarily supports commercial flight services. Massport also oversees various waterfront properties of the Port of Boston. The agency was created by the Commonwealth of Massachusetts in 1956. The governor of Massachusetts appoints the agency's board members.

Operations

Massport's business consists of two distinct operating departments: Aviation and the Port. Logan airport catered to 29.4 million aviation passengers and 369000 cruise passengers in 2013. Its shipping operations serviced more than 110000 containers of products at its port.

Financial Performance

Massport's net revenues have steadily climbed over the years. Revenues jumped 2% from $1.78 billion in 2012 to $1.83 billion in 2013 thanks mainly to parking concession ground services and other revenue from nearly 125000 more passengers at Logan. The overall revenue increase for 2013 was generated by operating revenues exceeding operating expenses by $2.4 million.

EXECUTIVES

CIO, Francis X. Anglin
Director Aviation, Edward C. Freni
CFO, John Pranckevicius
Chief Development Officer, James Doolin
CEO, Thomas P. Glynn
Chief of Staff, Elizabeth Morse
Port Director, Lisa Wieland
Vice President, George K Hertz
Chairman, Michael P. Angelini, age 72
Vice Chair, L. Duane Jackson
Secretary, Rita Hannon
Auditors: PRICEWATERHOUSECOOPERS LLP BO

LOCATIONS

HQ: MASSACHUSETTS PORT AUTHORITY
1 HARBORSIDE DR STE 200S, BOSTON, MA
021282905
Phone: 617 561-1600
Web: WWW.MASSPORT.COM

HISTORICAL FINANCIALS

Company Type: Private

Income Statement

FYE: June 30

	REVENUE ($ mil.)	NET INCOME ($ mil.)	NET PROFIT MARGIN	EMPLOYEES
06/07	526	49	9.3%	1,102
06/06*	497	74	15.0%	—
12/05	0	0	11.5%	—
06/04	414	0	—	—
Annual Growth	8.3%	—	—	—

*Fiscal year change

2007 Year-End Financials

Return on assets: 13.4%   Cash ($ mil.): 71
Return on equity: 9.3%
Current ratio: 0.40

MATTINGLY FOODS INC.

Mattingly Foods is a leading regional foodservice supplier that distributes food products and other goods to chain restaurant operators in more than a dozen states. It delivers a variety of dry goods along with frozen and refrigerated foods. In addition to its distribution business Mattingly Foods operates a cash & carry store where customers can purchase wholesale goods. Robert Mattingly started the family-owned business as Mattingly Seafood with his wife Bette in 1947.

LOCATIONS

HQ: MATTINGLY FOODS INC.
302 STATE ST, ZANESVILLE, OH 437013200
Phone: 740 454-0136
Web: WWW.MATTINGLYCASHNCARRY.COM

COMPETITORS

Dot Foods	Reinhart FoodService
Edward Don	Sysco
Ellenbee-Leggett	US Foods
Gordon Food Service	Van Eerden
I Supply	
Meadowbrook Meat Company	

HISTORICAL FINANCIALS
Company Type: Private

Income Statement
FYE: December 29

	REVENUE ($ mil.)	NET INCOME ($ mil.)	NET PROFIT MARGIN	EMPLOYEES
12/07	263	1	0.4%	240
12/06	290	1	0.4%	—
12/05	301	3	1.0%	—
12/04	309	0	—	—
Annual Growth	(5.2%)	—	—	—

2007 Year-End Financials
Return on assets: 4.3% Cash ($ mil.): —
Return on equity: 0.4%
Current ratio: 0.70

MAXIFACIAL DENTAL SURGERY

Auditors: ERNST & YOUNG US LLP INDIAN

LOCATIONS
HQ: MAXIFACIAL DENTAL SURGERY
1 MEDICAL CENTER DR, LEBANON, NH 037561000
Phone: 603 650-5000
Web: WWW.PATIENTS.DARTMOUTH-HITCHCOCK.ORG

HISTORICAL FINANCIALS
Company Type: Private

Income Statement
FYE: September 30

	REVENUE ($ mil.)	NET INCOME ($ mil.)	NET PROFIT MARGIN	EMPLOYEES
09/09	1,147	27	2.4%	7,500
09/06	913	15	1.7%	—
Annual Growth	7.9%	20.7%	—	—

2009 Year-End Financials
Return on assets: 4.9% Cash ($ mil.): 40
Return on equity: 2.4%
Current ratio: 1.10

MAXIM HEALTHCARE SERVICES INC.

Good health as the maxim goes is one of life's greatest blessings and Maxim Healthcare Services aims to promote that principle by offering medical staffing and home health care as well as immunizations and other wellness services to clients nationwide. The company provides medical and administrative personnel for hospitals school systems nursing homes and correctional facilities. The company's staffing division offers contract per diem and travel assignments. Maxim Healthcare's consultants are available 24 hours a day seven days a week to provide assistance for clients. The company which operates from more than 360 locations nationwide was established in 1988.

Operations

The company's Maxim Health Systems division established in 1996 provides immunizations health

screenings and health fairs. Each year the division's immunization program is responsible for vaccinating millions of people across more than 40000 clinics.

Other major Maxim Healthcare divisions include Maxim Staffing Solutions (Nurse Allied Health and Administrative Staffing) Maxim Government Services Maxim Physician Resources Timeline Recruiting Maxim Coders Maxim Pediatric Services; Logix Healthcare Search Partners and StaffAssist.

EXECUTIVES
CIO, Kevin Apperson
COO, Chris Powell
CEO, W. Bradley (Brad) Bennett
VP Chief Medical Officer and Chief Quality Officer, W. John Langley
CFO, Raymond (Ray) Carbone
Director Of Clinical Services, Denise Sutton
Director Of Clinical Services, Ann Lopez
Director Of Clinical Services, Lisa Malone
Director Of Clinical Services, Kathleen Burns
Director Of Clinical Services, Jolinda Jackson
Director of Clinical Services, Mandy Garcia
Area Vice President, Michael Rose
Vice President and General Counsel, Lisa Toni-Jean
Auditors: PRICEWATERHOUSECOOPERS LLP BA

LOCATIONS
HQ: MAXIM HEALTHCARE SERVICES INC.
7227 LEE DEFOREST DR, COLUMBIA, MD 210463236
Phone: 410 910-1500
Web: WWW.MAXIMHEALTHCARE.COM

PRODUCTS/OPERATIONS

Selected Services
Allied Health staffing
Facility nurse staffing
Flu and wellness services
Government services
Health information services
International nursing
Home healthcare
HME/pharmacy services
Habilitation services
Physician services
Travel nursing

Selected Divisions
CareFocus
CareFocus Companion Services
Centrus Premier Homecare
Logix Healthcare Search Partners
Maxim Coders
Maxim Government Services
Maxim Health Information Services
Maxim Health Systems
Maxim Healthcare Services (Homecare)
Maxim Home Health Resources
Maxim Pediatric Services
Maxim Physician Resources
Maxim Staffing Solutions - Administrative Staffing
Maxim Staffing Solutions - Allied Health
Maxim Staffing Solutions - Nurse Staffing
Orbis Clinical
Reflectx Services
StaffAssist
TimeLine Recruiting
TravelMax

COMPETITORS
American HomePatient	PHS Correctional Healthcare
Apria Healthcare	Team Health
Cross Country Healthcare	TeamStaff
MedStaff	
Medsearch Staffing Services	

HISTORICAL FINANCIALS
Company Type: Private

Income Statement
FYE: December 31

	REVENUE ($ mil.)	NET INCOME ($ mil.)	NET PROFIT MARGIN	EMPLOYEES
12/13	1,226	(1)	—	35,000
12/12	1,241	(21)	—	—
12/11	1,341	(12)	—	—
12/10	1,390	0	—	—
Annual Growth	(4.1%)	—	—	—

2013 Year-End Financials
Return on assets: 0.5% Cash ($ mil.): 15
Return on equity: (-0.1%)
Current ratio: 1.60

MAXOR NATIONAL PHARMACY SERVICES CORPORATION

Maxor National Pharmacy Services provides health care and pharmacy services including retail and mail order prescriptions (Maxor Pharmacies) pharmacy benefits management (MaxorPlus) pharmacy consulting (Maxor Pharmacy Consulting Services) and infusion and injection services (IV-Solutions). The company operates about a dozen Maxor Pharmacy stores mostly in Texas and Washington but also in Colorado and New York. Its correctional division provides services to more than 330000 offenders in more than 250 correctional facilities in 26 states through direct management contracts or via its pharmacy services division. Founded in 1926 as a single pharmacy in Amarillo Maxor put itself up for sale in 2013.

Change in Company Type

Privately-owned Maxor put itself up for sale seeking a private equity buyer in July 2013. Maxor's chairman and primary shareholder is looking to cash out of part of his investment and is seeking additional capital to grow the company.

Geographic Reach

Amarillo Texas-based Maxor has regional offices in Colorado Maryland New York Washington and South Texas. The company's drugstores are located in Texas New York Colorado and Washington. The firm also operates in Puerto Rico.

Operations

The company expanded its geographic and customer reach in 2011 when its Maxor Correctional Pharmacy Services business was awarded a contract worth $110 million over three years from the Michigan Department of Corrections. The contract guarantees that Maxor will provide pharmacy services for some 43000 prisoners at 31 correctional facilities and two residential facilities.

Maxor's specialty pharmacy business is growing. In mid-2013 the unit announced that the Jackson Health System (JHS) introduced its specialty pharmacy to patients employees and their families. Maxor currently manages five pharmacies for JHS in Miami-Dade County.

Strategy

Maxor sees great potential for its PickPoint technology division to expand in Puerto Rico over the next five years with the aim of becoming the dominant pharmacy solution there.

Mergers and Acquisitions

The company acquired California-based Pick-Point Corp. in 2011 to expand its technology services offering. PickPoint designs manufactures and distributes software that improves the accuracy safety and efficiency of medication delivery. Its Will Call System uses an LED light-guided system to easily identify prescription hangers via wireless technology.

Ownership

Maxor's primary shareholder is its chairman Jerry Hodge.

EXECUTIVES

Vice President Operations, Jan Robinson
Vice President, Heath Hodge
Vice President Correctional Administration, Allen (Al) Sapp
Vice President Of Operations, Angela Serioharney
Pharmacy Manager, Sandra Talbott
Treasurer, Cynthia Garner
Auditors: BROWN GRAHAM & COMPANY AMARIL

LOCATIONS

HQ: MAXOR NATIONAL PHARMACY SERVICES CORPORATION
320 S POLK ST STE 100, AMARILLO, TX 791011436
Phone: 806 324-5400
Web: WWW.MAXOR.COM

PRODUCTS/OPERATIONS

Selected Operations
IV Solutions (infusion therapy services)
Maxor Administrative Services (employee benefits)
Maxor Pharmacies (retail pharmacies)
MaxorPlus (pharmacy benefit management)
Maxor Specialty (specialty pharmaceuticals infusion therapy services chronic injectables)
PickPoint (pharmacy technology products)

COMPETITORS

CVS	Wal-Mart
H-E-B	Walgreen
Rite Aid	

HISTORICAL FINANCIALS

Company Type: Private

Income Statement

FYE: December 31

	REVENUE ($ mil.)	NET INCOME ($ mil.)	NET PROFIT MARGIN	EMPLOYEES
12/09	223	0	—	481
12/07	176	0	—	
12/06	0	0	—	
12/05	118	0	—	
Annual Growth 17.2%		—	—	—

2009 Year-End Financials

Return on assets: 6.9%   Cash ($ mil.): 8
Return on equity: —
Current ratio: 1.70

MAXYIELD COOPERATIVE

Auditors: MERIWETHER WILSON AND COMPANY

LOCATIONS

HQ: MAXYIELD COOPERATIVE
313 3RD AVE NW, WEST BEND, IA 505978572
Phone: 515 887-7211
Web: WWW.MAXYIELDCOOPERATIVE.COM

Income Statement

FYE: July 31

	REVENUE ($ mil.)	NET INCOME ($ mil.)	NET PROFIT MARGIN	EMPLOYEES
07/14	324	5	1.7%	157
07/13	372	7	2.1%	—
07/12	387	6	1.8%	—
07/11	241	0	—	—
Annual Growth 10.4%		—	—	—

2014 Year-End Financials

Return on assets: 12.2%   Cash ($ mil.): 26
Return on equity: 1.7%
Current ratio: 0.80

MAYER ELECTRIC SUPPLY COMPANY INC.

Mayer Electric Supply helps to light up those southern nights. The company is one of the nation's largest distributors of electrical supplies with about 50 branch locations in the southeastern US. It offers some 40000 items made by leading manufacturers such as 3M GE Littelfuse and Schneider Electric. Products include conduit circuit breakers controls and switches fire and safety products LED and low-voltage lighting systems motors power tools transformers and wire and cable. Mayer Electric supplies customers in the construction datacomm government industrial and utility industries. The Collat family including CEO Nancy Collat Goedecke owns Mayer Electric.

Geographic Reach

Mayer Electric serves customers through locations in Alabama Florida Georgia Mississippi the Carolinas Texas Tennessee and Virginia.

Operations

Besides distributing electrical supplies Mayer Electric offers several services. Its Mayer Project Management group works to lower cost for construction contractors by providing on-site storage and inventory management. Other services include lamp and battery recycling conduit bending and threading and wire and cable cutting. The company also specializes in factory automation energy efficiency and datacomm systems.

Sales and Marketing

The electrical supplies distributor serves multiple customer segments including those in the construction government industrial datacomm and utility industries through about 51 branch locations across US Southeast.

Strategy

Growing its geographic presence in 2013 Mayer Electric opened a branch location in the Houston area.

Mergers and Acquisitions

Looking to expand further in the southeastern US Mayer Electric in 2012 acquired Mustang Electric Supply based outside Dallas in Lewisville Texas. Established in 1998 Mustang Electric serves commercial and residential contractors across the Dallas and Fort Worth area allowing Mayer Electric to expand to the dynamic and lucrative Dallas market. The purchase included Mustang Electric's 40000-sq.-ft. facility in Lewisville.

Company Background

The recession hit companies like Mayer Electric hard as residential and commercial construction ef-

forts were backburnered. Sales for Mayer Electric dropped by about 21% in 2009 compared to the prior year. Rather than responding by laying off employees or shuttering branches the company planned for break-even results or a small loss for the year. Indeed the company made a small profit in 2009.

Mayer Electric was founded in 1930.

EXECUTIVES

Chairman Emeritus, Charles A. Collat Sr.
CFO, David L. Morgan
Chairman and CEO, Nancy Collat Goedecke
President, Wes Smith
EVP Sales and Marketing, Glenn Goedecke
Vice Chairman, Jim Summerlin
Chairman and CEO, Nancy Collat Goedecke
Auditors: WARREN AVERETT LLC BIRMINGHAM

LOCATIONS

HQ: MAYER ELECTRIC SUPPLY COMPANY INC.
3405 4TH AVE S, BIRMINGHAM, AL 352222300
Phone: 205 583-3500
Web: WWW.MAYERELECTRIC.COM

PRODUCTS/OPERATIONS

Selected Services
Basic distributor services
Construction partner
Maintenance repair and operations

Selected Products
Ballasts
Batteries
Cable and wire
Circuit breakers
Conduit
Factory automation products
Fan boxes
Fasteners
Fuses
LED lighting systems
Lenses
Lighting fixtures
Locks
Low-voltage lighting systems
Meters
Motors
Panelboards
Power supplies
Relays
Switches
Surge protection devices
Terminal blocks
Tools
Transformers
Voltage regulators

COMPETITORS

Anixter International	Independent Electric Supply
Consolidated Electrical	Rexel Inc.
Crescent Electric Supply	W.W. Grainger
Gexpro	WESCO International
Graybar Electric	Wholesale Supply Group

HISTORICAL FINANCIALS

Company Type: Private

Income Statement

FYE: December 28

	REVENUE ($ mil.)	NET INCOME ($ mil.)	NET PROFIT MARGIN	EMPLOYEES
12/13	672	6	1.0%	900
12/12	606	6	1.1%	—
12/11*	623	7	1.2%	—
01/11	565	0	—	—
Annual Growth 6.0%		—	—	—

*Fiscal year change

Return on assets: 6.0% Cash ($ mil.): 2
Return on equity: 1.0%
Current ratio: 1.70

MAYO CLINIC HEALTH SYSTEM-FRANCISCAN MEDICAL CENTER INC.

LOCATIONS

HQ: MAYO CLINIC HEALTH SYSTEM-FRANCISCAN
MEDICAL CENTER INC.
700 WEST AVE S, LA CROSSE, WI 546014783
Phone: 608 785-0940
Web: WWW.MAYOCLINICHEALTHSYSTEM.ORG

HISTORICAL FINANCIALS

Company Type: Private

Income Statement

FYE: December 31

	REVENUE ($ mil.)	NET INCOME ($ mil.)	NET PROFIT MARGIN	EMPLOYEES
12/08	363	0	—	3,300
12/05	223	200	89.5%	—
12/04	2,103	0	—	—
Annual Growth	—	—	—	—

2008 Year-End Financials

Return on assets: 22.0% Cash ($ mil.): —
Return on equity: —
Current ratio: 0.60

MAYVILLE ENGINEERING CO INC

Sometimes it's all right to get loaded. Mayville Engineering Company (MEC) manufactures shotshell reloading machinery and equipment used by hunters sport shooting enthusiasts and sporting goods stores. MEC also provides coating welding riveting painting manufacturing prototyping and mechanical assembly services. Its operations are divided across the main divisions of MEC Tube MEC Coatings MEC Fabrication and MEC Shooting Sports. Overall these divisions cater to the agricultural construction military medical and industrial markets.

Geographic Reach

MEC operates through 2 million sq. ft. of manufacturing space in nearly 15 facilities spanning five states including Michigan Mississippi South Carolina Virginia and Wisconsin.

Operations

In addition to MEC's manufacturing processes its MEC Coaters division offers coating services which include electrocoating shot blasting alodine conversion coating and liquid painting for military and other diverse commercial applications.

The company has partnered with the National Rifle Association to provide training to NRA instructors on the operations of their MEC reloaders. Reloading is an environmentally friendly prac-

tice since the hulls and brass are recycled in the process.

Sales and Marketing

MEC targets leading OEMs in the agricultural construction commercial vehicle power sports automotive mining and military sectors. Clients have included such big names as Deere & Company and Oshkosh Corporation.

Mergers and Acquisitions

MEC grows its divisions through the use of acquisitions and in investing in its capital. In 2013 it acquired Missouri-based clay trap machines manufacturer APEX Clay Traps in a deal that allowed MEC to launch a full line of clay target machines complementing the market presence of its MEC shotshell reloaders. To sell this new product line the company formed the MEC Shooting Sports group.

In 2012 MEC picked up Center Manufacturing a Michigan-based manufacturer of metal products. Center became a division of the MEC family of companies and provides additional products and processes through an expanded geographic footprint.

Company Background

Cousins Leo and Ted Bachhuber founded the employee-owned company in 1945 inside a rented garage in Mayville Wisconsin.

EXECUTIVES

Vice President Human Resources, Barry Hoopes
Vice President of Operations Phoenix Coaters Team, Ron Weber
Executive Vice President, Ed Paradowski
Vice President Of Strategic Planning, Jeff Pharris
CIO Chief Technology Officer Vice President Information Technology, Bob Kamphuis
Auditors: SCHENCK SC MILWAUKEE WISCO

LOCATIONS

HQ: MAYVILLE ENGINEERING CO INC
715 SOUTH ST, MAYVILLE, WI 530501823
Phone: 920 387-4500

PRODUCTS/OPERATIONS

Selected Products and Services
Assembly
Brake press
Coatings
Coatings
Equipment
Fabrication
Laser and Plasma Cutting
Machining and Turning
Metal Fastening
Punch press
Stamping
Tube Bending
Tube Bending and Forming
Welding

COMPETITORS

Kuhl Machine Shop	Quality Products
Kurt Manufacturing	Smith & Wesson Holding
MetoKote	Valmont Industries

HISTORICAL FINANCIALS

Company Type: Private

Income Statement

FYE: December 31

	REVENUE ($ mil.)	NET INCOME ($ mil.)	NET PROFIT MARGIN	EMPLOYEES
12/11	177	6	3.9%	1,925
12/10*	153	15	10.3%	—
03/10	1,003	0	—	—
Annual Growth	—23640.9%			

*Fiscal year change

Return on assets: 2.8% Cash ($ mil.): 7
Return on equity: 3.9%
Current ratio: 1.20

MCCARTHY BUILDING COMPANIES INC.

A company that was in construction before Reconstruction McCarthy Building Companies is one of the oldest and largest privately-held builders in the US. The general contractor and construction manager ranks among the top builders of health care education and green building facilities in the country. Contracts include heavy construction projects (bridges and water- and waste-treatment plants) commercial projects (retail and office buildings) and institutional projects (airports schools and prisons). Subsidiary MC Industrial handles energy auto and other manufacturing projects. Founded by Timothy McCarthy in 1864 the company is 100% employee owned and generates $3 billion in annual revenues.

OperationsAs of 2016 nearly half of the builder's project portfolio was made up of Construction Manager at Risk projects while around a quarter of the portfolio consisted of Hard Bid projects. The rest was made up of Design/Build Construction Manager Owner Agent and Negotiated General Contracting projects. About 70% of its work came from repeat clients.That year the company reported that it had 1600 full-time salaried and 1200 weekly payroll employees. Geographic Reach

Headquartered in Saint Louis McCarthy Building Companies has worked on projects in 44 US states. Its offices are in Newport Beach San Francisco Sacramento and San Diego California; Albuquerque New Mexico; Las Vegas; Phoenix; St. Louis; Atlanta; Dallas; Houston; and Illinois. It does business in about 45 states.

Sales and Marketing

The firm gets more than 70% of its work from repeat clients which have included Kaiser Permanente California State University and Bally's Casino Resort.

Financial Performance

Ranked among the Top 10 commercial builders in the US McCarthy generates about $3 billion in annual revenues (as of 2016).StrategyMcCarthy Building Companies has been steadily building its presence with new office openings in strong building markets across the US over the past few years with one of its most recent being an office in Lakewood Colorado in mid 2015. The company has also been growing through acquisitions of smaller companies that complement its existing service lines.

Some of the company's more recent contracts (around early 2016) include: the Genome Lab for J. Craig Venter Institute; the Chino Valley Solar project for Arizona Public Service; the Dallas City Performance Hall for the City of Dallas; the McCarran International Airport for Clark County; the Sacramento Recreation & Wellness Center for California State University; the San Diego and Paramount Unified School Districts in California; and the Lake Pleasant Water Treatment Plant for the City of Phoenix among others.Some of its past projects include The Platinum condominium/hotel tower in Las Vegas expansion at M.D. Anderson Cancer Center and renovation and expansion of the National Baseball Hall of Fame and Museum in Cooperstown New York.Mergers and AcquisitionsIn October 2014 McCarthy bought St. Louis-based Castle Contracting and its subsidiary CastleGPS. Castle provided turnkey civil services utilities earthwork and trenchless technology directly to owners general contractors and mechinncal electrical and plumbing contractors. Castle's GPS technology provides "industry-leading" subsurface 3-Dimensional utility mapping. The acquired company would continue using the Castle brand name.

Ownership

McCarthy Building Companies was sold it its employees in 2002 by the great grandson of the founder. The firm is now 100% employee owned.

EXECUTIVES

Chairman and CEO, Michael D. (Mike) Bolen
President and COO, Derek W. Glanvill
President Northern Pacific Division, Richard A. (Rich) Henry
President Southwest Region, Robert (Bo) Calbert
President Texas Region, Michael J. McWay
President Southeast Division, Kevin Kuntz
President MC Industrial, Tom Felton
Corporate President and COO, Scott Wittkop
EVP, Ray Sedey
EVP Operations, Robert Betz
VP and CIO, Mike Oster
CFO, Doug Audiffred
President Central Division, John Buescher
Vice President M E.p., Jaime Perera
Vice President of Operations Houston Office, Ben Johanneman
Auditors: RUBINBROWN LLP SAINT LOUIS M

LOCATIONS

HQ: MCCARTHY BUILDING COMPANIES INC.
 1341 N ROCK HILL RD, SAINT LOUIS, MO 631241441
Phone: 314 968-3300
Web: WWW.MCCARTHY.COM

PRODUCTS/OPERATIONS

Selected Markets
Commercial
Education K-12
Health care
Heavy/civil/transportation
Higher education
High performance/green
Hospitality/entertainment
Industrial
Native American
Parking structures
Science and technology
Water/wastewater

Selected Services
Negotiated general contracting
Construction management
Hard bid (lump sum contract for services)
Design/build
Construction management/general contracting

COMPETITORS

Alberici	Korte
Barton Malow	Peter Kiewit Sons'
Bechtel	Primus Builders
Clayco	S. M. Wilson
DPR Construction	Skanska
Gilbane	Swinerton
HBE Corporation	Turner Corporation
Hensel Phelps	Tutor Perini
Construction	

HISTORICAL FINANCIALS

Company Type: Private

Income Statement

FYE: December 31

	REVENUE ($ mil.)	NET INCOME ($ mil.)	NET PROFIT MARGIN	EMPLOYEES
12/13	2,991	0	—	2,438
12/12	2,816	0	—	—
12/11	2,331	0	—	—
12/10	2,379	0	—	—
Annual Growth	7.9%	—	—	—

2013 Year-End Financials

Return on assets: 16.1% Cash ($ mil.): 287
Return on equity: —
Current ratio: 1.30

MCCARTHY HOLDINGS INC.

Auditors: RUBINBROWN LLP CPAS SAINT LO

LOCATIONS

HQ: MCCARTHY HOLDINGS INC.
 1341 N ROCK HILL RD, SAINT LOUIS, MO 631241441
Phone: 314 968-3300
Web: WWW.MCCARTHY.COM

HISTORICAL FINANCIALS

Company Type: Private

Income Statement

FYE: December 31

	REVENUE ($ mil.)	NET INCOME ($ mil.)	NET PROFIT MARGIN	EMPLOYEES
12/13	3,229	0	—	2,699
12/12	3,008	0	—	—
12/11	2,379	0	—	—
12/10	0	0	—	—
Annual Growth	—	—	—	—

2013 Year-End Financials

Return on assets: 15.4% Cash ($ mil.): 52
Return on equity: —
Current ratio: 0.80

MCLAREN REGIONAL MEDICAL CENTER

Auditors: PLANTE & MORAN PLLC PORTAGE

LOCATIONS

HQ: MCLAREN REGIONAL MEDICAL CENTER
 401 S BALLENGER HWY, FLINT, MI 485323638
Phone: 810 342-2000
Web: WWW.MCLAREN.ORG

HISTORICAL FINANCIALS

Company Type: Private

Income Statement

FYE: September 30

	REVENUE ($ mil.)	NET INCOME ($ mil.)	NET PROFIT MARGIN	EMPLOYEES
09/13	408	41	10.1%	2,250
09/09	340	17	5.1%	—
09/08	317	14	4.7%	—
09/05	0	0	—	—
Annual Growth	169.8%	—	—	—

2013 Year-End Financials

Return on assets: 4.3% Cash ($ mil.): 20
Return on equity: 10.1%
Current ratio: 1.60

MCLEOD REGIONAL MEDICAL CENTER OF THE PEE DEE INC.

Auditors: DELOITTE TAX LLP ATLANTA GA

LOCATIONS

HQ: MCLEOD REGIONAL MEDICAL CENTER OF THE PEE DEE INC.
 555 E CHEVES ST, FLORENCE, SC 295062617
Phone: 843 777-7753
Web: WWW.BLOG.MCLEODHEALTH.ORG

HISTORICAL FINANCIALS

Company Type: Private

Income Statement

FYE: September 30

	REVENUE ($ mil.)	NET INCOME ($ mil.)	NET PROFIT MARGIN	EMPLOYEES
09/13	594	98	16.7%	5,000
09/09	537	24	4.5%	—
09/08	577	49	8.5%	—
09/06	473	0	—	—
Annual Growth	3.3%	—	—	—

2013 Year-End Financials

Return on assets: 7.5% Cash ($ mil.): 10
Return on equity: 16.7%
Current ratio: 0.30

MCNAUGHTON-MCKAY ELECTRIC CO.

Getting connected at work has a completely different meaning at McNaughton-McKay. Its more than 10000 customers can buy electrical supplies sensors and controls and automation and security software online or through 22 branches in five US states and two offices in Germany. One of the largest employee-owned companies in the US McNaughton-McKay distributes some 300 product lines from manufacturers such as Hubbell GE Brady Belden Coleman Cable Leviton Thomas & Betts Cognex Specter Instruments and Rockwell

Automation. It sells to the construction commercial government and industrial automation markets.

Geographic Reach

The company serves more than 10000 customers in the US and Germany.

Sales and Marketing

The company sells its products from its sales offices and as well as eSales Centers. In addition to the industrial automation commercial and construction markets McNaughton-McKay supports government customers on a Federal State and Local level by providing hundreds of electrical products and MRO supplies with local support and inventory. McNaughton-McKay's customers include supplyFORCE Vanguard National Alliance and Vantage Group.

Strategy

McNaughton-McKay —informally known as Mc-Mc —has grown by expanding its product lineup and increasing its purchasing power through buying and marketing groups such as Affiliated Distributors supplyFORCE and Vantage Group. The distributor has also added a group dedicated to green products primarily energy-efficient lighting and power distribution products along with an Engineered Solutions Group that sells and installs solar and wind energy through partnerships with companies that include Schletter and Ohio Green Wind.

Ownership

McNaughton-McKay is owned by its employees.

Company Background

Founded in 1910 the Bull and McNaughton families ran McNaughton-McKay until 2006. It established a sales office in Germany in 2004.

EXECUTIVES

EVP and, Donald D. (Don) Slominski

EVP Sales and Marketing, Richard (Rick) Dahlstrom

VP Information Technology, Gregory H. (Greg) Chun

Vice President Human Resources, John D. Kuczmanski

Corporate Purchasing Manager, Maridee Curry

Auditors: KPMG LLP

LOCATIONS

HQ: MCNAUGHTON-MCKAY ELECTRIC CO.
1357 E LINCOLN AVE, MADISON HEIGHTS, MI 480714126

Phone: 248 541-2805

Web: WWW.MC-MC.COM

PRODUCTS/OPERATIONS

Selected Products

Bar code scanners and systems
Communication input/output (I/O) networks
Computers and peripherals
Convenience panels (cables and equipment)
Cordsets
Data-collection terminals and software
Drives and motor controllers
Engineered products
I/O products (AC/DC modules)
Motion-control products
 CNC controls
 Servos
 Spindles
Motors (AC)
PLC processors
Radio-frequency identification (RFID) products
Safety products
 Gate switches
 Light curtains
 Mats
 Relays
Sensors
Software
Vision products (inspection equipment)

COMPETITORS

Anixter International	Kendall Electric
Border States Electric	Madison Electric
Consolidated	Medler Electric
Electrical	OneSource Distributors
Crescent Electric	Rexel Inc.
Supply	SUMMIT Electric Supply
Dealers Electrical	Steiner Electric
Electrocomponents	Stuart C. Irby
Graybar Electric	W.W. Grainger
Hite Company	WESCO International

HISTORICAL FINANCIALS

Company Type: Private

Income Statement

FYE: December 31

	REVENUE ($ mil.)	NET INCOME ($ mil.)	NET PROFIT MARGIN	EMPLOYEES
12/13	663	0	—	725
12/12	641	0	—	—
12/11	603	0	—	—
12/10	493	0	—	—
Annual Growth	10.4%	—	—	—

2013 Year-End Financials

Return on assets: 7.7%   Cash ($ mil.): 16
Return on equity: —
Current ratio: 1.50

MCNEILUS STEEL INC.

Auditors: MCGLADREY LLP ROCHESTER MIN

LOCATIONS

HQ: MCNEILUS STEEL INC.
702 2ND AVE SE, DODGE CENTER, MN 559278903

Phone: 507 374-6336

Web: WWW.MCNEILUS.COM

HISTORICAL FINANCIALS

Company Type: Private

Income Statement

FYE: September 30

	REVENUE ($ mil.)	NET INCOME ($ mil.)	NET PROFIT MARGIN	EMPLOYEES
09/13	441	22	5.1%	475
09/12	443	21	4.9%	—
09/11	360	22	6.3%	—
09/10	245	0	—	—
Annual Growth	21.6%	—	—	—

2013 Year-End Financials

Return on assets: 1.6%   Cash ($ mil.): 1
Return on equity: 5.1%
Current ratio: 1.60

MED AMERICA HEALTH SYSTEMS CORPORATION

LOCATIONS

HQ: MED AMERICA HEALTH SYSTEMS CORPORATION
1 WYOMING ST, DAYTON, OH 454092722

Phone: 937 223-6192

Web: WWW.MEDAMERICA.COM

HISTORICAL FINANCIALS

Company Type: Private

Income Statement

FYE: December 31

	REVENUE ($ mil.)	NET INCOME ($ mil.)	NET PROFIT MARGIN	EMPLOYEES
12/12	968	54	5.6%	4,700
12/11	919	24	2.7%	—
12/10	843	67	8.1%	—
12/08	790	0	—	—
Annual Growth	5.2%	—	—	—

2012 Year-End Financials

Return on assets: 3.9%   Cash ($ mil.): 29
Return on equity: 5.6%
Current ratio: 1.50

MEDCO L.L.C.

LOCATIONS

HQ: MEDCO L.L.C.
3700 DADEVILLE RD, ALEXANDER CITY, AL 35010

Phone: 256 215-3889

HISTORICAL FINANCIALS

Company Type: Private

Income Statement

FYE: June 30

	REVENUE ($ mil.)	NET INCOME ($ mil.)	NET PROFIT MARGIN	EMPLOYEES
06/09*	854	(173)	—	225
09/02	4	0	13.6%	—
09/00	2	0	13.7%	—
12/99	0	0	—	—
Annual Growth	—	—	—	—

*Fiscal year change

2009 Year-End Financials

Return on assets: —   Cash ($ mil.): —
Return on equity: (-20.3%)
Current ratio: 1.40

MEDICAL FACULTY ASSOCIATES INC.

LOCATIONS

HQ: MEDICAL FACULTY ASSOCIATES INC.
2150 PENNSYLVANIA AVE NW, WASHINGTON, DC 200373201

Phone: 202 741-3000

HISTORICAL FINANCIALS

Company Type: Private

Income Statement

FYE: June 30

	REVENUE ($ mil.)	NET INCOME ($ mil.)	NET PROFIT MARGIN	EMPLOYEES
06/13	329	0	0.1%	1,600
06/12	337	11	3.4%	—
06/11	292	13	4.7%	—
06/10	260	0	—	—
Annual Growth	8.2%	—	—	—

2013 Year-End Financials

Return on assets: —
Return on equity: 0.1%
Current ratio: 0.30

Cash ($ mil.): 4

MEGLOBAL AMERICAS INC.

LOCATIONS

HQ: MEGLOBAL AMERICAS INC.
3320 RIDGECREST DR # 100, MIDLAND, MI
486425864
Phone: 989 636-5393
Web: WWW.MEGLOBAL.BIZ

HISTORICAL FINANCIALS

Company Type: Private

Income Statement

FYE: December 31

	REVENUE ($ mil.)	NET INCOME ($ mil.)	NET PROFIT MARGIN	EMPLOYEES
12/13	596	10	1.7%	16
12/12	597	13	2.2%	—
12/11	743	20	2.7%	—
12/10	602	0	—	—
Annual Growth	(0.3%)	—	—	—

2013 Year-End Financials

Return on assets: 0.5%
Return on equity: 1.7%
Current ratio: 0.10

Cash ($ mil.): 5

MEMORIAL HEALTH SERVICES CORPORATION

Where do you go after you get sick riding the tea cups at Disneyland? Not-for-profit Memorial Health Services (known as MemorialCare) owns six hospitals in Southern California including Long Beach Memorial Medical Center Miller Children's Hospital Orange Coast Memorial Medical Center and Saddleback Memorial Medical Center. The facilities have a total of more than 1500 beds and offer a full spectrum of medical services including rehabilitation diagnostic/radiology and emergency services. MemorialCare also operates women's health facilities and other specialty and general practice clinics as well as home health and hospice programs. The organization was founded in 1907.

Operations

MemorialCare's outpatient facilities include the physician practices of the MemorialCare Medical Group the Memorial Prompt Care urgent care centers and the MemorialCare HealthExpress clinics. The network also includes the affiliated practices of the Greater Newport Physicians organization. In addition to inpatient outpatient and home medical care the organization provides clinical training and graduate medical education programs.

Altogether the system's facilities employ 2600 physicians and serve 70000 inpatients each year.

They also handle some 35000 surgeries 10000 births 200000 emergency room visits and 40000 home health visits.

Geographic Reach

MemorialCare's facilities are located in Los Angeles County and Orange County in Southern California.

Financial Performance

MemorialCare reported $1.9 billion in revenues and $83 million in net income in 2012. Most of the organization's revenues come from patient services.

Strategy

MemorialCare is expanding to meet continued demand throughout its service area. It has several projects either going on or recently completed that have added operating rooms neonatal beds more advanced technology and centers of excellence in imaging cardiac cancer and obesity at several of its hospitals. In 2014 it opened the new Lung Nodule Center at The MemorialCare Todd Cancer Institute part of Long Beach Memorial.

The organization is also expanding its outpatient care facilities. For instance MemorialCare has joined the growing trend of hospitals partnering with retailers to open in-store retail clinics (under the HealthExpress brand) that offer basic after-hours medical care through physicians and nurse practitioners. It has recently opened four new outpatient surgery centers and launched a couple of new physician locations in affiliation with UC Irvine Health.

EXECUTIVES

Senior Vice President Chief Financial Officer, Cheryl Sadro
President CEO, James Hobson
Information Technology Vice President, Steven (Steve) Beal
Vice President Information Systems, Wayne Sass
Medical Librarian, Veena Vyas
Medical Director, Robert Nagourney
Director, Keith Nelson
Secretary, Shoba Kumar
Board Member, Jaci Songstad
Secretary Department Medical, Tracie Keyes
Board Member, Sandy Longobardy
Auditors: PRICEWATERHOUSECOOPERS LLP L

LOCATIONS

HQ: MEMORIAL HEALTH SERVICES CORPORATION
17360 BROOKHURST ST # 160, FOUNTAIN VALLEY,
CA 927088003
Phone: 714 377-6748
Web: WWW.MEMORIALCARE.ORG

Selected Facilities

Long Beach Memorial Medical Center (Long Beach California)
Miller Children's Hospital (Long Beach California)
Community Hospital (Long Beach California)
Orange Coast Memorial Medical Center (Fountain Valley California)
Saddleback Memorial Medical Center (San Clemente California)
Saddleback Memorial Medical Center (Laguna Hills California)
MemorialCare Medical Group (regional)
MemorialCare HealthExpress (regional)
MemorialCare Imaging Centers (regional)
Memorial Prompt Care (regional)

PRODUCTS/OPERATIONS

Selected Services

Blood Donation
Diabetes Care
Heart and Vascular Care
Joint Replacement
Neonatal Intensive Care
Rehabilitation and Therapy
Wellness Care
Cancer Care
Gynecological Care
Imaging and Radiology
Maternity Care
Orthopedic Care
Stroke Care
Wound Healing
Breast Care
Express Care
Hyperbaric Medicine
Laboratory Services
Pediatric Care
Surgical Care
Women's Care

COMPETITORS

Adventist Health
Cedars-Sinai Medical Center
Childrens Hospital Los Angeles
Community Health Systems
Dignity Health
Good Samaritan Hospital (IN)
Good Samaritan Hospital (Los Angeles)
HCA
HealthCare Partners
Hollywood Presbyterian Medical Center
LifePoint Health
Los Angeles County Health Department
Methodist Hospital of Southern California
Pasadena Hospital Association
Prospect Medical
Providence Health & Services
St. Joseph Health System
St. Jude Medical Center
Sutter Health
Tenet Healthcare
Trinity Health (Novi)
Western Medical Center - Santa Ana

HISTORICAL FINANCIALS

Company Type: Private

Income Statement

FYE: June 30

	REVENUE ($ mil.)	NET INCOME ($ mil.)	NET PROFIT MARGIN	EMPLOYEES
06/13	2,094	284	13.6%	2,000
06/10	113	6	5.4%	—
06/09	90	0	—	—
Annual Growth	119.3%	—	—	—

2013 Year-End Financials

Return on assets: 5.2%
Return on equity: 13.6%
Current ratio: 1.00

Cash ($ mil.): 127

MEMORIAL HEALTH SYSTEM OF EAST TEXAS

Memorial Health System of East Texas operates deep in the heart of East Texas. The system is anchored by the 270-bed Memorial Medical Center-Lufkin a full-service general acute care hospital offering everything from rehabilitative and diabetes care to specialized centers in heart disease and cancer treatment. The Lufkin hospital also includes Memorial Specialty Hospital a long-term ward for critically ill patients. In addition Memorial Health System of East Texas features two critical access hospitals with limited services including emergency care and diagnostic imaging; it also has a clinic network. It is part of non-profit health care systems operator Catholic Health Initiatives(CHI).

Change in Company Type

In 2014 Colorado-based CHI purchased Memorial Health Systems of East Texas.

Operations

Specialty services provided by Memorial Health System of East Texas include orthopedics oncology wound care kidney treatment sleep disorder therapy women's health pediatrics stroke care robotic surgery and home health care. It also has diagnostic facilities including the Express Lab and the Temple Imaging Center. The organization handles about 245000 patient encounters each year including 65000 emergency room visits 9100 inpatient and outpatient surgeries and 1000 births.

Geographic Reach

The main hospital is in Lufkin Texas while Memorial Health System of East Texas' critical access facilities are located in Livingston and San Augustine. The system operates outpatient clinics in all three towns.

Financial Performance

Memorial Health System of East Texas reported an 2% decrease in 2013 revenues (to some $188 million) due to a decline in net patient service income and a reduced provision for uncollectable medical bills. Cash flow dropped by nearly $5 million due to a change in pension expenses and estimated third-party payer settlements.

Strategy

Memorial Health System of East Texas strives to reinvest all proceeds into the system. To that end it is expanding to meet the needs of its growing regional population. The system opened a new specialty medical center the Cardiovascular & Stroke Center of East Texas in 2012. To improve medical technologies the Memorial Medical Center purchased Texas' first DaVinci high-definition robotic surgery system and updated diagnostic systems to include new 4D ultrasound and cardiac imaging system equipment that year. Furthermore the Livingston campus invested $1.6 million in new imaging equipment during 2013.

Affiliations are also key to growth and in 2012 the organization created an affiliation with the Methodist Hospital of Houston to provide more comprehensive stroke care services. The following year it formed a cardiac care partnership with The Heart Institute of East Texas to open Memorial Cardiac Rehabilitation Center.

Company Background

The not-for-profit health system was founded in 1949.

EXECUTIVES

Director Of Pharmacy, Eric Ip
Executive Vice President, Don Morris
Auditors: AXLEY & RODE LLP LUFKIN TX

LOCATIONS

HQ: MEMORIAL HEALTH SYSTEM OF EAST TEXAS
1201 W FRANK AVE, LUFKIN, TX 759043357
Phone: 936 634-8111
Web: WWW.MEMORIALHEALTH.US

PRODUCTS/OPERATIONS

Selected Texas Locations
Memorial Medical Center-Livingston
Memorial Medical Center-Lufkin
Memorial Medical Center-San Augustine
Memorial Specialty Hospital (long-term acute care hospital)

Selected Services
Ambulatory Services
Cancer Center
Cardiovascular & Stroke Center
Diabetes
Emergency
Express Lab
Homecare
Inpatient & Outpatient Therapy
Imaging

Intensive Care
Infusion Center
Orthopedics
Robotic Surgery
SANE
Sleep Lab
Social Services
Stroke
Surgery
Women's & Children's Center
Wound Care & Hyperbaric Oxygen

COMPETITORS

Community Health Systems
East Texas Medical Center Regional Healthcare
Good Shepherd Health System
LifePoint Health
Trinity Mother Frances Hospital and Clinics
Wadley Regional Medical Center

HISTORICAL FINANCIALS
Company Type: Private

Income Statement
FYE: December 31

	REVENUE ($ mil.)	NET INCOME ($ mil.)	NET PROFIT MARGIN	EMPLOYEES
12/09	192	22	11.6%	940
12/08	8	0	—	—
/ 0	0	—	—	—
Annual Growth	—	—	—	—

2009 Year-End Financials
Return on assets: —
Return on equity: 11.6%
Current ratio: —
Cash ($ mil.): 55

MEMORIAL HEALTH UNIVERSITY MEDICAL CENTER INC.

Memorial Health University Medical Center wants to provide memorable health care to residents of Savannah Georgia and surrounding areas. An affiliate of Mercer University School of Medicine the tertiary care facility provides such services as cardiac and trauma care and rehabilitation. Also known as Memorial University Medical Center (MUMC) the hospital has some 620 beds and includes the MUMC Children's Hospital. It also operates specialty cancer care and women's health centers as well as research programs. Founded in 1955 MUMC is the flagship facility in a broader system of entities known as Memorial Health which includes affiliated primary and specialty care clinics in the region.

Geographic Reach

MUMC serves a 35-county region in southeastern Georgia and southern South Carolina. The medical center serves as a regional referral center for several smaller community hospitals in the area. Affiliates include Bacon County Hospital Evans Memorial Hospital and Liberty Regional Medical Center.

Operations

MUMC's cancer center the Curtis and Elizabeth Anderson Cancer Institute provides cancer treatment and surgical procedures; it also conducts research efforts to discover and develop new cancer therapies. The Women's Health Institute offers obstetrics gynecology and neonatology. MUMC also includes a level I trauma center and a Heart and

Vascular Institute as well as programs in orthopedics neurology gastroenterology urology and pulmonary care. The affiliated Memorial Health University Physicians (MHUP) group operates primary and specialty care offices in the area.

Strategy

In 2012 Memorial Health formed an affiliation with Novant Health. The partnership will help the MUMC organization cut costs provide for future growth opportunities and improve its operational infracturcture. By joining the Novant Health Shared Services group MUMC will gain access to a larger base of supply chain clinical engineering information technology and best practices resources.

EXECUTIVES

Director Community Benefits, Peter Doliber
SVP Oncology and Research, William (Bill) Hoskins
SVP Memorial Health Foundation, Hall Powell
SVP and Chief Medical Officer, Ramon V. Meguiar
President CEO and Director, Margaret (Maggie) Gill
VP Continuous Quality Improvement and Chief Patient Safety Officer, Frank Carlton
VP Women's and Children's Services, Jean Wright
VP Government Affairs, Amy H. Hughes
SVP Administration, S. Hart Williford
VP Clinical Oncology, Trib Vats
VP Finance and Associate CFO, Darcy J. Davis
SVP Physician Services, John Angstadt
Vice Chair, Kay A. Ford
SVP Chief Nursing Officer and COO, Mary Chatman
Ethics Officer, Mary Ann Bowman Beil
VP Strategy Business Development and The Children's Hospital, William (Bill) Lee III
VP Memorial Health Foundation, Phoenicia Miracle
VP Perioperative Services, Deborah (Debbie) Hattrich
Treasurer, Harry Haslam
Development Manager, Anne Cordeiro
Vice President for Oncology Programs, Guy Petruzzelli
Vice President Physician Services, Sharon Bromley
Senior Vice President Administration and General, Ira P. Berman
Chairman, Jacqueline Rabinowitz
Operations Manager, Monique Williams
Vice President Chief Communications Officer, Rebecca Keightley
Vice President of Finance, Laura Dow
Vice President Chief Information Officer, Robert Tynan
Vice President Memorial, Brett Waress
Director, Curtis G. Anderson, age 73
Director, Southwood J. (Woody) Morcott, age 76
Director, Jack M. Jones, age 75
President CEO and Director, Margaret (Maggie) Gill
Director, John R. Duttenhaver
Director, Gus H. Bell
Director, William J. Degenhart
Director, Helen Dean Downing
Director, Harold P. DuCloux Jr.
Director, Mark E. Murphy
Director, William L. (Bill) Lyght
Vice Chairman, William T. (Bill) Daniel
Director, Charles F. McMillan
Vice Chair, Kay A. Ford
Auditors: PERSHING YOAKLEY & ASSOCIATES

LOCATIONS

HQ: MEMORIAL HEALTH UNIVERSITY MEDICAL CENTER INC.
4700 WATERS AVE, SAVANNAH, GA 314046283
Phone: 912 350-8000
Web: WWW.MEMORIALHEALTH.COM

COMPETITORS

Appling
Beaufort Memorial
St. Joseph's/Candler Health System

Hospital	Tift Regional Medical
Doctors Hospital of Augusta	Center
Liberty Regional Medical Center	Universal Health Services
Redmond Regional Medical Center	University Health Services
South Georgia Medical Center	Walton Rehabilitation Hospital

HISTORICAL FINANCIALS

Company Type: Private

Income Statement
FYE: December 31

	REVENUE ($ mil.)	NET INCOME ($ mil.)	NET PROFIT MARGIN	EMPLOYEES
12/08*	453	(29)	—	5,000
06/05	447	39	8.8%	—
12/02	344	0	0.0%	—
Annual Growth	4.7%	—	—	—

*Fiscal year change

2008 Year-End Financials
Return on assets: 6.2%
Return on equity: (-6.5%)
Current ratio: 1.10
Cash ($ mil.): 16

MEMORIAL HERMANN HEALTH SYSTEM

LOCATIONS

HQ: MEMORIAL HERMANN HEALTH SYSTEM
909 FROSTWOOD DR STE 2100, HOUSTON, TX
770242301
Phone: 713 242-3000
Web: WWW.MEMORIALHERMANN.ORG

HISTORICAL FINANCIALS

Company Type: Private

Income Statement
FYE: June 30

	REVENUE ($ mil.)	NET INCOME ($ mil.)	NET PROFIT MARGIN	EMPLOYEES
06/13*	3,285	230	7.0%	14,000
09/09	3,195	(79)	—	—
06/09	3,195	(79)	—	—
Annual Growth	0.7%	—	—	—

*Fiscal year change

2013 Year-End Financials
Return on assets: 11.9%
Return on equity: 7.0%
Current ratio: 0.70
Cash ($ mil.): 434

MEMORIAL HERMANN HEALTHCARE SYSTEM

Memorial Hermann Healthcare System is a Texas-sized operation. As Houston's largest not-for-profit health care system it includes a dozen hospitals (one is a children's hospital) with more than 3500 beds and dozens of specialty treatment centers. The system also operates three managed acute care hospitals and a retirement community. Through Memorial Hermann Regional Healthcare Services the company is affiliated with more than 20 community hospitals and health centers most serving rural areas within 150 miles of the Houston area. Other services and programs include substance abuse treatment home health services air ambulances medical training and imaging; it also offers health insurance coverage.

Geographic Reach

Memorial Hermann's various facilities serve Southeast Texas and the Greater Houston community.

Operations

In the insurance arena the company's subsidiary MHealth provides health plans underwritten by UniCare Life & Health Insurance; it also offers administration of self-funded health care benefits and administers wellness programs. Memorial Hermann chose to start offering health care benefits as a way to help employers and individuals cut healthcare costs.

Memorial Hermann's 12 hospitals include three hospitals in the Texas Medical Center (Texas Trauma Institute – a level I trauma center which houses the Life Flight air ambulance; a hospital for children; and a rehabilitation hospital); eight suburban hospitals; and a second rehabilitation hospital in Katy. The system also operates three Heart & Vascular Institutes the Mischer Neuroscience Institute three Ironman Sports Medicine Institute locations cancer centers imaging and surgery centers sports medicine and rehabilitation centers outpatient laboratories a chemical dependency treatment center a home health agency a retirement community and a nursing home.

The company also offers employers health solutions and health benefit plans through Memorial Hermann Health Insurance Company. Memorial Hermann has 5500 affiliated physicians.

Sales and Marketing

Memorial Herman markets its services through a variety of outlets including social media which is somewhat unusual for a health care provider.

Financial Performance

Memorial Hermann's revenue increased by 7% to $3.6 billion in 2013 compared to 2012. The spike was largely due to increased net patient service revenue. Memorial Hermann's net income increased by 146% to $221 million in 2013 while cash flow increased by $375 million in 2013 due to a decline in investments.

Strategy

As Houston (one of the nation's largest cities) sprawls into the suburbs so has Memorial Hermann. The system's facilities were previously confined to the downtown medical plaza known as Texas Medical Center and other metropolitan locations but Memorial Hermann has branched out to serve the surrounding areas and now operates eight suburban hospitals. Partnerships with other area providers are another way in which Memorial Hermann enhances its service offerings.

In 2015 Memorial Hermann broke ground on a major medical campus in Cypress. The $168 million project is being constructed on a 32-acre site located on the northeast side of Highway 290 and the Grand Parkway between Mason Road and Mueschke Road.

In 2014 Memorial Hermann Katy Hospital also broke ground on a new six-story patient tower. To meet the wide-ranging health needs of families and businesses in 2014 Memorial Hermann broke ground on a $650 million expansion and renovation of its Houston campus (Texas Medical Center). The expansion also will provide the campus with an additional 1.34 million square feet; an additional 160 beds (plus 71 replacement beds); 24 new operating rooms; 16 additional emergency room bays; 750 new parking spaces; and a 333-seat café. The expansion is expected to be completed in 2018.

Memorial Herman is also upgrading information technology systems at its facilities to provide consistency of care across its network. For instance Memorial Hermann launched the first health information exchange (HIE) in the Houston area. Such systems are designed to let area health provider access a patient's medical history through electronic health records (EHRs) in order to make faster diagnoses and avoid unnecessary medical costs.

EXECUTIVES

President and CEO, Daniel J. Wolterman
COO, Charles D. (Chuck) Stokes, age 61
CEO Memorial Hermann Heart and Vascular Institute, Paul O'Sullivan
Assistant Vice President Information Systems, Emily Handwerk
Vice President Of Engineering, George Thomason
Secretary, Janet Mayo

LOCATIONS

HQ: MEMORIAL HERMANN HEALTHCARE SYSTEM
929 GESSNER RD STE 2600, HOUSTON, TX
770242593
Phone: 713 338-5555
Web: WWW.MEMORIALHERMANN.ORG

PRODUCTS/OPERATIONS

Selected Facilities
Children's Memorial Hermann Hospital
Memorial Hermann Katy Hospital
Memorial Hermann Memorial City Medical Center
Memorial Hermann Northeast Hospital
Memorial Hermann Northwest Hospital
 Memorial H
Memorial Hermann Southeast Hospital
Memorial Hermann Southwest Hospital
Memorial Hermann Sugar Land Health Center
Memorial Hermann - Texas Medical Center
Memorial Hermann The Woodlands Hospital
Memorial Hermann Wellness Center and Garden Spa
Neighborhood Health Center
TIRR Memorial Hermann (Houston)
University Place Retirement Community and Nursing Center (Houston)
Affiliates
Huntsville Memorial Hospital
Memorial Hermann Baptist Hospitals (Beaumont)
Triumph Healthcare (Houston)

COMPETITORS

CHRISTUS Health	Methodist Hospital
Dynacq Healthcare	System
HCA	St. Luke's Episcopal
LifePoint Health	Health System
MD Anderson Cancer Center	Tenet Healthcare
Memorial Sloan-Kettering	Texas Children's Hospital

HISTORICAL FINANCIALS

Company Type: Private

Income Statement
FYE: June 30

	REVENUE ($ mil.)	NET INCOME ($ mil.)	NET PROFIT MARGIN	EMPLOYEES
06/08	2,841	16	0.6%	16,505
06/07	2,506	209	8.4%	—
Annual Growth	13.4%	(92.3%)	—	—

2008 Year-End Financials
Return on assets: 4.0%
Return on equity: 0.6%
Current ratio: 1.20
Cash ($ mil.): 327

MERCY CORPS

Mercy Corps is dedicated to helping the poor and oppressed in developing countries. The not-for-profit organization offers emergency relief and economic support as well as assistance in building sustainable communities. It also develops curriculum guides to introduce students to various topics ranging from Kurdish history and Afghan henna art to the worldwide clean water campaign. Since its founding Mercy Corps programs have provided about $1.5 billion in assistance to people in 106 nations. Originally the organization was named Save the Refugees Fund when it was founded by Dan O'Neill in response to the plight of Cambodian refugees in 1979. Mercy Corps boasts offices in North America and Europe as well as several field offices in more troubled regions. The group's daily efforts reach more than 16 million people in some 35 countries.

EXECUTIVES

Senior Vice President, Paul Dudley-hart
Secretary, Barnes Ellis

LOCATIONS

HQ: MERCY CORPS
45 SW ANKENY ST, PORTLAND, OR 972043500
Phone: 503 796-6800
Web: WWW.MERCYCORPS.ORG

HISTORICAL FINANCIALS

Company Type: Private

Income Statement

	REVENUE ($ mil.)	NET INCOME ($ mil.)	NET PROFIT MARGIN	EMPLOYEES
06/13	236	(4)	—	450
06/12	232	(7)	—	
06/11	268	1	0.6%	
06/10	244	0	—	
Annual Growth	(1.2%)			

FYE: June 30

2013 Year-End Financials

Return on assets: —
Return on equity: (-2.0%)
Current ratio: —
Cash ($ mil.): 54

MERCY HEALTH CENTER INC.

Auditors: PLEUS AND COMPANY LLC CHESTER

LOCATIONS

HQ: MERCY HEALTH CENTER INC.
14528 S OUTER 40 RD STE 1, CHESTERFIELD, MO 630175785
Phone: 405 755-1515
Web: WWW.MERCY.NET

HISTORICAL FINANCIALS
Company Type: Private

Income Statement

FYE: June 30

	REVENUE ($ mil.)	NET INCOME ($ mil.)	NET PROFIT MARGIN	EMPLOYEES
06/10	312	16	5.2%	2,300
06/09	287	7	2.7%	
06/08	0	0		
Annual Growth	—	3037.1%	—	—

2010 Year-End Financials

Return on assets: —
Return on equity: 5.2%
Current ratio: 2.10
Cash ($ mil.): 12

MERCY HEALTH SERVICES INC.

Auditors: COHEN RUTHERFORD & KNIGHT PC

LOCATIONS

HQ: MERCY HEALTH SERVICES INC.
301 SAINT PAUL ST, BALTIMORE, MD 212022102
Phone: 410 332-9000
Web: WWW.MDMERCY.COM

HISTORICAL FINANCIALS
Company Type: Private

Income Statement

FYE: June 30

	REVENUE ($ mil.)	NET INCOME ($ mil.)	NET PROFIT MARGIN	EMPLOYEES
06/13	602	15	2.6%	—
06/10	1	0	42.6%	—
06/09	1	0	30.2%	—
Annual Growth	375.9%	157.7%	—	—

MERCY HEALTH SERVICES IOWA CORP

LOCATIONS

HQ: MERCY HEALTH SERVICES IOWA CORP
1000 4TH ST SW, MASON CITY, IA 504012800
Phone: 641 428-7000
Web: WWW.MERCYNORTHIOWA.COM

HISTORICAL FINANCIALS
Company Type: Private

Income Statement

FYE: June 30

	REVENUE ($ mil.)	NET INCOME ($ mil.)	NET PROFIT MARGIN	EMPLOYEES
06/11	649	17	2.7%	1
06/10	632	19	3.0%	—
Annual Growth	2.7%	(7.9%)	—	—

2011 Year-End Financials

Return on assets: —
Return on equity: 2.7%
Current ratio: 0.30
Cash ($ mil.): 10

MERCY HOSPITAL AND MEDICAL CENTER

Chicagoans in the loop know Mercy Hospital and Medical Center is the place to go for health care. The Catholic hospital located near Chicago's Loop (the historic downtown commercial district) has about 320 beds and operates a network of community clinics and occupational health facilities that provide employment-related services such as drug screening executive physicals and physical therapy. Other services include a cancer treatment center inpatient hospice care unit eye care center heart and vascular center diabetes treatment center stroke center and inpatient and outpatient chemical dependence recovery programs. Chicago's first teaching hospital it is owned by Ohio-based system Trinity Health.

Operations

The Illinois medical facility offers patients a Level II Trauma Center which includes the Mercy Foundation nearly a dozen auxiliary care facilities MercyWorks occupational health program and a pair of school-based health centers operating under the names Wendell Philips and Dunbar Vocational Career Academies.

The hospital's two on-site clinics —the Doctors Office Center and the Mercy Family Health Center —log some 65000 patient visits each year across every major specialty. Mercy's satellite clinics located throughout the Chicago area see upwards of 100000 patient visits a year.

It's affiliated with Gottlieb Memorial Hospital and Loyola University Medical Center.

Sales and Marketing

Mercy Hospital and Medical Center works to ensure its services are available to a variety of patient groups. To this end the hospital boasts a network of primary care clinics physician offices and satellite facilities.

Strategy

In recent years Mercy Hospital and Medical Center has focused on positioning its cardiovascular institute for growth. It has become the first Chicago hospital to have an FDA-approved carotid artery stenting procedure and was the first to perform Laparo-Endoscopic Single-Site surgeries. Additionally it introduced the HD 3D Laparoscopic Surgical Video System in its operating rooms.

Mercy plans to expand its critical care unit and gastrointestinal laboratory suites to accommodate increased patient demand.

In 2014 Mercy created Siouxland Surgery Center a joint venture with USP Health Ventures that provides surgeries and medical care in Dakota Dunes South Dakota.

Company Background

The hospital became Chicago's first chartered health care facility when it opened in 1852. Mercy Hospital and Medical Center became part of the Trinity Health network in 2012.

EXECUTIVES

V Pres, Susan (Sue) Gallagher
Vice President Spirituality and Mission, Martin (Marti) Hebda
Medical Director, Andrew Cha
Clinical Director, Cyndi Snodgrass
Vice President Of Patient Care Services, Carla Campbell
Vice President, Ronald Arnone
Vice President, Boomesma Jones
Vice President Support Services, Thomas Dohm
Vice President human resourcesrisk management, Nancy Hill-davis

Director of Operating Room, Mary Lindenmeyer
Secretary; Vice President, Nicholas Vogel
Auditors: MCGLADREY LLP CHICAGO IL

LOCATIONS

HQ: MERCY HOSPITAL AND MEDICAL CENTER
2525 S MICHIGAN AVE, CHICAGO, IL 606162332
Phone: 312 567-2201
Web: WWW.MERCY-CHICAGO.ORG

PRODUCTS/OPERATIONS

Selected Centers
The Birth Place
Cancer Center
Center for Weight Management
Comprehensive Breast and Women's Healthcare Center
Diabetes Treatment Center
Ear Nose & Throat Center
Heart & Vascular Center
Orthopedics
Spine & Back Care
Stroke Center

Selected Treatment Options
Cardiac rehabilitation
Clinical trials
Emergency medicine
Immediate care
Integrative medicine & wellness
Minimally invasive surgery
Pulmonary rehabilitation
Rehabilitation and therapy
Robotic surgery

Selected Specialty Care Centers
Behavioral health services
Center for urinary health
Diagnostic imaging/radiology
Dizziness & balance center
Eye center
Family health center
Gastroenterology
Laboratory & pathology
Lap-band program
Occupational health
Pain management
Pediatrics
Pre-birth center
Sleep center
Vitas hospice
Wound management

COMPETITORS
Covenant Ministries
NorthShore University HealthSystem
Northwestern Memorial HealthCare
Rush System for Health
Silver Cross Hospital
Sinai Health System
St. Bernard Hospital and Health Care Center
Swedish Covenant
SwedishAmerican Health System
University of Chicago Medical Center
Vanguard MacNeal Hospital
Weiss Memorial Hospital

HISTORICAL FINANCIALS
Company Type: Private

Income Statement
FYE: June 30

	REVENUE ($ mil.)	NET INCOME ($ mil.)	NET PROFIT MARGIN	EMPLOYEES
06/13	265	4	1.5%	1,550
06/10	250	9	3.6%	—
06/09	235	2	1.1%	—
06/08	1,500	0	—	—
Annual Growth	—	—	—	—

2013 Year-End Financials
Return on assets: 28.3%
Return on equity: 1.5%
Current ratio: 1.70
Cash ($ mil.): 81

MERCY HOSPITAL OF BUFFALO

LOCATIONS

HQ: MERCY HOSPITAL OF BUFFALO
565 ABBOTT RD, BUFFALO, NY 142202095
Phone: 716 826-7000
Web: WWW.MERCYHOSPFOUND.ORG

HISTORICAL FINANCIALS
Company Type: Private

Income Statement
FYE: December 31

	REVENUE ($ mil.)	NET INCOME ($ mil.)	NET PROFIT MARGIN	EMPLOYEES
12/12	337	13	4.0%	2,000
12/08	249	6	2.6%	—
12/05	205	6	3.2%	—
Annual Growth	7.4%	10.9%	—	—

2012 Year-End Financials
Return on assets: 4.9%
Return on equity: 4.0%
Current ratio: 1.10
Cash ($ mil.): 59

MERCY HOSPITAL ROGERS

Auditors: ERNST & YOUNG US LLP CLAYTON

LOCATIONS

HQ: MERCY HOSPITAL ROGERS
2710 S RIFE MEDICAL LN, ROGERS, AR 727581452
Phone: 479 338-8000

HISTORICAL FINANCIALS
Company Type: Private

Income Statement
FYE: June 30

	REVENUE ($ mil.)	NET INCOME ($ mil.)	NET PROFIT MARGIN	EMPLOYEES
06/09	343	0	—	760
06/08	253	(9)	—	—
06/05	0	0	—	—
Annual Growth	—	—	—	—

2009 Year-End Financials
Return on assets: 32.3%
Return on equity: —
Current ratio: 0.20
Cash ($ mil.): 9

MERCY HOSPITAL SPRINGFIELD

Mercy Hospital Springfield is an 890-bed acute-care hospital in the Mercy Health system. The facility provides health care to southwestern Missouri and northwestern Arkansas and includes the Mercy Children's Hospital Springfield. Other hospital specialties include cardiology and stroke care as well as women's and seniors' health cancer emergency trauma burn neuroscience rehabilitation and sports medicine. In addition to its hospital in Springfield Mercy Hospital Springfield operates a number of community clinics and specialty care centers in the area.

Geographic Reach

The hospital serves patients in southwest Missouri and northwest Arkansas.

Operations

Mercy Hospital Springfield has about 700 doctors on its medical staff. The center sees some 441000 outpatient visits per year as well as 94000 emergency room visits and 37000 surgeries. It also enables more than 3000 births Specialty units feature a level I trauma and burn center (the highest ranking in the US) a neonatal intensive care unit a nationally certified stroke center and high-tech surgery suites (including da Vinci robotic surgery and CyberKnife radiosurgery centers). It also operates an air ambulance service.

Financial Performance

The hospital's revenues decreased by 1% in 2014 due to 1% drop in net patient service revenue (which contributed 98% of the revenue) and a 11% decrease in revenues from other sources.

In 2014 the company provided charity care of about $26 million along with unreimbursed Medicaid expenses of around $17 million.

Strategy

That year Mercy Hospital Springfield opened the 60-bed Mercy Rehabilitation Hospital Springfield which is spread across a 63000-square-feet facility. The new $28 million building allows for more options for patient rehabilitation and will also serve as the region's only burn unit.

In 2014 the company also opened Phase II of its Betty and Bobby Allison Neonatal Intensive Care Unit (NICU) which expands the number of beds under NICU to 46. With this final phase complete Mercy permanently closed its former NICU.

Company Background

Formerly St. John's Regional Health Center the hospital's name changed to Mercy Hospital Springfield in 2012; the move coincided with the parent organization's efforts to to unify its brand identity. (The parent group's named changed as well from Sisters of Mercy Health System to Mercy Health.)

The hospital was founded in 1891 by the Sisters of Mercy.

EXECUTIVES

CEO St. John's Health System, Kim Day
COO, Michele Schaefer
Executive Vice President Chief Operating Officer, Michael McCurry
Executive Vice President Chief Financial Officer, Randy Combs
Executive Vice President Organizational Effectiveness, Shannon Sock
Auditors: ERNST & YOUNG US LLP CLAYTON

LOCATIONS

HQ: MERCY HOSPITAL SPRINGFIELD
1235 E CHEROKEE ST, SPRINGFIELD, MO 658042203
Phone: 417 820-8620
Web: WWW.MERCY.NET

PRODUCTS/OPERATIONS

Selected Services
Bariatric Surgery
Cancer Care
Children's Care
Heart Care
Integrative Medicine
Mother and Baby Care
Neurosciences

Orthopedic and Sport Care
Palliative Care
Pastoral Care
Senior Care
Trauma and Burn Care
Women' s Care

COMPETITORS

Ascension Health	HCA
BJC HealthCare	Heartland Health
Boone Hospital Center	Liberty Hospital
Catholic Health	Tenet Healthcare
Initiatives	Truman Medical Centers
Christian Hospital	University of Kansas
CoxHealth	Medical Center

HISTORICAL FINANCIALS

Company Type: Private

Income Statement

FYE: June 30

	REVENUE ($ mil.)	NET INCOME ($ mil.)	NET PROFIT MARGIN	EMPLOYEES
06/13	965	87	9.1%	4,400
06/12	968	112	11.6%	—
06/11	880	86	9.8%	—
06/10	68	0	—	—
Annual Growth	142.1%	—	—	—

2013 Year-End Financials

Return on assets: 14.0%   Cash ($ mil.): 12
Return on equity: 9.1%
Current ratio: 1.10

MERCY HOSPITALS EAST COMMUNITIES

LOCATIONS

HQ: MERCY HOSPITALS EAST COMMUNITIES
615 S NEW BALLAS RD, SAINT LOUIS, MO
631418221
Phone: 314 251-6000
Web: WWW.MERCY.NET

COMPETITORS

Ascension Health
BJC HealthCare
Memorial Hospital (Illinois)
SSM Health Care
St. Anthony' s Medical Center
St. Joseph' s Hospital of the Hospital Sisters
St. Luke' s Hospital (MO)

HISTORICAL FINANCIALS

Company Type: Private

Income Statement

FYE: June 30

	REVENUE ($ mil.)	NET INCOME ($ mil.)	NET PROFIT MARGIN	EMPLOYEES
06/13	840	82	9.8%	10,000
06/09	963	0	—	—
06/08	5	1	23.1%	—
06/05	3	0	—	—
Annual Growth	100.0%	—	—	—

2013 Year-End Financials

Return on assets: 2.2%   Cash ($ mil.): 10
Return on equity: 9.8%
Current ratio: 2.30

MERCY MEDICAL CENTER

Overlooking Long Island's Hempstead Lake State Park Mercy Medical Center offers healthcare services to patients just east of Manhattan. The not-for-profit Catholic hospital has expertise in weight loss and orthopedic surgeries mammograms and breast health and women's health services. It also provides outpatient services such as family and mental health care. With about 380 beds the medical center employs some 700 physicians who deliver about 1300 babies each year. Its acute care facilities include a suburban branch of Memorial Sloan-Kettering Cancer Center. Mercy Medical Center established in 1913 by the Sisters of the Congregation of the Infant Jesus is part of Catholic Health Services of Long Island.

EXECUTIVES

President and CEO, Alan D. Guerci
Director Public Relations and Marketing, Mel Granick
SVP and COO, Ron Steimel
Senior Vice President Chief Financial Officer, William Armstrong
EVP and Chief Administrative Officer, Aaron E. Glatt
Auditors: JH COHN LLP ROSELAND NJ

LOCATIONS

HQ: MERCY MEDICAL CENTER
1000 N VILLAGE AVE, ROCKVILLE CENTRE, NY 115701000
Phone: 516 562-6907
Web: WWW.CHSLI.ORG

PRODUCTS/OPERATIONS

Selected Services
Bariatric Surgery
Behavioral Health
Cancer Program
Cardiovascular Care
Drug and Alcohol
Emergency Care
Geriatrics
Mother Baby Services
Neurology
Neurosurgery
Orthopedic Surgery
Pediatrics
Physical Medicine and Rehabilitation
Podiatry
Procedures/Testing
Radiology and Imaging
Respiratory Health
Support Services
Surgery

COMPETITORS

Brookhaven Memorial Hospital Medical Center
Long Island College Hospital
Long Island Jewish Medical Center
New York City Health and Hospitals
NewYork-Presbyterian Healthcare
North Shore-Long Island Jewish Health System
Southside Hospital

HISTORICAL FINANCIALS

Company Type: Private

Income Statement

FYE: December 31

	REVENUE ($ mil.)	NET INCOME ($ mil.)	NET PROFIT MARGIN	EMPLOYEES
12/09	197	(8)	—	1,610
12/08	178	(8)	—	—
12/06	206	(3)	—	—
12/05	191	0	—	—
Annual Growth	0.8%	—	—	—

2009 Year-End Financials

Return on assets: —   Cash ($ mil.): 8
Return on equity: (-4.1%)
Current ratio: 0.20

MERCY MEDICAL CENTER INC.

Auditors: COHEN RUTHERFORD KNIGHT PC BE

LOCATIONS

HQ: MERCY MEDICAL CENTER INC.
345 SAINT PAUL PL, BALTIMORE, MD 212022123
Phone: 410 332-9000
Web: WWW.MDMERCY.COM

HISTORICAL FINANCIALS

Company Type: Private

Income Statement

FYE: June 30

	REVENUE ($ mil.)	NET INCOME ($ mil.)	NET PROFIT MARGIN	EMPLOYEES
06/10	387	36	9.3%	2,139
06/09	374	0	—	—
06/08	1,885	0	—	—
Annual Growth	(54.7%)	601050.8%	—	—

2010 Year-End Financials

Return on assets: —   Cash ($ mil.): 58
Return on equity: 9.3%
Current ratio: 0.10

MERCY MEDICAL CENTER INC.

Mercy Medical Center keeps patients doing the cancan in Canton. The facility is a 480-bed acute care hospital serving residents of five counties in southeastern Ohio. The Catholic medical center has 700 physicians and provides a comprehensive range of care including inpatient outpatient and rehabilitative services. It operates specialty care centers for cardiac vascular stroke and cancer treatment as well as trauma chest pain and rehabilitation units. Mercy Medical Center also operates outpatient health centers in the communities surrounding Canton Ohio. The facility is part of the Sisters of Charity Health System (SCHS) a not-for-profit ministry of the Sisters of Charity of St. Augustine.
Geographic Reach

Mercy Medical Center serves patients living in the Southeastern Ohio counties of Carroll Holmes Stark Tuscarawas and Wayne. In addition to the main hospital in Canton the health care provider operates outpatient centers in Carrollton Jackson Township Lake Township Louisville North Canton and Plain Township as well as Tuscarawas County.

Operations

Mercy Medical's center of excellence includes Mercy Heart Center Emergency Services/Trauma Center Emergency Chest Pain Center Mercy Cancer Center Mercy Rehabilitation Services Mercy Stroke Center and Mercy Vascular Center.

Sales and Marketing

The medical facility markets its services through social media and via TV commercials.

Financial Performance

Mercy Medical's total operating revenues were $275.1 million in fiscal 2012.

Strategy

Mercy Medical Center is focused on increasing operational efficiencies and pursuing growth opportunities including expanding services to patients. To that end the hospital in 2014 began to offer adult and pediatric therapy services in Western Stark County. It also launched an $80-million program in 2010 to invest in capital projects including facility improvements and equipment upgrades. The care provider also opened a new primary care office in Canton in 2012.

Company Background

Mercy Medical Center traces its roots to Mercy Hospital founded in 1908 in the former home of President William McKinley. The hospital was opened by the Sisters of Charity of St. Augustine which established SCHS as the parent company for its hospital operations in 1982. Between 1999 and 2009 SCHS operated the Mercy Medical Center and several other Ohio facilities through a joint venture with the University Hospitals Health System; however after 10 years full control of the facilities was reverted back to SCHS.

EXECUTIVES

Director Of Him, Lynne Shaffer
Director Of Respiratory Therapy, Larry Ramer
Vice President Fund Development and Government Relations, Thomas (Thom) Turner

LOCATIONS

HQ: MERCY MEDICAL CENTER INC.
1320 MERCY DR NW, CANTON, OH 447082641
Phone: 330 489-1000
Web: WWW.CANTONMERCY.ORG

Selected Facilities

Mercy Medical Center - Canton Ohio
Mercy Health Center of Alliance - Alliance Ohio
Mercy Health Center of Carroll County - Carrollton OH
Mercy Health Center of Lake - Uniontown OH
Mercy Health Center of Louisville - Louisville OH
Mercy Health Center of Jackson - Massillon OH
Mercy Health Center of North Canton - North Canton OH
Mercy Health Center of Plain - Canton OH
Mercy Health Center of Tuscarawas County - New Philadelphia OH
Mercy Medical Center at St. Paul Square - Canton Ohio

COMPETITORS

Akron Children' s Hospital
Akron General Health System
Aultman Health Foundation
Lake Health
OhioHealth
Parma Community General Hospital
Robinson Memorial Hospital
Summa Health System
The Cleveland Clinic
Trinity Health System
University Hospitals Health System

MERITER HEALTH SERVICES INC.

Meriter Health Services believes that the health concerns of its patients merits its careful attention. A teaching affiliate of the University of Wisconsin the Madison-based system serves residents of southern Wisconsin and northwestern Illinois. Its flagship facility is the 450-bed Meriter Hospital a not-for-profit community hospital providing general medical and surgical care as well as pediatric mental health services through its Child and Adolescent Psychiatric Hospital unit. Meriter Health Services also operates primary care clinics a home health care provider and clinical laboratories. It owns two-thirds of Physicians Plus Insurance a regional HMO.

Geographic Reach

In addition to its flagship hospital the company operates a network of clinics in the Greater Madison area which include DeForest-Windsor Clinic Deming Way Clinic Fitchburg Clinic McKee Clinic Middleton Clinic Monona Clinic Stoughton Clinic and West Washington Clinic.

Operations

Along with providing a full spectrum of medical services Meriter Health participates in an array of clinical research trials. Its trials include those for heart conditions mental health and vascular care as well as ways to improve information flow at the hospital.

Strategy

To advance its commitment to high-quality local patient care through shared best practices in 2014 the system affiliated with UnityPoint Health an integrated health system based in West Des Moines Iowa.

In 2013 Meriter Health won the National Research Corporation's Innovative Best Practice award Top Rated Adult Doctors award and Top Rated Pediatric Doctors award.

Meriter Health has been involved in a frenzy of expansion activity in recent years. In 2013 the system opened its three-story Birthing Center. In 2012 it opened one floor (5 North) in its Family Care Center with 24 private rooms and it also opened Meriter Stoughton a new clinic that is part of a growing group of eight primary care clinics located throughout the Madison-area.

Meriter Health also in 2012 adopted the technically advanced da Vinci Surgical System. It features high definition 3D vision wristed instrumentation and a natural motion enabling surgeons to perform with more agility. It also began offering neurology services that year.

Mergers and Acquisitions

At the beginning of 2012 Wisconsin Heart & Vascular Institute joined Meriter Medical Group. The practice which included 16 cardiologists vascular surgeons and mid-level providers experienced in all areas of cardiovascular care was subsequently renamed Meriter Wisconsin Heart.

Company Background

Meriter Health's roots can be traced all the way back to 1898 as Madison General Hospital. However it wasn't until 1987 that the hospital was given the Meriter moniker when General Health Services and Methodist Health Services (parent companies of Madison General Hospital and Methodist Hospital) merged to become Meriter Health Services. The combination of the two hospitals made Meriter Hospital.

In 2011 the company opened Meriter DeForest-Windsor a new clinic offering primary care medical imaging and lab and therapy services.

EXECUTIVES

Assistant Vice President For Information Systems, Denise Gomez
Vice President Professional Services, Sue Erickson
Auditors: KPMG LL MILWAUKEE WI

LOCATIONS

HQ: MERITER HEALTH SERVICES INC.
202 S PARK ST, MADISON, WI 537151507
Phone: 608 417-5800
Web: WWW.MERITER.COM

PRODUCTS/OPERATIONS

Selected Medical Services

Allergy and Immunology
Birthing Center
Dermatology
Digestive Health
Emergency Services
Endocrinology and Diabetes Care
General Surgery
Gynecology and Obstetrics
Heart and Vascular
Hospitalist Program
Laboratories
Medical Imaging Services
Medical Psychology
Home Health
Neuroscience
Newborn Intensive Care Unit
Oncology
Orthopedics
Palliative Care
Patient and Family Services
Pediatric Services
Plastic Surgery
Primary Care
Pharmacy
Psychiatry Program
Pulmonary Diagnostics
Sexual Assault Nurse Examiner Program
Sleep Clinic and Lab
Smoking Cessation Programs
Spiritual Care
Substance Use Treatment Program
Therapy for Adults
Therapy for Children
Women and Infants

COMPETITORS

Aspirus
Beaver Dam Community Hospitals
Beloit Health System
Dean Health Systems Inc.
Franciscan Skemp Healthcare
Marshfield Clinic Health System
Ministry Health Care
SSM Health Care
Stoughton Hospital
ThedaCare Inc.
Tomah Memorial Hospital
University of Wisconsin Hospital and Clinics

HISTORICAL FINANCIALS

Company Type: Private

Income Statement

FYE: December 31

	REVENUE ($ mil.)	NET INCOME ($ mil.)	NET PROFIT MARGIN	EMPLOYEES
12/13	283	10	3.6%	80
12/12	269	(14)	—	—
Annual Growth	5.1%	—	—	—

2013 Year-End Financials

Return on assets: 6.0%
Return on equity: 3.6%
Current ratio: 1.20
Cash ($ mil.): 15

HISTORICAL FINANCIALS

Company Type: Private

Income Statement

FYE: December 31

	REVENUE ($ mil.)	NET INCOME ($ mil.)	NET PROFIT MARGIN	EMPLOYEES
12/13	720	38	5.3%	3,330
12/12	774	12	1.6%	—
12/11	773	(16)	—	—
12/10	725	0	—	—
Annual Growth	(0.2%)	—	—	—

2013 Year-End Financials

Return on assets: 3.6%
Return on equity: 5.3%
Current ratio: 1.00

Cash ($ mil.): 79

MERITER HOSPITAL INC.

Auditors: KPMG LLP MILWAUKEE WI

LOCATIONS

HQ: MERITER HOSPITAL INC.
202 S PARK ST, MADISON, WI 537151596
Phone: 608 417-6000
Web: WWW.MERITER.COM

HISTORICAL FINANCIALS

Company Type: Private

Income Statement

FYE: December 31

	REVENUE ($ mil.)	NET INCOME ($ mil.)	NET PROFIT MARGIN	EMPLOYEES
12/13	454	56	12.5%	2,548
12/12	432	34	8.1%	—
12/11	402	(3)	—	—
12/10	365	0	—	—
Annual Growth	7.5%	—	—	—

2013 Year-End Financials

Return on assets: 4.9%
Return on equity: 12.5%
Current ratio: 1.50

Cash ($ mil.): 42

MERITUS HEALTH INC.

Meritus Health provides a wide range of medical services to patients living in western Maryland southern Pennsylvania and adjacent portions of West Virginia. The system's Meritus Medical Center has 250 beds and 40 bassinets and offers acute tertiary and long-term care including inpatient behavioral health services cardiac care obstetrics cancer treatment rehabilitation and trauma care. Meritus Health also operates the for-profit Meritus Enterprises a provider of outpatient health care including diagnostic imaging laboratory services and ambulatory surgery. In addition it provides general practice care at the Robinwood Professional Center.

Operations

The company's Meritus Medical Center Endowment Funds manages donations and also leases and manages real estate properties to other medical care providers while the Meritus Healthcare Foundation conducts endowment campaigns and other fundraising efforts. Another unit Meritus In-

surance Company is a captive provider of professional liability deductible and stop-loss coverage for the Meritus organization.

Each year the medical center has some 77000 emergency department visits 15000 admissions and performs some 4000 inpatient and 4700 outpatient surgeries.

Sales and Marketing

Reimbursement from Medicaid and Medicare plans account for about half of Meritus' annual patient service revenue.

Advertising costs totaled some $1.3 million in 2014 up from $1.1 million in 2013 but down from $1.7 million in 2012.

Financial Performance

Meritus Health reported a 3% decrease in 2014 annual revenues to some $360 million as net patient service revenues (which account for more than 90% of earnings) dipped. Lower equity earnings in affiliates also contributed to the decline. Despite that net income increased 6% to $19 million on higher investment returns and income tax benefits. Operating cash flow increased 99% to $32 million in 2014.

Strategy

To expand its services for area residents Meritus opened a new Center for Breast Health in 2013. The center includes radiation oncology pathology mental health physical and occupational therapy breast surgery and other services.

EXECUTIVES

Senior Vice President Operations Chief Operating Officer, Deborah (Deb) Samuels
Vice President Support Services, Lee Shaver
Vp And Chief Medical Officer, Heather N Lorenzo
Director of Health Information Systems, Shereen Martin
CQO Vice President Quality Management, Eileen Jaskuta
Secretary, Carolyn Jones
Auditors: GRANT THORNTON LLP BALTIMORE

LOCATIONS

HQ: MERITUS HEALTH INC.
11116 MEDICAL CAMPUS RD, HAGERSTOWN, MD 217426710
Phone: 301 790-8000
Web: WWW.MERITUSHEALTH.COM

PRODUCTS/OPERATIONS

2014 Sales

	% of total
Net patient service revenues less provision for bad debts	97
Other revenues	3
Total	**100**

Selected Centers and Services

Behavioral Health Services
Cardiac Services
Center for Bariatric Surgery
Center for Clinical Research
Center for Joint Replacement
Diagnostic Imaging Services
Endoscopy Center at Robinwood
Equipped for Life
Family Birthing Center
Hagerstown Medical Laboratory
Health@Work
Home Care Pharmacy
Home Health
Imaging Center
Infusion Services
John R. Marsh Cancer Center
The Learning Center
Meritus Imaging
Meritus NeuroRehab Foundation
Robinwood Professional Center
Robinwood Surgery Center
Special Care Nursery
Stroke Center
Total Rehab Care
Trauma Center

Vascular Center
Wound Center

COMPETITORS

Bon Secours Health	Sinai Hospital of
Civista Health	Baltimore
Frederick Memorial	St. Agnes HealthCare
Johns Hopkins Health	University of Maryland
System	Medical System
MedStar Health	

HISTORICAL FINANCIALS

Company Type: Private

Income Statement

FYE: June 30

	REVENUE ($ mil.)	NET INCOME ($ mil.)	NET PROFIT MARGIN	EMPLOYEES
06/13	374	17	4.7%	3,105
06/12	380	7	2.0%	—
06/11	0	0	—	—
06/10	0	0	—	—
Annual Growth	1112.5%	—	—	—

2013 Year-End Financials

Return on assets: 3.7%
Return on equity: 4.7%
Current ratio: 1.50

Cash ($ mil.): 18

MESSER CONSTRUCTION CO.

From casinos and courthouses to laboratories and dormitories Messer Construction has built them all. The builder provides commercial construction services (including design/build and project management) for projects in Indiana Kentucky Ohio North Carolina and Tennessee. Messer completes over $830 million worth of projects each year for clients in the life sciences higher education senior living commercial manufacturing/industrial public and health care sectors among others. Its projects have included one of the US's only LEED-certified research buildings (at the University of Louisville) and the Newport Aquarium in Kentucky. Founded in 1932 employee-owned Messer boasts a return-customer rate of 80%.

OperationsMesser Construction offers a range of commercial construction services including building information modeling cost planning and estimating integrated project delivery lean construction and safety programs. It also offers prefabrication services such as mechanical/electrical/plumbing services bathroom pods and health care headwall assemblies. Geographic Reach

Based in Cincinnati Ohio Messer operates regional offices in North Carolina (Charlotte) Ohio (Cincinnati Columbus and Dayton) Indiana (Indianapolis) Tennessee (Knoxville and Nashville) and Kentucky (Lexington and Louisville).Sales and MarketingMesser Construction has served customers from a variety of industries including clients such as: Aisin Automotive Casting Cummins DHL Express Dow AgroSciences Forest Pharmaceuticals Gannett Co General Motors Honda of America Praxair Procter & Gamble Sonoco and Worthington Steel.StrategyMesser continues to work on high-value projects across a wide range of industries in the Midwest particularly in secure industries such as healthcare government and education. During 2015 for example it worked on the 70000-square-foot expansion to Cincinnati Children's Hospital Medical Center (CCHMC) adding a fourth floor 30 beds kitchen full-service cafeteria expanded medical and surgery specialty clinics a gift shop and more. That year it also worked on the $24.1 million- expansion at the National Air and Space Intelligence Center's (NASIC) Foreign Materials Exploitation Laboratory in Dayton for the US Department of Defense as well as the University of Kentucky's $175 million- Student Center Transformation Project (to be completed in 2017) which will span 360000 square feet and include updated student activity and study spaces dining and retail outlets parking a bookstore and more.Company BackgroundFormerly known as Frank Messer & Sons Inc. the company changed its name to Messer Construction Co. in March 2002.

EXECUTIVES

Vice President, Robert (Bob) Verst
Vice President Operations, Mark Hill
Vice President Finance, Paul Hitter
Vice President, Bill Rutz
Vice President, John Megibben
Vice President Of Rental Division, Thomas Wall
Senior Vice President, Bernie Suer
Business Development Vice President, Matt Monnin
Vice President Operations, Kevin M Cozart
Vice President Operations, Douglas C (Doug) Downey
Vice President Operations, Tim Gusler
Vice President Operations, Richard (Dick) Zoller
Auditors: DELOITTE & TOUCHE LLP CINCINN

LOCATIONS

HQ: MESSER CONSTRUCTION CO.
5158 FISHWICK DR, CINCINNATI, OH 452162216
Phone: 513 242-1541
Web: WWW.MESSER.COM

PRODUCTS/OPERATIONS

Selected Projects
Health Care
  Norton Healthcare
  Knoxville Orthopedic Clinic
Life Sciences
  Indiana University
  University of Kentucky
Higher Education
  Xavier University
  Western Kentucky University
Senior Living
  Graceworks Lutheran Services
  Episcopal Retirement Homes
Commercial
  IGS Energy
  Penn National Gaming
Manufacturing & Industrial
  Aisin Automotive Casting Tennessee Inc.
  DHL Express Inc.
Public/Institutional
  The Ohio Building Authority
  Commonwealth of Kentucky

COMPETITORS

Albert M. Higley	Shook National
Danis	Skanska USA Building
F.A. Wilhelm	The Austin Company
Gray Construction	Turner Corporation
Hunt Construction	Tutor Perini
Pepper Construction	

HISTORICAL FINANCIALS
Company Type: Private

Income Statement
FYE: September 30

	REVENUE ($ mil.)	NET INCOME ($ mil.)	NET PROFIT MARGIN	EMPLOYEES
09/14	1,029	0	—	900
09/13	831	0	—	—
09/12	0	0	—	—
09/11	560	0	—	—
Annual Growth 22.5%		—	—	—

2014 Year-End Financials
Return on assets: 20.9%   Cash ($ mil.): 77
Return on equity: —
Current ratio: 1.10

METHODIST HOSPITAL OF SOUTHERN CALIFORNIA

If you're dehydrated in the Valley Methodist Hospital of Southern California can help. The hospital provides medical care to the residents of California's central San Gabriel Valley. The healthcare facility boasts some 600 beds and is part of Southern California Healthcare Systems. The not-for-profit hospital provides comprehensive acute care including surgical pediatric and intensive care units. It also offers a wide range of specialty services such as cardiology oncology neurology bariatrics and orthopedics. The hospital opened its doors in 1903 with five beds.

Geographic Reach

Methodist Hospital is located in Arcadia California in the northeastern corner of the Los Angeles metropolitan area; it serves patients from surrounding communities as well.

Operations

Methodist Hospital serves Arcadia Azusa Baldwin Park Bradbury Duarte El Monte Monrovia Pasadena Rosemead San Gabriel Sierra Madre and Temple City.

In addition to typical acute care services Methodist Hospital's cardiac care center provides complete cardiovascular services including open-heart surgery. The medical facility's intensive care units boast both neonatal and adult centers. Its cardiovascular stroke and cancer centers are certified by various national medical specialist organizations. The hospital employs about 630 medical staff members.

It also operates a rehabilitation clinic and a long-term recovery facility for patients requiring transitional care.

StrategyA grant from the H.N. and Frances C. Berger Foundation in 2012 has allowed the hospital to install a state-of-the-art hyperbaric (high-pressure oxygen) chamber in the hospital's Wound Healing Center. The chamber helps to treat diabetic patients suffering from chronic wounds as well as wounds resulting from immune deficiencies and assists patients suffering from decompression sickness or the "bends" as a result of diving accidents.In recent years Methodist Hospital has continued with its infrastructure expansion and improvement projects with a focus on expanding its emergency department in 2013 and opening a new GYN Oncology Institute in 2014. Each year the hospital serves 47000 emergency department visits 16800 outpatient visits 16600 inpatient admissions 5100 surgeries and 1800 deliveries.Financial PerformanceMethodist Hospital in fiscal 2013 boasted a $248 million total operating budget.

EXECUTIVES

Vice President, Clifford (Cliff) Daniels
Director Of Pharmacy, Dorothy Wong
Ambulatory Services Director, Barbara Murphy
Senior Management (Senior Vice President General Manager Director), Jeff Stack
Director of Medical Records, Bridgett Didier
Secretary, Debra Jones
Assistant Treasurer, Kay Berglund

LOCATIONS

HQ: METHODIST HOSPITAL OF SOUTHERN CALIFORNIA
300 W HUNTINGTON DR, ARCADIA, CA 910073402
Phone: 626 898-8000
Web: WWW.METHODISTHOSPITAL.ORG

PRODUCTS/OPERATIONS

Selected Services
Cardiology
Diabetes Services
Emergency Services
Gynecology
Maternal Child Health
Neurology
Oncology
Orthopedics
Outpatient Services
Rehabilitation Services
Senior Services
Surgical Services
Stroke
Transitional Care Unit
Weight Loss Surgery
Wound Healing Center

COMPETITORS

Citrus Valley Health Partners
Dignity Health
Glendale Adventist Medical Center
Good Samaritan Hospital (Los Angeles)
HCA
Hollywood Presbyterian Medical Center
Los Angeles County Health Department
Memorial Health Services
Newhall Memorial Hospital
Providence Saint Joseph Medical Center
St. Joseph Health System
Tenet Healthcare

HISTORICAL FINANCIALS
Company Type: Private

Income Statement
FYE: December 31

	REVENUE ($ mil.)	NET INCOME ($ mil.)	NET PROFIT MARGIN	EMPLOYEES
12/13	279	4	1.7%	2,200
12/12	281	0	0.3%	—
12/11	245	(4)	—	—
12/10	271	0	—	—
Annual Growth 1.0%		—	—	—

2013 Year-End Financials
Return on assets: 4.1%   Cash ($ mil.): 31
Return on equity: 1.7%
Current ratio: 1.50

METHODIST HOSPITALS OF DALLAS INC

Methodist Hospitals of Dallas serves the health care needs of North Texas —from Mansfield to McKinney. The church-affiliated organization which does business as Methodist Health System operates more than a dozen hospitals clinics and medical facilities in and around the area deemed by locals as Big D. The original hospital Methodist Dallas Medical Center opened in 1927. The 585-bed teaching and referral hospital boasts a Level II trauma center and an organ transplant program. Other facilities include the 269-bed Methodist Charlton Medical Center the 168-bed Methodist Mansfield Medical Center and the 209-bed Methodist Richardson Medical Center.

OperationsEach year the system oversees some 3000 births 64000 emergency department visits and 160000 outpatient visits. It has some 300 physicians.The Methodist Dallas liver kidney and pancreas transplant program is one of the largest and most active transplant centers in the southwestern part of the country performing hundreds of kidney pancreas and liver transplants each year.

Both Methodist Hospital for Special Surgery and Methodist McKinney are part of two separate joint venture agreements made between Methodist Health System and Nueterra Healthcare a health care facilities management and development company.

Geographic Reach

Methodist Hospitals of Dallas serves the residents of several communities located in and around the North Dallas area such as Midlothian Grand Prairie Cedar Hill Richardson Plano Garland Wylie and McKinney.

Strategy

In recent years Methodist Health System has grown through a series of acquisitions (such as the Methodist Mansfield Medical Center and the Methodist Richardson Medical Center) as well as through organic expansion efforts such as the construction of about 50 rooms and new surgery suites in the Methodist Charlton hospital.

In 2014 the health care provider opened its newly expanded Methodist Richardson Medical Center - Bush/Renner hospital. The new 125-bed hospital reaches four stories high and serves the northeast Dallas communities of Richardson Garland Murphy Plano Sachse Wylie and other surrounding areas. It boasts a women's pavilion a level III neonatal intensive care unit an advanced neurosciences program outpatient surgical services such as the robotic da Vinci surgical system and other specialty services.

EXECUTIVES

Rph Dph, Alan (Al) Roach
Assistant Vice President Corporate Tax Management, Dwight Williams
Senior Vice President Chief Human Resources Officer, Cheryl Flynn
Senior Vice President and Chief Nursing Officer; Chief Nursing Officer Methodist Dallas Medical Cen, Nancy Simon
Medical Director of INFECTION Control and INFECTIOUS DISEASES PHYSICIAN, Zakir Shaikh
Assistant Vice President, Monica Vehige
Vice President Of Revenue Cycle, Leslie Pierce
Vice President, Harold Kolni
Auditors: GRANT THORNTON LLP DALLAS TE

LOCATIONS

HQ: METHODIST HOSPITALS OF DALLAS INC
1441 N BECKLEY AVE, DALLAS, TX 752031201
Phone: 214 947-8181
Web: WWW.JOBS.METHODISTHEALTHSYSTEM.ORG

PRODUCTS/OPERATIONS

Selected Services
Back and Spine
Behavioral Health and Addiction Recovery
Cancer Services
Cardiovascular
da Vinci Surgical System
Diabetes
Digestive Diseases
Ear Nose & Throat (ENT) Services & Allergy Treatments
Emergency and Trauma Care
Fitness Programs
Home Health
Imaging and Radiology
The Liver Institute
Neurosurgery and Neurology
Ophthalmology
Orthopedics
Pain Management
Palliative Care
Physical Therapy and Rehabilitation
Prostate Screening and Awareness Program
Sleep Disorders
Transplant
Urology
Weight Management
Women and Children' s Services
Women' s Imaging and Mammography
Wound Care and Hyperbaric Center

Selected Facilities
Golden Cross Academic Clinic
Methodist Dallas Medical Center
Methodist Charlton Medical Center
Methodist Family Health Centers
 Cedar Hill
 Central Grand Prairie
 Dallas
 Midlothian
 South Grand Prairie
Methodist Hospital for Surgery
Methodist Mansfield Medical Center
Methodist McKinney Hospital
Methodist Midlothian Health Center (imaging)
Methodist Richardson Medical Center
Methodist Richardson Medical Center Bush/Renner
Methodist Rehabilitation Hospital

COMPETITORS

CHRISTUS Health
Children' s Medical Center of Dallas
Community Health Systems
Cook Children' s Health Care System
HCA
Harris Methodist Fort Worth Hospital
Hunt Memorial
JPS Health Network
NW Texas Healthcare
Parkland Health & Hospital System
Presbyterian Hospital of Dallas
Southwestern Medical Center
Tenet Healthcare
Texas Health Denton
Texas Health Resources

HISTORICAL FINANCIALS
Company Type: Private

Income Statement
FYE: September 30

	REVENUE ($ mil.)	NET INCOME ($ mil.)	NET PROFIT MARGIN	EMPLOYEES
09/13	1,038	132	12.8%	4,804
09/12	969	165	17.1%	—
09/11	985	51	5.3%	—
09/10	889	0	—	—
Annual Growth	5.3%	—	—	—

2013 Year-End Financials
Return on assets: 8.2%
Return on equity: 12.8%
Current ratio: 1.70
Cash ($ mil.): 663

METROPOLITAN UTILITIES DISTRICT OMAHA NEBRASKA.

The Metropolitan Utilities District (MUD) distributes natural gas and water in the Omaha Nebraska metropolitan area. The company serves some 220000 natural gas customers and more than 200000 water customers. It also collects sewer and trash fees for municipalities. Customer-owned MUD which claims to be the fifth-largest public gas utility in the nation is a political subdivision of the State of Nebraska. Its board members are elected by residents of its service territory.

Geographic Reach

MUD provides natural gas to customers in Omaha Bennington Fort Calhoun Springfield Yutan and Bellevue; its water operations cover Omaha Bellevue Bennington Carter Lake LaVista Ralston Waterloo and the Papio-Missouri Natural Resources District (which supplies water to Fort Calhoun).

Financial Performance

Overall revenue was down 6% in 2012 to about $293 million. A nearly 30% increase in water sales because of record-breaking demand during an unusually hot dry summer was not enough to offset a nearly 20% drop in natural gas sales. MUD's net income rose from $15 million to about $46 million that year however as operating expenses declined particularly the cost of natural gas.

Company Background

The Metropolitan Water District was created by the Nebraska Legislature in 1913. In 1918 state legislators authorized the City of Omaha to take charge of the gas system and the Metropolitan Water District subsequently was renamed as the Metropolitan Utilities District.

EXECUTIVES

Sr V Pres - Gen Council, Ron Bucher
Vice President Rates Regulatory Affairs and Revenues, Rhonda Chantry
Auditors: KPMG LLP OMAHA NE

LOCATIONS

HQ: METROPOLITAN UTILITIES DISTRICT OMAHA NEBRASKA.
1723 HARNEY ST, OMAHA, NE 681021960
Phone: 402 554-6666
Web: WWW.MYACOUNT.MUDOMAHA.COM

HISTORICAL FINANCIALS
Company Type: Private

Income Statement
FYE: December 31

	REVENUE ($ mil.)	NET INCOME ($ mil.)	NET PROFIT MARGIN	EMPLOYEES
12/13	341	47	13.7%	852
12/12	292	46	15.8%	—
12/11	311	15	4.9%	—
12/09	308	0	—	—
Annual Growth	2.6%	—	—	—

2013 Year-End Financials
Return on assets: 13.0%
Return on equity: 13.7%
Current ratio: 1.30
Cash ($ mil.): 64

MFA INCORPORATED

Agricultural cooperative MFA brings together 45000 farmers in Missouri and adjacent states. One of the US's oldest regional co-ops supplying its member/owners with agronomy distribution financing and purchasing services it runs more than 140 retail farm supply centers and works with independent dealers. MFA supplies animal feeds seed fertilizer and crop protection products. The co-op also provides its members with agronomy services animal-health products and farm supplies. It also offers marketing services and is the publisher of Today's Farmer. Agmo Corporation MFA's finance company provides co-op members longer credit terms for purchases made through MFA's retail outlets.

Geographic Reach

The company has fertilizer terminals on the Mississippi River as well as on the Missouri and Arkansas rivers.

Operations

MFA's plant food sales exceed one million tons each year.

Strategy

Part of MFA's strategy is to focus on growth initiatives and find opportunistic products and services to provide to its customers. Strategic river terminals and other bulk facilities give it capacity to deliver bulk quantities of plant food. It also invests in rolling stock trucks and application equipment to ensure bulk products are efficiently delivered to retail customers.

Mergers and Acquisitions

Expanding its assets in 2013 MFA acquired Producers Grain Company's assets in El Dorado Springs Walker Bronaugh and Nevada in Missouri.

Ownership

MFA is owned by it member/farmers.

Company Background

The co-op was established in 1914 when seven Missouri farmers got together to buy binder twine.

EXECUTIVES

SVP Corporate and Member Services, Janice Schuerman
SVP Corporate Operations, J. Brian Griffith
SVP Agri Services Division, Bill Streeter
VP Feed Division, Alan Wessler
SVP and CFO, Ernie Verslues
VP Plant Foods and Transportation, Bill Coen
VP Crop Protection Seed and Farm Supply, Don Houston
VP Agri Services, Craig Childs
Senior Vice President Corporate Operations, Brian Griffith
Vice President Mill Operations, Tom Staudt
Vice President Of Engineering, Todd Rauch
Second Vice President Finance, David (Dave) Moore
Vice Chairman, John Moffitt
Chairman, Don Mills
Treasurer, John Akridge
Assistant Secretary, Larna Lavelle
Treasurer, Patty Fuemmeler
Auditors: WILLIAMS KEEPERS LLC COLUMBIA

LOCATIONS

HQ: MFA INCORPORATED
201 RAY YOUNG DR, COLUMBIA, MO 652013599
Phone: 573 874-5111
Web: WWW.CALIFORNIAMFA.COM

COMPETITORS

ADM	GROWMARK
Andersons	Heartland Co-op
Cargill	Missouri Farm Bureau
Farm Service	Orscheln Farm and Home
Cooperative	Tennessee Farmers

Farmers Cooperative Company	Co-op United Producers

HISTORICAL FINANCIALS
Company Type: Private

Income Statement
FYE: August 31

	REVENUE ($ mil.)	NET INCOME ($ mil.)	NET PROFIT MARGIN	EMPLOYEES
08/14	1,510	18	1.2%	1,393
08/13	1,510	15	1.0%	—
08/12	1,470	22	1.5%	—
08/11	1,354	0	—	—
Annual Growth	3.7%	—	—	—

MFA OIL COMPANY

Many farmers appreciate MFA Oil. The energy cooperative controlled by its 40000 farmer-members produces fuel and lubrication products and manages bulk petroleum and propane plants in the Central and Western US. Operating 140 propane plants the company sells more propane for farm use and home heating than any other company in Missouri. It also operates nearly 100 oil and lubricant bulk plants and serves customers in Arkansas Iowa Kansas and Oklahoma. Additionally the company operates 76 convenience stores under the Break Time brand (in Arkansas and Missouri) more than 160 Petro-Card 24 fueling locations and owns 10 Jiffy Lube and a dozen Big O Tire franchises.

Geographic Reach

MFA Oil serves customers in Arkansas Colorado Kansas Kentucky Indiana Iowa Missouri Nebraska Oklahoma Virginia and Wyoming.

Strategy

While not a pure vertically integrated enterprise over time the cooperative has developed multiple complementary business lines to enable it to respond to a wide range of its members' fuel transportation and food service needs. In this tradition in 2011 MFA Oil teamed up with biofuel developer Aloterra Energy to form MFA Oil Biomass LLC. The partnership aims to help farmers to produce a renewable energy crop that can be used as biomass for an alternative cleaner burning energy supply for use in power generation plants as well as a liquid fuel. In 2011 about 250 farmers had signed letters of intent to grow miscanthus (a perennial grass) on more than 21000 acres as part of this initiative.

Mergers and Acquisitions

Expanding its geographic network in 2013 MFA Oil acquired Kansas-based American Petroleum Marketers which distributes fuel to more than 60 Cenex branded sites along with unbranded fuel in six states.

Ownership

The company is a cooperative owned by its farmer/members.

Company Background

MFA Oil has grown well beyond its Missouri roots where it was founded by farmers in 1929. The company's first bulk plant was located at Wright City Missouri.

EXECUTIVES

Senior Vice President of Retail, Curtis Chaney
Auditors: WILLIAMS KEEPERS LLC COLUMBIA

LOCATIONS

HQ: MFA OIL COMPANY
1 RAY YOUNG DR, COLUMBIA, MO 652013506
Phone: 573 442-0171
Web: WWW.MFAOIL.COM

COMPETITORS

Ag Processing Inc.	Lykins
Green Brick Partners	Shell Oil Products
Green Plains	Valero Energy
Jordan Oil Company	WilcoHess

HISTORICAL FINANCIALS
Company Type: Private

Income Statement
FYE: August 31

	REVENUE ($ mil.)	NET INCOME ($ mil.)	NET PROFIT MARGIN	EMPLOYEES
08/14	1,471	40	2.8%	1,500
08/13	1,300	55	4.2%	—
08/12	1,255	34	2.7%	—
08/11	1,275	0	—	—
Annual Growth	4.9%	—	—	—

2014 Year-End Financials
Return on assets: 3.4%   Cash ($ mil.): 39
Return on equity: 2.8%
Current ratio: 0.90

MIAMI UNIVERSITY

Not that Miami the other one. Named for the Miami Indian Tribe that inhabited the area now known as the Miami Valley Region of Ohio Miami University emphasizes undergraduate study at its main campus in Oxford (35 miles north of Cincinnati) as well as at commuter campuses in Hamilton Middletown and West Chester Ohio and a European Center in Luxembourg. The school offers bachelors masters and doctoral programs in areas including business administration arts and sciences engineering and education. Its student body includes more than 15000 undergraduates on the Oxford campus; 2500 graduate students; and another 5700 students attending satellite campuses. Miami University was established in 1809.

Financial Performance

Miami University's 2011 revenue increased 3% vs. 2010 due to a corresponding increase in undergraduate tuition on its three campuses and a rising rates for room and board. Net income at the public university rose 25% over the same period on higher revenue and lower operating expenses due primarily to a reduction in the number of positions and no salary increases. The rise in tuition for Ohio residents in 2011 was the first in four years. Also investment income rose in 2011 for the second consecutive year.

Company Background

Miami University celebrated its bicentennial in 2009. The school was chartered in February of 1809 by the State of Ohio but the first classses were not held until 1824.

EXECUTIVES

Division President, Jayne Whitehead
VP Information Technology, J. Peter Natale
Associate VP University Communications and Marketing, Deedie Dowdle
President, David C. Hodge
SVP Finance and Business Services and Treasurer, David Creamer
Dean School of Engineering and Computing, Marek Doll ̈r

Associate Provost and Dean College of Professional Studies and Applied Sciences, G. Michael Pratt
Provost and EVP Academic Affairs, Phyllis Callahan
Interim Dean College of Arts and Science, Chris Makaroff
Dean Farmer School of Business, Matthew B. Myers
Dean College of Creative Arts, Elizabeth R. Mullenix
Dean Graduate School, Jim Oris
Dean College of Education Health and Society, Michael Dantley
Vice President, Brenden Clinton
Assistant Vice President For Auxiliary Services, PETER C (Pete) MILLER
Associate Vice President and Deputy CIO, Alan (Al) Ferrenberg
Vice President For Student Affairs, Jayne Brownell
Senior Vice President Information Technology Programmer, Valerie (Val) Garnett
Vice President For Student Affairs, Barbara Jones
Associate Vice President Of Budgeting, David (Dave) Ellis
Associate Vice President For Enrollment Management, Michael (Mel) Kabbaz
Program Associate Vice President of Finance, Agnes A Shea
Co Vice President, Rory Ward
Associate Vice President for Finance and Associate Treasurer, Beverly Thomas
Interim Vice President for Information Technology, Debra Allison
Vice President Information Technology, Reid Christenberry
Vice President, Riley Kelly
Assistant Vice President Enterprise Operations Information Technology Services, Troy Travis
Vice President, Andrew (Andy) Hazel
Vice President of Public Relations, Jack Kellenberger
Vice President, Cameron Herring
Vice President, Emily Shindler
Executive Vice President, Ryan Koerner
Vice President, Mark Bennett
Vice President of Facilities Management, Eric Flynn
Vice President of Member Education, Duncan Rodts
Vice President, Rob Levoy
Vice President, Corinne Gilardi
Vice President, Annie Leanse
Vice President of Public Relations, Alexis DeBrunner
Vice President of Membership Development, Kasey Woomer
Vice President, Shannon Bradfield
Vice President of Community Service and Engagement, Leonard (Len) Awuah
Chairman, David H. Budig
Vice Chairman, Mark E. Ridenour
Treasurer, Sarah Brizzolara
Board Member, Phyllis Wykoff
Secretary, Chelsea Appiah
Auditors: MCGLADREY LLP CLEVELAND OHIO

LOCATIONS

HQ: MIAMI UNIVERSITY
501 E HIGH ST, OXFORD, OH 450561846
Phone: 513 529-1809

HISTORICAL FINANCIALS

Company Type: Private

Income Statement

FYE: June 30

	REVENUE ($ mil.)	NET INCOME ($ mil.)	NET PROFIT MARGIN	EMPLOYEES
06/13	443	93	21.1%	4,925
06/12	440	32	7.5%	—
06/11	418	120	28.8%	—
06/10	404	0	—	—
Annual Growth	3.1%	—	—	—

2013 Year-End Financials

Return on assets: 12.6%
Return on equity: 21.1%
Current ratio: 2.80

Cash ($ mil.): 312

MIAMI VALLEY HOSPITAL

Don't go to Florida looking for this hospital! Miami Valley Hospital (MVH) is an acute care facility serving the residents of Dayton Ohio and surrounding areas through two campuses. MVH and MVH South have roughly 950 beds and offer 50 primary and specialty care practices through its Regional Adult Burn Center the MVH Cancer Center MVH Sports Medicine Center and behavioral health units for outpatient and inpatient chemical dependency therapy and other psychiatric services. MVH also offers Level I trauma services Level III-B NICU adult burn center an air ambulance program and blood marrow and kidney transplant services. The hospital is part of the Premier Health Partners network.

Operations

In addition to MVH the Premier Health Partners network consists of Good Samaritan Hospital (also stationed in Dayton Ohio) Atrium Medical Center in nearby Middletown and Upper Valley Medical Center in Troy. Collectively the multi-hospital health system houses about 1800 inpatient beds and around 65 facilities.

MVH have more than 1100 physicians in more than 70 primary and specialty medical practice areas. It was a 2012 recipient of the HealthGrades Distinguished Hospital Award for Clinical Excellence placing it among the top 5% of hospitals in the US.In 2012 it had 41555 inpatient admissions; 164140 outpatient visits; 125622 emergency department visits; and oversaw 4000 births.

Financial Performance

Medicare accounted for 40% of the company's 2012 revenues; Medicaid 20%.

Strategy

Over the past few years MVH has focused on upgrading its infrastructure. It has built a $135 million 440000-sq. ft. 11-story heart tower on the south side of the campus and spent $19 million on renovating and expanding its neonatal intensive care unit.

In 2013 it opened its new $6 million 24-hour Emergency Center in Jamestown Ohio to meet the growing demand for emergency care.In 2013 MVH South opened a $20 million Comprehensive Cancer Center and (in 2012) a new maternity center

which includes five labor and delivery suites two surgical suites for c-section deliveries and 16 private after-birthing suites.

Company Background

MVH was formed in 1890.

EXECUTIVES

Medical Director Of Surgery, Marion Brown
Nursing Director, Jill Schneider
Vice President Hospital Operations, Diane Pleiman
Vice President Operations and Chief Nursing Officer, Deb Mals
Vice President, Mark Shaw
Medical Director, Daniel (Dan) Hood

LOCATIONS

HQ: MIAMI VALLEY HOSPITAL
1 WYOMING ST, DAYTON, OH 454092711
Phone: 937 208-8000
Web: WWW.MIAMIVALLEYHOSPITAL.ORG

PRODUCTS/OPERATIONS

Campus Locations
Miami Valley Hospital - Dayton OH
Miami Valley Hospital South - Centerville Ohio

Selected Services and Specialties
Ablation (Cardiology)
Access and Transfer Center (physicians)
Alcoholism Drug Dependency and Addiction Treatment
Aneurysm (Neurosciences)
Ankle Surgery
Arterial Interventions
Audiology
Bariatrics/Weight Loss Surgery
Behavioral Services
Biotherapy/Targeted Therapy
Blood and Marrow Transplant Program
Brachytherapy
Brain Conditions and Treatments
Brain Injury Rehabilitation
Breast Cancer Navigators
Breast Center
Breast Center
Brethen Center for Surgical Advancement (physicians)
Bull Family Diabetes Center
Burn Center
Cancer Care
Cancer Care (Oncology)
Cardiac Electrophysiology Lab
Cardiac Rehabilitation
Cardiology
Cardiology
Cardiothoracic Surgery
CareFlight - Medical Transportation
Catheterization Lab Procedures
Center for Sleep and Wake Disorders
Chemoembolization
Chemotherapy and Infusion Therapy
Childbirth Education
Colon Cancer
Colorectal Cancer
Complementary Medicine (Cancer)
Comprehensive Outpatient Rehab Program (CORP)
Counseling/Pastoral Care
Craniectomy (Neuroscience)
Craniotomy (Neuroscience)
Cryoablation
CT scan (Imaging)
Dental Center
Depression/Anxiety Treatment
Diabetes
Dialysis Services
Discectomy
Drug Addiction Treatment
Elder Care
Emergency & Trauma Center (ETC)
Foot Surgery
Fractures (Athletes)
Fusion (spinal treatment)
Gastric Bypass
Genetic Testing
Gynecologic Cancer
Gynecology
Hand Therapy
Head and Neck Cancer
Heart Care

Heart Surgery
High Risk Breast Cancer Center
Hip Surgery
Hormone Therapy
Hospitalists/Medical Professionals
Hyperbaric Oxygen Therapy Center
Image Guided Radiation Therapy (IGRT)
Injury Prevention Center
Inpatient Rehabilitation
Intensity Modulated Radiation Therapy (IMRT)
Intensive Care Unit (ICU)
Interventional Radiology
Joint replacements
Kidney Transplant
Knee Surgery
Kyphoplasty
Leukemia
Lung Cancer
Lymphoma
Mammography Screenings
Maternal-Fetal Medicine
Maternity
Maternity
Medical Professionals/Hospitalists
Medical Transportation - CareFlight
Mental Health Services
Minimally Invasive Surgery
Mother and Baby Services
MRI (Imaging)
Nanoknife
Neonatal Intensive Care
Neuro Rehabilitation
NeuroInterventional Center
Neuroscience
Neurosciences
Nutrition Services
OB-GYN
Obstetrics
Occupational Rehabilitation
Occupational Therapy
Oncology
Organ Transplant
Orthopedics
Orthopedics
Outpatient Physical Therapy
Pain Management
Palliative Care
Pancreatic Cancer
Perinatal Intensive Care
PET Scan (Imaging)
Pharmacy
Physiatry
Physical Therapy
Pre-Admission Testing
Premier HeartWorks
Preventive Cardiology
Prostate Cancer
Pulmonary Services
Radiofrequency ablation
Radiology
Radionuclide scan
Rehabilitation
Rehabilitation Institute of Ohio
Respiratory Care
Robotic Surgery
Shoulder Surgery
Shunt (Neuroscience)
Skin Cancer
Sleep Center
Solitaire Revascularization Device (Neurosciences)
Speech-Language Pathology
Spinal decompression surgery
Spinal disc replacement
Spinal fracture treatment
Spinal tumor surgery
Spine and back injuries (Orthopedics)
Spine Conditions and Treatments (Neuroscience)
Sports Medicine
Sports Medicine
Stereotaxis
Stomach Cancer
Stroke Treatments
Surgery Center
Surgical Oncology
Thoracic Surgery
Throat Cancer
Trauma
Ultrasound (Imaging)
Urological Cancer
Urology
Vascular Services

Venous Interventions
Vertebroplasty
Weight Loss Surgery (Bariatrics)
Weight Loss Surgery/Bariatrics
Wheelchair Clinic
Women's Health
Women's Heart Services
Women's Services
Wound Therapy
X-rays (Imaging)
Y-90 Radioembolization

COMPETITORS

Cincinnati Children's Hospital	OhioHealth
Deaconess Associations	The Christ Hospital Corporation
Good Samaritan Hospital (IN)	TriHealth
HealthSouth	UC Health
Kettering Health Network	

HISTORICAL FINANCIALS

Company Type: Private

Income Statement

FYE: December 31

	REVENUE ($ mil.)	NET INCOME ($ mil.)	NET PROFIT MARGIN	EMPLOYEES
12/12	773	77	10.0%	6,000
12/07	622	44	7.1%	—
12/05	502	(0)	—	—
Annual Growth	6.4%	—	—	—

2012 Year-End Financials

Return on assets: 4.4%
Return on equity: 10.0%
Current ratio: 1.80
Cash ($ mil.): 13

MICHIGAN MILK PRODUCERS ASSOCIATION

Ice cream and other dairy products might be missing a major ingredient without Michigan Milk Producers Association (MMPA). The dairy cooperative which serves more than 2100 farmers in Michigan Ohio Indiana and Wisconsin produces some 3.9 billion pounds of milk each year. Milk products include sweetened condensed milk instant nonfat milk and dried buttermilk as well as other items the likes of cream cheese butter and ice-cream mixes. With no consumer brands or products MMPA sells its products as ingredients to food makers who sell baby formulas candy ice cream and yogurt. Founded in 1916 the co-op operates a pair of Michigan plants and a merchandise facility.

Geographic Reach

From its headquarters in Novi Michigan MMPA operates solely in the state of Michigan where it has manufacturing plants in the villages of Ovid and Constantine and a merchandise facility in the Michigan city of Saint Louis. Its farmers are located in Michigan Ohio Indiana and Wisconsin.

Operations

As part of its business of serving member-farmers MMPA provides them with product quality incentives testing and customized blending as well as protection against loss from disaster.

EXECUTIVES

Vice President, Bob Kran
Auditors: CLIFTONLARSONALLEN LLP

LOCATIONS

HQ: MICHIGAN MILK PRODUCERS ASSOCIATION
41310 BRIDGE ST, NOVI, MI 483751302
Phone: 248 474-6672
Web: WWW.MIMILK.COM

PRODUCTS/OPERATIONS

Selected Products

Condensed skim milk
Condensed whole milk
Dried buttermilk
Dried whole milk
Ice cream mixes
Instant nonfat dry milk
Nonfat dry milk
Standardized cream
Standardized milk
Sweet condensed milk
Sweet cream butter

COMPETITORS

Associated Milk Producers	Land O' Lakes
Dairy Farmers of America	Main Street Ingredients
Dean Foods	Quality Chekd
Foremost Farms	Saputo

HISTORICAL FINANCIALS

Company Type: Private

Income Statement

FYE: September 30

	REVENUE ($ mil.)	NET INCOME ($ mil.)	NET PROFIT MARGIN	EMPLOYEES
09/12	854	5	0.7%	200
09/11	870	6	0.7%	—
09/10	698	6	1.0%	—
09/09	556	0	—	—
Annual Growth	15.3%	—	—	—

2012 Year-End Financials

Return on assets: 5.3%
Return on equity: 0.7%
Current ratio: 1.20
Cash ($ mil.): 17

MICHIGAN TECHNOLOGICAL UNIVERSITY

Michigan Technological University trains techies in the Wolverine State. A premier research university the school affectionately known as Michigan Tech offers a range of programs in computing engineering technology business and technology forest resources and environmental science social work sciences and arts and non-departmental sponsored educational programs. Based in Houghton the school has an enrollment of about 7000 undergraduate and graduate students and a faculty of almost 480 instructors. The company is considered to be a discrete component unit of the State of Michigan because its Board of Control is appointed by the Governor.

Operations

The university has 22 interdisciplinary research institutes and centers. In 2013-14 tuition was

$13470 per year for Michigan residents and $28350 for students from out of state.

Financial Performance

Michigan Technological University had total expenditures of $229.8 million in 2012-2013 of which $78.2 million was accounted for by tuition and fees.

Strategy

The university is focusing on expanding research service-learning and international opportunities for studentsstrengthening existing programs and developing new offerings in emerging interdisciplinary areas.

Company Background

Michigan Technological University was founded in 1885 as the Michigan Mining School.

EXECUTIVES

Vice President, Josh Loukus
Assistant Vice President, Eric Halonen
Assistant Vice President Student Life, Beth Lunde
Associate Vice President for Enrollment Marketing and Communication, John (Jack) Lehman
Vice President, Bryan Suits
Department Chair, Sean Kirkpatrick
Vice President, Karl Ahlem
Director Of Admissions, Allison Carter
Vice President, Devan Faust
Vice President, Morgan Davis
Vice President, Josh Socha
Vice President Advancement, Karla Aho
Vice President, Mariah Maggio
Vice President Communications, Chris Didur
Vice President Operations, Sean Butts
Vice President Operations, Jared Julien
Vice President, Helene Provost
Vice President, Nick Gravlin
Vice President, Dan Freiberg
Vice President Alumni Relations, Rand Lindner
Vice President, Michael Tiry
Department Chair Kinesiology And Integrative Physiology, Jason Carter
Vice President Research and Dean of Graduate School, David (Dave) DReed
Vice President of Administration Office, Gina Sayen
Second Vice President, Kathy Halvorsen
Secretary, Martin J Thompson
Vice Chair Board Of Control, Russell A Gronevelt
Secretary, Kyle Sutela
Treasurer, Magdalina Hildebrandt
Treasurer, Lynn Artman
Secretary, Kevin Halagan
Secretary, Karen Kangas
Treasurer, Roland Scott
Treasurer, Joel Mancewicz
Secretary, Lisa Fernstrum
Treasurer, Benjamin Mitchell
Secretary, Cherilynn Frost
Harc Chief Senior Operator And Secretary, Oliver Stocker
Board Member, Whitney Petersen
Secretary, Kathy Wollan
Secretary, Mary Rohrer
Board Member, Todd Schramke
Secretary, Nicole Kirch
Treasurer, Ryan Boivin
Vice President Governmental Relations and Secretary, Dale Tahtinen
Assistant Treasurer, Karen Wallace
Secretary, Joe Fedie
Auditors: REHMANN ROBSON LLC TRAVERSE

LOCATIONS

HQ: MICHIGAN TECHNOLOGICAL UNIVERSITY
1400 TOWNSEND DR, HOUGHTON, MI 499311200
Phone: 906 487-1885
Web: WWW.MTU.EDU

HISTORICAL FINANCIALS
Company Type: Private

Income Statement
FYE: June 30

	REVENUE ($ mil.)	NET INCOME ($ mil.)	NET PROFIT MARGIN	EMPLOYEES
06/13	155	3	1.9%	1,939
06/11	147	(0)	—	—
06/07	120	7	6.5%	—
06/06	104	0	—	—
Annual Growth	5.9%	—	—	—

2013 Year-End Financials
Return on assets: 3.1%   Cash ($ mil.): 7
Return on equity: 1.9%
Current ratio: 1.20

MIDDLE TENNESSEE STATE UNIVERSITY

Middle Tennessee State University (MTSU) founded in 1911 as a school for teacher training offers bachelor's and master's degrees through its eight university colleges. The educational institution boasts basic and applied sciences business education and behavioral science honors liberal arts mass communication and graduate studies. The school bestows master's degrees in eight areas including business and education. MTSU also confers a Specialist in Education degree and doctorate degrees. It has an enrollment of more than 25000 students. MTSU is part of the State University and Community College System of Tennessee.

Geographic Reach

With its campus in Murfreesboro Tennessee Middle Tennessee State University is the oldest and largest public university in Middle Tennessee with more than 500 acres.

Strategy

To expand the types of degrees it confers MTSU in recent years has added to its doctoral programs. Besides a doctorate in Philosophy it now offers a doctorate in Computational Science Molecular Biosciences and Math & Science Education.

Financial Performance

Revenue increased 7% in fiscal 2012 as compared to 2011 due to rising tuition and fees thanks to a nearly 10% fee increase for the 2011-2012 academic year as well as an increase in grants and contracts. Net income dropped by 85% however during the same reporting period attributable to rising operating expenses due to the completion of building projects and routine expenses. It also logged a decline in non-operating revenues and expenses attributable to lower capital appropriation.

Operations

Notable alumni include Nobel Laureate James Buchanan (class of '40) and the late Senator Albert Gore Sr. (class of '32).

EXECUTIVES

Associate Vice President for Information Technology, Tom Wallace
Administrative Coordinator Office of the Vice President, Tara Hollins
Vice President Marketing and Communications, Andrew (Andy) Oppmann
Assistant Vice President Human Resource Services, Kathy I Musselman
Campus Architect Assistantvice President Campus Planning, Patti Miller

Department Chair, Maria Bachman
Secretary 3 Assoc Vice President Marketing Communications, Tara Wann
Secretary 3 Biology, Virginia (Ginny) McKnight
Secretary 2 Student Support Services, Sherry House
Secretary 2 Housing Administration, Cynthia Phiffer
Secretary 3 Management and Marketing Faculty Staff, Judy Smith
Secretary 1 University Studies, Rhonda Drake
Secretary Infromation Technology, Eileen Chalmers

LOCATIONS

HQ: MIDDLE TENNESSEE STATE UNIVERSITY
1301 E MAIN ST, MURFREESBORO, TN 371320002
Phone: 615 898-2300
Web: WWW.CATALOG.MTSU.EDU

PRODUCTS/OPERATIONS

Selected Colleges
Basic and Applied Sciences
Behavioral and Health Sciences
Business
Education
Graduate Studies
University College
Liberal Arts
Mass Communication
University Honors

HISTORICAL FINANCIALS
Company Type: Private

Income Statement
FYE: June 30

	REVENUE ($ mil.)	NET INCOME ($ mil.)	NET PROFIT MARGIN	EMPLOYEES
06/13	190	46	24.6%	2,610
06/12	218	18	8.4%	—
06/06	5	0	—	—
06/05	5	0	—	—
Annual Growth	54.9%	—	—	—

2013 Year-End Financials
Return on assets: 2.1%   Cash ($ mil.): 65
Return on equity: 24.6%
Current ratio: 1.60

MIDDLESEX HOSPITAL

Auditors: KPMG LLP BOSTON MA

LOCATIONS

HQ: MIDDLESEX HOSPITAL
28 CRESCENT ST, MIDDLETOWN, CT 064573650
Phone: 860 358-6000
Web: WWW.MIDDLESEXHOSPITAL.ORG

HISTORICAL FINANCIALS
Company Type: Private

Income Statement
FYE: September 30

	REVENUE ($ mil.)	NET INCOME ($ mil.)	NET PROFIT MARGIN	EMPLOYEES
09/13	358	17	4.8%	2,632
09/09	327	17	5.5%	—
Annual Growth	2.3%	(1.2%)	—	—

2013 Year-End Financials
Return on assets: 4.7%   Cash ($ mil.): 39
Return on equity: 4.8%
Current ratio: 1.40

MIDMICHIGAN HEALTH

LOCATIONS

HQ: MIDMICHIGAN HEALTH
4000 WELLNESS DR, MIDLAND, MI 486702000
Phone: 989 839-3000
Web: WWW.MIDMICHIGAN.ORG

HISTORICAL FINANCIALS

Company Type: Private

Income Statement

FYE: December 31

	REVENUE ($ mil.)	NET INCOME ($ mil.)	NET PROFIT MARGIN	EMPLOYEES
12/14*	308	(17)	—	6,500
06/14	578	58	10.1%	—
06/13	569	46	8.1%	—
03/13	430	0	—	—
Annual Growth	(15.4%)	—	—	—

*Fiscal year change

2014 Year-End Financials

Return on assets: 7.9%   Cash ($ mil.): 11
Return on equity: (-5.8%)
Current ratio: 1.20

MIDMICHIGAN MEDICAL CENTER-MIDLAND

Auditors: ANDREWS HOOPER PAVLIK PLC SAG

LOCATIONS

HQ: MIDMICHIGAN MEDICAL CENTER-MIDLAND
4000 WELLNESS DR, MIDLAND, MI 486702000
Phone: 989 631-6030
Web: WWW.MIDMICHIGAN.ORG

HISTORICAL FINANCIALS

Company Type: Private

Income Statement

FYE: June 30

	REVENUE ($ mil.)	NET INCOME ($ mil.)	NET PROFIT MARGIN	EMPLOYEES
06/13	351	21	6.1%	1,404
06/09	281	(25)	—	—
06/08	294	32	10.9%	—
Annual Growth	3.6%	(7.8%)	—	—

2013 Year-End Financials

Return on assets: 6.8%   Cash ($ mil.): 1
Return on equity: 6.1%
Current ratio: 0.30

MIDWEST ENERGY INC.

Some rural residents of the Sunflower State rely on Midwest Energy for their power and gas needs. The multi-utility serves approximately 48000 electricity customers and 42000 natural gas customers in central and western Kansas. It also has some power generation operations; it purchases most of its electric supply from wholesale marketers. The company's Midwest United Energy subsidiary is a competitive natural gas supplier in four states and its WestLand Energy unit sells propane to Kansas consumers. Midwest Energy has seen its power sales grow by 23% since 2006 and its natural gas sales by 17%.

A strong advocate of green energy as a way to cut carbon emissions comply with regulations and conserve energy Midwest Energy got 9% of its power from wind-generated sources in 2011. It also offers its customers How$mart program which allows residents to pay for energy-saving projects with no upfront costs through utility bills.

Investing heavily infrastructure both to keep up with demand and to replace aging systems in 2011 the company invested more than $26 million in electric construction and about $3 million in gas construction.

Midwest Energy reported a 14% jump in revenues in 2011 led by higher rates and very hot summer which increased power demand. Its net margin went up 11% thanks to the higher revenues a drop in per-capita gas costs (due to lower gas prices) and lower interest expenses.

The Central Kansas Electric Cooperative was formed in 1939 to provide electric service to customers in the rural counties surrounding Great Bend Kansas. Midwest Energy was formed in 1981 when the Central Kansas Electric Cooperative acquired investor-owned Central Kansas Power.

EXECUTIVES

Vice President Customer Service, Pat Parke
Vice President Information Technology, Tim Flax
Vice President Of Operations Technical Support, Lynn Horner
Vice President, Phil Goodell
Auditors: BKD LLP OKLAHOMA OK

LOCATIONS

HQ: MIDWEST ENERGY INC.
1330 CANTERBURY DR, HAYS, KS 676012708
Phone: 785 625-3437
Web: WWW.MWENERGY.COM

COMPETITORS

AES	Great Plains Energy
Black Hills	Westar Energy
Edison International	

HISTORICAL FINANCIALS

Company Type: Private

Income Statement

FYE: December 31

	REVENUE ($ mil.)	NET INCOME ($ mil.)	NET PROFIT MARGIN	EMPLOYEES
12/13	202	14	7.1%	274
12/12	197	16	8.4%	—
12/11	197	14	7.5%	—
12/10	176	0	—	—
Annual Growth	4.7%	—	—	—

2013 Year-End Financials

Return on assets: 6.9%   Cash ($ mil.): —
Return on equity: 7.1%
Current ratio: —

MILES HEALTH CARE INC

Miles Health Care provides acute and specialty health care service to the residents of Maine's Lincoln County. The not-for-profit company operates Miles Memorial Hospital –known as LincolnHealth Miles Campus –a rural medical center with about 40 beds and has emergency intensive care surgery and birthing departments. In addition Miles Health Care operates outpatient and specialty practice clinics physician practice offices and home health rehabilitation and hospice programs. It also provides long-term senior care through its nursing assisted and independent living facilities. Miles Health Care is a member of Lincoln County Healthcare (LincolnHealth) which is part of the MaineHealth network.

Change in Company Type

In 2013 parent MaineHealth combined two of its hospitals –Miles Memorial Hospital and St. Andrews Hospital –to form the two-campus LincolnHealth organization. The merger aimed to reduce operating expenses by more than $6 million annually as well as a more than $5 million increase revenue due to the combined organization's new status as a critical access hospital (which leads to higher reimbursements from Medicare and Medicaid plans). The increased earnings will allow the LincolnHealth campuses to reduce the price of services including x-rays laboratory tests and minor surgeries and procedures.

Geographic Reach

The LincolnHealth Miles Campus is located in Lincoln County Maine in the town of Damariscotta (which is north of Portland). The LincolnHealth St. Andrews Campus is located in Boothbay Harbor.

Operations

In addition to the two main hospital campuses LincolnHealth includes physician practices operated by the Lincoln Medical Partners as well as family care and urgent care centers. It also continues to operate nursing home health hospice and assisted-living organizations.

Strategy

Both the Miles and St. Andrews medical centers began using electronic health record (EHR) systems in 2010 which allows doctors to access a patient's past medical and diagnostic experiences to make the best decisions on current treatment plans and avoid duplication. Such EHR systems are part of an initiative to lower the cost of medical care in the US.

Company Background

Miles Health Care was established in 1941. Miles has historically been governed by a board of trustees (the Lincoln County Healthcare Board of Trustees) that also oversee the nearby St. Andrews Hospital; as an independently governed member of MaineHealth Miles has received planning consulting capital and group purchasing benefits. In 2013 St. Andrews Hospital and Miles Memorial Hospital were officially merged to serve as dual campuses of the single LincolnHealth hospital.

EXECUTIVES

Director of Pharmacy Vice President Of Pharmacy Services, Karen Philbrick
Medical Director, Timothy (Tim) Fox

LOCATIONS

HQ: MILES HEALTH CARE INC
35 MILES ST, DAMARISCOTTA, ME 045434047
Phone: 207 563-1234
Web: WWW.MILESHEALTHCARE.ORG

PRODUCTS/OPERATIONS

Selected Centers and Services

Chase Point Adult Day Services
Chase Point Assisted Living
Cove' s Edge
Emergency Services
Family Support Services
General Surgery
Internal Medicine
Mammography

Miles & St. Andrews Home Health & Hospice
Miles Family Medicine
MMH BabyNet
Obstetrics
Orthopedic Services
Pediatric Services
Schooner Cove
Senior Services
Waldoboro Family Medicine
Wellness and Rehabilitation
Wiscasset Family Medicine
Women' s Services

COMPETITORS

Eastern Maine
  Healthcare Systems
MaineGeneral Health
Mercy Health System of
  Maine

Parkview Hospital
St. Joseph Healthcare

HISTORICAL FINANCIALS
Company Type: Private

Income Statement
FYE: September 30

	REVENUE ($ mil.)	NET INCOME ($ mil.)	NET PROFIT MARGIN	EMPLOYEES
09/09	1,042	12	1.2%	800
09/08	14	0	3.9%	—
09/06	58	3	5.9%	—
09/05	52	0	—	—
Annual Growth	111.6%	—	—	—

2009 Year-End Financials
Return on assets: —
Return on equity: 1.2%
Current ratio: 0.70

Cash ($ mil.): —

MILLER ELECTRIC COMPANY

Miller Electric Company flips the switch for projects primarily in the Southeast. The Florida-based electrical contractor provides services including construction installation renovation and maintenance of electrical systems. The company serves many industries including the communications construction health care and transportation segments. Outside of Florida the company has offices in Alabama Arkansas Georgia North Carolina Virginia Texas and Washington DC. Clients have included Anheuser Busch Bank of America Blue Cross and Blue Shield and the University of North Florida. Miller Electric was founded by Henry G. Miller in 1928.

Miller has found success by providing a myriad of installation services to the growing data center and Intelligent Transportation Systems (ITS) fields. ITS technologies are used to manage vehicle traffic and include intersection traffic signals dynamic message signs vehicle detection systems weather advisory systems and highway advisory radios. The company also installs the required power services and switching stations.

Most recently Miller also has diversified into the renewable energy market. In 2010 the company built a high tech solar project in Jacksonville that provides more than 12 megawatts of power for the city.

EXECUTIVES

Senior Vice President, Edward (Ed) Witt
Vice President, Ngoc Lai
Auditors: BISHOP & DRAPER JACKSONVILLE

LOCATIONS

HQ: MILLER ELECTRIC COMPANY
  2251 ROSSELLE ST, JACKSONVILLE, FL 322043125
Phone: 904 388-8000
Web: WWW.MECOJAX.COM

PRODUCTS/OPERATIONS

Selected Services
Access control
Audio/visual systems
Building Information Modeling (BIM)
Communications systems and services
Control systems
Electrical construction and repair
Fiber optic network installation
Fire protection systems
Maintenance Services
Network cabling installation and maintenance Specialty systems
Paging and intercom
Site lighting
UPS and generator installation and maintenance

COMPETITORS

Dycom
Edd Helms
Honshy Electric
Johnson Contractors

Megatran
Pike Corporation
Tri-City Electrical
  Contractors

HISTORICAL FINANCIALS
Company Type: Private

Income Statement
FYE: September 30

	REVENUE ($ mil.)	NET INCOME ($ mil.)	NET PROFIT MARGIN	EMPLOYEES
09/14	216	6	3.0%	691
09/13	204	2	1.3%	—
09/12	183	0	0.1%	—
09/11	183	0	—	—
Annual Growth	5.7%	—	—	—

2014 Year-End Financials
Return on assets: 11.3%
Return on equity: 3.0%
Current ratio: 1.60

Cash ($ mil.): 4

MILTON HERSHEY SCHOOL & SCHOOL TRUST

Auditors: GRANT THORNTON LLP PHILADELPH

LOCATIONS

HQ: MILTON HERSHEY SCHOOL & SCHOOL TRUST
  711 CREST LN, HERSHEY, PA 170338903
Phone: 717 520-1100

HISTORICAL FINANCIALS
Company Type: Private

Income Statement
FYE: July 31

	REVENUE ($ mil.)	NET INCOME ($ mil.)	NET PROFIT MARGIN	EMPLOYEES
07/12	386	180	46.7%	—
07/10	211	3	1.6%	—
Annual Growth	35.1%	634.4%	—	—

2012 Year-End Financials
Return on assets: —
Return on equity: 46.7%
Current ratio: —

Cash ($ mil.): 89

MILWAUKEE PUBLIC SCHOOLS

Auditors: BAKER TILLY VIRCHOW KRAUSE LL

LOCATIONS

HQ: MILWAUKEE PUBLIC SCHOOLS
  5225 W VLIET ST, MILWAUKEE, WI 532082698
Phone: 414 475-8345
Web: WWW.MPSFOUNDATION.NET

HISTORICAL FINANCIALS
Company Type: Private

Income Statement
FYE: June 30

	REVENUE ($ mil.)	NET INCOME ($ mil.)	NET PROFIT MARGIN	EMPLOYEES
06/11	1,292	(2)	—	14,154
06/09	1,237	(5)	—	—
06/05	1,122	(19)	—	—
06/04	0	0	—	—
Annual Growth	—	—	—	—

MINERS INCORPORATED

Miner's is a family-owned chain of about 30 grocery stores in Michigan North Dakota northern Minnesota and Wisconsin. Most of the company's stores fly the Super One Foods banner but there are a few under the U-Save Foods and Marketplace Foods names. Following the acquisition of seven Jubilee and Festival Foods stores in Minnesota from Plaza Holding Co. Miner's converted the stores to its Super One Foods banner most of which are located in Minnesota. Miner's also has a wholesale grocery operation in Duluth. Miner's was founded by Anton and Ida Miner who started out selling groceries out of their tavern in Grand Rapids Michigan in the 1930s. In 1943 they built the family's first store Miner's Market.

Geographic Reach
Minnesota is the regional grocery chain's largest market home to 21 of its 31 stores. Wisconsin and Michigan are each home to about five locations. The grocery chain has a single store North Dakota.

Financial Performance
Miner's rang up an estimated $437 million in sales in fiscal 2013 (ended June).

Strategy
Miner's takes a measured approach to growth combining occasional acquisitions with organic growth. Its newest location is a 59000-square-foot Super One Foods store slated to open in 2014 in Superior Wisconsin.

Mergers and Acquisitions
In May 2011 Miner's upped its store count with the acquisition of four family-owned Paulson's Super Valu grocery stores in northern Minnesota and Wisconsin.

Prevented by Minnesota law from selling alcohol in grocery stores the company recently bought two liquor stores in Cloquet and Duluth.

Ownership

Miner's is family owned and operated. Jim Miner Jr. is the company's CEO.

EXECUTIVES

Vice President Operations, Bob Halvorson
Vice President, Jim Miner
Auditors: MCGLADREY LLP DULUTH MINNESO

LOCATIONS

HQ: MINERS INCORPORATED
5065 MILLER TRUNK HWY, HERMANTOWN, MN 558111442
Phone: 218 729-5882
Web: WWW.SUPERONEFOODS.COM

2014 Stores

	No.
Minnesota	21
Michigan	5
Wisconsin	4
North Dakota	1
Total	**31**

PRODUCTS/OPERATIONS

2014 Stores

	No.
Super One Foods	27
U-Save Foods	2
Country Market	1
Marketplace Foods	1
Total	**31**

COMPETITORS

Cub Foods	Roundy's
IGA	SpartanNash
Kroger	Target Corporation
Meijer	Wal-Mart

HISTORICAL FINANCIALS

Company Type: Private

Income Statement

FYE: June 29

	REVENUE ($ mil.)	NET INCOME ($ mil.)	NET PROFIT MARGIN	EMPLOYEES
06/13	530	30	5.7%	2,300
06/12	501	31	6.3%	—
06/11	475	30	6.4%	—
06/10	463	0	—	—
Annual Growth	**4.6%**	—	—	—

2013 Year-End Financials

Return on assets: 3.6% Cash ($ mil.): 7
Return on equity: 5.7%
Current ratio: 0.30

MINNESOTA SOYBEAN PROCESSORS

LOCATIONS

HQ: MINNESOTA SOYBEAN PROCESSORS
121 ZEH AVE, BREWSTER, MN 561193009
Phone: 507 842-6677
Web: WWW.MNSOY.COM

HISTORICAL FINANCIALS

Company Type: Private

Income Statement

FYE: August 31

	REVENUE ($ mil.)	NET INCOME ($ mil.)	NET PROFIT MARGIN	EMPLOYEES
08/08	515	2	0.4%	80
08/05	207	(5)	—	—
08/04*	199	(2)	—	—
12/02	159	0	—	—
Annual Growth	**21.6%**			

*Fiscal year change

2008 Year-End Financials

Return on assets: 0.4% Cash ($ mil.): —
Return on equity: 0.4%
Current ratio: 0.80

MISSION HOSPITAL INC.

Its mission is clear and bold: Improve the health of all in western North Carolina. Mission Hospital is a 760-bed regional referral center serving the western quarter of North Carolina and portions of adjoining states. A not-for-profit community hospital system Mission is located in Asheville on two adjoining campuses: Memorial and St. Joseph's. It provides tertiary-level services in neurosciences cardiac care trauma care surgery pediatric medicine and women's services and has a medical staff of more than 540. It also includes the Mission Children's Hospital. Mission Hospitals is part of the Mission Health System which is made up of Blue Ridge Regional Hospital McDowell Hospital and other facilities.

Geographic Reach

The hospital system serves patients in western North Carolina.

Sales and Marketing

In 2014 Medicare accounted for 40% of Mission Hospital's net patient service revenue; Medicaid accounted for 28% and self-pay and other third-party payors accounted for 14% and 18% respectively.

Financial Performance

Revenue increased 6% to $119 million in 2014 on higher net patient service earnings. Those gains plus higher investment returns led to a 12% increase in net income to $1.2 million.

After posting an operating cash outflow in 2013 Mission Hospital had a cash inflow of $0.9 million in 2014 as less cash was used towards net patient accounts receivable.

Strategy

Mission Hospital has been actively expanding and modernizing its facilities in recent years. It built a surgery registration and waiting area to ease patient comfort as they wait to be seen at the Memorial Campus. It also opened a four-story facility to provide more surgery suites and patient beds for Mission Hospital. In order to increase patient satisfaction the hospital opened a new surgery registration and waiting area at its Memorial Campus.

Mission Hospital places great focus on genetic medicine. It has an entire department dedicated to the study of genetics genetic therapy and the study of fetal alcohol spectrum disorders.

Mission Health partnered with Western Carolina University to provide a graduate certification program in Healthcare Innovation Management. The program which began in 2013 is a component of Mission Health's budding Center for Innovation established to foster a spirit of advancement in healthcare throughout western North Carolina. The program consists of four courses over a period of 21 months and is open to all Mission Health employees. Students who complete the program which is fully funded by Mission Health will earn credit towards bachelor's and master's degrees.

Company Background

Mission Hospital was formed in 1996 from the partnership (and eventual merger) of Memorial and St. Joseph's hospitals.

EXECUTIVES

Senior Vice President For Patient Care Services, Kathy Guyette
Senior Vice President General Counsel, Ann Young
Director Of Pharmacy, Elizabeth Michalet
Senior Vice President Of Operations, Sonya Greck
Vice President Human Resources, Maria Roloff
Vice President Hr Mission Hospital & System Talent Mgmt, Sheila Meadows
Vice President Performance Improvement, Michael Creech
Vice President Chief Nursing Officer, Kathleen Culhane Guyette
Vice President Heart Services, Karen Lemieux

LOCATIONS

HQ: MISSION HOSPITAL INC.
509 BILTMORE AVE, ASHEVILLE, NC 288014601
Phone: 828 213-1111
Web: WWW.MISSIONHOSPITALS.ORG

PRODUCTS/OPERATIONS

Surgical Services
General Surgery
Minimally Invasive Surgery
Outpatient Surgery
Prepare for Surgery
Robotic Surgery
Surgery at Mission Hospital
Surgery Guide
Programs of Service
Endoscopy
Genetics
Integrative Healthcare
Mother and Baby
Outpatient Care Centers
Sleep Center
Urology
Weight Management Center
Wound Healing and Hyperbarics
Support Services
Chronic Medical Conditions
Long-Term Acute Care
Laboratory
Pastoral Care Services
Pharmacy
Psychiatric Services
Radiology (Imaging) Services
Rehabilitation Services
Research Institute
Respiratory Therapy
Senior Services and Geriatrics

COMPETITORS

Blue Ridge HealthCare
CaroMont
Carolinas HealthCare System
Duke University Health System
Haywood Regional
Presbyterian Healthcare
UNC Hospitals
Wake Forest University Baptist Medical Center

HISTORICAL FINANCIALS
Company Type: Private

Income Statement
FYE: September 30

	REVENUE ($ mil.)	NET INCOME ($ mil.)	NET PROFIT MARGIN	EMPLOYEES
09/13	942	71	7.6%	5,400
09/12	861	86	10.0%	—
09/06*	0	0	—	—
12/05	500	0	—	—
Annual Growth	8.2%	—	—	—

*Fiscal year change

2013 Year-End Financials
Return on assets: 1.8%
Return on equity: 7.6%
Current ratio: 1.50
Cash ($ mil.): —

MISSION HOSPITAL REGIONAL MEDICAL CENTER INC

Auditors: ERNST & YOUNG US LLP IRVINE

LOCATIONS
HQ: MISSION HOSPITAL REGIONAL MEDICAL CENTER INC
27700 MEDICAL CENTER RD, MISSION VIEJO, CA 926916426
Phone: 949 364-1400
Web: WWW.MISSION4HEALTH.COM

HISTORICAL FINANCIALS
Company Type: Private

Income Statement
FYE: June 30

	REVENUE ($ mil.)	NET INCOME ($ mil.)	NET PROFIT MARGIN	EMPLOYEES
06/10	500	50	10.1%	2,600
06/09	355	12	3.5%	—
06/08	829	0	0.0%	—
Annual Growth	(22.3%)	5451.5%	—	—

2010 Year-End Financials
Return on assets: —
Return on equity: 10.1%
Current ratio: 0.50
Cash ($ mil.): 66

MISSISSIPPI COUNTY ELECTRIC COOPERATIVE INC.

Like much of the rest of the state of Arkansas people in Mississippi County get their electricity from a cooperative. Mississippi County Electric Cooperative (MCEC) serves customers in the northeast corner of Arkansas about 60 miles north of Memphis. The area is home to two steel mills owned by Nucor Corporation that are powered by MCEC power; most customers are industrial or agricultural. The coop also offers Internet service via rural satellite broadband provider WildBlue and provides its customers with energy audits and information on saving energy. It is a member of Touchstone Energy a national alliance of electric cooperatives in nearly 40 states. MCEC was formed in 1938.

EXECUTIVES
President and CEO, Larry Hellums
SVP Cooperative Services, Pat O'Neal
VP Finance and Accounting, Mike Parrish
COO, Brad Harrison
Billing and Office Supervisor, Annette Parish
Operations Supervisor, Keeley Wheeler
Construction Supervisor, Tommy Jones
Chairman, Robert Davis
Secretary Treasurer, Steve West
Vice Chairman, Neil Burge

LOCATIONS
HQ: MISSISSIPPI COUNTY ELECTRIC COOPERATIVE INC.
510 N BROADWAY ST, BLYTHEVILLE, AR 723152732
Phone: 870 763-4563
Web: WWW.MCECI.COM

HISTORICAL FINANCIALS
Company Type: Private

Income Statement
FYE: December 31

	REVENUE ($ mil.)	NET INCOME ($ mil.)	NET PROFIT MARGIN	EMPLOYEES
12/13	157	0	0.2%	16
12/09	88	2	2.4%	—
12/08	150	4	3.1%	—
12/07	141	0	—	—
Annual Growth	1.7%			

2013 Year-End Financials
Return on assets: 8.6%
Return on equity: 0.2%
Current ratio: 1.40
Cash ($ mil.): 4

MISSOURI BAPTIST MEDICAL CENTER

LOCATIONS
HQ: MISSOURI BAPTIST MEDICAL CENTER
3015 N BALLAS RD, SAINT LOUIS, MO 631312374
Phone: 314 996-5000
Web: WWW.MISSOURIBAPTIST.ORG

HISTORICAL FINANCIALS
Company Type: Private

Income Statement
FYE: December 31

	REVENUE ($ mil.)	NET INCOME ($ mil.)	NET PROFIT MARGIN	EMPLOYEES
12/12	459	24	5.3%	1,670
12/08	388	(63)	—	—
Annual Growth	4.3%			

2012 Year-End Financials
Return on assets: 1.0%
Return on equity: 5.3%
Current ratio: 2.40
Cash ($ mil.): 3

MISSOURI STATE UNIVERSITY

When Missouri students say "show me" Missouri State University happily obliges. It is the state's second-largest university (after University of Missouri) with an enrollment of 23800 students. The school offers about 85 undergraduate majors 133 undergraduate minors and 50 graduate majors including 14 masters 3 doctoral degrees (audiology physical therapy and nurse practitioner) and one specialist degree. The university' coursework includes accounting biology criminology and physical geography. Missouri State awarded almost 4000 degrees in 2013. It also hosted some 16 NCAA Division One sports teams that year.

Geographic Reach

In addition to its main campus in Springfield the university has campuses in Mountain Grove and West Plains. Missouri State also operates various other special facilities including the Darr Agricultural Center (southwest Springfield) the Jordan Valley Innovation Center (downtown Springfield) the Bull Shoals Field Station near Forsyth Baker's Acres and Observatory near Marshfield and the Missouri State University Graduate Center in Joplin. The university also has a branch campus at Liaoning Normal University in Dalian China.

Operations

The university has six Academic colleges one School of Agriculture and one Graduate College. It has some 4000 faculty and staff members. The student-to-faculty ratio is approximately 19:1. Missouri State enrolls students from all 50 US states and 85 foreign countries. The Extended Campus provides learning opportunities through telecourses Internet-based instruction and through BearNet an interactive video network.

Financial Performance

Missouri State's revenues increased by 2% to $288 million in 2012 due to higher tuition and fees and better returns from sales and services and auxiliary enterprises. Organic growth helped to lift revenues every year between 2009 and 2012.

However net income dropped by 55% in 2012 due to a decline in non-operating revenues caused by a drop in state appropriations federal grants and contracts and investment income. The following year grants rose 6% to $20 million.

Strategy

The university's "Fulfilling Our Promise" initiative is centered around improving student learning expanding inclusive efforts and broadening the impact it has on the community and state. Among its goals are strengthening its undergraduate and graduate programs (and enroll more students) creating a more diverse student body and workforce and become an employer of choice. In 2013 the university opened the student-funded Foster Family Recreation Center for fitness and wellness. Also that year it introduced the Robert W. Plaster Center for Free Enterprise and Business Development which hosts programs including the cooperative engineering program shared with Missouri University of Science and Technology. Missouri State has also renovated numerous campus facilities.

Company Background

The school was founded in 1905 as the Fourth District Normal School a teacher training institution; it changed its name to Missouri State University 100 years later.

EXECUTIVES
Associate Vice President For International Programs, Steve Robinette

Department Head, Robert (Bob) Willenbrink
Vice President Adminstrative Info Services, KEN MCLURE
Vice President Of Communications, Rachel Elder
Associate Vice President for Academic Affairs, Kathy J Pulley
Vice President Marketing and Communications, Suzanne Shaw
Division President, Neosha Mackey
Department Head, Jason Jolley
Vice President Administrative Services and Information Services, Kenneth (Ken) McClure
Vice President Diversity inclusion, Kenneth (Ken) Coopwood
Vice President, Tessa Friedman
Assistant Vice President Multicultural Services, Juan Meraz
Department Head, Ardeshir J Dalal
Department Head, Ken Vollmar
Vice President University Advancement, Brent Dunn
Vice President Health System Facilities, Robert (Bob) Norton
Vice President of Operations, Andrea Green
Vice President of Recruitment, Ellie Edwards
Executive Board Member, George Wolf
Board Member, Marvin Prosono
Secretary, Pat Smith
Board Member, Walt Nelson
Auditors: BKD LLP SPRINGFIELD MO

LOCATIONS

HQ: MISSOURI STATE UNIVERSITY
901 S NATIONAL AVE, SPRINGFIELD, MO 658970001
Phone: 417 836-5000
Web: WWW.MISSOURISTATEBEARS.COM

HISTORICAL FINANCIALS
Company Type: Private

Income Statement
FYE: June 30

	REVENUE ($ mil.)	NET INCOME ($ mil.)	NET PROFIT MARGIN	EMPLOYEES
06/13	196	20	10.2%	2,066
06/12	201	16	8.4%	—
06/11	190	33	17.7%	—
06/10	189	0	—	—
Annual Growth	1.3%	—	—	—

2013 Year-End Financials
Return on assets: 5.1%   Cash ($ mil.): 70
Return on equity: 10.2%
Current ratio: 1.90

MISSOURI VALLEY PETROLEUM INC.

Auditors: EIDEBAILLY LLP BISMARCK NORT

LOCATIONS

HQ: MISSOURI VALLEY PETROLEUM INC.
1722 MANDAN AVE, MANDAN, ND 585542203
Phone: 701 663-5091
Web: WWW.MVPINC.NET

HISTORICAL FINANCIALS
Company Type: Private

Income Statement
FYE: December 31

	REVENUE ($ mil.)	NET INCOME ($ mil.)	NET PROFIT MARGIN	EMPLOYEES
12/13	320	1	0.3%	100
12/12	306	1	0.6%	—
Annual Growth	4.6%	(44.1%)		

2013 Year-End Financials
Return on assets: 4.1%   Cash ($ mil.): —
Return on equity: 0.3%
Current ratio: 0.80

MMR CONSTRUCTORS INC.

Auditors: MADDOX & ASSOCIATES APC CPAS

LOCATIONS

HQ: MMR CONSTRUCTORS INC.
15961 AIRLINE HWY, BATON ROUGE, LA 708177412
Phone: 225 756-5090
Web: WWW.MMRGRP.COM

HISTORICAL FINANCIALS
Company Type: Private

Income Statement
FYE: December 31

	REVENUE ($ mil.)	NET INCOME ($ mil.)	NET PROFIT MARGIN	EMPLOYEES
12/13	658	22	3.4%	2,500
12/12	483	20	4.3%	—
12/11	233	12	5.1%	—
12/01	0	0	—	—
Annual Growth	—	—	—	—

2013 Year-End Financials
Return on assets: 3.8%   Cash ($ mil.): 2
Return on equity: 3.4%
Current ratio: 2.10

MMR GROUP INC.

That murmur you hear could be the gentle hum of a properly functioning power system. MMG Group provides electrical and instrumentation construction maintenance management and technical services for clients in the oil and gas manufacturing chemical and power generation industries around the world. It also offers services in offshore marine and platform environments. Its Power Solutions division constructs onsite power-generation systems in industrial plants and other facilities. The group primarily operates in the Gulf of New Mexico. Founded in 1990 MMG is 100% management owned and has served such clients as Chevron Shell BP Merck Air Liquide DuPont and 3M.

OperationsMMR Group's provides four main services: electrical and instrumentation contracting safety services panel fabrication and communications.MMR's electrical and instrumentation contractors work on projects throughout the US and overseas. To ensure its projects are completed on time and within budget its personnel has support and management control systems and emphasizes planning scheduling progress tracking and labor analysis.The MMR Offshore Safety Services division specializes in disaster prevention and safety helping with navigation fire and gas detection suppression products paging and alarm systems level one cathodic protection inspections and other related services.For panel fabrication services MMR stages tests and designs control systems that best fit client needs. The MMR ProCom division is in charge of pre-commissioning commissioning and start-Up activities for both MMR Group construction projects and for outside clients interested in turning their facilities construction into a safe and reliable operation seamlessly. Geographic Reach-MMR operates out of some 20 offices spread across North and South America with most of its offices in Texas Louisiana and California. The company works on projects all over the world with foreign affiliate offices in Calgary Canada; Cartagena Colombia; Puerto la Cruz Venezuela; and Port of Spain Trinidad & Tobago.Sales and Marketing-MMR serves a variety of markets including: alternative energy exploration and production chemical and petrochemical industrial and manufacturing oil and gas power generation and waste and water treatment among others. Some of the company's panel fabrication clients have included Shell Pipeline Chevron Pipeline Enbridge Pipeline AGI Services Cimitation Engineering ExxonMobil Keystone Engineering W.S. Nelson Engineering and Entergy among others.Depending on the project and client's preference MMR operates on all types of fixed-price and cost-plus contracts.StrategyThe company continues to expand its operations to accommodate more projects. In 2014 the company built a 19-office administration building along with a 6000 square-foot warehouse facility to support the influx of new projects going on in the Golden Triangle area between Beaumont TX and Lake Charles LA.

EXECUTIVES

Vice President Manager Of Estimating, Darryl Clark
Auditors: MADDOX & ASSOCIATES APC BATO

LOCATIONS

HQ: MMR GROUP INC.
15961 AIRLINE HWY, BATON ROUGE, LA 708177412
Phone: 225 756-5090
Web: WWW.MMRGRP.COM

PRODUCTS/OPERATIONS

Selected Services
Instrumentation
  Air supply installation
  Control room equipment installation
  Instrument installation
  Process leads
  Panel fabrication
  Signal wiring
Electrical
  Controls
  Electrical equipment setting
  Grounding
  Lighting
  Power distribution
Technical
  Calibration
  Commissioning
  Detail design
  High voltage testing
  Instrument procurement
  Loop check
  Maintenance
  Start up assistance
  System analysis

Selected Divisions
MMR Constructors
MMR International
MMR Power Solutions
MMR Offshore Services
MMR Technical Services
Southwestern Power Group

COMPETITORS

Alberici	MYR Group
EMCOR	Matrix Service
Fisk Electric	Turner Industries
Industrial Specialty	
Contractors	

HISTORICAL FINANCIALS
Company Type: Private

Income Statement FYE: December 31

	REVENUE ($ mil.)	NET INCOME ($ mil.)	NET PROFIT MARGIN	EMPLOYEES
12/13	681	32	4.8%	2,500
12/12	501	19	3.9%	—
12/11	254	11	4.4%	—
12/10	0	0	—	—
Annual Growth	—	—	—	—

2013 Year-End Financials
Return on assets: 3.8%   Cash ($ mil.): 2
Return on equity: 4.8%
Current ratio: 2.10

MNP CORPORATION

If you are fascinated with fasteners then MNP will galvanize your senses. MNP manufactures a plethora of precision fasteners and cold formed components including screws rivets washers small stampings as well as screw machine parts. Its services range from plating to annealing flat-rolling pickling hot-dip galvanizing and coatings. General Fasteners Cadon Plating & Coatings Marathon Metals and Ohio Pickling & Processing are a few of MNP's affiliated companies that produce a medley of metal parts and jointly operate the GFC/MNP Engineering Center in Michigan. The company serves the automotive heavy truck military and industrial markets.

Geographic Reach

MNP is headquartered in Utica Michigan and operates throughout the company. It has 1220000 sq. ft. of space at its manufacturing warehousing and processing facilities. The company also has additional sourcing contacts in India Thailand Turkey Brazil Vietnam Malaysia Japan Israel and Europe.

Operations

MNP is considered a Tier One supplier to the Big Three automobile makers in Detroit and operates four production facilities within its Fastener Manufacturing division. The company has grown to encompass a dozen operating and support divisions and subsidiaries which provide steel and wire fabricating steel treating washer manufacture tool and die capabilities dip/spin coatings cold forming as well as engineering and design services.

Financial Performance

MNP reported $183 million in annual revenue for 2012 a 5% increase over 2011.

Strategy

MNP is counting on the prediction that fasteners for aerospace and construction (especially residential building) applications are expected to outpace standard fasteners. (It develops and manufactures fasteners for both applications.) The company's biggest competition comes from alternative fastening products such as industrial adhesives and clinching and welding. It also contends with falling raw material prices which cause fastener prices to decrease.

Company Background

MNP was founded in 1970 as Michigan Nut Products.

EXECUTIVES

Vice President Steel Services, Floyd Cushman
Vice President Quality, Chad Clifford
Vice President of Manufacturing and Distributi, Jan Klein
Auditors: UHY LLP FARMINGTON HILLS MIC

LOCATIONS

HQ: MNP CORPORATION
44225 UTICA RD, UTICA, MI 483175464
Phone: 586 254-1320
Web: WWW.MNP.COM

PRODUCTS/OPERATIONS

Selected Products and Services
Engineering and design
  Cold forming tooling
  Engineered product applications and solutions
  Alternative cam bolt assembly design
  Automated pre-assembly of fasteners and other cylindrical parts
  Bolt retainer
  Cold formed specials
  Isolator bolt
  Rotatable captured nut
  VTR bolt pre-located bolts for assembly
  Engineered stamping and fastener assemblies
  Joint design and problem solving
  Stamping tooling
Fastener and metal part coatings
  Organic coatings
  Phosphate based coatings
  Plating - mechanical and electroplated metals
Fastener and metal part heat treating
  Carburize
  Quench and temper
Male threaded fasteners
  Specialty engineered fasteners
  Standard fasteners
  Licenses
  Bolt Retainer
  Lo-Driv
  MAThread
  REMFORM
  Taptite
  Torx and Torx Plus
  VTR Bolt
Stampings
  Powder metal parts
  Small metal parts
  Washers
Steel sales and processing
  Rod and wire
Tooling and repair parts
  Machine repair

COMPETITORS

A. Raymond Tinnerman	MacLean-Fogg
AZZ Galvanizing	Metric & Multistandard
Services	Nucor
Ajax Metal Processing	Oneto Metal Products
Align Aerospace	Park-Ohio Holdings
Anixter Fasteners	PennEngineering
Chicago Rivet	Porteous Fastener
Federal Screw Works	Southco
Handy & Harman	TriMas
Illinois Tool Works	Valmont Industries
Kalamazoo Fabricating	Whitesell
LISI	Worthington Industries
Lawson Products	Wrth Group

HISTORICAL FINANCIALS
Company Type: Private

Income Statement FYE: November 30

	REVENUE ($ mil.)	NET INCOME ($ mil.)	NET PROFIT MARGIN	EMPLOYEES
11/13	181	13	7.3%	1,000
11/12	182	10	6.0%	—
11/11	173	8	4.7%	—
11/10	150	0	—	—
Annual Growth	6.5%	—	—	—

2013 Year-End Financials
Return on assets: 6.2%   Cash ($ mil.): —
Return on equity: 7.3%
Current ratio: 1.50

MOBILE INFIRMARY ASSOCIATION

LOCATIONS

HQ: MOBILE INFIRMARY ASSOCIATION
5 MOBILE INFIRMARY CIR, MOBILE, AL 366073513
Phone: 251 435-2400
Web: WWW.INFIRMARYHEALTH.ORG

HISTORICAL FINANCIALS
Company Type: Private

Income Statement FYE: March 31

	REVENUE ($ mil.)	NET INCOME ($ mil.)	NET PROFIT MARGIN	EMPLOYEES
03/13	411	27	6.6%	2,938
03/11	394	24	6.3%	—
03/10	351	12	3.5%	—
03/08	744	0	—	—
Annual Growth	(11.2%)	—	—	—

2013 Year-End Financials
Return on assets: 12.4%   Cash ($ mil.): 94
Return on equity: 6.6%
Current ratio: 2.50

MONMOUTH MEDICAL CENTER INC.

Monmouth Medical Center is a 530-bed tertiary care teaching hospital providing comprehensive health care to residents of central New Jersey. The not-for-profit medical center offers services ranging from orthopedics diagnostics and obstetric care to surgery dentistry and geriatric services. The medical center campus also includes a children's hospital a cancer center a neuroscience institute an outpatient care clinic and hospice and home health facilities. Monmouth Medical Center is a major teaching affiliate of the Drexel University College of Medicine in Philadelphia. The hospital is an affiliate of the Saint Barnabas Healthcare System.

Geographic Reach

Monmouth Medical Center is located on about 20 acres in Long Branch New Jersey near the Atlantic Ocean. The campus includes the main 16-wing hospital and and about 16 other buildings including resident physician dwellings a day care center a medical education and training facility and a Ronald McDonald House.

The hospital serves a territory consisting of Monmouth Ocean and Middlesex counties with a total of about one million residents. It has outpatient locations in Colts Neck Howell Long Branch Ocean Township and Shrewsbury.

Operations

Monmouth Medical Center handles 19000 inpatient admissions each year as well as 49000 emergency room visits. Its outpatient clinic handles some 126000 appointments annually. The hospital has 700 doctors representing 60 specialties on its staff.

Strategy

The hospital has conducted recent expansion projects including additions of new a new cancer center surgical suites and a family center. In 2013 it opened a new postpartum wing and newborn nursery as well as a larger neonatal ICU. Monmouth Medical Center also extended its pediatric and oncology programs by forming partnerships with other area hospitals in 2012.

Company Background

Monmouth Medical Center was founded in 1887. It has expanded over the years to provide a number of specialist services including high-tech offerings such as robotic surgery.

EXECUTIVES

Assistant Vice President, Sharon Holden
Vice President Quality Risk Management, Patricia Keating
Assistant Vice President Financial Services, James Alexander
Operational Vice President, Bill Arnold
Assistant Secretary, Denise Valentine
Auditors: WITHUMSMITHBROWN PC MORRISTOW

LOCATIONS

HQ: MONMOUTH MEDICAL CENTER INC.
300 2ND AVE, LONG BRANCH, NJ 077406395
Phone: 732 222-5200
Web: WWW.BARNABASHEALTH.ORG

PRODUCTS/OPERATIONS

Selected Centers and Services
Anesthesiology Services
Behavioral Health Network
Brain Tumor Center (David S. Zocchi)
The Breast Center (Jacqueline M. Wilentz Comprehensive)
Burn Center
Cancer Services
Cardiac Services
Cardiac Surgery
Children' s Hospital at Monmouth (Pediatrics)
Cleft Palate Center
Cord Blood Banking Program
Cosmetic Surgery
Cranmer Ambulatory Surgery Center
Critical Care Services
Diabetes Education - Center for Diabetes Education
Dental Medicine
Diagnostic Imaging Services
The Eisenberg Family Center
Emergency Services
Epilepsy Monitoring Program
Extracorporeal Membrane Oxygenation Program (ECMO)
The Gamma Knife Center
Geriatric Emergency Medicine (GEM) Unit
Geriatric Health Center
Head & Neck Surgery
Hernias Repair Institute for the Treatment of Complex
HIV/AIDS Program
Home Health Care
Home Infusion Care
Hospice
Hyperbaric Oxygen Therapy

Integrative Medicine (Center for)
Joint Replacement and Spine Center
Medical Records
Medical Alert/Lifeline
Medicine (Department of)
Minimally Invasive Surgery
Monmouth Family Health Center
Neonatal Intensive Care Unit (Regional Newborn Center)
Neuroscience Institute
Nutritional Counseling
Obstetrics/Gynecological Services
Occupational Medicine
Orthopaedic Services
Outpatient Services Location
Pain Management Program
Palliative Care
Pastoral Care
Pathology & Laboratory Services
Pediatric Services
Pediatric Subspecialty Center at Toms River The
Pediatric Surgery
Pharmacy Department
Plastic Surgery
Podiatry Services
Pre-Admission Testing Services
Psychiatric Services
Pulmonary Services
Radiation Oncology
Rehabilitation Services
Renal Services
Renal Transplantation
Respiratory Services
Robotic Surgery
Senior Services Program
Sleep Disorders Center
Spine Center
Surgical Services

Total	0	0

Urogynecology
Urology
Valerie Fund Cancer Center (Pediatrics)
Vascular Surgery
The Weight Loss Institute of New Jersey
Wound Treatment Center

COMPETITORS

Atlantic Health	Saint Peter' s
Bergen Regional	University Hospital
Medical	Shore Memorial
Capital Health System	Hospital
CentraState Healthcare	St. Joseph' s
System	Healthcare System
JFK Health System	Trinitas Regional
Meridian Health	Medical Center
Princeton HealthCare	Valley Health System

HISTORICAL FINANCIALS

Company Type: Private

Income Statement

FYE: December 31

	REVENUE ($ mil.)	NET INCOME ($ mil.)	NET PROFIT MARGIN	EMPLOYEES
12/09	287	14	5.0%	2,400
12/08	262	(11)	—	—
12/04	228	9	4.3%	—
12/03	221	0	—	—
Annual Growth	4.4%	—	—	—

MONMOUTH UNIVERSITY

Students looking for a monumental education might want to head to Monmouth University. The private institution offers more than 30 undergraduate and 20 graduate programs through eight schools that include business administration education humanities and social sciences and nursing and health sciences as well as graduate and honors schools. Founded in 1933 as the Monmouth Junior College Monmouth University has an enrollment of roughly an 6500 graduate and undergraduate students. The school's student-teacher ratio is about 14:1.

Geographic Reach

Monmouth University located in West Long Branch New Jersey.

Financial Performance

Revenues for 2012 were some $158 million while net income was about $7.1 million. Monmouth University has an endowment of some $60 million and an annual operating budget of some $153 million.

Strategy

To expand its academic offerings Monmouth University is working to offer a balanced ratio of liberal arts and professional programs to undergraduates. It is also strengthening its professional and disciplinary graduate programs and it is working to add extended programs.

To expand offerings for health professionals in 2013 Monmouth University formed a partnership with the University of Medicine and Dentistry of New Jersey's School of Health Related Professionals (UMDNJ-SHRP) which will allow eligible Monmouth students to participate in clinical trial science programs at UMDNJ-SHRP.

EXECUTIVES

Vice President Tech Campus PLNG, Richard (Dick) Kuntz
Vice President For External Affairs, Jason Kroll
Assistant Vice President Of University Engagement, Yasmin Neilsen
Secretary, Barbara (Barb) Santos
Secretary, Elaine Ponterio
Secretary Certification Field Placements And School Partners, Renee Bell
Auditors: GRANT THORNTON LLP NEW YORK

LOCATIONS

HQ: MONMOUTH UNIVERSITY
400 CEDAR AVE, WEST LONG BRANCH, NJ 077641898
Phone: 732 571-3400
Web: WWW.OUTLOOK.MONMOUTH.EDU

PRODUCTS/OPERATIONS

Selected Colleges and Schools
Graduate School
Honors School
Leon Hess Business School
School of Education
School of Science
School of Social Work
Marjorie K. Unterberg School of Nursing and Health Studies
Wayne D. McMurray School of Humanities and Social Sciences

HISTORICAL FINANCIALS

Company Type: Private

Income Statement

FYE: June 30

	REVENUE ($ mil.)	NET INCOME ($ mil.)	NET PROFIT MARGIN	EMPLOYEES
06/13	162	14	8.9%	1,000
06/10	145	18	12.6%	—
06/08	166	14	8.9%	—
06/07	0	0	—	—
Annual Growth	—	—	—	—

2013 Year-End Financials

Return on assets: 3.1%   Cash ($ mil.): 9
Return on equity: 8.9%
Current ratio: —

MONOGRAM FOOD SOLUTIONS LLC

Monogram Food Solutions is focused on M E A and T. As a manufacturer of meat and meat snack products the company produces beef jerky sausage hot dogs bacon and other processed food items. Its brands include Circle B King Cotton and Trail's Best Meat Snacks. Through several special licensing agreements Monogram Food Solutions also sells Jeff Foxworthy Jerky Products NASCAR Jerky and Steak Strips and Bass Pro Uncle Buck's Licensed Products. The company which distributes its products nationwide operates facilities in Minnesota Indiana and Virginia. Founded in 2004 Monogram Food Solutions was formed through the merger of assets (King Cotton and Circle B) previously owned by Sara Lee Corp.

Geographic Reach

From its headquarters in Memphis Tennessee Monogram Food Solutions directs the operation of additional facilities in (Chandler) Minnesota (Muncie and Bristol) Indiana and (Martinsville) Virginia. The company distributes its products nationwide.

Strategy

Licensing agreements have helped Monogram Food Solutions build a firm foundation for its business. Aside from its deal with Bass Pro Shops and Jeff Foxworthy the company enjoys licensing partnerships with Johnsonville Sausage and Glory Foods. Its alliance with Johnsonville Sausage inked in 2012 gave Monogram Food Solutions the go-ahead to produce and market Johnsonville Deli Bites Bacon Jerky and other meat snacks innovations.

Beginning in 2010 the company began manufacturing and selling meat snacks for the energy drink maker DNA Beverages Corporation under the DNA brand. Geared toward a younger consumer the DNA beef products gives Monogram a larger demographic for its products.

Mergers & Acquisitions

Since its founding the company has quickly built itself up by buying established meat product manufacturers and processing plants. In 2009 it acquired three companies including beef jerky maker Wild Bill's Foods and Al Pete's Meats (and the Pete's Pride brand name). It also acquired the Hannah's Bull's O'Brien's and Dakota meat snack brands from meat processing company American Foods Group.

In late 2012 Monogram Food Solutions purchased Hinsdale Farms of Bristol Indiana. As one of the nation's largest makers of corn dogs Hinsdale also has a hand in serving retail private label customers and co-packing for other manufacturers. The deal added a fourth manufacturing plant for processing meat. As part of the acquisition Monogram Food Solutions is working to integrate the Hinsdale business into its manufacturing and sales systems.

EXECUTIVES

Vice President National Accounts, Bill Schneider
Auditors: MAYER HOFFMAN MCCANN PC MEM

LOCATIONS

HQ: MONOGRAM FOOD SOLUTIONS LLC
930 S WHITE STATION RD, MEMPHIS, TN 381175703
Phone: 901 685-7167
Web: WWW.MONOGRAMFOODS.COM

PRODUCTS/OPERATIONS

Selected Brands
Circle B
Hannah's
King Cotton
O'Brien's Meat Snacks/Sausages
Wild Bill's

COMPETITORS

Bridgford Foods	Hormel
Carl Buddig	Jerky Snack Brands
Clemens Family	Link Snacks
Corporation	Oberto Sausage Company
ConAgra	Weaver Meats

HISTORICAL FINANCIALS

Company Type: Private

Income Statement				FYE: December 29
	REVENUE ($ mil.)	NET INCOME ($ mil.)	NET PROFIT MARGIN	EMPLOYEES
12/13	239	3	1.3%	790
12/12	197	1	0.9%	—
12/11	173	3	1.8%	—
Annual Growth	17.3%	2.5%		

2013 Year-End Financials

Return on assets: 8.2%   Cash ($ mil.): —
Return on equity: 1.3%
Current ratio: 0.70

MONTANA STATE UNIVERSITY INC

Montana State University helps develop young minds in Big Sky Country. The university located in Bozeman serves more than 14500 students most of whom are undergraduates from Montana. The school offers baccalaureate degrees in 60 fields master's degrees in 45 fields and doctoral degrees in about 20 fields. The school offers primarily a liberal arts education though it is also strong in agriculture and the fine arts. The university provides courses in fields ranging from English to political science to engineering. It has a teaching staff of more than 1150 including 781 full-time and 373 part-time faculty and department heads. Tuition and fees for a resident student is $6705; a non-resident $20062.

Geographic Reach

The university has campuses located in Bozeman Billings Great Falls and Havre as well as the Montana Agricultural Experiment Station Montana Extension Service and the Fire Services Training School.

Operations

Montana State University's expenditures from sponsored research programs reached $112 million in 2012. That year it had an enrollment of 14660 students and a faculty/student ratio of 17:1.

Financial Performance

The university saw a 5% increase in revenues in 2012 due to a rise in tuition and fees a growth in revenues from auxiliary enterprises and other revenues. These were partially offset by a decline in grant and contract operating revenues.

Net income grew by 46% in 2012 thanks to an increase in capital gifts grants and contributions partially offset by higher expenses and a decline in non-operating revenues.

Montana State University was supported by endowments of $7.8 million in 2012.

Higher tuition and fees helped to lift the university's revenues between 2009 and 2012.

Company Background

The university was founded in 1893.

Montana State University is one of only 108 institutions (out of 4600) designated as "very high research activity" by the Carnegie Foundation for the Advancement of Teaching.

EXECUTIVES

Associate Vice President Of Faculty And Staff Benefits, Brittany Nickolay
Department Head Civil Engineering, Brett Gunnink
Auditors: CINDY JORGENSON-LEGISLATIVE AU

LOCATIONS

HQ: MONTANA STATE UNIVERSITY INC
901 W GARFIELD ST, BOZEMAN, MT 59717
Phone: 406 994-4361
Web: WWW.MONTANA.EDU

PRODUCTS/OPERATIONS

Schools and Colleges
College of Agriculture
College of Arts & Architecture
College of Business
College of Education Health & Human Development
College of Engineering
College of Letters & Science
College of Nursing
Gallatin College
The Graduate School
University College

HISTORICAL FINANCIALS

Company Type: Private

Income Statement				FYE: June 30
	REVENUE ($ mil.)	NET INCOME ($ mil.)	NET PROFIT MARGIN	EMPLOYEES
06/13	333	(1)	—	2,500
06/12	334	24	7.4%	—
06/11	318	16	5.3%	—
06/08	302	0	—	—
Annual Growth	2.0%	—		

2013 Year-End Financials

Return on assets: —   Cash ($ mil.): 179
Return on equity: (-0.4%)
Current ratio: 2.50

MONTCLAIR STATE UNIVERSITY

With its roots as a teaching college it's fitting that today Montclair State University (MSU) is one of a handful of universities in the US offering a doctorate in pedagogy (the art and science of teaching). For more than 100 years MSU has provided a comprehensive curriculum for future educators as well as other students studying a variety of subjects. With an enrollment of some 20000 students MSU operates through six schools and colleges: College of the Arts College of Education and Human Services College of Humanities and Social Sciences College of Science and Mathematics School of Business and the Graduate School.

Operations

MSU's more than 400 fields of study include about 60 undergraduate and 50 graduate majors as well as numerous certificate programs and niche concentrations. Programs include molecular biology applied linguistics nutrition bioinformatics environmental management and justice studies. The university has a student-to-faculty ratio of 17:1.

Geographic Reach

MSU's main campus is located on 250-acres in Montclair New Jersey.

Financials

MSU's operating revenue for 2014 (ended June) was about $300 million an increase of $20.3 million over the previous year. Higher enrollments and tuition rates as well as increases in state grants and contracts boosted revenue.

Strategy

MSU is growing quickly and in recent years the school has spent more than $300 million on new buildings to accommodate that growth. It is building a Center for Environmental and Life Sciences that will house scientific research; a new School of Business building that will incorporate a mix of academic offices and classroom areas; and a new building for the School of Communication and Media that will offer students the latest tools for communications.

Company Background

MSU was founded in 1908 as a two-year college named Montclair State Normal School. It became a four-year institution in 1927 when it became known as Montclair State Teachers College; it gained its final name of Montclair State College in 1958.

EXECUTIVES

VP Finance and Treasurer, Donald D. Cipullo
President, Susan A. Cole
VP and CIO, Edward P. Chapel
VP Student Development and Campus Life, Karen Pennington
VP Human Resources, Judith Hain
VP University Advancement, Thomas Haynes
VP University Facilities, Gregory Bressler
Assistant VP Finance and Controller, Catherine A. Coryat
Provost and VP Academic Affairs, Willard P. Gingerich
VP University Advancement, John T. (Jack) Shannon
Auditors: O'CONNONR DAVIES LLP PARAMUS

LOCATIONS

HQ: MONTCLAIR STATE UNIVERSITY
1 NORMAL AVE, MONTCLAIR, NJ 070431624
Phone: 973 655-4000
Web: WWW.MONTCLAIR.EDU

PRODUCTS/OPERATIONS

Selected Schools and Colleges
College of the Arts
College of Education and Human Services
College of Humanities and Social Sciences
College of Science and Mathematics
School of Business
The Graduate School

HISTORICAL FINANCIALS
Company Type: Private

Income Statement
FYE: June 30

	REVENUE ($ mil.)	NET INCOME ($ mil.)	NET PROFIT MARGIN	EMPLOYEES
06/13	280	6	2.3%	2,000
06/12	266	29	11.0%	—
06/08	200	24	12.4%	—
06/07	179	0	—	—
Annual Growth	7.7%	—	—	—

2013 Year-End Financials
Return on assets: —   Cash ($ mil.): 51
Return on equity: 2.3%
Current ratio: 0.80

MOORE REGIONAL HOSPITAL

LOCATIONS

HQ: MOORE REGIONAL HOSPITAL
20 PAGE DR, PINEHURST, NC 283748847
Phone: 910 295-7888
Web: WWW.FIRSTHEALTH.ORG

HISTORICAL FINANCIALS
Company Type: Private

Income Statement
FYE: September 30

	REVENUE ($ mil.)	NET INCOME ($ mil.)	NET PROFIT MARGIN	EMPLOYEES
09/08	358	31	8.7%	1,400
09/05	326	45	13.9%	—
Annual Growth	3.1%	(11.8%)	—	—

2008 Year-End Financials
Return on assets: 3.1%   Cash ($ mil.): 4
Return on equity: 8.7%
Current ratio: 0.20

MORSE OPERATIONS INC.

Morse Operations (dba Ed Morse Automotive Group) has been selling cars and trucks long enough to know the code of the road. It owns about a dozen new car dealerships across Florida most of them operating under the Ed Morse name. Dealerships house more than 15 franchises and 10 domestic and import car brands including Cadillac Fiat Chevrolet Buick GMC Scion Honda Mazda and Toyota. The company's Bayview Cadillac in Fort Lauderdale is one of the world's largest volume sellers of Cadillacs. Morse Operations also sells used cars provides parts and service and operates a fleet sales division. Founder and auto magnate the late Ed Morse entered the automobile business in 1946 with a 20-car rental fleet.

Geographic Reach

The dealership network serves customers throughout Florida along the East and West coasts and in Central Florida.

Operations

Ed Morse Fleet Sales offers vehicles from about 10 different brands including Honda Cadillac Fiat Chevrolet Buick GMC Scion Mazda and Toyota. To date annual fleet sales have reached 100000 vehicles.

Fleet customers include daily rental companies such as National Car Rental Avis and Alamo Rent A Car.

EXECUTIVES

EVP and COO, Carmine Colella
President and CEO, Ted Morse
Auditors: CROWE HORWATH LLP FORT LAUDE

LOCATIONS

HQ: MORSE OPERATIONS INC.
2850 S FEDERAL HWY, DELRAY BEACH, FL 334833216
Phone: 561 276-5000
Web: WWW.EDMORSE.COM

PRODUCTS/OPERATIONS

Selected Dealerships
Brandon Auto Mall
Ed Morse Auto Plaza - Port Richey
Ed Morse Bayview Cadillac
Ed Morse Cadillac - Delray Beach
Ed Morse C
Ed Morse C
Ed Morse Delray Toyota/Scion
Ed Morse Honda Blue Heron
Ed Morse M
Ed Morse Sawgrass

COMPETITORS

AutoNation	JM Family Enterprises
Braman Management	March/Hodge
Buchanan Automotive	Penske Automotive
Ferman Automotive	Group
Holman Enterprises	Scott-McRae
Island Lincoln-Mercury	

HISTORICAL FINANCIALS
Company Type: Private

Income Statement
FYE: December 31

	REVENUE ($ mil.)	NET INCOME ($ mil.)	NET PROFIT MARGIN	EMPLOYEES
12/13	690	22	3.3%	1,295
12/12	604	(6)	—	—
12/11	513	4	0.8%	—
12/10	550	0	—	—
Annual Growth	7.9%	—	—	—

2013 Year-End Financials
Return on assets: 1.3%   Cash ($ mil.): 4
Return on equity: 3.3%
Current ratio: 0.10

MORTGAGE INVESTORS CORPORATION

Auditors: GRANT THORNTON LLP TAMPA FL

LOCATIONS

HQ: MORTGAGE INVESTORS CORPORATION
6090 CENTRAL AVE, SAINT PETERSBURG, FL 337071622
Phone: 727 347-1930
Web: WWW.MORTGAGEINVESTORS.COM

HISTORICAL FINANCIALS
Company Type: Private

Income Statement
FYE: December 31

	ASSETS ($ mil.)	NET INCOME ($ mil.)	INCOME AS % OF ASSETS	EMPLOYEES
12/12	115	75	65.8%	1,200
12/11	165	6	4.1%	—
12/10	120	23	19.5%	—
12/09	73	0	—	—
Annual Growth	16.5%	—	—	—

MORTON PLANT HOSPITAL ASSOCIATION INC.

Auditors: ERNST & YOUNG US LLP ATLANTA

LOCATIONS

HQ: MORTON PLANT HOSPITAL ASSOCIATION INC.
300 PINELLAS ST, CLEARWATER, FL 337563892
Phone: 727 462-7000
Web: WWW.MORTONPLANT.COM

HISTORICAL FINANCIALS

Company Type: Private

Income Statement
FYE: December 31

	REVENUE ($ mil.)	NET INCOME ($ mil.)	NET PROFIT MARGIN	EMPLOYEES
12/09	517	33	6.5%	3,000
12/08	0	(0)	—	—
12/05	521	(44)	—	—
12/04	477	0	—	—
Annual Growth	1.6%	—	—	—

2009 Year-End Financials

Return on assets: —   Cash ($ mil.): —
Return on equity: 6.5%
Current ratio: —

MOUNT AUBURN HOSPITAL

Auditors: KPMG LLP BOSTON MA

LOCATIONS

HQ: MOUNT AUBURN HOSPITAL
330 MOUNT AUBURN ST, CAMBRIDGE, MA 021385597
Phone: 617 492-3500
Web: WWW.MOUNTAUBURNHOSPITAL.ORG

HISTORICAL FINANCIALS

Company Type: Private

Income Statement
FYE: September 30

	REVENUE ($ mil.)	NET INCOME ($ mil.)	NET PROFIT MARGIN	EMPLOYEES
09/14	321	21	6.8%	1,700
09/13	289	27	9.4%	—
09/10	352	23	6.7%	—
09/09	335	0	—	—
Annual Growth	(0.9%)	—	—	—

2014 Year-End Financials

Return on assets: 6.4%   Cash ($ mil.): 40
Return on equity: 6.8%
Current ratio: 2.00

MOUNT CARMEL HEALTH SYSTEM

Mount Carmel Health System cares for the sick in the greater Columbus area and central Ohio. The health care system boasts 1500 physicians at three general hospitals and a specialty surgical hospital offering a comprehensive range of medical and surgical services including cardiovascular care. Mount Carmel Health also operates outpatient centers including primary care and specialty physicians' practices and it offers home health care services. The hospital group is part of Trinity Health one of the largest Catholic health care systems in the US.

Operations

Mount Carmel's facilities include the acute care Mount Carmel East Mount Carmel West and Mount Carmel St. Ann's hospitals as well as the Mount Carmel New Albany a surgical hospital specializing in orthopedic neurological and musculoskeletal treatments. The system also operates several freestanding emergency and surgery centers and other outpatient and community care centers. Its HealthProviders subsidiary manages about two dozen primary care and specialty practices with more than 100 physicians in central Ohio.

In the realm of education Mount Carmel Health operates six medical residency programs for physicians and its Mount Carmel College of Nursing is one of the largest in the state.

Strategy

In 2015 Mount Carmel announced that it was investing more than $700 million in a major expansion. The investment includes big projects at three Mount Carmel campuses: Mount Carmel East Mount Carmel Grove City and Mount Carmel West. Mount Carmel East will begin a $310 million modernization in 2015 to be completed in phases through 2019.That year the company signed an agreement with HealthSouth to begin construction on a new inpatient rehabilitation hospital in Westerville Ohio. The 60-bed hospital will be a joint venture between HealthSouth and Mount Carmel and will provide specialized rehabilitative care to patients who have experienced stroke trauma brain and orthopedic injuries or other major illnesses or injuries. Construction on the 60000-square-foot hospital is expected to be completed in early 2017. When the new hospital opens Mount Carmel will relocate its existing 24-bed unit at Mount Carmel West to the new facility.

Company Background

In 2012 the company launched a $110 million facilities improvement project (Project GRACE) which includes the renovation of the St. Ann's hospital. Mount Carmel Health plans for the upgraded St. Ann's facility to serve as a regional medical center.

In 2010 Mount Carmel completed construction of a new freestanding emergency center in the town of Canal Winchester through a partnership with Fairfield Medical Center. The center features both general emergency and pediatric urgent care facilities. In time the center might expand into a larger hospital facility.

Mother M. Angela and Sister M. Rufina Dunn of the Congregation of the Sisters of the Holy Cross of Notre Dame founded Mount Carmel in 1886.

EXECUTIVES

Vice President Patient Care Services Cno, Dina Bush
Pharmacy Manager, Megan (Meg) Kramer
Senior Vice President Stragety and System Development, Hugh Jones
Vice President Quality And Safety, Dawn Sorensen
Vice President of Marketing and Communications, Tessa Burke
Vice President, Christine Aucreman
Vice President, Jamie Bowman
Senior Vice President And Chief Compliance Officer, Dan Hackett
Treasurer, Michael Cooney

LOCATIONS

HQ: MOUNT CARMEL HEALTH SYSTEM
6150 E BROAD ST, COLUMBUS, OH 432131574
Phone: 614 234-6000
Web: WWW.MOUNTCARMELHEALTH.COM

PRODUCTS/OPERATIONS

Selected Facilities
Hospitals
Mount Carmel East
Mount Carmel New Albany
Mount Carmel St. Ann's
Mount Carmel West
Other Facilities
Anticoagulation Centers
Atrial Fibrillation Center
Cardiac Rehabilitation
Diley Ridge Medical Center
Mount Carmel Grove City Medical Center
Geriatrics Center
Health Centers
Heart Failure Centers
Home Medical Equipment
Imaging Centers
Mount Carmel Medical Group
Occupational Health Centers
Outpatient Cancer Treatment
Outpatient Labs
Physician Offices
Rehab and Sports Medicine Services
Sleep Medicine
Surgery Centers
Urgent Care Centers
Women's Health Centers
Wound Centers

COMPETITORS

Adena Health System	Mercy Health (OH)
Fairfield Medical Center	Nationwide Children's Hospital
Genesis HealthCare System (Ohio)	OhioHealth
Licking Memorial Health Systems	Regency Hospital

HISTORICAL FINANCIALS

Company Type: Private

Income Statement
FYE: June 30

	REVENUE ($ mil.)	NET INCOME ($ mil.)	NET PROFIT MARGIN	EMPLOYEES
06/13	1,195	89	7.5%	8,000
06/10	198	2	1.2%	—
06/09	167	0	—	—
06/05	1,088	0	—	—
Annual Growth	1.2%	—	—	—

2013 Year-End Financials

Return on assets: 10.2%   Cash ($ mil.): 21
Return on equity: 7.5%
Current ratio: —

MOUNT CLEMENS REGIONAL MEDICAL CENTER INC.

Mount Clemens Regional Medical Center (doing business as McLaren Medical Center-Macomb) is an general acute care hospital serving the Macomb County area of suburban Detroit. With about 290 beds the hospital offers such specialties as cardiac and cancer care family practice services home and hospice care and emergency care. The McLaren Health Care-controlled company also operates three prompt care centers in nearby townships as well as a wound treatment clinic. Of the more than 420 physicians on staff at the hospital more than 100 are family medicine and internal medicine specialists who provide primary care.

Geographic Reach

The hospital system serves Michigan patients in the Macomb County area of suburban Detroit.

Strategy

Growing its geographic network of services in 2012 McLaren Medical Center-Macomb opened a new facility in Richmond-Lenox its offers includes physical therapy X-ray/diagnostic imaging and a laboratory blood draw station.

That year it also expanded its technological capabilities with the addition of the da Vinci® Si HD Surgical System robotic technology. The acquisition was part of a long history of adopting surgical advancements.

Ownership

Mount Clemens Regional Medical Center was acquired by McLaren Health Care in 2006 to expand its reach into southeastern Michigan. In 2012 the medical center changed its name to McLaren Medical Center-Macomb.

Company Background

The hospital was founded in 1944.

EXECUTIVES

Medical Director, Michael Smith

LOCATIONS

HQ: MOUNT CLEMENS REGIONAL MEDICAL CENTER INC.
1000 HARRINGTON ST, MOUNT CLEMENS, MI 480432920
Phone: 586 493-8000

PRODUCTS/OPERATIONS

Selected Departments and Services
Bariatrics
Behavioral Health
Blood Conservation
Cancer Services
Cardiac
Diabetes
Diagnostic Imaging
Dialysis Services
Emergency Care
EMS
Family BirthPlace
Fitness Centers
Free Clinics
Health Insurance
Home Care
Hospice
Immunizations
Implantable Hearing Solutions
Infectious Disease
Infusion Center
Intensive Care
Internal Medicine
Laboratory and Pathology
Lifeline
Medical Library
Medical Supplies & Equipment
Neurosciences
Nutritional Counseling
Ophthalmology
Orthopedics
Pain Management
Pediatrics
Pharmacy Services
Primary Care
Proton Therapy
Pulmonary and Respiratory
Rehabilitaton and Therapy
Robotic Surgery
Sleep Medicine
Stroke Center
Surgical and Endoscopy Services
Trauma
Urology
Walk-in Clinics
Women' s Services
Wound Care

COMPETITORS

Beaumont Health System
Crittenton Hospital
St. John Hospital & Medical Center
St. John Macomb-Oakland Hospital

HISTORICAL FINANCIALS

Company Type: Private

Income Statement

FYE: September 30

	REVENUE ($ mil.)	NET INCOME ($ mil.)	NET PROFIT MARGIN	EMPLOYEES
09/13	303	18	6.1%	2,249
09/09	277	11	4.2%	—
09/08*	264	14	5.5%	—
05/05	0	0	—	—
Annual Growth	—	—	—	—

*Fiscal year change

2013 Year-End Financials

Return on assets: 10.0%
Return on equity: 6.1%
Current ratio: 0.20

Cash ($ mil.): 6

MULTICARE HEALTH SYSTEM

MultiCare Health System is a not-for-profit health system that serves the residents of four counties in the southern Puget Sound region and southwestern Washington. Altogether the system's five hospitals have more than 1100 beds. The largest facility Tacoma General boasts about 440 beds and provides specialized cancer cardiac orthopedic and trauma care in addition to general medical and surgical care. Other medical centers include Good Samaritan Hospital (with 286 beds) Allenmore Hospital (130 beds) Auburn Regional Medical Center (195 beds) and Mary Bridge Children's Hospital (82 beds).

Operations

MultiCare has more than 1000 staff physician specialists. In addition to its five hospitals the health system also operates dozens of primary care specialty care and urgent care clinics in the region as well as home health and hospice care agencies. Tacoma General Hospital operates the MultiCare Regional Cancer Center an obstetrics and neonatal intensive care unit the MultiCare Neuroscience Center of Washington orthopedics the MultiCare Surgical Care Center and the MultiCare Regional Heart & Vascular Center. Tacoma General also offers Level II Adult Trauma Center and Level IIIB neonatal intensive care unit. Mary Bridge Children's Hospital & Health Center operates a pediatric intensive care unit a pediatric heart center a Center for Childhood Safety child abuse intervention programs and outpatient specialty clinics.

In 2013 alone the company provided free and subsidized health care services at an estimated cost of $185 million.In 2013 MultiCare reported 217590 emergency department visits; 47138 admissions; 9616 inpatient surgeries 23502 outpatient surgeries and 5817 live births.

Geographic Reach

MultiCare serves patients in more than 130 locations in Washington's Pierce South King Thurston and Kitsap counties.

Strategy

The company is expanding its infrastructure to keep up with demand.

In 2014 MultiCare opened the 115929-sq.-ft. Rainier Pavilion as part of a $192 million project to expand services for women newborns and children at Tacoma General Hospital and Mary Bridge Children's Hospital. When the final phase is completed in 2015 the project will add 133919 sq. ft. of new space and 144835 sq. ft. of renovated space. Also that year MultiCare broke ground on a new hospital in Covington improving access to health care services in South King County. The new 24-bed three-story hospital (with the potential to expand to 58 beds) will open in 2016. Other new facilities that broke ground in 2013 and 2014 are a 120-bed psychiatric hospital in Tacoma (for which MultiCare is partnering up with CHI Franciscan Health to build) and a birth center at Tacoma General Hospital.On the technology front MultiCare uses technologies such as digital mammography CyberKnife Radiosurgery technology and Da Vinci Robotic Surgery to provide better service to the patients. In 2013 MultiCare Auburn Medical Center upgraded its billing processes to an electronic health record system.

EXECUTIVES

President and CEO, William G. (Bill) Robertson, age 55
EVP, Florence Chang
President East Pierce Region, Glenn Kasman
President West Pierce Region, Shelly Mullin
Chief Physician Officer, Claire Spain-Remy
VP Finance and Interim CFO, Anna Loomis
President South King Region, Hugh Kodama
CIO, Robert Biernbaum
Medical Director, Jeffrey J (Jeff) Whittall
Pharmd, Travis Smith
Nursing Director, Sharon Sterling
Clinical Director, Cathy Hanson
Pharmd, Emily Corgan
Clinic Supervisor, Alycia Harwood
AMBULATORY Services Director, Susan (Sue) Whitlock
Medical Records Director, Sherry Marrs
Occupational Medicine, Archie Adams
Medical Director Chief Medical Officer, Mario Alinea
Secretary to President, Lydia Wilke
Secretary, Cheryl Wamsley
Auditors: KPMG LLP SEATTLE WASHINGTON

LOCATIONS

HQ: MULTICARE HEALTH SYSTEM
315 MARTIN LUTHER KING, TACOMA, WA 984054234
Phone: 253 403-1000
Web: WWW.MULTICARE.ORG

PRODUCTS/OPERATIONS

Selected Facilities
Hospitals

Allenmore Hospital (Tacoma)
Auburn Medical Center (Auburn)
Good Samaritan Hospital (Puyallup)
Mary Bridge Children's Hospital and Health Center
(Tacoma)
Tacoma General Hospital (Tacoma)
Other facilities
Allenmore Medical Center
Auburn MultiCare Clinic
Covington MultiCare Clinic
Lakewood Urgent Care Clinic
Kent MultiCare Clinic
MultiCare Home Services
Spanaway MultiCare Clinic
Tacoma Family Medicine
University Place Urgent Care Clinic
Westgate Urgent Care Clinic

Selected Services

Adult Day Health
Behavioral Health
Boutique
Breast Health
Cancer Center
Center for Healthy Living
Children's Therapy Unit
Community Programs
CyberKnife Radiosurgery
Diabetes Services
Ear Nose and Throat
Emergency and Urgent Care
Family Birth Centers
Geriatric Psychiatric Center
Health Care Resource Center
Heart Care
Home Health and Hospice
Immunization Clinic
Infusion Center
Institute for Research & Innovation
Laboratories Northwest
Maternal-Fetal Medicine
Medical Imaging
Nephrology
Neonatal Intensive Care Unit
Neurosciences
Nutrition
OB/GYN
Occupational Medicine
Orthopedics
Pain Management
Palliative Medicine
Perinatal Outreach Program
Pharmacy
Physical Therapy
Podiatry
Primary Care Clinics
Pulmonary Care
Pulmonary Rehabilitation
Rehabilitation
Robotic Technology
Senior Services
Sexual Assault Services
Spa
Sports Medicine
Surgical Services
Tobacco Cessation
Transfusion Free Medical and Surgical Program
Urology
Weight Loss and Wellness
Wound Healing Center

COMPETITORS

Catholic Health
  Initiatives
Franciscan Health
  System
Harrison Medical
  Center
Overlake Hospital
PeaceHealth

Providence Health &
  Services
Seattle Children's
  Hospital
Swedish Health
  Services
Yakima Valley Memorial

HISTORICAL FINANCIALS
Company Type: Private

Income Statement
FYE: December 31

	REVENUE ($ mil.)	NET INCOME ($ mil.)	NET PROFIT MARGIN	EMPLOYEES
12/12	1,563	245	15.7%	6,510
12/11	1,384	27	2.0%	—
12/10	1,384	146	10.6%	—
12/09	1,094	0	—	—
Annual Growth	12.6%	—	—	—

2012 Year-End Financials

Return on assets: —
Return on equity: 15.7%
Current ratio: 1.10
Cash ($ mil.): 74

MUNSON MEDICAL CENTER

LOCATIONS

HQ: MUNSON MEDICAL CENTER
1105 SIXTH ST, TRAVERSE CITY, MI 496842386
Phone: 231 935-6000
Web: WWW.MUNSONHEALTHCARE.ORG

HISTORICAL FINANCIALS
Company Type: Private

Income Statement
FYE: June 30

	REVENUE ($ mil.)	NET INCOME ($ mil.)	NET PROFIT MARGIN	EMPLOYEES
06/10	441	28	6.4%	3,100
06/09	394	(0)	—	—
06/08	393	27	7.1%	—
06/06	334	0	—	—
Annual Growth	7.2%	—	—	—

2010 Year-End Financials

Return on assets: 2.6%
Return on equity: 6.4%
Current ratio: 2.10
Cash ($ mil.): 69

MUNSTER MEDICAL RESEARCH FOUNDATION INC

LOCATIONS

HQ: MUNSTER MEDICAL RESEARCH FOUNDATION INC
901 MACARTHUR BLVD, MUNSTER, IN 463212901
Phone: 219 836-1600
Web: WWW.COMHS.ORG

HISTORICAL FINANCIALS
Company Type: Private

Income Statement
FYE: June 30

	REVENUE ($ mil.)	NET INCOME ($ mil.)	NET PROFIT MARGIN	EMPLOYEES
06/13	449	23	5.2%	2,000
06/09	352	29	8.4%	—
06/08	337	24	7.1%	—
Annual Growth	5.9%	(0.4%)	—	—

2013 Year-End Financials

Return on assets: 10.2%
Return on equity: 5.2%
Current ratio: 1.50
Cash ($ mil.): 11

MUSCOGEE COUNTY SCHOOL DISTRICT

Auditors: ROBINSON GRIMES & COMPANY P

LOCATIONS

HQ: MUSCOGEE COUNTY SCHOOL DISTRICT
2960 MACON RD, COLUMBUS, GA 319062204
Phone: 706 748-2000
Web: WWW.MUSCOGEE.K12.GA.US

HISTORICAL FINANCIALS
Company Type: Private

Income Statement
FYE: June 30

	REVENUE ($ mil.)	NET INCOME ($ mil.)	NET PROFIT MARGIN	EMPLOYEES
06/08	373	24	6.6%	6,000
06/06	340	19	5.6%	—
06/05	0	0	—	—
Annual Growth	—	—	—	—

2008 Year-End Financials

Return on assets: —
Return on equity: 6.6%
Current ratio: 2.40
Cash ($ mil.): 125

MUSCULOSKELETAL TRANSPLANT FOUNDATION INC.

LOCATIONS

HQ: MUSCULOSKELETAL TRANSPLANT FOUNDATION INC.
125 MAY ST STE 300, EDISON, NJ 088373264
Phone: 732 661-0202
Web: WWW.MTFSPORTS.NET

HISTORICAL FINANCIALS
Company Type: Private

Income Statement
FYE: December 31

	REVENUE ($ mil.)	NET INCOME ($ mil.)	NET PROFIT MARGIN	EMPLOYEES
12/12	404	(16)	—	1,000
12/06	302	6	2.2%	—
12/05	271	0	0.0%	—
12/04	244	0	—	—
Annual Growth	6.5%	—	—	—

2012 Year-End Financials
Return on assets: —
Return on equity: (-4.1%)
Current ratio: 1.10

Cash ($ mil.): 24

MUSTANG FUEL CORPORATION

Like a good mustang Mustang Fuel is independent —an independent oil and gas exploration production transportation and marketing company that is. The company owns and operates 200 properties and owns non-operated interests in more than 1300 other properties. It also controls more than 100000 net undeveloped leasehold acres in a four-state service region. Mustang Fuel also owns natural gas gathering and transporting pipelines operates one of the largest gas processing facilities in Oklahoma and has a fleet of trucks that transports petroleum products. It also markets gas. Subsidiaries include Mustang Fuel Marketing Company and Mustang Gas Products LLC.

Geographic Reach

The company has operations in Kansas Oklahoma Texas and Utah.

Operations

Mustang Fuel operates upstream (exploration and production) and midstream assets.

Mustang Fuel Marketing Company (first formed in 1990 as Eagle Gas Marketing) serves several independent gas producers with a focus on the intrastate natural gas pipelines in Oklahoma.

Mustang Gas Products LLC (formed in 2002 to buy gas gathering and processing assets from ONEOK) operates five gas processing facilities in Oklahoma and owns more than 4000 miles of gas gathering pipeline. The unit's cryogenic gas plants daily process about 110 million cu. ft. of natural gas and 450000 gallons of natural gas liquids.

Strategy

The company has primarily grown through developing its own properties and by acquiring strategic complementary properties. It also pursues both oil and natural gas.

To better serve its customers in 2012 Mustang Gas Products expanded its Rodman gas gathering and processing capability in Kay and Noble counties in Oklahoma.

Company Background

Korean War veteran Edward Joullian III founded Mustang Fuel (as Westoc Oil & Gas Company) in 1949 and became chairman and president of the closely-held oil and gas company in 1964. He died in 2006. His son (E. Carey Joullian IV) took charge of the company

EXECUTIVES
Vice President And Controller, Carrie Brower
Vice President, Thomas Bennett

Vice President Gas Marketing, Paul Belflower
Vice President Of Gas Operations, John Hogsett
Vice President And Controller, Carrie Buchanan
Auditors: GRANT THORNTON LLP OKLAHOMA

LOCATIONS
HQ: MUSTANG FUEL CORPORATION
9800 N OKLAHOMA AVE, OKLAHOMA CITY, OK 731147406
Phone: 405 884-2092
Web: WWW.MUSTANGFUEL.COM

COMPETITORS
Anadarko Petroleum	Occidental Petroleum
Apache	Pioneer Natural
Chesapeake Energy	Resources
Newfield Exploration	SandRidge Energy
Noble Energy	Southwestern Energy
OGE Energy	

HISTORICAL FINANCIALS
Company Type: Private

Income Statement
FYE: December 31

	REVENUE ($ mil.)	NET INCOME ($ mil.)	NET PROFIT MARGIN	EMPLOYEES
12/09	240	13	5.7%	124
12/08	482	43	9.0%	—
12/05	441	24	5.6%	—
12/04	313	0	—	—
Annual Growth	(5.2%)	—	—	—

2009 Year-End Financials
Return on assets: 12.9%
Return on equity: 5.7%
Current ratio: 2.20

Cash ($ mil.): 37

MV TRANSPORTATION INC.

Need to supply transportation by bus? MV Transportation will run your bus system so you don't have to. The company operates more than 200 contracts to offer fixed-route and shuttle bus services as well as paratransit (transportation of people with disabilities) and transportation of Medicaid beneficiaries. Its customers consist primarily of transit authorities and other state and local government agencies responsible for public transportation. MV Transportation operates in more than 130 locations spanning 28 US states and in British Columbia Canada and Saudi Arabia; overall the company maintains a fleet of about 7000 vehicles. MV Transportation was founded in 1975.

Geographic Reach

MV Transportation and its subsidiaries joint ventures partnerships and affiliates operate more than 130 locations in 28 states the District of Columbia two Canadian Provinces and Saudi Arabia.

Sales and Marketing

The company provides its transportation services to cities counties municipalities and other jurisdictional entities as well as for private corporations non-profit agencies and community organizations. Some of its customers include Corpus Christi Regional Transportation Authority (B-Line paratransit and shuttle services) Ashland Public Transit (the curb-to-curb demand response transit service) Capital Area Transit System and Ashtabula County Transportation System (paratransit services).

Strategy

The company relies on the signing of year-long contracts and joint ventures for growth. In 2013 MV Transportation received a four-year contract to continue operation of the City of Irvine's iShuttle service; Irvine's iShuttle provides morning and evening peak-hour service along four routes connecting the Irvine Metrolink Station the Tustin Metrolink Station John Wayne Airport Irvine Spectrum and the Irvine Business Complex (IBC).

To expand its presence and experience in Qatar MV Transportation in 2013 opened its newest business venture in Doha Qatar: MV Global Transport Logistics WLL (MVGTL). In addition MVGTL signed an agreement with passenger transportation provider Mowasalat to provide planning scheduling and event management for the numerous events in Doha.

In early 2012 MV Transportation signed its first contract to manage a bus system outside North America when it made a two-year agreement to coordinate an operation of more than 400 buses carrying Saudi Arabian Oil employees in the Middle Eastern kingdom. Striving to extend its international reach even further the company purchased Transportation Management Services UK Limited (TMSUK) a few months later. The deal allowed MV Transportation to enter a niche market as TMSUK designs and operates transportation systems for special events worldwide.

EXECUTIVES
President and COO, Kevin A. Klika
CTO, Ray Lowrey, age 57
CEO, Brian Kibby
President Southwest Group, Douglas J. (Doug) Gies
SVP Fleet and Facilities, John Calame
EVP Risk Management, Bob Hargis
Chairman EVP and General Counsel, Lisa Winston Hicks
VP Information Technology, Mike Kopaczewski
EVP and CFO, Bob Pagorek

LOCATIONS
HQ: MV TRANSPORTATION INC.
5910 N CNTRL EXPY # 1145, DALLAS, TX 752065125
Phone: 972 391-4600
Web: WWW.MVTRANSIT.COM

PRODUCTS/OPERATIONS
Selected Services
Bid committee consultation
Emergency evacuation planning
Global mobility and unique technology assets
International transport and logistics solutions
Logistics and security staffing
Paratransit and multimodal transport
Parking management and valet services
Sustainability transport initiatives
Traffic control planning staffing and consultation
Transport planning and operations
VIP fleet services

COMPETITORS
Coach USA	National Express Group
FirstGroup America	Rural/Metro
LogistiCare	Veolia Transportation

HISTORICAL FINANCIALS
Company Type: Private

Income Statement
FYE: December 31

	REVENUE ($ mil.)	NET INCOME ($ mil.)	NET PROFIT MARGIN	EMPLOYEES
12/13	1,013	32	3.2%	12,389
12/09	706	23	3.3%	—
12/08	645	(2)	—	—
12/07	422	0	—	—
Annual Growth	15.7%	—	—	—

2013 Year-End Financials

Return on assets: 3.1% Cash ($ mil.): —
Return on equity: 3.2%
Current ratio: 0.60

NACA LOGISTICS (USA) INC.

LOCATIONS

HQ: NACA LOGISTICS (USA) INC.
857 E 230TH ST, CARSON, CA 907455003
Phone: 310 847-3000
Web: WWW.VANGUARDLOGISTICS.COM

HISTORICAL FINANCIALS

Company Type: Private

Income Statement

FYE: December 31

	REVENUE ($ mil.)	NET INCOME ($ mil.)	NET PROFIT MARGIN	EMPLOYEES
12/08	339	4	1.5%	681
12/07	261	2	0.9%	—
12/02	848	0	—	—
Annual Growth	—	625.4%		

2008 Year-End Financials

Return on assets: 3.5% Cash ($ mil.): 4
Return on equity: 1.5%
Current ratio: 0.70

NATIONAL CHRISTIAN CHARITABLE

LOCATIONS

HQ: NATIONAL CHRISTIAN CHARITABLE
11625 RAINWATER DR # 500, ALPHARETTA, GA
300098674
Phone: 404 252-0100
Web: WWW.NATIONALCHRISTIAN.COM

HISTORICAL FINANCIALS

Company Type: Private

Income Statement

FYE: December 31

	REVENUE ($ mil.)	NET INCOME ($ mil.)	NET PROFIT MARGIN	EMPLOYEES
12/11	665	141	21.3%	2
12/09	396	50	12.7%	—
Annual Growth	29.6%	67.9%	—	—

2011 Year-End Financials

Return on assets: — Cash ($ mil.): 302
Return on equity: 21.3%
Current ratio: 42.00

NATIONAL EDUCATION ASSOCIATION OF THE UNITED STATES

The National Education Association (NEA) is dedicated to promoting the cause of public education and the teaching profession. The organization boasts a membership of 3 million elementary and secondary teachers support professionals administrators higher education faculty and student teachers. It operates in all US states through affiliates. The group's key issues include the No Child Left Behind Act professional pay education funding minority community outreach dropout prevention achievement gaps and other matters facing America's schools. Founded in 1857 the NEA also hosts Read Across America a one-day reading event held on Dr. Seuss' birthday.

Operations

In 1966 the NEA merged with the American Teachers Association. Today it serves as the nation's largest teachers union followed by the American Federation of Teachers with its more than 1.5 million members.

Among the magazines newsletters and journals it publishes are NEA Today This Active Life and The NEA Almanac of Higher Education. The group's web site provides links to its publications as well as to lesson plans articles on classroom management and instruction methods professional development resources and additional online tools.

As part of its focus the organization also puts on regional leadership conferences American Education Week and National Teacher Day. It also partners with other causes and groups to reach out to parents families communities businesses foundations education groups and children's advocates. Some of its partnerships include New Jersey Center for Teaching and Learning (NJCTL) First Book Edward M. Kennedy Institute (EMK) and National PTA.

Geographic Reach

Based in Washington DC the NEA operates in all 50 states through affiliate organizations that altogether serve more than 14000 communities nationwide.

EXECUTIVES

Secretary and Treasurer, Rebecca Pringle

LOCATIONS

HQ: NATIONAL EDUCATION ASSOCIATION OF THE UNITED STATES
1201 16TH ST NW, WASHINGTON, DC 200363290
Phone: 202 833-4000
Web: WWW.NEA.ORG

PRODUCTS/OPERATIONS

Selected Key Issues
Achievement gaps
Dropout prevention
Education funding
Minority community outreach
No Child Left Behind Act
Professional pay

Selected Membership
Administrators
Elementary and secondary teachers Higher education faculty
Student teachers
Support professionals

HISTORICAL FINANCIALS

Company Type: Private

Income Statement

FYE: August 31

	REVENUE ($ mil.)	NET INCOME ($ mil.)	NET PROFIT MARGIN	EMPLOYEES
08/10*	376	16	4.3%	735
12/08	0	0	—	—
08/08	356	0	—	—
Annual Growth	—54061.2%	—	—	—

*Fiscal year change

2010 Year-End Financials

Return on assets: — Cash ($ mil.): 51
Return on equity: 4.3%
Current ratio: 2.30

NATIONAL FROZEN FOODS CORPORATION

Cool Beans! National Frozen Foods has made a name for itself as one of the nation's largest private-label frozen vegetable producers. The family-owned company's products which include peas sweet corn carrots squash and beans (green Italian lima and wax) as well as vegetable blends organic veggies and pureed items are available in grocery stores worldwide. National Frozen Foods also provides bulk and custom-packaging services. The company operates four processing plants in Washington and Oregon that offer a combined cold storage capacity for nearly 200 million pounds of frozen vegetables.

Geographic Reach

National Frozen Foods serves customers and consumers globally by offering private-label and custom-packing services to other companies. It's a frozen food leader not only nationwide but from Asia to Australia.

Operations

The company has four plants —in Albany Oregon and Chehalis Moses Lake and Quincy in Washington —which altogether freeze more than 400 million pounds of vegetables per year. National Frozen Foods uses technology to optimize productivity and ensure product quality. All of its plants use equipment and information technology systems including metal detection and electronic optical defect sorting equipment and warehouse management and electronic data interchange systems.

Strategy

The Pacific Northwest tolerated a damp chilly spring in 2011 driving farmers to delay planting that year. This move in turn made crop harvesting in the region late. In addition to the wet weather farmers had to decide how to apportion their limited acreage —from lower-priced lower-margin vegetables (such as sweet corn and peas —National's core products) to more expensive higher-margin vegetables (like field corn and wheat). Taken together these conditions left National Frozen Foods with a tight inventory for the year like other vegetable processing companies.

Company Background

National Frozen Foods was founded in 1912 by William McCaffray. It was originally named National Fruit Canning Company but the firm discontinued its canning operations in 1974 and later renamed itself.

NATIONAL GRAPE CO-OPERATIVE ASSOCIATION INC.

Well of course grape growers want to hang out in a bunch! The more than 1090 grower/owner-members of the National Grape Cooperative harvest Concord and Niagara grapes from almost 50000 acres of vineyards. The plucked produce supplies the coop's wholly owned subsidiary Welch Foods. Welch Foods makes and sells fruit-based juices jams jellies and spreads under the Welch's and Bama brands in the US and nearly 50 other countries. Offerings include fresh eating grapes distributed by C.H. Robinson Worldwide as well as dried fruit and frozen juice pops. The grape growers own vineyards in Pennsylvania Michigan New York Ohio Washington and Ontario Canada which produce some 300000 tons of grapes annually.

The entire business from growing to processing grapes is highly competitive and the difference between sales and cost of goods sold often so slim that earning a profit is challenging. Despite the economic downturn and soaring commodity costs in 2011 Welch's sustained less than a 10% decline in net income on a small slip in sales. The results reflect new value-priced product introductions coupled with an initiative started in 2009 to slash costs through concentrating production and distribution. Welch's initiative included adding a new bottle production facility to its plant in 2011 and cutting its workforce by 17% in early 2010.

The coop also realized a smaller crop in 2011 in part due to a decline in family-farmer owners. The 10% decrease in tons sold modestly reduced total net proceeds. Nonetheless net income on patron business grew boosted by a sizeable increase in distributable proceeds per ton.

HISTORY

Looking for a steady supply of grapes for his processing plant in 1945 Russian immigrant Jack Kaplan convinced 900 grape growers to join the newly formed National Grape Cooperative. Also that year Welch Foods' parent company decided to spin off its purple fruit interests and Kaplan purchased a controlling interest. Welch's —a competitor at the time —had been started in 1869 when Dr. Thomas Welch a tee totaling dentist created an unfermented Concord grape wine to be used for nonalcoholic communions. The juice was coolly received at first but the advent of Prohibition helped push the company to the forefront of the fruit-drink industry.

While Kaplan had purchased his interest in Welch's with the intention of combining it with the National Grape Co-op it wasn't until the mid-1950s that the two could agree on the acquisition. Welch's product line grew throughout the 1960s and 1970s including the 1972 introduction of red grape and white grape juices. A glut of grapes depressed prices in the 1980s but the co-op rebounded by the 1990s.

In 1994 the co-op acquired jam and jelly maker BAMA Foods from Borden. Daniel Dillon became CEO of Welch's in 1995 and Fredrick Kalian was named president of the co-op the next year. Yakima Valley Grape Producers joined National Grape Co-op in 1997 adding new growers and more grapes to meet a growing demand spurred in part by newly discovered health benefits of purple and white grape juice. (Welch's helped fund the research.)

New products and increased advertising helped boost juice sales dramatically in 1998 and 1999. Fresh table grapes distributed by C.H. Robinson Worldwide were also introduced in 1999 and by 2000 were available nationwide. In 2001 the company announced it would be cutting up to 100 jobs —its first layoffs in more than two decades —due to slowing sales.

In 2003 the company introduced new variations of its products including single-serving juices (Welsh Squeezables). This along with increased marketing and new packaging have seen its sales growing during the last two years. Expansion in grocery channels and the introduction of low-calorie items and shrink-pack products led to further sales gains in 2004.

EXECUTIVES

President and CEO Welch Foods, David J. Lukiewski, age 58
President and Director, Joseph C. Falcone
Chief Legal Officer and Assistant Secretary, Vivian S. Y. Tseng
General Manager COO and Treasurer, Brent J. Roggie

Secretary and Assistant Treasurer, Timothy A. Buss
First VP and Director, Timothy E. Grow
Assistant Treasurer, Thomas A. Bockhorst
Assistant Secretary, Mathew A. Aufman
Third VP and Director, Jon B. Hinkleman
Second VP and Director, Anthony J. Falcone Jr.
Financial and Accounting Officer, Michael J. Perda
President and Director, Joseph C. Falcone
Director, Richard A. Boushey
Director, Douglas R. Forraht
Director, Randolph H. Graham
Director, Jerry A. Czebotar
First VP and Director, Timothy E. Grow
Director, Jon B. Hinkleman
Director, Marvin D. Vining
Director, Gary R. Youngs
Director, William G. (Bill) Barker III, age 53
Third VP and Director, Jon B. Hinkleman
Director, Dennis C. Vacco
Second VP and Director, Anthony J. Falcone Jr.
Director, Thomas G. Wilkinson
Director, Ned R. Totzke
Auditors: KPMG LLP BOSTON MA

LOCATIONS

HQ: NATIONAL GRAPE CO-OPERATIVE ASSOCIATION INC.
2 S PORTAGE ST, WESTFIELD, NY 147871400
Phone: 716 326-5200
Web: WWW.WELCHS.COM

PRODUCTS/OPERATIONS

Selected Products

Food and snacks
  Dried fruit
  Fresh grapes
  Fruit ' N Y
  Fruit snacks mixed
  Welch' s frozen pops
  Welch' s soda
Jams jellies and spreads
Juice
  100% juices
  Concentrates
  Essentials fruit blends
  Fruit fizz sparkling juice beverage
  Light lower calorie
  Sparkling grape cocktails
  Refrigerator cocktails

COMPETITORS

B&G Foods	Hornell Brewing
Big Heart Pet Brands	IZZE
Chiquita Brands	Mondelez International
Coca-Cola	Monster Beverage
Constellation Brands	Nestl© USA
Cranberries Limited	Ocean Spray
Dole Food	PepsiCo
Dr Pepper Snapple Group	Procter & Gamble
Fresh Del Monte Produce	Smucker
	Snapple
Goya	Tropicana

HISTORICAL FINANCIALS

Company Type: Private

Income Statement

FYE: August 31

	REVENUE ($ mil.)	NET INCOME ($ mil.)	NET PROFIT MARGIN	EMPLOYEES
08/13	608	65	10.7%	1,325
08/12	649	74	11.5%	—
08/11	640	74	11.6%	—
08/10	658	0	—	—
Annual Growth	(2.6%)	—	—	—

2013 Year-End Financials

Return on assets: 3.6%   Cash ($ mil.): 5
Return on equity: 10.7%
Current ratio: 0.60

NATIONAL MARROW DONOR PROGRAM INC

LOCATIONS

HQ: NATIONAL MARROW DONOR PROGRAM INC
3001 BROADWAY ST NE, MINNEAPOLIS, MN
554132195
Phone: 612 627-5800

HISTORICAL FINANCIALS

Company Type: Private

Income Statement

FYE: September 30

	REVENUE ($ mil.)	NET INCOME ($ mil.)	NET PROFIT MARGIN	EMPLOYEES
09/13	389	26	6.8%	800
09/05	143	0	0.6%	—
Annual Growth	13.3%	53.4%	—	—

2013 Year-End Financials

Return on assets: 16.1%
Return on equity: 6.8%
Current ratio: 0.80

Cash ($ mil.): 52

NATIONAL PUBLIC RADIO INC.

This company helps keep radio listeners informed and entertained without commercial interruptions. National Public Radio (NPR) is a privately supported not-for-profit organization that produces and syndicates radio programming to 900 independently operated noncommercial radio stations including about 750 NPR member stations. Its shows include news programs Morning Edition and All Things Considered as well as cultural programs (Fresh Air) and entertainment shows (Car Talk; Wait Wait ... Don't Tell Me!). Founded in 1970 NPR is funded through private donations member station dues and grants from organizations such as the Corporation for Public Broadcasting and the National Science Foundation.

Geographic Reach

NPR is one of two major public radio networks in the US the other being Public Radio International. Many public radio stations are members of both networks selecting from their combined mix of programming.

Financial Performance

NPR depends on a variety of funding sources in order to maintain its high quality programming. Donations grants and underwriting from corporations and private organizations make up a large portion of NPR's funding as does individual donations from listeners. Its endowment fund is overseen by the NPR Foundation which also solicits private contributions and gifts.

EXECUTIVES

Vice President Distribution, Peter (Pete) Loewenstein
Executive Director Technology Research Center and NPR Labs, Mike Starling
SVP Marketing Communications and External Relations, Dana D. Rehm

VP Member and Audience Partnership and Chief of Staff, Joyce MacDonald
SVP News, Margaret Low Smith
Chief Administrative Officer and General Counsel, Joyce Slocum
EVP and Chief Content Officer, Kinsey Wilson
Vice President Policy and Re, Mike Riksen
Vice President Diversity in News and Operations, Keith Woods
Vice President Digital Strategy and Sponsorship Operations, Bryan Moffett
Vice President Content Strategy and Operations, Sarah Lumbard
Vice President General Manager Digital Services, Robert Kempf
General Counsel Vice President of Legal and Business Affairs, Terri Minatra
Senior Vice President National Public Media, Blake Truitt
Director, Eduardo Hauser, age 44
Director, Carol A. Cartwright, age 73
Director, Marita Rivero
Interim CEO and Director, Joyce Slocum
Director, Jon R. McTaggart
Director, JoAnn Urofsky
Director, John A. Herrmann Jr.
Director, Lyle L. Logan, age 53
Chair, Dave Edwards
Director, Steven Bass
Director, Jose A. Fajardo
Director, Rob Gordon
Director, Ellen Rocco
Director, Roger Sarow
Director; Chairman NPR Foundation, Antoine W. van Agtmael

LOCATIONS

HQ: NATIONAL PUBLIC RADIO INC.
1111 N CAPITOL ST NE, WASHINGTON, DC
200027502
Phone: 202 513-2000
Web: WWW.NPR.ORG

PRODUCTS/OPERATIONS

Selected Programming

Entertainment
  Car Talk
  Wait Wait ... Don' t Tell Me!
Music
  All Songs Considered
  From the Top
  Mountain Stage
  World Cafe
News and talk shows
  All Things Considered
  Fresh Air
  Morning Edition
  On The Media
  Talk of the Nation
  Weekend Edition

COMPETITORS

AP Broadcast	Public Radio
Pacifica	International
Premiere Radio	WestwoodOne
Networks	

HISTORICAL FINANCIALS

Company Type: Private

Income Statement

FYE: September 30

	REVENUE ($ mil.)	NET INCOME ($ mil.)	NET PROFIT MARGIN	EMPLOYEES
09/13	190	(18)	—	741
09/09*	148	(17)	—	—
12/07	170	26	15.8%	—
09/06	170	0	—	—
Annual Growth	1.6%	—	—	—

*Fiscal year change

NATIONAL RIFLE ASSOCIATION OF AMERICA

The NRA believes in the right to bear arms. With more than 5 million members The National Rifle Association (NRA) is the staunch defender of Second Amendment rights. It's a major player in the political arena and stands firm in its resolve to protect the right to keep and bear arms. The NRA offers a variety of educational and gun safety programs and publishes magazines (America's 1st Freedom American Hunter Women's Outlook). It also caters to more than one million youth through its shooting sports events and affiliated programs with the likes of 4-H the Boy Scouts of America and others. It also sells NRA merchandise. Union army veterans William Church and George Wingate founded the NRA in 1871.

Operations

The Institute for Legislative Action (ILA) established in 1975 is the lobbying arm of the NRA. With offices in Fairfax and Washington DC the ILA has a staff of more than 80 with a team of full-time lobbyists defending Second Amendment issues on Capitol Hill in state legislatures and in local government bodies. The NRA also operates the National Firearms Museum in Fairfax Virginia.

The NRA has made a commitment to training education and marksmanship. Its education and training department is supported by more than 65000 certified instructors who offer lessons to some 750000 gun owners each year. Through NRA's law enforcement division training program the NRA offers certified and standardized firearm instructor training and has trained over 50000 law enforcement firearm instructors.

Strategy

The NRA's membership ranks topped a record 5 million in 2013 as efforts to pass gun-control legislation following multiple mass shootings –including the Newtown Connecticut and Colorado movie theater tragedies — swelled the organization's ranks. About 500000 new members joined in 2013.

EXECUTIVES

Secretary, Edward J. Land
EVP, Wayne LaPierre
First VP, Sandra (Sandy) Froman
President, John C. Sigler, age 68
Executive Director General Operations, Kayne Robinson, age 71
Chief Lobbyist and Executive Director NRA Institute for Legislative Action, Chris W. Cox
Director Corporate and Foundation Relations Office of Advancement, Nicole Capossela
Southern Regional Director, Al Hammond
Manager Women's Programs, Rosemary E. Herr
Director Law Enforcement Activities, Glen Hoyer
President The NRA Foundation, Allen D. Cors
Executive Director The NRA Foundation, Wayne Sheets
Director Strategic Giving Office of Advancement, Frank L. Cerutti
Auditors: MCGLADREY & PULLEN LLP VIENNA

Return on assets: 15.6%
Return on equity: (-9.8%)
Current ratio: 0.10

Cash ($ mil.): 15

LOCATIONS

HQ: NATIONAL RIFLE ASSOCIATION OF AMERICA
11250 WAPLES MILL RD # 1, FAIRFAX, VA 220309400
Phone: 703 267-1000
Web: WWW.NRAILA.ORG

PRODUCTS/OPERATIONS

Selected Programs
Business Alliance & Clubs
NRA Sports
Competitions & Matches
Eddie Eagle GunSafe
Firearm Training
Hunter Services
Law Enforcement Services
Range Services
Women' s Programs
Friends of NRA Banquets
National Firearms Museum
NRA Headquarters Range
Gunsmithing Schools
NRA Recruiter
NRA Hunters Rights.
Youth
   National Youth Shooting Sports Cooperative Program
   Brownells/NRA Day Program
   Brownells/NRA Outstanding Achievement Youth Award
   Marksmanship Qualification Program
   Youth Hunter Education Challenge
   Brownells/NRA National Youth Shooting Sports
   Ambassador Program
   Youth Education Summit
   Resources & Information
   Youth Wildlife Art Contest
   Santioned Special Tournament
   Junior Membership
   InSights Magazine
   Email List Signup
   Youth Essay Contest
   Special Offers
   Volunteer State Coordinators
   NRA' s Home Air Gun Program
   Request for Eagle Scout Certificate
   National Junior Shooting Camps

HISTORICAL FINANCIALS
Company Type: Private

Income Statement
FYE: December 31

	REVENUE ($ mil.)	NET INCOME ($ mil.)	NET PROFIT MARGIN	EMPLOYEES
12/13	347	57	16.5%	500
12/09	237	1	0.5%	—
12/07	363	143	39.6%	—
12/06	758	0	—	—
Annual Growth	—	—	—	—

2013 Year-End Financials
Return on assets: 19.4%   Cash ($ mil.): 18
Return on equity: 16.5%
Current ratio: 0.60

NATIONAL RURAL ELECTRIC COOPERATIVE ASSOCIATION

Would it shock you to learn that consumer-owned cooperatives provide electricity to more than 42 million people in the US? The National Rural Electric Cooperative Association (NRECA) is the cooperatives' voice in politics and policymaking. It publishes a monthly magazine and a weekly newspaper sponsors conferences and seminars and represents about 900 rural electric co-ops (from 47 states) in the US Congress and state legislatures. As the nation embraces investor-owned utilities NRECA has been lobbying hard for more moderate approaches to deregulation in order to protect consumers from potential monopolies. The association also provides power assistance and technical advice to developing nations.

Financial Performance

NRECA generated nearly $304 million in total revenue in 2013 an increase of 6% versus 2012. While the co-op's net operating margin before board authorized payments increased from about $6.5 million in 2012 to $7.5 million in 2013 a one-time charge of $26.8 million to shore up its retirement security funding plan resulted in increased total board authorized payments resulting in a loss of $6.2 million for the year (versus a profit of about $4.5 million in 2012).

EXECUTIVES

Vice President, Scott Spencer
Vice President of Environmental Policy, Kirk Johnson
Auditors: BDO USA LLP BETHESDA MARYLA

LOCATIONS

HQ: NATIONAL RURAL ELECTRIC COOPERATIVE ASSOCIATION
4301 WILSON BLVD STE 1, ARLINGTON, VA 222031867
Phone: 703 907-5500
Web: WWW.NRECA.COOP

HISTORICAL FINANCIALS
Company Type: Private

Income Statement
FYE: December 31

	REVENUE ($ mil.)	NET INCOME ($ mil.)	NET PROFIT MARGIN	EMPLOYEES
12/12	208	4	2.2%	885
12/08	162	0	0.1%	—
12/06	139	3	2.5%	—
12/05	974	0	—	—
Annual Growth	—	—	—	—

2012 Year-End Financials
Return on assets: —   Cash ($ mil.): 77
Return on equity: 2.2%
Current ratio: 1.90

NATIONAL UNIVERSITY

National University is the flagship school of the National University System. The institution offers more than 150 undergraduate and graduate degrees and teacher credential and certificate programs. A not-for-profit institution National University programs range across fields including business engineering education media and human services. The university enrolls 23000 students at multiple locations in California and Nevada; it also offers about 70 online degree programs. The school conducts research through the National University Community Research Institute (NUCRI). National University was founded in 1971.

Geographic Reach

National University operates through about 45 locations in California and Nevada including regional campuses in Bakersfield Costa Mesa Fresno Los Angeles Ontario Oxnard Redding Sacramento San Bernardino San Diego San Jose Stockton Twentynine Palms and Woodland Hills California as well as Henderson Nevada. It also has offices in Dallas and Houston Texas and it operates online information centers in Florida Georgia Virginia and Washington State (in addition to numerous online information locations in California). Some of the university's satellite centers are located on military bases.

Operations

National University consists of five schools: Education; Professional Studies; Business and Management; Health and Human Services and Engineering Technology and Media. It also includes the College of Letters and Sciences. The university employs more than 250 full-time faculty members.

The National University System is a group of affiliated universities to meet educational demands for modern times. It was formed in 2001 and includes affiliates John F. Kennedy University City University of Seattle Spectrum Pacific Learning and WestMed College as well as National University International and National University Virtual High School.

Strategy

To meet the rising needs of a growing population National University has been adding new locations. For instance during 2012 it added new online information centers in Arcadia and San Francisco California and in Seattle Washington. It also added a new university campus in Rancho Cordova California and it expanded its San Diego locations by adding a new facility to house programs for its School of Business and Management and School of Professional Studies.

National University strives to provide learning opportunities to a diverse student population. It is a leading issuer of master' s degrees to minorities and women in California. It also serves a rising number of online students and is regularly adding new online courses to meet the needs of this audience.

Growing health care program demands prompted the university to add a Master of Healthcare Administration program at its Fresno campus in 2012. It also added bachelor's degree in allied health through a partnership with the San Mateo Community College District.

EXECUTIVES

Chancellor, Michael R. Cunningham
Vice President For Student Services, Kenneth Goldberg
Provost Vice President Academic Affairs, Thomas (Thom) Green
Associate Vice President, Vernon (Vern) Taylor
Interim President, Patricia (Pat) Potter
Vice Chair, Gerald M. Czarnecki, age 76
Vice Chairman, Donald Kripke
Admin Analyst And Secretary Specialist, Mei Lu-Beker
Auditors: JGD & ASSOCIATES LLP SAN DIEG

LOCATIONS

HQ: NATIONAL UNIVERSITY
11255 N TORREY PINES RD, LA JOLLA, CA 920371011
Phone: 858 642-8000
Web: WWW.NU.EDU

PRODUCTS/OPERATIONS

Selected Schools and Colleges
College of Letters and Sciences
School of Business and Management
School of Education
School of Engineering Technology and Media
School of Health and Human Services
School of Professional Studies

Company Type: Private

Income Statement
FYE: June 30

	REVENUE ($ mil.)	NET INCOME ($ mil.)	NET PROFIT MARGIN	EMPLOYEES
06/11	203	25	12.4%	1,954
06/10	178	18	10.3%	—
06/09	165	5	3.1%	—
06/02	126	0	—	—
Annual Growth	5.4%	—	—	—

2011 Year-End Financials

Return on assets: —
Return on equity: 12.4%
Current ratio: —
Cash ($ mil.): 38

NATIONWIDE CHILDREN'S HOSPITAL

Buckeye babies toddlers and teens don't have to travel the country to find pediatric care with Nationwide Children's Hospital at their disposal. The Columbus Ohio health care provider is one of the largest pediatric care centers in the US. The hospital has some 430 licensed beds and offers services in areas such as behavioral health cardiology hospice orthopedics and surgery. It has roughly 1100 health care providers on its medical staff and its emergency department treats more than 83000 patients each year. The hospital also operates outpatient and specialty clinics in the area and a research institute which is investigating gene therapy.

Geographic ReachNationwide Children's Hospital serves patients from 50 US states and 32 countries. The company is 68 facilities extending out across Ohio and beyond. The company's top ten outpatient visits counties are Franklin Delaware Fairfield Licking Clark Pickaway Madison Union Muskingum and Knox.

Operations

The hospital provides more than $122 million in charity care and community benefit services annually. It had more than 1 million patient visits and had more than 25000 surgery cases in 2014.

Sales and Marketing

Nationwide Children's Hospital payor mix in 2014 included commercial 43%; Medicaid managed care Cap 33%; and Medicaid 13%.

Strategy

In 2015 Nationwide Children's Hospital announced plans to adopt and integrate GenomeNext's genomic sequencing analysis platform for both clinical laboratory services and clinical research initiatives

In 2014 the company outlined numerous details of its $130 million campus expansion project. Its plans include an $85 million outpatient care building and a $45 million building to house faculty offices. The outpatient building called the Livingston Ambulatory Center will house primary care services dental services behavioral health dermatology adolescent medicine sports rehabilitation and various clinics. Both buildings will be six stories tall.

The hospital added helicopter medical transport service in 2013.

Company Background

The health system in 2012 completed a $740 million project to build a new main hospital and add 2 million sq. ft. of clinical research and support space. The expansion added about 100 new beds. Also in 2012 it opened an ambulatory surgery center in Westerville Ohio and a Close To Home lab and clinic in Springfield. In 2014 it opened the Sharon Woods Primary Care Center in north Columbus.

Nationwide Children's Hospital opened its doors in 1892.

EXECUTIVES

Vice President and Controller, Luke Brown
Medical Director Center For Child And Family Advocacy, Philip Scribano
Medical Director Clinical Informatics, Rich David
Chairman The Center for Family Safety and Healing, Abigail S. Wexner
EVP and CFO, Timothy C. Robinson
President and COO, Rick Miller
SVP and Chief Nursing Officer, Linda Stoverock
CEO, Steve Allen
President The Research Institute, John Barnard
President The Center for Family Safety and Healing, Karen Days
Chief Medical Officer, Richard J. Brilli
Surgeon-in-Chief, R. Lawrence Moss
Physician-in-Chief, J. Philip Saul
Chairman Nationwide Children's Hospital Foundation, Cheryl W. Lucks
Chairman The Research Institute, Donald P. McConnell
Vice President Basic Sciences Research, Lauren Bakaletz
Vice President, Karen Heiser
Vice President, William (Bill) Long
Vice President, Niki Shafer
Medical Director of The Research Institute, Grant Morrow
Medical Director, David (Dave) Axelson
Vice President Administration Surgical Services, Michelle (Mitch) Mckissick
Director of Operating Room, Robin Stewart
Vice President Revenue Cycle, Michael Hester
Vice President, Jeff Ziegler
Vice President Of Operations, Val Ruddock
Senior Vice President Of Ambulatory And Mental Health Services, Jack Clark
Physical Therapy, Helen Carey
Director Of Him, Jill Choi
Senior Management Senior Vice President General Manager Director, Phillip (Phil) Chanthasene
Vice President, Jennifer Voit
Senior Management Senior Vice President General Ma, Phillip Chanthasene
Vice President, Kevin Welch
Chairman, Alex Fischer
Vice Chairman, Kathleen Nicol
Secretary, Janet Tussing
Secretary, Wood Carol
Secretary, Kay McCann
Secretary, Heather Wildermuth
Secretary, Lisa Chaffee
Medical Coding Secretary, Marianne Clemons
Auditors: ERNST & YOUNG US LLP COLUMBUS

LOCATIONS

HQ: NATIONWIDE CHILDREN' S HOSPITAL
700 CHILDRENS DR, COLUMBUS, OH 432052639
Phone: 614 722-3040
Web: WWW.GIVING.NATIONWIDECHILDRENS.ORG

PRODUCTS/OPERATIONS

Selected Subsidiaries

Nationwide Children' s Hospital
Nationwide Children' s Behavioral Health
Nationwide Children' s Educational Institute
Nationwide Children' s Hospital Inc
Nationwide Children' s Hospital Homecare
Children' s Anesthesia Associates
Nationwide Children' s Hospital Foundation

Pediatric Academic Associates
Children' s Orthopedic Medical Center
Children' s Radiological Institute
Children' s Surgical Associates Corp.
The Research Institute at Nationwide Children' s Hospital
Pediatric Pathology Associates of Columbus
The Center for Family Safety and Healing at Nationwide Children' s Hospital

Selected Departments and Services

Adolescent Congenital Heart Disease
Adolescent Medicine
Adult Congenital Heart Disease
Adult Medicine and Hospital Pediatrics
Allergy/Immunology
Ambulatory Pediatrics
Anatomic Pathology
Anesthesiology & Pain Medicine
Asthma Program
Audiology
Bariatric Surgery
Battelle Center for Mathematical Medicine
Behavioral Health
Blood Conservation Program
Burn Program
Cancer
CAP4Kids
Cardiology
Cardiopulmonary Rehabilitation
Cardiothoracic Surgery
Center for Biobehavioral Health (Research)
Center for Cardiovascular and Pulmonary Research
Center for Childhood Cancer (Research)
Center for Clinical and Translational Research
Center for Colorectal and Pelvic Reconstruction
Center for Gene Therapy (Research)
Center for Healthy Weight and Nutrition
Center for Injury Research and Policy
Center for Innovation in Pediatric Practice
Center for Microbial Pathogenesis (Research)
Center for Molecular and Human Genetics (Research)
Center for Perinatal Research
Center for Vaccines and Immunity (Research)
Central Ohio Poison Center
Cerebral Palsy Program
Chest Wall Clinic
Child Development/Psychology
Child Life Specialists
ChildLab
Cleft Lip and Palate Center
Clinical Nutrition and Lactation
Clinical Services and Care Coordination
Clinical Studies
Clinical Therapies
Close To Home Centers
Community Relations
Congenital Heart Disease
Connecting Families
Critical Care
Cystic Fibrosis
Dentistry
Dermatology
Developmental/ Behavioral Pediatrics
Diabetes Clinic
Disorders of Sexual Development (DSD)
Ear Nose & Throat Services (Otolaryngology)
Early Childhood Development Program
Education Classes
Emergency Services
Endocrinology Metabolism & Diabetes
Family Advisory Council
Family AIDS Clinic and Educational Services (FACES)
Family Health Information Center
Family Practice
Family Resource Center
Fetal Diagnostics
Financial Matters
Gastroenterology Hepatology and Nutrition
Gender Concerns
General Pediatric Surgery
Genetics (Molecular and Human)
Gift Cards
Gift Shop
Government Relations
Health Info Library
Health Information Management (HIM)
Hearing Program
Heart Center
Hemangioma Vascular Anomalies
Hematology Oncology & BMT

HIV Program
Homecare
Hospice
Immunology
Infectious Diseases
Interdisciplinary Feeding Clinic
International Adoption Clinic
Interventional Radiology
Jeune's Syndrome
Laboratory Medicine/Reference Lab
Massage Therapy
Medical Records
Melanoma & Pigmented Lesion Clinic
Music Therapy
myChildren's
Neonatology
Nephrology
Neurodiagnostics/EEG
Neurology
Neuromuscular Disorders
Neurosciences Center
Neurosurgery
Nuclear Medicine
Nurse-Family Partnership
Occupational Therapy
Ophthalmology/Eye Clinic
Orthopedics
Outpatient Surgery
Pain Service Clinic
Palliative Care
Pastoral Care
Patient and Family Relations
Patient and Visitor Guide
Patient Financial Services
PediaCast: a pediatric podcast for parents
Pediatric and Adolescent Gynecology
Pediatric Psychiatry
Pediatric Psychology
Pharmacy Services (Outpatient)
Physical Medicine & Rehabilitation
Physical Therapy
Physical Therapy - Sports and Orthopedic
Plastic and Reconstructive Surgery
Prader-Willi Syndrome Clinic
Primary Care Centers
Pulmonary Medicine
Radiology
Reach Out and Read
Rehabilitation
Request an Appointment
Research at Children's
Resonance Disorders Program
Rheumatology
Robot-Assisted Surgery
Ronald McDonald House
School Program
Sibling Support (Children's Clubhouse)
Sleep Disorder Center
Social Work
Speech and Language Pathology
Spina Bifida Program
Sports Medicine
Surgical Services
Telehealth
The Center for Family Safety and Healing
Therapeutic Recreation
THRIVE Program (DSD & Complex Urological & Gender
   Concerns)
Toxicology
Transplant Program
Transport
Trauma
Urgent Care Services
Urology
Velopharyngeal Dysfunction Program
Weight Loss Surgery

COMPETITORS

Akron Children's Hospital	Licking Memorial Health Systems
Cincinnati Children's Hospital	Mount Carmel Health OhioHealth
Fairfield Medical Center	Select Medical
Genesis HealthCare System (Ohio)	Shriners Hospitals For Children

HISTORICAL FINANCIALS

Company Type: Private

Income Statement

FYE: December 31

	REVENUE ($ mil.)	NET INCOME ($ mil.)	NET PROFIT MARGIN	EMPLOYEES
12/13	1,658	334	20.1%	6,000
12/09	918	95	10.4%	—
12/08	1,059	(175)	—	—
Annual Growth	9.4%	—	—	—

2013 Year-End Financials

Return on assets: 2.6%   Cash ($ mil.): 291
Return on equity: 20.1%
Current ratio: 1.60

NCH CORPORATION

NCH has been cleaning up for years and like everyone else it's been using soaps and detergents to do so. The company makes and sells about 450 chemical maintenance repair and supply products including all kinds of cleaners for customers in more than 50 countries throughout the world. NCH markets its products through a direct sales force to companies in the agricultural home-improvement industrial recreational and utility markets. Other products include fasteners welding supplies pet care supplies plumbing parts lubricants and metal-working fluids.

Geographic Reach

NCH has operations in Asia Europe North America and Latin America. The company has representatives in 30 countries on five continents. The company's sales and service teams serve customers in North America Latin America Europe Asia Australia and India. NCH has wholly owned subsidiaries in more than 50 countries.

Operations

The company's major areas of focus include producing products for the industrial cleaning and maintenance pet care plumbing specialty industries supply and water treatment and remediation markets.

NCH's cleaning products include hand cleaners industrial cleaners and housekeeping supplies. Specialty chemical products including cleaning and water treatment chemicals deodorizers lubricants paints and paint strippers patching compounds and flooring and carpet treatments account for the majority of sales.

The company's divisions include: Water Treatment Solutions plumbing Pet Care (Simple Solutions® Bags on Board® Vet's Best® and OUT! Pet Care) Specialty Industrial Supplies (operates through Partsmaster) industrial and institutional maintenance oil and gas Parts Washing lubrication and biologicals.

NCH operates more than 40 separate business units. Subsidiary Supply Line Direct offers safety and maintenance products such as janitorial supplies safety signs first aid kits spills kits storage cabinets for hazardous chemicals and protective apparel. Its plumbing products group has plumbing supplies for OEM and retail consumer markets. Other subsidiaries include Pure Solve a parts washing service TERRA Services (which reduces hazardous chemicals used in the hydraulic fracturing process) and X-Chem an oil field services division.

Subsidiary companies in NCH's Chemical Specialties division produce a diverse array of maintenance chemicals that includes cleaners degreasers lubricants grounds care housekeeping and water treatment products. Companies in the Partsmaster group offer a wide variety of items for maintenance and repair including welding supplies and fasteners. The Plumbing Products Group provides plumbing supplies for the do-it-yourself retail consumer and the OEM market. The Retail Products Group markets a wide range of pet supplies.

Sales and Marketing

NCH sells its products directly through a number of wholly owned subsidiaries many of which are engaged in the maintenance products business. These include Bags on Board Partsmaster Chemsearch Chem-Aqua and Mantek.

Strategy

In 2012 subsidiaries Chem-Aqua and Nephros signed a non-exclusive distributor agreement for Chem-Aqua to distribute Nephros's innovative ultrafilters in North America. The addition of Nephros ultrafilters to Chem-Aqua's product line allows both companies to offer their institutional customers a comprehensive multi-barrier approach for the prevention of waterborne infection.

NCH continues to seek new opportunities in water treatment oil and gas and in driving innovation to help keep its facilities and equipment running in optimum condition while reducing costs.

Company Background

Descendants of founder Milton Levy own the company. NCH was established in 1919.

HISTORY

Salesman Milton Levy founded National Disinfectant Co. in Dallas in 1919 to make disinfectants insecticides and soaps. The company's offerings grew in the 1930s to include Everbrite a top-selling industrial floor wax. Levy's sons Irvin Lester and Milton Jr. worked for the company as teenagers and took over its management after their father's death in 1946.

National Disinfectant expanded geographically in the 1950s and 1960s opening its first branch office in St. Louis in 1956. The company changed its name to National Chemsearch in 1960 to reflect its diversity. It also expanded into Europe and Latin America. National Chemsearch went public in 1965. Acquisitions boosted its product line to about 250 items by 1970. The company shortened its name to NCH in 1978.

NCH expanded its marketing to include catalog sales direct mail and telemarketing in 1986. It opened a South Korean plant in 1992. Troubled economies in Mexico and Venezuela hurt profits in 1994 and the next year NCH began work on a long-term business strategy that envisioned third-generation Levy family members moving into higher executive ranks.

Softened currency rates in Europe and Asia contributed to a decrease in profits for fiscal 1999. That year NCH focused on strengthening its customer relationships by boosting sales staff training and implementing an Internet-based corporate network.

In 2000 Irvin Levy became the company's chairman and NCH sold its electronic components business. The next year the company shut down its direct broadcast satellite equipment operations. In February 2002 the Levys took the company private by purchasing the 43% of the company that they didn't already own. The brothers originally offered a 20% premium to buy the shares but were greeted by lawsuits from shareholders who claimed they were taking advantage of a depressed market. The Levys settled the suits by upping the offer by $120 million.

EXECUTIVES

Exec V Pres-cfo, Christopher T (Chris) Sortwell
Vice President In Charge Of Special Projects, Neil Struby

Senior Vice President Corporate Services
  Administration, Chris Zetena
Vice President Technology, Greg Swindle
Vice President Of Marketing, Kevin Jones
Vice President Information Technology, Brendan
  Coleman
Senior Vice President Sales, Brenda Sanders
Director Of Patient Relations and Regulatory
  Compliance, Rodney (Rod) Judd
Executive Vice President, Robert Levy
Vice President Operations, David (Dave) Evans
Vice President Global Travel Management, Ann
  Levy
Vice President Finance And Global Controller,
  John (Jack) Currie
Executive Vice President Customer Relationship,
  Susan Staples
Senior Vice President Training, John (Jack)
  Arakelian
Vice President Business Development, Rich
  Katzmann
Acting Vice President China, David (Dave)
  Kuntschik
Executive Vice President, Joe Osullivan
Executive Vice President, Mike Benton
Medical Director, Julie Allison
Vice President Of Marketing, Matt Smith
Vice President of Operations and Information
  Technology, Greg Groff
Senior Vice President, Earl Nicholson
Executive Vice President, Lester A Levy
Vice President of Operations, James (Jamie)
  Marshall
Vice President Finance, Tom Hetzer
Executive Vice President, Walter Levy
Vice President Treasurer, Irena Kildisas
Senior Vice President, John (Jack) Larsson
Vice President Research and Development, John
  (Jack) Roheim
Vice President, Dan Mason
Vice President Research and Development, Scott
  Boyette
Board Member, Marga Tubb
Board Member, Jim Hurt
Treasurer, Susan (Sue) Sullivan
Auditors: DELOITTE & TOUCHE LLP DALLAS

LOCATIONS

HQ: NCH CORPORATION
  2727 CHEMSEARCH BLVD, IRVING, TX 750626454
Phone: 972 438-0705
Web: WWW.US.CHEMSEARCH.COM

PRODUCTS/OPERATIONS

Selected Operations and Products
Chemical Specialties
  Cleaning chemicals
  Deodorizers
  Floor and carpet care products
  HVAC products
  Lubricants
  Oil production facility chemicals
  Paint
  Paint removers
  Water-treatment chemicals
Landmark Direct
  First-aid supplies
  Workplace signage and productivity products
Pet Care
Partsmaster Group
  Cutting tools
  Electrical products
  Fasteners
  Welding alloys
Plumbing Products Group
  Plumbing products for new construction
  Plumbing repair and replacement parts
Industrial and Institutional Maintenance
  Industrial and commercial cleaning
  Industrial Repair and maintenance
  Drains Grease Traps and lift stations
  Lubrication and coolants
  Equipment and supplies

Parts washing
Grounds Care
Personal hygiene
Pet Care
Training pads
Stain and Odor Removers
Cleaners and Disinfectants
Allergy Relief and shed Control
Grooming products
Plumbing
Sinks
Faucets
Tub & Showers
Toilets
Drains
Specialty Industrial Supply
High Performance Cutting Tools
Welding
Abrasives
Compounds
Fasteners
Electrical and Automotive
Shop Supplies
Storage Hardware
Tools
Water Treatment Solutions
Boiler
Cooling Towers
Colsed Recirculation Systems
Biocides and Algaecides
Cleaner/Descalers
Equipment
Wastewater and Bio Remediation

COMPETITORS

Church & Dwight	H.B. Fuller
Cintas	Illinois Tool Works
Clariant	Pioneer Corporation
Danaher	Quaker Chemical
Detrex	Safety-Kleen
Ecolab	

HISTORICAL FINANCIALS
Company Type: Private

Income Statement
FYE: April 30

	REVENUE ($ mil.)	NET INCOME ($ mil.)	NET PROFIT MARGIN	EMPLOYEES
04/13	1,018	3	0.3%	8,500
04/12	1,045	6	0.6%	—
04/11	952	6	0.7%	—
04/10	885	0	—	—
Annual Growth	4.8%	—	—	—

2013 Year-End Financials
Return on assets: 7.7%
Return on equity: 0.3%
Current ratio: 1.30
Cash ($ mil.): 11

NEBRASKA METHODIST HOSPITAL INC

LOCATIONS

HQ: NEBRASKA METHODIST HOSPITAL INC
  8303 DODGE ST, OMAHA, NE 681144108
Phone: 402 354-4540
Web: WWW.BESTCARE.ORG

HISTORICAL FINANCIALS
Company Type: Private

Income Statement
FYE: December 31

	REVENUE ($ mil.)	NET INCOME ($ mil.)	NET PROFIT MARGIN	EMPLOYEES
12/12	410	30	7.4%	2,635
12/08	347	19	5.7%	—
12/02	253	16	6.6%	—
12/01	390	0	—	—
Annual Growth	—	—	—	—

2012 Year-End Financials
Return on assets: 3.4%
Return on equity: 7.4%
Current ratio: 1.80
Cash ($ mil.): 42

NEIGHBORHOOD REINVESTMENT CORPORATION

Neighborhood Reinvestment Corporation (now dba NeighborWorks America) wants to be your neighbor. The not-for-profit organization supports more than 235 independent local organizations in suburban urban and rural communities across the country. Programs include building multi-family dwellings and helping low and middle income families with financing and insurance as well as job creation community facilities and economic development in rural areas. The organization also offers training for community leaders and would-be homeowners on community planning green building and financing among others. Established by Congress in 1978 NeighborWorks is funded by Congress private donations and corporate support.Geographic ReachNeighborWorks America operates a national office in Washgington DC and seven district offices in California Colorado Georgia. Massachusetts Missouri New York and Ohio.OperationsNeighborWorks America ranked third among nonprofit builders of affordable homes in 2012 on the Builder 100 list and for the fourth year it was ranked among the top 100 of all home builders with 608 closings in 2012. To date the organization has leveraged more than $16 billion to invest in America's communities through its work in more than 4400 urban suburban and rural communities in all 50 states the District of Columbia and Puerto Rico. Financial PerformanceCongressional appropriations account for close to 90% of the nonprofit's revenue; while contributions generated around 10%. Major contributors and partners for NeighborWorks include Bank of America Ford Foundation Fannie Mae JPMorgan Chase Morgan Stanley and Federal Home Loan Bank of Dallas. StrategyNeighborWorks America's strategic plan for 2012 through 2016 includes employing and promoting green and sustainable building practices for the long-term benefit of the residents and communities in which it operates. The plan also establishes two specific outcomes: moving the NeighborWorks network to adopt comprehensive green strategies by designing at least two-thirds of the network as a NeighborWorks Green Organization; and further reducing the environmental impact of its operations and training practices.

EXECUTIVES

CFO, Michael L. Forster
Senior Vice President Information Management, Damodar Konda
Senior Vice President Controller, Steve Slepian
Vice President Of Isles, Milton Sharp
Senior Vice President Public Relations, Christina McHenry
Vice Chairman, Rodney Hood
Treasurer, Jeff Marshall
Auditors: BDO USA LLP BETHESDA MD

LOCATIONS

HQ: NEIGHBORHOOD REINVESTMENT CORPORATION
999 N CAPITOL ST NE # 900, WASHINGTON, DC 200024684
Phone: 202 220-2300
Web: WWW.NW.ORG

HISTORICAL FINANCIALS

Company Type: Private

Income Statement

FYE: September 30

	REVENUE ($ mil.)	NET INCOME ($ mil.)	NET PROFIT MARGIN	EMPLOYEES
09/13	248	11	4.6%	260
09/10	312	2	0.8%	—
09/09*	359	7	2.0%	—
12/08	1	0	—	—
Annual Growth 197.0%				

*Fiscal year change

2013 Year-End Financials

Return on assets: 10.8%   Cash ($ mil.): 83
Return on equity: 4.6%
Current ratio: 1.10

NEMOURS FOUNDATION

Even if their offspring are fanatical about Finding Nemo parents of sick children may prefer finding Nemours. The Nemours Foundation operates the Nemours/Alfred I. duPont Hospital for Children in Wilmington Delaware; the Nemours Children's Hospital in Orlando Florida; and dozens of pediatric clinics in Delaware Florida New Jersey and Pennsylvania that treat acutely and chronically ill children. Specialties include orthopedics cardiology neurology and oncology. Nemours also has extensive research programs and it operates a clinic in Delaware that serves low-income elderly residents. The not-for-profit foundation was created in 1936 through the will of chemicals pioneer Alfred I. duPont.

Operations

Some of Nemours' facilities are operated in partnership with other health care providers. For example it runs pediatric programs with Bryn Mawr Hospital Lancaster General and Thomas Jefferson University Hospital in Pennsylvania as well as with AtlantiCare and Virtua Health in New Jersey.

Financial Performance

In 2013 Nemours posted a 14% increase in revenue from $861 million to $982 million mostly due to trust distributions and net assets released from restrictions but also from a bump in patient service revenue. Net income also rose from a loss of $71 million in 2012 to a positive $144 million from a pension liability adjustment. Cash from operations followed suit going from $5 million to $28 million.

Strategy

Nemours Foundation completed construction of a full-service children's hospital in Orlando Florida where it already operated a pediatric specialty clinic. The $400 million facility named Nemours Children's Hospital has 95 patient beds and emergency diagnostic specialty and outpatient units as well as educational and research centers. The foundation is also expanding the Nemours/Alfred I. duPont Hospital for Children in Delaware; the new patient tower a $256 million project is scheduled to open in 2014.

The Nemours Foundation has also invested in upgrading its information technology system. It uses a comprehensive electronic health record (EHR) system NemoursOne to connect all of its doctors and facilities with shared patient information. Some of the foundation's facilities participate in the state EHR network (Delaware Health Information Network).

EXECUTIVES

Special Project Office Of The Vice President Of Quality And Safety, Karen Hartis
Vice President Information Services, Bradley Robinson
Director of Nursing, Ann Hurst
Medical Librarian, Kristina Flathers
Clinical Director, Diana Corao
Managing Director, Lori Counts
Medical Director And Pediatrician In Chief, William B (Bill) Blanchard
Vice President Phys Prac Fl, Jay Cummings
Vice President Finance, Rodney (Rod) McKendree
Assistant Secretary, Marylynn Girouard
Auditors: KPMG LLP JACKSONVILLE FL

LOCATIONS

HQ: NEMOURS FOUNDATION
10140 CENTURION PKWY N, JACKSONVILLE, FL 322560532
Phone: 904 697-4100
Web: WWW.NEMOURS.ORG

PRODUCTS/OPERATIONS

2013 Sales

	% of total
Net patient revenue less provision for bad debts	75
Distribution from the Alfred I.duPont testamentary Trust	14
Net assets released from restrictions used for operations	5
Contract service revenue	2
Grant revenue	2
other income	2
Total	**100**

COMPETITORS

All Children's Hospital
Baptist Health System
Children's Hospital Boston
Children's Hospital of Philadelphia
Children's Hospital of Pittsburgh
Children's National Medical Center
Children's Specialized Hospital
Christiana Care
Cincinnati Children's Hospital
Florida Hospital Waterman
HCA
Mayo Clinic Jacksonville
Miami Children's Hospital
Orlando Health
Shriners Hospitals For Children
St. Jude Children's Research Hospital
UF&Shands

HISTORICAL FINANCIALS

Company Type: Private

Income Statement

FYE: December 31

	REVENUE ($ mil.)	NET INCOME ($ mil.)	NET PROFIT MARGIN	EMPLOYEES
12/08	160	(80)	—	4,400
12/07	635	53	8.5%	—
12/06	578	29	5.1%	—
12/05	546	0	—	—
Annual Growth (33.5%)				

2008 Year-End Financials

Return on assets: 4.6%   Cash ($ mil.): 164
Return on equity: (-50.5%)
Current ratio: 3.10

NEW ENGLAND PETROLEUM LIMITED PARTNERSHIP

Auditors: PRICEWATERHOUSECOOPERS LLP B

LOCATIONS

HQ: NEW ENGLAND PETROLEUM LIMITED PARTNERSHIP
6 KIMBALL LN STE 400, LYNNFIELD, MA 019402685
Phone: 617 660-7400
Web: WWW.GULFOIL.COM

HISTORICAL FINANCIALS

Company Type: Private

Income Statement

FYE: December 31

	REVENUE ($ mil.)	NET INCOME ($ mil.)	NET PROFIT MARGIN	EMPLOYEES
12/12	1,081	4	0.4%	25
12/11	998	3	0.3%	—
12/10	568	2	0.5%	—
12/09	397	0	—	—
Annual Growth 39.6%				

2012 Year-End Financials

Return on assets: 2.1%   Cash ($ mil.): 2
Return on equity: 0.4%
Current ratio: 1.20

NEW HANOVER REGIONAL MEDICAL CENTER AUXILIARY INC.

Those living in the Cape Fear area need not fear when it comes to accessing good medical care. Integrated health system New Hanover Regional Medical Center (NHRMC) serves the Wilmington and Cape Fear area of North Carolina through its flagship 855-bed New Hanover Regional Medical Center the 130-bed Cape Fear Hospital and the 85-bed Pender Memorial Hospital. NHRMC also operates a rehabilitation center a behavioral health facility and a women's and children's hospital as well as home health hospice EMS transport physician practice and outpatient care clinic locations. The not-for-profit health network is affiliated with the UNC-Chapel Hill School of Medicine.

Geographic Reach

NHRMC's hospitals serve southeastern North Carolina. Its main campus is in Wilmington; the health network also operates the Cape Fear Hospital in Wilmington and the Pender Memorial Hospital in Burgaw.

Operations

NHRMC's medical staff includes more than 550 physicians and 700 active volunteers.

NHRMC is part of the Coastal Carolinas Health Alliance a cooperative of regional hospitals that use their combined buying size to negotiate lower prices for hospital equipment and supplies. The group also works together to increase community access to health care and promote continuing medical education amongst its peers.

The company's orthopedic hospital performs 8000 orthopedic procedures a year including more than 2200 joint replacement surgeries.

Financial Performance

NHRMC's revenues grew by 5% in 2014 due to higher Net patient service revenues thanks to increased use of both inpatient and outpatient services. Net income increased by 5% as the result of higher revenues and a net increase in the fair value of investments.

NHRMC's operating cash flow decreased by 7% in 2014 due to an increase in cash used to pay suppliers for goods and services and employees for services.

Strategy

The medical center has consistently expanded services into the surrounding region to include construction of NHRMC ED-North a standalone emergency department that opened in May 2015. In 2015 NHRMC completed the construction of a new standalone emergency department in the northern part of New Hanover County. The 30000 square foot building has 10 treatment rooms and one critical care room and is staffed 24/7 by board-certified emergency physicians nurses certified in emergency care and a multidisciplinary support care team. The building designed by BBH Design and constructed by Brasfield & Gorrie cost $15.1 million to build and the project was funded from NHRMC's capital budget.

Company Background

In 2013 NHRMC expanded its EMS transportation services by expanding its AirLink program. The medical center added a second helicopter to provide services in Onslow and Columbus counties. The move will help the organization reduce response times and improve critical care services.

In addition the medical center expanded outpatient care services in 2012 through the addition of a multi-specialty physician group (Hanover Medical Specialists) to its physician practice group.

The medical network is governed by a board of trustees consisting of members appointed by the New Hanover County commissioners and representatives from the neighboring Pender County.

EXECUTIVES

President and CEO, Jack Barto
Treasurer, Ronald J. (Ron) Isyk
Chairman, John D. (Jack) Fuller
Executive Director of the NHRMC Foundation, Aline Lasseter
Trustee, Robert G. (Bobby) Greer
Trustee, Carl D. Brown
Trustees, Helyn R. Lofton

LOCATIONS

HQ: NEW HANOVER REGIONAL MEDICAL CENTER AUXILIARY INC.
2131 S 17TH ST, WILMINGTON, NC 284017407
Phone: 910 343-7001
Web: WWW.NHRMC.ORG

PRODUCTS/OPERATIONS

Selected Services

Bariatrics
Breast
Cancer Behavioral
Cancer
Children
Cardiology
Diabetes
Eye Care
Emergency
Gynecology
HIV Aids
Home Care
Heart
Maternity
Maxillofacial
Neonatology
Neurosurgery
Oral Surgery
Oncology
Orthopedics
Optometry
Occupational Therapy

Selected Locations

Behavioral Health Hospital (Wilmington North Carolina)
Betty H. Cameron Women's and Children's Hospital (Wilmington North Carolina)
Cape Fear Hospital (Wilmington North Carolina)
New Hanover Regional Medical Center (main campus; Wilmington North Carolina)
Pender Memorial Hospital (Burgaw North Carolina)
Rehabilitation Hospital (Wilmington North Carolina)

COMPETITORS

Blue Ridge HealthCare
Carolinas HealthCare System
Community Health Systems
Conway Medical Center
Grand Strand Regional Medical Center
High Point Regional Health System
Mission Hospitals
Novant Health
UNC Hospitals

HISTORICAL FINANCIALS

Company Type: Private

Income Statement
FYE: December 31

	REVENUE ($ mil.)	NET INCOME ($ mil.)	NET PROFIT MARGIN	EMPLOYEES
12/14*	200	26	13.1%	3,692
09/14	758	63	8.4%	—
09/13	687	50	7.3%	—
12/12	204	0	—	—
Annual Growth	(0.9%)	—	—	—

*Fiscal year change

2014 Year-End Financials

Return on assets: 13.7%
Return on equity: 13.1%
Current ratio: 1.40
Cash ($ mil.): 57

NEW JERSEY INSTITUTE OF TECHNOLOGY (INC)

A public research university New Jersey Institute of Technology (NJIT) offers about 100 undergraduate and graduate programs including about 20 doctoral programs in fields including architecture engineering computer science and liberal arts. The school also offers continuing education and distance courses. With some 500 full-time faculty members NJIT boasts a student-faulty ratio of 16:1. Its Albert Dorman Honors College provides students with individualized curricula and honors colloquia including travel and featured speakers. About 10000 students attend the NJIT which operates a single campus in Newark. NJIT was founded in 1881 as the Newark Technical School.

Operations

Newark's NJIT has some 7125 undergraduate and 2825 graduate students. Master's programs are offered across 56 specialties. The school also offers some 46 baccalaureate degree programs.

Strategy

Looking to provide additional capacity for students to reside on campus NJIT focuses on campus and area development. Through the efforts of three ongoing projects the university is working to enhance campus life for its students and increase its residential student numbers on campus by 600.

Financial Performance

Thanks to organic growth the university has logged revenue increases during the past three years. NJIT's revenue rose some 11% in 2011 vs. 2010 due to increases in tuition and fees and auxiliary enterprise revenues attributable to a boost in occupancy and residence hall charges and increases in federal state and other grants and contracts. Net income during the same reporting period increased by 61%. NJIT points to income from realized net gains on the sale of investments (partially offset by a decrease in interest and dividends) for the increases. Cash generated from tuition and fees and auxiliary enterprises contributed toward a cash flow bump of more than $20 million in 2011 vs. 2010.

EXECUTIVES

Vice President of Administration, Henry (Hal) Mauermayer
SVP Technology and Business Development, Donald H. Sebastian
President, Joel S. Bloom
Associate Provost Information Services and Technology and CIO, David F. Ullman
Provost and SEVP, Fadi P. Deek
SVP Finance and CFO, Edward J. Bishof
Borders Njit Vice President, Victor S Reynaga
Vice President For Academic Support And Student Affairs, Charles J (Chas) Fey
Vice President Finance, William Garcia
Executive Vice President Technology, Jerry Paris
Vice President for Human Resources, Theodore (Theo) Johnson
Vice President for Admin, Norma Montague
Chairman, Stephen P. DePalma
Advisory Board Member, Eseosa Eriamiato
Treasurer, Jason Cabrejos
Auditors: KPMG LLP SHORT HILLS NJ

LOCATIONS

HQ: NEW JERSEY INSTITUTE OF TECHNOLOGY (INC)
111 LOCK ST, NEWARK, NJ 071033540
Phone: 973 596-3000
Web: WWW.NJIT.EDU

PRODUCTS/OPERATIONS

Selected Colleges

Newark College of Engineering
College of Architecture and Design
College of Science and Liberal Arts
School of Management
Albert Dorman Honors College
College of Computing Sciences

HISTORICAL FINANCIALS

Company Type: Private

Income Statement

FYE: June 30

	REVENUE ($ mil.)	NET INCOME ($ mil.)	NET PROFIT MARGIN	EMPLOYEES
06/14	220	93	42.4%	1,047
06/13	210	17	8.3%	—
06/12	197	0	0.3%	—
06/11	184	0	—	—
Annual Growth	6.1%	—	—	—

2014 Year-End Financials

Return on assets: 15.0% Cash ($ mil.): 58
Return on equity: 42.4%
Current ratio: 1.50

NEW PRIME INC.

Check out this Prime number —more than 8200 remotely monitored temperature-controlled trailers. Specialized carrier New Prime (which does business simply as Prime) provides refrigerated flatbed and liquid bulk tanker trucking services throughout North America. The company operates in the US and Canada and serves Mexico through arrangements with other carriers. A subsidiary Prime Floral uses the parent company's refrigerated equipment and facilities to serve the flower industry. In addition to its freight-hauling operations Prime provides logistics services including freight brokerage.

Geographic Reach

The company serves customers in Canada Mexico and the US. Based in Springfield Missouri Prime operates two US terminals in Pennsylvania and Utah.

Operations

Prime which has a fleet of more than 4700 trucks operates through three divisions.

Prime's liquid bulk fleet (Tanker Division) consists of more than 200 trucks and more than 400 6800-gallon Walker Stainless MC407 trailers with air ride suspensions. The company's Refrigerated Division has a fleet of remotely monitored temperature-controlled trailers and serves businesses whose needs include transportation of fresh produce fresh cut floral produce pharmaceuticals fresh or frozen meats or any other dry or temperature controlled freight. Prime also has a Flatbed Division.

Its affiliates include Amber Aleri Prime Floral Prime Intermodal Prime Logistics and Trailer Skirt.

Sales and Marketing

Prime has hauled goods for such blue chip consumer goods makers as ConAgra Foods Kraft Foods and General Mills.

Strategy

Prime is shifting its strategy to align with customer preferences for shortening supply chain mileage and delivery time all of which is intended to offset lower consumer demand and volatile fuel costs.It is also using technology to enhance its position as an industry leader in the safe cost-effective transport of temperature-sensitive goods. The company has embraced modern technology like the QUALCOMM satellite system which benefits shippers by providing continuous communication from initial dispatch to final delivery. This option helps to monitor load temperatures set points alarm conditions connect and disconnect times and uses the QUALCOMM link present in every Prime tractor to transfer this important data.

Prime Position Tracking enables the company to locate tractors in real-time within a 600 foot radius at all times. Prime Mapping and Routing provides detailed Rand McNally and PC*Miler directions to driver associates to ensure that loads get to their destination in the quickest safest and most efficient manner.

To better serve its growing workforce in 2014 Prime selected Benefitfocus HR INTOUCH MARKETPLACE® to facilitate the compliance of its benefits administration with the Affordable Care Act. The software integrates all benefits-related data in a single portal that is accessible from any web-enabled device.

Company Background

Prime was founded in 1970 by Robert Low who continues to serve as Prime's president.

EXECUTIVES

National Account Manager, Jared Crutcher
Auditors: ERNST & YOUNG LLP KANSAS CITY

LOCATIONS

HQ: NEW PRIME INC.
2740 N MAYFAIR AVE, SPRINGFIELD, MO 658035084
Phone: 417 866-0001
Web: WWW.PRIMEINC.COM

COMPETITORS

Boyd Bros. Transportation
C.H. Robinson Worldwide
C.R. England
Central Refrigerated Service
Comcar
Frozen Food Express
KLLM Transport Services
Marten Transport
Quality Distribution
Stevens Transport

HISTORICAL FINANCIALS

Company Type: Private

Income Statement

FYE: March 29

	REVENUE ($ mil.)	NET INCOME ($ mil.)	NET PROFIT MARGIN	EMPLOYEES
03/13	1,164	70	6.0%	5,000
03/12*	1,022	60	6.0%	—
04/11	941	47	5.0%	—
03/10	844	0	—	—
Annual Growth	11.3%	—	—	—

*Fiscal year change

2013 Year-End Financials

Return on assets: 2.4% Cash ($ mil.): —
Return on equity: 6.0%
Current ratio: 0.80

NEW YORK BLOOD CENTER INC.

New York Blood Center (NYBC) holds a very literal interpretation of the meaning of life. It is a not-for-profit blood distribution and research organization serving New York City and its environs in New York State and New Jersey as well as parts of Connecticut and Pennsylvania. As one of the largest blood centers in the US NYBC provides nearly 1 million blood components to some 200 hospitals each year. The center's facilities collect blood from more than 2000 donors each day. It also operates the nation's oldest and largest public cord blood bank. In addition its Kimball Research Institute includes more than a dozen research laboratories which study the prevention and treatment of blood-related illnesses.

Geographic Reach

Based in New York NYBC offers its services throughout New York City Long Island the Hudson Valley and in Connecticut New Jersey and Pennsylvania.

OperationsAreas of research in the Kimball Research Institute include virology molecular genetics cell biology and signaling viral immunology and infectious disease prevention. It has been responsible for the development and licensing of solvent and detergent technology used to deactivate the potency of viruses in blood and blood products (such as plasma and platelets used in transfusions).NYBC's clinical services division acts as an adjunct and resource to hospitals throughout its service areas by providing expertise in transfusion medicine as well as delivering more than 8500 specialized procedures each year. In addition the center maintains a bone marrow donor registry for the New York area provides hemophilia services to some 1500 patients and offers screening and education programs for cholesterol high blood pressure and cardiovascular disease.

Strategy

Seeking greater breadth and financial stability NYBC announced it will combine its operations with Community Blood Center of Greater Kansas City (CBC) to form one of the leading blood centers serving patients and hospitals in the Northeast and Midwest. The combination is expected to be completed in mid-2014. The union of NYBC and CBC is expected to bring synergies in blood and laboratory services medical programs cell therapies and research.

Mergers and Acquisitions

In October 2013 NYBC acquired Coral Blood Services a subsidiary of HemaCare Corp. to advance its mission of providing innovative blood products and medical services to hospitals and patients throughout the Northeast. Coral Blood Services provides more than 2500 therapeutic apheresis procedures annually in New York New Jersey Connecticut and Pennsylvania.

EXECUTIVES

Vice President and Executive Director Hudson Valley Blood Services, Michele Shenfeld
Vice President and Director Lindsley F. Kimball Research Institute, Mohandas Narla
Vice President General Counsel Secretary, Jordana Schwartz
Vice President, Harvey Schaffler
Vice President Of Human Resources, Doriane Gloria
Senior Vice President Human Resources, Ollie Cheatham
Vice President, Charles (Chas) Grossenbacher
Vice President Program Director, Rubinstein Pablo
Adrp Treasurer Committee Oversight, Christine Foran
Auditors: BERDON LLP NEW YORK NY

LOCATIONS

HQ: NEW YORK BLOOD CENTER INC.
310 E 67TH ST, NEW YORK, NY 100656273
Phone: 212 570-3010
Web: WWW.NYBLOODCENTER.ORG

PRODUCTS/OPERATIONS

Selected Services
Blood products
Clinical services
Hemochromatosis phlebotomy program
Hemophilia services
Laboratory services
Ordertrak
Transfusion medicine services

HISTORICAL FINANCIALS

Company Type: Private

Income Statement

FYE: March 31

	REVENUE ($ mil.)	NET INCOME ($ mil.)	NET PROFIT MARGIN	EMPLOYEES
03/11	348	(11)	—	1,600
03/10	375	20	5.4%	—
Annual Growth	(7.3%)	—	—	—

2011 Year-End Financials

Return on assets: —   Cash ($ mil.): 38
Return on equity: (-3.4%)
Current ratio: 1.00

NEW YORK COMMUNITY TRUST AND COMMUNITY FUNDS INC

Auditors: KPMG LLP NEW YORK NY

LOCATIONS

HQ: NEW YORK COMMUNITY TRUST AND
COMMUNITY FUNDS INC
909 3RD AVE FL 22, NEW YORK, NY 100224752
Phone: 212 686-0010
Web: WWW.LICF.ORG

HISTORICAL FINANCIALS

Company Type: Private

Income Statement

FYE: December 31

	ASSETS ($ mil.)	NET INCOME ($ mil.)	INCOME AS % OF ASSETS	EMPLOYEES
12/13	2,443	302	12.4%	65
12/12	2,147	239	11.1%	—
12/11	1,908	17	0.9%	—
12/10	1,877	0	—	—
Annual Growth	9.2%	—	—	—

2013 Year-End Financials

Return on assets: 0.2%   Sales ($ mil): 451
Return on equity: 66.9%

NEW YORK METHODIST HOSPITAL

New York Methodist Hospital is a not-for-profit acute-care teaching hospital serving Brooklyn residents. Established in 1881 as the Methodist Episcopal Hospital the facility has more than 650 licensed beds. It offers a full range of medical services including primary and emergency care as well as specialty services such as women's health cancer cardiovascular pediatric geriatric and behavioral health. The hospital also operates satellite clinics in surrounding areas. A member of New York-Presbyterian Healthcare System New York Methodist is a teaching hospital affiliated with Cornell University's Weill Medical College.

Geographic Reach

New York Methodist Hospital's main campus is in the Park Slope neighborhood of Brooklyn. It has several outpatient centers in other parts of Brooklyn as well.

Operations

New York Methodist Hospital handles about 40000 inpatient admissions and 100000 emergency department visits each year as well as 24000 surgeries and 5000 births. It also processes about 200000 laboratory sample processes annually.

New York Methodist Hospital includes specialty institutes in about 10 fields including pulmonary medicine cancer care and vascular health. In addition to providing inpatient care the organization operates some 10 primary and specialty outpatient centers. It also runs a number of graduate medical programs including programs affiliated with professional training schools in the areas of radiography medical technology radiation therapy and paramedics.

Strategy

To expand care for area residents New York Methodist is adding new specialist programs and equipment. For instance in 2012 the hospital added a robotic-assisted surgery program for bariatric procedures. It also opened a new wound care and hyperbaric oxygen therapy center for hard-to-heal wounds. In addition in 2013 the hospital moved its sleep disorder center into a new facility.

EXECUTIVES

Senior Vice President, Lauren Yedvab
Vice President Planning Public Affairs and Development, Lyn Hill
President and CEO, Mark J. Mundy, age 74
SVP Nursing, Rebecca Flood
SVP Medical Affairs, Steven Silber
SVP Finance, Michael Fagan
President Medical Board, Prasad Gudavalli
Chairman, John E. Carrington
Board Member, James Perkins
Auditors: CHARLES A BARRAGATO & CO CPAS

LOCATIONS

HQ: NEW YORK METHODIST HOSPITAL
506 6TH ST, BROOKLYN, NY 112153609
Phone: 718 780-3000
Web: WWW.NYM.ORG

COMPETITORS

HISTORICAL FINANCIALS

Company Type: Private

Income Statement

FYE: December 31

	REVENUE ($ mil.)	NET INCOME ($ mil.)	NET PROFIT MARGIN	EMPLOYEES
12/13	810	115	14.2%	3,185
12/12	636	44	6.9%	—
12/09	516	4	0.9%	—
12/08	540	0	—	—
Annual Growth	8.4%	—	—	—

2013 Year-End Financials

Return on assets: 5.1%   Cash ($ mil.): 107
Return on equity: 14.2%
Current ratio: 1.20

NEW YORK POWER AUTHORITY

The hydropower generated by the mighty Niagara Falls is the real authority behind the New York Power Authority (NYPA). More than 70% of the power that NYPA produces is from hydropower resources. The company generates and transmits more than 20% of New York's electricity making it the largest state-owned public power provider in the US. It is also New York's only statewide electricity supplier. NYPA owns hydroelectric and fossil-fueled generating facilities (16 in total) that produce about 5700 MW of electricity and it operates more than 1400 circuit-miles of transmission lines. NYPA is owned by the State of New York.

Sales and Marketing

NYPA services more than 500 businesses and industrial customers including manufacturing companies such as Anchor Glass of Elmira and General Motors of Tonawanda and non-manufacturing companies like GEICO of Amherst and Yahoo! of Lockport and 114 government entities in New York City and Westchester County including New York City government the Metropolitan Transportation Authority The Port Authority of New York and New Jersey the New York City Housing Authority Westchester County government and most Westchester municipalities school districts and other public entities.

Financial Performance

In 2013 the company's revenues increased by 13% to more than $3 billion primarily due to higher prices on market-based sales of energy and capacity and a rise in sales volumes and from the recovery of higher purchased power and fuel costs.NYPA's net income increased by 30% to $228 million in 2013 from $175 million in 2012 thanks to higher sales and decreased non-operating expenses offset by higher operating expenses.The company's operating cash inflow increased to $513 million in 2013 from $391 million in 2012 as the result of higher market-based sales due to an increase in prices on energy and capacity sales partially offset by higher purchased power and fuel costs.

Strategy

NYPA receives no state funds or tax credits. Instead it finances new projects through bond sales.

Following its shift from a regulated monopoly to a competitor in an open power market NYPA is aiming to grow by reducing the cost of the energy it provides and by developing electric transportation (such as electric cars) and other energy-efficiency projects including installing emergency power generators in metropolitan buildings. It is also working to improve the state's transmission grid increase its generating capacity and help support the state's directive to get 45% of its power from clean energy sources by 2015 (include 100 MW of power from solar arrays at buildings across the state). NYPA has been tagged as the lead agency to reduce energy use at state facilities by 20% by 2020.

In 2014 NYPA completed the installation of solar thermal hot water systems at five New York City firehouses in the Rockaways section of Queens. The $550000 investment will reduce operating costs and could lead to the wider use of the clean energy-transfer technology in other city government facilities. The company's energy efficiency projects have saved New Yorkers more than $148 million a year cutting annual oil use by more than 2.7 million barrels and offsetting the release of approximately 890000 tons of greenhouse gases. Its clean transportation program has placed more than 1300 electric-drive vehicles into service.In 2013 The Village of Lake Placid unveiled a new hybrid-electric shuttle bus that will make commuting on public transportation quieter and cleaner. Financing for the bus was made possible through NYPA's Municipal Electric-Drive Vehicle Program which provides financial assistance to New York municipal utilities to facilitate the replacement of less fuel-efficient vehicles in order to advance the state's clean energy goals. That year NYPA added seven more hybrids and one more EV to its fleet bringing the total number of electric drive vehicles to 79. It also purchased just over 40000 gallons of B20 biodiesel which earned the Power Authority 17 Alternative Fuel Vehicle credits under the Department of Energy's Energy Policy Act that will be used to purchase additional hybrid and plug-in hybrid vehicles.

To improve its delivery of power the company is pursuing the development of a new cross-Hudson transmission line that will connect New York City customers to the PJM Interconnection power grid.

HISTORY

The Power Authority of the State of New York (aka New York Power Authority or NYPA) was established in 1931 by Gov. Franklin Roosevelt to gain public control of New York's hydropower resources. The utility's major power plants came on line with the opening of the St. Lawrence-Franklin D. Roosevelt Power Project (1958) and the Niagara Power Project (1961). The Blenheim-Gilboa Pumped Storage Power Project opened in 1973.

In the mid-1970s NYPA shifted to nuclear power when it opened the James A. FitzPatrick Nuclear Power Plant (1975) and the Indian Point 3 Nuclear Power Plant (1976). The company then opened gas- and oil-powered plants: the Charles Poletti Power Project (1977) and the Richard M. Flynn Power Plant (1994).

In 1998 the authority allocated low-cost electricity to five companies that planned to invest $104 million in business expansions in western New York. The company suffered a loss in 1999 in part from reduced hydro generation and a drop in investment earnings. In 2000 NYPA sold its two nuclear plants (1800 MW of capacity) to utility holding company Entergy for $967 million.

The company completed the installation of 11 gas-powered turbines at various locations in New York City and on Long Island in 2001; the program was initiated to prevent expected energy shortages that summer but it also helped maintain power in areas of the city during the September 11 terrorist attacks.

EXECUTIVES

COO, Edward A. (Ed) Welz
President and CEO, Gil C. Quiniones
EVP and CFO, Robert F. Lurie
Senior Vice President Power Supply, Thomas (Thom) Antenucci
Senior Vice President Strategic Planning, Robert Laurie
Vice President Environment Health And Safety, William Slade
Acting Senior Vice President of Enterprise Shared Services, Rocco Iannarelli
Chairman Board of Trustees, John R. Koelmel
Vice Chair Board of Trustees, Joanne M. Mahoney

Treasurer Corporate Finance, Brian McElroy
Auditors: KPMG LLP ALBANY NEW YORK

LOCATIONS

HQ: NEW YORK POWER AUTHORITY
123 MAIN ST STE 1600, WHITE PLAINS, NY 106013132
Phone: 914 681-6200
Web: WWW.NYPA.GOV

PRODUCTS/OPERATIONS

2014 Sales

	$ mil.	% of total
Power sales	2,396	76
Wheeling charges	614	19
Transmission charges	165	5
Total	**3,175**	**100**

Selected Operations

Transmission Control Facility
   Frederick R. Clark Energy Center (Oneida County)
Fossil-Fueled Plants
   Charles Poletti Power Project (New York City)
   Richard M. Flynn Power Plant (Suffolk County)
   PowerNow! Turbines (11 units in New York City and Long Island)
Hydropower Plants
   Blenheim-Gilboa Pumped Storage Power Project (Schoharie County)
   Niagara Power Project (Niagara County)
   St. Lawrence-Franklin D. Roosevelt Power Project (St. Lawrence County)
Small Hydropower Plants
   Ashokan Project (Ulster County)
   Crescent Plant (Albany and Saratoga Counties)
   Gregory B. Jarvis Plant (Oneida County)
   Kensico Project (Westchester County)
   Vischer Ferry Plant (Saratoga and Schenectady counties)

COMPETITORS

Avangrid	Entergy
CH Energy	National Grid USA
Con Edison	Rochester Gas and
Dynegy	Electric
Enbridge	TransCanada

HISTORICAL FINANCIALS
Company Type: Private

Income Statement
FYE: December 31

	REVENUE ($ mil.)	NET INCOME ($ mil.)	NET PROFIT MARGIN	EMPLOYEES
12/13	3,030	249	8.2%	4,450
12/12	2,673	175	6.5%	—
12/11	2,655	294	11.1%	—
Annual Growth	**6.8%**	**(8.0%)**	—	—

2013 Year-End Financials

Return on assets: —
Return on equity: 8.2%
Current ratio: —
Cash ($ mil.): 8

NEW YORK SOCIETY FOR THE RELIEF OF THE RUPTURED & CRIPPLED

Auditors: ERNST & YOUNG LLP NEW YORK

LOCATIONS

HQ: NEW YORK SOCIETY FOR THE RELIEF OF THE RUPTURED & CRIPPLED
535 E 70TH ST, NEW YORK, NY 100214823
Phone: 212 606-1000
Web: WWW.HSS.EDU

HISTORICAL FINANCIALS
Company Type: Private

Income Statement
FYE: December 31

	REVENUE ($ mil.)	NET INCOME ($ mil.)	NET PROFIT MARGIN	EMPLOYEES
12/07	441	(21)	—	1,238
12/05	376	14	3.9%	—
12/04	330	15	4.7%	—
12/02	249	0	—	—
Annual Growth	**12.1%**	—	—	—

2007 Year-End Financials

Return on assets: —
Return on equity: (-4.9%)
Current ratio: 0.80
Cash ($ mil.): 11

NEW YORK STATE CATHOLIC HEALTH PLAN INC

Fidelis Care hopes for always faithful health plan members. The New York State Catholic Health Plan which does business as Fidelis Care serves more than 921000 residents in some 60 counties across the state including the New York City area. The church-sponsored plan's provider network includes more than 63000 physicians hospitals and other health care professionals and facilities. Fidelis Care provides managed Medicaid Medicare and state-sponsored family and children's Health Plus plans as well as long-term care and behavioral health coverage.

Geographic Reach

Fidelis Care's regional offices are located in Rego Park Queens (Greater Metropolitan); Albany (Northeast); Syracuse (Central); and Buffalo (Western) with satellite offices in Poughkeepsie Rochester and Suffern.

Operations

The company boasts an overall statewide member retention rate of more than 78% with a s Child Health Plus retention rate of more than 85%.

Sales and Marketing

The health plan has expanded its membership by seeking new low-income patients who lack coverage. In addition to direct sales efforts Fidelis Care tries to maintain a presence at health centers frequented by its target audience partnering with neighborhood clinics to hold free health screenings and Health Plus enrollment information sessions.

Enroll NY a new website sponsored by not-for-profit organization Hudson Center for Health Equity & Quality is also connecting Fidelis Care and other Medicaid providers with potential customers. In 2013 Fidelis Care began selling through the New York State of Health insurance exchange marketplace.

To bosst membership in 2013 the company ran the "I Want Fidelis Care” campaign (which promoted Fidelis Care as a health care resource) in English and Spanish. TV was added to the media buy in the New York City and Buffalo regions. It also established a social media presence on Facebook Twitter YouTube and Google+.Financial Performance

Fidelis Care reported gross revenues of $4.1 billion in 2013 up from $3.3 billion in 2012.

Strategy

The company is expanding its office to keep up with demand. In 2014 it opened Ridgewood Community Office; in 2013 it completed ofﬁce expansion projects in the Albany and Syracuse regional ofﬁces and the satellite ofﬁce in Suffern and opened new community ofﬁces in Flushing (Queens) the Bronx and Bath (Steuben County).

Forecasting substantial growth in 2014 with the enrollment of more than 120000 new members the company announced plans to add more than 75 new information technology jobs at its Buffalo regional office.

In 2013 Fidelis Care moved into 12 new counties with the Medicare Advantage program highlighted by the opportunity to serve residents of western New York for the ﬁrst time. It also made plans to expand into Seneca Yates and Jefferson counties in 2014 and served additional Managed Long Term Care members as part of the State's phased-in expansion of mandatory enrollment in counties beyond New York City.

Fidelis Care has grown by expanding rapidly into new counties in New York including a number of growth measures in the Medicare marketplace during 2012 and 2013. The health plan's recent activity includes completing construction of Fidelis Care's new operations center and offices in Getzville (Erie County) and the launch of its new provider portal (Provider Access Online). Other growth measures include a 2012 partnership with DentaQuest to promote dental checkups; it also launched a new member portal for members to access benefit information. In 2013 the company gained approval to be a qualified health plan provider on the official New York State of Health marketplace.

Fidelis Care regularly evaluates and broadens its plan offerings. Recent additions include its Fidelis Care at Home managed long-term care offering; the behavioral health and developmental disabilities coverage options; and its fully integrated dual advantage plans (for consumers with both Medicare and Medicaid coverage).

Company Background

The church-sponsored plan was founded in 1993 by the bishops of New York's Roman Catholic dioceses and the Catholic Medical Center of Brooklyn and Queens.

EXECUTIVES

President and CEO, Mark L. Lane
Assistant Vice President Provider Relations, Maryjean Valigorsky
Assistant Vice President Corporate Communications And Advertising, Darla Skiermont
Vice President Finance, Dina Soroka
Vice President Marketing and Senior Programs, Pamela (Pam) Hassen
Auditors: DELOITTE TAX LLP JERICHO NY

LOCATIONS

HQ: NEW YORK STATE CATHOLIC HEALTH PLAN INC
9525 QUEENS BLVD STE 8, REGO PARK, NY 113744510
Phone: 888 343-3547
Web: WWW.FIDELISCARE.COM

PRODUCTS/OPERATIONS

Selected Plans
Child Health Plus
Dual Advantage
Family Health Plus
Fidelis Care at Home (managed long-term care)
Medicaid Advantage Plus (managed long-term care)
Medicaid Managed Care
Medicare Advantage
New York State of Health

COMPETITORS

Aetna
Affinity Health
Anthem
CIGNA
Capital District Physicians' Health Plan
EmblemHealth
Health Net
HealthPlus Amerigroup
Healthfirst
Healthplex
Humana
Independent Health
Lifetime Healthcare
MVP Health Plan
UnitedHealth Group
Vytra Healthcare
healthnow new york inc

HISTORICAL FINANCIALS
Company Type: Private

Income Statement
FYE: December 31

	REVENUE ($ mil.)	NET INCOME ($ mil.)	NET PROFIT MARGIN	EMPLOYEES
12/10	1,920	51	2.7%	1,625
12/09	1,435	27	1.9%	—
Annual Growth	33.8%	84.2%	—	—

2010 Year-End Financials

Return on assets: —
Return on equity: 2.7%
Current ratio: 0.80

Cash ($ mil.): 199

NEWARK BETH ISRAEL MEDICAL CENTER INC.

Part of the Saint Barnabas Health Care System Newark Beth Israel Medical Center is a 670-bed acute-care regional referral hospital. The facility serves residents of Newark and surrounding areas in northern New Jersey. The hospital offers services including primary diagnostic emergency surgical and rehabilitative care. It is home to specialized programs such as kidney transplantation cancer care dentistry sleep disorders geriatrics and women's health services. Newark Beth Israel Medical Center also houses the Children's Hospital of New Jersey and the Saint Barnabas Heart Center. The research and teaching hospital has a medical staff of more than 800 physicians.

Operations

Newark Beth Israel Medical Center along with sister hospital Saint Barnabas Medical Center has a teaching and research affiliation with the New Jersey Medical School (part of the University of Medicine and Dentistry of New Jersey). The hospital also has training programs with other regional schools.

Newark Beth Israel Medical Center handles about 25000 inpatient visits annually while the hospital's outpatient centers see some 300000 patients each year.

EXECUTIVES

Vice President Human Resources, Zachary (Zach) Lipner
Radiology Director, Michael Connely
Director Of Hospice Services, Jill Jackson
Director Of Radiology, Michael Abiri

LOCATIONS

HQ: NEWARK BETH ISRAEL MEDICAL CENTER INC.
201 LYONS AVE, NEWARK, NJ 071122027
Phone: 973 926-7000

PRODUCTS/OPERATIONS

Selected Departments and Centers
Barnabas Health Heart Center
Center for Geriatric Health Care
Center for Women' s Health
Children' s Hospital of New Jersey
Cohen Comprehensive Cancer and Blood Disorder Center
Lung Center
Pacemaker and Defibrillator Center
Palliative Care Program
Regional Perinatal Center
Radiology
Robotic Surgery Center
Renal Transplantation
Sleep Disorders Center

COMPETITORS

AtlantiCare
Atlantic Health
Bergen Regional Medical
CentraState Healthcare System
Children' s Specialized Hospital
Chilton Medical Center
East Orange General Hospital
Englewood Hospital and Medical Center
Hackensack University Medical Center
JFK Health System
Meridian Health
Newton Medical Center
Robert Wood Johnson University Hospital
Robert Wood Johnson University Hospital at Rahway
St. Joseph' s Healthcare System
The Valley Hospital
Virtua Health
Winthrop-University Hospital

HISTORICAL FINANCIALS
Company Type: Private

Income Statement
FYE: December 31

	REVENUE ($ mil.)	NET INCOME ($ mil.)	NET PROFIT MARGIN	EMPLOYEES
12/08*	438	(56)	—	3,000
06/05	441	0	—	—
12/03	641	0	0.0%	—
Annual Growth	(7.3%)	—	—	—

*Fiscal year change

2008 Year-End Financials

Return on assets: 9.6%
Return on equity: (-12.9%)
Current ratio: 0.40

Cash ($ mil.): 1

NEWPORT NEWS PUBLIC SCHOOL DISTRICT

Auditors: CHERRY BEKAERT LLP RICHMOND

LOCATIONS

HQ: NEWPORT NEWS PUBLIC SCHOOL DISTRICT
12465 WARWICK BLVD, NEWPORT NEWS, VA
236063041
Phone: 757 591-4500
Web: WWW.NN.K12.VA.US

HISTORICAL FINANCIALS
Company Type: Private

Income Statement				FYE: June 30
	REVENUE ($ mil.)	NET INCOME ($ mil.)	NET PROFIT MARGIN	EMPLOYEES
06/14	315	(2)	—	1,500
06/13	323	1	0.4%	—
06/12	329	(1)	—	—
06/11	324	0	—	—
Annual Growth	(0.9%)	—	—	—

NJVC LLC

Auditors: MCGLADREY LLP FREDERICK MARY

LOCATIONS

HQ: NJVC LLC
14295 PARK MEADOW DR, CHANTILLY, VA
201512220
Phone: 703 429-9000
Web: WWW.NJVC.COM

HISTORICAL FINANCIALS
Company Type: Private

Income Statement				FYE: September 30
	REVENUE ($ mil.)	NET INCOME ($ mil.)	NET PROFIT MARGIN	EMPLOYEES
09/13	443	17	3.9%	1,300
09/12	513	22	4.4%	—
09/11	542	44	8.1%	—
09/10	495	0	—	—
Annual Growth	(3.6%)	—	—	—

2013 Year-End Financials
Return on assets: 3.5%   Cash ($ mil.): —
Return on equity: 3.9%
Current ratio: 1.90

NOBLIS INC.

Noblis' noble pursuit is through its offering of science-related strategic and technology consulting services. The not-for-profit company which pledges to serve the public interest helps various government entities and other clients evaluate technology options and vendors as well as solve complex technical problems. Noblis provides strategic planning decision analysis and acquisition support services. The company addresses problems in areas such as criminal justice environment and energy health care homeland security public safety and transportation. Noblis has worked with such clients as the US Air Force Army Navy and Departments of Commerce and Defense.

Geographic Reach

Noblis has more than half a dozen offices located in Maryland Texas Virginia West Virginia and Washington DC.

Sales and Marketing

The company's product suite includes RASMAS a Web-based service allowing health care providers and suppliers to respond more efficiently to product recalls and AcquTrak an acquisitions support tool aimed at helping government entities reduce costs and schedule times.

Mergers and Acquisitions

In 2012 Noblis acquired ElanTech Systems a provider of government systems engineering program management and acquisition services to the intelligence community. The two companies made the deal because of the complementary strengths of their businesses; the acquisition expands Nobils' portfolio giving the firm a broader knowledge base and the ability to capitalize on emerging technology trends and bring innovative new capabilities to clients.

Company Background

The company was formed in 1996 as Mitretek Systems; it changed its name to Noblis in 2007.

EXECUTIVES

President and CEO, Amr A. ElSawy
VP CFO Secretary and Treasurer, Mark A. Simione
VP and CTO, H. Gilbert Miller
VP and CIO, Gail Hogan
President Noblis NSP, Ellen McCarthy
Vice President Engineering, Don Schaefer
Information Technology Management Executive Vice President S, Gerard Brosnan
Business Development Vice President, Diana Fossett
Vice President, Stacy Bunin
Chairman, Marion C. Blakey
Vice Chairman, Michael Chertoff
Board Member, Jean Cain
Assistant Treasurer, Pam Ware
Auditors: GRANT THORNTON LLP MCLEAN VA

LOCATIONS

HQ: NOBLIS INC.
3150 FAIRVIEW PARK DR, FALLS CHURCH, VA
220424504
Phone: 703 610-2000
Web: WWW.NOBLIS.ORG

COMPETITORS

Accenture	HP Enterprise Services
Bain & Company	IBM
Boston Consulting	McKinsey & Company
Deloitte Consulting	

HISTORICAL FINANCIALS
Company Type: Private

Income Statement				FYE: October 5
	REVENUE ($ mil.)	NET INCOME ($ mil.)	NET PROFIT MARGIN	EMPLOYEES
10/14*	252	16	6.7%	804
09/13	200	10	5.0%	—
09/12	199	12	6.4%	—
10/11	151	0	—	—
Annual Growth	18.6%	—	—	—
*Fiscal year change				

2014 Year-End Financials
Return on assets: 5.6%   Cash ($ mil.): 3
Return on equity: 6.7%
Current ratio: 1.00

NORDIC PCL CONSTRUCTION INC.

LOCATIONS

HQ: NORDIC PCL CONSTRUCTION INC.
1099 ALAKEA ST STE 1560, HONOLULU, HI
968134500
Phone: 808 541-9101
Web: WWW.ENTERPRISES.PCL.COM

HISTORICAL FINANCIALS
Company Type: Private

Income Statement				FYE: October 31
	REVENUE ($ mil.)	NET INCOME ($ mil.)	NET PROFIT MARGIN	EMPLOYEES
10/10	1,616	23	1.5%	150
10/09	1,467	6	0.4%	—
Annual Growth	10.2%	291.0%		

2010 Year-End Financials
Return on assets: 10.1%   Cash ($ mil.): 95
Return on equity: 1.5%
Current ratio: 0.90

NORKUS ENTERPRISES INC.

They sell pasta shells by the Jersey sea shore. Norkus Enterprises operates grocery stores under the Foodtown and Super Foodtown banners in Monmouth County and Ocean County New Jersey. The regional grocery chain also offers online shopping and home delivery. It was founded when Francis Norkus opened his first grocery store called Table Talk in Freehold New Jersey in 1935. Norkus Enterprises is a member of the Foodtown Supermarket cooperative. The company also owns four Max's Beer Wine & Liquor stores located in New Jersey. In 2011 Norkus sold five of its six Foodtown stores —located in Freehold Township Manalapan Neptune City Point Pleasant Beach and Long Branch —to The Stop & Shop Supermarket Company.

After the sale of its Foodtown stores Norkus Enterprises is left with one Foodtown store in Freehold and four Max's Beer Wine & Liquor stores.

EXECUTIVES

President, Gerard K. (Gerry) Norkus, age 66
VP, Stephen J. Norkus
VP, Mark Norkus
Controller, Jane Lemonde

LOCATIONS

HQ: NORKUS ENTERPRISES INC.
505 RICHMOND AVE, POINT PLEASANT BEACH, NJ
087422552
Phone: 732 899-8485

COMPETITORS

Acme Markets	Pathmark Stores
Costco Wholesale	Saker ShopRites
Empire Merchants	Wal-Mart
Food Circus Super Markets	Weis Markets

HISTORICAL FINANCIALS
Company Type: Private

Income Statement
FYE: April 25

	REVENUE ($ mil.)	NET INCOME ($ mil.)	NET PROFIT MARGIN	EMPLOYEES
04/09	157	0	0.4%	1,000
04/08	157	1	0.7%	—
04/07	153	0	0.6%	—
04/06	148	0	—	—
Annual Growth	2.0%	—	—	—

2009 Year-End Financials
Return on assets: 4.6%
Return on equity: 0.4%
Current ratio: 0.20
Cash ($ mil.): —

NORTH CAROLINA ELECTRIC MEMBERSHIP CORPORATION

It's a cooperative effort: North Carolina Electric Membership Corporation (NCEMC) generates and transmits electricity to the state's 26 electric cooperatives (more than 2.5 million people) in 93 of 100 North Carolina counties. The co-op owns more than 600 MW of generating capacity through four primarily natural gas peak load generators plus a 61.5% stake in Catawba Nuclear Station Unit 1 and a 31% stake in the Catawba Nuclear Station in South Carolina. It also buys power from Progress Energy American Electric Power and other for-profit utilities. NCEMC's member cooperatives serve more than 950000 metered businesses and homes in North Carolina. The wholesale co-op also operates an energy operations center.

NCEMC's cooperatives own operate and maintain more than 98000 miles of power lines primarily in rural areas of North Carolina. About 99% of co-op customers are residential (home owners and renters) and small businesses.

NCEMC members experienced an annual power delivery growth of 3.4% in the first decade of the 2000s and anticipated a 1.3% annual growth between 2012 and 2021.

To assist with local economic development projects NCEMC has teamed up with the USDA to give co-ops access to a $20 million federal rural development fund.

In August 2011 Hurricane Irene slammed into North Carolina causing serious disruption to the grid and cutting power to 152000 members. Despite major flood damage to some infrastructure power was restored to affected customers within a few days.

NCEMC (which was founded in 1949 with 17 co-op members) offers training programs engineering and construction management and power supply planning to member cooperatives.

EXECUTIVES
Vice President Wholesale Rates Billing and Settlement, Tim Bennett
Vice President Manager Director, Joy Hart
Vice President Of Finance, Liberache Harris
Vice President, Tim Eisel
Auditors: DELOITTE TAX LLP ATLANTA GA

LOCATIONS
HQ: NORTH CAROLINA ELECTRIC MEMBERSHIP CORPORATION
3400 SUMNER BLVD, RALEIGH, NC 276162950
Phone: 919 872-0800
Web: WWW.NCEMCS.COM

PRODUCTS/OPERATIONS

Subsidiaries
North Carolina Association of Electric Cooperatives (NCAEC training programs)
The Tarheel Electric Membership Association Inc. (TEMA purchasing and materials supply)
North Carolina Cooperatives
Albemarle Electric Membership Corporation
Blue Ridge Electric Membership Corporation
Brunswick Electric Membership Corporation
Cape Hatteras Electric Cooperative
Carteret-Craven Electric Cooperative
Central Electric Membership Corporation
Edgecombe-Martin County Electric Membership Corporation
EnergyUnited
Four County Electric Membership Corporation
French Broad Electric Membership Corporation
Halifax Electric Membership Corporation
Haywood Electric Membership Corporation
Jones-Onslow Electric Membership Corporation
Lumbee River Electric Membership Corporation
Pee Dee Electric Membership Corporation
Piedmont Electric Membership Corporation
Pitt & Greene Electric Membership Corporation
Randolph Electric Membership Corporation
Roanoke Electric Cooperative
Rutherford Electric Membership Corporation
South River Electric Membership Corporation
Surry-Yadkin Electric Membership Corporation
Tideland Electric Membership Corporation
Tri-County Electric Membership Corporation
Union Power Cooperative
Wake Electric Membership Corporation

COMPETITORS

AEP	Progress Energy
Dominion Resources	SCANA
Duke Energy	Santee Cooper
MEAG Power	TVA

HISTORICAL FINANCIALS
Company Type: Private

Income Statement
FYE: December 31

	REVENUE ($ mil.)	NET INCOME ($ mil.)	NET PROFIT MARGIN	EMPLOYEES
12/08	1,006	6	0.6%	150
12/07	942	2	0.3%	—
Annual Growth	6.8%	106.0%	—	—

2008 Year-End Financials
Return on assets: 9.5%
Return on equity: 0.6%
Current ratio: 0.80
Cash ($ mil.): 25

NORTH CENTRAL COOPERATIVE INC

Auditors: BLUE & CO LLC SEYMOUR INDIA

LOCATIONS
HQ: NORTH CENTRAL COOPERATIVE INC
2025 S WABASH ST, WABASH, IN 469924124
Phone: 260 563-9541
Web: WWW.NORTHCENTRALCOOP.COM

HISTORICAL FINANCIALS
Company Type: Private

Income Statement
FYE: August 31

	REVENUE ($ mil.)	NET INCOME ($ mil.)	NET PROFIT MARGIN	EMPLOYEES
08/14	402	16	4.2%	280
08/13	426	19	4.6%	—
08/12	411	14	3.5%	—
08/11	322	0	—	—
Annual Growth	7.6%	—	—	—

2014 Year-End Financials
Return on assets: 2.9%
Return on equity: 4.2%
Current ratio: 1.30
Cash ($ mil.): 9

NORTH CENTRAL FARMERS ELEVATOR

North Central Farmers Elevator's mission is to give its members a lift. The full-service member-owned agricultural cooperative located in South Dakota offers farm-support goods and services including feed seed and other farm supplies along with agronomy energy and marketing services. In conjunction with LOL Farmland Feeds and South Dakota Wheat Growers North Central Farmers Elevator owns Dakotaland Feeds which makes and markets feed to producers. It also has a marketing alliance with South Dakota Oilseed Processors to sell its member/farmer's soybean crops. The coop's 21 locations serve more than 2500 producer-members in north central South Dakota and south central North Dakota.

EXECUTIVES
Manager Grain Division, Mike Nickolas
Controller, Joe Zikmund
Director Grain Operations, David Dohman
Director Agronomy, Jim Kanable
Auditors: EIDE BAILLY LLP ABERDEEN SOU

LOCATIONS
HQ: NORTH CENTRAL FARMERS ELEVATOR
12 5TH AVE, IPSWICH, SD 57451
Phone: 605 447-5803
Web: WWW.NCFE.COOP

COMPETITORS

ADM	South Dakota Soybean
CHS	Processors
Cargill	South Dakota Wheat
Dow AgroSciences	Growers
DuPont Agriculture	

HISTORICAL FINANCIALS
Company Type: Private

Income Statement
FYE: December 31

	REVENUE ($ mil.)	NET INCOME ($ mil.)	NET PROFIT MARGIN	EMPLOYEES
12/07	281	2	1.0%	200
12/06	135	(1)	—	—
12/05	1,140	0	0.0%	—
Annual Growth	(50.3%)	15571.1%	—	—

2007 Year-End Financials
Return on assets: —
Return on equity: 1.0%
Current ratio: 0.10
Cash ($ mil.): 8

NORTH DAKOTA MILL & ELEVATOR ASSOCIATION INC

When bakeries need flour North Dakota Mill & Elevator rises to the occasion. The mill is a producer of wheat flour used specifically in breads and other baked goods like cookies and crackers. It processes more than 78000 bushels of wheat a day and ships most of its flour in bulk to wholesalers. It offers semolina flour as well as specialty products such as wholegrain wheat flour wheat germ and corn flour for tortillas. The mill also sells pancake mixes bread machine mixes and whole-wheat all-purpose and bread flours under the Dakota Maid brand to consumers through its online store. Owned by the State of North Dakota it contributes 50% of its profits to the North Dakota State General Fund.

The mill recently suffered the single largest quarterly loss in its history —down $12 million —in late 2008. Continuing to lose money in 2009 it stated that the losses were due to price instability in the wheat markets and a drop in demand for its products.

North Dakota Mill & Elevator operates six milling facilities a terminal elevator and a packing warehouse. Its customers include bakery and pasta manufacturers as well as retail food and foodservice suppliers.

The mill was founded in 1922 to serve as a buyer for wheat produced by the state's farmers.

EXECUTIVES

President and General Manager, Vance Taylor
Controller and Financial Manager, Ed Barchenger
Auditors: ROBERT R PETERSON STATE AUDI

LOCATIONS

HQ: NORTH DAKOTA MILL & ELEVATOR
ASSOCIATION INC
1823 MILL RD, GRAND FORKS, ND 582031535
Phone: 701 795-7000

COMPETITORS

ADM	Cooperative Elevator
BakeMark	General Mills
Bay State Milling	Gruma Corporation
Bob's Red Mill Natural	Hodgson Mill
Foods	Horizon Milling
Bunge Milling	Italgrani
C.H. Guenther & Son	King Arthur Flour
CGC	Organic Milling
CHS	Seaboard
Cargill	Smucker
Chelsea Milling	Star of the West

HISTORICAL FINANCIALS

Company Type: Private

Income Statement

	REVENUE ($ mil.)	NET INCOME ($ mil.)	NET PROFIT MARGIN	EMPLOYEES	FYE: June 30
06/14	256	9	3.6%	120	
06/13	268	5	2.1%	—	
06/12	262	3	1.4%	—	
06/11	228	0	—	—	
Annual Growth	3.9%	—	—	—	

2014 Year-End Financials

Return on assets: —
Return on equity: 3.6%
Current ratio: 1.10
Cash ($ mil.): —

NORTH DAKOTA UNIVERSITY SYSTEM FOUNDATION

Auditors: ROBERT R PETERSON BISMARCK

LOCATIONS

HQ: NORTH DAKOTA UNIVERSITY SYSTEM
FOUNDATION
600 E BOULEVARD AVE # 215, BISMARCK, ND
585050601
Phone: 701 328-2960
Web: WWW.NDCHOOSE.COM

HISTORICAL FINANCIALS

Company Type: Private

Income Statement

	REVENUE ($ mil.)	NET INCOME ($ mil.)	NET PROFIT MARGIN	EMPLOYEES	FYE: June 30
06/13	653	78	12.0%	26	
06/12	656	61	9.4%	—	
06/11	626	75	12.0%	—	
06/09	571	0	—	—	
Annual Growth	3.4%	—	—	—	

2013 Year-End Financials

Return on assets: —
Return on equity: 12.0%
Current ratio: 1.10
Cash ($ mil.): 106

NORTH KANSAS CITY HOSPITAL

LOCATIONS

HQ: NORTH KANSAS CITY HOSPITAL
2800 CLAY EDWARDS DR, NORTH KANSAS CITY, MO
641163220
Phone: 816 691-2000
Web: WWW.NKCH.ORG

HISTORICAL FINANCIALS

Company Type: Private

Income Statement

	REVENUE ($ mil.)	NET INCOME ($ mil.)	NET PROFIT MARGIN	EMPLOYEES	FYE: June 30
06/11	419	22	5.3%	3,100	
06/09	370	36	9.9%	—	
06/08	1,745	0	—	—	
Annual Growth	—	4643.9%	—	—	

2011 Year-End Financials

Return on assets: 3.4%
Return on equity: 5.3%
Current ratio: 1.50
Cash ($ mil.): 28

NORTH LA COUNTY REGIONAL CENTER INC

Auditors: LAUTZE & LAUTZE SAN FRANCISCO

LOCATIONS

HQ: NORTH LA COUNTY REGIONAL CENTER INC
15400 SHERMAN WAY STE 170, VAN NUYS, CA
914064272
Phone: 818 778-1900
Web: WWW.NLACRC.ORG

HISTORICAL FINANCIALS

Company Type: Private

Income Statement

	REVENUE ($ mil.)	NET INCOME ($ mil.)	NET PROFIT MARGIN	EMPLOYEES	FYE: June 30
06/14	318	(2)	—	350	
06/13	295	(0)	—	—	
06/12	274	(8)	—	—	
06/11	273	0	—	—	
Annual Growth	5.2%	—	—	—	

2014 Year-End Financials

Return on assets: 9.4%
Return on equity: (-0.7%)
Current ratio: 0.90
Cash ($ mil.): 11

NORTH MEMORIAL HEALTH CARE

North Memorial Health Care seeks victory over illness in the Twin Cities. Established in 1939 as Victory Hospital the healthcare network is home to North Memorial Medical Center a 520-bed hospital that features a Level I trauma center and the Humphrey Cancer Center. The hospital also operates specialty centers for cardiovascular care orthopedics pediatrics and women's health as well as an emergency vehicle fleet of more than 100 ambulances and nearly 10 helicopters. The adjacent outpatient center provides oncology radiation and imaging services. North Memorial Health Care also has a network of primary and specialty care clinics in the Twin Cities region and it provides home health and hospice services.

Geographic Reach

North Memorial Health Care's primary facility (North Memorial Medical Center) is located in Robbinsdale Minnesota. In partnership with Fairview Health Services the company operates the 130-bed Maple Grove Hospital in nearby Maple Grove Minnesota. Its ambulance division serves the northwestern Twin Cities area as well other portions of Minnesota and Wisconsin.

OperationsAs a regional trauma center North Memorial Medical Center must maintain a high level of technology resources and recruit skilled emergency room specialists. North Memorial's emergency fleet also adds to the facilities' capabilities as it is one of the largest hospital-based ambulance services in the country with eight helicopters and about 100 ground ambulances. Outpatient facilities include rehabilitation centers sleep diagnostic labs family practice offices imaging centers and mental health facilities.Boasting 75000 emergency room visits North Memorial Medical Center maintains more than 175 physicians. It has earned the designation of being a Level II Pediatric Trauma Center. StrategyThe health network is expanding its facilities to improve services for area residents. In 2013 North Memorial opened the Plymouth City Center primary care clinic in Plymouth as well as a new heart and vascular institute in Buffalo and an urgent care center in Blaine. In Golden Valley the health care system opened the new Sport Spine & Joint Clinic as well.Looking ahead the network broke ground in 2013 on the 63000-sq.-ft. Minnetonka Medical Center which will house a second Urgency Center.Financial PerformanceNorth Memorial Health Care which posted $736 million in revenue in fiscal 2013 logged flat revenue gains in 2013 vs. 2012 due to an increase in net patient revenues that were offset in part by the provision for bad debts.

EXECUTIVES

VP Emergency and Enterprise Operations, Mike Parrish

President North Memorial Medical Center, Gayle Mattson

CEO Maple Grove Hospital, Andy Cochrane

Chief Medical Officer and President Physician Organization, J. Kevin Croston

VP Patient Care, Tracy Kirby

Chief Information Officer, Pat Taffe

VP Operations, Jeff Wicklander

Chief Financial Officer, Todd Ostendorf

Vp Medical Affairs, Andrew Houlton

Cota, Arleen Arendt

Respiratory Therapy Director, Nick Kuhnley

Medical Director of Primary Care North Memorial, Robert (Bob) McDonald

Clinic Manager, Adelia Sims

Vice President Population Health And Ambulatory Services, Cory Olson

Auditors: BAKER TILLY VIRCHOW KRAUSE LLP

LOCATIONS

HQ: NORTH MEMORIAL HEALTH CARE
3300 OAKDALE AVE N, MINNEAPOLIS, MN 554222900
Phone: 763 520-5200
Web: WWW.NORTHMEMORIAL.COM

PRODUCTS/OPERATIONS

Selected Locations

Heart & Vascular Center - Maple Grove - Maple Grove Minnesota

Heart & Vascular Clinic - Buffalo - Buffalo Minnesota

Heart & Vascular Clinic - Monticello - Monticello Minnesota

Hope Chest Breast Center - Robbinsdale Minnesota

Humphrey Cancer Center - Robbinsdale Minnesota

Maple Grove Hospital - Maple Grove Minnesota

Maternal Fetal Medicine - Maple Grove - Maple Grove Minnesota

North Memorial Clinic Brooklyn Center - Brooklyn Center Minnesota

North Memorial Clinic Brooklyn Park - Brooklyn Park Minnesota

North Memorial Clinic Camden - Maple Grove - Maple Grove Minnesota

North Memorial Clinic Camden - Minneapolis - Minneapolis Minnesota

North Memorial Clinic Camden - Plymouth - Plymouth Minnesota

North Memorial Clinic Elk River - Elk River Minnesota

North Memorial Clinic Golden Valley - Golden Valley Minnesota

North Memorial Clinic Maple Grove - Maple Grove Minnesota

North Memorial Clinic Minnetonka - Minnetonka Minnesota

North Memorial Clinic Northeast - Minneapolis Minnesota

North Memorial Clinic Plymouth City Center - Plymouth Minnesota

North Memorial Clinic Silver Lake Clinic - St. Anthony - St. Anthony Minnesota

North Memorial Clinic Silver Lake Clinic - Blaine - Blaine Minnesota

North Memorial Medical Center - Robbinsdale Minnesota

North Memorial Urgent Care - Maple Grove - Maple Grove Minnesota

North Memorial Urgent Care - Roseville - Roseville Minnesota

Outpatient Imaging Center - Robbinsdale Minnesota

Outpatient Psychiatric Clinic - Robbinsdale Minnesota

Rehabilitation Services - Robbinsdale Minnesota

Rehabilitation Services - Maple Grove Minnesota

Rehabilitation Services - Elk River Minnesota

Residential Hospice - Brooklyn Center Minnesota

Sleep Health Center - Maple Grove Minnesota

Sleep Health Center - Robbinsdale Minnesota

Urgent Care - Blaine Minnesota

Selected Services

Acupuncture
Acute Concussion Clinic
Acute Inpatient Rehabilitation
Air Care
Ambulance Services
Anterior Hip Replacement
Balance Center
Breast Health
Breast Milk Depot
CACE Unit
Cancer Education & Support
Cancer Treatment
Cardiac Rehabilitation
Cardiology
Cardiology Clinic Services
Complex Heart Procedures and Interventional Services
Computed Tomography - CT
Dermatology
Diabetes Education
Domestic Abuse Victim Advocacy - SafeJourney
Emergency Department
EMS Education
Endovenous Laser Treatment (EVLT) for Varicose Veins
Family Birth Center
Family Medicine
Gastroenterology
General Radiology
Genetics Program
Geriatric Care
Gift Shop
Grief and Loss Support
Group Physical Therapy
Gynecology

COMPETITORS

Allina Hospitals
Bethesda Hospital
Catholic Health Initiatives
CentraCare Health
Children' s Hospitals and Clinics of Minnesota
Fairview Health
First Care
HealthEast Care System
Mayo Clinic
Methodist Hospital (MN)
Park Nicollet Health Services
Regions Hospital
SCMC
St. John' s Hospital (Minnesota)
St. Luke' s Hospital (MN)
University of Minnesota Medical Center

HISTORICAL FINANCIALS

Company Type: Private

Income Statement

FYE: December 31

	REVENUE ($ mil.)	NET INCOME ($ mil.)	NET PROFIT MARGIN	EMPLOYEES
12/13	735	51	7.0%	5,180
12/12	565	(4)	—	—
12/09	605	(17)	—	—
12/06	544	0	—	—
Annual Growth	4.4%	—	—	—

2013 Year-End Financials

Return on assets: 4.0%
Return on equity: 7.0%
Current ratio: 1.50

Cash ($ mil.): 35

NORTH MISSISSIPPI HEALTH SERVICES INC.

North Mississippi Health Services (NMHS) isn't contained by its name: The health system also provides health care to residents of northwestern Alabama. NMHS includes half a dozen community hospitals including its flagship North Mississippi Medical Center in Tupelo. North Mississippi Medical Clinics a regional network of more than 30 primary and specialty clinics; and nursing homes. Combined the facilities have nearly 1000 beds designated for acute long term and nursing care. Specialty services include home health and long-term care inpatient and outpatient behavioral health and treatment centers for cancer and digestive disorders. NMHS also operates outpatient care and wellness clinics in the region.

Geographic Reach

In all NMHS serves two dozen counties across the two states. In addition to its main hospital in Tupelo NMHS operates health centers in communities including Eupora Iuka Pontotoc and West Point Mississippi and in Hamilton Alabama. It also manages a center in Calhoun City Mississippi. Its Baldwyn Nursing Facility is located in Baldwyn Mississippi.

Operations

During 2014 NMHS handled about 30000 inpatient visits as well as more than 128000 emergency room visits and some 345000 outpatient care visits. It also conducted about 24000 surgeries at its various facilities. Its outpatient centers include more than 30 primary and specialty care clinics in Mississippi and Alabama operated through the North Mississippi Medical Clinics division as well as more than half a dozen wellness centers.

Financial Performance

Flagship North Mississippi Medical Center (NNMC)'s revenues increased by 6% due to a growth in net patient revenues. Medicare and Medicaid together accounted for about 50% of net patient revenues; managed care and commercial 25%; Blue Cross 14%; self-pay 10%; and Health Link 1%.

NNMC reported net loss of $14 million in 2014 over net income in 2013 due to pension-related changes.

NNMC's operating cash flow increased by 256% that year.

EXECUTIVES

Medical Director, Pamela Dykes
Medical Director, Fulton Thompson
Vice President Finance, Scott Edwards
Vice President, Bruce Toppin

LOCATIONS

HQ: NORTH MISSISSIPPI HEALTH SERVICES INC.
830 S GLOSTER ST, TUPELO, MS 388014934
Phone: 662 377-3000
Web: WWW.NMHS.NET

Selected Locations

Baldwyn Nursing Facility (Baldwyn Mississippi)
Calhoun County Medical Clinic (managed facility; Calhoun Mississippi)
NMMC-Eupora (Eupora Mississippi)
NMMC-Hamilton (Hamilton Alabama)
NMMC-Iuka (Iuka Mississippi)
NMMC-Pontotoc (Pontotoc Mississippi)
NMMC-Tupelo (Tupelo Mississippi)
NMMC-West Point (West Point Mississippi)
North Mississippi Medical Clinics (NMMCI regional)

PRODUCTS/OPERATIONS

Selected Facilities and Services
Acute Stroke Unit
Advanced Wound Center and Hyperbarics
Bariatric Center
Behavioral Health Center
Breast Care Center
Cancer Center
Center for Digestive Health
Community Health
Critical Care Unit
CRNA Program
Diabetes Treatment Center
Emergency Services
Family Medicine Residency Center
Heart Institute
Home Health and Hospice
Hospitalists
Joint Replacement Center
Le Bonheur Specialty Clinics
Medical Imaging
North Mississippi Surgery Center
Outpatient Infusion
Pain Management Center
Pastoral Care
Physician Specialties
Radiology
Rehabilitation Services
Respiratory Therapy
Skilled Nursing Facility
Sleep Disorders Center
Surgical Services
Tupelo Wellness Center
Vein Center
Volunteer Services
Women' s Hospital
Women' s and Children Services

COMPETITORS

Baptist Memorial Health Care
Community Health Systems
Delta Regional Medical Center
Forrest General Hospital
HCA
Memorial Hospital at Gulfport
Methodist Healthcare
Natchez Regional Medical Center
North Mississippi Medical
Shelby County Health Care
Southwest Mississippi Regional Medical Center

HISTORICAL FINANCIALS
Company Type: Private

Income Statement
FYE: September 30

	REVENUE ($ mil.)	NET INCOME ($ mil.)	NET PROFIT MARGIN	EMPLOYEES
09/14	779	(14)	—	6,000
09/13	735	82	11.3%	—
09/12	852	(3)	—	—
09/11	834	0	—	—
Annual Growth	(2.3%)	—	—	—

2014 Year-End Financials
Return on assets: 4.6%
Return on equity: (-1.8%)
Current ratio: 1.10
Cash ($ mil.): 80

NORTH MISSISSIPPI MEDICAL CENTER INC.

At North Mississippi Medical Center you might get some Mississippi Mud ice cream after your tonsils are removed. The full-service 650-bed regional referral hospital in Tupelo Mississippi is part of the North Mississippi Health Services system an affiliation of hospitals and clinics serving northern Mississippi northwestern Alabama and parts of Tennessee. It's the largest private not-for-profit hospital in Mississippi and the largest non-metropolitan hospital in America. Specialty services at the medical center include cancer treatment women's health care cardiology and behavioral health care. The hospital also operates a skilled-nursing facility and home health and hospice organizations.

Geographic Reach
North Mississippi Medical Center serves more than 700000 people across 24 counties in north Mississippi northwestern Alabama and portions of Tennessee.

Operations
Besides being a Mississippi State Department of Health-designated Level II trauma center North Mississippi Medical Center offers more than 40 specialties as well as centers for excellence in cardiac surgery cardiology research neurology neurosurgery pulmonology rehabilitation cancer treatment chemical dependency and neonatal programs.

The medical center's Home Health Agency canvases 17 counties in north Mississippi and provides complex and extremely high-tech procedures that can be performed in the home setting. It also operates Baldwyn Nursing Facility.

Strategy
In 2012 North Mississippi Medical Center - Hamilton opened a new pulmonary rehabilitation unit. Also the medical center's Outpatient Rehabilitation Center in 2012 became the first outpatient rehabilitation center in Mississippi to offer Fiberoptic Endoscopic Evaluation of Swallowing (FEES) to assess swallowing function.

Awards and Recognition
North Mississippi Medical Center's hospitalist program has been recognized by The American Journal of Medicine for providing cost-effective care to patients in the hospital. The program begun in 1997 serves hospitalized patients who do not have a primary care physician or whose primary care physicians do not have hospital practices.

Ownership
North Mississippi Medical Center is part of North Mississippi Health Services.

EXECUTIVES

Vice President Human Resources, Rodger Brown, age 63
Director Physician Recruitment, Stephanie Maxcy
Occupational Therapy Director, David Friloux
Medical Records Director, Sarah Beckham
Director Of Nursing, Wanda Turner
Physical Therapy Director, Kim Wade

LOCATIONS

HQ: NORTH MISSISSIPPI MEDICAL CENTER INC.
830 S GLOSTER ST, TUPELO, MS 388014934
Phone: 662 377-3000
Web: WWW.NMHS.NET

Selected Locations
Baldwyn Nursing Facility - Baldwyn Mississippi
NMMC - Eup
NMMC - Ham
NMMC - Iuk
NMMC - Pontotoc - Pontotoc Mississippi
NMMC - Tupelo - Tupelo Mississippi
NMMC - West Point - West Point Mississippi

PRODUCTS/OPERATIONS

Selected Programs & Services
Acute Stroke Unit
Advanced Wound Center and Hyperbarics
Bariatric Center
Behavioral Health Center
Breast Care Center
Cancer Center
Center for Digestive Health
Community Health
Critical Care Unit
CRNA Program
Diabetes Treatment Center
Emergency Services
Family Medicine Residency Center
Gift & Floral Shop
Heart Institute
Home Health and Hospice
Hospitalists
Joint Replacement Center
Le Bonheur Specialty Clinics
Medical Imaging
North Mississippi Surgery Center
Outpatient Infusion
Pain Management Center
Pastoral Care
Physician Specialties
Radiology
Rehabilitation Services
Respiratory Therapy
Skilled Nursing Facility
Sleep Disorders Center
Surgical Services
Tupelo Wellness Center
Vein Center
Volunteer Services
West Bedtower Project
Women' s Hospital
Women' s and Children Services

COMPETITORS

Community Health Systems
Delta Regional Medical Center
Forrest General Hospital
HCA
Memorial Hospital at Gulfport
Natchez Regional Medical Center
Southwest Mississippi Regional Medical Center

HISTORICAL FINANCIALS
Company Type: Private

Income Statement
FYE: September 30

	REVENUE ($ mil.)	NET INCOME ($ mil.)	NET PROFIT MARGIN	EMPLOYEES
09/13	537	2	0.5%	6,000
09/12	620	(6)	—	—
09/11	614	4	0.8%	—
09/10	585	0	—	—
Annual Growth	(2.8%)	—	—	—

2013 Year-End Financials
Return on assets: 4.9%
Return on equity: 0.5%
Current ratio: 1.00
Cash ($ mil.): 51

NORTH PACIFIC PAPER CORPORATION

The old adage "all the news fit to print" might not be possible without North Pacific Paper Corporation (NORPAC). The company a joint venture between Weyerhaeuser and Nippon Paper produces newsprint for newspaper publishers and commercial printers. NORPAC manufactures a variety of different paper grades including standard and lightweight newsprint and super- and ultra-lightweight stocks especially for the Japanese market. The company produces more than 250000 tons of newsprint annually at its manufacturing facility in Longview Washington. Its products are sent via truck and train to customers in the western US or are shipped by boat to customers in Japan.

Auditors: KPMG LLP SEATTLE WA

LOCATIONS

HQ: NORTH PACIFIC PAPER CORPORATION
3001 INDL WAY, LONGVIEW, WA 98632
Phone: 360 636-6400

PRODUCTS/OPERATIONS

Selected Products
Newsprint
  Lightweight
  Standard
  Super-lightweight
Printing and Publishing
  Norbite
  Norbrite Offset
  Norbrite Opaque
  Norbrite Plus
Other
  Groundwood forms
  Groundwood rotogravure
  Publication papers
  Super- and ultra-lightweight newsprint (for use in Japan)

COMPETITORS

Aylesford Newsprint	International Paper
Brant Industries	Norske Skog
Georgia-Pacific	Oji Holdings
Inland Empire Paper	Resolute Forest
Company	Products

HISTORICAL FINANCIALS

Company Type: Private

Income Statement

FYE: December 31

	REVENUE ($ mil.)	NET INCOME ($ mil.)	NET PROFIT MARGIN	EMPLOYEES
12/08	534	22	4.2%	410
12/07	474	(3)	—	—
12/06	2,040	0	—	—
Annual Growth	—	24921.7%	—	—

NORTHBAY HEALTHCARE GROUP

LOCATIONS

HQ: NORTHBAY HEALTHCARE GROUP
1200 B GALE WILSON BLVD, FAIRFIELD, CA
945333552
Phone: 707 646-5000
Web: WWW.NORTHBAY.ORG

HISTORICAL FINANCIALS

Company Type: Private

Income Statement

FYE: December 31

	REVENUE ($ mil.)	NET INCOME ($ mil.)	NET PROFIT MARGIN	EMPLOYEES
12/09	328	9	2.8%	1,200
12/08*	171	(10)	—	—
09/04	1,692	0	—	—
Annual Growth	—	666.7%	—	—

*Fiscal year change

2009 Year-End Financials

Return on assets: —
Return on equity: 2.8%
Current ratio: —

Cash ($ mil.): 7

NORTHEAST GEORGIA MEDICAL CENTER INC.

LOCATIONS

HQ: NORTHEAST GEORGIA MEDICAL CENTER INC.
743 SPRING ST NE, GAINESVILLE, GA 305013715
Phone: 770 219-9000
Web: WWW.NGHS.COM

HISTORICAL FINANCIALS

Company Type: Private

Income Statement

FYE: September 30

	REVENUE ($ mil.)	NET INCOME ($ mil.)	NET PROFIT MARGIN	EMPLOYEES
09/13	726	109	15.0%	3,053
09/05	400	8	2.0%	—
09/04	384	10	2.8%	—
Annual Growth	7.3%	29.5%	—	—

2013 Year-End Financials

Return on assets: 8.9%
Return on equity: 15.0%
Current ratio: 0.10

Cash ($ mil.): 5

NORTHEAST HEALTH SYSTEMS INC.

If a particularly beastly Nor'easter wreaks havoc on your immune system you might want to turn to Northeast Health System (NHS) for a little TLC. The organization provides a continuum of health services to residents of Massachusetts' North Shore communities through its network of hospitals outpatient care facilities and behavioral health and senior care centers. NHS' hospitals include Addison Gilbert Hospital a 60-bed full-service acute care facility; the 60-bed BayRidge Hospital a mental health and drug rehab facility; and Beverly Hospital with more than 220 beds. The company is a part of the Lahey Health System.

Operations

NHS provides primary care; acute medical and surgical care; outpatient and diagnostic services; physical therapy and rehabilitation services; wellness programs; substance abuse prevention and treatment; mental health services and treatment; senior health services specialty care and assisted living. The company has 600 physicians

In addition to its hospitals NHS owns a few nursing and assisted living homes as well as outpatient surgery and rehabilitation centers. Its services for seniors include The Center for Healthy Aging (outpatient and diagnostic services) Ledgewood and Seacoast short-term rehab and skilled nursing facilities Herrick House assisted living North Shore PRN and Northeast Homecare home health care and Spectrum Adult Day Health Center for those living with Alzheimer's.

Strategy NHS operates computerized physician order entry systems (CPOE) at all three of its primary hospitals allowing medical personnel to order everything from lab tests to medications electronically. The system helps reduce medical errors improve patient safety and reduce turnaround time for pharmacy orders meaning patients get their medications faster. Operating CPOEs also makes NHS eligible for certain incentive payments related to the federal economic stimulus bill (which also includes penalties for those hospitals that don't adopt CPOE technology). Hospitals able to meet requirements set by the American Reinvestment and Recovery Act are eligible for incentive payments. In order to expand its specialty care services NHS forms affiliations with local providers including Children's Hospital Boston (pediatrics) and Beth Israel Deaconess Medical Center (oncology).

Company Background

In 2012 the system joined the Lahey Health System.

Prior to its agreement with Lahey NHS had been looking to join up with one of the larger health care organizations in the region. NHS considered acquisition/merger proposals from Beth Israel Deaconess Medical Center Vanguard Health Systems (now part of Tenet Healthcare) and Steward Health Care System. The hospital system said it was not seeking financial stability necessarily but rather increased access to resources and broader geographic reach. Under terms of its agreement with Lahey Clinic (renamed Lahey Hospital and Medical Center) a new not-for-profit umbrella organization Lahey Health System was created.

EXECUTIVES

Senior Vice President Philanthropy, Susan Healey (Sue) Payson
Director of Radiology Md Specializes In Radiology, Christian Ecker
Vice President Finance, Gary Marlow
Vice President Human Resources and Development, Althea Lyons
Auditors: PRICEWATERHOUSECOOPERS LLP BO

LOCATIONS

HQ: NORTHEAST HEALTH SYSTEMS INC.
85 HERRICK ST, BEVERLY, MA 019151790
Phone: 978 922-3000
Web: WWW.BEVERLYHOSPITAL.ORG

PRODUCTS/OPERATIONS

Selected Facilities – Massachusetts
Addison Gilbert Hospital (Gloucester acute care hospital)
BayRidge Hospital (Lynn behavioral health hospital)
Beverly Hospital (Beverly acute care hospital)
Beverly Hospital at Danvers Medical and Day Surgery Center (Danvers medical center)
CAB Health & Recovery Services (Danvers behavioral health)
Health and Education Services (Beverly community-based indigent care)
Herrick House (Beverly senior living)
Ledgewood Rehabilitation & Skilled Nursing Center (Beverly)
Lifestyle Management Institute (Danvers chronic health care)
Northeast Senior Health (regional)
Seacoast Nursing and Rehabilitation Center (Gloucester)
The Herrick House (Beverly assisted living residence)

COMPETITORS

Beth Israel Deaconess Medical Center
Boston Medical Center
Brigham and Women's Hospital
Cambridge Health Alliance
Care New England
CareGroup
Children's Hospital Boston
Dana-Farber
Massachusetts General Hospital
Newton-Wellesley Hospital
Partners HealthCare
Southcoast Hospitals Group
Spaulding Rehabilitation Hospital
St. Elizabeth's Medical Center
Steward Health Care

HISTORICAL FINANCIALS
Company Type: Private

Income Statement
FYE: September 30

	REVENUE ($ mil.)	NET INCOME ($ mil.)	NET PROFIT MARGIN	EMPLOYEES
09/11	434	(12)	—	2,300
09/10	0	(0)	—	—
09/09	1,733	0	0.0%	—
Annual Growth	(49.9%)	—	—	—

2011 Year-End Financials
Return on assets: —
Return on equity: (-2.9%)
Current ratio: 1.30
Cash ($ mil.): 40

NORTHEAST HOSPITAL CORPORATION

LOCATIONS
HQ: NORTHEAST HOSPITAL CORPORATION
85 HERRICK ST, BEVERLY, MA 019151790
Phone: 978 922-3000
Web: WWW.BEVERLYHOSPITAL.ORG

HISTORICAL FINANCIALS
Company Type: Private

Income Statement
FYE: September 30

	REVENUE ($ mil.)	NET INCOME ($ mil.)	NET PROFIT MARGIN	EMPLOYEES
09/13	332	19	5.9%	2,800
09/08	296	(4)	—	—
09/07	291	296	101.6%	—
09/05	1,992	0	—	—
Annual Growth	—	—	—	—

2013 Year-End Financials
Return on assets: 9.2%
Return on equity: 5.9%
Current ratio: 0.40
Cash ($ mil.): 20

NORTHERN TIER ENERGY LP

Northern Tier Energy makes gasoline and sells it too. The company owns one of only two oil refineries in Minnesota and more than 260 SuperAmerica gas stations across Minnesota and Wisconsin. Its oil refinery produces 97800 barrels per day of gasoline diesel jet fuel and asphalt. The company also owns storage and transportation assets including terminals storage tanks rail loading and unloading facilities and a dock on the Mississippi River. In addition Northern Tier Energy owns a 17% stake in the 300-mile Minnesota Pipeline (Koch Industries owns the rest) that transports crude oil to its refinery.

Change in Company Type
In 2013 the company's controlling stockholders (ACON Investments and TPG Capital) sold their ownership in Northern Tier Energy to Western Refining for $775 million. As a result Western Refining owns 100% of the general partner or 38.7% of Northern Tier Energy.

Geographic Reach
The company has operations in Minnesota South Dakota and Wisconsin. Northern Tier also operates convenience stores and franchises convenience stores primarily in Minnesota and Wisconsin under the SuperAmerica trademark and owns a bakery and commissary under the SuperMom's brand.

Operations
Northern Tier Energy splits its operations into the refinery and retail businesses. Energy marketer J.P. Morgan Commodities Canada Corporation supplies the Minnesota refinery with crude oil under an agreement through 2015. Besides its SuperAmerica gas stations the refinery also supplies gas and diesel fuel to 90 Marathon-branded gas stations located in its marketing area.

The retail segment is made up of 165 company-owned SuperAmerica gas stations and 95 franchised stores (organized under SuperAmerica Franchising LLC) mostly located in Minnesota and Wisconsin but it does have two stores in South Dakota. The stores are supplied with general merchandise (tobacco and grocery items) by wholesaler Eby-Brown and with baked goods and other prepared food by its own SuperMom's Bakery.

Sales and Marketing
The company's refinery supplies almost all of the gasoline and diesel sold in company-operated and franchised convenience stores and in independently-owned and operated Marathon branded stores within its distribution area. Its retail customers primarily include retail end-users motorists and commercial drivers.

Asphalt and heavy fuel oil are sold to a broad customer base including asphalt paving contractors government entities (including states counties cities and townships) and to asphalt roofing shingle manufacturers.

Financial Performance
Northern Tier Energy's revenues have grown steadily since 2010. It grew by 7% by 11% in 2014 due to tincreased revenue from the refining segment offset by lower retail revenues. Refining revenues increased by 12% due to higher sales volumes of crude and refined products thanks to refinery capacity expansion completed in 2013 less unplanned maintenance at the St. Paul Park Refinery in the 2014.Retail revenues declined due to lower fuel prices.Northern Tier Energy's net income increased by 4% due to higher revenues lower turnaround and related costs and the absence of a loss from derivative activities and losses from early extinguishment of debt. In 2014 net cash provided by operating activities decreased by $10 million as a result of an increase in inventories a loss from from the change in fair value of outstanding derivatives and a loss from the lower cost of market inventory adjustment.

Strategy
The company's strategy is to grow its SuperAmerica branded retail business (to which it can supply transportation fuels from its refinery) by expanding its SuperAmerica franchise business. On the refining side it plans to continue its efforts to benefit from its access to cost-advantaged crude oil and increase refinery use with high-return capital projects that also improves yield of light products.A component of the company's growth strategy is to selectively consider accretive acquisitions within the refining industry and retail market which give it access to advantageous crude oil supplies distribution and logistics infrastructure and potential operating synergies.

Company Background
Northern Tier Energy went public with a $230 million IPO in 2012.

Following the IPO TPG and ACON Investments owned the majority of its voting power; each company also retained two seats on Northern Tier Energy's board of directors. Northern Tier Energy used the proceeds from its IPO to pay off Marathon Petroleum and its two investors.

Northern Tier Energy might be new but its properties are not. The company was formed by private investment firms TPG Capital and ACON Investments which bought the Minnesota oil refinery and SuperAmerica gas stations from Marathon for $608 million in October 2010. (Marathon Petroleum sold the properties in order to focus on the lower Midwest and Southeast.)

Without suspending operations TPG Capital and ACON Investments established Northern Tier Energy and its subsidiaries (Northern Tier Investments SuperMom's Bakery and SuperAmerica Franchising LLC) to own and manage the refinery and supply the gas stations.

EXECUTIVES
President CEO and Director, David L. (Dave) Lamp, $670,192 total compensation
VP Retail, Jack A. Helmick
EVP General Counsel and Secretary, Melissa M. Buhrig, $218,203 total compensation
VP Logistics, Jason Akey
VP St. Paul Park Refinery, Rick Hastings
SVP and Chief Commercial Officer, Scott L. Stevens, $169,231 total compensation
EVP and CFO, Karen Davis
Chairman, Paul L. Foster, age 57
Auditors: PRICEWATERHOUSECOOPERS LLP HO

LOCATIONS
HQ: NORTHERN TIER ENERGY LP
38C GROVE ST STE 1, RIDGEFIELD, CT 068774667
Phone: 203 244-6550
Web: WWW.NTENERGY.COM

PRODUCTS/OPERATIONS

2014 Sales

	$ mil.	% of total
Refining	5,097	79
Retail	1,390	21
Other	(932.1)	-
Total	**5,556**	**100**

COMPETITORS

7-Eleven	Holiday Companies
7-Eleven	Holiday Companies
BP	Kwik Trip
BP	Kwik Trip
CITGO	Marathon Petroleum
CITGO	Marathon Petroleum
Chevron	Shell Oil Products
Chevron	Shell Oil Products
ConocoPhillips	Sunoco
ConocoPhillips	Sunoco
Exxon Mobil	Tesoro
Exxon Mobil	Tesoro
Flint Hills	Valero Energy
Flint Hills	Valero Energy

HISTORICAL FINANCIALS
Company Type: Private

Income Statement
FYE: December 31

	REVENUE ($ mil.)	NET INCOME ($ mil.)	NET PROFIT MARGIN	EMPLOYEES
12/14	5,556	241	4.3%	642
12/13	4,979	231	4.6%	—
12/12	4,653	197	4.2%	—
Annual Growth	9.3%	10.6%	—	—

2014 Year-End Financials

Return on assets: 6.0%
Return on equity: 4.3%
Current ratio: 0.80

Cash ($ mil.): 87

NORTHERN VIRGINIA ELECTRIC COOPERATIVE

NOVEC is no novice when it comes to electricity distribution. Northern Virginia Electric Cooperative (NOVEC) is a member-owned not-for profit utility that serves more than 150000 residential commercial industrial and government customers in a 651-sq. ml. service area in northern Virginia. NOVEC which has more than 6790 miles of power lines receives its power supply from the PJM Interconnection marketplace. The company also markets natural gas to retail customers in Virginia and Maryland through its NOVEC Energy Solutions unit. Subsidiary NOVEC Solutions sells gas and electric water heaters and other energy appliances and provides optical data networking service for large businesses and government agencies.

Geographic Reach

NOVEC distributes power to customers in Clarke Fairfax Fauquier Loudoun Prince William and Stafford counties and the City of Manassas Park.

Sales and Marketing

The utility company's large commercial customers include AT&T Doane Food Products Potomac Mills Outlet Mall NOAA's Mount Weather Facility and Vulcan Materials Company. NOVEC Energy Solutions supplies natural gas service to 20000 primarily residential customers.

Financial Performance

Due to the lower costs of generating power because of low natural gas prices NOVEC cut rates in 2011 and implemented a power cost adjustment credit in 2012 reducing the amount that customers paid for NOVEC-supplied power. Revenues decreased by 14% in 2012; net margin by 49%.

Strategy

In 2012 NOVEC received $10 million from the Department of Energy as a part of Smart Grid Investment Grant program. The company uses the proceeds to automate of 38 of its 53 substations; replaced 19 outdated line-protective devices; install 164 capacitor banks with automatic switching devices; and install 14 remote-controlled motor-operated switches to isolate problems and help restore power quickly.

Ownership

The coop is owned by its members.

Company Background

NOVEC was formed in 1983 through the merger of Prince William Electric Cooperative and Tri-County Electric Cooperative.

EXECUTIVES

Assistant Vice President Customer Service, Diane Johnson
Vice President And Corporate Counsel, Patrick Toulme

LOCATIONS

HQ: NORTHERN VIRGINIA ELECTRIC COOPERATIVE
10323 LOMOND DR, MANASSAS, VA 201093113
Phone: 703 335-0500
Web: WWW.NOVEC.COM

Northern Virginia Electric Cooperative operates in rural areas in Clarke Fairfax Fauquier Loudoun Prince William and Stafford counties as well as in the Town of Clifton and the City of Manassas Park in northern Virginia.

PRODUCTS/OPERATIONS

Subsidiaries and Affiliates

NOVEC Energy Solutions (formerly America' s Energy Alliance retail gas marketing)
NOVEC Solutions (formerly NOVASTAR energy products and services)

COMPETITORS

AEP	Dominion Resources
AGL Resources	FirstEnergy
Chesapeake Utilities	NiSource
Constellation Energy Group	Pepco Holdings
Delmarva Power	WGL Holdings

HISTORICAL FINANCIALS

Company Type: Private

Income Statement

FYE: December 31

	REVENUE ($ mil.)	NET INCOME ($ mil.)	NET PROFIT MARGIN	EMPLOYEES
12/13	396	23	6.0%	275
12/09	419	50	12.2%	—
12/08	397	0	—	—
12/02	234	0	—	—
Annual Growth	4.9%	—	—	—

2013 Year-End Financials

Return on assets: 8.9%
Return on equity: 6.0%
Current ratio: 2.50

Cash ($ mil.): 54

NORTHSHORE UNIVERSITY HEALTHSYSTEM

NorthShore University HealthSystem provides care to residents of Chicago's north side and its suburbs. The health system operates hospitals a home care organization and a Medical Group with hundreds of primary and specialty care physicians. With about 355 beds the organization's flagship Evanston Hospital has teaching and research programs as well as capabilities for trauma cancer cardiology and women's health care. The system also includes Glenbrook Hospital (about 175 beds) while Highland Park Hospital (150 beds) and Skokie Hospital (more than 155 beds). The health care system is affiliated with the University of Chicago Pritzker School of Medicine.

Geographic Reach

Based in Evanston Illinois the company has more than 100 medical offices across the region.

Operations

Supported by more than 900 physicians each of NorthShore's hospitals is known for a certain specialty. Evanston for example specializes in cancer and cardiac care; Glenbrook Hospital is known for advanced technology for the treatment of gastrointestinal disorders; Highland Park Hospital is the site of the first open hear surgery in the region; and Skokie Hospital is known for its expertise in cancer and cardiac care as well as orthopedics.

Financial Performance

In 2014 NorthShore's net revenues increased by 6% due to higher net patient service and premium revenues and net assets released from restrictions used for operations.Net income decreased by 28% due to an increase in contributions and other.In 2014 NorthShore's cash from operating activities decreased by 30% as the result of the changes in patients accounts receivables and noncurrent assets and liabilities.

That year NorthShore contributed more than $268 million in charitable care and services to the community it serves.

Strategy

The company's health facility network has grown over the years through acquisitions. Some of NorthShore's notable buys include the Rush North Shore Medical Center in Skokie from the Rush System for Health for about $160 million. The hospital was renamed Skokie Hospital following the acquisition. The organization has also been working to expand its medical group to broaden its offering of specialized health care services.

NorthShore also widens its network and service offerings through organic growth. The health care provider regularly conducts expansion and remodeling projects at its facilities and has stepped up recruiting efforts to attract high-skill doctors. It has also been working to improve communication within its physician network by investing in information technology initiatives such as installing an electronic medical record system and has committed to spending $1 billion in capital improvements over the next five years.

Fortunately for NorthShore it thrives in an area where the population is young and poverty is limited. While the health system receives a good amount of revenue from Medicare and Medicaid it also receives income from commercial insurance payers with a low level of charity care despite economic turmoil in the US. This patient mix coupled with increased hospital capacity and occupancy rates (more than 70%) has allowed the company to maintain revenue and income growth as well as plenty of cash on hand to fund its expansion initiatives.

In 2014 in major strategic move to consolidate healthcare services in the region Northshore agreed to merge with Advocate Health Care to create Advocate NorthShore Health Partners (ANHP). When complete ANHP will be the largest integrated health care delivery system in Illinois (serving 3 million patients a year) and the 11th largest not-for-profit health care system in the US.

EXECUTIVES

Executive Vice President, Marsha Fache
Senior Vice President Of Business Services, Brian Washa
Assistant Vice President, Cheryl Singer
Executive Vice President Chief Financial Officer and Treasurer, Gary Weiss
Medical Director, Harry J Jaffe

LOCATIONS

HQ: NORTHSHORE UNIVERSITY HEALTHSYSTEM
1301 CENTRAL ST, EVANSTON, IL 602011613
Phone: 847 570-5295
Web: WWW.NORTHSHORE.ORG

PRODUCTS/OPERATIONS

Selected Hospitals

Evanston Hospital (Evanston Illinois)
Glenbrook Hospital (Glenview Illinois)
Highland Park Hospital (Highland Park Illinois)
NorthShore University HealthSystem Home and Hospice
NorthShore University HealthSystem Medical Group
NorthShore University HealthSystem Research Institute
Skokie Hospital (Skokie Illinois)

COMPETITORS

Advocate Health Care	Northwest Community
Central DuPage	Healthcare
Hospital	Northwestern Memorial
Children's Hopsital of	HealthCare
Chicago	Rockford Health System
KishHealth	Rush System for Health
Mercy Hospital and	Sherman Health Systems
Medical Center	University of Chicago
MetroSouth Medical	Medical Center

HISTORICAL FINANCIALS

Company Type: Private

Income Statement

FYE: September 30

	REVENUE ($ mil.)	NET INCOME ($ mil.)	NET PROFIT MARGIN	EMPLOYEES
09/09	1,085	(71)	—	9,000
09/08	26	0	0.4%	—
09/05	1,061	64	6.0%	—
09/04	1,015	0	—	—
Annual Growth	1.3%	—	—	—

2009 Year-End Financials

Return on assets: —
Return on equity: (-6.6%)
Current ratio: 0.20

Cash ($ mil.): 24

NORTHSIDE HOSPITAL INC.

Northside Hospital is no one-trick pony —it actually operates three hospitals serving Atlanta and surrounding areas. Also known as the Northside Healthcare Delivery System the Northside Hospital network includes some 840 licensed beds and more than 2500 physicians on multiple campuses with a host of outpatient health facilities including physician office parks and specialized cancer centers. All of Northside's hospitals are full-service acute-care facilities that provide specialty care including cancer care surgery radiology and women's health. Northside Hospital opened in 1970.

Operations

In addition to its 537-bed hospital in Sandy Springs Northside has hospitals in Cherokee and Forsyth counties as well as more than 120 outpatient centers across Georgia.

Northside Hospital handles about 700000 patient visits annually at its facilities. The organization's cancer treatment division partners with the Cancer Support Community of Atlanta to provide mental health social and educational services to cancer patients and survivors as well as family members and friends.

Geographic Reach

Northside Hospital's three campuses are located in Atlanta Forsyth and Cherokee Georgia. It also operate about 40 outpatient clinics and physician practices scattered across the northern Atlanta metropolitan area.

Strategy

Northside Hospital is conducting expansion and renovation efforts to meet the needs of area residents. It recently completed an expansion and relocation of its Cherokee County Spine & Pain Center (near the Cherokee hospital campus). In 2015 it expanded its radiology offerings with a new outpatient imaging center in Jasper.

The company is in talks with fellow Georgia-based hospital system Gwinnett Medical for a pos-

sible merger. The combined system would have nearly 3500 physicians and 1400 beds.

EXECUTIVES

Vice President Purchasing, Chuck Dalton
Medical Director Of The Sleep Disorders Center, Lisa Johnston
Pharmd, Aziza Aboubaker
Medical Records Director, Sharon Mullings
Director ICU Coronary Care Unit, Brandon Frady
Director of Respiratory Therapy, Rondi Wiggins
Rph, Patricia Boatright (Pat) Gilley
Vice President Marketing and Communications, Lee Echols
Respiratory Therapy Director, Larry Lindberg
Medical Director, Thomas Seay
Director Of Medical Records, Victoria Wyllieandrews
Vice President Planning And Real Estate, Doug Macdonald
Vice President Legal Risk Management and Anciliary Services, Susan (Sue) Sommers
Board Member, Kristina Brinkman
Auditors: DELOITTE & TOUCHE LLP ATLANTA

LOCATIONS

HQ: NORTHSIDE HOSPITAL INC.
1000 JOHNSON FY RD NE, ATLANTA, GA 303421611
Phone: 404 851-8000
Web: WWW.NORTHSIDE.COM

Selected Locations

Alpharetta Medical Campus
Dunwoody Cancer Center
Imaging at Peachtree Dunwoody
Medlock Bridge Imaging
Meridian Park Plaza
Northside Hospital Doctors Center
Northside Hospital-Atlanta
Northside Hospital-Cherokee
Northside Hospital Forsyth
Northside-Forsyth Outpatient Surgery Center
Northside Sugar Hill Imaging (Buford)
Pediatric Center at Northside/Alpharetta
Roswell Cancer Center
Townelake Medical Office/Riverstone Imaging

COMPETITORS

Children's Healthcare	Piedmont Healthcare
of Atlanta	Regency Hospital
DeKalb Medical	Shepherd Center
Emory Healthcare	SunLink Health Systems
Grady Health System	The Fulton-DeKalb
Gwinnett Health System	Hospital Authority
Northeast Georgia	WellStar Health System
Health System	

HISTORICAL FINANCIALS

Company Type: Private

Income Statement

FYE: September 30

	REVENUE ($ mil.)	NET INCOME ($ mil.)	NET PROFIT MARGIN	EMPLOYEES
09/13	1,253	109	8.7%	8,000
09/12	829	60	7.3%	—
09/09	1,002	8	0.8%	—
09/08	938	0	—	—
Annual Growth	6.0%	—	—	—

2013 Year-End Financials

Return on assets: 1.2%
Return on equity: 8.7%
Current ratio: 1.00

Cash ($ mil.): 147

NORTHSTAR GROUP SERVICES INC.

Asbestos lead-based paint nuclear materials and toxic mold don't scare LVI Services one of the top environmental contractors in the US with more than 30 offices across the country. The privately-held company provides integrated facility services such as remediation of hazardous materials decontamination and demolition. It caters to clients in a wide range of business segments from hotels and retail to commercial industrial and institutional. It also serves government and education segments. Customers have included AT&T IBM Marriott Prudential and Raytheon.

Geographic Reach

Headquartered in New York City the company works in all 50 US states. It has more than 30 offices nationwide.

Operations

LVI Services offers design-build general construction program management hazardous material and mold abatement infection control fireproofing demolition as wells as emergency response/disaster recovery and services.

Subsidiary NorthStar Recovery Services provides emergency response and recovery services that help clients minimize damage and disruption following disasters.

Sales and Marketing

LVI Services serves customers in the commercial education government health care hospitality industrial oil and gas power and retail segments.

Strategy

In addition to its core business activities LVI Services offers complementary services that leverage its expertise in remediation such as lead abatement decontamination and decommissioning and drying and dehumidification.

It has provided services to aid in detecting and interdicting nuclear and radioactive threats for three federal agencies: the US Department of Homeland Security the US Department of Energy and the US Customs and Border Protection Agency.

In 2012 LVI Services completed the decommissioning of the University of Arizona's 52-year-old Nuclear Reactor Laboratory.

Mergers and Acquisitions

In 2012 the company acquired Washington State-based Randolph Construction Services which provides design-build contracting services for commercial industrial and government clients.

Company Background

Major stockholder CHS Capital moved in 2010 to merge LVI Services with another of its companies Penhall International which specializes in highway excavations. However Penhall ran into debt problems which squelched the deal and sent LVI Services to the bond market to restructure its debt.

LVI Services was founded in 1986.

EXECUTIVES

President and CEO, Scott E. State
VP and Co-COO, John Leonard
VP and Co-COO, David P. Pearson
VP and Regional Manager New York and New Jersey, Frank Aiello
Director Mold Remediation and Infection Control, Alfred C. Draper
VP and CFO, Paul S. Cutrone
President Industrial Nuclear and Government Division, Richard McManus

VP Nuclear Decontamination and Decommissioning, Thomas W. Gilmore
VP Preconstruction Services, Michael Marcheschi
VP Federal Business Development, David Hicks
Auditors: GRANT THORNTON LLP NEW YORK

LOCATIONS

HQ: NORTHSTAR GROUP SERVICES INC.
150 W 30TH ST FL 8, NEW YORK, NY 100014151
Phone: 212 951-3660
Web: WWW.LVISERVICES.COM

PRODUCTS/OPERATIONS

Selected Services
Asbestos abatement
Demolition
Emergency/disaster response
Drying and dehumidification
Biological and chemical decontamination
Mold remediation
Infection control
Lead abatement
Decontamination and decommissioning
Fireproofing
Power and Petroleum

Selected Industries
Commercial
Government
Industrial
Retail
Health care
Education
Hospitality

COMPETITORS

Bechtel	ENSR International
CH2M HILL	ERM
Controlled Demolition	Fluor
Corvera Abatement	Native Environmental
Dallas Contracting	Parsons Corporation

HISTORICAL FINANCIALS

Company Type: Private

Income Statement

FYE: December 31

	REVENUE ($ mil.)	NET INCOME ($ mil.)	NET PROFIT MARGIN	EMPLOYEES
12/12	404	7	1.9%	3,500
12/11	339	(6)	—	—
12/10	1,589	0	0.0%	—
Annual Growth	(49.5%)	11626.6%	—	—

2012 Year-End Financials

Return on assets: 13.8%
Return on equity: 1.9%
Current ratio: 1.10
Cash ($ mil.): 2

NORTHWEST DAIRY ASSOCIATION

Northwest Dairy Association (NDA) members milk a lot of cows. The dairy cooperative's 550-plus member/farmers ship 7.2 billion pounds of milk annually which is processed by the co-op's subsidiary Darigold and packaged and sold under the Darigold label. NDA produces fluid and cultured dairy products including milk butter cottage cheese sour cream and yogurt that altogether generate some $2 billion in sales. It also makes bulk butter and cheese milk powder and whey products. The co-op caters to several sectors nationwide. Its customers include food retailers and wholesalers as well as foodservice and food-manufacturing

companies. The association's membership spans half a dozen US states.
Geographic Reach
NDA members are located in Washington Oregon Idaho Montana California and Utah.
Operations
The cooperative's Darigold subsidiary operates a dozen processing facilities across the Northwestern US.
Sales and Marketing
Through Darigold NDA makes and markets a full line of dairy-based products for retail foodservice and commodity and specialty markets.
Financial Performance
The dairy cooperative logged nearly $2.5 billion in revenue in 2012 up from just shy of $2.1 billion the prior year. While NDA earned more revenue its assets declined from $579 million to $548 million.
Mergers and Acquisitions
NDA added Country Classic Dairies to its operations in 2010. Its Montana-based business churn out Darigold-branded products with help from its 30 member/farmers. Securing the Country Classics business added some 160 million pounds of milk a year (more than half of Montana's milk supply) to the co-op's total production. NDA and Country Classic's union was the culmination of the two businesses' longtime working relationship (at one time Country Classic used the Darigold name to market its products).

EXECUTIVES

V Pres, Steve Rowe

LOCATIONS

HQ: NORTHWEST DAIRY ASSOCIATION
1130 RAINIER AVE S, SEATTLE, WA 981442842
Phone: 206 284-7220

PRODUCTS/OPERATIONS

Selected Products
Consumer
Butter
Buttermilk
Cottage cheese
Cream
Half and half
Milk
Sour cream
Whipping cream
Yogurt
Ingredients
Bleached sweet dry whey
Colored cheddar cheese
Cultured skim milk powder
Milk protein concentrate
Monterey Jack cheese
Nonfat dry milk
Salted sweet cream butter
Skim milk powder
Sweet cream buttermilk powder
Unsalted butter
Whey protein concentrate

COMPETITORS

Associated Milk Producers	Dean Foods
Berkeley Farms	Humboldt Creamery
California Dairies Inc.	Land O' Lakes
Dairy Farmers of America	Straus Family Creamery
	Tillamook County Creamery Association

HISTORICAL FINANCIALS

Company Type: Private

Income Statement

FYE: March 31

	REVENUE ($ mil.)	NET INCOME ($ mil.)	NET PROFIT MARGIN	EMPLOYEES
03/08	2,207	87	4.0%	1,300
03/07	1,450	12	0.9%	—
03/04	1,297	(6)	—	—
03/03	1,140	0	—	—
Annual Growth	14.1%	—	—	—

2008 Year-End Financials

Return on assets: 4.5%
Return on equity: 4.0%
Current ratio: 0.90
Cash ($ mil.): 10

NORTHWEST FARM CREDIT SERVICES ACA

Customer-owned financial cooperative Northwest Farm Credit Services is an agricultural lender that provides financial services to farmers ranchers agribusinesses commercial fishermen timber producers and rural home owners in Alaska Idaho Montana Oregon and Washington. The company has a network of around 45 branches and offers a broad range of flexible loan programs to meet the needs of people in the agriculture business. Northwest Farm Credit also provides leasing services appraisal services and life mortgage disability and crop insurance as well as legal advocacy and assistance to customers in need. It is part of the Farm Credit System a network of lenders serving the US agriculture industry.
Geographic Reach
Northwest Farm Credit serves customers through 45 branch offices located throughout the US Northwest and in Alaska.Operations
The credit union provides financing and related services to farmers ranchers agribusinesses commercial fishermen timber producers rural homeowners and crop insurance customers. Northwest Farm Credit provides $12 billion in loans. Farm Credit System a nationwide network of borrower-owned lending institutions of which it is part provides $205 billion in loans to rural America.Sales and Marketing
Northwest Farm Credit finances farmers ranchers agribusinesses commercial fishermen timber producers and rural homeowners as well as farm-related businesses agricultural cooperatives and rural utilities.
Financial Performance
The company has seen a slow decline in its revenues over the past few years. In 2013 Northwest Farm Credit's revenues dropped by 5% due to lower interest and noninterest income. Interest income declined as a result of a decrease in loan spread caused in part by greater prepayment expense competitive pressures and an increase in the average loan volume in lower spread lines of business. Noninterest income declined due to a refund received in 2012 from the Farm Credit System Insurance Corporation related to the Farm Credit Insurance Fund.However the company's net income increased by 27% in 2013 due to a benefit from the provision for credit losses and a decline in interest expenses. In 2013 Northwest Farm Credit's operating cash inflow decreased to $200.79 million (from $238.41 million in 2012)

due to a change in the company's current assets and liabilities.

Mergers and Acquisitions

In 2014 the company expanded its operations in Montana by buying Culbertson State Agency's crop insurance portfolio.

Company Background

The US Congress created the Farm Credit System in 1916 to meet the financial needs of farmers ranchers and cooperatives who invest as well as borrow from the institutions within the system. All Farm Credit System members are regulated by the Farm Credit Administration.

EXECUTIVES

EVP Financial Services, Fred (Fred) DePell
EVP and General Counsel, Thomas (Tom) Tracy
EVP Corporate Administration and Secretary, Joan E. Haynes
EVP CFO and CIO, Tom Nakano
Vice President, Marnie Vandenberg
Assistant Vice President country Home Lending, Matt Koch
Branch Manager Assistant Vice President, Jeffrey Rodenbaugh
Relationship Manager II Assistant Vice President, Natasha Jungers
Retiredf Vice President Credit, Val Warehime
Relationship Manager Vice President, Steve Smith
Assistant Vice President Operations, Jessi Dressen
Vice President Credit, Brandon Stacey
Vice President Credit Officer, Richard Harris
Assistant Vice President Loan Accounting, Sophie Conley
Regional Vice President, Lance Zollinger
Credit Manager And Assistant Vice President, Rick Guenther
Credit Officer And Assistant Vice President, Eric Gray
Vice President Agribusiness, Rich Fehringer
Relationship Manager And Assistant Vice President, Michael Mills
Relationship Manager Vice President Agribusiness, Tom Howard
Chairman, Drew Eggers
Vice Chairman, Kevin Riel

LOCATIONS

HQ: NORTHWEST FARM CREDIT SERVICES ACA
1700 S ASSEMBLY ST # 102, SPOKANE, WA
992242116
Phone: 509 838-2429

COMPETITORS

Bank of America
First Interstate
Idaho Independent Bank
KeyCorp
Northwest Bancorporation

U.S. Bancorp
Wells Fargo
Zions Bancorporation

HISTORICAL FINANCIALS

Company Type: Private

Income Statement				FYE: December 31
	ASSETS ($ mil.)	NET INCOME ($ mil.)	INCOME AS % OF ASSETS	EMPLOYEES
12/13	9,604	236	2.5%	500
12/12	9,471	187	2.0%	—
12/11	8,696	159	1.8%	—
12/10	8,705	0	—	—
Annual Growth	3.3%	—	—	—

2013 Year-End Financials

Return on assets: —
Return on equity: 51.5%
Sales ($ mil): 460

NORTHWESTERN MEMORIAL HOSPITAL

LOCATIONS

HQ: NORTHWESTERN MEMORIAL HOSPITAL
251 E HURON ST, CHICAGO, IL 606113055
Phone: 312 755-0604
Web: WWW.NMH.ORG

HISTORICAL FINANCIALS

Company Type: Private

Income Statement				FYE: August 31
	REVENUE ($ mil.)	NET INCOME ($ mil.)	NET PROFIT MARGIN	EMPLOYEES
08/10	1,380	64	4.7%	5,800
08/09	1,304	4	0.3%	—
Annual Growth	5.8%	1320.3%	—	—

2010 Year-End Financials

Return on assets: 4.2%
Return on equity: 4.7%
Current ratio: 0.60
Cash ($ mil.): 29

NOVA SOUTHEASTERN UNIVERSITY INC.

Nova Southeastern University (NSU) gives a whole new meaning to "school of sharks." NSU whose mascot is the deep sea predator has an enrollment of more than 27000 students and offers a variety of undergraduate graduate and professional academic programs. NSU offers degrees in several medical disciplines (osteopathic medicine pharmacy optometry nursing) marine biology business law education and computer sciences. The not-for-profit independent school operates four campuses in the Miami-Fort Lauderdale area several health centers and an oceanographic center. Founded in 1964 Nova University merged with Southeastern University of the Health Sciences in 1994 to become Nova Southeastern University.

Operations

In addition to its undergraduate and graduate programs NSU also operates The University School a pre-K through 12th grade college preparatory day school that draws part of its staff from NSU's School of Education and Human services. The university's Mailman Segal Institute for Early Childhood Studies serves the local community with programming for parents and educators.

Geographic Reach

NSU is a distance education pioneer (it was the first US university to offer graduate programs online) offering classes on the Internet as well as at six regional centers in Florida and Puerto Rico.

Finance

Continuing a trend of earnings growth over the last five years from organic growth measures NSU reported a 4% rise in revenues in 2014 to some $640 million. The growth was attributed to increased tuition and fee income as well as revenues from auxiliary enterprises and government grants.

Strategy

As universities do NSU regularly invests in facility upgrades to meet the growing needs of its students. In 2014 it broke ground on the NSU Center for Collaborative Research (CCR) that will house an IBM supercomputer a tech incubator one of the state's largest wet labs and space for guest researchers. Other CCR facilities will include cancer and neuro-immune institutes an incubator for security businesses and an entire floor for the US Geological Survey which will partner with the university on research into Everglades restoration projects.

EXECUTIVES

Intrm Vice President Information Technology, GREG HORNE
Associate Vice President Business Services and Director Purchasing, Marc C Crocquet
Associate Vice President Human Resources, Mark A Jones
Vice President Community Government Relations, Larry A Calderon
Associate Vice President Enrollment and Student Services, STEPHANIE G BROWN
Executive Vice Chancellor and Provost, Frederick Lippman
EVP and COO, George L. Hanbury
VP Finance, W. David Heron
Dean Student Affairs, Brad Williams
Director Alvin Sherman Library Research and Information Technology Center, Harriett MacDougall
Dean Shepard Broad Law Center, Athornia Steele
University Provost and EVP Academic Affairs, Frank DePiano
Dean University School, Jerome Chermak
Dean College of Health Care Sciences, Richard E. Davis
Dean Oceanographic Center, Richard E. Dodge
Dean Center for Psychological Studies, Karen Grosby
Dean College of Medical Sciences, Harold E. Laubach
Dean Mailman Segal Institute for Early Childhood Studies, Roni Leiderman
Dean College of Optometry, David S. Loshin
Dean College of Pharmacy, Andr ©Malav ©
Dean Farquhar College of Arts and Sciences, Don Rosenblum
Dean College of Osteopathic Medicine, Anthony J. Silvagni
Dean Fischler School of Education, H. Wells Singleton
Dean College of Dental Medicine, Robert A. Uchin
Dean Graduate School of Humanities and Social Sciences, Honggang Yang
EVP and COO, Jacqueline A. Travisano
Senior Executive Assistant President Manager, Shirley Naidoo
CEO Health Clinics, Robert S. Oller
VP Information Technology and CIO, Tom West
Executive Assistant Vice President, Katharine Perren
Medical Director Simulation and Standardized Patients Labs, Heather McCarthy
Pharmacy Manager, Todd Schmidt
Vice President Clinical Operations, Linda Smelser
Vice President Human Resources, Robert (Bob) Pietrykowski
Clinical Director, Albert Coombs
Vice President, Joseph P Degaetano
Vice President For Facilities Management, Pete Witschen
Vice President, Joanne Ferchland-Parella
Vice President Research And Technology Transfer, Gary Margules
Director Of Admissions, Regina Schawaroch
Associate Vice President, Barbara Packer
Vice President, Mary Laxton
Pharmacy Manager, Miguel Acosta
Chair Department of Clinics, Heidi Wagner
Vice President, Marie Cuneo

Director Of Clinical Services, Jessica Granata
Vice President Of Finance, David Heron
Vice President, Catalina Gonzalez
Vice President, Federica H Hulett
Co Vice President, Hilary Gerber
Vice President of Finance, David (Dave) Heron
Clinical Director, Amir Farhangpour
Vice President Programs, Jennifer (Jen) Donelson
Chair, Ronald G. Assaf
Vice Chair, Barry J. Silverman
Secretary, Jacquelyn Fisher
Treasurer, Tyler Lacertosa
Treasurer, Ari Lewit
Treasurer, Mary Tomaino
Treasurer, Ida Dumay
Secretary, Hannah (Hanna) Barr
Treasurer, Justin Arnold
Auditors: KPMG LLP GREENSBORO NC

LOCATIONS

HQ: NOVA SOUTHEASTERN UNIVERSITY INC.
3301 COLLEGE AVE, DAVIE, FL 333147796
Phone: 954 262-7300
Web: WWW.NSUNEWS.NOVA.EDU

COMPETITORS

Florida Atlantic
University
Florida International
University

University of Florida

HISTORICAL FINANCIALS

Company Type: Private

Income Statement

FYE: June 30

	REVENUE ($ mil.)	NET INCOME ($ mil.)	NET PROFIT MARGIN	EMPLOYEES
06/13	617	38	6.3%	2,500
06/12	689	48	7.1%	—
06/10	612	22	3.7%	—
06/09	595	0	—	—
Annual Growth	0.9%	—	—	—

2013 Year-End Financials

Return on assets: —
Return on equity: 6.3%
Current ratio: 0.60
Cash ($ mil.): 63

NOVELART MANUFACTURING COMPANY

Auditors: PITCHER ENDERS AND DROHAN CI

LOCATIONS

HQ: NOVELART MANUFACTURING COMPANY
2121 SECTION RD, CINCINNATI, OH 452373509
Phone: 513 351-7700
Web: WWW.TOPICZINC.COM

HISTORICAL FINANCIALS

Company Type: Private

Income Statement

FYE: September 30

	REVENUE ($ mil.)	NET INCOME ($ mil.)	NET PROFIT MARGIN	EMPLOYEES
09/14	359	0	—	160
09/13	330	0	—	
09/12	309	0	—	
09/11	284	0	—	
Annual Growth	8.2%	—	—	

2014 Year-End Financials

Return on assets: 1.5%
Return on equity: —
Current ratio: 1.40
Cash ($ mil.): —

NOVO CONSTRUCTION INC.

LOCATIONS

HQ: NOVO CONSTRUCTION INC.
1460 OBRIEN DR, MENLO PARK, CA 940251432
Phone: 650 701-1500
Web: WWW.NOVOCONSTRUCTION.COM

HISTORICAL FINANCIALS

Company Type: Private

Income Statement

FYE: October 31

	REVENUE ($ mil.)	NET INCOME ($ mil.)	NET PROFIT MARGIN	EMPLOYEES
10/13	404	4	1.1%	155
10/12	356	3	1.0%	
10/11	230	2	1.1%	
10/10	91	0	—	
Annual Growth	64.2%	—	—	

2013 Year-End Financials

Return on assets: —
Return on equity: 1.1%
Current ratio: 0.90
Cash ($ mil.): 47

NYSARC INC.

Auditors: BONADIO & CO LLP PITTSFORD

LOCATIONS

HQ: NYSARC INC.
393 DELAWARE AVE, DELMAR, NY 120543094
Phone: 518 439-8311
Web: WWW.NYSARC.ORG

HISTORICAL FINANCIALS

Company Type: Private

Income Statement

FYE: December 31

	REVENUE ($ mil.)	NET INCOME ($ mil.)	NET PROFIT MARGIN	EMPLOYEES
12/09	1,746	55	3.2%	28,000
12/08	0	0	—	
Annual Growth	21831162.5%	—	—	

2009 Year-End Financials

Return on assets: 3.5%
Return on equity: 3.2%
Current ratio: 0.40
Cash ($ mil.): 141

O'BRIEN & GERE LIMITED

O'Brien & Gere provides a range of engineering consulting and project management services throughout the US including wastewater management and water resources environmental compliance and remediation civil and facilities engineering and utility services. It also provides contract operations and maintenance. Employee-owned O'Brien & Gere serves municipal environmental manufacturing and federal clients. The company which employs hundreds of scientists engineers construction and other personnel operates nearly 30 offices in about a dozen states.

Operations

The company offers a broad range of services. With federal clients it helps to develop and manage infrastructure and facilities that improve efficiency safety and quality of life.

Its higher education services include collaborating with public and private higher education institutions supporting campus infrastructure and utility upgrades energy efficiency initiatives and environmental compliance programs.

O'Brien & Gere's industrial services include offering comprehensive project delivery services to advanced manufacturing clients through in-house skill-sets (ranging from engineering to fabrication) and control systems integration.

The company's municipal services provide energy water environmental and facilities services to municipalities state agencies and public and private water and sewer utilities.

Geographic Reach

The Syracuse New York-based firm has more than 27 branch offices in about a dozen states including Georgia Michigan New York Ohio Pennsylvania and Virginia.Sales and MarketingO'Brien & Gere mostly serves the Municipal Industrial Higher Education and Federal sectors. The company's public sector business accounted for roughly 25% of its total revenue in 2014.

Strategy

O'Brien & Gere has also been expanding into the New York metropolitan market where it believes more growth opportunities exist. In 2015 for example the company purchased Long Island-based Schuyler Engineering P.C. to extend its market reach into the New York and New Jersey markets while growing its client base at the same time. In 2013 the firm opened a new office in Utica New York as part of its strategic plan to expand services to clients across the Mohawk Valley and greater upstate New York regions.With a strengthening economy and a more sustainability-focused business environment O'Brien & Gere has also been positioned to pick up more projects and grow over the past few years. In 2014 O'Brien & Gere experienced growth in its water services business in the municipal market resulting from strong market demand in its wet infrastructure segment (including stormwater management); wastewater treatment (in response to growing require­ments for enhanced nutrient removal at wastewater treatment plants); and program and construction management (integrated operations and maintenance and commissioning services). In

2013 the company was awarded a project with Syracuse University to provide building commissioning services for the University's new bookstore fitness center and retail location. This $20 million mixed-use project would include a university-operated fitness center for students and employees and a bookstore with retail spaces.

Mergers and Acquisitions

The firm has made several acquisitions through the years in order to expand its geographic reach and grow its capabilities. In 2015 O'Brien & Gere purchased Long Island-based Schuyler Engineering P.C. an engineering firm that specialized in central utility plant and energy system design extending its market reach throughout the New York and New Jersey metropolitan markets. In 2012 the company acquired the remaining 55% of South Carolina-based architecture/engineering company Lindgergh & Associates.

Company Background

In 2014 O'Brien & Gere received a CCBJ award for Consulting & Engineering: Energy & Carbon Management. The firm was recognized for supporting development of the first comprehensive smart growth plan for regional energy and sustainability in Central New York.

The firm was formed by Earl O'Brien William Gere and Glenn Holmes as a water and wastewater engineering partnership in 1945.

EXECUTIVES

Senior Vice President Environmental Business Unit Leader, Thomas (Thom) Nowlan
Auditors: DANNIBLE & MCKEE LLP SYRACUSE

LOCATIONS

HQ: O' BRIEN & GERE LIMITED
333 W WASHINGTON ST # 400, SYRACUSE, NY 132025253
Phone: 315 437-6100
Web: WWW.OBG.COM

COMPETITORS

CH2M HILL	Jacobs Engineering
ENVIRON	Parsons Corporation
Fluor	

HISTORICAL FINANCIALS
Company Type: Private

Income Statement
FYE: December 28

	REVENUE ($ mil.)	NET INCOME ($ mil.)	NET PROFIT MARGIN	EMPLOYEES
12/13	219	2	1.1%	800
12/11	187	2	1.5%	—
12/06	125	1	1.1%	—
12/00	123	0	—	—
Annual Growth	4.5%	—	—	—

2013 Year-End Financials
Return on assets: 7.2%   Cash ($ mil.): 2
Return on equity: 1.1%
Current ratio: 1.00

O'CONNOR HOSPITAL

Auditors: GRANT THORNTON LLP SAN FRANCI

LOCATIONS

HQ: O' CONNOR HOSPITAL
2105 FOREST AVE, SAN JOSE, CA 951281471
Phone: 408 947-2500
Web: WWW.OCONNORHOSPITAL.ORG

HISTORICAL FINANCIALS
Company Type: Private

Income Statement
FYE: June 30

	REVENUE ($ mil.)	NET INCOME ($ mil.)	NET PROFIT MARGIN	EMPLOYEES
06/13	309	(25)	—	1,300
06/10	300	(6)	—	—
06/09	272	(9)	—	—
06/08	945	0	—	—
Annual Growth	—	—	—	—

2013 Year-End Financials
Return on assets: 5.0%   Cash ($ mil.): 32
Return on equity: (-8.2%)
Current ratio: 4.30

O'NEIL INDUSTRIES INC.

A family of construction companies O'Neil Industries has also built W.E. O'Neil Construction Company. The employee-owned company operates in Arizona California Colorado and Illinois providing general contracting construction management design/build and structural concrete services for commercial projects in the US and Canada. O'Neil Industries has worked on corporate offices manufacturing and distribution facilities and mixed-use centers for clients in the education gaming health care hospitality and retail industries. The company also serves the residential and senior living sectors. Clients have included Boeing DePaul University and The Nature Conservancy.

Geographic Reach

While O'Neil Industries is primarily US-centric with a headquarters office in Chicago and five operating units in Illinois (Chicago) Arizona (Tucson and Phoenix) California (Los Angeles) and Colorado (Denver) the construction company also boasts a presence in Ontario Canada.

Operations

Recent projects in Arizona include America West Airlines Flight Training Facility (in Phoenix) Arizona Cancer Center (in Tucson) and Air Center Scottsdale's McClain Street Facility (Scottsdale). In El Segundo California O'Neil Industries completed the Aerospace A6 PODS project.

The company transitioned its T.L. Roof & Associates business into its Tucson branch. Its O'Neil Construction Company unit serves as the company's concrete division. The company's Special Projects Group concentrates on small to midsized tenant improvement and facility- or campus-based projects.

Strategy

O'Neil Industries is focused on environmentally-friendly construction projects. To this end it has devoted 80 full-time staff members who deemed LEED Accredited Professionals. The company has been involved in more than 4 million sq. ft. of LEED-certified projects including BRE Park Viridian Apartments Columbia College Media Production Center and Haworth Permanent Showroom at the Merchandise Mart.

One of the company's most recent projects include a new Chapel at Carondelet St. Joseph's Hospital in Tucson Arizona which it completed in 2013. The 3000-sq.-ft. addition to the hospital's existing courtyard was developed through a partnership with designer Swaim Associates.

In 2013 its W.E. O'Neil Construction Company began a renovation and addition project on the Sun City Oro Valley Fitness Center.

The construction firm is also upgrading its technology.

Sales and Marketing

O'Neil Industries works to maintain high customer satisfaction. More than 80% of O'Neil Industries' clients are repeat customers. Such clients include Dessert Bloom OB & Gyn Peter Palumbo Exton City of West Hollywood and The Boeing Company.

EXECUTIVES

Vice President, Patrick J McGowan, age 60
Vice President Engineering Research and Development, Dean Arnold
Executive Vice President, Oleh Karawan
Vice President, Pat McGowan
Auditors: CROWE HORWATH LLP OAK BROOK

LOCATIONS

HQ: O' NEIL INDUSTRIES INC.
1245 W WASHINGTON BLVD, CHICAGO, IL 606071929
Phone: 773 244-6003
Web: WWW.WEONEIL.COM

PRODUCTS/OPERATIONS

Selected Delivery Methods
Construction Management
General Contracting
Design/Build

Selected Markets
Aerospace
Education
Green
Healthcare
Hospitality & Restaurants
Industrial
Infrastructure
Municipal
Office
Gaming & Recreation
Retail
Religious
Residential
Senior Living
Special Projects
Tribal

COMPETITORS

Bulley & Andrews	Leopardo
Clark Construction Group	McShane Construction
Gilbane Building Company	Pepper Construction
Graycor	Sundt
	The Austin Company
	Walsh Group

HISTORICAL FINANCIALS
Company Type: Private

Income Statement
FYE: December 31

	REVENUE ($ mil.)	NET INCOME ($ mil.)	NET PROFIT MARGIN	EMPLOYEES
12/13	458	2	0.5%	400
12/12	458	2	0.5%	—
12/11	458	2	0.5%	—
12/10	0	0	—	—
Annual Growth	—	—	—	—

2013 Year-End Financials
Return on assets: —   Cash ($ mil.): 31
Return on equity: 0.5%
Current ratio: 0.90

O. C. TANNER COMPANY

O.C. Tanner recognizes that it's nice to be appreciated. The company designs and helps implement employee recognition programs for customers around the world. Related services intended to help customers take full advantage of their investment in employee recognition include communication consulting research leadership training and social programs. The company which operates from offices in the US Canada and the UK has shipped awards to clients in about 150 countries. Over the years O.C. Tanner has counted numerous Fortune 100 companies among its clients.

Geographic Reach

O.C. Tanner serves global customers from its locations in Salt Lake City Utah (US); Burlington Ontario (Canada); and Loughton Essex (UK). Outside of the US its main markets are Australia Brazil Canada China Europe Hong Kong Japan India Mexico and Singapore.

Operations

In addition to its recognition programs Tanner provides ancillary products and services such as recognition publication and lecture series engagement studies and leadership recognition training. Tanner's roster of authors and speakers are available to give presentations on topics such as delivering appreciation strategies and the company hosts an annual Executive Recognition Summit where industry leaders come together to share insights into their companies' employee recognition practices.

Sales and Marketing

O.C. Tanner has served some 8500 businesses including about 35 Fortune 100 companies such as American Express Caterpillar Abbott Labs Chevron FedEx and Wells Fargo.

Strategy

O.C. Tanner seeks to cater its recognition programs to each client applying insights into the employees brands and cultures present within each customer's operations. Its packages include blends of recognition awards coaching communication solutions social tools and management assistance components and its services are available for smaller customers as well as multi-national corporations.

Company Background

Namesake Obert C. Tanner founded the company in 1927 by selling class rings and pins for school graduates.

Ownership

O.C. Tanner is owned by Obert's daughter and company chair Carolyn Tanner Irish.

EXECUTIVES

Vice President Business Development, Michelle (Mitch) Smith
Senior Vice President, Clark Campbell
Executive Vice President Marketing and Business Development, David (Dave) Sturt
Vice President Supply Chain, Paul Terry
General Counsel and Vice President, Brian Katz
Vice President and Consultant, Adrian Gostick
Vice President Creative Services, Steve Newman

LOCATIONS

HQ: O. C. TANNER COMPANY
1930 S STATE ST, SALT LAKE CITY, UT 841152383
Phone: 801 486-2430
Web: WWW.OCTANNER.COM

PRODUCTS/OPERATIONS

Selected Clients
Abbot
American Express
Bank of America
Caterpillar Inc.
Chevron Corporation
Comcast
ConocoPhillips
CVS
Dell
Dow Chemical
Express Scripts
FedEx
Freddie Mac
General Dynamics
HCA Corporate
Hess Corporation
Home Depot
Johnson Controls Inc.
JP Morgan Chase
Kraft Foods
The Kroger Co.
Marathon Petroleum
McKesson
Medco Health
Merck
Northrop Grumman
Raytheon
Safeway
State Farm Insurance
Sunoco Inc.
Sysco
Travelers
WellPoint
Wells Fargo

COMPETITORS

American Achievement	Pitney Bowes Marketing
CA Short	Solutions
ITAGroup	TharpeRobbins
LoyaltyOne	
Maritz Loyalty & Motivation	

HISTORICAL FINANCIALS
Company Type: Private

Income Statement
FYE: December 31

	REVENUE ($ mil.)	NET INCOME ($ mil.)	NET PROFIT MARGIN	EMPLOYEES
12/13	327	27	8.5%	1,700
12/12	316	19	6.3%	—
12/08	0	0	—	—
12/07	0	0	—	—
Annual Growth	—	—	—	—

O. C. TANNER RECOGNITION COMPANY

LOCATIONS

HQ: O. C. TANNER RECOGNITION COMPANY
1930 S STATE ST, SALT LAKE CITY, UT 841152311
Phone: 801 486-2430
Web: WWW.OCTANNER.COM

HISTORICAL FINANCIALS
Company Type: Private

Income Statement
FYE: December 31

	REVENUE ($ mil.)	NET INCOME ($ mil.)	NET PROFIT MARGIN	EMPLOYEES
12/13*	378	(2)	—	1,700
05/13	367	(2)	—	—
12/11	372	(1)	—	—
12/10	356	0	—	—
Annual Growth	2.1%	—	—	—
*Fiscal year change

OAKLAND UNIVERSITY

Oakland University is the OU of the North. The Michigan public university serves a student body of more than 20000 offering about 130 baccalaureate degree programs and more than 100 graduate degree and certificate programs. It boasts a student-to-faculty ratio of 22-to-1. In addition to academic and specialty programs in areas ranging from business and technology to nursing and athletics its faculty members also coordinate hands-on research projects for graduate students. The main university campus spans some 1400 acres that house seven academic schools and colleges in Rochester Michigan. Oakland University also has satellite campuses in Macomb County and a law school in Auburn Hills.

Geographic Reach

Located in Rochester Michigan Oakland University's main campus comprises seven academic schools and colleges. The educational institution also operates a law school in Auburn Hills and satellite campuses in Macomb County. About 70% of its students come from Oakland and Macomb counties. Out-of-state and foreign students comprise 4.3% of the student body.

Strategy

Oakland University works to expand and improve its programs and facilities to attract new students (it had more than 20000 students for the first time in the 2013-2014 year). In 2011 for instance it added two new bachelor's degree majors: one in creative writing and one in biomedical sciences. The school introduced a Master of Science in Engineering Management degree which help them better manage environmental resources and significantly reduce energy costs.. The university has also expanded its campus resources as it has increased enrollment levels during the past decade. In fall 2014 the university opened a $75 million 134000-square-foot building for the School of Engineering and Computer Science.

Financial Performance

Operating revenue was $212 million in 2014 (ended June) a 4% increase over 2013. A 2.3% enrollment increase boosted tuition (for which rates rose 3.7%). Operating expenses were about $283 million in 2014 compared to $275 million in 2013. The university's net position increased by almost $40 million with gains in investment income gifts and additions to permanent endowments.

Sales and Marketing

The university advertises through several mediums such as television radio websites social networking sites billboards magazines newspapers and journals.

Company Background

Oakland University was founded in 1957 by Alfred and Matilda Wilson who donated $2 million and their 1500-acre estate to Michigan State University to start a new college in Oakland County. Named Michigan State University Oakland the college enrolled its first students in 1959. The school's name changed to Oakland University in 1963 and it became an autonomous institution in 1970.

EXECUTIVES

Vice President Government Relations, Rochelle Black
Vice President Legal Affairs General Counsel and Secretary, Victor Zambardi
Associate Vice President, Terry Stollsteimer
Assistant Vice President Student Affairs and Dean of Students, Glenn Mcintosh
Executive Legal Secretary, Carolyn Hogan

Assistant Vice President Government And, Nicole
Stallworth
Assistant Vice President, Catheryn Cheal
Search Committee Chair Department Of
Biological Sciences, Anne Hitt
Board Of Directors, Amy Butler
Secretary Ii mathematics And Statistic, Alice M
Carleton
Secretary, Amber Hof
Secretary, Terese King
Secretary, Andrea Patton
Secretary, Dan Miller
Secretary, Sheri Rourke
Secretary I Communication And Journalism,
Debra Koehler
Secretary II University Housing, Susan (Sue) Tiley
Auditors: ANDREWS HOOPER PAVLIK PLC AU

LOCATIONS

HQ: OAKLAND UNIVERSITY
2200 N SQUIRREL RD, ROCHESTER, MI 483094401
Phone: 248 370-2100
Web: WWW.OAKLAND.EDU

PRODUCTS/OPERATIONS

Selected Schools
Beaumont School of Medicine
College of Arts and Sciences
Cooley Law School
Macomb Campuses
School of Business Administration
School of Education and Human Services
School of Engineering and Computer Science
School of Health Sciences
School of Nursing

HISTORICAL FINANCIALS

Company Type: Private

Income Statement   FYE: June 30

	REVENUE ($ mil.)	NET INCOME ($ mil.)	NET PROFIT MARGIN	EMPLOYEES
06/14	212	39	18.6%	2,650
06/13	203	27	13.3%	—
06/12	194	37	19.4%	—
06/10	172	0	—	—
Annual Growth	5.3%	—	—	—

2014 Year-End Financials
Return on assets: 17.3%   Cash ($ mil.): 28
Return on equity: 18.6%
Current ratio: 0.70

OBERLIN COLLEGE

Founded in 1833 Oberlin College was the first
college in the US to enroll women on an equal
basis with men. The school has a College of Arts
and Sciences (about 2300 enrollees) but may be
best known for its Conservatory of Music (about
600 enrollees) the oldest such institution in the US.
The College of Arts and Sciences offers nearly 50
undergraduate majors the Conservatory about 10.
Students can earn bachelor's degrees in either
program but can also earn a five-year double-de-
gree in both. In addition Oberlin offers master's degrees in opera theater conducting performance
historical performance historical instruments
music teaching and education. It has two-year certificate programs as well.

Strategy
In 2012 Oberlin launched a fundraising campaign called Oberlin Illuminate. The campaign aims
to raise $250 million to enhance academic pro-

grams as well as to support student access community and graduate placement initiatives.
Financial Performance
Oberlin increased revenues by 1% to $159 mil-
lion in 2012 due to increased income from student
tuition room and board. Student revenues make up
about more than 60% of sales; the rest comes
from investments gifts and auxiliary enterprises.
The school posted a net income loss however due
to higher operating expenses and decreased returns on investments.

The college has an endowment of some $679
million as of mid-2012 up nearly $20 million from
2011. Endowment levels remain low compared to
post-recession figures however and as a result
Oberlin continues to operate under tight spending
and budget guidelines.

EXECUTIVES

Vice President For Communications, Ben Jones
Vice President Finance and Administration, Mike
Frandsen
Auditors: MALONEY & NOVOTNY LLC CLEVELA

LOCATIONS

HQ: OBERLIN COLLEGE
173 W LORAIN ST, OBERLIN, OH 440741073
Phone: 440 775-8121
Web: WWW.BLOGS.OBERLIN.EDU

HISTORICAL FINANCIALS

Company Type: Private

Income Statement   FYE: June 30

	REVENUE ($ mil.)	NET INCOME ($ mil.)	NET PROFIT MARGIN	EMPLOYEES
06/14	171	119	69.6%	1,140
06/13	167	72	43.5%	—
06/09	147	(224)	—	—
06/07	137	0	—	—
Annual Growth	3.2%	—	—	—

2014 Year-End Financials
Return on assets: 5.6%   Cash ($ mil.): 9
Return on equity: 69.6%
Current ratio: 0.50

OCEAN BEAUTY SEAFOODS LLC

Prefer your piscatory purchase to be fresh frozen
or canned? Ocean Beauty Seafoods has it covered.
Doing no fishing of its own the company buys
seafood from commercial fishermen and then
processes sells and distributes its seafood products
in Alaska and across the continental US. Founded
in 1910 the company also exports seafood to Mexico Europe Asia Africa and the Middle East. Ocean
Beauty's specialty products include smoked
salmon smoked salmon spreads pickled and mar-
inated herring shrimp cocktail caviar and lobster
pâté. Nonprofit Bristol Bay Economic
Development Corporation owns 50% of Ocean
Beauty; individual investors own the rest.
Geographic Reach
Based in Washington Ocean Beauty enjoys a
global reach.
Operations
Boasting offices or plants in eight US states plus
overseas in Japan Ocean Beauty operates its own
fleet of seafood delivery trucks across the Western
US. The fleet makes regular stops at the seafood

company's distribution facilities located in Oregon
Idaho Texas Montana Utah and Washington. The
company operates six production sites in Alaska
in Alitak Cordova Excursion Inlet Kodiak Naknek
and Petersburg as well as a pair of production
sites in Seattle and Monroe Washington. Sales and
administration offices are located in Seattle and
Tokyo. Ocean Beauty exports its products to Mexico Europe Asia Africa and the Middle East.
Strategy
Ocean Beauty claims to be the first company to
vacuum pack Alaskan seafood (in 1954). The company's products are primarily caught in the waters
of the Pacific Northwest but Ocean Beauty also
purchases fish from harvesters worldwide. Its
major manufacturing facilities are certified against
the British Retail Consortium Audit Standards.
Ocean Beauty also voluntarily participates in the
US Department of Commerce's Hazard Actions
Critical Control Points (HACCP) Seafood Inspection Program for added assurance that its products
are safe wholesome and properly labeled. The company's production and distribution operations are
conducted in compliance with the US Food and
Drug Administration's HACCP regulations.
Sales and Marketing
Ocean Beauty sells its fresh and frozen seafood
products to both retail and foodservice customers.
The company maintains sales offices in the states
in Seattle and overseas in Tokyo.
Company Ownership
Individual investors and Bristol Bay Economic
Development Corporation a nonprofit each owns
a 50% stake in Ocean Beauty.

EXECUTIVES

Vice President, Tony Ross
Vice President Manufacturing Operations, David
(Dave) Forbush
Vice President Distribution, Jack Whitney

LOCATIONS

HQ: OCEAN BEAUTY SEAFOODS LLC
1100 W EWING ST, SEATTLE, WA 981191321
Phone: 206 285 6800
Web: WWW.OCEANBEAUTY.COM

PRODUCTS/OPERATIONS

Selected Brands
CircleSea
Commander
Deep Sea
Echo Falls
Icy Point
LASCCO
McGovern
Nathan's
Neptune
Ocean Beauty
Ocean Bonita
Pillar Rock
Pink Beauty
Pirate
Port Clyde
RITE
Royal Alaska
Sea Choice
Searchlight
Sound Beauty
St. Andrews
Surf King
Three Star
Tribe

Selected Products
Imported finfish
  Mahi mahi
  Sea Bass
  Shark
  Swordfish
  Tuna
North Pacific finfish
  Cod

Farm-raised
Flounder
Halibut
Perch
Pollock
Rockfish
Salmon
Sole
Sturgeon
Whiting
Shellfish
Coldwater shrimp meat
Clams
Crab
Mussels
Oysters
Prawns
Other products
Milt
Pickled herring
Roe
Surimi

COMPETITORS

Alaska Sausage	Maruha Nichiro
Alaska Seafood company	Orca Bay Seafoods
Alaskan Leader	Pacific Seafood Group
Fisheries	Peter Pan Seafoods
Arrowac Fisheries	Princes Limited
Banner Smoked Fish	Red Chamber Co.
Bumble Bee Foods	Salmolux
Chicken of the Sea	Santa' s Smokehouse
Gorton' s	Seafood Sales
High Liner Foods	StarKist
Icelandic Group	Trident Seafoods
Icicle Seafoods	

HISTORICAL FINANCIALS
Company Type: Private

Income Statement

	REVENUE ($ mil.)	NET INCOME ($ mil.)	NET PROFIT MARGIN	EMPLOYEES
				FYE: December 28
12/13	425	11	2.6%	18,000
12/12	409	8	2.0%	—
12/11	431	7	1.6%	—
12/08	418	0	—	—
Annual Growth	0.3%	—	—	—

2013 Year-End Financials

Return on assets: 3.5%
Return on equity: 2.6%
Current ratio: 0.40

Cash ($ mil.): 3

OCEAN DUKE CORPORATION

Ocean Duke maintains a regal demeanor in a fishy environment. The company is a seafood wholesaler offering a variety of frozen raw fish shrimp mollusks and crustaceans. Ocean Duke also sells breaded fish shrimp and squid. The company imports its products and serves foodservice food processing distribution and wholesale companies throughout the US.

LOCATIONS

HQ: OCEAN DUKE CORPORATION
3450 FUJITA ST, TORRANCE, CA 905054019
Phone: 310 326-3198
Web: WWW.OCEANDUKE.COM

COMPETITORS

Arista Industries	Florida Fresh Seafood
Caspian Trading	Corp.
Company	Orca Bay Seafoods

HISTORICAL FINANCIALS
Company Type: Private

Income Statement

	REVENUE ($ mil.)	NET INCOME ($ mil.)	NET PROFIT MARGIN	EMPLOYEES
				FYE: March 31
03/11	158	2	1.4%	25
03/02	191	0	0.5%	—
03/01	196	1	0.5%	—
03/00	0	0	—	—
Annual Growth	—	—	—	—

2011 Year-End Financials

Return on assets: 13.3%
Return on equity: 1.4%
Current ratio: 0.50

Cash ($ mil.): 1

OCHSNER CLINIC FOUNDATION

Auditors: DELOITTE TAX LLP NEW ORLEANS

LOCATIONS

HQ: OCHSNER CLINIC FOUNDATION
1514 JEFFERSON HWY, NEW ORLEANS, LA
701212483
Phone: 504 842-3000
Web: WWW.OCHSNER.ORG

HISTORICAL FINANCIALS
Company Type: Private

Income Statement

	REVENUE ($ mil.)	NET INCOME ($ mil.)	NET PROFIT MARGIN	EMPLOYEES
				FYE: December 31
12/12	4,829	12	0.3%	10,500
12/11	4,513	47	1.1%	—
12/09	3,484	55	1.6%	—
12/08	567	0	—	—
Annual Growth	70.8%	—	—	—

2012 Year-End Financials

Return on assets: —
Return on equity: 0.3%
Current ratio: 0.50

Cash ($ mil.): 147

OCLC ONLINE COMPUTER LIBRARY CENTER INCORPORATE

Working to reduce the cost of information OCLC Online Computer Library Center is a membership cooperative that provides access to the world's information. The group offers services and tools to some 74000 member libraries in about 170 countries. Services include computer-based cataloging preservation and library management. OCLC additionally facilitates interlibrary loan services administers the Dewey Decimal Classification system and operates the WorldCat database an online resource for finding library materials. OCLC

was founded in 1967 by presidents of the colleges and universities in Ohio. OCLC which stands for Ohio College Library Center opened its first location in Ohio State's main library.

Geographic Reach

OCLC operates in about 170 countries across the Americas Asia Pacific Europe the Middle East and Africa. The organization generates some 77% of its revenue from the Americas. The remainder comes from outside the US.

Financial Performance

OCLC's revenue increased by 2% in fiscal 2013 compared to the previous year. The company claimed $206.6 million in revenue for 2013 after reporting $203.4 million in 2012. The revenue growth was due to increased adoption of new services and a modest price increase.

Revenues from libraries and institutions outside of the US increased by $1.4 million to $54.8 million in fiscal 2013. The spike was primarily due to increased revenues from Bibliotheca in Germany.

Strategy

As part of its operations OCLC regularly maintains and enhances its existing services such as Connexion QuestionPoint CONTENTdm EZproxy and WorldCat through heavy investing activities. The company provides more than 5000 libraries in Africa Australia and Europe with integrated library management systems and works to release regular enhancements. The systems include Amlib Bibliotheca CBS LBS OLIB SunRise and TouchPoint.

OCLC also concentrates on expanding its capabilities with the addition of data centers. To this end it opened a new data center in Toronto in 2012 as part of a plan to operate local and global systems at Webscale service levels. The Toronto location is OCLC's fifth globally and allows the group to deliver its namesake WorldShare Management Services to member libraries in Canada. Soon after OCLC opened additional data centers in London and in Sydney Australia. It already has a pair of primary operations data centers in the US. In 2013 another data center came online in Europe.

EXECUTIVES

Vice President Global Product Management, Robin Murray
Vice President Research Chief Strategist, Lorcan Dempsey
Vice President Finance, Rick Schwieterma
Auditors: DELOITTE & TOUCHE LLP COLUMB

LOCATIONS

HQ: OCLC ONLINE COMPUTER LIBRARY CENTER INCORPORATE
6565 KILGOUR PL, DUBLIN, OH 430173395
Phone: 614 764-6000
Web: WWW.CONFERENCE-CENTER.OCLC.ORG

2013 Revenue

	% of total
Americas	77
Europe Middle East & Africa	19
Asia Pacific	4
Total	**100**

PRODUCTS/OPERATIONS

2013 Revenue

	$ mil.	% of total
Products & services	202	98
Grants	3	2
Research library partner dues	0	-
Total	**206**	**100**

Selected Services

Cataloging and Metadata
Digital Collection Management
Discovery
Electronic Collection Management

Library Management
Resource Sharing

Selected Products

Connexion
CONTENTdm
Dewey Services
Digital Search
FirstSearch
WorldCat

COMPETITORS

American Library	Informa
EBSCO	LexisNexis
FactSet	ProQuest
Google	

HISTORICAL FINANCIALS

Company Type: Private

Income Statement

FYE: June 30

	REVENUE ($ mil.)	NET INCOME ($ mil.)	NET PROFIT MARGIN	EMPLOYEES
06/14	213	21	10.3%	1,227
06/13	206	8	4.0%	—
06/12	203	(2)	—	—
06/11	205	0	—	—
Annual Growth	1.3%	—	—	—

2014 Year-End Financials

Return on assets: 2.9%   Cash ($ mil.): 13
Return on equity: 10.3%
Current ratio: 0.10

ODOM CORPORATION

The Odom Corporation wants you to drink up if you happen to be in the Pacific Northwest. The company distributes beer wine and spirits as well as sodas energy drinks and bottled waters from more than 500 domestic and foreign suppliers including Coca-Cola Diageo E. & J. Gallo MillerCoors and Pernod Ricard. The company serves retail customers throughout the northwestern US including those in Alaska Idaho Oregon and Washington. It also runs Odom-Southern Holdings a joint venture with Southern Wine and Spirits of America the #1 distributor of alcoholic beverages in the US. Milt Odom founded the company in 1933.

Since the mid-1990s Odom has largely expanded its operations through partnerships and more than 20 acquisitions. The company took a giant step forward in 2009 when it paired up with Miami-based Southern Wine and Spirits of America to form Odom-Southern Holdings. The partnership helped to expand Odom's wine and spirits distribution business in Alaska Idaho Montana Oregon Utah Washington and Wyoming. Following the joint venture's formation Odom-Southern Holdings acquired wine and spirits distribution rights for the state of Alaska from Alaska Distributors. In 2011 Odom-Southern Holdings acquired Washington-based wine wholesaler and distributor Cavatappi Distribuzione which sells wine from such countries as Australia France Italy and New Zealand.

In recent years Odom has upgraded its warehouse operations to boost efficiency and focus more on customer service. Its enhanced warehouse management system combines radio frequency technology and barcode scanning and has enabled the company to automate processes like inventory control order selection receiving shipping and returns processing. Such improvements are welcome at the high-volume distributor; Odom on average sells nearly 2 million cases of products monthly and processes some 4500 orders a day.

EXECUTIVES

Vice President, Bill Odom
Senior Vice President, Jim Odom
Vice President, Ron Young
Vice President Information Technology, Sweeney Phyllis
Auditors: GRANT THORNTON LLP SEATTLE W

LOCATIONS

HQ: ODOM CORPORATION
11400 SE 8TH ST STE 300, BELLEVUE, WA 980046409
Phone: 425 456-3535
Web: WWW.ODOMCORP.COM

PRODUCTS/OPERATIONS

Selected Brands

Beer
  Anchor Brewing
  Coors
  Fosters
  Green's
  Heineken
  Keystone
  Miller
  Pabst
  Red Stripe
  Samuel Adams
  Sierra Nevada
Energy Drinks
  Four Loko
  Full Throttle
  FUZE
  Honest Tea
  Nestea
  Rockstar
  V-8
  Viso
  VitaminWater
Sodas
  A&W
  Canada Dry
  Coca-Cola
  Crater Lake
  Dr. Pepper
  Fanta
  Fresca
  Sunkist
  Thomas Kemper
  Virgil's Rootbeer
Spirits
  Christian Brothers
  Finest Call
  O'maras
  Seagrams
  Smirnoff
Wine
  Arbor Crest
  Barefoot
  Barton & Guestier
  Concha y Toro
  Cupcake
  Franzia
  Newman's Own
  Purple Cowboy
  Red Bicyclette
  Sutter Home

COMPETITORS

Anheuser-Busch InBev	Monster Beverage
Columbia Distributing Company	Pepsi Amercias Beverages
Constellation Brands	PepsiCo
Jones Soda	

HISTORICAL FINANCIALS

Company Type: Private

Income Statement

FYE: December 31

	REVENUE ($ mil.)	NET INCOME ($ mil.)	NET PROFIT MARGIN	EMPLOYEES
12/07	337	2	0.9%	1,500
12/06	304	1	0.6%	—
12/04	211	3	1.8%	—
12/03	151	0	—	—
Annual Growth	22.1%	—	—	—

2007 Year-End Financials

Return on assets: 5.1%   Cash ($ mil.): 3
Return on equity: 0.9%
Current ratio: 0.70

OHIO STATE UNIVERSITY RESEARCH FOUNDATION

The Ohio State University Research Foundation was established in 1936 to function as a central agency for supporting research and development through grants management and information technology for Ohio State University one of the largest public universities in the US. The not-for-profit corporation provides administrative services for research programs including submitting support requests managing equipment and governmental and university compliance oversight. Ohio State University's total awards reached more than $37 million by July 2007 with some 330 awards.

EXECUTIVES

Senior Director Financial Services and Procurement, Jeffrey H. (Jeff) Kemper
President Board of Directors, Robert T. McGrath
Deputy Executive Director, Anne J.M. Moffat
Executive Director and Associate VP Research Administration, Robert A. Killoren

LOCATIONS

HQ: OHIO STATE UNIVERSITY RESEARCH FOUNDATION
1960 KENNY RD, COLUMBUS, OH 432101016
Phone: 614 688-8125

HISTORICAL FINANCIALS

Company Type: Private

Income Statement

FYE: June 30

	REVENUE ($ mil.)	NET INCOME ($ mil.)	NET PROFIT MARGIN	EMPLOYEES
06/13	498	0	0.2%	105
06/12	499	0	0.1%	—
06/11	485	0	0.1%	—
06/10	437	0	—	—
Annual Growth	4.5%	—	—	—

2013 Year-End Financials

Return on assets: —   Cash ($ mil.): 41
Return on equity: 0.2%
Current ratio: 2.90

OHIOHEALTH CORPORATION

Operating throughout the central part of the state OhioHealth aims to keep Buckeyes healthy. The not-for-profit system runs eight acute care hospitals and is affiliated with another 11 community hospitals and area health systems. All told OhioHealth has about 2000 staffed beds in and around Columbus. Additional facilities offer urgent care physical rehabilitation diagnostic imaging and sleep diagnostics services. Subsidiary HomeReach provides home health care and hospice care. Its WorkHealth program offers workers' compensation care management and occupational rehabilitation services. OhioHealth Group OhioHealth's joint venture with The Medical Group of Ohio operates the HealthReach PPO.

Operations

In addition to offering patient care OhioHealth also operates the The OhioHealth Research & Innovation Institute which coordinates research throughout the health system including conducting clinical trials of new drugs and medical devices. The system also operates The Center for Medical Education and Innovation a medical training facility that among other technologies offers human patient simulators on which medical professionals can practice new procedures in various clinical situations.

OhioHealth has some 28000 associates physicians and volunteers. Every year it facilitates approximately 2 million outpatient visits 95000 admissions 346000 emergency department visits 60000 surgeries and 13000 births.

Geographic Reach

OhioHealth operates in the Ohio communities of Athens Columbus Delaware Dublin Kenton Mansfield and Shelby.

Strategy

The company is focused on expanding geographically and capitalizing on opportunities due to population growth in the area. In 2013 it completed the construction of a new patient tower at its Riverside Methodist Hospital; the tower houses much of the company's Neuroscience Institute.

OhioHealth is now building an outpatient facility in Nelsonville which is expected to open sometime in 2017.

The system struck up a partnership with Berger Health System another Ohio-based health care network in 2014. The partners will explore ways to improve health care for the communities they serve.

Mergers and Acquisitions

In 2014 OhioHealth acquired O'Bleness Health System expanding its presence in southeastern Ohio. It also acquired MedCentral Health System.

Company Background

The health system traces its roots back to 1892 when Protestant Hospital (now known as Riverside Methodist Hospital) opened. The system initially organized as U.S. Health Corporation in 1984 later took on the OhioHealth name in 1997.

EXECUTIVES

Senior Vice President and Chief Communications Officer, Sue Jablonski
President and CEO, David P. Blom, age 61
EVP and COO, Michael W. (Mike) Louge
President Marion General Hospital, Bruce Hagen
President Riverside Methodist Hospital, Brian D. Jepson
Chief Medical Officer, Bruce Vanderhoff
SVP and CIO, Michael Krouse

SVP External Affairs; President OhioHealth Foundation, Karen Morrison
President Doctors Hospital, Mike Reichfield
President OhioHealth Physician Group, Hugh Thornhill
President OhioHealth Home Care, James P. Newbrough
President O'Bleness Hospital, Mark Seckinger
President Mansfield Hospital and Shelby Hospital, Jean Halpin
President OhioHealth Grant Medical Center, Vinson M. Yates
President Grant Medical Center, Michael Lawson
SVP and Chief Nursing Executive, Donna Hanly
President Dublin Methodist Hospital and Grady Memorial Hospital, Steve Bunyard
Sr V Pres, Michael Bernstein
Director Of Surgery Services, Les Hood
Vice President Business Development, Rick Goebel
Vice President Of Operations, Joe Hooper
Director Media Relations, Mark Hopkins
Medical Director, Matthew (Matt) Vail
Vice President, Arash Arshi
Evp And Coo, Robert P Millen, age 63
Medical Director Cme I, Brian Zeno
Vice President Finance (Multiple Hospitals), Troy Hammett
Director of Clinical Services, Lynn Shaffer
Senior Vice President Clinical Support Services, Cheryl Herbert
Vice President Marketing and Communications, Katy Dalton Rigsby
Vice President Client Products Services, Allen (Al) Heilman
Vice Chairman, John P. McConnell, age 61
Chairman, Steve Rasmussen
Auditors: DELOITTE TAX LLP CINCINNATI

LOCATIONS

HQ: OHIOHEALTH CORPORATION
180 E BRD ST, COLUMBUS, OH 432153707
Phone: 614 544-4455
Web: WWW.OHIOHEALTH.COM

PRODUCTS/OPERATIONS

Selected Facilities
Owned
Doctors Hospital (Columbus)
Doctors Hospital Nelsonville (Nelsonville)
Dublin Methodist Hospital (Dublin)
Grady Memorial Hospital (Delaware)
Grant Medical Center (Columbus)
Hardin Memorial Hospital (Kenton)
Marion General Hospital (Marion)
O' Bleness Memorial Hospital (Athens)
Riverside Methodist Hospital (Columbus)
Affiliated
Blanchard Valley Medical Center
Galion Community Hospital (Galion)
Genesis Healthcare System (Zanesville)
Knox Community Hospital
Morrow County Hospital (Mt. Gilead)
Samaritan Regional Health System (Ashland)
Southern Ohio Medical Center (Portsmouth)

COMPETITORS

Adena Health System
Fairfield Medical Center
Licking Memorial Health Systems
Mercy Health (OH)
Mount Carmel Health
Nationwide Children' s Hospital
Regency Hospital
Select Medical

HISTORICAL FINANCIALS

Company Type: Private

Income Statement

FYE: June 30

	REVENUE ($ mil.)	NET INCOME ($ mil.)	NET PROFIT MARGIN	EMPLOYEES
06/12	1,999	303	15.2%	15,000
06/11	2,328	412	17.7%	—
06/10	1,967	221	11.3%	—
06/09	1,794	0	—	—
Annual Growth	3.7%	—	—	—

2012 Year-End Financials

Return on assets: —
Return on equity: 15.2%
Current ratio: 0.30
Cash ($ mil.): 99

OLE' MEXICAN FOODS INC.

Its a wrap at Olé Mexican Foods. The company makes Mexican-American foods inducing tortillas and taco shells under brand names La Banderita La Centroamericana Olé and Verolé. The company also produces salsa sour cream Mexican cheeses and sausages tostadas and tortilla chips among other items. Its customers include retail food outlets and food service operations. Headquartered in Norcross Georgia the company has about a dozen distribution centers across the US. It serves customers across the continental US and Alaska as well as in Puerto Rico.

Geographic Reach

Olé Mexican Foods has about a dozen distribution centers in Arizona California Colorado Florida Illinois Kentucky North Carolina and Texas.

Strategy

To meet Americans' growing appetite for Mexican fare the company in 2013 opened a new production facility in Reno Nevada to serve the western US. The site is expected to create about 350 manufacturing and distribution jobs over the next several years. The new facility initially produced fried products adding tortilla production lines soon after. Catering to the health conscious Olé Mexican Foods makes multigrain whole wheat and spinach and herb wraps under the Xtreme Wellness brand.

EXECUTIVES

Vice President Sales and Marketing, Joe Ketchum
Auditors: WINDHAM BRANNON PC ATLANTA

LOCATIONS

HQ: OLE' MEXICAN FOODS INC.
6585 CRESCENT DR, NORCROSS, GA 300712901
Phone: 770 582-9200
Web: WWW.OLEMEXICANFOODS.COM

PRODUCTS/OPERATIONS

Selected Brands and Products
Consumer
La Banderita (corn tortillas flour tortillas tostadas cheese sausage)
La Centroamericana (corn tortillas)
Olé (corn tortillas flour tortillas tostadas cheese sausage pastry)
Olé Mexican Foods (flour tortillas cheese yogurt)
Verolé (corn tortillas flour tortillas)
Verolé Quesos (cheese)

Xtreme Wellness (multigrain whole wheat wraps)
Food service
Cheese
Flavor wraps
Flour tortillas
Low-carb tortillas
Tortilla chips
White corn tortillas
Yellow corn tortillas

COMPETITORS

Azteca Foods	Grupo Bimbo
Boar' s Head	H&H Meat Products
Cacique Inc	La Tortilla Factory
Casa de Oro Foods	Maseca
Cheesemakers Inc.	Patrick Cudahy
Chorizo De San Manuel	Roger Wood Foods
Don Miguel Mexican	Rose Packing
Foods	Ruiz Mexican Foods
Goya	Tumaro' s Gourmet
Gruma	Tortillas
Gruma Corporation	

HISTORICAL FINANCIALS

Company Type: Private

Income Statement

FYE: December 31

	REVENUE ($ mil.)	NET INCOME ($ mil.)	NET PROFIT MARGIN	EMPLOYEES
12/13	242	12	5.2%	500
12/03	65	5	9.0%	—
12/02	52	3	6.9%	—
12/01	988	0	—	—
Annual Growth	—	—	—	—

2013 Year-End Financials

Return on assets: 8.8%
Return on equity: 5.2%
Current ratio: 2.50

Cash ($ mil.): 14

OLMSTED MEDICAL CENTER

Olmsted Medical Center (OMC) provides general medical and surgical care to the Rochester Minnesota area. The not-for-profit hospital also partners with regional schools to provide medical nursing and technical training and it engages in clinical research programs. Specialty services include pediatrics neurology occupational medicine and orthopedics. In addition to its hospital OMC also operates several urgent care specialty and general practice clinics in the region. OMC was formed through the merger of Olmsted Community Hospital and Olmsted Medical Group in 1996.

Geographic Reach

In addition to the main hospital OMC operates 18 outpatient centers including two multi-specialty clinics a Level IV trauma hospital licensed for 61 beds with 24-hour emergency room two FastCare retail clinics (located inside Shopko stores) and a downtown Skyway Clinic in Rochester as well as 10 community clinics in 10 southeastern Minnesota municipalities (Byron Cannon Falls Chatfield Pine Island Plainview Preston Spring Valley St. Charles Stewartville and Wanamingo).

Operations

OMC sees some 286000 patients each year including more than 70000 overnight hospital patients (or inpatient visits). It handles some 30000 emergency room visits 4000 surgical procedures and 1000 births. The medical center employs 160 physicians (in more than 20 specialties) and 1000 other health care professionals at its inpatient and outpatient locations.

Financial Performance

OMC reported a 9% increase in revenues in 2013 to $179.6 million.

Strategy

The company is expanding its services and infrastructure to meet the growing needs of its patients.

OMC plans to add a new women's health wing to the main hospital building. The Women's Health Pavilion will cost $25 million to build and will be ready to serve patients in 2015.

In 2014 Olmsted Medical Center opened its 15000-sq.-ft $3.3-million Sports Medicine and Athletic Performance Facility. Services at the facility include clinical care rehabilitation services athletic performance training and education and one-on-one nutrition education.

In 2013 the medical center began expanding its emergency room and urgent care operations at existing facilities. OMC opened its new Skyway Clinic in downtown Rochester in 2012 to provide health care to students at the University of Minnesota Rochester campus as well as to the general public. The clinic provides non-emergency walk-in care.

The company is also enhancing customer service through online portals telehealth programming (virtual clinical visits) and care coordination programs. It is enhancing IT services by extending clinical electronic health record (EHR) systems to the main hospital facility as well.

In 2014 OMC and the OMC Regional Foundation teamed up with online solutions provider Geonetric to launch two new responsive websites. OMC's new website is built on Geonetric's VitalSite content management system and uses responsive design. The VitalSite CMS and new design/layout gives OMC more tools to help patients engage in their own healthcare management.

EXECUTIVES

Director of Health Information Management, Michelle (Mitch) Majerus
Director Of Nursing, Vicki Demmer
Auditors: RSM MCGLADREY INC ROCHESTER

LOCATIONS

HQ: OLMSTED MEDICAL CENTER
210 9TH ST SE STE 1, ROCHESTER, MN 559046400
Phone: 507 288-3443
Web: WWW.OLMMED.ORG

Selected Locations

Byron
Cannon Falls
Chatfield
Pine Island
Plainview
Preston
Spring Valley
St. Charles
Stewartville
Wanamingo

PRODUCTS/OPERATIONS

Selected Services

24-hour Emergency Care
Advanced Wound Healing Clinic
Anesthesiology
Anticoagulation Clinic
Asthma & Allergy
Audiology
Bariatrics
BirthCenter
Cardiology (non-invasive)
Center for Weight Loss and Wellness
Dermatology
Ear Nose & Throat
Emergency Medicine
Endocrinology
Family Medicine
FastCare Clinic
General Surgery
Health and Wellness
Hospitalist Services
Internal Medicine
Joint Replacement Center
Lactation Services
Neurology
Obstetrics & Gynecology
Occupational Medicine
Ophthalmology
Optical Center
Orthopedics & Sports Medicine
Pain Management
Pathology
Patient Account Services
Patient Education
Pediatrics
Perinatal Loss Support
Plastic Surgery
Podiatry
Prenatal & Family Education
Psychiatry
Radiology (Diagnostic)
Rehabilitation Services - Cardiopulmonary Rehabilitation
Rehabilitation Services - Industrial Rehabilitation
Rehabilitation Services - Occupational Therapy
Rehabilitation Services - Physical Therapy
Research
Skyway Clinic
Sleep Lab
Sleep Medicine
Social Services
Travel/Immunization Clinic
Urology
Vascular Ultrasound
Volunteer Chaplains
Women' s Services

COMPETITORS

Allina Hospitals	Gundersen Lutheran
CentraCare Health	Mayo Clinic
Fairview Health	Mayo Clinic Rochester
Franciscan Skemp	Park Nicollet Health
Healthcare	Services

HISTORICAL FINANCIALS

Company Type: Private

Income Statement

FYE: December 31

	REVENUE ($ mil.)	NET INCOME ($ mil.)	NET PROFIT MARGIN	EMPLOYEES
12/13	189	14	7.6%	950
12/09	144	12	8.6%	—
12/08	0	0	—	—
12/02	79	0	—	—
Annual Growth	8.2%	—	—	—

2013 Year-End Financials

Return on assets: 2.0%
Return on equity: 7.6%
Current ratio: 2.90

Cash ($ mil.): 85

OMNI CABLE CORPORATION

Omni Cable has it down to the wire. The company distributes electrical and electronic cables to wholesale customers in the US through 10 warehouses and distribution centers. Omni Cable also offers custom bundling coloring striping lashing twisting and imprinting of wires and cables. The employee-owned company was founded in 1977. Omni Cable has locations in Atlanta Boston

Chicago Denver Houston Los Angeles Philadelphia St. Louis San Francisco and Tampa. It is expanding its facilities within the regions served and has relocated and upgraded its San Francisco branch to serve the Bay Area better.

EXECUTIVES

Director Sales and Marketing, Peter J. Comber
EVP Sales Operations, Greg Donato
Vice President, Dan Trotta
National Accounts Manager, Mike Fitzpatrick
Vice President, John Russ

LOCATIONS

HQ: OMNI CABLE CORPORATION
2 HAGERTY BLVD, WEST CHESTER, PA 193827594
Phone: 610 701-0100
Web: WWW.OMNICABLE.COM

COMPETITORS

Gexpro   Sonepar USA
Premier Farnell

HISTORICAL FINANCIALS
Company Type: Private

Income Statement
FYE: December 31

	REVENUE ($ mil.)	NET INCOME ($ mil.)	NET PROFIT MARGIN	EMPLOYEES
12/11	256	0	—	216
12/10	202	12	5.9%	
12/09	2,116	0	—	
Annual Growth	—	—	—	—

2011 Year-End Financials
Return on assets: 3.2%   Cash ($ mil.): 14
Return on equity: —
Current ratio: 3.40

ON-SITE FUEL SERVICE INC.

When it comes down to gassing up the fleet On-Site Fuel Service delivers. The company specializes in dispensing fuel (diesel or regular) to corporate fleets in the most efficient location available. For most customers this means fueling their vehicles once the workday is complete (and eliminating fueling time from the workday). But the company also offers mobile fueling services allowing vehicles to be refueled in the field or at remote job sites. On-Site Fuel Service dispenses the fuel directly into each vehicle and also provides fueling data and reports for each vehicle (to comply with regulatory requirements when necessary). Its operations extend south from North Carolina to Florida and west to Arizona.

EXECUTIVES

Vice President Operations, Larry Rice
Auditors: SMITH TURNER & REEVES PA

LOCATIONS

HQ: ON-SITE FUEL SERVICE INC.
1089 OLD FANNIN RD STE A, BRANDON, MS 390479201
Phone: 601 353-4142
Web: WWW.ONSITEFUELSERVICE.COM

COMPETITORS

Sun Coast Resources

HISTORICAL FINANCIALS
Company Type: Private

Income Statement
FYE: December 31

	REVENUE ($ mil.)	NET INCOME ($ mil.)	NET PROFIT MARGIN	EMPLOYEES
12/13	238	(0)	—	85
12/07	119	(0)	—	
12/06	113	(0)	—	
12/02	0	0	—	
Annual Growth	—	—	—	—

2013 Year-End Financials
Return on assets: 1.9%   Cash ($ mil.): —
Return on equity: (-0.2%)
Current ratio: 0.60

OPEN SOCIETY INSTITUTE

LOCATIONS

HQ: OPEN SOCIETY INSTITUTE
224 W 57TH ST FRNT 1, NEW YORK, NY 100193212
Phone: 212 548-0600
Web: WWW.OPENSOCIETYFOUNDATIONS.ORG

HISTORICAL FINANCIALS
Company Type: Private

Income Statement
FYE: December 31

	REVENUE ($ mil.)	NET INCOME ($ mil.)	NET PROFIT MARGIN	EMPLOYEES
12/07	532	375	70.5%	445
12/03	156	25	16.0%	
Annual Growth	35.9%	96.8%	—	—

2007 Year-End Financials
Return on assets: 0.3%   Cash ($ mil.): 49
Return on equity: 70.5%
Current ratio: 0.40

OPERATION BLESSING INTERNATIONAL RELIEF AND DEVELOPMENT CORPORAT

Auditors: KPMG LLP MCLEAN VA

LOCATIONS

HQ: OPERATION BLESSING INTERNATIONAL RELIEF AND DEVELOPMENT CORPORAT
977 CENTERVILLE TPKE, VIRGINIA BEACH, VA 234631001
Phone: 757 226-3401
Web: WWW.OB.ORG

HISTORICAL FINANCIALS
Company Type: Private

Income Statement
FYE: March 31

	REVENUE ($ mil.)	NET INCOME ($ mil.)	NET PROFIT MARGIN	EMPLOYEES
03/09	407	0	0.1%	50
03/06	210	9	4.8%	
03/05	1,140	0	—	
Annual Growth	—	137.5%	—	—

2009 Year-End Financials
Return on assets: —   Cash ($ mil.): 5
Return on equity: 0.1%
Current ratio: 0.70

ORANGE COUNTY HEALTH AUTHORITY

Auditors: MC GLADREY & PULLEN LLP MINN

LOCATIONS

HQ: ORANGE COUNTY HEALTH AUTHORITY
505 CITY PKWY W, ORANGE, CA 928682924
Phone: 714 246-8500
Web: WWW.CALOPTIMA.ORG

HISTORICAL FINANCIALS
Company Type: Private

Income Statement
FYE: June 30

	REVENUE ($ mil.)	NET INCOME ($ mil.)	NET PROFIT MARGIN	EMPLOYEES
06/09	1,078	(17)	—	422
06/05	812	(24)	—	
06/04	0	0	—	
06/03	756	0	—	
Annual Growth	6.1%	—	—	—

2009 Year-End Financials
Return on assets: 0.3%   Cash ($ mil.): 81
Return on equity: (-1.6%)
Current ratio: 0.40

ORANGE COUNTY TRANSPORTATION AUTHORITY SCHOLARSHIP FOUNDATION IN

Public transportation in sunny Orange County California is overseen by the Orange County Transportation Authority (OCTA). The OCTA is the main provider of bus services in its 800-sq.-mi. territory which is home to more than 3 million people. In cooperation with the Southern California Regional Rail Authority the OCTA oversees

Metrolink commuter rail service in Orange County. The agency also operates a 10-mile toll road and issues permits to taxi operators. Revenue from a half-cent local sales tax allows the agency to pay for road improvement and mass transit projects.

Geographic Reach The company is located in Southern California - south of Los Angeles County north of San Diego County and west of Riverside and San Bernardino counties.

OperationsOCTA builds designs operates plans maintains and regulates the robust transportation network within Orange County. In addition to the four modes of transportation (transit driving bicycling and walking) OCTA oversees paratransit services taxi services light rail commuter rail and high‐occupancy managed lanes. It operates rail service for OCTA centers on Metrolink Southern California's commuter rail system linking residential communities to employment and activity centers. Metrolink is operated by the Southern California Regional Rail Authority — a joint powers authority of five member agencies representing the counties of Los Angeles Orange Riverside San Bernardino and Ventura. OCTA is one of the five member agencies that administers Orange County Metrolink activities.The 91 Express Lanes is a four-lane 10-mile toll road built in the median of California's Riverside Freeway (SR-91) between the Orange/Riverside County line and the SR-55.

Financial Performance

OCTA's rail budget for fiscal year 2015-16 consists of both operating and capital expenses. Operating expenses in FY 2015-16 are budgeted at $31.6 million while capital expenditures are anticipated to reach $100.4 million. The FY 2015-16 rail capital projects. The organization saw a decline in its budget for FY 2015-16 due to drop in passenger fares and state assistance federal capital assistance grants.(OCTA uses its revenue primarily in salaries and benefits professional services and capital expenditure).

Strategy

The 2014 – 2019 OCTA Strategic Plan takes a comprehensive forward-looking approach to address Orange County's transportation needs during the next five years.(OCTA maintains a Long-Range Transportation Plan updated every four years to account for new planning efforts as well as changes in demographics economic conditions and available sources of transportation funding).

In the FY 2015-16 budget $6.9 million of Measure M funds deposited in the General Fund are being used to fund the final work on the West County Connectors project.

After four years in the making OCTA marked the completion of the $297 million West County Connector project in 2014 which will bring congestion relief where three major freeways (Interstate 405 Interstate 605 and State Route 22) converge.In 2014 OCTA purchased 400 new buses for fixed-route and ACCESS services. This purchase combined with the in-process repainting of the existing fleet presents a cost-effective opportunity to explore new branding concepts for Orange County bus services.

Company Background

OCTA was formed in 1991 in a consolidation of seven transportation agencies.

EXECUTIVES

Director Motorist Services and Special Projects, Sue Zuhlke

Clerk of the Board, Wendy Knowles

Executive Director Finance and Administration, Ken Phipps

General Manager 91 Express Lanes and Treasurer, Kirk Avila

CIO, Bill Mao

Manager Accounting and Financial Reporting, Tom Wulf

Manager Financial Planning and Analysis, Andrew Oftelie

Director Contracts Administration and Materials Management, Virginia Abadessa

Manager Risk Management Human Resources, Al Gorski

Manager Training and Development, Julie Espy

Manager Metrolink Expansion, Dinah Minteer

Program Manager Construction, Charlie Guess

Executive Director Development, Kia Mortazavi

Executive Director External Affairs, Ellen S. Burton

Manager Marketing, Stella Lin

Manager Public Communications, Ted Nguyen

Chief Transit Police Services, Jim Rudy

General Manager Transit, Beth McCormick

Manager Service Planning and Customer Advocacy Transit, Scott Holmes

CEO, Will Kempton, age 68

Chairman, Jerry Amante

Vice Chair, Patricia (Pat) Bates

Executive Director Internal Audit, Kathleen O'Connell

Manager Labor and Employee Relations EEO, Sherry Bolander

Deputy CEO, Darrell Johnson

Program Manager Local Initiatives Rail, Jennifer Bergener

Program Manager SR-55 SR-57 SR-91 and Rail, Pradeep Gunaratne

Manager Human Resources, Lisa Arosteguy-Brown

Assistant to General Manager Transit, Erin Rogers

Executive Director Human Resources and Organizational Development, Patrick Gough

Manager Safety Human Resources, Angela Petrow

Section Manager General Services, Lori Parsel

Manager Contracts and Procurements, Carolina Coppolo

Project Manager Facilities Engineering Rail, Jim Kramer

Section Manager Metrolink Operations, Michael Litschi

Director Strategic Planning Development, Kurt Brotcke

Director Highway Project Delivery, Tom Bogard

Manager Planning and Analysis, Charlie Larwood

Section Manager Local and Capital Programs, Abbe McClenahan

Manager Regional Initiatives Development, Barry Engelberg

Program Manager I-5 and I-405 Development, Rose Casey

Section Manager Project Controls Development, Norbert Lippert

Manager Maintenance Transit, Tony Chavira

Manager Transit Program Management, Joeseph Vicente

Director, William J. (Bill) Dalton

Director, Bill Campbell

Director, Arthur C. (Art) Brown

Director, Carolyn V. Cavecche

Director, Richard T. Dixon

Director, Curt Pringle

Director, Miguel A. Pulido

Director, Gregory T. Winterbottom

Caltrans Director, Cindy Quon

Director, Peter Buffa

Vice Chair, Patricia (Pat) Bates

Director, Paul G. Glaab

Director, Allan Mansoor

Director, John Moorlach

Director, Don Hansen

Director, Janet Nguyen

Auditors: VAVRINEK TRINE DAY & CO LL

LOCATIONS

HQ: ORANGE COUNTY TRANSPORTATION AUTHORITY SCHOLARSHIP FOUNDATION IN
550 S MAIN ST, ORANGE, CA 928684506
Phone: 714 636-7433
Web: WWW.OCTA.NET

PRODUCTS/OPERATIONS

2014 Sales

	% of total
Sales taxes	93
Unrestricted investment earning	4
Property taxes	3
Other	-
Total	**100**

Selected Services

91 Express Lanes toll facility
Bus transit service
Freeway improvements funding
Freeway Service Patrol
Long-range planning
Measure M2 administration
Metrolink rail service
Rideshare options
Street and road improvements grants
Taxi administration program
Vanpool subsidies

HISTORICAL FINANCIALS

Company Type: Private

Income Statement

FYE: June 30

	REVENUE ($ mil.)	NET INCOME ($ mil.)	NET PROFIT MARGIN	EMPLOYEES
06/13	602	22	3.8%	1,050
06/12	609	23	3.8%	—
06/11	438	247	56.6%	—
06/10	421	0	—	—
Annual Growth	**12.6%**	—	—	—

OREGON HEALTH & SCIENCE UNIVERSITY MEDICAL GROUP

Oregon Health & Science University (OHSU) builds a bridge to medical education in the Beaver State. OHSU is the state's sole institution providing doctoral degrees in medicine dentistry and nursing. Its other two schools are science and engineering and in partnership with Oregon State University pharmacy. OHSU has about 2800 students. The university is also home to two hospitals (one a children's hospital) as well as specialty and primary care clinics research and interdisciplinary centers and community service programs. OHSU traces its roots to 1867 when members of the medical department at Willamette University began the first formal medical education program in Oregon.

Geographic Reach

OHSU's main campus includes about 40 buildings on 120 acres on Marquam Hill (overlooking downtown Portland). OHSU also operates two smaller research locations: The Schnitzer Campus in Portland and the West Campus in Hillsboro.

Operations

OHSU's medical school has a small student-teacher ratio at just 4:1. The organization is renowned for its research initiatives. It has about 3000 active research projects and produced about

120 inventions in 2012. OHSU receives about $350 million in research funding each year. The school engages in an array of multidisciplinary research projects including diseases of the central nervous system weight regulation cancer rare genetic disorders and infectious disease.

Much of the university's medical research is performed at or in concert with clinical care operations at the University Hospital the Doernbecher Children's Hospital and other family care and specialty centers. The medical centers care for some 250000 patients each year.

Researchers at OHSU's Stem Cell Center worked with the Oregon National Primate Research Center to pioneer the first successful cloned nonhuman primate embryonic stem cells. Such cells could help stem cell research gain acceptance as the human element that causes such controversy has been removed.

Financial Performance

OHSU reported a 5% increase in revenue to nearly $2 billion in 2012 due to higher net patient service revenues from higher patient volumes and complex procedures. Net income fell by 55% to $79 million due to higher operating expenses and lower state appropriations and investment returns. OHSU has an operating budget of some $2 billion.

Strategy

OHSU began construction of its collaborative life sciences building on the Schnitzer Campus in 2012. The building was scheduled to be completed in late 2013 and was built on land donated by the Schnitzer family in 2004. OHSU has purchased additional parcels of land in the area for future expansion efforts.

EXECUTIVES

Vice President Research, Daniel M Dorsa
Vice President and General Counsel, Amy M Wayson
EVP and Executive Director OHSU Hospitals and Clinics, Peter F. Rapp
President and Director, Joseph (Joe) Robertson
Dean School of Medicine, Mark Richardson
Senior Vice President, Constance French
Vice President Of Marketing, Sigrid Button
Director of Admissions, Debbie Melton
Vice President Pediatric Development, Mary Turina
Senior Vice President, Jack Friedman
Interim Associate Vice President For Faculty And Programs, Lauren Shatz
Vice President, Charissa Martin
Chairman, Charles A. Wilhoite
Vice Chairman, Jay Waldron
Treasurer, Thomas Hilton
Board Member, Sandra Gallagher
Auditors: KPMG LLP PORTLAND OR

LOCATIONS

HQ: OREGON HEALTH & SCIENCE UNIVERSITY MEDICAL GROUP
3181 SW SAM JACKSON PK RD, PORTLAND, OR 972393011
Phone: 503 494-8311
Web: WWW.OHSU.EDU

PRODUCTS/OPERATIONS

Selected schools
School of Dentistry
School of Medicine
School of Nursing
School of Pharmacy (with Oregon State University)
School of Science & Engineering

HISTORICAL FINANCIALS
Company Type: Private

Income Statement

FYE: June 30

	REVENUE ($ mil.)	NET INCOME ($ mil.)	NET PROFIT MARGIN	EMPLOYEES
06/13	2,169	221	10.2%	14,000
06/12	1,975	78	4.0%	—
06/06	1,257	140	11.2%	—
06/05	1,078	0	—	—
Annual Growth	9.1%	—	—	—

2013 Year-End Financials

Return on assets: —
Return on equity: 10.2%
Current ratio: 0.90
Cash ($ mil.): 96

OREGON UNIVERSITY SYSTEM

Auditors: CLIFTONLARSONALLEN LLP GREENW

LOCATIONS

HQ: OREGON UNIVERSITY SYSTEM
1401 WALNUT ST, EUGENE, OR 974032542
Phone: 541 346-5700
Web: WWW.OUS.EDU

HISTORICAL FINANCIALS
Company Type: Private

Income Statement

FYE: June 30

	REVENUE ($ mil.)	NET INCOME ($ mil.)	NET PROFIT MARGIN	EMPLOYEES
06/14	1,782	83	4.7%	26,000
06/13	1,701	14	0.8%	—
06/12	1,657	10	0.6%	—
06/08	1,251	0	—	—
Annual Growth	6.1%	—	—	—

2014 Year-End Financials

Return on assets: 9.8%
Return on equity: 4.7%
Current ratio: 1.30
Cash ($ mil.): 456

ORLANDO HEALTH INC.

It's not Disney World but for Floridians needing health care it is a prime destination. Orlando Health is a not-for-profit organization with a network of community and specialty hospitals with nearly 2300 beds in Central Florida. Its flagship facility the Orlando Regional Medical Center features a Level 1 trauma center and provides comprehensive acute care services in a range of specialties. Orlando Health also operates several community hospitals. Its specialty hospitals include the Arnold Palmer Hospital for Children and the Winnie Palmer Hospital for Women and Babies. It also operates the renowned M. D. Anderson Cancer Center Orlando (the first affiliate of Houston-based M. D. Anderson center).

Geographic Reach

Orlando Health operates throughout Orlando and in neighboring Clermont Longwood Ocoee and St. Cloud Florida.

Operations

In addition to the Orlando Regional Medical Center and three fully owned community hospitals the company operates two medical centers through partnerships. It holds a 50% stake in the South Lake Hospital and a 20% stake in the St. Cloud Regional Medical Center. It also operates physician practice associations and an emergency air transport service (Air Care).

Across its facilities Orlando Health has about 2000 affiliated physicians who provide a full spectrum of health care services. Areas of clinical excellence include heart and vascular care cancer care obstetrics and gynecology neonatology neurosciences surgery pediatric orthopedics and sports medicine. Annually Orlando Health serves more than 2 million residents of central Florida and 4500 international patients. The organization also provides between $250 and $300 million in community health programs each year.

As a statutory teaching hospital system Orlando Health also engages in medical training programs through affiliation agreements with the University of Central Florida College of Medicine and other institutions. Orlando Health offers a number of medical residency and fellowship programs; its seven residencies are offered to 250 participants and include programs in emergency medicine internal medicine OB-GYN orthopedic surgery pathology and pediatrics. The organization also conducts research studies and clinical trials through partnerships with educational and commercial organizations.

Financial Performance

The company's revenues increased by 9% in 2014 due to higher net patient service revenues and other revenues. Medicare accounted for 23% of the net patient revenues; Medicaid 19%. Orlando Health's net income grew by 349% due to higher revenues and investment income.Operating cash flow increased by 235% in 2014.

Strategy

Orlando Health is working to improve its operating model by improving the quality of patient outcomes; enhancing collaboration between physicians medical professionals hospitals research centers and other institutions; and increasing clinical integration of various disciplines to share resources and skills.

As an example of its collaborative and quality enhancement efforts Orlando Health is involved in the formation of a regional health information exchange to connect its electronic health record (EHR) systems with other Central Florida health providers and the public health department. The program aims to improve quality of care by eliminating redundant tests and other repeated efforts as well as by providing hospitals swift access to patient data.

Orlando Health is also focused on making improvements to its Orlando Regional Medical Center through a multi-year $297-million renovation project. In 2015 the company opened its new 245-bed 10-story 345000-square-foot North Tower's front entrance and its existing Orlando Regional Medical Center building now will be referred to as Orlando Regional Medical Center South Tower. The North Tower is part of the hospital's redesign and renovation project and includes an expanded emergency department cardiovascular service areas operating suites and other ancillary services located inside Orlando Regional Medical Center South Tower. The South Tower expansion is expected to was completed in 2015. That year the Orlando Regional Medical Center redesign and renovation project continued with its Surgical Services expansion and renovation. The 28000-square-foot addition includes 10 new operating rooms a new Post Anesthesia Care Unit area with 24 patient bays. Other planned projects include the expansion of the neonatal intensive care unit at Winnie Palmer Hospital for Women and Babies. In 2015 Orlando Health Physician Associates officially opened its doors in the Lake Nona area. That year the West Orange Healthcare District awarded a $13.8 million grant to Health Central Hospital to expand. The grant was the second largest in the history of the district and funded 75 percent of the total expansion costs. Orlando Health funded the remaining 25 percent. Upon completion the expansion project will add 40 rooms to Health Central Hospital increasing its bed count from 171 to 211 and enabling the further development of specialized care.

Mergers and Acquisitions

In 2015 Orlando Health Physician Associates acquired Pediatric Associates of Orlando. Founded in 1939 it was one of the first pediatric practices in Central Florida.

Company Background

In 2012 Arnold Palmer Hospital added an outpatient rehabilitation center.

The health system expanded its network in 2012 by acquiring the 170-bed Health Central Hospital and its associated facilities in Ocoee Florida for $181 million. Orlando Health further expanded through the purchase of Physician Associates a professional practice organization in 2013.

Orlando Health was founded in 1918.

EXECUTIVES

VP and CIO, Rick Schooler
President and CEO, David W. Strong
SVP; President Arnold Palmer Medical Center and Orlando Health Foundation, John Bozard
President Adult Hospitals Group, Shannon Elswick
President South Seminole Hospital, Steve Glazier
CFO, Bernadette Spong
VP; Executive Director Orlando Health Foundation, Karen Jensen
VP; President Dr. P. Phillips Hospital, Mark A. Jones
COO, Jessica Wertman
Svp Legal Affairs, Mildred Beam
Vice President Human Resources, Nancy Dinon
Vp Corporate Integrity, David (Dave) Huddleson
Vice President Orlando, Clarence Brown
Executive Vice President, Sherrie Mom
Vice President Safety, Linda Simmons
Medical Librarian, Richard Mercer
Medical Director of Population Health Management, Jonathan (Jon) Ware
Pharmacy Manager, Jeanette Bonstrom
Vp Patient Care And Chief Nursing Officer, Anne Peach
Vice President Operations, Myra Hancock
Vice President American, Luanne Lumpkins
Medical Director, Sam Venus
Vice President Human Resources, Willanne Colwell
Vice President, Lataydria Inmon
Vice President, Christopher Buffa
Medical Librarian, Aidy Silva-ortiz
Vice President Of Business Development, Jamie Barkley
Vice President Executive Director, Abe Lopman
Vice President Chief Marketing and Communications Officer, John (Jack) Marazano
Director of Respiratory Therapy, John (Jack) Albert
Chairman, Dianna Morgan
Treasurer and Director, Conrad Santiago
Board Of Directors, Howard Smith
Secretary, Jolene Guzman
Auditors: ERNST & YOUNG LLP TAMPA FL

LOCATIONS

HQ: ORLANDO HEALTH INC.
1414 KUHL AVE, ORLANDO, FL 328062008
Phone: 321 843-7000
Web: WWW.ORLANDOHEALTH.COM

PRODUCTS/OPERATIONS

2014 Sales

	% of total
Net patient service revenue less provision for bad debts	95
Other revenue	5
Net assets released from restrictions	
Total	**100**

Selected Facilities

Arnold Palmer Hospital for Children (Orlando)
Dr. P. Phillips Hospital (formerly Orlando Regional Sand Lake Hospital Orlando)
Health Central Hospital (Ocoee)
Lucerne Pavilion (Orlando)
M. D. Anderson Cancer Center Orlando
Orlando Health Heart Institute
Orlando Health Rehabilitation Institute
Orlando Regional Medical Center
South Lake Hospital (50% affiliate Clermont)
South Seminole Hospital (Longwood)
St. Cloud Regional Medical Center (20% affiliate)
Winnie Palmer Hospital for Women & Babies (Orlando)

Selected Specialties

Cancer care (at M. D. Anderson Cancer Center Orlando)
Emergency and trauma care
Heart and vascular
Neurosciences
Oncology/hematology
Orthopedic and sports medicine
Surgery
Women's services

Selected Services

Anesthesiology
Brain Injury Rehabilitation Center (BIRC)
Endocrinology (diabetes)
Endoscopy
Epilepsy care
Home health care
Infectious diseases
Internal medicine
Laboratory and pathology Services
Mammography
Memory Disorder Center
MRI
Multiple sclerosis treatment
Nephrology
Nuclear medicine
Ophthalmology
Otolaryngology (Ears Nose Throat)
Pain management
Patient and family counseling
Pediatric outpatient surgery
Pulmonary medicine
Radiology and diagnostic imaging
Rehabilitation and physical therapy

COMPETITORS

Adventist Health System Sunbelt Healthcare
All Children's Hospital
Baptist Health South Florida
Baptist Health System
Community Health Systems
Florida Hospital Heartland
Florida Hospital Waterman
HCA
Health First
Holmes Regional Medical Center
Mayo Clinic Jacksonville
Mount Sinai Medical Center of Florida
Munroe Regional Health System
Nemours Foundation
Ocala Regional Medical Center
Osceola Regional Medical Center
St. Vincent's Health System
UF&Shands

HISTORICAL FINANCIALS

Company Type: Private

Income Statement

FYE: September 30

	REVENUE ($ mil.)	NET INCOME ($ mil.)	NET PROFIT MARGIN	EMPLOYEES
09/13	1,576	115	7.3%	10,000
09/10	1,700	91	5.4%	—
09/09	1,637	76	4.7%	—
Annual Growth	(0.9%)	10.8%	—	—

2013 Year-End Financials

Return on assets: 3.8%
Return on equity: 7.3%
Current ratio: 1.30
Cash ($ mil.): 51

OROVILLE HOSPITAL

Auditors: MATSON AND ISOM

LOCATIONS

HQ: OROVILLE HOSPITAL
2767 OLIVE HWY, OROVILLE, CA 959666118
Phone: 530 533-8500
Web: WWW.OROVILLEHOSPITAL.COM

HISTORICAL FINANCIALS

Company Type: Private

Income Statement

FYE: November 30

	REVENUE ($ mil.)	NET INCOME ($ mil.)	NET PROFIT MARGIN	EMPLOYEES
11/13	761	2	0.3%	1,400
11/12	173	6	3.9%	—
11/11	150	3	2.4%	—
11/10	152	0	—	—
Annual Growth	70.8%	—	—	—

2013 Year-End Financials

Return on assets: 2.1%
Return on equity: 0.3%
Current ratio: 0.90
Cash ($ mil.): 8

OSC SPORTS INC.

Olympia Sports may not make you an Olympian but the company carries the gear to help you go for gold. The sporting goods retailer offers sports equipment fitness gear and apparel athletic shoes casual wear and sports accessories under such brands as Columbia Louisville Slugger Bauer PUMA Reebok and Teva. It sells merchandise through its website and via more than 225 banner stores across the Northeast and Mid-Atlantic states. In addition to its retail business the company oversees the private nonprofit Olympia Sports Foundation which runs a clothing bank and collaborates on projects with local charities and schools within its retail region. Founder and CEO Ed Manganello owns Olympia.

Geographic Reach

Based in Maine Olympia Sports operates sporting goods stores throughout the Northeast and the Mid-Atlantic states.

Operations

The regional retailer operates a website to sell its products to complement its portfolio of retail shops that serve those who reside in more than a dozen states.

Strategy

The company has been adding to its stores network in recent years. Olympia Sports has expanded into Maryland New York New Jersey Delaware Pennsylvania and Virginia.

Sales and Marketing

Besides its brick-and-mortar stores Olympia Sports sells name-brand sporting goods items through its website.

Company Ownership

Olympia Sports is owned by founder and CEO Ed Manganello.

EXECUTIVES

President of Olympia Sports, Ed Manganello
President, Dick Coffey
Training Coordinator, David Heath
Auditors: BAKER NEWMAN NOYES PORTLAND

LOCATIONS

HQ: OSC SPORTS INC.
5 BRADLEY DR, WESTBROOK, ME 040922013
Phone: 207 854-2794
Web: WWW.OLYMPIASPORTS.NET

2013 Stores

	No.
Massachusetts	63
New York	53
Maine	29
New Hampshire	21
Pennsylvania	20
Connecticut	14
Vermont	11
Rhode Island	5
Maryland	6
Virginia	5
New Jersey	2
Delaware	1
West Virginia	1
Total	**231**

PRODUCTS/OPERATIONS

Selected Brands

Adidas
Brooks
Champion
Columbia
Converse
Crocs
Easton
Etnies
Fathead
Life Is Good
Mizuno
Moving Comfort
New Balance
Nike
Oakley
Puma
Rawlings
Reebok
Saucony
SKLZ
Spalding
Teva

COMPETITORS

Dick's Sporting Goods	L.L. Bean
Dunham's	Modell's
Eastern Mountain Sports	REI
Finish Line	Sears
Foot Locker	Sports Authority
Hat World	Target Corporation
Kmart	Wal-Mart

HISTORICAL FINANCIALS

Company Type: Private

Income Statement

FYE: September 30

	REVENUE ($ mil.)	NET INCOME ($ mil.)	NET PROFIT MARGIN	EMPLOYEES
09/09	165	0	0.2%	2,000
09/08	191	4	2.3%	—
09/07	1,113	0	0.0%	—
Annual Growth	(61.4%)	2839.6%	—	—

2009 Year-End Financials

Return on assets: 7.7%   Cash ($ mil.): —
Return on equity: 0.2%
Current ratio: 0.10

OSF HEALTHCARE SYSTEM

OSF Healthcare helps patients who are feeling oh-so-frail in northern Illinois and southwestern Michigan. OSF Healthcare system includes 11 acute care hospitals and one long-term care facility that combined are home to more than 1500 beds and offer a full spectrum of inpatient and outpatient medical and surgical services. The system's primary care physician network consists of about 650 physicians at more than 105 locations throughout its service area. Subsidiary OSF Home Care provides hospice home visit and equipment services and OSF Saint Francis provides ambulance pharmacy and health care management services. The not-for-profit system is a subsidiary of the Sisters of The Third Order of St. Francis.

Operations Along with its various acute care hospitals OSF Healthcare provides urgent care through its OSF PromptCare locations. PromptCare administers a range of services including labs MRI ultrasound and primary and specialty care.

The company also has two colleges of nursing —Saint Francis Medical Center College of Nursing in Peoria Illinois; and the Saint Anthony College of Nursing in Rockford Illinois.

The system had some 58000 inpatient admissions; 1.3 million outpatient visits; and 254000 emergency department visits in 2014.

Financial Performance

In 2014 gross patient services revenue totaled $6.9 billion.

Strategy

OSF Healthcare has an incubation collaboration with the University of Illinois College of Medicine at Peoria. The venture dubbed Jump Trading Simulation and Education Center was established in 2013 to focus on advances in education research and innovation. It has been involved in such activities as funding 3-D printing for surgical procedures and exposing high school students to medical training experiences.

EXECUTIVES

Chairperson, Sister Judith Ann Duvall
SVP and CFO, Daniel Baker
SVP Medical Services, Gerald J. McShane
SVP Marketing and Communications, James G. Farrell
SVP Strategic Effectiveness, R. Michael Gulley
SVP and Chief Nursing Officer, Susan Campbell
SVP Government Relations, Tara D. Canty
CEO, Kevin D. Schoeplein
SVP and CIO, James J. Mormann

SVP Supportive Care, Robert Sawicki
SVP Care Management, Ralph R. Velazquez
President of the United, Wyatt Earp
Auditors: KPMG LLP COLUMBUS OH

LOCATIONS

HQ: OSF HEALTHCARE SYSTEM
800 NE GLEN OAK AVE, PEORIA, IL 616033200
Phone: 309 655-2850
Web: WWW.OSFHEALTHCARE.ORG

PRODUCTS/OPERATIONS

Selected Clinical Services

Cancer Care
Diabetes & Endocrinology
Emergency Services
Heart & Vascular
Home Health
Hospice
Neurosciences
Pediatrics
Primary Care
Rehabilitation
Surgery
Transplant Services
Weight Loss Management
Women's Health

Selected Support Services

Advance Care Planning
Clinical Research
Equipment Technology Services
Home Infusion Pharmacy
Home Medical Equipment
Mobile Medical Systems
OSF Life Flight
Retail Services
Skilled Nursing Network
System Laboratory
Telehealth

Selected Facilities

OSF Holy Family Medical Center (Monmouth IL)
OSF Saint Anthony Medical Center (Rockford IL)
OSF Saint Clare Home (Peoria Heights IL)
OSF Saint Elizabeth Medical Center (formerly Ottawa Regional Hospital Ottawa IL)
OSF Saint Francis Medical Center (Peoria IL)
OSF Saint James - John W. Albrecht Medical Center (Pontiac IL)
OSF St. Mary Medical Center (Galesburg IL)
OSF St. Francis Hospital (Escanaba MI)
OSF St. Joseph Medical Center (Bloomington IL)

COMPETITORS

Advocate BroMenn	Rush-Copley Medical
Centegra Health System	Center
Central DuPage	SwedishAmerican Health
Hospital	System
Covenant HealthCare	University of Chicago
Genesis Health System	Medical Center
McDonough District	University of Michigan
Hospital	Health System
Memorial Health System	Wheaton Franciscan
Northwestern Memorial	Services
HealthCare	

HISTORICAL FINANCIALS

Company Type: Private

Income Statement

FYE: September 30

	REVENUE ($ mil.)	NET INCOME ($ mil.)	NET PROFIT MARGIN	EMPLOYEES
09/13	1,893	105	5.6%	4,007
09/08	1,477	26	1.8%	—
09/06	1,481	58	4.0%	—
Annual Growth	3.6%	8.7%	—	—

2013 Year-End Financials

Return on assets: 8.6%   Cash ($ mil.): 228
Return on equity: 5.6%
Current ratio: —

OTTER PRODUCTS LLC

Otter Products' products keep your precious electronic devices safe and dry. The company which goes by OtterBox makes more than 250 models of protective cases for cell phones smart phones tablet computers and other portable electronics from Apple LG Corp BlackBerry Samsung and other manufacturers. It outsources production and sells its impact and water resistant Defender Reflex Commuter and Impact cases and watertight boxes at Best Buy Target and other retailers. OtterBox was formed in 1998 by CEO Curt Richardson and his wife Nancy who came up with the name after being inspired by otters' water-repellent skin and playful and creative attitudes.

Geographic Reach

Headquartered in Fort Collins Colorado Otterbox has other offices in San Diego; Boston; Cork Ireland; and Hong Kong. It has established distribution in 14 countries throughout the APAC region.Sales and MarketingMore than 75% of Otter Products' revenues were tied to Apple products in 2014 according to Moody's. The company's products are distributed through retailers including Verizon Best Buy AT&T Walmart Sprint Target T-Mobile and Amazon. The company distributes its products in other countries through distribution partners such as Ingram Micro (which distributes its products in China).Financial PerformanceWhile full details of the privately-held company were not available Otter Products reportedly grew its revenue by 180% from 2011 through 2014 making it one of Inc. 5000's fastest growing private companies in the nation. Its aggregate revenues were $205 billion over the period.

Strategy

OtterBox has been expanding its product distribution into Asia in recent years to capitalize on the growing affluence in markets in China and other developing countries. In mid-2014 for example OtterBox signed a distribution agreement with Ingram Micro the world's largest wholesale technology distributor to make OtterBox products available through Ingram Micro's vast retail network in China and through online retailers. The total smartphone shipments in China rose to 420 million at the end of 2014 a factor that OtterBox hopes to take advantage of in the coming years. Vietnam is another strategic market for OtterBox in Asia and presents significant opportunities as a result of the rapid growth of smartphone users within Vietnam. In 2013 OtterBox expanded into the Vietnam retail market through distribution partner Petrosetco Distribution Joint Stock Company (PSD).

Mergers and Acquisitions

In 2013 the company purchased San Diego-based TreeFrog Developments (dba LifeProof) for about $325 million. LifeProof makes complementary smartphone cases and accessories and Otter hopes the synergies and choices provided by the combined firm will drive its strategy of attracting and creating lifelong customers.

In 2012 OtterBox acquired Wrapsol and its family of premium protective film solutions for mobile devices.Company BackgroundOtterBox was formed in 1998 by CEO Curt Richardson and his wife Nancy who came up with the name after being inspired by otters' water-repellent skin and playful and creative attitudes; traits the company works to incorporate into its culture.

EXECUTIVES

National Account Manager, Nikki Street
Vice President, Danyel Day
Vice President, Tary Mauk
Vice President, Meghan Ledington
Vice President, Athena Woods
National Account Manager, Levi Sattler
National Account Manager, Ryan Sawyer
Vice President, Frank Herrera

LOCATIONS

HQ: OTTER PRODUCTS LLC
   209 S MELDRUM ST, FORT COLLINS, CO 805212603
Phone: 970 493-8446
Web: WWW.OTTERBOX.COM

COMPETITORS

Apple Inc.	Skullcandy
Coach Inc.	Tamrac
Eagle Creek Travel	Tenba
Gear	Tumi
Forward Industries	ZAGG
SKB Corporation	

HISTORICAL FINANCIALS
Company Type: Private

Income Statement

	REVENUE ($ mil.)	NET INCOME ($ mil.)	NET PROFIT MARGIN	EMPLOYEES
12/10	168	60	35.8%	320
12/09	48	15	31.7%	—
12/08	1,076	0	0.0%	—
Annual Growth	(60.4%)	325	63.6%	—

OUR LADY OF LOURDES MEDICAL CENTER INC

Our Lady of Lourdes Medical Center tends to the sick of southern New Jersey. The hospital is a general acute care facility with about 325 inpatient beds. In addition to general medical emergency and surgical care the hospital specializes in organ transplantation joint replacement rehabilitation dialysis treatment cardiac care and birthing care. The hospital also offers nursing and other medical training programs and it operates area clinics and provides community health and outreach services. Our Lady of Lourdes Medical Center part of Catholic Health East's Lourdes Health System is sponsored by the Franciscan Sisters of Allegany New York.

Operations

The medical center's specialty units include the New Jersey Heart Institute at Lourdes the Regional Perinatal Center and the Lourdes Rehabilitation Center as well as regional dialysis and organ transplant clinics. Besides offering primary and specialty care services in a variety of fields Our Lady of Lourdes Medical Center is a teaching and research facility through affiliations with area universities and health professional schools. It also operates its own nursing school.

The hospital had a total of 13682 admissions on 2014. Its physicians performed 3184 inpatient and 2392 outpatient surgeries.

Strategy

Our Lady of Lourdes Medical Center has undergone expansion efforts over the years to attract and retain customers in the region by continually upgrading its technology. The hospital also strives to expand services and resources for doctors and health professionals. In 2014 it became one of only a few hospitals in the South Jersey region to implant subcutaneous implantable defibrillators. The cardiac device is the first and only one of its kind that provides defibrillator therapy without touching the heart.

Lourdes Health System has also expanded by opening new outpatient care centers in Camden and the greater Philadelphia metropolitan area. It is the only hospital in the tri-state area (New Jersey Pennsylvania and Delaware) to have been awarded the American Hospital Association's top honor for excellence in community outreach services.

Company Background

In 2012 Our Lady of Lourdes Medical Center relocated and expanded its birthing center to include all-private rooms with improved family accommodations. It has also updated some of its medical equipment and energy systems including the addition of a new MRI imaging system during 2012 to improve patient comfort and diagnostic capabilities.

That year it enriched its educational programs by forming partnerships with the Immaculata University and Camden Community College to offer nursing bachelor's and master's degrees through its Our Lady of Lourdes School of Nursing.

EXECUTIVES

Radiology Director, Barbara Donnell
Director Of Medical Records, Octavia Gaston
Vice President Medical Affairs, Alan (Al) Pope
Vice President of Risk Management, Barbara (Barb) Holfelner

LOCATIONS

HQ: OUR LADY OF LOURDES MEDICAL CENTER INC
   1600 HADDON AVE, CAMDEN, NJ 081033101
Phone: 856 757-3500
Web: WWW.LOURDESNURSINGSCHOOL.ORG

PRODUCTS/OPERATIONS

Selected Services
Bariatric Surgery
Cardiac Services
Community Outreach
Dialysis
Emergency Services
Joint Replacement Center
Organ Transplantation
Rehabilitation Center
Senior Services
Stroke
Women and Children' s Services

COMPETITORS

Abington Memorial Hospital
Albert Einstein Healthcare Network
Aria Health
Christiana Care
Fox Chase Cancer Center
Inspira Health Network
Jefferson Health System
Kennedy Health System
Mercy Health System
North Philadelphia Health System
TUHS
Tenet Healthcare
The Cooper Health System
University of Pennsylvania Health System
Virtua Health

Company Type: Private

Income Statement FYE: December 31

	REVENUE ($ mil.)	NET INCOME ($ mil.)	NET PROFIT MARGIN	EMPLOYEES
12/12	271	30	11.1%	3,000
12/09	279	(21)	—	—
12/08	296	1	0.4%	—
12/03	243	0	—	—
Annual Growth	1.2%	—	—	—

2012 Year-End Financials

Return on assets: 3.3% Cash ($ mil.): 4
Return on equity: 11.1%
Current ratio: 1.20

OUR LADY OF LOURDES REGIONAL MEDICAL CENTER INC.

Established in 1949 as part of the not-for-profit Franciscan Missionaries of Our Lady Health System Our Lady of Lourdes Regional Medical Center is a hospital that provides medical care in southern Louisiana. The facility cares for denizens of the bayou with a medical staff of more than 400 physicians representing some 50 specialties including cardiology neurology and oncology. The medical center also offers oupatient care and urgent care as well as a general family practice and pediatric care. Our Lady of Lourdes extends its reach outside the facility into the Acadiana regional community by offering primary care physicians' offices home health care programs and occupational medicine.

EXECUTIVES

Medical Director, Kemp Corell
Auditors: KPMG LLC BATON ROUGE LA

LOCATIONS

HQ: OUR LADY OF LOURDES REGIONAL MEDICAL CENTER INC.
4801 AMBSSDOR CFFERY PKWY, LAFAYETTE, LA 705086917
Phone: 337 470-2000

COMPETITORS

Baton Rouge General	Our Lady of the Lake
CHRISTUS St. Frances	RMC
Cabrini Hospital	River Parishes
General Health System	Hospital
LHC Group	Terrebonne General
LSU System	Medical Center
Lafayette General	Woman's Hospital
Medical Center	
Lane Regional Medical	
Center	

Company Type: Private

Income Statement FYE: June 30

	REVENUE ($ mil.)	NET INCOME ($ mil.)	NET PROFIT MARGIN	EMPLOYEES
06/10	162	(9)	—	1,700
06/09	142	(58)	—	—
06/08	314	0	—	—
Annual Growth	—	—	—	—

2010 Year-End Financials

Return on assets: — Cash ($ mil.): 17
Return on equity: (-5.6%)
Current ratio: 0.20

OUR LADY OF THE LAKE HOSPITAL INC.

Our Lady of the Lake Regional Medical Center reaches out to Baton Rouge residents with a helping hand. Participating in teaching programs for LSU and Tulane medical schools the medical center has some 800 inpatient beds and includes trauma emergency surgery general medical and specialty care centers for conditions including heart disease cancer orthopedics and ENT (ear nose and throat) disorders. Our Lady of the Lake also includes a Children's Hospital two nursing homes and an independent-living facility and it offers outpatient services at its main campus and at satellite facilities throughout the greater Baton Rouge area.

Operations

The hospital's family of services include an 800-bed Regional Medical Center; a dedicated Children's Hospital; a 350-provider Physician Group primary care network free-standing emergency room in Livingston Parish; an outpatient imaging and surgery centers; Assumption Community Hospital; a network of urgent care clinics; and Our Lady of the Lake College. Our Lady of the Lake is a primary teaching site for graduate medical education programs and serves 45000 inpatients and 350000 outpatients a year. The company has more than 850 doctors. Some 70% of its physicians and other professional medical staff members are board certified and in nearly one-third of the hospital system's medical specialty areas 100% of the physicians and other professionals are board certified.

Strategy

As a major facility in the Baton Rouge area Our Lady of the Lake has been expanding its services in the region in recent years. In 2015 Our Lady of the Lake Children's Hospital opened its first pediatric specialty clinic outside of the Baton Rouge area offering specialized outpatient care for pediatric gastroenterology patients.In 2014 the company opened a new children's emergency room and expanded its adult emergency department.

Company Background

In 2012 the hospital constructed a freestanding emergency room facility in the suburban community of Livingston Louisiana. It is also building a new nine-story patient tower to the main hospital campus; the tower will house the heart and vascular center as well as an expanded ER and a new level 1 regional trauma center and will be completed in late 2013.

Our Lady of the Lake has also expanded its education programs. For instance it added a pediatric

residency program in 2010. The hospital also moved to extend its relationship with LSU that year by agreeing to become the primary clinical site for the LSU medical school. The agreement came as LSU considered whether to build a replacement hospital for its aging teaching facility and coincides with the Our Lady of the Lake expansion projects. The partnership launched a new psychiatric residency program in 2012.

Our Lady of the Lake was founded in 1923 by the Franciscan Missionaries of Our Lady.

EXECUTIVES

Vice President Finance, Barry Chambers
Vice President Medical Affairs, Rick Vath

LOCATIONS

HQ: OUR LADY OF THE LAKE HOSPITAL INC.
5000 HENNESSY BLVD, BATON ROUGE, LA 708084367
Phone: 225 765-7709
Web: WWW.OLOLCHILDRENS.COM

PRODUCTS/OPERATIONS

Selected Services
Advanced Wound and Ostomy Clinic
Cancer
Children's Hospital
Critical Care
Diabetes & Nutrition Center
Emergency Services
Endoscopy Center
Hearing and Balance Center
Heart & Vascular Institute
Imaging Services
Laboratory and Diagnostics
Lake Express Check-In
LSU Health Baton Rouge
Mental and Behavioral Health
Neurology Neurosurgery and Stroke
Orthopedics
Palliative Care
Pharmacy
Rehabilitation Center
Respiratory Care
Senior Services
St. Anthony's Home
Surgery
Trauma Center
Urgent Care
Voice Center
Weight Loss

COMPETITORS

CHRISTUS St. Frances	Our Lady of Lourdes
Cabrini Hospital	River Parishes
Dynacq Healthcare	Hospital
General Health System	Woman's Hospital
Lane Regional Medical	
Center	

HISTORICAL FINANCIALS

Company Type: Private

Income Statement FYE: June 30

	REVENUE ($ mil.)	NET INCOME ($ mil.)	NET PROFIT MARGIN	EMPLOYEES
06/11	826	214	26.0%	1,800
06/10	614	12	2.0%	—
06/08*	6	1	18.4%	—
12/05	0	0	—	—
Annual Growth	426.1%	—	—	—

*Fiscal year change

2011 Year-End Financials

Return on assets: — Cash ($ mil.): 200
Return on equity: 26.0%
Current ratio: 2.90

OVERLAKE HOSPITAL ASSOCIATION

LOCATIONS

HQ: OVERLAKE HOSPITAL ASSOCIATION
1035 116TH AVE NE, BELLEVUE, WA 980044604
Phone: 425 688-5000
Web: WWW.OVERLAKEHOSPITAL.ORG

HISTORICAL FINANCIALS

Company Type: Private

Income Statement
FYE: June 30

	REVENUE ($ mil.)	NET INCOME ($ mil.)	NET PROFIT MARGIN	EMPLOYEES
06/14	454	62	13.8%	—
06/13	427	42	9.9%	—
06/12	432	20	4.7%	—
06/11	9	0	—	—
Annual Growth	**263.3%**	—	—	—

2014 Year-End Financials

Return on assets: 2.9%   Cash ($ mil.): 34
Return on equity: 13.8%
Current ratio: 0.80

OVERLAKE HOSPITAL MEDICAL CENTER

Over the lake and through the sound to Overlake Hospital Medical Center we go! The not-for-profit hospital provides health care services to residents of Bellevue Washington in the Puget Sound region. The nearly 350-bed facility provides comprehensive inpatient and outpatient services ranging from cancer care and surgery to specialized senior care. Overlake also operates a number of outpatient clinics providing primary care urgent care and specialty care such as weight loss surgery. The organization also provides patients with health and wellness programs addressing issues like women's and children's health.

Operations

The medical center has more than 1000 physicians on staff and runs Centers of Excellence in cardiac care cancer care surgical services women's and infants' care and emergency and Level III trauma care. The facility is home to a 24-hour urgent care clinic an anticoagulation clinic and a breast screening center. Overlake also operates numerous outpatient clinics providing primary care urgent care and specialty care.

Geographic Reach

Overlake provides health care services to residents of Bellevue Washington and the entire Puget Sound region. It operates clinics on its main campus in Bellevue as well as in Redmond and in Issaquah and on Mercer Island.

Sales and Marketing

In 2014 Medicare payments accounted for 27% of net patient revenues followed by group health organizations (17%) Premera (13%) and Regence (12%).

Financial Performance

Overlake's revenues increased by 2% to $433 million in 2014 as the result of higher net patient revenues and contribution revenues.

Net income rose 50% to $60 million that year primarily due to income from change in net unrealized gains on investments. Cash flow from operations fell 3% to $47 million as more cash was used in net clinic accounts receivable pledges receivable prepaid expenses and other long-term receivables.

Strategy

Increasing demand in the region has led the hospital to invest in expansions and equipment upgrades that include more emergency treatment capabilities and an on-campus helistop for trauma patients being airlifted to the area.

Along with its expansion and construction projects Overlake is investing in new technology to keep the health system in line with its competitors and to improve patient care. It is adding endoscopic video towers to its operating rooms to facilitate improved views of surgical procedures and is also moving to digitize all of its facilities with electronic health records.

In 2013 it opened the new $17.4 million David and Shelley Hovind Heart & Vascular center. The new 19200-sq.-ft. facility brings cardiac and vascular services together in one location.

Overlake has also focused on adding new primary care clinics and expanding its physician network to serve patients in locations closer to where they live and work.

Company Background

Overlake founded in 1960 is led by CEO Craig Hendrickson a veteran health care executive.

EXECUTIVES

Director Of Radiology Director Of Radiology Servi, Brenda Rinehart
Chief Officer And Vp N, Alan (Al) Ertle
Chief Nursing Officer And Vice President Of Patient Care Services, Cathy Whitaker
Medical Librarian, Hazel Cameron
Medical Director Of Radiation Oncology, James (Jamie) Pelton
Auditors: KPMG LLP SEATTLE WA

LOCATIONS

HQ: OVERLAKE HOSPITAL MEDICAL CENTER
1035 116TH AVE NE, BELLEVUE, WA 980044687
Phone: 425 688-5000
Web: WWW.OVERLAKEHOSPITAL.ORG

Selected Locations

Outpatient Rehabilitation Services
Outpatient Surgery (park in the West Garage; Outpatient Surgery is located on the first floor of the West Garage.)
Overlake Bellevue Campus and Overlake Medical Clinics Medical Tower
Overlake Medical Clinics Downtown Bellevue
Overlake Medical Clinics Issaquah
Overlake Medical Clinics Kirkland
Overlake Medical Clinics Redmond
Urgent Care Clinic in Issaquah
Urgent Care Clinic in Redmond

PRODUCTS/OPERATIONS

2014 Sales

	% of total
Net patient service revenue	97
Other operating revenue	3
Contribution revenue	-
Total	**100**

Selected Medical Services

Breast Health Services
Cancer Center at Overlake
Cardiac Center at Overlake
Clinical Trials
Emergency & Trauma Center
Medical Imaging

Overlake Medical Clinics
Surgical Services
Weight Loss Surgery
Women's & Infants' Center

COMPETITORS

Catholic Health Initiatives
Franciscan Health System
Group Health Cooperative (Puget Sound)
Harrison Medical Center
MultiCare Health System
PeaceHealth
Providence Health & Services
Seattle Children's Hospital
Swedish Health Services
University of Washington
Yakima Valley Memorial

HISTORICAL FINANCIALS

Company Type: Private

Income Statement
FYE: June 30

	REVENUE ($ mil.)	NET INCOME ($ mil.)	NET PROFIT MARGIN	EMPLOYEES
06/14	450	59	13.3%	2,450
06/13	422	40	9.5%	—
06/12	427	18	4.4%	—
06/11	417	0	—	—
Annual Growth	**2.5%**	—	—	—

2014 Year-End Financials

Return on assets: 2.9%   Cash ($ mil.): 26
Return on equity: 13.3%
Current ratio: 0.80

OWENSBORO HEALTH INC.

Auditors: ERNST & YOUNG US LLP INDIANAP

LOCATIONS

HQ: OWENSBORO HEALTH INC.
1201 PLEASANT VALLEY RD, OWENSBORO, KY 423039811
Phone: 270 688-2000
Web: WWW.OWENSBOROHEALTH.ORG

HISTORICAL FINANCIALS

Company Type: Private

Income Statement
FYE: May 31

	REVENUE ($ mil.)	NET INCOME ($ mil.)	NET PROFIT MARGIN	EMPLOYEES
05/14	450	4	1.0%	3,200
05/13	420	2	0.7%	—
05/12	410	41	10.2%	—
05/10	416	0	—	—
Annual Growth	**2.0%**	—	—	—

2014 Year-End Financials

Return on assets: 11.3%   Cash ($ mil.): 23
Return on equity: 1.0%
Current ratio: 0.30

PACE UNIVERSITY

If you want to keep pace with your peers chances are you'll need a higher education. Pace University offers certificate programs as well as undergraduate graduate and doctoral degrees through half a dozen schools: arts and sciences business computer science and information systems education law and nursing. Altogether the school is home to 100 undergraduate majors offering roughly 30 undergraduate and graduate degrees 50 master's programs and four doctoral programs. Nearly 13000 students attend the university's three New York campuses (Lower Manhattan Pleasantville-Briarcliff and White Plains). It has a student-faculty ratio of about 18:1.

Geographic Reach
Pace boasts campus locations in New York City and in Westchester County.

Operations
The school has an endowment of more than $100 million. Besides its three New York campuses the university also offers courses online and at a location in midtown Manhattan.

Financial Performance
The university logged a 3% increase in revenue in 2012 as compared to 2011 due to a boost in contributions as well as tuition and fees net government grants and contracts. Net income meanwhile dropped by 160% during the same reporting period thanks to rises in expenses and unrealized depreciation in fair value of derivative instruments in 2012 vs. appreciation in 2011.

Company Background
Pace was founded in 1906 by the brothers Homer and Charles Pace as a co-educational business school called Pace Institute. It wasn't until 42 years later under Robert Pace that it began its transformation into its current incarnation as a liberal arts and sciences college.

EXECUTIVES

Associate Vice President for University Relations Marketing and Communications, Peter (Pete) Sikowitz
Assistant Vice President Government Community Ritns, Meghan Grench
Auditors: KPMG LLP NEW YORK NY

LOCATIONS

HQ: PACE UNIVERSITY
1 PACE PLZ, NEW YORK, NY 100381598
Phone: 212 346-1956
Web: WWW.PACE.EDU

PRODUCTS/OPERATIONS

Selected Colleges and Schools
Dyson College of Arts and Sciences
Lienhard School of Nursing
Lubin School of Business
School of Education
School of Law
Seidenberg School of Computer Science and Information Systems

HISTORICAL FINANCIALS
Company Type: Private

Income Statement
FYE: June 30

	REVENUE ($ mil.)	NET INCOME ($ mil.)	NET PROFIT MARGIN	EMPLOYEES
06/13	326	20	6.2%	1,862
06/12	310	(15)	—	—
06/11	300	26	8.9%	—
06/10	274	0	—	—
Annual Growth	6.0%	—	—	—

2013 Year-End Financials
Return on assets: —
Return on equity: 6.2%
Current ratio: —
Cash ($ mil.): 14

PACIFIC COAST PRODUCERS

Fruits seafood sauces and organic tomato puree —rather than movies —are the creative output of this particular group of Pacific Coast Producers. The cooperative markets the apricots grapes peaches pears and tomatoes grown by its approximately 160 California-based members. It turns the produce into private-label canned fruit sauces and juices and sells them to the retail and foodservice industries. Pacific Coast Producers typically serves retailers the likes of Albertson's Aldi Kroger Safeway SUPERVALU Whole Foods and Wal-Mart as well as the US Department of Agriculture. The company founded in 1971 operates three production sites and one distribution center in California.

Geographic Reach
From its base in Lodi California Pacific Coast Producers grows its fruits in California and sells them nationwide.

Operations
The cooperative boasts three food-processing facilities in California as well as distribution centers in California and Washington.

Strategy
Pacific Coast Producers has expanded its warehouse space in Lodi to improve efficiency and boost capacity. The move cost the company $23 million. It expanded its distribution center by 50% to meet rising demand for canned food.

The cooperative serves tomato processor Morning Star through a sales and marketing alliance it formed with the company in 2009. As part of the collaboration Pacific Coast Producers provides canned tomatoes to the retail and foodservice industries.

Sales and Marketing
Pacific Coast Producers sells the products it grows and processes to retailers and foodservice operators nationwide as well as to the US Department of Agriculture.

Financial Performance
As one of California's premier private label packers Pacific Coast Producers has logged annual sales in excess of $535 million plus $100 million in alliance income.

EXECUTIVES

Vice President Operations, Daniel Sroufe
Vice President General Counsel, Mona Shulman
Vice President Finance Chief Financial Officer, Mark Wahlman
Vice President Manager Director, Patricia Crowell
National Sales Manager, David Zuzich
Vice President Manager Director, George McMillan
Auditors: KPMG LLP SACRAMENTO CALIFORN

LOCATIONS

HQ: PACIFIC COAST PRODUCERS
631 N CLUFF AVE, LODI, CA 952400756
Phone: 209 367-8800
Web: WWW.CANNED-FRESH.COM

PRODUCTS/OPERATIONS

Selected Products
Apricots

Catsup
Chili Sauces
Chunky Mixed Fruit
Concentrated Crushed Tomatoes
Diced Style Tomatoes
Extra Heavy Concentrated Crushed Round Tomato Puree
Formulated Pizza Sauces
Fruit Cocktail
Fruit for Salad
Fruit Mix
Ground Tomatoes
Marinara Sauces
Non-Formulated Pizza Sauce
Organic Tomatoes
Peaches
Pears
Random Cut / Strip Style Tomatoes
Seafood Sauces
Stewed Style Tomatoes
Tomato Juice
Whole Peeled Tomatoes

COMPETITORS

Big Heart Pet Brands	Glory Foods
Campbell Soup	Hain Celestial
Cento	Hanover Foods
ConAgra	Heinz
Dole Food	NORPAC
Faribault Foods	Pictsweet
General Mills	Seneca Foods

HISTORICAL FINANCIALS
Company Type: Private

Income Statement
FYE: May 31

	REVENUE ($ mil.)	NET INCOME ($ mil.)	NET PROFIT MARGIN	EMPLOYEES
05/14	588	23	4.0%	1,000
05/13	534	18	3.5%	—
05/12	500	18	3.7%	—
05/11	498	0	—	—
Annual Growth	5.6%	—	—	—

2014 Year-End Financials
Return on assets: 6.9%
Return on equity: 4.0%
Current ratio: 0.40
Cash ($ mil.): 1

PACIFIC HIDE & FUR DEPOT

Pacific Steel & Recycling sells at one end of the steel mill and buys at the other. The company's Pacific Recycling unit supplies steel mills with scrap metal a key raw material. It operates about 35 recycling centers in the northwestern US and Canada that also handle cardboard and scrap paper in addition to metals. The company's Pacific Steel unit buys steel products and resells them from steel service centers and distribution centers in the northwestern US. Pacific Steel's facilities handle items such as bar products and structurals flat-rolled products reinforcing bar and tubing and pipe. The company offers a variety of processing services.

Pacific Steel & Recycling also sells livestock equipment (including gates feeders and fence wire) ornamental ironwork (handrails balusters and post tops) and trailer parts.

The company operates through several northwestern states in the US: Colorado Idaho Montana Nevada North Dakota South Dakota Utah Washington and Wyoming.

In 2012 the company acquired the assets of Canadian recycler Triple R Metals in Medicine Hat Alberta for an undisclosed amount. The acquisition was the first company outside of the US to be bought by Pacific Steel & Recycling. The metals recycling facility which has been in business for 10 years will operate under the name PHF Steel & Recycling.

The company has its roots in a fur-trading business that was founded in the 1880s.

EXECUTIVES

CIO, David (Dave) Richards
VP-Ops, Jeff Millhollin
Vice President Scrap Operations, Pat Kons
Vice President Business Development, Stuart (Stu) Boylan

LOCATIONS

HQ: PACIFIC HIDE & FUR DEPOT
5 RIVER DR S, GREAT FALLS, MT 594051872
Phone: 406 771-7222
Web: WWW.PACIFIC-STEEL.COM

COMPETITORS

Alaskan Copper   Ryerson
Reliance Steel

HISTORICAL FINANCIALS

Company Type: Private

Income Statement

	REVENUE ($ mil.)	NET INCOME ($ mil.)	NET PROFIT MARGIN	EMPLOYEES
08/10	301	34	11.0%	780
08/08	241	2	1.2%	—
08/07	2,109	0	—	—
Annual Growth	(47.7%)	15604.6%	—	—

2010 Year-End Financials

Return on assets: 1.4%   Cash ($ mil.): 38
Return on equity: 11.6%
Current ratio: 3.50

PALMETTO HEALTH

Palmetto Health provides health care in the Palmetto State. The not-for-profit organization administers a comprehensive range of medical services to residents of Columbia South Carolina and surrounding areas through a network of hospitals and other medical providers. The 1140-bed system includes a 650-bed teaching hospital Palmetto Health Richland which is affiliated with the University of South Carolina Medical School. Palmetto also operates the 490-bed Palmetto Health Baptist Columbia hospital as well as Baptist Health Easley a 110-bed general acute-care community hospital in the Appalachian highlands which it operates with Greenville Hospital System University Medical Center.

Operations

Two additional specialty hospitals provide pediatric and cardiac care. The system is also home to hospice facilities counseling centers and a network of affiliated physicians' practices.

Palmetto Health has about 1000 physicians on its medical staff. The system's emergency departments accommodate some 160000 visits each year. Additional divisions include home care agencies cancer and diagnostic centers and occupational health units. Palmetto Health's Parkridge Campus provides outpatient services including primary care diagnostics and ambulatory surgery.

Geographic Reach

The hospitals of Palmetto Health provide care for 70% of the residents of Richland County and more than 55% of the health care for the combined Richland/Lexington county area.

Strategy

The system is looking to expand to keep pace with a grwoing and aging population. In 2011 Palmetto Health held a groundbreaking for its $99 million hospital Palmetto Health Baptist Parkridge. The hospital scheduled to open in 2013 will be situated on 70 acres of property in one of the most rapidly growing areas of Northwest Columbia.

EXECUTIVES

Nursing Services Director, Patricia Robinson
Senior Vice President Of Human Resources, Willis Gregory
Auditors: GRANT THORNTON LLP COLUMBIA

LOCATIONS

HQ: PALMETTO HEALTH
1301 TAYLOR ST STE 8A, COLUMBIA, SC 292012955
Phone: 803 296-2100
Web: WWW.PALMETTOHEALTH.ORG

PRODUCTS/OPERATIONS

Selected Facilities – South Carolina

Palmetto Health Baptist Hospital Columbia
Palmetto Health Baptist Hospital Easley
Palmetto Health Children' s Hospital (Columbia)
Palmetto Health Heart Hospital (Columbia)
Palmetto Health HomeCare
Palmetto Health Hospice
Palmetto Health Parkridge (Columbia)
Palmetto Health Physician Practices
Palmetto Health Richland (Columbia)
Specialty Centers
Bariatric Services/Weight Management Center
Breast Center
Cancer Centers
Carolina Stone Center
Da Vinci Robotic Surgery Center
Gamma Knife Center
Stroke Center

Total	0	0
Trauma Center		

COMPETITORS

AnMed Health
Beaufort Memorial Hospital
Bon Secours Health
CaroMont
Carolinas HealthCare System
Carolinas Hospital System
Community Health Systems
Doctors Hospital of Augusta
Georgetown Hospital System

Grand Strand Regional Medical Center
Greenville Hospital System
HCA
Laurens County Hospital
Lexington Medical Center
McLeod Health
Novant Health
Spartanburg Regional Healthcare System

HISTORICAL FINANCIALS

Company Type: Private

Income Statement

	REVENUE ($ mil.)	NET INCOME ($ mil.)	NET PROFIT MARGIN	EMPLOYEES
09/08	1,188	0	—	10,200
09/07	1,131	41	3.6%	—
Annual Growth	5.0%	—	—	—

2008 Year-End Financials

Return on assets: 2.9%   Cash ($ mil.): 8
Return on equity: —
Current ratio: 2.00

PAN AMERICAN HEALTH ORGANIZATION INC

LOCATIONS

HQ: PAN AMERICAN HEALTH ORGANIZATION INC
525 23RD ST NW, WASHINGTON, DC 200372825
Phone: 202 974-3000
Web: WWW.PAHO.ORG

HISTORICAL FINANCIALS

Company Type: Private

Income Statement

FYE: December 31

	REVENUE ($ mil.)	NET INCOME ($ mil.)	NET PROFIT MARGIN	EMPLOYEES
12/09	1,268	101	8.0%	1,500
12/06	541	84	15.7%	—
Annual Growth	32.9%	6.2%	—	—

2009 Year-End Financials

Return on assets: 0.9%   Cash ($ mil.): 351
Return on equity: 8.0%
Current ratio: 14.00

PAPER CONVERTING MACHINE COMPANY

An empire built on paper: The Paper Converting Machine Company (PCMC) does just that — manufactures machinery for the converting packaging printing and laminating of paper. PCMC makes and sells equipment for tissue converting and packaging; wide-web flexo printing coating and laminating; coaters; roll engraving; and nonwoven converting. Its equipment is used by manufacturers of flexible packaging non-woven disposable products (wet wipes) and sanitary tissues. PCMC is a division of manufacturing technology supplier Barry-Wehmiller Companies.

Geographic Reach

PCMC is stationed in Green Bay Wisconsin. It has sales offices in Brazil China Germany Japan Mexico/Central America/the Caribbean Oceania Spain Switzerland and the UK. Additional locations reside in Wisconsin and Korea. The company has manufacturing and other sales facilities in Green Bay Wisconsin; Lucca Italy; Devon UK; and Duncansville Pennsylvania.

Sales and Marketing

The company serves primarily the flexible packaging tissue converting and packaging nonwovens prime label and carton converting industries. MPI Label Systems is a major customers.

Strategy

PCMC grows by adding to its product portfolio and attracting additional customers. In mid-2012 the company released a new mid-range inline flexographic press ELS MAX which combines technologies from both inline and wide web CI presses.

Company Background

PCMC traces its historical roots back to 1919. It was acquired by Barry-Wehmiller Companies in 2005.

EXECUTIVES

Vice President Research and Development, Craig Compton
Senior Vice President European and Asian Operations, Sergio Casella
Auditors: ERNST & YOUNG LLP ST LOUIS M

LOCATIONS

HQ: PAPER CONVERTING MACHINE COMPANY
2300 S ASHLAND AVE, GREEN BAY, WI 543045213
Phone: 920 494-5601
Web: WWW.PCMC.COM

PRODUCTS/OPERATIONS

Selected Products
Nonwoven converting
Printing
  Flexible packaging
  Labels and labeling
  Flexo
  Flexo and gravure
  Package printing
  Paper film and foil converting
Roll engraving
Tissue converting
  Accumulators
  Coaters
  Core machines
  Embossers
  Facial tissue machinery
  Laminators
  Printers
  Rewinders
  Saws
  Tail sealers
  Unwinds
Tissue packaging
  Tissue bundlers
  Tissue wrappers

COMPETITORS

Andritz AG	Polymer Group
James Cropper	Sandusky International
Norbord	Voith
Nordson	imagelinx

HISTORICAL FINANCIALS

Company Type: Private

Income Statement
FYE: September 30

	REVENUE ($ mil.)	NET INCOME ($ mil.)	NET PROFIT MARGIN	EMPLOYEES
09/12	251	0	—	1,304
09/11	215	0	—	—
09/10	196	0	—	—
09/06	194	0	—	—
Annual Growth	4.4%	—	—	—

2012 Year-End Financials

Return on assets: 10.1%
Return on equity: —
Current ratio: 0.70

Cash ($ mil.): 5

PARKLAND COMMUNITY HEALTH PLAN

Auditors: BRUCE E BERNSTEIN & ASSOC PC

LOCATIONS

HQ: PARKLAND COMMUNITY HEALTH PLAN
2777 N STEMMONS FWY, DALLAS, TX 752072277
Phone: 214 266-2100

HISTORICAL FINANCIALS

Company Type: Private

Income Statement
FYE: December 31

	REVENUE ($ mil.)	NET INCOME ($ mil.)	NET PROFIT MARGIN	EMPLOYEES
12/12	515	24	4.7%	2
12/11	470	39	8.4%	—
12/10	457	0	0.1%	—
12/09	402	0	—	—
Annual Growth	8.6%	—	—	—

2012 Year-End Financials

Return on assets: —
Return on equity: 4.7%
Current ratio: 2.60

Cash ($ mil.): 118

PARKS XANTERRA & RESORTS INC

LOCATIONS

HQ: PARKS XANTERRA & RESORTS INC
6312 S FIDDLERS GREEN CIR 600N, GREENWOOD VILLAGE, CO 801114943
Phone: 303 600-3400
Web: WWW.XANTERRA.COM

HISTORICAL FINANCIALS

Company Type: Private

Income Statement
FYE: December 25

	REVENUE ($ mil.)	NET INCOME ($ mil.)	NET PROFIT MARGIN	EMPLOYEES
12/13	304	11	3.7%	3,500
12/12	305	13	4.3%	—
12/11	301	7	2.4%	—
12/10	305	0	—	—
Annual Growth	(0.1%)	—	—	—

2013 Year-End Financials

Return on assets: —
Return on equity: 3.7%
Current ratio: 0.30

Cash ($ mil.): 18

PARKVIEW FOUNDATION INC

Auditors: CROWE HORWATH LLP SOUTH BEND

LOCATIONS

HQ: PARKVIEW FOUNDATION INC
2200 RANDALLIA DR, FORT WAYNE, IN 468054638
Phone: 260 373-4000
Web: WWW.PARKVIEW.COM

HISTORICAL FINANCIALS

Company Type: Private

Income Statement
FYE: December 31

	REVENUE ($ mil.)	NET INCOME ($ mil.)	NET PROFIT MARGIN	EMPLOYEES
12/08	459	39	8.6%	8
12/04	4	(0)	—	—
Annual Growth	215.1%			

PARKWEST MEDICAL CENTER

Parkwest Medical Center is a wholly-owned subsidiary of Covenant Health and the largest medical center in West Knoxville. Parkwest has more than 285 beds and provides health care services to patients of Knox County Tennessee. Its various specialties include cardiology orthopedics neurology and spine care women's services and bariatric surgery. Other services include cardiac rehabilitation diagnostic services outpatient surgery and senior health care. Parkwest's facilities include a 40-bed emergency care center a 30-bed critical care unit and a 20-suite childbirth center. The medical center also has a diabetes center and provides dental care.

Parkwest opened in 1973 as a joint venture between physicians and Hospital Corporation of America (HCA) the operating subsidiary of HCA Holdings Inc. In 1990 Parkwest became a part of the not-for-profit Fort Sanders Health System which in 1996 became Covenant Health.

Parkwest works to enhance its services to the community through improvements such as the addition of its Riverstone Tower a six-story addition that is part of a $100 million project that covers 326000 sq. ft. of new construction 45000 sq. ft. of renovated space and adds 214 beds.

Parkwest's Peninsula division provides inpatient and outpatient mental health and alcohol and drug crisis stabilization programs through Peninsula Hospital a 155-bed facility for adults adolescents and children and through outpatient centers that include its largest center Peninsula Lighthouse in Knoxville and freestanding facilities in Knox Blount Sevier and Loudon counties. Peninsula also provides support and aftercare services to support patient recovery and to help families. Its services include crisis intervention options for in-home treatment and supportive housing and employment programs to aid with maintaining healthy lifestyles and improving quality of life.

EXECUTIVES

Pharmd, Patty Strickler
Vice President Management, Linda Tillman

LOCATIONS

HQ: PARKWEST MEDICAL CENTER
9352 PARK WEST BLVD, KNOXVILLE, TN 379234387
Phone: 865 373-1000
Web: WWW.TREATEDWELL.COM

PRODUCTS/OPERATIONS

Selected Adult Specialties
Cancer
Cardiology and heart surgery
Diabetes and endocrinology
Ear nose and throat
Gastroenterology

Geriatrics
Gynecology
Nephrology
Neurology and neurosurgery
Orthopedics
Pulmonology
Urology

Selected Outpatient Centers
Parkwest Comprehensive Breast Center
Parkwest Cardiac Rehabilitation
Rehabilitation Outpatient Program
Parkwest Therapy Center

COMPETITORS

Baptist Memorial	Saint Thomas Midtown
Health Care	Hospital
Baptist Memorial	Saint Thomas
Hospital-Memphis	Rutherford Hospital
Blount Memorial	Tennova Healthcare
Hospital	University Health
East Tennessee	System Inc.
Children' s Hospital	Vanderbilt University
Erlanger Health System	Medical Center
Kindred Healthcare	Wellmont Health System
LifePoint Health	

HISTORICAL FINANCIALS
Company Type: Private

Income Statement
FYE: December 31

	REVENUE ($ mil.)	NET INCOME ($ mil.)	NET PROFIT MARGIN	EMPLOYEES
12/13	337	29	8.8%	1,300
12/05	172	5	3.1%	—
12/04	172	5	3.1%	—
12/03	384	0	—	—
Annual Growth	(1.3%)	—	—	—

PARSONS ENVIRONMENT & INFRASTRUCTURE GROUP INC.

A unit of Parsons Corporation Parsons Commercial Technology Group (PARCOMM) provides project management engineering construction design maintenance and related services for industrial and commercial projects. The company's clients include firms in the telecommunications health care manufacturing defense petroleum and chemical industries. PARCOMM also completes projects for schools colleges and government entities. Specialized services include industrial environmental remediation factory modernization and developing state vehicle inspection and compliance programs. PARCOMM operates throughout the US and the world.

LOCATIONS
HQ: PARSONS ENVIRONMENT & INFRASTRUCTURE GROUP INC.
4701 HEDGEMORE DR, CHARLOTTE, NC 282093281
Phone: 704 529-6246
Web: WWW.PARSONS.COM

COMPETITORS

Bechtel	Halliburton
Fluor	Jacobs Engineering

HISTORICAL FINANCIALS
Company Type: Private

Income Statement
FYE: July 29

	REVENUE ($ mil.)	NET INCOME ($ mil.)	NET PROFIT MARGIN	EMPLOYEES
07/14*	684	(12)	—	1,205
12/12	684	(12)	—	—
12/11	443	(57)	—	—
12/10	518	0	—	—
Annual Growth	7.2%	—	—	—
*Fiscal year change

2014 Year-End Financials
Return on assets: 8.2%   Cash ($ mil.): 24
Return on equity: (-1.8%)
Current ratio: 1.30

PARTNERSHIP FOR SUPPLY CHAIN MANAGEMENT INC.

Auditors: GELMAN ROSENBERG & FREEDMAN B

LOCATIONS
HQ: PARTNERSHIP FOR SUPPLY CHAIN MANAGEMENT INC.
1616 FORT MYER DR FL 12, ARLINGTON, VA 222093110
Phone: 571 227-8600
Web: WWW.PFSCM.ORG

HISTORICAL FINANCIALS
Company Type: Private

Income Statement
FYE: September 30

	REVENUE ($ mil.)	NET INCOME ($ mil.)	NET PROFIT MARGIN	EMPLOYEES
09/11	517	(2)	—	120
09/10	389	1	0.4%	—
09/09	0	0	—	—
Annual Growth	—	—	—	—

2011 Year-End Financials
Return on assets: —   Cash ($ mil.): 61
Return on equity: (-0.4%)
Current ratio: 0.60

PATERSON PUBLIC SCHOOL DISTRICT

Auditors: LERCH VINCI & HIGGINS LLP F

LOCATIONS
HQ: PATERSON PUBLIC SCHOOL DISTRICT
90 DELAWARE AVE, PATERSON, NJ 075031804
Phone: 973 321-1000
Web: WWW.INET.PATERSON.K12.NJ.US

HISTORICAL FINANCIALS
Company Type: Private

Income Statement
FYE: June 30

	REVENUE ($ mil.)	NET INCOME ($ mil.)	NET PROFIT MARGIN	EMPLOYEES
06/13	584	(5)	—	3,055
06/11	541	7	1.3%	—
06/05*	0	0	—	—
12/00	300	0	—	—
Annual Growth	5.7%	—	—	—
*Fiscal year change

2013 Year-End Financials
Return on assets: —   Cash ($ mil.): 83
Return on equity: (-1.0%)
Current ratio: —

PATTON BOGGS LLP

EXECUTIVES
Partner Washington D.C. and Co-Chairman Technology and Communications, Kevin J. Martin
Chairman, Thomas Hale Boggs Jr.
Director Professional Recruitment, Kara Reidy
Partner Washington D.C. and Co-Chairman Technology and Communications, Jennifer L. Richter
Vice Chairman, Donald V. Moorehead
Deputy Managing Partner, Charles P. (Charlie) Miller
Managing Partner Greater New York and New Jersey, James E. Tyrell Jr.
Managing Partner Northern Virginia, Douglas C. (Doug) Boggs
Managing Partner New Jersey, John McGahren
COO, Ralph E. Allen Jr.
Managing Partner Denver, Robert M. (Bob) Bearman
Managing Partner Anchorage, Walter T. Featherly
Senior Counsel Washington, Richard L. (Dick) Thompson
Founder of the firms, John F. Jonas
Director Public Relations and Communications, Elliott J. Frieder
Chairman CEO, Jamie Dimon
Owner, Fletcher Burlington
Vice President Broadcast Technology, Jay Adrick
President CEO, Lawrence B. Lindsey
Chairman of the Subcommittee on Commerce, Mary R-CA

LOCATIONS
HQ: PATTON BOGGS LLP
2550 M ST NW STE 200, WASHINGTON, DC 200371302
Phone: 202 457-6000
Web: WWW.PATTONBOGGS.COM

COMPETITORS

Arnold & Porter	Pillsbury Winthrop
Baker Donelson	Shaw Pittman
Covington &	Steptoe & Johnson
Burling	Venable LLP
Hogan Lovells	Vinson & Elkins

HISTORICAL FINANCIALS
Company Type: Private

Income Statement
FYE: December 31

	REVENUE ($ mil.)	NET INCOME ($ mil.)	NET PROFIT MARGIN	EMPLOYEES
12/12	326	130	40.0%	1,023
12/08	355	135	38.0%	—
12/07	310	139	45.1%	—
12/06	1,604	0	—	—
Annual Growth	—	—	—	—

2012 Year-End Financials
Return on assets: —
Return on equity: 40.0%
Current ratio: 1.20

Cash ($ mil.): 39

PAXTON MEDIA GROUP LLC

Paxton Media Group owns about 30 daily newspapers in the Midwest and South including its flagship The Paducah Sun (Kentucky) and The Herald-Sun (Durham North Carolina). The company also owns several dozen weekly papers and more than 100 free papers as well as a television station in Paducah Kentucky. W.F. Paxton launched The Paducah Sun in 1896; his family led by CEO David Paxton continues to run the publishing business.

EXECUTIVES
Publisher and Editor The Paducah Sun, James F. (Jim) Paxton, age 58
Director Human Resources, Eric Rudolph
CFO, Richard E. Paxton
Marketing Manager, Kendra Mitchell
Operations Manager, Tom Maher
Executive Assistant, Janice Johnson
General Manager, Gary Adkisson
Executive Editor, Duke Conover
Advertising Director, Carolyn Raney
Vice President of.., Mark Sheppard
Human resources Director, Mike Park
Auditors: WILLIAMS WILLIAMS & LENTZ CP

LOCATIONS
HQ: PAXTON MEDIA GROUP LLC
201 S 4TH ST, PADUCAH, KY 420031524
Phone: 270 345-3152
Web: WWW.CADIZRECORD.COM

COMPETITORS
Cox Newspapers	Raycom Media
McClatchy Company	Sinclair Broadcast
Media General	Group
News & Record	TEGNA

HISTORICAL FINANCIALS
Company Type: Private

Income Statement
FYE: December 28

	REVENUE ($ mil.)	NET INCOME ($ mil.)	NET PROFIT MARGIN	EMPLOYEES
12/08	188	0	—	2,000
12/06	204	0	—	—
12/05	0	0	—	—
12/03	0	0	—	—
Annual Growth	—	—	—	—

2008 Year-End Financials
Return on assets: 2.1%
Return on equity: —
Current ratio: 0.40

Cash ($ mil.): —

PCL CONSTRUCTION ENTERPRISES INC

PCL Construction Enterprises is the contractor to call on for commercial and civil construction concerns. The company serves as the parent to half a dozen US construction companies: PCL Construction Services PCL Civil Constructors PCL Construction PCL Industrial Services PCL Industrial Construction and Nordic PCL Construction. The companies serve as the operating entities for PCL one of Canada's largest general contracting groups. Having completed projects in nearly every US state PCL Construction Enterprises is active in the commercial institutional multi-family residential heavy industrial and civil construction sectors. PCL first entered the US construction market in 1975.

Geographic Reach

Denver-based PCL Construction Enterprises through its half a dozen operating units concentrates on commercial civil and industrial construction projects located in the US.

Its parent's work spans the US Canada the Caribbean and Australia.

Operations

PCL Construction Enterprises and its subsidiaries work on a variety of projects. PCL Construction Enterprises has completed bridges water and wastewater systems manufacturing plants office buildings and restaurants nationwide.

Like many construction companies PCL was hit by the economic recession. Backlogs were lacking and new projects became tougher to win due to an increase in competition. Contracts with water wastewater and renewable energy projects and universities have helped PCL Construction Enterprises through the downturn.

Sales and Marketing

PCL caters to customers in three primary sectors: commercial buildings civil infrastructure and heavy industrial construction. Clients have included the Alaska Railroad Corporation US Army Corps of Engineers Shaw Constructors and OUC-The Reliable One.

Its markets span big cities in Alaska Georgia California North Carolina Texas Colorado Hawaii Minnesota Florida Arizona and Washington.

EXECUTIVES
Vice President And District Manager, Dave Yount
Auditors: KPMG LLP EDMONTON CANADA

LOCATIONS
HQ: PCL CONSTRUCTION ENTERPRISES INC
2000 S COLOR BLVD TOWER T, DENVER, CO 80222
Phone: 303 365-6500
Web: WWW.ENTERPRISES.PCL.COM

PRODUCTS/OPERATIONS

Selected Operating Companies
Nordic PCL Construction Inc.
PCL Civil Constructors Inc.
PCL Construction Inc.
PCL Construction Services Inc.
PCL Industrial Construction Co.
PCL Industrial Services Inc.

COMPETITORS
Adolfson & Peterson Inc.	M. B. Kahn
Andersen Construction	Skanska USA Civil
Brasfield & Gorrie	Suffolk Construction
C.W. Driver	TIC Holdings
Dimeo Construction	Torix General
FCI Constructors	Contractors
Fluor	Turner Corporation
Gilbane Building Company	

HISTORICAL FINANCIALS
Company Type: Private

Income Statement
FYE: October 31

	REVENUE ($ mil.)	NET INCOME ($ mil.)	NET PROFIT MARGIN	EMPLOYEES
10/10	1,616	23	1.5%	3,300
10/09	2,182	52	2.4%	—
Annual Growth	(25.9%)	(55.3%)	—	—

2010 Year-End Financials
Return on assets: 10.1%
Return on equity: 1.5%
Current ratio: 0.90

Cash ($ mil.): 95

PCL INDUSTRIAL CONSTRUCTION CO.

Auditors: KPMG LLP EDMONTON CANADA

LOCATIONS
HQ: PCL INDUSTRIAL CONSTRUCTION CO.
6445 SHILOH RD STE E, ALPHARETTA, GA 300058407
Phone: 678 965-3100
Web: WWW.TETONINDUSTRIAL.COM

HISTORICAL FINANCIALS
Company Type: Private

Income Statement
FYE: October 31

	REVENUE ($ mil.)	NET INCOME ($ mil.)	NET PROFIT MARGIN	EMPLOYEES
10/09	313	20	6.6%	800
10/08	341	32	9.5%	—
10/03	1,417	0	0.0%	—
Annual Growth	(22.2%)	229.2%	—	—

2009 Year-End Financials
Return on assets: 4.0%
Return on equity: 6.6%
Current ratio: 1.00

Cash ($ mil.): 53

PDS TECH INC.

Need an IT pro to assist with your company's computer needs? PDS Tech wants to help. The company provides temporary technical industrial and general staffing services through more than 30 offices across the US with a concentration in Texas and on the East Coast. PDS Tech's specialties include aviation architecture engineering information technology administration and maritime staffing. Its PDS Engineering division handles engineering placement for the aerospace mechanical and structural engineering industries while the Information Services division offers technical consulting services in the IT and telecommunication industries. The company was founded in 1977 by aerospace engineer Art Janes.

EXECUTIVES

CEO, Arthur R. (Art) Janes
President CFO and General Counsel, Steven Cash Nickerson
Controller, Allen Wilson
VP Business Development, Rick Vogel
Auditors: BKM SOWAN & HORAN ADDISON TE

LOCATIONS

HQ: PDS TECH INC.
1925 W J CARPENTR FWY 5, IRVING, TX 75063
Phone: 214 647-9600
Web: WWW.PDSTECH.COM

PRODUCTS/OPERATIONS

PDS Operating Divisions
PDS Engineering
PDS Aviation
PDS Information Services
PDS Maritime
PDS Professional/General
Offload Engineering
Northwest

Selected Industries
Aerospace
Automotive
Civil/Architectural
Electronics
Energy
Financial Services
Government
Medical Defense/Military
Software
Telecommunications

COMPETITORS

Adecco	ManpowerGroup
Allegis Group	On Assignment
Butler America	StarTek
CDI	Volt Information
COMFORCE	

HISTORICAL FINANCIALS

Company Type: Private

Income Statement

FYE: December 29

	REVENUE ($ mil.)	NET INCOME ($ mil.)	NET PROFIT MARGIN	EMPLOYEES
12/13	373	1	0.3%	10,000
12/12	436	2	0.6%	—
12/11	397	5	1.3%	—
12/10	338	0	—	—
Annual Growth	3.3%	—	—	—

2013 Year-End Financials

Return on assets: 0.4%   Cash ($ mil.): 9
Return on equity: 0.3%
Current ratio: 4.10

PEACEHEALTH

PeaceHealth provides patients with a tranquil place to recover. Make that several tranquil places to recover. PeaceHealth serves residents in southeastern Alaska coastal regions of Washington and central portions of Oregon. Its medical centers include PeaceHealth Ketchikan Medical Center PeaceHealth St. Joseph Medical Center PeaceHealth St. John Medical Center Sacred Heart Medical Center (two campuses) Cottage Grove Community Hospital Peace Harbor Hospital PeaceHealth Peace Island Medical Center and PeaceHealth Southwest Medical Center. Other operations include physician practices community clinics hospices chemical dependency rehabilitation clinics and other outpatient facilities and services.

Operations

In all PeaceHealth has about 16000 acute beds and 30 nursing home beds. It has some 16000 caregivers and a multi-specialty medical group practice with more than 800 physicians. It also has 10 medical centers in both rural and urban communities throughout the Northwest.

In 2014 the system reported more than 72000 inpatient admissions and nearly 746000 outpatient registrations as well as 1.2 million patient encounters with its medical group. It had more than 8000 infant births and more than 302000 emergency department visits that year.

Sales and Marketing

Commercial and other payers accounted for 52% of net patient revenue in 2013 while Medicare accounted for 36%.

Financial Performance

Revenue decreased by just under 1% to $2.2 billion in 2013 due to a decline in premiums. However net income rose to $142 million (versus a net loss in 2012) due to an increase in investment returns and other changes. Cash flow from operations fell 1% to $174 million as more cash was used in accounts receivable.

Company Background

PeaceHealth was formed in 1923 by the Sisters of St. Joseph of Peace who opened the Little Flower Hospital in Ketchikan named after Saint Teresa. The Sisters of St. Joseph of Peace had previously opened St. Joseph Hospital in Bellingham in 1891.

PeaceHealth and Southwest Washington Health System merged in early 2011 boosting PeaceHealth's hospital holdings from six to eight with the addition of the two-campus Southwest Washington Medical Center in Vancouver Washington.

Under terms of the affiliation Southwest Washington Health System became part of PeaceHealth allowing Southwest to benefit from its larger peer's medical and financial resources. The move allows both health systems to increase the scope of services they offer in Washington State where Southwest Washington Health System also operates clinics a medical group and a foundation through which it conducts fundraising efforts.

EXECUTIVES

CEO, Liz Dunne, age 59
President PeaceHealth Medical Group, Michael Metcalf
SVP Ambulatory Services, Nancy Steiger
SVP and Interim CFO, Peggy Allen
System VP Marketing Communication and Public Affairs, Kathy Dean
COO, Beth O'Brien
President Hospital Services Northwest, Dale Zender
SVP and Chief Medical Officer, Michael Murphy
SVP and Chief Nursing Officer, Victoria King
SVP and CIO, Dan Hein
President Hospital Services Oregon, Rand O'Leary
Senior Vice President Knowledge and Information; CIO, Ryan Ball
Vice President Ambulatory Services, Michele Budd
Vice President Strategy Innovation and Development, Kristopher Kitz
Senior Vice President, Carol Aaron
Vice President of Operations NW Network, Stacey Zierath
Chairman, Andrea Nenzel
Auditors: KPMG LLP SEATTLE WA

LOCATIONS

HQ: PEACEHEALTH
1115 SE 164TH AVE # 334, VANCOUVER, WA 986839324
Phone: 425 747-1711
Web: WWW.PEACEHEALTH.ORG

PRODUCTS/OPERATIONS

2013 Sales

	$ mil.	% of total
Patient service revenue	1,984	92
Premium revenue	93	4
Other operating revenue	94	4
Total	**2,171**	**100**

Selected Hospitals

PeaceHealth Ketchikan Medical Center (Ketchikan Alaska)
Cottage Grove Community Hospital (Cottage Grove Oregon)
Peace Harbor Hospital (Florence Oregon)
PeaceHealth Peace Island Medical Center (Friday Harbor Washington)
PeaceHealth Southwest Medical Center (Vancouver Washington)
PeaceHealth St. John Medical Center (Longview Washington)
PeaceHealth St. Joseph Medical Center (Bellingham Washington)
Sacred Heart Medical Center at RiverBend (Springfield Oregon)
Sacred Heart Medical Center University District (Eugene Oregon)
Other Operations
PeaceHealth Laboratories (locations throughout Oregon and Washington)
PeaceHealth Medical Group (operates in Alaska Oregon and Washington)

COMPETITORS

Alaska Native Tribal Health Consortium	Providence Health & Services
Franciscan Health System	Seattle Children's Hospital
HCA	South Peninsula Hospital
Harrison Medical Center	Swedish Health Services
Immediate Care	
MultiCare Health System	Tenet Healthcare
Overlake Hospital	Yakima Valley Memorial

HISTORICAL FINANCIALS

Company Type: Private

Income Statement

FYE: June 30

	REVENUE ($ mil.)	NET INCOME ($ mil.)	NET PROFIT MARGIN	EMPLOYEES
06/09	1,372	(88)	—	6,690
06/06	1,048	103	9.8%	—
06/05	978	40	4.2%	—
06/04	885	0	—	—
Annual Growth	9.2%	—	—	—

2009 Year-End Financials

Return on assets: 4.0%   Cash ($ mil.): 145
Return on equity: (-6.5%)
Current ratio: 1.30

PEARCE INDUSTRIES INC.

LOCATIONS

HQ: PEARCE INDUSTRIES INC.
12320 MAIN ST, HOUSTON, TX 770356206
Phone: 713 723-1050
Web: WWW.WPI.COM

HISTORICAL FINANCIALS

Company Type: Private

Income Statement
FYE: March 31

	REVENUE ($ mil.)	NET INCOME ($ mil.)	NET PROFIT MARGIN	EMPLOYEES
03/14	515	16	3.3%	750
03/13	469	16	3.5%	—
03/03	240	(6)	—	—
03/02	266	0	—	—
Annual Growth	5.6%	—	—	—

2014 Year-End Financials
Return on assets: 9.9%   Cash ($ mil.): 8
Return on equity: 3.3%
Current ratio: 0.90

PENNINSULA REGIONAL MEDICAL CENTER

Auditors: ERNST & YOUNG LLP

LOCATIONS

HQ: PENNINSULA REGIONAL MEDICAL CENTER
10514 RACETRACK RD STE C, BERLIN, MD
218113241
Phone: 410 641-8585
Web: WWW.PENINSULA.ORG

HISTORICAL FINANCIALS

Company Type: Private

Income Statement
FYE: June 30

	REVENUE ($ mil.)	NET INCOME ($ mil.)	NET PROFIT MARGIN	EMPLOYEES
06/08	362	14	4.1%	8
06/05	274	18	6.7%	—
Annual Growth	9.7%	(6.7%)	—	—

2008 Year-End Financials
Return on assets: —   Cash ($ mil.): 29
Return on equity: 4.1%
Current ratio: 1.60

PEPPER CONSTRUCTION COMPANY

Auditors: DELOITTE & TOUCHE LLP CHICAGO

LOCATIONS

HQ: PEPPER CONSTRUCTION COMPANY
643 N ORLEANS ST, CHICAGO, IL 606543690
Phone: 312 266-4700
Web: WWW.PEPPERCONSTRUCTION.COM

HISTORICAL FINANCIALS

Company Type: Private

Income Statement
FYE: September 30

	REVENUE ($ mil.)	NET INCOME ($ mil.)	NET PROFIT MARGIN	EMPLOYEES
09/12	673	12	1.9%	900
09/11	668	4	0.6%	—
09/10	503	4	0.9%	—
09/09	592	0	—	—
Annual Growth	4.4%	—	—	—

2012 Year-End Financials
Return on assets: 16.5%   Cash ($ mil.): 25
Return on equity: 1.9%
Current ratio: 0.20

PEPPER CONSTRUCTION GROUP LLC

Pepper Construction Group spices up the construction business with a little of this and a pinch of that. The company provides general contracting and construction management services for commercial office education entertainment health care and institutional clients as well as waterworks projects. (Health care projects account for about 50% of Pepper's revenue.) Its client list includes UBS Northwestern University University of Notre Dame Texas Heart Institute Loyola University Medical Center and NASA. Pepper Construction Group has divisions in Illinois Indiana Ohio and Texas. Stanley F. Pepper founded the company in Chicago in 1927. The group is owned by his family and employees of the firm.

Geographic Reach

Chicago-based Pepper Construction comprises four geographic divisions: Illinois; Indiana; Ohio; and Texas. Overall the company is active in about 20 states mostly in the central and northeastern states.

Operations

The company's Pepper Environmental Technologies unit provides environmental services. Green building has become a large part of Pepper Construction's operations. Its Green Team of certified professionals have helped construct more than 2.9 million sq. ft. of eco-friendly space. The Green Team has built the Apple Computer flagship store HSBC Chicago North and Kohl's Children's Museum.

The firm's Pepper-Lawson Waterworks group constructs water purification plants for municipal clients including Houston and Missouri City Texas.

EXECUTIVES

SVP Marketing; President Pepper Environmental Technologies, Richard H. (Rich) Tilghman
Chairman and CEO, J. David (Dave) Pepper II
EVP and General Counsel, Thomas M. (Tom) O'Leary
SVP and CFO, Joel D. Thomason
President Pepper Construction Company of Indiana, William J. (Bill) McCarthy
President Emeritus Pepper-Lawson Construction Company in Texas, Paul E. Lawson
President and COO Pepper Construction Company, Kenneth A. (Ken) Egidi
VP of Information Technology, Howie Piersma
President Pepper Construction Company of Ohio, Paul Francois
CEO of Rivers Casino, Greg Carlin
Chairman, Neil Bluhm
President Pepper-Lawson Construction Company in Texas, Jason Lawson
Auditors: DELOITTE & TOUCHE LLP CHICAGO

LOCATIONS

HQ: PEPPER CONSTRUCTION GROUP LLC
643 N ORLEANS ST, CHICAGO, IL 606543690
Phone: 312 266-4703
Web: WWW.PEPPERCONSTRUCTION.COM

PRODUCTS/OPERATIONS

Selected Operations
Pepper Construction Group LLC (Chicago Illinois)
Pepper Construction Co. (Chicago Illinois)
Pepper Construction Co. of Indiana (Indianapolis Indiana)
Pepper Construction Co. of Ohio LLC (Dublin Ohio)
Pepper Environmental Technologies Inc. (Barrington Illinois)
Pepper-Lawson Construction LP (Houston Texas)
Pepper-Lawson Waterworks LLC (Houston Texas)

COMPETITORS

Barton Malow	Graycor
Bulley & Andrews	M. A. Mortenson
C. G. Schmidt	McCarthy Building
Charles Pankow Builders	Power Construction
Clark Enterprises	Turner Corporation
Gilbane	Walbridge Aldinger
	Walsh Group

HISTORICAL FINANCIALS

Company Type: Private

Income Statement
FYE: September 30

	REVENUE ($ mil.)	NET INCOME ($ mil.)	NET PROFIT MARGIN	EMPLOYEES
09/11	911	15	1.7%	1,100
09/10	911	15	1.7%	—
Annual Growth	(0.0%)	(0.0%)	—	—

2011 Year-End Financials
Return on assets: 0.1%   Cash ($ mil.): 1
Return on equity: 1.7%
Current ratio: 0.50

PEREZ TRADING COMPANY INC.

No matter how you say it paper or el papel Perez Trading has it. From its Miami warehouse the company distributes more than 15000 tons of paper and paperboard inventory including corrugated box equipment napkin paper printing paper and other printing and shipping equipment and supplies. Customers include commercial printers converters distributors and packaging manufacturers. Perez Trading imports and exports to nearly 30 countries encompassing the Caribbean Islands Central and South America Mexico and the US. Perez Trading has been family owned and operated since 1947.

EXECUTIVES

Vice President Marketing, Roberta Perez
Auditors: BERKOWITZ POLLACK BRANT MIAMI

LOCATIONS

HQ: PEREZ TRADING COMPANY INC.
 3490 NW 125TH ST, MIAMI, FL 331672412
Phone: 305 769-0761
Web: WWW.PEREZTRADING.COM

COMPETITORS

Georgia-Pacific   International Paper

HISTORICAL FINANCIALS

Company Type: Private

Income Statement   FYE: December 31

	REVENUE ($ mil.)	NET INCOME ($ mil.)	NET PROFIT MARGIN	EMPLOYEES
12/13	526	16	3.2%	148
12/12	570	20	3.6%	—
12/11	532	18	3.5%	—
12/10	492	0	—	—
Annual Growth	2.3%	—	—	—

2013 Year-End Financials

Return on assets: —
Return on equity: 3.2%
Current ratio: 1.50
Cash ($ mil.): —

PERISHABLE DISTRIBUTORS OF IOWA LTD.

Auditors: RSM MCCLADREY DES MOINES IOW

LOCATIONS

HQ: PERISHABLE DISTRIBUTORS OF IOWA LTD.
 2741 SE PDI PL, ANKENY, IA 500213958
Phone: 515 965-6300
Web: WWW.HY-VEE.COM

HISTORICAL FINANCIALS

Company Type: Private

Income Statement   FYE: September 29

	REVENUE ($ mil.)	NET INCOME ($ mil.)	NET PROFIT MARGIN	EMPLOYEES
09/13	1,056	25	2.4%	500
09/12*	1,007	22	2.3%	—
10/11	896	20	2.3%	—
10/10	835	0	—	—
Annual Growth	8.1%	—	—	—

*Fiscal year change

2013 Year-End Financials

Return on assets: 4.3%
Return on equity: 2.4%
Current ratio: 0.70
Cash ($ mil.): 17

PETERSBURG MOTOR COMPANY INC

Auditors: MITCHELL WIGGINS & COMPANY L

LOCATIONS

HQ: PETERSBURG MOTOR COMPANY INC
 100 MYERS DR, CHARLOTTESVILLE, VA 229011166
Phone: 434 951-1000
Web: WWW.COLONIALAUTOCENTER.COM

HISTORICAL FINANCIALS

Company Type: Private

Income Statement   FYE: December 31

	REVENUE ($ mil.)	NET INCOME ($ mil.)	NET PROFIT MARGIN	EMPLOYEES
12/13	319	4	1.4%	388
12/12	269	3	1.3%	—
12/11	204	3	1.6%	—
12/09	129	0	—	—
Annual Growth	25.4%	—	—	—

2013 Year-End Financials

Return on assets: 1.1%
Return on equity: 1.4%
Current ratio: 0.40
Cash ($ mil.): 7

PETR-ALL PETROLEUM CONSULTING CORP.

LOCATIONS

HQ: PETR-ALL PETROLEUM CONSULTING CORP.
 6567 KINNE RD, DE WITT, NY 132141923
Phone: 315 446-0125
Web: WWW.EXPRESSMART.COM

HISTORICAL FINANCIALS

Company Type: Private

Income Statement   FYE: December 31

	REVENUE ($ mil.)	NET INCOME ($ mil.)	NET PROFIT MARGIN	EMPLOYEES
12/13	482	0	0.0%	600
12/12	473	2	0.5%	—
12/11*	471	2	0.6%	—
07/11	400	0	—	—
Annual Growth	9.8%	—	—	—

*Fiscal year change

2013 Year-End Financials

Return on assets: 2.7%
Return on equity: —
Current ratio: 0.30
Cash ($ mil.): 2

PETRO STAR INC.

Petro Star is an oil refining and fuel marketing shining star that brings heating fuel and energy (diesel gasoline and aviation and marine fuel)s to the citizens of the communities in the vast cold and lonely expanses of the US' largest state Alaska. It operates refineries at North Pole and Valdez and distributes fuels and lubricants throughout Interior Alaska Dutch Harbor Kodiak and Valdez. Started in 1984 by a group of petroleum industry veterans the company built its first refinery operations along the Trans-Alaska Pipeline at North Pole Alaska. Petro Star is a subsidiary of Arctic Slope Regional Corp..

The company has expanded through acquisitions including fuel distribution firm Sourdough Fuel (in 1986) as well as the 1991 purchase of Alaska Lube and Fuel (now Petro Star Lubricants). Kodiak Sales (in 1997) and North Pacific Fuel (in 1998).

In 2008 Petro Star secured a $158.7 million aviation fuel contract from the Defense Logistics Agency.

EXECUTIVES

VP Heating Fuel and Marine, Don Castle
Director North Pacific Fuel Operations, Mark Hughes

LOCATIONS

HQ: PETRO STAR INC.
 3900 C ST STE 802, ANCHORAGE, AK 995035963
Phone: 907 339-6600
Web: WWW.PETROSTAR.COM

COMPETITORS

Exxon Mobil   Valero Energy
Tesoro

HISTORICAL FINANCIALS

Company Type: Private

Income Statement   FYE: December 31

	REVENUE ($ mil.)	NET INCOME ($ mil.)	NET PROFIT MARGIN	EMPLOYEES
12/08	992	0	—	300
12/03	291	3	1.2%	—
12/02	267	1	0.7%	—
12/01	279	0	—	—
Annual Growth	19.9%	—	—	—

2008 Year-End Financials

Return on assets: 7.0%
Return on equity: —
Current ratio: 1.50
Cash ($ mil.): 106

PETROCARD INC.

LOCATIONS

HQ: PETROCARD INC.
 730 CENTRAL AVE S, KENT, WA 980326109
Phone: 253 852-7801
Web: WWW.PETROCARD.COM

HISTORICAL FINANCIALS

Company Type: Private

Income Statement   FYE: March 31

	REVENUE ($ mil.)	NET INCOME ($ mil.)	NET PROFIT MARGIN	EMPLOYEES
03/13	1,097	5	0.5%	190
03/12	1,173	0	0.1%	—
03/11	948	3	0.4%	—
03/10	791	0	—	—
Annual Growth	11.5%	—	—	—

2013 Year-End Financials
Return on assets: 1.9%   Cash ($ mil.): 2
Return on equity: 0.5%
Current ratio: —

PETROLEUM TRADERS CORPORATION

Petroleum Traders Corporation barters with fuel. The company provides wholesale gasoline diesel fuel and heating oil to fuel distributors government agencies and other large consumers of fuel such as businesses with vehicle fleets. The largest pure wholesale fuel distributor in the country Petroleum Traders operates and trades in 44 US states. It supplies #1 and #2 low sulfur diesel fuels biodiesel high sulfur heating oil and kerosene and conventional ethanol and reformulated blends of gasoline in regular midgrade and premium octane ratings.

Operations

Petroleum Traders focuses on supplying wholesale diesel and gasoline exclusively in the US offering a range of turnkey wholesale diesel fuel and wholesale gasoline fuel services.

Sales and Marketing

The company provides discount fuel to commercial government and wholesale customers. In the commercial space it services the trucking construction railroad mining and manufacturing industries as well as utilities and private fleets.

Strategy

Petroleum Traders parlays its hedging experience into fuel cost management for its customers via firm pricing cap programs collars and fuel swaps.

Company Background

The company was founded in 1979.

EXECUTIVES

Vice President, Vicky Himes
Auditors: BADEN GAGE & SCHROEDER LLC

LOCATIONS

HQ: PETROLEUM TRADERS CORPORATION
7120 POINTE INVERNESS WAY, FORT WAYNE, IN
468047928
Phone: 260 432-6622
Web: WWW.PETROLEUMTRADERS.COM

COMPETITORS

George Warren	Petro Holdings
Gulf Oil	Sun Coast Resources
Martin Resource Management	

HISTORICAL FINANCIALS

Company Type: Private

Income Statement

FYE: June 30

	REVENUE ($ mil.)	NET INCOME ($ mil.)	NET PROFIT MARGIN	EMPLOYEES
06/14	2,670	14	0.6%	110
06/13	3,066	24	0.8%	—
06/12	2,796	13	0.5%	—
06/11	2,470	0	—	—
Annual Growth	2.6%	—	—	—

2014 Year-End Financials

Return on assets: 1.5%   Cash ($ mil.): 9
Return on equity: 0.6%
Current ratio: 1.90

PHELPS MEMORIAL HOSPITAL ASSOCIATION

If you happen to spot the headless horseman in Sleepy Hollow it's possible he's on his way to Phelps Memorial Hospital for some medical treatment. The 240-bed hospital provides both physical and mental health care services to residents of Sleepy Hollow and Westchester County New York. Specialized services include cardiology emergency care orthopedics and psychiatry. It also includes a satellite location of the Memorial Sloan-Kettering Cancer Center and it provides geriatric health services through a partnership with Mount Sinai Hospital and operates a senior retirement community with Kendal Corporation. Phelps Memorial is one of four hospitals that make up the Stellaris Health Network.

Geographic Reach

Phelps Memorial is located on a 70-acre campus on the banks of the Hudson River in Sleepy Hollow. The company serves Westchester County and surrounding communities in Rockland Putnam and Dutchess Counties in New York and Fairfield County in Connecticut.

Operations

Phelps Memorial Hospital handles some 27000 emergency room visits each year. Its maternity wing also managed more than 1000 birthing procedures and the hospital's counseling unit saw about 18000 patients. Other specialty divisions provide stroke care and home health and hospice services. The medical center operates family and specialty physician practices and mental health clinics in the region.

Through its affiliation with Mount Sinai Hospital (and therefore the Sinai Health System) Phelps Memorial's patients and physicians have access to specialized services from Mount Sinai Hospital. It also provides prenatal and high-risk pregnancy care in partnership with area providers Open Door Family Medical Centers and Westchester Medical Center. The hospital is a teaching facility for family medicine and dental residency programs through an affiliation with New York Medical College.

The other hospitals in the Stellaris network are Lawrence Hospital Center Northern Westchester Hospital and White Plains Hospital Center. The medical centers operate independently but pool resources in areas including information technology procurement and best practices.

The company's 500 medical staff members represent 60 medical specialties.

Strategy

The hospital's primary goals include enhancing the convenience of its services and increasing patient satisfaction. Phelps Memorial has gone through major renovations in recent years more than doubling its size with the addition of a new emergency department new offices more inpatient beds and an inpatient pediatrics unit.

In 2014 Phelps Memorial opened its new SurgiCenter in New York State. That year it also established the Phelps Balance Center to offer comprehensive testing and rehabilitation for individuals who have problems with dizziness and imbalance.

In 2013 it expanded services by launching new asthma treatment and lung nodule screening programs; it also opened a new family and diagnostic facility (Phelps at Croton) that year.

Company Background

Phelps Memorial restructured its west wing in 2011; the facility now houses its pre-surgical assessment pain management registration and outpatient laboratory departments.

The hospital was first opened in 1955.

EXECUTIVES

Vice President Support Services, Kerry Pisano
Assistant Vice President Quality and Case Management, William (Bill) Reifer
Medical Director of the Thoracic Center, Avraham Merav
Senior Vp, Dan Blum
Respiratory Therapy Director, Mike McGrath
Admissions Director, Patricia Espinoza
Medical Director Physical Medicine And Rehabilita, Wei Liu
Infection Control Director, Anita Watson
Ambulatory Services Director, Martha Maresco
Auditors: JH COHN LLP NEW YORK NY

LOCATIONS

HQ: PHELPS MEMORIAL HOSPITAL ASSOCIATION
701 N BROADWAY, SLEEPY HOLLOW, NY 105911096
Phone: 914 366-3000
Web: WWW.PHELPSHOSPITAL.ORG

PRODUCTS/OPERATIONS

Selected Services
Alcohol & Substance Abuse Treatment
Behavioral Health
Blood Donor Services
Bone Densitometry
Cardiac Rehabilitation
Cardiovascular Laboratory
Cardiovascular Risk Assessment
Critical Care Unit
Decontamination Unit
Diabetes -
Diabetes -
Electroconvulsive Therapy
Emergency Services
Emergency Training Services
Endoscopy
Gastroenterology
Geriatrics
Hand Therapy
Health Management
Hearing (Audiology)
Hernia Center
Hip
Hospice
Hyperbaric Medicine
Incontinence
Infusion Center
Laboratory Services
Lung Nodule Center
Lymphedema
Mammography
Maternity
Memory Loss
Mental Health Services
MRI
Nutrition Counseling for Outpatients
Oncology - Memorial Sloan-Kettering Cancer Center
Orthopedics
Ostomy - O
Pain Center
Palliative Care
Pediatric Endocrinology
Pediatrics
Pharmacy
Physical Rehabilitation
Psychiatry
Pulmonology & Respiratory
Radiology
Respiratory Care
Respite
Senior Health & Internal Medicine
Sleep Disorders
Speech
Stroke Center
Swallowing Disorders

COMPETITORS

Bergen Regional Medical	Montefiore Medical
Burke Rehabilitation	Nyack Hospital
	The Valley Hospital

Hospital
Englewood Hospital and
Medical Center
Greenwich Hospital

Valley Health System
Westchester Medical
Center

HISTORICAL FINANCIALS
Company Type: Private

Income Statement
FYE: December 31

	REVENUE ($ mil.)	NET INCOME ($ mil.)	NET PROFIT MARGIN	EMPLOYEES
12/09	182	5	3.2%	1,200
12/06	135	5	4.0%	—
12/05	129	5	4.4%	—
12/04	124	0	—	—
Annual Growth	7.9%	—	—	—

2009 Year-End Financials
Return on assets: —
Return on equity: 3.2%
Current ratio: 0.80
Cash ($ mil.): 13

PHILLIPS AND JORDAN INCORPORATED

While some like to clear the air Phillips and Jordan (P&J) prefers to clear the land. Founded in 1952 as a small land clearing firm P&J is a general and specialty contractor that still provides land clearing services in addition to industrial commercial and residential site development and heavy civil construction on dams highways bridges railroads and waterways. P&J also performs reclamation landfill and disaster recovery services. The latter includes handling some of the nation's worst disaster cleanups including hurricanes floods toxic spills and land and rock slides. P&J operates about a dozen offices in eight states. The Phillips family owns and runs the company.

Geographic Reach

Knoxville Tennessee-based Phillips and Jordan has about a dozen offices in North Carolina and in California Florida North Dakota Tennessee and Wyoming.

Operations

Phillips and Jordan operates a fleet of more than 850 pieces of heavy and specialized equipment including excavators graders loaders tractors and trucks. The firm performs projects across the US.

True to its roots the company has built a reputation for taking on difficult land clearing jobs. With a fleet of specialized equipment P&J clears and grubs swamp forest mountain and agricultural land to make way for reservoirs pipelines power transmission lines railways and roadways. Clients come from both the public and private sectors.

Strategy

The booming oil and gas industry in Wyoming has drawn P&J to the state where in late 2013 it opened two rock pits in the Douglas area. The pits are managed from the firm's Douglas office. Also in 2013 P&J partnered with North Creek Energy to form a joint venture company Solar Jack LLC to market a system that offers oil and gas producers the opportunity to capture the regenerated energy from their pump jacks combined with solar energy to reduce energy consumption and costs. Previously the firm expanded its operations near Williston North Dakota opening an equipment maintenance shop and offices there in 2012.

EXECUTIVES
Vice President Nc Clearing Div, Randy Jordan
Vice President, Morgan Pierce
Vice President Fl Heavy Div, Stanley (Stan) Croy
Vice President of Information Technology and Technical Operations, Ronald W (Ron) Oakley
Vice President Human Resources, Jolana Carpenter
Auditors: RODEFER MOSS & CO PLLC KNOXVI

LOCATIONS
HQ: PHILLIPS AND JORDAN INCORPORATED
10201 PARKSIDE DR STE 300, KNOXVILLE, TN
379221983
Phone: 865 688-8342
Web: WWW.PANDJ.COM

PRODUCTS/OPERATIONS

Selected Services
Apartment site development
Debris management
Disaster recovery
Earthmoving & erosion control
Heavy civil construction
Industrial and commercial site development
Land clearing
Landfill and liner design
Reclamation and mitigation
Storm drainage
Subdivision site development

COMPETITORS

Boh Bros Construction
Clarkson Construction
Environmental Safety & Health
Hardaway Construction

McCarthy Building
Peter Kiewit Sons'
Rentenbach Constructors

HISTORICAL FINANCIALS
Company Type: Private

Income Statement
FYE: December 31

	REVENUE ($ mil.)	NET INCOME ($ mil.)	NET PROFIT MARGIN	EMPLOYEES
12/13	215	4	2.1%	650
12/12	284	11	4.0%	—
12/11	356	12	3.4%	—
12/10	261	0	—	—
Annual Growth	(6.3%)	—	—	—

2013 Year-End Financials
Return on assets: 3.1%
Return on equity: 2.1%
Current ratio: 2.00
Cash ($ mil.): 13

PHOENIX CHILDREN'S HOSPITAL INC.

Phoenix Children's Hospital (PCH) invests in the health of the next generation. Founded in 1983 the hospital provides a comprehensive range of medical services specifically for children and adolescents in the greater Phoenix area. The hospital has about 360 beds and provides care in a number of pediatric sub-specialties including childhood cancers hematology neuroscience heart disease trauma and orthopedics. In addition to a newborn intensive care unit (NICU) at its main campus PCH operates a second NICU on the campus of Banner Good Samaritan Regional Medical Center (a member of Banner Health).

Geographic Reach

PCH has several pediatric outpatient care centers in surrounding Phoenix suburbs.

Financial Performance

The hospital's revenue increased by 33% to $669 million in fiscal 2012 compared to fiscal 2011. Its net income was $28 million in fiscal 2012.

Strategy

To meet population growth levels in the region PCH is working to expand its medical center facilities. For instance in 2012 the hospital completed a multi-year $588 million construction project; the effort started in 2008 and increased the number of hospital beds from 350 to to 465. Capacity for specialties that include ICU operating rooms trauma care neurology sports medicine and pediatric research were also added in the new patient tower. The expansion efforts also allow PCH to accommodate patients from other areas of Arizona and surrounding states in the Southwest.

PCH added further to its research and educational operations by forming an affiliation with University of Arizona's College of Medicine in 2010. The two entities collaborate on research projects and physician training programs. PCH has additional clinical and non-clinical research collaborations with other institutions to make advances in pediatric care such as Mayo Clinic Translational Genomics Institute and the Children's Oncology Group.

EXECUTIVES
President and CEO, Robert L. Meyer
VP and Chief Medical Officer, Murray M. Pollack
EVP Phoenix Children?s Medical Group and Surgeon-in-Chief, Dennis P. Lund
EVP Finance and CFO, Craig L. McKnight
EVP and COO, Betsy Kuzas
SVP and Chief Information Officer, David Higginson
SVP Patient Care and Chief Nursing Officer, Pamela J. Carlson
VP and Chief Medical Information Officer, Vinay Vaidya
SVP and Chief Administrative Officer Phoenix ChildrenÂ's Medical Group, Roger Logan
President Phoenix Children's Medical Staff, Jeffrey P. Morray
Chairman Phoenix Children's Hospital Foundation Board of Directors, Brian Swartz
Vice President Managed Care, Ethel Hoffman
Vice President Information Technology, Brian Meyer
Vice President Employee Relations, Mark Thomas
Radiology Director, William Barta
Vice President Quality And Risk Management, Tamara Johnson
Senior Vice President Business Development and Chief Strategy Officer, Robert (Bob) Campbell
Director Of Radiology Services, John Underwood
Respiratory Therapy Director, Christine Tenaglia
Vice President of Critical Care Services, Julie Bowman
Medical Director of Research for Gastroenterology, Mitchell (Mitch) Shub
Chairman, Mark B. Bonsall
Vice Chairman, Jon Hulburd
Auditors: ERNST & YOUNG US LLP PHOENIX

LOCATIONS
HQ: PHOENIX CHILDREN' S HOSPITAL INC.
1919 E THOMAS RD, PHOENIX, AZ 850167710
Phone: 602 546-1000
Web: WWW.SURGERY4CHILDREN.COM

COMPETITORS

Banner Health
Dignity Health
Flagstaff Medical Center
John C. Lincoln Health

Scottsdale Healthcare
Shriners Hospitals For Children
University of Arizona Health Network

Network
Northern Arizona
Healthcare

HISTORICAL FINANCIALS
Company Type: Private

Income Statement
FYE: December 31

	REVENUE ($ mil.)	NET INCOME ($ mil.)	NET PROFIT MARGIN	EMPLOYEES
12/13	655	31	4.9%	3,000
12/11	498	(5)	—	—
12/09	408	106	26.1%	—
12/08	424	0	—	—
Annual Growth	9.1%	—	—	—

2013 Year-End Financials
Return on assets: 15.3%   Cash ($ mil.): 64
Return on equity: 4.9%
Current ratio: 0.20

PIEDMONT HEALTH CARE AUTHORITY

LOCATIONS
HQ: PIEDMONT HEALTH CARE AUTHORITY
  30 ROUNDTREE DR, PIEDMONT, AL 362725892
Phone: 256 447-8258
Web: WWW.PIEDMONTHC.COM

HISTORICAL FINANCIALS
Company Type: Private

Income Statement
FYE: June 30

	REVENUE ($ mil.)	NET INCOME ($ mil.)	NET PROFIT MARGIN	EMPLOYEES
06/09	579	25	4.3%	135
06/98	2	0	3.3%	—
06/97	2	(0)	—	—
06/96	0	0	—	—
Annual Growth	—	—	—	—

2009 Year-End Financials
Return on assets: —   Cash ($ mil.): 1
Return on equity: 4.3%
Current ratio: 3.60

PIGGLY WIGGLY ALABAMA DISTRIBUTING CO. INC.

Auditors: DENT BAKER & COMPANY LLP BI

LOCATIONS
HQ: PIGGLY WIGGLY ALABAMA DISTRIBUTING CO. INC.
  2400 J TERRELL WOOTEN DR, BESSEMER, AL 350202272
Phone: 205 481-2300
Web: WWW.PWADC.COM

HISTORICAL FINANCIALS
Company Type: Private

Income Statement
FYE: July 27

	REVENUE ($ mil.)	NET INCOME ($ mil.)	NET PROFIT MARGIN	EMPLOYEES
07/12	733	0	0.1%	500
07/11	772	0	0.1%	—
07/10	837	0	0.0%	—
07/09	830	0	—	—
Annual Growth	(4.1%)	—	—	—

2012 Year-End Financials
Return on assets: 3.1%   Cash ($ mil.): 6
Return on equity: 0.1%
Current ratio: 0.20

PIKEVILLE MEDICAL CENTER INC.

Taking a nasty fall while hiking the rugged Appalachians will likely land you at Pikeville Medical Center (PMC). Serving patients in eastern Kentucky the hospital boasts more than 260 beds and provides a full range of inpatient outpatient and surgical services. PMC's centers and departments handle a number of specialties such as diagnostic imaging echocardiogram neurosurgery cancer care and bariatric surgery. Employing some 350 physicians PMC also operates a rehabilitation hospital a home health agency and outpatient family practice and specialty clinics as well as a physician residency program. PMC first opened on Christmas Day in 1924.

Operations
Pikeville Kentucky-based PMC offers more than 400 services.

Strategy
PMC is rapidly expanding its services and facilities to keep pace with the needs of area residents. In recent years it has added such new services as pulmonary rehabilitation plastic surgery and orthopedic trauma. In addition the hospital launched a $150 million expansion project that will add an 11-story outpatient center (including physician practices and surgery suites) and a 10-story parking garage. Additional expansion efforts have included opening new outpatient cancer diagnostic pain management and primary care clinics.

An active participant in clinical trials and studies PMC works to expand its research opportunities for patients and physicians. In 2013 the hospital began new treatment for patients with Paroxysmal Atrial Fibrillation (Afib) using Medtronic's Arctic Front Advance Cardiac Cryoballoon System. Since 2012 when it inked a Medicaid contract with Coventry PMC has contracts with all three providers: Coventry Wellcare and Kentucky Spirit. PMC become member of the Mayo Clinic Care Network in 2013. The agreement gives PMC providers access to Mayo Clinic resources including its online point-of-care information system and its electronic consulting process that connects physicians with Mayo Clinic specialists on questions of diagnosis therapy or care management.

EXECUTIVES
Assistant Vice President Clinical Financial Integration, Melissa (Mel) Thacker
Vice President of Physician Services, Peggy Justice
Adm Ast To The Assistant Vice President of Marketing, Shaundra Adkins
Director Of Nursing, Kathy Khoshreza
Vice President Professional Services, Patty Thompson
Vice President And Nurse Executive, Cheryl Hickman

LOCATIONS
HQ: PIKEVILLE MEDICAL CENTER INC.
  911 BYPASS RD, PIKEVILLE, KY 415011689
Phone: 606 218-3500
Web: WWW.PIKEVILLEHOSPITAL.ORG

PRODUCTS/OPERATIONS

Selected Services
Bariatric Surgery
Breast Care Center
Critical Care
Diagnostics
Diabetes Education
Ear Nose & Throat (Otolaryngology)
Emergency
Endocrinology
Family Practice
Gastroenterology
Gynecology/Obstetrics
Family Practice Clinic
Heart Institute
Heart Failure/Coumadin Clinic
Home Health
Home Medical Equipment
Inpatient
Infectious Disease
Laboratory Services
Leonard Lawson Cancer Center
Neonatology
Nephrology
Neurosurgery
Ophthalmology
Other Patient Services
Orthopedic Surgery
Palliative Care
Pediatrics
Pharmacy
Plastic & Reconstructive Surgery
Pulmonary Clinic
Radiology
Rehabilitation
Residency Program
Rheumatology
Sleep
Urology
Women and Childrens' Services
Wound Care Center

COMPETITORS
Appalachian Regional Healthcare
Clinch Valley Medical Center
Community Health Systems
Highlands Health
Norton Community Hospital
Norton Healthcare
Russell County Medical Center
University of Kentucky Chandler Hospital

HISTORICAL FINANCIALS
Company Type: Private

Income Statement
FYE: September 30

	REVENUE ($ mil.)	NET INCOME ($ mil.)	NET PROFIT MARGIN	EMPLOYEES
09/13	394	2	0.7%	1,025
09/09	267	27	10.2%	—
09/03	132	12	9.3%	—
09/02	127	0	—	—
Annual Growth	10.8%	—	—	—

2013 Year-End Financials
Return on assets: 3.7%   Cash ($ mil.): 126
Return on equity: 0.7%
Current ratio: 4.10

PINNACLE HEALTH HOSPITAL

LOCATIONS

HQ: PINNACLE HEALTH HOSPITAL
4300 LONDONDERRY RD, HARRISBURG, PA
171095317
Phone: 717 782-3131
Web: WWW.PINNACLEHEALTH.ORG

HISTORICAL FINANCIALS
Company Type: Private

Income Statement

FYE: June 30

	REVENUE ($ mil.)	NET INCOME ($ mil.)	NET PROFIT MARGIN	EMPLOYEES
06/13	733	105	14.4%	4,800
06/08	0	0	14.6%	—
06/05*	0	0	—	—
07/98	48	0	—	—
Annual Growth	19.9%	—	—	—

*Fiscal year change

2013 Year-End Financials

Return on assets: 19.5% Cash ($ mil.): 1
Return on equity: 14.4%
Current ratio: 0.20

PINNACLE HEALTH HOSPITALS

Auditors: PARENTEBEARD LLC YORK PA

LOCATIONS

HQ: PINNACLE HEALTH HOSPITALS
409 S 2ND ST STE 1C, HARRISBURG, PA 171041612
Phone: 717 782-5678
Web: WWW.PRIMARY.PINNACLEHEALTH.ORG

HISTORICAL FINANCIALS
Company Type: Private

Income Statement

FYE: June 30

	REVENUE ($ mil.)	NET INCOME ($ mil.)	NET PROFIT MARGIN	EMPLOYEES
06/10	559	14	2.5%	4,500
06/09	538	0	—	—
06/08	513	(14)	—	—
06/06	482	0	—	—
Annual Growth	3.8%	—	—	—

2010 Year-End Financials

Return on assets: — Cash ($ mil.): —
Return on equity: 2.5%
Current ratio: 0.10

PITT COUNTY MEMORIAL HOSPITAL INCORPORATED

Vidant Medical Center is an acute health services facility that serves the vibrant community of Greenville North Carolina and surrounding areas. The 909-bed regional referral hospital's specialty divisions include Vidant Children's Hospital East Carolina Heart Institute a rehabilitation center and the outpatient Vidant SurgiCenter. Other services include oncology transplant women's health orthopedic behavioral care and home health and hospice care units. The center also serves as a teaching facility for East Carolina University's Brody School of Medicine. Vidant Medical Center (formerly Pitt County Memorial Hospital) is a member of University Health Systems of Eastern Carolina (dba Vidant Health).

Geographic Reach

Vidant Medical Center provides care to patients in a 29-county service territory in eastern North Carolina. It operates as a regional referral center for smaller community hospitals in the area taking on complex care cases in its specialized fields of medicine.

Operations

In addition to serving as a primary teaching facility for the Brody School of Medicine Vidant Medical Center provides clinical training for East Carolina University's allied health and nursing programs. About 2000 students complete clinical programs at the medical center and its affiliated Vidant Health facilities each year.

Its subsidiary PMI Inc. offers property management services.

Altogether Vidant Medical Center serves more than 1.4 million people across its 29-county service area. Boasting a clinical staff of more than 500 physicians and 1200 nurses the medical center in 2013 tended to more than 46000 inpatients and more than 275000 outpatients. Its emergency department visits reached 121000-plus in 2013.

Strategy

To enhance its service offerings to area residents the Vidant Health organization regularly updates its facilities through capital improvement projects. In addition to basic equipment and infrastructure upgrades in 2011 the hospital completed phase one of an expansion project at the Vidant Medical Center that aims to improve the hospital's pediatric and cancer care capabilities.

To signify its mission to enhance the quality of life in its service territories in 2012 University Health Systems of Eastern Carolina began operating as Vidant Health and the Pitt County Memorial Hospital was renamed as Vidant Memorial Hospital.

EXECUTIVES

Director Of Pharmacy, Angela (Angie) Hardy
Executive Vice President, Travis Douglass
Medical Records Director, Jean Foster
Senior Vice President, Reggie Pearson
Assistant Vice President Perioperative, Steve Butler
Senior Vice President, Paul Shackelford
Vice President Information Systems Pitt County Memorial Hospital, Ben Aycock
Board Member, Caleb Forbes
Board Member, Beverly Venters

LOCATIONS

HQ: PITT COUNTY MEMORIAL HOSPITAL INCORPORATED
2100 STANTONSBURG RD, GREENVILLE, NC
278342832
Phone: 252 847-4100
Web: WWW.VIDANTHEALTH.COM

PRODUCTS/OPERATIONS

Selected Services
Asthma Program (Pediatric)
Audiology
Behavioral & Mental Health
Cancer Care
Child Life
Children's Care
Children's Emergency Department
Children's Hospital
Community Health Programs
CyberKnife
Diagnostic Imaging
Diabetes
Emergency Services
Endoscopy Services
Gamma Knife

COMPETITORS
Adventist Health System Sunbelt Healthcare
Bon Secours Health
Carolinas HealthCare System
Duke University Health System
Greenville Hospital System
Novant Health
Sentara Healthcare
Tenet Healthcare
UNC Hospitals
Wake Forest University Baptist Medical Center

HISTORICAL FINANCIALS
Company Type: Private

Income Statement

FYE: September 30

	REVENUE ($ mil.)	NET INCOME ($ mil.)	NET PROFIT MARGIN	EMPLOYEES
09/13*	1,031	91	8.9%	8,373
12/12	395	19	4.8%	—
09/09	878	26	3.0%	—
09/08	796	0	—	—
Annual Growth	5.3%	—	—	—

*Fiscal year change

2013 Year-End Financials

Return on assets: 5.2% Cash ($ mil.): 17
Return on equity: 8.9%
Current ratio: 1.40

PITT-OHIO EXPRESS LLC

Primarily a regional less-than-truckload (LTL) freight carrier Pitt Ohio operates a fleet of about 1000 tractors and 3100 trailers. (LTL carriers consolidate freight from multiple shippers into a single truckload.) It maintains straight trucks and vans in its fleet. Pitt Ohio additionally provides truckload (TL) transportation through ECM Transport. It operates a network of about 20 terminals primarily in the Midwest and Mid-Atlantic US. Beyond freight hauling Pitt Ohio provides specialized logistics services for shippers. The family of Charles Hammel III owns Pitt Ohio which has grown from a business established by Hammel's grandfather in 1919.

Geographic Reach

Pitt Ohio is headquartered in Pittsburgh and operates across the Mid-Atlantic and Mid-West regions through more than 20 terminals and 12 truckload locations. It caters to Canada Mexico and other parts of the US through its affiliation with The Reliance Network.

Operations

Pitt Ohio is not historically a third-party logistics (3PL) provider but as the economy recovers the trend toward blending logistics and transportation is on the rise and the company recognizes that. What makes shippers seek a 3PL in the first place is usually for convenience. Given its experience through perhaps the worst recession in the trucking industry and its willingness to evolve Pitt Ohio is moving with the times and incorporating specialized logistics services for its dedicated accounts.

To extend its service throughout the US and Canada Pitt Ohio is part of The Reliance Network (TRNET) a group of regional LTL carriers. TRNET which serves all of North America includes Lakeville Motor Express Averitt Express Canadian Freightways/Epic Express DATS Trucking and Land Air Express. TRNET has the ability to bid jointly on LTL contracts as one entity. Alliances such as TRNET are important as freight companies search for ways to boost profitability and offset losses.

Financial PerformancePitt Ohio has experienced continued growth over the last five years. In fiscal 2014 the company's revenue increased by 16% to $498 million.

Strategy

Pitt Ohio expands by opening new facilities in key markets. In 2014 the company opened two new terminals at Chicago and Cincinnati. The Ohio facility includes 71 dock doors and serves Ohio Indiana and Kentucky whereas the Illinois facility includes 55 dock doors and serves Illinois. In addition in 2014 Pitt Ohio relocated its Norristown Pennsylvania terminal to a new larger facility to serve the rising demand in the Philadelphia region. The facility includes 66 dock doors.

Company Background

The company was originally known as Pitt Ohio Express referring to its travel between Pittsburgh and Ohio. When it began to offer more services than just freight hauling the company decided in 2010 to brand itself and adopt a new name —Pitt Ohio.

EXECUTIVES

President, Charles L. (Chuck) Hammel
EVP and Chief Marketing Officer, Geoffrey (Geoff) Muessig
CFO and CIO, Scott R. Sullivan
COO, James P. (Jim) Fields
Vice President Operations, Brad Caven
Human Resources Director And Vice President, Penny Pilafas

LOCATIONS

HQ: PITT-OHIO EXPRESS LLC
15 27TH ST, PITTSBURGH, PA 152224729
Phone: 412 232-3015
Web: WWW.PITTOHIO.COM

PRODUCTS/OPERATIONS

Selected Services
Ground transportation (small package shipping)
Less-than-truckload transportation
Supply chain services
  Distribution
  Fleet and asset management
  Management consulting
  Transportation
Truckload transportation

COMPETITORS

A. Duie Pyle Inc.	Ryder System
Estes Express	Schneider National

J.B. Hunt — UPS Freight
Landstar System — USF Holland
New Penn Motor Express — Ward Trucking
Old Dominion Freight

HISTORICAL FINANCIALS

Company Type: Private

Income Statement

FYE: December 31

	REVENUE ($ mil.)	NET INCOME ($ mil.)	NET PROFIT MARGIN	EMPLOYEES
12/07	261	18	7.2%	3,000
12/06	243	24	10.1%	—
12/04	221	22	10.0%	—
12/02	205	0	—	—
Annual Growth	5.0%	—	—	—

2007 Year-End Financials

Return on assets: 1.0%   Cash ($ mil.): 1
Return on equity: 7.2%
Current ratio: 1.30

PJM INTERCONNECTION LLC

Interdependence is a given at PJM Interconnection which oversees a 62555-mile section of the North American power transmission grid that spans 13 northeastern and midwestern states and the District of Columbia. The regional transmission organization monitors and coordinates the movement of wholesale electricity in its service territory; its 850 members have a combined generating capacity of 185600 MW. Sanctioned by the Federal Energy Regulatory Commission PJM is charged with ensuring fair competition among power purchasers sellers and traders; it also is responsible for the reliable delivery of distributed electricity to 61 million consumers in its territory.

Geographic Reach

PJM coordinates the movement of wholesale electricity in all or parts of Delaware Illinois Indiana Kentucky Maryland Michigan New Jersey North Carolina Ohio Pennsylvania Tennessee Virginia West Virginia and the District of Columbia. Its total service area covers 214000 square miles.

Operations

PJM's members include power generation companies transmission owners electricity distributors power marketers and large industrial consumers.

The organization is structured to secure independence and neutrality in its business operations. It has a two-tier committee structure consisting of 10-person Board of Managers (made up of individuals with no financial interests in PJM market participants) and a Members Committee which represents the interests of participating members. The structure is designed to secure that individual members have strong input on issues while protecting the neutrality of PJM's decision-making process.

In addition to overseeing and maintaining the generation and transmission reliability of the electric system the enterprise is also responsible for maintaining the integrity of the regional power grid as it accommodates new generating plants and other equipment such as substations and transmission lines. PJM also analyzes and forecasts the future power needs of the region and develops renewable energy resources as a way to expand power supply options and keep prices competitive.

Its Markets and Operations unit has expertise in Energy Marketing Reliability Pricing Model Financial Transmission Rights Demand Response Financial Credit Ancillary Services Synchronized Reserve and Regulation.PJM subsidiary PJM Environmental Information Services reports and tracks emissions data and Renewable Energy Credits.PJM Settlement a Pennsylvania nonprofit corporation handles all of PJM's financial credit settlement activities.PJM Technologies provides services to existing and emerging energy markets system operators and regional transmission operators.

Financial Performance

The company reported a slight revenue dip in 2013 due to lower interest income and other income partially offset by higher deferred regulatory income service and membership fees. PJM posted net income growth that year of 16% due to higher income tax benefits.

Strategy

The company grows through organic expansion and by absorbing the operations of power transmission and distribution companies. To upgrade its infrastructure in 2013 PJM authorized $1 billion in improvements to its high-voltage electric transmission system that serves the Mid-Atlantic and all or parts of other states between the Mid-Atlantic and Chicago.

Generation owners plans to retire more than 14000 MW of coal-fired generation by the end of 2015. PJM is dealing effectively with this rapid transformation and has three-year forward capacity marketattracting resources of all kinds – combined-cycle gas generators renewable resources demand response and energy efficiency – that enhance competition and ensure reliability. In 2013 it had more than 169000 MW committed for future service including 5400 MW of new generation and more than 12400 MW of demand response

Mergers and Acquisitions

In 2013 the integration of East Kentucky Power Cooperative and PJM brought 3099 MW of generating capacity and 2797 miles of transmission lines into the PJM grid.

Company Background

Growing its geographic coverage in 2012 PJM assumed operational control of the transmission systems of Duke Energy Ohio and Duke Energy Kentucky.

In 2011 PJM integrated FirstEnergy's Ohio and Pennsylvania power utilities' transmission assets into its system.

In a move to improve the efficiency and reliability of its operations in 2010 PJM teamed up with Midwest ISO to coordinate the installation of synchrophasors to improve their operators' visibility of the grid. The upgrade is funded by the Department of Energy's $3.4 billion smart grid program. In 2010 the company also connected the system to more than 1500 MW of renewable power including more than 1030 MW of wind energy. That year it also formed a new subsidiary to provide an auction platform for trading solar renewable energy certificates.

PJM was formed in 1927 when three utilities interconnected to share resources thus creating the world's first continuing power pool. In 1997 PJM became the first independent system operator.

EXECUTIVES

President CEO, W. Terry Boston
EVP and COO, Michael J. Kormos
VP CFO and Treasurer, Suzanne Daugherty
President and CEO, Andrew L. Ott
VP Information and Technology Services, Thomas F. O'Brien
Vice President Operations, Bruce Balmat
Vice President Pjm Eis, Jaclynn Lukach

Vice Chairman, Ake Almgren, age 69
Chairman, Howard Schneider
Auditors: PRICEWATERHOUSECOOPERS LLP P

LOCATIONS

HQ: PJM INTERCONNECTION LLC
955 JEFFERSON AVE, NORRISTOWN, PA 194032410
Phone: 610 666-8980
Web: WWW.PJMSETTLEMENT.COM

Operating Areas
Delaware
District of Columbia
Illinois
Indiana
Kentucky
Maryland
Michigan
New Jersey
North Carolina
Ohio
Pennsylvania
Tennessee
Virginia
West Virginia

HISTORICAL FINANCIALS

Company Type: Private

Income Statement

	REVENUE ($ mil.)	NET INCOME ($ mil.)	NET PROFIT MARGIN	EMPLOYEES
				FYE: December 31
12/12	324	0	0.3%	600
12/08	241	0	0.3%	—
12/06	274	0	0.2%	—
Annual Growth	2.8%	9.4%	—	—

2012 Year-End Financials

Return on assets: —
Return on equity: 0.3%
Current ratio: 0.90
Cash ($ mil.): 1,119

PLACID HOLDING COMPANY

Auditors: HEIN & ASSOCIATES LLP DALLAS

LOCATIONS

HQ: PLACID HOLDING COMPANY
1601 ELM ST STE 3900, DALLAS, TX 752014708
Phone: 214 880-8479

HISTORICAL FINANCIALS

Company Type: Private

Income Statement

	REVENUE ($ mil.)	NET INCOME ($ mil.)	NET PROFIT MARGIN	EMPLOYEES
				FYE: December 31
12/13	4,929	47	1.0%	2
12/02	532	3	0.6%	—
12/01	579	18	3.1%	—
12/00	564	0	—	—
Annual Growth	18.1%	—	—	—

2013 Year-End Financials

Return on assets: 4.2%
Return on equity: 1.0%
Current ratio: 1.10
Cash ($ mil.): 51

PLACID REFINING COMPANY LLC

A calm presence in the volatile oil and gas industry Placid Refining owns and operates the Port Allen refinery in Louisiana which converts crude oil into a number of petroleum products including diesel ethanol gasoline liquid petroleum gas jet fuel and fuel oils. Placid Refining's refinery has the capacity to process 80000 barrels of crude oil per day. The company is one of the largest employers and taxpayers in West Baton Rouge Parish. Placid Refining which is controlled by Petro-Hunt distribute fuels across a dozen states in the southeastern US from Texas to Virginia and is a major supplier of jet fuel to the US military.

Placid Refining's refinery (purchased in 1975) is strategically located on a 80-plus acre lot near the Mississippi River and about two miles from Interstate Highway 10 and about 10 minutes by car from downtown Baton Rouge.

To meet growing demand the Placid Refining invested $300 million in the late 2000s to expand the Port Allen refinery's throughput capacity from 55000 barrels per day to 80000 barrels per day. As part of this process in 2009 the company completed a 20000 barrels per day fluidized catalytic cracker gasoline hydrotreater.

In 2011 Placid Refining agreed to reduce the nitrogen oxide and sulfur dioxide emissions from its Port Allen refinery and agreed to pay $675000 to the State of Louisiana to settle previous emission violations.

EXECUTIVES

V Pres, Ron Hurst
Treasurer, Barry Joffrion
Auditors: HEIN & ASSOCIATES LLP DALLAS

LOCATIONS

HQ: PLACID REFINING COMPANY LLC
1601 ELM ST STE 3400, DALLAS, TX 752017201
Phone: 214 880-8479
Web: WWW.PLACIDREFINING.COM

COMPETITORS

CITGO Refining and Chemicals
NuStar Energy
United Refining
Valero Energy

HISTORICAL FINANCIALS

Company Type: Private

Income Statement

	REVENUE ($ mil.)	NET INCOME ($ mil.)	NET PROFIT MARGIN	EMPLOYEES
				FYE: December 31
12/13	4,929	47	1.0%	200
12/11	4,699	4	0.1%	—
12/10	3,686	39	1.1%	—
12/06	2,925	0	—	—
Annual Growth	7.7%	—	—	—

2013 Year-End Financials

Return on assets: 4.2%
Return on equity: 1.0%
Current ratio: 1.10
Cash ($ mil.): 42

PLAINS COTTON COOPERATIVE ASSOCIATION

Plainly speaking most of the US cotton used by textile mills worldwide starts with the Plains Cotton Cooperative Association (PCCA). The farmer-owned co-op markets millions of bales annually for members in Oklahoma Kansas and Texas. To obtain a competitive price for their cotton PCCA takes advantage of Telmark LP's access to The Seam an online cotton marketplace that continually updates cotton prices buyer data and more. The co-op operates cotton warehouses in Texas Oklahoma and Kansas. PCCA sold its textile and apparel operations in 2014 to focus exclusively on cotton marketing and warehousing. Formed in 1953 PCCA's customers include Replay Urban Outfitters and Abercrombie & Fitch.

Geographic Reach
Lubbock Texas-based Plains Cotton Cooperative Association owns half a dozen cotton warehouses in Kansas Oklahoma and Texas. Its Telmark LP business is also headquartered in Lubbock.

Operations
PCCA is a member of the American Apparel Producers' Network Amcot the National Cotton Council of America the National Council of Textile Organizations the Texas Agricultural Coop Council and The International Cotton Association.

Financial Performance
The cooperative which distributed more than $22 million to its members posted total net margins of $10.4 million from its fiscal 2012-2013 operations. Despite a small crop during the reporting period PCCA saw its cotton marketing and warehouse divisions post profits. It was also helped by its IT division and support services. Feeling the drag of the US economy and unemployment the co-op's textile and apparel division focused on cutting costs.

Strategy
To better focus on its core cotton marketing and warehousing businesses PCCA sold its textile and apparel division to American Textile Holdings LLC (AmTex) in June 2014. The sale gave AmTex control of all the operations of American Cotton Growers (ACG) denim mill in Littlefield Texas and Denimatrix S.A. in Guatemala.

EXECUTIVES

Corporate Secretary, John Johnson
VP Information Systems, Joe Tubb
VP Administration and Human Resources, Jim Taylor
VP Finance and Treasurer, Sam Hill
VP Fabric Sales and Product Development, Jack Mathews
President CEO, Wallace L. (Wally) Darneille
VP Marketing, Lonnie Winters
Vice Chairman, David Pearson
VP TELMARK, Stan Kirby
VP Grower Services, Dean Church
VP Textile Manufacturing, Bryan Gregory
Domestic Sales Manager, Chris Ford
Director Sales, Grady Martin
Export Sales Manager, Carlos Garcia
Chairman, Bob McGinnis
Vice President of Services, Greg Bell
V.P. of Warehouse Operations, Jay Cow
Auditors: CROWE HORWATH LLP DALLAS TEX

LOCATIONS

HQ: PLAINS COTTON COOPERATIVE ASSOCIATION
3301 E 50TH ST, LUBBOCK, TX 794044331
Phone: 806 763-8011
Web: WWW.PCCA.COM

PRODUCTS/OPERATIONS

Selected Sales and Services
Buying cotton
Cotton gins
  Gin bookkeeping
  Gin patronage
  Marketing and invoicing
  Scale ticket software
  Support and training
  Technology solutions
Cotton producers
  Agent gins
  Cash marketing
  marketing contracts
  Pool marketing
Warehousing

COMPETITORS

Alabama Farmers Cooperative	J.G. Boswell Co. Parkdale Mills
Calcot	Staplcotn
Dunavant Enterprises	Weil Brothers Cotton
Greenwood Mills	
International Cotton Marketing	

HISTORICAL FINANCIALS

Company Type: Private

Income Statement

FYE: June 30

	REVENUE ($ mil.)	NET INCOME ($ mil.)	NET PROFIT MARGIN	EMPLOYEES
06/14	947	(36)	—	800
06/13	1,080	10	1.0%	—
06/12	793	8	1.1%	—
06/11	1,835	0	—	—
Annual Growth	(19.8%)	—	—	—

2014 Year-End Financials

Return on assets: 0.6%   Cash ($ mil.): 28
Return on equity: (-3.9%)
Current ratio: 0.80

PLAN INTERNATIONAL INC.

Auditors: DYL & PERILLO INC PROVIDENCE

LOCATIONS

HQ: PLAN INTERNATIONAL INC.
155 PLAN WAY STE A, WARWICK, RI 028861099
Phone: 401 294-3693
Web: WWW.PLAN-INTERNATIONAL.ORG

HISTORICAL FINANCIALS

Company Type: Private

Income Statement

FYE: June 30

	REVENUE ($ mil.)	NET INCOME ($ mil.)	NET PROFIT MARGIN	EMPLOYEES
06/12	601	29	4.9%	7
06/10	531	93	17.6%	—
06/08	514	39	7.6%	—
06/01	245	0	—	—
Annual Growth	8.5%			

2012 Year-End Financials

Return on assets: —   Cash ($ mil.): 252
Return on equity: 4.9%
Current ratio: 4.40

POLK COUNTY SCHOOL DISTRICT

LOCATIONS

HQ: POLK COUNTY SCHOOL DISTRICT
1915 S FLORAL AVE, BARTOW, FL 338307124
Phone: 863 534-0500
Web: WWW.POLK-FL.NET

HISTORICAL FINANCIALS

Company Type: Private

Income Statement

FYE: June 30

	REVENUE ($ mil.)	NET INCOME ($ mil.)	NET PROFIT MARGIN	EMPLOYEES
06/14	871	(5)	—	—
06/13	827	(40)	—	—
06/12	821	(42)	—	—
Annual Growth	3.0%	—	—	—

2014 Year-End Financials

Return on assets: 1.8%   Cash ($ mil.): 69
Return on equity: (-0.6%)
Current ratio: —

POMP'S TIRE SERVICE INC..

If by circumstance you have a flat tire in the Midwest limp on over to Pomp's Tire Service. The company sells tires for agricultural commercial and industrial vehicles as well as everyday cars and trucks from more than 75 locations in eight Midwestern states. (More than half are located in Wisconsin and Illinois.) Brands include Bridgestone Goodrich Goodyear and Michelin. Pomp's Tire Service also offers roadside assistance and retread services and it has extensive contracts with the US Army for vehicle parts. Originally called Pomprowitz Tire Co. the company was founded in 1939 by Andrew "Sparky" Pomprowitz. It is owned by the family of Roger Wochinske who bought the firm in 1964.

Geographic Reach

Green Bay Wisconsin-based Pomp's Tire Service has stores in Wisconsin Illinois Indiana Iowa Michigan Minnesota Nebraska and South Dakota.

Operations

In addition to its retail commercial and wholesale tire businesses Pomp's provides services to its customers such as alignments engine diagnostics fuel system cleaning oil changes and radiator and transmission services. It also operates about a dozen retread plants a wheel manufacturing facility and a pair of original equipment manufacturing (OEM) plants that employ more than 1100 workers.

Strategy

In 2013 Pomp's began construction of a new storage building to house tires that are currently stores outside. The 4800-squre-foot cold storage building is located in Monona Wisconsin.

Ownership

The company is owned by the Wochinske family.

EXECUTIVES

V Pres, Garry Glime, age 74
Vice President, Theresa Chapman
Auditors: SCHENCK SC GREEN BAY WISCONS

LOCATIONS

HQ: POMP' S TIRE SERVICE INC..
1123 CEDAR ST, GREEN BAY, WI 543014703
Phone: 920 435-8301
Web: WWW.POMPSTIRE.COM

PRODUCTS/OPERATIONS

Selected Brands
Bandag
Bridgestone
Firestone
General
Goodrich
Goodyear
Kelly
Michelin
Yokohama

COMPETITORS

Bauer Built	Sears
Discount Tire	TBC
Pep Boys	TCI Tire Centers

HISTORICAL FINANCIALS

Company Type: Private

Income Statement

FYE: December 31

	REVENUE ($ mil.)	NET INCOME ($ mil.)	NET PROFIT MARGIN	EMPLOYEES
12/12	427	15	3.5%	1,200
12/11	398	12	3.2%	—
12/10	342	11	3.2%	—
12/09	284	0	—	—
Annual Growth	14.5%	—	—	—

2012 Year-End Financials

Return on assets: 19.2%   Cash ($ mil.): —
Return on equity: 3.5%
Current ratio: 0.70

POPULATION SERVICES INTERNATIONAL

Population Services International (PSI) goes far beyond the scope of its name. Founded in 1970 to promote global family planning PSI has established social programs that use local networks in low-income regions to distribute such lifelines as insecticide-treated mosquito nets iodized salt snake boots and insect repellent along with condoms contraceptives and pregnancy test kits. The group prides itself on using business principals to confront health issues in more than 65 countries worldwide. It reportedly has averted 4.2 million unintended pregnancies some 29 million malaria cases and provided 1.8-plus million clients with of HIV testing and counseling. PSI is also active ensuring safe water supplies.

PSI's social franchise network has grown to more than 10000 franchise sites in 21 countries. Each social franchise is steered by a network of health practitioners that have contracted to provide a level of quality services under a common brand. The top products and services found to be most effective in preventing disease include long-lasting insecticidal nets and male condoms. PSI has also had some success with pre-packaged malaria treatment various contraceptives and a basic are package for people living with HIV.

Geographically PSI in 2010 focused on health issues in Africa primarily East Africa. The organization's intervention programs also gained a considerable footing in West and Central Africa and Southern Africa. (Progress is based on years of healthy life added which refers to a metric of years the illness or death was averted through PSI product and service intervention.)

During the last three years PIS has reported consistent gains in revenue. In 2010 revenues increased by 12% over the prior year less than the more than 25% jump posted in 2009 over 2008. Major donors include the US government which accounts for more than 30% of annual revenues and the governments of Germany the Netherlands and the UK. In addition PIS has received donations from several United Nations agencies and private foundations including the Bill & Melinda Gates Foundation corporations and individuals. More than 93% of the revenues in 2010 were used to fund PIS's programs. Management and general expenditures were less than 7% of all expenses and fundraising less than 1%.

The nonprofit in 2010 targeted in five health areas with the greatest impact on malaria and reproductive health followed by HIV and tuberculosis. Child survival in terms of years of healthy life added was least affected. PSI measures the effectiveness of its intervention in years of healthy life added or disability-adjusted life year (DALY). The metric adds one year of healthy life with every year of illness or death averted attributable to the intervention.

EXECUTIVES

Managing Director, Anders Dejgaard

LOCATIONS

HQ: POPULATION SERVICES INTERNATIONAL
1120 19TH ST NW STE 600, WASHINGTON, DC
200363605
Phone: 202 785-0072
Web: WWW.PSI.ORG

HISTORICAL FINANCIALS

Company Type: Private

Income Statement

	REVENUE ($ mil.)	NET INCOME ($ mil.)	NET PROFIT MARGIN	EMPLOYEES
12/13	584	4	0.8%	250
12/01	121	(0)	—	—
12/00	96	3	3.4%	—
Annual Growth	14.8%	2.9%	—	—

FYE: December 31

2013 Year-End Financials

Return on assets: 10.1%   Cash ($ mil.): 210
Return on equity: 0.8%
Current ratio: 0.60

PORT OF HOUSTON AUTHORITY

Houston is too far inland to be a port city by the strictest of definitions but don't try to tell that to the Port of Houston Authority. The agency manages the Port of Houston complex including the Barbours Cut Container Terminal one of the busiest in the US. Port of Houston facilities are arrayed along the Houston Ship Channel which connects Houston with Galveston Bay and the Gulf of Mexico and with intracoastal waterways. The Port of Houston Authority itself operates more than 40 cargo wharves; however most of the terminal facilities along the ship channel are managed by private companies. The ship channel was opened in 1914; the Port of Houston Authority was created by the Texas Legislature in 1927.

Besides cargo operations the Port of Houston Authority oversees the Bayport Cruise Terminal which breifly served Carnival Cruise Lines when Hurricane Ike diverted the cruise operator from the Port of Galveston. The $81 million-terminal built in 2008 hasn't secured a permanent tenant.

The economic downturn has hammered all those connected to the cargo transportation industry including the Port of Houston Authority. In 2009 some 25000 fewer automobiles were offloaded in the Port of Houston and steel imports plunged. In response the authority is not hiring vacant positions in its administrative offices and raised some of its cargo-moving fees. (The authority's revenue comes from harbor and docking fees as well as tax from Harris County Texas property owners.)

In the midst of the downturn the port authority is looking to the future. To alleviate pressure on the extremely busy Barbours Cut Container Terminal the port authority is building the Bayport Container and Cruise Terminal. The $1.4 billion project which will double the port's container capacity is expected to be completed in 2014 —the same year an expansion of the Panama Canal will boost container trade.

H. Thomas Kornegay executive director of the Port of Houston Authority retired in January 2009 after almost 40 years of service. He was replaced in September 2009 by Alec Dreyer former CEO of Horizon Wind Energy.

EXECUTIVES

COO, Thomas J. Heidt
Executive Director, Roger Guenther
Chief Commercial Officer, Ricky W. Kunz
CIO, Charles T. Thompson
Chief Port Operations Officer, Jeff Davis
CFO, Tim Finley
Vice President Student Affairs Dean of Students,
 David (Dave) Buckingham
Chairman, Janiece M. Longoria, age 62
Auditors: GRANT THORTON LLP HOUSTON TE

LOCATIONS

HQ: PORT OF HOUSTON AUTHORITY
111 EAST LOOP N, HOUSTON, TX 770294326
Phone: 713 670-2400
Web: WWW.PORTOFHOUSTON.COM

COMPETITORS

Alabama State Docks	The Port of New
Port of Corpus Christi	Orleans

HISTORICAL FINANCIALS

Company Type: Private

Income Statement

	REVENUE ($ mil.)	NET INCOME ($ mil.)	NET PROFIT MARGIN	EMPLOYEES
12/13	233	67	29.0%	595
12/12	225	54	24.1%	—
12/11	206	33	16.0%	—
12/10	186	0	—	—
Annual Growth	7.8%	—	—	—

FYE: December 31

POTANDON PRODUCE L.L.C.

Auditors: RUDD & COMPANY IDAHO FALLS I

LOCATIONS

HQ: POTANDON PRODUCE L.L.C.
1210 PIER VIEW DR, IDAHO FALLS, ID 834024966
Phone: 208 419-4200
Web: WWW.POTANDON.COM

HISTORICAL FINANCIALS

Company Type: Private

Income Statement

	REVENUE ($ mil.)	NET INCOME ($ mil.)	NET PROFIT MARGIN	EMPLOYEES
12/13	396	1	0.5%	100
12/12	369	0	—	—
12/11	433	5	1.3%	—
12/10	350	0	—	—
Annual Growth	4.2%	—	—	—

FYE: December 31

2013 Year-End Financials

Return on assets: 12.0%   Cash ($ mil.): —
Return on equity: 0.5%
Current ratio: 0.70

POWER ENGINEERS INCORPORATED

Auditors: DELOITTE & TOUCHE LLP BOISE

LOCATIONS

HQ: POWER ENGINEERS INCORPORATED
3940 GLENBROOK DR, HAILEY, ID 833338446
Phone: 208 788-3456
Web: WWW.POWERENG.COM

HISTORICAL FINANCIALS

Company Type: Private

Income Statement

FYE: December 31

	REVENUE ($ mil.)	NET INCOME ($ mil.)	NET PROFIT MARGIN	EMPLOYEES
12/13	329	8	2.4%	803
12/12	298	9	3.1%	—
12/10	203	6	3.2%	—
12/09	210	0	—	—
Annual Growth	11.9%	—	—	—

2013 Year-End Financials

Return on assets: 2.9%
Return on equity: 2.4%
Current ratio: 1.10
Cash ($ mil.): 14

POWERSOUTH ENERGY COOPERATIVE

Several hundred thousand Alabamans and Floridians get their electric power courtesy of the work of PowerSouth Energy Cooperative which provides wholesale power to its member-owners (16 electric cooperatives and four municipal distribution utilities). Its distribution members provide electric services to almost 417200 customer meters in central and southern Alabama and western Florida. PowerSouth operates a more than 2200-mile power transmission system and has more than 2000 MW of generating capacity from interests in six fossil-fueled and hydroelectric power plants.

Geographic Reach

PowerSouth serves customers in Alabama (39 counties) and Florida (10 counties).

Operations

The company owns and operates six generation facilities and holds ownership interest in an additional facility. Its diverse generating fuel mix includes natural gas coal and water (hydro). It also has compressed air energy storage technology and a disciplined fuel supply hedging program that minimizes the impact of fuel cost increases. In addition PowerSouth maintains long-term purchased power agreements to ensure economic and reliable power supply for its members.

PowerSouth serves the wholesale energy needs of electric cooperatives and municipal electric systems in Alabama and northwest Florida who in turn serve more than a million consumers. PowerSouth is dedicated to providing reliable energy at the lowest possible cost to its members.

Financial Performance

The company's revenues increased by 3% in 2013 primarily due to an increase in member revenues as a result of an increase in energy sales. The remaining increase was due to the surcharges added to the excess demand rate during 2013.That year PowerSouth's net income decreased by 6% as the result of increased operating costs caused by higher distribution costs and administration and general expenses.Its operating cash inflow increased to $63.5 million in 2013 (compared to $38.3 million in 2012) due to a rise in account receivables and inventories.

Strategy

To meet future demand and tightening environmental regulations the company is looking to diversify and expand its power production assets with an emphasis on cleaner energy plants. Pow-

erSouth's long-term energy plans include a 20-year contract for 125 MW of nuclear power from two Vogtle Units being built by the Municipal Energy Authority of Georgia near Augusta and due to come onstream in 2016 and 2017. The company is also investing in wind power and biomass-to-energy initiatives.

Company Background

PowersSouth is owned and managed by it 20 distribution members.

The company once provided propane but sold its Cooperative Propane unit in 2011 to focus on its core power businesses.

In 2008 Alabama Electric Cooperative changed its name to PowerSouth Energy Cooperative to better reflect its service territory (Alabama and Florida) and its opportunities for future growth.

Founded in 1941 as Alabama Electric Cooperative the coop promotes a strong economic development program aimed at bringing industry into both Alabama and Florida.

EXECUTIVES

Vice President Information Technology, Lewis Jeffers
Vice President, Elizabeth (Beth) Woodard
Vice President Power Delivery, Larry Auery
Vice President Of Power Production Mcintosh Plant, Lee Davis
Secretary, Gary Herrison
Board Member, Ben Floyd
Auditors: DELOITTE & TOUCHE LLP ATLANT

LOCATIONS

HQ: POWERSOUTH ENERGY COOPERATIVE
2027 E THREE NOTCH ST, ANDALUSIA, AL 364212427
Phone: 334 222-2571
Web: WWW.POWERSOUTH.COM

PRODUCTS/OPERATIONS

View Archived What Charts | Edit 2013 Sales

	% of total
Electric Cooperatives	93
Municipalities	6
Other	1
Total	**100**

HISTORICAL FINANCIALS

Company Type: Private

Income Statement

FYE: December 31

	REVENUE ($ mil.)	NET INCOME ($ mil.)	NET PROFIT MARGIN	EMPLOYEES
12/13	609	25	4.1%	600
12/12	591	26	4.5%	—
12/11	640	28	4.4%	—
12/10	673	0	—	—
Annual Growth	(3.3%)	—	—	—

2013 Year-End Financials

Return on assets: 7.3%
Return on equity: 4.1%
Current ratio: 0.10
Cash ($ mil.): 16

PRAIRIE FARMS DAIRY INC.

Prairie Farms Dairy is very cooperative. With some 700 dairy farmer/members the cooperative

offers a full line of retail and food service dairy products. It turns raw milk into fresh fluid cultured and frozen dairy products under the Prairie Farms label. It also makes juices and ice cream novelties. The company's customers include food drug and convenience stores mass merchandisers schools restaurants and other food service operators. Located in Carlinville Illinois it is the managing partner for joint ventures with smaller regional dairies. It makes its products at 24 Prairie Farms-owned plants and 13 joint-venture plants which are located throughout the midwestern and southern areas of the US.

Geographic Reach

Prairie Farms and its subsidiaries manufacture dairy products at 24 co-op-owned plants as 13 joint venture plants in Arkansas Illinois Indiana Iowa Kansas Kentucky Michigan Mississippi Missouri Nebraska Oklahoma Ohio and Tennessee.

Operations

To get its dairy products to market the co-op relies on subsidiaries Hawthorne-Mellody Distributors in Chicago and Tom David & Sons in Detroit.

In addition to manufacturing dairy foods co-packing is a big part of Prairie Farms' operation. Approximately 50% of the co-operative's sales come from packing non-Prairie Farm brands. The co-op's PFD Supply and GMS Transportation non-dairy subsidiaries distribute products for fast-food chains including McDonald's Dairy Queen and Church's Chicken.

Company Background

The cooperative dates back to 1932 when Illinois farmers formed a statewide organization Illinois Producers Creameries to market and sell cream. In 1938 it became Prairie Farms Dairy.

EXECUTIVES

Vice President Human Resources Labor Relations, Ray Silvey
Vice President Procurement, Gary Lee
National Sales Manager, Gary Davis
Auditors: BKD LLP ST LOUIS MISSOURI

LOCATIONS

HQ: PRAIRIE FARMS DAIRY INC.
1100 BROADWAY, CARLINVILLE, IL 626261183
Phone: 217 854-2547
Web: WWW.PRAIRIEFARMS.COM

Selected Areas of Distribution

Arkansas
Illinois
Indiana
Iowa
Kansas
Kentucky
Michigan
Mississippi
Missouri
Nebraska
Ohio
Oklahoma
Tennessee

PRODUCTS/OPERATIONS

Branded Partners

Belfonte Ice Cream & Dairy Foods Company
Coleman Dairy
Hiland Dairy Foods Company
Hiland-Roberts Ice Cream Company
Ice Cream Specialties
LuVel Dairy Products
Madison Farms Butter
Muller-Pinehurst Dairy
Roberts Dairy Company
Southern Belle Dairy
Swiss Valley Farms
Turner Dairy

Selected Products

Butter
Cultured dairy products
  Cottage cheese (regular low fat and fat-free; small and
  large curd)
  Dips
  Sour cream
  Yogurt (regular low fat and fat-free)
Fluid milk products
  Buttermilk
  Cream
  Egg nog (seasonal)
  Milk (regular low fat and fat-free)
  Flavored milk
Frozen desserts
  Frozen yogurt
  Ice cream (regular low fat and fat-free)
  Novelties
  Sherbet
Juices drinks and iced tea

COMPETITORS

Associated Milk	Foremost Farms
Producers	Friendly's Ice Cream
Dairy Farmers of	HP Hood
America	Land O' Lakes
Darigold Inc.	Quality Chekd
Dean Foods	Rockview Dairies
Dreyer's	Wells' Dairy
Farmland Dairies	

HISTORICAL FINANCIALS

Company Type: Private

Income Statement

FYE: September 30

	REVENUE ($ mil.)	NET INCOME ($ mil.)	NET PROFIT MARGIN	EMPLOYEES
09/14	1,878	(5)	—	1,965
09/13	1,721	14	0.8%	—
09/12	1,649	38	2.4%	—
09/11	1,607	0	—	—
Annual Growth	5.3%	—	—	—

2014 Year-End Financials

Return on assets: 9.6%   Cash ($ mil.): 10
Return on equity: (-0.3%)
Current ratio: 0.90

PREMIER PURCHASING PARTNERS L.P.

LOCATIONS

HQ: PREMIER PURCHASING PARTNERS L.P.
13034 BALNTYN CORP PL, CHARLOTTE, NC
282771498
Phone: 704 357-0022
Web: WWW.PREMIERINC.COM

HISTORICAL FINANCIALS

Company Type: Private

Income Statement

FYE: June 30

	REVENUE ($ mil.)	NET INCOME ($ mil.)	NET PROFIT MARGIN	EMPLOYEES
06/13	663	371	56.0%	199
06/12	590	326	55.3%	—
06/11	679	311	45.8%	—
06/09	411	0	—	—
Annual Growth	12.7%	—	—	—

2013 Year-End Financials

Return on assets: 1.8%   Cash ($ mil.): 195
Return on equity: 56.0%
Current ratio: 5.30

PRESBYTERIAN HOSPITAL

LOCATIONS

HQ: PRESBYTERIAN HOSPITAL
200 HAWTHORNE LN, CHARLOTTE, NC 282042528
Phone: 704 384-4000
Web: WWW.NOVANTHEALTH.ORG

HISTORICAL FINANCIALS

Company Type: Private

Income Statement

FYE: December 31

	REVENUE ($ mil.)	NET INCOME ($ mil.)	NET PROFIT MARGIN	EMPLOYEES
12/09	688	68	10.0%	3,100
12/08	500	18	3.7%	—
Annual Growth	37.6%	270.7%	—	—

2009 Year-End Financials

Return on assets: —   Cash ($ mil.): —
Return on equity: 10.0%
Current ratio: —

PRESBYTERIAN INTERCOMMUNITY HOSPITAL INC.

LOCATIONS

HQ: PRESBYTERIAN INTERCOMMUNITY HOSPITAL
INC.
12401 WASHINGTON BLVD, WHITTIER, CA
906021006
Phone: 562 698-0811
Web: WWW.WHITTIERPRES.COM

HISTORICAL FINANCIALS

Company Type: Private

Income Statement

FYE: September 30

	REVENUE ($ mil.)	NET INCOME ($ mil.)	NET PROFIT MARGIN	EMPLOYEES
09/13	491	81	16.7%	2,000
09/12	419	69	16.6%	—
09/09	383	28	7.4%	—
09/08	401	0	—	—
Annual Growth	4.1%	—	—	—

2013 Year-End Financials

Return on assets: —   Cash ($ mil.): —
Return on equity: 16.7%
Current ratio: 0.60

PRESBYTERIAN MEDICAL CENTER OF THE UNIVERSITY OF PENNSYLVANIA HE

LOCATIONS

HQ: PRESBYTERIAN MEDICAL CENTER OF THE
UNIVERSITY OF PENNSYLVANIA HE
51 N 39TH ST, PHILADELPHIA, PA 191042692
Phone: 215 662-8000
Web: WWW.PENNMEDICINE.ORG

HISTORICAL FINANCIALS

Company Type: Private

Income Statement

FYE: June 30

	REVENUE ($ mil.)	NET INCOME ($ mil.)	NET PROFIT MARGIN	EMPLOYEES
06/13	429	7	1.7%	1,370
06/05	301	(1)	—	—
06/02	213	(16)	—	—
06/01	212	0	—	—
Annual Growth	6.1%	—	—	—

2013 Year-End Financials

Return on assets: 3.2%   Cash ($ mil.): 1
Return on equity: 1.7%
Current ratio: 0.40

PRESIDENT AND FELLOWS OF MIDDLEBURY COLLEGE

President and Fellows of Middlebury College operates Middlebury College a private liberal arts school in Vermont that offers courses of study in the arts humanities literature foreign languages social sciences and natural sciences. About 2450 undergraduates are enrolled at the educational institution. Founded in 1800 it is home to the Bread Loaf School of English known for its summer graduate courses in literature as well as instruction in creative writing and theatre. Bread Loaf is located in the Green Mountains a dozen miles east of Middlebury. Every summer Middlebury College also opens the Language Schools from which the college provides instruction in 10 languages to more than 2000 students.

Geographic Reach

The Vermont liberal arts college boasts a global footprint with schools located in China Egypt France Germany Israel Italy Japan Jordan Russia Spain Brazil Argentina Uruguay Chile and Mexico. Its summer programs are taught in Vermont New Mexico North Carolina and the UK.

Operations

Middlebury College offers its 2450 undergraduates more than 850 courses across some 45 majors. Typically offering small class sizes its student-faculty ratio is 9:1. Nearly an equal number of students attend Middlebury College during the summer to take advantage of its foreign language courses in French German Italian Russian and Spanish offered at both the undergraduate and graduate levels. Undergraduate students also have access to Arabic Chinese Japanese Portuguese and Hebrew there.

For more than 40 years iconic author Robert Frost spent his summers at the Bread Loaf School of English. Outside Vermont Bread Loaf maintains satellite summer sessions in the US in New Mexico and North Carolina as well as in the UK at the University of Oxford.

Strategy

Middlebury College has earned a global presence through its alliances with other universities. Through a partnership established in 2011 with Brandeis University Middlebury College offers the only study-abroad program in Israel designed to be experienced in Hebrew. Based in the city of Be'er Sheva the program is affiliated with Ben-Gurion University of the Negev and began offering classes in spring 2012.

The college entered South Asia in 2012 through its existing C.V. Starr-Middlebury School Abroad program. The program will begin offering classes in fall 2013 at the University of Delhi's St. Stephen's College or its Lady Shri Ram College for Women. Previously Middlebury College established a program at the University of Jordan that began offering classes in fall 2011.

Financial Performance

Thanks to an increase in operating revenues and other support and sponsored activities Middlebury College logged a 1% increase in 2012 revenue as compared to 2011. Net income however decreased some 119% during the same reporting period. The institution points to rising operating expenses due to increases in total educational and general expenses for the declines. Decreases in non-operating activities in 2012 vs. 2011 also contributed to the net income dip primarily due to endowment return declines net of distribution. Increases in cash used for operating activities caused cash flow during the reporting period to decrease some $2.3 million. This was partially offset by decreases in realized and unrealized gains on investments.

EXECUTIVES

Vice President College Advancement, Michael Schoenfeld
Associate Vice President for Alumni Relations, Meg Groves
Co President, Sarah Cohen
V Pres, Brook Escobedo
Associate Vice President for Human Resources and Organizational Development, Drew Macan
Assoc. Vice President for Advancement Operations, Jami Black
Executive Vice President And Treasurer, F Robert Huth
Secretary of the College, Eric Davis
Advisory Board Member, Ernie Parizeau
Auditors: PRICEWATERHOUSECOOPERS LLP A

LOCATIONS

HQ: PRESIDENT AND FELLOWS OF MIDDLEBURY COLLEGE
38 COLLEGE ST, MIDDLEBURY, VT 05753
Phone: 802 443-5000
Web: WWW.MIDDLEBURY.EDU

Selected Locations
Center for the Comparative Study of Race and Ethnicity
Chellis House
Middlebury College Snow Bowl
Ralph Myhre Golf Course
Rikert Nordic Center
Rohatyn Center for International Affairs
Scott Center for Spiritual & Religious Life

HISTORICAL FINANCIALS
Company Type: Private

Income Statement
FYE: June 30

	REVENUE ($ mil.)	NET INCOME ($ mil.)	NET PROFIT MARGIN	EMPLOYEES
06/13	260	113	43.4%	1,000
06/12	233	(24)	—	—
06/08	278	50	18.3%	—
06/06	181	0	—	—
Annual Growth	5.3%	—	—	—

2013 Year-End Financials
Return on assets: 16.0%
Return on equity: 43.4%
Current ratio: —
Cash ($ mil.): 29

PRESSURE VESSEL SERVICE INC.

LOCATIONS

HQ: PRESSURE VESSEL SERVICE INC.
10900 HARPER AVE, DETROIT, MI 482133364
Phone: 313 921-1200
Web: WWW.PVSCHEMICALS.COM

HISTORICAL FINANCIALS
Company Type: Private

Income Statement
FYE: December 31

	REVENUE ($ mil.)	NET INCOME ($ mil.)	NET PROFIT MARGIN	EMPLOYEES
12/13	549	12	2.3%	800
12/12	566	21	3.8%	—
12/11	461	12	2.6%	—
12/10	356	0	—	—
Annual Growth	15.5%	—	—	—

PRIDGEON & CLAY INC.

A moving target not a sitting duck Pridgeon & Clay (P&C) takes on all rivals within the metal forming industry. An independent manufacturer and supplier of stamped and fine blanked components the family-owned company designs and produces an array of parts for auto assembly plants across the US. Its lineup includes steering column lock nuts brackets for headlights to engines control arms flanges exhaust parts and muffler shields. Stamping equipment runs from fine blanking presses to high tonnage and progressive presses. P&C also makes blanks for equipment in other industries. The company touts hand assembly spot welding and tapping services along with a global sales force.

Geographic ReachP&C has more than 100 stamping presses. Its operations are supplemented by PC NAVA a Mexico-based joint venture between P&C and NAVA Hermanos S.A. P&C also runs five manufacturing facilities in the US (Grand Rapids; and Franklin Indiana) Mexico Germany Hungary and a joint venture in Poland as well as engineering and sales branches in North America Germany and China.

Operations

The company's Advanced Engineering Lab is an American Association for Laboratory Accreditation accredited independent testing facility.

Sales and Marketing

Serving both OEM and Tier 1 manufacturers the company provides services to a large variety of industries including agriculture automobiles and heavy trucks fuel cells and batteries hardware and appliances marine craft medical supply motorcycles and solar and wind energy.

Strategy

Outlasting the automotive industry's melt down and even the bankruptcies of a couple of its major customers P&C has reached out for new markets. The company is investing in research and development of stamped components for customers in commercial hardware and wind power industries. P&C is also branching out into medical supply.

Company Background

P&C was founded in 1948 by John Pridgeon and Don Clay.

EXECUTIVES

Vice President Marketing and Product Development, Bill McKibben
President and COO, Michael J. Alcala
Owner And Vice President Of Administrati, Clay Donald
Vice President Of Global Operations, Keith O'Brien
Vice President Marketing, William (Bill) Mckibben
Vice President Fin, D B Penno
Auditors: PLANTE & MORAN PLLC GRAND RA

LOCATIONS

HQ: PRIDGEON & CLAY INC.
50 COTTAGE GROVE ST SW, GRAND RAPIDS, MI 495071685
Phone: 616 241-5675
Web: WWW.PRIDGEONANDCLAY.COM

PRODUCTS/OPERATIONS

Selected Products
Axle Components
Brake Components
Chassis Frame and Body
Class 8 Truck Parts
Cones
Exhaust Components
Flanges
Non Automotive Parts
Transmission Components

Selected Services
Advanced Engineering and Design
Assembly
De-burring
Deep Drawn Stamping
Distribution Center
Fine Blanking
In-die Sensoring and Welding
Package and Distribution
Progressive Die Stamping
Prototyping
Resistance Welding
Riveting
Robotic MIG Welding
Studding
Tool Design and Build
Transfer Press Stamping
Truck Fleet
Wide Variety of Secondary Services

COMPETITORS

Batesville Tool & Die	Mid-South Industries
Defiance Metal Products	Ohio Stamping and Machine LLC
Exact Tool	Precision Resource
Hannibal Industries	Steel Technologies
Martinrea International	Talan Products

HISTORICAL FINANCIALS
Company Type: Private

Income Statement
FYE: December 31

	REVENUE ($ mil.)	NET INCOME ($ mil.)	NET PROFIT MARGIN	EMPLOYEES
12/13	287	7	2.5%	600
12/12	294	1	0.4%	—
12/11	267	5	1.9%	—
12/10	220	0	—	—
Annual Growth	9.3%	—	—	—

2013 Year-End Financials
Return on assets: 7.7% Cash ($ mil.): 1
Return on equity: 2.5%
Current ratio: 1.40

PRINCE GEORGE'S COUNTY PUBLIC SCHOOLS

Auditors: BERT SMITH & CO WASHINGTON D

LOCATIONS
HQ: PRINCE GEORGE'S COUNTY PUBLIC SCHOOLS
14201 SCHOOL LN, UPPER MARLBORO, MD
207722866
Phone: 301 952-6000

HISTORICAL FINANCIALS
Company Type: Private

Income Statement
FYE: June 30

	REVENUE ($ mil.)	NET INCOME ($ mil.)	NET PROFIT MARGIN	EMPLOYEES
06/13	1,966	43	2.2%	18,000
06/11	1,855	3	0.2%	—
06/07	1,627	13	0.8%	—
06/06	1,553	0	—	—
Annual Growth	3.4%	—	—	—

2013 Year-End Financials
Return on assets: — Cash ($ mil.): 246
Return on equity: 2.2%
Current ratio: —

PRINCE WILLIAM COUNTY PUBLIC SCHOOLS

Auditors: CHERRY BEKAERT & HOLLAND LLP

LOCATIONS
HQ: PRINCE WILLIAM COUNTY PUBLIC SCHOOLS
14800 JOPLIN RD, MANASSAS, VA 201123909
Phone: 703 791-8308
Web: WWW.PWCS.EDU

HISTORICAL FINANCIALS
Company Type: Private

Income Statement
FYE: June 30

	REVENUE ($ mil.)	NET INCOME ($ mil.)	NET PROFIT MARGIN	EMPLOYEES
06/13	1,048	23	2.3%	8,000
06/12	968	(18)	—	—
06/11	887	(66)	—	—
06/10	0	0	—	—
Annual Growth	—	—	—	—

PRINCETON HEALTHCARE SYSTEM A NEW JERSEY NONPROFIT CORPORATION

Auditors: PRICEWATERHOUSECOOPERS LLP P

LOCATIONS
HQ: PRINCETON HEALTHCARE SYSTEM A NEW
JERSEY NONPROFIT CORPORATION
253 WITHERSPOON ST STE 1, PRINCETON, NJ
085403211
Phone: 609 497-4000
Web: WWW.PRINCETONHCS.ORG

HISTORICAL FINANCIALS
Company Type: Private

Income Statement
FYE: December 31

	REVENUE ($ mil.)	NET INCOME ($ mil.)	NET PROFIT MARGIN	EMPLOYEES
12/08	310	(26)	—	12
12/06	283	17	6.2%	—
Annual Growth	4.6%	—	—	—

2008 Year-End Financials
Return on assets: 5.2% Cash ($ mil.): 21
Return on equity: (-8.6%)
Current ratio: 1.60

PRO PETROLEUM INC.

Auditors: GARRETT AND SWANN LLP LUBBOCK

LOCATIONS
HQ: PRO PETROLEUM INC.
4710 4TH ST, LUBBOCK, TX 794164900
Phone: 806 795-8785
Web: WWW.PROPETROLEUM.COM

HISTORICAL FINANCIALS
Company Type: Private

Income Statement
FYE: December 31

	REVENUE ($ mil.)	NET INCOME ($ mil.)	NET PROFIT MARGIN	EMPLOYEES
12/13	1,815	12	0.7%	150
12/12	1,830	12	0.7%	—
12/11	1,856	6	0.3%	—
12/10	1,132	0	—	—
Annual Growth	17.0%	—	—	—

2013 Year-End Financials
Return on assets: 1.1% Cash ($ mil.): 15
Return on equity: 0.7%
Current ratio: 0.90

PRODUCERS RICE MILL INC.

These producers aren't just milling about they're about milling. Producers Rice Mill dries mills and markets more than 50 million bushels of rice each year which it sells both domestically and overseas. The growers' cooperative is one of the largest private-label producers of rice in the US packaging more than 100 brands for the foodservice retail private label export and industrial industries. Its brands include ParExcellence LeGourment Golden Harvest Classic Grains Granada Mandalay Bamboo 103 Calrose and Thai Orchard. It also processes rice for animal feeds such as Buck Grub deer feed and Equi-Jewel horse feed.

Geographic Reach

In addition to its corporate headquarters and production facilities in Stuttgart Arkansas the co-operative has receiving operations in Arkansas Mississippi and Texas. It has plants in DeWitt Eudora Fair Oaks Pine Bluff Stuttgart Tyronza Wilmot Wilson and Wynne in Arkansas; Boyle and Greenville in Mississippi; and DeWitt in Texas. About 15% of US milled grains like rice are exported to countries such as Canada Mexico Japan Haiti and Iraq.

Operations

Along with bagged and bulk rice Producers also offers parboiled rice and seasoned rice mixes and processes rice for animal feed. During 2012-13 Producers' mills processed 64.3 million bushels of rice up 14% from the previous year.

Sales and Marketing

The company serves foodservice retail private label export and industrial customers. Ahold U.S.A. Federated Nash Finch and SUPERVALU have been long-term customers.

Strategy

The USDA projects a demand in US rice exports over the next several years. Milled rice will have a higher demand which will directly benefit the US rice industry.

Ownership

Producers is a farmer-owned cooperative.

Company Background

The cooperative was founded in 1943.

EXECUTIVES

V Pres-oprs, Ken Dryden, age 72
Vice President Of Operations, Steven Caver
Auditors: ERWIN & COMPANY LITTLE ROCK

LOCATIONS

HQ: PRODUCERS RICE MILL INC.
518 E HARRISON ST, STUTTGART, AR 721603700
Phone: 870 672-4420
Web: WWW.PRODUCERSRICE.COM

COMPETITORS

ADM	Goya
American Rice	Mars Incorporated
CHS	Mondelez International
Cargill	PepsiCo
Cereal Byproducts	RiceX
Farmers Rice Milling	Riceland Foods
Farmers' Rice Cooperative	Specialty Rice

HISTORICAL FINANCIALS

Company Type: Private

Income Statement
FYE: July 31

	REVENUE ($ mil.)	NET INCOME ($ mil.)	NET PROFIT MARGIN	EMPLOYEES
07/14	546	327	59.9%	730
07/13	568	368	64.8%	—
07/12	478	302	63.3%	—
07/11	499	0	—	—
Annual Growth	3.0%	—	—	—

2014 Year-End Financials

Return on assets: 2.2%   Cash ($ mil.): 1
Return on equity: 59.9%
Current ratio: 0.90

PRODUCTION TOOL SUPPLY COMPANY LLC

Production Tool Supply totes the tools of the trade —and it distributes them to customers worldwide. With nine showrooms in Michigan and Ohio the company (PTS) distributes brand-name discount industrial tools and machinery. It markets approximately 235000 products through a 1700-page catalog on the Internet and through independent distributors. Products include cutting tools carbide tools abrasives measuring tools clamps and vises power tools tool safety products and power machinery by blue chip OEMs such as Bosch Porter-Cable and Sandvik. D. Dan Kahn founded PTS in 1951 to serve small factories and shops in the Detroit area. The Kahn family still controls the company.

Geographic Reach

The company has store locations in Grand Rapids Jackson Lansing Madison Heights Novi Redford Roseville Michigan; and Cleveland. It has more than 400000 sq. ft. of manufacturing space.

Sales and Marketing

Products are sold under such brand names as Brands A-9 Accu-Lube Accurate Acer Acu-Rite Eagle Eagle-Rock Ecco Tool Co Inc Edge Z-Drive Zebra Skimmers.

EXECUTIVES

Vice President Sales, Kim Zrepskey
Senior Vice President Management Information Syste, Richard Caliandro
Auditors: BAKER TILLY VIRSCHOW KARAUSE L

LOCATIONS

HQ: PRODUCTION TOOL SUPPLY COMPANY LLC
8655 E 8 MILE RD, WARREN, MI 480894030
Phone: 586 755-2200
Web: WWW.PTS-TOOLS.COM

PRODUCTS/OPERATIONS

Selected Products
Abrasives
  Abrasives
  Diamond tools
  Grinding-wheel dressers
  Wire brushes
Cutting Tools
  Countersinks and counterbores
  Drills
  Reamers
  Saw blades
  Taps and dies
  Threading tools and accessories
Fluids
  Adhesives/sealants
  Cleaning/lubricants
  Machining fluids/applicators
  Marking/paint
Hand Tools
  Cutting
  Edge deburring
  Electrical tools
  Fastening
  Fastener drive tools
  Hand files
  Marking labeling etching
  Pliers/cutters
  Plumbing tools
  Pullers/heaters
  Scribers and tweezers
  Striking tools
Machinery
  Bandsaws
  CNC machinery
  Cut-off saws
  Drill presses
  Lathes
  Milling machines
  Sandblasters
Material handling
  Furniture
  Handling equipment
  Storage
Measuring Tools
  Comparators/magnifiers
  Gages
  Indicators
  Precision tools
  Service plates
  SPC equipment
MRO/Safety Tools
  Brushes
  Cabinets
  Extension cords
  Fans
  Gloves
  Lamps and lights
  Vacuums
Power Tools
  Air tools
  Electric power tools
  Marking and etching tools
Work-Holding Tools
  Boring heads
  Chucks
  Collet fixtures
  Magnetic chucks
  Quick-change tooling
  Tapping heads
  Vises

COMPETITORS

AIS Construction Equipment	J. O. Galloup
Carbide Tool Services	MSC Industrial Direct
Carlson Systems	Michigan Tractor
DXP Enterprises	Total Plastics
Fastenal	W.W. Grainger
Industrial Distribution Group	

HISTORICAL FINANCIALS

Company Type: Private

Income Statement
FYE: December 31

	REVENUE ($ mil.)	NET INCOME ($ mil.)	NET PROFIT MARGIN	EMPLOYEES
12/13*	228	23	10.3%	357
10/10	129	14	11.6%	—
10/09	117	10	9.2%	—
10/08	1,519	0	—	—
Annual Growth	—	—	—	—

*Fiscal year change

2013 Year-End Financials

Return on assets: 0.8%   Cash ($ mil.): 6
Return on equity: 10.3%
Current ratio: 6.00

PROHEALTH CARE INC

That cheddar-and-beer diet take a toll on your health? Might be time to turn your health over to the pros. ProHealth Care provides health care services to southeastern Wisconsin through a network of three hospitals (Waukesha Memorial Oconomowoc Memorial and the Rehabilitation Hospital of Wisconsin) about two dozen clinics assisted living facilities (Regency Senior Communities) a rehabilitation partnership home health care services and a hospice facility. The community-based organization's specialized services include advanced cancer care cardiology orthopedic and obstetrical and neonatal intensive care.

Operations

ProHealth Care's total operations include Waukesha Memorial Hospital Oconomowoc Memorial Hospital Rehabilitation Hospital of Wisconsin (RHOW) ProHealth Care Medical Associates ProHealth Home Care and Hospice West Wood Health & Fitness Center and senior living facilities.

The RHOW is a 40-bed hospital that is the result of a partnership between ProHealth Care and Centerre Healthcare to meet the increased rehabilitation needs of the region.

Oconomowoc Memorial Hospital has 58 available beds and provides general acute care and support activities in Oconomowoc Wisconsin and surrounding communities.

Financial Performance

In 2014 ProHealth Care's net sales increased by 3% due to higher sales from net patient service revenues less provision for bad debts. Patient service revenues net of contractual allowances and discounts was comprised of $657.9 million from third party payors and $7.3 from self-pay payors.Net income decreased by $107.1 million in 2014 due to lower excess of revenues over expenses (due to unrealized investment loss and change in interest rate swap value) and pension-related changes other than net periodic benefit cost partially offset by increased revenues.Net cash provided by the operating activities increased by 16% due to changes in patient accounts receivable and accounts payable.

Company Background

ProHealth Care in 2012 merged the foundations serving its two hospitals in Waukesha County in an effort to optimize the efficiency of its operations. With the merger the Waukesha Memorial Hospital Foundation and Oconomowoc Memorial Hospital Foundation became the ProHealth Care Foundation. The integration combined the foundation boards donors and volunteers into one organization.

ProHealth Care was established as a not-for-profit corporation in 1998.

EXECUTIVES

Vice President Procurement, Melissa Anderson
Director Of Nursing, Betty Heater
Director Of Nursing, Katie Quintanilla
Board Member, Kathy Ricco
Board Member, Martha Gleisner
Auditors: PLANTE & MORAN PLLC GRAND RA

LOCATIONS

HQ: PROHEALTH CARE INC
N57W 24950 N CORP CIR N 57 W, SUSSEX, WI 53089
Phone: 262 544-2011
Web: WWW.PROHEALTHCARE.ORG

PRODUCTS/OPERATIONS

2014 Sales

	%		
Net patient service revenues	91		
Other operating revenues	9		
Total		0	100

Selected Medical Services

Allergies
Birthing
Bones Joints and Muscles
Brain and Nerves
Breast Health
Cancer
CyberKnife
Diabetes
Diagnostic Services
Digestive
Ear Nose and Throat
Emergency Services/Urgent Care
Eyes and Vision
Gastrointestinal Services
Hearing
Heart and Vascular
Home Care and Hospice
Integrative Medicine
Kidneys and Urinary System
MAKOplasty
Mammography
Men's Health
Mental Health
Multiple Sclerosis
Occupational Health Services
Orthopedic
Pain
Palliative Medicine
Primary Care
Physical Therapy and Rehabilitation Services
Senior Services
Sleep
Spine Care
Stroke
Travel Medicine
Weight Loss
Women's Health
Women's Sexual Health
Wound Care

COMPETITORS

Beaver Dam Community Hospitals
Children's Hospital and Health System
Columbia St. Mary's
FHN
Froedtert Hospital
Hospital Sisters Health System
KishHealth
Ministry Health Care
Rockford Health System
SwedishAmerican Health System
UW Medical Foundation
University of Wisconsin Hospital and Clinics

HISTORICAL FINANCIALS
Company Type: Private

Income Statement
FYE: December 31

	REVENUE ($ mil.)	NET INCOME ($ mil.)	NET PROFIT MARGIN	EMPLOYEES
12/14*	186	14	8.0%	3,000
09/14	710	58	8.2%	—
09/13	687	97	14.1%	—
09/12	702	0	—	—
Annual Growth (48.5%)	—	—	—	—

*Fiscal year change

2014 Year-End Financials

Return on assets: 14.2%   Cash ($ mil.): 75
Return on equity: 8.0%
Current ratio: 2.00

PROTESTANT MEMORIAL MEDICAL CENTER INC.

With more than 315 beds Memorial Hospital has plenty of space to take care of Prairie Staters. The Bellevue Illinois-based hospital is owned and operated by Protestant Memorial Medical Center a community-based not-for-profit organization. Memorial Hospital provides general medical surgical and emergency care as well as pediatric home health and cardiovascular care. Specialty services include treatment for sleep disorders and women's health. The hospital also operates Memorial Convalescent Center a nearly 110-bed skilled nursing facility and the Belleville Health and Sports Center which provides fitness facilities to promote community health.

Geographic Reach

In addition to its main facility in the Belleville neighborhood Memorial Hospital has diagnostic centers in O'Fallon Illinois and an off-campus physical therapy center in east Belleville.

Operations

Memorial Hospital has a medical staff with more than 350 members representing 42 specialties. It provides access to new imaging technology though the Southern Illinois Positive Emission Tomography Imaging Center in Swansea (a joint venture between Memorial and St. Elizabeth's hospitals).

The hospital collaborates with the Southern Illinois University School of Medicine for certain research programs and services. Memorial Hospital is a part of the Memory and Aging Network at the school of medicine as a designated Alzheimer's Disease Primary Provider Site. The program includes a network of about 35 provider sites that collect data on the frequency type and progression of dementia.

Strategy

Memorial Hospital is building a $118 million satellite hospital in nearby Shiloh called Memorial Hospital - East. The new facility will include 94 beds private patient rooms surgical suites a cardiac catheterization lab as well as an intensive care unit and an obstetrics unit. The hospital is expected to open in 2016. When the new hospital opens hospital officials expect the main campus in Belleville to reduce its capacity and convert all patient rooms to single occupancy.

In 2014 CEP America a physician-owned organization which had staffed and managed physician coverage for Memorial Hospital's Emergency

Department also began to provide hospitalist services for the hospital's inpatients.

Memorial Hospital has also expanded its services to Memorial Healthcare Center in O'Fallon to provide general x-ray services state-of-the-art CT scanning MRI and physical therapy.

Company Background

The hospital first opened its doors in 1958.

EXECUTIVES

Vice President of Nursing, Nancy Weston
Vice President, Ruth Holmes
Director Of Pharmacy, Lori Adams
Director Icu Coronary Care Unit, Barb Jany
Director Of Nursing, Anne Crook
Vice President Of General Services, John Kessler
Vice President of Finance, Joe Lanius
Auditors: BKD LLP ST LOUIS MISSOURI

LOCATIONS

HQ: PROTESTANT MEMORIAL MEDICAL CENTER INC.
4500 MEMORIAL DR, BELLEVILLE, IL 622265360
Phone: 618 233-7750
Web: WWW.MEMHOSP.COM

PRODUCTS/OPERATIONS

Selected Services

Advanced Interventional Pain
Belleville Health and Sports Center
Breast Health Center
Cancer Treatment Center
Cardiovascular
Center for Diabetes Education
Emergency Department
Family Care Birthing Center
Gastroenterology Lab
Home Care
Laboratory
Memorial Care Center
Orthopedics
Palliative Care
Pulmonary and Respiratory
Radiology
Rehab Services
Senior Care
Sleep Disorders Center
Surgical Services

COMPETITORS

Ascension Health   RehabCare
BJC HealthCare   St. Anthony's Medical
Barnes-Jewish Hospital   Center
Christian Hospital

HISTORICAL FINANCIALS
Company Type: Private

Income Statement
FYE: December 31

	REVENUE ($ mil.)	NET INCOME ($ mil.)	NET PROFIT MARGIN	EMPLOYEES
12/13	256	(36)	—	2,344
12/12	263	15	6.0%	—
12/11	259	9	3.7%	—
12/09	248	0	—	—
Annual Growth	0.8%	—	—	—

2013 Year-End Financials

Return on assets: —   Cash ($ mil.): 8
Return on equity: (-14.1%)
Current ratio: 2.10

PROVIDENCE COLLEGE

Students don't need divine intervention to get into Providence College they just need good grades and an interest in liberal arts. The Catholic institution of higher education offers undergraduate and graduate degrees at its four schools: Arts and Sciences Business Continuing Education and Professional Studies. It offers degrees in about 50 academic disciplines including biology business education marketing politics and psychology. It has a student-to-faculty ratio of 12:1 with students primarily coming from New England and the Midwest and Mid-Atlantic regions. Providence College was founded in 1917 by the Dominican Friars of the Province of St. Joseph and the Diocese of Providence.

EXECUTIVES

Associate Vice President For Finance Assistant Tre, Jacqueline White
Assistant Vice President, Joseph (Jo) Carr
Assistant Vice President For Development, William O'Neil
Department Chair, Helen Caldwell
Associate Vice President, Rafael Zapata
Vice President Class, Katie Tripp
Auditors: KPMG LLP BOSTOM MA

LOCATIONS

HQ: PROVIDENCE COLLEGE
1 CUNNINGHAM SQ, PROVIDENCE, RI 029180001
Phone: 401 865-1000
Web: WWW.SUPPORT.PROVIDENCE.EDU

HISTORICAL FINANCIALS
Company Type: Private

Income Statement
FYE: June 30

	REVENUE ($ mil.)	NET INCOME ($ mil.)	NET PROFIT MARGIN	EMPLOYEES
06/13	237	22	9.4%	800
06/11	216	24	11.2%	—
06/10	145	24	16.5%	—
06/09	142	0	—	—
Annual Growth 13.6%	—	—	—	—

2013 Year-End Financials
Return on assets: 6.6%
Return on equity: 9.4%
Current ratio: 0.20
Cash ($ mil.): 22

PROVIDENCE HOSPITAL

Providence Hospital and Medical Centers provides health care in the Motor City and surrounding areas. The main Providence Hospital is a 408-bed teaching facility that has been recognized for its cardiology program and clinical expertise in behavioral medicine. It offers a variety of other services ranging from cancer treatment and neurosurgery to orthopedics and women's health. The network also includes dozens of affiliated general practice and specialty health clinics. The not-for-profit medical center founded in 1845 as St. Vincent's Hospital in Detroit by the Daughters of Charity is part of Catholic health ministry St. John Health (itself a subsidiary of Ascension Health).
Operations
As part of its health care system Providence Hospital and Medical Centers operates a host of hospitals and medical centers across the metropolitan Detroit area. They include Providence Southfield and four namesake Providence Medical Center locations in Farmington Hills Livonia Dearborn Heights and South Lyon. Across its system the medical facilities employ some 1500 physicians and enlist the help of about 300 active volunteers.

Carroll Manor is a skilled nursing center that provides short- and long-term medical care and rehabilitation services. The system's behavioral health division Seton House provides alcohol and addiction treatment in Washington DC.
Providence Hospital and Medical Centers had more than 41600 emergency department visits in 2013.
Strategy
In order to provide better services the hospital renovated and expanded its emergency department in 2014. Also that year its family medicine division opened a new office in the Glenn Dale/Bowie area.

EXECUTIVES

Director Of Radiology, Alfred Coccaro

LOCATIONS

HQ: PROVIDENCE HOSPITAL
16001 W 9 MILE RD, SOUTHFIELD, MI 480754803
Phone: 248 849-3000
Web: WWW.PROMEDICA.ORG

Selected Hospitals and Medical Centers
Providence Southfield-Southfield
Providence Medical Center-Farmington Hills
Providence Medical Center-Livonia
Providence Medical Center-Dearborn Heights
Providence Medical Center-South Lyon

PRODUCTS/OPERATIONS

Selected Primary Services
Cancer clinical trials
Cardiac rehabilitation
Childbirth
Congenital heart disease clinic
Emergency
Oncology
Orthopedics
Senior services
Surgery
Women's health

COMPETITORS

Beaumont Health System	McLaren Health Care
Crittenton Hospital	Oakwood Healthcare
Detroit Medical Center	Trinity Health (Novi)
Henry Ford Health System	University of Michigan Health System

HISTORICAL FINANCIALS
Company Type: Private

Income Statement
FYE: June 30

	REVENUE ($ mil.)	NET INCOME ($ mil.)	NET PROFIT MARGIN	EMPLOYEES
06/11	706	27	3.9%	4,700
06/10	593	1	0.3%	—
06/09*	532	(53)	—	—
12/08	0	0	—	—
Annual Growth 101319.4%	—	—	—	—

*Fiscal year change

2011 Year-End Financials
Return on assets: —
Return on equity: 3.9%
Current ratio: 2.20
Cash ($ mil.): 26

PROVIDENCE HOSPITAL

Providence Hospital is a pillar in the health care community of Washington DC. The oldest continuously operating hospital in our nation's capitol the 410-bed facility provides a full spectrum of

services from behavioral health to women's services. It also administers programs for sleep disorders geriatric care and palliative care in addition to its comprehensive medical and surgical services. Providence Hospital's affiliates include the adjacent Carroll Manor Nursing and Rehabilitation Center a 250-bed facility for long-term and rehabilitative care as well as several outpatient family behavioral and occupational health clinics in the region. Providence Hospital is part of the Ascension Health network.
Operations
The main hospital and rehab facility includes the OB/GYN Center for Life a pharmacy and a wellness center. In addition area facilities operated by the hospital include the Seton House behavioral health center several Senior Wellness centers the Fort Lincoln Family Medicine Center (which serves Colmar Manor Maryland) and the Perry Family Health Center.
Company Background
Chartered by President Abraham Lincoln in 1861 Providence Hospital is the longest continuously operating hospital in the US capital.

EXECUTIVES

Vice President Finance, James W (Jamie) Rohrbaugh
Senior Vice President Patient Care Servi; Senior Vice President Patient Care, Thedosia Munford
Operating Room Director, Ulanders Craig
Senior Vice President Operations, Marc Edelman
Nursing Services Director, Denise Gaston
Vice Chair, Mary Bader
Auditors: DELOITTE TAX LLP CINCINNATI

LOCATIONS

HQ: PROVIDENCE HOSPITAL
1150 VARNUM ST NE, WASHINGTON, DC 200172104
Phone: 202 269-7000
Web: WWW.PROVHOSP.ORG

Selected Facilities
Carroll Manor Nursing And Rehabilitation Center (Washington DC)
Congress Heights Senior Wellness Center (Washington DC)
Model Cities Senior Wellness Center (Washington DC)
Hattie Holmes Senior Wellness Center (Washington DC)
Fort Lincoln Family Medicine Center (Colmar Manor Maryland)
Perry Family Health Center (Washington DC)
Police and Fire Clinic (Washington DC)
Seton House (Washington DC; behavioral health services)
Wellington Pharmacy (Washington DC)
Wellness Institute (Washington DC)

COMPETITORS

Adventist HealthCare	Fauquier Hospital
Children's National Medical Center	HSC Pediatric Center
Dimensions Healthcare	MedStar Health
Doctors Community Hospital	Sibley Memorial Hospital
	Suburban Hospital

HISTORICAL FINANCIALS
Company Type: Private

Income Statement
FYE: June 30

	REVENUE ($ mil.)	NET INCOME ($ mil.)	NET PROFIT MARGIN	EMPLOYEES
06/13	198	(8)	—	2,517
06/10	235	8	3.5%	—
06/09	230	(13)	—	—
06/08	0	0	—	—
Annual Growth	—	—	—	—

2013 Year-End Financials
Return on assets: 16.9%
Return on equity: (-4.2%)
Current ratio: 0.90
Cash ($ mil.): 5

PSCU INCORPORATED

Credit unions turn to PSCU to provide key card services. Ass one of the nation's largest credit union service organizations PSCU (short for Payment Systems for Credit Unions) provides credit debit ATM and prepaid card servicing as well as electronic banking bill payment risk management specialized marketing and contact center services to credit unions across the US. The not-for-profit cooperative serves more than 1300 institutions nationwide which combined represent more than 18 million cardholder accounts and one million online bill payment subscribers. PSCU is owned by about 800 member credit unions.

Operations

The centers perform new member enrollment automated lending collections cardholder support cross-selling and customer service. Its four contact centers handle more than 18 million inquiries a year.

Geographic Reach

PSCU operates four Contact Centers covering three major US regions: the Eastern US with one center located in St. Petersburg Florida; the Western US with one center in Phoenix Arizona; and the Midwest with two centers in Detroit Michigan.Sales and MarketingPSCU's clients have included: Redwood Credit Union State Department Federal Credit Union Corporate One Federal Credit Union Advantis Credit Union and the Indiana Credit Union League.

Strategy

PSCU has taken a string of steps to help its partnering credit unions adopt newer safer digital payment technologies in recent years. In early 2015 for example it helped its clients Redwood Credit Union and State Department Federal Credit Union implement access to the smartphone-based Apple Pay platform so their cardholders could make digital payments using their iPhones and iPads. In 2013 the company expanded its Phoenix site to house its PSCU technology-based services and developed six new mobile apps to help clients' members interact with their core deposit prepaid credit card and rewards accounts via smart phone technology. It also introduced the CardLock solution (which works in tandem with PSCU's fraud detection and prevention platform) to enable cardholders to block and unblock authorizations on cards they register with the service. In 2012 the company became the first to issue VISA Prepaid EMV (Europay MasterCard and Visa) cards in the US.

PSCU also continues to lock in its long-term contracts with existing and new clients to keep business growing. In late 2014 the company signed a five-year renewal agreement with the $4.2 billion Corporate One Federal Credit Union to continue providing its credit and debit processing services. In mid-2014 PSCU signed a two new long-term contracts including: a five-year agreement with the $1.1 billion Advantis Credit Union in Portland and secured another long-term agreement with the Indiana Credit Union League.

Company Background

PSCU was formed in 1977 by leaders from Pinellas County Teachers Credit Union and the federal credit unions of GTE Publix Employees Suncoast Schools and Railroad and Industrial.

EXECUTIVES

Senior Vice President Chief Risk Officer, Steve Ruwe
Executive Vice President, Steve Salzer
President and CEO, Michael J. (Mike) Kelly

EVP Credit Debit Prepaid eCommerce Contact Center and Information Technology, Tom Gandre
EVP Credit Union Experience, Fredda McDonald
EVP Human Resources, Lynn Heckler
Executive Vice President & Chief Financial Officer, Brian Caldarelli
Executive Vice President Chief Information Officer, Sam Esfahani
Senior Vice President & Chief Marketing Officer, Dan Csont
Senior Vice President Operations Service Delivery, Jack Lynch
Senior Vice President of Product, Dave Stafford
Vice President Application Development and Delivery, Adam Kreuger
Vice President Advisors Plus Marketing, Michelle (Mitch) Hillenbrand
Vice President Card Solutions, Kent Potterton
Area Vice President Card Services, John (Jack) McPherson
Vice President Strategic Innovation, Mark Welch
Area Vice President Of Sales, Norma Martinez
Vice President Account Management, Joe Poulliott
Senior Vice President Of Innovation, Kristin Scharf
Vice President Account Management, Brenden McGinness
Area Vice President Total Member Care, Micah Washinski
Area Vice President, Ron Metsker
Vice President Business Development, Sam Snyder
Senior Vice President Vendor Alliance Partnerships, David Hall
Area Vice President, Steven (Steve) Mathias
Area Vice President, Francine Fern
Vice President Talent And Organizational Development, John (Jack) Buschiazzo
Vice President Financial Operations, Keith Rolleston
Vice President Key Accounts, Leslie Reistrup
Vice President of Human Resources Strategy, Chris Sierra
Chairman, Craig Esrael
Vice Chairman, Mike Valentine
Board Member, Margie Phillips
Board Member, Henderson Smith
Board Member, John (Jack) Thompson
Auditors: PRICEWATERHOUSECOOPERS LLP TA

LOCATIONS

HQ: PSCU INCORPORATED
560 CARILLON PKWY, SAINT PETERSBURG, FL 337161294
Phone: 727 572-8822
Web: WWW.PSCU.COM

PRODUCTS/OPERATIONS

Selected Services
Advisors Plus
Credit Solutions
Debit Solutions
eCommerce Solutions
EMV
Prepaid Solutions
Risk Management Solutions

Total	0	0

Technology Tools
PSCU Partnerships/Sponsorships
Credit Union Cherry Blossom Run
Credit Union Student Choice
Filene Research Institute
Financial Service Center Cooperatives (FSCC)
Ongoing Operations
The Colonial Williamsburg Foundation

COMPETITORS

CUSO Financial Services	Raymond James Financial
Fidelity National Information Services	Southwest Corporate FCU
LPL Financial	U.S. Central

HISTORICAL FINANCIALS
Company Type: Private

Income Statement

	REVENUE ($ mil.)	NET INCOME ($ mil.)	NET PROFIT MARGIN	EMPLOYEES
09/13*	388	41	10.6%	1,400
12/12	377	38	10.2%	—
12/11	425	29	6.9%	—
12/10	662	0	—	—
Annual Growth	(16.3%)	—	—	—

FYE: September 30
*Fiscal year change

2013 Year-End Financials

Return on assets: 8.8%   Cash ($ mil.): 124
Return on equity: 10.6%
Current ratio: 0.80

PUBLIC BROADCASTING SERVICE

You might say these shows get a lot of public support. Public Broadcasting Service (PBS) is a non-profit organization that provides educational and public interest programming to more than 350 member public TV stations in the US. In addition to such programs as NOVA This Old House and Downton Abbey it provides related services such as distribution fundraising support and technology development. PBS gets its revenue from underwriting membership dues federal funding (including grants from the not-for-profit Corporation for Public Broadcasting) royalties license fees and product sales. The organization was founded in 1969 to provide cultural and educational programming.

Geographic Reach

PBS reaches about 120 million people through television and nearly 28 million people online each month.

Operations

PBS operates through more than 350 member public TV stations across the US.

Financial Performance

PBS saw is revenue decrease by almost 17% during fiscal year 2011 as compared to 2010.

Strategy

While PBS —and its federal funding —regularly finds itself caught in the crossfire between liberal and conservative political groups supporters of the non-profit trumpet the benefits of publicly-funded television programming created to serve groups often overlooked by commercial broadcasters.

PBS' children's programming and news shows such as Frontline and PBS NewsHour (formerly The NewsHour with Jim Lehrer) are often touted as examples of how public broadcasting can fill voids left by the major networks.

The organization has also been looking to capitalize on new distribution channels to get its programming to the public. PBS sells its programs on DVD and through Apple's iTunes store. It has also ramped up its online video efforts.

EXECUTIVES

SVP CFO and Interim EVP PBS Businesses, Barbara L. Landes
COO, Jonathan Barzilay
SVP and General Manager PBS Digital, Ira Rubenstein
President CEO and Director, Paula A. Kerger

Executive Director PBS Foundation, Brian J. Reddington

CTO, Mario Vecchi

Chief Programming Executive and General Manager General Audience Programming, Beth Hoppe

SVP Marketing and Communications; General Manager Children's Programming, Lesli Rotenberg

Vice President, Joseph (Jo) Campbell

Vice President Government Affairs And Associate General Counsel, William (Bill) Weber

Senior Vice President Station Services, Juan Seplveda

Vice President and Controller, Pete Quinlivan

Coordinator Assistant To Assistant Vice President, Julianne Menassian

Vice President Human Resources, Carole Dickert-scherr

Vice President Digital Marketing and Services, Don Wilcox

Chairman, Donald A. (Don) Baer

Director, Tom Axtell

Auditors: BDO USA LLP BETHESDA MD

LOCATIONS

HQ: PUBLIC BROADCASTING SERVICE
2100 CRYSTAL DR STE 100, ARLINGTON, VA 222023784
Phone: 703 739-5000
Web: WWW.PBS.ORG

PRODUCTS/OPERATIONS

Selected Programming
Antiques Roadshow
Austin City Limits
Barney
Downton Abbey
Frontline
Juila Child: Lessons with Master Chefs
Live from Lincoln Center
Masterpiece Theatre
Mister Rogers' Neighborhood
MotorWeek
Mystery!
Nature
NOVA
NOW
P.O.V.
PBS NewsHour
Reading Rainbow
Sesame Street
Teletubbies
This Old House
Victory Garden
Washington Week
ZOOM

COMPETITORS

ABC Cable Networks	HBO
ABC Inc.	MTV Networks
AMC Networks	NBC
BBC Worldwide	Scripps Networks
CBS	Turner Broadcasting
Current Media	
Discovery Communications	

HISTORICAL FINANCIALS

Company Type: Private

Income Statement FYE: June 30

	REVENUE ($ mil.)	NET INCOME ($ mil.)	NET PROFIT MARGIN	EMPLOYEES
06/10	505	28	5.6%	507
06/09	502	(80)	—	—
06/08	0	0	—	—
Annual Growth	—	4045.9%	—	—

2010 Year-End Financials

Return on assets: —   Cash ($ mil.): 7
Return on equity: 5.6%
Current ratio: 0.30

PUBLIC HEALTH SOLUTIONS

Public Heath Solutions (formerly Medical and Health Research Association of New York City) is here to help. Public Health Solutions (PHS) is a not-for-profit organization that works with the NYC Department of Health to create and administer projects aimed at providing better healthcare to the city's low-income at-risk population. It helps about 200000 people a year with studies like the Human Papillomavirus Screening Project and others looking at disease awareness and prevention in minority groups. Services include women's and children's health HIV/AIDS health care smoking cessation counseling and access to health care. The organization was founded in 1957 to conduct health research projects.

EXECUTIVES

Vice President and General Counsel, Jane (Ginny) Levine

Vice President Public Health Programs, Louise Cohen

Auditors: JH COHN LLP NEW YORK NY

LOCATIONS

HQ: PUBLIC HEALTH SOLUTIONS
40 WORTH ST FL 5, NEW YORK, NY 100132955
Phone: 646 619-6400
Web: WWW.HEALTHSOLUTIONS.ORG

HISTORICAL FINANCIALS

Company Type: Private

Income Statement FYE: December 31

	REVENUE ($ mil.)	NET INCOME ($ mil.)	NET PROFIT MARGIN	EMPLOYEES
12/07	225	7	3.3%	650
12/06	214	(2)	—	—
12/05	1,130	0	0.0%	—
Annual Growth	(55.3%)	2019.1%	—	—

2007 Year-End Financials

Return on assets: —   Cash ($ mil.): 20
Return on equity: 3.3%
Current ratio: 0.30

PUBLIC UTILITIES BOARD

This PUB has no beer. Brownsville Public Utilities Board (Brownsville PUB) is a municipally-owned utility company providing electric water and wastewater services to residential and commercial customers in Brownsville Texas. Brownsville PUB serves 46000 with electric service and 47000 with water and wastewater service. The utility's two water treatment plants have the capacity to provide 40 million gallons of treated water per day. It gets its water supply from the Rio Grande. The utility's wastewater system has 174 lift stations and two treatment plants.

Brownsville PUB is challenged to keep pace with explosive population growth in Brownsville (2.5% a year since 2000). In 2012 its major growth initiatives included bringing water to a colonias (un-developed but populated rural community) on the edge of Brownsville a seawater desalination plant a filtration project and sewer overflow remediation.

Customer growth and higher power water and wastewater demand lifted the utility's revenues by more than 8% in 2011 while the robust revenues and lower fuel costs (due to low natural gas prices) and a drop in depreciation and other costs helped the company to report a 52% jump in operating income for the year.

The utility got it start in 1907 after local residents voted for the issuance of bonds to build electric and water plants and construct a utility system.

In the 1960s Brownsville citizens narrowly defeated a bid by electrical provider Central Power & Light Co. to buy the Brownsville utility. Following this the city set up Brownsville PUB as a municipally owned utility giving customers control over the management of their utility.

EXECUTIVES

CEO General Manager and Director, John S. Bruciak

Director Environmental Services, Albert Gomez

Director Water and Wastewater Engineering Operations, Genoveva G. Gomez

Director Communications and Administrative Services, Lucila Cano Hernandez

Director Transmission and Distribution, James McCann

Assistant General Manager Chief Operating Officer, Fernando Saenz

Director Purchasing, Diane Solitaire

Manager Customer Service, Susan Walker

Chief Financial Officer, Leandro G. Garcia

Human Resources Manager, Emilia Guerra

Account Manager, Ana I. Lozano

Chairman, David S. Morales

CEO General Manager and Director, John S. Bruciak

Auditors: PATTILLO BROWN & HILL LLP

LOCATIONS

HQ: PUBLIC UTILITIES BOARD
1425 ROBINHOOD ST, BROWNSVILLE, TX 785214230
Phone: 956 350-8819
Web: WWW.BROWNSVILLE-PUB.COM

HISTORICAL FINANCIALS

Company Type: Private

Income Statement FYE: September 30

	REVENUE ($ mil.)	NET INCOME ($ mil.)	NET PROFIT MARGIN	EMPLOYEES
09/09	163	10	6.3%	482
09/08	209	34	16.6%	—
09/06	421	0	—	—
Annual Growth	—	2707.7%	—	—

2009 Year-End Financials

Return on assets: 9.2%   Cash ($ mil.): 10
Return on equity: 6.3%
Current ratio: 0.70

PULSE ELECTRONICS INC.

Auditors: KPMG LLP SAN DIEGO CALIFORNI

LOCATIONS

HQ: PULSE ELECTRONICS INC.
12220 WORLD TRADE DR, SAN DIEGO, CA
921283765
Phone: 858 674-8100
Web: WWW.PULSEELECTRONICS.COM

HISTORICAL FINANCIALS

Company Type: Private

Income Statement
FYE: December 27

	REVENUE ($ mil.)	NET INCOME ($ mil.)	NET PROFIT MARGIN	EMPLOYEES
12/13	355	(27)	—	12,000
12/12	373	(32)	—	
Annual Growth	(4.7%)	—	—	—

2013 Year-End Financials

Return on assets: 19.9%   Cash ($ mil.): 26
Return on equity: (-7.6%)
Current ratio: 0.70

PYCO INDUSTRIES INC.

Ginning up business is the secret to this vegetable oil producer's success. PYCO Industries is said to be the largest cotton seed co-op to serve the southern US. The Texas-based cooperative comprising more than 60-member gins processes cottonseed for a broad market through two cottonseed oil mills. Its cottonseed oil is shipped to food manufacturers and other foodservice customers across the country. The co-op also markets whole cottonseed as well as the by-products of crushing cottonseed such as cottonseed hulls and cottonseed meal for beef and dairy cattle feed. Cottonseed linters another byproduct are used by manufacturers of mattresses and upholstery padding paper and plastics and other products.

PYCO's operations include subsidiary Plainsman Switching Company (PSC) a shortline railroad connection with the BNSF Railroad and the Union Pacific Railroad. PSC ships and receives a variety of commodities in Lubbock including grain chemicals lumber as well as cotton seed and cottonseed oil. It also handles wind turbine components used to construct wind energy farms.

In early 2010 PYCO sold its Greenwood Mississippi-based cottonseed oil mill shutdown since early 2009. Mississippi cotton gin Delta Oil Mill acquired the plant along with its storage facilities.

In 2011 a historic drought drove the worst dryland cotton crop on record. The impact rippled across the industry. PYCO reported enough carryover seed from prior plentiful crops along with the immediate meager turnout to keep running. However the downturn in production coupled with another year of rain-starved crops threatens to force a cut to operations by some 50%. The tight situation follows increasing interest in the culinary and textile application of cottonseed oil and the by-products fueled by episodes on the History Channel and America's Heartland a nationally distributed program.

EXECUTIVES

President, Gail Kring
VP Finance, Tony Morton
Director Information Technology, Jeff Tucker
SVP Marketing, Robert Lacy
VP Oil Trading and Packaged Oil, Ronnie Gilbert
Manager Marketing and Transportation, Kelly Jack
Mid-South Division Manager, John Stewart
Controller Mid-South Division, Kathy Garrett

Traffic and Sales Mid-South Division, Willie Willis
Chairman, Thomas W. Horsford
Oil Administrator and Logistics, Lisa Buxton
Sales Manager, Seth Terrell
Auditors: D WILLIAMS & CO LUBBOCK TX

LOCATIONS

HQ: PYCO INDUSTRIES INC.
2901 AVENUE A, LUBBOCK, TX 794042231
Phone: 806 747-3434
Web: WWW.PYCOINDUSTRIESINC.COM

PRODUCTS/OPERATIONS

Selected Products

Hulls
  Feed for cattle
  Furfural
  Oil well drilling mud
Linters
  Cellulose esters and ethers
  Cellulose nitrate
  Felts
  Films
  Food casings
  Medical grade cotton
  Paper
  Yarns
Meal
  Feed
  Fertilizer
Oil
  Fatty acids
  Glycerine
  Refined
Whole seed
  Feed for cattle

COMPETITORS

ADM   Cargill

HISTORICAL FINANCIALS

Company Type: Private

Income Statement
FYE: September 30

	REVENUE ($ mil.)	NET INCOME ($ mil.)	NET PROFIT MARGIN	EMPLOYEES
09/14	184	22	12.4%	160
09/13	176	18	10.6%	
09/12	196	11	5.8%	
09/06	234	0		
Annual Growth	(2.9%)	—	—	—

2014 Year-End Financials

Return on assets: 1.1%   Cash ($ mil.): 34
Return on equity: 12.4%
Current ratio: 1.20

QUAKER VALLEY FOODS INC.

Quaker Valley Foods (QVF) is known by friends high and low for its take-out fresh and frozen staples. The food distributor makes daily deliveries of meat and other provisions to foodservice customers across the Northeast US. QVF a member of the UNIPRO Foodservice coop offers beef pork poultry frozen seafood imported meats (mutton and goat) cheeses salads and other items from its Philadelphia warehouse. Customers range from wholesalers and jobbers to independent retail and wholesale groceries and major supermarket chains. Its vendors include Hormel Swift Packerland Carolina Turkey Tyson Alpine Lace and Land O'

Lakes. QVF was started by two brothers-in-law in 1975 and is led by its founders' sons.

EXECUTIVES

President, Wayne Hudis
VP Operations, Kenneth Fleekop
Auditors: KREISCHER MILLER HORSHAM PA

LOCATIONS

HQ: QUAKER VALLEY FOODS INC.
2701 RED LION RD, PHILADELPHIA, PA 191141019
Phone: 215 992-0900
Web: WWW.QUAKERVALLEYFOODS.COM

PRODUCTS/OPERATIONS

Selected Products

Beef
Deli and provisions
Goats
Lamb
Mutton imported
Pork
Poultry
Seafood frozen

COMPETITORS

Associated Wholesale Grocers	SUPERVALU
C&S Wholesale	Schiff's
Feesers	Sysco
McLane	US Foods
Meadowbrook Meat Company	Vista Food Exchange

HISTORICAL FINANCIALS

Company Type: Private

Income Statement
FYE: December 31

	REVENUE ($ mil.)	NET INCOME ($ mil.)	NET PROFIT MARGIN	EMPLOYEES
12/11*	195	0	0.2%	145
01/11	177	0	0.2%	—
01/10	1,546	0	0.0%	
Annual Growth	(64.4%)	3198.3%	—	—

*Fiscal year change

2011 Year-End Financials

Return on assets: —   Cash ($ mil.): —
Return on equity: 0.2%
Current ratio: 0.60

QUALITY OIL COMPANY LLC

With more services than your average oil company Quality Oil helps its customers get fueled up cooled off and well rested. And they can smoke if they want to. The company distributes fuel oil and propane to customers in the Winston-Salem area of North Carolina. Quality Oil provides air conditioning and heating equipment service operates 47 convenience stores (Quality Marts) and about 20 service stations and owns hotels in five southern states. In addition the company operates 60 Quality Plus locations at which drivers can buy cigarettes at discount prices. The company also provides Right-a-Way oil change services at many of its gas stations.

Geographic Reach

Quality Oil owns and operates four Hampton Inns two Hampton Inn & Suites and one Homewood Suites in the Carolinas Florida Georgia and

Virginia. Affiliate Reliable Tank Line LLC transports petroleum products and provides fleet fueling services at 10 locations in North Carolina northern South Carolina eastern Virginia and eastern Tennessee. Quality Oil Heating-Cooling has assets throughout North Carolina and parts of South Carolina Virginia Florida and Tennessee and serves Forsyth County Stokes County Davie County Davidson County Yadkin County Rowan County and Iredell County.

Operations

In addition the company's real estate unit (Quality Oil Real Estate) operates a diverse portfolio of retail and hotel sites industrial units residential subdivision developments and a shopping center. Quality Marts and Quality Plus also provide heating and cooling and fleet fueling services.

Sales and Marketing

The company markets Shell oil products.

Strategy

To sharpen its competitive edge in 2013 Quality Oil created a new department —Retail Technology —to maintain PDI Pricebook and POS Systems and test and implement future technological developments.

To increase operational efficiency in 2012 Quality Oil installed Professional Datasolutions Inc. (PDI) scanning software at all of its retail outlets.

Mergers and Acquisitions

To complement its existing oil and propane business in 2012 Quality Oil acquired regional gas station and convenience store operator Horn Oil Co. in Mocksville North Carolina.

Company Background

Expanding its store network in 2011 the company opened Quality Mart locations #46 and #47 in Kernersville and Morrisville.

Quality Oil was founded in 1929 by Joe Glenn and Bert Bennett as a Shell oil products distributor and is still owned and operated by descendants of the founders.

EXECUTIVES

Senior Vice President Construction, Ernie Rhymer
Vice President Shell Stations, Danny Brown
Senior Vice President Hotel Division, Rob Hill
Senior Vice President Real Estate, Jim Slate
Senior Vice President, Tracy Harmon
Senior Vice President, Tim Lowman
Senior Vice President, Andy Sayles
Auditors: BUTLER & BURKE LLP WINSTON-S

LOCATIONS

HQ: QUALITY OIL COMPANY LLC
1540 SILAS CREEK PKWY, WINSTON SALEM, NC 271273705
Phone: 336 722-3441
Web: WWW.QUALITYOILNC.COM

PRODUCTS/OPERATIONS

Selected Brands
Hampton Inn
Quality Heating and Air Conditioning
Quality Mart
Quality Oil Appliance Sales and Service
Quality Oil Commercial Heating and On-Site Fueling
Quality Oil Fuel Oil
Quality Oil Gas Logs and Heaters
Quality Oil Propane
Quality Plus
Reliable Tank Line
Shell Oil products

Selected Mergers and Acquisitions

COMPETITORS

A.T. Williams	Marriott
Cumberland Farms	Racetrac Petroleum
E-Z Mart Stores	WilcoHess
Hyatt	

HISTORICAL FINANCIALS
Company Type: Private

Income Statement
FYE: December 31

	REVENUE ($ mil.)	NET INCOME ($ mil.)	NET PROFIT MARGIN	EMPLOYEES
12/09	634	11	1.9%	1,000
12/08	806	27	3.4%	—
12/07	619	10	1.8%	—
12/06	542	0	—	—
Annual Growth	5.4%	—	—	—

2009 Year-End Financials
Return on assets: 3.5%
Return on equity: 1.9%
Current ratio: 0.70
Cash ($ mil.): 11

QUEEN OF THE VALLEY MEDICAL CENTER

The Queen of the Valley Medical Center reigns over the whole of Napa Valley. The 190-bed hospital provides acute and tertiary care to the residents of California's Napa County. It operates a level III trauma center and provides emergency surgery and wound care services as well as specialty family work health nutritional and rehabilitation services. "The Queen" as it is known colloquially operates regional cancer orthopedic women's and heart centers as well as the Napa Valley Imaging Center and the Napa Valley Women's Healthcare Center. Queen of the Valley Medical Center is part of St. Joseph Health.

Current expansion efforts at Queen of the Valley Medical Center include construction of a $30 million three-story diagnostic and surgical pavilion. The new center will add high-tech surgical suites and diagnostic laboratory and imaging facilities as well as private ICU rooms. The hospital is also developing a new neuroscience center.

The medical center was founded in 1958 by the Sisters of St. Joseph of Orange. It expanded its facilities a number of times over the years. For instance in 2006 the hospital added a wellness center and a unit dedicated to maternal and infant care. These expansion efforts prompted a name change from Queen of the Valley Hospital to Queen of the Valley Medical Center in 2007 to reflect the facility's expanded offerings and its emphasis on not just medical care but also community-based outreach and prevention services.

EXECUTIVES

Vice President Mission Integration, Marian Schubert
Vice President Marketing Private Programs, Joseph (Jo) Carrillo
Auditors: ERNST & YOUNG US LLP IRVINE

LOCATIONS

HQ: QUEEN OF THE VALLEY MEDICAL CENTER
1000 TRANCAS ST, NAPA, CA 945582906
Phone: 707 251-1761
Web: WWW.THEQUEEN.ORG

COMPETITORS

Adventist Health
Community Hospital of the Monterey Peninsula
Dignity Health
HCA
John Muir Health
Providence Health & Services

Stanford Hospital and Clinics
Sutter Health
Tenet Healthcare
UCSF Medical
Western Medical Center - Santa Ana

HISTORICAL FINANCIALS
Company Type: Private

Income Statement
FYE: June 30

	REVENUE ($ mil.)	NET INCOME ($ mil.)	NET PROFIT MARGIN	EMPLOYEES
06/13	285	23	8.1%	1,070
06/10	276	25	9.1%	—
06/09	242	(5)	—	—
06/08	333	0	—	—
Annual Growth	(3.0%)	—	—	—

2013 Year-End Financials
Return on assets: 11.1%
Return on equity: 8.1%
Current ratio: 4.50
Cash ($ mil.): 111

QUINNIPIAC UNIVERSITY

At Quinnipiac University the first thing you may have to learn is how to pronounce it (for the record it's KWIN-uh-pe-ack). The private university offers a variety of liberal arts undergraduate programs as well as graduate programs in selected professional fields (business education health sciences communications arts and sciences nursing and law) to some 9000 students with a student-to-faculty ration of 16 to 1. It often appears on lists of top colleges including those published by U.S. News & World Report. The university known to political junkies and others for its polling operation includes eight schools and colleges across three Connecticut campuses (Mount Carmel York Hill and North Haven).

Operations

Quinnipiac offers more than 50 undergraduate majors and more than 20 graduate programs. For fiscal year 2015-2016 its tuition and fees are $42270.

Geographic Reach

The school's York Hill campus is home to the TD Bank Sports Center; its North Haven campus houses the Center for Medicine Nursing and Health Sciences which includes the School of Health Sciences the Frank H. Netter MD School of Medicine and the School of Nursing.

Strategy

In 2014 Quinnipiac launched an online graduate business program as well as a master's program in sports journalism. With the 2013 opening of the Frank H. Netter MD School of Medicine the university became one of fewer than 100 with both a law school and a medical school on campus.

Company BackgroundOriginally named the Connecticut College of Commerce the school was founded in 1929 by Samuel W. Tator as a small business college awarding associate's degrees. The college changed its name in 1951 to Quinnipiac College commemorating the early Indian settlers who made their home in and around the New Haven Connecticut harbor area.

EXECUTIVES

Vice Chairman, Carlton L. Highsmith, age 61
President and Trustee, John L. Lahey, age 68

SVP Finance, Patrick J. Healy, age 70
Vice President for public affairs, Lynn M. Bushnell
VP and Dean of Students, Manuel Carreiro
VP and Dean of Admissions, Joan Isaac Mohr
Chairman, Terry W. Goodwin
Dean Academic Services and Research Support, Linda K. Broker
Director Admissions, Carla May Knowlton
Director Admissions for Transfer and Part-Time Students, Mary E. Wargo
Director Arnold Bernhard Library, Charles M. Getchell
Director Athletics and Recreation, John J. McDonald
senior Vice President for academic and student affairs, Mark A. Thompson
Associate Dean School of Business, Charles M. Brooks
Dean School of Communications, David Donnelly
Vice President for development and alumni affairs, Donald J. Weinbach
Associate VP Development and Alumni Affairs, Dianna Pategas
Associate VP Facilities Administration, Joseph D. Rubertone
Associate Director Facilities, Keith Woodward
Director Administrative Services, John J. Meriano
Director Human Resources, Anna M. Spragg
Senior Director Financial Aid, Dominic R. Yoia
Senior Associate Director Financial Aid, Laurie Folsom
Director Graduate Admissions, Scott Farber
Director Marketing Communications for Admissions, Louise M. Howe
Director Graduate Financial Aid, Heather Hamilton
Director Student Health Services, Katheryn B. Macaione
VP CIO and CTO, Richard C. Ferguson
Dean School of Law, Brad Saxton
Director Learning Center, Andrew Delohery
Dean College of Arts and Sciences, Johannes D. (Hans) Bergmann
Registrar, Dorothy M. Lauria
Director Residential Life, Cindy Long Porter
Chief of Security and Safety, John R. Twining
Dean Academic Technology, John Paton
Bursar, Valerie Carbone
Controller, Daniel Johnson
Interim Dean School of Health Sciences, Edward R. O'Connor
Dean Division of Education, Cynthia K. Dubea
Managing Director, David M. Darst
Vice President for human resources, Ronald Mason
VP CIO and CTO, Fred Tarca
Dean School of Communications, Lee Kamlet
Dean School of Education, Kevin Basmadjian
Vice President executive associate to the president, Jean Husted
Trustee, William G. Spears, age 75
Trustee, William C. (Bill) Weldon, age 64
Vice Chairman, Carlton L. Highsmith, age 61
President and Trustee, John L. Lahey, age 68
Trustee, David R. Nelson
Trustee, William L. (Bill) Ayers Jr.
Trustee, Frederick J. Mancheski
Vice Chairman, Murray Lender
Secretary and Trustee, Robert J. Hauser Jr.
Trustee, Alexander Alexiades
Trustee, John R. Antonino
Trustee, Anthony J. Baudanza
Trustee, Patrick Baumgarten
Trustee, Donald P. Calcagnini
Trustee, Albert Canosa
Trustee, Peter R. DeGeorge
Trustee, Gabriel Ferrucci
Trustee, Dennis P. Flanagan
Trustee, Mary-Jane Foster, age 62
Trustee, Hugh F. Keefe
Trustee, Richard G. Kelley
Trustee, Marcus R. McCraven

Trustee, John F. Meuser
Trustee, Paula Moynahan
Trustee, Donald L. Perlroth
Trustee, Jonathan M. Reeves
Trustee, Arthur H. Rice
Trustee, Edward L. Scalone

LOCATIONS

HQ: QUINNIPIAC UNIVERSITY
275 MOUNT CARMEL AVE, HAMDEN, CT 065181908
Phone: 203 582-8200
Web: WWW.QUINNIPIAC.EDU

PRODUCTS/OPERATIONS

Selected Schools
College of Arts and Sciences
Schools of Business and Engineering
School of Communications
School of Education
School of Law
School of Health Sciences
School of Nursing

HISTORICAL FINANCIALS
Company Type: Private

Income Statement   FYE: June 30

	REVENUE ($ mil.)	NET INCOME ($ mil.)	NET PROFIT MARGIN	EMPLOYEES
06/13	376	45	12.2%	900
06/10	290	45	15.6%	—
06/09	235	(0)	—	—
Annual Growth	12.4%	—	—	—

2013 Year-End Financials
Return on assets: 14.7%   Cash ($ mil.): 5
Return on equity: 12.2%
Current ratio: —

R. E. MICHEL COMPANY

Blowing hot and cold is good for R.E. Michel. The company is one of the nation's largest wholesale distributors of heating air-conditioning and refrigeration (HVAC-R) equipment parts and supplies. The family-owned and operated firm offers more than 16000 items through about 2 sales offices located across the Southern Mid-Atlantic and Northeastern regions of the country. R.E. Michel ships more than 20000 items each day from its 900000-sq.-ft. distribution center in Maryland. Its Exclusive Supplier Partnership (ESP) program offers customers inventory control advertising and marketing support. R.E. Michel was founded in 1935 as a supplier to the home heating oil burner industry.

Geographic Reach
The HVAC wholesaler maintains a handful of offices to cater to customers located in the Southern US as well as in the Mid-Atlantic and Northeastern regions. Most recently opened offices reside in Ohio California Virginia Florida South Carolina Arizona and Tennessee.

Sales and Marketing
R.E. Michel uses up to 50 trailers to ship its more than 10000 items each day. To this end the company also ships more than 3200 items via the United Parcel Service each week. As part of its business it publishes a 1300 page catalog that includes 20000 catalog line items.

EXECUTIVES

President, Butch Michel
Vice President Of Marketing, Mike Michel

Vice President Of Fin Human Resources, Holly Porter
Vice President Operations, Harry Tate
Vice President Of Sales, Glen Baker
Treasurer, Ron Miller
Auditors: CLIFTONLARSONALLEN LLP BALTIM

LOCATIONS

HQ: R. E. MICHEL COMPANY
1 RE MICHEL DR, GLEN BURNIE, MD 210606408
Phone: 410 760-4000
Web: WWW.REMICHEL.COM

PRODUCTS/OPERATIONS

Selected Products & Services
Air conditioning & heating
Indoor air quality
Boilers
Water heating equipment
Hydronic & steam systems
Valves
Pipe & fittings
Fuel oil systems
Gas systems
Chemicals
Refrigeration equipment & supplies
Controls
Electrical supplies
Motors
Air handling products
Venting products
Duct registers & grilles
Tools & test instruments
O.E.M. Parts

COMPETITORS

Emco Corporation	Lowe's
Ferguson Enterprises	MSC Industrial Direct
Gensco	W.W. Grainger
HD Supply	WinWholesale

HISTORICAL FINANCIALS
Company Type: Private

Income Statement   FYE: December 31

	REVENUE ($ mil.)	NET INCOME ($ mil.)	NET PROFIT MARGIN	EMPLOYEES
12/13	685	31	4.6%	1,674
12/12	611	3	0.6%	—
12/11	606	8	1.4%	—
12/10	593	0	—	—
Annual Growth	4.9%	—	—	—

2013 Year-End Financials
Return on assets: 12.2%   Cash ($ mil.): —
Return on equity: 4.6%
Current ratio: 0.60

R. L. JORDAN OIL COMPANY OF NORTH CAROLINA INC.

R. L. Jordan Oil Company takes gas from hot spots and sells it —and lots more —at Hot Spots. The company operates a chain of more than 50 convenience stores and gas stations under the Hot Spots banner as well as about 10 fast food restaurants under the Hardee's and Subway names. It operates in the Carolinas. About 75% of the company's stores are located in South Carolina. The family-owned and -operated company was founded by its namesake and former chairman in 1950 the late R. L. Jordan. As part of its operations the Jordan family also owns a real estate business Jordan Properties which operates several hotels and properties in North Carolina.

Operations

Besides convenience stores with gas stations and fast food establishments Jordon Oil Company extends its reach into the real estate business. The company manages properties such as the Crown Reef Resort Mountain High Motel and Tropical Seas Hotel.

Strategy

In recent years the convenience store operator has braced for the impact of a state cigarette tax hike of 50 cents per pack in South Carolina. (The price of a pack of cigarettes in the state has risen from $4.09 in 2009 to $5.21 on July 1 2010 as a result of recent federal and state tax increases.) The tax hike which took effect in July 2010 is expected to have a negative impact on sales. According to Jordan Oil cigarettes account for about 25% of sales at its South Carolina Hot Spot stores.

History

The foundation of Jordan Oil Company was built in 1950 from a small country store in Franklin North Carolina. Under the name Jordan's Self Serve the company represented the first gasoline station in its market to provide less expensive and unbranded gasoline.

EXECUTIVES

Vice President, Jeanne Cook
Auditors: SCOTT TAYLOR WHITE & WINGO S

LOCATIONS

HQ: R. L. JORDAN OIL COMPANY OF NORTH CAROLINA INC.
1451 FERNWOOD GLENDALE RD, SPARTANBURG, SC 293073044
Phone: 864 585-2784
Web: WWW.RLJOC.COM

2012 Stores

	No.
South Carolina	41
North Carolina	13
Total	**54**

COMPETITORS

7-Eleven	Mountain Empire Oil
Colonial Group	Quiznos
Cumberland Farms	Racetrac Petroleum
Exxon Mobil	Spinx
McDonald's	The Pantry

HISTORICAL FINANCIALS

Company Type: Private

Income Statement

FYE: September 30

	REVENUE ($ mil.)	NET INCOME ($ mil.)	NET PROFIT MARGIN	EMPLOYEES
09/07	278	(0)	—	900
09/06	270	(1)	—	—
09/05	1,428	0	—	—
Annual Growth	—	—	—	—

2007 Year-End Financials

Return on assets: 1.8%
Return on equity: (-0.1%)
Current ratio: 0.60
Cash ($ mil.): 4

R. M. PARKS INC.

Auditors: GUMBINER SAVETT INC

LOCATIONS

HQ: R. M. PARKS INC.
1061 N MAIN ST, PORTERVILLE, CA 932571686
Phone: 559 784-2384
Web: WWW.RMPARKSINC.COM

HISTORICAL FINANCIALS

Company Type: Private

Income Statement

FYE: October 31

	REVENUE ($ mil.)	NET INCOME ($ mil.)	NET PROFIT MARGIN	EMPLOYEES
10/14	612	0	0.0%	4
10/13	615	0	0.1%	—
10/12	623	0	0.1%	—
10/11	583	0	—	—
Annual Growth	1.6%	—	—	—

2014 Year-End Financials

Return on assets: 1.6%
Return on equity: —
Current ratio: 0.70
Cash ($ mil.): 2

R.S. HUGHES COMPANY INC.

R.S. Hughes distributes the stuff that holds the world together –duct tape that is –plus a lot more. Established in 1954 the employee-owned company maintains some 45 warehouse locations in the US and Mexico. It supplies adhesives (epoxies aerosols hot glues silicones) electrical specialties (tubing terminals films tape and barriers) safety products (glasses ear plugs masks) tapes (masking foam vinyl cloth foil duct joining) and abrasives (roll disc brush wheel belt and air tools). R.S. Hughes also distributes labels and signs (printable labels and tags safety signs) and aerosols and coatings (WD-40 paints lubricants oils cleaners).

EXECUTIVES

CEO, Robert McCollum
CFO, Gail Zimmerman
President and COO, Pete Biocini
Director Human Resources, Janet Coronado
VP Sales and Marketing, Pete Brocini
Auditors: MOSS ADAMS LLP CAMPBELL CALI

LOCATIONS

HQ: R.S. HUGHES COMPANY INC.
1162 SONORA CT, SUNNYVALE, CA 940865378
Phone: 408 739-3211
Web: WWW.RSHUGHES.COM

PRODUCTS/OPERATIONS

Selected Products

Adhesives
Abrasive power tools
Aerosol paints and lubricants
Coatings
Labels
Printers
Sealants
Tapes

COMPETITORS

DXP Enterprises	Plymouth Rubber
HD Supply	W.W. Grainger
Industrial Distribution Group	

HISTORICAL FINANCIALS

Company Type: Private

Income Statement

FYE: September 28

	REVENUE ($ mil.)	NET INCOME ($ mil.)	NET PROFIT MARGIN	EMPLOYEES
09/14	302	15	5.1%	460
09/13	281	15	5.5%	—
09/12*	253	15	6.2%	—
10/11	231	0	—	—
Annual Growth	9.2%	—	—	—

*Fiscal year change

2014 Year-End Financials

Return on assets: 3.2%
Return on equity: 5.1%
Current ratio: 2.70
Cash ($ mil.): 10

RADY CHILDREN'S HOSPITAL-SAN DIEGO

Rady Children's Hospital-San Diego handles the big injuries of pint-sized patients. Serving as the region's only pediatric trauma center the nonprofit hospital boasts more than 520 beds. As part of its services Rady Children's Hospital-San Diego offers comprehensive pediatric care including surgical services convalescent care a neonatal intensive care unit and orthopedic services. Across its service area the hospital also operates about 25 satellite centers that provide such primary and specialized care services as physical therapy and hearing diagnostics. Rady Children's Hospital a teaching hospital affiliated with the University of California San Diego Medical School was founded in 1954.

Operations

Rady Children's operates its own 36-bed emergency department –The Sam S. and Rose Stein Emergency Care Center –that each day sees up to 300 patients. It is the only regional emergency center solely dedicated and equipped to care for children. The hospital also operates California's only pediatric skilled nursing facility –The Helen Bernardy Center –to provide 24-hour care to disabled and medically fragile children in a homelike environment.

For treating non-life-or-limb-threatening injuries and illnesses the hospital operates neighborhood urgent care centers in Escondido La Mesa Oceanside and San Diego.

Through its medical school affiliation Rady Children's engages in nearly 500 clinical trials in all pediatric specialties. It collaborates with University of California San Diego the Sanford-Burnham Medical Research Institute The Scripps Research Institute the Salk Institute for Biological Studies and St. Jude Children's Research Hospital. Specialized research facilities on campus include the Autism Discovery Institute the Blair L. Sadler Center for Quality and the Child and Adolescent Services Research Center.

The hospital operates a LEED-certified Acute Care Pavilion which holds a neonatal intensive care unit the Peckham Center for Cancer and Blood Disorders and the Warren Family Surgical

Center. It serves those suffering from eating disorders through its inpatient center to allow for intensive psychiatric therapy for patients with anorexia and bulimia and to aid families with home care.

In 2014 the hospital had 18782 inpatient admissions 230383 outpatient visits nearly 85000 emergency department visits and more than 54000 urgent care visits. It performed about 20000 surgeries.

Geographic Reach

Rady Children's Hospital serves as the pediatric medical center that caters to the California region of San Diego Imperial and southern Riverside counties. It has more than 30 offices throughout San Diego and southern Riverside counties with satellite locations in Chula Vista El Centro Encinitas Escondido La Jolla La Mesa Murrieta Oceanside San Diego and Solana Beach.

EXECUTIVES

Chairman Rady Pediatric Genomics and Systems Medicine Institute, David F. Hale, age 66
President and CEO Rady Pediatric Genomics and Systems Medicine Institute, Stephen Kingsmore
EVP and Chief Administrative Officer, Margareta E. (Meg) Norton
President and CEO, Donald Kearns
VP and CIO, Albert Oriol
VP and Chief Nursing Executive, Mary Fagan
Chief Medical Officer, Irvin A. Kaufman
SVP and COO, Nicholas Holmes
Executive Director Rady Children's Hospital Foundation and SVP Rady Children's Hospital, Stephen Jennings
Physician-In-Chief and Chief Scientific Officer and Chairman of Pediatrics UC San Diego, Gabriel G. Haddad
SVP Rady Children's Specialists of San Diego, Herb Kimmons
Respiratory Therapy Director, Toni Popien
Vice President Human Resources, Mamoon Syed
Director Of Radiology, Bruce Bower
Executive Vice President, Michelle Deitz
Vice President Information Technology, Chana Dean
Director Media Relations, Ben Metcalf
Vice President Human Resources, Ruth Wilson
Medical Director, Robert Newbury
Medical Director of Pediatric Medicine, Cynthia Kuelbs
Pharmacy Manager, Michael Clark
Vice President Development, Carol Damon-Scherer
Medical Director, Ghazala Sharieff
Medical Director Cme, Keith Vaux
Managed Care Director, Bobbi Gomez
Vice Chairman, Michael P. (Mike) Peckham
Chairman, Theodore D. (Ted) Roth, age 64
Secretary, Anthony Magit
Board Member, Joe Bezdek
Secretary, Heidie Ellis
Auditors: KPMG LLP LOS ANGELES CA

LOCATIONS

HQ: RADY CHILDREN' S HOSPITAL-SAN DIEGO
3020 CHILDRENS WAY, SAN DIEGO, CA 921234223
Phone: 858 309-7701
Web: WWW.RCHSD.ORG

Selected Satellite Locations
Chula Vista
El Centro
Encinitas
Escondido
La Jolla
La Mesa
Murrieta
Oceanside
San Diego
Solana Beach

PRODUCTS/OPERATIONS

Selected Services
Allergy/Immunology
Attention Deficit Hyperactivity Disorder
Audiology/Hearing
Autism Discovery Institute
Behavioral Health
Brachial Plexus Clinic
Cancer & Blood Disorders
Cardiology
Cardiovascular Surgery
Celiac Disease Clinic
Center for Healthier Communities
Cerebral Palsy Center
Chadwick Center For Children & Families
Child & Adolescent Psychiatry Services (CAPS)
Child & Adolescent Services Research Center (CASRC)
Child Life Services
Children' s Care Connection (C3)
Children' s Hospital Emergency Transport (CHET)
Cleft Palate Clinic
Craniofacial Disorders
Critical Care
Cystic Fibrosis Center
Dental Surgery
Dermatology
Developmental Evaluation Clinic
Developmental-Behavioral Pediatrics
Developmental Screening & Enhancement Program (DSEP)
Developmental Services
Down Syndrome Center
Eating Disorders/
Medical-Behavioral Disorders Unit
Emergency Medicine
Endocrinology/Diabetes
Fatty Liver Clinic
Feeding Team
Gastroenterology Hepatology & Nutrition
Genetics/Dysmorphology
Heart Institute
Helen Bernardy Center for Medically Fragile Children
Hematology/Oncology
HomeCare
Hospice
Infectious Diseases
Kawasaki Disease Clinic
Kidney/Liver Tranplant Program
Kidney Disease
Laboratory Services/Pathology
Liver Disease
Liver Transplant
Muscle Disease Clinic
Metabolic Medicine
Neonatology
Nephrology
Neurology
Neurosurgery
Newborn Screening Program
Nutrition Clinic
Occupational Therapy
Ophthalmology
Orthopedics
Otolaryngology/ENT
Pain Services
Palliative Care
Pediatric Surgery
Pediatrics & Hospital Medicine
Pharmacy Services
Physical Therapy
Prader-Willi Syndrome Clinic
Psychiatry
Pulmonary/Respiratory Medicine
Radiology
Rehabilitation Medicine
Rheumatology
Sleep Center
Speech/Language Pathology
Spiritual Care
Sports Medicine
Surgery
Toddler School (Alexa' s PLAYC)
Trauma Center
Urgent Care
Urology
Weight & Wellness Center

COMPETITORS

All Children' s Hospital
Children' s Health System
Children' s Hospital & Research Center at Oakland
Children' s Hospital of Orange County
Children' s Hospital of Philadelphia
Children' s Hospital of Richmond
Children' s Specialized Hospital
Childrens Hospital Los Angeles
Cook Children' s Health Care System
Dell Children' s Medical Center
Nationwide Children' s Hospital
Palomar Health
Scripps health
Seattle Children' s Hospital
Sharp HealthCare
Shriners Hospitals For Children
St. Jude Children' s Research Hospital
Sutter Health
Tri-City Healthcare District
UCSD Medical
UCSF Medical

HISTORICAL FINANCIALS

Company Type: Private

Income Statement

FYE: June 30

	REVENUE ($ mil.)	NET INCOME ($ mil.)	NET PROFIT MARGIN	EMPLOYEES
06/13	818	117	14.4%	2,313
06/10	619	42	6.9%	—
06/09	490	(56)	—	—
Annual Growth	13.6%	—	—	—

2013 Year-End Financials

Return on assets: 15.7%
Return on equity: 14.4%
Current ratio: 0.30
Cash ($ mil.): 32

RALEY'S

Raley's has to stock plenty of fresh fruit and great wines —it sells to the people that produce them. The company operates about 130 supermarkets and superstores in California and Nevada. In addition to about 80 flagship Raley's Superstores the company operates about 20 Bel Air Markets (in the Sacramento area) Nob Hill Foods (an upscale Bay Area chain with more than 20 locations) and nearly 10 discount warehouse stores under the Food Source banner in Northern California and Nevada. Raley's stores typically offer groceries natural foods and liquor as well as instore pharmacies. Founded during the Depression by Thomas Porter Raley the company is owned by Tom's daughter Joyce Raley Teel.

Operations

In addition to supermarkets Raley's operates about a dozen Aisle 1 full-service fuel stations in Northern California and Nevada.

Raley's three smaller chains serve different markets. Bel Air Markets are located in the greater Sacramento area. Nob Hill Foods stores are located along the Central Coast region of California and in the Bay Area. Food Source stores caters to customers in Hayward California the Sacramento area and northern Nevada.

EXECUTIVES

Vice President Information Technology, Jeff Szczesny
President and CEO, Michael J. (Mike) Teel
SVP Store Operations, Kevin Konkel

SVP Sales Merchandising Marketing and Advertising, Kevin Curry
CFO and Controller, Ken Mueller
COO, Keith Knopf, age 48
Vice President Finance, Jeff Cummings
Vice President, Lee Worthy
Executive Vice President, Tom Kees
Pharmacy Manager, Chona Sabistina
Pharmacy Manager, Rose Barnes
Vice President Real Estate, Linda Kelly
Senior Vice President Operations, Kavin Kunkel
Co Chairman and Owner, Joyce Raley Teel
Treasurer, Lisa Johnson
Member Board Of Directors, Tim Branigan
Board Of Directors, Dale Henley

LOCATIONS

HQ: RALEY' S
500 W CAPITOL AVE, WEST SACRAMENTO, CA
956052696
Phone: 916 373-3333
Web: WWW.RALEYS.COM

2013 Stores

	No.
California	124
Northern Nevada	16
Total	**140**

PRODUCTS/OPERATIONS

2013 Stores

	No.
Supermarkets	
Raley's	78
Nob Hill	22
Bel Air	20
Food Source	8
Aisle 1 fuel stations	12
Total	**140**

COMPETITORS

Andronico' s Market	Safeway
Costco Wholesale	Save Mart
Food 4 Less Holdings	Trader Joe' s
Grocery Outlet	Wal-Mart
Kroger	Whole Foods
Lunardi' s Super Market	WinCo Foods
Ralphs Grocery	

HISTORICAL FINANCIALS

Company Type: Private

Income Statement

FYE: June 29

	REVENUE ($ mil.)	NET INCOME ($ mil.)	NET PROFIT MARGIN	EMPLOYEES
06/13	3,054	(8)	—	14,000
06/12	3,162	(1)	—	—
06/10	3,064	0	—	—
06/09	0	0	—	—
Annual Growth	—	—	—	—

2013 Year-End Financials

Return on assets: 4.8%
Return on equity: (-0.3%)
Current ratio: 0.30
Cash ($ mil.): 21

RAPPAHANNOCK ELECTRIC COOPERATIVE

Like the river it's named after the Rappahannock Electric Cooperative (REC) keeps the power running smoothly. The consumer-owned cooperative provides electricity to homes businesses and industries in parts of 22 counties from the Blue Ridge Mountains to the mouth of the Rappahannock River in eastern Virginia. REC supplies power to more than 157000 members over more than 16000 miles of power line. REC offers surge protection internet services and home security plans to entice customers as competition from other suppliers arrives. Once rural in nature the cooperative's territory has seen large pockets of suburban growth.

Geographic Reach

The company serve members in 22 Virginia counties: Albemarle Caroline Clarke Culpeper Essex Fauquier Frederick Goochland Greene Hanover King and Queen King William Louisa Madison Orange Page Rappahannock Rockingham Shenandoah Spotsylvania Stafford and Warren.

Sales and Marketing

REC's largest customer is Bear Island Paper Company the second largest power consumer in the state of Virginia. Other major customers include DuPont GE Kings Dominion Amusement Park and Merillat Industries.

Financial Performance

In 2012 the company reported revenues of $405.6 million (1% down on 2011). Residential customers accounted for more than half of the REC's total sales in 2012.

Strategy

REC is also pursuing ways to help its customers to become more energy efficient to help them save money and to help the cooperative trim its power capacity growth plans. Supported by a $16 million federal green energy grant the company has replaced customers' older meters with smart (automated efficient) ones.

In 2012 REC and Old Dominion Electric Cooperative offered a pilot energy efficiency program (energy retrofits) for REC's members in Albemarle Louisa Greene Madison and Orange counties.

Company Background

REC was formed when the Virginia Electric Cooperative in Bowling Green and the Northern Piedmont Electric Cooperative in Culpeper merged in 1980.

Dramatically growing its business in 2010 the company and fellow co-op Shenandoah Valley Electric Cooperatives acquired Potomac Edison (Allegheny Energy's electric distribution operations in Virginia) for about $340 million. The expansion increased REC's coverage from 16 counties to 22 and its customer base by about 50%.

EXECUTIVES

Vice President Customer Service, David Koogler
Vice President, Brian Wolfe

LOCATIONS

HQ: RAPPAHANNOCK ELECTRIC COOPERATIVE
247 INDUSTRIAL CT, FREDERICKSBURG, VA
224082443
Phone: 540 898-8500
Web: WWW.MYREC.COOP

COMPETITORS

Dominion Virginia Power	Pepco Energy Services
	WGL Holdings

HISTORICAL FINANCIALS

Company Type: Private

Income Statement

FYE: December 31

	REVENUE ($ mil.)	NET INCOME ($ mil.)	NET PROFIT MARGIN	EMPLOYEES
12/13	400	15	3.8%	423
12/12	4	16	352.0%	—
12/11	410	17	4.2%	—
12/10	352	0	—	—
Annual Growth	4.3%	—	—	—

2013 Year-End Financials

Return on assets: 10.2%
Return on equity: 3.8%
Current ratio: 0.10
Cash ($ mil.): 7

RARITAN BAY MEDICAL CENTER.

Health care is not rare at Raritan Bay Medical Center (RBMC). The not-for-profit center operates two hospitals in central New Jersey: Its Perth Amboy campus has about 390 beds and its Old Bridge campus has more than 110 beds. RBMC provides acute care and emergency services as well as ambulatory care through its outpatient clinics. Its Perth Amboy location provides specialized care in fields including women's and children's health. RBMC is affiliated with the University of Medicine and Dentistry of New Jersey - Robert Wood Johnson Medical School as well as the Cancer Institute of New Jersey.

Geographic Reach

RBMC serves residents of Monmouth and Middlesex counties in New Jersey.

Operations

With more than 600 physicians on its staff RBMC offers a broad range of services including general medical and surgical maternity pediatric diagnostic imaging laboratory emergency and critical care. It also provides diagnostic imaging and lab services as well as specialist units for cardiac stroke wound healing bariatric pulmonary sleep medicine rehabilitation and behavioral health care services.

An affiliate of Joslin Diabetes Center RBMC provides some of the latest advances for treating diabetes and its complications as well as patient education and related support services.

Strategy

To expand its services in the region in 2013 RBMC began construction of a new $45 million medical office building at the Perth Amboy campus. The program is part of the health network's ongoing growth and renewal project. The new building features an imaging center including women's imaging inpatient and ambulatory surgery centers and physician offices and will also allow for the expansion of the emergency department.On the technology front to enable patient to to better manage their health RBMC has launched a new online patient portal to provide patients access to their medical test results allowing them to share results digitally with physicians and family.In 2013 RBMC began to provide access to pricing of common bariatric procedures on its mobile site to better enable patients in New Jersey and in the New York metro area to make informed decisions. In addition it launched a new content-rich mobile website for use on smartphones and other mobile devices.

To help fuel efforts to increase efficiencies and improve quality and cost structures the RBMC organization announced that it entered talks to partner with hospital management group Prospect Medical Holdings in 2013.

Company Background

The Perth Amboy hospital opened its doors in 1902 with 12 beds and a six-member medical staff; the nursing school opened in 1903.

EXECUTIVES

Senior Vice President Patient Care Ser, Joan Harewood
V President, Andrew M Citron
Director Of Pharmacy, Denise Reisert
Vice President Marketing And Sales and Marketing, Lynette Davis
Vice President Of Community Relations, Lynette King-davis
Executive Vice President, Nancy Barone
Vice President Human Resources, Vincent Constantino
Vpma Acting Chief Marketing Officer, Michael (Mel) Ciencewicki
Vice President human Resources, Vincent Costantino
Vice Chairman, Joseph Jankowski

LOCATIONS

HQ: RARITAN BAY MEDICAL CENTER.
530 NEW BRUNSWICK AVE, PERTH AMBOY, NJ 088613685
Phone: 732 442-3700
Web: WWW.RBMC.ORG

PRODUCTS/OPERATIONS

Selected Centers and Services

Bay Family Medicine
Bay Obstetrics and Gynecology
Behavioral Health
Cardiology Diagnostic and Treatment Center
CareOne at Raritan Bay Medical Center
Center for Balance
Center for Sleep Medicine
Center for Women
Center for Wound Healing
Diagnostic Radiology
Dr. Sam Gordon Berkow Maternity Pavilion
Emergency Medical Services
Human Motion Institute
Infectious Diseases and Immunology
Institute for Weight Loss
Integrative Medicine
Laboratory Services
Medical Pavilion at Woodbridge
Pediatrics
Physical Medicine and Rehabilitation
Pulmonary Rehabilitation
Renal Dialysis
Same Day Surgery
Stroke Center

COMPETITORS

Atlantic Health
Barnabas Health
Beth Israel Medical Center
Catholic Healthcare System
CentraState Healthcare System
Children's Specialized Hospital
East Orange General Hospital
Hackensack University Medical Center
JFK Health System
Jersey City Medical Center
Maimonides Medical Center
Memorial Sloan-Kettering
Newark Beth Israel Medical Center
Robert Wood Johnson University Hospital
Robert Wood Johnson University Hospital at Rahway
Saint Peter's University Hospital
St. Joseph's Healthcare System
Staten Island University Hospital
The Valley Hospital
Trinitas Regional Medical Center
Valley Health System

HISTORICAL FINANCIALS

Company Type: Private

Income Statement

FYE: December 31

	REVENUE ($ mil.)	NET INCOME ($ mil.)	NET PROFIT MARGIN	EMPLOYEES
12/08	228	(6)	—	1,970
12/06	232	3	1.5%	—
12/05	230	(2)	—	—
12/04	240	0	—	—
Annual Growth	(1.3%)	—	—	—

2008 Year-End Financials

Return on assets: 11.3%   Cash ($ mil.): —
Return on equity: (-3.0%)
Current ratio: 0.50

RAYBURN COUNTRY ELECTRIC COOPERATIVE INC

This is indeed Sam Rayburn country. Rayburn Country Electric Cooperative (Rayburn Electric) operates in the old stomping grounds of the legendary Texas politician and former speaker of the US House of Representatives. Rayburn Electric is a power generation and transmission organization that supplies wholesale power to five rural distribution cooperatives operating in 16 counties in north central and northeastern Texas. Five distribution cooperatives (Fannin County Electric Coop Farmers Electric Coop Grayson-Collin Electric Coop Lamar Electric Coop and Trinity Valley Electric Coop) collectively own the company.

EXECUTIVES

President and General Manager, John W. Kirkland
Operations Manager, Eddy Reece
Administrative Director, Annette K. Kirkland
Communications Manager, Jack Hodges

LOCATIONS

HQ: RAYBURN COUNTRY ELECTRIC COOPERATIVE INC
980 SIDS RD, ROCKWALL, TX 750326512
Phone: 972 771-1336
Web: WWW.RAYBURNELECTRIC.COM

COMPETITORS

Bluebonnet Electric   TMPA
Brazos Electric

HISTORICAL FINANCIALS

Company Type: Private

Income Statement

FYE: December 31

	REVENUE ($ mil.)	NET INCOME ($ mil.)	NET PROFIT MARGIN	EMPLOYEES
12/13	301	0	0.0%	8
12/11	316	0	—	—
12/10	238	1	0.7%	—
12/09	238	0	—	—
Annual Growth	6.0%	—	—	—

2013 Year-End Financials

Return on assets: 8.7%   Cash ($ mil.): 33
Return on equity: —
Current ratio: —

RAYMOURS FURNITURE COMPANY INC.

Raymours Furniture is heating up the oft-chilly Northeast doing business as Raymour & Flanigan. The company operates in several states through 94 retail stores including nearly a dozen clearance centers. It sells furniture for just about every room in the house (bedroom dining room home office living room) offering such pieces as bookcases entertainment centers headboards mattresses nightstands recliners sofas and tables. Brands such as Broyhill La-Z-Boy Natuzzi and Tempur Sealy are represented. Raymours is run by founding Goldberg family.

Geographic Reach

Based in New York Raymours has become the largest furniture retailer in the Northeast. Through a contractor it provides furniture delivery across the continental US.

Sales and Marketing

Raymours sells its furniture and accessories through its retail stores and online.

Operations

The company boasts 94 full-line showrooms about a dozen clearance centers 15 customer service centers and four distribution centers in New York New Jersey Pennsylvania Connecticut Massachusetts Delaware and Rhode Island. Raymours also operates more than a dozen customer distribution centers. Its one warehouse property is located in Quakertown Pennsylvania.

Strategy

Following significant expansion in 2008 Raymours has focused in recent years on expanding its presence on the Internet to entice more customers to shop. It added rugs and home decor items such as lamps throw pillows wall art and silk florals to its online furniture catalog. It also extended its furniture delivery area to all states within the continental US through a partnership with a contracted delivery service.

Raymours also expanded its existing partnership with Kathy Ireland Worldwide (led by its namesake model-actress) by adding 10 upholstered pieces to its Kathy Ireland Home furniture collection. The Kathy Ireland pieces are sold exclusively through Raymours.

The company has been expanding its New York distribution center in Rockland County spending some $46 million to purchase and renovate the 839000-sq.-ft. facility which will serve as its primary regional warehouse and distribution hub for the New York New Jersey and Connecticut areas.

In 2015 Raymours purchased the North Oaks Shopping Plaza. The majority of the complex located at 1345 Route 1 South in North Brunswick had been vacant for years. Raymours will become the plaza's new anchor.

Since 2013 Raymours has been prudently adding furniture showrooms in New York one in Brooklyn in 2013 on Fulton Street and another in 2014 in Queens which spans 22000 sq. ft. on multiple levels.

Company Background

Founded in 1947 by brothers Arnold and Bernard Goldberg Raymour & Flanigan is run by president and CEO Neil Goldberg and EVPs Michael and Steven.

EXECUTIVES

Senior Vice President Logistics, Jeff Lanier
Executive Vice President Sales and Marketing, Michael (Mel) Goldberg
Auditors: GREEN & SEIFTER SYRACUSE NEW

LOCATIONS

HQ: RAYMOURS FURNITURE COMPANY INC.
7248 MORGAN RD, LIVERPOOL, NY 130904535
Phone: 315 453-2500
Web: WWW.RAYMOURFLANIGAN.COM

PRODUCTS/OPERATIONS

Selected Products
Accents
Area Rugs
Bedrooms
Dining Rooms
Entertainment
Home Decor
Home Office
Living Rooms
Mattresses
Youth Bedrooms

Selected Brands
Berkline
Bernhardt
Broyhill
Cindy Crawford Home
Kathy Ireland Home
La-Z-Boy
Natuzzi
Rowe
Sealy
Stanley Furniture
Stearns & Foster
Tempur-Pedic

COMPETITORS

ABC Home Furnishings
American Signature
Bassett Furniture
Bob' s Discount Furniture Bob' s Discount Furnitu
Crawford Furniture
Dillard' s
Ethan Allen
Euromarket Designs
IKEA
Jennifer Convertibles
La-Z-Boy
Room & Board
Rooms To Go
Williams-Sonoma

HISTORICAL FINANCIALS

Company Type: Private

Income Statement

FYE: December 29

	REVENUE ($ mil.)	NET INCOME ($ mil.)	NET PROFIT MARGIN	EMPLOYEES
12/07	881	30	3.4%	4,400
12/06	780	23	3.0%	—
12/05	46	0	—	—
Annual Growth	—46328.7%	—	—	—

2007 Year-End Financials

Return on assets: 6.0%
Return on equity: 3.4%
Current ratio: 0.20
Cash ($ mil.): —

RDO EQUIPMENT CO

RDO Equipment has built a business herding Deere in a big way. The company sells and rents new and used trucks and heavy equipment to customers in the agriculture and construction industries. As the largest independent dealer of John Deere equipment RDO Equipment operates 70 locations in nearly 10 states. Of these 10 locations are dedicated Vermeer dealerships while its RDO Truck Centers offer heavy-duty Volvo GMC Isuzu

and Mack trucks. RDO Integrated Controls is the company's acquisitive positioning division. RDO also supplies lawn and garden equipment and provides maintenance and repair services and replacement parts. Ronald Offutt founded the family owned and operated company in 1968.

Geographic Reach

North Dakota-based RDO Equipment has stores in Arizona California Minnesota Montana North Dakota Oregon South Dakota Texas and Washington. Outside the US the company operates through partnerships in Australia Mexico Russia and Ukraine.

Operations

The company owns and operates 75-plus dealerships in almost 10 US states. It specializes in selling some of the nation's top brands such as John Deere Vermeer and Topcon. Through international partnerships RDO Equipment operates in Mexico Russia Ukraine and Australia.

Strategy

RDO has grown its network of dealerships and menu of services primarily through acquisitions. The company's positioning division —RDO Integrated Controls —has been busy during the past couple years inking deals to expand its territory as a top dealer of Topcon-branded positioning products.

In 2015 the company opened a new store in McKinney Texas adding to the half a dozen locations it already operates in the state. The McKinney location offers sales parts services and rental of John Deere heavy construction equipment.

Mergers and Acquisitions

In March 2013 RDO Integrated Controls added South Dakota to the map of territories where it provides Topcon-branded construction supplies with the purchase of the Topcon Survey Contract for the state of South Dakota from Mathison's Co. The deal extended RDO's reach in the Dakotas Minnesota Montana and Wyoming. Also in November 2013 RDO acquired Water Tech Ag Supply a California-based company that provides agricultural irrigation systems. The company has half a dozen locations in California and one in Yuma Arizona.

EXECUTIVES

Senior Vice President Special Projects, Larry Scott
Chair and CEO, Christi J. Offutt
VP Organizational Development, Gean Zimmerman
EVP and CFO, David Frear
President; Chief Content Officer, Scott Greenstein
EVP with responsibility for the company&rsquo, Ryan Offutt
COO, Chris Cooper
Vice President Midwest Construction, Lon Kindseth
Vice President Special Projects, Skip Klinkhammer
Vice President, Ronald (Ron) Offutt
Auditors: PRICEWATERHOUSECOOPERS LLP MI

LOCATIONS

HQ: RDO EQUIPMENT CO
700 7TH ST S, FARGO, ND 581032704
Phone: 701 239-8700
Web: WWW.RDOEQUIPMENT.COM

PRODUCTS/OPERATIONS

Selected Brands
Hitachi
John Deete
Sakai
Topcon
Vermeer
Wirtgen

Selected Products
Balers
Chippers

Combines
Dozers
Drills
Excavators
Planters
Scrapers
Tractors
Trenchers
Wheel loaders

COMPETITORS

Briggs Equipment	Komatsu America
Hertz	Mustang CAT
Home Depot	Scott Equipment

HISTORICAL FINANCIALS

Company Type: Private

Income Statement

FYE: January 31

	REVENUE ($ mil.)	NET INCOME ($ mil.)	NET PROFIT MARGIN	EMPLOYEES
01/14	1,698	82	4.9%	1,500
01/13	1,650	82	5.0%	—
01/12	1,251	63	5.1%	—
01/11	1,000	0	—	—
Annual Growth	19.3%	—	—	—

2014 Year-End Financials

Return on assets: 0.9%
Return on equity: 4.9%
Current ratio: 0.20
Cash ($ mil.): —

READING HOSPITAL

No it's not a square on the game of Monopoly but The Reading Hospital and Medical Center does treat patients in Berks County Pennsylvania and the surrounding area. Operating as Reading Health System the not-for-profit 735-bed medical center provides acute care and rehabilitation programs as well as behavioral and occupational health services. Specialty units include cancer cardiovascular weight management diabetes orthopedic trauma (level II) and women's health centers. In addition to the main hospital the Reading Health System includes Reading Health Rehabilitation Hospital and medical centers in nearby communities as well as laboratory imaging and outpatient centers throughout its region.

Operations

The system also delivers academic clinical training through its School of Health Sciences and Residency programs and operates the 113-acre Highlands at Wyomissing retirement community.

Altogether Reading Health System operates more than 45 locations with roughly 800 combined beds including primary and specialty care centers operated by Reading Health Physician Partners Reading Health Medical Services and the Quick Care and Urgent Care organizations. It employs some 1000 physicians and serves a population of more than 750000 residents. The Reading Health System served about 124400 emergency room patients during 2014; it also handled more than 31000 inpatient discharges and 19000 surgeries.

More than 90% of the company's revenues come from patient care services while residential (rehabilitation) and other services account for the rest.

Geographic Reach

Reading Health System's main hospital campus is located on a 22-building campus on 36 acres in West Reading Pennsylvania.

The system serves Berks County and the surrounding area.

Financial Performance

Reading Health System reported revenues of $901.1 million in fiscal 2014 (ended June) with net income of $62.8 million. Cash flow from operations totaled $30.2 million.

Strategy

Like most other hospitals Reading Health System sees its fair share of uninsured or underinsured patients seeking care at the ER for problems that are often not emergencies which can put a strain on hospital finances. Reading works to divert these patients to its Quick Care and Urgent Care Centers to help reduce some of that burden. The organization is also working to increase the size of its primary care network.

Within the main hospital Reading Health System is working to add new specialists such as interventional neuroradiologists and pediatric hospitalists as well as physicians who specialize in cardiac revascularization and robotic surgery procedures. It is also working to modernize technologies build new facilities and expand partnerships with area health care organizations. For example in 2013 it implemented its Reading HealthConnect electronic health record (EHR) system.

In addition the network broke ground on a $354 million expansion at the main West Reading hospital campus. The facility which is expected to open in 2016 will include new surgery and emergency treatment capacity and will add 150 private patient rooms; the project also includes conversion of existing rooms to private status. In 2015 Reading Health System opened a new family health care center; a new medical facility (featuring primary care physicians' offices imaging services and a laboratory) in Douglassville is also in the works.

Company Background

The Reading Hospital and Medical Center was founded in 1868 as The Reading Dispensary.

EXECUTIVES

VP and Chief Nursing Officer, Donna Weber
VP, Margaret M. Bligh
SVP Business Development and Planning, Richard Mable
VP, Carl Seidl
Assistant VP Quality Management, Debra Levengood
Director Communication Services, Wendie Waschitsch
CEO, Clint Matthews
Chairman, C. Thomas Work
Chair Department of Obstetrics and Gynecology and Director, A. George Neubert
Chair Department of Medicine and Director, Cecilia M. Smith
COO, Therese Sucher
VP Trauma and Surgical Services, James Demetriades
VP Support Services, Paul Toburen
VP Finance, Dan Cochran
SVP and and Chief Medical Officer, M. Joseph Grennan Jr.
President Medical Staff and Director, Brent J. Wagner
VP and CFO, Richard W. Jones
Chief Compliance Officer, Kathleen Wetzel
Director, Jay S. Sidhu, age 62
Director, Bruce P. Bengtson
Director, Barbara Arner
Director, Theodore W. Auman
Director, J. Marc Aynardi
Director, Elizabeth Ehrlich
Director, Bernard Fromm
Director, Robert J. Gibble
Director, Victor Hammel
Director, Samuel A. McCullough
Director, Terrence J. McGlinn

Director, Marlin Miller Jr.
Chair Department of Obstetrics and Gynecology and Director, A. George Neubert
Director, Richard M. Palmer Jr.
Director, G. David Reynolds Jr.
Director, David H. Roland
Director, Thomas P. Handwerk
Director, John Roland
Director, Elizabeth B. Rothermel
Director, Julia H. Klein
Director, Sidney D. Kline Jr.
Director, Chris G. Kraras
Director, Edward T. Lentz
Chair Department of Medicine and Director, Cecilia M. Smith
Director, James R. Stoudt
Director, David L. Thun
Director, Mary Ellen Batman
President Medical Staff and Director, Brent J. Wagner
Auditors: PRICEWATERHOUSECOOPERS LLP PH

LOCATIONS

HQ: READING HOSPITAL
6TH AND SPRUCE ST, READING, PA 196111428
Phone: 484 628-8000
Web: WWW.READINGHEALTH.ORG

Selected Pennsylvania Operations

The Reading Health Dispensary (Reading)
The Reading Hospital (West Reading)
Reading Health Medical Services
Reading Health Medical Services at Muhlenberg (Reading)
Reading Health Medical Services at Northern Berks (Hamburg)
Reading Health Medical Services at Spring Ridge (Wyomissing)
Reading Health Medical Services at Wyomissing (Wyomissing)
Reading Health Medical Services at Wyomissing Plaza (Reading)
Reading Health Physicians
Reading Health Rehabilitation Hospital (Wyomissing)
QuickCare Centers (regional)
Urgent Care Centers (regional)

Selected Services

Audiology
Behavioral Health Services
Behavioral Medicine Pain Management
Center for Public Health
Chaplaincy Services
Chest Pain Center
Cleft Palate Clinic
Cochlear Implant Program
da Vinci Surgical System
Diabetes Center
Emergency Services
Epilepsy Monitoring Unit
Family Risk Assessment Program (FRAP)
HelpLine
Hospitalist Program
Infusion Center
Interventional Radiology
Laboratory Services
Library Services
Mammography Services
Nutrition Services
Occupational Health Services
Occupational Therapy
Pain Management
Palliative Care Program
Pediatrics - St' Chris Care
PET/CT Imaging
Physical Therapy
QuickCare -Reading Health Physician Network
Radiology Services
Rehabilitation Services
Respiratory Care
Senior Assessment Program
Sleep Center
Social Service
Speech and Hearing Center
Stroke Center
The Reading Hospital Home Care
Tobacco-Free Wellness Program
Travel Immunization Service

Women' s Health Services
Wound Healing and Hyperbaric Medicine Center

COMPETITORS

Ascension Health
Doylestown Hospital
Jefferson Health System
Lancaster General
Lehigh Valley Health Network
Moses Taylor Hospital
Sacred Heart Hospital of Allentown
St. Luke' s University Health Network
Universal Health Services
University of Pennsylvania Health System
Wyoming Valley Health Care System

HISTORICAL FINANCIALS

Company Type: Private

Income Statement

FYE: June 30

	REVENUE ($ mil.)	NET INCOME ($ mil.)	NET PROFIT MARGIN	EMPLOYEES
06/09	675	42	6.2%	5,500
06/08	640	50	7.8%	—
06/06	0	0	—	—
Annual Growth	—	—	—	—

2009 Year-End Financials

Return on assets: 4.2%
Return on equity: 6.2%
Current ratio: 1.40

Cash ($ mil.): 43

REDNER'S MARKETS INC.

Redner' s Markets operates about 45 warehouse club-style supermarkets under the Redner' s Warehouse Markets banner and more than a dozen Quick Shoppe convenience stores. Most of the company' s stores are located in eastern Pennsylvania but the regional grocer also operates several locations in Maryland and Delaware having closed its one New York supermarket. Redner' s Warehouse Markets house bakery deli meat produce and seafood departments as well as in-store banks. The employee-owned company was founded by namesake Earl Redner in 1970. It is still operated by the Redner family including chairman and CEO Richard and COO Ryan Redner.

Financial Performance

Redner' s Markets rang up an estimated $865 million in sales in fiscal 2012 (ends September) up from about $859 million in sales the previous year.

Strategy

Redner' s has been tinkering with its store portfolio shuttering underperforming locations including several in its core Pennsylvania market while building new stores in existing and new markets. The regional chain has grown to four stores each in Delaware and Maryland since entering those markets in 2008 and 2005 respectively. Redner' s is also growing its Web presence doubling its online traffic in the first year of a digiral shopper marketing program conducted in partnership with Google Shopping Network.

EXECUTIVES

Vice President Of Finance, Michael McNaney
Vice President Operations, Gary O'Brien
Vice President Information Technology, Joseph (Jo) Hayes

Vice President Human Resources, Robert McDonough

Vice President Construction Real Esta, Doug Emore

LOCATIONS

HQ: REDNER' S MARKETS INC.
3 QUARRY RD, READING, PA 196059787
Phone: 610 926-3700
Web: WWW.REDNERSMARKETS.COM

2012 Warehouse Market Stores

	No.
Pennsylvania	36
Delaware	4
Maryland	4
Total	**44**

PRODUCTS/OPERATIONS

2012 Stores

	No.
Redner's Warehouse Market	44
Quick Shoppe	14
Total	**58**

COMPETITORS

7-Eleven	Wal-Mart
A&P	Wawa Inc.
Cumberland Farms	Wegmans
Giant Food Stores	Weis Markets
Sheetz	

HISTORICAL FINANCIALS

Company Type: Private

Income Statement

FYE: September 27

	REVENUE ($ mil.)	NET INCOME ($ mil.)	NET PROFIT MARGIN	EMPLOYEES
09/14	902	1	0.2%	4,800
09/13*	892	4	0.5%	—
12/12	0	0	23.4%	—
10/10	831	0	—	—
Annual Growth	**2.1%**	—	—	—

*Fiscal year change

2014 Year-End Financials

Return on assets: 3.4%   Cash ($ mil.): 42
Return on equity: 0.2%
Current ratio: 1.20

REGIONS HOSPITAL FOUNDATION

If you live around the Twin Cities Regions Hospital can help with your medical needs. The not-for-profit hospital has more than 450 beds and provides acute medical and emergency care services as well as specialty programs in areas including behavioral health rehabilitation burn care cancer cardiovascular orthopedic pediatrics and women's care. Regions Hospital is one of a handful of level I trauma centers in Minnesota and is also a teaching and residency center for the University of Minnesota Medical School. Regions Hospital is part of HealthPartners which operates a network of medical centers and a health plan in the Twin Cities area.

Geographic Reach

Regions Hospital serves the St. Paul Minnesota metropolitan area as well as patients from other areas across Minnesota and in western Wisconsin. It also sees visitors from other Midwest states.

Operations

In 2012 Regions Hospital operated at a 78% occupancy rate with some 25000 inpatient visits. It also handled 78000 emergency center visits 13000 surgeries and some 2500 births. It has about 650 physicians on its staff plus another 800 affiliated doctors who are members of the HealthPartners Medical Group physician practice organization.

The hospital provided some $56 million in community benefits during 2012 including charity care and outreach programs.

Strategy

The hospital has expanded its facilities in recent years to meet the demands of a growing Twin Cities population and address certain underserved community health needs. For instance in 2012 Regions Hospital completed construction of a new $36 million eight-story inpatient mental health center with about 100 beds designed to replace its aging mental health facility. In addition in 2009 the hospital wrapped up a $180 million expansion and renovation project that gave it a new 10-story patient tower with 20 new operating rooms more than 35 private patient beds and shell space for further expansion in the future.

In addition the hospital looks to enhance services through new equipment and procedural offerings as well as through partnerships with other area providers.

Ownership

Parent HealthPartners is a not-for-profit cooperative organization. Other HealthPartners facilities include Lakeview Hospital (Stillwater Minnesota) Hudson Hospital (Hudson Wisconsin) and Westfields Hospital (New Richmond Wisconsin). It also operates health clinics and urgent care centers in the area.

In 2013 HealthPartners merged with another Twin Cities hospital operator Park Nicollet Health Services. The combined organization continues to operate under the HealthPartners name. The merger created the second-largest hospital group in Minnesota giving the combined organization a broader operational base through which it aims to provide high-quality accountable care in the region. The organization's operations are gradually being combined following the transaction. Regions Hospital will become part of a new hospital division Park Nicollet HealthPartners Care Group.

Company Background

Established in 1872 Regions Hospital became part of the HealthPartners network in 1993.

EXECUTIVES

President CEO, Brock D. Nelson, age 63
CFO, Heidi Conrad
Vice President Patient Care Services, Christine Boese

LOCATIONS

HQ: REGIONS HOSPITAL FOUNDATION
640 JACKSON ST, SAINT PAUL, MN 551012595
Phone: 651 254-3456
Web: WWW.REGIONSHOSPITAL.COM

PRODUCTS/OPERATIONS

Selected Specialties and Divisions

Behavioral Health
Birth Center
Breast Health Center
Burn Center
Cancer Care Center
Center for Dementia and Alzheimer' s Care
Digestive Care Center
Emergency Center
Heart Center
Level I Trauma Center
Level I Pediatric Trauma Center
Neurosciences
Orthopedics
Palliative Care Unit

Rehabilitation Institute
Spine Center
Stroke Center
Surgery Center

COMPETITORS

Allina Hospitals
Amery Regional Medical Center
Catholic Health Initiatives
CentraCare Health
Children' s Hospitals and Clinics of Minnesota
Fairview Health
Gillette Children' s
HealthEast Care System
Mayo Clinic
North Memorial Health Care
Olmsted Medical
Paynesville Area Healthcare System

HISTORICAL FINANCIALS

Company Type: Private

Income Statement

FYE: December 31

	REVENUE ($ mil.)	NET INCOME ($ mil.)	NET PROFIT MARGIN	EMPLOYEES
12/12	581	36	6.3%	3,000
12/06	413	4	1.0%	—
12/05	430	12	2.8%	—
12/04	7	0	—	—
Annual Growth	**71.3%**	—	—	—

2012 Year-End Financials

Return on assets: 6.2%   Cash ($ mil.): 64
Return on equity: 6.3%
Current ratio: 1.70

REID HOSPITAL & HEALTH CARE SERVICES INC.

Auditors: BKD LLP INDIANAPOLIS IN

LOCATIONS

HQ: REID HOSPITAL & HEALTH CARE SERVICES INC.
1100 REID PKWY, RICHMOND, IN 473741157
Phone: 765 983-3000
Web: WWW.REIDHOSPITAL.ORG

HISTORICAL FINANCIALS

Company Type: Private

Income Statement

FYE: December 31

	REVENUE ($ mil.)	NET INCOME ($ mil.)	NET PROFIT MARGIN	EMPLOYEES
12/13	339	47	14.1%	1,800
12/12	351	22	6.4%	—
12/11	294	(47)	—	—
12/10	294	0	—	—
Annual Growth	**4.9%**	—	—	—

2013 Year-End Financials

Return on assets: 4.6%   Cash ($ mil.): 11
Return on equity: 14.1%
Current ratio: 1.70

REIF OIL COMPANY

Auditors: CPA ASSOCIATES PC BURLINGTON

LOCATIONS

HQ: REIF OIL COMPANY
   801 N 3RD ST, BURLINGTON, IA 526015006
Phone: 319 758-1240
Web: WWW.REIFOIL1.COM

HISTORICAL FINANCIALS

Company Type: Private

Income Statement

FYE: December 31

	REVENUE ($ mil.)	NET INCOME ($ mil.)	NET PROFIT MARGIN	EMPLOYEES
12/13	316	(0)	—	100
12/12	369	0	0.0%	—
12/09	214	0	0.5%	—
12/08	312	0	—	—
Annual Growth	0.2%	—	—	—

2013 Year-End Financials

Return on assets: 2.4%   Cash ($ mil.): —
Return on equity: (-0.1%)
Current ratio: 0.50

RENFRO CORPORATION

For those who tend to misplace their socks Renfro can foot the bill. The company designs and manufacturers hundreds of styles of socks and legwear products and markets them in North America through department stores specialty stores and e-commerce sites. Renfro's products are sold under several brands including Carhartt Fruit of the Loom Dr. Scholl's Copper Sole Polo Work King and Wrangler among others. The company also sells its owns brands K. Bell and Hot Sox. The clothing company's customers include well-known retailers such as Costco Kmart J.C. Penney Target and Wal-Mart.

Geographic Reach

North Carolina-based Renfro makes and distributes socks from its facilities in five US states Canada Mexico India Pakistan and China. It operates sales offices throughout North America Europe and Asia.

Operations

Renfro specializes in developing making and marketing socks under its own brands including K. Bell and Hot Sox and via private label for others. It licenses Fruit of the Loom Dr. Scholl's Ralph Lauren Cooper Sole Wrangler and Carhartt.

Sales and Marketing

The clothing company serves some of the world's biggest retailer including Wal-Mart Kmart Macy's Costco J.C. Penney Sears and Target among others.

Strategy

With the fashionable return of Sperry Top-Siders to wardrobes the company is expanding beyond its iconic loafers to a number of items including socks. Renfro will be making men's and women's socks under the Sperry brand. This comes on top of recent editions from Richlu (Canadian brands Tough Ducks and Work King under license) and Fruit of the Loom (Renfro purchased Fruit of the Loom maker DeSoto Mills).

In 2014 Renfro signed a licensing agreement with New Balance Athletic Shoe to design manufacture and market new lines of New Balance socks as well as manufacture the brand's current lines.

Company Background

The company was founded in 1921.

EXECUTIVES

Vice President Procurement, Ronnie Wheeler
Sr V Pres-v Pres, Charlie M Nichols
SVP and CFO, Andrew L. Kilby
Vice President Manufacturing, Norman Smith
Vice President Of International Marketing, Peter Worcester
Vice President Of Marketing, Dan Harrison
Vice President Accounting, George Doehner
National Account Manager, Lennie Averna
Vice President International Sourcing, Harold Amos
National Account Manager, Laura Brim
Vice President Sourcing Renfro, Jay Plumback
Vice President Of Marketing, Dean Parker
Vice President of Sales, Ian Beckstead
Vice President Business Development, Brad Ballentine
Vice President of Sales, Doug Lindner
Vice President of International Business Development, Beckstead Ian
Vice President Planning, Pickett Tim

LOCATIONS

HQ: RENFRO CORPORATION
   661 LINVILLE RD, MOUNT AIRY, NC 270303101
Phone: 336 719-8000
Web: WWW.RENFRO.COM

PRODUCTS/OPERATIONS

Selected Brands

Carhartt
Copper Sole
Dr. Scholl' s
Fruit of The Loom
Hot Sox
K. Bell
Polo
Ralph Lauren/Lauren
Spalding
Sperry
Wrangler

COMPETITORS

Gildan Activewear	The Gap
Hanesbrands	Triumph Apparel
Jockey International	Under Armour
MAST	VF Corporation
Russell Brands	

HISTORICAL FINANCIALS

Company Type: Private

Income Statement

FYE: January 29

	REVENUE ($ mil.)	NET INCOME ($ mil.)	NET PROFIT MARGIN	EMPLOYEES
01/11	390	9	2.5%	5,000
01/10	375	11	3.1%	—
01/08	593	0	0.0%	—
Annual Growth	(13.1%)	2454.2%	—	—

2011 Year-End Financials

Return on assets: 6.5%   Cash ($ mil.): 9
Return on equity: 2.5%
Current ratio: 1.20

REPLACEMENT PARTS INC.

Replacement Parts works Bumper to Bumper. The company's subsidiary Crow-Burlingame operates about 160 stores under the Bumper To Bumper banner in Arkansas Louisiana Mississippi Missouri Oklahoma and Texas. Replacement Parts also distributes auto parts through three Parts Warehouses in Arkansas Louisiana and Oklahoma. The company was founded in 1919 by grocer J.G. Burlingame and candy salesman William Robert Crow grandfather of president Fletcher Lord Jr. The duo first entered the auto business by purchasing new cars in St. Louis and driving them around Little Rock to attract buyers. Employees own about 15% of the company through its stock ownership program.

EXECUTIVES

President and CEO, William (Bill) Schlatterer
Vice President Operation, Tom Singleton

LOCATIONS

HQ: REPLACEMENT PARTS INC.
   1901 E ROOSEVELT RD, LITTLE ROCK, AR 722062533
Phone: 501 375-1215
Web: WWW.REPLACEMENTPARTS.COM

COMPETITORS

Advance Auto Parts	Goodyear Tire & Rubber
AutoZone	O' Reilly Automotive
CARQUEST	Pep Boys
Discount Tire	Sears
General Parts	Wal-Mart
Genuine Parts	

HISTORICAL FINANCIALS

Company Type: Private

Income Statement

FYE: December 31

	REVENUE ($ mil.)	NET INCOME ($ mil.)	NET PROFIT MARGIN	EMPLOYEES
12/07	187	3	1.7%	1,115
12/06	179	5	2.8%	—
12/04	149	2	1.9%	—
12/03	137	0	—	—
Annual Growth	8.0%	—	—	—

2007 Year-End Financials

Return on assets: 7.8%   Cash ($ mil.): —
Return on equity: 1.7%
Current ratio: 0.80

RESEARCH TRIANGLE INSTITUTE INC

The scientists at Research Triangle Institute address the problems of a sphere (the planet). Operating mainly under its trade name RTI International (RTI) the not-for-profit enterprise conducts research in such areas as advanced technologies environmental resources and medicine. It provides such services as certification and materials testing as well as software used in laboratories and research projects. Serving the US federal government other governments nonprofits and for-profit companies RTI offers analytical perspectives on public policy and has more than 3740 researchers working in offices around the world.

Geographic Reach

RTI serves clients in more than 75 countries. It has eight US offices and offices in China El Salvador India Indonesia Kenya Spain Sweden the UAE and the UK.

Operations

The company offers analytical perspectives on public policy. Its staff members represent more than 80 nationalities and speak nearly 90 languages enabling RTI to communicate and collaborate effectively with peer researchers clients and stakeholders around the world.

Sales and Marketing

The organization works with clients in government industry academia and public service. RTI's main clients are the Department of Health and Human Services and the US Agency for International Development. RTI's private sector clients have included 3M Chevron Cisco Systems GE and Sanofi-Aventis.

Financial Performance

During fiscal 2013 RTI reported revenue totaling $783 million. The institute reinvests its net income in programs facilities and new capabilities.

EXECUTIVES

Vice President, Jerry Rench
EVP and COO, James J. (Jim) Gibson
EVP RTI Health Solutions, Allen W. Mangel
President and CEO, E. Wayne Holden
EVP International Development Group, Aaron S. Williams
EVP Social Statistical and Environmental Sciences, Timothy J. (Tim) Gabel
EVP and CFO, Michael H. (Mike) Kaelin
Chair Fellow Program and Distinguished Fellow Early Childhood Development, Don Bailey
Vice President Business Development and Program Development Office, David M (Dave) Sotolongo
Vice President of Research Computing, Karen Davis
Vice President Health Economics, Josephine Mauskopf
Vice President Marketing, Susana Gutthann
Vice President Information Technology, Wayne Holdn
Executive Vice President, Satinder Sethi
Vice President Finance, Francis (Fran) Neary
Senior Vice President Secretary and Chief Legal Officer, Scott Merrell
Vice President Contracts, Mary Reiss
Vice President Information Technology, Jeff Lowe
Senior Vice President General Counsel, Greg Story
Vice President Facility Strategic Services, Dennis Naugle
Senior Vice President, Edward (Ed) Story
Vice President Compensation And Benef, Kristen Vosburgh
Vice President Of Operations, Lynn Soby
Vice President Faciilties Strategic Service, Allwyne Richards
Vice President Strategic Energy Initiatives, James (Jamie) Trainham
Senior Vice President General Counsel and Corporate Secretary, G Story
Vice Chairman, Peter M. Scott
Chairman, William M. Moore
Treasurer, Rick Sisson
Treasurer, Edward (Ed) Lilly
Auditors: PRICEWATERHOUSECOOPERS LLP RA

LOCATIONS

HQ: RESEARCH TRIANGLE INSTITUTE INC
3040 CORNWALLIS RD, DURHAM, NC 277090128
Phone: 919 541-6000
Web: WWW.RTI.ORG

PRODUCTS/OPERATIONS

Selected Research Areas
Advanced technology research and development
Drug discovery and development
Economic and social
Education and training
Energy
Environmental
Health
International development
Laboratory and chemistry
Statistics
Survey

COMPETITORS

Argonne National Laboratory	Sandford Burnham Institute
Battelle Memorial	Urban Institute
QSS Group	

HISTORICAL FINANCIALS
Company Type: Private

Income Statement
FYE: September 30

	REVENUE ($ mil.)	NET INCOME ($ mil.)	NET PROFIT MARGIN	EMPLOYEES
09/13	782	37	4.8%	2,680
09/12	733	11	1.6%	—
09/11	777	24	3.1%	—
09/10	758	0	—	—
Annual Growth	1.0%	—	—	—

2013 Year-End Financials
Return on assets: 7.4%
Return on equity: 4.8%
Current ratio: 0.80
Cash ($ mil.): 78

REX HEALTHCARE INC.

Rex is a king of health care in Raleigh. Part of the UNC HealthCare System Rex Healthcare is a not-for-profit health care provider that serves residents of Raleigh and the rest of Wake County North Carolina. Founded in 1894 Rex Healthcare includes the more than 430-bed acute-care Rex Hospital and two nursing homes with nearly 230 beds as well as primary and specialty care clinics throughout the area. Specialty centers and clinics provide services such as birthing cancer treatment same-day surgery heart and vascular care pain management and sleep disorder therapy. Rex also provides home health and mobile emergency medical services. UNC HealthCare also includes affiliate UNC Hospitals.

Operations

The healthcare system employs a medical staff of more than 1100 physicians and 1700 nurses. Its operations consist of an acute care hospital five wellness centers a pair of skilled nursing facilities (for rehabilitation and long-term nursing care) six suburban campuses and freestanding outpatient diagnostic urgent care and surgery centers.

In 2013 Rex had about 34000 in-patient visits discharged 30778 welcomed 5292 babies conducted 30628 surgeries and handled 57944 emergency room visitors.

Geographic Reach

Rex Healthcare operates facilities in Wake County North Carolina in the cities of Apex Cary Garner Holly Springs Knightdale Wakefield and Raleigh.

Financial Performance

In 2013 Rex renegotiated some payor contracts and as a result it reported a 4% increase in revenue for the year. A larger number of patients also contributed to the growth.

Strategy

Looking to provide the most promising innovations among new medical services tools and technologies Rex Healthcare in 2012 funded the newly launched Rex Strategic Innovations with an initial $10 million investment. Venture capital investment fund Rex Health Ventures plans to invest in researchers entrepreneurs and inventors and support start-up companies.

In 2013 it submitted permit applications and plans to the North Carolina Department of Health Service Regulation in hopes of adding about 200 beds to various facilities. While waiting it also opened a new orthopedic surgery center moved its Breast Care Center to a larger facility and opened a bariatric surgery center. In late 2014 Rex begins construction on its new $200 million eight-story cardiac care tower.

Company Background

In 2011 rival WakeMed offered to buy Rex Healthcare for about $750 million. WakeMed says the purchase would eliminate duplicate services from the regions the two health care providers serve. Rex Healthcare responded by saying it's not for sale and considers the offer "hostile." WakeMed previously filed a complaint with the state against Rex Healthcare saying it was creating duplicative services especially in the areas of surgery and cardiac care.

EXECUTIVES

VP Ambulatory Services, Tom Williams
SVP CFO and Interim CIO, Bernadette Spong
SVP Patient Services and Chief Nursing Officer, Mary Lou Powell
Interim President and COO, Steve Burriss, age 48
SVP Heart and Vascular Services UNC Health Care System, R. Erick Hawkins
VP Surgical Services, Jane Byrd
VP Rex Physician Services and Executive Operations Director University of North Carolina Physician Network, Bob Ricker
VP Post Acute Services UNC Health Care System, Tamie Stanton
VP Medical Affairs Chief Medical Officer and Chief Medical Information Officer, Linda Butler
Vice President Oncologist, Charles (Chas) Scarantino
Director Of Pharmacy, Jane Green
Occupational Therapy Director, Michael Anglin
Pharmacy Manager, Christine Zone
Vice President Patient Care Services Cno, Joel Ray
Director Of Radiology, Kent Davis
Pharmacy Manager, Jim Hall
Director Of Operating Room, Ruth Nelson-mustard
Director of Radiology, Gregory Hinn
Chairman, A. Dale Jenkins
Secretary, Alberta Sanders
Auditors: CLIFTONLARSONALLEN CHARLOTTE

LOCATIONS

HQ: REX HEALTHCARE INC.
4420 LAKE BOONE TRL, RALEIGH, NC 276077505
Phone: 919 784-3100
Web: WWW.REXHEALTH.COM

PRODUCTS/OPERATIONS

2013 Sales

	% of total
Net patient service revenue	96
Other operating revenue	4
Total	**100**

Selected Specialty Services
Oncology
Heart and vascular
Surgical Services: Bariatric Heartburn and GI
Orthopedic Neuro and Spine

Rehabilitation
Emergency and Urgent Care
Women's Services
Wound Healing

COMPETITORS

Carolinas HealthCare System
Cone Health
Cumberland County Hospital System
Danville Regional Medical Center
Duke University Health System
FirstHealth of the Carolinas
Morehead Memorial Hospital
Novant Health
Vidant Health
Wake Forest University Baptist Medical Center
WakeMed

HISTORICAL FINANCIALS

Company Type: Private

Income Statement

	REVENUE ($ mil.)	NET INCOME ($ mil.)	NET PROFIT MARGIN	EMPLOYEES
06/13	731	8	1.2%	5,500
06/12	719	34	4.8%	—
06/11	628	69	11.0%	—
06/10	571	0	—	—
Annual Growth	8.6%	—	—	—

FYE: June 30

2013 Year-End Financials

Return on assets: —
Return on equity: 1.2%
Current ratio: 1.30
Cash ($ mil.): 74

REX HOSPITAL INC.

Auditors: LARSONALLEN LLP CHARLOTTE NO

LOCATIONS

HQ: REX HOSPITAL INC.
4420 LAKE BOONE TRL, RALEIGH, NC 276076599
Phone: 919 784-3100
Web: WWW.REXHEALTH.COM

HISTORICAL FINANCIALS

Company Type: Private

Income Statement

	REVENUE ($ mil.)	NET INCOME ($ mil.)	NET PROFIT MARGIN	EMPLOYEES
06/13	701	7	1.0%	3,500
06/08	460	6	1.4%	—
06/07	426	31	7.3%	—
06/05	1,847	0	—	—
Annual Growth	(11.4%)	—	—	—

FYE: June 30

2013 Year-End Financials

Return on assets: 14.8%
Return on equity: 1.0%
Current ratio: 0.60
Cash ($ mil.): 66

RHODE ISLAND HOSPITAL

LOCATIONS

HQ: RHODE ISLAND HOSPITAL
593 EDDY ST, PROVIDENCE, RI 029034923
Phone: 401 444-4000
Web: WWW.LIFESPAN.ORG

HISTORICAL FINANCIALS

Company Type: Private

Income Statement

	REVENUE ($ mil.)	NET INCOME ($ mil.)	NET PROFIT MARGIN	EMPLOYEES
09/13	1,048	49	4.7%	6,200
09/07	918	110	12.0%	—
09/06	876	74	8.5%	—
09/05	794	0	—	—
Annual Growth	3.5%			

FYE: September 30

2013 Year-End Financials

Return on assets: 4.6%
Return on equity: 4.7%
Current ratio: 1.20
Cash ($ mil.): 18

RICELAND FOODS INC.

Handling more than 125 million bushels of grain a year Riceland Foods is ingrained in its business. The agricultural cooperative processes and markets the rice soybeans and wheat grown by its 9000 member/owners who farm in Arkansas Louisiana Mississippi Missouri and Texas. One of the world's largest rice millers it sells white and brown rice plus flavored rices and meal kits under the Riceland and private-label brands. The co-op sells to food retailers and food service and food manufacturing companies worldwide. Riceland also makes cooking oils and processes soybeans bran and lecithin and offers rice bran and hulls to pet food makers and livestock farmers as feed and bedding.

Geographic Reach

Arkansas-based Riceland provides marketing services to farmers in its home state as well as Louisiana Mississippi Missouri and Texas.Riceland markets rice products under the Riceland label private labels as ingredients and in bulk. Riceland's products are sold across the US and in more than 75 foreign destinations.

OperationsRiceland's Research and Technical Center (Stuttgart Arkansas) is staffed by scientists and technicians with experience in rice edible oil and lecithin chemistry applications and process engineering.The facility houses separate soybean and rice research laboratories to conduct product development product and process improvement and customer support. Riceland's business lines are supported by on-site analytical food applications and regulatory compliance labs consumer and foodservice test kitchens and a well-equipped pilot plant. An ongoing research program reinforces Riceland's position as a premier supplier of rice edible oils and lecithin.

In addition to being a leader in rice milling the cooperative is a major soybean processor. Indeed its soybean processing plant in Stuttgart provides high-protein soybean meal and soybean mill run to poultry catfish and other livestock producers in the Mississippi Delta region and southwestern US.Sales and Marketing

A major rice exporter and edible oil producer Riceland markets its rice and oil products under the Riceland and Chefway (vegetable oil and shortening) labels. Its products are sold nationwide and to more than 75 foreign destinations.

Rice and oil products are supplied to many of America's leading restaurants fast-food chains cafeterias and military installations. Packaged and flavored rice products are marketed under the Riceland brand. Vegetable oil and shortening products are sold under Riceland and private label brands. Wheat is exported to Mexico and Egypt. Soybeans are sold to US buyers. Rough rice is sold to Mexico and Central America.

Financial Performance

In 2014 Riceland Foods' revenues topped more than $1 billion for the seventh consecutive year. However its net sales for the year were down about 12% due to a decline in prices for rice and soybeans.

Strategy

A key business objective for Riceland is to increase the number of value-added products (such as Riceland Rice ‘N Easy flavored rice mixes Riceland Turkey Fry Oil and Fish Fry Oil) and the level of its value added marketing. In 2014 a new riceland.com website went online allowing Riceland customers worldwide access to product information and sales personnel. The website brings consumers face-to-face with some Riceland farmer-members discussing their farming operations. It also includes cooking videos by Georgia Pellegrini a celebrity chef and author of “Modern Pioneering.” The websiteIn 2015 Sage V Foods of Boulder Colorado has sold its interest in an instant rice production facility in Little Rock to Best Rice LLC which is jointly owned by Riceland Foods and Producers Rice Mill both based in Stuttgart.

EXECUTIVES

Vice President International Marketing, Dwight Hill
District Manager Brinkley (AR), Opal Derrick
Director New Madrid (MO) Operations, Ed Williams
District Manager Gillett and Dumas (AR), David Curtis
District Manager Newport and Tuckerman (AR), Alvin Mullins
District Manager Jonesboro (AR), Freddie Gahr
Vice President Of Operations, Scott Johnson
Vice President Engineering, Don McCaskill
Vice President Application Development, Todd Thompson
Vice President Of Rice MILLI, Rick Rorex
Vice President, Betty Stepe
Sr Vp Admin & Secretary, Terry L Richardson
Auditors: BKD LLP LITTLE ROCK ARKANSA

LOCATIONS

HQ: RICELAND FOODS INC.
2120 S PARK AVE, STUTTGART, AR 721606822
Phone: 870 673-5500
Web: WWW.RICELAND.COM

PRODUCTS/OPERATIONS

Selected Products
Consumer
Saffron Yellow Rice Mix
Rice N Easy Mix Wild Rice
Long Grain & Wild Mix Rice N Easy Mix
Broccoli & Cheese Rice N Easy Mix
Spanish Rice Mix Rice N Easy Mix
Chicken Rice Mix Rice N Easy Mix
Long Grain Rice Riceland Extra Long Grain Rice
Riceland GOLD Perfected Rice

Riceland Jasmine Rice
Riceland Natural Brown Rice
Riceland Plump & Tender Medium Grain Rice
Food Service
  Oil
  Rice
Food Ingredients
  Long grain milled rice
  Long grain brown rice
  Medium grain milled rice
  Parboiled rice
  Broken grains

COMPETITORS

AarhusKarlshamn	Goya
American Rice	JFC International
CHS	Lotus Foods
Cereal Byproducts	Louis Dreyfus Group
Connell Company	Producers Rice Mill
Ebro Foods	Riviana Foods
Farmers Rice Milling	Specialty Rice
Farmers' Rice	
Cooperative	

HISTORICAL FINANCIALS

Company Type: Private

Income Statement

FYE: July 31

	REVENUE ($ mil.)	NET INCOME ($ mil.)	NET PROFIT MARGIN	EMPLOYEES
07/14	1,148	2	0.2%	1,646
07/13	1,314	58	4.4%	—
07/12	1,159	1	0.1%	—
07/11	1,107	0	—	—
Annual Growth	1.2%	—	—	—

2014 Year-End Financials

Return on assets: 1.1%
Return on equity: 0.2%
Current ratio: 1.20
Cash ($ mil.): 5

RICH PRODUCTS CORPORATION

Starting in 1945 with "the miracle cream from the soya bean" Rich Products has grown from a niche maker of soy-based whipped toppings and frozen desserts to a global US frozen foods maker. The family-owned business has developed other products such as toppings and icings and Coffee Rich (nondairy coffee creamer). It has expanded its product line to include frozen bakery and pizza doughs and ingredients for the food service and in-store bakery markets plus appetizers baked goods seafood meatballs and barbecue meat. Rich Products markets more than 2000 frozen food items that are sold in more than 110 countries; it has kitchens and bakeries around the world including about 50 locations on six continents.

Operations

Rich Products offers a variety of food items including topping and icings breads and rolls finished desserts pizza doughs bakery products appetizers and snacks BBQ meatballs and pasta and gluten-free and all-natural products.

Beyond food the Rich family through Rich's Entertainment Group owns the Buffalo Bisons the Jamestown Jammers and the Northwest Arkansas Naturals minor league baseball teams. It also owns and operates a number of catering operations and restaurants in New York and Florida through its Be Our Guest group. In addition the family owns a corporate and leisure travel management and event-planning business called The Travel Team; Roar Logistics which offers truck and rail shipping solutions; and the Palm Beach National Gold & Country Club.

Geographic Reach

Rich Products has operations in 20 countries worldwide including the US and Canada Argentina Australia Brazil China India Korea Mexico Russia South Africa Turkey United Arab Emirates the UK and Vietnam. Altogether the company sells its products in 112 countries.

Sales and Marketing

In addition to serving the restaurant and retail industries Rich Products sells to the logistics travel and hospitality sectors.

Financial Performance

Rich Products boasts $3.5 billion in annual sales and more than 9000 employees worldwide.

Strategy

While the company has developed a history in the states Rich Products has focused on expanding globally in recent years primarily in the Asia/Pacific region. It operates in Australia through wholesale bakery manufacturer VSE International which boasts a portfolio of 800 products. The company is also expanding in emerging markets in western Asia. Turkey serves as a base from which to reach customers in Iran Iraq Syria Bulgaria and Azerbaijan.

As part of its strategy Rich Products works to keep up with popular food trends such as gluten-free products as it jockeys for market share in the baked goods category. As early as 2010 the company began offering gluten-free items such as Parisian cakes.

Spending some $11 million the company is expanding its food manufacturing facility in Georgia by 40% to grow its capacity by 30%.

EXECUTIVES

Vice President Procurement And Inventory Planning Consumer Brands Division, Gary Bunn
Vice President Finance, Mary Kiener
President and CEO, William G. (Bill) Gisel, age 62
EVP Global Business Development and Director, Kevin R. Malchoff
President Rich's Entertainment Group, Melinda R. (Mindy) Rich, age 58
Executive VP Chief Financial Officer, James R. (Jim) Deuschle
Executive VP Chief Operating Officer, Richard M. Ferranti
Vice President Of National Account Sales, Paul Rich
Executive Vice President, Jonathan Dandes, age 63
Vice President Communications, Dwight Gram
Vice President Engineering, Tim Falken
Senior Vice President Of Operations, Dave Konst
Vice President Information Technology, Kevin Ridlon
National Account Manager, Corey Williamson
Vice President, Marty Hurley
Vice President Marketing Isb, Trish Hudson
National Account Manager, Rick Johnson
Vice President Marketing, Nick Stambula
Executive Vice President, Edward (Ed) Moore
Vice President Marketing, Deborah Andrews
Vice President Operations, Jay Lin
Vice President Senior Vice President Finance Director, Bob Pavone
Vice President Finance and Business Development, David (Dave) Faturos
National Accounts Manager, Stubblefield Sammy
Executive Vice President, Jonathan (Jon) Dandes
Senior Vice President Customer Experience, Ted Rich
Chairman, Robert E. (Bob) Rich
Assistant Treasurer, Ryan Trapper

LOCATIONS

HQ: RICH PRODUCTS CORPORATION
  1 ROBERT RICH WAY, BUFFALO, NY 142131701
Phone: 716 878-8422
Web: WWW.RICHS.COM

PRODUCTS/OPERATIONS

Selected Product Categories

Appetizers and snacks
Bakery products
BBQ
Breads and rolls
Cakes & desserts
Cooking creams
Gluten-free and all-natural
Meatballs and pasta
Pizza
Shrimp and seafood
Syrups and soaked cakes
Toppings and icings

Selected Consumer Brands

Byron' s
Carvel
Casa
Coffee Rich
Farm Rich
Freal
French Meadow Bakery
Rich' s
SeaPak

COMPETITORS

BakeMark	Gorton' s
Campbell Soup	Heinz
Canada Bread Company	Hom/Ade Foods
ConAgra	Kraft Foods Group Inc.
Dawn Food Products	Nestl©
Dean Foods	Pinnacle Foods
General Mills	Schwan' s
Gonnella Baking	Windsor Foods

HISTORICAL FINANCIALS

Company Type: Private

Income Statement

FYE: December 31

	REVENUE ($ mil.)	NET INCOME ($ mil.)	NET PROFIT MARGIN	EMPLOYEES
12/12	2,858	0	—	8,400
12/11	2,736	0	—	—
12/10	2,465	0	—	—
Annual Growth	7.7%	—	—	—

RICHMOND SCHOOL INC.

LOCATIONS

HQ: RICHMOND SCHOOL INC.
  301 N 9TH ST, RICHMOND, VA 232191933
Phone: 804 780-7710
Web: WWW.RICHMONDSCHOOL.NET

HISTORICAL FINANCIALS
Company Type: Private

Income Statement				FYE: June 30
	REVENUE ($ mil.)	NET INCOME ($ mil.)	NET PROFIT MARGIN	EMPLOYEES
06/11	308	2	0.7%	4,200
06/07	319	0	0.2%	—
06/06	0	0	—	—
06/05	0	0	—	—
Annual Growth	329.4%	—	—	—

2011 Year-End Financials
Return on assets: 1.5% Cash ($ mil.): —
Return on equity: 0.7%
Current ratio: —

RIGGINS INC.

LOCATIONS
HQ: RIGGINS INC.
3938 S MAIN RD, VINELAND, NJ 083607743
Phone: 856 825-7600
Web: WWW.RIGGINSOIL.COM

HISTORICAL FINANCIALS
Company Type: Private

Income Statement				FYE: December 31
	REVENUE ($ mil.)	NET INCOME ($ mil.)	NET PROFIT MARGIN	EMPLOYEES
12/13	456	0	0.0%	105
12/12	491	0	0.0%	—
12/11	471	0	0.0%	—
12/10	327	0	—	—
Annual Growth	11.7%	—	—	—

2013 Year-End Financials
Return on assets: 1.7% Cash ($ mil.): 1
Return on equity: —
Current ratio: 1.00

RIP GRIFFIN TRUCK SERVICE CENTER INC.

Rip Griffin Truck Service Center tries to make sure you never go hungry again (in Scarlett O'Hara's words) at least when you're driving on the highways of North Texas. Rip Griffin's network of about 10 travel centers offers truckers tour buses and other travelers a smorgasbord of features such as convenience stores fuel game rooms laundry facilities restaurants and showers. Locations also offer truck maintenance and repair services. In addition to its travel center business Rip Griffin sells Freightliner trucks through two Texas dealerships and provides fuel transportation services. In 2004 CEO Rip Griffin sold the company to Ohio-based TravelCenters of America.

EXECUTIVES
President, Mark Griffin
Auditors: GARRETT AND SWANN LLP LUBBOC

LOCATIONS
HQ: RIP GRIFFIN TRUCK SERVICE CENTER INC.
4710 4TH ST, LUBBOCK, TX 794164900
Phone: 806 795-8785
Web: WWW.RIPGRIFFIN.COM

COMPETITORS
Allsup's	Pilot Corporation
Chevron	Racetrac Petroleum
E-Z Mart Stores	Stuckey's
Love's Country Stores	Valero Energy

HISTORICAL FINANCIALS
Company Type: Private

Income Statement				FYE: December 31
	ASSETS ($ mil.)	NET INCOME ($ mil.)	INCOME AS % OF ASSETS	EMPLOYEES
12/13	126	3	2.6%	88
12/12	122	4	3.4%	—
12/11	119	3	2.6%	—
12/10	114	0	—	—
Annual Growth	3.4%	—	—	—

2013 Year-End Financials
Return on assets: 8.3% Sales ($ mil): 211
Return on equity: 1.5%

RIVER CITY PETROLEUM INC.

Auditors: BROWN FINK BOYCE & ASTLE LLP

LOCATIONS
HQ: RIVER CITY PETROLEUM INC.
840 DELTA LN, WEST SACRAMENTO, CA 956912801
Phone: 916 371-4960
Web: WWW.RCPFUEL.COM

HISTORICAL FINANCIALS
Company Type: Private

Income Statement				FYE: December 31
	REVENUE ($ mil.)	NET INCOME ($ mil.)	NET PROFIT MARGIN	EMPLOYEES
12/13	655	1	0.2%	55
12/12	579	1	0.2%	—
12/11	656	2	0.4%	—
12/10	488	0	—	—
Annual Growth	10.3%	—	—	—

2013 Year-End Financials
Return on assets: 3.0% Cash ($ mil.): 4
Return on equity: 0.2%
Current ratio: 0.80

RIVER VALLEY COOPERATIVE

LOCATIONS
HQ: RIVER VALLEY COOPERATIVE
102 S MAIN ST, WALCOTT, IA 527737761
Phone: 563 284-6223
Web: WWW.RIVERVALLEYCOOP.COM

HISTORICAL FINANCIALS
Company Type: Private

Income Statement				FYE: June 30
	REVENUE ($ mil.)	NET INCOME ($ mil.)	NET PROFIT MARGIN	EMPLOYEES
06/09	410	8	2.1%	84
06/08	276	5	1.8%	—
06/07	1,159	0	—	—
Annual Growth	—	29738.0%	—	—

2009 Year-End Financials
Return on assets: 2.0% Cash ($ mil.): —
Return on equity: 2.1%
Current ratio: 0.40

RIVERSIDE HEALTHCARE ASSOCIATION INC.

Extra! Extra! Read all about it! Residents of Newport News (and about a dozen other cities in Eastern Virginia) Turn to Riverside Health for Medical Care. The not-for-profit health care provider administers general emergency and specialty medical services from five hospitals Riverside Regional Medical Center Riverside Walter Reed Hospital Riverside Tappahannock Hospital and Riverside Shore Memorial Hospital and Riverside Doctors Hospital as well as a psychiatric hospital a physical rehabilitation facility and retirement communities. Riverside also operates physician offices and medical training facilities. Specialty centers provide home and hospice care cancer treatment and dialysis.

Geographic Reach

It serves Eastern Virginia including cities of Gloucester Hampton Newport News Poquoson Richmond Tappahannock West Point Williamsburg and Yorktown; Eastern Shore Area of Virginia; Counties of Essex Gloucester Isle of Wight James City King and Queen King William Lancaster Mathews Middlesex New Kent Northumberland Richmond and Surry.

Operations

Combined Riverside's hospitals (including rehabilitation and psychiatric) are home to nearly 1000 beds. Its major hospitals include Riverside Regional Medical Center (450-bed flagship hospital); Riverside Walter Reed Hospital (67-bed acute care facility); Riverside Tappahannock Hospital (67-bed serving the Northern Neck rural area); Riverside Shore Memorial Hospital (143-bed facility); and Riverside Doctors' Hospital Williamsburg (40 private rooms). It also operates specialty medical facilities including a psychiatric hospital a physical rehabilitation facility and retirement communities.

Strategy

To keep up with demand Riverside Health has been upgrading its older facilities and building new ones.

In 2013 the company opened a new hospital the Doctors Hospital in Williamsburg. The 40 room hospital provides acute and emergency care as well as specialty services including cardiology neurology and pulmonary care.

That year Riverside broke ground on the new Riverside Shore Memorial Hospital in Onley which is expected to be completed in late 2015. It will have 57 private inpatient rooms with the ability to add 12 more in the future.In 2012 Riverside Walter Reed Hospital opened a new intensive care unit.

It is also investing in technology physician expertise and patient services. In 2013 Riverside Shore Medical Center at Metompkin converted to digital mammography equipment offering patients a superior diagnostic tool to film mammograms.

Company Background

The original charter for Riverside dates back to 1915 when the company began as one hospital founded by the community. In 1962 the hospital was relocated to the present site in central Newport News.

EXECUTIVES

President, Charles R. Revere
Managing Partner, Julie Rautio
Executive Vice President And Chief Medical Officer; Director, Barry L Gross
Auditors: ERNST & YOUNG LLP RICHMOND

LOCATIONS

HQ: RIVERSIDE HEALTHCARE ASSOCIATION INC.
701 TOWN CENTER DR # 1000, NEWPORT NEWS, VA 236064286
Phone: 757 534-7000

Selected Facilities – Virginia
HOSPITALS
Riverside Behavioral Health Center (Hampton)
Riverside Doctors' Hospital (Williamsburg)
Riverside Regional Medical Center (Newport News)
Riverside Rehabilitation Institute (Williamsburg)
Riverside Tappahannock Hospital (Tappahannock)
Riverside Shore Memorial Hospital (Nassawadox)
Riverside Walter Reed Hospital (Gloucester)
RETIREMENT COMMUNITIES
Patriots Colony (Williamsburg)
Sanders (Gloucester)
Warwick Forest (Newport News)
SURGERY CENTERS
Doctors Surgery Center (Williamsburg)
Peninsula Surgery Center (Newport News)
Riverside Hampton Surgery Center (Hampton)

COMPETITORS

Alleghany Regional Hospital
Bon Secours Health
Carilion Clinic
Centra Health Inc.
Children' s Hospital of The King' s Daughters
Franklin Hospital Corp.
Novant Health
Sentara Healthcare
Wake Forest University Baptist Medical Center

HISTORICAL FINANCIALS
Company Type: Private

Income Statement

	REVENUE ($ mil.)	NET INCOME ($ mil.)	NET PROFIT MARGIN	EMPLOYEES
12/13	1,017	101	10.0%	8,000
12/12	948	41	4.4%	—
12/11	952	(25)	—	—
12/10	872	0	—	—
Annual Growth	5.3%	—	—	—

FYE: December 31

2013 Year-End Financials
Return on assets: 4.2%
Return on equity: 10.0%
Current ratio: 1.20
Cash ($ mil.): 40

RIVERSIDE HOSPITAL INC.

Riverside Hospital operates as Riverside Regional Medical Center a 450-bed acute-care facility that serves the residents of Newport News Virginia. Founded in 1916 the hospital moved to its current 72-acre campus in 1963 providing more than 30 medical specialties including cancer treatment cardiology birthing and diagnostic imaging. It specializes in cardiovascular and neurological surgeries and provides radiosurgery (radiation surgery) through a partnership with the University of Virginia Health System. Its emergency department is a 42-room Level II Trauma Center that treats more than 57000 patients each year. Riverside Hospital is part of the Riverside Health System.

Geographic Reach

Riverside Hospital serves the health care needs of those who reside in and around Newport News Virginia.

Operations

As part of its operations Riverside Hospital operates a heart center neonatal center 18-bed neonatal intensive care unit cancer care center and radiosurgery center through a partnership with Chesapeake Regional and the University of Virginia Health System. Riverside Hospital works to prevent diagnose and treat diseases of the stomach intestines esophagus pancreas gall bladder liver and biliary tract through its Peninsula Gastroenterology & Riverside Endoscopy Center.

EXECUTIVES

Physical Therapy Director, Doug Culbert
Medical Director, Patrick (Paddy) Harding
Medical Director, Bharati Srivastava
Secretary and Treasurer Medical Staff, Ken Jones
Auditors: ERNST YOUNG RICHMOND VA

LOCATIONS

HQ: RIVERSIDE HOSPITAL INC.
500 J CLYDE MORRIS BLVD, NEWPORT NEWS, VA 236011929
Phone: 757 594-2000
Web: WWW.RIVERSIDEONLINE.COM

PRODUCTS/OPERATIONS

Selected Services
Diagnostic Services
Cardiac testing
CT
Digital mammography
Electrocardiography
Magnetic resonance imaging
Nuclear medicine
PET
Ultrasound
Nutrition Services
Radiosurgery Center
Leksell Gamma Knife Synergy S Radiosurgery
Gastroenterology Procedures
Colonoscopy and polypectomy
Flexible sigmoidoscopy
Upper endoscopic exams and therapy
Endoscopic retrograde cholangiopancreatography (ERCP)
Percutaneous endoscopic gastrostomy (PEG)
Capsule/Cam (M2A) study of the small intestine
Esophageal dilation

Esophageal and anal manometry
BRAVO pH study of the esophagus
Pulmonary Rehabilitation
Surgical Services

COMPETITORS

Alleghany Regional Hospital
Bon Secours Health
Carilion Clinic
Centra Health Inc.
Children' s Hospital of The King' s Daughters
Franklin Hospital Corp.
Novant Health
Sentara Healthcare
Wake Forest University Baptist Medical Center

HISTORICAL FINANCIALS
Company Type: Private

Income Statement

	REVENUE ($ mil.)	NET INCOME ($ mil.)	NET PROFIT MARGIN	EMPLOYEES
12/12	479	70	14.7%	8,000
12/11	466	36	7.8%	—
12/10	429	20	4.9%	—
12/09	413	0	—	—
Annual Growth	5.0%	—	—	—

FYE: December 31

2012 Year-End Financials
Return on assets: 3.3%
Return on equity: 14.7%
Current ratio: 5.40
Cash ($ mil.): 214

ROBERT WOOD JOHNSON UNIVERSITY HOSPITAL

Robert Wood Johnson University Hospital (RWJUH) is the flagship facility of the Robert Wood Johnson Health System and Network. The medical center offers patients acute and tertiary care including cardiovascular services organ and tissue transplantation pediatric care (at The Bristol-Myers Squibb Children's Hospital) Level I trauma care cancer treatment (at the Cancer Hospital of New Jersey) women's health and emergency medicine. Founded in 1884 the 600-bed facility serves as a teaching center for the Robert Wood Johnson Medical School (RWJMS). The Robert Wood Johnson Health System plans to merge with fellow New Jersey hospital system Barnabas Health.

Geographic Reach

RWJUH has locations in New Brunswick Hamilton and Rahway New Jersey.

Operations

More than 1300 physicians affiliated with RWJUH treat some 200000 patients each year. The hospital handles some 17000 inpatient admissions each year as well as 48000 emergency visits. The hospital's cancer unit is the flagship partner of the Cancer Institute of New Jersey a research and treatment center located adjacent to RWJUH that is the only National Cancer Institute-designated cancer center in New Jersey. In addition the Bristol-Myers Squibb Children's Hospital works in tandem with the Child Health Institute of New Jersey (also located on the integrated medical campus).

Its RWJMS-partnered educational programs include residency programs for some 300 to 400 students. The hospital's nursing program covers 500 students and is affiliated with five schools; RWJUH also offers allied health professional training programs in fields including pharmacy; radiology; dental technology; dietary health; emergency medicine; and physical occupational speech/hearing and respiratory therapy.

For six straight years from 2007 through 2012 RWJUH was listed among U.S. News & World Report's "America's Best Hospitals."

Other members of the Robert Wood Johnson Health System include Robert Wood Johnson University Hospital Rahway Robert Wood Johnson University Hospital Hamilton and the Children's Specialized Hospital. The Robert Wood Johnson Health Network is an affiliated group of health care providers including hospitals nursing homes and health clinics which are located throughout New Jersey.

Strategy

The medical center's affiliation with the Robert Wood Johnson Medical School was transformed in 2012 when the school's operator —University of Medicine and Dentistry of New Jersey (UMNDJ) — agreed to merge with with Rutgers University. State officials believe a union between the two schools will raise New Jersey's profile as an academic destination which would benefit the programs at RWJUH as well.

To further enhance its diagnostic services the hospital opened a new satellite laboratory patient service location in New Brunswick in 2013 after redesigning the central clinical lab in 2012. It also opened a new satellite center for wound healing during 2013. In addition the RWJMH level I trauma center received the added designation of pediatric trauma center by the American College of Surgeons in 2012.

Mergers and Acquisitions

In mid-2015 Barnabas Health and the Robert Wood Johnson Health System agreed to join forces in a merger that will create the largest hospital system in New Jersey. The combined entity will operate under the name RWJ Barnabas Health and will include 11 hospitals. The deal is just one of a series of consolidation deals that have been taking place in New Jersey as companies work to remain competitive in the wake of the passing of the Affordable Care Act.

EXECUTIVES

Asst V Pres, Moira Burns
Head Nurse, Natalia Diaz
Vice President Of Human Resources, Martin Everhart
Head Nurse, Sarah Lawrence
Head Nurse, Rebecca Ramos
Director Of Nursing, Billie Bellamy
Nursing Director, Leigh Schmidt
Head Nurse, Maryjane Germek
Head Nurse, Jessica Bankowski
Head Nurse, Arlene McKnight
Vice President, Lori Colineri
Rph, Katherine Mundhenk
Pharm D, Isabel Caratenuto
Head Nurse, Crystal Walden
Head Nurse, Jennifer Mackown
Nursing Director, David Pinsky
Vice President Oncology Services, David Fernandez
Assistant Vice President Nursing, Kari Mastro
Nursing Director, Regina Ciambrone
Nursing Director Peds Or, Christopher (Chris) Rodgers
Vice President IS, Robert (Bob) Irwin
Nursing Director, Richard Bush
Head Nurse, Jennifer Bentley
Director Of Pharmacy, John Yanoschak
Vice President Critical Care, Julie Arsenault

Nursing Director PICU, Linda Palkoski
Vice President Human Resources, Lorin Rizco
Secretary, Stephanie Weldon

LOCATIONS

HQ: ROBERT WOOD JOHNSON UNIVERSITY HOSPITAL
1 ROBERT WOOD JOHNSON PL, NEW BRUNSWICK, NJ 089011928
Phone: 732 828-3000
Web: WWW.RWJUH.EDU

PRODUCTS/OPERATIONS

Selected Services

Bariatric Surgery
Bloodless Surgery
Cardiothoracic Surgery
Colorectal Surgery
Comprehensive Sleep Disorders Center
Diabetes
Digestive Disorders
Emergency Department
Executive Health Program
Heart Transplantation
Injury Prevention
Kidney and Pancreas Transplantation
Lab Services (blood work and blood collection)
Level 1 Trauma Center
Neurosciences
  Clinical Neurosciences Center
  Deep Brain Stimulation for Movement Disorders
  Laser Ablation for Brain Tumor Treatment
  Neurosurgery
  New Jersey Brain Aneurysm & AVM Program
  Parkinson's Disease Information and Referral Center
  Stroke Center
  The Gamma Knife Center: Advanced Treatment for Brain and Spine
New Jersey Pain Institute at RWJUH
Orthopedic Surgery
Outpatient Radiology: University Radiology at Robert Wood Johnson
Palliative Care Program
Pastoral Care
Pelvic Floor and Incontinence Program
Physical and Occupational Therapy
Prostate Cancer Surgery
Radiation Oncology
  Gynecologic Brachytherapy
  Prostate Brachytherapy
  TomoTherapy
  Total Skin Electron Beam Therapy
Radiology (including CT MRI and ultrasound)
Speech and Hearing Program
The Center for Wound Healing
The Limb Preservation Program
Therapeutic Apheresis
Thoracic Surgery
Vascular Surgery

COMPETITORS

Barnabas Health	Saint Peter's
Bergen Regional	University Hospital
Medical	Somerset Medical
Capital Health System	Center
JFK Health System	St. Joseph's
Princeton HealthCare	Healthcare System
Raritan Bay Medical	
Center	

HISTORICAL FINANCIALS

Company Type: Private

Income Statement

FYE: December 31

	REVENUE ($ mil.)	NET INCOME ($ mil.)	NET PROFIT MARGIN	EMPLOYEES
12/14	1,043	83	8.0%	4,674
12/13	833	108	13.0%	—
12/12*	823	83	10.2%	—
09/12	622	0	—	—
Annual Growth	29.4%	—	—	—

*Fiscal year change

ROBERTS DAIRY COMPANY LLC

Holy cow! Roberts Dairy Foods is a leading producer of fluid cultured and frozen dairy products. It offers milk yogurt sour cream cottage cheese and other dairy products. A division of Hiland Dairy the firm operates production plants in Omaha and Kansas City and 10 distribution centers located in the Midwest. The company markets its products under the Roberts and Hiland-Dairy brands; it also provides private-label services and school milk. Through a joint venture named Hiland-Roberts the company makes ice cream products from a facility in Norfolk Nebraska. Founded as a milk route by J.R. Roberts in 1906 Roberts Dairy Foods serves retail food and food service customers throughout the Midwest.

Geographic Reach

Roberts Dairy Foods has two production plants and 10 distribution centers in Nebraska Iowa Kansas and Missouri. Roberts Dairy serves a region that includes Nebraska Iowa Missouri Kansas and parts of Colorado Illinois and South Dakota.

Strategy

In 2011 the company changed its name from Roberts Dairy to Roberts Dairy Foods to reflect its expansion beyond milk. It also adopted a new logo that year to emphasize the freshness of its products. Non-dairy products include juices lemonade fruit punches and teas. Other specialty markets for the company include kosher and gluten-free products.

EXECUTIVES

President, Jeff Powell
Manager Corporate Marketing, Al Streeter
General Manager Sales Kansas City, Jon Behermeyer

LOCATIONS

HQ: ROBERTS DAIRY COMPANY LLC
2901 CUMING ST, OMAHA, NE 681312108
Phone: 402 344-4321
Web: WWW.ROBERTSDAIRYEFCU.ORG

PRODUCTS/OPERATIONS

Selected Products

Butter
Cottage cheese
Cream
Dips
Egg nog
Half-and-half
Ice cream
Juice & lemonade
Milk
Sour cream
Yogurt

COMPETITORS

Associated Milk	Organic Valley
Producers	Sunkist
Dairy Farmers of	Swiss Valley Farms
America	Tree Top
Dean Foods	Tropicana
Land O' Lakes	Welch's

HISTORICAL FINANCIALS
Company Type: Private

Income Statement
FYE: September 30

	REVENUE ($ mil.)	NET INCOME ($ mil.)	NET PROFIT MARGIN	EMPLOYEES
09/08	359	0	0.2%	320
09/07	319	2	0.7%	—
09/06	591	0	—	—
Annual Growth	—	8220.6%		

2008 Year-End Financials
Return on assets: 2.1%   Cash ($ mil.): 3
Return on equity: 0.2%
Current ratio: 0.10

ROBINSON OIL CORPORATION

Like Hamlet's Denmark something's rotten in the state of Robinson Oil. The company owns and operates Rotten Robbie a regional brand of independent gas stations that caters to consumer and commercial motorists. The chain consists of some 35 stops in Northern California mainly around the San Francisco Bay Area. Some stops are kiosks; about half are larger with Mrs. Robbie's Markets a food store and several offer commercial fleet fueling services affiliated with Pacific Pride and other cardlock networks. Diesel is available at all locations and at certain stores kerosene propane and biodiesel. Founded in the 1930s as a private-label fuel retailer Robinson Oil is a fourth-generation family-owned business.

Robinson Oil purchases products refined by one of five San Francisco Bay Area refineries: Chevron Conoco-Phillips Shell Tesoro and Valero. Most of the crude oil originates in California or Alaska.

Robinson Oil's growth strategy is based upon selling high volumes of fuel at a competitive price. When gas is abundant it is able to target car and truck drivers with prices considerably lower than major service stations. The strategy however is impacted by volatile fuel costs attributable to the capacity of state refineries known to fall short of demand coupled with the limited number of refineries elsewhere that make California's special reformulated blend. In August 2012 a fire at the state's Chevron refinery the largest in Northern California cut production to about 60% choking gas supplies and sending up prices at the pump. The event forced stations to battle over both supplies and the price for a fill-up.

Robinson Oil co-founder the late Herb Richards in 1948 pioneered the self-service gas station (and selling gas for less than other stations) against a backlash of concern over the safety in drivers pumping their own gas. Richards created the Rotten Robbie banner in 1973 intending that customers would not assume the worse and remember the best about his stations. He also boosted the company's presence by giving away a Cadillac every few weeks and offering free merchandise stamps to collect and redeem for discounts on groceries.

LOCATIONS
HQ: ROBINSON OIL CORPORATION
  955 MARTIN AVE, SANTA CLARA, CA 950502608
Phone: 408 327-4300
Web: WWW.ROBINSONOILCORP.COM

PRODUCTS/OPERATIONS

Selected Products
BioDiesel
Commercial fleet fueling
  CFN (Commercial Fueling Network)
  FleetWide Corp.
  Pacific Pride (PacPride)
Convenience store
Diesel
Kerosene
Lotto
Propane
  Blue Rhino
  Bulk

COMPETITORS
7-Eleven	Couche-Tard
Chevron	Flyers Energy

HISTORICAL FINANCIALS
Company Type: Private

Income Statement
FYE: December 31

	REVENUE ($ mil.)	NET INCOME ($ mil.)	NET PROFIT MARGIN	EMPLOYEES
12/13	468	8	1.9%	250
12/12	464	10	2.3%	—
12/09	292	8	2.8%	—
12/08	409	0	—	—
Annual Growth	2.7%	—	—	—

2013 Year-End Financials
Return on assets: 1.8%   Cash ($ mil.): 10
Return on equity: 1.9%
Current ratio: 1.20

ROCHESTER CITY SCHOOL DISTRICT

Auditors: FREEDMAXICK CPAS PC ROCHES

LOCATIONS
HQ: ROCHESTER CITY SCHOOL DISTRICT
  131 W BROAD ST, ROCHESTER, NY 146141103
Phone: 585 262-8100
Web: WWW.RCSDK12.ORG

HISTORICAL FINANCIALS
Company Type: Private

Income Statement
FYE: June 30

	REVENUE ($ mil.)	NET INCOME ($ mil.)	NET PROFIT MARGIN	EMPLOYEES
06/14	756	(127)	—	5,470
06/13	708	74	10.6%	—
06/11	681	(19)	—	—
06/06	448	0	—	—
Annual Growth	6.8%	—	—	—

2014 Year-End Financials
Return on assets: 9.7%   Cash ($ mil.): 197
Return on equity: (-16.9%)
Current ratio: —

ROCHESTER GENERAL HOSPITAL INC

Auditors: ERNST & YOUNG LLP HARTFORD

LOCATIONS
HQ: ROCHESTER GENERAL HOSPITAL INC
  1425 PORTLAND AVE, ROCHESTER, NY 146213095
Phone: 585 922-4101
Web: WWW.ROCHESTERGENERAL.ORG

HISTORICAL FINANCIALS
Company Type: Private

Income Statement
FYE: December 31

	REVENUE ($ mil.)	NET INCOME ($ mil.)	NET PROFIT MARGIN	EMPLOYEES
12/09	637	33	5.3%	3,100
12/08	551	(6)	—	—
12/06	1,726	0	—	—
Annual Growth	—	4322.9%		

2009 Year-End Financials
Return on assets: —   Cash ($ mil.): 53
Return on equity: 5.3%
Current ratio: 0.80

ROCHESTER INSTITUTE OF TECHNOLOGY (INC)

The Rochester Institute of Technology (RIT) is a privately-endowed university with nine colleges focused on providing career-oriented education to about 18000 students. The school which has a student-faculty ratio of about 14:1 offers more than 90 bachelor's degree programs in art and design business engineering science and hotel management. RIT also confers master's and doctorate degrees. The university's National Technical Institute for the Deaf is the first and largest technological college for learners who suffer from hearing loss. RIT which traces its roots back to 1829 counts among its alumni the CEOs of Kodak and The Associated Press.

Operations

Spanning some 1300 acres in Rochester New York RIT's campus serves 15000 undergraduate and 2900 graduate students with help from its faculty and staff of more than 4000. Approximately 1300 deaf and hard-of-hearing students live study and work alongside hearing students on the RIT campus. Tuition runs nearly $33000 for general students and more than $12000 for deaf and hard-of-hearing students.

RIT operates a campus in Dubai's Silicon Oasis a government owned high tech complex. The campus serves the university's goal of growing its reputation worldwide and expanding international opportunities for students. RIT Dubai offers undergraduate and graduate degree programs in engineering business information technology and leadership.

Financial Performance

RIT logged a 4% revenue rise in 2012 as compared to 2011 due to an increase in tuition and fees net of scholarships and sales and services of auxiliaries and private contributions. Meanwhile net income decreased by 84% during the same reporting period attributable to increased operating expenses and loss from investment returns and other non-operating activities. As a result of cash provided by operating activities RIT's cash outflow dropped $7.8 million in 2012 vs. 2011.

Sales and Marketing

The university sources its students globally from all 50 US states and from more than 100 countries.

EXECUTIVES

SVP Finance and Administration, James H. Watters
Dean Kate Gleason College of Engineering, Harvey Palmer
President, William W. (Bill) Destler
Dean College of Applied Science and Technology, H. Fred Walker
SVP Academic Affairs and Provost, Jeremy A. Haefner
VP and Dean Institute of Health Sciences and Technology, Daniel B. Ornt
Dean College of Imaging Arts & Sciences, Lorraine Justice
Dean College of Liberal Arts, James J. Winebrake
Dean College of Science, Sophia Maggelakis
Dean and President National Technical Institute for the Deaf, Gerard J. Buckley
SVP Enrollment Management and Career Services, James Miller
Dean B. Thomas Golisano College of Computing and Information Sciences, Anne Haake
Dean Saunders College of Business, Jacqueline Mozrall
Dean Graduate Studies, Hector Flores
SVP Student Affairs, Sandra Johnson
Secretary of the Institute and Chief of Staff, Karen Barrows
Provost-v Pres, Stanley D (Stan) Mckenzie
Vice President Community Relations, Richard Demartino
Associate Vice President for Development, Craig Smith
Assistant Vice President For Development, Kimberly Slusser
Assistant Vice President And Director Fin Aid And Scholarship, Verna Hazen
Student Affairs Vice Presidents Office, Kathy Routly
Vice President Dean Rit, James (Jamie) Decaro
ACADEMIC AFFIARS Vice President S OFFICE, Lynne Mazadoorian
Assistant Vice President Housing Operations, Howard Ward
Executive Vice President, Adrianne Carageorge
Assistant Vice President To the Provost, Susan (Sue) Provenzano
Interim Senior Vice President Student Affairs, Heath Boice-pardee
Associate Vice President for Academic Affairs, Stephen (Steve) Aldersley
Vice President For Academic Affairs, Katherine (Kate) Mayberry
Director Of Clinical Services, Mark Miles
Assistant Vice President Human Resources, Judy Bender
Department Chair, John (Jack) Morelli
STUDENT AFFIARS Vice President S OFFICE, Nicole Boulais
Vice President Research, Donald Boyd
Associate Vice President of Academics and Student Affairs, Muhieddin Amer
Department Chairman, Roy Czernikowski
Controller and Assistant Treasurer, Lyn Kelly
Secretary of Chinese Culture Club, Yan Li
Vice Chairman, Joyce Hertzson
Auditors: PRICEWATERHOUSECOOPERS LLP A

LOCATIONS

HQ: ROCHESTER INSTITUTE OF TECHNOLOGY (INC)
1 LOMB MEMORIAL DR, ROCHESTER, NY 146235698
Phone: 585 475-2411
Web: WWW.RIT.EDU

PRODUCTS/OPERATIONS

Selected Colleges
College of Applied Science and Technology
  School of Engineering Technology
  School of International Hospitality and Service Innovation
E. Philip Saunders College of Business
B. Thomas Golisano College of Computing and Information Sciences
Kate Gleason College of Engineering
College of Health Sciences and Technology
College of Imaging Arts and Sciences
  School for American Crafts
  School of Art
  School of Design
  School of Film and Animation
  School of Media Sciences
  School of Photographic Arts and Sciences
College of Liberal Arts
National Technical Institute for the Deaf
College of Science

Selected Graduate & Undergraduate Programs
Accounting
Applied Networking & Systems Administration
Applied Statistics
Biochemistry
Business
Civil Engineering Technology
Clinical Chemistry
Computer Integrated Machining Technology
Computer Science
Digital Imaging & Publishing Technology
Electrical/Mechanical Engineering Technology
Environmental Science
Finance
Glass & Glass Sculpture
Health Systems Administration
Healthcare Billing & Coding Technology
Imaging Arts: Photography
Industrial & Systems Engineering
Instruction Technology
Management
Medical Illustration
Metals/Jewelry Design
Ophthalmic Optical Finishing Technology
Print Media
Psychology
Service Leadership and Innovation
Voice Communication
Woodworking and Furniture Design

HISTORICAL FINANCIALS
Company Type: Private

Income Statement
FYE: June 30

	REVENUE ($ mil.)	NET INCOME ($ mil.)	NET PROFIT MARGIN	EMPLOYEES
06/13	504	52	10.4%	2,400
06/12	490	16	3.4%	—
06/06	370	45	12.2%	—
06/05	350	0	—	—
Annual Growth	4.6%	—	—	—

2013 Year-End Financials
Return on assets: 9.1%
Return on equity: 10.4%
Current ratio: —
Cash ($ mil.): 67

ROCKFORD MEMORIAL HOSPITAL

LOCATIONS

HQ: ROCKFORD MEMORIAL HOSPITAL
2400 N ROCKTON AVE, ROCKFORD, IL 611033681
Phone: 815 971-5000

HISTORICAL FINANCIALS
Company Type: Private

Income Statement
FYE: December 31

	REVENUE ($ mil.)	NET INCOME ($ mil.)	NET PROFIT MARGIN	EMPLOYEES
12/13	346	49	14.2%	2,800
12/12	307	63	20.5%	—
12/08	0	0	—	—
12/07	310	0	—	—
Annual Growth	1.8%	—	—	—

2013 Year-End Financials
Return on assets: 24.3%
Return on equity: 14.2%
Current ratio: 0.70
Cash ($ mil.): 43

ROCKHILL MENNONITE HOME

Auditors: BERGEY YODER & ASSOCIATES PC

LOCATIONS

HQ: ROCKHILL MENNONITE HOME
3250 STATE RD, SELLERSVILLE, PA 189601624
Phone: 215 257-2751
Web: WWW.ROCKHILLMENNONITE.ORG

HISTORICAL FINANCIALS
Company Type: Private

Income Statement
FYE: June 30

	REVENUE ($ mil.)	NET INCOME ($ mil.)	NET PROFIT MARGIN	EMPLOYEES
06/09	1,416	52	3.7%	225
06/98	8	0	9.1%	—
Annual Growth	59.8%	47.2%	—	—

2009 Year-End Financials
Return on assets: 0.1%
Return on equity: 3.7%
Current ratio: 0.10
Cash ($ mil.): —

ROCKVIEW DAIRIES INC.

Got organic milk? Rockview Dairies does. Doing business as Rockview Farms the company produces milk and other dairy products under brand names Rockview Farms and Good Heart Organic Milk. Bucking modern trends the dairy owns its own farms and cows which have not been treated with bovine growth hormones. Rockview Dairies processes packages and distributes its own milk. It also offers eggs dressings fruit drinks and desserts. The company wholesales its products to food retailers and foodservice operators and as a bonus offers home-delivery service. Established in 1927 by Bob Hops Rockview Dairies serves Southern California. It has been owned and operated by the DeGroot family since 1965.

Geographic Reach

Rockview Dairies operates one of the few family-owned and independently-operated fluid milk plants in Southern California. It primarily serves customers in Los Angeles and Orange counties and operates farms and processing facilities in Southern California Nevada Texas and Kansas.

Sales and Marketing

Rockview Dairies provides its milk yogurt cottage cheese and other products to independent supermarkets convenience stores drive-through dairies and foodservice operators. It delivers its dairy items to customers' homes as well.

Operations

Thanks to a growing movement to eat local and organic foods Rockview Dairies has developed a successful milk-delivery business. The dairy partners with delivery companies to deliver milk and other dairy products to more than 7500 homes located in Los Angeles and Orange counties. Milk is delivered fewer than 48 hours after milking.

It has grown to become one of the largest dairies in the state to own its own cows and process package and distribute its own milk.

LOCATIONS

HQ: ROCKVIEW DAIRIES INC.
7011 STEWART AND GRAY RD, DOWNEY, CA 902414347
Phone: 562 927-5511
Web: WWW.ROCKVIEWFARMS.COM

PRODUCTS/OPERATIONS

Selected Products
Butter
Buttermilk
Cottage cheese
Cream
Half & half
Milk
Juice
Sour cream
Yogurt

COMPETITORS

Aurora Organic Dairy	Garelick Farms
California Dairies Inc.	Kemps LLC
	Land O' Lakes
Dairy Farmers of America	Oberweis Dairy
	Organic Valley
Dean Foods	Roberts Dairy
Farmland Dairies	Springfield Creamery
Foster Dairy Farms	Stonyfield Farm
Friendship Dairies	Turkey Hill Dairy

HISTORICAL FINANCIALS
Company Type: Private

Income Statement
FYE: March 31

	REVENUE ($ mil.)	NET INCOME ($ mil.)	NET PROFIT MARGIN	EMPLOYEES
03/08	333	8	2.4%	250
03/07	265	3	1.5%	—
03/06	2,112	0	—	—
Annual Growth	—13235.1%	—	—	—

2008 Year-End Financials
Return on assets: 3.9% Cash ($ mil.): 3
Return on equity: 2.4%
Current ratio: 0.90

ROGERS PETROLEUM INC.

LOCATIONS

HQ: ROGERS PETROLEUM INC.
1634 W 1ST NORTH ST, MORRISTOWN, TN 378143709
Phone: 423 581-7460
Web: WWW.ROGERSPETRO.COM

HISTORICAL FINANCIALS
Company Type: Private

Income Statement
FYE: March 31

	REVENUE ($ mil.)	NET INCOME ($ mil.)	NET PROFIT MARGIN	EMPLOYEES
03/13	425	1	0.3%	200
03/12	445	1	0.2%	—
03/11	371	0	0.1%	—
03/10	288	0	—	—
Annual Growth	13.8%	—	—	—

2013 Year-End Financials
Return on assets: 3.6% Cash ($ mil.): 1
Return on equity: 0.3%
Current ratio: 0.10

RONILE INC.

Ronile can spin a yarn –a textile one that is. The company manufactures custom-dyed accent yarns including twisted space-dyed air-ply and heatset yarns. Ronile's slew of finished yarn goods include nylon polyester acrylic and other wool fibers which are marketed to carpet rug home furnishings craft and automotive markets. Ronile also operates through subsidiary Bacova Guild Ltd. a manufacturer and supplier of printed accent rugs room-size rugs and bath ensembles to US retail chains and Gulistan a division supplying broadloom carpet. Employee-owned the company is led by its founder's son Phillip Essig.

Ronile was founded in 1984 as a yarn spinning company by Abe and Elinor Essig. The company's name derives from "Elinor" spelled backward.

EXECUTIVES

Vice President Sales, Ron Martin
Auditors: SMITH LEONARD ACCOUNTANTS AND

LOCATIONS

HQ: RONILE INC.
701 ORCHARD AVE, ROCKY MOUNT, VA 241511848
Phone: 540 483-0261
Web: WWW.RONILE.COM

COMPETITORS

Beaulieu of America	Mohawk Industries
Interface Inc.	Shaw Industries

HISTORICAL FINANCIALS
Company Type: Private

Income Statement
FYE: June 30

	REVENUE ($ mil.)	NET INCOME ($ mil.)	NET PROFIT MARGIN	EMPLOYEES
06/07*	232	0	—	1,383
07/06	245	0	—	—
07/05	597	0	0.0%	—
Annual Growth	(37.6%)	—	—	—

*Fiscal year change

2007 Year-End Financials
Return on assets: 8.6% Cash ($ mil.): —
Return on equity: —
Current ratio: 1.00

ROPER HOSPITAL INC.

LOCATIONS

HQ: ROPER HOSPITAL INC.
316 CALHOUN ST, CHARLESTON, SC 294011125
Phone: 843 724-2800
Web: WWW.RSFH.COM

HISTORICAL FINANCIALS
Company Type: Private

Income Statement
FYE: December 31

	REVENUE ($ mil.)	NET INCOME ($ mil.)	NET PROFIT MARGIN	EMPLOYEES
12/13	392	54	14.0%	2,100
12/09	450	48	10.8%	—
12/08	618	(51)	—	—
12/06	353	0	—	—
Annual Growth	1.5%	—	—	—

2013 Year-End Financials
Return on assets: 0.3% Cash ($ mil.): —
Return on equity: 14.0%
Current ratio: 49.50

ROSE INTERNATIONAL INC.

Rose International keep its customers' tech gardens in bloom. The company provides outsourced IT services including database performance optimization application development and project management to businesses and government agencies in the US. Other services include vendor management payroll processing training and staffing and call center operations. Rose —its name is an acronym for "reliable open systems engineering" — serves customers in the financial services energy technology telecommunications and health care industries. Its software development activities in Missouri and India are overseen by subsidiary Rose I.T. Solutions.

Geographic Reach

Rose International has about 20 offices located across the US and one in New Delhi India.

Sales and Marketing

The company serves more than 130 customers in the energy entertainment financial and healthcare industries and government agencies. Some of its commercial customers have included Square D UniGroup Boeing Southwestern Bell and Maritz. In addition to commercial clients the company's government clients have included the US Air Force Army and Navy the State of Missouri and the USDA.

Rose International has sales and service partnerships with IT vendors IBM Microsoft and Cisco Systems.

Company Background

Established in 1993 as Rose Imaging the company (a minority- and woman-owned business) is controlled by founder Himanshu (Sue) Bhatia.

EXECUTIVES

Vice President Finance, Larry Crane
Senior Vice President Sales and Marketing, Eric Token
Vp Western Region, Harish Vakharia
Vice President Contingent Workforce Services, Phil Black
Auditors: BROWN SMITH WALLACE LLC ST LO

LOCATIONS

HQ: ROSE INTERNATIONAL INC.
16401 SWINGLEY RIDGE RD, CHESTERFIELD, MO 630170757
Phone: 636 532-3126
Web: WWW.ROSEINT.COM

PRODUCTS/OPERATIONS

Selected Services
Application Development
Database Performance Optimization Practice
Operations Maintenance and Support
Project Management and PMI Training
Workforce Solutions

Selected Industries Served
Energy
Entertainment
Financial
Government Agencies
Healthcare
Retail and Consumer
Technology and Telecommunication

COMPETITORS

Accenture	Infosys
Analysts International	Leidos
Capgemini	Maryville Data Systems
Computer Sciences Corp.	S2 Tech
	Tata Consultancy
HP Enterprise Group	Unisys
IBM Global Services	World Wide Technology

HISTORICAL FINANCIALS
Company Type: Private

Income Statement
FYE: December 31

	REVENUE ($ mil.)	NET INCOME ($ mil.)	NET PROFIT MARGIN	EMPLOYEES
12/12	357	11	3.2%	6,000
12/11	357	13	3.8%	—
12/10	228	9	4.0%	—
12/09	161	0	—	—
Annual Growth	30.5%	—	—	—

2012 Year-End Financials
Return on assets: 1.9%   Cash ($ mil.): 1
Return on equity: 3.2%
Current ratio: 3.00

ROSELAND PARTNERS L.L.C.

LOCATIONS

HQ: ROSELAND PARTNERS L.L.C.
233 CANOE BROOK RD, SHORT HILLS, NJ 070781013
Phone: 973 218-2300

HISTORICAL FINANCIALS
Company Type: Private

Income Statement
FYE: December 31

	ASSETS ($ mil.)	NET INCOME ($ mil.)	INCOME AS % OF ASSETS	EMPLOYEES
12/09	1,458	2	0.1%	350
12/08	1,056	16	1.6%	—
Annual Growth	38.1%	(87.7%)	—	—

2009 Year-End Financials
Return on assets: 57.2%   Sales ($ mil): 71
Return on equity: 2.9%

ROSEN HOTELS AND RESORTS INC.

Want to make your Florida stay a little rosy? Rosen Hotels & Resorts owns and operates seven hotels in Orlando collectively totaling more than 6300 rooms and suites. Its properties are located near major area attractions such as Disney World (from Walt Disney Parks) and Universal Studios Orlando (from Universal Parks & Resorts). Its portfolio consists of hotels such as the Rosen Plaza Hotel and Rosen Inn. Three of its hotels are home to major Orlando convention centers: Rosen Plaza Rosen Centre and Rosen Shingle Creek. In addition subsidiary Millennium Technology Group manages computer systems for its hotels. The family-owned Rosen Hotels & Resorts was founded by president Harris Rosen in 1974.

Geographic Reach

The company is Florida's largest independent hotel chain.

Company Background

Harris Rosen a former manager at Hilton and executive at Disney has made a name for himself as a prominent Orlando businessman. Among his notable achievements are providing employees with healthcare via onsite clinics and the donation of a site to the University of Central Florida for the Rosen College of Hospitality Management.

EXECUTIVES

CFO, Frank A. Santos
President and COO, Harris Rosen
VP Sales and Marketing, Leslie Menichini
Director of IT, Mike Lewis
National Sales Manager Southeast, Lilianne Murr
National Sales Manager, Andrew (Andy) Halsey

LOCATIONS

HQ: ROSEN HOTELS AND RESORTS INC.
8990 INTL DR STE 200, ORLANDO, FL 328199321
Phone: 407 996-1706
Web: WWW.ROSENHOTELS.COM

PRODUCTS/OPERATIONS

Selected Properties
Rosen Shingle Creek
Rosen Centre Hotel
Rozen Plaza Hotel
Clarion Inn Lake Buena Vista
Rosen Inn at Pointe Orlando
Rosen Inn
Rosen Inn International
Rosen's Perfect ProductsPerfect PizzaAlligator DroolRosen Perfect Bars

COMPETITORS

Central Florida Investments Inc.	Orange Lake Country Club
Disney Parks & Resorts	Peabody Management
Larry Blumberg and Associates	Starwood Hotels & Resorts
Marriott Vacations	Wyndham Vacation

HISTORICAL FINANCIALS
Company Type: Private

Income Statement
FYE: January 31

	REVENUE ($ mil.)	NET INCOME ($ mil.)	NET PROFIT MARGIN	EMPLOYEES
01/14	268	76	28.5%	3,420
01/13	268	76	28.5%	—
01/12	8	0	—	—
01/11	8	0	—	—
Annual Growth	216.0%	—	—	—

2014 Year-End Financials
Return on assets: 4.2%   Cash ($ mil.): —
Return on equity: 28.5%
Current ratio: —

ROTH STAFFING COMPANIES L.P.

Roth Staffing Companies L.P. offers temporary and temp-to-hire staffing and permanent placement services through its specialized business lines. Ultimate Staffing Services specializes in administrative customer service clerical manufacturing & production positions. Ledgent Finance & Accounting focuses on accounting and finance professionals while Ledgent Technology & Engineering concentrates on professionals in those fields. Adams & Martin Group recruits legal professionals. The company serves clients in 21 US states and Washington DC through more than 100 branches and a number of on-premise locations.

Operations

The company has six specialized business lines: Ultimate Staffing Service (the 11th largest administrative/clerical staffing company in the US) Ledgent Finance & Accounting Adams & Martin Group Ledgent Technology & Engineering and About Talent. The organization is also affiliated with Ultimate Locum Tenens.

In addition to staffing Roth Staffing Companies L.P. offers executive search services recruitment process outsourcing 1099 (independent contractor) management and payroll services.

Company Background

The company was founded in 1994 by CEO Ben Roth. Roth Staffing Companies stands as the only firm in the industry ever ranked #1 on the Inc. 500 list of fastest-growing privately-owned companies.

EXECUTIVES

Senior Vice President Of Professional Services, Julie Porter
Founder and CEO, Ben Roth
SVP; President Ultimate Staffing Services, Pam Sexauer
President and COO, Adam Roth
VP Accounting and Finance, Pauline Francis
Sr. VP of Professional Services, Julie Hagan
VP Ledgent Technology, Brett Roth
Senior Vice President Finance and Accounting, Mimi Taylor
Senior Vice President General Counsel, Jennifer Jech (Jen) Simonson

LOCATIONS

HQ: ROTH STAFFING COMPANIES L.P.
333 CITY BLVD W STE 100, ORANGE, CA 928682952
Phone: 714 939-8600
Web: WWW.ADAMSMARTINGROUP.COM

COMPETITORS

Adecco	On Assignment
Allegis Group	Randstad Holding
Kelly Services	Robert Half
Kforce	TrueBlue
ManpowerGroup	Volt Information

HISTORICAL FINANCIALS

Company Type: Private

Income Statement

FYE: December 31

	REVENUE ($ mil.)	NET INCOME ($ mil.)	NET PROFIT MARGIN	EMPLOYEES
12/13	258	0	—	500
12/12	244	0	—	—
12/11	244	0	—	—
12/10	202	0	—	—
Annual Growth	8.6%	—	—	—

2013 Year-End Financials

Return on assets: 0.3%   Cash ($ mil.): —
Return on equity: —
Current ratio: 2.20

ROUSE'S ENTERPRISES L.L.C.

Auditors: TS KEARNS & CO THIBODAUX

LOCATIONS

HQ: ROUSE' S ENTERPRISES L.L.C.
1301 SAINT MARY ST, THIBODAUX, LA 703016527
Phone: 985 447-5998
Web: WWW.SHOP.ROUSES.COM

HISTORICAL FINANCIALS

Company Type: Private

Income Statement

FYE: December 29

	REVENUE ($ mil.)	NET INCOME ($ mil.)	NET PROFIT MARGIN	EMPLOYEES
12/10	691	24	3.5%	5,200
12/09	689	21	3.1%	—
12/06	1,452	0	0.0%	—
Annual Growth	(16.9%)	519.4%	—	—

2010 Year-End Financials

Return on assets: 1.8%   Cash ($ mil.): 8
Return on equity: 3.5%
Current ratio: 0.30

RUMSEY ELECTRIC COMPANY

This company delivers the juice and it's not O.J. Rumsey Electric distributes electrical construction equipment utility products and services and systems for relay and power and lighting for retailers. Operating through one central distribution facility and a dozen branches the company caters to construction and industrial businesses and utilities as well as OEMs institutions and commercial Mid-Atlantic markets. It is the authorized distributor of Rockwell Automation a large industrial automation firm. Employee-owned Rumsey Electric has been in business for over 110 years.

Geographic Reach

Rumsey operates through its 135000 sq. ft. central distribution facility and 11 branch locations primarily located in Delaware Pennsylvania and New Jersey.

Strategy

Rumsey grows by adding products to its portfolio and launching additional locations in key markets. In 2013 it announced the opening of a new retail sales office and regional distribution center with a 40000 sq. ft. capacity in Atlantic City New Jersey. It 2012 it opened a new 15000 sq. ft. facility in Malvern Pennsylvania.

EXECUTIVES

President and CEO, Gerald M. (Jerry) Lihota, age 68
EVP and CFO, Scott M. Cutler, age 65
SVP Logistics Purchasing and Operations, Paul Esterheld
Manager Information Technology, Matt Prior
Vice President of Sales Development, Elliot Levine
Vice President Of Sales, Pat Melvin
Vice President of Utility Sales, George Strasbaugh
Vice President, Steven Cabibbo
Vice President, Jim Presto
Auditors: RAINER & COMPANY NEWTON SQUAR

LOCATIONS

HQ: RUMSEY ELECTRIC COMPANY
15 COLWELL LN, CONSHOHOCKEN, PA 194281878
Phone: 610 832-9000
Web: WWW.RUMSEY.COM

PRODUCTS/OPERATIONS

Selected Products
Automation and controls
Ballasts
Control panel components
Enclosures
Energy saving components
Fixtures
Lamps
Lighting
Lighting controls
Lighting services
Mechanical components
Metering
Power distribution
Process components
Protection and control products
Relay and power systems
Safety and supply parts
Switchgear
Tools
Transformers

COMPETITORS

Anixter International	Fromm Electric
Billows Electric Supply	Gexpro
Colonial Electric Supply	Graybar Electric
	Rexel Inc.
	United Electric Supply

Consolidated Electrical	WESCO International

HISTORICAL FINANCIALS

Company Type: Private

Income Statement

FYE: December 31

	REVENUE ($ mil.)	NET INCOME ($ mil.)	NET PROFIT MARGIN	EMPLOYEES
12/13	225	9	4.1%	284
12/12	197	10	5.4%	—
12/11	196	2	1.0%	—
12/10	187	0	—	—
Annual Growth	6.4%	—	—	—

2013 Year-End Financials

Return on assets: 8.6%   Cash ($ mil.): 14
Return on equity: 4.1%
Current ratio: 2.20

RUSAL AMERICA CORP.

LOCATIONS

HQ: RUSAL AMERICA CORP.
500 MMARONECK AVE STE 102, HARRISON, NY 10528
Phone: 914 670-5771

HISTORICAL FINANCIALS

Company Type: Private

Income Statement

FYE: December 31

	REVENUE ($ mil.)	NET INCOME ($ mil.)	NET PROFIT MARGIN	EMPLOYEES
12/12	683	0	0.1%	11
12/11	611	0	0.1%	—
12/10	525	0	0.1%	—
12/08	1,009	0	—	—
Annual Growth	(9.3%)	—	—	—

2012 Year-End Financials

Return on assets: 0.1%   Cash ($ mil.): 7
Return on equity: 0.1%
Current ratio: 0.30

RUSH UNIVERSITY MEDICAL CENTER

LOCATIONS

HQ: RUSH UNIVERSITY MEDICAL CENTER
1653 W CONGRESS PKWY, CHICAGO, IL 606123833
Phone: 312 942-5000
Web: WWW.TRANSFORMING.RUSH.EDU

HISTORICAL FINANCIALS
Company Type: Private

Income Statement
FYE: June 30

	REVENUE ($ mil.)	NET INCOME ($ mil.)	NET PROFIT MARGIN	EMPLOYEES
06/13	1,583	124	7.9%	214
06/12	1,449	33	2.3%	—
06/11	1,441	290	20.2%	—
06/10	1,395	0	—	—
Annual Growth	4.3%	—	—	—

2013 Year-End Financials
Return on assets: 22.9% Cash ($ mil.): 172
Return on equity: 7.9%
Current ratio: 0.30

RUSH-COPLEY MEDICAL CENTER INC.

People in a rush to get healthy can find help at Rush-Copley Medical Center. A member of the Rush System for Health family the medical center serves Illinois' Fox Valley area. The hospital has about 210 beds and provides acute and tertiary medical services including cardiac care cancer treatment neurology women's services neonatal care and health education programs. Its Rush-Copley Surgery Center performs both day surgeries and inpatient procedures while its nearby Rush-Copley Healthcare Center houses doctors' offices and offers outpatient diagnostic imaging services. Other programs include a neuroscience center a home health care agency and its Healthplex fitness center.

Geographic Reach

With facilities in Aurora and Yorkville Rush-Copley provides medical services to residents of Kane County and Kendall County in Illinois. It also serves small portions of other counties including DeKalb DuPage Grundy LaSalle and Will.

Operations

Rush-Copley employs 500 doctors and sees about 80000 patients each year. It handles about 70000 emergency room visits as well as more than 3000 births. The hospital operates the only level III neonatal intensive care unit in the county. Rush-Copley spends about $50 million each year to provide care for uninsured or under-insured patients.

The medical center's campus includes Fox Valley Dialysis Ltd Rush-Copley Healthplex Fitness Center and Waubonsee Community College.

Strategy

As a strategic collaborator with Rush University Medical Center Rush-Copley is actively participating in initiatives that improve care reduce costs and enhance patient access to both local community care as well as academic medicine.

The hospital has outlined a plan to expand its services in key areas. In addition to increasing its inpatient bed capacity and growing the size of its medical staff Rush-Copley plans to expand its cardiovascular oncology neurology emergency and women's health departments as well as its outpatient care centers. It also plans to upgrade its technology systems to improve caregiver communication capabilities and qualify for meaningful use guidelines as outlined in the American Recovery and Reinvestment Act of 2009.Rush-Copley is undergoing a major $53 million construction project to improve care and comfort for patients and vis-

itors. The expansion consists of a major addition and renovation to its surgery center including three additional operating rooms. The project will also add a new non-denominational chapel an expanded gift shop a new lobby and a main entrance that will feature comfortable waiting areas.

Company Background

In 2012 the organization widened outpatient services when it opened a new emergency clinic in Yorkville; the Rush-Copley Emergency Center also offers laboratory imaging and occupational health services. Also in 2012 the Rush-Copley Medical Group physician organization opened a new sports medicine office in Aurora.

The hospital was founded in 1886.

EXECUTIVES
Senior Vice President Strategy, Gail Bumgarner
Svp Finance; Cfo, Brenda Van Wyhe
Vice President, Vijay Shah
Vice President Finance, Brenda VanWyhe
Auditors: DELOITTE & TOUCHE LLP CHICAG

LOCATIONS
HQ: RUSH-COPLEY MEDICAL CENTER INC.
2000 OGDEN AVE, AURORA, IL 605045893
Phone: 630 978-6200
Web: WWW.RUSHCOPLEY.COM

PRODUCTS/OPERATIONS

Selected Services
Advance Directives
Allergy and Immunology
Anterior Cervical Disectomy and Fusion (ACDF)
Arrhythmia
Asthma
Audiology
Cancer Care
Capsule Endoscopy
Cardiology
Cardiovascular and Thoracic Surgery
Celiac Disease
Cervical Stenosis and Myelopathy
Child Passenger Safety
Cirrhosis
Colonoscopy
Concussion Management
Convenient Care
Crohn' s Disease
Same Day Sick Visits
School and Sports Physicals
Sleep Medicine
Smoking Cessation
Spinal Surgery
Spondylolisthesis
Sports Medicine
Stroke
Support Groups
Surgery Center

COMPETITORS

Central DuPage Hospital	OSF Healthcare System
Dreyer Clinic	University of Chicago Medical Center
Morris Hospital	Wheaton Franciscan Services
Northwestern Memorial HealthCare	

HISTORICAL FINANCIALS
Company Type: Private

Income Statement
FYE: June 30

	REVENUE ($ mil.)	NET INCOME ($ mil.)	NET PROFIT MARGIN	EMPLOYEES
06/13	319	41	12.9%	2,000
06/12	296	17	6.0%	—
06/11	0	0	—	—
06/10	0	0	—	—
Annual Growth	—	—	—	—

2013 Year-End Financials
Return on assets: 4.2% Cash ($ mil.): 23
Return on equity: 12.9%
Current ratio: 0.70

RUSSELL & SMITH FORD INC.

Auditors: SVADLENAK SEE & COMPANY PC

LOCATIONS
HQ: RUSSELL & SMITH FORD INC.
3440 SOUTH LOOP W, HOUSTON, TX 770255296
Phone: 713 663-4111
Web: WWW.RSFORD.COM

HISTORICAL FINANCIALS
Company Type: Private

Income Statement
FYE: May 31

	REVENUE ($ mil.)	NET INCOME ($ mil.)	NET PROFIT MARGIN	EMPLOYEES
05/14	304	4	1.5%	310
05/13	265	3	1.3%	—
05/12	222	2	0.9%	—
05/11	194	0	—	—
Annual Growth	10.1%	—	—	—

2014 Year-End Financials
Return on assets: 3.0% Cash ($ mil.): 7
Return on equity: 1.5%
Current ratio: 0.20

RUSSELL SIGLER INC.

Russell Sigler has built a business providing a rather cool service in a hot region. Through about 30 offices located primarily in California and Arizona (but also in Idaho Nevada New Mexico and Texas) the company provides commercial and residential air conditioning contractors with equipment parts supplies and technical support. Its brands include Carrier Bryant and Payne. Russell Sigler has distributed Carrier products for more than 60 years. As part of its business the company also operates a residential and commercial distribution joint venture with industry giant Carrier. Russell Sigler owns a 60% stake while Carrier holds 40%.

Geographic Reach

Based in Tolleson Arizona Russell Sigler has branch locations in Arizona California Idaho Nevada New Mexico and Texas.

Sales and Marketing

Russell Sigler provides its products to retail stores and to dealers.

EXECUTIVES
Vice President Of Human Resources, Pat Crocker
Auditors: MCGLADREY LLP PHOENIX ARIZON

LOCATIONS
HQ: RUSSELL SIGLER INC.
9702 W TONTO ST, TOLLESON, AZ 853539703
Phone: 623 388-5100
Web: WWW.SIGLERS.COM

COMPETITORS

Chas Roberts Air Conditioning
Ferguson Enterprises
Gustave A. Larson Company
HD Supply
Johnstone Supply
US Airconditioning Distributors
Watsco
WinWholesale

HISTORICAL FINANCIALS

Company Type: Private

Income Statement

FYE: December 31

	REVENUE ($ mil.)	NET INCOME ($ mil.)	NET PROFIT MARGIN	EMPLOYEES
12/13	488	6	1.3%	550
12/09	140	(0)	—	—
12/08	176	1	0.8%	—
12/06	2,141	0	—	—
Annual Growth (19.0%)	—	—	—	—

2013 Year-End Financials

Return on assets: 3.3%
Return on equity: 1.3%
Current ratio: 1.30
Cash ($ mil.): —

RUTLAND HOSPITAL INC.

For those seeking health care in the New England region Rutland Regional Medical Center (RRMC) just might be the destination for you. Part of Rutland Regional Health Services it runs a hospital that boasts more than 120 beds and serves patients in Vermont and eastern New York. RRMC offers about 40 medical specialties including cancer care diabetes treatment and total joint replacement. The acute-care facility also has centers dedicated to cardiac rehabilitation and women's health. To meet growing community medical needs RRMC also operates a prostate care unit and a 30-bed psychiatric unit. Along with a range of specialty care options RRMC administers primary care and emergency medical transport.

Geographic Reach

RRMC serves communities in Rutland County and surrounding portions of southern and central Vermont as well as eastern New York. It operates about 25 locations in Rutland Vermont as well as single facilities in towns including East Dorset Killington and Poultney Vermont.

Operations

Established in 1896 RRMC gets nearly half of its patient income from Medicare accounts about 20% from Blue Cross and Blue Shield contracts and the balance from a mix of commercial managed care contracts Medicaid and self-pay patients. The facility provides about $6 million in charity care each year.

Providing preventive diagnostic acute and rehabilitative services RRMC is the second largest hospital in Vermont and is a not–for–profit organization dedicated to improving the health of families and individuals. The 123-bed hospital employs more than

1600 professional and support staff including 227 providers trained in 36 specialty areas.

Affiliated facilities in the RRMC network include an orthopedic clinic a sports medicine center a health plan and a health foundation as well as two long-term care centers. The Center has some 33900 Emergency visits 412 new births and 230600 inpatients and outpatients registrations a year.

Financial Performance

In fiscal 2014 (September year end) the company reported a 4% revenue increase. Net Patients revenues accounted for 95% of the total. Medicare Medicaid and commercial accounted for 32% 17% and 15% of total net patient's revenues respectively.

The company net profits declined by 15% that year.

StrategyIn fiscal 2016 RRMC plans to seek input from community members on their health concerns to help identify the top health issues facing Rutland County through a Community Health Needs Assessment. (The company undertake this work every three years to collect input toward a county-wide health improvement plan based on data such as illness injury and death rates community opinions and resources available. Information from regional state and national reports along with input from consumers and community leaders is compiled and analyzed for this purpose).

To further improve efficiencies and reduce medical spending RRMC is participating in Vermont's Blueprint for Health program which seeks to coordinate care between various medical providers. For instance through the program the hospital is helping to implement a care management infrastructure for patients with chronic diseases.

Company Background

To expand services in the region RRMC expanded into new markets and entered into collaborations with other area providers. It also increased its specialist offerings; in 2012 for instance RRMC added a wing with six private patient rooms for inpatient psychiatric care. In 2013 it also announced plans to open an outpatient center for addiction recovery.

The hospital in 2011 upgraded its information systems through a 20-month $10 million initiative to install an electronic health record (EHR) system that now manages the clinical administrative human resources and financial aspects of RRMC's daily operations. What helped to fund its IT initiatives was RRMC's decision to shutter its 12-unit inpatient rehabilitation facility which was completed in late 2012. The move is expected to save the hospital some $3 million annually. The hospital took other restructuring measures to shore up its finances in 2012 due to a budget gap created by state caps on expenses.

EXECUTIVES

Director Of Pharmacy, Ji Chen
Vice President Of Human Resources, Allison Wollen
Vice President Clinical Services, Barbara (Barb) Robinson
Auditors: BKD LLP SPRINGFIELD MO

LOCATIONS

HQ: RUTLAND HOSPITAL INC.
160 ALLEN ST, RUTLAND, VT 057014595
Phone: 802 775-7111
Web: WWW.RRMC.ORG

PRODUCTS/OPERATIONS

2014 Sales

	% of total
Net patients revenue	95
Other revenue	5
Total	**100**

Selected Services

Acute care
Cancer
Cardiology
Diagnostic imaging
ENT and audiology
Laboratory
Orthopedics
Preventative care
Surgery
Women's health

COMPETITORS

Ellis Hospital
Fletcher Allen Health Care
New England Alliance for Health
Southwestern Vermont Health Care
Springfield Hospital

HISTORICAL FINANCIALS

Company Type: Private

Income Statement

FYE: September 30

	REVENUE ($ mil.)	NET INCOME ($ mil.)	NET PROFIT MARGIN	EMPLOYEES
09/13	213	8	4.0%	1,350
09/10	181	(1)	—	—
09/09	172	(18)	—	—
09/08	1,267	0	—	—
Annual Growth (30.0%)	—	—	—	—

2013 Year-End Financials

Return on assets: 4.7%
Return on equity: 4.0%
Current ratio: 1.10
Cash ($ mil.): 5

RYAN LLC

The professionals at Ryan aren't too concerned when clients notice their SALT-y language. One of the US's largest state and local tax (SALT) consulting firms Ryan provides tax advice preparation and planning for major corporations and other businesses. It also offers advice on federal and international tax issues. The firm specializes in consulting services such as audit defense dispute resolution strategic planning tax process efficiencies and tax recovery. Ryan serves customers through some 65 offices in more than 20 US states and 40 countries including Canada and Europe.

Operations

Ryan is the sixth largest corporate tax practice in the US equipped with a multidisciplinary team of more than 1900 professionals and associates.

The company is also the largest global provider of property tax services the largest indirect tax services provider in North America and one of the largest unclaimed property practices in the US.

Geographic Reach

Dallas-based Ryan has some 65 offices across the US and in 40 countries including Australia Canada India Ireland the Netherlands Singapore and the UK. The firm is active in Latin America through its partnership with Godoy & Hoyos Abogados.

Sales and Marketing

Ryan serves more than 9000 clients primarily in the business services construction financial services and food services industries in 40 countries. The company's clients include BASF Cara Chrysler and CBS.Financial PerformanceWhile full financials were not available for the privately-held company Ryan reported that its 2013 revenue exceeded $390 million –a company record for annual revenue and EBITDA performance. The firm ended 2013 as the sixth-largest corporate tax services firm in the US.

Strategy

Ryan likes to acquire specialized firms to broaden the scope of its services and geographic reach. In 2014 for example the company purchased three different tax and consulting firms that not only expanded its reach into Canada but also deepened its expertise in international tax Canadian sales tax and unclaimed property practices and added significantly to its client roster in these practices as well.Beyond acquisitions Ryan seeks partnerships to grow. In 2013 the company formed a strategic alliance with Colombia-based Godoy & Hoyos Abogados to support the expansion of its international tax practice in Latin America. That year it also formed a strategic alliance with Santiago Chile-based Garnham Abogados.

Ryan extended its services into Europe as it formed a strategic alliance with Altalex a tax advisory and legal firm based in Barcelona Spain. In 2012 Ryan opened offices in Sydney Australia and Singapore. It also launched a Latin American Business Center based in Fort Lauderdale Florida to lead the Ryan's delivery of value-added tax international income tax transfer pricing and tax technology services to multinational clients operating in Central and South America.

Mergers and Acquisitions

In 2014 Ryan acquired fast-growing independent tax agency WTP Advisors to expand its international tax expertise add more names to Fortune 500 client relationship ranks and expand its reach into New York and California. It also bought Canadian tax professional Definitive Consulting Services which greatly expanded its expertise in Canadian sales tax practice and significantly helped pad its list of respected Canadian clients. Additionally in 2014 it purchased Unclaimed Property Compliance business from StoneRiver which quadrupled the number of client relationships that Ryan had in its Abandoned and Unclaimed Property practice. In 2013 the company purchased the Thomson Reuters Property Tax Services business adding 600 property tax and unclaimed property professionals. The move makes Ryan the largest global provider of property tax services and North America's largest indirect tax practice. As part of the agreement Ryan will operate a Center for Tax Excellence in India staffed by some 145 professionals. The center serves as a foundation for building Ryan's business in South Asia and extends the reach of its indirect tax practice to China's emerging markets.

That year the company also acquired SR&ED ONE a full-service consulting firm specializing in Scientific Research & Experimental Development tax credits and Burke & Associates LLC which added more than 100 new client relationships to Ryan's Property Tax practice.

In mid-2012 Ryan acquired The TAARP Group LLP the leading tax and penalty review firm in the US. The move added specialized federal income tax expertise and a number of Fortune 500 firms to Ryan's client roster.

EXECUTIVES

Evp Chief Legal Officer And Secretary, Gregory S Weiss

President Global Shared Services, Delta Emerson

Chairman and CEO, G. Brint Ryan, age 51

President U.S. Operations and Principal, Ginny Buckner Kissling

EVP and Vice Chairman Emerging Businesses and Principal, Gerry L. Ridgely

SVP and CFO, David English, age 47

SVP and CIO, Ray Ann Cacheria

President Europe Asia and Latin America Operations, Brendan F. Moore

President Canadian Operations and Principal, Garry Round

EVP and Vice Chairman Chief Market Strategy Officer and Principal, Jon C. Sweet

EVP Principal, Joe Mulcahy

Senior Vice President Operations And Business Planning, Joe Mileti

Vice President Operations, Grant Sheppard

Vice President Legal, Richard (Dick) Nearhood

Svp And Chief Human Resources Officer, Adrianne Court, age 45

Senior Vice President, Marykay Manning

Vice President Finance and Corporate Controller, Chris Belknap

Vice President Finance, Louis Galvao

Executive Vice President Chief Operating Officer And Treasurer, Gerry Jr

Vice President Senior Vice President Finance Director, Luke Branyan

Vice President of Information Technology, Danny Ladouceur

Treasurer, Jim Aubele

Board Member, Duane DuCharme

Auditors: WHITLEY PENN LLP DALLAS TEXA

LOCATIONS

HQ: RYAN LLC
13155 NOEL RD STE 100, DALLAS, TX 752405050
Phone: 972 934-0022
Web: WWW.RYAN.COM

Selected Locations
Atlanta
Austin TX
Baton Rouge LA
Boston
Calgary AB
Charlotte NC
Chicago
Cleveland
Columbus
Dallas
Denver
Detroit
Downers Grove IL
El Paso TX
Ft. Lauderdale FL
Houston
Indianapolis
Jacksonville FL
Kansas City KS
Lansing MI
London
Los Angeles
Lubbock TX
Minneapolis
Montreal
Nashville TN
New Orleans
New York
Philadelphia
Pittsburgh
Providence RI
Sacramento CA
Salt Lake City
San Antonio
San Francisco
San Jose CA
Seattle
St. Louis
Tampa
Toronto
Washington DC

PRODUCTS/OPERATIONS

Selected Services
Alternative compliance procedures
Audit representation
Audit sampling analysis and evaluation
Captive insurance
Strategic planning
Tax compliance outsourcing
Tax refunds
Tax research
Tax systems implementation
Utility exemption studies
Voluntary disclosure and registration
Strategic alliances

Selected Industries Served
Business services
Construction
Financial services
Food services
Health care and pharmaceuticals
Manufacturing
Retail
Telecommunications
Transportation
Utilities

COMPETITORS

CliftonLarsonAllen	SALT Group
Management Insights	SC&H Group
Moss Adams LLP	UHY Advisors TX
Peisner Johnson & Company	

HISTORICAL FINANCIALS
Company Type: Private

Income Statement
FYE: December 31

	REVENUE ($ mil.)	NET INCOME ($ mil.)	NET PROFIT MARGIN	EMPLOYEES
12/13	382	39	10.4%	1,595
12/12	241	9	4.1%	—
12/11	225	25	11.2%	—
12/10	212	0	—	—
Annual Growth 21.7%	—	—	—	—

2013 Year-End Financials
Return on assets: 7.9% Cash ($ mil.): 1
Return on equity: 10.4%
Current ratio: 0.80

S.D. DEACON CORP.

Auditors: ZEZOFF YUEN & CO CITRUS HEI

LOCATIONS

HQ: S.D. DEACON CORP.
7745 GREENBACK LN STE 250, CITRUS HEIGHTS, CA 956105865
Phone: 916 969-0900
Web: WWW.SDDEACON.COM

HISTORICAL FINANCIALS
Company Type: Private

Income Statement
FYE: October 31

	REVENUE ($ mil.)	NET INCOME ($ mil.)	NET PROFIT MARGIN	EMPLOYEES
10/13	388	1	0.4%	340
10/12	384	7	1.9%	—
10/11	212	1	0.8%	—
10/10	168	0	—	—
Annual Growth 32.2%	—	—	—	—

2013 Year-End Financials
Return on assets: 24.0% Cash ($ mil.): 19
Return on equity: 0.4%
Current ratio: 1.00

SABRA HEALTH CARE REIT INC.

Sabra Health Care REIT doesn't mind a little healthy competition in the real estate sector. The company invests in income-producing health care facilities in the US. The REIT's investment portfolio includes about 120 properties most of which are skilled nursing/post-acute centers. It also invests in assisted living and independent living facilities and hospitals. Sabra's facilities house more than 12300 beds and are located in more than 25 states. Substantially all of the properties are leased to and operated by subsidiaries of Sun Healthcare Group which spun off its real estate assets to form Sabra Health Care REIT in 2010.

Geographic Reach

The REIT has licensed beds in 27 US states including New Hampshire Kentucky and Connecticut its three largest markets.

Financial Performance

Sabra's revenue jumped 22% in 2012 versus 2011 due to an increase in rental income partially offset by a decline in interest income. The lion's share of the $21 million increase in rental income is due to acquisitions made in 2011 and 2012. Net income climbed 52% in 2012 compared with 2011 primarily on rising rental income.

Strategy

Sabra aims to profit from the aging of the US population and increasing life expectancies both of which are driving demand for long-term care services. The REIT is focused on growing its geographically diverse portfolio primarily through the purchase of senior housing and memory care facilities with a secondary emphasis on acquiring skilled nursing homes.

Mergers and Acquisitions

In 2012 the firm invested nearly $207 million to acquire 10 skilled nursing facilities and 13 senior living facilities. In 2011 the REIT acquired the Cadia portfolio Texas Regional Medical Center at Sunnyvale the Aurora portfolio the Encore portfolio Oak Brook Health Care Center and Creekside Senior Living for an aggregate cost of about $204.5 million.

Ownership

The Vanguard Group owns about 12% of the company's shares.

EXECUTIVES

Chairman and CEO, Richard K. Matros, age 61, $725,000 total compensation
Chief Investment Officer, Talya Nevo-Hacohen, $350,000 total compensation
EVP and CFO, Harold W. Andrews, age 51, $350,000 total compensation
Chief Technology Officer, Galen Warren
Chief Operating Officer, Nick Cafferillo
Acquisition Vice President, Tri Tran

LOCATIONS

HQ: SABRA HEALTH CARE REIT INC.
18500 VON KARMAN AVE # 550, IRVINE, CA 926120504
Phone: 949 255-7100
Web: WWW.SABRAHEALTH.COM

COMPETITORS

Extendicare	Omega Healthcare
Extendicare	Investors
HCP	Omega Healthcare
HCP	Investors
Healthcare Realty	Senior Housing
Trust	Properties
Healthcare Realty	Senior Housing
Trust	Properties
LTC Properties	Ventas
LTC Properties	Ventas
National Health	Welltower
Investors	Welltower
National Health	
Investors	

HISTORICAL FINANCIALS
Company Type: Private

Income Statement
FYE: December 31

	ASSETS ($ mil.)	NET INCOME ($ mil.)	INCOME AS % OF ASSETS	EMPLOYEES
12/14	2,064	46	2.3%	10
12/13	1,197	33	2.8%	—
12/12	916	19	2.1%	—
12/11	749	0	—	—
Annual Growth 40.2%				

2014 Year-End Financials
Return on assets: 17.3%   Sales ($ mil): 183
Return on equity: 25.6%

SACRED HEART HOSPITAL INC.

Sacred Heart Hospital not only cares for hearts that are holey but also for the rest of what ails residents of western Wisconsin. The more than 300-bed medical center provides specialized services that include cardiology cancer care pediatrics and emergency medicine. The hospital provides community-wide care through affiliations with the Marshfield Clinic (a provider network with more than 700 physicians) Oakleaf Medical Network (an organization of providers and clinics) and Infinity Healthcare and Pathology Services (supplies the hospital with medical x-ray professionals). Founded in 1889 by the Hospital Sisters of the Third Order of St. Francis the center is part of the Hospital Sisters Health System.

Sacred Heart Hospital is also associated with St. Francis Apartments an independent-living apartment complex located directly behind the hospital. St. Francis Apartments provides seniors above the age of 62 a place to live that is in close proximity to the hospital without being an assisted living facility. Additionally many of the residents at St. Francis serve as volunteers at the hospital.

Sacred Heart Hospital is helmed by Steve Ronstrom president of the western Wisconsin division of Hospital Sisters Health System. Ronstrom also oversees the operations of St. Joseph's Hospital in Chippewa Falls Wisconsin.

EXECUTIVES

Health Care Director, Lynn Gullicksrud

LOCATIONS

HQ: SACRED HEART HOSPITAL INC.
900 W CLAIREMONT AVE, EAU CLAIRE, WI 547015105
Phone: 715 839-4121

COMPETITORS

Abbott Northwestern Hospital
Allina Hospitals
Amery Regional Medical Center
Aspirus
Bethesda Hospital
Children's Hospitals and Clinics of Minnesota
Fairview Health
Franciscan Skemp Healthcare
Gundersen Lutheran
HealthEast Care System
Luther Midelfort
Methodist Hospital (MN)
North Memorial Health Care
Tomah Memorial Hospital

HISTORICAL FINANCIALS
Company Type: Private

Income Statement
FYE: June 30

	REVENUE ($ mil.)	NET INCOME ($ mil.)	NET PROFIT MARGIN	EMPLOYEES
06/13	234	41	17.5%	1,000
06/08	174	22	12.7%	—
06/05	144	19	13.4%	—
06/03	1,258	0	—	—
Annual Growth	—	—	—	—

2013 Year-End Financials
Return on assets: 10.5%   Cash ($ mil.): —
Return on equity: 17.5%
Current ratio: 0.30

SADDLEBACK MEMORIAL MEDICAL CENTER

Saddleback Memorial Medical Center part of Memorial Health Services (MHS) serves the residents of southern Orange County in California. With some 325 beds the not-for-profit medical center provides general medical and surgical services as well as specialty care in areas such as cancer heart disease and physical rehabilitation. It operates two campuses one in Laguna Hills and one in San Clemente. The medical center also features several facilities for women's health including the Saddleback Women's Hospital and the Memorial-Care Breast Center. In addition Saddleback Memorial provides home health care and hospice services.

Operations

Saddleback Memorial Center sees about 16000 inpatients each year. It also handles some 48000 emergency room visits and 6900 inpatient and outpatient surgeries.

The main hospital campus —Saddleback Memorial-Laguna Hills —is home to the Saddleback Women's Hospital and the MemorialCare Cancer Institute while both the Laguna Hills and San Clemente locations house MemorialCare Breast Center and Memorial Heart and Vascular Institute sites. The Saddleback Memorial-San Clemente campus offers additional specialty services such as weight-loss surgery and infusion therapy. Saddleback Memorial Medical Center is recognized in its industry for its care services in areas including endocrinology (diabetes) gastroenterology and orthopedics.

Strategy

As part of parent MHS' efforts to provide quality care and reduce medical expenses in the California health care market Saddleback Memorial has expanded and upgraded its facilities and partnered with area physicians' groups. In 2014 it opened the new MemorialCare Cancer Institute near its Laguna Hills location; the center features the TrueBeam radiation system a more accurate and powerful machine than the ones Saddleback used previously.

EXECUTIVES

CEO, Steve Geidt
Administrator, Liz Bear
CFO, John Bishop
Director Human Resources, Ron Salzberg

LOCATIONS

HQ: SADDLEBACK MEMORIAL MEDICAL CENTER
24451 HEALTH CENTER DR, LAGUNA HILLS, CA
926533689
Phone: 949 837-4500
Web: WWW.MEMORIALCARE.ORG

COMPETITORS

Children' s Hospital of
Orange County
Hoag Memorial Hospital
Southwest Healthcare
St. Joseph Hospital of
Orange

Tenet Healthcare
UC Irvine Medical
Center
Western Medical Center
- Santa Ana

HISTORICAL FINANCIALS

Company Type: Private

Income Statement

FYE: June 30

	REVENUE ($ mil.)	NET INCOME ($ mil.)	NET PROFIT MARGIN	EMPLOYEES
06/08	364	32	8.8%	1,209
06/01	170	4	2.5%	—
06/99	2,141	0	0.0%	—
Annual Growth	(17.9%)	261.8%	—	—

2008 Year-End Financials

Return on assets: 13.0%
Return on equity: 8.8%
Current ratio: 0.60
Cash ($ mil.): —

SAINT AGNES MEDICAL CENTER

Protecting and caring for the vulnerable Saint Agnes continues to ward off death for the patients at Saint Agnes Medical Center. The medical center provides healthcare to Valley residents of Fresno California through a 436-bed acute care hospital. Along with general surgery the hospital offers a variety of services including asthma management bariatric surgery (for which it has scored state-wide accolades) cardiac rehabilitation hospice care and home care. The facility also has centers dedicated to cancer child development and women's health. The hospital is part of Trinity Health one of the largest Catholic health care systems in the US.

Operations
Saint Agnes Medical Center is a 436-bed medical campus that has some 2500 staff members. In fiscal 2015 (ended June) the center had more than 20300 admissions and 222170 outpatient visits.

Geographic Reach
Saint Agnes Medical Center provides care to residents of the Fresno California area (Fresno and Madera counties).

Financial Performance
In fiscal 2015 (ended June) the center had operating revenues of $487 million.

Strategy
Saint Agnes Medical Center has launched a new state-of-the-art Electronic Medical Record (EMR) system. The new EMR system replaced paper medical records and streamlined patient care. In 2013 Saint Agnes became the first medical center in

greater Fresno to receive American College of Radiology accreditations in Breast MRI and Nuclear Medicine.

In 2015 the hospital did not renew the sub-lease for a building it owns in northwest Fresno County (which had been leased to physician group Northwest Medical Group). It plans to utilize the space for future expansion in the area.

Ownership
Saint Agnes Medical Center is owned by Trinity Health.

Company Background
The hospital system was established in 1929 by nine Holy Cross Sisters.

Saint Agnes Medical Center sponsors a number of community outreach programs throughout the Valley including adult day care senior activity programs health care clinics for the uninsured and services for poor and homeless women.

EXECUTIVES

Chief Financial Officer Senior Vice President, Derek Miller
Medical Director, Stephen Soldo
Pharm D, Tai Kosiyangkakul
Director Of Home Healthcare Services, Ronda Pistoresi
Vice President Of Information Technology, Richard Blanks
Medical Director, Lesley Hanes
Vice President Of Mission Integration, Susie Kuszmar
Vice President Operations, Jim Vandevelde
Director Of Pharmacy, Lloyd Smith
Vice President Management, Amy Schneider
Vice President, Debbie Chappell
Medical Director, Michael G (Mel) Saul
Treasurer, Andrea Lanier
Secretary And Treasurer, William Lyles

LOCATIONS

HQ: SAINT AGNES MEDICAL CENTER
1303 E HERNDON AVE, FRESNO, CA 937203309
Phone: 559 450-3000
Web: WWW.SAMC.COM

PRODUCTS/OPERATIONS

Selected Programs and Services
Cancer Services
Emergency Services
Endoscopy
Heart & Vascular
Home Health Care
Hospice
Imaging Services
Laboratory Services
Neuroscience
Occupational Health Center
Orthopaedics
Surgery
Palliative Care
Pulmonary Rehabilitation
Women' s Services
Wound Care Hyperbaric Medicine and Amputation
Prevention

Selected Facilities
Breast Center
Cancer Center
The California Eye Institute at Saint Agnes
Child Development Center
Home Health and Hospice
Medical Library
Occupational Health Center
Outpatient Surgery North
Satellite Labs
Wound Care Hyperbaric Medicine and Amputation
Prevention

COMPETITORS

Community Medical
Centers
Dignity Health
HCA

Memorial Hospitals
Association
Northern Inyo Hospital
Tenet Healthcare

HISTORICAL FINANCIALS

Company Type: Private

Income Statement

FYE: June 30

	REVENUE ($ mil.)	NET INCOME ($ mil.)	NET PROFIT MARGIN	EMPLOYEES
06/13	503	19	3.8%	2,400
06/10	438	8	1.8%	—
06/09	394	(52)	—	—
06/08	223	0	—	—
Annual Growth	17.6%	—	—	—

2013 Year-End Financials

Return on assets: 7.6%
Return on equity: 3.8%
Current ratio: 2.30
Cash ($ mil.): 20

SAINT ALPHONSUS REGIONAL MEDICAL CENTER INC.

Saint Alphonsus Regional Medical Center makes medical care its primary mission. The 384-bed hospital provides Boise Idaho and the surrounding region (including eastern Oregon and northern Nevada) with general acute and specialized health care services. Its facilities and operations include a level II trauma center an orthopedic spinal care unit an air transport service and a home health and hospice division. Saint Alphonsus Regional Medical Center is part of Trinity Health's four-hospital Saint Alphonsus Health System which serves Boise and Nampa in Idaho and Ontario and Baker City in Oregon. The Sisters of the Holy Cross founded the hospital in 1894.

Operations
Saint Alphonsus Regional Medical Center provides outpatient services through the 70 affiliated physician practices that make up the Saint Alphonsus Medical Group. It also operates the Saint Alphonsus Health Plaza which provides urgent care and outpatient surgery laboratory rehabilitation and primary care services.

The hospital also offers rural or homebound patients telemedicine services through which remote physician visits are conducted using audio or video.

Geographic Reach
Saint Alphonsus Regional Medical Center serves a territory that includes portions of southwestern Idaho northern Nevada and eastern Oregon.

Strategy
Saint Alphonsus Regional Medical Center expands its facilities to improve medical care in its service territory. In 2014 it opened its newly expanded and renovated emergency department which included a 30% increase in square footage. Also that year it became the first hospital in the region to utilize the EndoWrist Stapler technology on the da Vinci robotic system for minimally invasive surgeries.

EXECUTIVES

Director of HIM, Karen Fleming
Vice President Marketing and Community Development, Linda Smith
Infection Control Director, Aline Lee
Medical Director of Physician Relations, Patrice Burgess

Vice President Corporate Development Marketing, Jean Basom
Vice President, Pamela Thomas
Medical Director, Beth Malasky
Vice President and General Counsel, Stephanie Westermeier
Director of Surgery, John (Jack) Hiltibidal
Nursing Director, Karen Hodge
Vice President Patient Care Services Chief Nursing Officer, Dina Ellwanger
Vice President Finance, Lannie Checketts
Clinic Manager, Donna Whalen
Vice President Finance Saint Alphonsus Medical Group, Rick Presnell
Treasurer, Richard (Dick) Presnell

LOCATIONS

HQ: SAINT ALPHONSUS REGIONAL MEDICAL CENTER INC.
1055 N CURTIS RD, BOISE, ID 837061309
Phone: 208 367-2121
Web: WWW.SAINTALPHONSUS.ORG

COMPETITORS

Ascension Health
HCA
Intermountain Health Care
St. Luke' s Health System

HISTORICAL FINANCIALS
Company Type: Private

Income Statement
FYE: June 30

	REVENUE ($ mil.)	NET INCOME ($ mil.)	NET PROFIT MARGIN	EMPLOYEES
06/13	545	43	7.9%	3,500
06/10	449	13	3.1%	—
06/09	428	(8)	—	—
06/08	0	0	—	—
Annual Growth	—	—	—	—

2013 Year-End Financials
Return on assets: 16.0%
Return on equity: 7.9%
Current ratio: 0.90
Cash ($ mil.): 4

SAINT ELIZABETH MEDICAL CENTER INC.

It doesn't have much to do with the Holy Trinity except for the fact that St. Elizabeth Medical Center (operating as St. Elizabeth Healthcare) does business in a trinity of states. The system provides health care services to residents in Kentucky Ohio and West Virginia. St. Elizabeth Healthcare's programs include stroke and cardiac care hospice services and neurosurgery. The system is home to six hospitals with about 1200 beds and dozens of primary care offices. St. Elizabeth Healthcare was formed through a merger between St. Elizabeth Medical and nearby St. Luke Hospitals. The organization has one board of directors and one management structure and is sponsored by the Catholic Diocese of Covington.

St. Elizabeth Healthcare owned and operated ambulance services company TransCare of Kentucky until 2010 when it agreed to sell the provider of emergency and non-emergency ambulance services in Northern Kentucky to Rural/Metro Corporation one of the nation's largest of ambulance and private fire protection services. St. Elizabeth Healthcare made the sale to expand ambulance

services in Northern Kentucky.St. Elizabeth's opened The Regional Diabetes Center at its Covington campus. With this expansion St. Elizabeth has more endocrinologists in one center than nearly anywhere else in the eastern US that specializes in diabetes management and other endocrine disorders.Also in 2010 the health system began development of a Neonatal Intensive Care Unit (NICU) at St. Elizabeth Edgewood. The hospital completed the first phase of a major renovation of the OB and NICU space to provide higher levels of neonatal care with about 20 newly-built private NICU beds and post-partum rooms that were upgraded and expanded.2010 was a busy year for St. Elizabeth which also formed the St. Elizabeth Physicians group by merging with Summit Medical Group and PatientFirst. St. Elizabeth Physicians is home to roughly 160 physicians and mid-level providers and nearly 1000 total employees.

The St. Elizabeth Business Health Division offers health care services to employers and their employees to try to cut down on lost production due to sick days. The division focuses on wellness and prevention as well as personalized exercise plans drug screening and injury/care prevention.

EXECUTIVES

President and Trustee, Joseph W. Gross
Interim President and CEO, Garren Colvin
CIO, Alex Rodriguez
Pharmd, Andrea Schumann
Vice President Business Development, Julie Siemer
Vice President Of Call Centre, Richard Heap
Admissions Director, Bobbi Jones
Assistant Vice President, Vera Hall
Vice President Of Finance, Lori Ritchey
Vice President Telecommunications, Glenda Harned
Medical Records Director, Cindy Stroud
Director of Nursing, Judy Schneider
Vice President Information Services, Tammy Herd
Vice President Of Sales, Cynthia Glass
Chairman, Barry Wendt
Secretary, Barbara (Barb) Krohman
Secretary to Director, Lisa Robinson
Auditors: ERNST & YOUNG LLP CINCINNATI

LOCATIONS

HQ: SAINT ELIZABETH MEDICAL CENTER INC.
1 MEDICAL VILLAGE DR, EDGEWOOD, KY 410173403
Phone: 859 301-2000
Web: WWW.SAINTE.PPS-INC.COM

Selected locations
St. Elizabeth Covington (Covington Kentucky)
St. Elizabeth Edgewood (Edgewood Kentucky)
St. Elizabeth Grant (Williamstown Kentucky)
St. Elizabeth Ft. Thomas (St. Thomas Kentucky)
St. Elizabeth Florence (Florence Kentucky)
St. Elizabeth Falmouth (Falmouth Kentucky)

COMPETITORS

Adventist Health System Sunbelt Healthcare
Bethesda North
Catholic Health Initiatives
Cincinnati Children' s Hospital
Deaconess Associations
HCA
Kettering Health Network
Mercy Health (OH)
Mount Carmel Health
OhioHealth
Regency Hospital
Tenet Healthcare
The Christ Hospital Corporation
TriHealth
UC Health
Universal Health Services

HISTORICAL FINANCIALS
Company Type: Private

Income Statement
FYE: December 31

	REVENUE ($ mil.)	NET INCOME ($ mil.)	NET PROFIT MARGIN	EMPLOYEES
12/08	623	(32)	—	6,227
12/06	483	49	10.2%	—
12/05	520	0	0.0%	—
Annual Growth	6.2%	—	—	—

2008 Year-End Financials
Return on assets: 7.1%
Return on equity: (-5.2%)
Current ratio: 1.10
Cash ($ mil.): 53

SAINT ELIZABETH REGIONAL MEDICAL CENTER

Saint Elizabeth Regional Medical Center a Catholic Health Initiatives (CHI) affiliate is a 260-bed acute care hospital that serves the Lincoln Nebraska area. The not-for-profit hospital also known as CHI Health St. Elizabeth provides a variety of services such as obstetrics bariatrics cancer care burn and wound care and cardiac and pulmonary care. Some 430 physicians are affiliated with the facility. The hospital also operates community health clinics urgent care centers and physical therapy clinics as well as home health and hospice organizations. CHI Health St. Elizabeth was originally founded as a simple frontier hospital in 1889 by the Sisters of St. Francis of Perpetual Adoration.

Operations

CHI Health St. Elizabeth is one of several affiliate and subsidiary hospitals of CHI operating in Nebraska. The medical center boasts a network of family practice and internal medicine clinics including stand-alone urgent care centers and offsite physical therapy clinics. Its locations include St. Mary's Community Hospital in Nebraska City Good Samaritan Hospital in Kearney and Saint Francis Medical Center in Grand Island as well as the Alegent Health network in Omaha.

Each year the hospital has some 33000 emergency department visits some 13000 admissions and more than 10000 surgical procedures.

Geographic Reach

Saint Elizabeth Regional Medical Center serves those who reside in and around Lincoln Nebraska.

Strategy

As part of the CHI network these hospitals work together to coordinate administrative technology and clinical resources with the goal of increasing efficiency and quality of care in their respective communities. For example in 2013 CHI Health St. Elizabeth partnered with CHI Nebraska Lincoln and the Lincoln YMCA to provide a community wellness program.

Company Ownership

CHI Health St. Elizabeth is part of Denver-based Catholic Health Initiatives.

EXECUTIVES

Director Of Radiology, Mike Hopkins
Director Of Operating Room, Nancy Gondringer
Vp Operational Finance, Dan Schonlau
Radiology Director, John Speaker

Vice President Clinical And Support Services,
Patrick Gilles
Medical Records Director, Elizabeth (Beth) Bechtle
Vice President Mission and Human Resource,
John (Jack) Dumonceaux
Medical Director of the Saint Elizabeth Bariatric
Surgery Program, Benjamin J (Ben) Hung

LOCATIONS

HQ: SAINT ELIZABETH REGIONAL MEDICAL CENTER
555 S 70TH ST, LINCOLN, NE 685102462
Phone: 402 219-5200
Web: WWW.SAINTELIZABETHONLINE.ORG

PRODUCTS/OPERATIONS

Selected Specialty Areas

Bariatric Surgery - Weight-Loss Surgery
Breast Care Center
Burn and Wound Care
Cancer Institute
Cardiovascular Services
Colorectal Cancer
Company Care
Continuing Care Network
CyberKnife
Diabetes Center
Emergency Care
Home Care Services
Home Medical Equipment
Hospitalists
Intensivists
Maternal Fetal Medicine
Neonatal Intensive Care Unit (NICU)
Neurology
Occupational Therapy
Orthopaedics
Palliative Care
Pediatrics
Physical Therapy
Pulmonary Services
Radiology
Research & Clinical Trials
Robotic Surgery Center
Sleep Disorders Center
Speech Therapy
Stroke Center
The Advanced Baby Center

COMPETITORS

BryanLGH Medical
Center
Children's Hospital &
Medical Center
Fremont Area Medical
Center
Madonna Rehabilitation
Hospital

Methodist Health
System
Nebraska Medical
Center
Tenet Healthcare
University of Nebraska

HISTORICAL FINANCIALS

Company Type: Private

Income Statement

	REVENUE ($ mil.)	NET INCOME ($ mil.)	NET PROFIT MARGIN	EMPLOYEES
06/13	268	27	10.3%	1,825
06/10	1	0	32.7%	—
06/09	251	(5)	—	—
06/08	1,071	0	—	—
Annual Growth	(24.2%)	—	—	—

FYE: June 30

2013 Year-End Financials

Return on assets: 5.3%   Cash ($ mil.): 9
Return on equity: 10.3%
Current ratio: 3.00

SAINT EUGENE MEDICAL CENTER

LOCATIONS

HQ: SAINT EUGENE MEDICAL CENTER
301 E JACKSON ST, DILLON, SC 295362509
Phone: 843 774-4111
Web: WWW.BLOG.MCLEODHEALTH.ORG

HISTORICAL FINANCIALS

Company Type: Private

Income Statement

FYE: September 30

	REVENUE ($ mil.)	NET INCOME ($ mil.)	NET PROFIT MARGIN	EMPLOYEES
09/12	514	152	29.6%	300
09/00	26	1	5.9%	—
09/99	20	1	8.1%	—
09/98	20	0	—	—
Annual Growth	25.9%	—	—	—

2012 Year-End Financials

Return on assets: 3.6%   Cash ($ mil.): 54
Return on equity: 29.6%
Current ratio: 1.40

SAINT FRANCIS HOSPITAL AND MEDICAL CENTER FOUNDATION INC.

Saint Francis takes care of the hearts of Hartford Connecticut. The Saint Francis Hospital and Medical Center also known as Saint Francis Care is a regional medical center with some 620 beds. The hospital specializes in cardiology oncology neurology orthopedics and women's and children's health services. It also offers behavioral health weight management trauma care and injury rehabilitation programs. Saint Francis serves as a teaching hospital affiliated with the University of Connecticut Schools of Medicine and Dentistry. It also operates the nearby Mount Sinai Rehabilitation Hospital a 60-bed facility that provides brain trauma sports medicine and orthopedic care.

Operations
Saint Francis' on-campus specialty centers include the Hoffman Heart Institute which specializes in open-heart surgeries and catheterization procedures and the Saint Francis/Mount Sinai Regional Cancer Center. In addition to its main campuses (Saint Francis and Mount Sinai Rehabilitation) Saint Francis operates health clinics and medical offices in about a dozen surrounding communities. The medical center also operates specialty clinics such as radiology and imaging centers and it maintains a medical laboratory in a joint venture with nearby Bristol Hospital.

Financial Performance
During fiscal 2012 and fiscal 2011 approximately 40% respectively of net patient service revenue was received under the Medicare program;

about 15% under the Medicaid program; and almost 20% came from from Blue Cross. The hospital's net loss decreased by 65% in fiscal 2012 compared to the previous year due to net gain on investments and increased income from gifts contributions and donations.

Strategy
Saint Francis has initiated a number of internal cost-reduction efforts to keep its operations and finances healthy. It is also improving its internal information management systems to increase efficiencies at its facilities.

As a sign of economic troubles and health care reform changes in the US market Saint Francis is exploring affiliations with other regional hospitals to improve care and control medical costs. As example: in 2012 Saint Francis established an affiliation with nearby Johnson Memorial Medical Center. It is also involved in efforts by the Connecticut legislature to form a UConn Health Network with the University of Connecticut Health Center and other area providers.

Company Background
Established in 1897 Saint Francis began an affiliation with Mount Sinai Hospital in 1990 and merged with it in 1995. Mount Sinai Hospital originally founded in 1923 was then converted from an acute care center into the Mount Sinai Rehabilitation Hospital.

EXECUTIVES

Vice President Financial Standards and Compliance Chief Compliance Officer, Jennifer J (Jen) Schneider
President and CEO, Christopher M. (Chris) Dadlez
Chief Medical Officer and SVP Medical Affairs, Rolf W. Knoll
EVP and COO, Kathleen M. (Kate) Roche
VP Facilities Support Services and Construction, Robert J. (Bob) Falaguerra
EVP and Chief Physician Executive, Arthur W. DeTore
President and CEO Saint Francis HealthCare Partners Inc., Jess Kupec
VP and CIO, Linda Shanley
SVP; Chief Development Officer; President Saint Francis Foundation, E. Merritt Donough
SVP and CFO, John N. Giamalis
Physical Therapy, Dan Henck
Medical Director, James Mazo
Senior Vice President Marketing, James (Jim) Schepker
Senior Vice President Chief Human Resources Officer, Dawn L Bryant
Vice President, Diane Bertrand
Vice President Mission Integration, Stephen T Surprenant
Vice President Of Mission Integration, Judith Carey
Senior Vice President Marketing, Jim Schepker
SR.v.p., Chris Hartley
Operating Room Director, Shirley Thomas
Secretary, Cathy Hebert
Secretary, Donna Fitzpatrick
Board Member, Joyce Mandell
Board Member, Jean-Pierre Van Rooy
Auditors: ERNST & YOUNG LLP HARTFORD C

LOCATIONS

HQ: SAINT FRANCIS HOSPITAL AND MEDICAL CENTER FOUNDATION INC.
114 WOODLAND ST, HARTFORD, CT 061051208
Phone: 860 714-4006
Web: WWW.SAINTFRANCISCARE.COM

COMPETITORS

Backus
Bristol Hospital
Connecticut Children's Medical Center
Griffin Health

Hartford Health Care
Hospital of Central Connecticut
Lawrence & Memorial Hospital
MidState Medical Center
Stamford Health
University of Connecticut Health Center
Yale New Haven Health System

HISTORICAL FINANCIALS
Company Type: Private

| Income Statement | | | FYE: September 30 |
| | NET | NET | |
REVENUE ($ mil.)	INCOME ($ mil.)	PROFIT MARGIN	EMPLOYEES
09/10	651	(10)	—	3,270
09/09	638	(16)	—	—
09/08	1,016	0	0.0%	—
Annual Growth (19.9%)	—	—	—

2010 Year-End Financials

Return on assets: 6.8%   Cash ($ mil.): 117
Return on equity: (-1.7%)
Current ratio: 1.40

SAINT FRANCIS HOSPITAL INC.

Auditors: ERNST & YOUNG LLP COLUMBUS

LOCATIONS

HQ: SAINT FRANCIS HOSPITAL INC.
6161 S YALE AVE, TULSA, OK 741361992
Phone: 918 502-2050
Web: WWW.SAINTFRANCIS.COM

HISTORICAL FINANCIALS
Company Type: Private

| Income Statement | | | FYE: June 30 |
| | NET | NET | |
REVENUE ($ mil.)	INCOME ($ mil.)	PROFIT MARGIN	EMPLOYEES
06/13	910	190	21.0%	4,000
06/12*	838	157	18.7%	—
09/11	18	3	21.5%	—
06/09	675	0	—	—
Annual Growth 7.7%	—	—	—

*Fiscal year change

2013 Year-End Financials

Return on assets: 7.6%   Cash ($ mil.): 326
Return on equity: 21.0%
Current ratio: 1.40

SAINT JOSEPH REGIONAL MEDICAL CENTER-SOUTH BEND CAMPUS INC

LOCATIONS

HQ: SAINT JOSEPH REGIONAL MEDICAL CENTER-SOUTH BEND CAMPUS INC
5215 HOLY CROSS PKWY, MISHAWAKA, IN 465451469
Phone: 574 335-5000
Web: WWW.SJMED.COM

HISTORICAL FINANCIALS
Company Type: Private

| Income Statement | | | FYE: June 30 |
| | NET | NET | |
REVENUE ($ mil.)	INCOME ($ mil.)	PROFIT MARGIN	EMPLOYEES
06/13	300	11	3.9%	680
06/12	77	(6)	—	—
06/06	81	(2)	—	—
06/05	80	0	—	—
Annual Growth 18.0%	—	—	—

2013 Year-End Financials

Return on assets: 6.1%   Cash ($ mil.): 8
Return on equity: 3.9%
Current ratio: 2.60

SAINT JOSEPH'S HOSPITAL OF MARSHFIELD INC.

LOCATIONS

HQ: SAINT JOSEPH' S HOSPITAL OF MARSHFIELD INC.
611 N SAINT JOSEPH AVE, MARSHFIELD, WI 544491832
Phone: 715 387-1713
Web: WWW.MINISTRYHEALTH.ORG

HISTORICAL FINANCIALS
Company Type: Private

| Income Statement | | | FYE: September 30 |
| | NET | NET | |
REVENUE ($ mil.)	INCOME ($ mil.)	PROFIT MARGIN	EMPLOYEES
09/10	348	31	9.2%	2,200
09/09	342	21	6.4%	—
09/08	1,063	0	—	—
Annual Growth (42.7%)	136954.4%	—	—

2010 Year-End Financials

Return on assets: —   Cash ($ mil.): 85
Return on equity: 9.2%
Current ratio: 4.10

SAINT JOSEPH'S UNIVERSITY

Saint Joseph's University (SJU) has been educating Joes and Janes for more than 150 years. The Catholic Jesuit university provides higher education for about 8000 students a year from its campus on the outskirts of Philadelphia. It has more than 300 full-time faculty members and offers 50 undergraduate majors and 40 graduate and professional study areas including an Ed.D. in Educational Leadership. About 650 undergraduates attend its College of Professional and Liberal Studies; the remainder attend the College of Arts and Sciences and the Haub School of Business. SJU also conducts study abroad honors service and faith learning and other special study programs. It was founded in 1851 by the Society of Jesus.

Operations

SJU's academic centers include the Center for Food Marketing the Arrupe Center for Business Ethics the Catholic Bioethics Institute the Kinney Center for Autism Education and the Richard Johnson Institute for Anti-Violence. Such centers support SJU's commitment to provide specialized learning programs through community engagement.

Financial Performance

SJU had a budget of some $213 million for fiscal 2014. The university's endowment funds totaled about $193 million as of mid-2013. Undergraduate tuition runs at about $38900 per year.

EXECUTIVES

Assistant Vice President Marketing Communications, Joe Lunardi
Vice President Financial Affairs, Louis Mayer
Vice President Administrative Services, Kevin W Robinson
Assistant Vice President Government and Community Relations, Wadell Ridley
Vice President For Development, Martin F (Marti) Farrell
Associate Vice President Development Office of Development Operations, Theresa Travis
Vice President Student, Cary Anderson
Associate Vice President and Athletic Director, Dominick J Dijulia
Associate Vice President For Financial Affairs, Stephanie Pricken
Senior Vice President Interim, John Smithson
Vice President External Affairs, Joan Chrestay
Executive Vice President, Sean Sweeney
Vice President of Pledge Education, Alana Whitmarsh
Vice President of Fundraising, Kristin Thompson
Vice President of Chapter Operations, Brittney Welde
Vice President of Finance, Juan Giron
Vice President of Professional Activities, Vincent Alibrandi
Vice President of Alumni Relations, Rebecca Rosati
Vice President of Scholarship and Awards, Samantha Melnick
Vice President of Marketing, Allison Quillty
Secretary, Jean Murray
Secretary, Paul Gronski
Auditors: DELOITTE TAX LLP PHILADELPHIA

LOCATIONS

HQ: SAINT JOSEPH' S UNIVERSITY
5600 CITY AVE, PHILADELPHIA, PA 191311376
Phone: 610 660-1000
Web: WWW.SJU.EDU

PRODUCTS/OPERATIONS

Selected Schools and Colleges
College of Arts and Sciences
College of Professional and Liberal Studies
Haub School of Business

HISTORICAL FINANCIALS
Company Type: Private

Income Statement
FYE: May 31

	REVENUE ($ mil.)	NET INCOME ($ mil.)	NET PROFIT MARGIN	EMPLOYEES
05/11	267	9	3.6%	1,138
05/10	246	18	7.5%	—
05/09	0	0	—	—
Annual Growth	—	2331.4%	—	—

2011 Year-End Financials
Return on assets: —
Return on equity: 3.6%
Current ratio: —
Cash ($ mil.): 91

SAINT LOUIS UNIVERSITY

This university gives students a SLU of opportunities. Saint Louis University (SLU) is a Jesuit Catholic school offering about 100 undergraduate 70 graduate and a host of professional degree programs through about a dozen schools and colleges including a school of medicine and a campus in Madrid Spain. Most programs require core classes in philosophy and theology. SLU has an enrollment of about 9000 undergraduate and 5000 graduate and professional students. Its student-teacher ratio is 12:1. Saint Louis University was founded in 1818 by Reverend Louis William Du Bourg Catholic Bishop of Louisiana.

Geographic Reach

SLU's students hail from all 50 states and about 70 foreign countries. In addition to its main campus in St. Louis Missouri the university operates a campus in Madrid Spain.

Operations

In addition to its extensive educational programs SLU's students and staff are involved in a number of research projects in areas including cancer molecular biology cardiovascular disease biodefense and neurology and aging.

SLU also operates primary and specialty medical care clinics (some through its SLU Physicians organization) on its medical school campus. The medical campus also includes the SLU Hospital which is owned by Tenet Healthcare but which serves as a primary teaching facility for the university.

Financial Performance

SLU is supported by an endowment of some $880 million as of mid-2011. About two-thirds of the university's revenues come from educational activities (including student tuition and fees) while another third comes from patient care at the medical center campus. It also receives about $62 million in research funding from external partners including government agencies (like the National Institutes of Health) and private foundations.

Strategy

In 2011 SLU completed the construction of its new Health Sciences Education Union building; the center includes an auditorium and medical simulation labs. The university also opened its new

Hotel Ignacio a Midtown boutique hotel designed to enhance the neighborhood where its main campus is located.

In addition to expanding its physical facilities the university grows or rearranges its academic departments to meet the needs of students in a changing society and economy. In 2012 it established a College for Public Health and Social Justice combining its previous schools of public health and social work to increase the focus on social justice. It also upgraded its neurosurgery division to an independent department in 2011 due to strong growth in the program. SLU also occasionally partners with other area universities on special degree programs.

To expand its research programs SLU established a cancer education prevention and research center for minority patient groups in late 2012.

Mergers and Acquisitions

SLU added about 20 acres to its campus in 2011 by purchasing several properties to expand its medical center campus. It also acquired a building to expand its Madrid campus.

EXECUTIVES

Vice President Academic Affairs, LISA DORSEY
Vice President Of Student Development, Kent Porterfield
Vice President Publications Communications, Jody Smith
Vice President For Research, Raymond Tait
Assistant Vice President, Jill Carnaghi
Co Director, Richard Lee
Associate Vice President ALUMNI Relations INTERIM, Meg Connolly
Associate Vice President, Edwin Kidd
Vice President Of Human Resources, Michael Luna
Interim Vice President Human Services, PATTY HABERBERGER
Vice President, Phil Clerc
Secretary Medical, Mary Streif
Auditors: KPMG LLP COLUMBUS OH

LOCATIONS

HQ: SAINT LOUIS UNIVERSITY
1 N GRAND BLVD, SAINT LOUIS, MO 631032006
Phone: 314 977-2500
Web: WWW.CONCENTRA.COM

PRODUCTS/OPERATIONS

Colleges Schools and Degree Granting Centers
Advanced Dental Education Center for (CADE)
Arts and Sciences College of
Business John Cook School of
Education and Public Service College of
Engineering Aviation and Technology Parks College of
Health Care Ethics Albert Gnaegi Center for
Health Sciences Doisy College of
Law School of
Madrid Spain Campus
Medicine School of
Nursing School of
Outcomes Research Center for (SLUCOR)
Philosophy and Letters College of
Professional Studies School for
Public Health School of
Social Work School of

HISTORICAL FINANCIALS
Company Type: Private

Income Statement
FYE: June 30

	REVENUE ($ mil.)	NET INCOME ($ mil.)	NET PROFIT MARGIN	EMPLOYEES
06/10	750	28	3.8%	7,500
06/09	697	0	—	—
Annual Growth	7.6%	—	—	—

2010 Year-End Financials
Return on assets: —
Return on equity: 3.8%
Current ratio: —
Cash ($ mil.): 141

SAINT LUKE'S HOSPITAL OF BETHLEHEM PENNSYLVANIA

Auditors: JOSEPH SZEMANEK DOYLESTOWN P

LOCATIONS

HQ: SAINT LUKE'S HOSPITAL OF BETHLEHEM PENNSYLVANIA
801 OSTRUM ST, BETHLEHEM, PA 180151000
Phone: 484 526-4000
Web: WWW.SLHN.ORG

HISTORICAL FINANCIALS
Company Type: Private

Income Statement
FYE: June 30

	REVENUE ($ mil.)	NET INCOME ($ mil.)	NET PROFIT MARGIN	EMPLOYEES
06/13	741	42	5.8%	2,958
06/09	647	(26)	—	—
06/08	600	14	2.4%	—
Annual Growth	4.3%	24.0%	—	—

2013 Year-End Financials
Return on assets: 24.5%
Return on equity: 5.8%
Current ratio: —
Cash ($ mil.): 46

SAINT LUKE'S HOSPITAL OF KANSAS CITY

LOCATIONS

HQ: SAINT LUKE'S HOSPITAL OF KANSAS CITY
4401 WORNALL RD, KANSAS CITY, MO 641113241
Phone: 816 932-2000
Web: WWW.SAINTLUKESHEALTHSYSTEM.ORG

HISTORICAL FINANCIALS
Company Type: Private

Income Statement
FYE: December 31

	REVENUE ($ mil.)	NET INCOME ($ mil.)	NET PROFIT MARGIN	EMPLOYEES
12/08	409	(61)	—	5,000
12/02	38	4	11.0%	—
Annual Growth	48.4%	—	—	—

2008 Year-End Financials
Return on assets: 4.3%
Return on equity: (-14.9%)
Current ratio: 4.40
Cash ($ mil.): 154

SAINT TAMMANY PARISH HOSPITAL SERVICE DISTRICT 1

St. Tammany Parish Hospital serves communities in St. Tammany Parish and Washington Parish along the northern shores of Lake Ponchartrain in eastern Louisiana. The not-for-profit hospital has about 240 beds and offers acute care diagnostic rehabilitation and community wellness services. It also includes centers and clinics specializing in surgery breast care cardiology and sleep disorders. In addition St. Tammany Parish Hospital operates a home health and hospice agency an outpatient services center and a primary care physicians' office. The company's facilities are served by doctors in St. Tammany Physicians Network.

Geographic Reach

The hospital serves patients in St. Tammany Parish and Washington Parish in southeastern Louisiana.

Financial Performance

More than half of St. Tammany Parish Hospital's billable revenues in 2012 came from insurance companies; Medicare makes up one third while Medicaid and self-pay patients account for about 10% of sales.

Strategy

In response to growing demand for primary care on the North Shore of Lake Ponchartrain in 2013 the hospital broke ground on a $21 million project that will expand the emergency department to treat more mental health-related emergencies.Company Background

The hospital opened its doors in 1954.

EXECUTIVES

President CEO, Patti Ellish
SVP and COO, Sharon A. Toups
SVP and Chief Medical Officer, Robert Capitelli
SVP and Chief Nursing Officer, Kerry Milton
Sr. VP Chief Financial Officer, Tim C. Lessing
Auditors: LAPORTE APAC METAIRIE LA

LOCATIONS

HQ: SAINT TAMMANY PARISH HOSPITAL SERVICE DISTRICT 1
1202 S TYLER ST, COVINGTON, LA 704332330
Phone: 985 898-4000
Web: WWW.STPH.ORG

PRODUCTS/OPERATIONS

Selected Services and Facilities
Adult Rehabilitation
Adult Rehabilitation Outpatient
Adult Weight Management
Angiography
Breast Center
Bronchoscopy
Cardiac Care (Heart)
Cardiac Cath Lab
Cardiac Rehab Outpatient
Cardiac Rehabilitation
Cardiology
Cardiology Non-Invasive
Center for Wound Care and Hyperbaric Medicine
Colonoscopy
Community Wellness Center
Coumadin Clinic
Covington Surgery Center
Critical Care
CT Scan
Diabetes Education Program
Diagnostic X-ray
EGD (Esophagogastroduodenoscopy)

Embolizations Emergency Services
Endoscopic Retrograde Cholangioancreatography
Endoscopy
ERCP
Esophageal Motility Studies
Family Medical Clinic Franklinton
Fluoroscopy
Gynecologic Surgery
Hospital Medicine
Hospitalist
Hyperbaric Medicine
Intensive Care Unit (ICU)
Interventional Radiology
Kyphoplasty
Labor & Delivery Suite
Lymphedema Management
Mammography
Mary Bird Perkins Cancer Center
MaternalChild Services
Medical Nutrition Therapy
Medical Surgical Nursing Care
MRI
Neonatal Intensive Care Unit
Nephrostograms
New Family Center
Nuclear Medicine
Occupational Therapy
Oncology Nursing Care
Outpatient Pavilion
Pacemaker Clinic
Parenting Center
Pediatric Care
Pediatric Rehabilitation Outpatient
Pediatric Unit
Physical Therapy
Post-Operative Care
Pre-Operative Care
Primary Care Physicians
Prostate Cancer
Prostatectomy
Pulmonary Rehab
Radio Frequency Ablation
Radiology/Imaging
Respiratory Services
Rehabilitation Services
Robotic Surgery
Sigmodoscopy
Sleep Disorders Center
Speech Therapy
St. Tammany Physician's Network Covington
St. Tammany Physician's Network Mandeville
St. Tammany Physician's Network Masonville
Surgery Inpatient
Surgery Outpatient
Ultrasound
Urologic Surgery
Vertebroplasty
Wellness Works
Women's Health
Wound Care

COMPETITORS

Ascension Health	Regency Hospital
Baton Rouge General	River Parishes
Dynacq Healthcare	Hospital
General Health System	West Jefferson Medical
HCA	Center
Medical Properties Trust	Woman's Hospital
Our Lady of the Lake RMC	

HISTORICAL FINANCIALS
Company Type: Private

Income Statement
FYE: December 31

	REVENUE ($ mil.)	NET INCOME ($ mil.)	NET PROFIT MARGIN	EMPLOYEES
12/12	225	13	6.1%	1,520
12/11	223	16	7.6%	—
12/09	200	8	4.2%	—
12/08	1	0	—	—
Annual Growth	270.6%	—	—	—

SAINT TAMMANY PARISH SCHOOL BOARD

Auditors: LAPORTE APAC COVINGTON LA

LOCATIONS

HQ: SAINT TAMMANY PARISH SCHOOL BOARD
321 N THEARD ST, COVINGTON, LA 704332835
Phone: 985 892-2276
Web: WWW.STPSB.NET

HISTORICAL FINANCIALS
Company Type: Private

Income Statement
FYE: June 30

	REVENUE ($ mil.)	NET INCOME ($ mil.)	NET PROFIT MARGIN	EMPLOYEES
06/14	464	24	5.2%	4,400
06/13	457	(0)	—	—
06/12	455	(22)	—	—
06/11	445	0	—	—
Annual Growth	1.4%	—	—	—

2014 Year-End Financials
Return on assets: 0.5%   Cash ($ mil.): 81
Return on equity: 5.2%
Current ratio: —

2012 Year-End Financials
Return on assets: 3.3%   Cash ($ mil.): 44
Return on equity: 6.1%
Current ratio: 2.50

SAINT THOMAS HEALTH SERVICES INC.

Auditors: DELOITTE TAX LLP CINCINNATI

LOCATIONS

HQ: SAINT THOMAS HEALTH SERVICES INC.
4220 HARDING PIKE, NASHVILLE, TN 372052005
Phone: 615 222-2111
Web: WWW.SAINTTHOMASHEART.COM

HISTORICAL FINANCIALS
Company Type: Private

Income Statement
FYE: June 30

	ASSETS ($ mil.)	NET INCOME ($ mil.)	INCOME AS % OF ASSETS	EMPLOYEES
06/13	1,967	(28)	—	4,650
06/10	79	(20)	—	—
06/09	95	(25)	—	—
06/08	8	0	—	—
Annual Growth	200.7%	—	—	—

SAINT THOMAS HOSPITAL

LOCATIONS

HQ: SAINT THOMAS HOSPITAL
4220 HARDING PIKE, NASHVILLE, TN 372052095
Phone: 615 222-5976

HISTORICAL FINANCIALS

Company Type: Private

Income Statement

FYE: June 30

	REVENUE ($ mil.)	NET INCOME ($ mil.)	NET PROFIT MARGIN	EMPLOYEES
06/11	493	60	12.2%	99
06/10	455	60	13.3%	—
Annual Growth	8.4%	(0.2%)	—	—

2011 Year-End Financials

Return on assets: —
Return on equity: 12.2%
Current ratio: 2.10

Cash ($ mil.): 35

SALEM HOSPITAL

Salem Hospital serves the healthcare needs of residents in and around Oregon's Willamette Valley. The acute care hospital boasts about 455 beds and a medical staff of 440-plus physicians that represents some 45 specialty areas such as oncology joint replacement obstetrics diabetes weight loss and mental health among others. The not-for-profit hospital offers a range of services from emergency and critical care to rehabilitation and community wellness programs. Its Center for Outpatient Medicine provides cancer care outpatient surgery and imaging services and has a sleep disorders center. Salem Hospital is part of Salem Health which also includes West Valley Hospital and Willamette Health Partners.

Operations

The Oregon hospital also has a Family Birth Center that offers family-health education services and neonatal intensive-care services. Additionally it provides space to community support services to benefit families.Salem Hospital operates under the guidance of a 15-member volunteer Board of Trustees.

Strategy

As with many healthcare institutions in this age of reform Salem Hospital is working hard to improve patient experience and the quality of healthcare it provides while reducing the cost of care and eliminating waste within its systems. It has been improving clinical documentation to ensure payments are received standardizing care processes improving scheduling of surgeries leaving 30 open positions unfilled and cutting another 30 positions.

Inspired by Toyota's lean production processes the hospital entered into a five-year contract with John Black and Associates in 2010 to begin what it projects to be a transformation that will be accomplished incrementally over the next 20 years. Its goal is to improve care using a holistic patient-centered approach and reduce waste in terms of waits inventory and other day-to-day processes.

Salem Hospital set a goal of becoming a Magnet hospital in 2003 and accomplished the feat in 2010. (Only 6% of hospitals in the US have achieved Magnet status.) Magnet certification is awarded to hospitals that meet a set of criteria that measures the quality and strength of their nursing staffs as set by the American Nurses' Credentialing Center an affiliate of the American Nurses Association. Criteria includes patient outcomes job satisfaction and low turnover.In 2009 the hospital opened a new patient tower. In 2010 it sold its money-losing home care department to LHC Group as a way of cutting operating costs.

EXECUTIVES

Director Of Nursing, Marsha Radford
Vice President Human Resources, Laurie Barr
Medical Director, Richard Segal
Vice President Cmo, Anne Theis
Auditors: AKT LLP SALEM OR

LOCATIONS

HQ: SALEM HOSPITAL
890 OAK ST SE, SALEM, OR 973013905
Phone: 503 561-5200
Web: WWW.SALEMHEALTH.ORG

PRODUCTS/OPERATIONS

Selected Services

Bariatrics
Cancer
Diabetes
Gynecology
Heart
Joint replacement
Neurosciences
Obstetrics
Orthopedics
Pain management
Psychiatric medicine
Psychology
Rehabilitation
Spine
Sleep
Stroke
Weight-loss surgery
Wound care

COMPETITORS

Adventist Health
Asante Health System
Kadlec Regional Medical Center
Kaiser Foundation Hospitals
Legacy Emanuel Hospital and Health Center
Legacy Health System
Oregon Health & Science University
PeaceHealth Southwest Medical Center
Providence Health & Services

HISTORICAL FINANCIALS

Company Type: Private

Income Statement

FYE: September 30

	REVENUE ($ mil.)	NET INCOME ($ mil.)	NET PROFIT MARGIN	EMPLOYEES
09/13	531	61	11.6%	3,400
09/09	493	20	4.2%	—
09/08	2	(1)	—	—
09/04	321	0	—	—
Annual Growth	5.7%	—	—	—

2013 Year-End Financials

Return on assets: 6.3%
Return on equity: 11.6%
Current ratio: 1.00

Cash ($ mil.): 2

SALEM-KEIZER SCHOOL DISTRICT 24 J

LOCATIONS

HQ: SALEM-KEIZER SCHOOL DISTRICT 24 J
2450 LANCASTER DR NE # 100, SALEM, OR 973051130
Phone: 503 399-3036
Web: WWW.SALKEIZ.K12.OR.US

HISTORICAL FINANCIALS

Company Type: Private

Income Statement

FYE: June 30

	REVENUE ($ mil.)	NET INCOME ($ mil.)	NET PROFIT MARGIN	EMPLOYEES
06/13	428	(21)		4,000
06/06	319	8	2.7%	—
06/04	319	8	2.7%	—
06/03	279	0	—	—
Annual Growth	4.4%	—	—	—

SAM LEVIN INC.

Founded in 1920 as a furniture and hardware store by the husband-and-wife team Sam and Jessie Levin Sam Levin (dba Levin Furniture) sells a wide variety of dining room bedroom living room and office furniture as well as mattresses at about a dozen retail locations in northeastern Ohio and southwestern Pennsylvania. It also operates a Sleep Center bedding store in Pennsylvania and a clearance outlet in Ohio. The family-owned-and-run-company offers self-service kiosks in its showrooms and creative exhibits that include sports- and Wizard of Oz-themed displays. Robert Levin Sam and Jessie's grandson is president of the company.

EXECUTIVES

Vice President Of Operations, Ward Dingman
Vice President Human Resources, Irene Fostyk
Auditors: SCHNEIDER DOWNS & CO INC P

LOCATIONS

HQ: SAM LEVIN INC.
301 FITZ HENRY RD, SMITHTON, PA 154798715
Phone: 724 872-2055
Web: WWW.LEVINFURNITURE.COM

2009 Stores

	No.
Ohio	7
Pennsylvania	7
Total	**14**

COMPETITORS

Ashley Furniture	J. C. Penney
Bassett Furniture	Macy's
Havertys	Rooms To Go

HISTORICAL FINANCIALS
Company Type: Private

Income Statement
FYE: December 31

	REVENUE ($ mil.)	NET INCOME ($ mil.)	NET PROFIT MARGIN	EMPLOYEES
12/13	188	7	3.8%	400
12/12	187	7	4.1%	—
12/11	170	11	6.8%	—
12/10	145	0	—	—
Annual Growth	8.8%	—	—	—

2013 Year-End Financials
Return on assets: 2.6%
Return on equity: 3.8%
Current ratio: 0.60
Cash ($ mil.): 13

SAM SWOPE AUTO GROUP LLC

Sam Swope Auto Group has plenty of new cars for old Kentucky. The company owns about two dozen automobile dealerships in the Blue Grass State. Located in Louisville Lexington Radcliff and Elizabethtown Swope dealerships sell General Motors cars including Buicks Cadillacs GMC trucks and Saturns. Other company dealerships sell BMW Honda Lexus Toyota and Volvo models. Sam Swope Auto Group also sells used cars and offers parts and service. In 1952 founder Sam Swope parlayed his love of cars into his first dealership which sold Plymouth and Dodge cars in Elizabethtown Kentucky. The company is still owned and managed by the Swope family.

Financial Performance

The rebounding economy has increased demand for new vehicles. Sales and leases of new cars and trucks at Sam Swope Auto Group's dealerships were up by about 20% in 2012 to 8750 vehicles while the company sold 24% fewer pre-owned cars in 2012 than in 2011. The company's recovery has accelerated since 2009 with 2012 its best year since the crash.

Mergers and Acquisitions

Buoyed by increasing sales Sam Swope Auto Group has been making acquisitions. In October 2012 the company acquired Clapp Volkswagen in Clarksville. In August 2011 it purchased the Cardinal Jeep Dodge Ram dealership from Pittman Automotive Inc.

Company Background

The company also operates the Swope's Cars of Yesteryear Auto Museum in Elizabethtown. The museum has a working garage and sells vintage and classic cars.

EXECUTIVES
Vice President of Used Car Vehicle Operations,
Cary Donovan
Vice President And General Manager, J%2ER%2E Hage

LOCATIONS
HQ: SAM SWOPE AUTO GROUP LLC
10 SWOPE AUTOCENTER DR, LOUISVILLE, KY 402991806
Phone: 812 282-8285
Web:
WWW.SAMSWOPEAUTOGROUP.WISEBUYINGMALL.COM

PRODUCTS/OPERATIONS

Dealerships
Lexus of Louisville
Richmond Honda
Sam Swope Buick GMC Auto Center
Sam Swope Buick GMC Clarksville
Sam Swope Buick GMC On Dixie
Sam Swope Cadillac
Sam Swope Chrysler Jeep Dodge Ram
Sam Swope Honda World
Sam Swope Infiniti
Sam Swope Mitsubishi
Sam Swope Volkswagen of Clarksville
Scion of Louisville
Toyota of Louisville

COMPETITORS

AutoNation
Jeff Wyler Automotive
Martin Management Group
Penske Automotive Group
Sonic Automotive

HISTORICAL FINANCIALS
Company Type: Private

Income Statement
FYE: December 31

	REVENUE ($ mil.)	NET INCOME ($ mil.)	NET PROFIT MARGIN	EMPLOYEES
12/07	444	59	13.4%	900
12/06	434	57	13.2%	—
12/05	1,598	0	0.0%	—
Annual Growth	(47.2%)	66206.2%	—	—

2007 Year-End Financials
Return on assets: 0.2%
Return on equity: 13.4%
Current ratio: 0.50
Cash ($ mil.): 12

SAMARITAN'S PURSE

Auditors: DIXON HUGHES GOODMAN LLP CHA

LOCATIONS
HQ: SAMARITAN' S PURSE
801 BAMBOO RD, BOONE, NC 286078721
Phone: 828 262-1980
Web: WWW.SAMARITANSPURSE.COM

HISTORICAL FINANCIALS
Company Type: Private

Income Statement
FYE: December 31

	REVENUE ($ mil.)	NET INCOME ($ mil.)	NET PROFIT MARGIN	EMPLOYEES
12/13	473	59	12.5%	525
12/12	389	(35)	—	—
12/11	388	38	9.8%	—
12/08	313	0	—	—
Annual Growth	8.6%	—	—	—

2013 Year-End Financials
Return on assets: 3.1%
Return on equity: 12.5%
Current ratio: 2.20
Cash ($ mil.): 53

SAMPSON-BLADEN OIL COMPANY INCORPORATED

LOCATIONS
HQ: SAMPSON-BLADEN OIL COMPANY INCORPORATED
520A E RAILROAD ST, CLINTON, NC 283284304
Phone: 910 592-4177
Web: WWW.SBOIL.COM

HISTORICAL FINANCIALS
Company Type: Private

Income Statement
FYE: October 31

	REVENUE ($ mil.)	NET INCOME ($ mil.)	NET PROFIT MARGIN	EMPLOYEES
10/09	308	(0)	—	280
10/08	449	7	1.7%	—
10/07	1,996	0	—	—
Annual Growth	—	—	—	—

2009 Year-End Financials
Return on assets: 5.0%
Return on equity: (-0.2%)
Current ratio: 0.80
Cash ($ mil.): 11

SAN ANDREAS REGIONAL CENTER

Auditors: LAUTZE & LAUTZE SAN FRANCISCO

LOCATIONS
HQ: SAN ANDREAS REGIONAL CENTER
300 ORCHARD CY DR STE 170, CAMPBELL, CA 95008
Phone: 408 374-9960
Web: WWW.REGIONALCENTER.ORG

HISTORICAL FINANCIALS
Company Type: Private

Income Statement
FYE: June 30

	REVENUE ($ mil.)	NET INCOME ($ mil.)	NET PROFIT MARGIN	EMPLOYEES
06/14	310	(0)	—	272
06/13	299	0	0.1%	—
06/12	282	(0)	—	—
06/11	283	0	—	—
Annual Growth	3.1%	—	—	—

2014 Year-End Financials
Return on assets: 0.3%
Return on equity: —
Current ratio: 1.00
Cash ($ mil.): 9

SAN BERNARDINO COUNTY SCHOOL DISTRICT

LOCATIONS

HQ: SAN BERNARDINO COUNTY SCHOOL DISTRICT
601 N E ST, SAN BERNARDINO, CA 924150020
Phone: 909 386-2417
Web: WWW.SBCSS.K12.CA.US

HISTORICAL FINANCIALS

Company Type: Private

Income Statement

FYE: June 30

	REVENUE ($ mil.)	NET INCOME ($ mil.)	NET PROFIT MARGIN	EMPLOYEES
06/07*	414	20	4.9%	1,700
12/05	301	0	—	—
06/02	301	7	2.5%	—
06/01	256	0	—	—
Annual Growth	8.3%	—	—	—

*Fiscal year change

2007 Year-End Financials

Return on assets: —
Return on equity: 4.9%
Current ratio: —

Cash ($ mil.): 76

SANFORD CLINIC NORTH

Auditors: EIDE BAILLY LLP MINNEAPOLIS

LOCATIONS

HQ: SANFORD CLINIC NORTH
737 BROADWAY N, FARGO, ND 581024421
Phone: 701 234-2000
Web: WWW.SANFORDHEALTH.ORG

HISTORICAL FINANCIALS

Company Type: Private

Income Statement

FYE: June 30

	REVENUE ($ mil.)	NET INCOME ($ mil.)	NET PROFIT MARGIN	EMPLOYEES
06/09	431	(24)	—	7,000
06/08	401	(20)	—	—
06/05	0	0	—	—
06/04	8	0	—	—
Annual Growth	119.0%	—	—	—

2009 Year-End Financials

Return on assets: —
Return on equity: (-5.6%)
Current ratio: 0.50

Cash ($ mil.): —

SANFORD HEALTH

Auditors: DELOITTE & TOUCHE LLP MINNEAP

LOCATIONS

HQ: SANFORD HEALTH
1305 W 18TH ST, SIOUX FALLS, SD 571050401
Phone: 605 333-1720
Web: WWW.SANFORDHEALTH.ORG

HISTORICAL FINANCIALS

Company Type: Private

Income Statement

FYE: June 30

	REVENUE ($ mil.)	NET INCOME ($ mil.)	NET PROFIT MARGIN	EMPLOYEES
06/13	3,105	133	4.3%	2,939
06/12	2,516	72	2.9%	—
06/11	2,312	264	11.5%	—
06/10	96	0	—	—
Annual Growth	218.2%	—	—	—

2013 Year-End Financials

Return on assets: 2.2%
Return on equity: 4.3%
Current ratio: 1.50

Cash ($ mil.): 85

SANFORD NORTH

LOCATIONS

HQ: SANFORD NORTH
801 BROADWAY N, FARGO, ND 581023641
Phone: 701 234-6000
Web: WWW.SANFORDHEALTH.ORG

HISTORICAL FINANCIALS

Company Type: Private

Income Statement

FYE: June 30

	REVENUE ($ mil.)	NET INCOME ($ mil.)	NET PROFIT MARGIN	EMPLOYEES
06/10	677	(15)	—	7,200
06/08	112	2	2.0%	—
Annual Growth	145.1%	—	—	—

2010 Year-End Financials

Return on assets: 0.7%
Return on equity: (-2.3%)
Current ratio: 1.30

Cash ($ mil.): —

SANTA BARBARA COTTAGE HOSPITAL FOUNDATION

LOCATIONS

HQ: SANTA BARBARA COTTAGE HOSPITAL FOUNDATION
400 W PUEBLO ST, SANTA BARBARA, CA 931054353
Phone: 805 682-7111
Web: WWW.SBCH.ORG

HISTORICAL FINANCIALS

Company Type: Private

Income Statement

FYE: December 31

	REVENUE ($ mil.)	NET INCOME ($ mil.)	NET PROFIT MARGIN	EMPLOYEES
12/12	569	16	2.8%	1,786
12/08	0	(0)	—	—
12/02	203	(51)	—	—
12/01	358	0	—	—
Annual Growth	—	—	—	—

2012 Year-End Financials

Return on assets: 10.0%
Return on equity: 2.8%
Current ratio: 0.40

Cash ($ mil.): 77

SANTA ROSA MEMORIAL HOSPITAL INC

Auditors: ERNST & YOUNG US LLP IRVINE

LOCATIONS

HQ: SANTA ROSA MEMORIAL HOSPITAL INC
1165 MONTGOMERY DR, SANTA ROSA, CA 954054897
Phone: 707 546-3210
Web: WWW.STJOSEPHHEALTH.ORG

HISTORICAL FINANCIALS

Company Type: Private

Income Statement

FYE: June 30

	REVENUE ($ mil.)	NET INCOME ($ mil.)	NET PROFIT MARGIN	EMPLOYEES
06/10	357	(1)	—	2,100
06/09	319	5	1.8%	—
06/08	2,028	0	—	—
Annual Growth	—	—	—	—

2010 Year-End Financials

Return on assets: —
Return on equity: (-0.6%)
Current ratio: 0.70

Cash ($ mil.): 70

SAPP BROS. INC.

Need air in those 18 wheels? Sapp Bros Travel Centers (formerly Sapp Bros Truck Stops) has the usual air gas food but also offers human conveniences such such as laundry rooms mailbox rentals private showers and TV lounges. The company operates a chain of some 15 truck stops —readily identifiable by the giant red-and-white coffeepot logo —along interstate highways from Utah to Pennsylvania; with a concentration in Nebraska. Half of the locations also operate service centers offering oil changes new tires and safety checks. Its sister company Sapp Bros Petroleum distributes fuels and lubricants to more than 200 retailers. The firm is run by CEO Bill Sapp one of the four founding Sapp brothers.

Geographic Reach

Omaha-based Sapp Bros. has travel centers in eight states: Nebraska Iowa Utah Colorado Wyoming Kansas Illinois and Pennsylvania.

Strategy

To raise its profile and rev up its business Sapp Bros. in 2013 joined the roster of VP Racing Fuels's retail brand partners. The benefits of the affiliation include association with an attractive retail image competitive credit card rates and the ability to source unbranded fuel for its travel centers.

EXECUTIVES

CFO Secretary and Treasurer, Allen Marsh
President, Don Quinn
Auditors: KPMG LLP OMAHA NE

LOCATIONS

HQ: SAPP BROS. INC.
 9915 S 148TH ST, OMAHA, NE 681383876
Phone: 402 895-7038
Web: WWW.SAPPBROSTRUCKSTOPS.COM

2012 Locations

	No.
Nebraska	8
Iowa	2
Colorado	1
Illinois	1
Kansas	1
Pennsylvania	1
Utah	1
Wyoming	1
Total	**16**

COMPETITORS

Exxon Mobil	Stuckey's
Love's Country Stores	TravelCenters of
Pilot Flying J	America

HISTORICAL FINANCIALS

Company Type: Private

Income Statement

FYE: September 30

	REVENUE ($ mil.)	NET INCOME ($ mil.)	NET PROFIT MARGIN	EMPLOYEES
09/14	1,566	12	0.8%	1,115
09/13	1,483	14	1.0%	—
09/12	1,677	13	0.8%	—
09/11	1,271	0	—	—
Annual Growth	**7.2%**	**—**	**—**	**—**

2014 Year-End Financials

Return on assets: 3.0%   Cash ($ mil.): 2
Return on equity: 0.8%
Current ratio: 0.90

SAPP BROS. PETROLEUM INC.

There have been few poor saps in this family since the Sapp brothers made a go of their petroleum products business. Sapp Bros Petroleum distributes petroleum products such as fuels lubricants propane antifreeze absorbents additives and equipment through more than 10 locations in Nebraska and western Iowa. It has a sideline selling used computer parts such as modems processors and keyboards. The regional fuel distributor was founded by the four Sapp brothers in 1980 and is run by CEO Bill Sapp who also runs sister company Sapp Bros Truck Stops.

EXECUTIVES

Vice President, Kay Hayes
Auditors: KPMG LLP OMAHA NE

LOCATIONS

HQ: SAPP BROS. PETROLEUM INC.
 9915 S 148TH ST STE 2, OMAHA, NE 681383876
Phone: 402 895-2202
Web: WWW.SAPPBROSPETRO.COM

COMPETITORS

Exxon Mobil	Shell Oil Products

HISTORICAL FINANCIALS

Company Type: Private

Income Statement

FYE: October 31

	REVENUE ($ mil.)	NET INCOME ($ mil.)	NET PROFIT MARGIN	EMPLOYEES
10/09	563	5	1.0%	285
10/08	922	3	0.3%	—
10/07	1,566	0	—	—
Annual Growth	**—19890.6%**	**—**	**—**	**—**

2009 Year-End Financials

Return on assets: 3.1%   Cash ($ mil.): 2
Return on equity: 1.0%
Current ratio: 1.10

SARAH BUSH LINCOLN HEALTH CENTER

With the moniker of the Illinois' favorite son's stepmother (Sarah Bush Lincoln) who wouldn't want to go to this health center? And apparently the locals agree since Sarah Bush Lincoln Health Center (SBLHC) has a market share of about 44% in its seven-county service area in east-central Illinois and an inpatient market share for Coles County of nearly 80%. SBLHC has 128 beds and provides a wide range of health care services including emergency medicine behavioral health care surgical services and cancer treatment. Its network also includes about 30 clinics doctors' offices and hospice centers. The hospital also offers support groups and continuing education classes. Operations

SBLHC has a staff of active and consulting physicians totaling 145 providers with nearly 30 specialties. Each year it has some 7000 admissions and performs 1000 inpatient and 5000 outpatient surgeries.Geographic ReachThe regional hospital is centrally located in east-central Illinois' Coles County and serves seven counties. Home health services extend to the surrounding 19 counties in east-central and southern Illinois.StrategyAs part of an ongoing expansion drive SBLHC broke ground on a new regional cancer center in 2015. The center located on the front lawn of the main campus will feature 17 individual chemotherapy areas and will span 21000 sq. ft. of space. They hospital is also building a new clinic in Tuscola Illinois.Company BackgroundSBLHC opened its doors in 1977. It was named after President Abraham Lincoln's stepmother Sarah Bush Lincoln.

EXECUTIVES

Vice President of Patient Care, Mary Lou Randolph
Director Of Infection Control, Ramona Tomshack
Vice President Finance, John Riley
Nursing Director, Mary Wild

Vice President Of Is, Maggie Ratliss
Director of Nursing, Cathy Alexander
Vice President System Practices, Jerry Esker
Director ICU Coronary Care Unit, Joyce Cottingham
Vice President Medical Affairs, James (Jamie) Hildebrandt
Auditors: BKD LLP ST LOUIS MO

LOCATIONS

HQ: SARAH BUSH LINCOLN HEALTH CENTER
 1000 HEALTH CENTER DR, MATTOON, IL 619389261
Phone: 217 258-2525
Web: WWW.SARAHBUSH.ORG

PRODUCTS/OPERATIONS

Selected Programs/Services

Advanced Wound Center
Audiology
Center for Interventional Pain
Emergency Department
EMS
Gastroenterology
Heart Center
Hospitalist Program
Laboratory
Lifeline
Lincolnland Hospice
Lincolnland Home Care
Orthopedics and Sports Medicine
Outpatient Surgery Center
Patient Care
Physical Medicine & Rehabilitation
Psychiatry and Counseling
Radiology
Regional Cancer Center
Women and Children's Center

COMPETITORS

Carle Hospital	Memorial Health System
Crawford Memorial	(Colorado)
Hospital	Memorial Medical
Decatur Memorial	Center
Hospital	St. John's Hospital
Hospital Sisters	(Illinois)
Health System	
Iroquois Memorial	
Hospital	

HISTORICAL FINANCIALS

Company Type: Private

Income Statement

FYE: June 30

	REVENUE ($ mil.)	NET INCOME ($ mil.)	NET PROFIT MARGIN	EMPLOYEES
06/11	195	14	7.2%	1,543
06/09	132	(6)	—	—
06/08	699	0	0.0%	—
Annual Growth	**(34.6%)**	**849.5%**	**—**	**—**

2011 Year-End Financials

Return on assets: —   Cash ($ mil.): 47
Return on equity: 7.2%
Current ratio: 3.10

SARGENT ELECTRIC COMPANY

Sargent Electric Company has earned its stripes providing electrical services for its customers. Founded in 1907 to serve Pittsburgh's steel industry the electrical contractor performs construction work for utilities foundries oil refineries chemical processing firms and steelmakers. Clients have included Allegheny Energy Duquesne Light General

Electric and United States Steel. The company also provides electric service and maintenance services to residential commercial and government customers. Its service area encompasses about 20 states in the eastern half of the US. Sargent Electric is owned and managed by the Sargent family.

EXECUTIVES

COO, Gary W. Groom
President and CEO, Stephan H. (Steve) Dake
CFO, Elizabeth A. (Beth) Lawrence
CEO Sargent Safety Services, Gregory A. (Greg) Woodworth
SVP Operations, Richard S. (Dick) Rectenwald
General Manager Northwest Indiana, Thomas (Tom) Frame
General Manager Terre Haute, Charles E. (Chuck) Wheat
General Manager Commercial, Mark Staudt
General Manager Industrial, Jim Voss
Auditors: HILL BARTH & KING LLC WEXFOR

LOCATIONS

HQ: SARGENT ELECTRIC COMPANY
2767 LIBERTY AVE, PITTSBURGH, PA 152224703
Phone: 412 338-8480
Web: WWW.SARGENT.COM

COMPETITORS

EMCOR
Fisk Electric
Integrated Electrical Services
Limbach Facility Services
MYR Group
Miller Electric
Miller Electric Co

HISTORICAL FINANCIALS

Company Type: Private

Income Statement

	REVENUE ($ mil.)	NET INCOME ($ mil.)	NET PROFIT MARGIN	EMPLOYEES
12/13	187	10	5.5%	400
12/11	89	0	0.4%	—
12/10	79	0	0.8%	—
12/09	107	0	—	—
Annual Growth	14.9%	—	—	—

2013 Year-End Financials

Return on assets: 2.6%
Return on equity: 5.5%
Current ratio: 1.70
Cash ($ mil.): —

SATTERFIELD AND PONTIKES CONSTRUCTION INC.

Satterfield & Pontikes Construction (S&P) provides general contracting consultation and construction management services primarily in the Gulf Coast region of Texas and Louisiana. The company often works on buildings for the commercial retail industrial educational entertainment and recreational sectors. High profile projects include the Texas A&M University Health Science Center and the expansion of the World War II Museum in New Orleans. S&P specializes in concrete work and early-stage site work as well as 3-D modeling and virtual design. The company was founded in 1989 and is headed by majority owner and CEO George Pontikes.

S&P works from offices in Houston Dallas/Fort Worth New Orleans San Antonio and Austin.

The firm has looked outside of the Gulf Region for work. In 2011 it was chosen by Delta Air Lines to work on the $1.2 billion expansion of a terminal and the demolition of another at JFK International airport in New York.

EXECUTIVES

Vice President, Bo Smith
Vice President, Brad Shearer
Senior Vice President, Jason Haralson
Vice President Contract Administration, Pete Lozada
Senior Vice President, Frank Roetzel
Vice President, Kenneth Smith
Auditors: MELTON & MELTON LLP CPAS HO

LOCATIONS

HQ: SATTERFIELD AND PONTIKES CONSTRUCTION INC.
11000 EQUITY DR STE 100, HOUSTON, TX 770418235
Phone: 210 637-5250
Web: WWW.SATPON.COM

PRODUCTS/OPERATIONS

Selected Services
Building information modeling
Construction
Construction management
Design build
Development
Green building
Practical Project Delivery

COMPETITORS

Balfour Beatty Construction
C.F. Jordan
Falkenberg Construction
Skanska USA Building
Spawglass Holding
Turner Corporation

HISTORICAL FINANCIALS

Company Type: Private

Income Statement

	REVENUE ($ mil.)	NET INCOME ($ mil.)	NET PROFIT MARGIN	EMPLOYEES
12/13	373	(7)	—	300
12/12	377	(8)	—	—
12/11	388	0	0.1%	—
12/10	445	0	—	—
Annual Growth	(5.7%)	—	—	—

2013 Year-End Financials

Return on assets: 25.6%
Return on equity: (-2.1%)
Current ratio: 1.00
Cash ($ mil.): 20

SAVE THE CHILDREN FEDERATION INC.

Save the Children helps poor and malnourished children in some 15 US states and nearly 120 countries focusing on such areas as health and nutrition economic development education child protection and HIV/AIDS. The humanitarian organization also participates in international disaster relief efforts focusing on children and their families. Save the Children spends about 90% of its budget on program services with the rest allocated to administration and fundraising. The group was founded in 1932 inspired by the international children's rights movement begun in the UK in 1919 by Eglantyne Jebb founder of the British Save the Children Fund. It is a member of the International Save the Children Alliance.

Geographic Reach

Save the Children operates programs in some 120 countries including the US. It comprises 29 member organizations worldwide.

Operations

Some 43% of the humanitarian organization's work is centered in Asia with 34% in Africa. Save the Children spends the rest of its time in the US Latin America and the Middle East.

In 2012 alone Save the Children helped 125 million girls and boys worldwide.

Financial Performance

The global aid organization's revenue declined by 3.5% in 2012 versus 2011 due largely to a 12% drop in private gifts grants and contributions which account for nearly half of its total revenue. Save the Children directed 89% of its expenses to programs which benefit children and allow the humanitarian organization to keep private costs (includes fundraising and management and general) at about 10% —one of the best ratios for nonprofit organizations.

Strategy

With about 28% of its program services devoted to emergencies and 20% to education Save the Children in 2014 partnered with The Malala Fund to help vulnerable Syrian and Jordanian children return to school. As part of the partnership Save the Children is launching a pair of education projects. Another large portion of Save the Children's program services are focused on Health and Nutrition (25%) and Hunger & Livelihoods (10%).

EXECUTIVES

Associate Vice President Office, David (Dave) Oot
Vice President, Gary Shaye
Associate Vice President International, Greg Ramm
Assistant Vice President Finance, Rick Trowbridge
Vice President And Managing Director Development P, Diana Myers
Associate Vice President and Deputy General Counsel, Brian White
Secretary, Andrea Williamson-hughes

LOCATIONS

HQ: SAVE THE CHILDREN FEDERATION INC.
501 KINGS HWY E STE 400, FAIRFIELD, CT 068254861
Phone: 203 221-4000
Web: WWW.SAVETHECHILDREN.ORG

Selected Countries of Operation
Australia
Brazil
Canada
Denmark
Dominican Republic
Fiji
Finland
Germany
Guatemala
Honduras
Hong Kong
Iceland
India
Italy
Japan
Jordan
Korea
Lithuania
Mexico
Netherlands
New Zealand
Norway
Romania

South Africa
Spain
Swaziland
Sweden
Switzerland
United Kingdom
United States

HISTORICAL FINANCIALS
Company Type: Private

Income Statement
FYE: December 31

	REVENUE ($ mil.)	NET INCOME ($ mil.)	NET PROFIT MARGIN	EMPLOYEES
12/13*	657	4	0.6%	3,000
09/07	356	9	2.8%	—
09/06	332	20	6.3%	—
09/05	1,710	0	—	—
Annual Growth	(11.3%)	—	—	—

*Fiscal year change

2013 Year-End Financials
Return on assets: 4.0% Cash ($ mil.): 79
Return on equity: 0.6%
Current ratio: 0.70

SAWNEE ELECTRIC MEMBERSHIP CORPORATION

Sawnee Electric Membership Corporation (Sawnee EMC) wasn't around on the night the lights went out in Georgia but it plans to make sure they stay on. The electric distribution cooperative serves about 152000 residential commercial and industrial meters in a seven-county area of northern Georgia comprised of Cherokee Dawson Forsyth Fulton Gwinnett Hall and Lumpkin counties. Residential customers in the area (which includes the sprawling Atlanta suburbs) account for two-thirds of electricity usage. While small and medium users must get their electricity from Sawnee potential customers with loads exceeding 900 kilowatts can shop around. Sawnee EMC distributes electricity over 9970 miles of power line.

The cooperative provides its members with the option of gas service through a partnership with Coweta-Fayette EMC Natural Gas a subsidiary of fellow Georgia-based power co-op Coweta-Fayette EMC. In 2010 it had 16000 Sawnee EMC customers participating in this arrangement.

As part of its commitment to green energy Sawnee EMC has also teamed up with Green-e Energy a leading national renewable energy certification and verification program to offer certified renewable power to Sawnee EMC members. It is encouraging its members to conserve energy and help keep down costs offering home energy audits installing Smart meters and encouraging the use of energy-efficient light bulbs.

In 2010 Sawnee EMC reported a jump in revenues and operating income thanks to a growth in its membership and higher energy use due to a hotter-than-usual summer.

The company was founded as the Forsyth County Electric Membership Corporation in 1938 as part of the Roosevelt government's national rural electrification drive. It was renamed for local landmark Sawnee Mountain in 1950.

EXECUTIVES
Vice President, Gary Mauldin
Auditors: MCNAIR MCLEMORE MIDDLEBROOKS

LOCATIONS
HQ: SAWNEE ELECTRIC MEMBERSHIP CORPORATION
543 ATLANTA RD, CUMMING, GA 300402701
Phone: 770 887-2363
Web: WWW.SAWNEE.COM

COMPETITORS
Cobb EMC
Georgia Power
Jackson Electric Membership

HISTORICAL FINANCIALS
Company Type: Private

Income Statement
FYE: December 31

	REVENUE ($ mil.)	NET INCOME ($ mil.)	NET PROFIT MARGIN	EMPLOYEES
12/13	335	0	—	300
12/12	325	0	—	—
12/08	0	(0)	—	—
12/03	201	0	—	—
Annual Growth	5.2%	—	—	—

2013 Year-End Financials
Return on assets: 10.0% Cash ($ mil.): 23
Return on equity: —
Current ratio: 1.10

SCHAUMBOND GROUP INC.

LOCATIONS
HQ: SCHAUMBOND GROUP INC.
225 S LAKE AVE STE 300, PASADENA, CA 911013009
Phone: 626 215-4998

HISTORICAL FINANCIALS
Company Type: Private

Income Statement
FYE: December 31

	ASSETS ($ mil.)	NET INCOME ($ mil.)	INCOME AS % OF ASSETS	EMPLOYEES
12/07	65	4	7.5%	550
12/06	50	4	9.6%	—
Annual Growth	28.2%	(0.0%)	—	—

2007 Year-End Financials
Return on assets: 0.1% Sales ($ mil): 2,200
Return on equity: 0.2%

SCHOOL BOARD OF BREVARD COUNTY

Auditors: ERNST & YOUNG LLP ORLANDO FL

LOCATIONS
HQ: SCHOOL BOARD OF BREVARD COUNTY
2700 JDGE FRAN JMESON WAY, MELBOURNE, FL 329406699
Phone: 321 633-1000

HISTORICAL FINANCIALS
Company Type: Private

Income Statement
FYE: June 30

	REVENUE ($ mil.)	NET INCOME ($ mil.)	NET PROFIT MARGIN	EMPLOYEES
06/09	613	(19)	—	9,031
06/06	628	100	15.9%	—
Annual Growth	(0.8%)	—	—	—

2009 Year-End Financials
Return on assets: — Cash ($ mil.): 29
Return on equity: (-3.1%)
Current ratio: —

SCHOOL BOARD OF ORANGE COUNTY FLORIDA

Auditors: ERNST & YOUNG LLP ORLANDO FL

LOCATIONS
HQ: SCHOOL BOARD OF ORANGE COUNTY FLORIDA
445 W AMELIA ST LBBY, ORLANDO, FL 328011153
Phone: 407 317-3200
Web: WWW.ORANGECOUNTYFL.NET

HISTORICAL FINANCIALS
Company Type: Private

Income Statement
FYE: June 30

	REVENUE ($ mil.)	NET INCOME ($ mil.)	NET PROFIT MARGIN	EMPLOYEES
06/13	1,877	110	5.9%	25,000
06/12	1,823	30	1.7%	—
06/11	1,895	24	1.3%	—
06/05	1,570	0	—	—
Annual Growth	2.3%	—	—	—

2013 Year-End Financials
Return on assets: — Cash ($ mil.): 204
Return on equity: 5.9%
Current ratio: —

SCHOOL DISTRICT 1J MULTNOMAH COUNTY OREGON (INC)

Auditors: TALBOT KORVOLA & WARWICK LLP

LOCATIONS

HQ: SCHOOL DISTRICT 1J MULTNOMAH COUNTY
OREGON (INC)
501 N DIXON ST, PORTLAND, OR 972271804
Phone: 503 916-2000
Web: WWW.PPS.K12.OR.US

HISTORICAL FINANCIALS

Company Type: Private

Income Statement

FYE: June 30

	REVENUE ($ mil.)	NET INCOME ($ mil.)	NET PROFIT MARGIN	EMPLOYEES
06/14	661	(0)		5,244
06/13	578	118	20.6%	—
06/12*	574	(4)		—
05/12	527	0		—
Annual Growth	11.9%	—		—

*Fiscal year change

2014 Year-End Financials

Return on assets: 2.8%
Return on equity: (-0.1%)
Current ratio: 1.40

Cash ($ mil.): 98

SCHWAB CHARITABLE FUND

Auditors: DELOITTE & TOUCHE LLP SAN FRA

LOCATIONS

HQ: SCHWAB CHARITABLE FUND
211 MAIN ST, SAN FRANCISCO, CA 941051905
Phone: 415 667-9131
Web: WWW.ABOUTSCHWAB.COM

HISTORICAL FINANCIALS

Company Type: Private

Income Statement

FYE: June 30

	REVENUE ($ mil.)	NET INCOME ($ mil.)	NET PROFIT MARGIN	EMPLOYEES
06/12	722	172	23.9%	26
06/11	822	308	37.5%	—
06/10	937	506	54.1%	—
06/09	496	0		—
Annual Growth	13.3%	—		—

2012 Year-End Financials

Return on assets: —
Return on equity: 23.9%
Current ratio: —

Cash ($ mil.): 3

SCIENCE AND ENGINEERING SERVICES LLC

LOCATIONS

HQ: SCIENCE AND ENGINEERING SERVICES LLC
6992 COLUMBIA GATEWAY DR # 200, COLUMBIA,
MD 210462985
Phone: 443 539-0139
Web: WWW.SESI-MD.COM

HISTORICAL FINANCIALS

Company Type: Private

Income Statement

FYE: December 31

	REVENUE ($ mil.)	NET INCOME ($ mil.)	NET PROFIT MARGIN	EMPLOYEES
12/08	345	18	5.3%	700
12/06	240	6	2.6%	—
12/05	46	0		—
Annual Growth	—	13034.8%		—

2008 Year-End Financials

Return on assets: 8.2%
Return on equity: 5.3%
Current ratio: 1.00

Cash ($ mil.): 2

SCIENTIFIC RESEARCH CORP

Scientific Research Corporation (SRC) doesn't limit its services to the laboratory. The government contractor provides a wide variety of engineering and research services including consulting systems engineering project management network design hardware and software development prototyping testing and evaluation systems integration and training. Its expertise encompasses communications and intelligence systems electronic warfare simulation and instrumentation systems. In some cases SRC works as a subcontractor for larger companies such as Booz Allen. SRC's clients include the US government and military state agencies and private sector businesses.

Operations The company's integrated systems and solutions division specializes in software development network engineering systems automation digital signal processing production engineering and logistical support services for intelligence systems. It also provides other IT and wireless network support services. SRC's simulation test and instrumentation division offers products and engineering services to support surveillance radar and instrumentation systems. It also develops sensor systems and provides interoperability testing services for military weapons systems. The company's communications networks and electronics unit provides research and development systems integration design deployment and support services for military and commercial communications and network systems.

Geographic Reach SRC operates from about 15 offices located mainly in the southern and eastern US; it also has a few facilities in the Southwest and in California.

EXECUTIVES

Vice President Human Resources, Sandra Holtzclaw
Vice President Operations, Alan Harris
Vice President Business Development Federal Programs, Mark Pelletier
Executive Vice President, James Ward
Auditors: DIXON HUGHES GOODMAN LLP ATL

LOCATIONS

HQ: SCIENTIFIC RESEARCH CORP
2300 WINDY RIDGE PKWY SE 400S, ATLANTA, GA
303395665
Phone: 770 859-9161
Web: WWW.SCIRES.COM

COMPETITORS

Boeing	ManTech
CACI International	Northrop Grumman
Computer Sciences	QinetiQ
Corp.	Raytheon
HP Enterprise Services	Research Triangle
Leidos	Institute
Lockheed Martin	Serco Inc.
Long Wave	

HISTORICAL FINANCIALS

Company Type: Private

Income Statement

FYE: December 31

	REVENUE ($ mil.)	NET INCOME ($ mil.)	NET PROFIT MARGIN	EMPLOYEES
12/13	372	24	6.7%	1,006
12/12	360	26	7.3%	—
12/11	326	21	6.7%	—
12/10	322	0		—
Annual Growth	4.9%	—		—

2013 Year-End Financials

Return on assets: 7.6%
Return on equity: 6.7%
Current ratio: 1.40

Cash ($ mil.): 26

SCL HEALTH - FRONT RANGE INC.

Exempla aims to provide exemplary health care to residents in the Denver area. The Exempla medical network operating as Exempla Healthcare includes three hospitals: Exempla Saint Joseph Hospital (570 beds) Exempla Lutheran Medical Center (400 beds) and Good Samaritan Medical Center (more than 230 beds). It also operates the Exempla Physician Network a chain of primary care clinics. The company employs more than 2100 physicians. Among its specialties are cardiovascular services and surgeries rehabilitation cancer care orthopedics and women's and children's services. Exempla Healthcare is sponsored by the Catholic faith-based Sisters of Charity of Leavenworth Health System (SCL Health System).

Strategy

Exempla is investing in expansion of the facilities at Lutheran Medical Center. It is also constructing a new building for Saint Joseph Hospital that is set to open in 2015.

Ownership

Exempla Healthcare was sponsored by two not-for-profit organizations —SCL Health System and the Lutheran-sponsored Community First Foundation —until 2012 when SCL Health System acquired the CFF interest in a deal worth some $275 million. SCL Health System had already gained management oversight of the Exempla facilities in 2009.

Company Background

Exempla Healthcare was formed in 1998 when Saint Joseph Hospital and Lutheran Medical Center combined.

EXECUTIVES

Vice President Finance, Judy Boller
Evp And Chief Population Health Officer, Richard T Lopes
Evp And Cfo, Lydia W Jumonville
Vice President Human Resources, Scott Day
Svp Chief Communications And Marketing Officer, Christine Woolsey
Vice President Of Human Resources, Amy Pacey
Vice President Payer Strategies Legislative Affairs, Debbie Welle-Powell
Medical Records Director, Bob Manner
Vice President and Chief Nursing Officer, Susan (Sue) Kerschen
Vice President of Information Technology, Benjamin (Ben) Malanga
Auditors: ERNST & YOUNG US LLP PHOENIX

LOCATIONS

HQ: SCL HEALTH - FRONT RANGE INC.
2420 W 26TH AVE STE 100D, DENVER, CO 802115302
Phone: 303 813-5000

PRODUCTS/OPERATIONS

2009 Revenues

	$ mil.	% of total
Exempla Saint Joseph Hospital	377	40
Exempla Lutheran Medical Center	302	32
Exempla Good Samaritan Medical Center	217	23
Exempla Physician Network	22	2
Colorado Lutheran Home & Exempla West Pines Behavioral Health	22	2
Exempla Lutheran Collier Hospice	6	1
Total	948	100

COMPETITORS

Catholic Health Initiatives
Centura Health
Denver Health and Hospital Authority
HealthONE
Porter Adventist Hospital
Presbyterian/St. Luke's Medical Center
Rose Medical Center
University of Colorado Hospital

HISTORICAL FINANCIALS

Company Type: Private

Income Statement
FYE: December 31

	REVENUE ($ mil.)	NET INCOME ($ mil.)	NET PROFIT MARGIN	EMPLOYEES
12/09	597	7	1.3%	5,300
12/05	472	30	6.5%	—
12/04	335	37	11.2%	—
12/02	267	0	—	—
Annual Growth	12.2%	—	—	—

2009 Year-End Financials

Return on assets: —
Return on equity: 1.3%
Current ratio: 0.40
Cash ($ mil.): 53

SCOTT & WHITE HEALTH PLAN

The Scott & White Health Plan (SWHP) works to keep its members Safe & Well. The not-for-profit company provides health insurance plans and related services to more than 200000 members across some 50 counties in and around Central Texas. Owned by the Scott & White network of hospitals and clinics SWHP has employer-sponsored plans (including HMO PPO and consumer choice options) as well as several choices for individuals and families. It also offers COBRA state-administered continuation plans the Young Texan Health Plan for children Medicare and dental and vision benefits. The company began offering its services in 1982. Owner Scott & White is exploring a merger with Baylor Health Care System.

In late 2012 the boards of Scott & White and Baylor Health Care System signed an agreement of their intent to merge to form a $7.7 billion organization called Baylor Scott & White Health. The combined organization will be the largest not-for-profit health system in Texas with 42 hospitals more than 350 patient care sites more than 4000 active physicians 34000 employees and the Scott & White Health Plan.

EXECUTIVES

Associate Vice President Marketing Communications And Brand Strategy, Sarah Mackey
Auditors: ERNST & YOUNG US LLP INDIANAP

LOCATIONS

HQ: SCOTT & WHITE HEALTH PLAN
1206 WEST CAMPUS DR, TEMPLE, TX 765027124
Phone: 254 298-3000
Web: WWW.SW.ORG

PRODUCTS/OPERATIONS

Selected Products

Employer plans
Individual and family plans
Medicare plans
Vital Care programs

COMPETITORS

Aetna
Blue Cross and Blue Shield of Texas
CIGNA
Centene
Humana
Texas Health Resources
USHEALTH Group
UnitedHealth Group

HISTORICAL FINANCIALS

Company Type: Private

Income Statement
FYE: December 31

	REVENUE ($ mil.)	NET INCOME ($ mil.)	NET PROFIT MARGIN	EMPLOYEES
12/09	660	13	2.0%	426
12/08	621	(4)	—	—
12/07	586	8	1.4%	—
12/06	557	0	—	—
Annual Growth	5.8%	—	—	—

2009 Year-End Financials

Return on assets: —
Return on equity: 2.0%
Current ratio: 1.40
Cash ($ mil.): 8

SCOTT EQUIPMENT COMPANY L.L.C.

Scott Equipment Company sells and rents construction and farm equipment through some 25 locations located in the South and Midwest. The company also offers parts and service financing and insurance. Scott Equipment is part of the Scott family of companies which also includes Scott Toyota Lift (material handling) Scott Irrigation (pivot irrigation systems) and Scott Truck (sales leasing and service). The company's beginnings date back to 1939 when Tom Scott founded Scott Truck & Tractor. It is operated by descendants of the founder. Scott Equipment has shut down several agricultural stores (Scott Tractor) to focus on its Construction Equipment division.

EXECUTIVES

Vice President, Jesse Fallin
Vice President, Jay Lee
Vice President, Lance Pankey

LOCATIONS

HQ: SCOTT EQUIPMENT COMPANY L.L.C.
1000 MARTIN LUTHER KING J, MONROE, LA 712035543
Phone: 318 387-4160
Web: WWW.SCOTTCOMPANIES.COM

COMPETITORS

Briggs Equipment	Komatsu America
Deere	Mustang CAT
H&E Equipment	Rain Bird Corporation
J. A. Riggs Tractor	Van Keppel

HISTORICAL FINANCIALS

Company Type: Private

Income Statement
FYE: December 31

	REVENUE ($ mil.)	NET INCOME ($ mil.)	NET PROFIT MARGIN	EMPLOYEES
12/08	317	12	4.0%	525
12/07	323	17	5.5%	—
12/06	299	6	2.1%	—
12/05	265	0	—	—
Annual Growth	6.1%	—	—	—

2008 Year-End Financials

Return on assets: 2.9%
Return on equity: 4.0%
Current ratio: 0.20
Cash ($ mil.): —

SCOTTSDALE HEALTHCARE CORP.

Scottsdale Healthcare a not-for-profit organization serves the health care needs of central Arizona residents. Its operations include three acute care hospitals that combined boast some 900 beds. Scottsdale Healthcare also operates other campuses that offer physician offices a cancer center home health and other health care services. It conducts clinical research through the Scottsdale Healthcare Research Institute. The group's Essential Touch Wellness Center and Boutique provides spa-like stress-reduction therapies. With nearly 2000 medical and surgical staff members the company offers some 35 medical specialties. Scottsdale Healthcare is an affiliate of Scottsdale Lincoln Health Network along with John C. Lincoln Health Network.

Operations

The group's hospitals are Scottsdale Healthcare Osborn Medical Center (trauma orthopedics neurosurgery cardiovascular and critical care) Scottsdale Healthcare Shea Medical Center (full-service hospital including emergency medical and surgical critical care cardiovascular and oncology services) and Scottsdale Healthcare Thompson Peak (patient-family centered medical/surgical hospital). Additionally Scottsdale Healthcare operates five Urgent Care Plus clinics the Piper Outpatient Surgery Center at the Shea Medical Center the Greenbaum Surgical Specialty Hospital at Osborn Medical center and the Scottsdale Healthcare Primary Care network of primary care physicians.

Geographic Reach

Scottsdale Healthcare serves central Arizona specifically in an around the entire Northeast Valley as well as the area north of Loop 101.

Strategy

Since 2012 the health care network has been expanding into Northeast Phoenix to deepen its relationships with community physicians and diversify beyond its three-hospital Scottsdale campuses. To this end it opened new Scottsdale Healthcare Primary Care physician offices in 2013 —one each in Phoenix and Tempe —to join existing locations in Arcadia Scottsdale and Grayhawk.

What makes Scottsdale Healthcare stand out is its military training program the only one of its kind in the country. Its Readiness Skill Sustainment Training Program gives National Guard Air Force Reserve and nearby Air Force base personnel 12 days of training in treating trauma burns and other wounds they might encounter when deployed in a war zone. Participants also work in intensive care ride along with EMS personnel and get orthopedics and operating room practice. It has since expanded the program to include a $1.6-million military trauma training center which serves military medical personnel with classroom and simulation training and trains civilian paramedics and firefighters.

The organization performs clinical research through the Scottsdale Healthcare Research Institute. Through the institute the organization conducts clinical trials in a range of disciplines including cancer and other complex diseases.

In 2014 Scottsdale Healthcare formed an affiliation with John C. Lincoln Health Network. The combined networks operating under the moniker Scottsdale Lincoln Health Network include five hospitals with some 3700 affiliated physicians and an extensive outpatient services network.

The group opened a new 28-bed unit at its Scottsdale Healthcare Thompson Peak Hospital in 2013. The unit provides care to orthopedic and spine surgery patients.

Company Background

Scottsdale Healthcare was established in 1962 as City Hospital of Scottsdale.

EXECUTIVES

Senior Vice President Medical Affairs, James (Jamie) Burke
Vice President Integrated Delivery Network, Lois Uniat
Vice President Clinical Service Lines Business Development, Dean Thomas
Vice President Marketing and Business Development, Dave Barber
Director Of Nursing, Jody Fay
Senior Vice President Chief Talent Officer, Carol Henderson
Director of Nursing, Susan (Sue) Angelides

Vice President Information Systems and Information Technology, Thomas (Thom) Sadvary
Senior Vice President and Chief Clinical Officer, Joanne Clavelle
Vice President and Chief Nurse Executive, Kathi Zarubi
Vice President and Administrator Thompson Peak Hospital, Kim Post
Senior Vice President General Counsel, Alan (Al) Kelly
Executive Vice President Healthcare Operations, Gary Baker
Vice President Research, Mark Slater
Vice President Operations Osborn Campus, Vikki Noyes
Vice Chairman, Brad Gazaway
Auditors: ERNST & YOUNG LLP PHOENIX AZ

LOCATIONS

HQ: SCOTTSDALE HEALTHCARE CORP.
8125 N HAYDEN RD, SCOTTSDALE, AZ 852582463
Phone: 480 882-4000
Web: WWW.SHC.ORG

PRODUCTS/OPERATIONS

Selected Services
Bariatric Weight Loss Surgery
Cancer Care
Community Health
Corporate Health
Diabetes Management
Diagnostic Imaging Services
Digestive Health
Emergency Services
Heart & Vascular
Home Health Services
Infusion & Treatment Services
Minimally Invasive Surgery
Neurosciences
Nutrition Services
Orthopedic Services
Outpatient Therapy Services
Pediatrics
Sleep Disorders Center
Trauma Center
Wound Management
Urgent Care Plus
Urology Services

COMPETITORS

Banner Health
Community Health Systems
Dignity Health
Flagstaff Medical Center
Iasis Healthcare
Mayo Clinic
Phoenix Children's Hospital

St. Joseph Health System
Sun Health
Universal Health Services
University of Arizona Health Network
Yuma Regional Medical Center

HISTORICAL FINANCIALS
Company Type: Private

Income Statement
FYE: September 30

	REVENUE ($ mil.)	NET INCOME ($ mil.)	NET PROFIT MARGIN	EMPLOYEES
09/13	862	33	3.9%	6,500
09/09	808	11	1.5%	—
09/07	748	67	9.0%	—
Annual Growth	2.4%	(10.9%)	—	—

2013 Year-End Financials
Return on assets: 6.6%
Return on equity: 3.9%
Current ratio: 2.20
Cash ($ mil.): 18

SCOTTSDALE HEALTHCARE HOSPITALS

Auditors: ERNST & YOUNG US LLP PHOENI

LOCATIONS

HQ: SCOTTSDALE HEALTHCARE HOSPITALS
7400 E OSBORN RD, SCOTTSDALE, AZ 852516432
Phone: 480 882-4000
Web: WWW.SHC.ORG

HISTORICAL FINANCIALS
Company Type: Private

Income Statement
FYE: September 30

	REVENUE ($ mil.)	NET INCOME ($ mil.)	NET PROFIT MARGIN	EMPLOYEES
09/09	847	4	0.5%	3,500
09/08*	812	(17)	—	—
06/06	528	0	—	—
Annual Growth	17.1%	—	—	—

*Fiscal year change

2009 Year-End Financials
Return on assets: —
Return on equity: 0.5%
Current ratio: 2.10
Cash ($ mil.): 37

SCRIPPS HEALTH

Scripps Health houses many a script-writing physician in its hospitals. The not-for-profit health system serves the San Diego area through four acute-care hospitals on five campuses. Altogether the health system is home to 1400 inpatient beds and a network of outpatient clinics. The system also offers home health care and operates community outreach programs. Its hospitals along with more than 20 outpatient Scripps Clinic and Scripps Coastal Medical Center locations employ more than 2600 affiliated general practice and specialty physicians. The Scripps Health Foundation raises philanthropic funds for Scripps Health is affiliated with biomedical research center The Scripps Research Institute.

Operations

The health network's facilities include the 700-bed Scripps Mercy Hospital which has a main campus in San Diego and a satellite campus in Chula Vista as well as Scripps Green Hospital (173 beds in La Jolla) Scripps Memorial Hospital Encinitas (160 beds) and Scripps Memorial Hospital La Jolla (382 beds). Scripps Health is also the official health care provider for the San Diego Padres baseball team.

Financial Performance

The not-for-profit Scripps Health organization reported about $2.6 billion in revenues in 2013 (up 2% on 2012) thanks to an increase of $20 million received from theCapitation premium. Net assets-released revenues rose by 43% compared to 2012.Scripps Health's net income decreased by 9% in 2013 due to higher operating expenses (an increase in wages and benefits expenses of $30 million together with higher services expenses partially offset by higher sales and gains from investment income).Driven by higher current assets and account payable and accrued liabilities the health network's cash flow in operating activities rose to $299.4 million in 2013 (from $145.9 million in 2012).

Strategy

The health system's overall strategy is to remain on the cutting edge of technology in order to treat patients more effectively therefore reporting better patient outcomes (making itself eligible for certain government incentives). It also aims to make itself the destination of choice for patients (both locally and globally) for heart cancer care and other types of specialty care. While Scripps Health continues to grow the company keeps an eye on its bottom line continuing to evaluate its budget on a regular basis to reduce expenses when necessary.

As a major provider in the larger San Diego area Scripps Health is constantly evaluating its scope of services to meet ever-increasing demand for health care. The company is building several outpatient clinics including cancer treatment and cardiac care centers. It is also expanding and upgrading its hospitals; for instance the La Jolla hospital is adding a $456 million 170-bed cardiovascular institute (scheduled to open in 2015). In 2014 the health network opened the Leichtag Foundation Critical Care Pavilion a $94 million emergency department and inpatient care facility on the campus of Scripps Memorial Hospital Encinitas.

In addition Scripps Health has launched an initiative to increase the number of clinical trials conducted at its facilities in partnership with pharmaceutical and medical device companies. In 2014 Scripps Health teamed up with SCAN Health Plan in a co-branding agreement to explore and develop new products and services designed to serve the growing senior population by launching of the SCAN Medicare Advantage plan in San Diego County.

HISTORY

Scripps Health was founded by Ellen Browning Scripps in 1924 when the Scripps Memorial Hospital and Scripps Metabolic Clinic opened in La Jolla.

The network grew through the opening of Scripps Green Hospital in 1977 and the Scripps Memorial Hospital Encinitas campus was added through the purchase of San Dieguito Hospital the following year.

Scripps Mercy Hospital which was first established in 1890 in San Diego joined the Scripps network in 1995.

The Scripps Health system expanded once again when it acquired the Scripps Mercy Hospital Chula Vista campus in 2004.

EXECUTIVES

SVP and Chief Executive Scripps Green Hospital, Robin B. Brown
SVP and Chief Executive Scripps Memorial Hospital La Jolla, Gary G. Fybel
SVP and Chief Executive Scripps Mercy Hospital and Scripps Memorial Hospital Chula Vista, Tom Gammiere
Corporate EVP and CFO, Richard K. Rothberger
SVP and Chief Executive Scripps Memorial Hospital Encinitas, Carl J. Etter
President and CEO, Christopher D. Van Gorder
Corporate SVP and Chief Medical Officer, James LaBelle
SVP and Chief Executive Scripps Medical Foundation, Shiraz M. Fagan
Corporate SVP and CIO, Andy Crowder
Director of Physical Therapy, Alan (Al) Ferrarelli
Director Of Radiology, William Marshall

Medical Director, Renee Smilde
Vice President Of Financial Services, David (Dave) Cohn
Vice President Medical Services Regional Sites, Peter D (Pete) Aldrich
Vice President Medicine Services and Academic Affairs, Gary W Williams
Senior Vice President Human Resources and Interim Employee Training and Devel, Vic Buzachero
Corporate Senior Vice President General Counsel and Corporate Secretary, Richard (Dick) Sheridan
Vice Chair, Maureen A Stapleton
Auditors: ERNST & YOUNG LLP SAN DIEGO

LOCATIONS

HQ: SCRIPPS HEALTH
4275 CAMPUS POINT CT, SAN DIEGO, CA 921211513
Phone: 858 678-7000
Web: WWW.SCRIPPS.ORG

Selected California Facilities
Scripps Clinic (outpatient centers)
Scripps Coastal Medical Center (outpatient centers formerly Scripps Mercy Medical Group)
Scripps Green Hospital (La Jolla)
Scripps Memorial Hospital Encinitas
Scripps Memorial Hospital La Jolla
Scripps Mercy Hospital (San Diego)
Scripps Mercy Hospital Chula Vista

PRODUCTS/OPERATIONS

2013 Sales

	$ mil.	% of total
Patient service (net)	2,249	85
Capitation (contract) premium	250	11
Net assets released	19	1
Meaningful use	20	1
Other	68	2
Total	**2,609**	**100**

COMPETITORS

Adventist Health
Cedars-Sinai Medical Center
Community Health Systems
Dignity Health
Good Samaritan Hospital (IN)
Grossmont Hospital
HCA
Los Angeles County Health Department
Mayo Clinic
Palomar Health
Paradise Valley Hospital
Prospect Medical
Providence Saint Joseph Medical Center
Rady Children' s Hospital
Sharp HealthCare
St. Joseph Health System
Tenet Healthcare
Tri-City Healthcare District
UCSD Medical

HISTORICAL FINANCIALS
Company Type: Private

Income Statement
FYE: September 30

	REVENUE ($ mil.)	NET INCOME ($ mil.)	NET PROFIT MARGIN	EMPLOYEES
09/13	2,654	311	11.7%	13,445
09/08	1,953	18	0.9%	—
09/07	1,781	223	12.6%	—
Annual Growth	**6.9%**	**5.7%**	**—**	**—**

2013 Year-End Financials
Return on assets: 13.7%
Return on equity: 11.7%
Current ratio: 0.80
Cash ($ mil.): 640

SEACOAST NURSING AND REHABILITATION CENTER INC

Auditors: PRICEWATERHOUSECOOPERS LLP LO

LOCATIONS

HQ: SEACOAST NURSING AND REHABILITATION CENTER INC
292 WASHINGTON ST, GLOUCESTER, MA 019304832
Phone: 978 283-0300
Web: WWW.BEVERLYHOSPITAL.ORG

HISTORICAL FINANCIALS
Company Type: Private

Income Statement
FYE: September 30

	REVENUE ($ mil.)	NET INCOME ($ mil.)	NET PROFIT MARGIN	EMPLOYEES
09/09	1,421	69	4.9%	172
09/08	14	0	4.9%	—
09/02	9	0	4.9%	—
09/01	8	0	—	—
Annual Growth	**88.6%**	**—**	**—**	**—**

2009 Year-End Financials
Return on assets: —
Return on equity: 4.9%
Current ratio: 2.30
Cash ($ mil.): 2

SEALASKA CORPORATION

Sealaska Corporation is a native-owned investment firm active in natural resources manufacturing services and gaming. The holding company owns land in southeastern Alaska home to the Tlingit Haida and Tsimshian peoples. Sealaska core holdings include Sealaska Timber Corporation Alaska Coastal Aggregates Sealaska Constructors Sealaska Environmental Services and Colorado-based information technology services provider Managed Business Solutions. Subsidary End-to-End Enterprises manages the company's gaming business. Sealaska's subsidiaries operate throughout North America and around the world. Its companies often win government contracts for construction environmental and engineering projects.

Geographic Reach

Juneau-based Sealaska has offices through the US and several other countries including Canada and Mexico as well as Europe.

Operations

About 60% of Sealaska's revenues come from its services segment which includes subsidiary Sealaksa Environmental Services Sealaksa Constructors Synergy Systems and Managed Business Solutions.

More than 25% of Sealaska's revenues are earned by its natural resources business which oversees land management and stewardship functions for all Sealaska lands. Sealaska owns about 290000 acres of timberland as well as the minerals rights to construction-grade aggregates on more than 565000 acres. Sealaska Timber harvest timber and markets logs for the domestic and export markets.

The company's manufacturing arm consists mainly of injection-molded plastics maker Nypro Kánaak which is a joint venture with Massachusetts-based Nypro. The division grew its revenue by 30% in 2011 after landing two major clients (Clorox and SC Johnson). Kraft also is another major client. In 2011 Sealaska shut down its mechanical parts manufacturer Olympic Fabrication.

The company also invests in stocks bonds and private equity.

Financial Performance

Sealaska reported revenue of $165 million in 2013 a 22% decline versus 2012. The double-digit decline was primarily due to falling revenue in the service business resulting from a decrease in civil construction in Hawaii offset partially by progress in other regions. (The firm is attempting to minimize its losses in Hawaii.) Revenue from Sealaska's natural resources business also fell year over year while gaming posted a gain. The gaming business segment produced revenues of $374000 in 2013 up from $343000 in 2012.

The company swung to a net loss of $33.3 million in 2013 compared with a profit of $13.4 million in 2012 dragged down by construction costs on two projects in Hawaii in the amount of $26 million. Cash from operating activities decreased to $15.6 million in 2013 over $39.6 million the prior year due to a loss on the sale of its interest in its Nypro Kánaak joint venture.

Strategy

In 2012 the company adopted a five-year plan designed to transform Sealaska into a financially sustainable and profitable company driven by its core cultural values. To that end in 2013 the company sold its interest in its Nypro Kánaak joint venture and the Sealaska Global Logistics business and exited the security guard services business (acquired in 2010) to support future acquisitions.

Subsidiary Haa Aaní (meaning "our land") was established in 2009 as a way to promote the culture social and economic viability of Southeast Alaska. Haa Aaní has assisted tribal members with their efforts to establish businesses such as a new oyster farms in southeastern Alaska. Haa Aaní also promotes renewable energy initiatives such as a biomass heating system for commercial buildings. In 2012 Haa Aaní launched a non-profit community development financial institution in order to provide financing and promote economic development.

Sealaska's also is developing a gaming casino and resort in Cloverdale California north of San Francisco. The corporation through its End-to-End Enterprises subsidiary is partners with the Pomo Indians of California on the project.

Company Background

Sealaska is the largest of 13 corporations formed under the Alaska Native Claims Settlement Act (ANCSA) of 1971 which promised some 44 million acres of land to Alaska natives. The company is owned by some 21600 tribal member shareholders.

EXECUTIVES

EVP, Richard P. (Rick) Harris, $240,000 total compensation
President and CEO, Chris E. McNeil, $350,000 total compensation
Manager Information Systems, Robert (Rob) Johnson
VP and CFO, Doug Morris
President & CEO Haa Aan LLC, Russell A. Dick
President and CEO, Anthony Mallott
Manager Natural Resources, Ron Wolfe

President and CEO Sealaska Timber Corporation (STC), Wade Zammit
President and CEO Sealaska Environmental Services, Derik Frederiksen
President and CEO Managed Business Solutions (MBS) and MBS Systems, Jon Duncan
COO, Terry Downes
COO Sealaska Environmental Services, Lewis Ivers
General Counsel And Vice President, Jaeleen Araujo
Chairman, Albert M. Kookesh, age 66
Vice Chair, Rosita F. Worl, age 77
Board Member, Bill Thomas
Auditors: KPMG LLP ANCHORAGE ALASKA

LOCATIONS

HQ: SEALASKA CORPORATION
1 SEALASKA PLZ STE 400, JUNEAU, AK 998011276
Phone: 907 586-1512

PRODUCTS/OPERATIONS

2013 Sales

	$ mil.	% of total
Services	102	62
Natural Resources	45	28
Investments	16	10
Gaming	0	-
Corporate & other	0	-
Total	**164**	**100**

Selected Subsidiaries

Alaska Coastal Aggregates
End-to-End Enterprises LLC (gaming)
Haa Aaní LLC
Managed Business Solutions (majority owned)
Sealaska Constructors LLC
Sealaska Environmental Services
Sealaska Timber Corporation

COMPETITORS

Plum Creek Timber	West Fraser Timber
Tembec	chugach alaska

HISTORICAL FINANCIALS

Company Type: Private

Income Statement

FYE: December 31

	REVENUE ($ mil.)	NET INCOME ($ mil.)	NET PROFIT MARGIN	EMPLOYEES
12/13	164	(33)	—	1,400
12/12	311	13	4.3%	—
12/11	259	8	3.2%	—
12/10	223	0	—	—
Annual Growth	(9.7%)	—	—	—

2013 Year-End Financials

Return on assets: 5.3%
Return on equity: (-20.2%)
Current ratio: 0.40
Cash ($ mil.): 32

SEALY & SMITH FOUNDATION

Auditors: HEAD MAXWELL & MCKENNA PC

LOCATIONS

HQ: SEALY & SMITH FOUNDATION
2200 MARKET ST STE 500, GALVESTON, TX 775501532
Phone: 409 762-8666

HISTORICAL FINANCIALS

Company Type: Private

Income Statement

FYE: December 31

	ASSETS ($ mil.)	NET INCOME ($ mil.)	INCOME AS % OF ASSETS	EMPLOYEES
12/13	1,065	52	5.0%	6
12/10	832	14	1.8%	—
12/09	767	12	1.6%	—
12/08	1	0	—	—
Annual Growth	268.8%	—	—	—

2013 Year-End Financials

Return on assets: 0.2%
Return on equity: 80.0%
Sales ($ mil): 65

SEATTLE CANCER CARE ALLIANCE

Auditors: CLARK NUBER PS BELLEVUE WA

LOCATIONS

HQ: SEATTLE CANCER CARE ALLIANCE
825 EASTLAKE AVE E, SEATTLE, WA 981094405
Phone: 206 288-7222
Web: WWW.SEATTLECCA.ORG

HISTORICAL FINANCIALS

Company Type: Private

Income Statement

FYE: June 30

	REVENUE ($ mil.)	NET INCOME ($ mil.)	NET PROFIT MARGIN	EMPLOYEES
06/13	392	27	6.9%	745
06/10	0	(2)	—	—
06/09	234	20	8.6%	—
06/08	268	0	—	—
Annual Growth	7.9%	—	—	—

2013 Year-End Financials

Return on assets: 14.1%
Return on equity: 6.9%
Current ratio: 0.60
Cash ($ mil.): 48

SEATTLE CHILDREN'S HOSPITAL

Children's Hospital and Regional Medical Center was a big name for little kids so they changed it to what everyone already used: Seattle Children's. The hospital which has some 325 beds serves children and infants of all ages. Its specialty units include psychiatric care neonatal intensive care and rehabilitation for children disabled by injuries illness or congenital complications. In addition to its primary campus Seattle Children's Hospital operates numerous outpatient clinics in the

Puget Sound area. It also provides outreach services throughout the Pacific Northwest as well as in Alaska and Montana. Seattle Children's Hospital provides telemedicine services in Idaho.

Geographic Reach

Seattle Children's Hospital serves the largest landmass of any children's hospital in the country (Washington Alaska Montana and Idaho).

Its outreach clinics in Alaska and Montana provide specialty care through physicians and nurses who travel to rural communities in each state. In Idaho videoconferencing brings specialty services to rural communities that would not otherwise have access to them.

Sales and Marketing

The hospital runs a program called the Medical-Legal Partnership for Children that provides assistance to low-income families with children receiving medical treatment at its Odessa Brown Children's Clinic (OBCC) or its Harborview Children and Teens Clinic (HCTC).

Through the project patients facing family law issues such as custody domestic abuse or access to public benefits are provided an attorney through the Northwest Justice Project. In addition a staff attorney trains physicians and social workers to recognize legal problems that may affect a child's health and also provide direct legal services and referrals for patients at OBCC and HCTC.

Strategy

Seattle Children's keeps expanding throughout its service areas by opening additional clinics (urgent care specialty and primary care). The hospital is also increasing the size of its main hospital by adding an additional 350 beds in four phases over the next two decades. Once the project is complete Seattle Children's will house roughly 600 beds —something the medical providers there will welcome since the hospital operates at near capacity the majority of the time.

EXECUTIVES

CEO, Thomas N. Hansen
President Seattle Children's Research Institute, James B. Hendricks
SVP and CFO, Kelly Wallace
SVP and Chief Academic Officer, F. Bruder Stapleton
SVP and Surgeon-in-Chief; President CUMG, Robert S. Sawin
SVP Hospital Operations, Cindy Evans Gazecki
SVP and Chief Nursing Officer, Susan Heath
President Seattle Children's Hospital and Research Foundation, Douglas Picha
Chief Data Officer, Eugene Kolker
SVP and Chief Administrative Officer, Lisa Brandenburg
Chief Medical Information Officer, Troy L. McGuire
Chief Information Security Officer, Cris V. Ewell
SVP and Chief Medical Officer, Mark A. Del Beccaro
SVP and CIO, Jeff Brown
Director Of Radiology, Kim Cecil
Director Of Radiology, Christopher Anton
Chief Academic Officer And Senior Vice President, F Stapleton
Chairman, Judy Holder

LOCATIONS

HQ: SEATTLE CHILDREN' S HOSPITAL
4800 SAND POINT WAY NE, SEATTLE, WA 981053901
Phone: 206 987-2000
Web: WWW.UWMEDICINE.ORG

Selected Locations – Washington State
After Hours Clinic
Bellevue Clinic and Surgery Center
Children' s at Overlake
Everett Clinic
Federal Way Clinic
Odessa Brown Children' s Clinic
Olympia Clinic

Seattle Children' s Hospital
Tri-Cities Clinic

PRODUCTS/OPERATIONS

Selected Specialty Programs
Audiology
Dental Medicine
Endocrinology and Diabetes
Gastroenterology
Genetics
Neurodevelopmental
Neurology
Otolaryngology
Psychiatry and Behavioral Medicine
Radiology
Urology

COMPETITORS

Franciscan Health System
Group Health Cooperative (Puget Sound)
Harrison Medical Center
MultiCare Health System
Overlake Hospital
PeaceHealth
Providence Health & Services
Shriners Hospitals For Children
Swedish Health Services
Yakima Valley Memorial

HISTORICAL FINANCIALS
Company Type: Private

Income Statement

	REVENUE ($ mil.)	NET INCOME ($ mil.)	NET PROFIT MARGIN	EMPLOYEES
				FYE: September 30
09/13	1,018	192	18.9%	2,800
09/12	814	150	18.5%	—
Annual Growth	25.1%	27.9%	—	—

2013 Year-End Financials

Return on assets: 4.3%   Cash ($ mil.): 32
Return on equity: 18.9%
Current ratio: 1.20

SEATTLE UNIVERSITY

Seattle University isn't very big but as one of 28 Jesuit universities in the US it is part of a Roman Catholic teaching legacy that spans the country and the world. With an enrollment of about 7500 students the school offers 64 undergraduate more than 35 graduate degree programs and 28 certificate programs through its eight schools (College of Arts and Sciences Albers School of Business and Economics College of Education School of Law Matteo Ricci College College of Nursing College of Science and Engineering and School of Theology and Ministry).

Operations

In 2012 Seattle University had 4589 undergraduate students and 1933 graduate students. Some 40% of the first year students were from Washington State and some 7% of all students were from outside the US.

The average class size is 19 and the faculty-to-student ratio is 1 to 13.

Financial Performance

In 2012 the university reported a 10% decrease in revenues due to a drop in investment income a loss incurred in net realized and unrealized losses on investments and a change in value of interest rate swap agreements.

Its net income declined by 90% in 2012 due to a decrease in revenues and an increase in expenses

attributed largely to higher costs for instruction academic support and auxiliary enterprises.

StrategyGrowing its portfolio of degree programs in 2012 Seattle University's Albers School of Business and Economics added the Bridge MBA to its family of graduate degrees.

Company Background

Seattle University was founded in 1891 by two Jesuit priests.

EXECUTIVES

Executive Vice President, Stephen (Steve) Sundborg
Vice President For Communications, Scott McClellan
Executive Vice President Timothy P. Leary, Timothy (Tim) Leary
Executive Vice President, Tram Le
Associate Vice President for Development, Kim Isaac
Vice President, Amy Matsunaga
Vice President Of Ambiance Choir, Mara Silvers
Associate Vice President for Finance and Investments, Andrew (Andy) O'Boyle
Associate Vice President Of Facilities, Robert (Bob) Schwartz
Senior Management (Senior Vice President General Manager Director), Valerie Ross
Executive Vice President, Matthew Frix
secretary of Girl Up, Rukhsar Palla
Advisory Board Member, Jeff Bottorff

LOCATIONS

HQ: SEATTLE UNIVERSITY
901 12TH AVE, SEATTLE, WA 981224411
Phone: 206 296-6150
Web: WWW.LAW.SEATTLEU.EDU

PRODUCTS/OPERATIONS

Schools and Colleges
Albers School of Business and Economics
College of Arts and Sciences
College of Education
College of Nursing
College of Science and Engineering
Matteo Ricci College
School of Law
School of Theology and Ministry

COMPETITORS

University of Washington
Washington State University
Western Washington University

HISTORICAL FINANCIALS
Company Type: Private

Income Statement

	REVENUE ($ mil.)	NET INCOME ($ mil.)	NET PROFIT MARGIN	EMPLOYEES
				FYE: June 30
06/13	277	1	0.5%	1,100
06/10	236	11	4.9%	—
06/09	236	0	—	—
06/08	0	0	—	—
Annual Growth	—	—	—	—

2013 Year-End Financials

Return on assets: 9.5%   Cash ($ mil.): 45
Return on equity: 0.5%
Current ratio: 0.30

SECURITIES INVESTOR PROTECTION CORPORATION

Securities Investor Protection Corporation (SIPC) is an industry-financed insurance plan that protects clients of most broker-dealers registered with the US Securities and Exchange Commission (SEC). SIPC insures customers' securities (up to $500000 per account) against losses due to the financial failure of brokerage firms. Losses caused by fluctuations in market value are not protected. The not-for-profit membership corporation was mandated by the Securities Investor Protection Act and has more than 6000 members. Its board is appointed by the US president the treasury secretary and the Federal Reserve Board. Assessments from members and investments in government securities provide money for the SIPC Fund.

While SIPC will replace missing cash and hard securities (stocks and bonds) it doesn't protect less tangible investments such as commodity futures or investment contracts. Nor does it insure against fraud.

As investment firms imploded throughout 2008 SIPC shifted into high gear to process more than 900000 claims from customers and creditors of Lehman Brothers and more than 15000 claims from investors in Bernard L. Madoff Investment Securities. By late 2009 SIPC was looking at potential payouts of $534 million to former Madoff investors —greater than the sum total of its payouts since it was created in 1970.

During 2011 the firm disagreed with the SEC's efforts to make it pay customers of fraudster R. Allen Stanford. SIPC contends that while Stanford Group was a member of SIPC the defrauded customers didn't lose their money in a failed brokerage.

EXECUTIVES

Vice President Operations, Karen Saperstein

LOCATIONS

HQ: SECURITIES INVESTOR PROTECTION CORPORATION
805 15TH ST NW STE 800, WASHINGTON, DC
200052207
Phone: 202 371-8300
Web: WWW.SIPC.ORG

HISTORICAL FINANCIALS

Company Type: Private

Income Statement

	ASSETS ($ mil.)	NET INCOME ($ mil.)	INCOME AS % OF ASSETS	EMPLOYEES
12/12	1,912	512	26.8%	35
12/11	1,606	131	8.2%	—
12/10	1,382	(271)	—	—
12/09	1,307	0	—	—
Annual Growth	13.5%	—	—	—

2012 Year-End Financials

Return on assets: —
Return on equity: 113.2%
Sales ($ mil): 452

SECURITY FINANCE CORPORATION OF SPARTANBURG

Folks looking for a little financial security just might turn to Security Finance Corporation of Spartanburg. Founded in 1955 the consumer loan company provides personal loans typically ranging from $100 to $600 (some states however allow loan amounts as high as $3000). Customers can also turn to Security Finance for credit reports and tax preparation services. The company operates approximately 900 offices in more than 15 states that are marketed under the Security Finance Sunbelt Credit and PFS banner names. A subsidiary of Security Group the financial institution also has locations operating as Security Financial Services in North Carolina and Longhorn Finance in Texas.

Geographic Reach

From its headquarters in South Carolina Security Finance boasts offices in more than 15 states nationwide.

Operations

Security Finance boasts some 900 offices nationwide that operate under the Security Finance Sunbelt Credit and PFS names. The company specializes in offering consumers loans to individuals. It also provides consumer credit reports and assistance as well as tax preparation services.

Company Background

Security Finance exited Colorado in 2010 after the state's attorney general general office filed a compliant that the company had been refinancing some consumer loans more than three times a year (the limit under Colorado law). The company agreed to repay acquisition fees that it had charged the customers for refinancing the loans.
Auditors: ELLIOTT DAVIS LLC GREENVILLE

LOCATIONS

HQ: SECURITY FINANCE CORPORATION OF SPARTANBURG
181 SECURITY PL, SPARTANBURG, SC 293075450
Phone: 864 582-8193
Web: WWW.SECURITY-FINANCE.COM

Selected Locations

Alabama
Florida
Georgia
Idaho
Illinois
Louisiana
Missouri
Nevada
New Mexico
North Carolina
Oklahoma
South Carolina
Tennessee
Texas
Utah
Wisconsin

PRODUCTS/OPERATIONS

Selected Banners

Longhorn Finance (Texas)
PFS
Security Finance
Security Financial Services (North Carolina)
Sunbelt Credit

COMPETITORS

1st Franklin Financial	EZCORP
ACE Cash Express	First Cash Financial
Advance America	Services

Bank of America	GE Capital
Capital One	OneMain Financial
Cash America	Springleaf
Cash Plus	Value Financial
Community Choice	Services
Financial	World Acceptance
DFC Global	

HISTORICAL FINANCIALS

Company Type: Private

Income Statement
FYE: December 31

	ASSETS ($ mil.)	NET INCOME ($ mil.)	INCOME AS % OF ASSETS	EMPLOYEES
12/13	616	62	10.2%	2,500
12/12	461	53	11.6%	—
12/11	322	42	13.1%	—
12/10	495	0	—	—
Annual Growth	7.6%	—	—	—

2013 Year-End Financials

Return on assets: —
Return on equity: 12.9%
Sales ($ mil): 485

SECURITY GROUP INC.

LOCATIONS

HQ: SECURITY GROUP INC.
181 SECURITY PL, SPARTANBURG, SC 293075450
Phone: 864 582-8193

HISTORICAL FINANCIALS

Company Type: Private

Income Statement
FYE: December 31

	ASSETS ($ mil.)	NET INCOME ($ mil.)	INCOME AS % OF ASSETS	EMPLOYEES
12/13	1,263	107	8.5%	2,500
12/12	1,198	96	8.1%	—
12/11	983	81	8.3%	—
12/10	876	0	—	—
Annual Growth	13.0%	—	—	—

2013 Year-End Financials

Return on assets: —
Return on equity: 16.4%
Sales ($ mil): 653

SECURITY HEALTH PLAN OF WISCONSIN INC.

Security Health Plan of Wisconsin provides health insurance coverage and related services to some 200000 members in more than 35 Wisconsin counties. Its managed network of providers includes more than 4000 physicians 40 hospitals and health care facilities as well as 55000 pharmacies across the US. Security Health Plan provides policies for groups and individuals. Its products include HMO coverage plans and supplemental Medicare plans as well as prescription drug and equipment coverage disease management programs and administration services for self-funded plans. Established in 1986 the company is the managed healthcare arm of Marshfield Clinic which operates medical practices across the state.

Geographic Reach

Headquartered in the town of Marshfield Security Health Plan serves the counties of Adams Ashland Barron Bayfield Burnett Chippewa Clark Columbia Dane Douglas Dunn Eau Claire Forest Iron Jackson Juneau Langlade Lincoln Marathon Marquette Monroe Oneida Pepin Portage Price Rusk Sauk Sawyer Shawano Taylor Trempealeau Vilas Washburn Waupaca Waushara and Wood.

Operations

Since it is affiliated with a medical care provider Security Health Plan's coverage decisions are directly impacted by the practicing physician. The company's provider network consists of independent physician locations and parent Marshfield Clinic's more than 50 locations in Wisconsin.

In addition to HMO plans the firm's comprehensive medical coverage plans include POS (point of service) and high-deductable offerings. Security Health Plan offers health care reimbursement accounts through third-party provider agreements with Employee Benefits Corporation and Diversified Benefits Services. In addition the company provides community education and wellness programs.

Sales and Marketing

Security Health Plan serves individuals families and small to large employer groups.

Strategy

Originally started in 1986 as an offshoot of the Greater Marshfield Community Health Plan Security Health Plan's service territory has grown over the years. For instance in 2012 the company extended its Advocare Medicare Advantage plan offering into several new counties. Security Health Plan also regularly adds primary care and specialty providers to its network to provide a broader range of accessible care services to its members as well as to strengthen its operations in underserved regions. The company is also looking to enhance its IT systems to allow for greater information access communication methods and collaboration among its providers and members.

EXECUTIVES

Chief Marketing and Operations Officer, John Kelly
CEO, Julie Brussow
CIO, Dave Marksteiner
Controller Accounting/Finance, Geri Batten
Auditors: KPMG LLP COLUMBUS OH

LOCATIONS

HQ: SECURITY HEALTH PLAN OF WISCONSIN INC.
1515 N SAINT JOSEPH AVE, MARSHFIELD, WI
544491343
Phone: 715 387-5621
Web: WWW.SECURITYHEALTH.ORG

COMPETITORS

Aetna
Blue Cross Blue Shield of Wisconsin
CIGNA
Centene
Dean Health Plan
Group Health Cooperative
Gundersen Lutheran
Humana
UnitedHealth Group
Unity Health Plans Insurance
WEA Trust
Wisconsin Physicians Service Insurance Corporation

HISTORICAL FINANCIALS

Company Type: Private

Income Statement

FYE: December 31

	REVENUE ($ mil.)	NET INCOME ($ mil.)	NET PROFIT MARGIN	EMPLOYEES
12/09	814	27	3.4%	1,006
12/05	385	0	—	—
12/04	369	17	4.7%	—
12/02	285	0	—	—
Annual Growth	16.1%	—	—	—

2009 Year-End Financials

Return on assets: —
Return on equity: 3.4%
Current ratio: 0.70
Cash ($ mil.): 38

SELECT ENERGY SERVICES LLC

LOCATIONS

HQ: SELECT ENERGY SERVICES LLC
1820 N INTERSTATE 35, GAINESVILLE, TX
762402179
Phone: 940 668-1818
Web: WWW.SELECTENERGYSERVICES.COM

HISTORICAL FINANCIALS

Company Type: Private

Income Statement

FYE: December 31

	REVENUE ($ mil.)	NET INCOME ($ mil.)	NET PROFIT MARGIN	EMPLOYEES
12/10	502	55	11.0%	3,700
12/09	115	11	10.4%	—
Annual Growth	336.8%	364.4%		

2010 Year-End Financials

Return on assets: 2.0%
Return on equity: 11.0%
Current ratio: 1.40
Cash ($ mil.): 22

SELECTRANSPORTATION RESOURCES LLC

Auditors: DOERENMAYHEW HOUSTON TEXAS

LOCATIONS

HQ: SELECTRANSPORTATION RESOURCES LLC
9550 NORTH LOOP E, HOUSTON, TX 770291230
Phone: 713 672-4115
Web: WWW.SELECTRANSPORTATION.COM

HISTORICAL FINANCIALS

Company Type: Private

Income Statement

FYE: December 31

	REVENUE ($ mil.)	NET INCOME ($ mil.)	NET PROFIT MARGIN	EMPLOYEES
12/13	331	0	—	366
12/12	274	0	—	—
12/11	274	0	—	—
12/10	152	0	—	—
Annual Growth	29.6%	—	—	—

2013 Year-End Financials

Return on assets: 3.3%
Return on equity: —
Current ratio: 0.90
Cash ($ mil.): 19

SELLEN CONSTRUCTION CO. INC.

Auditors: MOSS ADAMS

LOCATIONS

HQ: SELLEN CONSTRUCTION CO. INC.
227 WESTLAKE AVE N, SEATTLE, WA 981095217
Phone: 206 682-7770
Web: WWW.SELLEN.COM

HISTORICAL FINANCIALS

Company Type: Private

Income Statement

FYE: December 31

	REVENUE ($ mil.)	NET INCOME ($ mil.)	NET PROFIT MARGIN	EMPLOYEES
12/12	396	4	1.0%	600
12/11	426	9	2.3%	—
12/10	600	17	2.9%	—
12/09	478	0	—	—
Annual Growth	(6.1%)	—	—	—

2012 Year-End Financials

Return on assets: 14.2%
Return on equity: 1.0%
Current ratio: 1.20
Cash ($ mil.): 32

SEMINOLE ELECTRIC COOPERATIVE INC.

This Seminole is not only a native Floridian but it has also provided electricity in the state since 1948. Seminole Electric Cooperative generates and transmits electricity for 10 member distribution cooperatives that serve 1.4 million residential and business customers in 42 Florida counties. Seminole Electric has more than 3350 MW of primarily coal-fired generating capacity. The cooperative also buys electricity from other utilities and independent power producers and it owns 350 miles of transmission lines. Some 90% of its power load uses the transmission systems of other utilities through long-term contracts.

Geographic Reach

The company serves customers in 45 counties in northeast south central and southeast Florida.

Operations

Seminole Electric's primary resources include the 1300 MW Seminole Generating Station and the 810 MW Richard J. Midulla Generating Station. The coop's renewable energy resources include waste-to-energy facilities landfill gas-to-energy facilities and a biomass facility. It also buys power as needed on the market.

Seminole Electric has more than 350 miles of transmission line.

Financial Performance

In 2013 the coop's revenues declined by 1% due to lower rates and as well as a reduction in Member energy requirements and lower volumes sold to Non-Members.Seminole Electric's net income increased by 48% in 2013 thanks to lower operating costs as a result of the absence of asset impairment costs and a drop in interest expenses.The company's operating cash inflow increased to $86.05 million in 2013 (from $34.81 million in 2012) primarily due to improved net income and a change in working capital.

Strategy

The coop is seeking to respond to the State of Florida's push to get more power generation from renewable sources. In 2014 the company generating about 58% of its electricity from coal 35% from natural gas and 7% from green energy sources (up from 5.5% in 2011 making Seminole Electric one of the largest green energy providers in Florida).

Company Background

In 2012 it also made major environmental improvements to its main power plant the coal-fired Seminole Generating Station. In 2011 Seminole Electric boosted its portfolio of purchased green energy to more than 140 MW (including 113 MW from waste-to-energy facilities).

Seminole Electric was formed in 1948 to aggregate the power demands of its members and is governed by a board of trustees representing the 10 member utilities. The cooperative built its first power plant in the 1970s.

EXECUTIVES

Vice President Technical Services, Michael (Mel) Opalinski
Executive Vice President, Steve Wallace
Vice President Of Administration, Al Garcia
Senior Vice President Of Strategic Services, Mike Opalinski

LOCATIONS

HQ: SEMINOLE ELECTRIC COOPERATIVE INC.
16313 N DALE MABRY HWY, TAMPA, FL 336181427
Phone: 386 328-9255
Web: WWW.SEMINOLE-ELECTRIC.COM

PRODUCTS/OPERATIONS

Members
Central Florida Electric Cooperative
Clay Electric Cooperative
Glades Electric Cooperative
Lee County Electric Cooperative
Peace River Electric Cooperative
Sumter Electric Cooperative
Suwannee Valley Electric Cooperative
Talquin Electric Cooperative
Tri-County Electric Cooperative
Withlacoochee River Electric Cooperative

COMPETITORS

Duke Energy	JEA
Duke Energy	NextEra Energy
Florida Power & Light	NextEra Energy
Florida Power & Light	Progress Energy
Florida Public	Progress Energy
Utilities	Southern Company
Florida Public	Southern Company
Utilities	TECO Energy
JEA	TECO Energy

HISTORICAL FINANCIALS

Company Type: Private

Income Statement

FYE: June 30

	REVENUE ($ mil.)	NET INCOME ($ mil.)	NET PROFIT MARGIN	EMPLOYEES
06/14*	1,179	28	2.4%	528
03/14	1,199	6	0.6%	—
12/13	1,213	17	1.5%	—
09/13	957	0	—	—
Annual Growth	23.2%	—	—	—

*Fiscal year change

2014 Year-End Financials

Return on assets: 4.2%
Return on equity: 2.4%
Current ratio: 0.80

Cash ($ mil.): 43

SENTARA HEALTHCARE

Sentara Healthcare is not-for-profit organization that operates a network of hospitals and other health facilities primarily in the coastal Hampton Roads area of southeastern Virginia. The system includes a dozen acute care hospitals housing a total of more than 2000 beds. One of its hospitals Sentara Norfolk includes a dedicated cardiac hospital with more than 100 beds. In addition to its acute care facilities Sentara Healthcare operates several outpatient care facilities as well as nursing homes rehab centers medical practices imaging centers and home health agencies. Its Optima Health unit provides HMO PPO and other health insurance products to about 450000 Virginians.

Operations

Across the Sentara Healthcare system the organization boasts a medical staff of about 3800. The medical system's multi-specialty physicians group the Sentara Medical Group has more than 380 primary care and specialty physicians. Its Sentara Senior Services unit operates about 10 nursing and assisted living centers.

The health care group also runs the 160-bed Sentara Princess Anne Hospital an acute care facility located on the Princess Anne outpatient campus in Virginia Beach. Opened in mid-2011 it operates through a 70%-owned joint venture with Bon Secours Health System. The $145 million facility encompasses five stories and offers comprehensive surgical procedures intensive care advanced cardiac care and a maternity center.

Geographic Reach

Sentara Healthcare is the region's largest integrated health care provider serving more than 2 million residents. Its facilities serve customers throughout southeastern and northern Virginia as well as in northeastern North Carolina. It operates in the Virginia cities of Alleghany Charlottesville Hampton Roads Harrisonburg Richmond and Roanoke. In North Carolina Sentara has a presence in Currituck and Elizabeth City.

Financial Performance

The system's revenues increased 9% to $4.7 billion in 2014 due to an increase in net patient services revenues and other operating revenues. Net income fell 82% to $156 million though as salaries and wages increased medical claims and other operating expenses rose and investment gains declined. Cash flow from operations decreased 25% that year to $318 million as a result of the lower net income plus an increase in cash used in receiv-

ables and changes in employee compensation and benefits.

Strategy

While it is already one of the largest health care organizations in the state Sentara Healthcare continues to grow through acquisitions construction (both expansions and new buildings) and mergers. In 2014 it acquired the assets and operations of Albemarle Hospital Albemarle Physician Services and Regional Medical Services through a 30-year capital lease agreement with Pasquotank County and Albemarle Hospital Authority. The businesses were combined into newly formed subsidiary SAMC. In 2015 Sentara Leigh Hospital opened a new tower as part of a larger renovation project.

Also in 2015 the system launched a new retail website shopsentara.com which offers over-the-counter health care products including medications vitamins exercise equipment diabetic care supplies and educational books.

Company Background

Sentara Healthcare was founded in 1888 as Norfolk's 25-bed Retreat for the Sick.

EXECUTIVES

Vice President Human Resources, Michael (Mel) Taylor
President and COO, Howard P. Kern
SVP and CIO, Bertram S. (Bert) Reese
CEO, David L. Bernd
SVP and CFO, Robert A. (Rob) Broerman
SVP; President Sentara Health Plans and Optima Health, Michael M. Dudley
President Sentara Leigh Hospital, Teresa L. (Terrie) Edwards
President Sentara CarePlex Hospital, Debra A. Flores
Corporate VP Sentara Norfolk General Hospital Sentara CarePlex Hospital and Sentara Williamsburg Regional Medical Center, Mary L. Blunt
President Sentara Martha Jefferson Hospital, Jonathan S. Davis
President Sentara Virginia Beach General Hospital, Elwood B. (Bernie) Boone
Chief Nursing Officer, Genemarie McGee
SVP and Chief Medical Officer, Terry Gilliland
President Sentara Williamsburg Regional Medical Center, David J. (Dave) Masterson
President Sentara Norfolk General Hospital, Kurt Hofelich
President Sentara Life Care Corporation, Bruce Robertson
President Sentara Princess Anne Hospital, Thomas B. Thames
Corporate VP; President Sentara RMH Medical Center, Jim Krauss
Corporate VP; President Sentara Medical Group, Robert (Doug) Culling
Corporate VP, Michael Gentry
President Sentara Enterprises, Linda R. Huffer
President Sentara Obici Hospital, Steve Julian
President Sentara Halifax Regional Hospital, Chris A. Lumsden
Corporate VP; President Sentara Northern Virgnia Medical Center, Stephen D. Porter
President Sentara Albemarle Medical Center, Coleen Santa Ana
Senior Vice President Sales and Marketing, John (Jack) Degruttola
Vice President Coporate Strategy, Grace Hines
Vice President And President Martha Jefferson Hospital, James (Jamie) Haden
Vice President Of Corporate Finance, Vikki Lorenz
Vice President Managed Care Contracting, Lance Torcom
Medical Director, Frank Barch
Vice President Of Operations, Chet Hart
Medical Director, Scott James
Director Of Pharmacy, Margaret Rosner

Vice President of Medical Affairs Administration
Sentara Norfolk General Hospital, Paul Chidester
Vice President And Nurse Executive Swrmc,
Donna Wilmoth
Director Of Pharmacy, Betsy Early
Vice President Business Development, Katherine
Harrison
Senior Vice President Clinical Effectiveness Chief
Marketing Officer, Dale Carroll
Chairman, Bob Fort
Vice Chairman, Henry (Sandy) Harris
Auditors: KPMG LLP NORFOLK VA

LOCATIONS

HQ: SENTARA HEALTHCARE
6015 POPLAR HALL DR, NORFOLK, VA 235023819
Phone: 757 455-7000
Web: WWW.SENTARA.COM

PRODUCTS/OPERATIONS

2014 Sales

	% of total
Net patient service revenue less provision of bad debts	65
Premium & capitation revenue	32
Other operating revenue	3
Net assets released from restrictions for operations	
Total	**100**

Mergers and Acquisitions
FY2011
   Martha Jefferson Hospital
FY2010
   RMH Healthcare (Rockingham Memorial Hospital
   wellness center and physicians group)
FY2009
   Bath Community House Home Health and Hospice of
   the Highlands
   Potomac Hospital

Selected Hospitals

Charlottesville
   Martha Jefferson Hospital
   MJH Outpatient Care Center
   Health Services at Proffit Road
   Health Services at Spring Creek
   Sentara Home Care Services
   Optima Health
Hampton Roads
   Sentara CarePlex Hospital
   Sentara Heart Hospital
   Sentara Leigh Hospital
   Sentara Norfolk General Hospital
   Sentara Obici Hospital
   Sentara Princess Anne Hospital
   Sentara Virginia Beach General Hospital
   Sentara Williamsburg Regional Medical Center
   Orthopaedic Hospital at Sentara CarePlex
   Sentara Northern Virginia Medical Center
   Martha Jefferson Hospital
   RMH Healthcare
Harrisonburg
   RMH Healthcare
   Optima Health
Northern Virginia
   Sentara Northern Virginia Medical Center
   Sentara Lake Ridge
   Sentara Medical Group physicians
   Sentara Home Care Services
   Sentara Heart and Vascular Center
   Optima Health

Selected Services

Cancer
Cardiac (Heart)
Digestive (Colorectal)
Home Care
Imaging
Maternity
Neurosciences
Rehabilitation
Seniors
Thoracic
Transplant
Trauma/Emergency Services
Urology
Vascular
Weight Loss Surgery
Women' s

COMPETITORS

Aetna
Anthem Health Plans of Virginia
Bon Secours Health
CIGNA
Carilion Clinic
Centra Health Inc.
Children' s Hospital of The King' s Daughters
Franklin Hospital Corp.
HCA Capital Division
Humana
Inova
Kaiser Foundation Health Plan of the Mid-Atlantic
Norton Community Hospital
Novant Health
Riverside Health System (Virginia)
Twin County Regional Healthcare
UnitedHealth Group
Wake Forest University Baptist Medical Center

HISTORICAL FINANCIALS

Company Type: Private

Income Statement

FYE: December 31

	REVENUE ($ mil.)	NET INCOME ($ mil.)	NET PROFIT MARGIN	EMPLOYEES
12/13	4,298	861	20.0%	22,000
12/12	4,068	307	7.6%	—
12/11	3,930	103	2.6%	—
12/10	3,385	0	—	—
Annual Growth	**8.3%**	**—**	**—**	**—**

2013 Year-End Financials

Return on assets: —
Return on equity: 20.0%
Current ratio: 1.80

Cash ($ mil.): 936

SENTARA RMH MEDICAL CENTER

Sentara RMH Medical Center (RMH) formerly
known as Rockingham Memorial Hospital serves
residents in Virginia's Shenandoah Valley offering
some 240 beds. In addition to emergency services
and general surgeries and care procedures RMH
offers specialized services including cardiovascular
care cancer treatment sleep disorder diagnosis behavioral health care medical imaging orthopedic
procedures obstetrics and rehabilitation as well as
home health hospice and wellness services.
Founded in 1912 RMH is part of the Sentara
Healthcare system.
Operations
Sentara RMH Medical Center is part of Sentara
Healthcare a 125-year old non-profit system which
operates more than 100 care sites across Virginia
and North Carolina including 12 acute care hospitals.
Geographic Reach
Sentara RMH Medical Center is located in Harrisonburg Virginia and serves residents in seven
surrounding counties.
Strategy
Sentara RMH Medical Center continues to be
recognized for its specialty care in recent years. In
late 2014 the U.S. News and World Report
awarded the Sentara RMH Medical Center "high
performing" status in three specialty areas —gastroenterology and GI surgery pulmonology and
geriatrics —and ranked it the 15th best hospital in
Virginia out of nearly 130 hospitals.
Ownership

Sentara RMH Medical Center became part of regional health system Sentara Healthcare in May
2011 when its parent organization RMH Healthcare was acquired by Sentara.

EXECUTIVES

Vice President Human Resources Development
and Support Services, Mark Zimmerman
Director of Pharmacy, Betsy Early
Vice President Business Development, Kay
Harrison
Medical Director, Jerome McDonald
Pic Phcy Ops Mgr, John (Jack) Lubkowski

LOCATIONS

HQ: SENTARA RMH MEDICAL CENTER
2010 HEALTH CAMPUS DR, HARRISONBURG, VA
228018679
Phone: 540 433-4100
Web: WWW.RMHONLINE.COM

PRODUCTS/OPERATIONS

Selected Services

Bariatric Surgery
Behavioral Health
Blood Donor Center
Business Office
Center for Sleep Medicine
Chaplain Services
Childcare Connection
Community Health
East Rockingham Health Center
Emergency Department
Family Birthplace
Gifts & Floral
Grief and Loss Services
Hahn Cancer Center
Healthsource
Heart and Vascular Center
Home Care Services
Hospice
Hospitalists
Image Recovery Center
Imaging Services
Joint Services
Laboratory Services
Lifeline
Luray Health Center
Mount Jackson Health Center
New Market Health Center
Occupational Health Center
Orthopedics and Sports Medicine
Palliative Care
Pharmacy
Physician Billing
Pulmonary Services
Rehab Services
Security
Senior Advantage
South Main Health Center
Surgical Services
Valley Behavioral Medicine
Virginia Funkhouser Health Sciences Library
Volunteer Services
Wellness Center
Women' s Center

COMPETITORS

Carilion Clinic
Centra Health Inc.
HCA Capital Division
Loudoun Healthcare
MedStar Health

University of Virginia
   Health System
Valley Health
Virginia Hospital &
   Healthcare

HISTORICAL FINANCIALS
Company Type: Private

Income Statement
FYE: December 31

	REVENUE ($ mil.)	NET INCOME ($ mil.)	NET PROFIT MARGIN	EMPLOYEES
12/08	264	10	3.8%	1,892
12/06	229	18	7.8%	—
12/05	214	5	2.5%	—
12/04	188	0	—	—
Annual Growth	8.9%	—	—	—

2008 Year-End Financials
Return on assets: 12.4% Cash ($ mil.): 55
Return on equity: 3.8%
Current ratio: 1.00

SERVCO PACIFIC INC.

Servco Pacific's business flows through an ocean's worth of enterprises. The company sells passenger vehicles (including Toyota Subaru Suzuki and Chevrolet models) and commercial trucks through dealerships in Hawaii and Australia. In addition Servco Home & Appliance wholesales kitchen and bath products to building professionals throughout the South Pacific; Servco Raynor Overhead Doors installs residential and commercial garage doors; Servco Insurance Services offers insurance coverage for businesses and individuals; and Servco School & Office Furniture outfits educational institutions and government agencies with desks seating and other furnishings. Servco Pacific was founded by Peter Fukunaga in 1919.

Geographic Reach

Honolulu-based Servco Pacific has insurance offices in Seattle and Tacoma Washington. Its other businesses operate in Hawaii (Kauai Maui Oahu and the Big Island); and Australia (New South Wales Queensland).

Operations

The diversified firm sells insurance through Servco Insurance Services (SIS) in Washington state. It clients are in the fishing shipping and cargo industries in several states including Alaska. SIS also operates in Hawaii where sister chains Servco Home & Appliance Servco Forklift & Industrial Equipment and Servco Automotive also operate. Servco Tire Company sells tires on Maui and in Honolulu.

Financial Performance

The private company reports revenue of approximately $800 million annually.

Strategy

Servco Pacific through its Australian subsidiary has been expanding its Toyota dealer operations in recent years. During 2010 the company acquired majority stakes in Sunshine Toyota of Queensland and Dubbo City Toyota of New South Wales. It also purchased Pacific Toyota in Cairns in 2009. The deals have significantly grown Servco Pacific's business in Australia part of a bid to strengthen its international presence; altogether Servco Pacific owns five dealerships in the country. The firm started operating in Australia in late 2007 with the acquisition of a Toyota dealership in Brisbane. Closer to home Servco is acquiring dealerships in Hawaii amid a influx of off-island businesses including Lithia Motors to Hawaii.

Mergers and Acquisitions

In February 2014 Servco acquired the assets of Maui's Island Subaru dealership in Kahului. The newly-acquired dealership will operate as Servco Subaru.

EXECUTIVES
Senior Vice President, Glenn Inouye
Senior Vice President, Brian Horikami
Vice President Finance, Craig Mishina
Vice President and Director of Variable Operations, Kyle Shirakata

LOCATIONS
HQ: SERVCO PACIFIC INC.
2850 PUKOLOA ST STE 300, HONOLULU, HI 968194475
Phone: 808 564-1300
Web: WWW.SERVCO.COM

PRODUCTS/OPERATIONS

Selected Operations
Automotive
 Rex Tire and Supply
 Scion Dealers of Hawaii
 Subaru Dealers of Hawaii
 Suzuki Dealers of Hawaii
 Servco Australia
 Servco Chevy
 Servco Lexus
 Servco Truck & Commercial
 Toyota Dealers of Hawaii
Servco Home and Appliance Distribution
Servco Insurance Services
Servco Raynor Overhead Doors
Servco School and Office Furniture

COMPETITORS

AutoNation	HD Supply
Citigroup	Inchcape
Fletcher Jones	Lithia Motors

HISTORICAL FINANCIALS
Company Type: Private

Income Statement
FYE: June 30

	REVENUE ($ mil.)	NET INCOME ($ mil.)	NET PROFIT MARGIN	EMPLOYEES
06/13*	1,094	20	1.9%	925
12/12	923	15	1.7%	—
/	0	0	—	—
Annual Growth	—	—	—	—

*Fiscal year change

2013 Year-End Financials
Return on assets: —   Cash ($ mil.): 16
Return on equity: 1.9%
Current ratio: 0.30

SES HOLDINGS LLC

Auditors: KPMG LLP DALLAS TX

LOCATIONS
HQ: SES HOLDINGS LLC
114 E FORELINE ST, GAINESVILLE, TX 762403320
Phone: 940 668-0251
Web: WWW.SES-HOLDINGS.COM

HISTORICAL FINANCIALS
Company Type: Private

Income Statement
FYE: December 31

	ASSETS ($ mil.)	NET INCOME ($ mil.)	INCOME AS % OF ASSETS	EMPLOYEES
12/13	892	(32)	—	4,200
12/12	941	2	0.3%	—
12/11	1,019	131	12.9%	—
12/10	617	0	—	—
Annual Growth	13.1%	—	—	—

2013 Year-End Financials
Return on assets: 2.5%   Sales ($ mil): 843
Return on equity: (-3.9%)

SETON HALL UNIVERSITY

Seton Hall University is a Catholic institution with an enrollment of almost 10000 students (5500 undergraduates and 4300 graduates) who hail from 70 countries. The university offers more than 90 undergraduate and graduate degree programs as well as more than a dozen doctoral programs at eight colleges and schools including the Whitehead School of Diplomacy and International Relations Stillman School of Business and Immaculate Conception Seminary School of Theology. Seton Hall also offers degree and certificate programs online. Seton Hall is the US' oldest diocesan university and is under purview of the Archdiocese of Newark.

Geographic Reach

Seton Hall's campus is in a South Orange New Jersey suburban setting about 30 minutes from New York City.

Operations

Some 80% of its undergraduate student live on campus.

Seton Hall has a student-to-faculty ratio of 14:1. About 97% of its students receive financial aid.

Strategy

Expanding its academic profile in 2015 Seton Hall and Hackensack University Health Network agreed to form a new four-year school of medicine. This partnership will establish the first private school of medicine in New Jersey and provide a major economic boost to the region.

Company Background

Formed in 1856 Seton Hall University was named after Mother Elizabeth Ann Seton the first American-born saint (and an aunt of school founder Bishop James Roosevelt Bayley). Originally called Seton Hall College it became a university in 1950 and became coeducational in 1968.

EXECUTIVES
Vice President for Administration at Seton Hall University, Dennis Garbini
CFO, Stephen A. Graham
EVP and Provost, Larry A. Robinson
Dean School of Theology, Joseph R. Reilly
Dean School of Health and Medical Sciences, Brian B. Shulman
CIO, Stephen G. Landry
President, A. Gabriel Esteban
Dean School of Diplomacy and International Relations, Andrea Bartoli
Dean College of Education and Human Services, Grace M. May

Dean of Students, Karen Van Norman
Dean Stillman School of Business, Joyce Strawser
Dean University Libraries, John E. Buschman
Dean College of Nursing, Marie Foley
Dean School of Law, Kathleen M. Boozang
Dean Continuing Education and Professional Studies, Karen Passaro
Interim Dean College of Arts and Sciences, Chrysanthy M. Grieco
Interim Dean College of Communication and the Arts, Deirdre Yates
Provost and Executive Vice President Academic Affairs, Gabriel Esteban
Associate Vice President for Development, Brigette Bryant
Chairman, John J. Myers
Vice Chairman, Bernard A. Hebda
Secretary, Joann DeBerto
Secretary To the Vice President, Ellen Schoch
Secretary Government Relations, Annette Manso
Auditors: GRANT THORNTON LLP EDISON NE

LOCATIONS

HQ: SETON HALL UNIVERSITY
400 S ORANGE AVE, SOUTH ORANGE, NJ 070792697
Phone: 973 761-9000

PRODUCTS/OPERATIONS

Selected Schools & Colleges
College of Arts and Sciences
College of Education and Human Services
College of Nursing
Immaculate Conception Seminary School of Theology
School of Health and Medical Sciences
School of Law
Stillman School of Business
Whitehead School of Diplomacy & International Relations

HISTORICAL FINANCIALS

Company Type: Private

Income Statement

	REVENUE ($ mil.)	NET INCOME ($ mil.)	NET PROFIT MARGIN	EMPLOYEES
06/14	270	52	19.4%	2,700
06/13	269	38	14.5%	—
06/12	256	(0)	—	—
06/11	256	0	—	—
Annual Growth	1.9%	—	—	—

2014 Year-End Financials
Return on assets: 17.0%   Cash ($ mil.): 31
Return on equity: 19.4%
Current ratio: —

SEYFARTH SHAW LLP

Every day is labor day at law firm Seyfarth Shaw which specializes in handling employment-related matters for its clients. The firm divides its numerous practices into four main areas: business services employee benefits labor and employment and litigation. Overall Seyfarth Shaw has about 800 attorneys in 14 offices –ten spread throughout the US plus four international outposts. Seyfarth Shaw draws clients from industries such as financial services life sciences and telecommunications. Henry Seyfarth Lee Shaw and Owen Fairweather founded the firm in 1945.

Geographic Reach

The firm maintains offices in Atlanta Boston Chicago Houston London Los Angeles Melbourne New York Sacramento San Francisco Shanghai Sydney and Washington DC. It extends its offerings through alliances with other firms in leading business centers around the world.

Sales and Marketing

Seyfarth's clients have included more than 300 companies from the FORTUNE 500.

Strategy

The firm has been expanding its real estate practice.

EXECUTIVES

Chairman Intellectual Property Practice Group, Brian L. Michaelis
Office Managing Partner Chicago, David J. Rowland
National Chairman Real Estate Department, Paul P. Mattingly
National Chairman Seyfarth's Labor & Employment Department, Lisa J. Damon
Managing Partner San Francisco, Nick C. Geannacopulos
Chairman National Wage and Hour Litigation Practice Group, Richard L. Alfred
Managing Partner and the Chairman Houston, Mark W. Coffin
Managing Partner, Russell B. Swapp
Chairman Asia Pacific Transactional Practice, Craig Carracher
CIO, Andrew D. Jurczyk
Managing Director, Philippe Weiss
Senior Legal Project Manager, Jenny L. Lee
CEO SeyfarthLean Consulting, Robert Saccone
Legal Secretary, Ellen Ferebee
Legal Secretary, Antoinette Riebling
Legal Secretary, June Daniel
Legal Secretary, Carol Alaniz
Vice President Research Director, Athena Goehl
Legal Secretary, Venessa Brown
Legal Secretary, Diana Gomez
Legal Secretary, Marylou Vaughan
Senior Vice President, Ronald Swanstrom
Secretary, Rebecca Ortega
Secretary, Patricia Thurman
Secretary, Laura Henderson
Secretary, Melanie Alexander
Secretary, Veronica Gavin
Secretary, Maridith Winter
Secretary, Margaret (Peg) Brueck
Secretary, Theresa Ponds
Secretary, Fiona Moyes
Secretary, Eloisa Flores
Secretary, Kathy Olson
Secretary, Deborah Hodgson
Secretary, Lynne Mateja
Secretary, Nancy Hull
Secretary, Sharon Jordan
Secretary, Carla Bryant

LOCATIONS

HQ: SEYFARTH SHAW LLP
131 S DEARBORN ST # 2400, CHICAGO, IL 606035863
Phone: 312 460-5000
Web: WWW.SEYFARTH.COM

PRODUCTS/OPERATIONS

Selected Practice Areas
Bankruptcy workouts and business reorganization
Commercial class action defense
Commercial litigation
Construction
Corporate
E-discovery
Employee benefits and executive compensation
Environmental safety and toxic torts
Government contracts
Intellectual property
International
Labor and employment
Product liability
Real estate
Securities and financial litigation
Tax
Trade secrets computer fraud and non-competes

Selected Industries Served
Financial services
Health care
Hospitality
Insurance
Life sciences: pharmaceuticals biotechnology and medical devices
Media
Professional services
Retail
Technology
Telecommunications
Trusts and estates

COMPETITORS

Baker & McKenzie	McDermott Will & Emery
Baker Botts	Ogletree Deakins
Hinshaw & Culbertson	Paul Hastings
Jones Day	Proskauer Rose
Kirkland & Ellis	Sidley Austin
Littler Mendelson	Skadden Arps
Mayer Brown	Winston & Strawn

HISTORICAL FINANCIALS

Company Type: Private

Income Statement
FYE: December 31

	REVENUE ($ mil.)	NET INCOME ($ mil.)	NET PROFIT MARGIN	EMPLOYEES
12/08	462	146	31.7%	1,608
12/07	431	141	32.9%	—
12/06	385	136	35.3%	—
12/05	332	0	—	—
Annual Growth	11.7%	—	—	—

2008 Year-End Financials
Return on assets: —   Cash ($ mil.): 41
Return on equity: 31.7%
Current ratio: 3.30

SGT INC.

Like its acronym name suggests SGT (aka Stinger Ghaffarian Technologies) is used to taking military orders; in this case very specific technical ones. An engineering services firm SGT provides aerospace engineering project management IT systems development and related services to NASA the US Navy the US Air Force and other primarily military-related government entities through contracts. The company also offers science-related services such as earth climate and planetary modeling and analysis. SGT's facilities are located near airfields and other military facilities.

Geographic Reach

SGT operates a more than dozen offices including in Houston Cleveland and Los Angeles White Sands (New Mexico) and Wallops Island (Virginia).

Strategy

In 2013 the company formed a new subsidiary Houston-based engineering products subsidiary Intuitive Machines Inc. The partnership leverages synergies between control systems motor control robotics advanced manufacturing mechanics electronics software computational analysis sensing and other core competencies to address significant challenges across a range of industries.

In 2014 SGT was awarded a five-year contract by the Naval Research Laboratory (NRL). Under the agreement SGT will develop space science instruments and experimental payloads for NRL's Space Science Division.

Company Background

SGT was founded in 1994 by Harold Stinger and CEO Kam Ghaffarian.

EXECUTIVES

President and CEO, Kam Ghaffarian
CFO, Joe Morway
SVP NASA Business Unit, Dave Wolt
VP Business Operations, Matt Yetman
Senior Vice President, Jerry Mayefskie
Vice President Finance Chief Financial Officer, Mike Gigliotti
Vice President sls, Ron Marinzel
Chairman, Harold Stinger
Secretary, Matthew (Matt) Davis

LOCATIONS

HQ: SGT INC.
7701 GREENBELT RD STE 400, GREENBELT, MD 207706521
Phone: 301 614-8600
Web: WWW.SGT-INC.COM

COMPETITORS

Ball Aerospace
CACI International
CDI Government Services
Digital Fusion
Lockheed Martin Space Systems
QSS Group
Sierra Nevada Corp
Techshot
United Space Alliance

HISTORICAL FINANCIALS

Company Type: Private

Income Statement

FYE: September 30

	REVENUE ($ mil.)	NET INCOME ($ mil.)	NET PROFIT MARGIN	EMPLOYEES
09/14	453	17	3.9%	1,500
09/13	416	15	3.7%	—
09/12	374	9	2.4%	—
09/08	292	0	—	—
Annual Growth	7.5%	—	—	—

2014 Year-End Financials

Return on assets: 8.4%
Return on equity: 3.9%
Current ratio: 1.20
Cash ($ mil.): —

SHAMROCK FOODS COMPANY

You might say Shamrock Foods is milking the food service business for all it's worth. Distribution business Shamrock Foods ranks in the top 10 US food services companies while its Shamrock Farms unit represents one of the largest dairy operators in the southwestern US. The company's distribution operations supply food and related products to food service operators in 10 states in the Intermountain region through a handful of distribution centers. Shamrock Farms home to more than 10000 cows produces and offers a full line of dairy products including fluid milk half and half and ice cream. Founded in 1922 as a mom-and-pop dairy Shamrock Foods is still owned and operated by the founding McClelland family.

Geographic Reach
The Phoenix-based company's distribution area spans Arizona California Colorado Kansas New Mexico Nevada Nebraska Texas Utah and Wyoming. It supplies its customers from distribution centers in Denver Phoenix and Albuquerque.

Operations
Shamrock Foods carries some 16000 food service products including fresh produce dry groceries frozen foods ethnic specialties meat seafood and beverages along with Shamrock Farms' dairy products. It also carries cleaning and paper products and other supplies and equipment. Its customers include restaurants fast-food outlet schools hospitals and institutions in 10 states.

Strategy
Looking to extend its reach eastward Shamrock Foods in 2013 broke ground on a $50 million manufacturing facility in Virginia where it will process milk and other dairy products.

The company works to develop new products and maintains relationships with other businesses to keep its products in front of customers. Shamrock Farms sells Rockin' Refuel a protein-fortified chocolate milk that the company says helps rebuild and repair muscles after exercise. In addition to its Shamrock-branded dairy products the dairy company offers private-label services and is the milk supplier for all US Subway sandwich shops.

EXECUTIVES

President Shamrock Farms Company, Norman McClelland
National Sales Manager, Paul Hohmann
SVP CFO Secretary and Treasurer, F. Phillips (Phil) Giltner
President, Kent McClelland
VP & CIO, Rob Baxter
Senior Vice President, F Giltne
Vice President Of Operations, Mark Sherman
Vice President Operations, Jeff Patterson

LOCATIONS

HQ: SHAMROCK FOODS COMPANY
3900 E CAMELBACK RD # 300, PHOENIX, AZ 850182614
Phone: 602 477-2500
Web: WWW.SHAMROCKFARMS.NET

PRODUCTS/OPERATIONS

Selected Products

Beverages
Center of the plate
Dairy
Cleaning supplies
Dry goods and groceries
Frozen foods
Mexican foods
Pacific rim foods
Paper and disposable products
Produce
Specialty produce
Seafood
Supplies and equipment

Selected Brands

Aspen Gold
Brickfire Bakery
Chef Mark
Emerald Valley Ranch
Gold Canyon
Katy's Kitchen
Lotus Garden
Prairie Creek
Pro Clean
Proware
Shamrock Farms
Silverbrook
Southern Pearl
Villa Frizzoni

COMPETITORS

Blue Bell
C&S Wholesale
California Dairies Inc.
Dairy Farmers of America
Dean Foods
Services Group of America
Stonyfield Farm
Sysco
US Foods
United Dairymen of Arizona
Land O' Lakes
McLane
Meadowbrook Meat Company
Wells' Dairy

HISTORICAL FINANCIALS

Company Type: Private

Income Statement

FYE: September 30

	REVENUE ($ mil.)	NET INCOME ($ mil.)	NET PROFIT MARGIN	EMPLOYEES
09/14	2,433	0	—	2,600
09/13	1,353	0	—	—
09/12	1,353	0	—	—
09/11	1,353	0	—	—
Annual Growth	21.6%	—	—	—

2014 Year-End Financials

Return on assets: 6.1%
Return on equity: —
Current ratio: 0.70
Cash ($ mil.): 13

SHAMROCK TRADING CORPORATION

Auditors: BKD LLP KANSAS CITY MO

LOCATIONS

HQ: SHAMROCK TRADING CORPORATION
8601 MONROVIA ST, SHAWNEE MISSION, KS 662154501
Phone: 913 310-2200
Web: WWW.RYANTRANS.COM

HISTORICAL FINANCIALS

Company Type: Private

Income Statement

FYE: December 31

	REVENUE ($ mil.)	NET INCOME ($ mil.)	NET PROFIT MARGIN	EMPLOYEES
12/10	1,468	10	0.7%	200
12/09	938	5	0.6%	—
Annual Growth	56.5%	74.0%	—	—

2010 Year-End Financials

Return on assets: 0.1%
Return on equity: 0.7%
Current ratio: 1.30
Cash ($ mil.): —

SHANDS JACKSONVILLE MEDICAL CENTER INC.

Close to the shifting sands of the northern Florida coast Shands Jacksonville Medical Center (doing business as UF Health Jacksonville) offers a range of services to the 19 counties it serves in Florida and southern Georgia. The 695-bed hospital includes a cardiovascular center Level III neonatal intensive care unit and a Level I trauma center. It also operates primary and specialty clinics in the Jacksonville area. The medical center is affiliated with the University of Florida and is the largest of seven hospitals in the Shands HealthCare family.

Geographic Reach

UF Health Jacksonville's facilities are located in Jacksonville Florida and surrounding areas of northeastern Florida and southeastern Georgia.

Operations

UF Health Jacksonville operates about 40 outpatient care centers. Overall its facilities handle some 34000 inpatient visits and 600000 outpatient visits per year. The hospital's affiliation with the University of Florida (UF) includes collaborative treatment and research programs in areas including cancer cardiovascular neurology orthopedic and pediatric care.

Together with its UF colleagues and affiliates UF Health Jacksonville provides a wide range of health care services across the continuum of care on an inpatient and outpatient basis. Backed by a team of more than 400 faculty physicians it offers nearly 100 specialty services.

Financial Performance The company's revenues increased by 3% in 2014 due to growth in net patient service revenues as a result of a growth in inpatient and outpatient volumes. Medicare accounted for 25% net patient revenues; Medicaid 31%.UF Health Jacksonville reported net income of $3 million in 2014 over a net loss in 2013 due to higher interest and a loss on the disposal of capital assets.Operating cash flow in 2014 decreased by 8% due to higher payments to suppliers and vendors.

Strategy

UF Health Jacksonville has plans to build a second campus on the north side of Jacksonville to meet the needs of a growing community. It's also exploring ways to increase clinical efficiencies such as implementing an electronic health record (EHR) system (with help from federal stimulus funding); it also is looking to maximize funding opportunities for its research programs.

The company is looking to develop a Health Science Center Medical Education on Jacksonville Regional Campus including undergraduate graduate and health-related professions.

It also plans to build a 92-bed hospital wing for the North Campus which will provide greater access to more health care services for the center's residents as well as those living in surrounding communities. Construction is scheduled to begin in 2015 with completion in 2017.In 2015 UF Health North opened the six-story 210000-square-foot outpatient medical complex in North Jacksonville which includes a 28-bed emergency room advanced imaging a midwife-led birth center rehabilitation services and more than 20 specialty services.

Company Background

In 2010 in the midst of economic challenges parent Shands HealthCare aligned UF Health Jacksonville's administration more closely with its other academic hospital Shands at the University of Florida in Gainesville. The sister hospitals continue to operate independently but benefit from a shared academic and research focus; the hospitals are working together to increase operational efficiency and flexibility within the system.

Company Background

Founded in 1870 as the Duval Hospital and Asylum UF Health Jacksonville started the first cancer program in Florida in 1948.

EXECUTIVES

Vp Primary Care Services, Rita A James
Vice President of Human Resources, Lesli Ward
Vice President Of Government Affairs, Penny Thompson
Director Of Admissions, Dan Kurmaskie
Board Member, Manish Patel
Auditors: PRICEWATERHOUSECOOPERS LLP T

LOCATIONS

HQ: SHANDS JACKSONVILLE MEDICAL CENTER INC.
655 W 8TH ST, JACKSONVILLE, FL 322096511
Phone: 904 244-5576
Web: WWW.RAINBOW.JAX.UFL.EDU

PRODUCTS/OPERATIONS

Selected Services
Cancer services
Cardiovascular services
Neuroscience services
Orthopaedic services
Pediatrics
Poison Center
Trauma and critical care services
Women and families

COMPETITORS

Baptist Health System	Ocala Regional Medical
Bay Medical Center	Center
Brooks Rehabilitation	Orange Park Medical
Florida Hospital Tampa	Orlando Health
Bay Division	Palms West Hospital
Mayo Clinic	St. Vincent' s Health
Jacksonville	System
Nemours Foundation	
North Florida Regional	
Medical Center	

HISTORICAL FINANCIALS

Company Type: Private

Income Statement FYE: June 30

	REVENUE ($ mil.)	NET INCOME ($ mil.)	NET PROFIT MARGIN	EMPLOYEES
06/10	592	19	3.2%	3,000
06/09	591	7	1.2%	—
06/08	1,174	0	—	—
Annual Growth	—23854.6%	—	—	—

2010 Year-End Financials
Return on assets: —   Cash ($ mil.): 58
Return on equity: 3.2%
Current ratio: 1.30

SHARI'S MANAGEMENT CORPORATION

This Shari keeps the kitchen open all day and all night. Shari's Management Corporation owns and operates more than 100 Shari's family restaurants in six states (primarily in the Northwest) that serve breakfast lunch and dinner 24 hours a day. The chain of eateries offers standard American fare such as pancakes and eggs sandwiches and burgers and beef chicken and pasta dishes as well as a selection of appetizers and desserts through a menu of about 120 items. The company is owned by a group of private investors led by Circle Peak Management. Ron and Sharon (Shari) Berquist opened the first Shari's in Hermiston Oregon in 1978.

Geographic Reach

The chain's 100 locations are located throughout California Idaho Nebraska Oregon Washington and Wyoming.

Operations

In a given year Shari's pours over 50000 cups of coffee serves 4000 dozen eggs grills a mile of sausage links and toasts nearly 50000 slices of bread.

Strategy

Shari's Management has continued to expand slowly with funding from its private equity investors. As it grows outside of its core market the company faces the challenge of creating a brand identity in a segment crowded with national chains such as Denny's and IHOP (owned by DineEquity). Shari's expanded into the San Francisco market in 2009 when it purchased and converted four Bakers Square locations from troubled VICORP Restaurants.

EXECUTIVES

Vice President Marketing, Michael Kiriazis

LOCATIONS

HQ: SHARI' S MANAGEMENT CORPORATION
9400 SW GEMINI DR, BEAVERTON, OR 970087105
Phone: 503 605-4299
Web: WWW.SHARIS.COM

Selected Locations
California
Idaho
Nebraska
Oregon
Washington
Wyoming

COMPETITORS

Brinker	McMenamins
Carlson Restaurants	OSI Restaurant
Catalina Restaurant	Partners
Group	Panera Bread
Darden	Perkins & Marie
Denny' s	Callender' s
DineEquity	Red Robin
Elmer' s Restaurants	Ruby Tuesday
Golden Corral	The Holland Inc.

HISTORICAL FINANCIALS

Company Type: Private

Income Statement FYE: January 2

	REVENUE ($ mil.)	NET INCOME ($ mil.)	NET PROFIT MARGIN	EMPLOYEES
01/08	170	1	0.9%	4,000
01/07	165	40	24.3%	—
Annual Growth	3.0%	(96.2%)	—	—

2008 Year-End Financials
Return on assets: 3.4%   Cash ($ mil.): 1
Return on equity: 0.9%
Current ratio: 0.10

SHARP CHULA VISTA MEDICAL CENTER

Auditors: ERNST & YOUNG US LLP SAN DIEG

LOCATIONS

HQ: SHARP CHULA VISTA MEDICAL CENTER
8695 SPECTRUM CENTER BLVD, SAN DIEGO, CA 921231489
Phone: 858 499-5150
Web: WWW.SHARP.COM

HISTORICAL FINANCIALS

Company Type: Private

Income Statement

FYE: September 30

	REVENUE ($ mil.)	NET INCOME ($ mil.)	NET PROFIT MARGIN	EMPLOYEES
09/13	319	12	4.0%	99
09/09	251	2	1.2%	—
Annual Growth	6.1%	45.0%	—	—

2013 Year-End Financials

Return on assets: 8.0%   Cash ($ mil.): 2
Return on equity: 4.0%
Current ratio: 1.90

SHARP CHULA VISTA MEDICAL CENTER

LOCATIONS

HQ: SHARP CHULA VISTA MEDICAL CENTER
751 MEDICAL CENTER CT, CHULA VISTA, CA
919116617
Phone: 619 502-5800
Web: WWW.MYECARE.SHARP.COM

HISTORICAL FINANCIALS

Company Type: Private

Income Statement

FYE: September 30

	REVENUE ($ mil.)	NET INCOME ($ mil.)	NET PROFIT MARGIN	EMPLOYEES
09/13	304	19	6.5%	1,600
09/12	298	25	8.6%	—
09/04	156	(6)	—	—
09/03	144	0	—	—
Annual Growth	7.8%	—	—	—

2013 Year-End Financials

Return on assets: 2.9%   Cash ($ mil.): 1
Return on equity: 6.5%
Current ratio: 0.90

SHARP HEALTHCARE

Sharp HealthCare stands on the cutting edge of health care delivery in Southern California. The system of not-for-profit hospitals and health care facilities is the largest in the San Diego area. The network includes four acute-care hospitals (Sharp Chula Vista Sharp Coronado Sharp Grossmont and Sharp Memorial) as well as three specialty hospitals for women's care psychiatry and chemical dependence. It also operates two physician medical groups and a number of urgent care and outpatient facilities and clinics. With some 2100 beds and about 2600 physicians Sharp HealthCare offers cancer and cardiac care fertility and maternity services surgical procedures and hospice care.

Geographic Reach

In addition to its operating bases in San Diego Sharp HealthCare has California facilities in Carmel Valley Chula Vista El Cajon La Mesa Mira Mesa Otay Ranch Point Loma Rancho Bernado San Diego Scripps Ranch Serra Mesa and Sorrento Mesa.

Operations

Altogether the Sharp HealthCare facilities handle 1600 surgeries each year. In addition to medical services the organization operates its own health plan; the Sharp Health Plan is a not-for-profit HMO serving tens of thousands of members in and around San Diego.

The Sharp Grossmont hospital which serves eastern San Diego County is run by Grossmont Hospital Corporation a subsidiary holding a 30-year lease to manage the facility. One of the system's specialty operations Sharp Mary Birch Hospital for Women & Newborns claims to deliver more babies than any other hospital in California. Sharp's two medical groups are Sharp Community and Sharp Rees-Stealy which between them comprise more than 1100 doctors providing both primary and specialty care.

Financial Performance

Sharp's net revenues have trended upward in recent years. The company's revenues grew by $100 million in 2014 due to increase in net patient revenue and premiums. Revenues from the Medicare and Medi-Cal programs accounted for 30% and 24% respectively of Sharp's gross patient charges. The company's net income decreased by 4% due to pension-related changes other than net periodic pension cost and increase in employee benefits and medical fees expenses.Sharp's operating cash flow decreased by 48% in 2014.

Strategy

Sharp HealthCare improves its services to area residents through facility upgrades.

In 2015 the company launched Sharp Health News an online news site featuring engaging and original stories about medical breakthroughs new technology and health and wellness. In 2014 Sharp HospiceCare opened its newest hospice residence BonitaView the first facility of its kind in the South Bay area of San Diego County for end-of-life care designed around the needs of patients and their families.

The organization installed new imaging equipment at the Sharp Memorial Outpatient Pavilion in 2013 and a opened the new Sharp Rees-Stealy center in Del Mar in 2014.

Company Background

In 2011 the system doubled the capacity of Sharp Chula Vista Medical Center's emergency department at a cost of $12 million and in 2012 the Chula Vista hospital opened a new cancer center.

The system began as a single hospital in 1955 named for a local pilot who died in WWII.

EXECUTIVES

Senior Vice President Human Resources, Ky Lewis
President and CEO, Michael W. (Mike) Murphy
SVP and CIO, William A. (Bill) Spooner
SVP Finance and CFO, Ann Pumpian
SVP and CEO Sharp Grossmont Hospital, Michele Tarbet
EVP Hospital Operations, Daniel L. (Dan) Gross
CEO Sharp HealthCare Foundation, Bill Littlejohn
President and CEO Sharp Health Plan, Melissa Hayden-Cook
SVP and CEO Sharp Mesa Vista and Sharp McDonald Center, Kathi Lencioni
CEO Sharp Community Medical Group, John Jenrette
SVP and CEO Sharp Memorial Hospital, Tim Smith
SVP and CEO Sharp Chula Vista Medical Center, Pablo Velez
SVP and CEO Sharp Coronado Hospital, Susan Stone
CEO Sharp Rees-Stealy Medical Group, Stacey Hrountas
SVP and CEO Sharp Mary Birch Hospital for Women & Newborns, Trisha Khaleghi
Vice President Patient Financial Services, Gerilynn Sevenikar
Legal Secretary, Jenna Haynes
Director Of Nursing and Patient Care Services, Maryjo Webb
Vice President Business Development, Donna Thompson
Vice President Clinical Informatics, Julie McCoy
Director Of Clinical Services, Tracy Kaiser
Vice President, Jerlyn Yusi
Vice President Cardiovascular Service Line, Paul Patchen
Vice President, Joshua Stopper
Vice President, Claudia Mills
Vice President Corporate Compliance, Paul Belton
Physical Therapy Director, Jerome Stenehjem
Vice President Of Finance, Donna Serpico
Pharmacy Manager, Mike Elyea
Senior Vice President, Randi Larsson
Senior Vice President And Chief Executive Officer Sharp Mary Birch Hospital For Women, Mary Henrikson
Vice President Patient Financial Services, Gerilynn Wagner
Vice President Workforce Support Services, Anne Davis
Treasurer, James Brown
Board Member, Shawna Fallon
Auditors: ERNST & YOUNG US LLP SAN DIEG

LOCATIONS

HQ: SHARP HEALTHCARE
8695 SPECTRUM CENTER BLVD, SAN DIEGO, CA
921231489
Phone: 858 499-4000
Web: WWW.MYECARE.SHARP.COM

PRODUCTS/OPERATIONS

2014 Sales

	% of total
Net patient revenue	62
Premium	35
Other	3
Total	**100**

Selected Programs and Services

Alcohol and drug dependency
Bloodless medicine
Cancer treatment
Complimentary and alternative medicine
Diabetes
Ear nose and throat
Eating disorders
Emergency and trauma
Endoscopy
Executive health
Eye care
Flu care
Health and wellness
Heart and vascular care
   Heart valve surgery
Home care
Hospice
Integrative and complementary medicine
International patient services
Laboratory services
Men's health
Mental health
Neurology
Nutrition
Occupational health
Orthopedics
Pediatrics
Pregnancy and childbirth
Primary care and family health
Radiology and diagnostic imaging
Rehabilitation and physical therapy
Robotic surgery
Safety and injury prevention
Senior care and services
Skilled nursing
Sleep disorders

Stroke and neurology
Transplant
Travel medicine
Urgent care
Weight loss
  Weight management support
  Weight-loss surgery (bariatric)
Women' s care
Worksite wellness
Wound care and hyperbaric medicine

Selected Facilities

Sharp Chula Vista Medical Center (340 beds)
Sharp Coronado Hospital (180 beds)
Sharp Grossmont Hospital (540 beds La Mesa)
Sharp Mary Birch Hospital for Women & Newborns (170 beds San Diego)
Sharp McDonald Center (20 beds San Diego)
Sharp Memorial Hospital (675 beds San Diego)
Sharp Mesa Vista Hospital (150 beds San Diego)

COMPETITORS

Adventist Health	Scripps health
Dignity Health	Sutter Health
HCA	Tenet Healthcare
Palomar Health	Tri-City Healthcare
Paradise Valley	District
Hospital	UCSD Medical
Rady Children' s	
Hospital	

HISTORICAL FINANCIALS

Company Type: Private

Income Statement

FYE: September 30

	REVENUE ($ mil.)	NET INCOME ($ mil.)	NET PROFIT MARGIN	EMPLOYEES
09/13	1,158	(11)	—	13,000
09/09	897	(0)	—	—
09/06	1,790	42	2.4%	—
09/05	1,663	0	—	—
Annual Growth	(4.4%)	—	—	—

2013 Year-End Financials

Return on assets: 13.7%
Return on equity: (-1.0%)
Current ratio: 0.30

Cash ($ mil.): 178

SHARP MEMORIAL HOSPITAL

The docs and the scalpels are sharp at Sharp Memorial Hospital. The flagship facility of Sharp HealthCare the not-for-profit hospital has roughly 675 beds and is a designated trauma center for San Diego County. Specialties include cardiac care women's health multi-organ transplantation and cancer treatment. It also provides skilled nursing home health and hospice services. Sharp Memorial Hospital first opened in 1955. Sharp Health-Care completed reconstruction efforts on the Sharp Memorial facility in 2009; the new hospital has improved inpatient surgery emergency trauma and intensive care facilities.

Operations

Along with a full range of inpatient services Sharp Memorial's Outpatient Pavilion provides patients with cancer care women's imaging and endoscopy services. The center also conducts outpatient surgery procedures ranging from LASIK to orthopedic surgeries. More and more hospitals are adding outpatient services to their roster because they tend to be reimbursed at higher rates. The fa-

cility also provides patient education services such as community health classes.

Sharp Memorial which provides some $199 million in community benefits (including charity care and outreach efforts) each year is affiliated with a number of other hospitals clinics and physician groups through its parent organization.

EXECUTIVES

Pharmd, Leola Hau
Director Of Nursing, Angel Akabane
Vice President Finance, Staci Dickerson
Vice President Operations, Robert Wherry
Vice President Supply Chain, Kathryn Hanna
Pharmacy Manager, Kim Allen

LOCATIONS

HQ: SHARP MEMORIAL HOSPITAL
  7901 FROST ST, SAN DIEGO, CA 921232701
Phone: 858 939-3636
Web: WWW.SHARP.COM

COMPETITORS

Adventist Health	Scripps health
Grossmont Hospital	Tenet Healthcare
Palomar Health	Tri-City Healthcare
Rady Children' s	District
Hospital	UCSD Medical

HISTORICAL FINANCIALS

Company Type: Private

Income Statement

FYE: September 30

	REVENUE ($ mil.)	NET INCOME ($ mil.)	NET PROFIT MARGIN	EMPLOYEES
09/13	992	183	18.5%	3,500
09/12	965	194	20.2%	—
09/09	734	49	6.7%	—
09/08	670	0	—	—
Annual Growth	8.2%	—	—	—

2013 Year-End Financials

Return on assets: 2.4%
Return on equity: 18.5%
Current ratio: 1.50

Cash ($ mil.): 1

SHAWMUT WOODWORKING & SUPPLY INC.

Shawmut Woodworking & Supply which does business as Shawmut Design and Construction provides beginning-to-end construction services from preconstruction planning to post-construction quality assurance checks. The $860 million national construction management firm has experience building retail hotel gaming spa sports restaurant education banking healthcare and life science facilities. It also handles corporate interiors and high-end residential construction and boasts expertise in cultural and historical preservation projects. Founded in 1982 by Jim Ansara the employee-owned company serves clients nationwide from offices in a handful of US states.

OperationsShawmut's operations are divided into several groups including the design and construction of Academic Projects; Commercial Projects; Corporate Interiors Projects; Cultural and Historic Projects; Gaming Projects; Healthcare and Science Projects; Hotel Projects; Restaurant Proj-

ects; Retail Projects; Spas and Health Clubs Projects; and Sports Venues Projects.Geographic Reach

Shawmut Woodworking & Supply operates from offices in Boston; New York; Los Angeles; Las Vegas; Providence Rhode Island; New Haven Connecticut; Miami Florida; and West Springfield Massachusetts.

Sales and Marketing

Shawmut Woodworking & Supply serves a range of markets with varying needs with projects involving corporate interiors cultural and historic structures healthcare and science restaurants retail spas and health clubs sports venues and universities.Its clients have included Harvard University Massachusetts Institute of Technology Babson College Bank of America Accenture Mercantile Bank Cisco Systems the Nantucket Whaling Museum Harry Winston Hard Rock Cafe and Ruth's Hospitality Group.

Strategy

Shawmut Woodworking & Supply has been busy taking on high-value projects over the past few years. In early 2015 it completed its work on Boston's $115-million Dudley Municipal Building. In 2014 Shawmut's growing Healthcare and Life Sciences division started two new projects for two top clients. This included the renovation of clinical and support spaces in the health center a new wellness center and construction for additional examination rooms for Beth Israel Deaconess Medical Center; and a 35000-square-foot addition to a building at the Boston Medical Center.

The company has also been building high-end retail stores for top name clients in New York and elsewhere in recent years. Projects have included boutiques for Gucci Chanel and Juicy Couture.To keep its business growing in more areas Shawmut Woodworking & Supply has extended its operations across the US in recent years. In 2013 the firm added new offices on both US coasts with an office in Los Angeles and another in West Springfield Massachusetts.

EXECUTIVES

CEO, Les Hiscoe
VP and CFO, Roger C. Tougas
VP Chief Legal Officer and CIO, Doug Lareau
Vice President, Kevin Sullivan
Vice President Field Operations, Paul Doherty
Vice President Chief Legal Officer, Douglas (Doug) Laueau
Auditors: FEELEY & DRISCOLL PC BOSTO

LOCATIONS

HQ: SHAWMUT WOODWORKING & SUPPLY INC.
  560 HARRISON AVE STE 200, BOSTON, MA 021182632
Phone: 617 338-6200
Web: WWW.SHAWMUT.COM

PRODUCTS/OPERATIONS

Selected Markets
Academic
Commercial
Corporate interiors
Cultural and historic
Gaming
Healthcare and science
Restaurants
Retail
Spas and healthclubs
Sports venues

Selected Services
Services
  Pre-Construction
  Master planning services
  Master project scheduling
  Lease review
  Value engineering

Feasibility studies
Green design services
Drawing reviews
Facilities audits and campus assessments
Collaborative approach with architect/design team
Comprehensive conceptual estimating
BIM and virtual construction
In-house M/E/P expertise
Bid packages
Constructability reviews
Due diligence and site surveys
Pre-qualification of subcontractors
Management of permitting and approvals
Development of specific phasing schedules and delivery methods
Open book subcontractor bidding
Logistics planning
National purchasing power
Construction
Master project scheduling
Weekly project team meetings
Sites monitored by a Safety Manager
Zero-tolerance safety program
BIM and virtual construction services
LEED documentation certification and green building techniques
Permitting services
Design/build services
Communication with surrounding community
Coordination of owner-supplied items and vendors
Procurement solutions
Schedule and budget controls
24-hour/7 days-a-week emergency services
Specialized services for program clients
Indoor air quality management
Construction and demolition waste recycling
Customized waterproofing details
Post-Construction
Commissioning and close-out services
O&M manuals and training
Project services division
1-year warranty walkthrough

COMPETITORS

Andrew Velez Construction	Conti Enterprises
BBL Construction Services	E.W. Howell
	Skanska USA Building
Barr & Barr	Structure Tone
	Turner Corporation

HISTORICAL FINANCIALS

Company Type: Private

Income Statement

FYE: November 30

	REVENUE ($ mil.)	NET INCOME ($ mil.)	NET PROFIT MARGIN	EMPLOYEES
11/12	680	4	0.6%	711
11/11	662	3	0.6%	—
11/09*	618	(21)	—	—
12/05	440	0	—	—
Annual Growth	6.4%	—	—	—

*Fiscal year change

2012 Year-End Financials

Return on assets: 18.2%   Cash ($ mil.): 75
Return on equity: 0.6%
Current ratio: 1.10

SHAWNEE MISSION MEDICAL CENTER INC.

Shawnee Mission Medical Center (SMMC) cares for Kansas City residents primarily on the Kansas-side. The health care facility located in the city's southwest suburbs has some 500 inpatient beds. It also offers outpatient surgery and other health services in areas such as pediatrics rehabilitation oncology and radiology. The medical center's emergency department receives some 50000 visits each year. SMMC also operates satellite facilities including the Shawnee Mission Outpatient Pavilion in nearby Lenexa which offers emergency and outpatient diagnostic general practice and surgical care. SMMC is part of Adventist Health System.

Operations

SMMC handles some 20000 inpatient admissions each year as well as some 200000 outpatient visits. Its staff includes about 700 physicians who specialize in about 50 fields of medicine. Specialist care centers include a Chest Pain Emergency Center and the Center for Women's Health. The hospital also provides primary and specialty care through the Shawnee Mission Physicians Group including after-hours clinical care and cardiology and reproductive medicine services. SMMC delivers more babies per year than any other hospital in the metropolitan area.

Geographic Reach

SMMC is located on a more than 50-acre campus in Shawnee Mission (near Kansas City) in Johnson County Kansas and serves the surrounding area. The main hospital campus includes a free-standing surgery center six physician practice buildings a child-care center for associates and a community health center.

Strategy

The SMMC organization looks at community needs to determine where it should grow. In 2013 the hospital opened a $44 million new birthing center to meet the growing need for obstetric services in the Kansas City area. The expansion effort tripled the size of the medical center's labor and delivery and postpartum rooms allowing it to accommodate up to 5000 births annually and added a level III neonatal intensive care unit.

The facility is also adding to its technological abilities to better serve the community. In late 2014 it deployed the eMediTrack platform to help document and analyze data for compliance and accreditation readiness.

Company Background

SMMC is part of a network of more than 500 health care facilities sponsored by the Seventh-day Adventist Church.

EXECUTIVES

Vice President Taxation, Maxine Grassinger
Operating Room Director, Monica Powers
Medical Director Chest Pain Unit, Steven (Steve) Rowe
Executive Vice President Human Resources, Brad Hoffman

LOCATIONS

HQ: SHAWNEE MISSION MEDICAL CENTER INC.
9100 W 74TH ST, SHAWNEE MISSION, KS 662044004
Phone: 913 676-2000
Web: WWW.SHAWNEEMISSION.ORG

PRODUCTS/OPERATIONS

Selected Centers and Services
Bariatric Surgery
Behavioral Health
Britain Center (Cancer)
Center for Pain Medicine
CorporateCare
Diabetes
Emergency Services
Express Care
GI Services
Hand Specialty Center
HEALTHaware
Heart and Vascular Center
Home Health Care
Maternity
Holistic Care
Men's Health Program
Neurology
Nutrition and Weight Loss
Orthopedics
Plastic Surgery
Radiology
Rehabilitation Services
Reproductive Medicine
Robotic Surgery
Sleep Disorders Center
SM Outpatient Pavilion
SportsCare
Support Groups
Surgical Services
TherapyPlus
Transfer Center Urgent Care
Weight Loss Surgery
Women's Health
Wound Care Center

COMPETITORS

Ascension Health	Sisters of Charity of
Children's Mercy Hospital	Leavenworth
	Stormont-Vail
CoxHealth	HealthCare
HCA	Truman Medical Centers
Heartland Health	University of Kansas
Mercy Health	Medical Center
Saint Luke's Health System	Via Christi Health System

HISTORICAL FINANCIALS

Company Type: Private

Income Statement

FYE: December 31

	REVENUE ($ mil.)	NET INCOME ($ mil.)	NET PROFIT MARGIN	EMPLOYEES
12/12	343	30	9.0%	1,850
12/09	358	24	6.7%	—
12/08	304	19	6.4%	—
Annual Growth	3.0%	12.1%	—	—

2012 Year-End Financials

Return on assets: 5.6%   Cash ($ mil.): 236
Return on equity: 9.0%
Current ratio: 4.60

SHAWNEE MISSION UNIFIED SCHOOL DISTRICT 512

Auditors: MIZE HOUSER & COMPANY PA TOP

LOCATIONS

HQ: SHAWNEE MISSION UNIFIED SCHOOL DISTRICT 512
7235 ANTIOCH RD, SHAWNEE MISSION, KS 662041758
Phone: 913 993-6478
Web: WWW.SMSD.ORG

HISTORICAL FINANCIALS

Company Type: Private

Income Statement

FYE: June 30

	REVENUE ($ mil.)	NET INCOME ($ mil.)	NET PROFIT MARGIN	EMPLOYEES
06/14	317	15	4.9%	4,132
06/13	314	(11)	—	—
06/12	325	(8)	—	—
06/11	320	0	—	—
Annual Growth	(0.3%)	—	—	—

2014 Year-End Financials

Return on assets: 1.1%
Return on equity: 4.9%
Current ratio: 2.50

Cash ($ mil.): 97

2013 Year-End Financials

Return on assets: —
Return on equity: (-2.8%)
Current ratio: —

Cash ($ mil.): 35

EXECUTIVES

Senior Vice President Corporate Development and Managed Care, Mitchell (Mitch) Fillhaber
Vice President And Executive Director, Scott Sikes
Infection Control Director, Polly Hogue
Radiology Director, Deoarn Clinton
Medical Records Director, Lydia Williams
Vice President Of Marketing, Mitch Fillhaber
Board Member and Secretary, Stephen (Steve) Goot
Board Member, James D Thompson
Auditors: BENNETT THRASHER PC ATLANTA

SHEA HOMES LIMITED PARTNERSHIP A CALIFORNIA LIMITED PARTNERSHIP

Auditors: ERNST & YOUNG LLP LOS ANGELE

LOCATIONS

HQ: SHEA HOMES LIMITED PARTNERSHIP A CALIFORNIA LIMITED PARTNERSHIP
655 BREA CANYON RD, WALNUT, CA 917893078
Phone: 909 594-9500
Web: WWW.SHEAHOMES.COM

HISTORICAL FINANCIALS

Company Type: Private

Income Statement

FYE: December 31

	REVENUE ($ mil.)	NET INCOME ($ mil.)	NET PROFIT MARGIN	EMPLOYEES
12/14	1,140	133	11.7%	1,200
12/13	930	125	13.5%	—
12/12	680	29	4.3%	—
12/99	1,793	0	—	—
Annual Growth	(3.0%)	—	—	—

2014 Year-End Financials

Return on assets: 5.9%
Return on equity: 11.7%
Current ratio: 0.30

Cash ($ mil.): 236

SHELBY COUNTY BOARD OF EDUCATION

Auditors: WATKINS UIBERALL BANKS FINLEY

LOCATIONS

HQ: SHELBY COUNTY BOARD OF EDUCATION
160 S HOLLYWOOD ST, MEMPHIS, TN 381124801
Phone: 901 321-2500
Web: WWW.SCSK12.ORG

HISTORICAL FINANCIALS

Company Type: Private

Income Statement

FYE: June 30

	REVENUE ($ mil.)	NET INCOME ($ mil.)	NET PROFIT MARGIN	EMPLOYEES
06/13	391	(10)	—	4,800
06/12	422	(13)	—	—
06/11	414	(24)	—	—
06/10	395	0	—	—
Annual Growth	(0.3%)	—	—	—

SHEPHERD CENTER INC.

Here to shepherd those with catastrophic injuries back to good health is Shepherd Center. The not-for-profit hospital specializes in medical treatment research and rehabilitation for people with spinal cord and brain injuries as well as patients with neuromuscular disorders (such as spina bifida) and chronic pain. Shepherd Center boasts more than 150 beds and a 10-bed intensive care unit. Of its patients who have suffered injuries about 60% have been in car accidents. The hospital conducts neurological and neuromuscular research through its Virginia C. Crawford Research Institute.

Geographic Reach
Based in Atlanta Shepherd Center serves not only its home state of Georgia but the entire nation as one of the leading rehabilitation hospitals in the US.

Operations
Aside from its primary Shepherd Hospital Shepherd Center operates the Shepherd Pain Institute and the Andrew C. Carlos Multiple Sclerosis Institute.

Shepherd Center employs more than 1500 people. Seeing some 6600 people on an outpatient basis each year the center admits more than 960 patients to its inpatient programs and another 570 to its programs for day patients.

It conducts up to 50 research projects annually and is a Spinal Cord Injury Model Center as designated by the National Institute on Disability and Rehabilitation Research.

Strategy
In 2015 the company opened patient enrollment in a Phase 1/2a clinical trial to study an investigational product called AST-OPC1 (oligodendrocyte progenitor cells) in newly injured patients with sensory and motor-complete cervical spinal cord injury.

Expanding geographically to increase its services in 2014 Shepherd Center expanded to Nashville. That year the also hospital also announced plans for a $12.8 million project to expand and update its lab pharmacy and MRI suite. In 2014 AT&T gave $50000 to Shepherd Center to assist researchers in the Rehabilitation Engineering Research Center for Wireless Technologies by launching a series of seminars to help consumers with disabilities uncover the range of accessibility features found on their mobile devices.In 2013 Parker Hannifin formalized its collaboration with the Shepherd Center for the commercialization of Parker Hannifin's exoskeleton device Indego.

Company Background
The hospital is ranked by U.S. News & World Report magazine as one of the top 10 rehabilitation hospitals in the nation. It sponsors 11 wheelchair sports teams and has served as official sponsor of the wheelchair division of the Peachtree Road Race since 1984.

In 2012 the company continued or initiated 17 externally funded projects (totaling $2.4 million) and had 15 ongoing clinical trials sponsored by pharmaceutical and biotechnology companies.

Shepherd Center was founded in 1975 by James Shepherd (who was paralyzed in a bodysurfing accident) and his family.

LOCATIONS

HQ: SHEPHERD CENTER INC.
2020 PEACHTREE RD NW, ATLANTA, GA 303091465
Phone: 404 352-2020
Web: WWW.SHEPHERD.ORG

PRODUCTS/OPERATIONS

Selected Facilities

Andrew C. Carlos Multiple Sclerosis Institute
Shepherd Hospital
Shepherd Pain Institute

Selected Programs

Beyond Therapy
Brain Injury Rehabilitation
Care for U.S. Service Members
Chronic Pain
Disorders of Consciousness
Locomotor Training
Multiple Sclerosis
Outpatient Clinics
Patient Care
Secondary Complications
Shepherd Step
Spinal Cord Injury Rehabilitation
Stroke Rehabilitation
Ventilator Programs

Selected Services

Brain injury
Chronic Pain
Multi Specialty
Multiple Sclerosis
Spinal cord injury
Upper Extremity
Urology
Wound

COMPETITORS

DeKalb Medical	Regency Hospital
Emory Healthcare	Southern Regional
Grady Health System	Medical Center
Northside Hospital	WellStar Health System
Piedmont Healthcare	

HISTORICAL FINANCIALS

Company Type: Private

Income Statement

FYE: March 31

	REVENUE ($ mil.)	NET INCOME ($ mil.)	NET PROFIT MARGIN	EMPLOYEES
03/14	170	27	15.9%	800
03/13	168	23	13.9%	—
03/12	159	23	14.8%	—
03/11	134	0	—	—
Annual Growth	8.1%	—	—	—

2014 Year-End Financials

Return on assets: 2.2%
Return on equity: 15.9%
Current ratio: 3.20

Cash ($ mil.): 21

SHEPHERD ELECTRIC COMPANY INCORPORATED

For well over a hundred years Shepherd Electric has steered customers through a range of electrical needs. The company supplies a variety of electrical products to wholesale and retail customers primarily to the commercial construction market but it also serves government entities industrial firms and OEMs. Shepherd Electric carries products from major manufacturers such as 3M Brady Eaton Hadco Fluke General Electric and Thomas & Betts among many others. The company was founded in 1892 by Ernest Fluharty and Henry Shepherd. Shepherd Electric is owned by the Vogel family which has had a controlling interest in the company since 1931.

Shepherd Electric operates from four locations in the Baltimore and Washington DC area. Some of the lighting and switchgear projects that the company has been involved with include working with the US Chamber of Commerce Johns Hopkins Cancer Center University of Maryland Medical System and The Baltimore Museum of Art.

EXECUTIVES

CEO, Charles C. Vogel III, age 84
President, Stuart L. Vogel, age 58
VP and General Manager, Jim Shearer
Auditors: STEGMAN & COMPANY BALTIMORE

LOCATIONS

HQ: SHEPHERD ELECTRIC COMPANY INCORPORATED
7401 PULASKI HWY, BALTIMORE, MD 212372542
Phone: 410 866-6000
Web: WWW.SHEPHERDELEC.COM

COMPETITORS

Billows Electric Supply	Fromm Electric Gexpro
Colonial Electric Supply	Graybar Electric Rumsey Electric
Consolidated Electrical	United Electric Supply W.W. Grainger
Dominion Electric Supply	WESCO International

HISTORICAL FINANCIALS

Company Type: Private

Income Statement

FYE: December 31

	REVENUE ($ mil.)	NET INCOME ($ mil.)	NET PROFIT MARGIN	EMPLOYEES
12/13	188	3	1.6%	185
12/12	183	5	3.0%	—
12/11	163	2	1.8%	—
12/10	151	0	—	—
Annual Growth	7.5%	—	—	—

2013 Year-End Financials

Return on assets: 8.4%
Return on equity: 1.6%
Current ratio: 1.80
Cash ($ mil.): 5

SHEPPARD AND ENOCH PRATT FOUNDATION INC.

Auditors: KPMG LLP BALTIMORE MD

LOCATIONS

HQ: SHEPPARD AND ENOCH PRATT FOUNDATION INC.
6501 N CHARLES ST STE 242, BALTIMORE, MD 212046819
Phone: 410 938-3000
Web: WWW.SHEPPARDPRATT.ORG

HISTORICAL FINANCIALS

Company Type: Private

Income Statement

FYE: June 30

	REVENUE ($ mil.)	NET INCOME ($ mil.)	NET PROFIT MARGIN	EMPLOYEES
06/13	318	56	17.7%	1,399
06/12	281	(17)	—	—
06/11	273	44	16.4%	—
06/10	264	0	—	—
Annual Growth	6.4%	—	—	—

2013 Year-End Financials

Return on assets: 2.2%
Return on equity: 17.7%
Current ratio: 2.10
Cash ($ mil.): 68

SHI INTERNATIONAL CORP.

Businesses that need more than boxes of hardware and software can call SHI International. The company distributes scores of computer hardware and software products from suppliers such as Adobe Cisco HP Microsoft and McAfee. It resells PCs networking products data storage systems printers software and keyboards among other items. SHI offers a range of professional services including software licensing asset management managed desktop services systems integration and vocational training. The company serves corporate government and health care customers from more than 30 offices across the US Canada the UK Germany France and Hong Kong. SHI was founded in 1989 by Chairman Koguan Leo.

Geographic Reach

Based in Somerset New Jersey SHI has a global reach through its 30-plus offices located across the US Canada the UK Germany France and Hong Kong. In the US the company operates primarily in Texas and California but also in Arizona Colorado Florida Georgia Illinois Indiana Kansas Massachusetts Michigan Minnesota Missouri New Jersey New York Pennsylvania Virginia and Washington. Specifically its cloud briefing center is housed in New York City and its corporate call center runs from Austin Texas. The company's 420000-sq.-ft. headquarters operates beside its 140000-sq.-ft. Integration Center in Somerset New Jersey.

Operations

SHI serves several sectors and verticals. The company specializes in software and hardware procurement deployment planning configuration data center optimization IT asset management and cloud computing as well as custom IT solutions.

Financial Performance

SHI International rang up $5 billion in sales in 2013 a 15% increase versus the prior year. SHI's public sector corporate and enterprise commercial sales divisions each surpassed $1 billion in sales for the first time in 2013. Combined the strategic enterprise and international divisions accounted for an additional $2 billion in revenue for the year.

The seller of IT products and services boasts a 99% annual customer retention rate.

Strategy

The company has transformed itself from a $1 million regional reseller of software to a $5 billion global provider of information technology products and services. To this end SHI has invested some $20 million in a new data center that provides cloud services specifically what the company terms infrastructure-as-a-service (IaaS). The data center is one of six in the US that houses virtual machines for IT professionals to provide services such as application deployment disaster recovery software-as-a-service (SaaS). It also offers on-demand burst computing services where customers use the additional bandwidth to handle peaks in demand. HP Networking provides the network infrastructure for the data center which became operational in 2011.

SHI's professional services unit already provides some cloud services and data center consulting. SHI sees IaaS as a logical extension of the software asset management (SAM) service it already provides. Under the SAM program SHI handles software deployment licensing compliance and inventories across a business.

SHI partners with Omaha Nebraska-based information security software specialist Solutionary to manage data security services using its ActiveGuard software product to block computer network security breaches as data center security is one of the biggest concerns for businesses in a cloud computing environment.

Awards and Recognition

SHI is the largest minority and women-owned Business Enterprise (MWBE) in the US. The company's ranked 17th on CRN's 2013 Solution Provider 500 list of the largest IT solution providers in North America.

EXECUTIVES

President and CEO, Thai Lee, age 58
VP Finance and Corporate Secretary, Paul Ng
VP and General Manager, Hal Jagger
Chief Technology Officer, Richard (Rich) Taggart
Vice President Material Handling Division, Pete Hackett
National Account Manager, Thomas Miner
Vice President Information Technology, Sam Mourad
Vice President COMMERCIAL and INDUSTRIAL PROPERTIES, Nehal Patel
Vice President New Business Development, Celeste Lee
Chairman, Koguan Leo
Auditors: COHN REZNICK LLP NEW YORK NE

LOCATIONS

HQ: SHI INTERNATIONAL CORP.
290 DAVIDSON AVE, SOMERSET, NJ 088734145
Phone: 732 764-8888
Web: WWW.SHI.COM

PRODUCTS/OPERATIONS

Selected Products
Accessories

Peripherals
Hardware
Memory
Software

Selected Services
Cloud services
Computer vocational training services
Data center services
Events
Hardware services
Networking
POLARIS Software asset management
Storage
Strategic consulting
Webinars

COMPETITORS

ASI Computer	Computacenter
Technologies	Ingram Micro
Agilysys	Insight Enterprises
Arrow Electronics	PC Mall
Avnet	Softchoice
CDW	Tech Data
CompuCom	

HISTORICAL FINANCIALS
Company Type: Private

Income Statement
FYE: December 31

	REVENUE ($ mil.)	NET INCOME ($ mil.)	NET PROFIT MARGIN	EMPLOYEES
12/13	5,003	74	1.5%	2,500
12/12	4,389	61	1.4%	—
12/11	3,757	35	1.0%	—
12/08	0	0	—	—
Annual Growth	—	—	—	—

2013 Year-End Financials
Return on assets: 14.4%
Return on equity: 1.5%
Current ratio: 1.20
Cash ($ mil.): 96

SHIRES HOUSING INC.

Auditors: OTIS ATWELL SOUTH PORTLAND M

LOCATIONS

HQ: SHIRES HOUSING INC.
302 SOUTH ST, BENNINGTON, VT 052012844
Phone: 802 442-8139
Web: WWW.RAHCBENNINGTON.ORG

HISTORICAL FINANCIALS
Company Type: Private

Income Statement
FYE: September 30

	REVENUE ($ mil.)	NET INCOME ($ mil.)	NET PROFIT MARGIN	EMPLOYEES
09/13	448	(400)	—	3
09/12	0	(0)	—	—
09/11	0	(0)	—	—
09/10	0	0	—	—
Annual Growth	747.7%	—	—	—

2013 Year-End Financials
Return on assets: 14.9%
Return on equity: (-89.2%)
Current ratio: 0.50
Cash ($ mil.): 286

SHORE MEMORIAL HOSPITAL

You might be able to get a room with a view of the ocean at Shore Memorial Hospital. Operating as Shore Medical Center the facility is a not-for-profit community hospital with some 300 beds. It offers acute care services and more than 35 specialized care programs including oncology cardiology neurology obstetrics and orthopedic care. Shore Medical Center is affiliated with The University of Pennsylvania Health System and The Children's Hospital of Philadelphia. In addition to the hospital Shore Medical Center operates community-based health and fitness centers.

Geographic Reach

Shore Medical Center is located in Somers Point New Jersey which is located about 60 miles southeast of downtown Philadelphia.

Operations

Shore Medical Center has some 370 physicians on its staff which handles some 11000 inpatient visits per year. The hospital also manages some 6000 surgeries 1000 births and 47000 emergency room visits per year. Inpatient services account for about half of annual operating revenues while outpatient and emergency services each account for between 15% and 20% of sales.

As part of its affiliation with The University of Pennsylvania Health System Shore Medical Center has access to larger neuroscience and cardiovascular care programs among other specialties. It partners with the Children's Hospital of Philadelphia to provide pediatric services.

Financial Performance

Shore Medical Center reported a slight 3% dip in revenue for 2013 down to $15.4 million from $16 million.

Strategy

To expand its services for children and infants in 2013 Shore Medical Center formed a partnership with Onsite Neonatal Partners. Through the collaboration Onsite will provide staff for Shore Medical Center's 24-hour neonatal and pediatric care divisions.

In the realm of medical education Shore Medical Center strengthened its position by teaming up with Drexel University's College of Medicine to provide clinical education programs beginning in 2012. Through the partnership Drexel students will be able to conduct one-month rotations at the hospital in about 10 medical fields.

Shore Memorial Hospital adopted the Shore Medical Center brand after it completed a $125 million expansion project in 2011. The project included a new surgical pavilion that expanded its cardiovascular surgery and endoscopy centers as well as other specialist departments and diagnostic exam and laboratory units. Expansion efforts also included the opening of a new pediatric care center. The change in branding reflects the facility's broader service offerings and its connections to other health providers in the region.

EXECUTIVES

Assistant Vice President Surgical, Robin Keyack
Director Of Pharmacy and Pgy1 Program, Matt Piskun
Secretary, Diane Severino
Secretary Radiology School, Kristin Dennis

LOCATIONS

HQ: SHORE MEMORIAL HOSPITAL
100 MEDICAL CENTER WAY, SOMERS POINT, NJ 082442389
Phone: 609 653-3800
Web: WWW.SHOREMEDICALCENTER.ORG

PRODUCTS/OPERATIONS

2012 Operating Revenues

	% of total
Inpatient	50
Outpatient services	19
Emergency department	15
Same day surgery	6
Dialysis	4
Observation	2
Other	4
Total	**100**

Selected Departments and Services
Anesthesiology
Balance Care
Blood Bank
Cancer Center
CardioVascular Institute
Critical Care Center
Diabetes Education
Emergency Department
Endoscopy
Give To Shore
Hospitalist Services
Laboratory Services
Maternal-Fetal Medicine
Maternity Care Center
Neurosciences Center
Outpatient Testing Centers
Palliative Care
Pediatrics
Pulmonary Diagnostic Center
Quick Care Center
Radiology & Diagnostic Imaging
Rehabilitation Services
Respiratory Care
Sleep Medicine
Social Services
Spine and Orthopedic
Stroke Services
Surgical Services
Tele-ICU
Wound Care and Hyperbaric Medicine

COMPETITORS

AtlantiCare	Jefferson Health
Capital Health System	System
Christiana Care	Kennedy Health System
Crozer-Keystone Health	Princeton HealthCare
System	The Cooper Health
Doylestown Hospital	System
Inspira Health Network	Virtua Health

HISTORICAL FINANCIALS
Company Type: Private

Income Statement
FYE: December 31

	REVENUE ($ mil.)	NET INCOME ($ mil.)	NET PROFIT MARGIN	EMPLOYEES
12/12	202	(3)	—	1,600
12/09	202	5	2.6%	—
12/08	180	(7)	—	—
12/07	183	0	—	—
Annual Growth	2.0%	—	—	—

2012 Year-End Financials
Return on assets: 8.7%
Return on equity: (-1.7%)
Current ratio: 0.50
Cash ($ mil.): —

SHRIEVE CHEMICAL COMPANY

Auditors: BRIGGS & VESELKA CO HOUSTON

LOCATIONS

HQ: SHRIEVE CHEMICAL COMPANY
1755 WOODSTEAD CT, SPRING, TX 773800964
Phone: 281 367-4226
Web: WWW.SHRIEVE.COM

HISTORICAL FINANCIALS

Company Type: Private

Income Statement

FYE: December 31

	REVENUE ($ mil.)	NET INCOME ($ mil.)	NET PROFIT MARGIN	EMPLOYEES
12/13	372	21	5.7%	77
12/12	372	21	5.7%	—
12/11	328	20	6.1%	—
12/10	173	0	—	—
Annual Growth 29.0%		—	—	—

2013 Year-End Financials

Return on assets: 7.3% Cash ($ mil.): 4
Return on equity: 5.7%
Current ratio: 1.20

SIGNAL INTERNATIONAL LLC

LOCATIONS

HQ: SIGNAL INTERNATIONAL LLC
601 BAYOU CASOTTE PKWY, PASCAGOULA, MS
395819600
Phone: 228 762-0010
Web: WWW.SIGNALINT.COM

HISTORICAL FINANCIALS

Company Type: Private

Income Statement

FYE: December 31

	REVENUE ($ mil.)	NET INCOME ($ mil.)	NET PROFIT MARGIN	EMPLOYEES
12/07	398	40	10.1%	2,750
12/06	285	30	10.6%	—
12/04	82	6	7.4%	—
12/03	0	0	—	—
Annual Growth	—	—	—	—

2007 Year-End Financials

Return on assets: 3.4% Cash ($ mil.): 6
Return on equity: 10.1%
Current ratio: 1.10

SIGNATURE CONSULTANTS LLC

Signature Consultants wants your John Hancock when it comes to signing up for its staffing services. The company provides information technology staffing services to clients from a variety of industries. Signature places IT professionals with expertise in areas like project management Web application development database administration storage and network security. The firm has experience placing IT professionals across such industries as aerospace automotive banking and financial services education electronics government technology pharmaceutical and manufacturing.

Geographic Reach

Signature provides information technology staffing services from more than 15 locations throughout the US. The company has its National Service Center in Boston Massachusetts and Regional Service Centers in Charlotte North Carolina; Orlando Florida; Fort Lauderdale Florida; and Boston Massachusetts.

Operations

Signature has more than 1100 IT consultants to support run and manage clients' technology needs.

Company Background

The privately owned company was founded in 1996.

EXECUTIVES

President and CEO, Jay Cohen
COO, Mark Nussbaum
CFO, Philip Monti
CIO, Chris Tyrell
President National Accounts, Geoff Gray
National Account Manager, Chad Kelly
National Account Manager, Sasha Anderson
Senior Vice President Of Human Resources, Candace Whitaker
National Accounts Manager, Debbie Robertson
National Account Manager, Michael Goad
Auditors: MAYER HOFFMAN MCCANN PC BOC

LOCATIONS

HQ: SIGNATURE CONSULTANTS LLC
2101 W COML BLVD STE 3000, FORT LAUDERDALE, FL 33309
Phone: 954 677-1020
Web: WWW.SIGCONSULT.COM

COMPETITORS

Adecco	Kelly Services
Allegis Group	Motion Recruitment
Butler America	Partners
CDI	RCM Technologies
COMFORCE	Technisource

HISTORICAL FINANCIALS

Company Type: Private

Income Statement

FYE: December 31

	REVENUE ($ mil.)	NET INCOME ($ mil.)	NET PROFIT MARGIN	EMPLOYEES
12/13	202	3	1.9%	1,450
12/12	153	(1)	—	—
12/09	106	3	3.1%	—
12/08	127	0	—	—
Annual Growth 9.7%		—	—	—

2013 Year-End Financials

Return on assets: — Cash ($ mil.): —
Return on equity: 1.9%
Current ratio: 1.30

SIGNATURE HEALTHCARE CORPORATION

Auditors: PRICEWATERHOUSECOOPERS LLP B

LOCATIONS

HQ: SIGNATURE HEALTHCARE CORPORATION
680 CENTRE ST, BROCKTON, MA 023023308
Phone: 508 941-7000
Web: WWW.SIGNATURE-HEALTHCARE.ORG

HISTORICAL FINANCIALS

Company Type: Private

Income Statement

FYE: September 30

	REVENUE ($ mil.)	NET INCOME ($ mil.)	NET PROFIT MARGIN	EMPLOYEES
09/14	304	11	3.8%	1,500
09/13	1	0	61.1%	—
09/09	0	0	42.9%	—
09/08	1	0	—	—
Annual Growth 149.1%		—	—	—

2014 Year-End Financials

Return on assets: 6.7% Cash ($ mil.): 20
Return on equity: 3.8%
Current ratio: 1.20

SILVER BLUFF LLC

LOCATIONS

HQ: SILVER BLUFF LLC
100 SILVER BLUFF DR, CANTON, NC 287166350
Phone: 828 648-2044
Web: WWW.SILVERBLUFFVILLAGE.COM

HISTORICAL FINANCIALS

Company Type: Private

Income Statement

FYE: September 30

	REVENUE ($ mil.)	NET INCOME ($ mil.)	NET PROFIT MARGIN	EMPLOYEES
09/09	891	66	7.5%	200
09/07	8	0	5.5%	—
09/06	8	0	5.4%	—
09/05	8	0	—	—
Annual Growth 216.7%		—	—	—

2009 Year-End Financials

Return on assets: — Cash ($ mil.): —
Return on equity: 7.5%
Current ratio: 2.00

SILVER CROSS HOSPITAL AND MEDICAL CENTERS

Silver Cross Hospital and Medical Centers serve the Illinois counties of Will Grundy and Cook through its 290-bed main hospital campus and nine satellite facilities throughout the area. Services provided by the medical facility include cardiovascular care women's health rehabilitation and behavioral health care. Its outpatient facilities provide primary and specialty care services such as medical imaging and dialysis. The Silver Cross Hospital and Medical Centers name comes from the emblem (the Maltese Cross) of the Christian organization that founded the not-for-profit hospital the International Order of The King's Daughters and Sons.

Geographic Reach

Silver Cross Hospital and Medical Centers serves patients in the Illinois counties of Cook Grundy and Will.

Operations

Thomson Reuters' Truven a leading source of healthcare intelligence has named Silver Cross Hospital and Medical Centers one of the "100 Top Hospitals" in the nation for seven consecutive years.

The Illinois medical facility maintains a staff of more than 100 physicians. It specializes in offering diagnostic imaging rehabilitation therapy dialysis women's health services and emergency services.

Strategy

In 2012 the hospital opened a replacement facility in New Lenox to house its main hospital and to keep pace with population growth in its service territory. The $400-million Silver Cross Hospital facility has about 290 private patient rooms. The 70-acre New Lenox campus also includes two medical offices buildings and the University of Chicago Medicine Comprehensive Cancer Center.

Silver Cross Hospital and Medical Centers also collaborates with the Rehabilitation Institute of Chicago to provide outpatient rehabilitation services at four of the health system's locations.

It added a sleep disorders center in 2012 at its New Lenox (Route 6) location.

Company Background

Silver Cross Hospital admitted its first patient in Joliet Illinois in 1895.

EXECUTIVES

Infection Control Director, Margaret Rodeghero
Pharm D, Nneka Okafo
Auditors: ERNST & YOUNG US LLP INDIAN

LOCATIONS

HQ: SILVER CROSS HOSPITAL AND MEDICAL CENTERS
1900 SILVER CROSS BLVD, NEW LENOX, IL 604519509
Phone: 815 740-1234
Web: WWW.SILVERCROSS.ORG

Selected Locations
Headquarters
  New Lenox Illinois
Locations with Silver Cross Services
  East Joliet
  Homer Glen
  New Lenox (Route 6)
  New Lenox (Route 30)
  West Joliet

Professional Office Buildings with Silver Cross Medical Staff
  East Joliet
  Frankfort
  Home Glen
  Lemont
  New Lenox (Route 6)
  New Lenox (Route 30)
  West Joliet

PRODUCTS/OPERATIONS

Selected Departments/Facilities
Behavioral Health/Chemical Dependency
Birthing Center
Cancer Center
Cardiology
Center for Women' s Health
Colon Cancer Screening
Diagnostic Imaging
Diabetes
Dialysis
Encore Shop
Emergency Department
Free-Standing Emergency Care Center
Home Health Care
Incontinence & Pelvic Floor Disorders
Interventional Radiology
Joint Replacement Education
Intensive Care
Outpatient Infusion Center
Pediatric Services
Pet Therapy
Prostate Health
Pulmonary Program
  Rehabilita
Surgery - Same Day
Surgery - Using the da Vinci Robot
Senior Advantage
Silver Cross Emergency Medical Services System
Sleep Disorders Center
Weight Loss Surgery
Wound Healing & Treatment Center

Selected Services
Behavioral health care
Birthing services
Cancer care
Cardiovascular care/Cath Lab
Cardiopulmonary Rehabilitation
Chemical Dependency Services
Chemo and Radiation
Colon cancer screening/Colonoscopies
Da Vinci Robotic Surgery
Diabetes management
Diagnostic testing and imaging (ultrasound x-ray MRI PET/CT scan etc.)
Dialysis
Dietary Counseling
Emergency care
Health educational programs and screenings
Home health care
Hospitalists
Infusion Therapy (chemotherapy etc.)
Incontinence Care
Intensive care
Laboratory testing
Lifeline Emergency Personal Response Service
Mammography
Medical/Surgical inpatient care
Neonatal care
Neurology/Neurosurgery
Obstetrical/gynecological care
Orthopedic care
Pain management
Pastoral care
Pediatric care
Pulmonary care
Rehabilitation (physical speech occupational)
Senior Advantage Program
Sleep Disorders Carre
Support Groups
Stroke care
Surgery (outpatient & inpatient)
Weight Loss Surgery
Women' s Health
Wound care

COMPETITORS

Adventist Health System Sunbelt Healthcare
Advocate Health Care
Covenant Ministries
Elmhurst Memorial Healthcare
Mercy Hospital and Medical Center
Northwestern Memorial HealthCare
Sinai Health System
St. Bernard Hospital and Health Care Center
University of Chicago Medical Center

HISTORICAL FINANCIALS
Company Type: Private

Income Statement

FYE: September 30

	REVENUE ($ mil.)	NET INCOME ($ mil.)	NET PROFIT MARGIN	EMPLOYEES
09/13	306	6	2.1%	1,700
09/08	244	21	8.6%	—
09/06*	187	13	7.3%	—
12/05	601	0	—	—
Annual Growth	(8.1%)	—	—	—

*Fiscal year change

2013 Year-End Financials
Return on assets: 10.5%
Return on equity: 2.1%
Current ratio: 0.20
Cash ($ mil.): 10

SILVER TOWNE L.P.

Auditors: DRUMM & COMPANY MUNCIE INDIA

LOCATIONS

HQ: SILVER TOWNE L.P.
120 E UNION CITY PIKE, WINCHESTER, IN 473948383
Phone: 765 584-7481
Web: WWW.SILVERTOWNEMINT.COM

HISTORICAL FINANCIALS
Company Type: Private

Income Statement

FYE: December 31

	REVENUE ($ mil.)	NET INCOME ($ mil.)	NET PROFIT MARGIN	EMPLOYEES
12/13	342	0	0.2%	80
12/12	319	0	0.1%	—
12/11	509	4	0.8%	—
12/09	259	0	—	—
Annual Growth	7.2%	—	—	—

2013 Year-End Financials
Return on assets: 0.2%
Return on equity: 0.2%
Current ratio: 0.30
Cash ($ mil.): —

SINAI HOSPITAL OF BALTIMORE INC

Sinai Hospital of Baltimore part of the LifeBridge Health network provides medical care in northwestern Baltimore. The 470-bed hospital is a not-for-profit medical center that includes such facilities as a heart center a children's hospital a cancer institute and a rehab center. Other specialties include orthopedics neurology and women's care. Medical students from Johns Hopkins University and the University of Maryland do some of their training at the hospital. Sinai Hospital of Baltimore was founded in 1866 as the Hebrew Hospital and Asylum and became a subsidiary of LifeBridge when it merged with other area providers in 1998.

Operations

The Sinai Hospital of Baltimore handles about 26000 inpatient admissions and some 75000 emergency room visits per year. It also conducts about 20000 inpatient and outpatient surgeries annually.

The medical center conducts a number of education and training programs including residencies and fellowships for about 400 medical students each year. It is a designated training site for the Johns Hopkins University's ambulatory and internal medicine clerkships.

Strategy

Sinai Hospital of Baltimore has completed several expansion efforts in recent years. In 2012 it opened a new dedicated inpatient hospice unit as well as a new center for geriatric surgery. In addition the 20-bed Friedman Neurological Rehabilitation Center was completed that year.

EXECUTIVES

President, Amy Perry
Senior Vice President President and Chief Executive Officer LifeBridge Health, Neil M. Meltzer, $343,251 total compensation
SVP Finance and CFO, Charles (Chuck) Orlando
VP Marketing and Public Relations, Rudy Miller
Patient Safety Officer, Tina Gionet
VP Human Resources, Taylor Foss
Coordinator Auxiliary Services, Sharon Rosen
President Medical Staff, Joel Pleeter
Physician-in-Chief, Steven Gambert
VP, Barbara Epke
VP and Chief Nursing Officer, Diane Johnson
VP, Lorrie Liang
SVP Finance and CFO, Chuck Orlando
VP, Ida Samet
COO Practice Dynamics, Jeff Watson
Senior Vice President Chief Financial Officer, David Krajewski
Senior Vice President President - Levindale, Aric Spitulnik
Senior Vice President President - Northwest Hospital, Brian White
Chair, Brian L. Moffet
Vice Chair, Robin Weiman
Vice President Chief Information Officer, Tressa Springmann
Auditors: KPMG LLP BALTIMORE MD

LOCATIONS

HQ: SINAI HOSPITAL OF BALTIMORE INC
2401 W BELVEDERE AVE, BALTIMORE, MD 212155270
Phone: 410 601-5678
Web: WWW.LIFEBRIDGEHEALTH.ORG

PRODUCTS/OPERATIONS

Selected Centers

Alvin & Lois Lapidus Cancer Institute at LifeBridge Health
Center for Joint Preservation and Replacement
Children's Hospital at Sinai
ER-7 Emergency Center
Heart Center at Sinai
International Center for Limb Lengthening
Krieger Eye Institute
Louis and Phyllis Friedman Neurological Rehabilitation Center
Rubin Institute for Advanced Orthopedics
Sandra and Malcolm Berman Brain & Spine Institute
Sinai Rehabilitation Center
The Spine Center at Sinai

Selected Services

Allergy and Immunology
Anesthesia
Cardiology
Cancer/Medical Oncology
Dermatology
Dialysis
Emergency Medicine
Endocrinology and Metabolism
Family Medicine
Gastroenterology
General Internal Medicine
Geriatric Medicine
Infectious Diseases
Nephrology (kidneys)
Pulmonary and Critical Care Medicine
Rheumatology (joints tendons)
Neurology
Neurosurgery
Obstetrics and Gynecology
Ophthalmology (eye care)
Oral and Maxillofacial Surgery and Dentistry
Orthopedic Surgery
Otolaryngology (ear nose & throat)
Pathology
Pediatrics
Pharmacy
Physical Medicine and Rehabilitation
Psychiatry
Radiation Oncology
Radiology
Surgery
Urology

COMPETITORS

Anne Arundel Medical Center	Johns Hopkins Health System
Ascension Health	MedStar Health
Bon Secours Health	Meritus Health
Franklin Square Hospital Center	University of Maryland Medical System
GBMC	

HISTORICAL FINANCIALS

Company Type: Private

Income Statement

FYE: June 30

	REVENUE ($ mil.)	NET INCOME ($ mil.)	NET PROFIT MARGIN	EMPLOYEES
06/13	742	32	4.3%	1,403
06/11	691	36	5.3%	—
06/10	665	14	2.1%	—
06/09	1,237	0	—	—
Annual Growth	—	—	—	—

2013 Year-End Financials

Return on assets: 12.4%
Return on equity: 4.3%
Current ratio: 1.60
Cash ($ mil.): 106

SINGING RIVER HEALTH SYSTEM

LOCATIONS

HQ: SINGING RIVER HEALTH SYSTEM
2809 DENNY AVE, PASCAGOULA, MS 395815301
Phone: 228 809-5251
Web: WWW.MYSRHS.COM

HISTORICAL FINANCIALS

Company Type: Private

Income Statement

FYE: September 30

	REVENUE ($ mil.)	NET INCOME ($ mil.)	NET PROFIT MARGIN	EMPLOYEES
09/13	359	2	0.6%	2,100
09/12	366	5	1.6%	—
09/05	259	12	4.7%	—
09/02	224	0	—	—
Annual Growth	4.4%	—	—	—

2013 Year-End Financials

Return on assets: 25.5%
Return on equity: 0.6%
Current ratio: 1.50
Cash ($ mil.): 38

SLOAN IMPLEMENT COMPANY INC.

There's no slowin' down at Sloan Implement. The company provides the tools of trade for farmers in Illinois. Headquartered in Assumption Illinois Sloan is an authorized dealer of John Deere equipment and new and used parts. Founded in 1931 the company sells and services new and used Deere equipment including combines tractors manure spreaders tillers earth moving and lawn machinery and grain-handling equipment at five locations in Wisconsin and at 11 locations in Illinois; it also ships products nationwide and to international customers.

EXECUTIVES

President, Jim Steck
Parts Manager, Dustin Duduit
Manager Service, Chuck Standley
Store Manager Atwood (IL), Craig Wynne
Store Manager Carlinville (IL), Greg McCallum
Store Manager Effingham (IL), Larry Probst
Store Manager Taylorville (IL), Rod Carls
Store Manager Shelbyville (IL), Gary Patterson
Store Manager Virden (IL), Roger Spires
Service Manager, Bill Winstead
Office Manager, Chris McMahon
Service Manager Trucking, Shawn Jordan

LOCATIONS

HQ: SLOAN IMPLEMENT COMPANY INC.
120 N BUSINESS 51, ASSUMPTION, IL 625101120
Phone: 217 226-4411
Web: WWW.SLOANS.COM

COMPETITORS

Evergreen FS	Two Rivers FS
Southern FS	

HISTORICAL FINANCIALS

Company Type: Private

Income Statement

FYE: December 31

	REVENUE ($ mil.)	NET INCOME ($ mil.)	NET PROFIT MARGIN	EMPLOYEES
12/07	217	9	4.3%	350
12/06	146	4	3.0%	—
12/05	150	5	3.4%	—
12/04	159	0	—	—
Annual Growth	10.8%	—	—	—

SMDC MEDICAL CENTER

Auditors: ERNST & YOUNG US LLP ATLANTA

LOCATIONS

HQ: SMDC MEDICAL CENTER
502 E 2ND ST, DULUTH, MN 558051913
Phone: 218 726-4000
Web: WWW.SMDC.ORG

HISTORICAL FINANCIALS
Company Type: Private

Income Statement
FYE: June 30

	REVENUE ($ mil.)	NET INCOME ($ mil.)	NET PROFIT MARGIN	EMPLOYEES
06/12	372	5	1.4%	750
06/11	373	13	3.7%	—
06/10	365	12	3.4%	—
06/09	208	0	—	—
Annual Growth	21.3%	—	—	—

2012 Year-End Financials
Return on assets: —   Cash ($ mil.): 126
Return on equity: 1.4%
Current ratio: —

SMO INCORPORATED

LOCATIONS

HQ: SMO INCORPORATED
6355 CRAIN HWY, LA PLATA, MD 206464267
Phone: 301 932-3600
Web: WWW.WILLSGROUP.COM

HISTORICAL FINANCIALS
Company Type: Private

Income Statement
FYE: September 30

	REVENUE ($ mil.)	NET INCOME ($ mil.)	NET PROFIT MARGIN	EMPLOYEES
09/10	496	6	1.3%	25
09/09	395	8	2.1%	—
09/06	0	0	—	—
09/05	0	0	—	—
Annual Growth	—	—	—	—

2010 Year-End Financials
Return on assets: 1.1%   Cash ($ mil.): 6
Return on equity: 1.3%
Current ratio: 1.00

SNAKE RIVER SUGAR COMPANY

Auditors: EIDEBAILLY LLP BOISE IDAHO

LOCATIONS

HQ: SNAKE RIVER SUGAR COMPANY
1951 S SATURN WAY STE 100, BOISE, ID 837092924
Phone: 208 383-6500
Web: WWW.SRCOOP.COM

HISTORICAL FINANCIALS
Company Type: Private

Income Statement
FYE: August 31

	REVENUE ($ mil.)	NET INCOME ($ mil.)	NET PROFIT MARGIN	EMPLOYEES
08/12	936	31	3.4%	2,500
08/11	876	13	1.5%	—
08/10	839	18	2.2%	—
08/09	658	0	—	—
Annual Growth	12.4%	—	—	—

2012 Year-End Financials
Return on assets: —   Cash ($ mil.): 28
Return on equity: 3.4%
Current ratio: 0.10

SNAPPING SHOALS ELECTRIC TRUST INC.

Named after a geographic area that sounds like an angler's dream Snapping Shoals Electric Membership Corporation (Snapping Shoals EMC) distributes electricity to 95000 residential commercial and industrial customers in an 8-county region in the southeastern portion of the Atlanta metropolitan area. The member-owned cooperative also provides competitive retail natural gas supply services to customers through Snapping Shoals Energy Management Company a partnership with SCANA. Snapping Shoals EMC also offers security systems surge protection services and security lighting options.

The cooperative is also a member of Green Power EMC which analyzes and negotiates power purchase agreements with Georgia-based renewable resource providers to allow member EMCs to access "greener" power supplies in order to conserve energy and help protect the environment.

Formed in 1938 as part of the national rural electrification drive Snapping Shoals EMC's service territory covers parts of Butts DeKalb Henry Jasper Morgan Newton Rockdale and Walton counties.

EXECUTIVES

President and CEO, Randall G. Meadows
VP Energy Services, Terry Clark
VP Engineering Services, Brad Thomas
VP Line Services, Charles Woodward
VP Corporate Services, Randy Shaw
Manager Engineering, Melvin Allen
Manager MIS, Louise Blackman
Manager Member Services, Randy Price
Manager Human Resources, Margie Rowe
Manager Economic Development, Danny Stone
Manager Consumer Services, Dennis Thompson
Executive Assistant, Cathy Dyer
Chairman, James I. White
Vice Chairman, Olin Bonner
Secretary Treasurer and Director, Anthony Norton
Assistant Secretary Assistant Treasurer and Director, Joseph Sharp
Secretary Treasurer, Brenda Mason
Accounting Supervisor, Katie Johnston
President CEO of Snapping Shoals EMC, Brad Thomas
Assistant Secretary Treasurer, Walter Johnson
Vice Chairman, Olin Bonner
Secretary Treasurer and Director, Anthony Norton
Assistant Secretary Assistant Treasurer and Director, Joseph Sharp
Director, Ruby Woods
Director, Brenda Mason
Director, D. L. (Pete) Knox
Director, Jarnett W. Wigington
Director, James Sockwell
Director, Lewis Washington
Auditors: MCNAIR MCLEMORE MIDDLEBROOKS

LOCATIONS

HQ: SNAPPING SHOALS ELECTRIC TRUST INC.
14750 BROWN BRIDGE RD, COVINGTON, GA 300164113
Phone: 770 786-3484
Web: WWW.CO.HENRY.GA.US

HISTORICAL FINANCIALS
Company Type: Private

Income Statement
FYE: December 31

	REVENUE ($ mil.)	NET INCOME ($ mil.)	NET PROFIT MARGIN	EMPLOYEES
12/12	170	2	1.2%	270
12/11	176	2	1.6%	—
12/10	186	4	2.4%	—
12/09	179	0	—	—
Annual Growth	(1.8%)	—	—	—

2012 Year-End Financials
Return on assets: 6.4%   Cash ($ mil.): 2
Return on equity: 1.2%
Current ratio: 0.50

SOMERSET TIRE SERVICE INC.

Somerset Tire Service (STS) operates about 145 tire and auto centers throughout New Jersey New York and Pennsylvania. The company primarily sells tires auto parts batteries and accessories under such top brand names as Bridgestone Firestone Michelin Toyo Pirelli Goodyear Yokohama and Continental. Operating under the banner STS Tire & Auto Centers the company's locations feature a window between the store and service bays so customers can watch the work being done on their cars. STS has grown by acquiring other regional tire and service centers with hopes of saturating the Northeast before moving outside its home region. Founded in 1958 the company is employee-owned.

Geographic Reach

Based in New Jersey STS operates more than 80 of its stores in its home state as well as 30 stores each in New York and Pennsylvania. The company is the largest independent tire and automotive service company in the Northeast.

Operations

To support its distribution business STS in 2010 began operations at a 200000-sq.-ft. warehouse in Bridgewater Township New Jersey which today represents its largest location and boasts 20 loading docks as well as the capability to store 350000 tires. The facility serves the company's retail stores and wholesale customers on the East Coast.

Strategy

In recent years STS has concentrated on expanding its retail footprint with an ultimate goal of reaching a network that numbers some 150 stores. In 2014 the firm opened a location in Whiting New Jersey. Previous expansion efforts include opening about 25 stores in its tri-state market of New York New Jersey and Pennsylvania in 2012. It opened another handful of stores in 2013.

Company Background

STS is recognized for its environmental commitment due to events that occurred many years ago. The company began work on a warehouse facility in 2005 having owned the land on which the facility was built since 1971. It had not started construction until decades later because the land was classified as "brownfield" (for high arsenic levels) and required substantial cleanup to be usable. (STS did not know the extent of the pollution at the time of purchase.) The cleanup efforts were substantial.

EXECUTIVES

Vice President, Mark Reiner
Vice President Of Information Technology, Mike Cardali
Vice President, Robert (Bob) Glotfelty
Board Member, Deo Ganesh
Board Of Directors, Frank Andolino
Auditors: WITHUM SMITH+BROWN PC RED BA

LOCATIONS

HQ: SOMERSET TIRE SERVICE INC.
1 STS DR BLDG STE 1, BRIDGEWATER, NJ 08807
Phone: 732 356-8500
Web: WWW.STSTIRE.COM

2014 Stores

	No.
New Jersey	85
New York	30
Pennsylvania	30
Total	**145**

PRODUCTS/OPERATIONS

Selected Services
Battery
Brakes
Engines
General maintenance
Seasonal service
Shocks
Struts
Tire services

Selected Brands
Bridgestone
Continental
Firestone
Goodyear
Michelin
Pirelli
Toyo Tires
Yokohama

COMPETITORS

Advance Auto Parts
AutoZone
Bridgestone Retail Operations
CARQUEST
Goodyear Tire & Rubber
Monro Muffler Brake
Pep Boys
Precision Auto
Sears
Wal-Mart

HISTORICAL FINANCIALS
Company Type: Private

Income Statement				FYE: December 31
	REVENUE ($ mil.)	NET INCOME ($ mil.)	NET PROFIT MARGIN	EMPLOYEES
12/13	214	9	4.6%	800
12/12	203	7	3.8%	—
12/11	201	8	4.3%	—
12/10	189	0	—	—
Annual Growth	**4.4%**	**—**	**—**	**—**

2013 Year-End Financials

Return on assets: 6.2% Cash ($ mil.): 2
Return on equity: 4.6%
Current ratio: 0.30

SOUTH DAKOTA STATE UNIVERSITY

South Dakota State University (SDSU) is big on education in the Mount Rushmore State. The college offers undergraduate graduate and pre-professional programs to some 13000 students. Academic offerings include agriculture engineering and pharmacy courses. Its SDSU Sioux Falls Program targets non-traditional students (such as students with jobs and families) by providing evening and weekend classes. Notable SDSU alumni include former US Senator Tom Daschle and professional football players Adam Timmerman and Adam Vinatieri. SDSU a public school governed by the South Dakota Board of Regents was founded as a land grant college in 1881.

Geographic Reach

The university's main campus is located in Brookings South Dakota. SDSU's four attendance centers (where select courses are offered) are located in Pierre Rapid City Sioux Falls and Watertown. It also has eight extension offices across the state.

Operations

SDSU students can choose from more than 180 areas of study including about 70 undergraduate majors 30 master's degree programs 15 doctoral degrees and 10 certificates. Its classes are organized under colleges of agriculture and biological sciences; arts and sciences; education and human sciences; nursing; pharmacy; and engineering. The university also operates a university college a graduate school and an honors college.

SDSU receives grants and contracts to help fund research programs in fields including agriculture engineering geospatial data environmental science energy human health and pharmaceutical studies. Agricultural research is a core field of exploration for university students primarily through the school's South Dakota Agricultural Experiment Station.

With a student-to-faculty ratio of about 19:1 SDSU operates with an annual budget of $299 million.

Financial Performance

The university's operating revenue was reported at some $199 million in fiscal 2012 an increase of 4% over fiscal 2011 due to higher tuition fees and state support as well as other sources of income. Increase in net assets declined 44% to $17.7 million on higher expenses from supplies and contractual services as well as the lack of certain federal appropriations.

Strategy

SDSU's core operating goals are to provide quality academic programs through environment innovative staff and engaged students; offer support for research creativity and scholarship through facilities services and infrastructure; and to create beneficial partnerships with government community and global organizations to enhance academic opportunities.

Program and facility enhancements include the establishment of a new center for Agribusiness and Food Systems Management in 2013. It also opened several new residence halls that year. Projects under construction include new learning and research spaces for the engineering and architecture departments.

EXECUTIVES

EVP Administration, Michael (Mike) Reger
VP Academic Affairs and Provost, Carol J. Peterson
Vice President for Research and Dean of Graduate School, Kevin D. Kephart
Grants Administrator, Jacqueline Nelson
Director Human Resources, David Hanson
President CEO, Dick McComish
Vice President for Academic Affairs, Laurie Nichols

LOCATIONS

HQ: SOUTH DAKOTA STATE UNIVERSITY
2201 ADMINISTRATION LANE, BROOKINGS, SD 570070001
Phone: 605 688-6101
Web: WWW.SDBOR.EDU

PRODUCTS/OPERATIONS

Select Colleges
College of Agriculture & Biological Sciences
College of Arts & Sciences
College of Education & Human Sciences
College of Nursing
College of Pharmacy
Graduate School
Jerome J. Lohr College of Engineering
University College
Van D. & Barbara B. Fishback Honors College

HISTORICAL FINANCIALS
Company Type: Private

Income Statement				FYE: June 30
	REVENUE ($ mil.)	NET INCOME ($ mil.)	NET PROFIT MARGIN	EMPLOYEES
06/13	195	17	8.9%	2,000
06/12	198	17	8.9%	—
06/11	190	31	16.5%	—
06/08	134	0	—	—
Annual Growth	**7.7%**	**—**	**—**	**—**

2013 Year-End Financials

Return on assets: 4.2% Cash ($ mil.): 38
Return on equity: 8.9%
Current ratio: 1.50

SOUTH DAKOTA WHEAT GROWERS ASSOCIATION

Who loves you a bushel and a peck? South Dakota Wheat Growers may; it is an agricultural co-op comprising some 5400 member-farmers. It provides a grain warehouse along with grain marketing services intended to compete with big food and ag companies. In addition to storage and drying Wheat Growers offers agronomy spreading and spraying and transportation. It supplies feed fertilizer chemicals and other farm-related provisions for members in and around counties in North and South Dakota. Wheat Growers generates more than half of its revenues through marketing some 160 million bushels of grain (corn wheat and soybeans) each year. Remaining revenues are made through agronomy and retail sales and services.

EXECUTIVES

Senior Vice President Agronomy and Corporate Marketing, Steve Briggs
Chief Executive Officer, Dale Locken
Senior Vice President Grain, Roger Krueger
VP Operartions, Roger Price
Vice President Human Resources and Organizational Development, Judy Stulken
Senior Vice President Operations, Chris Pearson
Chief Financial Officer, Blake Bomesberger
Auditors: GARDINER THOMSEN PC

LOCATIONS

HQ: SOUTH DAKOTA WHEAT GROWERS ASSOCIATION
908 LAMONT ST S, ABERDEEN, SD 574015515
Phone: 605 225-5500
Web: WWW.WHEATGROWERS.COM

Selected Counties of Operation
North Dakota
  Dickey
  LaMoure
  Stutsman
South Dakota
  Aurora
  Beadle
  Brown
  Brule
  Clark
  Corson
  Day
  Edmunds
  Faulk
  Hand
  Hyde
  Jerauld
  Lyman
  Marshall
  Sanborn
  Spink

COMPETITORS

ADM
CHS
Cargill
Country Pride
North Central Farmers Elevator
Northern Growers

HISTORICAL FINANCIALS
Company Type: Private

Income Statement

	REVENUE ($ mil.)	NET INCOME ($ mil.)	NET PROFIT MARGIN	EMPLOYEES
07/14	1,498	20	1.4%	638
07/13	1,847	20	1.1%	—
07/12	1,667	16	1.0%	—
07/10	1,020	0	—	—
Annual Growth	10.1%	—	—	—

FYE: July 31

2014 Year-End Financials
Return on assets: 1.0%
Return on equity: 1.4%
Current ratio: 0.60
Cash ($ mil.): 143

SOUTH MIAMI HOSPITAL INC.

South Miami Hospital offers primary and tertiary health care services to the residents living near the University of Miami. The hospital has about 470 beds and is one of the largest members of Baptist Health South Florida a top regional health system. Specialty services include emergency care cardiovascular services oncology neurology women's health metabolic care and rehabilitation. It operates an addiction treatment residential facility provides home health care and provides child development diagnostic and early intervention services. South Miami Hospital was founded in 1960.

Operations
South Miami Hospital handles 15000 inpatient admissions each year as well as 30000 emergency room visits 5000 outpatient surgeries and 4000 births. It has about 1300 physicians on its medical staff.

As part of the broader Baptist Health South Florida system South Miami Hospital benefits from shared resources including procurement administration and technology the coordination of which helps the member facilities control costs during times of economic trouble and rising medical care expenses in the US.

Strategy
The Baptist Health system facilities including South Miami Hospital are installing electronic health record (EHR) systems to manage patient records across the system. Such EHR systems are designed to improve quality and lower expenses by facilitating communication between care providers and increasing patient involvement in condition management.

In addition South Miami Hospital has improved its services through expansion and renovation projects. It has added specialty units for robotic surgery birthing heart care and neonatal intensive care. In addition it completed an $80 million two-story construction in 2013 that enhanced the medical center's emergency surgery and imaging departments.

EXECUTIVES

Director of Pharmacy, Judy Tseng
Ambulatory Services Director, Carmen Rodriguez
Vice President Human Resources, Melissa (Mel) Lupisella

LOCATIONS

HQ: SOUTH MIAMI HOSPITAL INC.
6200 SW 73RD ST, SOUTH MIAMI, FL 331434679
Phone: 786 662-4000
Web: WWW.BAPTISTHEALTH.NET

COMPETITORS

Adventist Health System Sunbelt Healthcare
Broward Health
H. Lee Moffitt Cancer Center & Research Institute
HCA
Jackson Health System
Larkin Community Hospital
Miami Children's Hospital
Mount Sinai Medical Center of Florida
South Broward Hospital District
UF&Shands
University of Miami Hospital

HISTORICAL FINANCIALS
Company Type: Private

Income Statement

	REVENUE ($ mil.)	NET INCOME ($ mil.)	NET PROFIT MARGIN	EMPLOYEES
09/13	484	59	12.3%	2,205
09/12	484	36	7.6%	—
Annual Growth	(0.0%)	63.1%	—	—

FYE: September 30

2013 Year-End Financials
Return on assets: —
Return on equity: 12.3%
Current ratio: 0.80
Cash ($ mil.): —

SOUTH MISSISSIPPI ELECTRIC POWER ASSOCIATION

LOCATIONS

HQ: SOUTH MISSISSIPPI ELECTRIC POWER ASSOCIATION
7037 U S HIGHWAY 49, HATTIESBURG, MS 394029128
Phone: 601 579-0215
Web: WWW.SMEPA.COOP

HISTORICAL FINANCIALS
Company Type: Private

Income Statement

	REVENUE ($ mil.)	NET INCOME ($ mil.)	NET PROFIT MARGIN	EMPLOYEES
12/13	811	0	—	238
12/12	771	0	—	—
12/11	766	0	—	—
Annual Growth	2.9%	—	—	—

FYE: December 31

2013 Year-End Financials
Return on assets: 8.6%
Return on equity: —
Current ratio: 0.80
Cash ($ mil.): 19

SOUTH NASSAU COMMUNITIES HOSPITAL INC

Auditors: ERNST & YOUNG LLP NEW YORK

LOCATIONS

HQ: SOUTH NASSAU COMMUNITIES HOSPITAL INC
1 HEALTHY WAY, OCEANSIDE, NY 115721551
Phone: 516 632-3000
Web: WWW.SOUTHNASSAU.ORG

HISTORICAL FINANCIALS

Company Type: Private

Income Statement
FYE: December 31

	REVENUE ($ mil.)	NET INCOME ($ mil.)	NET PROFIT MARGIN	EMPLOYEES
12/13	421	111	26.4%	2,800
12/12	400	(3)	—	—
12/11	386	(49)	—	—
12/10	383	0	—	—
Annual Growth	3.2%	—	—	—

2013 Year-End Financials

Return on assets: 3.6%
Return on equity: 26.4%
Current ratio: 0.70
Cash ($ mil.): 27

SOUTH SHORE HOSPITAL INC.

LOCATIONS

HQ: SOUTH SHORE HOSPITAL INC.
55 FOGG RD, SOUTH WEYMOUTH, MA 021902455
Phone: 781 624-8000
Web: WWW.SOUTHSHOREHOSPITAL.ORG

HISTORICAL FINANCIALS

Company Type: Private

Income Statement
FYE: September 30

	REVENUE ($ mil.)	NET INCOME ($ mil.)	NET PROFIT MARGIN	EMPLOYEES
09/14	495	30	6.1%	2,375
09/13	479	21	4.4%	—
09/12	426	4	1.0%	—
09/08	359	0	—	—
Annual Growth	5.5%	—	—	—

2014 Year-End Financials

Return on assets: 12.1%
Return on equity: 6.1%
Current ratio: 1.40
Cash ($ mil.): 34

SOUTH TEXAS ELECTRIC COOPERATIVE INC.

Auditors: BUMGARDNER MORRISON & COMPANY

LOCATIONS

HQ: SOUTH TEXAS ELECTRIC COOPERATIVE INC.
2849 FM 447, NURSERY, TX 77976
Phone: 361 575-6491
Web: WWW.STEC.ORG

HISTORICAL FINANCIALS

Company Type: Private

Income Statement
FYE: December 31

	REVENUE ($ mil.)	NET INCOME ($ mil.)	NET PROFIT MARGIN	EMPLOYEES
12/13	359	19	5.3%	145
12/12	320	23	7.4%	—
12/11	320	21	6.8%	—
12/10	328	0	—	—
Annual Growth	3.0%	—	—	—

2013 Year-End Financials

Return on assets: 22.2%
Return on equity: 5.3%
Current ratio: 0.50
Cash ($ mil.): 69

SOUTHCO DISTRIBUTING COMPANY

This company makes sure you can get subs on the go from the convenience store. Southco Distributing is a leading convenience food supplier that distributes prepackaged sandwiches and other products to retail stores in seven states in the Southeast and Midwest. In addition to prepackaged foods Southco provides branded quick-service kiosks and equipment that allow convenience stores and other retailers to offer food on the go. Its foodservice programs are branded under the names AutoFry Pizza Primo Sub Express and Squawkers.

Southco's sales and distribution areas primarily include in Georgia North Carolina South Carolina Ohio Tennessee Virginia and West Virginia.

The company provides other services such as store set-up and re-set including installing produce racks and arranging produce within the available space. Through the company's inventory management system customers have the capability of tracking prepackaged items print inventory sheets create and send orders and receive email confirmation of processed orders.

EXECUTIVES

Executive Vice President Of Sales, Blount Craft
Vice President Marketing, Blount Kraft
Auditors: PARKER & PARKER PA GOLDSBOR

LOCATIONS

HQ: SOUTHCO DISTRIBUTING COMPANY
2201 S JOHN ST, GOLDSBORO, NC 275307163
Phone: 919 735-8012
Web: WWW.SOUTHCODISTRIBUTING.COM

COMPETITORS

Core-Mark	Perky' s Pizza
Eby-Brown	Pizza Pro
Hot Stuff Foods	Sysco
Marketfare Foods	US Foods
McLane	

HISTORICAL FINANCIALS

Company Type: Private

Income Statement
FYE: December 28

	REVENUE ($ mil.)	NET INCOME ($ mil.)	NET PROFIT MARGIN	EMPLOYEES
12/12	397	2	0.7%	225
12/06	253	1	0.4%	—
12/05	0	0	—	—
12/00	203	0	—	—
Annual Growth	5.7%	—	—	—

2012 Year-End Financials

Return on assets: 1.3%
Return on equity: 0.7%
Current ratio: 1.00
Cash ($ mil.): —

SOUTHCOAST HOSPITALS GROUP INC.

When you feel more than a little physically washed up get to one of the Southcoast Hospitals Group facilities. The not-for-profit company provides medical services in the southeastern corner of Massachusetts and in Rhode Island. Its primary facilities in Massachusetts are the Charlton Memorial Hospital (with about 330 beds) in Fall River St. Luke's Hospital (420 beds) in New Bedford and Tobey Hospital (65 beds) in Wareham which provide acute medical care and specialty services including cardiology neurology orthopedics and women's care. Southcoast Hospitals Group also operates about 20 ancillary facilities including nursing and assisted-living facilities and home health and hospice agencies.

Company Background

Charlton Memorial was founded in 1885 as Fall River Hospital. St. Luke's was established in 1884 and Tobey Hospital was founded in 1938. The three community hospitals merged under the Southcoast organization in 1996.

EXECUTIVES

Medical Director, Beth Herrick
Nursing Director, Denise Mercier
Medical Director, Peter (Pete) Martelly
Vice President Human Resources, Patricia (Pat) Roberts
Director Of Operating Room, Deb Rideout
Intrim Vice President Primary Care, Martin Oneill
Secretary For Engineering, Jane (Ginny) Bernier
Auditors: DELOITTE & TOUCHE LLP

LOCATIONS

HQ: SOUTHCOAST HOSPITALS GROUP INC.
363 HIGHLAND AVE, FALL RIVER, MA 027203703
Phone: 508 679-3131
Web: WWW.SOUTHCOAST.ORG

COMPETITORS

Baystate Health	Partners HealthCare
Boston Medical Center	Roger Williams Medical Center
Care New England	
CareGroup	Steward Health Care
Hallmark Health	Yale New Haven Health System
Lifespan Corporation	
McLean Hospital	
Memorial Hospital of Rhode Island	

HISTORICAL FINANCIALS
Company Type: Private

Income Statement

FYE: September 30

	REVENUE ($ mil.)	NET INCOME ($ mil.)	NET PROFIT MARGIN	EMPLOYEES
09/13	687	22	3.3%	3,853
09/12	704	49	7.0%	—
09/06	506	14	2.8%	—
09/04	445	0	—	—
Annual Growth	4.9%	—	—	—

2013 Year-End Financials
Return on assets: 6.9% Cash ($ mil.): 6
Return on equity: 3.3%
Current ratio: 0.60

SOUTHEAST MISSOURI HOSPITAL ASSOCIATION

Auditors: KERBER ECK & BRAECKEL LLP CAR

LOCATIONS
HQ: SOUTHEAST MISSOURI HOSPITAL ASSOCIATION
1701 LACEY ST, CAPE GIRARDEAU, MO 637015230
Phone: 573 651-5560
Web: WWW.SEHEALTH.ORG

HISTORICAL FINANCIALS
Company Type: Private

Income Statement

FYE: December 31

	REVENUE ($ mil.)	NET INCOME ($ mil.)	NET PROFIT MARGIN	EMPLOYEES
12/09	311	19	6.1%	2,000
12/08	277	8	3.2%	—
12/05	0	0	15.2%	—
12/04	177	0	—	—
Annual Growth	11.9%	—	—	—

2009 Year-End Financials
Return on assets: — Cash ($ mil.): 18
Return on equity: 6.1%
Current ratio: 0.50

SOUTHEAST PETRO DISTRIBUTORS INC.

Auditors: JAMES MOORE & CO PL GAINE

LOCATIONS
HQ: SOUTHEAST PETRO DISTRIBUTORS INC.
402 HIGH POINT DR STE A, COCOA, FL 329266600
Phone: 321 631-0245
Web: WWW.SOUTHEASTPETRO.COM

HISTORICAL FINANCIALS
Company Type: Private

Income Statement

FYE: December 31

	REVENUE ($ mil.)	NET INCOME ($ mil.)	NET PROFIT MARGIN	EMPLOYEES
12/11	553	5	1.0%	12
12/10	416	5	1.3%	—
12/09	331	4	1.5%	—
12/02	57	0	—	—
Annual Growth	28.6%	—	—	—

2011 Year-End Financials
Return on assets: — Cash ($ mil.): 8
Return on equity: 1.0%
Current ratio: 1.10

SOUTHERN BAPTIST HOSPITAL OF FLORIDA INC.

Auditors: ERNST & YOUNG LLP JACKSONVIL

LOCATIONS
HQ: SOUTHERN BAPTIST HOSPITAL OF FLORIDA INC.
800 PRUDENTIAL DR, JACKSONVILLE, FL 322078202
Phone: 904 202-2000
Web: WWW.BAPTISTHEALTH.NET

HISTORICAL FINANCIALS
Company Type: Private

Income Statement

FYE: September 30

	REVENUE ($ mil.)	NET INCOME ($ mil.)	NET PROFIT MARGIN	EMPLOYEES
09/09	793	(21)	—	4,000
09/08	1,007	82	8.1%	—
Annual Growth	(21.3%)	—	—	—

2009 Year-End Financials
Return on assets: — Cash ($ mil.): 4
Return on equity: (-2.7%)
Current ratio: 0.90

SOUTHERN MAINE HEALTH CARE

Southern Maine Medical Center (SMMC) provides health care services to the residents of York County Maine. The central facility of the not-for-profit medical organization is its 150-bed full-service hospital. Founded in 1906 the medical center also operates a home health care service and outpatient diagnostic and therapy centers. Specialty services include pediatrics cardiology oncology and emergency care. The medical center has a staff of about 200 physicians. SMMC is a member of MaineHealth a network of area hospitals and health clinics.

SMMC became a full member of the Maine-Health network in 2009 a move that gave it access to the MaineHealth administrative and group purchasing services. SMMC which retains its status as an independently operated organization was already an affiliate of the MaineHealth system.

In 2008 the hospital completed a $26 million expansion project to increase the capacity of its emergency department. The new emergency center was named the Dorothy Walker Bush Pavilion after President George H. W. Bush's mother.

EXECUTIVES
Vice President Human Resource, Lorraine Bouchard
Vice President Support Services, Marc Fournier

LOCATIONS
HQ: SOUTHERN MAINE HEALTH CARE
1 MEDICAL CENTER DR, BIDDEFORD, ME 040059422
Phone: 207 283-7000

COMPETITORS
Eastern Maine Healthcare Systems
Franklin Community Health Network
MaineGeneral Health
Mercy Health System of Maine
Parkview Hospital

HISTORICAL FINANCIALS
Company Type: Private

Income Statement

FYE: September 30

	REVENUE ($ mil.)	NET INCOME ($ mil.)	NET PROFIT MARGIN	EMPLOYEES
09/13*	171	5	3.0%	1,000
04/09	3	0	—	—
03/09	0	(0)	—	—
04/07	95	0	—	—
Annual Growth	—	—	—	—

*Fiscal year change

2013 Year-End Financials
Return on assets: 6.7% Cash ($ mil.): 4
Return on equity: 3.0%
Current ratio: 0.90

SOUTHERN METHODIST UNIVERSITY INC

What do former first lady Laura Bush actress Kathy Bates and NFL Hall-of-Famer Doak Walker have in common? They're all graduates of Southern Methodist University (SMU). Founded in 1911 by what is now The United Methodist Church SMU is a nonsectarian private institution offering undergraduate graduate and professional degrees in arts business engineering humanities law science and theology through seven schools. It's one of a handful of schools nationwide to offer an academic major in human rights. Some 11000 students attend the university which has a student-faculty ratio of 11:1. About 85% of the 700-member full-time faculty hold the doctorate or highest degree in their fields.

Geographic Reach

SMU is housed in more than 75 buildings. The Texas university operates through a main campus located in University Park within Dallas County. Also in Texas it maintains property in Dallas (19 acres) Highland Park (2 acres) and Plano (25 acres). In Taos New Mexico SMU holds 423 acres.

Operations

The university offers more than 120 undergraduate degrees and about 130 graduate degrees through seven schools. SMU also offers more than two dozen doctorates. Most of the its degrees are conferred in the humanities and sciences and business.

Sales and Marketing

SMU's enrollment includes international students from 90 countries. The largest numbers of students in descending order are from India China Saudi Arabia Mexico Korea Taiwan (Province of China) Guatemala Thailand Iran and Canada.

Financial Performance

Endowment gifts from donors reached $14.9 million in 2012. The private university's revenue decreased by 9% in 2012 as compared to 2011 due to dips in tuition and fees net realized and unrealized gains grants and contracts. Net income also decreased by 44% during the same reporting period. Revenue declines and increases in program expenses contributed to the net income woes.

EXECUTIVES

Vice President Development and External Affairs, Brad Cheves

V Pres Legal Affairs & Govt Re, Paul Ward

Vice President Executive Affairs, Thomas Barry

Assistant Vice President Executive Director Lecture Programs, Lisa Chou

Vice President Programming, Alex Munoz

Department Chairman, Dennis Ippolito

Vice President Of Staff Development, Cindy Gautreaux

Department Chair and O. Paul Corley Distinguished Chair in Organizational Behavior, Miguel Quinones

Vice President, Andrea Smith

Managing Director, Jeff Noland

Department Chairman, Mark Chancey

Vice President Operations, George Utkov

Vice President Of Programming, Bo Kamensky

Provost Vice President Academic Affair, Ross Murfin

Vice President Of Marketing And Communications, Cathy Heckman

Vice President Office Coordinator, Martha Mendez

Co President, Kristina Lackey

Associate Vice President Information Technology Services, George Chrisman

Vice President, Cchea Nugent

Vice President CSI Delivery, Klyne Smith

Vice President, Lori Brakhage

Assistant Vice President of Student Affairs;, Joanne Vogel

Department Chair and Robert, Hemang Ph

Secretary, Debra McDowell

Secretary, David Kuczer

Secretary Admissions Office, Uanna Alves

General Vice Chair, Bezalel Gavish

Secretary, Suzanne Nelsen

LOCATIONS

HQ: SOUTHERN METHODIST UNIVERSITY INC
6425 BOAZ LN, DALLAS, TX 75205
Phone: 214 768-2000
Web: WWW.SMU.EDU

PRODUCTS/OPERATIONS

Selected Schools and Divisions

Annette Caldwell Simmons School of Education and Human Development
Bobby B. Lyle School of Engineering
Cox School of Business
Dedman College of Humanities and Sciences
Dedman School of Law
Meadows School of the Arts
Perkins School of Theology

HISTORICAL FINANCIALS
Company Type: Private

Income Statement FYE: May 31

	REVENUE ($ mil.)	NET INCOME ($ mil.)	NET PROFIT MARGIN	EMPLOYEES
05/13	563	115	20.5%	2,200
05/11	602	58	9.6%	
05/09	236	(171)	—	
Annual Growth	24.3%	—	—	—

2013 Year-End Financials

Return on assets: 33.1%   Cash ($ mil.): 290
Return on equity: 20.5%
Current ratio: —

SOUTHERN NEW HAMPSHIRE MEDICAL CENTER

Southern New Hampshire Medical Center (SNHMC) provides medical care for the residents of the Nashua New Hampshire area and surrounding region through Southern New Hampshire Medical Center and Foundation Medical Partners. The two-campus hospital which has about 190 beds and is part of the Southern New Hampshire Health System offers centers for cancer treatment diabetes education fertility and childbirth obesity sleep disorders trauma and other programs. Outpatient and rehabilitation services are offered through several clinic locations. SNHMC is also affiliated with physician practice organization Foundation Medical Partners and it is a teaching facility for the Dartmouth Medical School.

Geographic Reach

SNHMC's main campus is located in the heart of downtown Nashua New Hampshire and serves patients in the Greater Nashua area.

Operations

The Medical Center has a medical staff of more than 500 primary and specialty care providers from Foundation Medical Partners Dartmouth-Hitchcock Nashua and local independent practices. The Centers partnerships and affiliations include Dartmouth Medical School Dartmouth-Hitchcock Medical Center Lahey Clinic and the Children's Hospital in Boston.In 2013 SNHMC reported 8830 admissions (adult/pediatric/newborn); 5432 total surgical procedures (inpatient and outpatient); 1395 total births (newborn and NICU admits); 42974 emergency department visits; and 225127 outpatient visits.The Center provided $53 million for community benefit in 2013.

Financial Performance

The organization's revenues grew by 4% to $286 million in 2013. Net income decreased by 7% to $22 million that year.

Strategy

SNHMC is expanding its network of medical facilities to keep pace wth demand.In 2013 the system opened its fifth Immediate Care of Southern New Hampshire location at newly constructed medical facilities in Nashua. In 2012 Foundation Medical Partners opened Southern New Hampshire Health System at Pelham.

It is also growing via partnerships. In 2013 Dartmouth-Hitchcock Nashua SNHMC and St. Joseph Healthcare teamed up to establish The Surgery Center of Greater Nashua to bring cost-effective options for surgery patients. The Surgery Center of Greater Nashua's services include orthopedics; sports medicine; general surgery; ear nose and throat; plastic surgery; podiatry; and endoscopy.Upgrading its technology in 2012 SNHMC introduced the da Vinci Surgical System to strengthen its surgical services.

Company Background

In 2011 SNHMC opened Hudson and Merrimack locations to meet the growing needs of the greater Nashua community.

The company was founded as an 8-bed emergency hospital in 1893.

EXECUTIVES

President and CEO, Thomas E. (Tom) Wilhelmsen

SVP; President and CEO Foundation Medical Partners, Susan M. DeSocio

VP Medical Affairs and Chief Medical Officer, Stephanie Wolf-Rosenblum

VP Patient Care Services and Chief Nursing Officer, Colette D. Tilton

SVP and CFO, Michael S. Rose

Chief Surgical Officer, Kenneth F. Howe

VP Information Technology and Chief Medical Information Officer, Andrew Watt

VP Marketing, Suzanne Tammaro

Medical Director Of The Sleep Center, Matthew (Matt) Curley

Vice President Of Sales, Theresa Hebert

Executive Vice President Of Information Technology, Eugene Lesser

Vice President Operations, Michael Barb

Vice President Operations, Dagan Cloutier

Medical Records Director, Craig Warner

Auditors: BAKER NEWMAN & NOYES MANCHEST

LOCATIONS

HQ: SOUTHERN NEW HAMPSHIRE MEDICAL CENTER
8 PROSPECT ST, NASHUA, NH 030603925
Phone: 603 577-2000
Web: WWW.SNHHS.ORG

PRODUCTS/OPERATIONS

Selected Medical Services

Aesthetics
Allergy and Immunology
Anesthesia and Pain Management
Arthritis
Asthma
Audiology (Hearing Evaluations for Children)
Auditory Brainstem Response
Clinical Trials and Open Protocols
Ear Nose and Throat
Endocrinology
Family Practice
Genetic Counseling
Geriatric Medicine and Services
Hematology
Hospice Care
Hospitalist Program
Internal Medicine
Kidney Care
Maternity
Nephrology
Neurology
Neurosurgery
Nutrition
Pathology
Plastic Surgery
Podiatry
Pulmonary Medicine
Psychiatry
Pulmonary Rehab Program
Renal Dialysis
Rheumatology
Sleep Center
Sports Medicine
Stroke
Urology
Vascular Services
Specialty Medical Services
Behavioral Health

Cancer Care
Diabetes Care
Digestive Health
Dermatology
Emergency Department
Heart Care
Immediate Care
Laboratory Services
Orthopedics
Pediatric Services
Radiology Services
Rehabilitation Services
Spine and Brain Care
Surgical Services
Women's Services

COMPETITORS

Catholic Medical Center
Concord Hospital
Elliot Health System
Exeter Health Resources
Frisbie Memorial Hospital
Steward Health Care

HISTORICAL FINANCIALS

Company Type: Private

Income Statement

FYE: September 30

	REVENUE ($ mil.)	NET INCOME ($ mil.)	NET PROFIT MARGIN	EMPLOYEES
09/13	285	32	11.4%	1,200
09/12	194	16	8.3%	—
09/11	274	(4)	—	—
09/10	214	0	—	—
Annual Growth	10.0%	—	—	—

2013 Year-End Financials

Return on assets: —
Return on equity: 11.4%
Current ratio: 1.20

Cash ($ mil.): 41

SOUTHERN NEW HAMPSHIRE UNIVERSITY

LOCATIONS

HQ: SOUTHERN NEW HAMPSHIRE UNIVERSITY
2500 N RIVER RD, MANCHESTER, NH 031061018
Phone: 603 668-2211
Web: WWW.SNHU.EDU

HISTORICAL FINANCIALS

Company Type: Private

Income Statement

FYE: June 30

	REVENUE ($ mil.)	NET INCOME ($ mil.)	NET PROFIT MARGIN	EMPLOYEES
06/14	305	44	14.6%	1,000
06/13	202	29	14.8%	—
06/12	166	10	6.0%	—
06/11	142	0	—	—
Annual Growth	28.9%	—	—	—

2014 Year-End Financials

Return on assets: 13.7%
Return on equity: 14.6%
Current ratio: —

Cash ($ mil.): 57

SOUTHERN OHIO MEDICAL CENTER

LOCATIONS

HQ: SOUTHERN OHIO MEDICAL CENTER
1805 27TH ST, PORTSMOUTH, OH 456622640
Phone: 740 354-5000
Web: WWW.SOMC.ORG

HISTORICAL FINANCIALS

Company Type: Private

Income Statement

FYE: June 30

	REVENUE ($ mil.)	NET INCOME ($ mil.)	NET PROFIT MARGIN	EMPLOYEES
06/12	301	15	5.3%	2,100
06/10	292	17	6.0%	—
06/09	246	5	2.1%	—
06/08	435	0	—	—
Annual Growth	(8.8%)	—	—	—

2012 Year-End Financials

Return on assets: —
Return on equity: 5.3%
Current ratio: 0.30

Cash ($ mil.): 15

SOUTHERN PIPE & SUPPLY COMPANY INC.

Southern Pipe and Supply Co. sells pipes and anything that connects to them. Serving everyone from contractors and homeowners to commercial real estate property owners Southern Pipe sells plumbing heating and air-conditioning supplies through more than 90 stores located throughout seven southeastern states. The company operates a central distribution center and a handful of Southern Bath & Kitchen showrooms that feature various products for homeowners. Southern Pipe's vendors include dozens of supply companies and manufacturers such as MOEN Kohler and Amana Heating and Air Conditioning. Southern Pipe and Supply Co. was founded in 1938.

Geographic Reach

Mississippi-based Southern Pipe and Supply Co. operates about 25 locations in Mississippi and about 65 others across Alabama Arkansas Florida Georgia Louisiana and Tennessee.

Sales and Marketing

As part of its business Southern Pipe and Supply Co. serves as a distributor for some of the industry's most well-known names such as Kohler Delta Elkay Pfister Rheem Watts Zurn Lennox and Ridgid.

Operations

The company's Central Distribution Center which averages some 70000 transactions monthly boasts an error rate of less than 1% on orders shipped to its branches. For its designated more than 900 critical-service items the center has reached a near perfect fill rate of 99.7%.

EXECUTIVES

Chairman, Marty Davidson

Manager Central Distribution Center, Charles Johnson
Auditors: DELOITTE & TOUCHE LLP BIRMING

LOCATIONS

HQ: SOUTHERN PIPE & SUPPLY COMPANY INC.
4330 HIGHWAY 39 N, MERIDIAN, MS 393011082
Phone: 601 693-2911
Web: WWW.SOUTHERNPIPE.COM

Selected Locations

	No.
Mississippi	26
Alabama	17
Louisiana	16
Georgia	14
Arkansas	10
Florida	4
Tennessee	3
Total	**90**

PRODUCTS/OPERATIONS

Selected Products

Heating & cooling equipment
Kitchen & bath fixtures
Plumbing
Residential & commercial pipe valves & fittings
Tools & safety equipment
Water metering fire hydrants & fittings
Waterworks

COMPETITORS

Baker Distributing
Ferguson Enterprises
HD Supply
Lowe's
Stuart C. Irby
WinWholesale
Wolverine Tube

HISTORICAL FINANCIALS

Company Type: Private

Income Statement

FYE: December 31

	REVENUE ($ mil.)	NET INCOME ($ mil.)	NET PROFIT MARGIN	EMPLOYEES
12/10	284	6	2.1%	767
12/09	261	3	1.3%	—
12/00	1,879	0	—	—
Annual Growth	—	231.4%	—	—

2010 Year-End Financials

Return on assets: 5.7%
Return on equity: 2.1%
Current ratio: 1.40

Cash ($ mil.): 5

SOUTHFRESH AQUACULTURE LLC.

Auditors: MCGLADREY & PULLEN LLP ORLAN

LOCATIONS

HQ: SOUTHFRESH AQUACULTURE LLC.
1792 MCFARLAND BLVD N B, TUSCALOOSA, AL 354062185
Phone: 205 247-4490
Web: WWW.SOUTHFRESH.COM

HISTORICAL FINANCIALS

Company Type: Private

Income Statement

FYE: July 31

	REVENUE ($ mil.)	NET INCOME ($ mil.)	NET PROFIT MARGIN	EMPLOYEES
07/11*	450	9	2.0%	250
12/08	0	0	—	—
05/03	54	1	2.4%	—
05/02	52	0	—	—
Annual Growth	27.0%			

*Fiscal year change

2011 Year-End Financials

Return on assets: 3.7%   Cash ($ mil.): 13
Return on equity: 2.0%
Current ratio: 0.70

SOUTHLAND INDUSTRIES

Southland Industries designs builds and maintains a variety of mechanical systems for facilities around North America. The employee-owned mechanical engineering firm provides design construction fabrication and maintenance of plumbing process piping fire protection HVAC and controls and automation systems. Southland Industries' clients are in the health care life sciences hospitality industrial education government and telecommunication sectors. Projects include the renovation of the Pentagon following the terrorist attacks of September 11 and the M Resort in Las Vegas. Founded in 1949 Southland Industries has offices in the Northern California Southern California Mid-Atlantic and Southwest regions.

Geographic Reach

Southland Industries has about a half-dozen offices in California Maryland Nevada Virginia and Baltimore.

Financial Performance

Revenues had been slipping every year since they'd peaked at $471 million in fiscal 2008 (ended September). However earnings rebounded and surpassed that figure in fiscal 2014 when revenue totaled $517 million.

Strategy

To broaden its service offerings the company launched subsidiary Envise in 2015. That unit specializes in building management systems with capabilities in analytics and equipment lifecycle management.

EXECUTIVES

Chairman President and CEO, Andrew A. Fimiano
Chief Business Development Officer, Joseph G. Cvetas
CFO, Jon Spallino
COO, Chuck Allen
Chief Design Officer, Peter Pobjoy
Northern California Division Leader, Rick Blazier
Mid-Atlantic Division Leader, Mike Miller
CEO, Ted Lynch
Southern California Division Leader, Christopher Taylor
Southwest Division Leader, Nicolas Sfeir
Vice President Of Human Resources, Gregory Michaud
Vice President Of Energy Services Tags, Natasha Shah
Vice President, Michael Miller
Auditors: MOSS ADAMS LLP IRVINE CALIFO

LOCATIONS

HQ: SOUTHLAND INDUSTRIES
7390 LINCOLN WAY, GARDEN GROVE, CA 928411427
Phone: 714 901-5800
Web: WWW.SOUTHLANDIND.COM

PRODUCTS/OPERATIONS

Selected Projects

Carl R. Darnall Army Medical Center
Kaiser Downey Hospital
MLK Hospital Renovation
Palo Alto Medical Foundation
UHS Temecula Hospital

Selected Services

Controls and automation
Energy analysis
Fire protection
HVAC
Planning and development
Plumbing
Process piping
Project management
Maintenance
Repair and retrofit

COMPETITORS

ACCO
Atlas Comfort Systems
Comfort Systems USA
EMCOR
Kinetics
Limbach Facility Services
University Mechanical & Engineering

HISTORICAL FINANCIALS

Company Type: Private

Income Statement

FYE: September 30

	REVENUE ($ mil.)	NET INCOME ($ mil.)	NET PROFIT MARGIN	EMPLOYEES
09/13	362	10	2.8%	1,900
09/11	407	61	15.0%	—
09/08	471	44	9.4%	—
09/07	363	0	—	—
Annual Growth	(0.1%)	—	—	—

2013 Year-End Financials

Return on assets: 4.9%   Cash ($ mil.): 13
Return on equity: 2.8%
Current ratio: 0.20

SOUTHWEST CATHOLIC HEALTH NETWORK CORPORATION

Southwest Catholic Health Network (SCHN) which does business as Mercy Care Plan is a not-for-profit provider of managed health care services in Arizona. The Mercy Care Plan provides these services under a contract with the Arizona Health Care Cost Containment System the state of Arizona's Medicaid program. The plan provides health coverage and prescription drug benefits to some 300000 members. The company founded in 1985 is affiliated with St. Joseph's Hospital & Medical Center (which is part of Catholic Healthcare West) Dignity Health and Carondelet Health Network. The plan is administered by health care management firm Schaller Anderson.

Geographic Reach

SCHN serves the Arizona counties of Maricopa Pima Graham Greenlee and Cochise providing covered services to enrolled members.

Sales and Marketing

As part of its business SCHN provides patients with prescriptions through retail pharmacies mail order pharmacies home infusion pharmacies long-term care pharmacies and Indian Health Service/Tribal/Urban Indian Health Program (I/T/U) pharmacies.

Financial Performance

SCHN logged a 10% decline in revenue in 2012 as compared to 2011. The provider points to a decrease in capitation premiums delivery/HIV AIDS supplement reinsurance and third-party recoveries for the double-digit drop. During the same reporting period SCHN posted a $7.5 million net loss thanks to revenue decreases paired with increases in investment fees and unrealized losses on investments incurred by the company during 2012.

Operations

SCHN provides coverage to families children the elderly and the developmentally disabled. In addition to traditional HMO coverage the company also offers disease management and preventative health care services.

Along with the Centers for Medicare & Medicaid Services (CMS) SCHN provides qualified members with medical and prescription drug benefits. Its Mercy Care Long Term Care (MCLTC) offers services to those covered by the AHCCCS Arizona Long Term Care System (ALTCS) which accounts for 22% of revenue.

The Division of Developmental Disabilities Long Term Care serves members who are enrolled through the Arizona Department of Economic Security/Division of Development Disabilities (DES/DDD) which generates approximately 2% of SCHN's revenue. Through a contract with the DES/DDD the company provides medical care to qualified members.

EXECUTIVES

Chief Operating Officer for Mercy Care Plan, Mark Fisher
Chief Financial Officer, Chuck Sowers
Vice President of Medicare Products Mercy Care Plan, Matt Cowley
Vice President Strategy and Development, Christi Lundeen
Chief Operating Officer, Lorry Bottrill
Chief Medical Officer, Charlton Wilson

LOCATIONS

HQ: SOUTHWEST CATHOLIC HEALTH NETWORK CORPORATION
4350 E COTTON CENTER BLVD, PHOENIX, AZ 850408852
Phone: 602 230-9921
Web: WWW.MERCYCAREPLAN.COM

PRODUCTS/OPERATIONS

2012 Revenue

	% of total
Acute	57
DES/DDD	2
HCG	1
ALTCS	22
Medicare	18
Total	100

COMPETITORS

Aetna
Blue Cross Blue Shield of Arizona
CIGNA HealthCare of Arizona
Health Net
UnitedHealth Group

HISTORICAL FINANCIALS

Company Type: Private

Income Statement

FYE: June 30

	REVENUE ($ mil.)	NET INCOME ($ mil.)	NET PROFIT MARGIN	EMPLOYEES
06/12	1,747	28	1.6%	500
06/11	1,939	58	3.0%	—
06/10	1,904	49	2.6%	—
06/09	1,814	0	—	—
Annual Growth	(1.3%)	—	—	—

2012 Year-End Financials

Return on assets: —
Return on equity: 1.6%
Current ratio: 0.80
Cash ($ mil.): 147

SOUTHWEST LOUISIANA ELECTRIC MEMBERSHIP CORPORATION

Southwest Louisiana Electric Membership Corporation (SLEMCO) is no slowpoke when it comes to serving more than 93400 power customers in eight Louisiana parishes. SLEMCO provides regulated power transmission and distribution services via 9000 miles of power lines to its residential commercial and industrial members. It also provides energy conservation and street and security lighting services. SLEMCO extended assistance to help repair the badly damaged infrastructure in parishes from New Orleans to the Mississippi border following the devastation caused by Hurricane Katrina.

The Enterprise Center of Louisiana a small business incubator project was spearheaded by SLEMCO in the 1980s (and is still supported by the company) to help fledgling businesses with potential establish themselves and mature into successful job-creating enterprises.

SLEMCO was formed in 1937 as a private membership corporation as part of the nationwide push to bring affordable electricity to rural areas.

EXECUTIVES

General Manager and CEO, J. U. Gajan
Director Marketing and Communications, George Fawcett
Director Engineering, Jim Laque
CFO, Gary Smith
Director Operations, Glenn Tamporello
Dispatch Supervisor, Merlin Alleman

LOCATIONS

HQ: SOUTHWEST LOUISIANA ELECTRIC MEMBERSHIP CORPORATION
3420 NE EVANGELINE TRWY, LAFAYETTE, LA 705072554
Phone: 337 896-5384
Web: WWW.SLEMCO.COM

SOUTHWEST RESEARCH INSTITUTE INC

If you're looking for research at an institute in the Southwest look no further. Founded in 1947 by oilman and rancher Thomas Slick Jr. Southwest Research Institute (SwRI) is an independent not-for-profit research and development institution that contracts to explore subjects in areas including automation and data systems applied physics space science and engineering and chemistry. SwRI has about 2700 scientists engineers and support staff at some 40 laboratories and offices in the US China and the UK. Customers include the private sector and government agencies. SwRI's Signature Science subsidiary researches national security environmental management and biotechnology.

Geographic Reach

The company is based in San Antonio Texas and the Institute has technical offices and laboratories in Ann Arbor Michigan.; Beijing China; Boulder Colorade; Hill Air Force Base (Ogden) Utah; Hanover and Rockville Maryland.; Minneapolis Minnesota; Oklahoma City Oklahoma.; Warner Robins Georgia; and Durham New Hampshire.

Operations

SwRI provides contract research and development services to industrial and government clients. It keeps the scope of its work confidential and assigns patent rights arising from its sponsored research to the client. SwRI generally retains rights to Institute-funded advancements and holds more than 900 patents awarded to staff members.

The company operates through nearly a dozen technical divisions including Aerospace Electronics; Systems Engineering & Training; Applied Physics Chemistry & Chemical Engineering; Engine Emissions & Vehicl; Research; Geosciences & Engineering; Mechanical Engineering; and Space Science & Engineering.

Strategy

SwRI's current projects include cooperative research focusing on safe reliable cost-effective energy storage systems for electric and hybrid-electric vehicle applications. In addition it has formed a consortium to conduct research and code development and apply advanced ROS (Robot Operating System)software to industrial applications.

EXECUTIVES

Vp Aerospace Electronics And Information Technology, Rick Somers
Vice President Engine And Vehicle Research Division, Nigel Gale

HISTORICAL FINANCIALS

Company Type: Private

Income Statement

FYE: December 31

	REVENUE ($ mil.)	NET INCOME ($ mil.)	NET PROFIT MARGIN	EMPLOYEES
12/13	198	(0)	—	270
12/08	161	9	5.7%	—
12/07	152	10	6.9%	—
12/06	1,743	0	—	—
Annual Growth	—	—	—	—

2013 Year-End Financials

Return on assets: 9.2%
Return on equity: (-0.1%)
Current ratio: 1.50
Cash ($ mil.): 15

Assistant Vice President Administration, Bruce Bykowski
V Pres-applied Power, Mary Massey
V Pres-signal Exploitation & G, Nils Smith
Vp Geosciences And Engineering, Wesley Patrick
Assistant Vice President Facilities And General, Paul Easley
Executive Manager, Steven Fritz
Associate Vice President Research and Development, Alan (Al) Stern
Senior Management Senior Vice President General Manager Director, Christopher (Chris) Freitas
Treas-asst Sec, Linda M Boehme
Treasurer, Debra Streeter
Secretary, Crystal Moczygemba
Board Member, Pete Rivera

LOCATIONS

HQ: SOUTHWEST RESEARCH INSTITUTE INC
6220 CULEBRA RD, SAN ANTONIO, TX 782385100
Phone: 210 684-5111
Web: WWW.SWRI.ORG.CN

PRODUCTS/OPERATIONS

Selected Technical Divisions
Aerospace Electronics and Information Technology
Applied Physics
Applied Power
Automation and Data Systems
Chemistry and Chemical Engineering
Engine Emissions and Vehicle Research
Fuels and Lubricants Research
Geosciences and Engineering
Mechanical Engineering
Signal Exploitation and Geolocation
Space Science and Engineering
Training Simulation and Performance Improvement

COMPETITORS

Argonne National Laboratory	Lawrence Livermore Lab
Battelle Memorial	QinetiQ
Berkeley Lab	Southern Research Institute
Brookhaven Lab	

HISTORICAL FINANCIALS

Company Type: Private

Income Statement

FYE: September 26

	REVENUE ($ mil.)	NET INCOME ($ mil.)	NET PROFIT MARGIN	EMPLOYEES
09/14	548	7	1.4%	2,973
09/13	569	29	5.2%	—
09/12	584	36	6.2%	—
09/11	581	0	—	—
Annual Growth	(1.9%)	—	—	—

2014 Year-End Financials

Return on assets: 3.9%
Return on equity: 1.4%
Current ratio: 0.20
Cash ($ mil.): 21

SOUTHWEST WASHINGTON HEALTH SYSTEM

LOCATIONS

HQ: SOUTHWEST WASHINGTON HEALTH SYSTEM
400 NE MOTHER JOSEPH PL, VANCOUVER, WA
986643200
Phone: 360 514-2000
Web: WWW.PEACEHEALTH.ORG

HISTORICAL FINANCIALS
Company Type: Private

Income Statement
FYE: December 31

	REVENUE ($ mil.)	NET INCOME ($ mil.)	NET PROFIT MARGIN	EMPLOYEES
12/09	601	9	1.5%	3,500
12/08*	110	(38)	—	—
09/08	0	0	—	—
Annual Growth	—27017547.1%	—	—	—

*Fiscal year change

2009 Year-End Financials
Return on assets: —
Return on equity: 1.5%
Current ratio: 1.10
Cash ($ mil.): 13

SOUTHWIND NURSING AND REHABILITATION CENTER INC

LOCATIONS

HQ: SOUTHWIND NURSING AND REHABILITATION
CENTER INC
804 CROWLEY RAYNE HWY, CROWLEY, LA
705268208
Phone: 337 783-2740

HISTORICAL FINANCIALS
Company Type: Private

Income Statement
FYE: December 31

	REVENUE ($ mil.)	NET INCOME ($ mil.)	NET PROFIT MARGIN	EMPLOYEES
12/09	411	9	2.2%	405
12/97	2	0	9.3%	—
Annual Growth	54.0%	36.5%	—	—

2009 Year-End Financials
Return on assets: —
Return on equity: 2.2%
Current ratio: 2.20
Cash ($ mil.): —

SPAW GLASS HOLDING L.P.

Deep in the heart of Texas SpawGlass Holding is busy providing general building and construction management services for commercial and institutional projects through its SpawGlass Construction and SpawGlass Contractors subsidiaries. The group also offers design/build delivery and tenant finish-out services. Among its landmark projects is the interior restoration of the Texas State Capitol. It also worked on the NASA Shuttle Flight Training Facility near Houston and the University of Texas Health Science Center at San Antonio. Louis Spaw and Frank Glass formed SpawGlass in 1953. The company now employee-owned has offices in Austin Houston San Antonio and the Rio Grande Valley in Texas.

EXECUTIVES

SVP Senior Living and Campus Housing, John English
VP Human Resources, Laurie Dralle
VP Estimating, Doug Worrell
Auditors: PADGETT STRATEMANN & CO LL

LOCATIONS

HQ: SPAW GLASS HOLDING L.P.
9331 CORPORATE DR, SELMA, TX 781541250
Phone: 210 651-9000
Web: WWW.SPAWGLASS.COM

COMPETITORS

Beck Group	Structure Tone
Cadence McShane	Southwest
Harvey Builders	Tellepsen Builders
Linbeck	Turner Corporation
Manhattan Construction	W.S. Bellows
Satterfield & Pontikes	

HISTORICAL FINANCIALS
Company Type: Private

Income Statement
FYE: December 31

	REVENUE ($ mil.)	NET INCOME ($ mil.)	NET PROFIT MARGIN	EMPLOYEES
12/13	442	3	0.9%	450
12/09	460	8	1.9%	—
12/07	336	5	1.8%	—
12/06	1,121	0	—	—
Annual Growth	—	—	—	—

2013 Year-End Financials
Return on assets: 12.4%
Return on equity: 0.9%
Current ratio: 0.20
Cash ($ mil.): 18

SPECTRUM HEALTH HOSPITALS

LOCATIONS

HQ: SPECTRUM HEALTH HOSPITALS
100 MICHIGAN ST NE MC-498, GRAND RAPIDS, MI
495032560
Phone: 616 391-1774

HISTORICAL FINANCIALS
Company Type: Private

Income Statement
FYE: June 30

	REVENUE ($ mil.)	NET INCOME ($ mil.)	NET PROFIT MARGIN	EMPLOYEES
06/13	1,742	171	9.8%	11,000
06/08	2,595	(21)	—	—
06/06	1,013	77	7.6%	—
Annual Growth	8.1%	12.0%	—	—

2013 Year-End Financials
Return on assets: 9.6%
Return on equity: 9.8%
Current ratio: 0.20
Cash ($ mil.): 26

SPECTRUM HEALTH PRIMARY CARE PARTNERS DBA

Auditors: CROWE HORWATH LLP CHICAGO IL

LOCATIONS

HQ: SPECTRUM HEALTH PRIMARY CARE PARTNERS
DBA
1840 WEALTHY ST SE, GRAND RAPIDS, MI
495062921
Phone: 616 774-7322

HISTORICAL FINANCIALS
Company Type: Private

Income Statement
FYE: June 30

	REVENUE ($ mil.)	NET INCOME ($ mil.)	NET PROFIT MARGIN	EMPLOYEES
06/13	391	2	0.6%	4
06/11	222	5	2.4%	—
06/10	75	3	4.7%	—
Annual Growth	73.0%	(10.9%)	—	—

2013 Year-End Financials
Return on assets: 11.7%
Return on equity: 0.6%
Current ratio: 0.30
Cash ($ mil.): —

SPECTRUM HEALTH SYSTEM

Offering more health services than colors in the rainbow Spectrum Health is a regional health system serving western Michigan. The not-for-profit network operates 12 hospitals that boast more than 1900 beds. Its health system provides a variety of services from general surgery to specialized cancer care. Besides its Spectrum Health Medical Group and West Michigan Heart Spectrum Health also operates Priority Health a health plan with 648000 members and Helen Devos Children's Hospital. The group runs more than 170 service sites including urgent care centers primary care physician offices community clinics rehabilitation and other outpatient facilities and continuing care residences for the elderly.

Operations

Spectrum Health's other hospitals include Blodgett Hospital Butterworth Hospital Kelsey Hospital Reed City Hospital and United Hospital.

Spectrum Health conducts hundreds of research studies each year through its Institutional Review Board. The organization has more than 300 physicians involved in research as investigators and at least 6000 patients enrolled in heart and cancer clinical studies.

The company is western Michigan's largest provider of post-acute care. It provided some $294.6 million in community benefits during fiscal 2014.

Geographic Reach

Spectrum Health provides patient services at community hospitals in Big Rapids East Grand Rapids Fremont Greenville Lakeview Ludington Reed City and Zeeland.

Sales and Marketing

Managed care and other represented more than half of the organization's net patient revenues in 2014; Medicare accounted for 26% and Medicaid represented another 15%.

Financial Performance

Spectrum Health's revenues increased 5% to $4.1 billion in fiscal 2014 (versus $3.9 billion in fiscal 2013) due to increases in net patient revenues and revenues from health plans. Net income rose by less than half of a percent to $377 million; impacting net income growth were factors including a decline in non-operating revenue and an increase in operating expenses.

Cash flow from operations rose a modest 2% to $181 million in 2014 due to changes in accounts payable accrued salaries and wages health care claims payable and other operating liabilities.

Strategy

The health system regularly expands its footprint. In 2015 Spectrum Health began construction on its newest integrated care campus. The new 10000 square foot facility will be located in front of the Meijer store at 2770 South State Road in Berlin Township near Ionia.

In also recently opened a 14-story building for its Helen DeVos Children's Hospital. The health network is also focused on expanding its health plan operations which account for about half of annual revenues. To this end Priority Health has added about 100000 customers in recent years by offering plans in eight new counties in northern Michigan and by adding the Bronson Healthcare provider network in southwestern Michigan. In 2015 Spectrum Health and Munson Healthcare agreed to form a joint venture between Aero Med's northern operations and North Flight EMS Air Division. The new organization will enhance critical care air emergency transport services in northern Michigan. Aero Med will continue to serve West Michigan from its operations based at the Gerald R. Ford International Airport in Grand Rapids. North Flight's fleet of ground ambulances in northern Michigan will continue to operate as North Flight EMS.

Spectrum Health also focuses on recruiting new physicians and strengthening its community hospital offerings. In 2014 it announced plans for new construction and renovation at its Rehab and Nursing Center in Grand Rapids. It is also building office space in the same city that will house some 200 employees.

Mergers and Acquisitions

The company has expanded its health network in recent years through acquisitions.

In 2015 Pennock Hospital become part of Spectrum Health and renamed Spectrum Health Pennock. Pennock and Spectrum will work in partnership with physicians to develop a new strategic plan which will include the expansion of services.

In 2014 Gynecologic Oncology of West Michigan joined the group. Prior to that Spectrum Health bought Gerber Memorial Health Services operator of a 60-bed hospital near the company's service area; the facility now operates as Spectrum Health Gerber Memorial.

Company Background

Spectrum Health was formed through the 1997 merger of Blodgett Hospital and Butterworth Hospital. Kent Community Hospital joined the organization in 1999 and the United Memorial Health System (Kelsey Hospital and United Hospital) became a member in 2003.

HISTORY

.

EXECUTIVES

President and CEO, Richard C. (Rick) Breon
EVP and CFO; President and CEO Priority Health, Michael P. (Mike) Freed
SVP and CIO, Patrick J. O'Hare
EVP Spectrum Health Delivery System, Matthew G. (Matt) Van Vranken
EVP and Chief Strategy Officer, John B. Mosley
President Blodgett Hospital, James (Jim) Wilson, age 59
President Helen DeVos Children's Hospital, Robert H. (Bob) Connors
Chief Clinical Systems and Improvement Officer, James M. Tucci
President Spectrum Health Grand Rapids, Kevin Splaine
SVP and Chief Human Resource Officer, Roger E. Jansen
President Spectrum Health Hospital Group, Tina Freese-Decker
Chief Medical Officer; President Spectrum Medical Group, Seth W. Wolk
President Spectrum Health Big Rapids and Reed City Hospitals, Mary Kay VanDriel
COO Spectrum Health Grand Rapids, Gwen G. Sandefur
Vp Facilities, Jonathan (Jon) Flyte
Executive Vice President Of Medical Affairs, Lowell Bursch
Assistant Vice President Nursing, Jodi Boyce
Vice President Of Sales, Kathy Alarie
Vice President of Facilities and Real Estate, Rick Redetzke
Vice President Supply Chain, Christopher (Chris) Baskel
Vice President Information Technology, Scott Dresen
Senior Vice President Community Relations, Steven (Steve) Heacock
Vice President Human Resources, David Beach
Medical Director Chronic Disease Management, Robert K (Bob) Jarve
Pharmacy Manager, Heather Christensen
Vice President Performance Improvement and Patient Affairs, Kurt Knoth
Vice President Of Human Resources, Thea Reigler
Vice President Clinical Integration, Jan Stone
Director of Finance Vice President Of Finance, Ron Knauf
Medical Director, David Start
Vice President Operations, Karen Pakkala
Medical Director, Christopher Barnes
Orthopaedic Surgeon Medical Director Sports Medicine SHMG, James (Jamie) Lebolt
Vice President Human Resources Sh System, Julie Lepzinski
Senior Vice President IT, Mike Feed
Vice President Finance, Polly M Krywanski
Vice President Community and Home Based Services, Mark Guzicki
Vice President Of Operations, Matt Davis
Vice President Nursing, Shari SchwanzlBsnMba
Cota L, Leigh Moulton
Auditors: ERNST & YOUNG LLP GRAND RAPID

LOCATIONS

HQ: SPECTRUM HEALTH SYSTEM
100 MICHIGAN ST NE, GRAND RAPIDS, MI 495032560
Phone: 616 391-1774
Web: WWW.SPECTRUMHEALTH.ORG

PRODUCTS/OPERATIONS

2014 Sales

	% of total
Health plan	52
Net patient service revenue	45
Other	3
Total	**100**

Selected Services

Cancer
Continuing care
Digestive disease
Heart & vascular
Neurosciences
Orthopedics
Outpatient
Pediatric
Rehabilitation
Transplant
Women's health

Selected Operations

Helen DeVos Children's Hospital
Priority Health
Spectrum Health Blodgett Hospital
Spectrum Health Butterworth Hospital
Spectrum Health Continuing Care
Spectrum Health Kent Community Campus
Spectrum Health Gerber Memorial Hospital
Spectrum Health Pennock Hospital
Spectrum Health Reed City Hospital
Spectrum Health Special Care Hospital
Spectrum Health United Memorial
Kelsey Hospital
United Hospital

COMPETITORS

Ascension Health	Health Alliance Plan
Blue Cross Blue Shield	of Michigan
of Michigan	McLaren Bay
Borgess Health	McLaren Health Care
Bronson Battle Creek	Mercy Health Hackley
Bronson Health Care	Munson Healthcare
CareSource	OmniCare Health Plan
Covenant HealthCare	Sheridan Community
Great Lakes Health	Hospital
Plan	Total Health Care
Hayes Green Beach	Zeeland Community
Memorial Hospital	Hospital

HISTORICAL FINANCIALS
Company Type: Private

Income Statement
FYE: June 30

	REVENUE ($ mil.)	NET INCOME ($ mil.)	NET PROFIT MARGIN	EMPLOYEES
06/10	1,446	142	9.9%	16,996
06/09	1,266	0	—	—
Annual Growth	14.2%	—	—	—

2010 Year-End Financials
Return on assets: —
Return on equity: 9.9%
Current ratio: 0.20

Cash ($ mil.): 5

SPF ENERGY INC.

Super-jobber SPF Energy is also a super-pumper of petroleum. The company's Super-pumper subsidiary runs a chain of about 15 convenience stores and gas stations in Minnesota Montana and North Dakota under the Cenex Conoco Exxon SinclairTesoro and Shell banners. Its Farstad Oil subsidiary offers bulk transportation of petroleum products including the annual distribution of about 250 million gallons of gas 20 million gallons of propane and 2.5 million gallons of lubricants. The Farstad fleet serves businesses and government agencies from Montana to eastern Minnesota and from northern Wyoming to the Canadian border. SPF Energy is owned by North American fuel wholesaler Parkland Fuel Corporation.

Change in Company Type

Parkland Fuel Corporation acquired SPF Energy in 2014 for CAD $113 million. It bought the Superpumper and Farstad Oil operator for its growth potential in the northwestern US and annual production of 1.1 million liters of refined petroleum product.

Operations

SPF Energy operates Superpumper which runs convenience stores and gas stations under a variety of big-name banners in Minnesota Montana and North Dakota.

The company also serves all of North Dakota and Montana as well as portions of Minnesota South Dakota and Wyoming through its Farstad Oil business. The unit maintains a fleet of more than 50 trucks.

Altogether SPF Energy services more than 200 independent gasoline stations 60 of which operate under a major brand name.

Auditors: BRADY MARTZ & ASSOCIATES PC

LOCATIONS
HQ: SPF ENERGY INC.
100 27TH ST NE, MINOT, ND 587035164
Phone: 701 852-1194
Web: WWW.SPFENERGY.COM

PRODUCTS/OPERATIONS

Selected Brands
Cenex
Conoco
Exxon
Shell
Sinclair
Tesoro

COMPETITORS
BP
Redwood Coast Petroleum
Wilson Oil

HISTORICAL FINANCIALS
Company Type: Private

Income Statement
FYE: December 31

	REVENUE ($ mil.)	NET INCOME ($ mil.)	NET PROFIT MARGIN	EMPLOYEES
12/14	1,026	16	1.6%	300
12/13	1,012	8	0.9%	—
12/12	1,062	5	0.5%	—
12/11	1,078	0	—	—
Annual Growth	(1.6%)	—	—	—

2014 Year-End Financials
Return on assets: 2.0%
Return on equity: 1.6%
Current ratio: 1.80

Cash ($ mil.): 12

SPORTS INC.

Auditors: JUNKEMIER CLARK CAMPANELLA

LOCATIONS
HQ: SPORTS INC.
333 2ND AVE N, LEWISTOWN, MT 594572700
Phone: 406 538-3496
Web: WWW.SPORTSINC.COM

HISTORICAL FINANCIALS
Company Type: Private

Income Statement
FYE: December 31

	REVENUE ($ mil.)	NET INCOME ($ mil.)	NET PROFIT MARGIN	EMPLOYEES
12/13	757	0	0.0%	40
12/12	568	0	0.0%	—
12/11	446	0	0.0%	—
12/10	442	0	—	—
Annual Growth	19.6%	—	—	—

2013 Year-End Financials
Return on assets: 12.5%
Return on equity: —
Current ratio: 1.10

Cash ($ mil.): —

SRC TEC INC.

Auditors: ERNST & YOUNG LLP SYRACUSE N

LOCATIONS
HQ: SRC TEC INC.
5801 E TAFT RD STE 7, SYRACUSE, NY 132123273
Phone: 315 452-8700
Web: WWW.SRCINC.COM

HISTORICAL FINANCIALS
Company Type: Private

Income Statement
FYE: September 30

	REVENUE ($ mil.)	NET INCOME ($ mil.)	NET PROFIT MARGIN	EMPLOYEES
09/10	583	42	7.3%	275
09/09	365	19	5.4%	—
Annual Growth	59.7%	115.0%	—	—

2010 Year-End Financials
Return on assets: 14.3%
Return on equity: 7.3%
Current ratio: 1.30

Cash ($ mil.): 44

SRI INTERNATIONAL

SRI International sometimes called "Silicon Valley's soul" is a not-for-profit think tank pondering advances in biotechnology chemicals and energy computer science electronics and public policy — and ways to commercialize those advances. It focuses on technology research and development business strategies and analysis. The organization has patents and patent applications in IT communications robotics and pharmaceuticals. SRI's clients have included Samsung General Motors and AT&T. The artificial intelligence it designed for the Department of Defense became Apple's Siri. Originally founded in 1946 as Stanford Research Institute SRI became fully independent in 1970.

Operations

SRI has conceived such innovations as the computer mouse magnetic encoding for checks and high-definition television not to mention some of the foundations of personal computing the Internet and stealth technology. It also provides basic and applied research laboratory and advisory services tech development and venture opportunities.

Geographic Reach

SRI operates 17 offices across the US (California Connecticut Florida Maryland Michigan Montana New Jersey Pennsylvania Texas and Virginia) along with four international offices in Puerto Rico Dubai Japan and Greenland. The organization's 2500 employees (including about 1000 scientists and researchers) work at research centers worldwide.

Sales and Marketing

SRI brings its research and development innovations to the marketplace by licensing its intellectual property and creating new ventures. SRI has created and launched more than 50 ventures with a total market capitalization exceeding $20 billion. It has conducted more than $4 billion in R&D since the early 2000s for clients and partners and worked with government partners including the National Institutes of Health and the Defense Advanced Research Projects Agency for more than 50 years. In fact Department of Defense clients contributed about 63% of sales in 2013. Its venture partners include Draper Fisher Jurvetson Horizon Ventures Intel Capital Khosla Ventures Kleiner Perkins Caufield & Byers and Mayfield Fund.

Financial Performance

After years of climbing revenue SRI reported an 8% drop in 2013 from $585 to $540.

Strategy

SRI continues to invest in R&D on behalf of its clients. In 2013 it completed a new $2.8 million 40000-square-foot bioscience research and development facility in Virginia.

In 2014 the company sold its fourth artificial intelligence platform Desti a smart travel planner to mobile device maker Nokia. Other AI projects include Siri content discovery engine Trapit and productivity app Tempo AI; together they brought SRI more than $20 billion.

HISTORY

In the 1920s Stanford University professor Robert Swain envisioned a research center devoted to chemistry physics and biology. Swain received support from university president Ray Lyman and alumnus Herbert Hoover but the Great Depression and WWII postponed the venture.

Finally in 1946 the Stanford Research Institute was formed in conjunction with the university. That year the David Sarnoff Research Center invented the color TV tube under the wing of RCA Laboratories.

During Stanford Research's early years it worked on such projects as logistics for Disneyland magnetic ink for character recognition and strategies for combating air pollution. The think tank was the focus of student protests in the 1960s because of its defense work. In 1969 Stanford Research Institute was one of four nodes on the first computer network the ARPANET. It became fully independent in 1970 as SRI International.

During the 1960s and 1970s SRI won large contracts from the US Department of Defense for research in such areas as radar speech recognition and noise cancellation technologies. It got a tremendous boost in 1987 when longtime client General Electric gave SRI the Sarnoff Research Center (as a tax write-off) plus $250 million in business along with $65.2 million in cash.

In 1993 SRI founded Pangene to commercialize gene cloning and analysis technology. The next year it founded GeneTrace to develop genetics-related products for biomedical research and Nuance Communications to commercialize speech-recognition products. Intuitive Surgical which develops minimally invasive surgical technologies was formed in 1995.

SRI developed two key components for use in an improved mail sorting program which the US Postal Service announced in 1997 it would use to save millions in processing costs. The David Sarnoff Research Center changed its name to Sarnoff Corporation that year.

In 1998 SRI and the National Science Foundation teamed to develop innovative science and math teaching programs. The following year SRI began working with network equipment leader Cisco Systems and the US Army to develop a voice and multimedia communications system for the military. In 2001 SRI partnered with SPEEDCOM Wireless to co-develop wireless technology.

In order to complement its biosciences division SRI bought Quality Clinical Labs (QCL) a few years later. QCL was a California-based clinical pathology analysis center specializing in clinical hematology and chemistry evaluations.

SRI's former subsidiary the Sarnoff Corporation fully integrated into SRI's operations during 2011.

EXECUTIVES

Vice President Legal Business Affairs General Counsel, Richard (Dick) Abramson
Vice President Policy Division, Dennis Beatrice
President Information and Computing Sciences Division and VP SRI International, William Mark
VP Corporate and Marketing Communications, Alice R. Resnick
VP and President SRI Biosciences, Walter H. Moos, age 60
VP Mission Solutions and COO, John W. Prausa
VP and President Advanced Technology and Systems, Scott Seaton
VP and President Global Partnerships, Stephen J. (Steve) Ciesinski
President and CEO, William Jeffrey
VP and President Products and Solutions, Mark A. Clifton
VP Information Technology and CIO, Michael Page
VP CFO and Treasurer, Luther Lau
VP and President SRI Ventures, Manish Kothari
President SRI Education and VP SRI International, Denise Glyn Borders
Vp Human Resources, Jeanie Tooker
Vice President Human Resources, Jean Tooker

Vice President, Eric Pearson
Chairman, Mariann Byerwalter, age 55
Board Of Directors, Sybil Vasche
Auditors: PRICEWATERHOUSECOOPER LLP SA

LOCATIONS

HQ: SRI INTERNATIONAL
333 RAVENSWOOD AVE, MENLO PARK, CA 940253493
Phone: 650 859-2000
Web: WWW.SRI.COM

PRODUCTS/OPERATIONS

Selected Research Areas
Automation and robotics
Automotive and commercial equipment technologies
Chemistry materials and applied physics
Communications
Defense and intelligence
Homeland defense and national security
Information science and software development
Medical devices
Product engineering
Pharmaceutical services
Policy
Sensors and measurement systems

COMPETITORS

Aerospace Corporation	Quintiles
Battelle Memorial	Transnational
Bayer Corp.	RAND Corporation
CACI International	Research Triangle
Charles Stark Draper	Institute
Laboratory	SwRI
DaVinci Institute	University of
DuPont	California
MIT	Wellcome Trust
MITRE	Westat
PAREXEL	

HISTORICAL FINANCIALS

Company Type: Private

Income Statement
FYE: December 28

	REVENUE ($ mil.)	NET INCOME ($ mil.)	NET PROFIT MARGIN	EMPLOYEES
12/13	547	(5)	—	2,437
12/12	560	(5)	—	—
12/11	585	14	2.5%	—
12/10	502	0	—	—
Annual Growth	2.9%	—	—	—

2013 Year-End Financials
Return on assets: —
Return on equity: (-1.0%)
Current ratio: 1.30
Cash ($ mil.): 26

ST AGNES HOSPITAL OF FOND DU LAC WISC INC

LOCATIONS

HQ: ST AGNES HOSPITAL OF FOND DU LAC WISC INC
430 E DIVISION ST, FOND DU LAC, WI 549354597
Phone: 920 929-2300
Web: WWW.AGNESIAN.COM

HISTORICAL FINANCIALS

Company Type: Private

Income Statement
FYE: June 30

	REVENUE ($ mil.)	NET INCOME ($ mil.)	NET PROFIT MARGIN	EMPLOYEES
06/13	312	36	11.8%	2,700
06/09	255	1	0.6%	—
06/08*	2	1	83.2%	—
09/06	0	0	—	—
Annual Growth	—	—	—	—

*Fiscal year change

2013 Year-End Financials
Return on assets: 3.2%
Return on equity: 11.8%
Current ratio: 1.60
Cash ($ mil.): 10

ST BARNABAS MEDICAL CENTER INC

Part of the Saint Barnabas Health Care System Saint Barnabas Medical Center is a 600-bed acute-care hospital that provides a full range of health services to residents of Livingston New Jersey and surrounding areas. The not-for-profit medical center provides general inpatient and outpatient care programs as well as burn and perinatal care. It also houses units specializing in organ transplant stroke care cardiac surgery and comprehensive cancer treatment. Its Institute for Reproductive Medicine and Science provides assisted reproductive technology services. Saint Barnabas Medical Center treats some 35000 inpatients and more than 85000 emergency-room patients each year.

OperationsIn combination with its satellite Saint Barnabas Ambulatory Care Center the medical center serves about 300000 outpatients per year. Saint Barnabas Medical Center is also a teaching affiliate of several regional schools including the University of Medicine and Dentistry of New Jersey and Drexel University College of Medicine.

Company BackgroundNew Jersey's first hospital Saint Barnabas Medical Center was founded in 1865 in a private home.

EXECUTIVES

Infection Control Director, Eileen Yaney
Vice President Of Patient Care Services, Sari Kaplon
Vice President Financial Management, John (Jack) Doll
Auditors: WITHUMSMITHBROWN PC MORRISTOW

LOCATIONS

HQ: ST BARNABAS MEDICAL CENTER INC
94 OLD SHORT HILLS RD # 1, LIVINGSTON, NJ 070395668
Phone: 973 322-5000
Web: WWW.NJBURNCENTER.COM

COMPETITORS

Atlantic Health
Children's Specialized Hospital
Chilton Medical Center
East Orange General Hospital
Hackensack University Medical Center
JFK Health System
JFK Medical Center
Meridian Health
Newark Beth Israel Medical Center

Raritan Bay Medical Center
Robert Wood Johnson University Hospital
Robert Wood Johnson University Hospital at Rahway
Saint Peter's University Hospital
St. Joseph's Healthcare System
Trinitas Regional Medical Center
Virtua Health

HISTORICAL FINANCIALS
Company Type: Private

Income Statement
FYE: December 31

	REVENUE ($ mil.)	NET INCOME ($ mil.)	NET PROFIT MARGIN	EMPLOYEES
12/12	652	74	11.5%	479
12/08	510	(4)	—	—
12/05	438	9	2.1%	—
12/03	1,550	0	—	—
Annual Growth	(9.2%)	—	—	—

2012 Year-End Financials
Return on assets: 7.8%   Cash ($ mil.): —
Return on equity: 11.5%
Current ratio: 0.30

ST FRANCIS HOSPITAL

Sure St. Francis Hospital can handle your gall bladder and sinus difficulties but it's really on top of your heart problems. The hospital's Heart Center – New York State's only specially designated cardiac center –provides surgical diagnostic and treatment services. The 365-bed St. Francis Hospital also has centers for ENT (ear nose and throat) orthopedic vascular prostate cancer gastrointestinal and general surgery services. As part of Catholic Health Services of Long Island St. Francis opened its doors in 1954 to children and adults. It was originally established as St. Francis Hospital and Sanatorium for Cardiac Children in 1936.

Geographic Reach

St. Francis Hospital is located in Roslyn New York. In addition it has satellite New York locations in Greenvale (DeMatteis Center for Cardiac Research and Education) West Islip (South Bay Cardiovascular Center) and Hicksville (Bishop McHugh Health Center) as well as administrative offices in Port Washington.

Operations

St. Francis Hospital's Heart Center performs about 8000 cardiac catheterizations 3000 coronary angioplasties and about 1500 open-heart operations every year. The center's DeMatteis Center for Cardiac Research and Education works to develop improved techniques for heart disease diagnosis including conducting clinical trials through partnerships with device and equipment makers and provides patient education and fitness programs.

Strategy

St. Francis Hospital has expanded in recent years to keep up with growing patient demand. It opened the Bishop McHugh Health Center to provide outpatient primary care services for uninsured and underinsured patients in 2012.

The hospital completed its largest expansion project to date in 2009 with the construction of the $190 million Nancy and Frederick DeMatteis Pavilion; the project increased the hospital's clinical space by about 40% and added 85 beds.

EXECUTIVES
Infection Control Director, Mary Solliday
Auditors: JH COHN LLP ROSELAND NJ

LOCATIONS
HQ: ST FRANCIS HOSPITAL
  100 PORT WASHINGTON BLVD, ROSLYN, NY
  115761353
Phone: 516 627-3813
Web: WWW.STFRANCISHEARTCENTER.COM

PRODUCTS/OPERATIONS

Selected Services
Anesthesiology
Breast Surgery
Cardiology
Cardiothoracic Surgery
Diabetes Care Center
Emergency Medicine
Gastroenterology
General Surgery
Hematology/Oncology
Nephrology
Neurology
Orthopedic Surgery
Otolaryngology
Podiatry
Psychiatry
Pulmonary Medicine
Radiology
Rehabilitation
Urology
Vascular Services
Women's Center

COMPETITORS

Bronx-Lebanon Hospital
Brookhaven Memorial Hospital Medical Center
Calvary Hospital
Continuum Health Partners
Franklin Hospital
Huntington Hospital
Mather Memorial Hospital
MediSys Health Network
Memorial Sloan-Kettering
New York City Health and Hospitals
NewYork-Presbyterian Healthcare
North Shore-Long Island Jewish Health System
NuHealth

HISTORICAL FINANCIALS
Company Type: Private

Income Statement
FYE: December 31

	REVENUE ($ mil.)	NET INCOME ($ mil.)	NET PROFIT MARGIN	EMPLOYEES
12/08	385	28	7.4%	2,184
12/04	366	47	12.9%	—
12/02	828	0	—	—
Annual Growth	—	606.6%	—	—

2008 Year-End Financials
Return on assets: 9.2%   Cash ($ mil.): 117
Return on equity: 7.4%
Current ratio: 2.20

ST JOHN MEDICAL CENTER INC

LOCATIONS
HQ: ST JOHN MEDICAL CENTER INC
  1923 S UTICA AVE, TULSA, OK 741046520
Phone: 918 744-2828
Web: WWW.STJOHNHEALTHSYSTEM.COM

HISTORICAL FINANCIALS
Company Type: Private

Income Statement
FYE: September 30

	REVENUE ($ mil.)	NET INCOME ($ mil.)	NET PROFIT MARGIN	EMPLOYEES
09/13	511	86	16.9%	3,187
09/12	436	71	16.3%	—
09/09	510	(33)	—	—
09/08	448	0	—	—
Annual Growth	2.6%	—	—	—

2013 Year-End Financials
Return on assets: 2.4%   Cash ($ mil.): 2
Return on equity: 16.9%
Current ratio: 1.60

ST JOHN'S UNIVERSITY NEW YORK

No university is an island but one of St. John's campuses is on Manhattan Island. A private co-educational Roman Catholic school St. John's University offers undergraduate and graduate programs in more than 100 majors through five colleges a law school and a distance learning program. St. John's has more than 20000 students at five campuses (Queens Staten Island and Manhattan in New York City one in Oakdale New York and one graduate center in Rome). The school has a 17-to-1 student-faculty ratio. More than 80% of its graduates reside in the New York region including notable alumni such as former New York governors Hugh Carey and Mario Cuomo. The school was founded in 1870 by the Vincentian Community.

EXECUTIVES

Secretary III Department Of Facilities Services, Barbara (Barb) Kucija
Secretary, Sandra Dobbins
Secretary III English, Lana Umali
Department Assistant Treasurer, Marie Sloan
Secretary Iicps Criminal Justice And Legal Studies, Elana Pirov
Secretary, Linda Gonsalves
Secretary, Kathy Briscoe
Secretary III Athletic Department, Rosemarie Bendel
Auditors: KPMG LLP NEW YORK NY

LOCATIONS
HQ: ST JOHN'S UNIVERSITY NEW YORK
  8000 UTOPIA PKWY, JAMAICA, NY 114399000
Phone: 718 990-6161
Web: WWW.STJOHNS.EDU

PRODUCTS/OPERATIONS

Selected Colleges and Schools
College of Pharmacy and Allied Health Professions
College of Professional Studies
The Peter J. Tobin College of Business
St. John's College of Liberal Arts and Sciences
St. John's Distance Learning
The School of Education
School of Law

HISTORICAL FINANCIALS
Company Type: Private

Income Statement
FYE: May 31

	REVENUE ($ mil.)	NET INCOME ($ mil.)	NET PROFIT MARGIN	EMPLOYEES
05/13	473	64	13.5%	3,310
05/12	471	2	0.6%	—
05/11	450	82	18.4%	—
05/10	440	0	—	—
Annual Growth	2.4%	—	—	—

2013 Year-End Financials
Return on assets: —
Return on equity: 13.5%
Current ratio: —

Cash ($ mil.): 7

ST JOHNS HOSPITAL SISTERS OF THE THIRD ORDER OF ST FRANCIS

Truck-struck Homer Simpson might use his last gasp trying to blurt out "St. John's Hospital of the Hospital Sisters of the Third Order of St. Francis-Springfield" to his ambulance driver but he might be better off using the hospital's more common name St. John's. D'oh! The 440-bed St. John's Hospital serves residents of central and southern Illinois with general and specialized health care services. The teaching hospital affiliated with Southern Illinois University's School of Medicine has centers devoted to women and children's health trauma cardiac care cancer orthopedics and neurology. It also operates area health clinics. Founded in 1875 St. John's is part of the Hospital Sisters Health System.

Operations

The facility is Hospital Sisters Health System's flagship hospital. It has grown to boast about 700 physicians podiatrists and dentists from more than 30 specialties. In addition to educating medical students through Southern Illinois University's School of Medicine St. Johns also supports those working on careers in nursing through its own nursing school St. John's College. It also offers courses in pharmacy pathology respiratory therapy and electroneurodiagnostics (brain disorder diagnostics) professions.

St. John's physicians perform more than 15000 surgical procedures each year. It also receives some 54000 emergency department visits and helps deliver about 2000 babies annually.

Financial Performance

In 2014 revenue fell 26% to $450 million; this was primarily due to an 89% decline in contributions investments and foundation assets.

Strategy

The hospital has been expanding its offerings to provide more specialized services to area residents. Recent additions include 3-D mammographies and expanded children's surgical services. St. John's is also focused on improving access to health care through technology such as telemedicine. In 2014 it partnered with Greenville Regional Hospital to provide advanced treatment to stroke patients at their home hospital through STAT Stroke TeleMedicine.

Other strategic initiatives at the hospital include increasing doctor and nurse retention rates grow-ing nursing school enrollment rates and increasing patient satisfaction scores. Part of its efforts to reach more patients has led St. John's to open new outpatient health centers in areas near the main hospital facility. The hospital has also renovated its main buildings including the revamp of its day surgery and intermediate care departments.

EXECUTIVES
President CEO and Director, Robert P. (Bob) Ritz, age 52

LOCATIONS
HQ: ST JOHNS HOSPITAL SISTERS OF THE THIRD ORDER OF ST FRANCIS
800 E CARPENTER ST, SPRINGFIELD, IL 627690002
Phone: 217 544-6464
Web: WWW.STJOHNSCOLLEGESPRINGFIELD.EDU

PRODUCTS/OPERATIONS

2014 Sales

	% of total
Amount generated for taking care patients excluding provision	95
Other contributions	5
Other	.
Total	**100**

Selected Services
AthletiCare
Behavioral Health Services
Birth Center
Cancer Institute
Center for Living
Children' s Hospital
Connect
Emergency/Trauma Care
Gastroenterology
Health Centers | Priority Care
Home Health
Hospice
Intensive Care Unit
Lab
Neurosciences Institute
Orthopedics
Pain Management Center
Prairie Heart Institute
Radiology
Regional Wound Care Center
Sleep Center
Stroke Treatment
Surgery | daVinci
TherapyCare | Rehab
Third Age Living
Women' s Services

COMPETITORS

Advocate Health Care	Memorial Health System
Blessing Hospital	Memorial Hospital
Community Health Systems	(Illinois)
Decatur Memorial Hospital	Southern Illinois Healthcare

HISTORICAL FINANCIALS
Company Type: Private

Income Statement
FYE: June 30

	REVENUE ($ mil.)	NET INCOME ($ mil.)	NET PROFIT MARGIN	EMPLOYEES
06/08	393	(8)	—	3,000
06/05	387	50	13.1%	—
06/04	1,737	0	—	—
Annual Growth	—	—	—	—

2008 Year-End Financials
Return on assets: 9.4%
Return on equity: (-2.2%)
Current ratio: 0.20

Cash ($ mil.): —

ST JOSEPH OF THE PINES INC

Auditors: BERNARD ROBINSON & COMPANY LL

LOCATIONS
HQ: ST JOSEPH OF THE PINES INC
100 GOSSMAN RD STE B, SOUTHERN PINES, NC 283872282
Phone: 910 246-1000
Web: WWW.SJP.ORG

HISTORICAL FINANCIALS
Company Type: Private

Income Statement
FYE: September 30

	REVENUE ($ mil.)	NET INCOME ($ mil.)	NET PROFIT MARGIN	EMPLOYEES
09/09*	2,285	(571)	—	300
12/06	28	2	8.6%	—
12/05	26	0	2.7%	—
12/04	26	0	—	—
Annual Growth	144.0%	—	—	—

*Fiscal year change

2009 Year-End Financials
Return on assets: —
Return on equity: (-25.0%)
Current ratio: 0.70

Cash ($ mil.): 1

ST LUKE'S METHODIST HOSPITAL INC

LOCATIONS
HQ: ST LUKE' S METHODIST HOSPITAL INC
1026 A AVE NE, CEDAR RAPIDS, IA 524025074
Phone: 319 369-7211
Web: WWW.STLUKESCR.ORG

HISTORICAL FINANCIALS
Company Type: Private

Income Statement
FYE: December 31

	REVENUE ($ mil.)	NET INCOME ($ mil.)	NET PROFIT MARGIN	EMPLOYEES
12/09	312	15	4.9%	2,000
12/08	262	1	0.7%	—
12/05	277	15	5.5%	—
12/04	210	0	—	—
Annual Growth	8.2%	—	—	—

2009 Year-End Financials
Return on assets: —
Return on equity: 4.9%
Current ratio: 2.10

Cash ($ mil.): 44

ST PATRICK HOSPITAL CORPORATION

Feeling a little green? St. Patrick Hospital and Health Sciences Center is there to help. The not-for-profit hospital boasts some 250 beds (acute-care and transitional) and serves nearly 20 counties in and around Missoula Montana. Its specialty services include cancer treatment surgery and occupational health. The center also provides Life Flight air transport to critically ill or injured patients. The hospital provides outpatient primary and specialty care through a host of affiliated physician practices and clinics throughout the area. St. Patrick Hospital and Health Sciences Center is part of Providence Health & Services which has two hospitals and more than 40 clinics across Montana.

Geographic Reach

St. Patrick Hospital and Health Sciences Center serves those who reside in Missoula Montana and the surrounding counties which generate 95% of its patient volume.

Operations

The center's facility annual admits more than 7900 patients and logs more than 37900 days of patient care. Its physician offices and outpatient services are located adjacent to the hospital. They comprise the Western Montana Clinic the Montana Neuroscience Institute the Montana Cancer Center and the International Heart Institute. Outpatient services provided by St. Patrick Hospital and Health Sciences Center include physical occupational speech diabetic and cardiac rehabilitation.

In 2013 the hospital was awarded Magnet recognition by the American Nurses Credentialing Center's Magnet Recognition Program.

Strategy

St. Patrick Hospital and Health Sciences Center is looking to expand its comprehensive women's and children's services. Its new services will include inpatient obstetrical and newborn care (with a Level 2 neonatal intensive care unit); an expanded inpatient and outpatient pediatric program; and outpatient obstetrical/gynecological and perinatology care.

Company Background

St. Patrick Hospital and Health Sciences Center was founded in 1873 by the Sisters of Providence.

EXECUTIVES

Vice President of Finance and Information, Joel Lankford
Vice President Human Resources Services, Kerry Schultz

LOCATIONS

HQ: ST PATRICK HOSPITAL CORPORATION
500 W BROADWAY ST, MISSOULA, MT 598024008
Phone: 406 543-7271
Web: WWW.SAINTPATRICK.ORG

PRODUCTS/OPERATIONS

Selected Services
Cardiology
Cancer Center
Diabetes Care Center
Diagnostic Imaging
Emergency Department
First STEP
Joint Replacement
Laboratory
Life Flight
Neurobehavioral Medicine
Neurology
Broadway Pharmacy
Rehabilitation
Sleep Center
Stroke Center
Surgery

COMPETITORS

Billings Clinic
Glendive Medical Center
St. Alexius Medical Center
St. James Healthcare
Wyoming Medical Center

HISTORICAL FINANCIALS

Company Type: Private

Income Statement FYE: December 31

	REVENUE ($ mil.)	NET INCOME ($ mil.)	NET PROFIT MARGIN	EMPLOYEES
12/12	227	37	16.6%	1,460
12/05	191	8	4.3%	—
12/04	163	6	3.8%	—
12/02	1,361	0	—	—
Annual Growth	(16.4%)	—	—	—

2012 Year-End Financials

Return on assets: 3.9%
Return on equity: 16.6%
Current ratio: 1.60

Cash ($ mil.): 1

ST PETER'S MEDICAL CENTER

Serving the central portions of the Garden State Saint Peter's University Hospital has about 480 beds. The facility is sponsored by the Roman Catholic Diocese of Metuchen New Jersey and provides patients with a staff of more than 900 physicians and dentists. Saint Peter's also offers one of the country's largest Neonatal Intensive Care Units minimally invasive surgical (MIS) procedures and specialized cancer diabetes and geriatric care. In affiliation with the Children's Hospital of Philadelphia Saint Peter's provides cardiac care for infants and children. The teaching hospital is also affiliated with the Drexel University College of Medicine.

Geographic Reach

Saint Peter's serves the residents of central New Jersey from its New Brunswick campus.

Operations

Saint Peter's is a state-designated children's hospital and a regional perinatal center and is a regional specialist in geriatrics oncology orthopedics women's services and ambulatory care. As part of the Saint Peter's Healthcare System the non-profit acute care facility performs some 30000 inpatient treatments and more than 200000 outpatient procedures each year. It also delivers some 6100 newborns annually and is a state-designated children's hospital and regional perinatal center. Supported by 2800 healthcare professionals Saint Peter's University Hospital serves as a regional specialist in geriatrics oncology orthopedics women's services and ambulatory care. It offers both adults and children cancer care services including inpatient care and outpatient radiation and infusion. The hospital performs single-incision robotic-assisted surgery using the da Vinci Si Surgical System.

Strategy

In 2013 Saint Peter's opened a redesigned and expanded perinatal center that houses both maternal-fetal medicine and antenatal testing services. Some 500 low-birth-weight babies are delivered at the hospital each year. The facility also logs more than 2200 high-risk obstetrics clinic visits each year.

In 2012 Saint Peter's opened a hospice program for adults in association with Bloomfield-based Hospice of New Jersey one of the oldest and largest providers of hospice care in the US. The year the hospital has launched a two-and-half-year-long building project to enlarge its emergency department and expand emergency services. When completed the Saint Peter's emergency department will have grown in size from 18000 sq. ft. to 29000 sq. ft. and will be able to treat 70000 to 75000 patients a year.

Saint Peter's also sponsors residency programs in obstetrics and gynecology pediatrics and internal medicine as a regional medical campus of Drexel University College of Medicine. The medical institution also sponsors a residency program in orthopedic surgery in affiliation with the University of Medicine and Dentistry of New Jersey-Robert Wood Johnson Medical School. It has agreements with Rutgers University and Kean University to enhance its educational programs.

Company Background

Additionally Saint Peter's is recognized as a magnet hospital for nursing excellence by the American Nurses Credentialing Center. It has won the Beacon Award for Critical Care Excellence in Nursing and is recognized by the American Diabetes Association in every area of diabetes education.

The hospital was established in 1907.

EXECUTIVES

Senior Vice President, John Rauner
Director Of Radiology, Lauris Beam
Director Icu Coronary Care Unit, Pam Harmon
Vice President Finance, John Green
Assistant Vice President, Joan Scott
Assistant Vice President, Doreen Stevenson
Vice President, Elizabeth Wykpisz
Director of Surgery Department, Isaak Kruger
Assistant Secretary trustee, Kathleen Killion

LOCATIONS

HQ: ST PETER' S MEDICAL CENTER
254 EASTON AVE, NEW BRUNSWICK, NJ 089011766
Phone: 732 745-8600
Web: WWW.SAINTPETERSHCS.COM

PRODUCTS/OPERATIONS

Selected Services
Adult care
Cancer care
Community health
Diagnostic technology
Heart health
Maternity
Meet the staff
Movement sports rehabilitation
Nicu
Nursing at saint peters
Nutrition and weight
Outreach
Parent education
Pediatric and adolescent
Support groups
Surgery
Womens health
Adult and Family Health Services
Adult Intensive Care
Audiology
Emergency Medicine
Endocrinology
Hospice Program (Inpatient)
Intensive Care
Interstitial Cystitis Support Group
Lithotripsy
Ophthalmology
Osteoporosis/Bone Density
Pain Management
Primary Care
Pulmonary Medicine

Rheumatology
Sleep and Breathing Disorders
Thyroid
Urology
Wound Care and Hyperbaric Services
Adult Day Center
Allergy and Immunology
Dermatology
Dialysis
Emergency Medicine Physicians
Endoscopy/Same Day Services
Gastroenterology
Geriatric Medicine
Infectious Diseases
Internal Medicine
Interventional Radiology
Memory Assessment
Orthopedics
Otolaryngology (Ear Nose and Throat)
Pulmonary Function Laboratory Services
Respiratory Care Services
Skilled Nursing Care
Stroke
Urinary Incontinence and Pelvic Pain Program
Vascular Disease

COMPETITORS

CentraState Healthcare System
JFK Medical Center
Princeton HealthCare
Raritan Bay Medical Center
Robert Wood Johnson University Hospital
Robert Wood Johnson University Hospital at Rahway
Saint Barnabas Medical
Somerset Medical Center

HISTORICAL FINANCIALS

Company Type: Private

Income Statement

FYE: December 31

	REVENUE ($ mil.)	NET INCOME ($ mil.)	NET PROFIT MARGIN	EMPLOYEES
12/08	391	(34)	—	2,475
12/06	392	4	1.0%	—
12/05	373	4	1.1%	—
12/04	351	0	—	—
Annual Growth	2.7%	—	—	—

2008 Year-End Financials

Return on assets: 9.8% Cash ($ mil.): —
Return on equity: (-8.8%)
Current ratio: 0.90

ST. ALBANS COOPERATIVE CREAMERY INC

Auditors: DOPKINS & COMPANY LLP BUFFAL

LOCATIONS

HQ: ST. ALBANS COOPERATIVE CREAMERY INC
140 FEDERAL ST, SAINT ALBANS, VT 054782000
Phone: 802 524-9366

Income Statement

FYE: October 31

	REVENUE ($ mil.)	NET INCOME ($ mil.)	NET PROFIT MARGIN	EMPLOYEES
10/13	387	2	0.7%	70
10/12	353	5	1.6%	—
10/11	361	5	1.4%	—
10/10	293	0	—	—
Annual Growth	9.7%	—	—	—

2013 Year-End Financials

Return on assets: 7.1% Cash ($ mil.): 4
Return on equity: 0.7%
Current ratio: 0.80

ST. ALEXIUS MEDICAL CENTER

Auditors: DELOITTE TAX LLP CHICAGO IL

LOCATIONS

HQ: ST. ALEXIUS MEDICAL CENTER
1555 BARRINGTON RD BLDG 1, HOFFMAN
ESTATES, IL 601691099
Phone: 847 884-9800

HISTORICAL FINANCIALS

Company Type: Private

Income Statement

FYE: June 30

	REVENUE ($ mil.)	NET INCOME ($ mil.)	NET PROFIT MARGIN	EMPLOYEES
06/13*	327	29	9.1%	1,500
12/08	280	21	7.7%	—
12/04	189	33	17.9%	—
12/03	1,789	0	—	—
Annual Growth	(17.2%)	—	—	—

*Fiscal year change

2013 Year-End Financials

Return on assets: 4.8% Cash ($ mil.): 18
Return on equity: 9.1%
Current ratio: 3.60

ST. ALEXIUS MEDICAL CENTER

Established in 1885 CHI St. Alexius Health (formerly St. Alexius Medical Center) has been serving the health care needs of those who reside in the Dakotas and Montana longer than any other area hospital. The medical facility with more than 300 beds caters to central and western North Dakota and parts of South Dakota and Montana. Specialty services include cancer care trauma care geriatrics orthopedics and rehabilitation. As part of its operations the longtime hospital also owns and manages a handful of smaller regional hospitals and community clinics. In 2014 St. Alexius joined the Catholic Health Initiatives health care system.
Operations

In 2014 the hospital performed 3372 inpatient and 7611 outpatient surgeries. It reported 57021 emergency department visits.

Affiliated organizations include Northland Pace Northland Health Care Alliance Primcare Health Group and Bismarck Cancer Center.
Geographic Reach

In addition to its main campus in Bismarck North Dakota CHI St. Alexius Health owns and operates hospitals in Garrison North Dakota; and Turtle Lake North Dakota. It manages hospitals and clinics owned by Mobridge Regional Hospital in South Dakota; and owns and operates a primary care clinic in Mandan North Dakota. Finally the hospital owns and operates specialty and primary care clinics in Minot North Dakota.
Strategy

CHI St. Alexius Health opened a new dialysis unit in Dickinson North Dakota in 2015.

EXECUTIVES

Radiology Medical Director, Douglas (Doug) Peterson
Pharmd, Carrie Sorenson
Vice President Material and Facility Resources, Frank Kilzer
Department Chairman, Elizabeth (Beth) Hughes
Vice President Medical Affairs, S Hyder
Auditors: EIDEBAILLY LLP FARGO NORTH

LOCATIONS

HQ: ST. ALEXIUS MEDICAL CENTER
900 E BROADWAY AVE, BISMARCK, ND 585014520
Phone: 701 530-7000
Web: WWW.ST.ALEXIUS.ORG

PRODUCTS/OPERATIONS

Selected Services
Acceleration
Arthritis Clinic
Balance and Dizziness Center
Behavioral and Mental Health
Cardiac Rehabilitation
Clinical Research Services
Community Health
Community Pharmacy
Deep Brain Stimulation
Dialysis
EAP
Emergency & Trauma
Family Practice Clinic
Geriatrics (Older Adults)
Heart and Vascular Center
Home Care and Hospice
Human Performance Center
Kidney Dialysis
Mandan Clinic
Minot Medical Clinic
Neonatology Clinic
Nephrology Clinic
Neurology
Neuroscience
Neurosurgery
Occupational Health and Wellness
Occupation
Orthopedics
Pediatric Cardiology Clinic
Pediatric Neurology Clinic
Physical Medicine & Rehabilitation
Physical T
Radiology Services
Rehabilita
Spine Center
Stroke Center
Surgical Services
Telemedicine and Videoconferencing Services
Therapy at HPC
Urology Clinic
Women's Health

COMPETITORS

Altru Health   Sanford
Avera Health   Health-MeritCare
Billings Clinic

Catholic Health
Initiatives

HISTORICAL FINANCIALS
Company Type: Private

Income Statement
FYE: June 30

	REVENUE ($ mil.)	NET INCOME ($ mil.)	NET PROFIT MARGIN	EMPLOYEES
06/13	291	(1)	—	1,947
06/12	294	11	3.7%	—
06/11	275	12	4.6%	—
06/10	243	0	—	—
Annual Growth	6.2%	—	—	—

2013 Year-End Financials

Return on assets: 13.2%   Cash ($ mil.): 36
Return on equity: (-0.7%)
Current ratio: 0.90

ST. ANTHONY'S MEDICAL CENTER

St. Anthony's Medical Center applies its skills to medical cases in the Midwest. The hospital serves residents in the areas surrounding St. Louis Missouri as well as portions of southwestern Illinois. With about 770 beds and some 800 affiliated physicians the hospital provides a comprehensive offering including inpatient and outpatient medical surgical diagnostic and behavioral health care. The hospital operates a level II trauma center cancer and chest pain units and a pediatric emergency center as well as several urgent care facilities. It also offers home health hospice laboratory and pharmacy services. St. Anthony's Medical Center was founded in 1900 by the Franciscan Sisters of Germany.

Operations

St. Anthony's Medical Center's ER is staffed by an independently owned group of emergency physicians (Emergency Physicians of St. Louis) who provide services to the hospital on a contract bases. The physician-group model of employment aims to improve patient flow and reduce waiting times at the ER.

In fiscal 2015 (ended June) the hospital had some 27000 inpatient admissions and more than 77700 emergency department visits delivered more than 1100 babies and performed more than 13000 surgeries.

Geographic Reach

St. Anthony's Medical Center is one of the largest hospitals in the St. Louis metropolitan area. It serves a population base of more than 900000 people in 10 counties in Missouri and Illinois. It also operates four urgent care centers in surrounding communities of Arnold Big Bend Fenton and Lemay.

Strategy

In 2014 St. Anthony's Medical Center became one of the first hospitals in the nation to implant the newly approved Medtronic Reveal LINQ Insertable Cardiac Monitor System a miniature cardiac monitor in a stroke patient.

EXECUTIVES

Vice President Of Quality, Jim Tune
Executive Vice President And Cho, Michalene Maringer
Director Of Pharmacy, David Palmer
Board Member, Jeff Randall
Auditors: BKD LLP ST LOUIS MISSOURI

LOCATIONS

HQ: ST. ANTHONY'S MEDICAL CENTER
    10010 KENNERLY RD, SAINT LOUIS, MO 631282106
Phone: 314 525-1000
Web: WWW.STANTHONYSMEDCENTER.COM

PRODUCTS/OPERATIONS

Selected Services
Acute Rehabilitation
Audiology/Hearing
Behavioral Health
Breast Center
Cancer Care Center
Diabetes Education
Emergency/Trauma
Heart Specialty Center
Home Care
Hospice Field Program
Hyland Behavioral Health
Long-term Acute Care
Neuroscience and Stroke
Occupational Medicine
Oncology
Orthopedics
Ostomy Clinic
Outpatient Imaging
Pediatric Services
Physical Therapy
Pregnancy and Birth
Pharmacy
Pulmonary
Radiology/Imaging Centers
Rehabilitation (cardiac and acute)
Senior Services
Sleep Disorder Center
Social Services (Care Management)
Speech Therapy
Sports & Therapy
Stroke
Surgery
Urgent Care Centers
Urological Gynecology
Vestibular Rehab
Weight Management
Women's Medical/Surgical Unit
Wound Treatment

COMPETITORS

Ascension Health	Mercy Hospital St.
BJC HealthCare	Louis
Barnes-Jewish Hospital	RehabCare
Christian Hospital	SSM Health Care
CoxHealth	Saint Francis Medical
HCA	Center
Memorial Hospital	St. Luke's Hospital
(Illinois)	(MO)
Mercy Health	Tenet Healthcare

HISTORICAL FINANCIALS
Company Type: Private

Income Statement
FYE: June 30

	REVENUE ($ mil.)	NET INCOME ($ mil.)	NET PROFIT MARGIN	EMPLOYEES
06/13	443	38	8.7%	3,900
06/12	467	(29)	—	—
06/11	473	53	11.3%	—
06/10	439	0	—	—
Annual Growth	0.3%	—	—	—

2013 Year-End Financials

Return on assets: 2.4%   Cash ($ mil.): 23
Return on equity: 8.7%
Current ratio: 1.40

ST. BERNARD'S HOSPITAL INC.

Auditors: BKD LLP LITTLE ROCK AR

LOCATIONS

HQ: ST. BERNARD'S HOSPITAL INC.
    225 E JACKSON AVE, JONESBORO, AR 724013119
Phone: 870 972-4100

HISTORICAL FINANCIALS
Company Type: Private

Income Statement
FYE: September 30

	REVENUE ($ mil.)	NET INCOME ($ mil.)	NET PROFIT MARGIN	EMPLOYEES
09/13	305	19	6.3%	2,000
09/12	291	17	6.0%	—
09/11	264	7	2.9%	—
09/10	260	0	—	—
Annual Growth	5.4%	—	—	—

2013 Year-End Financials

Return on assets: 6.5%   Cash ($ mil.): 43
Return on equity: 6.3%
Current ratio: 3.20

ST. CLOUD HOSPITAL

Auditors: ERNST & YOUNG US LLP ROSEVILL

LOCATIONS

HQ: ST. CLOUD HOSPITAL
    1406 6TH AVE N, SAINT CLOUD, MN 563031901
Phone: 320 251-2700
Web: WWW.CENTRACARE.COM

HISTORICAL FINANCIALS
Company Type: Private

Income Statement
FYE: June 30

	REVENUE ($ mil.)	NET INCOME ($ mil.)	NET PROFIT MARGIN	EMPLOYEES
06/13	717	70	9.9%	4,738
06/12	686	85	12.4%	—
06/11	657	82	12.5%	—
06/10	604	0	—	—
Annual Growth	5.9%	—	—	—

2013 Year-End Financials

Return on assets: 62.5%   Cash ($ mil.): 50
Return on equity: 9.9%
Current ratio: 0.30

ST. DOMINIC-JACKSON MEMORIAL HOSPITAL

LOCATIONS

HQ: ST. DOMINIC-JACKSON MEMORIAL HOSPITAL
969 LAKELAND DR, JACKSON, MS 392164606
Phone: 601 200-6776
Web: WWW.STDOM.COM

HISTORICAL FINANCIALS

Company Type: Private

Income Statement

FYE: December 31

	REVENUE ($ mil.)	NET INCOME ($ mil.)	NET PROFIT MARGIN	EMPLOYEES
12/12	376	12	3.3%	2,400
12/08	337	(51)	—	—
12/03	228	6	2.8%	—
12/02	765	0	—	—
Annual Growth	—	—	—	—

2012 Year-End Financials

Return on assets: 4.9%   Cash ($ mil.): 66
Return on equity: 3.3%
Current ratio: 3.10

ST. JOHN HEALTH SYSTEM INC.

St. John Health System aims to bring health into the lives of the ill. The not-for-profit system provides health care services to residents of Tulsa and surrounding areas in northeastern Oklahoma and southern Kansas. In addition to flagship facility St. John Medical Center it owns or manages eight other community hospitals as well as urgent care and long-term care facilities. St. John Health System provides primary and specialty medical care through OMNI Medical Group and offers health insurance through CommunityCare health plan. Established in 1926 by the Sisters of the Sorrowful Mother the health system is part of Marian Health.

Operations

Facilities owned managed or sponsored by St. John Health System include hospitals Oklahoma State University Medical Center St. John Sapulpa St. John Owasso St. John Broken Arrow Pawhuska City Hospital Sedan City Hospital Nowata Hospital and Jane Phillips Medical Center. The company's senior living facilities include Franciscan Villa Frances Streitel Villa Heartsworth House and Rosewood Terrace.

Strategy

St. John Health System will periodically add services to its offerings to meet community demand. In early 2011 St. John Health opened the St. John Weight Management Institute to offer its patients weight loss options including bariatric surgery. The health system's newest hospital St. John Broken Arrow near Tulsa was constructed in 2009.

In 2012 Marian Health entered talks with another Catholic health system operator Ascension Health over the possibility of merging St. John Health System and other Marian organizations into the Ascension organization.

EXECUTIVES

Vice President Medical Affairs, William (Bill) Allred
Corporate Vice President, Randy Hamil
Vice President, Gwen Moudry
Medical Director, Alfred Vitanza
Director Physician Recruitment Retention And Practice Development, Krista Thacker
Vice President Human Resources, Page Bachman
Vice President Of Properties A, Dewey Davis
Medical Director of Stroke Service, Anna Wanahita
Treasurer, Donna Butler
Auditors: KPMJ LLP TULSA OK

LOCATIONS

HQ: ST. JOHN HEALTH SYSTEM INC.
1923 S UTICA AVE, TULSA, OK 741046520
Phone: 918 744-2180
Web: WWW.STJOHNPROVIDENCE.ORG

PRODUCTS/OPERATIONS

Selected Facilities and Operations – Oklahoma
CommunityCare (health plan)
Jane Phillips Medical Center (Bartlesville)
Nowata Hospital
Oklahoma State University Medical Center (managed facility in Tulsa)
OMNI Medical Group (physicians group)
Pawhuska City Hospital
Regional Medical Laboratory (clinical lab testing)
Sedan City Hospital
St. John Broken Arrow Hospital
St. John Medical Center (Tulsa)
St. John Owasso Hospital
St. John Physicians
St. John Sapulpa Hospital

COMPETITORS

Anthem	INTEGRIS Health
Ardent Health Services	Kindred Healthcare
CIGNA	Marian Health System
Catholic Health Initiatives	Norman Regional Health Presbyterian
Community Health Systems	Healthcare Services
Deaconess Health Care	SSM Health Care
HCA	Saint Francis Health System
Hillcrest Medical Center	UnitedHealth Group

HISTORICAL FINANCIALS

Company Type: Private

Income Statement

FYE: June 30

	REVENUE ($ mil.)	NET INCOME ($ mil.)	NET PROFIT MARGIN	EMPLOYEES
06/14*	1,056	79	7.5%	4,011
09/12	977	74	7.7%	—
09/11	895	17	2.0%	—
09/10	919	0	—	—
Annual Growth	3.5%	—	—	—

*Fiscal year change

2014 Year-End Financials

Return on assets: 8.6%   Cash ($ mil.): 44
Return on equity: 7.5%
Current ratio: 1.30

ST. JOHN'S UNIVERSITY

LOCATIONS

HQ: ST. JOHN' S UNIVERSITY
8000 UTOPIA PKWY, JAMAICA, NY 114399000
Phone: 718 990-2000
Web: WWW.STJOHNS.EDU

HISTORICAL FINANCIALS

Company Type: Private

Income Statement

FYE: May 31

	REVENUE ($ mil.)	NET INCOME ($ mil.)	NET PROFIT MARGIN	EMPLOYEES
05/13	473	64	13.5%	—
05/12	652	30	4.7%	—
Annual Growth	(27.4%)	107.4%	—	—

2013 Year-End Financials

Return on assets: —   Cash ($ mil.): 7
Return on equity: 13.5%
Current ratio: —

ST. JOSEPH HEALTH SYSTEM

St. Joseph Health System has earned a medal for decades by caring for patients on the West Coast and more recently the South Plains. The health care network includes 16 acute care hospitals home health agencies hospice care outpatient services skilled nursing facilities community clinics and physician organizations throughout California and in eastern New Mexico and West Texas. In its primary market of California the health system has some 2900 beds at 10 hospitals. Its Covenant Health System unit operates in Texas and New Mexico with about 1200 beds in its network of some 50 primary care facilities. St. Joseph is merging with fellow not-for-profit Providence Health & Services.

Operations

In 2013 the system discharged more than 142000 patients and had more than 4 million outpatient and 513000 emergency department visits.

Geographic Reach

The network operates acute care hospitals home health agencies urgent care centers and other health care delivery organizations throughout California and in eastern New Mexico and West Texas. Based in Irvine St. Joseph serves 10 communities in its operating regions.

Sales and Marketing

Government payments accounted for 44% of net patient revenue in 2013 while private payers accounted for 42%.

Financial Performance

Revenue increased 14% to $5.6 million due to an increase in patient service earnings. Net income decreased 83% though to $353 million as salary and benefits expenses increased. Operating cash flow fell 38% to $327 million that year.

Strategy

Already one of the largest health systems on the West Coast St. Joseph continues to grow thanks principally to its proficient fundraising.

The system invests regularly in network and facility expansion efforts. In 2013 it formed an affiliation with Hoag Memorial Hospital Presbyterian which operates two hospitals in Orange County. The Hoag operations are being combined with five of St. Joseph's area hospitals to form a new network called Covenant Health Network. The affiliated facilities will provide comprehensive care in the region while retaining their respective identities and religious affiliations.

In 2014 St. Joseph entered a collaborative care initiative with Cigna to improve access to health care and enhance care coordination.

In 2015 the system agreed to merge with Providence Health & Services which operates more than 30 hospitals in five western states. The combination will create a larger provider network of hospitals physician groups and outpatient centers eliminating some overhead expenses in the process. Furthermore by creating economies of scale the new organization will be better positioned to negotiate with health plans.

Company Background

St. Joseph Health System traces its roots back to 1920 when St. Joseph Hospital in Eureka California was first established. The health care system was officially organized in 1982 as it expanded and took on additional health care facilities. The system is a ministry of The Sisters of St. Joseph of Orange which itself was organized in 1912.

EXECUTIVES

President and CEO Redwood Memorial Hospital and St. Joseph Hospital Eureka, Joe Mark
EVP Mission Integration, Marian Schubert
EVP West Texas and Southern New Mexico, Richard H. Parks
EVP Strategic Services, Annette M. Walker
EVP Northern California Region, Kevin Klockenga
Chief Financial Officer, Jo Escasa-Haigh
Vice President Performance Improvement, Mary Ann Vincent
Vice President Quality And Medical Affairs, Mark Montgomery
Assistant Vice President Executive Architect, Wesley Okamoto
Vice President Revenue Cycle, Kimberly Sullivan
Senior Vice President Governance, Suzanne Sassus
Director Of Medical Records, Daniel Pothen
Senior Vice President General Counsel, Shannon Dwyer
Information Technology Executive Vice President, Bill Murin
Medical Records Director, Sandy Barber
Assistant Vice President Of Information Technology Solutions Delivery, Jeff Allport
Vice President Shared Operations Revenue Cycle Se, Debbie Salas
Vice President Clinical Informatics, Joon Saddul
Vice President Mission Integration, John Perring-mulligan
Assistant Vice President, Kevin Murphy
Senior Vice President Of Human Resources, Ryan Faulkner
Vice President and General Manager, Karen Wilson
Assistant Vice President Risk Management, Lisa Ramthun
Assistant Vice President, Ronald Scott
Senior Vice President Ministry Integrity, Margaret Hambleton
Senior Vice President Operations, Toni Small
Vice President Human Resources, Stephen Eckberg
Vice President Of Strategic Services, Ned Laubacher
Vice President IS Strategy, Larry Stofko
Chairman, Walter W. (Bill) Noce
Controller And Treasurer, Darren Montalvo
Secretary, Denise Blanchard
Board of Directors, Kathleen Kelly
Auditors: ERNST & YOUNG LLP IRVINE CA

LOCATIONS

HQ: ST. JOSEPH HEALTH SYSTEM
3345 MICHELSON DR STE 100, IRVINE, CA 926120693
Phone: 949 381-4000
Web: WWW.STJHS.ORG

Selected Operations
Northern California
Petaluma Valley Hospital
Queen of the Valley Medical Center (Napa)
Redwood Memorial Hospital (Fortuna)
St. Joseph Home Care Network (Sonoma)

St. Joseph Hospital (Eureka)
Santa Rosa Memorial Hospital
Southern California
Mission Hospital (Mission Viejo)
Mission Hospital Laguna Beach
St. Joseph Hospital (Orange)
St. Jude Medical Center (Fullerton)
St. Mary Medical Center (Apple Valley)
West Texas/Eastern New Mexico
Covenant Health System
Artesia General Hospital (New Mexico)
Covenant Hospital Levelland (Texas)
Covenant Hospital Plainview (Texas)
Covenant Medical Center (Lubbock TX)
Nor-Lea General Hospital (Lovington NM)
Roosevelt General Hospital (Portales NM)

PRODUCTS/OPERATIONS

2014 Sales

	% of total
Net patient service net of provision for doubtful accounts	76
Premium	20
Other	4
Total	**100**

COMPETITORS

Adventist Health	Los Angeles County
Arrowhead Medical	Health Department
Center	Memorial Health
Banner Health	Services
Catholic Health	Pasadena Hospital
Initiatives	Association
Cedars-Sinai Medical	Prospect Medical
Center	Scripps health
Citrus Valley Health	Sutter Health
Partners	Tenet Healthcare
City of Hope	Western Medical Center
Dignity Health	- Santa Ana
HCA	
Loma Linda University	
Medical Center	

HISTORICAL FINANCIALS

Company Type: Private

Income Statement

FYE: June 30

	REVENUE ($ mil.)	NET INCOME ($ mil.)	NET PROFIT MARGIN	EMPLOYEES
06/14	5,631	353	6.3%	21,500
06/13	4,955	2,082	42.0%	—
06/10	4,268	268	6.3%	—
06/08	3,943	0	—	—
Annual Growth	**6.1%**	**—**	**—**	**—**

2014 Year-End Financials
Return on assets: 2.4%   Cash ($ mil.): 269
Return on equity: 6.3%
Current ratio: 0.90

ST. JOSEPH HOSPITAL OF ORANGE

If you're feeling green or blue in Orange County St. Joseph Hospital of Orange is there to help get back to feeling pink and rosy. The California hospital provides general medical and surgical services as well as specialty care such as women's health mental health services oncology cardiology and physical rehabilitation. Part of the St. Joseph Health System the hospital provides primary care and specialty outpatient services through a network of affiliated physician practices. It also operates low-income and mobile clinics. The hospital

has about 468 beds and a medical staff of some 1000.

Geographic Reach

St. Joseph Hospital serves Orange County California and the greater Los Angeles metropolitan area.

Operations

In addition to physician group affiliates St. Joseph Hospital Affiliated Physicians and St. Joseph Heritage Medical Group the hospital also partners with the Childrens Hospital of Orange County to help expand pediatric care throughout the region. The hospital has more than 20100 inpatient discharges and about 290400 outpatient visits a year.

Strategy

St. Joseph Hospital has been working to expand its community outreach programs related to cancer through a number of projects including offering improved access to clinical trials; providing better overall access to cancer care; and implementing measures to garner support for the implementation of cancer electronic health records. St. Joseph Hospital is using stimulus money and about a $3 million award from the National Cancer Institute Community Cancer Centers Program to help fund its various projects.

Company Background

The company was founded in 1929 by the Sisters of St. Joseph of Orange.

EXECUTIVES

Vice President Operations, Tom Hill
Director Of Nursing, Linda Simon
Clinic Manager, Gioconda Martinez
Vice President Finance, Melinda Evans
Co Medical Director Palliative Care Program, Melvyn Sterling
Auditors: ERNST & YOUNG US LLP IRVINE

LOCATIONS

HQ: ST. JOSEPH HOSPITAL OF ORANGE
1100 W STEWART DR, ORANGE, CA 928683891
Phone: 714 633-9111
Web: WWW.SJO.ORG

PRODUCTS/OPERATIONS

Selected Services
Bariatric Surgery
Behavioral Health
Cancer
Nasal & Sinus Center
Heart & Vascular Center
Kidney Dialysis Center
Maternity
Orthopedic Services
Sleep Disorders Center

COMPETITORS

Anaheim Regional	Southwest Healthcare
Medical Center	Sutter Health
Children' s Hospital of	Tenet Healthcare
Orange County	Torrance Memorial
Citrus Valley Health	Medical Center
Partners	Trinity Health (Novi)
Hoag Memorial Hospital	UC Irvine Medical
Memorial Health	Center
Services	Western Medical Center
Pasadena Hospital	- Santa Ana
Association	
Providence Health &	
Services	

Income Statement

FYE: June 30

	REVENUE ($ mil.)	NET INCOME ($ mil.)	NET PROFIT MARGIN	EMPLOYEES
06/13	668	47	7.2%	3,300
06/12	645	23	3.6%	—
06/11	661	32	4.9%	—
06/10	638	0	—	—
Annual Growth	1.6%	—	—	—

2013 Year-End Financials

Return on assets: 9.6% Cash ($ mil.): 49
Return on equity: 7.2%
Current ratio: 1.80

ST. JOSEPH'S HOSPITAL AND MEDICAL CENTER

LOCATIONS

HQ: ST. JOSEPH' S HOSPITAL AND MEDICAL CENTER
703 MAIN ST, PATERSON, NJ 075032691
Phone: 973 754-2000
Web: WWW.STJOSEPHSHEALTH.ORG

HISTORICAL FINANCIALS

Company Type: Private

Income Statement

FYE: December 31

	REVENUE ($ mil.)	NET INCOME ($ mil.)	NET PROFIT MARGIN	EMPLOYEES
12/12	666	(17)	—	4,000
12/08	472	(41)	—	—
12/06	437	17	3.9%	—
12/05	0	0	—	—
Annual Growth	—	—	—	—

2012 Year-End Financials

Return on assets: 6.4% Cash ($ mil.): 57
Return on equity: (-2.6%)
Current ratio: 1.00

ST. JOSEPH'S HOSPITAL HEALTH CENTER

With about 430 inpatient beds St. Joseph's Hospital Health Center serves the residents of 16 central New York counties. The not-for-profit hospital system provides general emergency and surgical care as well as specialty services in areas such as obstetrics cardiology dialysis and wound care. In addition to its inpatient facilities the organization operates a home health agency a nursing school medical and dental residency programs and several outpatient care centers. Its Franciscan Companies affiliate offers some ancillary services including the provision of medical supplies home health equipment and senior services. St. Joseph's Hospital Health Center was founded in 1869.

Operations

With a total of some 800 physicians St. Joseph's Hospital Health Center admits some 28000 inpatients each year. It also handles some 957000 emergency room visits and about 640000 outpatient visits annually. The hospital provides about $22 million in charity and community care each year as well.

Geographic Reach

St. Joseph's Hospital Health Center's service territory includes the New York counties of Broome Cayuga Chenango Cortland Delaware Herkimer Jefferson Lewis Madison Oneida Onondaga Oswego Otsego St. Lawrence Tioga and Tompkins.

Financial Performance

In 2013 revenue rose 7% to $626 million as patient and other revenue grew. Net income also improved by 33% due to better investment returns.

Strategy

St. Joseph's Hospital Health Center is conducting a massive $220 million expansion program at its main campus. The first phase opened in 2011 and includes a larger emergency room facility with chest pain and psychiatric units. The hospital broke ground on the second phase of the project in 2012. The program will add a new patient tower surgery facilities a sterilization center and an intensive care unit. In 2013 it opened a sleep center and a new surgical suite at the hospital. The following year St. Joseph's expanded its primary care center in west Syracuse and launched it electronic health record system.

Mergers and Acquisitions

In 2013 the center purchased Upstate Surgical Group creating a general surgery group in St. Joseph's ambulatory surgery group.

In late 2010 St. Joseph's Hospital Health Center boosted its physician network significantly by acquiring North Medical a physician practice organization that operates five practices: Family Physicians Urgent Care Orthopedics & Rehabilitation The Women's Place and Living Proof Longevity Centre. Its practices are home to about 80 physicians and mid-level practitioners.

EXECUTIVES

Senior Vice President System Development and Ambulatory Care Leadership, Mark Murphy
Director Of Medical Records, Michelle Degraff
Vice President of Spiritual Car, Rose Renna
Vice President Clinical Services, Karin Kolisz
Vice President Of Support Services, Mary Obrist
Radiology Director, Stephen (Steve) Swierczek
Board Member, Mary Ryan
Board Member, Susan Lamanna
Auditors: FUST CHARLES CHAMBERS LLP SYR

LOCATIONS

HQ: ST. JOSEPH' S HOSPITAL HEALTH CENTER
301 PROSPECT AVE, SYRACUSE, NY 132031899
Phone: 315 448-5111
Web: WWW.SJHSYR.ORG

PRODUCTS/OPERATIONS

Selected Services
Centers of Excellence
  Cardiac Services
  The Center for Orthopedic and Spine Care
  Vascular Services
  Women and Children' s Services
  Wound Care
  Home Care
  Dialysis
  Bariatric (Weight Loss) Services
Other Services and Centers
  Aesthetic Services
  Behavioral Health
  da Vinci Robotic Surgery
  Emergency Services
  Imaging
  Infusion (CPEPCNY)
  Interventional Radiology

Medical Equipment
Obstetric Services
Palliative Care
Pharmacy
Physical Medicine & Rehabilitation
Pulmonary Services
Sleep Laboratory
Social Adult Day Care
Surgical Services
Urology Services
Outpatient Services
  Dental Services
  Family Medicine Center
  Obstetrics and Gynecology
  Pediatric Office
  Physician Health
  Primary Care
  Westside Family Health Center

COMPETITORS

Catholic Health System
Ellis Hospital
Kaleida Health
Lifetime Health
Oneida Healthcare Center
SUNY Upstate Medical University
United Health Services Hospitals
Upstate University Hospital at Community General

HISTORICAL FINANCIALS

Company Type: Private

Income Statement

FYE: December 31

	REVENUE ($ mil.)	NET INCOME ($ mil.)	NET PROFIT MARGIN	EMPLOYEES
12/09	436	5	1.2%	3,300
12/08	399	6	1.6%	—
12/05	363	11	3.2%	—
12/98	221	0	—	—
Annual Growth	6.4%	—	—	—

2009 Year-End Financials

Return on assets: — Cash ($ mil.): 5
Return on equity: 1.2%
Current ratio: 0.50

ST. JOSEPH'S HOSPITAL INC.

Auditors: ERNST & YOUNG US LLP ATLANTA

LOCATIONS

HQ: ST. JOSEPH' S HOSPITAL INC.
3001 W DR MRTN LTHR KNG B MARTIN LUTHER,
TAMPA, FL 33607
Phone: 813 554-8500
Web: WWW.STJOSEPHSCHILDRENS.COM

HISTORICAL FINANCIALS

Company Type: Private

Income Statement

FYE: December 31

	REVENUE ($ mil.)	NET INCOME ($ mil.)	NET PROFIT MARGIN	EMPLOYEES
12/09	719	75	10.4%	300
12/08	663	29	4.5%	—
12/06	565	63	11.2%	—
12/05	0	0	—	—
Annual Growth	—	—	—	—

2009 Year-End Financials

Return on assets: — Cash ($ mil.): —
Return on equity: 10.4%
Current ratio: 0.60

ST. JUDE CHILDREN'S RESEARCH HOSPITAL INC.

St. Jude Children's Research Hospital studies and treats catastrophic diseases in children especially pediatric cancers. The hospital which only has about 80 beds annually treats more than 7800 children most of whom are treated on an outpatient basis as part of its research efforts into finding cures and more effective treatments. The hospital not only helps children with their health it also helps their parents: It pays all expenses that are not covered by insurance and doesn't require payment from patients without insurance. St. Jude Children's Research Hospital was founded in 1962.

Operations

St. Jude Children's Research Hospital has a 2.5-million-sq.-ft. campus for its research clinical and administrative operations. It is the only pediatric cancer center to be designated as a Comprehensive Cancer Center by the National Cancer Institute.

While it is best known for its research in pediatric cancers St. Jude Children's Research Hospital also treats children with genetic immune defects and pediatric AIDS and it has one of the largest pediatric sickle cell programs in the US.

As part of the organization's education mission it provides about 350 postdoctoral fellowships to those doctors who seek to specialize in pediatric medicine. St. Jude Children's Research Hospital is affiliated with the University of Tennessee Health Sciences Center at Memphis. Along with offering fellowships it serves as the training site for medical students and residents learning a variety of disciplines.

Geographic Reach

St. Jude Children's Research Hospital is located in Memphis Tennessee. The facility has affiliations with six other US hospitals in Alabama Illinois Louisiana Missouri and Tennessee. It shares its research findings with scientific and medical organizations worldwide.

Financial Performance

The hospital's revenues increased 23% to $1.5 billion in fiscal 2014 primarily due to increased support and investment earnings. The rise in revenues drove a 66% increase in net income which totaled $587 million in 2014; this was partially offset by an increase in patient care service expenses.

Cash flow from operations also increased rising 39% to $356 million.

Public contributions cover most of St. Jude Children's Research Hospital operating costs of $1.8 million a day.

Strategy

Throughout the year St. Jude Children's Research Hospital coordinates events to raise funds and awareness - from golf tournaments and triathlons to radiothons and telethons.

In 2015 the hospital added its seventh affiliate clinic –the St. Jude Affiliate Clinic at Novant Health Hemby Children's Hospital in Charlotte North Carolina. Affiliate clinics provide treatment to St. Jude patients allowing the number of children enrolled in its clinical trials to grow.

The Marlo Thomas Center for Global Education and Collaboration opened on the St. Jude campus in 2014.

Company Background

Entertainer Danny Thomas founded St. Jude in 1962; Thomas also founded the fundraising organization for the hospital the American Lebanese Syrian Associated Charities (ALSAC).

EXECUTIVES

CEO, James Downing
SVP Patient Care Services and Chief Nursing Officer, Pam Dotson
Chair Biostatistics, James Boyett
Co-Chair Oncology, Amar Gajjar
Chair Immunology, Doug Green
Chair Genetics, Gerard Grosveld
Chair Chemical Biology and Therapeutics, Kip Guy
Chair Biochemistry, James Ihle
EVP and Clinical Director, Larry E. Kun
Chair Developmental Neurobiology, James Morgan
Chair Oncology, Ching-Hon Pui
Chair Pharmaceutical Sciences, Mary Relling
Chair Epidemiology and Cancer Control, Les Robison
Chair Tumor Cell Biology, Charles Sherr
Chair Infectious Diseases, Elaine Tuomanen
Chair Structural Biology, Stephen White
CFO, Pat Keel
Chair Surgery, Andrew Davidoff
EVP Director Comprehensive Cancer Center, Richard J. Gilbertson
Chair Pathology, David Ellison
Chair Psychology, Sean Phipps
CIO, Keith Perry
Senior Vice President Patient Care Services Chief Nursing Officer, Pamela (Pam) Dotson
Vice President Of Communications, Kelly Schulz
Pharm D, Julie Richardson
Director Managed Care, Jane (Ginny) Fache
Board Member, David (Dave) Kalwinsky
Auditors: DELOITTE TAX LLP MEMPHIS TN

LOCATIONS

HQ: ST. JUDE CHILDREN' S RESEARCH HOSPITAL INC.
262 DANNY THOMAS PL, MEMPHIS, TN 381053678
Phone: 901 595-3300
Web: WWW.STJUDE.ORG

PRODUCTS/OPERATIONS

2014 Sales

	% of total
Support revenue	62
Net investment income	25
Net patient service revenue	6
Research grants	5
Other	2
Total	**100**

Selected US Affiliate Clinics

Children' s Hospital of Illinois (OSF Healthcare System) University of Illinois College of Medicine at Peoria
Feist-Weiller Cancer Center LSU Health Sciences Center (Shreveport Louisiana)
Huntsville Hospital (Huntsville Alabama)
Johnson City Medical Center East Tennessee State University
Our Lady of the Lake Regional Medical Center (Baton Rouge Louisiana)
St. John' s Health System (Springfield Missouri)

Selected International Outreach Partner Sites

American University of Beirut/Children' s Cancer Center of Lebanon (Beirut Lebanon)
Beijing Children' s Hospital (Beijing)
Davao Medical Center (Philippines)
Hospital 20 Aout 1953 (Casablanca Morocco)
Hospital Benjamin Bloom (San Salvador El Salvador)
Hospital Civil de Guadalajara (Guadalajara Mexico)
Hospital de Especialidades Pediatricas (Maracaibo Venezuela)
Hospital de la Sociedad de Lucha Contra el Cancer Nucleo de Quito (Quito Ecuador)
Hospital de Ninos Baca Ortiz (Quito Ecuador)
Hospital de Ninos J.M. de los Rios (Caracas Venezuela)
Hospital d' Enfants (Rabat Morocco)
Hospital Escuela Materno Infantil (Tegucigalpa Honduras)
Hospital Luis Calvo Mackenna (Santiago Chile)
Hospital Nacional de Ninos (San Jose Costa Rica)
Hospital Pediatrico de Sinaloa (Culiacan Mexico)
King Hussein Cancer Center (Amman Jordan)
Our Lady' s Hospital for Sick Children (Dublin Ireland)
Shanghai Children' s Medical Center (Shanghai)
Unidad de Oncologia Pediatrica - Instituto Materno Infantil de Pernambuco; Centro de Hematologia e Oncologia Pediatrica (Recife) - Brazil
Unidad Nacional de Oncologia Pediatrica (Guatemala City Guatemala)

COMPETITORS

Ascension Health
Baptist Memorial Health Care
Children' s Medical Center of Dallas
Children' s National Medical Center
Cincinnati Children' s Hospital
City of Hope
Damon Runyon Cancer Research
Dana-Farber
Fox Chase Cancer Center
H. Lee Moffitt Cancer Center & Research Institute
HCA
LifePoint Health
MD Anderson Cancer Center
Memorial Sloan-Kettering
Mercy Health (OH)
Methodist Healthcare
Nationwide Children' s Hospital
Roswell Park Cancer Institute
Shelby County Health Care
Shriners Hospitals For Children
Tenet Healthcare
UT Medical Group

HISTORICAL FINANCIALS
Company Type: Private

Income Statement
FYE: June 30

	REVENUE ($ mil.)	NET INCOME ($ mil.)	NET PROFIT MARGIN	EMPLOYEES
06/11	573	(26)	—	2,500
06/10	589	(5)	—	
Annual Growth	(2.7%)	—	—	—

2011 Year-End Financials

Return on assets: —
Return on equity: (-4.6%)
Current ratio: 0.30
Cash ($ mil.): 12

ST. JUDE HOSPITAL

St. Jude Medical Center gets sickly Southern Californians on their feet again. The faith-based not-for-profit acute care facility with some 385 beds serves the residents of Orange County. The medical center provides an onsite cancer center (the Virginia K. Crosson Cancer Center) and a heart institute that offers cardiac surgeries and rehabilitation programs. It also provides inpatient and outpatient physical rehabilitation services and a variety of community outreach programs. Established by the Sisters of St. Joseph of Orange religious order in the 1950s St. Jude Medical Center is part of the St. Joseph Health System.

Geographic Reach

St. Jude serves residents in communities in California's Orange County including Brea Buena Park Fullerton La Habra Placentia and Yorba Linda.

Operations

Beyond the medical center's campus St. Jude operates its Heritage Medical Group with outpatient locations throughout its region. The medical group includes specialists in plastic surgery rheumatology and gastroenterology. Altogether St.

Jude employs some 700 physicians. It handles more than 17000 inpatient admissions each year as well as 13000 surgeries 2000 births and 54000 emergency room visits.

The organization spends some $47 million in community benefits including outreach and charity care. Its mobile and fixed-site community clinics offer medical dental and preventative care services for low-income residents.

Strategy

St. Jude is expanding its facilities through the construction of a new $312 million patient tower schedule to open in late 2014. The Northwest Tower will feature private patient rooms as well as enhanced surgical and data management capabilities. Other improvement measures include technology upgrades such as a new neurovascular surgical system added in 2012.

In October 2011 St. Jude Medical Center closed its 12-bed pediatric unit and redirected patients younger than 16 to nearby Children's Hospital of Orange County. St. Jude's NICU (neonatal intensive care unit) remains open and the hospital continues to provide emergency and outpatient services to children.

EXECUTIVES

Vice President Medical Affairs, Joseph S Lawton
Vice President Of Information Technology, Dennis Briley
Operating Room Director, Joanne Bonnot
Medical Librarian, Carol Schecter
Medical Records Director, Pamela Frey
Respiratory Therapy Director, Lori Auw
Auditors: ERNST & YOUNG LLP IRVINE CA

LOCATIONS

HQ: ST. JUDE HOSPITAL
101 E VALENCIA MESA DR, FULLERTON, CA
928353875
Phone: 714 871-3280
Web: WWW.STJUDEMEDICALCENTER.ORG

COMPETITORS

Anaheim Regional Medical Center	UC Irvine Medical Center
Children's Hospital of Orange County	Western Medical Center - Santa Ana
Hoag Memorial Hospital	
Memorial Health Services	

HISTORICAL FINANCIALS

Company Type: Private

Income Statement
FYE: June 30

	REVENUE ($ mil.)	NET INCOME ($ mil.)	NET PROFIT MARGIN	EMPLOYEES
06/13	476	62	13.2%	2,600
06/10	492	61	12.4%	—
06/09	412	0	—	—
06/08	21	0	—	—
Annual Growth	—	—	—	—

ST. LUKE'S EPISCOPAL-PRESBYTERIAN HOSPITALS

St. Luke's Episcopal-Presbyterian Hospital doing business as St. Luke's Hospital provides health care services to St. Louis residents and surrounding areas of eastern Missouri. The medical center houses more than 490 beds and offers general medical and surgical care as well as specialty services in areas such as heart disease cancer neuroscience orthopedics pediatrics and women's health. St. Luke's also operates half a dozen urgent care clinics in St. Louis and St. Charles counties providing treatment for minor emergencies such as cuts and animal bites as well as a skilled-nursing facility rehabilitation hospital and several diagnostic imaging centers. The not-for-profit hospital was founded in 1866.

Operations

In 2014 St. Luke's Hospital had more than 18000 inpatients and 315000 outpatients performed some 17500 surgeries facilitated 1800 births and had more than 30000 emergency department visits.

Financial Performance

In fiscal 2014 (ended June) operating revenue in excess of expense totaled $20.4 million. Total operating revenue grew 4% to $478 million that year.

Strategy

St. Luke's Hospital continues to grow via expansion projects. In 2013 the medical center renovated its neonatal special care nursery adding six private rooms and areas for twins and other multiples to stay together. The following year it opened a new urgent care center and a new facility with the state's only Open Upright MRI scanner. Other urgent care centers and physicians' offices are in the works. In 2015 the hospital broke ground on a $40 million outpatient building on its campus; it is expected to open in late 2016.

The company also grows by adding physicians to its network. During 2014 it added 34 new physicians to its staff with specializations in the areas of primary care neurology oncology cardiovascular orthopedics and others. In all the medical staff has more than 60 specialties.

EXECUTIVES

Vice President Marketing, Jan Hess
Director of HIM, Bonnie Lehmann
Secretary, Linda Moreland

LOCATIONS

HQ: ST. LUKE'S EPISCOPAL-PRESBYTERIAN HOSPITALS
232 S WOODS MILL RD, CHESTERFIELD, MO
630173417
Phone: 314 434-1500
Web: WWW.STLUKES-STL.COM

PRODUCTS/OPERATIONS

Selected Services
Brain and spine
Cardiac
Orthopedic
Pulmonary
Sleep medicine
Women's services

COMPETITORS

Barnes-Jewish Hospital	St. Anthony's Medical Center
CHRISTUS Health	Tenet Healthcare
Mercy Health	
SSM Health Care	

HISTORICAL FINANCIALS

Company Type: Private

Income Statement
FYE: June 30

	REVENUE ($ mil.)	NET INCOME ($ mil.)	NET PROFIT MARGIN	EMPLOYEES
06/13	415	25	6.1%	3,000
06/04	274	11	4.1%	—
06/03	263	9	3.5%	—
06/02	1,170	0	—	—
Annual Growth	—	—	—	—

2013 Year-End Financials
Return on assets: 7.8%   Cash ($ mil.): 165
Return on equity: 6.1%
Current ratio: 1.60

ST. LUKE'S HEALTH SYSTEM FOUNDATION

LOCATIONS

HQ: ST. LUKE'S HEALTH SYSTEM FOUNDATION
6624 FANNIN ST STE 1100, HOUSTON, TX
770302323
Phone: 832 355-1000

HISTORICAL FINANCIALS

Company Type: Private

Income Statement
FYE: December 31

	REVENUE ($ mil.)	NET INCOME ($ mil.)	NET PROFIT MARGIN	EMPLOYEES
12/08	1,078	1,155	107.2%	6,000
12/07	1,128	26	2.3%	—
12/06	1,078	1,155	107.2%	—
12/04	0	0	—	—
Annual Growth	494.9%	—	—	—

2008 Year-End Financials
Return on assets: 11.1%   Cash ($ mil.): 153
Return on equity: 107.2%
Current ratio: 0.90

ST. LUKE'S HOSPITAL OF DULUTH

St. Luke's cares for colds cancers and other conditions in the chilly northern US. St. Luke's Hospital provides a variety of health care services to patients in northeastern Minnesota northwestern Wisconsin and parts of Michigan. The medical center has some 270 beds and a staff of about 370 physicians. Services include cardiology emergency medicine pediatrics oncology rehabilitation and vascular surgery. In addition to acute care services the organization offers primary and specialty health care services through a network of outpatient clinics.

Geographic Reach

St. Luke's serves a 17-county region in three states —encompassing northeastern Minnesota northwestern Wisconsin and the western Upper Peninsula of Michigan —through its acute care hospital in Duluth Minnesota and about 40 outpatient clinics providing primary and specialty care services.

Operations

The medical system consists of two hospitals (St. Luke's Hospital and Lake View Hospital) 14 primary care clinics 24 specialty clinics and two pharmacies.

St. Luke's handles about 11000 inpatient visits per year as well as 900 births 10300 surgeries and 73600 emergency room or urgent care visits. Its emergency room serves as a regional trauma center. St. Luke's also sees about 485000 patients annually at its primary and specialty care clinics. Its outpatient service divisions include Q Care (express medical clinic) St. Luke's Orthopedics and St. Luke's Infusion Therapy Clinic. The hospital conducts medical studies through a partnership with the Whiteside Institute for Clinical Research; it also has collaborative care relationships with the Pavilion Surgery Center and the Lake View Memorial Hospital.

Financial Performance

St. Luke's reported $823.5 million in patient services revenue in 2013. After contractual deductions and other obligations total revenues were reported at about $355 million.

Strategy

In 2013 St. Luke's Laurentian Medical Clinic completed a $2 million dollar expansion increasing its size by 60% allowing it to become an ambulatory care center. The clinic offers primary care visiting specialists urgent care and imaging services including low dose CT ultrasound MRI scans and mobile echocardiography.

To expand its services for area residents in 2012 St. Luke's completed construction of a new medical office building which is located adjacent to the main hospital facilities and will include centers for sports medicine pediatrics neurosurgery and plastic surgery. Also that year St. Luke's opened its da Vinci Si surgical system suite which allows surgeons to conduct minimally invasive surgical procedures using the robotic system.

St. Luke's launched its iPad Project in the Birthing Center allowing new mothers and families can check out an iPad for the duration of their stay. The $100000 project was funded by St. Luke's Foundation's annual Circle of Light event and individual donors.

In 2012 the health system added two urgent care clinics: The Northland Obstetrics & Gynecology Lake View Pharmacy opened as part of the Lake View campus in Two Harbors; St. Luke's Campus Building A opened expanding patient access to specialty care.

Company Background

In 2011 St. Luke's formed a new maternal child health department to improve its birthing services; the new unit provides labor and delivery nursery and pediatric services.

St. Luke's Hospital was founded in 1881. What was established as a typhoid response clinic became the city of Duluth's first hospital.

EXECUTIVES

President ; Sandra Barkley, John Strange
VP Clinics, Sandra Barkley
VP Finance and CFO, James (Jim) Wuellner
VP Support Services, Ron Franzen
VP Network Development and Chief Nursing Officer, Jo Ann Hoag
VP Medical Affairs and Medical Director, Gary Peterson
VP and CEO Lakeview Memorial Hospital, Brian Carlson
Marketing Specialist, Mary Greene
Chief of Staff, Ann Rock
Founder, Joseph Pilates
Treasurer, Melinda Machones

LOCATIONS

HQ: ST. LUKE' S HOSPITAL OF DULUTH
915 E 1ST ST, DULUTH, MN 558052193
Phone: 218 726-5555
Web: WWW.SLHDULUTH.COM

Selected Services Centers and Affiliates
Birthing Center
Breast Center
Cardiac Care
Cancer Care
Diagnostic Imaging
Emergency Care
Family Medicine
Laboratory Services
Lake View Pharmacy
Lake View Memorial Hospital
Northland Pharmacy
Pavilion Outpatient Surgery Center
Physical Rehabilitation Services
Sleep Center
St. Luke' s Center for Diagnostic Imaging
St. Luke' s Foundation
Surgery
Urgent Care
Whiteside Institute for Clinical Research

COMPETITORS

Allina Hospitals	North Memorial Health
CentraCare Health	Care
First Care	Sanford Bemidji
Gillette Children' s	Spectrum Health
Howard Young Health	
Care	

HISTORICAL FINANCIALS
Company Type: Private

Income Statement
FYE: December 31

	REVENUE ($ mil.)	NET INCOME ($ mil.)	NET PROFIT MARGIN	EMPLOYEES
12/13	377	2	0.8%	2,200
12/09	307	8	2.6%	—
12/08	276	1	0.6%	—
12/06	264	0	—	—
Annual Growth	5.2%	—	—	—

2013 Year-End Financials
Return on assets: 9.5%
Return on equity: 0.8%
Current ratio: 0.50
Cash ($ mil.): 13

ST. LUKE'S REGIONAL MEDICAL CENTER LTD.

Auditors: DELOITTE TAX LLP SAN FRANCISC

LOCATIONS

HQ: ST. LUKE' S REGIONAL MEDICAL CENTER LTD.
190 E BANNOCK ST, BOISE, ID 837126241
Phone: 208 381-2222
Web: WWW.SLRMC.ORG

HISTORICAL FINANCIALS
Company Type: Private

Income Statement
FYE: September 30

	REVENUE ($ mil.)	NET INCOME ($ mil.)	NET PROFIT MARGIN	EMPLOYEES
09/13	1,121	(19)	—	4,500
09/08	898	44	4.9%	—
09/07	832	64	7.7%	—
Annual Growth	5.1%	—	—	—

2013 Year-End Financials
Return on assets: 7.0%
Return on equity: (-1.7%)
Current ratio: 1.70
Cash ($ mil.): 145

ST. MARY MEDICAL CENTER

LOCATIONS

HQ: ST. MARY MEDICAL CENTER
1201 LANGHORNE NEWTOWN RD, LANGHORNE, PA 190471295
Phone: 215 710-2000
Web: WWW.STMARYHEALTHCARE.ORG

HISTORICAL FINANCIALS
Company Type: Private

Income Statement
FYE: December 31

	REVENUE ($ mil.)	NET INCOME ($ mil.)	NET PROFIT MARGIN	EMPLOYEES
12/11	438	35	8.1%	2,400
12/09	372	44	11.9%	—
12/08	1,204	0	—	—
Annual Growth	—	4261.0%	—	—

2011 Year-End Financials
Return on assets: 3.8%
Return on equity: 8.1%
Current ratio: 3.30
Cash ($ mil.): 137

ST. MARY'S HOSPITAL & MEDICAL CENTER INC

LOCATIONS

HQ: ST. MARY' S HOSPITAL & MEDICAL CENTER INC
2635 N 7TH ST, GRAND JUNCTION, CO 815018209
Phone: 970 244-2273
Web: WWW.STMARYSMADISON.COM

HISTORICAL FINANCIALS
Company Type: Private

Income Statement
FYE: December 31

	REVENUE ($ mil.)	NET INCOME ($ mil.)	NET PROFIT MARGIN	EMPLOYEES
12/09	360	50	13.9%	2,000
12/05*	0	0	17.9%	—
05/03	107	0	0.0%	—
Annual Growth	18.9%	874.5%	—	—

*Fiscal year change

2009 Year-End Financials
Return on assets: —
Return on equity: 13.9%
Current ratio: 0.60
Cash ($ mil.): 6

ST. MARY'S MEDICAL CENTER

Auditors: ERNST & YOUNG US LLP COLUMBUS

LOCATIONS

HQ: ST. MARY' S MEDICAL CENTER
407 E 3RD ST, DULUTH, MN 558051984
Phone: 218 786-4000
Web: WWW.SMDC.ORG

HISTORICAL FINANCIALS

Company Type: Private

Income Statement
FYE: June 30

	REVENUE ($ mil.)	NET INCOME ($ mil.)	NET PROFIT MARGIN	EMPLOYEES
06/13	419	65	15.6%	4,209
06/12	373	38	10.3%	—
06/11	387	52	13.5%	—
06/10	365	0	—	—
Annual Growth	4.7%	—	—	—

2013 Year-End Financials

Return on assets: 7.0% Cash ($ mil.): 75
Return on equity: 15.6%
Current ratio: 4.50

ST. MARY'S MEDICAL CENTER

Nobody wants to get sick but if you're ailing in West Virginia St. Mary's Medical Center wants you to know you are in good hands. The not-for-profit 395-bed medical facility serves patients in areas such as cardiac emergency neuroscience and cancer treatment. The largest health care facility in the tri-state region St. Mary's Medical Center is also a teaching facility affiliated with Joan C. Edwards Marshall University School of Medicine. St. Mary's Home Health Services administers care for patients in a six county area in Ohio and West Virginia. Services include IV therapy and occupational and physical therapies. St. Mary's Medical Center was founded in 1924.

Geographic Reach
With a campus in West Virginia St. Mary's Medical Center serves a tri-state region across some 20 counties.

Operations
The campus also houses St. Mary's School of Nursing the St. Mary's School of Medical Imaging and the St. Mary's School of Respiratory Care. St. Mary's Centers of Excellence includes cardiac care cancer treatment emergency/trauma services neuroscience and orthopedics.

Strategy
Following years of collaboration with area homeowners and businesses St. Mary's Medical Center opened a new $18.5-million Ironton campus in 2012 that boasts a 24-hour emergency room imaging and lab services family care and specialty doctors the likes of pediatricians and dentists.

EXECUTIVES

SVP and COO, Todd Campbell
President and CEO, Michael G. Sellards

President St. MaryÂ's Medical Center Foundation, David Sheils
CEO, Gabrielle Finley-Hazle
VP Finance and CFO, Angie Swearingen
Vice President, Vera Rose
Vice President of Support Services Planning and Development, Tim Parnell
Vice President of Marketing, Doug Korstanje
Ambulatory Services Director, Tammy Nimmo
Vice President of Medical Affairs, Lee Taylor
Cfe And Medical Librarian, Suzanne Bunten
Vice President, Chris Trotter
Contract Analyst and Vice President of Purchasing, Lavona Turvey
Vice President of Human Resources, Susan (Sue) Robinson

LOCATIONS

HQ: ST. MARY' S MEDICAL CENTER
2900 1ST AVE, HUNTINGTON, WV 257021241
Phone: 304 526-1234
Web: WWW.STMARYS.ORG

COMPETITORS

Adena Health System	Highlands Health
CAMC Health	Pikeville Medical
Clinch Valley Medical Center	Center
Fairfield Medical Center	

HISTORICAL FINANCIALS

Company Type: Private

Income Statement
FYE: September 30

	REVENUE ($ mil.)	NET INCOME ($ mil.)	NET PROFIT MARGIN	EMPLOYEES
09/14	401	10	2.7%	2,000
09/13	366	31	8.7%	—
09/09	341	1	0.5%	—
09/07	289	0	—	—
Annual Growth	4.8%	—	—	—

2014 Year-End Financials

Return on assets: 7.9% Cash ($ mil.): 16
Return on equity: 2.7%
Current ratio: 2.00

ST. OLAF COLLEGE

The hills of Northfield Minnesota are alive with the sounds of St. Olaf College. The private liberal arts university offers undergraduate and pre-professional education to more than 3000 students offering degrees in about 45 academic focus areas. The school has a faculty of more than 250 teachers and is recognized for its choral and orchestral music programs as well as its mathematics department. Other popular majors include English psychology biology economics social services theology language medical science and chemistry. St. Olaf College was founded in 1874 by Norwegian immigrants and is affiliated with the Evangelical Lutheran Church of America.

Geographic Reach
An early adopter of international education principals St. Olaf College conducts about 110 international and off-campus programs in more than 45 countries around the globe. More than two-thirds of its students participate in study abroad programs. The college's students hail from all 50 US states and more than 60 other countries.

Operations

St. Olaf College confers Bachelor of Arts (BA) and Bachelor of Music (BM) degrees. The school's student-to-teacher ratio is 12:1 and its most popular majors fall in the fields of biology mathematics economics chemistry and psychology. St. Olaf has a high success rate (about 28%) for students who go on to earn doctoral degrees at other institutions. It also has a positive record for turning out Rhodes Scholars Fulbright Fellows and Peace Corps volunteers.

Financial Performance
St. Olaf College has an operating budget of about $123.4 million (based on figures for fiscal 2013). Its programs are supported by an endowment of some $330 million. Annual tuition and fees for each student averages about $40000 with room and board bringing in another $9000.

In fiscal 2012 the college reported a 3% increase in revenues to some $124.6 million due to higher earnings from net tuition auxiliary enterprises (sales and services) and private gifts and grants. However the company's profits declined 118% leaving St. Olaf to report a loss of some $10.7 million due to increased operating expenses primarily attributed to net investment losses.

EXECUTIVES

V Pres-treas, Alan (Al) Norton
Department Chair And Associate Profess, Karen Wilson
Vice President Technology, Craig Rice
Department Chair, Dolores Peters
Director of Admissions, Dan Franklin
Board Member, Judith Stoutland
Secretary, Michelle Bayer
Auditors: BAKER TILLY VIRCHOW KRAUSE LLP

LOCATIONS

HQ: ST. OLAF COLLEGE
1520 SAINT OLAF AVE, NORTHFIELD, MN 550571574
Phone: 507 786-2222
Web: WWW.STOLAFTELEPHONE.COM

HISTORICAL FINANCIALS

Company Type: Private

Income Statement
FYE: May 31

	REVENUE ($ mil.)	NET INCOME ($ mil.)	NET PROFIT MARGIN	EMPLOYEES
05/13	193	22	11.5%	800
05/12	124	(10)	—	—
05/11	121	60	49.7%	—
05/10	116	0	—	—
Annual Growth	18.4%	—	—	—

2013 Year-End Financials

Return on assets: 8.9% Cash ($ mil.): 22
Return on equity: 11.5%
Current ratio: 0.20

ST. PETER'S HEALTH PARTNERS

St. Peter's Health Partners (formerly St. Peter's Health Care Services) is a not-for-profit health care system that serves northeastern New York. It includes health networks Seton Health and Northeast Health. Its primary facility St. Peter's Hospital has more than 440 acute-care beds and a medical staff of more than 600 physicians. Specialty services include emergency medicine cancer and cardiovascular care and women's health. St.

Peter's also operates community health clinics long-term care facilities mental health centers and home health and hospice agencies. Founded by the Religious Sisters of Mercy in 1869 St. Peter's operates from more than 125 locations and is a subsidiary of Catholic Health East.

Change in Company Type

Following its 2011 merger with Seton Health and Northeast Health St. Peter's Health Care was renamed St. Peter's Health Partners and continued to be owned by not-for-profit hospital operator Catholic Health East. By merging the systems aim to better meet the challenges of federal health reform measures and have greater operational flexibility although full integration may take up to three years.

Operations

St. Peter's Health Partners is the parent company for four hospitals: St. Peter's Hospital the Albany Memorial and Samaritan Hospitals of Northeast Health and Seton's St. Mary's Hospital. It also includes the Sunnyview Rehabilitation Hospital the Community Hospice and the Eddy Visiting Nurses Association which provides skilled nurses for home health and senior services.

Strategy

To better serve Troy and Rensselaer counties St. Peter's Health Partners has undertaken a 13-year $150-million master facilities plan for Samaritan and St. Mary's Hospitals. The project includes constuction renovation and modernization of inpatient facilites at Samaritan and outpatient facilities at St. Mary's. The project aims to fulfill a promise of the 2011 merger with Seton Health and Northeast Health: to improve health care facilities and programs in Troy.

EXECUTIVES

Vice President Human Resources, Barbara (Barb) Mccandless

Vice President Facilities Management And Supply Chain, Mike Whelan

LOCATIONS

HQ: ST. PETER' S HEALTH PARTNERS
315 S MANNING BLVD, ALBANY, NY 122081707
Phone: 518 525-1111
Web: WWW.CHE.ORG

PRODUCTS/OPERATIONS

Selected Operations
Albany Memorial Hospital
The Community Hospice
Eddy Visiting Nurses Association
Samaritan Hospital (Troy)
St. Mary' s Hospital (Troy)
St. Peter' s Hospital (Albany)
Sunnyview Rehabilitation Hospital (Schenectady)

COMPETITORS

Albany Medical Center
Ellis Hospital
Oneida Healthcare Center
SUNY Upstate Medical University
St. Joseph' s Hospital Health Center
United Health Services Hospitals
Upstate University Hospital at Community General

HISTORICAL FINANCIALS

Company Type: Private

Income Statement

	REVENUE ($ mil.)	NET INCOME ($ mil.)	NET PROFIT MARGIN	EMPLOYEES
06/14	1,185	48	4.1%	12,000
06/13*	571	23	4.2%	—
12/12	1,069	61	5.7%	—
Annual Growth	10.8%	(20.9%)	—	—

*Fiscal year change

2014 Year-End Financials

Return on assets: 4.4% Cash ($ mil.): 114
Return on equity: 4.1%
Current ratio: 1.30

ST. VINCENT HEALTHCARE

LOCATIONS

HQ: ST. VINCENT HEALTHCARE
1233 N 30TH ST, BILLINGS, MT 591010127
Phone: 406 657-7000
Web: WWW.STVINCENTHEALTHCARE.ORG

HISTORICAL FINANCIALS

Company Type: Private

Income Statement
FYE: December 31

	REVENUE ($ mil.)	NET INCOME ($ mil.)	NET PROFIT MARGIN	EMPLOYEES
12/12*	314	15	4.8%	1,800
05/01	176	17	10.1%	—
05/00	165	14	9.1%	—
05/99	458	0	—	—
Annual Growth	(2.7%)	—	—	—

*Fiscal year change

ST. VINCENT HOSPITAL

Auditors: ERNST & YOUNG US LLP HOUSTON

LOCATIONS

HQ: ST. VINCENT HOSPITAL
455 SAINT MICHAELS DR, SANTA FE, NM 875057663
Phone: 505 983-3361
Web: WWW.STVIN.ORG

HISTORICAL FINANCIALS

Company Type: Private

Income Statement
FYE: June 30

	REVENUE ($ mil.)	NET INCOME ($ mil.)	NET PROFIT MARGIN	EMPLOYEES
06/13	368	3	1.0%	1,555
06/10	299	21	7.1%	—
06/09*	288	18	6.5%	—
03/09	0	0	—	—
Annual Growth	—	—	—	—

*Fiscal year change

2013 Year-End Financials

Return on assets: 12.6% Cash ($ mil.): 2
Return on equity: 1.0%
Current ratio: 1.00

ST. VINCENT HOSPITAL OF THE HOSPITAL SISTERS OF THE THIRD ORDER

Auditors: KPMG LLP COLUMBUS OH

LOCATIONS

HQ: ST. VINCENT HOSPITAL OF THE HOSPITAL SISTERS OF THE THIRD ORDER
835 S VAN BUREN ST, GREEN BAY, WI 543013575
Phone: 920 433-0111
Web: WWW.STVINCENTHOSPITAL.ORG

HISTORICAL FINANCIALS

Company Type: Private

Income Statement
FYE: June 30

	REVENUE ($ mil.)	NET INCOME ($ mil.)	NET PROFIT MARGIN	EMPLOYEES
06/11	424	26	6.3%	2,360
06/10	376	16	4.4%	—
06/09	247	0	—	—
06/08	261	0	—	—
Annual Growth	17.5%	—	—	—

2011 Year-End Financials

Return on assets: — Cash ($ mil.): 21
Return on equity: 6.3%
Current ratio: 2.20

ST. VINCENT'S BIRMINGHAM

LOCATIONS

HQ: ST. VINCENT' S BIRMINGHAM
810 SAINT VINCENTS DR, BIRMINGHAM, AL 352051601
Phone: 205 939-7000

HISTORICAL FINANCIALS

Company Type: Private

Income Statement
FYE: June 30

	REVENUE ($ mil.)	NET INCOME ($ mil.)	NET PROFIT MARGIN	EMPLOYEES
06/13	386	38	10.0%	1,478
06/10	371	29	8.0%	—
06/08	302	8	2.8%	—
06/06	1,679	0	—	—
Annual Growth	(18.9%)	—	—	—

2013 Year-End Financials

Return on assets: 5.3% Cash ($ mil.): —
Return on equity: 10.0%
Current ratio: 2.20

ST. VINCENT'S MEDICAL CENTER

LOCATIONS

HQ: ST. VINCENT'S MEDICAL CENTER
2800 MAIN ST, BRIDGEPORT, CT 066064292
Phone: 203 576-6000
Web: WWW.STVINCENTS.ORG

HISTORICAL FINANCIALS

Company Type: Private

Income Statement — FYE: September 30

	REVENUE ($ mil.)	NET INCOME ($ mil.)	NET PROFIT MARGIN	EMPLOYEES
09/13*	438	43	9.9%	1,900
12/05	0	0	19.1%	—
09/03	224	(0)	—	—
09/02	197	0	—	—
Annual Growth	7.5%	—	—	—

*Fiscal year change

2013 Year-End Financials

Return on assets: 10.4%   Cash ($ mil.): 3
Return on equity: 9.9%
Current ratio: 0.70

ST. VINCENT'S MEDICAL CENTER INC

Auditors: DELOITTE TAX LLP CINCINNATI

LOCATIONS

HQ: ST. VINCENT'S MEDICAL CENTER INC
4205 BELFORT RD STE 4030, JACKSONVILLE, FL
322161475
Phone: 904 308-7300
Web: WWW.JAXHEALTH.COM

HISTORICAL FINANCIALS

Company Type: Private

Income Statement — FYE: June 30

	REVENUE ($ mil.)	NET INCOME ($ mil.)	NET PROFIT MARGIN	EMPLOYEES
06/13	455	42	9.3%	3,535
06/10	448	34	7.7%	—
06/09	377	(32)	—	—
06/08	1,690	0	—	—
Annual Growth	—	—	—	—

2013 Year-End Financials

Return on assets: 6.1%   Cash ($ mil.): 2
Return on equity: 9.3%
Current ratio: 2.50

STAN BOYETT & SON INC.

LOCATIONS

HQ: STAN BOYETT & SON INC.
601 MCHENRY AVE, MODESTO, CA 953505411
Phone: 209 577-6000
Web: WWW.BOYETT.NET

HISTORICAL FINANCIALS

Company Type: Private

Income Statement — FYE: December 31

	REVENUE ($ mil.)	NET INCOME ($ mil.)	NET PROFIT MARGIN	EMPLOYEES
12/08	656	0	0.1%	170
12/07	559	0	0.0%	—
12/06	475	0	0.1%	—
12/05	416	0	—	—
Annual Growth	16.4%	—	—	—

2008 Year-End Financials

Return on assets: 1.8%   Cash ($ mil.): 2
Return on equity: 0.1%
Current ratio: 0.90

STANDARD ELECTRIC COMPANY

Standard Electric and its affiliates distribute electrical and electronic products and supplies to customers through about 30 locations in Michigan. The company was founded in 1929 by Samuel Cohen and brothers Morris and Max Blumberg. The Blumberg brothers earlier established another Michigan-based electrical distributor Madison Electric an affiliate of Standard Electric with 10 Michigan locations. Another affiliated firm U.P. Electric/Wittock Supply Co. is a distributor of electrical and mechanical products with four locations on the upper Michigan peninsula. The company is owned by its directors and their families.

EXECUTIVES

Vice President Sales, Fred Forsgard
Executive Vice President, Bill Gray
Auditors: GORDON ADVISORS PC TROY M

LOCATIONS

HQ: STANDARD ELECTRIC COMPANY
2650 TRAUTNER DR, SAGINAW, MI 486049599
Phone: 989 497-2100
Web: WWW.STANDARDELECTRICCO.COM

COMPETITORS

Kendall Electric	Utility Supply and
McNaughton-McKay	Construction
Medler Electric	Werner Electric Supply

HISTORICAL FINANCIALS

Company Type: Private

Income Statement — FYE: February 28

	REVENUE ($ mil.)	NET INCOME ($ mil.)	NET PROFIT MARGIN	EMPLOYEES
02/14	159	1	1.1%	250
02/13	152	1	1.0%	—
02/12	155	1	1.1%	—
02/11	132	0	—	—
Annual Growth	6.5%	—	—	—

2014 Year-End Financials

Return on assets: 8.8%   Cash ($ mil.): —
Return on equity: 1.1%
Current ratio: 0.80

STANFORD HEALTH SERVICES

Auditors: PRICEWATERHOUSECOOPERS LLP BO

LOCATIONS

HQ: STANFORD HEALTH SERVICES
300 PASTEUR DR, STANFORD, CA 943052200
Phone: 650 723-4000
Web: WWW.STANFORDHOSPITAL.ORG

HISTORICAL FINANCIALS

Company Type: Private

Income Statement — FYE: August 31

	REVENUE ($ mil.)	NET INCOME ($ mil.)	NET PROFIT MARGIN	EMPLOYEES
08/11	2,510	415	16.6%	4
08/10	2,141	186	8.7%	—
Annual Growth	17.2%	123.2%	—	—

2011 Year-End Financials

Return on assets: —   Cash ($ mil.): 395
Return on equity: 16.6%
Current ratio: 0.50

STANLEY STEEMER INTERNATIONAL INC.

Carpet stains don't startle this Stanley. Stanley Steemer International provides residential and commercial carpet and upholstery cleaning through more than 300 franchise and corporate locations in 48 states. In addition to cleaning carpets the company provides cleaning services for tile and grout and air ducts as well as cars boats and RVs. The company which is known for its fleet of yellow vans sells its own brand of cleaning products through an online store. Founded by Jack Bates in 1947 when he established his own one-man carpet cleaning business Stanley Steemer is owned by his descendants including CEO Wesley Bates and President Justin Bates.

Geographic Reach

From its headquarters in Dublin Ohio Stanley Steemer boasts both franchised and corporate locations in nearly all 50 states nationwide.

Operations

Stanley Steemer has built a longtime business providing residential and commercial deep cleaning services offering 24-hour emergency water restoration services. Its staff of trained technicians also clean upholstery tile grout hardwood and air ducts.

Company Ownership

Stanley Steemer is a family-owned and -operated company led by the third generation of the founding Bates family.

EXECUTIVES

Chairman and CEO, Wesley C. Bates
CFO, Mark Bunner
EVP, Phillip P. Ryser
Director MIS, Dale Bevins
Senior Vice President Of Sales, Jeff Schneider
Vice President, Dana Beck
Vice President of Marketing Communications,
 Brenda Smittle
Auditors: GBQ PARTNERS LLC COLUMBUS OH

LOCATIONS

HQ: STANLEY STEEMER INTERNATIONAL INC.
 5800 INNOVATION DR, DUBLIN, OH 430163271
Phone: 614 764-2007
Web: WWW.STANLEYSTEEMER.COM

PRODUCTS/OPERATIONS

Selected Products
Gonzo Pet Hair Lifter
Handi Brush
Pet-Mess Solution Kit
Stanley Steemer Door Mat
Stanley Steemer Hardwood Floor Cleaner Kit
Stanley Steemer Neutral Tile & Grout Cleaner
Stanley Steemer Odor Out Plus
Stanley Steemer Red Wine Remover
Stanley Steemer Spot Remover

Selected Services
Residential Cleaning
 Carpet Cleaning
 Furniture Cleaning
 Tile & Grout Cleaning
 Hardwood Floor Services
 Air Duct Cleaning
 Water Damage Restoration
 Area Rug Cleaning
 Autos Boats & RVs
 Insurance Services
Commercial Cleaning
 Carpet Cleaning
 Furniture Cleaning
 Tile & Grout Cleaning
 Hardwood Floor Services
 Air Duct Cleaning
 Water Damage Repair
 National Accounts

COMPETITORS

Dwyer Group
Maid to Perfection
Molly Maid

ServiceMaster
The BMS Enterprises

HISTORICAL FINANCIALS

Company Type: Private

Income Statement   FYE: December 31

	REVENUE ($ mil.)	NET INCOME ($ mil.)	NET PROFIT MARGIN	EMPLOYEES
12/13	199	18	9.2%	2,000
12/12	192	10	5.5%	—
12/11	191	11	6.3%	—
12/10	186	0	—	—
Annual Growth	2.3%	—	—	—

Return on assets: 1.1%   Cash ($ mil.): 26
Return on equity: 9.2%
Current ratio: 1.20

STAPLE COTTON CO-OPERATIVE ASSOCIATION

Referred to as Staplcotn the Staple Cotton Cooperative has been a staple of its member-producers' business lives since 1921. One of the oldest and largest cotton marketing co-ops in the US it provides domestic and export marketing cotton warehousing and agricultural financing to some 9730 members in 47 states. As of 2011 the co-op handles nearly 14000 farm accounts in 10 states. Staplcotn's inventory is consigned by member-producers and averages from 2.5 million to 3 million bales of cotton a year. The co-op operates though 15 warehouses serving the mid-south and southeastern US to supply more than 25% of the cotton consumed by the US textile industry as well as the needs of textile mills overseas.

Staplcotn's operations currently draw members from all 11 cotton-producing states east of Texas. Georgia is the co-op's second largest in cotton production behind Texas. Staplcotn also holds 50% of the Mississippi crop market fourth in production nationwide in 2011. Members sign an agreement passing title for any cotton they produce on a particular farm to Staplcotn. The cotton is marketed in Staplcotn's name through the Mill Sales Program where large lots of cotton are offered for sale to attract better commodity prices.

The co-op's subsidiary Stapldiscount finances crops as well as farm equipment land purchases and improvements cotton gins and warehouses flying services and seed processors. It operates on a non-profit basis averaging a net interest rate less than the New York Prime Rate. Its accounts dot five states: Mississippi Louisiana Arkansas Tennessee and Missouri.

Although the co-op's cotton is sold mainly to domestic customers a decrease in demand for cotton in the US has led Staplcotn to pursue foreign sales mainly in Asia. In 2012 it was among several merchants that signed deals with Chinese mill owners for 220000 tons of cotton. Staplcotn's end-customers have included such clothing giants as Fruit of the Loom Levi Strauss and Hanes.

EXECUTIVES

Vice President Of Sales Operations, David Camp
Vice President Customer Service and Support,
 Sterling Jones

LOCATIONS

HQ: STAPLE COTTON CO-OPERATIVE ASSOCIATION
 214 W MARKET ST, GREENWOOD, MS 389304329
Phone: 662 746-4941
Web: WWW.STAPLCOTN.COM

PRODUCTS/OPERATIONS

Selected Services
Cotton services
 Loans
 Mill Sales Program
Marketing
Stapldiscount
Warehouse

COMPETITORS

Alabama Farmers
 Cooperative
Calcot
Cargill
Dunavant Enterprises
International Cotton
 Marketing
J.G. Boswell Co.
JB Cotton

King Ranch
Louis Dreyfus Group
Noble Group
Olam
Plains Cotton
Southern States
Tennessee Farmers
 Co-op
Weil Brothers Cotton

HISTORICAL FINANCIALS

Company Type: Private

Income Statement   FYE: August 31

	REVENUE ($ mil.)	NET INCOME ($ mil.)	NET PROFIT MARGIN	EMPLOYEES
08/14	865	807	93.3%	187
08/13	1,138	5	0.5%	—
08/12	1,236	8	0.7%	—
08/11	963	0	—	—
Annual Growth	(3.5%)	—	—	—

Return on assets: —   Cash ($ mil.): 138
Return on equity: 93.3%
Current ratio: 0.90

STAR OF THE WEST MILLING COMPANY

All hands are on the mill floor at Star of the West Milling. The company operates five flour mills in four US states an about 10 storage elevators. The mills and elevators store and process wheat corn and soybeans. Its flour milling capacity is about 20000 lbs. per day. North Star Bean a division of Star of the West processes beans such as navy pinto kidney and black beans into dry commodity products. The company also owns Eastern Michigan Grain an elevator that offers grain handling and marketing services. Star of the West Milling sells its flour and beans worldwide to canning and packaging customers the likes of Kellogg General Mills Nabisco and Pepperidge Farm.

Geographic Reach

Michigan-based Star of the West Milling has operations in Indiana Michigan Ohio New York and North Dakota. It has five flour mills in four different states and nine country elevators.

Strategy

The company in mid-2013 announced it will spend about $3 million to expand its facility in Rapson Michigan. The project includes a new fertilizer plant dry bean receiving facility and more space for grain storage. Star of the West Milling has grown steadily without any devastating blows to its bottom line during the economic slump. Also instead of setting aside cash for a rainy day or paying off debt Star of the West Milling in 2011 invested more than $8 million in new equipment and building additions in an effort to boost production and improve sales. The new machinery cleans and separates wheat and uses optical sorting to identify and remove imperfect kernels. Star of the West Milling in turn hopes to expand its capabilities further to include whole wheat production to cater to customer requests.

Company Background

Star of the West Milling was founded by the Hubinger family in 1870; its name was taken from a side-wheel merchant steamer of the same name that secretly transported soldiers and supplies to Fort Sumpter site of the first battle of the Civil War.

EXECUTIVES

President, Art Loeffler
Vice President Flour Milling Division, Mike Fassezke
VP Edible Bean Marketing, Joe Cramer
Controller, Eric Bushey
Director Information Technology, Jim Koski
VP Grain Marketing, Gary Kaufman
VP Elevator Division, Jim Howe
Human Resources, Tim Brooks
Plant Manager, Mark Kern
Manager Maintenance, Frank Frysh
Manager Customer Service Flour Department, Janice Weiss
Director Safety, Wayne Bauer
Office Manager, Anne Stesny
Technical Director, Laurie Murphy
Head, Keith Weber
Operations Manager, Joe Ignash
Auditors: YEO & YEO PC SAGINAW MI

LOCATIONS

HQ: STAR OF THE WEST MILLING COMPANY
121 E TUSCOLA ST, FRANKENMUTH, MI 487341731
Phone: 330 673-2941
Web: WWW.STAROFTHEWEST.COM

PRODUCTS/OPERATIONS

Selected Products

Beans
  Black beans
  Cranberry beans
  Dark red kidney beans
  Great northern beans
  Light red kidney beans
  Navy beans (pea beans)
  Pink beans
  Pinto beans
  Small reds
  Small white beans
  Yelloweye beans
Flour
  Cardinal flour
  Cracked wheat
  Crushed wheat
  Heavy bran flakes
  Heritage Brand All Purpose
  Light bran
  Patriot whole wheat flour
  Peerless flour
  Perfection pretzel flour
  Soft wheat flour and specialty products
  Special soft white wheat cake flour
Grain
  Corn
  Soybeans
  Wheat
Plant food

COMPETITORS

Bay State Milling   Italgrani
Bunge Milling   Kelley Bean
C.H. Guenther & Son   North Dakota Mill
CGC   Seaboard
Chippewa Valley Bean   US Soy
DeBruce Grain   Wilkins Rogers
Horizon Milling

HISTORICAL FINANCIALS

Company Type: Private

Income Statement

	REVENUE ($ mil.)	NET INCOME ($ mil.)	NET PROFIT MARGIN	EMPLOYEES	FYE: December 31
12/13	416	15	3.7%	239	
12/12	444	17	3.9%	—	
12/11	394	15	4.0%	—	
12/10	294	0	—	—	
Annual Growth	12.3%	—	—	—	

2013 Year-End Financials

Return on assets: 10.3%   Cash ($ mil.): 43
Return on equity: 3.7%
Current ratio: 1.40

STEEL RESOURCES LLC

Auditors: KPMG LLP MIAMI FL

LOCATIONS

HQ: STEEL RESOURCES LLC
9155 S DADELAND BLVD # 1800, MIAMI, FL 331562737
Phone: 305 591-9792
Web: WWW.STEELRESOURCES.COM

HISTORICAL FINANCIALS

Company Type: Private

Income Statement

	REVENUE ($ mil.)	NET INCOME ($ mil.)	NET PROFIT MARGIN	EMPLOYEES	FYE: December 31
12/10	418	5	1.3%	36	
12/09	285	(2)	—	—	
Annual Growth	46.8%	—	—	—	

2010 Year-End Financials

Return on assets: —   Cash ($ mil.): 1
Return on equity: 1.3%
Current ratio: 1.80

STEIN FIBERS LTD.

Auditors: TEAL BECKER & CHIARAMONTE AL

LOCATIONS

HQ: STEIN FIBERS LTD.
4 COMPUTER DR W STE 200, ALBANY, NY 122051630
Phone: 518 489-5700
Web: WWW.STEINFIBERS.COM

HISTORICAL FINANCIALS

Company Type: Private

Income Statement

	REVENUE ($ mil.)	NET INCOME ($ mil.)	NET PROFIT MARGIN	EMPLOYEES	FYE: August 31
08/14	309	1	0.6%	61	
08/13	314	2	0.7%	—	
08/07	294	4	1.7%	—	
08/06	271	0	—	—	
Annual Growth	1.7%	—	—	—	

2014 Year-End Financials

Return on assets: 7.4%   Cash ($ mil.): —
Return on equity: 0.6%
Current ratio: 0.40

STEPHEN GOULD CORPORATION

Others can worry about what's inside –Stephen Gould Corporation concentrates on the package. The company provides a full range of packaging-related design and printing services for customers worldwide. Its products include gift packaging point-of-purchase displays product merchandising and retail and industrial packaging. Stephen Gould Corporation also provides graphic design and package-engineering services as well as assembly and fulfillment. The company was originally founded in 1939 by Stephen Gould David Golden and Leonard Beckerman.

Geographic Reach

Stephen Gould Corporation operates from about 40 facilities; branches are located primarily in the US (more than 20 states) but also in China Ireland Malaysia and Mexico.

EXECUTIVES

Vice President Business Development, Bob Challinor
Vice President Human Resources, Tammy Pombo

LOCATIONS

HQ: STEPHEN GOULD CORPORATION
35 S JEFFERSON RD, WHIPPANY, NJ 079811043
Phone: 973 428-1510
Web: WWW.STEPHENGOULD.COM

PRODUCTS/OPERATIONS

Selected Products and Services

Products
  Aerospace reusable cases
  Corrugated containers
  Gift packaging
  Industrial packaging
  Point of sale packaging
  Protective packaging
Services
  Creative services
  Logistics & facilities
  Package design & engineering

COMPETITORS

Consolidated   Gibraltar Packaging
  Carqueville   Metro Packaging and
Focus Packaging &   Imaging
  Display group   R.R. Donnelley
Fort Dearborn   WS Packaging Group

HISTORICAL FINANCIALS

Company Type: Private

Income Statement

	REVENUE ($ mil.)	NET INCOME ($ mil.)	NET PROFIT MARGIN	EMPLOYEES	FYE: December 31
12/13	526	3	0.7%	325	
12/12	526	3	0.7%	—	
12/11	519	4	0.8%	—	
12/10	500	0	—	—	
Annual Growth	1.7%	—	—	—	

2013 Year-End Financials

Return on assets: —   Cash ($ mil.): 9
Return on equity: 0.7%
Current ratio: 1.50

STEPHENSON WHOLESALE COMPANY INC.

Buying a candy bar and a box of nails is made easier thanks to Stephenson Wholesale. Operating through subsidiaries Indian National Wholesale Company and GLC Marketing the company is a leading supplier of food and non-food goods to convenience stores and other retail outlets in Oklahoma and Texas. It also distributes goods to snack bars concessions operators and tribal smoke shops. The family-owned company was founded in 1953 by Ralphen Cross.

EXECUTIVES

Vice President Purchasing and Marketing, Becky Spellman

Auditors: BDO USA LLP DALLAS TEXAS

LOCATIONS

HQ: STEPHENSON WHOLESALE COMPANY INC.
230 S 22ND AVE, DURANT, OK 747015646
Phone: 580 920-0125
Web: WWW.INWSUPPLY.COM

COMPETITORS

Associated Wholesale Grocers	Eby-Brown
C&S Wholesale	GSC Enterprises
Core-Mark	H. T. Hackney
	McLane

HISTORICAL FINANCIALS

Company Type: Private

Income Statement

	REVENUE ($ mil.)	NET INCOME ($ mil.)	NET PROFIT MARGIN	EMPLOYEES
12/13	369	2	0.8%	305
12/12	395	2	0.8%	—
12/11	404	3	0.9%	—
12/10	401	0	—	—
Annual Growth	(2.7%)	—	—	—

FYE: December 31

2013 Year-End Financials

Return on assets: 0.7%
Return on equity: 0.8%
Current ratio: 1.50
Cash ($ mil.): 3

STEVENS INSTITUTE OF TECHNOLOGY (INC)

Even before the advent of the internal combustion engine Stevens Institute of Technology was educating students in science technology and engineering. Founded in 1870 through an endowment from engineer Edwin Stevens the university offers undergraduate master's and doctoral degrees in engineering science humanities computer science and technology management. The school enrolls roughly 3000 undergraduates and some 3500 graduate students. Stevens Institute teams up with corporate and military institutions to provide students with hands-on research experience; Stevens Technologies a for-profit subsidiary of the school licenses and sells the technological fruits of these partnerships.

Operations

Stevens Institute has about 400 faculty members and a student-to-teacher ratio of 10:1 for undergrads and 10:1 for graduate students. It offers more than 35 undergraduate 40 master's and 20 Ph.D. degree programs as well as 100-plus graduate certificates.

The university includes three national research centers of excellence and its annual research budget is about $27 million. Research programs are conducted in fields including medicine energy finance defense and STEM (science technology engineering and mathematics) fields. Stevens Institute collaborates with the University of Southern California on the Systems Engineering Research Center (SERC) which develops and tests complex defense systems for the Department of Defense. The center is located on the Stevens Institute campus.

In addition to Stevens Technologies Stevens Institute has for profit operations through its real estate investment subsidiary Ravenswood Corporation. It also owns Castle Point Holdings which provides a corporate interface between Stevens and startup companies.

Financial Performance

Stevens Institute reported a 6% rise in revenue to $197.6 million in 2014 thanks mostly to higher tuition and fees (which account for about two-thirds of earnings) but also thanks to higher operation-supporting investment returns higher revenue from state-sponsored activity and increased auxiliary enterprise income. Despite higher revenue net assets fell by 4% to $32 million as the university collected fewer non-operating activity contributions and paid higher expenses related to salaries benefits and supplies. Operations provided $27.2 million or 74% more cash than in 2013 mostly as the university collected significantly more from its contribution receivable accounts.

Strategy

Stevens Institute forms partnerships with other universities and commercial and government entities to expand both its educational and research programs. In 2014 for example it partnered with Scivantage to encourage the creation of startups in financial technology. That year it also launched a research and education collaboration with Accenture to focus on analytics for the financial services industry. As part of the three-year partnership agreement and as part of the its 2015 Financial Services Analytics (FSA) Graduate Certificate Program Stevens will conduct advanced analytics research projects and workshop sessions with Accenture's financial services clients.

In 2012 Stevens partnered with Seton Hall University to offer a joint legal degree with Hackensack University Medical Center to conduct biomedical clinical education programs and with mPhase Technologies on battery technology research projects.

The university also widens its offerings through organic measures. For instance in 2012 it launched a new graduate program in enterprise project management and opened a new financial teaching and research facility (the Hanlon Financial Systems Lab).

EXECUTIVES

VP Information Technology and CIO, David Dodd
VP Finance Treasurer and CFO, Randy L. Greene
Professor Provost and University Vice President, George P. Korfiatis
Dean Academic Administration, Siva Thangam
President, Nariman Farvardin
VP Communications and Marketing, Edward Stukane
Dean Schaefer School of Engineering and Science, Michael Bruno
Dean School of Systems and Enterprises, Dinesh Verma
Dean Howe School of Technology Management, Gregory Prastacos
Dean College of Arts and Letters, Lisa M. Dolling
Vice President General Counsel and Secretary, Kathy Schulz
Assistant Vice President For Finance, Mary Wheeler
Vice President, Mary Rediger
Director Of Admissions, Shane Topping
Assistant Vice President Communications And Marketing, Anastasia Greene
Vice President and Chief Administrative Officer, Maureen Weatherall
Assistant Vice President, Mary Wheeleri
Vice President for the Research Enterprise, Joseph (Jo) Mitola
Vice President Human Resources, Taylor Race
Assistant Vice President for Financial Planning Budgeting and Analysis, Justin Oates
Vice President Human Resources And Administration, Sabrina Sanichar
Vice President, Hiral Shah
Vice President, Kelvin Caraballo
Vice President General Counsel and Secretary, Kathryn Schulz
Chairman, Virginia P. Ruesterholz, age 53
Board Member, Edward (Ed) Foster
Secretary, Chris Pilusa
Secretary Of The Graduate Student Council, Yue Sun
Secretary Treasurer, Gabrielle Czernik
Auditors: GRANT THORNTON LLP NEW YORK

LOCATIONS

HQ: STEVENS INSTITUTE OF TECHNOLOGY (INC)
1 CASTLE POINT TER, HOBOKEN, NJ 070305906
Phone: 201 216-5000
Web: WWW.DC.STEVENS.EDU

PRODUCTS/OPERATIONS

2014 Sales

	$ mil.	% of total
Net tuition and fees	127	63
Sponsored activity revenue	28	16
Auxiliary enterprises	26	14
Contribution	4	2
Investment return in support of operations	6	3
Other revenue	3	2
Grants	0	-
Total	**197**	**100**

Selected Schools and Colleges

Charles V. Schaefer Jr. School of Engineering and Science
College of Arts and Letters
School of Systems and Enterprises
Wesley J. Howe School of Technology Management

HISTORICAL FINANCIALS

Company Type: Private

Income Statement

	REVENUE ($ mil.)	NET INCOME ($ mil.)	NET PROFIT MARGIN	EMPLOYEES
06/13	259	29	11.3%	500
06/10	211	8	4.0%	—
06/08	168	(1)	—	—
06/07	0	0	—	—
Annual Growth	—	—	—	—

FYE: June 30

2013 Year-End Financials

Return on assets: 6.2%
Return on equity: 11.3%
Current ratio: 0.50
Cash ($ mil.): 29

STEVENS TRANSPORT INC.

Staying cool is a must for Stevens Transport. An irregular-route refrigerated truckload carrier (or reefer) Stevens hauls temperature-controlled cargo throughout the US covering the 48 contiguous states. Through alliances Stevens also covers every province in Canada and every state in Mexico. The company operates a fleet of about 2000 Kenworth and Peterbuilt tractors and 3500 Thermo King refrigerated trailers from a network of more than a dozen service centers. Partnerships with railroads allow Stevens to arrange intermodal transport of temperature-controlled cargo. The company also provides third-party logistics services. Stevens Transport was founded in 1980.

Geographic Reach

Stevens Transport maintains its operations across Canada Mexico and the US through its partnerships with BNSF Norfolk Southern CSX and Union Pacific. It has 13 logistics offices located in Canada and throughout the US.

Operations

The company owns 49% of B2B Transport which provides an array of transportation related services to large mid-sized and small companies throughout North America.

Sales and Marketing

Stevens has provided refrigerated shipping services for such big names as General Mills Kraft Foods M&M Mars Procter & Gamble and Wal-Mart.

Strategy

Even in a US economy ripe with unpredictable fuel costs and a decline in consumer confidence one thing has always worked in Stevens' favor: people will always need their food. The company has managed to maintain a steady growth rate by keeping costs down updating the technology of its trucking equipment and maintaining an efficient operating structure. Along these lines in 2012 it implemented new mobile computing platforms across its fleet of tractors to enhance its customer services and optimize productivity.

EXECUTIVES

Sr V Pres, Todd Aaron, age 54
Vice President Risk Management, William (Bill) Tallent
Vice President Fleet Sales, Morrow Ryan
Executive Vice President of Stevens Transport, Mike Richey
Auditors: SADDOCK & CO PLLC DALLAS T

LOCATIONS

HQ: STEVENS TRANSPORT INC.
9757 MILITARY PKWY, DALLAS, TX 752274805
Phone: 972 216-9000
Web: WWW.STEVENSTRANSPORTTL.COM

PRODUCTS/OPERATIONS

Selected Services
Intermodal
International
Logistics
Truckload

COMPETITORS

C.R. England	Marten Transport
Central Refrigerated Service	Navajo Shippers
	Prime Inc.
Comcar	Southern Refrigerated
Covenant	Transport
Transportation	TransAm Trucking

Frozen Food Express
Henderson Trucking
Jim Palmer Trucking
KLLM Transport Services
Watkins Associated Industries
Willis Shaw Express

HISTORICAL FINANCIALS
Company Type: Private

Income Statement
FYE: December 31

	REVENUE ($ mil.)	NET INCOME ($ mil.)	NET PROFIT MARGIN	EMPLOYEES
12/13	636	84	13.3%	2,100
12/12	607	85	14.0%	—
12/11	566	76	13.5%	—
12/08	0	0	—	—
Annual Growth	—	—	—	—

2013 Year-End Financials

Return on assets: 0.9%
Return on equity: 13.3%
Current ratio: 2.20
Cash ($ mil.): 64

STEWARD HEALTH CARE SYSTEM LLC

Steward Health Care System is a steward of its patients' good health. With a total of 2100 beds Steward Health operates 10 hospitals including Carney Hospital Good Samaritan Medical Center Holy Family Hospital Norwood Hospital St. Elizabeth's Medical Center and Saint Anne's Hospital. Several of the hospitals are affiliated with Boston-area medical schools. The company is a top health care provider in New England; its territory ranges from Rhode Island to eastern Massachusetts and southern New Hampshire. In addition to hospitals Steward Health also includes a physician practice organization an outpatient clinic network and a home care and hospice agency. Steward is owned by Cerberus Capital Management.

Operations

Steward Health is a community-based accountable care organization that offers a full range of health care services to patients in Massachusetts. Its operations include 3000 physicians 10 hospital campuses 24 affiliated urgent care providers 6 ambulatory surgery centers home care hospice and other services. The three main components of the system are: Steward Medical Group (which provides 1 million patient encounters per year in 152 sites and manages Steward Home Care and Hospice with 300000 and 35000 encounters respectively);Steward Health Care Network (a fully integrated care management company with 3000 physician and 4 million patient encounters per year and affiliates or joint ventures with 24 urgent care centers); andSteward Hospital Group (which includes Saint Anne's Hospital in Fall River Holy Family Hospital in Methuen St. Elizabeth's Medical Center in Brighton Norwood Hospital Carney Hospital in Dorchester Good Samaritan Medical Center in Brockton Nashoba Valley Medical Center in Ayer Holy Family-Haverhill Campus Morton Hospital in Taunton and New England Sinai Hospital in Stoughton).

Other operations include Por Cristo a charitable organization providing services in Ecuador and Labouré College a medical school that confers bachelor's degrees in nursing.

Strategy

Steward Health is widely recognized as a US leader in implementing a new model of health care delivery. As an integrated care organization with over 90% of its commercial lives under risk and more than 75000 Medicare members in the Medicare Pioneer ACO under full financial and clinical risk Steward Health provides care for patients across the care spectrum. By providing health care services in a coordinated and more efficient manner Steward Health is able to control costs and improve quality eliminate care fragmentation and reduce duplication of services in the delivery of health care.

In 2014 Steward Health transitioned care at Quincy Medical Center (QMC) to a more sustainable outpatient health care delivery network in Quincy. The new outpatient delivery system includes a new 24-hour Emergency Department; a separately sited state-of-the-art urgent care center; multi-specialty clinic in Quincy; radiological services including X-ray mammography CT and ultrasound; as well as a multi-point transportation plan.That year Steward Health announced a new clinical affiliation with AFC Doctors Express Urgent Care (Doctors Express) the largest urgent care provider in New England. The partnership added nine in-network urgent care centers available to Steward Health patients. As part of this clinical affiliation Doctors Express physicians have access to Steward's patient portal to evaluate a patient's clinical history prior to commencing treatment. In 2014 Steward Health also moved to integrate Merrimack Valley Hospital and Holy Family Hospital. This integration puts Merrimack Valley and Holy Family Hospital on stronger financial footing while maintaining the same level of acute care services offered at their current locations. The two hospitals already share an integrated leadership team so this is an extension of a successful partnership between the two hospitals.

Company Background

Acquisitions in 2011 and 2012 included five Massachusetts hospitals: Merrimack Valley Hospital (120 beds) Nashoba Valley Medical Center (60 beds formerly part of Essent Healthcare) Morton Hospital (150 beds) Quincy Medical Center (200 beds) and New England Sinai Hospital (210 postacute care beds).

The company changed its name from Caritas Christi to Steward Health after being acquired by Cerberus Capital Management in 2010; it had previously been operated by the Catholic Archdiocese of Boston. The acquisition by Cerberus was worth some $895 million and provided operational funding and capital for hospital improvement projects; it also helped pay down debt obligations. As a result of the transaction Steward Health became a for-profit corporation; however a stipulation of the deal mandated that the health system's hospitals retain their pastoral and charitable care policies. The sale to Cerberus was not the first attempt by the Archdiocese of Boston to sell the ailing Caritas Christi system which had been suffering from financial troubles for several years prior to the deal.

EXECUTIVES

Vice President Corporate Financial Services, Jill Moretto
Senior Vice President Of Physicians And, Timothy (Tim) Crowley
Vice President of Medical Affairs at Saint Anne's Hospital, Harvey Kowaloff
Vice President Allied Health Services, Alan (Al) Rosenfeld
System Vice President, Georgann Bruski
Vice President of Employee Health, Kim Wedge
Vice President Of Medical Management, Scott Stewart

Director of Pharmacy Rehab and Resp Services, Nancy Huff
Vice President Finance, Dave Fielding
Vice President, Neville Zar
Vice President of Medical Affairs, Paul Allen
Vice President Ambulatory Care St Anne, John (Jack) Jurczyk
Vice President Human Resources Shared Services, Melinda Braithwaite
System Vice President Employee Health Management, Kimberly Wedge
Corp. Vice President of Patient Access, Kathy Fehser
Director Media Relations, Chris Murphy
Medical Director Local Chapter, Anthony Sposato
Vice President Of Information Technology, Daniel Oniel
Medical Director, Vijay Sudheendra
Infection Control Director, Kathleen Malm
Vice President Of Medical Affairs Quality And Safety, John (Jack) Alexander
System Vice President of Pharmacy, Ernie Anderson
Vice President Learning And Training, Davor Kvaternik
Secretary, Lisa Hanscom
Board Member, Judith (Judi) Waterston

LOCATIONS

HQ: STEWARD HEALTH CARE SYSTEM LLC
500 BOYLSTON ST, BOSTON, MA 021163740
Phone: 617 419-4700
Web: WWW.STEWARD.ORG

Services
Behavioral Health Services
Centers for Cancer Care
Center for Advanced Cardiac Surgery
Centers for Cardiac and Vascular Care
Centers for Weight Control
Home Care and Hospice
MAKOplasty® Services
Maternity Services

Selected Hospitals – Massachusetts
Carney Hospital (Dorchester)
Good Samaritan Medical Center (Brockton)
Holy Family Hospital (Methuen)
Merrimack Valley Hospital (Haverhill acquired in 2011)
Morton Hospital (Taunton acquired in 2011)
Nashoba Valley Medical Center (Ayer acquired in 2011)
New England Sinai Hospital (Stoughton acquired in 2012)
Norwood Hospital (Norwood)
Quincy Medical Center (Quincy acquired in 2011)
Saint Anne' s Hospital (Fall River)
St. Elizabeth' s Medical Center (Brighton)

COMPETITORS

Berkshire Health Systems
Boston Medical Center
Cambridge Health Alliance
Cape Cod Healthcare
Care New England
CareGroup
Children' s Hospital Boston
Emerson Hospital
Hallmark Health

Lahey Health System
New England Alliance for Health
Northeast Health System
Partners HealthCare
Southcoast Hospitals Group
Southern New Hampshire Medical Center
Winchester Healthcare

HISTORICAL FINANCIALS
Company Type: Private

Income Statement
FYE: September 30

	REVENUE ($ mil.)	NET INCOME ($ mil.)	NET PROFIT MARGIN	EMPLOYEES
09/07	1,240	30	2.5%	12,000
09/06	1,220	47	3.9%	—
Annual Growth	1.7%	(35.9%)	—	—

2007 Year-End Financials
Return on assets: —   Cash ($ mil.): 73
Return on equity: 2.5%
Current ratio: 0.80

STEWART BUILDERS INC.

Concrete is the key to Stewart Builders' success in the construction industry. Stewart Builders through main subsidiaries Keystone Concrete Placement and Keystone Structural Concrete provides concrete construction services for commercial industrial and institutional facilities as well as for residential markets primarily serving working on projects in the Lone Star State. Other subsidiaries do site work and construct basements. President Don Stewart and his sons founded the firm in 1993. The company has operations in Austin Georgetown Houston and San Antonio Texas.

EXECUTIVES

Vice President Finance, Sean McGarity
Vice President, Craig Stewart
Vice President, Rodney Horn
Sec-treas, Mark Stewart

LOCATIONS

HQ: STEWART BUILDERS INC.
16575 VILLAGE DR, JERSEY VILLAGE, TX 770401124
Phone: 713 983-8002
Web: WWW.KEYSTONECONCRETE.COM

COMPETITORS

American Pan & Engineering
Baker Concrete
Ceco Concrete

KHS&S
United Forming
Western Construction

HISTORICAL FINANCIALS
Company Type: Private

Income Statement
FYE: December 31

	REVENUE ($ mil.)	NET INCOME ($ mil.)	NET PROFIT MARGIN	EMPLOYEES
12/13	236	10	4.3%	1,400
12/12	206	5	2.4%	—
12/10	144	0	—	—
12/09	169	0	—	—
Annual Growth	8.7%	—	—	—

2013 Year-End Financials
Return on assets: 9.6%   Cash ($ mil.): 8
Return on equity: 4.3%
Current ratio: 0.20

STEWART'S SHOPS CORP.

I scream you scream we all scream for Stewart's ice cream —especially if we live in upstate New York or Vermont home to some 330 Stewart's Shops. The chain of convenience stores sells more than 3000 products across 30-plus counties. They include dairy items groceries food to go (soup sandwiches hot entrees) beer coffee gasoline and of course ice cream. In addition to its retail business the company owns about 100 rental properties including banks hair salons and apartments near its stores. Stewart's Shops formerly known as Stewart's Ice Cream Company was established in 1945. The founding Dake family owns about two-thirds of the company; employee compensation plans own the rest.

Geographic Reach

Based in New York Stewart's Shops operates a chain of convenience stores across upstate New York and in Vermont.

Operations

The convenience store chain which spans New York and Vermont offers consumers milk ice creams coffee to-go foods beer gasoline and groceries. As part of its business Stewart's Shops also acquires and develops (preferably adjacent) properties the likes of shops banks hair salons and apartments that it then leases or sells.

Stewart's Shops makes its own dairy products including its own ice cream in more than 50 flavors that are hand-dipped and packaged. Recognized for its quality products the company relies on a group of about 45 farmers in New York to supply its milk.

The vertically-integrated company which makes about 75% of the items it sells also offers private-label goods and national brands in its stores. Its private-label brands extend far beyond dairy products to include soda chips bread and juices.

Sales and Marketing

Stewart's Shops serves consumers through its New York and Vermont shops; two-thirds of its stores sell gas.

Strategy

The convenience store operator regularly extends its reach. In 2014 it's focused on Syracuse New York following several store openings in 2013 in Keeseville Herkimer Rotterdam and Heuvelton New York. The latter shops boast an expanded cooler walk-in beer cave and seating.

The company is also investing in environmentally friendly facilities. In 2013 for instance it had 2400 solar panels installed at its manufacturing and distribution center. Stewart's Shops anticipates that the effort will save nearly $40000 a year in energy costs at the plant after about a 5-year period.

It enlisted the help of Paragon Software in 2014 to automate the planning of daily and seasonal deliveries. In turn Stewart's Shops aims to lower mileage reduce fuel usage and improve truckload efficiencies.

EXECUTIVES

Senior Vice President Of Information Technology Operations, Dave Caruso
Treasurer, David (Dave) Farr
Auditors: BOLLAM SHEEDY TORANI & CO

LOCATIONS

HQ: STEWART' S SHOPS CORP.
2907 ROUTE 9, BALLSTON SPA, NY 12020
Phone: 518 581-1201
Web: WWW.STEWARTSSHOPS.COM

PRODUCTS/OPERATIONS

Selected Products
Beverages
Coffee
Ice Cream
Food to go
Gasoline
Groceries
Milk

COMPETITORS

7-Eleven
Ahold U.S.A.
Ben & Jerry' s

Hannaford Bros.
Kroger
McDonald' s

Carvel
Cumberland Farms
Exxon Mobil
Friendly's Ice Cream
Golub

Pathmark Stores
Sunoco
TravelCenters of
America

HISTORICAL FINANCIALS

Company Type: Private

Income Statement

FYE: December 29

	REVENUE ($ mil.)	NET INCOME ($ mil.)	NET PROFIT MARGIN	EMPLOYEES
12/13	1,577	73	4.7%	3,800
12/12*	1,528	64	4.2%	—
01/11	1,296	53	4.2%	—
01/10	1,187	0	—	—
Annual Growth	7.3%	—	—	—

*Fiscal year change

2013 Year-End Financials

Return on assets: 4.0%
Return on equity: 4.7%
Current ratio: 0.60

Cash ($ mil.): 34

STG INC.

STG provides technical TLC to government agencies. Serving the US Defense Department and about 50 other federal agencies the company provides information technology services such as project management application development network implementation security systems support and IT systems integration. It also offers data security assessment and compliance reporting services as well as foreign language translation and transcription. In addition to the DOD STG counts the US departments of State and Agriculture among its clients as well as Fortune 100 companies. Internationally the company has worked with NATO the Korea Airports Authority and other agencies.

Geographic Reach

The company serves customers at more than 250 locations around the world. It has offices in Reston Virginia; Aberdeen Maryland; Warrenton Virginia; North Charleston South Carolina; Dayton Ohio; and Sierra Vista Arizona.

Operations

STG serves as a prime contractor on a number of government programs. Its key areas of specialty are enterprise network operations cyber security financial services systems engineering and integration software engineering and linguistics and intelligence software development.

Financial Performance

According to a 2013 Washington Technology ranking STG revenues in from prime contracts with defense and civilian customers dropped about $8 million (to $217.4 million) from 2012 to 2013. Defense revenue was $126.9 million and civilian was $90.5 million.

Strategy

Responding to the increasing complex needs of its customers STG has expanded its core competencies to be adapt in making innovative responses to new challenges such as engineering solutions for rapid prototyping and battlefield support niche scientific solutions for specialized agency mission and the development of unique name searching algorithms for six language groups.

In 2014 STG was named a prime contractor for a project from the Department of Homeland Security. The contract includes work in integration software design and development and operations and maintenance over a possible 7-year duration.

In 2013 STG secured the two-year US Army's Noncombatant Evacuation Operation Tracking System Support contract for the Eighth Army. That year it was also awarded a task order to provide network operations center support services for the Department of Homeland Security and Customs and Border Protection.

In a major move in 2012 the National Institutes of Health awarded STG an up to $20 billion 10-year contract for the NIH Information Technology Acquisition and Assessment Center. The contract supports the federal enterprise architecture the Department of Defense enterprise architecture and the federal health architecture.

Company Background

STG was founded in 1986 by Chairman and CEO Simon Lee.

EXECUTIVES

Chairman and CEO, Simon S. Lee
SVP Civil Agencies Sector, Paul A. Fernandes
Senior Vice President Defense Sector, Glenn W. Davis
Chief Financial Officer, Patrick G. Attilio
SVP Financial Services Practice, Paul G. Hudecek
Chief Technology Officer and Senior Vice President, Bill B. Perlowitz
SVP Strategy and Business Growth, Dale E. Luddeke
Senior Vice President Civil Agencies Sector, Mark Jendzejec, age 60

LOCATIONS

HQ: STG INC.
12011 SUNSET HILLS RD, RESTON, VA 201905918
Phone: 703 691-2480
Web: WWW.STG-INC.COM

PRODUCTS/OPERATIONS

Solutions
Enterprise Network Operations
Program & Project ManagementEnterprise & IT SupportApplication & Web DevelopmentSecurity ManagementKey Programs
Cyber Security
Financial Services
Capabilities
Systems Engineering and Integration
Technical Assistance
Software Engineering
Linguistics and Intelligence Solutions

COMPETITORS

Accenture
BAE Systems Inc.
Booz Allen
CACI International
Computer Sciences Corp.
General Dynamics Information Technology
HP Enterprise Services
IBM Global Services
Jacobs Engineering
Leidos
Lockheed Martin Information Systems
ManTech
Northrop Grumman
Raytheon
Unisys

HISTORICAL FINANCIALS

Company Type: Private

Income Statement

FYE: December 31

	REVENUE ($ mil.)	NET INCOME ($ mil.)	NET PROFIT MARGIN	EMPLOYEES
12/14	209	4	2.1%	1,250
12/13	248	3	1.5%	—
12/12	212	5	2.8%	—
12/11	261	0	—	—
Annual Growth	(7.0%)	—	—	—

2014 Year-End Financials

Return on assets: 3.0%
Return on equity: 2.1%
Current ratio: 1.20

Cash ($ mil.): —

STM INDUSTRIES INC.

Auditors: MCGLADREY & PULLEN LLP CHARLO

LOCATIONS

HQ: STM INDUSTRIES INC.
1985 TATE BLVD SE STE 2, HICKORY, NC 286021433
Phone: 828 322-2700
Web: WWW.SHURTAPE.COM

HISTORICAL FINANCIALS

Company Type: Private

Income Statement

FYE: January 1

	REVENUE ($ mil.)	NET INCOME ($ mil.)	NET PROFIT MARGIN	EMPLOYEES
01/11	374	20	5.4%	1,125
01/10*	374	20	5.4%	—
12/08	1,090	0	—	—
Annual Growth	—23064.0%	—	—	—

*Fiscal year change

2011 Year-End Financials

Return on assets: 5.8%
Return on equity: 5.4%
Current ratio: 1.30

Cash ($ mil.): 2

STORMONT-VAIL HEALTHCARE INC.

Auditors: BERBERICH TRAHAN & CO PA TOPE

LOCATIONS

HQ: STORMONT-VAIL HEALTHCARE INC.
1500 W 10TH ST, TOPEKA, KS 66604
Phone: 785 354-6000
Web: WWW.STORMONTVAIL.ORG

HISTORICAL FINANCIALS

Company Type: Private

Income Statement

FYE: September 30

	REVENUE ($ mil.)	NET INCOME ($ mil.)	NET PROFIT MARGIN	EMPLOYEES
09/13	510	68	13.4%	3,557
09/12	576	50	8.7%	—
09/08	5	4	72.0%	—
09/04	273	0	—	—
Annual Growth	7.2%	—	—	—

2013 Year-End Financials

Return on assets: 3.2%
Return on equity: 13.4%
Current ratio: 2.40

Cash ($ mil.): 90

STRACK AND VAN TIL SUPER MARKET INC

One of Chicagoland's leading grocery chains Strack & Van Til operates more than 35 supermarkets in and around Chicago and northern Indiana. Stores operate under the banners of Strack & Van Til Town & Country Food Market and Ultra Foods. The regional grocery chain offers fresh and packaged foods and has delicatessen and bakery divisions in each of its stores. Its websites offer weekly circulars and coupons as well as feature recipes cooking videos meal planners and food-related articles. The company is owned by Chicago-based grocery distributor Central Grocers which also operates supermarkets under the Berkot's and Key Market banners.

Strategy

Strack & Van Til and its regional rivals are facing increased competition from national chains including Wal-Mart and Trader Joe's moving into the market while taking advantage of the woes of smaller ones. Rather than retreat the grocery chain is pursuing a growth strategy acquiring seven stores in its market area in late 2012. (With Safeway-owned Dominick's Supermarkets on the block its stores are in play.) It is also investing in its existing stores and stocking more organic foods to compete with the likes of Whole Foods. The company is revamping supermarkets in Valpariso Hobart and Chesterton was well as an Ultra Foods store in Highland Strack's supermarkets in Munster and Schereville and an Ultra in Lansing are slated for upgrades as well.

Wal-Mart which had been expanding aggressively in the Chicago suburbs has begun opening supercenters and smaller Walmart Express stores within the city limits. Its arrival has sparked fierce price competition among area grocers. Other relative newcomers to the Illinois grocery market include Roundy's and non-traditional grocery chains such as SuperTarget stores and limited-assortment ALDI. To take on nationwide retailers Strack & Van Til bands together with other independent stores as members of the Central Grocers cooperative. The combined buying power helps the stores to offer competitive pricing and product selection.

In late 2013 the grocery chain launched a new marketing campaign I'm a Strack & Van Til Shopper to appeal to a wide audience while maintaining the company's value proposition.

Mergers and Acquisitions

In December 2012 Strack & Van Til acquired seven grocery stores from Indiana-based WiseWay Supermarkets. Four of the stores were converted to the Strack & Van Til banner while three became Ultra Foods stores. Like Strack & Van Til WiseWay was also supplied by Central Grocers.

EXECUTIVES

Vice President Operations, Andy Raab
Auditors: MCGLADREY & PULLEN LLP CHICAG

LOCATIONS

HQ: STRACK AND VAN TIL SUPER MARKET INC
9632 CLINE AVE, HIGHLAND, IN 463223094
Phone: 219 924-7588
Web: WWW.STRACKANDVANTIL.COM

COMPETITORS

ALDI	Target Corporation
Jewel Osco	Trader Joe's
Kmart	Wal-Mart
Meijer	Whole Foods
Roundy's	

HISTORICAL FINANCIALS

Company Type: Private

Income Statement

FYE: August 1

	REVENUE ($ mil.)	NET INCOME ($ mil.)	NET PROFIT MARGIN	EMPLOYEES
08/10	961	15	1.7%	2,300
08/09	995	13	1.4%	—
Annual Growth	(3.4%)	16.1%	—	—

2010 Year-End Financials

Return on assets: 3.5%
Return on equity: 1.7%
Current ratio: 0.20

Cash ($ mil.): 10

STRIKE LLC

Strike Construction aims to strike it rich by constructing installing and testing pipelines for the oil and gas industry. The family-owned contracting firm builds and repairs onshore pipelines and meter stations for customers the likes of Kinder Morgan SandRidge Energy and TransCanada. It also performs state-mandated integrity tests to ensure pipeline safety and offers remediation services in case a pipe should require repairs. Subsidiary Pickett Systems designs and installs flow measurement systems for onshore and offshore use; it also offers fabrication services. Strike Construction is licensed to work in about 30 states but the bulk of its business is concentrated in oil-rich Texas and along the Gulf Coast.

Geographic Reach

Based near Houston Strike Construction serves clients nationwide primarily in Texas and Louisiana. It boasts about a dozen locations in these states.

Sales and Marketing

Strike Construction's customer base includes more than 200 pipeline producer and engineering firms.

Operations

Strike Construction provides services in a range of sectors of the oil gas utility and power industries through five business units: Pickett Systems Strike Testing Strike Industrial Strike Instrumentation & Electrical and Strike Oilfield.

Pickett Systems focuses on flow measurement systems and offers fabrication services.

Strike Testing provides a full turnkey service from beginning to end and from 4-inch to 42-inch pipe.Strike Industrial represents the diversified heavy industrial arm of Strike serving Texas's oil gas power utility and chemical industries.Strike Instrumentation & Electrical provides industrial trade-certified and tested instrument technicians and electricians for project completion and start-up solutions.Strike Oilfield offers rig and tank cleaning roustabout services and a variety of other critical functions.

EXECUTIVES

CEO, Steve Pate
EVP Special Projects, Kacey Smart
EVP Western Operations, Jarvie Arnold
SVP, Jason Heckt
SVP, Kevin Pate
Chief Financial Officer, Douglas Jones
Auditors: UHY LLP CPAS HOUSTON TX

LOCATIONS

HQ: STRIKE LLC
5170 WESTWAY PARK BLVD, HOUSTON, TX 77041
Phone: 281 362-9708
Web: WWW.STRIKECONSTRUCTION.COM

PRODUCTS/OPERATIONS

Selected Business Units

Pickett Systems
Strike Testing
Strike Industrial
Strike Instrumentation and Electrical
Strike Oilfield

Selected Services

Pipeline Construction
Facilities Services
Pipeline Integrity
Operations and Maintenance
Industrial Services
Oilfield Services
Instrumentation and Electrical
Fabrication and Measurement
Hydrostatic Testing

COMPETITORS

B. L. Harbert	TIC Holdings
Bechtel	Technip USA
Fluor	Tellepsen Builders
Holloman	Willbros
Southwest Gas	Zachry Inc.

HISTORICAL FINANCIALS

Company Type: Private

Income Statement

FYE: December 31

	REVENUE ($ mil.)	NET INCOME ($ mil.)	NET PROFIT MARGIN	EMPLOYEES
12/12	545	47	8.6%	1,000
12/10	192	7	4.1%	—
12/08	114	7	6.8%	—
12/07	58	0	—	—
Annual Growth	56.5%	—	—	—

2012 Year-End Financials

Return on assets: 12.7%
Return on equity: 8.6%
Current ratio: 1.50

Cash ($ mil.): —

STURDY MEMORIAL HOSPITAL INC.

Sturdy Memorial Hospital has been a stalwart provider of health care to southeast Massachusetts and Rhode Island since 1913. In addition to comprehensive medical surgical and emergency care the hospital offers cardiac and pulmonary rehabilitation women's health services diagnostic imaging and a center devoted to treating multiple sclerosis patients. It also operates pain management cancer and wound care centers. In 2014 Sturdy Memorial admitted some 7000 patients facilitated around 700 births and had some 51000 emergency department visits. The not-for-profit hospital employs more than 150 physicians.

EXECUTIVES

Director Of Nursing, David Spoor
Auditors: GRANT THORNTON LLP WESTBOROU

LOCATIONS

HQ: STURDY MEMORIAL HOSPITAL INC.
211 PARK ST, ATTLEBORO, MA 027033137
Phone: 508 222-5200
Web: WWW.STURDYMEMORIAL.ORG

PRODUCTS/OPERATIONS

Selected Services
Allergy
Anesthesiology
Dentistry
Dermatology
Endocrinology
Gastroenterology
Hematology
Nephrology
Neurology
Neurosurgery
Ophthalmology
Orthopedics
Otolaryngology
Pathology
Urology

COMPETITORS

Care New England	Memorial Hospital of
Caritas Norwood	Rhode Island
Hospital	Milford Regional
Kent Hospital	Medical Center
Lifespan Corporation	Southcoast Health

HISTORICAL FINANCIALS

Company Type: Private

Income Statement

FYE: September 30

	REVENUE ($ mil.)	NET INCOME ($ mil.)	NET PROFIT MARGIN	EMPLOYEES
09/14	161	22	13.8%	1,300
09/13	158	74	46.8%	—
09/12	164	30	18.4%	—
09/11	155	0	—	—
Annual Growth	1.2%	—	—	—

2014 Year-End Financials

Return on assets: 3.3%
Return on equity: 13.8%
Current ratio: 1.00

Cash ($ mil.): 9

SUFFOLK CONSTRUCTION COMPANY INC.

Suffolk Construction Company provides construction services from top to bottom. The company kicks off the building process with pre-construction services and follows through with design/build general contracting and construction management. Suffolk Construction builds for both the public and private organizations in the science and technology health care education government and commercial sectors operating in the Northeast Mid-Atlantic Southeast and West Coast regions of the US. Founded in 1982 the privately-held firm is owned by president and CEO John Fish whose family has been in construction for four generations.

Geographic Reach

The Boston-based construction firm operates nationwide across the Northeast Mid-Atlantic Southeast and West Coast regions. Its offices are located Boston; Miami; Los Angeles; San Diego; San Francisco; Tarrytown New York; and Estero Florida.

Sales and Marketing

Suffolk Construction offers its services for projects in the assisted living aviation and transportation commercial education entertainment government healthcare hospitality non-profit residential retail and science and technology sectors. The company has also worked on projects for federal and local governments. In the past Suffolk has built for the Army Corps of Engineers the US Marine Corps and US Navy.Strategy

Suffolk reemphasized its "Build Smart" approach in 2015 which is designed to boost productivity and cut costs in the construction management process on every project. Before the company breaks ground at a job site it uses technologies such as virtual models and Building Information Modeling (BIM) to build projects virtually. The practice minimizes risk lessens design conflicts and issues and lowers costs for Suffolk Construction clients.Suffolk Construction serves several sectors to keep the company thriving even in challenging times. The firm extended its reach into the growing health care sector by launching National Healthcare Group which specializes in building health care projects nationwide.

Company Background

Already a successful builder in the New England area Suffolk Construction has expanded nationally in the past through acquisitions. In 2009 it bought Massachusetts-based William A. Berry & Son creating Suffolk's Berry Division which specializes in health care and biomedical projects.

Suffolk Construction also acquired The Dietze Construction Group based in Ashburn Virginia in 2010. The deal strengthened Suffolk's position in the Mid-Atlantic region and expanded its ability to serve the government health care education science/technology and commercial sectors. Giving the company a boost in the West Suffolk Construction acquired Southern California-based ROEL Construction in 2011.

EXECUTIVES

Chairman and CEO, John F. Fish
President West Region, Andrew J. (Andy) Ball
EVP and CFO, Michael (Mike) Azarela
President and General Manager Northeast Region, Mark L. DiNapoli
President & General Manager Southeast Region, Rex B. Kirby
General Manager San Diego, Wayne Hickey
General Manager Retail and Interiors, Michael (Mike) DiNapoli
Executive Vice President Work Acquisition Northeast Region, Peter Welsh
President Healthcare/Science and Technology & Chief Innovation Officer, Peter Campot
Vice President and Chief Information Officer, Corren Collura
EVP and General Manager Mid-Atlantic Region, Stephen Skinner
Vice President & Chief Operating Officer Commercial Education and Government Northeast Region, Angus Leary
Executive Vice President of National Business Development, Christopher Woods
Vice President of Marketing and Communications, Dan Antonellis
Executive Vice President Marketing And Work Acquisi, Andrea L Bruce
Vp And Regional Director Of Ne, Mark Sanborn
Vice President Sales and Marketing, David (Dave) Passafaro
Senior Vice President, Vin Murphy
Vice President of Risk Management, Chris Debruin
Executive Vice President and General Manager, Jeffrey (Jeff) Gouveia
Vice President, Min Zavarella
Vice President, Diana Martinez
Vice President Of Strategic Planning, Nicole Mills
Vice President Of Business Development, Rick Kolb
Executive Vice President, James K (Jamie) Mcelwee
Vice President Finance, Christina DeGroote
Vice President Of Estimating, Richard Armsworthy
Senior Vice President Chief Information Officer, Kevin McDonough
Executive Vice President And General Manager, Jeffrey Gouveia
Vice President Retail, Mike DiNapoli
Executive Vice President, Jim D'Agostino
Vice President Miami, John (Jack) Planz

LOCATIONS

HQ: SUFFOLK CONSTRUCTION COMPANY INC.
65 ALLERTON ST, BOSTON, MA 021192923
Phone: 617 445-3500
Web: WWW.SUFFOLKCONSTRUCTION.COM

PRODUCTS/OPERATIONS

Selected Services
Building information modeling
Construction management
Design/build
General contracting
Preconstruction
Sustainable building

COMPETITORS

Balfour Beatty	Pepper Construction
Construction	Swinerton
Clark Enterprises	Turner Corporation
DooleyMack	Tutor Perini
Kraus-Anderson	Walsh Group
McCarthy Building	Whiting-Turner

HISTORICAL FINANCIALS

Company Type: Private

Income Statement

FYE: August 31

	REVENUE ($ mil.)	NET INCOME ($ mil.)	NET PROFIT MARGIN	EMPLOYEES
08/14	1,761	0	—	1,150
08/13	1,825	0	—	—
08/12	1,349	0	—	—
08/11	1,290	0	—	—
Annual Growth	10.9%	—	—	—

2014 Year-End Financials

Return on assets: 16.3%
Return on equity: —
Current ratio: 0.20

Cash ($ mil.): 111

SUFFOLK UNIVERSITY

Suffolk University provides a well-rounded education around the Athens of America and abroad. From its main campus in Boston and its satellite and branch campuses across Massachusetts as well as through study abroad programs the university provides undergraduate and graduate degrees in more than 70 areas of study through the College of Arts and Sciences Sawyer Business School and Suffolk Law School. It also runs about 25 institutes and research centers. More than 9000 students attend the private university which has a 12:1 student-to-faculty ratio and offers courses taught by about 900 faculty members. The university was founded in 1906 as the Suffolk School of Law.

Geographic Reach

Suffolk University's main campus consists of 16 buildings on Beacon Hill and in downtown Boston; the university also operates a branch campus in Madrid Spain as well as offers degree programs at two satellite sites in Massachusetts (Cape Cod Community College and the MBA-North facility in Lawrence). Students from all 50 states and more than 100 countries around the globe attend the university.

Financial Performance

Suffolk University reported a 2% increase in revenues to some $237 million in 2012 due to higher tuition fee income and endowment-sourced funding. Net income decreased 66% however to about $12 million due to lower investment returns.

Strategy

Suffolk University is enhancing student opportunities especially for international learning opportunities such as seminars study tours and service-learning and study abroad programs. It is also working to expand its interdisciplinary study programs such as entrepreneurship public policy and intellectual property. Other strategic initiatives include renovating and enhancing campus facilities and increasing career opportunities for graduates. Suffolk University is also working to increase budget transparency and to diversify its revenue sources.

EXECUTIVES

Vice President Of External Affairs, John Nucci
Acting Vice President, Danielle Manning
Assoc Vice President Advancement, STEPHANIE MORAN
Managing Director Alumni Engagement, Elizabeth (Beth) Conley
Assistant Vice President of Finance, Maureen Stewart
Vice President Marketing Comm, Greg Gatlin
Controller and Treasurer, Sandra Scott
Secretary To The Law Library Director, Deborah L (Deb) Whelton
Treasurer, Elif Armbruster
Board Member, Gerard Clark
Secretary World Languages and Cultural Studies, Madelyn Soto
Auditors: KPMG LLP BOSTON MA

LOCATIONS

HQ: SUFFOLK UNIVERSITY
8 ASHBURTON PL, BOSTON, MA 021082770
Phone: 617 573-8000
Web: WWW.LAW.SUFFOLK.EDU

PRODUCTS/OPERATIONS

Selected Colleges Schools Institutes and Research Centers
Colleges and Schools
  College of Arts and Sciences
  Sawyer Business School
  Suffolk Law School
Institutes and Research Centers
  Beacon Hill Institute
  Center for Advanced Legal Studies
  Center for Crime & Justice Policy Research
  Center for Entrepreneurship
  Center for Global Business Ethics and Law
  Center for Global Enterprise
  Center for Innovation & Change Leadership
  Center for Restorative Justice
  Center for Teaching Excellence
  Center for Women's Health and Human Rights
  Friedman Field Station
  Institute for Executive Education and Lifelong Learning
  Institute for Public Service
  John Joseph Moakley Archive and Institute
  Juvenile Justice Center
  Knowledge Globalization Institute
  Macaronis Institute for Trial and Appellate Advocacy
  McDonnell International Business Institute
  Moakley Center for Public Management

Moakley Institute on Public Policy and Political Leadership
Poetry Center
Political Research Center
Rappaport Center for Law and Public Service
Rosenberg Institute for East Asian Studies
Sagan Energy Research Laboratory

HISTORICAL FINANCIALS
Company Type: Private

Income Statement
FYE: June 30

	REVENUE ($ mil.)	NET INCOME ($ mil.)	NET PROFIT MARGIN	EMPLOYEES
06/14	235	35	15.0%	800
06/13	236	28	12.1%	—
06/11	298	5	1.8%	—
06/10	282	0	—	—
Annual Growth	(4.5%)	—	—	—

2014 Year-End Financials
Return on assets: 13.1%   Cash ($ mil.): 2
Return on equity: 15.0%
Current ratio: —

SUMMA HEALTH SYSTEM

Acute care hospitals plus a network of outpatient and primary care clinics plus a health care plan yields the sum of Summa Health System. The not-for-profit system serves the residents of the greater Akron Ohio area through five acute care hospitals and a whole slew of other health care sites. It also has an affiliation and management agreement with the nearby Robinson Memorial Hospital. Together its hospitals are home to more than 2000 beds. In addition to general medical and surgical care Summa's key services include cardiac stroke behavioral health cancer care emergency services and women's health.

Geographic Reach

Summa is expanding its services through locations in the Ohio counties of Summit Portage and Medina.

Operations

Summa's medical facilities include Summa Akron City Hospital Summa St. Thomas Hospital Summa Western Reserve Hospital Summa Barberton Hospital Summa Wadsworth-Rittman Hospital Summa affiliate Robinson Memorial Hospital and joint venture Crystal Clinic Orthopaedic Center. In addition outpatient care is extended throughout the area through a network of community health centers. Summa also operates home health and hospice organizations. Altogether Summa serves about 1 million patients each year.

The system's health care plan called SummaCare offers HMO PPO and POS (point of service) health insurance products to employer groups individuals and Medicare recipients in northern Ohio. It also administers health plans for self-funded groups through its Apex Benefit Services unit. SummaCare covers about 230000 members. Its services are accepted at 50 hospitals and about 7000 providers.

Several of Summa's facilities are teaching hospitals and as such support the education of the organization's physicians and health care professionals. For instance Summa Western Reserve Hospital provides osteopathic medicine training programs through an affiliation with Ohio University. Akron

City Hospital and St. Thomas Hospital are teaching affiliates of the Northeastern Ohio Universities College of Medicine and offer about 15 accredited residency training programs.

The health system invests about $10 million each year in research support for many areas including cardiology cancer and geriatrics. It is a founding member of Akron's Austen BioInnovation Institute. Major research programs are supported by grants from institutions such as the National Institutes of Health and the Department of Defense. Summa also spends more than $100 million on community care programs each year.

Financial Performance

Summa reported revenues of about $1.6 billion in 2012. The organization estimates that it makes a $2.8 billion business impact on the Ohio economy as well as a $99 million impact on the state government's revenue.

Strategy

Summa has conducted growth efforts in recent years to expand its presence and service offerings in the region through organic growth efforts and partnership formations. For instance the organization opened a new Summa Rehab Hospital through a partnership with Vibra; the $25 million facility consists of a 70000-sq. ft. freestanding medical building. The Summa network also invested in expanding new emergency care clinics in Green and Medina and it consolidated its home health and hospice organizations to improve profitability.

Also in 2012 Summa formed a joint management services organization with two affiliated physician organizations: Community Health Care and Pioneer Physicians Network. Together the organizations aim to streamline clinical processes.

In 2013 Summa also entered talks to form a partnership with hospital group Catholic Health Partners (CHP). The strategic partnership would give CHP a minority stake in the Summa network. Through the deal Summa hopes to expand its strategic initiatives and strengthen its finances.

Summa invests heavily in the latest technology continually seeking out the latest treatment options for some of today's most serious medical conditions. Company BackgroundThe company was formed in 1989 through the merger of Akron City Hospital and St. Thomas Hospital.

EXECUTIVES

SVP and Chief Medical Officer, Erik Steele
SVP and COO SummaCare, Claude Vincenti
SVP and CIO, Gregory Kall
SVP and COO, Valerie Gibson
SVP and Chief Nursing Officer, Lanie Ward
SVP and CFO, Brian Derrick
President and Chief Development Officer Summa Foundation, Phylis Ferrara
President and CEO, Thomas Malone, age 58
President Summa Physicians, Lydia Cook
President NewHealth Collaborative, Mark Terpylak
SVP Hospital Operations and Site Administration, Jason Niehaus
SVP Strategy and Performance Management, Ben Sutton
Vice President, Robert Kent
Medical Director, Stephen (Steve) Fannin
Medical Director, Stephen (Steve) Heupler
Medical Director, Mark Iler
Medical Director, Joseph (Jo) Restivo
Vice President of Sales and Marketing, Shawn Johnson
Vice President Integrated Innovations and Strategy, Benjamin (Ben) Sutton
Vice President, Kathy Blake
Medical Director, Kevin H Silver
Medical Director of Clinical Research, Otto Costantini
Senior Vice President, David Biats
Director Of Medical Records, Dianna Earnest

Medical Director, Marvin Cohen
Medical Director, Ihsan Haque
Chairman, James McIlvaine
Secretary, Donna Hinkle
Secretary, Dawn Pamer
Secretary, Jessica Nickles
Secretary, Teresa Murphy
Secretary, Susanne Kerrigan
Secretary, Winifred Kelleher
Secretary, Christina Thompson
Auditors: ERNST & YOUNG US LLP INDIANAP

LOCATIONS

HQ: SUMMA HEALTH SYSTEM
  95 ARCH ST STE G50, AKRON, OH 443041477
Phone: 330 375-3000
Web: WWW.SUMMAHEALTH.ORG

PRODUCTS/OPERATIONS

2012 Payers

	% of total
Medicare	47
Commercial/Managed care/Other	31
Medicaid	15
Self-pay	7
Total	**100**

Selected Ohio Facilities

Hospitals
  Akron City Hospital (Akron)
  Barberton Hospital (Barberton)
  Cuyahoga Falls General Hospital (aka Western Reserve
    Hospital Cuyahoga Falls)
  Robinson Memorial Hospital (affiliate Ravenna)
  St. Thomas Hospital (Akron)
  Wadsworth-Rittman Hospital (Wadsworth)
Other facilities
  Crystal Clinic Orthopaedic Center (Akron)
  Natatorium Rehabilitation and Wellness Center
    (Cuyahoga Falls)
  Summa Health Center at Cuyahoga Falls (Cuyahoga
    Falls)
  Summa Health Center at Green (Uniontown)
  Summa Health Center at Lake Medina
  Summa Health Center at Western Reserve (Hudson)
  Summa Health Center at White Pond/Park West
    (Akron)
  Summa Rehabilitation Services at White Pond (Akron)
  Summa Wellness Institute at Western Reserve
    (Hudson)
  Specialty Surgery Center (Akron)

COMPETITORS

Akron Children' s Hospital	Mercy Medical Center (OH)
Akron General Health System	Parma Community General Hospital
Aultman Health Foundation	Regency Hospital
Humana Health Plan of Ohio	The Cleveland Clinic
	Trinity Health System
Kaiser Foundation Health Plan of Ohio	United Healthcare of Ohio
Lake Health	University Hospitals Health System
Medical Mutual	

HISTORICAL FINANCIALS

Company Type: Private

Income Statement

	REVENUE ($ mil.)	NET INCOME ($ mil.)	NET PROFIT MARGIN	EMPLOYEES
12/09	168	6	3.8%	7,406
12/08	1,264	(75)	—	—
12/07	940	71	7.6%	—
12/06	797	0	—	—
Annual Growth	(40.4%)	—	—	—

FYE: December 31

2009 Year-End Financials

Return on assets: —
Return on equity: 3.8%
Current ratio: —
Cash ($ mil.): 28

SUMMIT ELECTRIC SUPPLY CO. INC

SUMMIT continues its ascent within the electronics distribution sector. SUMMIT Electric Supply distributes goods from manufacturers such as Dialight Eaton Fluke and Thomas & Betts. Products include cable conduits switches fuses lamps light fixtures instruments and safety equipment. The company offers in-house marine cable braiding for offshore oil and gas customers. SUMMIT also sells to electrical contractors government agencies construction firms and public utilities. It has nearly 25 branches located in New Mexico Arizona Louisiana Oklahoma and Texas and a service center in Dubai.

Geographic Reach

SUMMIT has locations in about 25 locations across Arizona Louisiana New Mexico Oklahoma and Texas. It also has a marine division based in New Orleans a Latin American sales office and a service center in Dubai UAE.

Sales and Marketing

The company caters to the construction; engineering; maintenance repair and operation (MRO); original equipment manufacturer; government; oil and gas exploration; petrochemical; and mining industries. Summit ships its products into 75 countries around the world.

Financial Performance

SUMMIT's sales have rebounded from the drubbing they took during the global economic downturn when electrical wholesalers were hit hard as construction slowed and businesses cut back on expansion plans. Indeed SUMMIT's 2012 sales exceeded their pre-recession high. The $385 million in sales the electrical wholesaler rang up in 2012 was a 7% increase vs. the prior year.

The next year it generated about $$406 million in annual revenue an increase of 5%. The growth for 2013 was due to expansion of its operations fueled by the acquisition of Central Electrical Supply. The company is also benefiting from its aggressive expansion in such growth markets as Latin America and the Middle East.

Strategy

In order to grow SUMMIT launched new facilities in key growth regions. Throughout 2012 it opened new service centers in Waynoka Oklahoma; Kenedy Texas; Pearsall Texas; and Abilene Texas. In 2013 the company opened a new Victoria Texas-based service center.

Mergers and Acquisitions

In an effort to grow its level of service in East Texas and provide better coverage to the Bryan/College Station electrical communities SUMMIT in 2013 acquired Central Electrical Supply a Bryan Texas-based wholesale distributor.

EXECUTIVES

President and CEO, Victor R. Jury
Service Center Leader Albuquerque and Santa Fe, Wiley Shaw
Regional VP Southwest Region, Scott Cogan
Service Center Leader Farmington, Kenneth King
Service Center Leader Corpus Christi and Kenedy, Ted Mendoza
Service Center Leader Fort Worth and Waynoka, Richard Efurd
VP Operations, Cole Harrison
Director Marine Division, Ed Dowey
VP IT and CIO, David Wascom
Regional VP Gulf Coast Region, Dan Ferrari
Service Center Leader Phoenix, Craig Rusk
Service Center Leader San Antonio and Pearsall, Allen O'Dell
Service Center Leader Clute, Steve Lincoln
Service Center Leader El Paso, Chris Gallegos
Service Center Leader Houston, Rodney Ilseng
Director EP&C Division, Ralph Mouret
Service Center Leader Austin, Jack Cogwin
Service Center Leader Broussard, Leland M. Sonnier
Service Center Leader Bryan College Station, Jim Suttle
Service Center Leader Dallas and Waco, Todd Bockenfeld
Service Center Leader Gonzales, Chip Shows
Director International Division, Will Gonzalez
VP Finance and CFO, Thomas Klemp
Vice President Of Sales, Jack Barnes
National Account Manager, Jon Borgeson
Auditors: REDW LLC ALBUQUERQUE NEW ME

LOCATIONS

HQ: SUMMIT ELECTRIC SUPPLY CO. INC
  2900 STANFORD DR NE, ALBUQUERQUE, NM
  871071814
Phone: 505 346-2900
Web: WWW.SUMMIT.COM

PRODUCTS/OPERATIONS

Selected Products

Ballasts
Box hangers
Brackets
Cable
Chemicals
Conduit
Drills
Enclosures
Fasteners
Fuses and fuse kits
Gaskets
Gloves
Goggles
Hand tools
Installation tools
Junction boxes
Lamps (HID and incandescent)
Light fixtures
Lubricants
Outlet boxes
PVC pipe
Power tools
Raceway
Receptacles
Safety equipment
Saws
Screws
Switches
Terminals
Test equipment
Transformers
Uninterruptible power supplies
Wire
Wire guards

COMPETITORS

Border States Electric	Kirby Risk
Consolidated Electrical	Rexel Inc.
Crescent Electric Supply	Sonepar USA
Graybar Electric	Stuart C. Irby
Hisco	W.W. Grainger
	WESCO International

HISTORICAL FINANCIALS

Company Type: Private

Income Statement

FYE: December 31

	REVENUE ($ mil.)	NET INCOME ($ mil.)	NET PROFIT MARGIN	EMPLOYEES
12/13	405	12	3.1%	497
12/12	384	10	2.6%	—
12/11	358	7	2.1%	—
12/10	301	0	—	—
Annual Growth	10.4%	—	—	—

2013 Year-End Financials

Return on assets: 8.9% Cash ($ mil.): 1
Return on equity: 3.1%
Current ratio: 1.20

SUMMIT HEALTH

Auditors: SMITH ELLIOTT KEARNS & COMPANY

LOCATIONS

HQ: SUMMIT HEALTH
112 N 7TH ST, CHAMBERSBURG, PA 172011720
Phone: 717 267-3000
Web: WWW.SUMMITHEALTH.ORG

HISTORICAL FINANCIALS

Company Type: Private

Income Statement

FYE: June 30

	REVENUE ($ mil.)	NET INCOME ($ mil.)	NET PROFIT MARGIN	EMPLOYEES
06/13	424	69	16.4%	2,150
06/12	393	(39)	—	—
06/11	401	53	13.4%	—
06/08	333	0	—	—
Annual Growth	4.9%	—	—	—

2013 Year-End Financials

Return on assets: 1.9% Cash ($ mil.): 41
Return on equity: 16.4%
Current ratio: 1.20

SUMMIT MATERIALS LLC

Auditors: KPMG LLP MCLEAN VIRGINIA

LOCATIONS

HQ: SUMMIT MATERIALS LLC
1550 WYNKOOP ST FL 3, DENVER, CO 802021130
Phone: 303 893-0012
Web: WWW.SUMMIT-MATERIALS.COM

HISTORICAL FINANCIALS

Company Type: Private

Income Statement

FYE: December 27

	REVENUE ($ mil.)	NET INCOME ($ mil.)	NET PROFIT MARGIN	EMPLOYEES
12/14	1,204	(6)	—	3,300
12/13	916	(103)	—	—
Annual Growth	31.4%	—	—	—

2014 Year-End Financials

Return on assets: 6.5% Cash ($ mil.): 13
Return on equity: (-0.5%)
Current ratio: 0.70

SUN COAST RESOURCES INC.

Breaking the glass ceiling with large containers of Texas tea woman-owned Sun Coast Resources buys refined oil and sells it to more than 10000 third-party customers such airlines and construction educational energy industrial and retail companies in about 40 states. The company has an extensive truck fleet (more than 1000 vehicles) and delivers gasoline and diesel fuels marine and aviation fuels and lubricants. It also provides oilfield transportation and services onsite and fleet fueling petroleum tanks and generator fueling services. In 2013 the Houston Chronicle ranked Sun Coast as the 8th largest private company based in Houston.

Geographic Reach

Sun Coast owns and operates 18 offices in Arkansas New Mexico Mississippi Oklahoma Texas and Louisiana. It also has more than of 350000 sq. ft. of office and warehouse space in nine facilities in Texas. It markets its products in 40 US states. Sun Coast also provides equipment and services in fast-growing shale plays including the Eagle Ford Eagle Ford Bryan Permian Haynesville Cline Woodford and Marcellus.

Operations

Sun Coast carries a full line of Chevron oils and lubricants and is one of Chevron's largest lubricant distributors in the US. Other Sun Coast services include additive packages bulk storage and warehousing a computerized fleet tracking system and customized schedule and deliveries. The company has 1.5 million gallons of bulk fuel storage more than 10000 fuel and lubricant tanks including skid tanks aviation certified tanks emergency ISO tanks and others. Its truck fleet includes bobtails lowboys lube trucks pick-ups roll-backs and vacuum trucks.

Its transport trucks are capable of hauling 7500 gallons of diesel fuel and 8600 gallons of gasoline. Its bobtails are used for orders of less than 4500 gallons. Sun Coast's lubricant trucks are capable of hauling 2000 gallons of bulk lubricants as well as drums totes and other packaged products.

The company's products include aviation gasoline (avgas) gasoline jet fuel kerosene marine diesel ultra-low sulfur diesel fuel and Chevron Conoco Mystik Phillips 66 and TOTAL lubrication products. It also offers services card lock service filtration and fluid purification fleet fueling and mobile on-site fueling spill response and other services.

Sun Coast's crude/condensate segment serves more than 300 well sites and numerous gathering facilities and transports more 37000 barrels per day (more than 10 million barrels a year).

Sales and Marketing

Sun Coast provides fuel supply services and related equipment to communication companies delivery services firms government entities utilities and other fleet operators.

Financial Performance

Buoyed by higher oil prices and the rapid growth of company assets in 2013 Sun Coast's revenues rose to $2 billion up from $1.94 billion in 2012.

Strategy

The company pursues a strategy of organic growth supplemented by complementary acquisitions in its core geographic markets.

Mergers and Acquisitions

It expanded into Louisiana in 2012 with the purchase of St. Martin Oil and Gas which operated a small fleet of fuel transportation trucks from two bulk storage facilities in St. Martinville and Denham Springs.

Further expanding its portfolio in 2012 the company acquired assets from bankrupt SMF Energy including its wholly owned affiliate H&W Petroleum Co. Properties included more than 100 fuel trucks and support vehicles previously used by SMF's mobile refueling operations outside of Texas and about 100 fuel and chemical transportation and support vehicles from H&W its Lufkin blending facility and fuel storage tanks across Texas.

That year Sun Coast further expanded its branded and unbranded fuel and lubricant distribution business by buying Houston-based ADA Resources.

Company Background

In 2011 the company bought the commercial fuel and disaster response businesses of Cypress Texas-based Roy Moffitt Customized Fueling.

Sun Coast was founded in 1985 by president and CEO Kathy Lehne with $2000 in start-up capital.

EXECUTIVES

CEO, Kathy Lehne
VP Sales and Marketing, Kyle Lehne
Director Information Technology, Bryan Frazier
President and CFO, Sheila Kahanek
Operations Manager, Larry Bothmann

LOCATIONS

HQ: SUN COAST RESOURCES INC.
6405 CAVALCADE ST BLDG 1, HOUSTON, TX 770264315
Phone: 713 844-9600
Web: WWW.SUNCOASTRESOURCES.COM

PRODUCTS/OPERATIONS

Selected Products

Petroleum Products
  Aviation gasoline
  High sulfur diesel fuel
  Jet fuel
  Kerosene
  Lubricants
  Marine fuels
  Mid-grade fuel
  Low sulfur diesel fuel
  Premium low sulfur diesel fuel
  Premium unleaded gasoline
  Unleaded gasoline
Oils and Lubricants
  Automatic transmission fluid
  Chain oils
  Food-grade oils
  Fuel Additives
  Gear oils
  Greases
  Heat transfer oils
  Hydraulic oils
  Metal-working oils
  Motor oils
  Refrigeration oils
  Solvents and chemicals

Selected Mergers and Acquisitions

COMPETITORS

George Warren	Martin Resource
Global Partners	Management
Gulf Oil	Mercury Air Group
J.A.M. Distributing	

HISTORICAL FINANCIALS

Company Type: Private

Income Statement

FYE: December 31

	REVENUE ($ mil.)	NET INCOME ($ mil.)	NET PROFIT MARGIN	EMPLOYEES
12/07	1,064	2	0.3%	1,649
12/06	864	7	0.8%	—
12/05	867	13	1.6%	—
12/04	697	0	—	—
Annual Growth	15.1%	—	—	—

2007 Year-End Financials

Return on assets: 2.6%
Return on equity: 0.3%
Current ratio: 3.10

Cash ($ mil.): —

SUN MAR MANAGEMENT SERVICES

LOCATIONS

HQ: SUN MAR MANAGEMENT SERVICES
3050 SATURN ST STE 201, BREA, CA 928216278
Phone: 714 577-3880
Web: WWW.SUN-MAR.COM

HISTORICAL FINANCIALS

Company Type: Private

Income Statement

FYE: March 31

	REVENUE ($ mil.)	NET INCOME ($ mil.)	NET PROFIT MARGIN	EMPLOYEES
03/09*	742	0	0.1%	395
12/08		6	(0)	—	—
Annual Growth	**********%			

*Fiscal year change

SUN-MAID GROWERS OF CALIFORNIA

The Sun-Maid's basket runneth over. Sun-Maid Growers is the producer of Sun-Maid Raisins. Packaged in the familiar red boxes with the smiling red-sunbonneted maid Lorraine Collett Petersen offering her basket laden with grapes the brand is seen in just about every food store in the US. In addition to offering every toddler's (and moms of toddlers) favorite little-red-boxed snack the grower-owned cooperative manufactures industrial and food service products and exports to more than 50 countries. The company's other dried fruits include pitted prunes currants apricots cranberries figs dates apples fruit bits and tropical fruit mixtures. Founded in 1912 the coop is owned by 750 family farmers.

Geographic Reach

Headquartered in Kingsburg California Sun-Maid's facilities are located in California's Central Valley —the world's largest raisin producing area

—where vineyards belonging to some 750 family farmers span approximately 50000 acres.

Operations

Sun-Maid whose growers harvest some 200 million pounds of grapes every year also licenses its brand for products including raisin bread raisin muffins and raisin cookie mix as well as chocolate- and vanilla yogurt-covered raisins. Retail products make up about half of the co-op's sales; ingredient products comprise the rest.

Sales and Marketing

In 2013 Sun-Maid Growers hired San Francisco-based Baker Street Advertising as its agency of record. The agency's responsibilities for the brand include marketing strategy research and creative development for advertising and communications across all media channels including broadcast print online social media and event marketing.

EXECUTIVES

Vice President Distillery and By Products, Charles (Chas) Feaver
Vice President Of Sales, Tomo Naito
Vice President, Rick Bruno
Vice President Customer Service, John (Jack) Slinkard
Auditors: DELOITTE & TOUCHE LLP FRESNO

LOCATIONS

HQ: SUN-MAID GROWERS OF CALIFORNIA
13525 S BETHEL AVE, KINGSBURG, CA 936319212
Phone: 559 897-6235
Web: WWW.SUNMAID.COM

PRODUCTS/OPERATIONS

Selected Products

Bakery
  Oatmeal raisin cookie mix
  Raisin bread
  Raisin muffins
Dried apples
Dried California apricots
Dried Calimyrna figs
Dried chopped dates
Dried cranberries
Dried fruit bits
Dried golden raisins and cherries
Dried Mediterranean apricots
Dried mission figs
Dried mixed fruit
Dried pitted dates
Dried pitted plums
Dried tropical trio
Raisins
  Baking raisins
  Chocolate yogurt-covered raisins
  Chocolate-covered raisins
  Golden raisins
  Jumbo raisins
  Vanilla yogurt-covered raisins
  Zante currents

COMPETITORS

Cherry Central Cooperative Inc.	Meridian Nut Growers
Dole Food	Multiple Organics
Encore Fruit Marketing	National Raisin
Florida Food Products Inc	Pinnacle Foods
	Riviana Foods
Fresh Del Monte Produce	Shoreline Fruit
	SunOpta
General Mills	Sunview Vineyards
Gold Harbor	Tree Top
Golden West Nuts	Tropical Nut & Fruit
Graceland Fruit	United Natural
Kendall Frozen Fruits	Valley Fig Growers
Lion Raisins	Waymouth Farms
	Welch' s

HISTORICAL FINANCIALS

Company Type: Private

Income Statement

FYE: July 31

	REVENUE ($ mil.)	NET INCOME ($ mil.)	NET PROFIT MARGIN	EMPLOYEES
07/14	389	11	3.0%	800
07/13	360	15	4.3%	—
07/12	360	8	2.3%	—
07/11	352	0	—	—
Annual Growth	3.4%	—	—	—

2014 Year-End Financials

Return on assets: 8.0%
Return on equity: 3.0%
Current ratio: 0.30

Cash ($ mil.): —

SUNDT CONSTRUCTION INC.

LOCATIONS

HQ: SUNDT CONSTRUCTION INC.
2620 S 55TH ST, TEMPE, AZ 852821903
Phone: 480 293-3000
Web: WWW.SUNDT.COM

HISTORICAL FINANCIALS

Company Type: Private

Income Statement

FYE: September 30

	REVENUE ($ mil.)	NET INCOME ($ mil.)	NET PROFIT MARGIN	EMPLOYEES
09/14	823	0	—	1,000
09/13	895	0	—	—
09/12	0	0	—	—
09/11	0	0	—	—
Annual Growth	—	—	—	—

2014 Year-End Financials

Return on assets: 16.7%
Return on equity: —
Current ratio: 1.40

Cash ($ mil.): 115

SUNFLOWER ELECTRIC POWER CORPORATION

Rural Kansans bloom under the light provided by Sunflower Electric Power an electricity generation and transmission cooperative. The utility has interests in six fossil-fueled generation facilities (600 MW of capacity) and operates a more-than-1150-mile transmission system with 76 substations. Sunflower Electric Power provides electricity to its owners six member distribution cooperatives which collectively have more than 51000 customers in western Kansas; it also indirectly serves a further 10000 meters as wholesale power suppliers to regional cities and towns.

Expanding its geographic coverage in 2007 Sunflower Electric Power purchased the Kansas electric properties of Aquila. In 2009 the Kansas Corporation Commission approved ITC Great

Plains' plan to build a 345 kV transmission line extending 89 miles between Spearville and Hays. In addition to increasing power supply to Sunflower Electric Power's customers in Western Kansas the new line offers infrastructure support for the development of wind farms in the region a growth industry in the area.

Sunflower Electric Power was organized in 1957 to provide reliable long-term power supply to its six member distribution cooperatives at the lowest possible costs.

EXECUTIVES

Vice President Power Supply Delivery, Corey
Linville
Auditors: KPMG LLP KANSAS CITY MISSOUR

LOCATIONS

HQ: SUNFLOWER ELECTRIC POWER CORPORATION
301 W 13TH ST, HAYS, KS 676013087
Phone: 785 628-2845
Web: WWW.SUNFLOWER.NET

COMPETITORS

AES
Constellation Energy
Group

HISTORICAL FINANCIALS

Company Type: Private

Income Statement				FYE: December 31
	REVENUE ($ mil.)	NET INCOME ($ mil.)	NET PROFIT MARGIN	EMPLOYEES
12/10	213	21	10.2%	215
12/09	195	16	8.2%	—
12/08	1,440	0	0.0%	—
Annual Growth	(61.5%)	15493.7%	—	—

2010 Year-End Financials

Return on assets: 3.8%   Cash ($ mil.): 17
Return on equity: 10.2%
Current ratio: 0.90

SUNKIST GROWERS INC.

Sunkist Growers is one business that is least susceptible to an outbreak of scurvy among its employees. America's oldest continually operating citrus cooperative the company is owned by California and Arizona citrus growers who farm some 300000 acres of citrus trees. Sunkist offers traditional and organic fresh oranges lemons limes grapefruit and tangerines worldwide. The co-op which operates some 20 packing facilities also makes juice and cut fruit packaged in jars. Fruit that doesn't meet fresh market standards is turned into oils and peels for use in food products made by other manufacturers. Sunkist's customers include food retailers and manufacturers and foodservice providers worldwide.

Geographic Reach

California-based Sunkist operates in the Americas Europe the Middle East and Asia Pacific.

Sales and Marketing

Sunkist regularly advertises worldwide to encourage use of its citrus products and build its brand. Additionally the company leverages television to get its name out such as its alliance with the NBC motivational weight loss competition The Biggest Loser.

Sunkist which has operated a centralized sales organization since 2009 sells its products primarily to food retailers and manufacturers as well as to foodservice providers worldwide. The company is the largest marketing cooperative in the global fruit and vegetable industry.

Financial Performance

Gross annual sales of Sunkist-brand products exceed $1.2 billion worldwide.

Operations

The cooperative's seasonal citrus includes Meyer lemons mandarin oranges Clementine oranges blood oranges and tangelos. Sunkist is one of the most recognized brand names in the world.

Through some 40 licensing agreements the Sunkist name appears on more than 600 beverages and other products –from vitamins to candy to soda to pistachios. It offers Sunkist Fruit Gems (gummie candies) made for the company by the Jelly Belly Candy Company.

Some 45% of Sunkist's fresh fruit sales revenues come from markets outside the US as well as more than 20% of its processed products revenues. To maintain its reach abroad Sunkist works with the US government and the governments of foreign countries to open new markets that are off limits to Western citrus growers.

Strategy

The company has been focused on market and portfolio expansion and getting the most from its citrus juice and oils and for-profit businesses. It is working to extend its reach to new markets such as India the Middle East and Eastern Europe where its core product has not historically been traded. To reach beyond citrus and expand its products portfolio Sunkist is concentrating on table grapes. Through a pilot program with its existing citrus growers the company markets Sunkist-branded California table grapes grown by them.

It also worked in recent years to improve the productivity of its Tipton juice processing plant. To this end Sunkist in 2012 entered a 50:50 joint venture agreement with fellow juice processor Ventura Coastal. Under the name Ventura Coastal LLC the entity operates the Ventura Coastal plant in Visalia and the Sunkist plant in Tipton. Beginning in 2013 Sunkist also partnered with Greene River Marketing to sell its Florida citrus in promising domestic and export markets.

The 2011-2012 growing season got off to a late start thanks to slow maturing fruit. Its navel orange crop grew to a manageable 88 million cartons as compared to a challenging 93-million-carton crop the previous year. Lemons started slowly as well but both demand and price picked up. Protected groves fared well during the year while unprotected ones –those outside the traditional growing areas –did not. More susceptible to the cold mandarins crops have suffered.

HISTORY

Sunkist Growers was founded in the early 1890s as the Pachappa Orange Growers a group of California citrus farmers determined to control the sale of their fruit. Success attracted new members and in 1893 the Southern California Fruit Exchange was born. The name "Sunkissed" was coined by an ad copywriter in 1908 and it was soon reworked into "Sunkist" and registered as a trademark becoming the first brand name for a fresh produce item. Eventually the co-op renamed itself after its popular brand: It became Sunkist Growers in 1952. Sunkist began licensing its trademark to other companies in the early 1950s.

As early as 1916 efforts to increase citrus consumption included designing and marketing glass citrus juicers and encouraging homemakers to "Drink an Orange." The co-op also promoted the practice of putting lemon slices in tea or water and funded early research on the health benefits of vitamins (vitamin C in particular). In 1925 tissue wrappers gave way to stamping the Sunkist name directly on each piece of fruit.

Although Sunkist pioneered bottled orange juice in 1933 its juice marketing efforts were never as successful as those of its Florida competitors. Florida oranges are drippy and dowdy and thus better suited for juicing. Capitalizing on this aspect Florida growers dominated the market for fresh and frozen juice.

In 1937 Congress created a system of citrus shipment quotas and limits (known as "marketing orders") that ultimately proved most beneficial to large citrus cooperatives. By the early 1990s the marketing order system was under political attack and in 1992 the Justice Department filed civil prosecution against Sunkist alleging that the co-op had reaped unfair extra profits by surpassing its lemon shipment limits. In 1994 after much legal wrangling the quotas were abolished and the Justice Department dropped its case against Sunkist.

Inconveniently warm weather and increasing competition from imported citrus marked the harvests of 1996. That year the co-op had trouble maintaining discipline among its members; some undercut Sunkist price levels while others flooded the market to sell their fruit at the higher early market prices creating a supply surplus. Also that year the co-op relinquished the marketing of all Sunkist juices in North America to Florida-based Lykes Bros. in a licensing agreement.

The co-op agreed in 1998 to distribute grapefruit from Florida's Tuxedo Fruit providing Sunkist with a winter grapefruit supply and increasing its year-round consumer a-peel. Also in 1998 Russell Hanlin Sunkist president and CEO since 1978 was succeeded by Vince Lupinacci. Lupinacci who had held positions with Pepsi and Six Flags became the first person from outside the citrus business to hold Sunkist's top post.

In 1998 the company sold 90 million cartons of fresh citrus –the greatest volume in its history –despite increased competition from imported Latin American South African and Spanish crops a damaging California freeze and the ill effects of El Niño. The next year production was almost halved because of adverse weather.

Lupinacci resigned in 2000 citing personal and family reasons. Chairman emeritus James Mast then took the helm as acting president. Although the company grew its market through exports to China in 2000 its profits were squeezed that year by increasing foreign competition a citrus glut and lessened demand. In mid-2001 Jeff Gargiulo replaced Mast as Sunkist's president and CEO.

In 2003 Sunkist formed a joint venture with strawberry shipper Coastal Berry Co. to market strawberries under the Sunkist label year-round. (Coastal Berry's president and CEO John Gargiulo and Sunkist's former president and CEO Jeff Gargiulo are brothers.) Also that year Sunkist began offering pre-cut bagged fruit to retail customers and restaurants in order to keep up with a changing market and consumer demand.

In retrospect 2006 was an eventful year for Sunkist. The co-op's largest producer and 16-year-member Paramount Citrus Association left the organization. In addition chairman and CEO David Krause stepped down and president Jeff Gargiulo left the company. Krause was replaced as chairman by Nicholas Bozick president of produce grower/packer Richard Bagdasarian Inc. Sunkist veteran and former president of Fruit Growers Supply Company Timothy Lindgren was appointed president and CEO. And citing expense as the determining factor the co-op discontinued marketing berries (strawberries blueberries and raspberries) in 2006. Lindgren retired in 2008; he was replaced by EVP Russ Hanlin.

EXECUTIVES

Managing Director Sunkist Global, Michael Nomoto
Senior Vice President, Al Cachofa

LOCATIONS

HQ: SUNKIST GROWERS INC.
14130 RIVERSIDE DR, SHERMAN OAKS, CA
914232392
Phone: 818 986-4800
Web: WWW.SUNKIST.COM

PRODUCTS/OPERATIONS

Selected Products
Fresh fruit
  Grapefruit
    Melo Golds
    Oro Blancos
    Pummelos
    Sweeties
    Texas Rio Star
    Western
  Lemons
    Eureka/Lisbon
    Meyer
  Limes
    Key
    Persian
  Mandarins
    Clementine
    Honey
    Royal
    Satsuma
    Shasta Gold
  W. Murcott
  Oranges
    Cara Cara
    Moro
    Navel
    Valencia
    Tangelos
    Minneola
    Orlando
    Tangerines
    Dancy
    Fairchild
    Pixie
Packaged fruit
  Beverage concentrates
  Carbonated beverages (under license)
  Chilled fruit jellies (under license)
  Fruit juice
  Fruit juice drinks
  Fruit snacks (under license)
  Powdered fruit drinks
  Vitamins (under license)

COMPETITORS

Alico Inc.	Lionel Hitchen
Big Heart Pet Brands	Louis Dreyfus Group
Chiquita Brands	M&B Products
Citrus World	Old Orchard
Coca-Cola	Orchard House Foods
Dole Food	R & Z Ventures
Dundee Citrus Growers	Silver Springs
Edinburg Citrus	Southern Gardens
Fresh Del Monte	Citrus
Produce	Sunny Delight
Freshco	Tropicana
Great Western Juice	U.S. Sugar
King Ranch	Wonderful Company
Lake Placid Groves	

HISTORICAL FINANCIALS

Company Type: Private

Income Statement — FYE: October 31

	REVENUE ($ mil.)	NET INCOME ($ mil.)	NET PROFIT MARGIN	EMPLOYEES
10/14	1,234	6	0.5%	500
10/13	1,046	33	3.2%	—
10/12*	1,003	6	0.6%	—
12/09	0	0	—	—
Annual Growth	—	—	—	—

---

*Fiscal year change

2014 Year-End Financials

Return on assets: 1.2%   Cash ($ mil.): 2
Return on equity: 0.5%
Current ratio: 1.10

SUNRUN INSTALLATION SERVICES INC.

REC Solar is helping its customers to say "So long!" to fossil fuel-buring power dependence. The company designs and installs solar electric systems for residential small commercial government and utilty customers in six states —Arizona California Colorado Hawaii New Jersey and Oregon. Its systems range from simple rooftop panel displays for residential customers to industrial solar electric systems for Costco. REC Solar uses solar panels manufactured by Kyocera Mitsubishi Sanyo and Sharp and components by Satcon SMA Solar Technology and Xantrex.

Geographic Reach

REC Solar serves customers in Arizona California Colorado Hawaii New Jersey and Oregon.

Strategy

The company is focused on making solar power affordable and simple and specializes in residential business government and utility projects offering a local presence in all major solar markets in the US. Since its founding in 1997 REC Solar has installed more than 8000 systems nationwide (with more than 100 MW of total capacity).

In 2012 REC Solar established itself as one of the top solar companies in Florida's emerging solar market with work on five installations at IKEA and Department of Veteran's Affairs Medical Center locations totaling almost 5 MW. All told REC Solar has installed solar panels at 13 IKEA locations across the US.

Ownership

Investment group Mainstream Energy owns both REC Solar and AEE Solar.

EXECUTIVES

CEO, Paul J. Detering
CFO, Betsy Wallace
VP Sales and Marketing, Mark Bettis
Auditors: KPMG SAN FRANSCISCO CA

LOCATIONS

HQ: SUNRUN INSTALLATION SERVICES INC.
775 FIERO LN STE 200, SAN LUIS OBISPO, CA
934017904
Phone: 805 528-9705
Web: WWW.RECSOLAR.COM

PRODUCTS/OPERATIONS

Utility Services
Development
  Co-development support
  Engineering and design
  Financing Option
Construction
  Project Management
  Procurement and logistics
  Full turnkey installation
Operation
  On-going service and support
  Full Operations and maintenance service
  System monitoring
Business/Government Services
Development
  Feasibility

Engineering and design
  Financing and Incentives
Construction
  Project Management
  Sourcing and Procurement
  Installation
Operation
  Operations and Maintenance
  System monitoring
  Solar marketing and PR

COMPETITORS

Andalay Solar	Real Goods Solar
Conergy Inc.	SolarCraft Services
Entech Solar	

HISTORICAL FINANCIALS

Company Type: Private

Income Statement — FYE: December 31

	REVENUE ($ mil.)	NET INCOME ($ mil.)	NET PROFIT MARGIN	EMPLOYEES
12/08*	155	(3)	—	350
04/06	5	1	24.8%	—
Annual Growth	200.5%	—	—	—

*Fiscal year change

2008 Year-End Financials

Return on assets: 10.7%   Cash ($ mil.): 11
Return on equity: (-2.2%)
Current ratio: 1.00

SUNSWEET GROWERS INC.

Being all dried up is a good thing at Sunsweet Growers. The more than 400 member/grower-owned cooperative processes and markets dried fruit. Sunsweet produces one-third of the world's prunes (it processes more than 50000 tons of prunes each year). Its other fruit products include prune and other juices as well as dried apples apricots dates cranberries blueberries mangoes peaches pears pineapples and more. Sunsweet which has gotten into dietary supplement beverages supplies its products to retail food and foodservice outlets worldwide. Sunsweet produces some 40000 cases of dried fruit products every day. The co-op was founded in 1917 as the California Prune and Apricot Growers Association.StrategyTo diversify its business and give its bottom line a boost Sunsweet in 2011 acquired California-based Function Drinks known for making functional beverages that have added nutrition. As part of the transaction Sunsweet rolled Function Drinks into a newly formed subsidiary Disruptive Beverages Inc. (DBI). The cooperative is using DBI as the foundation for expanding its beverages portfolio.

EXECUTIVES

Vice President, Deb Macias
Secretary, Mark Ramos
Auditors: MOSS ADAMS LLP STOCKTON CALI

LOCATIONS

HQ: SUNSWEET GROWERS INC.
901 N WALTON AVE, YUBA CITY, CA 959939370
Phone: 530 674-5010
Web: WWW.SUNSWEET.COM

PRODUCTS/OPERATIONS

Selected Products and Brands

Juices
  Amazing Prune Light
  Juicers
  PlumSmart
  PlumSmart Light
  Prune Juice
  Prune Juice with Pulp
Prunes
  60 CALORIE PACKS
  Amazins
  BITE SIZE PRUNES
  D' NOIR PRUNES
  ESSENCE
  Lighter Bake
  PREMIUM PRUNES
  WHOLE PRUNES
Specialty Fruits
  Antioxidant Blend
  Berry Blend
  Blueberries
  Cherries
  Cranberries
  Dates
  Jumbo Red Raisins
  Mediterranean Apricots
  Philippine Mangos
  Philippine Pineapple
  PlumSweets

COMPETITORS

Big Heart Pet Brands	Ocean Spray
Cherry Central	Pro-Fac
Cooperative Inc.	Seneca Foods
Chiquita Brands	Shoreline Fruit
Dole Food	Stewart & Jasper
Fresh Del Monte	Orchards
Produce	Sunkist
Graceland Fruit	Tropical Nut & Fruit
Maui Land & Pineapple	Valley Fig Growers
Meridian Nut Growers	Waymouth Farms
Naturipe Farms	

HISTORICAL FINANCIALS
Company Type: Private

Income Statement
FYE: July 31

	REVENUE ($ mil.)	NET INCOME ($ mil.)	NET PROFIT MARGIN	EMPLOYEES
07/14	261	81	31.3%	700
07/13	266	71	26.7%	—
07/12	281	64	22.8%	—
07/11	245	0	—	—
Annual Growth	2.1%	—	—	—

2014 Year-End Financials
Return on assets: 8.5%   Cash ($ mil.): 7
Return on equity: 31.3%
Current ratio: 0.40

SUPERIOR BULK LOGISTICS INC.

Superior Bulk Logistics through subsidiaries Superior Carriers and Carry Transit hauls liquid and dry bulk cargo including both chemical and food-grade products. Overall the trucking units of Superior Bulk Logistics operate a fleet of some 875 tractors and 2000 trailers. The company's SuperFlo unit provides transloading services —the transfer of cargo between railcars and trucks. Superior Bulk Logistics' Sanicare Wash Systems unit cleans tank truck trailers and other bulk contain-

ers used for food products. Superior Bulk Logistics offers service between Mexico and the US and Canada through a partnership with Transpormex a division of Grupo Dexel.

Geographic Reach

Stationed in Illinois Superior Bulk Logistics delivers more than 8 billion pounds or products and provides its services in the US Canada and Mexico while driving nearly 75 million miles.

Operations

The company's subsidiaries include Superior Carriers SuperFlo and Carry Transit. Superior Carriers transports and transloads hazardous non-hazardous liquid and dry bulk chemicals throughout the US Canada and Mexico. It delivers over 5 billion pounds. SuperFlo provides bulk distribution services and transloads a wide range of bulk commodities liquid and dry food grade and chemicals hazardous and nonhazardous. Operating in the US Canada and Mexico Carry Transit provides transportation and transloading of liquid and dry bulk food grade kosher and pharmaceutical products. It delivers 3 billion pounds.

EXECUTIVES

Vice President Business Development, Joseph Nolan
Vice President of Operations Carry Transit, Douglas (Doug) Bell
Executive Vice President Sales, W Wes Stone

LOCATIONS

HQ: SUPERIOR BULK LOGISTICS INC.
1711 JORIE BLVD STE 101N, OAK BROOK, IL 605232285
Phone: 630 573-2555
Web: WWW.SUPERIORBULKLOGISTICS.COM

COMPETITORS

A&R Logistics	Quality Distribution
Bulkmatic	Ruan Transportation
Groendyke Transport	Management Systems
InterBulk Group	Schneider National
Kenan Advantage Group	Trimac

HISTORICAL FINANCIALS
Company Type: Private

Income Statement
FYE: December 31

	REVENUE ($ mil.)	NET INCOME ($ mil.)	NET PROFIT MARGIN	EMPLOYEES
12/09	188	2	1.1%	1,160
12/07	234	7	3.1%	—
12/06	457	0	0.0%	—
Annual Growth	(25.6%)	1546.7%	—	—

2009 Year-End Financials
Return on assets: 5.2%   Cash ($ mil.): 1
Return on equity: 1.1%
Current ratio: 0.50

SUPERIOR OIL COMPANY INC

Despite the name Superior Oil actually distributes industrial products and provides chemical and waste services. Superior's solvents and chemicals division supplies manufacturers of paints and coatings pharmaceuticals fabricated metal products and adhesives. The fiberglass and resins unit sells to clients that make products ranging from parts for recreational vehicles to bathtubs and showers.

Superior Oil also provides blending solvent reclamation and hazardous waste removal services. The company has nine stocking facilities and a fleet of trucks trailers and tankers. The company is owned by members of its management team.

EXECUTIVES

Vice President, Thomas (Thom) Fleming
Vice President, Scott Cox

LOCATIONS

HQ: SUPERIOR OIL COMPANY INC
1402 N CAPITOL AVE # 100, INDIANAPOLIS, IN 462022375
Phone: 574 264-0161
Web: WWW.SUPERIORSOLVENTS.COM

PRODUCTS/OPERATIONS

Selected Products and Services

Acetate esters
Alcohols
Aliphatic naphthas
Aromatic hydrocarbons
Caustic soda
Chelating agents
Compliance management
Equipment programs
Glycol ethers
Glycols
Heat exchange fluids
Ketones
Lacquer thinners
Paint strippers
Plasticizers
Professional waste services
Recycling programs
Regulatory services
Silicones
Technical support
Terpenes
Transportation

COMPETITORS

Aceto	ICC Chemical
Brenntag North America	Univar USA
HallStar	Wego Chemical &
Harcros Chemicals	Mineral

HISTORICAL FINANCIALS
Company Type: Private

Income Statement
FYE: December 31

	REVENUE ($ mil.)	NET INCOME ($ mil.)	NET PROFIT MARGIN	EMPLOYEES
12/13	211	0	—	250
12/12	202	0	—	—
12/11	191	0	—	—
12/10	167	0	—	—
Annual Growth	8.2%	—	—	—

2013 Year-End Financials
Return on assets: 5.4%   Cash ($ mil.): —
Return on equity: —
Current ratio: 1.00

SUTTER GOULD MEDICAL FOUNDATION

Auditors: ERNST & YOUNG US LLP ROSEVILL

LOCATIONS

HQ: SUTTER GOULD MEDICAL FOUNDATION
1700 MCHENRY AVE STE 60B, MODESTO, CA
953504333
Phone: 209 526-4500
Web: WWW.SUTTERGOULD.ORG

HISTORICAL FINANCIALS

Company Type: Private

Income Statement				FYE: December 31
	REVENUE ($ mil.)	NET INCOME ($ mil.)	NET PROFIT MARGIN	EMPLOYEES
12/11	305	(8)	—	4
12/09	288	(7)	—	
Annual Growth	2.8%			

2011 Year-End Financials

Return on assets: 0.7%   Cash ($ mil.): 23
Return on equity: (-2.6%)
Current ratio: 1.00

SUTTER MEDICAL FOUNDATION

Auditors: ERNST & YOUNG LLP ROSEVILLE

LOCATIONS

HQ: SUTTER MEDICAL FOUNDATION
2800 L ST FL 7, SACRAMENTO, CA 958165616
Phone: 916 454-6640
Web: WWW.SUTTERHEALTH.ORG

HISTORICAL FINANCIALS

Company Type: Private

Income Statement				FYE: December 31
	REVENUE ($ mil.)	NET INCOME ($ mil.)	NET PROFIT MARGIN	EMPLOYEES
12/09	505	(21)	—	700
12/02	111	(7)	—	—
12/01	679	0	—	—
Annual Growth	—	—	—	—

2009 Year-End Financials

Return on assets: —   Cash ($ mil.): 30
Return on equity: (-4.3%)
Current ratio: 0.80

SWEDISH HEALTH SERVICES

Swedish Health Services doing business as Swedish Medical Center hopes that the Swedish reputation for good health is transferred to its patients in the Pacific Northwest. The largest not-for-profit health provider in the greater Seattle area Swedish Health operates five acute care hospitals. It also runs two ambulatory care centers and the Swedish Medical Group physician practice organization which has more than 100 primary and specialty care offices in the greater Puget Sound region. Swedish Health is affiliated with Providence

Health & Services a Catholic not-for-profit organization with about 30 hospitals in five states.

Operations

Swedish Medical has more than 2800 physicians and its hospitals are home to more than 1500 beds. The network's facilities see over 57000 inpatients per year as well as 175000 emergency room visits more than 9000 births and about 39000 surgeries. Swedish Medical operates numerous institutes across its campuses including its Cancer Institute Heart and Vascular Institute Neuroscience Institute and Orthopedic Institute. Other medical specialties include transplants pediatrics and women's health.

Swedish Medical also conducts clinical research programs with as many as 700 trials being conducted at one time making it one of the largest clinical trial sites in the US. The network's research programs are supported by government and commercial partners.

Geographic Reach

Swedish Medical has three hospital locations in Seattle as well as hospitals in Edmonds and Issaquah Washington. Its ambulatory centers (with emergency and specialty facilities) are located in Redmond and Everett Washington.

Financial Performance

In 2013 the system reported $2 billion in revenue (96% of which came from patient care services) and $59 million in net operating income.

Strategy

The company grows both organically and through partnerships. Through its affiliation with Providence Health & Services Swedish Medical combined with Providence's Washington facilities under a new not-for-profit holding company. The two health systems retain their independent identities but share clinical and IT resources to work towards reducing medical costs and increasing the quality of care in the region.

The company announced a $63.5 million expansion to its Swedish Edmonds hospital campus in 2014. The two-story expansion will include a new emergency department and an outpatient diagnostic imaging center.

Also in 2014 Swedish Medical launched a hematologic malignancies program to research and treat blood-based cancers such as leukemia multiple myeloma and lymphoma.

To balance the costs of growth Swedish Medical occasionally exits underperforming businesses. In 2012 for instance the company ceased operations of its Swedish Visiting Nurse Services program which provide home health care hospice and therapy services. The unit had incurred continuous losses since 2009.

Company Background

Not-for-profit Swedish Medical began in 1910 as a single hospital with 24 beds.

EXECUTIVES

Chief Executive Swedish Suburban Hospitals and Affiliates, Marcel Loh
CEO, Anthony A. (Tony) Armada
Chief Medical Officer, John H. Vassall
CEO Issaquah, Rayburn S. Lewis
Chief Development Officer; President Swedish Medical Center Foundation, Don Theophilus
CEO Edmonds, David E. Jaffe
SVP Physician Services; Chief Executive Swedish Medical Group, Ralph Pascualy
Chief Nursing Officer; COO Swedish Seattle, June Altaras
COO, Bryan Mueller
CEO First Hill and Cherry Hill, Todd Strumwasser
CFO, Dan Harris
Chief Strategy Officer, Heidi Aylsworth
CEO Nurse Executive Ballard, Jennifer Graves
Interim Information Services Strategic Partner, Shannon Diede

Medical Director, Jon Younger
Director Of Respiratory Therapy, Christopher Meyer
Vice President Of Development For The Foundation, Becca Kelly
Assistant Chair Department Of Ob Gyn, Sarah Delatorre
Medical Director, Enrico Versace
Vice President of Patient Care Services Chief Nursing Officer, Nancy Wood
Medical Director, Claire Frost
Medical Director, Julie Hubble
Medical Director, Belinda Fu
Medical Director, Mimi Nguyen
Medical Director, John Stevens
Medical Director Liver Program; Transplant Hepatologist, Thomas Amankonah
Senior Vice President Chief Administrative Officer Swedish Edmonds, Mike Carter
Chairman, Michael J. Hart
Vice Chairman, Teresa Bigelow
Auditors: KPMG LLP SEATTLE WA

LOCATIONS

HQ: SWEDISH HEALTH SERVICES
747 BROADWAY, SEATTLE, WA 981224379
Phone: 206 386-6000

PRODUCTS/OPERATIONS

Selected Washington Facilities
Ballard Campus (Seattle)
Cherry Hill Campus (Seattle)
Edmonds Campus (Edmonds)
First Hill Campus (Seattle)
Issaquah Campus (Issaquah)
Mill Creek Campus (ambulatory center in Everett)
Redmond Campus (ambulatory center in Redmond)

Selected Institutes and Services
Cancer Institute
Emergency Services
Heart and Vascular Institute
Neuroscience Institute
Orthopedic Institute
Pediatric Specialty Care
Primary Care
Pregnancy and Childbirth
Surgical Services
Transplant Program
Women's Health

COMPETITORS

Franciscan Health System	Seattle Children's Hospital
Harrison Medical Center	University of Washington
MultiCare Health System	Wenatchee Valley Medical Center
Overlake Hospital	Yakima Valley Memorial
PeaceHealth	

HISTORICAL FINANCIALS

Company Type: Private

Income Statement				FYE: December 31
	REVENUE ($ mil.)	NET INCOME ($ mil.)	NET PROFIT MARGIN	EMPLOYEES
12/07	1,153	78	6.8%	6,916
12/06	1,087	56	5.2%	—
Annual Growth	6.1%	40.5%	—	—

2007 Year-End Financials

Return on assets: 6.1%   Cash ($ mil.): 43
Return on equity: 6.8%
Current ratio: 1.40

SWEDISHAMERICAN HOSPITAL

Auditors: MCGLADREY LLP CHICAGO IL

LOCATIONS

HQ: SWEDISHAMERICAN HOSPITAL
1401 E STATE ST, ROCKFORD, IL 611042315
Phone: 815 968-4400
Web: WWW.SWEDISHAMERICAN.ORG

HISTORICAL FINANCIALS

Company Type: Private

Income Statement

FYE: May 31

	REVENUE ($ mil.)	NET INCOME ($ mil.)	NET PROFIT MARGIN	EMPLOYEES
05/13	465	21	4.6%	1,599
05/11	450	15	3.5%	—
05/10	420	13	3.2%	—
05/09	1,243	0	—	—
Annual Growth	(21.8%)	—	—	—

2013 Year-End Financials

Return on assets: 9.3%   Cash ($ mil.): 26
Return on equity: 4.6%
Current ratio: 0.50

SWINERTON BUILDERS

Swinerton Builders a subsidiary of Swinerton focuses on commercial and sustainable construction and renovation projects. Operating primarily in the western US its interiors group offers interior tenant finishes and remodeling working on such projects as high-tech and lab renovations hospitals retail facilities and seismic upgrades. The employee-owned company's building group focuses on new construction and retrofitting for such projects as the San Francisco Museum of Modern Art a Lockheed Martin launch vehicle assembly plant in Colorado and the Bay Bridge toll operations building in San Francisco. Swinerton Builders operates from offices in California Colorado Hawaii Texas New Mexico and Washington.

Operations
As part of its business Swinerton Builders is involved in high-tech and lab renovations hospitals retail facilities and seismic upgrades as well as new construction and retrofitting projects.

Swinerton Builders also constructs many buildings to meet environmental standards. Green projects have ranged from fire stations and retail outlets to college facilities and hotels. Swinertons' own corporate offices in California are solar powered.

Geographic Reach
The building arm of Swinerton serves the western US through offices in California Colorado Hawaii Texas Oregon and Washington. Its offices are located across California as well as in Austin Texas; Denver Colorado; Portland Oregon; Seattle Washington; and Honolulu Hawaii.

Sales and Marketing
Swinerton Builders serves a variety of sectors involving: critical facilities education government healthcare hospitality interiors multi-family residential native American and renewable energy projects. Its clients have included NASA the Fed-

eral Aviation Administration Bureau of Indian Affairs and several military and governmental entities including the US Air Force US Army US Department of Agriculture US Department of Homeland Security and the US National Park Service.

Strategy
Swinerton Builders continues to work on high-value projects around the country. In 2015 after being selected from a two-phase best value selection process the company secured a contract to lead the design-build construction project of a $46 million parking building (with some 1795 parking spaces) at the Denver International Airport (DIA) in Colorado. The company's Swinerton Renewable Energy unit which builds and offers services to the solar utility industry expanded its capabilities in 2013 by adding comprehensive operations and maintenance (O&M) services for any solar facility across North America. The unit also launched a monitoring platform named SOLV to manage all the operational needs of customers with solar utility plants.

Company Ownership
Swinerton Builders is a subsidiary of Swinerton.

EXECUTIVES

V Pres, Ray Haj
V Pres, George W Hershman
V Pres, Scott Conrad
Vice President, Robert Dymond
Vice President, Tony Williamson
Asst Sec, Mark S Catel
Asst Sec, Lisa M Telles
Auditors: GALLINA LLP WALNUT CREEK CAL

LOCATIONS

HQ: SWINERTON BUILDERS
260 TOWNSEND ST, SAN FRANCISCO, CA 941071719
Phone: 415 421-2980
Web: WWW.SWINERTON.COM

PRODUCTS/OPERATIONS

Selected Services
BIM/VD&C
Corporate Services
Critical Facilities
General Contracting
Government Construction
Management & Consulting
Preconstruction
Renewable Energy
Sustainable Construction/LEED

COMPETITORS

Andersen Construction	Hensel Phelps
Charles Pankow	Construction
Builders	J.F. Shea
Clark Builders Group	Jaynes Companies
Cordoba	Kitchell
DPR Construction	Torix General
Devcon Construction	Contractors
Gilbane Building	Turner Corporation
Company	W. L. Butler
Hathaway Dinwiddie	Webcor Builders
Construction	Whiting-Turner

HISTORICAL FINANCIALS

Company Type: Private

Income Statement

FYE: December 31

	REVENUE ($ mil.)	NET INCOME ($ mil.)	NET PROFIT MARGIN	EMPLOYEES
12/13	1,674	4	0.3%	900
12/12	1,429	6	0.4%	—
12/11	948	0	—	—
12/10	796	0	—	—
Annual Growth	28.1%	—	—	—

2013 Year-End Financials

Return on assets: —   Cash ($ mil.): 28
Return on equity: 0.3%
Current ratio: 0.10

SWINERTON INCORPORATED

Swinerton is building up the West just as it helped rebuild San Francisco after the 1906 earthquake. One of the largest contractors in California the construction group builds commercial industrial and government facilities including resorts subsidized housing public schools soundstages hospitals and airport terminals. Through its subsidiaries (including Swinerton Builders) Swinerton offers general contracting and design/build services as well as construction and program management. The firm also provides property management for conventional subsidized and assisted living residences and is active in the renewable energy sector. The 100% employee-owned company traces its roots to 1888.

OperationsSwinerton has a special renewable energy division (Swinerton Renewable Energy) focused on solar and wind projects.For North American solar power facilities the company also offers comprehensive operations and maintenance (O&M) services which include performance monitoring and alerting parts management service ticketing reporting preventive and corrective maintenance warranty administration and site maintenance (including vegetation mitigation and module washing).Swinerton also has a special division to handle government construction projects delivering large-scale complex design and construction services for government agencies. Through the division Swinerton has worked on federal courthouses and administrative buildings training centers VA hospitals and military housing projects.Geographic Reach

San Francisco-based Swinerton has more than a dozen offices throughout California Colorado Hawaii Texas Oregon and Washington.

Financial Performance
With the California construction market experiencing some of the strongest growth the industry has seen since 2008 Swinerton posted nearly $1.8 billion in revenue in 2013 about $1.4 billion of which was rung up in California.

Strategy
Swinerton's renewable energy division has been busy with a series of projects and new services coming to the fold in recent years. In 2014 Duke Energy awarded Swinerton a contract to develop a pair of 20-megawatt solar farms called the Pumpjack and Wildwood solar power projects which will power some 10000 households in central California once they're completed. In 2013 the company began offering comprehensive operations and maintenance (O&M) services for any North American solar facility. The company also continues to work on other projects in recent years. In 2014 it started building the five-story 117000-square-foot building on behalf of the developer Breevast which secured a 12-year lease agreement on the building with file-sharing service provider Dropbox. In 2013 it started work on Telecom Real Estate Services' Block Data Center in Las Vegas with the goal of turning an existing warehouse facility into a Tier III modular data center. That year it also began construction on Chevron's 340000 square-foot office complex and campus in Midland Texas.

As one of the top waste-reducing companies in California Swinerton employs green building construction and design practices to conserve resources reduce waste and create healthier environments. The company's own headquarters building in San Francisco received Gold LEED-EB (Leadership in Energy & Environmental Design for Existing Buildings) –a top certification from the U.S. Green Building Council. Swinerton also built the LEED platinum rated NASA Ames Research Center Sustainability Base the greenest government building in history.

EXECUTIVES

V Pres, Charlene M Atkinson
Exec V Pres, Eric Foster
V Pres, Brenda E Reimche
Vice President, Kerry Atkinson
Vice President General Counsel, Sheriann Murphy
Vice President Manager Director, Glenna Kelly
Vice President Manager Director, Gretchen Baker
Vice President Manager Director, Karen Moro
Vice President Manager Director, Charlene Chopnak
Legal Secretary, Marissa Otellini
Vice President Manager of Treasury Services Swinerton Inc., Phyllis Smith
Vice President and Director of Operations, Ray Haj
Vice President and General Manager, Jeff Gee
Vice President Operations Manager, Gerald (Jerry) Mejia
Asst Sec, Lisa M Telles
Auditors: GALLINA LLP WALNUT CREEK CAL

LOCATIONS

HQ: SWINERTON INCORPORATED
260 TOWNSEND ST, SAN FRANCISCO, CA 941071719
Phone: 415 421-2980
Web: WWW.SWINERTON.COM

PRODUCTS/OPERATIONS

Selected Companies and Divisions
Cameron Swinerton
Harbison-Mahony-Higgins Builders Inc. (HMH general contracting)
Swinerton Builders (general contracting)
Swinerton Government Services
Swinerton Management & Consulting (property assessment)
Swinerton Property Services (property management)
William P. Young Construction (engineering and civil construction)

Selected Projects
100 Montgomery
AECOM
Agilent Technologies
Andaz Wailea Resort & Villas
Avaya Research & Development
Bank of New York Mellon Newport Beach
Bank of New York Mellon San Francisco
Bright Horizons Colorado
Bright Horizons South Lake Union
Bruceville | 19.15 MWdc
Cache Creek Casino Resort
CalSTRS Office Headquarters
Caltech Solar Project | 1.10 MWdc
Cathedral of the Blessed Sacrament
Christopher High School
Cinépolis Del Mar
City Center Plaza and Entry Upgrades
City Target at the Metreon
CNET Headquarters
Columbia 3 | 11.06 MWdc Columbia Sportswear
de Young Museum
Delta Airlines Sky Club
Dillard | 12.03 MWdc

COMPETITORS

A.G. Spanos	J.F. Shea
Bechtel	JCM Partners
Beck Group	Kitchell
Charles Pankow	McCarthy Building
Builders	Menas Realty
Clark Construction	PCL Construction

Group
Cordoba
DPR Construction
Devcon Construction
Gilbane
Hathaway Dinwiddie Construction
Hensel Phelps Construction

Enterprises
Rudolph & Sletten
Skanska USA Building
Sundt
Turner Corporation
Tutor-Saliba
Webcor Builders
Western National Group
Whiting-Turner

HISTORICAL FINANCIALS
Company Type: Private

Income Statement
FYE: December 31

	REVENUE ($ mil.)	NET INCOME ($ mil.)	NET PROFIT MARGIN	EMPLOYEES
12/13	1,681	6	0.4%	900
12/12	1,506	0	—	—
12/11	1,080	0	—	—
12/10	981	0	—	—
Annual Growth 19.7%		—	—	—

2013 Year-End Financials
Return on assets: —
Return on equity: 0.4%
Current ratio: 0.20
Cash ($ mil.): 72

SYRACUSE UNIVERSITY

Syracuse University is a serious school with a silly mascot. While it wasn't until 1995 that Otto the Orange was officially adopted as the school's mascot Syracuse's tradition of quality higher education dates back to 1870. The school enrolls more than 21000 undergraduate and graduate students and has some 1000 full-time faculty members on its campus in central New York State. It offers about 500 degree programs in areas such as communications computer science engineering psychology art mathematics music and information. Notable alumni include Dick Clark Ted Koppel Joyce Carol Oats Joe Biden and Aaron Sorkin.

Geographic Reach

Syracuse's student population includes residents of all 50 US states and international students from about 125 countries. In addition to its main campus in central New York State the university also has satellite campuses in New York City Los Angeles and Washington DC. It also has an extensive study abroad program with some 40% of its student body enrolling in curriculum programs in countries including Chile China France Italy Spain Turkey and the UK.

Operations

Syracuse's degree programs are organized under 13 schools in the fields of architecture arts and sciences education engineering and computer science graduate studies sports information law management public affairs communication visual and performing arts and continuing education.

Several of the colleges have research centers in areas such as accounting pop culture investment biomaterials health engineering energy technology business management and public affairs. Overall the university has sponsored programs in research teaching and other areas with a total of about $80 million in funding much of which comes from the federal and state governments.

Financial Performance

Syracuse reported a 3% decrease in revenues to $819 million in 2012 due to lower gains on investment transactions (slightly offset by higher tuition and fees). However net income in 2012 dipped into the red due to investment losses increased ex-

penses and interest rate swap and currency forward agreements.

Student tuition and fees are the largest component of university revenues accounting for about 55% of earnings. Syracuse charges full-time undergraduate tuition of some $38000 per year. Auxiliary enterprises including room board bookstore sales and parking fees account for about a quarter of annual revenues.

Syracuse has a total endowment worth some $940 million as of mid-2012.

Company Background

Syracuse is an education corporation that operates under the direction of an independent board of trustees under the New York Not-for-Profit Corporation Law. The university was granted a charter by the state of New York in 1870.

EXECUTIVES

CIO and VP Information Technology, Samuel Scozzafava
Senior Vice President For Human Capital Development, Kal Alston
Student Government Vice President, Evan Advises
Vice President Of Computational Technology, Jeff Saltz
Associate Vice President Enrollment Mana, Ryan Williams
Vice President, Patrick Kelly
Vice President And Chief Development Officer, Elizabeth O'Rourke
Assistant Vice President for, Larry Martin
Assistant Vice President of Institutional Research and Assessment, LaVonda Reed
Vice President Judicial Affairs, Lewis Paulino
Assistant Secretary, Michael (Mel) Cox
Auditors: KPMG LLP SYRACUSE NY

LOCATIONS

HQ: SYRACUSE UNIVERSITY
900 S CROUSE AVE STE 620, SYRACUSE, NY 132440001
Phone: 315 443-1870
Web: WWW.SYR.EDU

PRODUCTS/OPERATIONS

Selected Academic Units
College of Arts and Sciences
College of Law
College of Visual and Performing Arts
University College
David B. Falk College of Sports and Human Dynamics
Graduate School
L.C. Smith College of Engineering and Computer Science
Martin J. Whitman School of Management
Maxwell School of Citizenship and Public Affairs
School of Architecture
School of Education
School of Information Studies
S.I. Newhouse School of Public Communications

HISTORICAL FINANCIALS
Company Type: Private

Income Statement
FYE: June 30

	REVENUE ($ mil.)	NET INCOME ($ mil.)	NET PROFIT MARGIN	EMPLOYEES
06/13	869	136	15.7%	4,350
06/12	818	(73)	—	—
06/11	839	145	17.3%	—
06/10	978	0	—	—
Annual Growth (3.9%)		—	—	—

2013 Year-End Financials
Return on assets: —
Return on equity: 15.7%
Current ratio: 0.80
Cash ($ mil.): 138

TALLAHASSEE MEMORIAL HEALTHCARE INC.

Tallahassee Memorial HealthCare (TMH) aims to take the hassle out of health care. The community health system serves residents of Florida's state capital and its surrounding communities. The system is anchored by Tallahassee Memorial Hospital a not-for-profit facility with more than 770 beds and about 560 physicians on staff who represent some 50 different specialties. TMH provides general medical and surgical care as well as specialty care in areas such as oncology rehabilitation women's and children's health obesity and diabetes. TMH also has a trauma center offers a family practice residency program and provides primary medical care through a handful of regional clinics.

Geographic Reach

TMH serves 17 counties across North Florida and South Georgia.

Operations

TMH is Florida's eighth-largest hospital boasting more than 24000 inpatient admissions per year. As part of its operations TMH has a 60-bed psychiatric hospital and offers adult day care and home health care services. It operates the only Level II trauma center in the region which benefits from newly added telemedicine equipment that includes videoconferencing. Trauma centers are specially trained and equipped to handle severe injuries and all such patients in the area are routed to trauma certified facilities.

The system partners with the H. Lee Moffitt Cancer Center & Research Institute in Tampa to allow cancer patients to participate in clinical trials and other experimental and research opportunities.

The system offers a range of cardiovascular services from diagnostic procedures to open-heart surgery a designated acute brain and spinal cord injury center and a 110000-sq.-ft. childbirth facility –the region's only Level Three Neonatal Intensive Care Unit.

In 2014 the hospital had 122100 emergency and urgent care visits and 29586 general admissions.

Financial Performance

In 2014 TMH's net revenues increased by 7% due to higher net patient service revenues (net of contractual allowances and discounts). The company's net income rose by 15% due to higher net revenues and a decrease in interest. TMH's operating cash inflow in 2014 increased by 16%.

Strategy

The medical facility operates the Tallahassee Memorial Transition Center created in partnership with Capital Health Plan and Florida State University College of Medicine. The center was designed to improve wellness through new approaches and collaborative research. Looking to position itself as a regional center for healthcare Tallahassee Memorial has plans to roll out more new services and add physicians.

In 2015 the hospital and Apalachee Center expanded their agreement to include administrative management of Tallahassee Memorial behavioral health services by Apalachee Center to improve behavioral health services in the community. As part of an earlier agreement the company will continue to provide some psychiatric medical coverage for Apalachee Center's inpatient services as well as providing all psychiatric medical services at the Tallahassee Memorial Behavioral Health Center. In 2014 TMH and Doctors' Memorial Hospital signed an agreement to create an equal governance partnership between the two institutions that will ultimately enhance services to Doctors' Memorial Hospital and expand its role in Taylor County's health care system.

To expand its capabilities TMH opened the Tallahassee Memorial Emergency Center - Northeast in mid-2013 and broke ground in 2013 on a new surgery and adult intensive care facility that's anticipated to cost as much as $175 million.

Company Background

TMH was founded in 1948.

EXECUTIVES

Chief Communications Officer and Vice President of Public Relations, Warren Jones
Chief Improvement and Planning Officer and Vice President, Cynthia Blair
Medical Director Internist, David (Dave) Robinson
Treasurer and Director, Frank Gredler

LOCATIONS

HQ: TALLAHASSEE MEMORIAL HEALTHCARE INC.
1300 MICCOSUKEE RD, TALLAHASSEE, FL
323085054
Phone: 850 431-1155
Web: WWW.TMH.ORG

PRODUCTS/OPERATIONS

2014 sales

	% of total
Hospitals	97
TMHV	1
Medicus	2
Total	**100**

Selected Services

Behavioral Health Center
Rehabilitation Center
Cancer Center
Bixler Emergency Center
Heart & Vascular Center
Diabetes Center
Orthopedic Center
NeuroScience Center
Surgical Services
Women's Pavilion
Home Health Care
Clinical Genetics Center
Bariatric Center
Chronic Pain Management
Lipid Center

COMPETITORS

Adventist Health System Sunbelt Healthcare
Baptist Health System
Bay Medical Center
H. Lee Moffitt Cancer Center & Research Institute
HCA
Jackson County Hospital of Florida
Munroe Regional Health System
Sacred Heart Health System
UF&Shands

HISTORICAL FINANCIALS

Company Type: Private

Income Statement

FYE: September 30

	REVENUE ($ mil.)	NET INCOME ($ mil.)	NET PROFIT MARGIN	EMPLOYEES
09/13	566	31	5.6%	6,430
09/12	479	40	8.4%	—
09/09	435	24	5.7%	—
09/08	411	0	—	—
Annual Growth	**6.6%**	**—**	**—**	**—**

2013 Year-End Financials
Return on assets: 7.8%   Cash ($ mil.): 156
Return on equity: 5.6%
Current ratio: 1.40

TAUBER OIL COMPANY

No liquid petrochemical product is taboo for oil refiner and marketer Tauber Oil. The family owned company markets refined petroleum products carbon black feedstocks liquefied petroleum gases chemicals and petrochemicals (including benzene styrene monomer and methanol). Tauber Oil is one of the US's leading suppliers of feedstocks for reforming and olefin cracking. It also has oil and gas exploration and production operations. Subsidiary Tauber Petrochemical was created in 1997 to beef up the company's international petrochemical business. Tauber Oil which is owned by David and Richard Tauber maintains a fleet of more than 500 rail cars to supply its customers.

Geographic Reach

The company's rail and barge fleet moves products from inland to Gulf Coast markets. It gathers blends and distributes out of tankage in Houston Texas City and on the Mississippi River. Tauber Oil's has oil and gas exploration and production operations in the East Texas South Texas the Gulf Coast of Texas Southern Louisiana and Oklahoma. (Additionally Tauber participates in 3-D seismic projects lease acquisitions and funding for geological and geophysical projects). Its Canadian Crude group works with heavy crude oil producers.

Operations

Tauber Oil's blending group works with refineries and producers to create a market for by-product/co-product streams. It also supplies liquid petroleum products to marine diesel customers fuel to power generators cutters for bunker blending clients and a number of other fuel applications.

The company's natural gas liquids department works with producers and consumers to create a market; the refined products department trades refined products with refiners traders distributors and other customers.

Tauber Petrochemical markets a range of products including alkylate benzene C9 aromatics ethyl benzene pyrolysis gasoline styrene monomer toluene and xylene.

Strategy

Unlike most other oil and gas suppliers Tauber Oil does not rely on a financial speculation strategy (the buying and selling of contracts for petroleum products). The company primarily plays the role of the middleman and more than 90% of the company's businesses involve the actual delivery of petroleum products and gas liquids.

Price volatility goes with Tauber Oil's territory and the company relies on its track record of reliable service and long-term relationships with customers to weather downturns in the market.

To strengthen its finances and to focus on its core oil chemical and petrochemical businesses in 2012 the company merged its natural gas division with Interconn Resources Inc. to form Interconn Resources LLC. Interconn Resources specializes in delivering competitively priced natural gas to municipal industrial retail and governmental customers across the southeastern US.

In order to develop and grow new operations the company enters into partnerships collaborations joint ventures and acquisition arrangements. Tauber Oil is partnered with Rio Energy International to provide adequate storage tank capacity at multiple terminals which helps it to maintain low cost train operations from Western Canada to the US Gulf Coast.

Company Background

Tauber Oil was founded in 1953 by O. J. Tauber Sr. He gained his oil and petroleum products trading experience working for a small Houston refinery called Eastern States Refining.

His son (and company executive) Richard Tauber is also the president of a small affiliated oil company Tauber Exploration and Production.

EXECUTIVES

VP Credit Finance, Stephen E. Hamlin
Owner and Principal, David W. Tauber, age 65
Owner and Principal, Richard E. Tauber
Vice President, Ed Naspinski
Vice President Intermediate and Heavy Feedstocks, Gerald (Jerry) Applestein
Vice President Blending Components, John (Jack) Wakefield
Vice President Of Refined Products, Curtis Cox
Vice President Supply and Marketing Carbon Black Feedstocks, Bobby Combs
Executive Vice President, J Podsednik
Vice President, Mauricio Ruiz
Auditors: MOHLE ADAMS

LOCATIONS

HQ: TAUBER OIL COMPANY
55 WAUGH DR STE 700, HOUSTON, TX 770075837
Phone: 713 869-8700
Web: WWW.TAUBEROIL.COM

PRODUCTS/OPERATIONS

Selected Products:
Natural Gas Liquids
  Butane
  Ethane
  Isobutane
  Propane
Petrochemicals
  Benzene
  Methanol
  MTBE
  Styrene monomer
  Toluene
  Xylene
Refined
  Aviation jet fuel
  Kerosene
  Low sulfur diesel
  No. 2 fuel oil

COMPETITORS

Cabot Oil & Gas	Marathon Oil
Devon Energy	Occidental Petroleum
Exxon Mobil	Tesoro
George Warren	Valero Energy
Global Partners	

HISTORICAL FINANCIALS

Company Type: Private

Income Statement

FYE: December 31

	REVENUE ($ mil.)	NET INCOME ($ mil.)	NET PROFIT MARGIN	EMPLOYEES
12/13	4,769	16	0.3%	135
12/12	5,088	21	0.4%	—
12/11	4,427	7	0.2%	—
12/10	3,155	0	—	—
Annual Growth 14.8%		—	—	—

2013 Year-End Financials

Return on assets: —
Return on equity: 0.3%
Current ratio: 0.70
Cash ($ mil.): 26

TEAM INDUSTRIES INC.

It takes a team TEAM Industries to make the drivetrains that and other vehicles parts. The Ricke family owned company designs tests manufacturers and assembles powertrain transmissions drivetrains gear sets and chassis components for snowmobile all-terrain vehicle lawn mowers and other vehicles through partnerships with CNH Ford Honda Ingersoll-Rand Kawasaki Textron Yamaha and other OEMs. TEAM maintains half a dozen facilities throughout Minnesota and North Carolina; its manufacturing capabilities run from ductile iron and shaft machining to aluminum die-casting and gear/spline making. The company also offers engineering R&D and testing services.

Geographic Reach

TEAM operates six manufacturing facilities five in Minnesota (Audubon Bagley Cambridge Detroit Lakes and Park Rapids) and one in North Carolina (Andrews) with more than 850000 sq. ft. of total manufacturing space.

Operations

The company sells its products through six locations: TEAM Andrews acts as its precision machining gear manufacturing and metallurgical lab; TEAM Audubon specializes in gear cutting and heat treating; TEAM Bagley is its corporate headquarters; TEAM Detroit Lakes has expertise in aluminum die casting; TEAM Park Rapids works with CNC (computer numerical control) machining and loctite (a brand of adhesives) impregnation casting; and Motek-TEAM Industries is another metallurgical lab with a focus on induction hardening.

Ownership

TEAM is owned by its founding family the Rickes.

Company Background

The company was established in 1967 as Motek Engineering and Manufacturing by Don and Bea Ricke.

EXECUTIVES

Vice President Safety, Gene Bullis
Auditors: PEFFER & WALLACE LTD CAMBRI

LOCATIONS

HQ: TEAM INDUSTRIES INC.
105 PARK AVE NW, BAGLEY, MN 566219558
Phone: 218 694-3550
Web: WWW.TEAM-IND.COM

PRODUCTS/OPERATIONS

Selected Products
Axle assemblies and housings (spiral straight bevel or hypoid gearing)
Continuously variable transmissions (10-200 horsepower & up to 10000 rpm)
Differentials (with a variety of traction control mechanisms)
Gear sets
Transaxles (for a variety of electric or gas powered vehicles)
Transmissions and gear boxes (using parallel axis gears crossed axis gears worm sets planetary)
Wet brake assemblies

Selected Market Applications
Agricultural
All-terrain vehicles
Alternative on-road vehicles
Automotive
Golf carts
Lawn & garden
Marine
Motorcycles
Off-highway construction & others
Personal watercraft
Snowmobiles
Turf care
Utility vehicles

COMPETITORS

American Axle & Manufacturing	GKN
BorgWarner	Lippert Components
Dana Holding	Magna International
Federal-Mogul	Meritor
	Visteon

HISTORICAL FINANCIALS

Company Type: Private

Income Statement

FYE: September 28

	REVENUE ($ mil.)	NET INCOME ($ mil.)	NET PROFIT MARGIN	EMPLOYEES
09/13	291	21	7.3%	1,100
09/12	288	25	8.8%	—
09/11	251	22	9.1%	—
09/10	193	0	—	—
Annual Growth 14.8%		—	—	—

2013 Year-End Financials

Return on assets: 8.0%
Return on equity: 7.3%
Current ratio: 1.10
Cash ($ mil.): 15

TEKNOR APEX COMPANY

The apex of Teknor Apex's business model is to serve its customers by offering a wide-ranging portfolio of chemicals plastic and rubber. The company's business divisions provide chemicals (plasticizers and toll compounding) garden hoses and rubber products (custom mixed and molded rubber compounds). Teknor Apex also manufactures bioplastics color concentrates for plastics (Teknor Color Company) thermoplastic elastomers and vinyl (custom PVC compounds); it also provides specialty compounding (custom thermoplastic compound manufacturing and toll compounding of plastics).

Geographic Reach

The company has manufacturing plants for its nine divisions in eight locations in the US (in California Kentucky Massachusetts North Carolina Rhode Island South Carolina Tennessee Texas and Vermont) and one each in Belgium China Singapore and the UK.

Operations

Teknor Apex operates eight divisions: Bioplastics (thermoplastic starch compounds with polymers); Chemical; Garden Hose; Nylon; Teknor Color Company (custom and standard colors and additives as well as special effects); Thermoplastic Elastomer (specialty resins); Toll and Specialty Compounding; and Vinyl (specialty PVC compounds).

Strategy

Teknor Apex is broadening its offerings as well as its geographic reach. To better serve the wind energy market that year the company launched two high-performance vinyl jacketing compounds that can withstand extreme cold exposure to lubricants and other harsh conditions.

Ownership

The founding Fain family owns a controlling interest in Teknor Apex.

Company Background

The company was founded in 1924 as a tire distributor and retreader.

EXECUTIVES

Vice President Human Resources, Laurie Meisner

Vice President Of Information Technology, Craig White
Vice President and Business Manager Vinyl Division, Lou Cappucci
Senior Vice President of Manufacturing, Bill Murray
Assistant Treasurer, Shauneen Bourgeois

LOCATIONS

HQ: TEKNOR APEX COMPANY
505 CENTRAL AVE, PAWTUCKET, RI 028611900
Phone: 401 725-8000
Web: WWW.BIOVINYL.COM

PRODUCTS/OPERATIONS

Selected Products and Services
Chemicals and Colorants
  Color concentrates
  Custom compounds
  Dry colors
  High-performance colors
  Plasticizers (trimellitates adipates phthalates sebacates and azelates)
  Pulverized colors
  PVC compounds
  Thermoplastic elastomers
Garden Hose Products
  Cord hose and rope organizers
  Residential and commercial hoses
Rubber Products
  Custom rubber mixing
  Custom rubber molding

COMPETITORS

DuPont	RB Rubber
GLS	Synthomer
NatureWorks	Tekni-Plex
PMC Global	Vulcan International
PolyOne	

HISTORICAL FINANCIALS
Company Type: Private

Income Statement
FYE: July 31

	REVENUE ($ mil.)	NET INCOME ($ mil.)	NET PROFIT MARGIN	EMPLOYEES
07/14	996	50	5.0%	2,500
07/05	574	0	—	—
Annual Growth	6.3%	—	—	—

2014 Year-End Financials
Return on assets: 6.8%   Cash ($ mil.): 74
Return on equity: 5.0%
Current ratio: 2.40

TEKSYSTEMS INC.

TEKsystems a subsidiary of staffing giant Allegis provides IT consulting and staffing services from locations in North America and Europe. Considered one of the nation's largest IT staffing firms the company places more than 70000 technical professionals each week who work in a variety of fields including biotechnology telecommunications and construction and engineering. TEKsystems has 100 offices serving more than 6000 clients. In addition the company runs the thingamajob.com website which is an online job board for technical staff. Spinning off of fellow Allegis unit Aerotek TEKsystems was formed in 1994 to focus on the IT needs of clients.Geographic ReachThe company has 100 locations throughout North America Europe and Asia.Sales and MarketingTEKsystems works to help its clients control cost mitigate risk and deliver quality product outcomes.StrategyThe

company has used strategic partnerships to grow its business.

EXECUTIVES

President, Keith Bozeman
Vice President Of Financial Operations, Brad Curtis
Vice President, Mark Cooper
Auditors: PRICEWATERHOUSECOOPERS LLP BA

LOCATIONS

HQ: TEKSYSTEMS INC.
7437 RACE RD, HANOVER, MD 210761112
Phone: 410 579-3000
Web: WWW.TEKSYSTEMS.COM

PRODUCTS/OPERATIONS

Selected Services
Component services
Staffing services
Team services
Workforce management services

Selected Markets Served
Communications
Information technology
Financial services
Government

COMPETITORS

Acro Service	Info Technologies
Adecco	Kelly Services
CDI	ManpowerGroup
CorSource Technology Group	Prosum
	Robert Half

HISTORICAL FINANCIALS
Company Type: Private

Income Statement
FYE: December 31

	REVENUE ($ mil.)	NET INCOME ($ mil.)	NET PROFIT MARGIN	EMPLOYEES
12/13	3,551	0	—	2,900
12/12	3,319	328	9.9%	—
12/11	2,987	195	6.5%	—
12/10	2,632	0	—	—
Annual Growth	10.5%	—	—	—

2013 Year-End Financials
Return on assets: 2.1%   Cash ($ mil.): 41
Return on equity: —
Current ratio: 2.80

TELAMON CORPORATION

Auditors: BKD LLP INDIANAPOLIS INDIAN

LOCATIONS

HQ: TELAMON CORPORATION
1000 E 116TH ST, CARMEL, IN 460323416
Phone: 317 818-6888
Web: WWW.TELAMON.COM

HISTORICAL FINANCIALS
Company Type: Private

Income Statement
FYE: September 30

	REVENUE ($ mil.)	NET INCOME ($ mil.)	NET PROFIT MARGIN	EMPLOYEES
09/13	782	8	1.1%	585
09/10	423	3	0.8%	—
09/09	303	0	0.1%	—
09/08	81	0	—	—
Annual Growth	57.0%	—	—	—

2013 Year-End Financials
Return on assets: 19.8%   Cash ($ mil.): 11
Return on equity: 1.1%
Current ratio: 0.10

TEMPLE UNIVERSITY HEALTH SYSTEM INC.

Temple University Health System (TUHS) is a network of academic and community hospitals associated with the Temple University School of Medicine. It provides primary secondary and tertiary care to residents in the Philadelphia County (Pennsylvania) area. The system includes 730-bed Temple University Hospital (a Level 1 trauma center) and a pair of community-based hospitals that provide acute and emergency care as well as the Jeanes Hospital and TUH-Episcopal Hospital (home to a 120-bed behavioral health unit). TUHS supports programs in pediatric and adult cardiology organ transplantation oncology and pulmonary disease. TUHS also includes a community-wide network of primary care physicians.

Geographic Reach
Temple University Health System serves the residents of Philadelphia.

Operations
The $1.4-billion academic health system comprises Temple University Hospital TUH-Episcopal Campus TUH-Northern Campus Fox Chase Cancer Center Jeanes Hospital Temple Transport Team and Temple Physicians. It's affiliated with Temple University School of Medicine. Bermuda-based TUHS Insurance Company Ltd. is a captive insurance company established to reinsure the professional liability claims of TUHS subsidiaries.

It offers everything from specialized cardiac care and spinal rehabilitation to a lung care center a burn center and stroke treatments.

Medicare and Medicaid account for 65% of net patient revenues.

Sales and Marketing
TUHS markets itself through TV commercials and print and billboard advertising.

Financial Performance
In fiscal 2012 revenue rose by 37% to $1.35 billion vs. 2011. It attributes the double-digit gains to increases in net patient service revenue research revenue and other revenue. The system logged $107 million in net income during the reporting period as compared to a net loss in 2011.

Strategy
TUHS concentrates on adding services and expanding its geographic reach. It added Fox Chase Cancer Center in 2012; opened the women's care center in Elkins Park Pennsylvania in 2012; opened a third urgent care facility in Jenkintown Pennsylvania in 2013; and expanded into new

markets by opening the Temple Health Center City facility.

EXECUTIVES

VP and COO, Robert E. Pezzoli
VP Human Resources, Robert Birnbrauer
VP and CFO, Robert H. Lux
VP and CIO, Arthur Papacostas
VP Communications and External Affairs, David Newell
CEO and Executive Director Jeanes Hospital, Linda Grass
CEO and Executive Director Northeastern Hospital, John Buckley
Executive Director Temple University Hospital - Episcopal Campus, Kathleen Barron
CEO Temple Physicians, Eric Mankin
Director Public Relations, Rebecca Harmon
Chief Counsel, Beth Koob
Manager Internal Communications, Steve Bates
Coordinator Public Relations, Thomas Mitchell
VP and Chief Medical Officer, Calvin B. Johnson
Auditors: DELOITTE & TOUCHE LLP PHILADE

LOCATIONS

HQ: TEMPLE UNIVERSITY HEALTH SYSTEM INC.
2450 W HUNTING PARK AVE, PHILADELPHIA, PA 191291302
Phone: 215 707-0900
Web: WWW.TEMPLE.EDU

PRODUCTS/OPERATIONS

Selected Facilities
Esther Boyer Pavilion (outpatient pediatric care)
Jeanes Hospital
Temple University Hospital
Temple University Hospital (TUH) Episcopal Campus

COMPETITORS

Albert Einstein Healthcare Network
Aria Health
Children's Hospital of Philadelphia
Community Health Systems
Crozer-Keystone Health System
Doylestown Hospital
Jefferson Health System
Mercy Health System
North Philadelphia Health System
Northwestern Human Services
Our Lady of Lourdes Medical Center
Pennsylvania Hospital
The Magee Memorial Hospital for Convalescents
Thomas Jefferson University Hospital
University of Pennsylvania Health System

HISTORICAL FINANCIALS

Company Type: Private

Income Statement

FYE: June 30

	REVENUE ($ mil.)	NET INCOME ($ mil.)	NET PROFIT MARGIN	EMPLOYEES
06/13	1,355	107	7.9%	7,573
06/12	1,004	(48)	—	—
06/11	994	45	4.6%	—
06/09	0	0	—	—
Annual Growth	888.5%	—	—	—

2013 Year-End Financials

Return on assets: 5.3%   Cash ($ mil.): 110
Return on equity: 7.9%
Current ratio: 1.10

TEMPLE UNIVERSITY-OF THE COMMONWEALTH SYSTEM OF HIGHER EDUCATION

Temple University's owl mascot reflects its start as a night school but the owl's sagacity also points to the school's educational credentials. More than 36000 students are enrolled in Temple's 320 academic programs. Its Health Sciences Center includes Temple University Hospital and schools that teach medicine and dentistry. Part of Pennsylvania's Commonwealth System of Higher Education Temple has nine different campuses in the Philadelphia area as well as in Tokyo and Rome and educational programs in China Greece France Israel and the UK. The system has a student-teacher ratio of about 15:1. Dr. Russell Conwell founded the university in 1884; it was incorporated as Temple University in 1907.

Operations
Temple's campus in suburban Ambler Pennsylvania offers programs in community and regional planning horticulture and landscape architecture. Together all of its campuses offer a combined total of about 140 bachelor's 125 master's 60 doctoral and nearly 10 professional degrees. Students can obtain professional degrees in dentistry law medicine pharmacy and podiatric medicine among others.

Financial Performance
Temple's revenue increased 9% for its 2014-2015 years compared to the previous period. Undergraduate tuition increased about 6%.

Strategy
Temple finalized in 2014 a plan to erect new buildings on campus including a signature library in the middle of campus. Also recommended according to the 10-year plan are a new interdisciplinary sciences building an expanded College of Engineering and consolidation of the College of Public Health. Outside the main campus the plan calls for investing in the university campus in Philadelphia's Center City campus and maintaining the School of Podiatric Medicine's campus at 8th and Race streets in Philadelphia and in Harrisburg.

EXECUTIVES

Dean Fox School of Business and Management, M. Moshe Porat, age 68
VP Computer Services and CIO, Timothy C. O'Rourke
Dean Katz School of Medicine, Larry R. Kaiser
Provost and SVP Academic Affairs, Hai-Lung Dai
Dean Boyer College of Music and Dance, Robert T. Stroker
VP CFO and Treasurer, Ken Kaiser
President, Neil D. Theobald
Dean of Students, Stephanie Ives
Interim Dean Tyler School of Art, Hester Stinnett
Dean Kornberg School of Dentistry, Amid I. Ismail
Dean College of Education, Gregory Anderson
Dean Beasley School of Law, JoAnne A. Epps
Dean School of Media and Communication, David Boardman
Dean School of Pharmacy, Peter Doukas
Dean School of Podiatric Medicine, John A. Mattiacci
Dean College of Public Health, Laura A. Siminoff

Dean College of Science and Technology, Michael L. Klein
Associate Vice President and Controller, Frank Annunziato
Department Chair, Alice Hausman
Vice President, Michael Guglielmo
Associate Vice President Care Management, Steven (Steve) Carson
Associate Vice President for Student Success, Laurel Harrish
Assistant Vice President, Anne Nadol
Assistant Vice President, Shawn Kleitz
Assistant Vice President For Operations, Michelle (Mitch) Lai
Senior Vice President For Institutional Advancement, David Unruh
Vice President, Ryan Olson
Assistant Vice President, Nnadozie Ibeh
Assistant Vice President Government Affairs, George Kenney
Associate Vice President, Timm Rinehart
Senior Vice President For Government C, Karin Mormando
Vice President Campus Safety, William (Bill) Bergman
Associate Vice President Institutional D, Rhonda Brown
Associate Vice President University Relations, George Ingram
Vice President of Professional Development, Haoren Yu
Associate Vice President Business Services, Richard (Dick) Rumer
Associate Vice President for Budget, Jaison Kurichi
Vice President Of Finance, Hong Tran
Associate Vice President Budget and Planning, Rick Chant
Vice President, Robert Salomon
Vice President, Deanna Geddes
Associate Vice President Organizational Development And Training, Karen Cherwony
Vice President, Kimberly Benns
Associate Vice President Strategic Marketing and Communications, Emily Spitale
Assoc Vice President Acad Computing Service, SHERI STAHLER
Vice President Events, Mohnish Nair
Chairman, Patrick J. (Pat) O'Connor
Vice Chairman, Anthony J. Scirica
Secretary, Djuna Witherspoon
Secretary, Rosa Grier
Assistant Secretary, Janet Carruth
Board Member, Joe Siderowicz
Treasurer, Dolores Zygmont
Board Member, Harris Webber
Executive Board Member, Camillia Keach
Secretary, Vernell Ross
Secretary, Pamela Smallwood
Secretary, Ruby Hammond
Secretary, Lydia Young
Secretary, Kristen Tamburini
Auditors: DELOITTE & TOUCHE LLP PHILADE

LOCATIONS

HQ: TEMPLE UNIVERSITY-OF THE COMMONWEALTH SYSTEM OF HIGHER EDUCATION
1801 N BROAD ST, PHILADELPHIA, PA 191226003
Phone: 215 204-1380
Web: WWW.WRTI.ORG

Selected Campuses
Philadelphia
  Ambler
  Center City
  Fort Washington
  Harrisburg
  Main
  Podiatric Medicine
  Health Sciences Center
International
  Japan
  Rome Italy

HISTORICAL FINANCIALS

Company Type: Private

Income Statement
FYE: June 30

	REVENUE ($ mil.)	NET INCOME ($ mil.)	NET PROFIT MARGIN	EMPLOYEES
06/14	2,723	181	6.7%	9,061
06/13	2,635	192	7.3%	—
06/12	2,254	(37)	—	—
06/08	2,034	0	—	—
Annual Growth	5.0%			

2014 Year-End Financials

Return on assets: 14.2%
Return on equity: 6.7%
Current ratio: 1.30
Cash ($ mil.): 182

TENASKA MARKETING VENTURES

LOCATIONS

HQ: TENASKA MARKETING VENTURES
14302 FNB PKWY, OMAHA, NE 681544446
Phone: 402 758-6100
Web: WWW.TENASKA.COM

HISTORICAL FINANCIALS

Company Type: Private

Income Statement
FYE: December 31

	REVENUE ($ mil.)	NET INCOME ($ mil.)	NET PROFIT MARGIN	EMPLOYEES
12/07	10,309	0	—	91
12/05	9,470	0	—	—
12/04	0	0	—	—
12/03	4,940	0	—	—
Annual Growth	20.2%	—	—	—

TERRACON CONSULTANTS INC.

Employee-owned Terracon Consultants provides geotechnical environmental construction material evaluation pavement engineering and construction management and facilities engineering services. One of the nation's top design firms the company serves the agriculture energy telecommunications commercial development and transportation sectors as well as government clients. The company has more than 140 offices in some 40 US states. Terracon serves more than 160 clients. It helps its customers comply with new building codes and environmental regulations assess environmental hazards and tackle the problem of aging structures.

Geographic Reach

Kansas-based Terracon has operations throughout the US.

Strategy

Continuing its efforts to expand in the Northeast in 2013 Terracon opened an office in South Plain-field (New Jersey) to serve the New York and Philadelphia markets.

Going forward the company is looking shift its primary acquisition strategy away from filling in geographic gaps to strengthening its service lines.

Mergers and Acquisitions

Terracon has expanded its geotechnical environmental engineering and testing capabilities with a string of recent purchases.

In 2013 it expanded its presence in the Northeast with the acquisition of New Hampshire-based environmental consulting firm New England EnviroStrategies Inc.

In 2012 Terracon acquired California-based Earthtec Inc. a provider of geotechnical environmental special inspection and other services to clients in Northern California. Also in 2012 it purchased Utah-based IHI Environmental a provider of industrial hygiene occupational safety and environmental consulting services to public and private sector clients across the western US. Previously Terracon bought Colorado firm Geotechnical Engineering Group boosting its presence in the West; and Stafford Consulting Engineers a building envelope system specialist with a presence in the Southeast. Also that year Terracon acquired Dressler Consulting Engineers a building forensics engineering firm based in Kansas and Nodarse & Associates a Florida-based environmental geotechnical and construction materials engineering firm.

Company Background

Terracon is owned by its employees. The firm was ranked 51st on the Employee Ownership 100 the list of the top 100 largest majority employee-owned companies in the US in 2012.

The company was founded in Iowa in 1965 as a joint venture between Shive Hall and Hattery (civil consulting) Soil Testing Services (geotechnical testing) and Gerald Olson P.E. (the company's founder and a project engineer).

EXECUTIVES

President and CEO, David Gaboury
CFO, Roger R. Herting
EVP and Director, Dan Israel
Vice President, Jack Scott
Vice President Human Resources and Organizational Development, Robert (Bob) Bergeson
Senior Vice President, David Harwood
Auditors: BKD LLP KANSAS CITY MISSOUR

LOCATIONS

HQ: TERRACON CONSULTANTS INC.
18001 W 106TH ST STE 300, OLATHE, KS 660616447
Phone: 913 599-6886
Web: WWW.TERRACON.COM

PRODUCTS/OPERATIONS

Selected Services
Materials
Special InspectionsOn-site Observation and MonitoringConstruction Quality Control and Quality Assurance ProgramsField and Laboratory Testing and AnalysisDesign and Review of Concrete Grout and Asphaltic Concrete MixesStructural Steel Nondestructive Testi
Geotechnical
Subsurface exploration and testing
Foundation analysis and design
Soil stabilization
Groundwater control
Pavement design
Environmental
Site assessment
Industrial hygiene and occupational safety
Regulatory compliance
Solid waste planning and design
Facilities
Roof/waterproofing consulting
Foundation/structural consulting
Life cycle cost analysis
Peer reviews
Seismic risk assessments
Construction administration

Selected Markets
Agriculture
Commercial/Retail
Energy
Federal
Financial
Industrial
Telecommunications
Transportation/Infrastructure

COMPETITORS

AECOM	Jacobs Engineering
Fluor	KBR
HNTB Companies	

HISTORICAL FINANCIALS

Company Type: Private

Income Statement
FYE: December 31

	REVENUE ($ mil.)	NET INCOME ($ mil.)	NET PROFIT MARGIN	EMPLOYEES
12/13	419	10	2.6%	2,823
12/12	380	10	2.7%	—
12/11	353	8	2.5%	—
12/10	319	0	—	—
Annual Growth	9.5%	—	—	—

2013 Year-End Financials

Return on assets: 3.1%
Return on equity: 2.6%
Current ratio: 0.90
Cash ($ mil.): 4

TEXAS A&M FOUNDATION

Auditors: PWC HOUSTON TX

LOCATIONS

HQ: TEXAS A&M FOUNDATION
401 GEORGE BUSH DR, COLLEGE STATION, TX 778402811
Phone: 979 845-8161
Web: WWW.TAMU.EDU

HISTORICAL FINANCIALS

Company Type: Private

Income Statement
FYE: June 30

	ASSETS ($ mil.)	NET INCOME ($ mil.)	INCOME AS % OF ASSETS	EMPLOYEES
06/13	1,505	97	6.5%	95
06/12	1,313	66	5.0%	—
06/11	1,313	43	3.3%	—
06/10	1,238	0	—	—
Annual Growth	6.7%	—	—	—

2013 Year-End Financials

Return on assets: 1.1%
Return on equity: 52.3%
Sales ($ mil): 186

TEXAS AROMATICS LP

Auditors: WEAVER AND TIDWELL LLP HOUSTO

LOCATIONS

HQ: TEXAS AROMATICS LP
3555 TIMMONS LN STE 700, HOUSTON, TX
770276450
Phone: 713 520-2900
Web: WWW.TEXASAROMATICS.COM

HISTORICAL FINANCIALS

Company Type: Private

Income Statement

FYE: December 31

	REVENUE ($ mil.)	NET INCOME ($ mil.)	NET PROFIT MARGIN	EMPLOYEES
12/13	1,033	13	1.3%	17
12/12	1,073	18	1.7%	—
12/11	928	10	1.2%	—
12/10	782	0	—	—
Annual Growth	9.7%			

2013 Year-End Financials

Return on assets: 3.4%
Return on equity: 1.3%
Current ratio: 1.50

Cash ($ mil.): 28

TEXAS CHRISTIAN UNIVERSITY INC

Home of the Horned Frogs (the school mascot) Texas Christian University (TCU) offers bachelor's master's and doctorate degrees in more than 200 fields of study. More than 10300 undergraduate and graduate students attend the university's nine colleges and schools the cover fields of study ranging from liberal arts to engineering to business. TCU has about 550 full-time faculty members and a student-to-faculty ratio of 13:1. It also has one of the NCAA's top football programs. TCU is affiliated with the Disciples of Christ a Protestant denomination.

Geographic Reach

TCU's campus takes up about 280 acres about five miles from downtown Fort Worth.

Operations

The TCU academic programs are organized under nine schools in fields including liberal arts communication education fine arts science and engineering nursing and health and business. It offers 117 bachelors 62 masters and 25 doctoral degrees.

Tuition fees room and board and books cost about $50940 per year.

Financial Performance

The university reported a 2014-2015 annual budget of $547 million. It had total investments (as at June 30 2014) of $1.44 billion.

Strategy

TCU is investing in facility upgrades and enhancement efforts as part of its strategic plan entitled Academy of Tomorrow. Over the past few years the school has invested about $430 million in upgrading academic administrative recreational and residence facilities including the construction of a new commons building on the eastern end of its campus. In 2014 it began work on a new library.

TCU also expands its academic programs; in 2013 it added new master's degrees in social work and criminal justice and criminology. .

Company Background

Brothers Addison and Randolph Clark established the school in 1873 as Addran Male and Female College (the school changed its name to Texas Christian University in 1902).

EXECUTIVES

Chancellor, Victor J. Boschini
Vice Chancellor Academic Affairs and Provost, R. Nowell Donovan
Vice Chancellor Finance and Administration, Brian G. Gutierrez
Chief Investment Officer, James R. Hille
Dean Mary Couts Burnett Library, June Koelker
Director Technical Services, Bryan Lucas
Dean Harris College of Nursing and Health Sciences, Paulette Burns
Dean AddRan College of Liberal Arts, F. Andrew Schoolmaster
Dean Neeley School of Business, O. Homer Erekson
Dean College of Communication, David Whillock
Dean College of Fine Arts, Scott A. Sullivan
Dean College of Science and Engineering, Philip S. Hartman
Dean Brite Divinity School, Joretta Marshall
Division President, Kathy Cavins-Tull
Director of Admissions, Sandra Mackey
Department Chair, Harry Parker
Vice President Of New, Leah Reynolds
Financial Vice President Of Delta Sigma Pi, Julie Brandenburg
Panhellenic Vice President Recruitment, Simone Elices
Vice President, Dillon Cook
Sigma Kappa Vice President Of Communication, Alexandra Kester
Sigma Phi Epsilon Vice President Of Communications, Dillon Smith
Department Chairman, William Graham
Executive Vice President And Dean, Nancy Ramsay
Vice President Finance, Carol Campbell
Student Body Vice President For External Affairs, Hillary Shepheard
Vice President Sales Operations, Eric Davis
Chairman, Clarence Scharbauer
Vice Chairman, Mark L. Johnson
Board Member, Julie O'Neil
Treasurer, Hillary Roberts
Auditors: PRICEWATERHOUSECOOPERS LLP FO

LOCATIONS

HQ: TEXAS CHRISTIAN UNIVERSITY INC
2800 S UNIVERSITY DR, FORT WORTH, TX
761290002
Phone: 817 257-7000
Web: WWW.TCU.EDU

PRODUCTS/OPERATIONS

Selected Colleges and Schools

AddRan College of Liberal Arts
College of Communication
College of Education
College of Fine Arts
College of Science and Engineering
Harris College of Nursing and Health Sciences
John V. Roach Honors College
Neeley School of Business
Relationship with Brite Divinity School

HISTORICAL FINANCIALS

Company Type: Private

Income Statement

FYE: May 31

	REVENUE ($ mil.)	NET INCOME ($ mil.)	NET PROFIT MARGIN	EMPLOYEES
05/13	401	270	67.3%	3,400
05/12	441	(4)	—	—
05/09	263	0	—	—
05/05	216	0	—	—
Annual Growth	8.0%	—	—	—

2013 Year-End Financials

Return on assets: —
Return on equity: 67.3%
Current ratio: —

Cash ($ mil.): 3

TEXAS COUNTY AND DISTRICT RETIREMENT SYSTEM

LOCATIONS

HQ: TEXAS COUNTY AND DISTRICT RETIREMENT SYSTEM
901 S MO PAC EXPY IV500, AUSTIN, TX 787465776
Phone: 512 328-8889
Web: WWW.TCDRS.ORG

HISTORICAL FINANCIALS

Company Type: Private

Income Statement

FYE: December 31

	ASSETS ($ mil.)	NET INCOME ($ mil.)	INCOME AS % OF ASSETS	EMPLOYEES
12/11	17,828	(101)	—	108
12/10	18,116	2,178	12.0%	—
12/09	16,287	3,503	21.5%	—
12/08	12,833	0	—	—
Annual Growth	11.6%			

2011 Year-End Financials

Return on assets: —
Return on equity: (-14.1%)

Sales ($ mil.): 718

TEXAS GUARANTEED STUDENT LOAN CORPORATION

TG may sound like a college fraternity but it's more about tuition and books than togas and beer. Texas Guaranteed Student Loan Corporation commonly known as TG was formed by the Texas legislature in 1979 to administer the Federal Family Education Loan Program (FFELP) in the Lone Star State. However the FFELP was eliminated in 2010 and private borrowers can no longer originate government-sponsored student loans which are now provided exclusively through the US Department of Education. TG continues to service and provide support for the approximately $26 billion worth of loans in its existing portfolio. TG is a public not-for-profit corporation that receives no state funding.

Financial Performance

TG is comprised of two funds: the Operating Fund which is the property of TG and the Federal Fund considered the property of the US government. In fiscal 2012 (ended September) TG's total revenue increased by 17% to $134.3 million versus $115.2 million in fiscal 2011. Of that revenue from the Operating Fund accounted for 88% of the total with the Federal Fund representing the rest.

Total assets in fiscal 2012 were $832.1 million versus $828.6 million the prior year.

EXECUTIVES

Assistant Vice President Research and Analytical Services, Jeff Webster
Assistant Vice President Congressional And Legislative Relations, George Torres
Vice President Manager Director, Dianne Ivy
Assistant Vice President and Portfolio Manager, Cal Abbott
Vice President Policy Compliance, Carol Lindsey
Senior Vice President General counsel Chief Ethics Officer, Deanne Varner
Vice President, Andy Levy
Assistant Vice President Customer Assistance, Sam Wilson
Vice President Customer Focus, Kim Alexander
Vice President Manager Director, Janet Langley
Assistant Vice President Enterprise Project Management Office, Jim Zimmerman

LOCATIONS

HQ: TEXAS GUARANTEED STUDENT LOAN CORPORATION
301 SUNDANCE PKWY, ROUND ROCK, TX 786818004
Phone: 512 219-5700
Web: WWW.TGSLC.ORG

COMPETITORS

Brazos Higher Education Service Corp.
Nelnet
Sallie Mae

HISTORICAL FINANCIALS

Company Type: Private

Income Statement   FYE: September 30

	ASSETS ($ mil.)	NET INCOME ($ mil.)	INCOME AS % OF ASSETS	EMPLOYEES
09/13	551	(210)	—	600
09/08	783	(64)	—	—
09/05	520	60	11.6%	—
09/04	459	0	—	—
Annual Growth	2.0%	—	—	—

2013 Year-End Financials

Return on assets: 25.8%   Sales ($ mil): 165
Return on equity: (-127.6%)

TEXAS HEALTH HARRIS METHODIST HOSPITAL FORT WORTH

Harris Methodist Fort Worth Hospital is the largest and busiest hospital in Fort Worth. It is a private not-for-profit almost 730-bed tertiary care hospital serving the residents of Tarrant County and nearby communities in Texas. Harris Methodist provides both inpatient and outpatient care through its main medical center and on-site health clinics. Specialized services include emergency medicine trauma care orthopedics occupational health women's health oncology and rehabilitation. Its Harris Methodist Heart Center has about 100 beds. The hospital is the flagship facility of the Texas Health Resources hospitals system.

Operations

Harris Methodist also known as Texas Health Harris Methodist Hospital Fort Worth serves as a regional referral center. The hospital employs a medical staff of about 1000 physicians.

Sales and Marketing

To promote its services to area residents Harris Methodist uses a range of marketing avenues including print television online radio and outdoor advertising.

Strategy

To meet the growing needs of Fort Worth area residents in 2012 Harris Methodist launched a $58 million construction project to add a new emergency care center adjacent to the medical center campus. The 75000-sq. ft. center scheduled for completion in 2014 will increase the hospital's emergency room capacity from about 60 beds to 90 beds. A sky bridge will connect the new emergency care center to the main hospital.

Mergers and Acquisitions

To further expand outpatient services in 2012 Harris Methodist acquired the Clear Fork Surgery Center (now named Texas Health Outpatient Surgery Center Fort Worth). The ambulatory surgery center is located on the Harris Methodist hospital campus and was previously operated through a venture with Symbion and a group of physicians. The center performs about 10000 procedures per year.

Company Background

The organization opened its doors in 1930 the leadership of Dr. Charles Harris and the Methodist Church.

EXECUTIVES

Managing Director, Joe Lacy
Respiratory Therapy Director, Gloria Boyer
Auditors: TEXAS HEALTH RESOURCES ARLING

LOCATIONS

HQ: TEXAS HEALTH HARRIS METHODIST HOSPITAL FORT WORTH
1301 PENNSYLVANIA AVE, FORT WORTH, TX 761042122
Phone: 817 250-2000
Web: WWW.TEXASHEALTH.ORG

PRODUCTS/OPERATIONS

Selected Centers and Services
Breast Center
Breastfeeding Resource Center
Business Health Services
Cancer
Complementary or Alternative Medicine
Diabetes
Emergency Trauma Services
Executive Health Program
Fitness Center
Heart and Vascular
Gastroenterology
Home Health
Hospitalist Program
Imaging
Infertility
Mobile Health Unit
Neurosciences
Occupational Health
Orthopedics
Outpatient Physical Therapy
Respiratory
Weight Loss
Texas Health Physician Offices Saginaw
Palliative Care
Rehabilitation
Sports Medicine
Primary Stroke Center
Surgery
Texas Health Physician Offices Keller
Vascular and Interventional Radiology
Women and Infants
Wound Care

COMPETITORS

Baylor University Medical Center
JPS Health Network
Parkland Health &

Cook Children's Health Care System
HCA
HealthSouth
Hospital System
Tenet Healthcare
The Methodist Health System

HISTORICAL FINANCIALS

Company Type: Private

Income Statement   FYE: December 31

	REVENUE ($ mil.)	NET INCOME ($ mil.)	NET PROFIT MARGIN	EMPLOYEES
12/13	713	59	8.4%	3,500
12/06	548	36	6.7%	—
12/05	501	56	11.3%	—
12/04	1,131	0	—	—
Annual Growth	—	—	—	—

2013 Year-End Financials

Return on assets: 11.3%   Cash ($ mil.): 1
Return on equity: 8.4%
Current ratio: 1.30

TEXAS STATE UNIVERSITY

Texas State University-San Marcos is saddled up and ready to rope some graduates. The school has about 37000 students pursuing degrees in about 100 undergraduate programs nearly 90 graduate programs and a dozen doctoral programs. Comprising eight colleges as well as a graduate school Texas State is the largest school in the Texas State University system which includes Angelo State University Lamar University Sam Houston State University and Sul Ross State University. It also offers bachelor's and graduate-level courses at a campus in Round Rock.

Geographic Reach

Texas State's main campus in the Central Texas community of San Marcos consists of some 490 acres. The university also operates some 5000 acres of recreational and instruction properties in the area.

Strategy

As Texas State is ranked among the top US colleges for awarding degrees to bachelor's degrees to Hispanic students the university targets a portion of its marketing efforts towards minority students. About 35% of its student body is composed of ethnic minorities. Texas State also enrolls student through international efforts.

To accommodate its growing student base Texas State has been expanding its campus facilities. For instance it opened its Performing Arts Center in 2014.

Also that year the school became a member of the American Academic Research Institute in Iraq (TAARII) which promotes scholarly research on Iraq and ancient Mesopotamia by providing graduate and post-graduate fellowships for Americans and Iraqis. Other TAARII members include Columbia University Georgetown University and Harvard.

Company Background

The former Southwest Texas State University (the name was changed in 2003) was originally a teacher's college founded by the state legislature in 1903.

EXECUTIVES

Vp Finance And Support Services, William Nance

Vice President of Academic Affairs, Robert (Bob) Gratz

Associate Vp Planning, Nancy Nusbaum

President, Denise M. Trauth

VP Student Affairs, Joanne Smith

Provost and VP Academic Affairs, Eugene J. (Gene) Bourgeois

VP University Advancement, Barbara Breier

VP Finance and Support Services, Eric Algoe

VP Information Technology, Ken Pierce

Presidential Fellow, Lisa Kay Lloyd

Dean College of Applied Arts, Jaime Chahin

Dean McCoy College of Business Administration, Denise T. Smart

Dean College of Education, Stan Carpenter

Dean College of Fine Arts and Communication, John Fleming

Dean College of Health Professions, Ruth B. Welborn

Dean Honors College, Heather C. Galloway

Dean College of Liberal Arts, Michael J. Hennessy

Interim Dean College of Science and Engineering, Robert Habingreither

Dean University College, Daniel A. Brown

Dean The Graduate College, Andrea Golato

Associate Vice President Technology Resources T, Mark Hughes

V Pres-financial Services, Terry Ondreyka

Assoc Vice President Facilities, Juan Guerra

Associate Vice President University Library, Joan Heath

Assistant Vice President Development, Ted Mckinnon

Assistant Vice President For Fin Services Treasurer, VALERIE R (Val) VAN VLACK

Associate Vice President Instructional Technologies Support T, Milt Nielsen

Associate Vice President Academic Affairs, Debbie Marie Thorne

Associate Vice President For Student Affairs and Dean of Students, Margarita Arellano

Vice President For Information Technology, CARL V VAN WYATT

Assistant Vice President For Research, Michael Blanda

Vice President Of Alumni Affairs, Eva Garza

Vice President, Nathan Salazar

Vice President Student Affairs, James Studer

Assistant Vice President Enrollmt Management Undgrad Admis, Stephanie J Anderson

Vice President Information Technology, C Van Wyatt

Assistant Vice President, T Cay Rowe

Associate Vice President For Research And Federal, Billy Covington

Vice President For Finance Support Services, William A (Bill) Nance

LOCATIONS

HQ: TEXAS STATE UNIVERSITY
601 UNIVERSITY DR, SAN MARCOS, TX 786664684
Phone: 512 245-2111
Web: WWW.CAREERSERVICES.TXSTATE.EDU

PRODUCTS/OPERATIONS

Schools and Colleges
College of Applied Arts
College of Education
College of Fine Arts and Communication
College of Health Professions
College of Liberal Arts
College of Science
The Graduate College
McCoy College of Business Administration
University College (general studies)

HISTORICAL FINANCIALS
Company Type: Private

Income Statement
FYE: August 31

	REVENUE ($ mil.)	NET INCOME ($ mil.)	NET PROFIT MARGIN	EMPLOYEES
08/14	377	73	19.4%	3,156
08/13	329	61	18.6%	—
08/12	330	19	5.8%	—
08/11	313	0	—	—
Annual Growth	6.4%	—	—	—

2014 Year-End Financials
Return on assets: 8.2%
Return on equity: 19.4%
Current ratio: 1.20
Cash ($ mil.): 250

THE AEROSPACE CORPORATION

A not-for-profit company The Aerospace Corporation provides space-related research development and advisory services primarily for US government programs. Its chief sponsor is the US Air Force and its main customers have included the Space and Missile Systems Center of Air Force Space Command and the National Reconnaissance Office. Other clients have included NASA and the National Oceanic and Atmospheric Administration as well as commercial enterprises universities and international organizations. Areas of expertise include launch certification process implementation systems engineering and technology application. The Aerospace Corporation was established in 1960 and operates through about 20 offices.

Geographic Reach

The US relies on space systems for intelligence communications navigation and weather making Aerospace's mission assurance and systems engineering services vital to national security.

Operations

Officially The Aerospace Corporation operates a federally funded research and development center or FFRDC for the Air Force. The Aerospace FFRDC is one of more than 40 established to help government agencies with tasks related to aviation defense energy health and human services space and tax administration.

Strategy

Among the company's projects are work on the next generation of satellites including the Global Positioning System IIF Space Based Space Surveillance Advanced Extremely High Frequency Wideband Global Satcom and Space Based Infrared System programs. These new satellites will provide new capabilities and replace systems from the 1970s and 1980s.

Scientists at The Aerospace Corporation also have been developing a nanosatellite to test high-efficiency solar cells under space conditions. Solar cells made by Spectrolab (a subsidiary of Boeing Space and Intelligence Systems) and EMCORE convert sunlight into electricity. The nanosatellite only 14 pounds is one of many such small satellites pioneered by Aerospace. Compared to larger satellites nanosatellites are less expensive to launch and operate.

EXECUTIVES

Senior Vice President General Counsel Secretary, Gordon L Louttit, age 69

President and CEO, Wanda M. Austin

EVP, David J. Gorney

General Manager Computers and Software, William C. (Willie) Krenz

Acting Principal Director Finance Directorate Assistant CFO and Assistant Treasurer, Ellen M. Beatty

SVP Operations and Support Group, Wayne H. Goodman

VP Space Launch Operations, Randolph L. (Randy) Kendall

VP Space Program Operations, Malina M Hills

Vice President Of Marketing, Diana Cannon

Vice President Director Manager, Mindy Dayton

Vice President Director Manager, Marsha Pradia

Vice President, Gary P Pulliam

Vice President Technology, Sherrie Zacharius

Vice President Space Program Operations, Stephen Burrin

Executive Vice President, Michael Daugherty

Senior Vice President Systems Planning And Engineering, Rodney C (Rod) Gibson

Vice President Director Manager, Moria Cunningham

Vice President of Strategic Space Operations, Glenn Davis

Vice President Director Manager, James (Jamie) Jusko

Vice President Director Manager, Catherine A (Cathy) James

Vice President, George Paulikas

Senior Vice President Technology, John (Jack) Parsons

Vice President, Shirley Dohzen

Vice President Technology, Lawrence Greenberg

Vice President And Associate General C, Malissia Clinton

Chairman, Barbara M. Barrett, age 63

Vice Chairman, Gen. George K. Muellner

Assistant Secretary, Mabel Oshiro

Board Member, Kathryn Brenan

Auditors: DELOITTE & TOUCHE LLP LOS ANG

LOCATIONS

HQ: THE AEROSPACE CORPORATION
2310 E EL SEGUNDO BLVD, EL SEGUNDO, CA 902454609
Phone: 310 336-5000
Web: WWW.AEROSPACE.ORG

PRODUCTS/OPERATIONS

Selected Services
Civil and Commercial
CORDS
Cyber Security
Labs
Launch Support
Mission Assurance
Systems Engineering
Technical Resources

COMPETITORS

AKKA Technologies
Orbital Research
QinetiQ

HISTORICAL FINANCIALS
Company Type: Private

Income Statement
FYE: September 30

	REVENUE ($ mil.)	NET INCOME ($ mil.)	NET PROFIT MARGIN	EMPLOYEES
09/14	881	5	0.6%	3,920
09/13	868	0	0.0%	—
09/12	903	4	0.5%	—
09/11	939	0	—	—
Annual Growth	(2.1%)	—	—	—

Return on assets: 3.5% Cash ($ mil.): 14
Return on equity: 0.6%
Current ratio: 0.20

THE ALICE BYRD TAWES NURSING HOME INC

Auditors: SCOTT TAWED & ASSOCIATES PA

LOCATIONS

HQ: THE ALICE BYRD TAWES NURSING HOME INC
201 HALL HWY, CRISFIELD, MD 218171237
Phone: 410 968-1200
Web: WWW.MCCREADYFOUNDATION.ORG

HISTORICAL FINANCIALS
Company Type: Private

Income Statement
FYE: June 30

	REVENUE ($ mil.)	NET INCOME ($ mil.)	NET PROFIT MARGIN	EMPLOYEES
06/09	478	9	2.0%	280
06/01	3	0	0.9%	—
06/00	2	(0)	—	—
06/99	2	0	—	—
Annual Growth 68.5%		—	—	—

2009 Year-End Financials

Return on assets: — Cash ($ mil.): —
Return on equity: 2.0%
Current ratio: 0.30

THE AMALGAMATED SUGAR COMPANY LLC

The Amalgamated Sugar Company with roots reaching back to 1915 turns beets into sweets. It's the second-largest US sugar producer processing sugar beets grown on about 180000 acres in Idaho Oregon and Washington. The company manufactures granulated coarse powdered and brown consumer sugar products marketed under the brand White Satin. It also makes products for retail grocery chains under private labels. The sugar company produces beet pulp molasses and other beet by-products for use by food and animal-feed manufacturers. Since 1997 Amalgamated Sugar has been owned by the Snake River Sugar Company a cooperative that comprises sugar beet growers in Idaho Oregon and Washington.

Geographic Reach
The Idaho-based company's sugar beets which are grown in Idaho Oregon and Washington are processed through the three sugar processing facilities it operates in Idaho. The Amalgamated Sugar Company's warehouses and bulk transfer stations are strategically located from the Midwest to the West Coast.

Operations
The Amalgamated Sugar Company processes up to 1.6 billion pounds of sugar each year. Along with processing the cooperative's crops the company provides its owner-farmers with agronomy advice and services runs workshops and seminars operates a co-op store and sells used equipment.

The company's key management team is employed on a contract basis. A seven-member Management Committee oversees the management team. The committee comprises members of the cooperative's board of directors.

Strategy
The industry's return to the use of real sugar in soft drinks and other beverages has become a boon for The Amalgamated Sugar Company. To this end Pepsi Bottling Ventures has tapped the sugar beet processor to supply the bottler with granulated sugar. During the past few decades more beverage makers have moved to using lesser-expensive high fructose corn syrup (HFCS) to sweeten their beverages as a way to cut costs and boost profits but the shift spurred by consumers to return to sugar-sweetened drinks has become profitable for sugar processors the likes of The Amalgamated Sugar Company.

Sales and Marketing
The Amalgamated Sugar Company markets its sugar primarily in the nation's North Central Intermountain and Northwest regions. The company competes with not only cane sugar refiners but also manufacturers of other forms of sweeteners such as regular and high fructose corn syrup (HFCS) and non-nutritive high intensity sweeteners the likes of aspartame.

Financial Performance
The Amalgamated Sugar Company generates some 90% of its annual sales through the sale of refined sugar. The balance of its revenue comes from animal feed derived from beet pulp and molasses and other by-products as a result of sugar beet processing.

Company Ownership
The company is owned by Snake River Sugar Company a sugar beet grower cooperative operating in three US states.

EXECUTIVES

VP and COO, Joe Huff
President and CEO, John McCreedy
VP Finance and CFO, John Landis
Chairman, Duane Grant
General Counsel and Secretary, Scott Blickenstaff
Auditors: EIDE BAILLY LLP BOISE IDAHO

LOCATIONS

HQ: THE AMALGAMATED SUGAR COMPANY LLC
1951 S SATURN WAY STE 100, BOISE, ID 837092924
Phone: 208 658-2243
Web: WWW.AMALGAMATEDSUGAR.COM

PRODUCTS/OPERATIONS

Selected Products
Bakers' special sugar
Brown sugar
Dark brown sugar
Extra-fine granulated sugar
Fine granulated sugar
Gel gran granulated sugar
Industrial coarse sugar
Powdered sugar 10x and 12x
Sugar packets
Sugar standards
Type 50 medium invert sugar
Type O liquid sucrose (66.5 brix)
Type O liquid sucrose (67.5 brix)

COMPETITORS

Alico Inc.
American Crystal Sugar
Associated British Foods
C&H Sugar
Cosun
Cumberland Packing
Eurosugar
Florida Crystals

Imperial Sugar
Ingredion
M. A. Patout
Merisant
Michigan Sugar Company
Minn-Dak Co-op
Nippon Beet Sugar
Nordzucker
NutraSweet
SMBSC
Sterling Sugars
Sugar Cane Growers Cooperative of Florida
Sdzucker
U.S. Sugar
Western Sugar Cooperative

HISTORICAL FINANCIALS
Company Type: Private

Income Statement
FYE: December 31

	REVENUE ($ mil.)	NET INCOME ($ mil.)	NET PROFIT MARGIN	EMPLOYEES
12/13	953	62	6.6%	1,500
12/12	907	14	1.6%	—
12/11	886	46	5.3%	—
12/10	841	0	—	—
Annual Growth 4.2%		—	—	—

2013 Year-End Financials

Return on assets: — Cash ($ mil.): 1
Return on equity: 6.6%
Current ratio: 0.10

THE AMERICAN MUSEUM OF NATURAL HISTORY

The American Museum of Natural History is one of the world's foremost scientific museums. Its landmark building on New York's Central Park West showcases parts of its immense collections of anthropological and zoological specimens along with meteorites gemstones dinosaur fossils and a butterfly conservatory. The museum which is also home to the Rose Center for Earth and Space and the Hayden Planetarium and a top-flight research library conducts many educational programs offers an IMAX theater and publishes Natural History magazine. The American Museum of Natural History is part of the University of the State of New York. The museum was chartered by the New York legislature in 1869.

Geographic Reach
More than 4 million people visit the museum each year more than a third of which are international tourists.

Operations
Behind the scenes at the American Museum of Natural History more than 200 scientists work in its anthropology vertebrate and invertebrate zoology paleontology and physical sciences divisions. Also the museum boasts the Richard Gilder Graduate School which is authorized to grant the Ph.D. degree in comparative biology.

Sales and Marketing
Many of the museum's exhibits are marketed towards children.

EXECUTIVES

President, Ellen V. Futter, age 66

SVP and CFO, Ellen Gallagher
Senior Management (Senior Vice President General Manager Director), Michael (Mel) Benedetto
Vice Chairman, Richard S. LeFrak, age 68
Chairman, Lewis W. Bernard, age 72
Vice Chairman, Fiona Druckenmiller
Vice Chairman, Louis V. Gerstner
Vice Chairman, David S. Gottesman
Vice Chairman, Linda R. Macaulay
Vice Chairman, Christopher Davis
Vice Chairman, Roberto Mignone
Treasurer, Sue Rudavsky
Auditors: GRANT THORNTON LLP NEW YORK

LOCATIONS

HQ: THE AMERICAN MUSEUM OF NATURAL HISTORY
CENTRAL PARK W AT 79TH ST, NEW YORK, NY 10024
Phone: 212 769-5000
Web: WWW.AMNH.ORG

HISTORICAL FINANCIALS
Company Type: Private

Income Statement
FYE: June 30

	REVENUE ($ mil.)	NET INCOME ($ mil.)	NET PROFIT MARGIN	EMPLOYEES
06/13	197	7	4.0%	1,262
06/09	135	(53)	—	—
06/07	163	100	61.3%	—
06/06	0	0	—	—
Annual Growth	—	—	—	—

2013 Year-End Financials
Return on assets: 17.5% Cash ($ mil.): 50
Return on equity: 4.0%
Current ratio: 0.20

THE ANNENBERG FOUNDATION

Auditors: GRANT THORNTON LLP LOS ANGEL

LOCATIONS

HQ: THE ANNENBERG FOUNDATION
101 W ELM ST STE 324, CONSHOHOCKEN, PA 194282075
Phone: 610 397-1800
Web: WWW.ANNENBERG.ORG

HISTORICAL FINANCIALS
Company Type: Private

Income Statement
FYE: June 30

	ASSETS ($ mil.)	NET INCOME ($ mil.)	INCOME AS % OF ASSETS	EMPLOYEES
06/11	1,720	136	7.9%	45
06/10	1,616	(22)	—	—
06/06	278	0	—	—
Annual Growth	43.9%	—	—	—

2011 Year-End Financials
Return on assets: 1.6% Sales ($ mil): 249
Return on equity: 54.6%

THE ASSOCIATED PRESS

This just in: The Associated Press (AP) is reporting tonight and every night wherever news is breaking. AP is one of the world's largest news gathering organizations with news bureaus in about 100 countries. It provides news photos graphics and audiovisual services that reach people daily through print radio TV and the Web. It also offers advertising management and distribution services. The not-for-profit cooperative is owned by 1500 US daily newspaper members. A group of New York newspapers founded the AP in 1846 in order to chronicle the US-Mexican War more efficiently. Founding papers include The New York Sun The Journal of Commerce The Courier and Enquirer The New York Herald and The Express.

Geographic Reach

The Associated Press is headquartered in New York City. The AP serves 1700 newspapers and 5000 radio and television outlets in the US many of which are members.

Operations

The AP has about 3200 employees globally working around 280 locations worldwide.

Financial Performance

In fiscal 2014 the AP's total annual revenue increased by 1% to $604 million compared to $595 million in fiscal 2013. The company's net income increased dramatically to $140 million in fiscal 2014 compared to $3.26 million in fiscal 2013 mainly due to increased gross revenue and interest income.

Strategy

In recent years the AP has shifted its focus away from providing content to newspapers and towards serving online media sources; some of the company's biggest customers now include media outlets such as Google MSN and Yahoo!. It has also focused on developing AP Direct its live video news agency service. It sells its back catalog of video through AP Video Archives.

To cope with the decline in print readership the news co-op is continuing to invest in digital initiatives. It is currently undergoing a multimillion-dollar upgrade of its newsgathering infrastructure to increase its video coverage of global events. It is also pushing to increase its high definition footage to broadcast and digital markets and ensure that its video and images integrate seamlessly with new digital workflows to drive value for customers.

HISTORY

The Associated Press traces its roots to 1846 when New York Sun publisher Moses Yale Beach agreed to share news arriving by telegraph about the Mexican-American War with four other New York newspapers. The cooperative news gathering effort was later established as the AP which began selling wire reports to other papers and started creating regional associations. Adapting to changing technologies and public interests AP began covering sports financial and public interest stories in the 1920s and was selling news reports to radio stations in the 1940s. Advancements during WWII included using transatlantic cable and radio-teletype circuits to deliver news and photos.

In the late 1960s AP and Dow Jones introduced services to improve business and financial reporting. AP improved photo delivery reception and storage in the 1970s with the advent of Laserphoto and the Electronic Darkroom. It began transmitting news by satellite and offering color photographs to newspapers in the 1980s. In 1985 Louis Boccardi took over the job as president and CEO of AP.

AP adjusted to the media-heavy culture of the 1990s by launching the APTV international news video service and the All News Radio network in 1994. It then moved onto the Internet with The WIRE in 1996 and began offering online access to its Photo Archive in 1997. It bought Worldwide Television News in 1998 combining it with APTV to form AP Television News Limited (APTN). The following year it purchased the radio news contracts of UPI after the rival organization announced it was getting out of broadcast news.

In 2000 AP created an Internet division AP Digital to focus on marketing news to online providers. The cooperative continued its Internet focus the following year launching AP Online en Español (news for Spanish-language websites) and AP Entertainment Online (multimedia entertainment news for websites). Also that year AP bought the Newspaper Industry Communication Center from the Newspaper Association of America.

In 2002 the company launched an expanded editorial partnership with Dow Jones Newswires increasing the amount of financial news distributed on AP wires. Later that year it acquired Capitolwire a provider of state government news. Boccardi stepped down as CEO in 2003 handing the reins to former USA TODAY publisher Tom Curley.

AP relocated in 2004 from Rockefeller Plaza (its home for 65 years) to a new headquarters on the west side of Manhattan that features a 105000-sq.-ft. newsroom and serves as a central hub of digital news streams.

The organization moved to strengthen its sports information coverage in 2005 merging its AP MegaSports operation with News Corporation's STATS Inc. to form STATS LLC a 50-50 joint venture that provides sports-related information content and statistical applications.

The following year AP launched The Online Video Network (OVN) service to provide news video to AP member and customer websites. The co-op responded to the harsh economy by cutting costs in 2008 with consolidation of its print broadcast and digital sales and marketing units. It continued its cost-cutting efforts in 2009 when it cut some 90 jobs instituted a hiring freeze and bought out about 100 employees.

EXECUTIVES

Vice President Global Security, Danny Spriggs
Vice President Business Operations Global Newspaper Markets, Joy Jones
Vice President Ap Images, Fernando Ferre
Vice President Global Development, Joy Jackson
Vice President Of AP Images, Fernando Ferer

LOCATIONS

HQ: THE ASSOCIATED PRESS
450 W 33RD ST FL 16, NEW YORK, NY 100012626
Phone: 212 621-1500
Web: WWW.AP.ORG

PRODUCTS/OPERATIONS

Selected Products and Services
AP Digital News (Internet and wireless news delivery)
AP Images (photo services)
AP Mobile (mobile applications)
APTN (AP Television News international television news service)
ENPS (electronic news production system)
Online Video Network (video content distribution)

COMPETITORS

Agence France-Presse	GlobeNewswire
Bloomberg L.P.	Marketwire
Business Wire	New York Times
Comtex News	PR Newswire
Corbis	Reuters
Dow Jones	TEGNA

E. W. Scripps Tribune Media
Getty Images   UPI

HISTORICAL FINANCIALS
Company Type: Private

Income Statement
FYE: December 31

	REVENUE ($ mil.)	NET INCOME ($ mil.)	NET PROFIT MARGIN	EMPLOYEES
12/13	595	3	0.5%	3,533
12/12	622	(25)	—	—
12/11	627	(193)	—	—
12/10	630	0	—	—
Annual Growth	(1.9%)	—	—	—

2013 Year-End Financials
Return on assets: 1.7% Cash ($ mil.): 14
Return on equity: 0.5%
Current ratio: 0.60

THE BIG TEN CONFERENCE INC

Auditors: RSM MCGLADREY INC CHICAGO IL

LOCATIONS
HQ: THE BIG TEN CONFERENCE INC
 1500 HICCINS RD, PARK RIDGE, IL 600685735
Phone: 847 696-1010

HISTORICAL FINANCIALS
Company Type: Private

Income Statement
FYE: June 30

	REVENUE ($ mil.)	NET INCOME ($ mil.)	NET PROFIT MARGIN	EMPLOYEES
06/13	318	5	1.9%	25
06/11	265	(0)	—	—
06/10	232	(4)	—	—
06/09	221	0	—	—
Annual Growth	9.4%	—	—	—

2013 Year-End Financials
Return on assets: 1.9% Cash ($ mil.): 35
Return on equity: 1.9%
Current ratio: 1.90

THE BOLDT GROUP INC

Auditors: SCHENCK SC CPAS APPLETON WI

LOCATIONS
HQ: THE BOLDT GROUP INC
 2525 N ROEMER RD, APPLETON, WI 549118623
Phone: 920 739-7800

HISTORICAL FINANCIALS
Company Type: Private

Income Statement
FYE: December 31

	REVENUE ($ mil.)	NET INCOME ($ mil.)	NET PROFIT MARGIN	EMPLOYEES
12/13	715	0	—	1,500
12/12	624	0	—	—
12/11	640	6	1.0%	—
12/10	0	0	—	—
Annual Growth				

2013 Year-End Financials
Return on assets: 13.3% Cash ($ mil.): 41
Return on equity: —
Current ratio: 1.10

THE BRANCH GROUP INC

It's not going out on a limb to say that The Branch Group has paved a lot of roads and built a lot of structures up and down the Atlantic Seaboard. The company through its subsidiaries provides heavy/highway construction (Branch Highways and E.V. Williams) building construction (Branch & Associates and R.E. Daffan) and mechanical/electrical construction services (G.J. Hopkins). The group has paved roads for highway departments built hospitals schools factories and infrastructure projects. The employee-owned company began in 1963 as Branch & Associates Inc. but traces its roots to 1955 when Billy Branch and C. W. McAlister paired up to provide road and site construction services.

EXECUTIVES
Vice President Administration, Melanie Wheeler
Auditors: KPMG LLP ROANOKE VIRGINIA

LOCATIONS
HQ: THE BRANCH GROUP INC
 442 RUTHERFORD AVE NE, ROANOKE, VA
 240162116
Phone: 540 982-1678
Web: WWW.BRANCHGROUP.COM

PRODUCTS/OPERATIONS

Selected Subsidiaries
Branch & Associates Inc. (builder construction services)
Branch Highways Inc. (highway bridge airport infrastructure and site development)
E.V. Williams Inc. (highway site development and concrete paving construction servives)
G.J. Hopkins Inc. (mechanical and electrical construction services)
R. E. Daffan (construction and architectural services)

COMPETITORS

Bechtel	KBS
English Construction Company	S. W. Rodgers
Fluor	Tetra Tech Tesoro
K3 Construction	Turner Corporation
	Whiting-Turner

HISTORICAL FINANCIALS
Company Type: Private

Income Statement
FYE: December 31

	REVENUE ($ mil.)	NET INCOME ($ mil.)	NET PROFIT MARGIN	EMPLOYEES
12/13	326	0	—	800
12/12	271	0	—	—
12/11	238	0	—	—
12/10	228	0	—	—
Annual Growth	12.7%	—	—	—

2013 Year-End Financials
Return on assets: 15.0% Cash ($ mil.): 43
Return on equity: —
Current ratio: 0.80

THE BROAD INSTITUTE INC

Auditors: PRICEWATERHOUSECOOPERS LLP BO

LOCATIONS
HQ: THE BROAD INSTITUTE INC
 7 CAMBRIDGE CTR 7034, CAMBRIDGE, MA
 021421401
Phone: 617 714-7000
Web: WWW.BROADINSTITUTE.ORG

HISTORICAL FINANCIALS
Company Type: Private

Income Statement
FYE: June 30

	REVENUE ($ mil.)	NET INCOME ($ mil.)	NET PROFIT MARGIN	EMPLOYEES
06/13	356	73	20.6%	800
06/10	785	549	70.0%	—
Annual Growth	(23.1%)	(48.8%)	—	—

2013 Year-End Financials
Return on assets: 16.1% Cash ($ mil.): 56
Return on equity: 20.6%
Current ratio: 0.20

THE BROTHER'S BROTHER FOUNDATION

He ain't heavy he's my brother's brother. The lyrics aren't quite right but the sentiment is the same. The not-for-profit Brother's Brother Foundation (BBF) provides emergency and nonemergency medical supplies textbooks food shoes and other humanitarian supplies to people in some 120 countries using a combination of gifts from the general public corporations and the US government. BBF is a gift-in-kind charity meaning the bulk of the donations are goods rather than money. The organization was established in 1958 by the renowned anesthesiologist Robert Hingson as Brother's Keeper but later changed its name. Hingson invented the jet inoculation gun used to provide 1000 inoculations per hour.

EXECUTIVES

V Pres, Bill Davis
Auditors: SCHNEIDER DOWNS & CO INC PITT

LOCATIONS

HQ: THE BROTHER'S BROTHER FOUNDATION
1200 GALVESTON AVE, PITTSBURGH, PA 152331604
Phone: 412 321-3160
Web: WWW.BROTHERSBROTHER.ORG

HISTORICAL FINANCIALS

Company Type: Private

Income Statement

FYE: December 31

	REVENUE ($ mil.)	NET INCOME ($ mil.)	NET PROFIT MARGIN	EMPLOYEES
12/13	243	5	2.4%	12
12/12	295	10	3.7%	—
12/11	242	7	3.0%	—
12/10	273	0	—	—
Annual Growth	(3.7%)	—	—	—

2013 Year-End Financials

Return on assets: 0.1%   Cash ($ mil.): 1
Return on equity: 2.4%
Current ratio: 11.00

THE CALIFORNIA ENDOWMENT

The California Endowment awards grants to health care providers in the Golden State. Funding is directed to not-for-profit organizations particularly those that work with the state's poor and underserved communities as well as studies of the state's health care industry. Its advocacy interests include health care access culturally competent health systems and elimination of health disparities. A private foundation The California Endowment has awarded more than $1.5 billion in grants since it was established in 1996. It has regional offices in Fresno Los Angeles Sacramento San Diego and San Francisco.

EXECUTIVES

Senior Vice President Healthy California, Daniel (Dan) Zingale
Vice President Human Resources, Brytain Ashford
Senior Vice President Healthy Communities, Anthony Iton
Board Member, Marion Standish
Auditors: PRICEWATERHOUSECOOPERS LLP W

LOCATIONS

HQ: THE CALIFORNIA ENDOWMENT
1000 N ALAMEDA ST, LOS ANGELES, CA 900121804
Phone: 213 628-1001
Web: WWW.TCENEWS.CALENDOW.ORG

HISTORICAL FINANCIALS

Company Type: Private

Income Statement

FYE: March 31

	REVENUE ($ mil.)	NET INCOME ($ mil.)	NET PROFIT MARGIN	EMPLOYEES
03/13	159	(58)	—	110
03/12*	206	41	20.3%	—
02/09	0	0	—	—
02/05	345	0	—	—
Annual Growth	(9.2%)	—	—	—

*Fiscal year change

2013 Year-End Financials

Return on assets: 5.1%   Cash ($ mil.): 71
Return on equity: (-36.7%)
Current ratio: 1.00

THE CARLE FOUNDATION

Auditors: KPMG LLP MILWAUKEE WI

LOCATIONS

HQ: THE CARLE FOUNDATION
611 W PARK ST, URBANA, IL 618012529
Phone: 217 383-3311
Web: WWW.CARLE.ORG

HISTORICAL FINANCIALS

Company Type: Private

Income Statement

FYE: December 31

	REVENUE ($ mil.)	NET INCOME ($ mil.)	NET PROFIT MARGIN	EMPLOYEES
12/12	1,690	91	5.4%	5,284
12/11*	1,608	0	0.0%	—
06/10	135	72	53.3%	—
06/09	0	0	—	—
Annual Growth	—	—	—	—

*Fiscal year change

2012 Year-End Financials

Return on assets: 1.1%   Cash ($ mil.): 47
Return on equity: 5.4%
Current ratio: 0.30

THE CARTER-JONES LUMBER COMPANY

Carter Lumber has the answer when new home construction has you hollering "timber!" The company owns and operates about 145 lumber and home improvement stores in a dozen states from Michigan to South Carolina. The company caters to both contractors and do-it-yourselfers supplying them with lumber plywood roofing windows doors plumbing and electrical products heating equipment tools siding and other products. The home improvement retailer also owns Carter-Jones Lumber which runs a 17-acre lumberyard and custom millwork facilities in Ohio. The company was founded by Warren E. Carter in 1932 and it continues to be a family-owned business.

Geographic Reach

Carter Lumber operates stores in 12 states: Illinois Indiana Kentucky Maryland Michigan North Carolina Ohio Pennsylvania South Carolina Georgia Virginia and West Virginia. Ohio is the company's largest market home to about 80 of its stores. Indiana and Pennsylvania are also big markets for Carter Lumber each with about 20 stores.

Operations

In addition to Carter-Jones Lumber the company operates half a dozen other divisions that also specialize in providing building materials.

These include Ohio-based Holmes Lumber a building materials supplier with two stores in Ohio (acquired in 2004); Kight Home Centers with five stores in Indiana and Kentucky (acquired in 2005); Griggs Lumber with three locations along the Outer Banks of North Carolina; and Kempsville Building Materials with two locations in Virginia.

Strategy

Looking to expand its operations Carter Lumber in 2013 opened its first store in the Atlanta area adding Georgia to its list of states. It also purchased Athens Building Supply in Winder Georgia to boost its presence. The company also added new stores in Maryland Ohio Virginia Indiana Pennsylvania North Carolina and Washington DC. When the company adds new stores and new markets it makes a point to hire employees from the lumberyard industry who understand its business platform and know the market and its customers.

To expand Carter Lumber has had to contract. It shuttered 26 stores as it focused on growth in larger markets. Keeping the company lean has been key to surviving recessionary times. To this end Carter Lumber has transformed itself from a $500 million traditional lumberyard to a near-$1 billion professional lumberyard.

It works to be #1 in every market in which it operates. It achieves this by realigning its field operations and expanding its footprint in the Midwest Mid-Atlantic and South regions.

Mergers and Acquisitions

Adding to its operations in Ohio Carter Lumber acquired the assets of DSD Builders Supply of Canton Ohio a former subsidiary of Stark Truss. The asset purchase of DSD Builders Supply included the inventory rolling stock and equipment.

EXECUTIVES

President Carter Lumber Company, Neil C. Sackett
SVP COO and CFO, Jeffrey S. (Jeff) Donley

LOCATIONS

HQ: THE CARTER-JONES LUMBER COMPANY
601 TALLMADGE RD, KENT, OH 442407331
Phone: 330 673-6100
Web: WWW.CARTERLUMBER.COM

PRODUCTS/OPERATIONS

Selected Subsidiaries

Carter Components Plan
Carter Custom Millwork
Carter Lumber
Carter-Jones Lumber Company
Carter-Jones Timber (CDC)
Griggs Lumber
Holmes Lumber
Kempsville Building Materials
Kight Home Center

COMPETITORS

84 Lumber
ABC Supply
BlueLinx
Guardian Building Products Distribution
HD Supply
Lowe's
Menard
Pro-Build
Stock Building Supply
Weekes Forest Products

HISTORICAL FINANCIALS
Company Type: Private

Income Statement
FYE: December 31

	REVENUE ($ mil.)	NET INCOME ($ mil.)	NET PROFIT MARGIN	EMPLOYEES
12/10	334	(4)	—	1,575
12/09	314	(4)	—	—
12/08	2,083	0	—	—
Annual Growth	—	—	—	—

2010 Year-End Financials
Return on assets: 1.7%
Return on equity: (-1.4%)
Current ratio: —
Cash ($ mil.): 2

THE CATHOLIC UNIVERSITY OF AMERICA

The Catholic University of America (CUA) established in 1887 by US bishops has an enrollment of more than 7000 students from all 50 states and nearly 100 countries. With graduate and undergraduate programs in 13 colleges CUA offers degrees in such fields as architecture and planning arts and sciences engineering music and nursing; it's expanding into business and economics. CUA is the only US university with ecclesiastical faculties granting canonical degrees in canon law philosophy and theology. Some 80% of undergraduates and nearly 60% of graduate students are Catholic. The University's Theological College prepares men for the priesthood serving dioceses nationwide.

Geographic Reach
The university's 193-acre campus is located north of Capitol Hill in Washington D.C. The campus comprises more than a dozen schools and nearly two dozen research facilities.

Operations
As part of its operations CUA offers its students several areas of study. It boasts schools in architecture and planning arts and sciences business and economics canon law engineering law library and information sciences music nursing philosophy professional studies social services and theology and religious studies. Its architecture program is the largest in the D.C. area and the legal clinic at its Columbus School of Law is rated among the top 12 in the nation.

The university which has a student-faculty ratio is 9:1 grants undergraduate degrees in 72 programs master's degrees in 103 programs and doctoral or terminal degrees in 66 programs.

Strategy
To cater to those who have requested an increased focus on business education CUA added a School of Business and Economics. Instead of focusing on theories the school offers students an education model based on Catholic social doctrine and the natural law.

Sales and Marketing
CUA sources its students from all 50 states and nearly 100 countries.

EXECUTIVES
Vice President Finance and Treasurer, Cathy Wood
Vice President Fac Operations, Jerry Conrad

Associate Vice President For Enrollment Services And University Registrar, Julie Isha
Assoc Vice President Student Life Dean Students, Jonathan (Jon) Sawyer
Vice President Enrollment Management and Marketing, Christopher (Chris) Lydon
Assistant Vice President for University Relations for University Events, Suzanne McCarthy
Vice President, Michael Kushner
Vice President, Caitlin Jones
Assistant Vice President Finance, Rachel Battles
Secretary to the Director, Judy Blower
Auditors: PRICEWATERHOUSECOOPERS LLP MC

LOCATIONS
HQ: THE CATHOLIC UNIVERSITY OF AMERICA
620 MICHIGAN AVE NE, WASHINGTON, DC
200640002
Phone: 202 319-5000
Web: WWW.CUA.EDU

PRODUCTS/OPERATIONS

Selected Schools
Benjamin T. Rome School of Music
Columbus School of Law
Metropolitan School of Professional Studies
National Catholic School of Social Service
School of Architecture and Planning
School of Arts and Sciences
School of Business and Economics
School of Canon Law
School of Engineering
School of Library and Information Science
School of Nursing
School of Philosophy
School of Theology and Religious Studies

HISTORICAL FINANCIALS
Company Type: Private

Income Statement
FYE: April 30

	REVENUE ($ mil.)	NET INCOME ($ mil.)	NET PROFIT MARGIN	EMPLOYEES
04/14*	222	28	12.7%	4,239
06/13	342	57	16.8%	—
04/13	217	17	8.3%	—
04/09	0	0	—	—
Annual Growth	655.8%	—	—	—

*Fiscal year change

2014 Year-End Financials
Return on assets: 12.5%
Return on equity: 12.7%
Current ratio: —
Cash ($ mil.): 39

THE CHILDREN'S HOSPITAL CORPORATION

Children's Hospital Boston is an elder in the world of pediatric care. The 400-bed hospital offers acute health care and specialty services for children from birth to age 21. The medical center is also Harvard Medical School's main teaching hospital for children's health care and it is the world's largest pediatric research center. Its John F. Enders Pediatric Research facility provides research for the treatment of childhood diseases. Specialty services include cardiovascular surgery digestive care neurology oncology ophthalmology orthopedics transplants blood diseases and fetal

care. The not-for-profit hospital was founded in 1869.

Operations
Children's Hospital Boston handles about 25000 inpatient visits per year as well as 27000 surgeries and 160000 radiological exams. Its 200+ specialized clinical programs handle about 560000 appointments annually. The hospital is considered a safety-net hospital and as such is one of the largest providers of medical care to low-income children in the state. About 30% of the hospital's patients are either uninsured or have health care coverage through public assistance.

In addition to its educational and research partnerships with Harvard the medical center collaborates with other universities as well as drugmakers medical equipment firms and research institutes. Altogether it has some 1100 scientists at its research centers including the Enders Pediatric Research Laboratories and the Karp Family Research Laboratories. Children's Hospital Boston receives some $225 million in research funding per year.

Along with the main hospital the system operates a handful of primary and specialty care centers throughout the Boston area. It also provides services collaborative pediatric care at about a dozen area hospitals including Good Samaritan Medical Center in Brockton and Holy Family Hospital in Methuen. It also operates a cancer clinic within the main Children's Hospital Boston facilities through a partnership with the Dana Farber Cancer Institute.

Geographic Reach
The hospital has satellite locations and affiliates throughout Massachusetts. In addition to its main campus in Boston it has satellites in Lexington Peabody and Waltham; doctors' offices in Brockton Milford North Dartmouth Norwood and Weymouth; and affiliates in Beverly Jamaica Plain New Bedford South Weymouth and Winchester.

Strategy
Due to increasing economic troubles and health reform measures in the US Children's Hospital Boston has been working to cut costs. Despite the cost-control efforts the main Children's Hospital Boston campus is undergoing expansion and renovation efforts as part of a 10-year expansion plan.

One way to increase research funding is to increase external partnerships. Children's Hospital Boston formed a research collaboration with diagnostic and lab supply firm Life Technologies to develop new gene sequencing workflows. In 2013 the two companies expanded their relationship by forming Claritas Genomics; the venture was established to develop new genetic and genomic-based diagnostic tests.

EXECUTIVES
Senior Vice President of Patient Care Operations, Eileen Sporing
Senior Vice President Patient Safety, Kathy Jenkins
Medical Director Lung Transplant, Gary Visner
Medical Director, Mustafa Sahin
Vice President For Research Chief Scientific Off, Bruce Zetter
Director of Medical Records, Mary Radley
Medical Director, Sharon Levy
Medical Director, Lauren Garcia
Vice President Medical Staff Affairs, Patricia Derusso
Medical Director, John Hickey
Medical Director, James Wall
Vice President Human Resources, Inez Stewart
Vice President Research Administration, August Cervini
Icu Intensitvist Vice President Of Cardiology, Patricia (Pat) Hickey
Senior Vice President Network Development and Strategic Partnerships, Warring Wendy

Treasurer, David Rodriguez
Secretary, Cynthia Dube
Secretary, Linda Willis
Auditors: ERNST & YOUNG LLP BOSTON MA

LOCATIONS

HQ: THE CHILDREN' S HOSPITAL CORPORATION
300 LONGWOOD AVE, BOSTON, MA 021155737
Phone: 617 355-6000

PRODUCTS/OPERATIONS

Selected Services
Major centers
  Brain Center
  Cancer and Blood Diseases Center
  Heart Center
  Orthopedic Center
  Transplant Center
Other Services
  Airway breathing and lungs
  Allergies and asthma
  Anatomy and function
  Bone joint and muscle
  Brain and nervous system
  Cancer and blood disorders
  Common childhood health topics and conditions
  Craniofacial anomalies
  Diet and nutrition
  Digestive metabolic and renal disorders
  Ears nose and throat
  Emergency medicine and trauma
  Eyes and vision
  Genetic disorders and birth defects
  Heart blood and circulation
  International patient care
  Medical tests
  Newborns
  Psychiatric (mental) conditions
  Reproductive and urinary conditions
  Skin and vascular
  Viruses and infections

COMPETITORS

Baystate Medical
  Center
Beth Israel Deaconess
  Medical Center
Boston Medical Center
Cambridge Health
  Alliance
Cape Cod Hospital
CareGroup
Children' s Hospital of
  Philadelphia

Dana-Farber
Nemours Foundation
Newton-Wellesley
  Hospital
Northeast Health
  System
Partners HealthCare
Shriners Hospitals For
  Children
Steward Health Care
Sturdy Memorial

HISTORICAL FINANCIALS
Company Type: Private

Income Statement
FYE: September 30

	REVENUE ($ mil.)	NET INCOME ($ mil.)	NET PROFIT MARGIN	EMPLOYEES
09/13	940	157	16.8%	8,000
09/09*	1,348	94	7.0%	—
06/05	4	0	13.0%	—
09/03	695	0	—	—
Annual Growth	3.1%	—	—	—

*Fiscal year change

2013 Year-End Financials
Return on assets: 14.2%   Cash ($ mil.): —
Return on equity: 16.8%
Current ratio: 0.40

THE CHILDREN'S HOSPITAL OF ALABAMA

Auditors: WARREN AVERETT LLC BIRMINGHAM

LOCATIONS

HQ: THE CHILDREN' S HOSPITAL OF ALABAMA
1600 7TH AVE S, BIRMINGHAM, AL 352331711
Phone: 205 939-9100
Web: WWW.AMELIACENTER.COM

HISTORICAL FINANCIALS
Company Type: Private

Income Statement
FYE: December 31

	REVENUE ($ mil.)	NET INCOME ($ mil.)	NET PROFIT MARGIN	EMPLOYEES
12/12	561	103	18.4%	3,329
12/09	488	35	7.2%	—
12/05	319	22	6.9%	—
12/04	315	0	—	—
Annual Growth	7.5%	—	—	—

2012 Year-End Financials
Return on assets: 8.1%   Cash ($ mil.): 68
Return on equity: 18.4%
Current ratio: 1.20

THE CHILDRENS HOSPITAL LOS ANGELES

Childrens Hospital Los Angeles (CHLA) is dedicated to treating the youngest critical care patients in the region. The about 570-bed hospital specializes in treating seriously ill and injured children from its neonatal intensive care unit to its pediatric organ transplant center. CHLA's pediatric specialists also provide care at its ambulatory care center in Arcadia and through about 40 off-site practice sites. The hospital's pediatric specialties include cancer kidney failure and cystic fibrosis care. CHLA serves more than 107000 children every year. It is one of only 12 children's hospitals in the nation (and the only one in California) ranked in all 10 pediatric specialties by U.S. News & World Report.

Operations
The CHLA medical staff includes about 600 physicians most of which are members of the CHLA Medical Group. Its emergency department treats some 71000 patients and the hospital sees more than 343000 outpatients annually. Nearly 50% of its patients are under the age of four. CHLA is also the only freestanding level I Pediatric Trauma Center in LA County approved by the Committee on Trauma of the American College of Surgeons and among only 5% of US hospitals to be designated as a Magnet Hospital by the American Nurses Credentialing Center.

It is also a teaching hospital through its affiliation with the Keck School of Medicine of the University of Southern California and is home to the Saban Research Institute which conducts biomedical research into pediatric diseases. CHLA's training programs include 575 medical students 85 full-time residents three chief residents and 98 fellows.

Financial Performance
Revenue decreased 7% to $803 million in 2014 due to a decline in net patient service revenue. Also that year the company reported a net loss of $30 million due to the decline in revenue and higher operating expenses.

Strategy
CHLA is expanding its facilities to keep up with demand. In 2015 it opened the doors of a new outpatient center in Encino.

Company Background
Although it sometimes operates as Children's Hospital Los Angeles the absent apostrophe in the legal Childrens Hospital of Los Angeles name is no accident. The intentional spelling honors the original incorporation documents filed in 1901 when the institution was founded as Childrens Hospital Society of Los Angeles.

EXECUTIVES

Director of Health Information Director of Him
  Director Health Info Management, Ruth Hauser
Assistant Vice President Development, Robert
  (Bob) Weiner
Vice President and Surgeon in Chief, Henri Ford
Vice President Human Resources, Deann Marshall
Senior Vice President and General Counsel,
  Lawrence L Foust
Asociate Vice President Foundation Relations,
  Anna Weiser
Assistant Vice President Development, Rita
  Terterian
Pharmacy Manager, Ferguson Deborah
Auditors: DELOITTE TAX LLP SAN DIEGO C

LOCATIONS

HQ: THE CHILDRENS HOSPITAL LOS ANGELES
4650 W SUNSET BLVD, LOS ANGELES, CA
900276062
Phone: 323 660-2450
Web: WWW.CHLA.ORG

COMPETITORS

Cedars-Sinai Medical Center
Children' s Hopsital of Chicago
Children' s Hospital & Research Center at Oakland
Children' s Hospital Boston
Children' s Hospital of Orange County
Children' s Hospital of Philadelphia
Children' s National Medical Center
Cincinnati Children' s Hospital
Cook Children' s Health Care System
Dignity Health
Good Samaritan Hospital (Los Angeles)
Hollywood Presbyterian Medical Center
Los Angeles County Health Department
Nationwide Children' s Hospital
Shriners Hospitals For Children

HISTORICAL FINANCIALS
Company Type: Private

Income Statement
FYE: June 30

	REVENUE ($ mil.)	NET INCOME ($ mil.)	NET PROFIT MARGIN	EMPLOYEES
06/13	869	36	4.2%	3,000
06/10	564	(34)	—	—
06/09	405	(94)	—	—
06/08	589	0	—	—
Annual Growth	8.1%	—	—	—

2013 Year-End Financials
Return on assets: 9.6%   Cash ($ mil.): 27
Return on equity: 4.2%
Current ratio: 0.30

THE CHRISTIAN BROADCASTING NETWORK INC

Standards & Practices probably won't find much wrong with these TV programs. The Christian Broadcasting Network (CBN) is one of the leading producers of religious television programming in the country offering news and entertainment shows with a spiritual message. Its centerpiece is The 700 Club a daily show featuring a mix of news and commentary interviews feature stories and Christian ministry co-hosted by CBN founder Pat Robertson. The company's programs are syndicated to broadcast and cable TV outlets that reach audiences around the world. CBN generates most of its revenue through ministry donations.

Geographic ReachCBN programs have aired in 108 languages (from Mandarin to Spanish and from Turkish to Welsh) in 218 different countries and territories. It currently broadcasts in 139 countries with programs and content translated into 62 languages. The company has offices in Africa Asia Europe the Middle East North America (Canada and US) and Russia and the Commonwealth of Independent States.OperationsCBN has a broad portfolio of ministries and services.This portfolio includes The 700 Club & Prayer Center. CBN's The 700 Club program brings a magazine-style mix of news interviews testimonies and insights from Christian leaders. CBN's Prayer Center provides prayer as well as biblical guidance and resources to callers.   The 700 Club Interactive is a show designed for viewer interaction and uses a chat community Skype live phone calls and social networking.   CBN is launching a massive media campaign to promote the Bible under the brand Superbook.   Orphan's Promise ministers to the physical spiritual and educational needs of orphaned and vulnerable children.CBN's Operation Blessing International's core programs include disaster relief medical aid hunger relief orphan care water wells and community development. CBN.com offers streaming video teaching; in-depth discipleship courses; Online Bible; CBN Radio; Bible teachings; my.CBN.com a social network; and free downloads of videos widgets and articles.

Financial PerformanceThe company's revenue increased to $542 million during fiscal 2013 a 11% increased from previous year's $487 million. The spike was largely due to increases in revenue from Gifts in kind by 24% to $245 million in fiscal 2013 compared to $197 million in fiscal 2012 and additional investment gain and other revenues.

EXECUTIVES

Vice President Of Human Resources, Barbara (Barb) Ritter
Vice President Marketing, John Turver
Vice President Digital Media, Michael (Mel) Stonecypher
Auditors: KPMG LLP NORFOLK VA

LOCATIONS

HQ: THE CHRISTIAN BROADCASTING NETWORK INC
977 CENTERVILLE TPKE, VIRGINIA BEACH, VA
234631001
Phone: 757 226-3030
Web: WWW.CBN.COM

COMPETITORS

Eden Communications	Thomas Nelson
Guideposts	Trinity Broadcasting
Integrity Media	Zondervan

Salem Media

HISTORICAL FINANCIALS
Company Type: Private

Income Statement
FYE: March 31

	REVENUE ($ mil.)	NET INCOME ($ mil.)	NET PROFIT MARGIN	EMPLOYEES
03/11	285	6	2.4%	941
03/10	283	8	3.0%	—
03/09	2,135	0	0.0%	—
Annual Growth	(63.5%)	1932.4%	—	—

2011 Year-End Financials
Return on assets: —
Return on equity: 2.4%
Current ratio: 0.60
Cash ($ mil.): 18

THE CLEVELAND FOUNDATION

Auditors: ERNST & YOUNG US LLP INDIANAP

LOCATIONS

HQ: THE CLEVELAND FOUNDATION
1422 EUCLID AVE STE 1300, CLEVELAND, OH
441152063
Phone: 216 861-3810
Web:
WWW.EDUCATIONBLOG.CLEVELANDFOUNDATION.
ORG

HISTORICAL FINANCIALS
Company Type: Private

Income Statement
FYE: December 31

	ASSETS ($ mil.)	NET INCOME ($ mil.)	INCOME AS % OF ASSETS	EMPLOYEES
12/09	1,445	(18)	—	75
12/08	2	0	—	—
12/04	1,632	103	6.3%	—
12/03	1,520	0	—	—
Annual Growth	(0.8%)	—	—	—

2009 Year-End Financials
Return on assets: —
Return on equity: (-23.4%)
Sales ($ mil): 78

THE COMMUNITY HOSPITAL GROUP INC

JFK Medical Center plays a central role in health care in central New Jersey. The medical center is an acute care facility with some 500 beds and 950 physicians providing emergency surgical trauma and other inpatient services. The hospital includes the JFK New Jersey Neuroscience Institute which treats stroke and other neurological conditions and the JFK Johnson Rehabilitation Institute which treats traumatic injuries. JFK Medical Center also offers diagnostic imaging cancer care senior and hospice care and family practice services. It is also a teaching hospital affiliated with several area uni-

versities. The hospital is part of the JFK Health System.
Strategy
To expand its capacity for emergency services JFK Medical Center launched construction of a new ER pavilion in 2013. The project includes the addition of a three-story structure above the existing ER facilities. To keep pace with cutting-edge medical technologies the hospital has also made recent investments in upgrades to its diagnostic imaging cardiac catheterization and wound healing equipment.

EXECUTIVES

Vice President Rehab Services, Anthony Cuzzola
Auditors: PARENTE BEARD LLC CLARK NEW

LOCATIONS

HQ: THE COMMUNITY HOSPITAL GROUP INC
98 JAMES ST STE 400, EDISON, NJ 088203902
Phone: 732 321-7000

PRODUCTS/OPERATIONS

Selected Centers and Affiliates
Adult Medical Day Program
Haven Hospice
JFK at Home
JFK Dental Clinic
JFK Family Medicine Center
JFK Hartwyck Nursing Convalescent and Rehabilitation Centers
JFK Johnson Rehabilitation Institute (JRI)
JFK Mediplex Surgery Center
JFK New Jersey Neuroscience Institute
JFK Medical Center Muhlenberg Campus/JFK-Muhlenberg Snyder Schools
Whispering Knoll Assisted Living

COMPETITORS

Ball Memorial Hospital	Newton Medical Center
Barnabas Health	Princeton HealthCare
Bergen Regional Medical	Robert Wood Johnson University Hospital
Capital Health System	Saint Peter's
CentraState Healthcare System	University Hospital St. Joseph's
Henry County Memorial Hospital	Healthcare System
Monmouth Medical Center	

HISTORICAL FINANCIALS
Company Type: Private

Income Statement
FYE: December 31

	REVENUE ($ mil.)	NET INCOME ($ mil.)	NET PROFIT MARGIN	EMPLOYEES
12/10	427	(17)	—	3,000
12/09	423	(37)	—	—
12/06	388	0	0.0%	—
Annual Growth	2.4%	—	—	—

2010 Year-End Financials
Return on assets: 6.8%
Return on equity: (-4.1%)
Current ratio: 1.20
Cash ($ mil.): 24

THE COOPER HEALTH SYSTEM

The Cooper Health System keeps folks along the Delaware River shoreline feeling fine. The not-for-profit organization includes clinics and hospitals located throughout southern New Jersey and the Delaware Valley including the 600-bed Cooper University Hospital and The Children's Regional Hospital. Cooper University Hospital is a teaching campus for the University of Medicine and Dentistry of New Jersey providing training for medical students nurses residents fellows and health professionals. Its more than 700 physicians operate in about 80 specialties. Founded in 1887 the health care system provides trauma cancer cardiology neuroscience psychiatric and orthopedic specialty centers.

Operations

Cooper Health System is home to the area's Level I Southern New Jersey Regional Trauma Center; the Cooper Cancer Institute the Cooper Heart Institute the Cooper Bone & Joint Institute the Cooper Neurosciences Institute and critical care medicine. Carrying the Level 1 moniker means that Cooper Health System will be the referral of hospital of choice for patients' with massive injuries in the service area.

In 2013 Cooper Health System had 26600 hospital admissions and 81000 emergency department visits.

Geographic Reach

The Cooper Health System operates clinics hospitals and home health services in New Jersey Pennsylvania and Delaware. Cooper University Hospital serves as Southern New Jersey's major tertiary-care referral hospital for specialized services.

Sales and Marketing

HMO payments accounted for 34% of Cooper's net patient revenue in 2013 while commercial payments accounted for 27%.

Financial Performance

The system's revenue increased 6% to $874 million in 2013 as net patient service earnings rose. Net income rose 57% to $90 million on increased investment returns and contributions for capital acquisitions.

Cash flow from operations declined 26% to $47 million that year due to changes in prepaid expenses and a decline in accrued payable and accrued expenses.

Strategy

As demand for health care services has grown in the areas in which Cooper Health System serves Cooper University Hospital itself has also been forced to expand. Additions include all private rooms more operating suites intensive care and laboratory units and a new larger lobby area. Cooper Health System also built a new emergency department.

In 2014 the system's university health care division established a partnership with Kennedy Health System to expand cardiac services in Gloucester County. The partners opened a Cardiac Catheterization Laboratory at Kennedy University Hospital that year.

Mergers and Acquisitions

Cooper University Health Care acquired a 20% interest in AmeriHealth New Jersey in 2014. Cooper and AmeriHealth plan to work together to develop co-branded health products.

EXECUTIVES

Vice President Marketing, Jill Lawlor
President and CEO Cooper University Health Care, Adrienne Kirby
EVP Government Relations and Public Policy, Gary S. Young
President CEO and Director, John P. Sheridan
SVP Operations, Maureen P. Barnes
SEVP and General Counsel, Gary J. Lesneski
SEVP and CFO, Douglas E. Shirley
President Director Population, Louis S. Bezich
SVP Patient Care Services and Chief Nursing Officer, Dianne Charsha

Interim Chief Medical Officer; Chair of the Radiology Department, Raymond L. Baraldi
Director Of Pharmacy, Jaqueline Sutton
Vice President, Adrienne Elberfeld
Clinical Director Obstetrical Units, Nancy Mimm
Senior Vice President of Ambulatory Operations, Barbara H (Barb) Smith
Vice President, Dorothy Duffy
Director Of Radiology Services, Gerard Mullen
Clinical Director, Joanna Horst
Clinical Director, Jeanne Greer
Medical Director, Andrew Farkas
Clinical Director, Joanne Fox
Clinical Director, Karen Gruber
Clinical Director, Linda Williams
Vice President, Beth Green
Assistant Vice President Surgical Services, Lisa Laphan-morad
Clinical Director, Cynthia Refolo
Clinical Director, Michael Pizzuto
Clinical Director, Lisa Geoghegan
Vice President Business Development, Jerome Check
Medical Director, Magdy Takla
Director Of Him, Dana Clark
Clinical Director And System Administrator, MJ Tiedeken
Clinical Director, MaryJo Cimino
Clinical Director, D Rn
Director of Respiratory Therapy, Rrt Lofland
Chairman, George E. Norcross, age 59
Vice Chairman, Joan S. Davis

LOCATIONS

HQ: THE COOPER HEALTH SYSTEM
1 COOPER PLZ, CAMDEN, NJ 081031461
Phone: 856 342-2000
Web: WWW.COOPERHEALTH.ORG

PRODUCTS/OPERATIONS

2013 Net Patient Revenue

	%of total
HMO	34
Commercial	27
Medicare	19
Blue cross	13
Self-pay	3
Medicaid	4
Total	**100**

Selected Services

Adult Health Institute
Bariatric and Metabolic Surgery Center
Joint Replacement and Reconstruction Program
Manual Physical Therapy Program
Musculoskeletal Ultrasound
Neuromuscular Program
Orthopaedic Trauma Program
Otology/Neurotology
Pituitary Tumor and Neuroendocrine Program
Podiatry
Pulmonary Medicine
Rhinology / ENT Allergy / Skull-Base Surgery
Spine Center
Sports Medicine
Urogynecology
Urology
Women's Heart Program

COMPETITORS

Abington Memorial Hospital
Albert Einstein Healthcare Network
Aria Health
AtlantiCare
Capital Health System
Children's Hospital of Philadelphia
Crozer-Keystone Health System
Inspira Health Network
Kennedy Health System
Lourdes Health
Main Line Health
Mercy Health System
North Philadelphia Health System

Princeton HealthCare
Shore Memorial Hospital
Universal Health Services
University of Pennsylvania Health System
Virtua Health

HISTORICAL FINANCIALS
Company Type: Private

Income Statement FYE: December 31

	REVENUE ($ mil.)	NET INCOME ($ mil.)	NET PROFIT MARGIN	EMPLOYEES
12/14	944	60	6.4%	4,900
12/13	874	0	—	
12/12	823	46	5.7%	
12/11	775	0	—	
Annual Growth	6.8%	—	—	—

2014 Year-End Financials

Return on assets: 1.8% Cash ($ mil.): 166
Return on equity: 6.4%
Current ratio: 1.90

THE CORPORATION OF GONZAGA UNIVERSITY

Gonzaga University is a private liberal arts institution providing instruction to more than 7800 undergraduate graduate doctoral and law students. The school offers about 75 undergraduate majors two dozen master's degree programs and two leadership study doc at its six colleges and schools. The university offers a juris doctorate degree at its School of Law. The Roman Catholic university is run by the Society of Jesus —the Jesuits —and is named after a sixteenth-century Italian Jesuit Aloysius Gonzaga the patron saint of youth. The university was founded in 1887 as a men's college.

Geographic Reach

The university's main 130-acre campus in Spokane Washington contains more than 100 buildings and is located near the Spokane River about half a mile from downtown. In addition Gonzaga University has a campus in Florence Italy where Aloysius Gonzaga lived as a student.

Operations

Gonzaga University has more than 400 faculty members and a student-to-faculty ratio of 11:1. Areas of study include business education law politics arts engineering and science. It also enrolls students in a number of internship research and community outreach programs.

Financial Performance

Gonzaga University reported operating revenue of $257 million for fiscal 2012. Most of the university's revenues come from student tuition and fees; other sources of income include auxiliary enterprises endowment income and government grants and contracts. The university is supported by endowment funds totaling some $148 million.

Strategy

In 2013 the university launched a construction project to add a $60 million 170000-sq. ft. University Center to the Gonzaga campus. It also built a new $6 million tennis and golf center.

Gonzaga also adds new educational programs to enhance services for students. For instance it launched a new nursing doctorate program in 2013.

EXECUTIVES

Vice President For Finance, Charles J Murphy

Vp University Relations, Margot Stanfield
Executive Vice President, Earl Martin
University Vice President, Harry Sladich
Vp Student Life, Sue D Weitz
Associate Vice President of Finance, Joe Smith
Assistant Vice President For Mission, James (Jamie) Voiss
Vice President for Advancement, Danny Costello
Honors Council Vice Chair, Tabitha Lovell

LOCATIONS

HQ: THE CORPORATION OF GONZAGA UNIVERSITY
502 E BOONE AVE, SPOKANE, WA 992581774
Phone: 509 328-4220
Web: WWW.GONZAGA.EDU

PRODUCTS/OPERATIONS

Selected Schools and Colleges
College of Arts and Sciences
School of Business Administration
School of Education
School of Engineering
School of Law
School of Professional Studies

HISTORICAL FINANCIALS

Company Type: Private

Income Statement

FYE: May 31

	REVENUE ($ mil.)	NET INCOME ($ mil.)	NET PROFIT MARGIN	EMPLOYEES
05/14	193	38	20.0%	650
05/13	191	56	29.5%	—
05/12	194	12	6.4%	—
05/11	186	0	—	—
Annual Growth	1.3%	—	—	—

2014 Year-End Financials

Return on assets: 8.9%
Return on equity: 20.0%
Current ratio: —
Cash ($ mil.): 34

THE CORPORATION OF MERCER UNIVERSITY

Mercer University covers a lot of Georgia with one campus in Macon another in Atlanta and a third in Savannah. The main campus in Macon includes the Walter F. George School of Law (one of the nation's oldest law schools) while The Cecil B. Day Graduate and Professional campus in Atlanta includes schools of theology pharmacy and nursing. Savannah is home to a new four-year M.D. program at the Mercer School of Medicine at Memorial University Medical Center. The university which has a total enrollment of more than 8300 students also has educational centers in Douglas County Henry County and Eastman. Mercer was founded in 1833 by Jesse Mercer a prominent Georgia Baptist.

EXECUTIVES

Vice President And Dean, Rhonda Lidstone
Vice President, Douglas Pearson
Vice President, John (Jack) Patterson
Director of Admissions and Financial Aid, Leah Aiken
Associate Vice President Student Financial Planning, Carol Williams
Director Of Admissions, Jordana Berry
Physical Therapy, Leslie Taylor

Executive Vice President for Administration and Finance, Barbara (Barb) Short
Associate Vice President For University Advancement, Allen (Al) Wallace
Executive Vice President Technology, Emily Myers
Dean and Vice President for the Health Sciences, Ted Matthews
Vice President, Jay Stroman
Senior Vice President Marketing Communications, Debra Leahy
Assistant Vice President For Creative Services, Steven Mosley
Vice President For External Relations, Hugh Sosebee
Assistant Vice President Budget And Analysis, Christa Ward
Assoc. Vice President Of Advancement, Shawna Dooley
Senior Vice President University Advancement, Richard (Dick) Swindle
Executive Vice President and Provost, Horace Fleming
Vice President, Rick Cameron
Treasurer And Associate Vice President For Finance, Julie Davis
Treasurer, Hiral Patel
Auditors: KPMG LLP GREENSBORO NC

LOCATIONS

HQ: THE CORPORATION OF MERCER UNIVERSITY
1400 COLEMAN AVE, MACON, GA 312070001
Phone: 478 301-2700
Web: WWW.MERCER.EDU

COMPETITORS

Baylor University	Kennesaw State University
Benedict College	
Clark Atlanta University	Morris College
	Spelman College
Georgia Southern University	University of Mobile
Interdenominational Theological Center	University of West Georgia

HISTORICAL FINANCIALS

Company Type: Private

Income Statement

FYE: June 30

	REVENUE ($ mil.)	NET INCOME ($ mil.)	NET PROFIT MARGIN	EMPLOYEES
06/13	297	8	2.8%	1,658
06/11	270	8	3.0%	—
06/10	255	0	0.2%	—
06/09	235	0	—	—
Annual Growth	6.0%	—	—	—

2013 Year-End Financials

Return on assets: 4.2%
Return on equity: 2.8%
Current ratio: 0.30
Cash ($ mil.): 45

THE DAVID AND LUCILE PACKARD FOUNDATION

One of the wealthiest philanthropic organizations in the US The David and Lucile Packard Foundation primarily provides grants to not-for-profit entities. The foundation focuses on operating in three areas: conservation and science; children families and communities; and population. The David and Lucile Packard Foundation boasts approximately $4.6 billion in assets. In 2009 the

organization committed $100 million for the expansion of the Lucile Packard Children's Hospital at Stanford. The late David Packard (co-founder of Hewlett-Packard) and his wife the late Lucile Salter Packard created the foundation in 1964. Their children run the organization.

In 2006 it awarded about $225 million in national and international grants with an extra focus on Northern California's Monterey San Mateo Santa Clara and Santa Cruz counties.

EXECUTIVES

Director Organizational Effectiveness, Stephanie McAuliffe
VP and CFO, George A. Vera, age 66
Vice Chairman, Julie E. Packard
Vice Chairman, Nancy Packard Burnett
Chairman, Susan Packard Orr
President and CEO, Carol S. Larson, age 52
Director Children Families and Communities, Lois Salisbury
VP and Director Communications, Chris DeCardy
Senior Program Manager Population, Sono Aibe
Director Conservation and Science, Walter Reid
Chief Investment Officer, John H. Moehling
Director Program-Related Investments, Mary Anne Rodgers
Director Local Grantmaking, Irene Wong
Director Evaluation, Gale Berkowitz
Director Population, Musimbi Kanyoro
Controller, Kenneth (Ken) Tsuboi
Director Operations and Technology, Matthew D. (Matt) Sharp
Vice President Chief Financial Officer, Craig Neyman
Vice Chairman, Julie E. Packard
Vice Chairman, Nancy Packard Burnett
President and CEO, Carol S. Larson, age 52
Auditors: PRICEWATERHOUSECOOPERS LLP

LOCATIONS

HQ: THE DAVID AND LUCILE PACKARD FOUNDATION
300 2ND ST, LOS ALTOS, CA 940223694
Phone: 650 917-7167
Web: WWW.PACKARD.ORG

HISTORICAL FINANCIALS

Company Type: Private

Income Statement

FYE: December 31

	REVENUE ($ mil.)	NET INCOME ($ mil.)	NET PROFIT MARGIN	EMPLOYEES
12/10	701	412	58.8%	85
12/09	398	74	18.8%	—
12/06	809	587	72.6%	—
12/05	0	0	—	—
Annual Growth	302.5%	—	—	—

2010 Year-End Financials

Return on assets: —
Return on equity: 58.8%
Current ratio: 1.60
Cash ($ mil.): 213

THE DELONG CO INC

Auditors: BAKER TILLY VIRCHOW KRAUSE LL

LOCATIONS

HQ: THE DELONG CO INC
513 FRONT ST, CLINTON, WI 53525
Phone: 608 676-2255
Web: WWW.DELONGCOMPANY.COM

Income Statement

FYE: September 30

	REVENUE ($ mil.)	NET INCOME ($ mil.)	NET PROFIT MARGIN	EMPLOYEES
09/14	1,306	19	1.5%	250
09/13	1,326	25	1.9%	—
09/12	0	22	—	—
09/11	995	0	—	—
Annual Growth	9.5%	—	—	—

2014 Year-End Financials

Return on assets: 2.2%   Cash ($ mil.): 16
Return on equity: 1.5%
Current ratio: 0.90

THE DREES COMPANY

The Drees Company is a big homebuilder in Cincinnati and one of the nation's top private builders. Drees targets first-time and move-up buyers with homes that are priced from about $100000 to more than $1 million. Drees also builds condominiums townhomes and patio homes. Its homes portfolio ranges from its former Zaring Premier Homes luxury division to the company's more financially accessible and modest Marquis Homes division. Drees is active in Florida Indiana Kentucky Maryland North Carolina Ohio Tennessee Texas Virginia and Washington DC. The family-owned firm was founded in 1928.

OperationsIn addition to home building architecture energy efficiency upgrades and design services Drees also provides new construction financing solutions through its subsidiary and mortgage lending business First Equity Mortgage which has closed more than $1 billion in loans.Geographic ReachHeadquartered in Fort Mitchell Kentucky Drees operates across nearly 10 states in cities including Cincinnati and Cleveland Ohio; Indianapolis; Nashville; Raleigh North Carolina; Jacksonville Florida; Austin Houston and Dallas Texas; and the Greater Washington DC area.Sales and MarketingIn recent years Drees has concentrated on the fast-growing "move up" segment market targeting home buyers looking to upgrade into larger houses.In 2012 Drees converted its longtime Zaring Premier Homes luxury brand name to its flagship Drees Homes brand. While the move required rebranding in the greater Cincinnati area Drees is banking on its brand reputation and recognition. It also allowed the residential homebuilder to consolidate its advertising sales and marketing efforts. Financial PerformanceWhile full details of the private company could not be found Drees' CEO David Drees announced in July 2013 that he expected the company to reach $629 million in revenue by April 1 2014. Looking further back Drees had revenues as high as $1.2 billion in 2006 which slid dramatically following the financial crisis to $490 million in revenue in 2010. To its benefit Texas markets —specifically Austin and Dallas —remained active throughout the recession. Drees was also helped by entering the recession with a relatively low debt load of $364 million. By March 2013 Drees had sold land to generate cash flow and reduced its debt to $125 million. StrategyRanked among the top 25 largest national homebuilders by BUILDER Magazine Drees has been steadily expanding over the past few years to capitalize on an improving housing market. In recent years Drees has concentrated on the fast-growing and lucrative "move up" segment of the homebuyer's market targeting home owners that are looking to upgrade to larger houses with higher-end amenities. In late 2014 the company landed a $100 million contract to build 237 homes in three Cincinnati-based residential communities with the average house priced between $307000 and $360000. In September 2014 the company entered its first ever foray into the Houston Texas market with plans to price its houses there for more than $300000 —prime pricing to lure these "move up" buyers.Company BackgroundA family-operated enterprise since its founding by immigrant Theodore Drees in 1928 the company is run by the third generation of the Drees family.

EXECUTIVES

Vice President Marketing, Barbara (Barb) Drees-Jones
Vice President Human Resources, Effie McKeehan
Vice President Strategic Marketing, Douglas Hinger
Vice President Marketing, Barbara (Barb) Drees
Vice President Human Resources, Effie Mc Keehan
Treasurer, Lawrence Herbst
Auditors: DELOITTE & TOUCHE LLP CINCINN

LOCATIONS

HQ: THE DREES COMPANY
211 GRANDVIEW DR STE 300, FORT MITCHELL, KY 410172790
Phone: 859 578-4200
Web: WWW.DREESHOMES.COM

Selected Locations

Florida
  Jacksonville
Indiana
  Indianapolis
Kentucky
  Fort Mitchell
Maryland
  Frederick
North Carolina
  Raleigh
Ohio
  Cincinnati
  Cleveland
  Dayton
Tennessee
  Nashville
Texas
  Austin
  Dallas
Washington DC

COMPETITORS

D.R. Horton	Lennar
Fischer Homes	M/I Homes
KB Home	PulteGroup

HISTORICAL FINANCIALS
Company Type: Private

Income Statement

FYE: March 31

	REVENUE ($ mil.)	NET INCOME ($ mil.)	NET PROFIT MARGIN	EMPLOYEES
03/14	683	35	5.3%	850
03/13	584	19	3.3%	—
03/12	548	14	2.6%	—
03/11	536	0	—	—
Annual Growth	8.4%	—	—	—

2014 Year-End Financials

Return on assets: 3.9%   Cash ($ mil.): 5
Return on equity: 5.3%
Current ratio: —

THE FIRST DISTRICT ASSOCIATION

LOCATIONS

HQ: THE FIRST DISTRICT ASSOCIATION
101 S SWIFT AVE, LITCHFIELD, MN 553552800
Phone: 320 693-3236
Web: WWW.FIRSTDISTRICT.COM

HISTORICAL FINANCIALS
Company Type: Private

Income Statement

FYE: September 30

	REVENUE ($ mil.)	NET INCOME ($ mil.)	NET PROFIT MARGIN	EMPLOYEES
09/14	745	27	3.7%	150
09/13	627	16	2.6%	—
09/12	523	18	3.6%	—
09/11	476	0	—	—
Annual Growth	16.1%	—	—	—

THE FISHEL COMPANY

The Fishel Company reels in revenues by laying out lines. The company (also known as Team Fishel) provides engineering construction management and maintenance services for electric and gas utility and communications infrastructure projects. The aerial and underground utility contractor designs and builds distribution networks for telecommunications cable and broadband television gas transmission and distribution and electric utilities throughout the US. It also counts municipalities state and federal agencies universities commercial building owners financial services companies health care providers manufacturers and residential real estate developers among its clients.
Geographic Reach
The Fishel Company is licensed to do business in some two dozen states. It operates from 32 offices located in about 15 states including Arkansas Arizona California Florida Georgia Kentucky Nevada New Mexico Ohio Oklahoma Pennsylvania Tennessee Texas and Virginia.
Operations
The company's products and services include Structured Cabling Systems Data Center buildouts Wireless Networks and Building Security and Automation. It has installed more than 16000 communications networks for the healthcare financial education manufacturing logistics and government sectors.
Sales and Marketing
The company's power customers include American Electric Power Arizona Public Service Arkansas Valley Electric Dayton Power & Light Dominion Virginia Power Duke Energy Entergy and First Electric Cooperative among others.
In addition to utilities and power coops the company serves other markets including Repair and Planning Broadband Broadband Network Services Enterprise Solutions and Advanced Technology Services.
Strategy
Fishel Company is tracking its business to a Vision 2020 initiative which has a three-pronged goal of customer development operational excellence and teammate development. Its customer de-

velopment focus involves natural gas distribution power transmission and distribution (T&D) construction and fiber network installation. Operational excellence goals are centered on bidding and pricing project management and being accident-free. Its teammate management focus comprises leadership development performance management workforce planning and continuous improvement.

The company has strategic business relationships with TE Connectivity Andrews Wireless Belden Commscope Corning Cable Systems Legrand Ortronics Leviton Nexans Berktek OASIS and Panduit.

Company Background

Kenneth Fishel founded the firm in 1936 as an underground contractor for telephone companies.

EXECUTIVES

President and CEO, John E. Phillips
VP and CFO, Paul R. Riewe
VP Western Region, William E. (Bill) Pauley
VP Technologies, Ken E. Katz
Regional Director Florida, Vance Mauldin
VP Midwest Region, Scott Homberger
EVP and COO, Randy Blair
VP Central Region, Scott Keeler
Vice President, Joe Mayhew
Chairman, Diane Fishel Keeler
Auditors: CROWE HORWATH LLP COLUMBUS O

LOCATIONS

HQ: THE FISHEL COMPANY
1366 DUBLIN RD, COLUMBUS, OH 432151093
Phone: 614 274-8100
Web: WWW.TEAMFISHEL.COM

Selected Locations
Arizona
Arkansas
California
Florida
Georgia
Kentucky
Nevada
New Mexico
Ohio
Oklahoma
Pennsylvania
Tennessee
Texas
Virginia

PRODUCTS/OPERATIONS

Selected Services
Emergency restoration repair & maintenance
Fiber overbuilds
GPS survey
Network installation
Permitting
Project management
Right of way
Site Design
Utility construction

Selected Markets
Commercial industrial advanced logistics
Electric Distribution & Transmission
Financial & health care
Gas distribution & transmission pipeline
Telecom & broadband cable
Wireless backhaul

COMPETITORS

Dycom	MYR Group
EMCOR	MasTec
Integrated Electrical Services	Pike Corporation
	Quanta Services
MDU Construction Services	

Company Type: Private

Income Statement FYE: December 31

	REVENUE ($ mil.)	NET INCOME ($ mil.)	NET PROFIT MARGIN	EMPLOYEES
12/13	306	10	3.4%	1,400
12/12	281	(2)	—	—
12/11	174	7	4.5%	—
12/09	162	0	—	—
Annual Growth	17.1%	—	—	—

2013 Year-End Financials
Return on assets: 4.2%   Cash ($ mil.): 3
Return on equity: 3.4%
Current ratio: 0.80

THE FLORIDA SCHOOL CHOICE FUND INC

Auditors: NATHERSON & COMPANY PA SAR

LOCATIONS

HQ: THE FLORIDA SCHOOL CHOICE FUND INC
337 S PLANT AVE, TAMPA, FL 336062325
Phone: 813 258-2700
Web: WWW.STEPUPFORSTUDENTS.ORG

HISTORICAL FINANCIALS
Company Type: Private

Income Statement FYE: June 30

	REVENUE ($ mil.)	NET INCOME ($ mil.)	NET PROFIT MARGIN	EMPLOYEES
06/14	333	47	14.4%	17
06/13	311	97	31.4%	—
06/09	33	(8)	—	—
06/08	42	0	—	—
Annual Growth	41.2%	—	—	—

2014 Year-End Financials
Return on assets: 0.3%   Cash ($ mil.): 61
Return on equity: 14.4%
Current ratio: 57.20

THE G W VAN KEPPEL COMPANY

If you ask The G. W. Van Keppel Co. being stuck in the middle isn't half bad. The company touts its role as a middle man matching original equipment manufacturers with operators of their heavy duty workhorses. Founded in 1926 it has grown to distribute a slew of construction aggregate and material handling equipment under blue chip brands including Volvo Hyster and Champion Motor Graders. The company also offers repair and maintenance services rental equipment and aftermarket parts for its equipment. G. W. Van Keppel is led by its founder's third generation chairman and president Bill Walker.

Geographic Reach

The company operates through 15 locations crossing Arkansas Iowa Kansas Oklahoma Missouri Wisconsin and Texas.

Operations

G. W. Van Keppel operates through the divisions of Bobcat of Springfield Construction Equipment Material Handling Peerless Conveyor Quarry Supplies and Trench Safety.

Sales and Marketing

The company sells its products through dealers and sales representatives in the US. It targets the aggregate construction mining and material handling markets.

EXECUTIVES

President, William S. (Bill) Walker
EVP, Kevin Kientz
Treasurer, Rick Krause
General Manager Material Handling Division, Jared (JW) Ward
General Manager Quarry Supply/Trench Safety, Michael Murray
VP Product Support, Brian Loderhose
Auditors: BKD KANSAS CITY MO

LOCATIONS

HQ: THE G W VAN KEPPEL COMPANY
1801 N 9TH ST, KANSAS CITY, KS 661012023
Phone: 913 281-4800
Web: WWW.VANKEPPEL.COM

COMPETITORS

Briggs Equipment	John Henry Foster
DXP Enterprises	Maxim Crane Works
Duncan Industrial Solutions	Rocky Duron & Associates
HOLT Texas	Victor L. Phillips
J. A. Riggs Tractor	Warren CAT

HISTORICAL FINANCIALS
Company Type: Private

Income Statement FYE: November 30

	REVENUE ($ mil.)	NET INCOME ($ mil.)	NET PROFIT MARGIN	EMPLOYEES
11/07	163	1	0.8%	200
11/05	139	20	14.8%	—
11/04	115	2	2.1%	—
11/02	106	0	—	—
Annual Growth	9.0%	—	—	—

2007 Year-End Financials
Return on assets: 3.5%   Cash ($ mil.): 1
Return on equity: 0.8%
Current ratio: 0.30

THE GARDEN CITY CO-OP INC

Auditors: LINDBURG VOGEL PIERCE FARIS D

LOCATIONS

HQ: THE GARDEN CITY CO-OP INC
106 N 6TH ST, GARDEN CITY, KS 678465545
Phone: 620 275-6161
Web: WWW.GCCOOP.COM

HISTORICAL FINANCIALS

Company Type: Private

Income Statement

FYE: August 31

	REVENUE ($ mil.)	NET INCOME ($ mil.)	NET PROFIT MARGIN	EMPLOYEES
08/08	425	13	3.2%	23
08/07	237	5	2.4%	—
08/06	0	0		—
Annual Growth	—	—	—	—

2008 Year-End Financials

Return on assets: —
Return on equity: 3.2%
Current ratio: 0.20

Cash ($ mil.): —

THE GEORGE J FALTER COMPANY

The George J. Falter Company is a leading independent wholesale distributor of food and merchandise serving grocery stores convienience stores and other retailers throughout Maryland. It supplies customers with such goods as beverages dry goods and frozen foods as well as health and beauty items tobacco products and other merchandise. In addition George J. Falter distributes candy for fund raising activities. The company has delivery operations as well as a cash & carry outlet in Baltimore. The family-owned business was founded in 1878 as a candy distributor.

Auditors: GROSS MENDELSOHM & ASSOCIATES

LOCATIONS

HQ: THE GEORGE J FALTER COMPANY
3501 BENSON AVE, BALTIMORE, MD 212271098
Phone: 410 646-3641
Web: WWW.FALTERFUNDRAISING.COM

COMPETITORS

Atlantic Dominion	Eby-Brown
C&S Wholesale	H. T. Hackney
Century Distributors	McLane
Core-Mark	

HISTORICAL FINANCIALS

Company Type: Private

Income Statement

FYE: December 31

	REVENUE ($ mil.)	NET INCOME ($ mil.)	NET PROFIT MARGIN	EMPLOYEES
12/09	188	0	0.3%	130
12/08*	181	0	0.4%	—
06/07	1,295	0		—
Annual Growth	— 4433.1%	—	—	—

*Fiscal year change

2009 Year-End Financials

Return on assets: 2.2%
Return on equity: 0.3%
Current ratio: 0.80

Cash ($ mil.): 1

THE GOLUB CORPORATION

Supermarket operator The Golub Corporation offers tasty come-ons such as table-ready meals gift certificates automatic discount cards and a hotline where cooks answer food-related queries. Golub operates about 135 Price Chopper supermarkets and market 32 stores in six states in the northeastern US (New York is its largest market.) About 80 of the locations have in-store pharmacies and some New York stores provide shopping and delivery service through the Shops4U program. The founding Golub family runs the company and owns about 45% of the regional grocery chain; employees own slightly more than 45%.

Geographic Reach

Golub's Price Chopper chain is active in six US states. New York accounts for more than 60% of its locations while Massachusetts and Vermont each contribute more than 10%. It also has locations in Connecticut Pennsylvania and New Hampshire.

Financial Performance

While privately-held Golub doesn't publish sales results for its Price Chopper chain its supermarkets ring up an estimated $3.5 billion in annual revenues.

Sales and Marketing

The company sells its products in its stores and online.

Strategy

Golub continues to invest in its future through new locations improved products and services customer engagement and health and wellness initiatives environmental sustainability activities progressive technology digital marketing e-commerce and social networking. In 2015 Price Chopper Supermarkets launched a specialty pharmacy program with Aureus Health Services a specialty pharmacy and health management company.

In 2014 the company announced plans to rebrand about 135 Price Chopper supermarkets under a new banner Market 32. The conversions will take place over the next several years. More than half of the conversions will be completed within five years representing a $300 million investment. The renamed stores will will include expanded food service options an enhanced product mix and an emphasis on customer service. The new name references 1932 the year the company was founded.

In late 2013 Golub invested some $10 million to relaunch a Latham New York store as Market Bistro by Price Chopper. The 87000-square-foot revamped location features a New York-style deli pizza counter cooking classes and indoor and outdoor patios.

Company Background

Like many other retailers the company is experimenting with new formats. In May 2012 it opened its first small-format store known as Price Chopper Limited. The 19000-square-foot store (about a third of the size of a typical Price Chopper supermarket) is located in a residential neighborhood in downtown Saratoga Springs New York. The "Limited" store offers an edited selection of Price Chopper's most popular products a bakery full-service meat deli and seafood departments and a cafe with eat-in or take-out meals.

In fall 2011 Price Chopper launched a new online ordering and home delivery program called Price Chopper Shops4U. The service charges a service fee of $10 with an additional $6 fee for delivery. Customers can either pick up their orders at the store or have them delivered.

Brothers Bill and Ben Golub founded the company in 1932.

EXECUTIVES

President and CEO, Jerel T. (Jerry) Golub, age 57
VP Public Relations and Consumer Services, Mona J. Golub, age 51
SVP Administration, David Golub, age 54
VP Produce & Floral Merchandising, Rick Reed
Director Of Pharmacy, Toni Shields
Vice President Advertising, Shawn Gonzalez
Vice President Meat Merchandising, Jason Resner
Vice President Talent Management, Paul Rollins
Senior Vice President Chief Information Officer, Richard Bauer
Vice President Construction and Engineering, Bill Sweet
Senior Vice President Fin Chief Financial Officer, John J (Jack) Endres
Vice President of Real Estate and Construction, Don Orlando
Chairman and CEO, Neil M. Golub, age 78

LOCATIONS

HQ: THE GOLUB CORPORATION
461 NOTT ST, SCHENECTADY, NY 123081812
Phone: 518 355-5000
Web: WWW.PRICECHOPPER.COM

2013 Stores

	No.
New York	81
Massachusetts	16
Vermont	15
Connecticut	8
Pennsylvania	8
New Hampshire	4
Total	**132**

COMPETITORS

7-Eleven	Gerrity's
A&P	Hannaford Bros.
ALDI	Shaw's
BJ's Wholesale Club	Stewart's Shops
Big Y Foods	Stop & Shop
CVS	TOPS Markets
Costco Wholesale	Target Corporation
Cumberland Farms	Wal-Mart
DeMoulas Super Markets	Wegmans

HISTORICAL FINANCIALS

Company Type: Private

Income Statement

FYE: April 27

	REVENUE ($ mil.)	NET INCOME ($ mil.)	NET PROFIT MARGIN	EMPLOYEES
04/14	3,472	18	0.5%	21,741
04/13	3,484	24	0.7%	—
04/12	3,627	37	1.0%	—
04/11	3,459	0	—	—
Annual Growth	0.1%			

2014 Year-End Financials

Return on assets: 5.2%
Return on equity: 0.5%
Current ratio: 0.30

Cash ($ mil.): 24

THE HEALTHCARE AUTHORITY FOR BAPTIST HEALTH AND AFFILIATE OF UAB

LOCATIONS

HQ: THE HEALTHCARE AUTHORITY FOR BAPTIST HEALTH AND AFFILIATE OF UAB
2105 E SOUTH BLVD, MONTGOMERY, AL 361162409
Phone: 334 286-2987
Web: WWW.BAPTISTFIRST.ORG

HISTORICAL FINANCIALS
Company Type: Private

Income Statement
FYE: June 30

	REVENUE ($ mil.)	NET INCOME ($ mil.)	NET PROFIT MARGIN	EMPLOYEES
06/13	543	24	4.6%	1,550
06/05	360	21	6.0%	—
Annual Growth	5.3%	1.8%	—	—

2013 Year-End Financials
Return on assets: —
Return on equity: 4.6%
Current ratio: 0.90
Cash ($ mil.): 8

THE HENRY M JACKSON FOUNDATION FOR THE ADVANCEMENT OF MILITARY M

Auditors: GRANT THORNTON LLP MCLEAN VA

LOCATIONS

HQ: THE HENRY M JACKSON FOUNDATION FOR THE ADVANCEMENT OF MILITARY M
6720A ROCKLEDGE DR # 100, BETHESDA, MD 208171888
Phone: 240 694-2000
Web: WWW.HJF.ORG

HISTORICAL FINANCIALS
Company Type: Private

Income Statement
FYE: September 30

	REVENUE ($ mil.)	NET INCOME ($ mil.)	NET PROFIT MARGIN	EMPLOYEES
09/13	441	12	2.9%	2,200
09/10	402	7	1.9%	—
09/08	268	2	1.0%	—
09/07	120	0	—	—
Annual Growth	24.1%	—	—	—

2013 Year-End Financials
Return on assets: 10.8%
Return on equity: 2.9%
Current ratio: 0.20
Cash ($ mil.): 10

THE HOWARD UNIVERSITY

Howard University is a predominantly African-American university enrolling some 11000 students in Washington DC. The university offers undergraduate graduate and professional degrees in 120 areas including engineering education divinity dentistry law medicine history political science music and social work through its 12 schools and colleges. It has about 1000 full-time faculty members and has a low student-to-teacher ratio of about 8:1. Established in 1867 the school was named after one of its founders General Oliver O. Howard a Civil War hero who was commissioner of the Freedman's Bureau.OperationsMedical students at Howard University have the convenience of using Howard University Hospital (located right on the school's campus) for their training and residency programs. The not-for-profit hospital offers students training in a full range of medical specialties including Level 1 Trauma care. The hospital is also a research facility giving students the opportunity to participate in clinical and research work.

Notable alumni at Howard University include choreographer Debbie Allen former US Supreme Court Justice Thurgood Marshall former New York City mayor David Dinkins Nobel laureate Toni Morrison and singer Roberta Flack.

Financial Performance

Howard University reported a 2% increase in revenue to some $851 million in 2012 due to higher tuition and fees patient services and other income. The university reported net income losses of $149 million that year (it also posted a loss in 2011) due to higher operating expenses and restructuring costs as well as lower investment returns.

Howard University's endowment is about $400 million. Its operating budget is nearly $885 million.

EXECUTIVES

Associate Vice President of Clinical Affairs and Quality Improvement, Jeanette Gibbs
Vice President, Cicely Cottrell
Senior Vice President, Florence Prioleau
Assistant Vice President University Communications and Marketing, Kerry-Ann Hamilton
Auditors: PRICEWATERHOUSECOOPERS LLP MC

LOCATIONS

HQ: THE HOWARD UNIVERSITY
2400 6TH ST NW, WASHINGTON, DC 200590002
Phone: 202 806-6100
Web: WWW.HOWARD.EDU

PRODUCTS/OPERATIONS

Selected Schools and Colleges
Arts and Sciences
Business
Communications
Dentistry
Divinity
Education
Engineering Architecture and Computer Sciences
Graduate School
Law
Medicine
Nursing and Allied Health Sciences
Pharmacy
Social Work

HISTORICAL FINANCIALS
Company Type: Private

Income Statement
FYE: June 30

	REVENUE ($ mil.)	NET INCOME ($ mil.)	NET PROFIT MARGIN	EMPLOYEES
06/13	843	202	24.0%	5,600
06/12	1,000	(148)	—	—
06/11	989	11	1.2%	—
06/10	941	0	—	—
Annual Growth	(3.6%)	—	—	—

2013 Year-End Financials
Return on assets: —
Return on equity: 24.0%
Current ratio: —
Cash ($ mil.): 34

THE HUMANE SOCIETY OF THE UNITED STATES

The Humane Society of the United States (HSUS) is a watchdog for dogs and all sorts of other domestic animals and wildlife. Founded in 1954 HSUS is the country's largest animal protection organization with 11 million members and constituents. The organization supports the work of local humane societies and implements a variety of investigative educational advocacy and legislative programs to promote animal welfare. Its campaigns have addressed such issues as animal fighting factory farming animal testing the fur trade and hunting practices. Most of HSUS's revenue comes from contributions and grants. An affiliate Humane Society International takes the cause to other countries.

Operations

The HSUS operates through a network of animal sanctuaries and rescue efforts to provide emergency care and homes for animals nationwide. The organization runs an online store –in place of a catalog –that offers products for pets and people with pets. HSUS sets aside a portion of the online sales to fund its programs.

The organization supports public policy corporate reforms and major campaigns to confront animal cruelty. It provides training and services to local shelters and rescue groups supports spay/neuter and adoption initiatives and offers tips on caring for pets.

In addition to Humane Society International HSUS maintains affiliate relationships with Doris Day Animal League Humane Society Veterinary Medical Association Humane Society University The Fund for Animals Humane Society Wildlife Land Trust and South Florida Wildlife Center. While the organization operates independently from local humane societies and SPCAs it shares similar goals and supports and serves in a number of outreach areas.

Geographic Reach

Based in Washington DC HSUS has regional representatives throughout the US. States with the largest number of constituents are California Florida Illinois Massachusetts Michigan New Jersey New York Ohio Pennsylvania and Texas. It operates wildlife sanctuaries in 35 states.

Financial Performance

HSUS generates revenue from a variety of sources including contributions and grants (77%) bequests investment income and other income.

More than 80% of its operating and supporting expenses goes toward animal protection programs.

Strategy

Americans have become increasingly concerned about a wide range of issues that reach far beyond direct animal abuse. HSUS cites progress on several fronts such as the fact that nearly 50 fast food chains grocers pork producers and food service providers have committed to phasing out gestation crates that help to immobilize breeding sows. It also assisted in the rescue of hundreds of animals from coastal New York and New Jersey neighborhoods impacted by Hurricane Sandy in 2012.

The group's lobbying efforts aided in the passing of around 100 pro-animal state laws per year including ones that have banned hound hunting of bears and bobcats in California and private ownership in Ohio of animals deemed too dangerous. HSUS is also behind the USDA's efforts to establish mandatory minimum penalties for Horse Protection Act violations. Previously HSUS was party to a landmark agreement with the United Egg Producers trade association to support federal legislation banning the confinement of hens to a battery cage.

To its benefit the organization is steered by individuals with a diverse pool of talent that lobby and develop policies that take on big industries and interests. To this end HSUS attracts attorneys undercover investigators academics and veterinarians. It is also experienced in gaining news coverage to expose cruel practices and the parties responsible. HSUS' future is global as it seeks to develop a network that tackles the fur trade in China elephant poaching in Africa and factory farming in Brazil and India to name a few.

EXECUTIVES

Chief International Officer and Chief Scientific Officer; President and CEO Humane Society International, Andrew N. Rowan
President and CEO, Wayne Pacelle
SVP Campaigns and Outreach, Heidi Prescott
SVP Animal Protection Litigation and Investigations, Jonathan Lovvorn
CFO and Treasurer, G. Thomas Waite
Vice Chair, Jennifer Leaning
Chair, Eric L. Bernthal
Second Vice Chair, Jason Weiss

LOCATIONS

HQ: THE HUMANE SOCIETY OF THE UNITED STATES
2100 L ST NW STE 500, WASHINGTON, DC
200371595
Phone: 202 452-1100
Web: WWW.HUMANESOCIETY.ORG

PRODUCTS/OPERATIONS

Selected Affiliates
Doris Day Animal League
Humane Society International
Humane Society Legislative Fund
Humane Society University
Humane Society Veterinary Medical Association
Humane Society Wildlife Land Trust
The Fund for Animals

Selected Areas of Focus
Campaigns
  Adopt a shelter pet
  Chimps deserve better
  End animal cruelty and fighting
  Farm animal protection
  Fur-Free
  Protect seals
  Stop puppy mills
  Wildlife abuse
  Wild horses
Issues
  Animal cruelty and fighting
  Animal rescue
  Animals in laboratories

Captive wildlife
Equine protection
Factory farming
Fur
Opposition
Pet protection
Threats to wildlife
Wildlife abuse
Wildlife management

HISTORICAL FINANCIALS
Company Type: Private

Income Statement

	REVENUE ($ mil.)	NET INCOME ($ mil.)	NET PROFIT MARGIN	EMPLOYEES
12/13	169	21	12.6%	440
12/11	133	5	4.3%	—
Annual Growth	12.8%	91.8%	—	—

2013 Year-End Financials

Return on assets: —
Return on equity: 12.6%
Current ratio: —

Cash ($ mil.): 21

THE INGALLS MEMORIAL HOSPITAL

Ingalls Memorial Hospital serves Chicago's south suburbs. With more than 560 beds the main hospital offers a variety of acute and tertiary health care services including cancer treatment cardiovascular care orthopedic surgery rehabilitation services neurosurgery women's health and other clinical services. It also includes specialty centers in areas such as sleep therapy and addiction treatment. Ingalls Memorial Hospital also acts as a health system operating outpatient offices and clinics and providing home health and hospice services in the area.

Geographic Reach

Ingalls Memorial Hospital's main campus encompasses some 22 acres in the south suburbs of Chicago. Its family and urgent care centers are located in Calumet City Flossmoor Matteson and Tinley Park. The system also includes rehabilitation centers in Calumet City and South Holland; a wellness center in Homewood; and a cancer and surgery center in Tinley Park.

Operations

Ingalls Memorial Hospital employs 450 physicians who specialize in 30 fields. The medical center sees about 18000 inpatient admissions per year. It also handles about 1100 births and more than 50000 emergency department visits annually.

In addition to the hospital the health system includes a handful of family care centers and several urgent care and surgery clinics as well as outpatient rehabilitation wellness and cancer support centers. Ingalls Health System also operates home health and hospice agencies and it provides community health screenings and other outreach programs.

Each year Ingalls hosts more than 200 free health screenings educational programs and health fairs that reach nearly 50000 individuals. These include free or discounted mammograms; free prostate screenings; and free or deeply discounted children's physicals and immunizations for hundreds of area children preparing for school.Ingalls Health System also includes a Wellness Center in

Homewood; Cancer Care Center and Same Day Surgery in Tinley Park; Ingalls Center for Outpatient Rehabilitation in Calumet City; and Ingalls Home Care & Hospice which provides skilled nursing support and therapy services throughout the Southland.

Strategy

To improve primary care services Ingalls Memorial Hospital has conducted expansion and renovation efforts at several of its family clinic locations in recent years. It is also growing its range of advanced cancer treatment offerings.

In 2015 Ingalls opened its intensive outpatient program at the Ingalls Family Care Center in Tinley Park. A short-term behavioral health treatment program for adults ages 18 and above the program treats individuals struggling with depression stress and anxiety. It expanded its services to Tinley Park to serve more patients in need of outpatient therapy west of the hospital's main campus in Harvey. The program helps participants take charge of their own well-being through skill development in areas like positive lifestyle changes self-image stress management problem solving communication and relationships.In 2015 Ingalls also launched an online risk assessment to screen for depression.

Company Background

The company's infusion center was the first Chicago-area cancer center to administer a new prostate cancer drug Provinge in 2012. Ingalls first introduced intensive outpatient therapy at its Flossmoor Family Care Center in 2012.

Ingalls Health System was founded by Chicago-area industrialist Frederick Ingalls in 1923.

EXECUTIVES

Nursing Director, Gregory Biedron
Corporate Vice President Marketing And Planning, Susan (Sue) Fine
Rph, Martha Jelski
Nursing Director, Jill Zaki

LOCATIONS

HQ: THE INGALLS MEMORIAL HOSPITAL
1 INGALLS DR, HARVEY, IL 604263558
Phone: 708 333-2300
Web: WWW.INGALLSHEALTHSYSTEM.ORG

PRODUCTS/OPERATIONS

Selected Services
Advanced Orthopedic Institute
  Joint Center
  Spine Center
  Sports Medicine
  Rehabilitative Services
Behavioral Health
  Inpatient Adult Care
  Addictions
  Adolescent
  Depression Risk
Cancer Care
  Newly Diagnosed
  Research
  Technology and Treatments
Heart and Vascular
  Diabetes
  Heart Care Center
  Leg Veins
  Stroke
Home Care and Hospice
  Palliative Care
Interventional Radiology
  Interventional Oncology
  Uterine Fibroids
  Vein Clinic
Irwin Retina Center
  Clinical Research
  Diabetic Retinopathy
  Macular Degeneration
Neurosciences
  Stroke
  Concussion Program

Sleep Centers
Occupational Health
  Employer Resource Center
  Worksite Wellness and Prevention
Outpatient Services
  Advanced Imaging
  Pharmacy
  Same Day Surgery
  Urgent Aid
Rehabilitation Services
  Acute Care
  Day Rehabilitation
  Home Care
  Inpatient Rehabilitation
  Outpatient Rehabilitation
Wellness
  Complementary Medicine
  Nutrition and Weight Management
Women's Services
  Breast Center
  Maternity Unit
  Osteoporosis
  Uterine Fibroids
Additional Services
  Complementary Medicine
  Dermatology
  Diabetes
  Dialysis
  Ear/Nose/Throat
  Gastroenterology
  Occupational Health
  Ophthalmology
  Pain Management
  Pediatrics
  Rheumatology
  Therapies
  Urinary Incontinence
  Weight Management
  Wound Care

COMPETITORS

Advocate Health Care
Alexian Brothers Health System
Loyola University Health System
MetroSouth Medical
Mount Sinai Hospital
NorthShore University HealthSystem
Rush System for Health
Saint Margaret Mercy Healthcare
St. Bernard Hospital and Health Care Center
Vanguard MacNeal Hospital
WellGroup HealthPartners

HISTORICAL FINANCIALS

Company Type: Private

Income Statement

FYE: September 30

	REVENUE ($ mil.)	NET INCOME ($ mil.)	NET PROFIT MARGIN	EMPLOYEES
09/13	290	34	11.8%	2,296
09/12	293	36	12.6%	—
09/09	267	(15)	—	—
09/08	270	0	—	—
Annual Growth	1.4%	—	—	—

2013 Year-End Financials

Return on assets: 6.7%   Cash ($ mil.): 22
Return on equity: 11.8%
Current ratio: 1.20

THE JACKSON LABORATORY

The Jackson Laboratory (JAX) was into genetics before genetics was cool. Founded in 1929 the not-for-profit organization is a leading researcher of human diseases their causes and their potential cures. Much of its research into mammalian genetics is focused on mice which share a similar genetic makeup to humans. In addition to its own research in areas such as cancer immunology and metabolic disease the organization maintains colonies of mice and supplies them under the brand name JAX to other laboratories around the globe. Additionally JAX offers educational programs –including internships workshops and predoctoral programs –for both current and future scientists.

Geographic Reach

The organization has one location in Sacramento California and two each in Farmington Connecticut and Bar Harbor Maine.

Financial Performance

JAX receives operating revenue from public sector support in the form of federal grants private sector support in the form of private foundation grants philanthropic contributions and resource revenue in the form of cost and fees collected for JAX Mice & Services its service for supplying mice models used for research. The organization's operating revenue increased by 5% from $230 million to $240 million in 2013 over 2012; about 75% of it from National Institutes of Health grants.

Strategy

JAX has spent a couple of years and at least $227 million acquiring and upgrading facilities at its California and Maine locations. Part of the organization's mandate is educating scientists. To that end in 2013 it purchased a website content and assets from the National Coalition of Health Professional Education in Genetics and hired three of its employees.

The following year JAX and Chinese company Wuhan Frasergen Bioinformatics created a cancer research facility in Wuhan China that will let Chinese researchers use the Laboratory's cancer tools.

EXECUTIVES

EVP and COO, Charles E. Hewett
VP Research, Robert (Bob) Braun
CFO, Linda Jensen
President and CEO, Edison T. Liu
Scientific Director The Jackson Laboratory for Genomic Medicine, Charles Lee
General Manager Jax Mice Clinical and Research Services, Auro Nair
Vice President, Carol Lamb
Medical Librarian, Douglas (Doug) Macbeth
Chairman, David J. Roux, age 58
Vice Chairman, Weslie R. Janeway
Assistant Secretary, Jana Robinson
Auditors: KPMG LLP BOSTON MA

LOCATIONS

HQ: THE JACKSON LABORATORY
  600 MAIN ST, BAR HARBOR, ME 046091500
Phone: 207 288-6000
Web: WWW.LIBRARY.JAX.ORG

PRODUCTS/OPERATIONS

2013 Sources of Revenue

	% of total
Genetic resources and services	69
Grants	29
Contributions	1
Other	1
Total	**100**

Selected Services

Breeding and rederivation services
Cryopreservation & recovery services
Genome science services
In Vivo pharmacology services
Surgical and preconditioning services

COMPETITORS

Charles River Laboratories
Deltagen

Harlan Laboratories
Howard Hughes Medical Institute
Taconic Farms
Whitehead Institute for Biomedical Research

HISTORICAL FINANCIALS

Company Type: Private

Income Statement

FYE: May 31

	REVENUE ($ mil.)	NET INCOME ($ mil.)	NET PROFIT MARGIN	EMPLOYEES
05/10	200	29	14.9%	1,300
05/09	166	(25)	—	—
05/08	143	0	—	—
Annual Growth	—	4163.0%	—	—

2010 Year-End Financials

Return on assets: —   Cash ($ mil.): 74
Return on equity: 14.9%
Current ratio: 0.70

THE JEFFERSON COUNTY ASSISTED HOUSING CORPORATION

Auditors: DIPIAZZA LAROCCA HEETER & CO L

LOCATIONS

HQ: THE JEFFERSON COUNTY ASSISTED HOUSING CORPORATION
  500 OFFICE PARK DR # 300, MOUNTAIN BRK, AL 352232437
Phone: 205 445-2800

HISTORICAL FINANCIALS

Company Type: Private

Income Statement

FYE: December 31

	REVENUE ($ mil.)	NET INCOME ($ mil.)	NET PROFIT MARGIN	EMPLOYEES
12/09	407	6	1.7%	83
12/08	17	8	47.8%	—
12/07	14	8	56.2%	—
12/05	22	0	—	—
Annual Growth	106.9%	—	—	—

2009 Year-End Financials

Return on assets: —   Cash ($ mil.): 23
Return on equity: 1.7%
Current ratio: —

THE JERRY BROWN CO INC

Auditors: JONES & ROTH PC EUGENE OR

LOCATIONS

HQ: THE JERRY BROWN CO INC
  2690 PRAIRIE RD, EUGENE, OR 974029747
Phone: 541 998-2300
Web: WWW.JBCO.COM

HISTORICAL FINANCIALS
Company Type: Private

Income Statement
FYE: December 31

	REVENUE ($ mil.)	NET INCOME ($ mil.)	NET PROFIT MARGIN	EMPLOYEES
12/10	379	2	0.6%	60
12/09	316	2	0.7%	—
12/08	1,532	0	—	—
Annual Growth	(50.3%)	24239.9%	—	—

2010 Year-End Financials

Return on assets: 2.8%
Return on equity: 0.6%
Current ratio: 1.00

Cash ($ mil.): 2

THE JEWISH GUILD FOR THE BLIND

Auditors: LORES & TROPER LLP NEW YORK

LOCATIONS

HQ: THE JEWISH GUILD FOR THE BLIND
15 W 65TH ST, NEW YORK, NY 100236601
Phone: 212 769-6200
Web: WWW.JGB.ORG

HISTORICAL FINANCIALS
Company Type: Private

Income Statement
FYE: December 31

	REVENUE ($ mil.)	NET INCOME ($ mil.)	NET PROFIT MARGIN	EMPLOYEES
12/13	691	65	9.5%	712
12/12	64	9	15.2%	—
12/11	57	9	16.4%	—
12/10	304	0	—	—
Annual Growth	31.4%	—	—	—

2013 Year-End Financials

Return on assets: 1.1%
Return on equity: 9.5%
Current ratio: 0.20

Cash ($ mil.): 16

THE JUDGE GROUP INC

If your business requires staffing technology consulting or training services The Judge Group will be predisposed to render a verdict in your favor. The company offers temporary and permanent employee placement services in a wide variety of service and manufacturing sectors but specializes in technology staffing. The company's technology consulting services address such areas as enterprise content management and strategy. It also offers training for IT-related and other professional functions through its Berkeley division. Martin Judge founded the company in 1970.

Geographic Reach

The Judge Group operates from a network of more than 30 offices throughout the US and has locations in Asia and Canada.

Strategy

The company's growth strategy revolves around the opening of offices in select markets and by entering alliances with other human resources services firms. Over the last few years it has launched offices in Baltimore Houston Milwaukee and Phoenix. In 2013 it opened its newest office in Ottawa Ontario. Throughout 2015 it opened new US offices in Oregon Connecticut and Maryland.

The Judge Group has also expanded its international reach by launching Judge China a firm which provides clients with consulting expertise for accessing markets in the most populous country in the world through offices in Beijing and Shanghai.

EXECUTIVES

COO, Katy A. Wiercinski
CFO, Robert G. Alessandrini, $137,308 total compensation
CEO, Martin E. Judge, $588,665 total compensation
President Direct Placement, Stephen D. Green
EVP, Gary R. Morris
President North America, Brian T. Anderson
EVP Talent Acquisition, Dennis F. Judge
President Berkeley Training, Peter Pedone
President Technology Solutions/Unified Communications, James D. Miner
EVP Sales, Michael Tedesco
President Judge Healthcare, Mick J. Angelichio
EVP and Chief Marketing Officer, Peter L. Fong
VP Training and Development and CIO, Kenneth F. (Ken) Krieger
Managing Vice President, Frank Santoro
Vice President Of Workflow Consulting, John Judge
Vice President Recruiting, Brian Blasko
Vice President, Linda Wertman
Vice President, Lisa Vaillette
Auditors: GRANT THORNTON LLP PHILADELPH

LOCATIONS

HQ: THE JUDGE GROUP INC
300 CONSHOHOCKEN STATE RD # 300, CONSHOHOCKEN, PA 194283801
Phone: 610 667-7700
Web: WWW.JUDGE.COM

PRODUCTS/OPERATIONS

Selected Services
Corporate training
  Custom content development
  Information technology training
  Professional development
  Project staffing and logistics
Enterprise-wide staffing
  Financial services
  Food/beverage
  Government
  Health care
  Insurance
  Manufacturing
  Pharmaceutical
  Retail/supermarkets
  Technology
  Utilities/telecom
  Wholesale distribution
Technology consulting
  Application design and development
  Audio visual design and implementation
  E-discovery and compliance
  Enterprise content management
  Research validation and compliance
  SAP implementation services
  Technology strategy and architecture

COMPETITORS

Accenture	Kenexa
Adecco	Kforce
Aquent	ManpowerGroup
Butler America	NTT Data
CDI	RCM Technologies
IBM Global Services	Unisys
Kelly Services	

HISTORICAL FINANCIALS
Company Type: Private

Income Statement
FYE: September 30

	REVENUE ($ mil.)	NET INCOME ($ mil.)	NET PROFIT MARGIN	EMPLOYEES
09/13	273	1	0.4%	570
09/12	251	2	1.2%	—
09/11	222	2	1.2%	—
09/08	188	0	—	—
Annual Growth	7.8%	—	—	—

2013 Year-End Financials

Return on assets: 6.8%
Return on equity: 0.4%
Current ratio: 2.10

Cash ($ mil.): 3

THE KLEINFELDER GROUP INC

The Kleinfelder Group isn't afraid to get its hands dirty. Since its start as a materials testing lab in 1961 the company has expanded to become one of the largest engineering consulting and design groups in the US. Kleinfelder's operating subsidiaries offer soils and materials testing geotechnical engineering construction management and environmental services. With about 50 domestic offices and locations in Australia and Guam the group targets the energy transportation water commercial/industrial government and education markets; projects run the gamut from building underground parking garages to establishing wind farms. Jim Kleinfelder who retired in 1993 founded the employee-owned company.

Geographic Reach

Kleinfelder has operations in the US and Calgary Canada. It opened offices in Australia and Guam in 2010.

Strategy

Kleinfelder is expanding at home and abroad though organic growth and frequent acquisitions of environmental services firms. It entered Canada in 2012 with an office in Calgary and continued its expansion in Australia (begun in 2010) with a pair of acquisitions there.

In 2011 the firm introduced a program to certify greenhouse gas emissions to help clients remain compliant in clean air regulations. Two years earlier it launched a nuclear services division to serve the uranium mining and milling power generation and spent-fuel storage sectors.

Mergers and Acquisitions

In 2012 Kleinfelder acquired two Australian environmental services firms: Ecobiological Group and Alliance Environmental Engineering and Consulting Pty Ltd.. The twin purchases strengthen Kleinfelder's position in the retail petroleum assessment and remediation market there and help the company grow its multinational client list throughout Australia and the Asia-Pacific Region.

Closer to home Kleinfelder in 2013 purchased Simon Wong Engineering (SWE) a San Diego-based firm providing project management structural and bridge engineering services construction management and inspection services and public relations support to the transportation and water markets in California to strengthen its resources to serve its global clients. The SWE purchase followed two domestic acquisitions: Omni Environmental in Princeton New Jersey and Houston-based Corrigan Consulting in 2012. In 2011 it purchased InSite Environmental in Stockton California.

Ownership

The Kleinfelder Group is owned by its employees.

EXECUTIVES

Vice President of Health and Safety, Robert (Bob) Benamati
Vice President Project Management, Richard B (Dick) McCain
Vice President Major Accounts, Larry Vandeventer
Vice President, William (Bill) Golightly
Vice President, Mark Creveling
Senior Principal Vice President President Engineer, Dahlen Keith
Vice President and General Counsel, Chuck Alpert
Vice President Program Management, Douglas Gilkey
Vice President, Timothy (Tim) Bradley
Vice President Principal, Raymond Ferrara
Vice President Of Application Services, Bill Corley

LOCATIONS

HQ: THE KLEINFELDER GROUP INC
550 W C ST STE 1200, SAN DIEGO, CA 921013532
Phone: 858 320-2000
Web: WWW.KLEINFELDER.COM

PRODUCTS/OPERATIONS

Selected Acquisitions

COMPETITORS

AECOM	Leighton Group
ATC Associates	Ninyo & Moore
CH2M HILL	Precision Assessment
Cadmus Group	Technology
Dudek	Professional Service
Geocon Group	Industries
HNTB Companies	RECON Environmental
Holguin Fahan &	SCS Tracer
Associates	Environmental
Jacobs Engineering	USA Environmental
LCS Constructors	

HISTORICAL FINANCIALS

Company Type: Private

Income Statement
FYE: March 31

	REVENUE ($ mil.)	NET INCOME ($ mil.)	NET PROFIT MARGIN	EMPLOYEES
03/14	243	1	0.7%	1,522
03/13	224	1	0.5%	—
03/12	216	5	2.5%	—
03/11	222	0	—	—
Annual Growth	3.0%	—	—	—

2014 Year-End Financials

Return on assets: 10.0%   Cash ($ mil.): 2
Return on equity: 0.7%
Current ratio: 0.90

THE LANCASTER GENERAL HOSPITAL

Lancaster General Health (LG Health) is a 690-bed integrated health care delivery system serving residents of Lancaster County Pennsylvania and surrounding areas. Its flagship Lancaster General Hospital (LGH) - opened in 1893 - is known for its cardiology orthopedic and intensive care special-ties. A separate Women & Babies hospital cares for those just making it into the world. The not-for-profit system also includes multiple outpatient clinics a rehab hospital home care services and a nursing center and health care college as well as a medical group of more than 300 physicians operating at more than 40 practices throughout the region.

Operations

Facilities in the LG Health system include the 533-bed flagship LGH the 98-bed Women & Babies Hospital the 59-bed Lancaster Rehabilitation Hospital and 14 outpatient centers. Specialty services include open-heart surgery obstetrics neurosurgery trauma care and behavioral health. The system also operates a number of outpatient programs such as a diabetes and nutritional Center and a sleep medicine center.

Every year LG Health sees some 972000 outpatients delivers some 4000 babies and performs around 38000 surgeries.

Geographic Reach

The system serves Pennsylvania's Lebanon Berks Dauphin York Chester and Lancaster counties.

Sales and Marketing

Commercial and HMO payments together account for about 40% of net patient revenues; Medicare accounts for another 35% while Medicaid accounts for some 10%.

Financial Performance

LG Health's revenue rose 5% to $969 million in fiscal 2014 (ended June) on higher net patient revenue and medical services revenue. However net income fell 51% to $117 million as income from contributions and gifts declined; a change in pension liability also hurt the system's bottom line.

Cash flow from operations declined 43% to $43 million in fiscal 2014 as more cash was used in patient accounts receivable and changes were made in prepaid expenses assets and benefits.

Strategy LG Health continues to make strategic investments to better serve its patients and the community. In 2013 the health system completed construction on the Ann B. Barshinger Cancer Center which opened its doors that year. Two years later it announced plans to expand LGH in a $60 million project that will add a new eight-story patient tower. With the addition of 60 new private rooms and the space for 80 more rooms as demand requires the hospital will have the room to convert its existing semi-private rooms to private rooms.

The system also partners with others in the community to improve patient care. In 2014 it formed an alliance with the University of Pennsylvania Health System to develop innovative care research and education programs.

EXECUTIVES

Senior Vice President Business Development, Susan Wynne
SVP and CIO, Gary Davidson
EVP Chief Population Health Officer; President LG Health Innovation Solutions Inc., Marion A. McGowan
President and CEO, Thomas E. (Tom) Beeman
EVP Chief Administrative and Legal Officer and Corporate Secretary, Robert P. Macina
SVP Post-Acute Care, Geoffrey W. Eddowes
EVP and CFO, Dennis R. Roemer
SVP Chief Physician Executive and Chief Medical Officer, Lee M. Duke
SVP Hospital Operations and Nurse Executive; President Lancaster General Hospital, Karen Flaherty-Oxler
Senior Vice President, Joseph (Jo) Puskar
Executive Vice President Sales And Marketing, Joel Perlish
Vice President Of Operations, Christopher Maley

Vice President General Manager, Norma Ferndinand
Operating Room Director, Donna Straley
Vice President Legal Services, Margaret F (Peg) Costella
Medical Director of Perinatology, Philip Bayliss
Vice President Of Operations, Rich Paoletti
Vice President Of Customer Service, Carolyn Carlson
Vice President Risk Management And Corporate Compliance, Elizabeth H (Beth) Katz
Medical Director, Jeffrey Hardin
Senior Vice President Human Resources, Regina Mingle
Vice President and Controller, Doug Rinehart
Chairman, C. Clair McCormick
Vice Chairman, Philip R. Wenger
Board Member, Christine Vlassis
Secretary, Jennifer Edmonds
Secretary Community Health And Wellness, Susan (Sue) Strickler
Secretary, Pamela Miller

LOCATIONS

HQ: THE LANCASTER GENERAL HOSPITAL
555 N DUKE ST, LANCASTER, PA 176022207
Phone: 717 544-5511
Web: WWW.LANCASTERGENERALHEALTH.ORG

PRODUCTS/OPERATIONS

2014 Sales

	% of total
Net patient services revenue less provision for bad debts	95
Medical services	4
Other revenue	1
Other	.
Total	**100**

Selected Specialties

Cardiology
Emergency medical
Intensive care
Neurology
Oncology
Radiology
Rehabilitation
Urology

COMPETITORS

Altoona Regional
Ascension Health
Catholic Health Initiatives
Evangelical Community Hospital
Hanover Healthcare
Holy Spirit
Jefferson Health System
Lewistown Hospital
Memorial Hospital (PA)
PinnacleHealth System
Saint Vincent Health System
St. Luke's University Health Network
University of Pennsylvania Health System
WellSpan Health

HISTORICAL FINANCIALS

Company Type: Private

Income Statement
FYE: June 30

	REVENUE ($ mil.)	NET INCOME ($ mil.)	NET PROFIT MARGIN	EMPLOYEES
06/14	867	(13)	—	5,000
06/13	823	(15)	—	—
06/12	852	31	3.7%	—
06/11	838	0	—	—
Annual Growth	1.2%	—	—	—

2014 Year-End Financials

Return on assets: 3.7%   Cash ($ mil.): 4
Return on equity: (-1.6%)
Current ratio: 1.20

THE LANE CONSTRUCTION CORPORATION

Lane likes people to be in the fast lane. For more than a century the heavy civil contractor and its affiliates have been widening paving and constructing lanes for highways bridges runways railroads dams and mass transit systems in the eastern and southern US. The group also produces bituminous and precast concrete and mines aggregates at plants and quarries in the northeastern mid-Atlantic and southern US. Additionally it sells and leases construction equipment. Founded in 1902 Lane Construction has offices in more than 20 states and is owned by descendants of Lane and employees.

Operations

Lane Construction specializes in heavy civil construction services and products in the transportation infrastructure and energy industries. During the past decade Lane Construction has participated in more than 70 design-building projects with a combined value of more than $4 billion. Beyond its construction projects Lane operates divisions that manufacture bituminous and precast concrete with mine aggregates at 70 plants and 12 quarries throughout the U.S.Lane's business divisions are spread across the US and include: Civil Wall Solutions Cold River Materials Prestress of the Carolinas Senate Asphalt Virginia Paving Company and Virginia Sign & Lighting Company.

Lane affiliates include New Hampshire-based Cold River Materials Senate Asphalt of Washington D.C. and Virginia Paving and Virginia Sign & Lighting Co. among about a half a dozen others. In 2013 its Rea Contracting division in the Carolinas changed its name to Lane Construction Corp.

Geographic Reach

Lane Construction has offices in more than 20 US states including Florida Illinois Maine North Carolina Pennsylvania Texas and Virginia. While most of Lane's projects take place along the East Coast it also operates in the South/Southwest and has international operations —under the Lane Worldwide Infrastructure Inc. name —in the Middle East.

Financial Performance

While full financials of the privately-held company were not available Lane Construction has posted annual revenues of more than $1 billion since 2010.

Strategy

The company continues to work for both public and private entities on a variety of high-value projects. In early 2015 the contractor was working on a joint-venture project with Skanska and Granite Construction Company on the $2.3 billion "I-4 Ultimate project" which involves design build finance operating and maintenance work on 21 miles of Interstate 4 from Orange County to Seminole County in Florida. Also as of early 2015 Lane reported that it recently completed its $1.5-billion construction project on the I-495 Express Lanes in Virginia in one of the largest public-private joint ventures in the US. The same team also completed a $722 million expansion and improvement project on 29 miles of the I-95 Express (high occupancy toll road) lanes in Virginia. Both of these Virginia-based projects were completed ahead of schedule.

EXECUTIVES

Principal and Vice President of Legal and Safety, Jay Cruickshank
Secretary, Ann Falsey
Auditors: PRICEWATERHOUSECOOPERS LLP H

LOCATIONS

HQ: THE LANE CONSTRUCTION CORPORATION
90 FIELDSTONE CT, CHESHIRE, CT 064101212
Phone: 203 235-3351
Web: WWW.LANECONSTRUCT.COM

PRODUCTS/OPERATIONS

Selected Projects
Airports
Bridges
Design-Build
Federal
Heavy Civil
Highways
Public Private Partnerships
Plants & Paving
Rail
Specialty Paving

Selected Divisions
Civil Wall Solutions
Cold River Materials Prestress of the Carolinas
Senate Asphalt
Sunquip
Sunrise Materials
Virginia Paving Company
Virginia Sun & Lighting Company
Wardwell
White Bros.

COMPETITORS

Angelo Iafrate	Sargent Corp
Austin Industries	Skanska USA Civil
Balfour Beatty Inc	The Middlesex
Bechtel	Corporation
Clark Enterprises	Turner Corporation
Granite Construction	Tutor-Saliba
J.F. White Contracting	Vecellio & Grogan
MBC Holding	Walsh Group
Peter Kiewit Sons'	

HISTORICAL FINANCIALS

Company Type: Private

Income Statement				FYE: December 31
	REVENUE ($ mil.)	NET INCOME ($ mil.)	NET PROFIT MARGIN	EMPLOYEES
12/13	1,091	(22)	—	3,500
12/12	1,229	26	2.2%	—
12/11	1,002	20	2.0%	—
12/09	848	0	—	—
Annual Growth	6.5%	—	—	—

2013 Year-End Financials
Return on assets: 6.5% Cash ($ mil.): 15
Return on equity: (-2.1%)
Current ratio: 0.90

THE LEGAL AID SOCIETY

Serving as a law firm for many of New York City's less fortunate residents The Legal Aid Society represents people who could not otherwise afford a lawyer in civil criminal and juvenile rights cases. The society has a staff of some 1100 lawyers. It also draws upon the work of more than 700 investigators social workers and paralegals who combined handle about 300000 individual cases and matters each year. A not-for-profit organization The Legal Aid Society receives government money for its work in criminal and some juvenile matters and it counts on donations to support its efforts in civil cases. The Legal Aid Society was founded in 1876.

Geographic Reach

The Legal Aid Society operates from about 25 facilities in all five boroughs of New York City (The Bronx Brooklyn Manhattan Queens and Staten Island).

Operations

The society handles about 300000 individual cases and matters annually and provides a comprehensive range of legal services in three areas: civil criminal and juvenile rights.

Sales and Marketing

Clients have included Arnold & Porter Cooley Goodwin Procter Mayer Brown and White & Case.

Financial Performance

The society's revenue for fiscal year 2012 increased by 7% compared to 2011.

EXECUTIVES

Vice President Of Human Resources, Adriene Holder
Treasurer, George Albro
Auditors: MCGLADREY LLP NEW YORK NY

LOCATIONS

HQ: THE LEGAL AID SOCIETY
199 WATER ST FRNT 3, NEW YORK, NY 100383526
Phone: 212 577-3346
Web: WWW.LEGAL-AID.ORG

Selected Service Area
Bronx
Brooklyn
Manhattan
Queens
Staten Island

PRODUCTS/OPERATIONS

Selected Cases
Juvenile Rights
Civil
Criminal

HISTORICAL FINANCIALS

Company Type: Private

Income Statement				FYE: June 30
	REVENUE ($ mil.)	NET INCOME ($ mil.)	NET PROFIT MARGIN	EMPLOYEES
06/13	217	8	3.9%	1,600
06/12	189	0	0.1%	—
06/11	175	0	0.3%	—
06/10	169	0	—	—
Annual Growth	8.6%	—	—	—

2013 Year-End Financials
Return on assets: 12.8% Cash ($ mil.): 37
Return on equity: 3.9%
Current ratio: 1.40

THE MARY IMOGENE BASSETT HOSPITAL

Auditors: KPMG LLP ALBANY NY

LOCATIONS

HQ: THE MARY IMOGENE BASSETT HOSPITAL
1 ATWELL RD, COOPERSTOWN, NY 133261394
Phone: 607 547-3456
Web: WWW.BASSETT.ORG

HISTORICAL FINANCIALS

Company Type: Private

Income Statement

	REVENUE ($ mil.)	NET INCOME ($ mil.)	NET PROFIT MARGIN	EMPLOYEES
12/09	366	1	0.5%	3,200
12/08	336	8	2.6%	—
12/07	312	(2)	—	—
12/06	301	0	—	—
Annual Growth	6.7%	—	—	—

FYE: December 31

2009 Year-End Financials

Return on assets: —
Return on equity: 0.5%
Current ratio: 0.60
Cash ($ mil.): 12

THE MEDICAL CENTER

Auditors: PERSHING YOAKLEY & ASSOCIATES

LOCATIONS

HQ: THE MEDICAL CENTER
710 CENTER ST, COLUMBUS, GA 319011547
Phone: 706 660-6255
Web: WWW.CRHS.NET

HISTORICAL FINANCIALS

Company Type: Private

Income Statement

	REVENUE ($ mil.)	NET INCOME ($ mil.)	NET PROFIT MARGIN	EMPLOYEES
06/10	316	15	4.9%	1,500
06/08	283	12	4.5%	—
06/05	1,059	0	—	—
Annual Growth	— 1124.8%	—	—	—

FYE: June 30

2010 Year-End Financials

Return on assets: —
Return on equity: 4.9%
Current ratio: —
Cash ($ mil.): 52

THE MEDICAL COLLEGE OF WISCONSIN INC

Auditors: KPMG LLP MILWAUKEE WI

LOCATIONS

HQ: THE MEDICAL COLLEGE OF WISCONSIN INC
8701 W WATERTOWN PLANK RD, MILWAUKEE, WI 532263548
Phone: 414 456-8296
Web: WWW.MCW.EDU

HISTORICAL FINANCIALS

Company Type: Private

Income Statement

	REVENUE ($ mil.)	NET INCOME ($ mil.)	NET PROFIT MARGIN	EMPLOYEES
06/13	926	123	13.4%	4,700
06/11	936	63	6.8%	—
06/10	839	20	2.5%	—
06/09	751	0	—	—
Annual Growth	5.4%	—	—	—

FYE: June 30

2013 Year-End Financials

Return on assets: 5.7%
Return on equity: 13.4%
Current ratio: —
Cash ($ mil.): 96

THE MERCHANTS COMPANY

The Merchants Company which does business as Merchants Foodservice is a leading foodservice supplier that serves more than 6000 customers in 10 Southeastern states. From a handful of distribution warehouses in Alabama Georgia Mississippi and South Carolina the company supplies a wide range of food and non-food items to restaurants hospitals schools and other foodservice operations. The company was founded in 1904 as Fain Grocery Co. a wholesale grocery distributor and changed its name to Merchants Company in 1927. It began focusing on foodservice distribution in 1982 and was acquired by family owned holding company Tatum Development in 1988.

The company's Sunrise Fresh Produce subsidiary acquired a 47000-sq.-ft. produce distribution center in 2012 renaming it Sunrise Fresh Produce of Jacksonville Florida. The climate-controlled warehouse represents the subsidiary's second produce distribution center.

EXECUTIVES

President and CEO, Andrew B. (Andy) Mercier
VP and CFO, Jarrod Gray
Auditors: MCARTHUR THAMES SLAY AND DEW

LOCATIONS

HQ: THE MERCHANTS COMPANY
1100 EDWARDS ST, HATTIESBURG, MS 394015511
Phone: 601 353-2461
Web: WWW.THEMERCHANTSCOMPANY.COM

COMPETITORS

Ben E. Keith	Quirch Foods
Cheney Brothers	Reinhart FoodService
MAINES	Services Group of
McLane Foodservice	America
Meadowbrook Meat	Sysco
Company	US Foods

HISTORICAL FINANCIALS

Company Type: Private

Income Statement

	REVENUE ($ mil.)	NET INCOME ($ mil.)	NET PROFIT MARGIN	EMPLOYEES
09/11	489	2	0.5%	500
09/10	441	5	1.2%	—
09/08	2,033	0	—	—
Annual Growth	— 2341.1%	—	—	—

FYE: September 30

2011 Year-End Financials

Return on assets: 3.4%
Return on equity: 0.5%
Current ratio: 1.00
Cash ($ mil.): —

THE METHODIST HOSPITAL

Houston Methodist (formerly The Methodist Hospital) owns and operates seven Houston-area medical centers including the flagship location which has more than 800 beds and is known for innovations in urology and neurosurgery among other specialties. Other hospitals include Houston Methodist West Houston Methodist Sugar Land Houston Methodist San Jacinto Houston Methodist Willowbrook Houston Methodist St. John and Houston Methodist St. Catherine. Together the hospitals have nearly 2000 beds and employ more than 4500 physicians. In addition to hospitals the organization operates emergency care imaging outpatient and rehab centers and manages a physician organization of nearly 400.

Operations

The health system has been recognized for high performance in several specialty areas including cancer diabetes nephrology pulmonology and geriatrics. It's also been lauded for its specialties in cardiology and heart surgery endocrinology gastroenterology and GI surgery gynecology neurology and neurosurgery orthopedics and urology.Houston Methodists family of hospitals include the main Houston Methodist Hospital Sugar Land Hospital West Hospital San Jacinto Hospital Willowbrook Hospital St. John Hospital St. Catherine Hospital. It also has long-term acute care facilities emergency care centers imaging centers and a research institute.

The hospital has educational and research affiliations with Cornell University's Weil Cornell Medical College the New York-Presbyterian Hospital University of Houston Baylor College of Medicine Texas A&M and other organizations.Geographic ReachOperating mostly in and around Houston Texas Houston Methodist has hospitals and medical facilities in Sugar Land Missouri City the Woodlands Baytown Nassau Bay Pearland Clear Lake and Katy.

Strategy

To widen its capacity for medical care Houston Methodist has been expanding its service network around the Houston area in recent years. In early 2015 it opened a new 36-bed patient care unit in the Houston Methodist Willbrook Hospital's North Pavilion. Houston Methodist's primary care group also broke ground on a new 7200-square-foot primary care practice which will be staffed with six board-certified primary care physicians who will serve adults and children in the Northwest Houston area starting in May 2015.

In 2014 Houston Methodist began work on a new patient tower at its Sugar Land Hospital which will add 104 beds (mostly for intensive care and medical/surgical patients)as part of its $131 million expansion effort at that location. The group also started working on a 390-bed hospital in The Woodlands Texas with completion expected in 2017. Also scheduled for completion in 2017 is a new patient tower with advanced heart and neurosurgery operating rooms at the main Houston Methodist Hospital location.

EXECUTIVES

Vice President, David P (Dave) Bernard
Senior Vice President, Edward (Ed) Tyrrell
President and CEO, Marc L. Boom
CEO Houston Methodist Sugar Land Hospital, Chris Siebenaler
CEO San Jacinto Methodist Hospital, Donna Gares
CEO Houston Methodist Willowbrook Hospital; SVP Houston Methodist, Beryl Ramsey
President and CEO Houston Methodist Research Institute, Mauro Ferrari
SVP Houston Methodist; CEO Houston Methodist West Hospital, Wayne Voss
Respiratory Therapy Director, Ken Hargett
Medical Director, Philip Cagle
Pharmacy Residency Program Director Pharmd Mba Bcps, Thomas E (Thom) Schwartz
Vice President Of Quality, Thomas W Knight
Vice President Legal Services, Lee Schwartz
Health Care Director, Linney Girouard
Vice President Legal Servicea, Mark Easterly
Vice President, Charles (Chas) Millikan
Nursing Director, Denene Williams
Vice President Infrastructure Services, Steve Burns
Pharmacy Residency Program Director Pharmd Bcps, William Musick
Vice President Operations and Chief Nursing Executive, Anne Scanlon-mcginity
Vice President Supply Chain Management, Gary Wagner
Pharmacy Residency Program Director Pharmd Ms, Alex Varkey
Vice President Managed Care Administration, Vivian Rose
Medical Librarian, Robert Bartlett
Vice President Of Operations, J Elliott
Vice President Operations, Stephen Spielman
Vice President Finance, Lowell Stanton
Pharmacy Residency Program Director Bs Pharmd Bcop, Jose Murillo
Director Of Pharmacy, Dan Metzen
Secretary, Gregory V Nelson
Chairman, Ewing Werlein
Vice Chairman, David M. Underwood
Board Of Directors, Lawrence Kellner
Secretary Of Facilities Management, Caroline Browder
Auditors: DELOITTE & TOUCHE LLP HOUSTON

LOCATIONS

HQ: THE METHODIST HOSPITAL
6565 FANNIN ST, HOUSTON, TX 770302707
Phone: 713 790-3311
Web: WWW.METHODISTHEALTH.COM

PRODUCTS/OPERATIONS

Selected Houston-Area Hospitals
Houston Methodist Hospital - Texas Medical Center (Houston)
Houston Methodist Sugar Land Hospital
Houston Methodist Willowbrook Hospital (Houston)
Houston Methodist West Hospital (Houston)
Houston San Jacinto Methodist Hospital (Baytown)
Houston Methodist St. John Hospital (Texas)
Houston Methodist St. Catherine Hospital (Texas)

Selected Services
Cancer / Oncology
Diabetes / Endocrinology
Digestive Diseases
Ear Nose & Throat
Emergency Care
Heart & Vascular
Imaging / Radiology
Internal Medicine
Neurology
Neurosurgery
Obstetrics & Gynecology
Ophthalmology
Oral and Maxillofacial Surgery & Dentistry
Orthopedics & Sports Medicine
Otolaryngology Head & Neck Surgery
Pathology & Genomic Medicine
Plastic & Reconstructive Surgery
Psychiatry
Rehabilitation
Robotic Surgery
Transplant
Urology
Weight Management
Wellness

COMPETITORS

CHRISTUS Health
Dynacq Healthcare
HCA
Johns Hopkins Medicine
MD Anderson Cancer Center
Mayo Clinic
Memorial Hermann Healthcare
St. Luke' s Episcopal Health System
Tenet Healthcare
Texas Children' s Hospital
Texas Health Resources
Tomball Regional
Universal Health Services

HISTORICAL FINANCIALS

Company Type: Private

Income Statement

FYE: December 31

	REVENUE ($ mil.)	NET INCOME ($ mil.)	NET PROFIT MARGIN	EMPLOYEES
12/13	2,616	683	26.1%	14,000
12/12	2,331	386	16.6%	—
12/11	2,284	101	4.4%	—
12/10	2,115	0	—	—
Annual Growth	7.3%	—	—	—

2013 Year-End Financials

Return on assets: 15.1%
Return on equity: 26.1%
Current ratio: 0.20

Cash ($ mil.): 71

THE METHODIST HOSPITALS INC

The Methodist Hospitals Inc. is a not-for-profit community-based health care system that provides medical care to Indiana residents. More than 580 physicians representing some 60 specialties serve its two campus hospitals which have a combined total of about 640 beds. The system provides care for a range of specialized areas from neurology and neurosurgery oncology and home health and hospice to rehabilitation and orthopedics. The emergency department treats more than 59000 patients a year. The system also provides screenings charitable care and community education programs. The Methodist Hospitals established in 1923 reinvests all of its profits to improve patient care.

Operations

The system operates two main hospitals - Northlake in Gary and Southlake in Merrillville. The two campuses which are 14 miles apart are both full-service facilities. It also runs the Midlake Campus an outpatient facility with physician offices and other services in Gary a gastro-intestinal specialty center in Southlake and addiction treatment and inpatient Geriatric Behavioral Health Services units at its Northlake campus.

In 2012 The Methodist Hospitals invested more than $60 million in equipment technology and patient programs.

Geographic Reach

Methodist' s main service areas include Lake and Porter counties extending west to the border east to LaPorte and south to Lowell.

Financial Performance

In 2012 the hospitals reported their fourth consecutive year of increasing profitability with $303 million in net revenue.

Strategy

The system keeps its not-for-profit operations profitable by investing in technology and facilities. After major upgrades at both hospitals and the installation of a state-of-the-art computer-assisted operating suite The Methodist Hospitals in 2013 opened an addiction treatment facility in Northlake and a GERD (gastroesophageal reflux disease) center in Southlake.

EXECUTIVES

Medical Records Director, Patrick Lester
Vice President Marketing and Human Resources, Alex Horvath
Operating Room Director, Nada Orlich
Vice Chairman, Mamon Powers
Secretary, Barbara Kennedy
Secretary, Charlotte Davis

LOCATIONS

HQ: THE METHODIST HOSPITALS INC
600 GRANT ST, GARY, IN 464026001
Phone: 219 886-4000
Web:
WWW.METHODISTCMS.METHODISTHOSPITALS.OR
G

PRODUCTS/OPERATIONS

Selected Services
Behavioral health sciences
Bloodless medicine (surgery without blood transfusions)
Cardiovascular
  Cardiopulmonary rehabilitation
Diabetes Center
Emergency/trauma services
Home health
Maternity
NeuroScience Institute
  Gamma Knife (non-invasive brain surgery)
  Multiple Sclerosis Center
  Spine Care Center
  Stroke Center
Oncology Institute
Orthopedic services
Outpatient
Rehabilitation
Surgical weight loss/ bariatric services
Women' s services
  Advanced obstetrical services
Wound Center

Selected Affiliations
American Cancer Society
American Heart Association
American Lung Association
Anthem Coronary Service Network
Edgewater Systems for Balanced Living
Gary Career Center
Gary Southshore Railcats
Indiana State Medical Association
Indiana University Northwest Campus
  Medical School
  Radiological Tech Program
  Respiratory Program
  School of Nursing
International Association for Healthcare Security and Safety
Ivy Technical Vocational School
Lakeshore Kids Immunization Fair
March of Dimes
Multiple Sclerosis Society
National Alliance for Mentally Ill (NAMI)
Purdue University Calumet Campus
  School of Nursing
Purdue University North Central Campus
  School of Nursing
Valparaiso University
  School of Nursing
Rosalind Franklin University

HISTORICAL FINANCIALS

Company Type: Private

Income Statement

FYE: December 31

	REVENUE ($ mil.)	NET INCOME ($ mil.)	NET PROFIT MARGIN	EMPLOYEES
12/09	291	5	2.0%	3,260
12/04	310	9	3.2%	—
12/03	298	7	2.5%	—
12/02	267	0	—	—
Annual Growth	1.3%	—	—	—

2009 Year-End Financials

Return on assets: —
Return on equity: 2.0%
Current ratio: 0.80
Cash ($ mil.): 51

THE METROHEALTH SYSTEM

Helping Cleveland's metropolitan citizens stay healthy (and healing them when they aren't) is what MetroHealth System is all about. At the center of the system is MetroHealth Medical Center a level I trauma center and acute care hospital that serves as a teaching affiliate for Case Western Reserve University. Services include oncology behavioral health vascular care orthopedics burn care and pediatrics. The system also operates outpatient clinics long-term care facilities a regional rehabilitation clinic a heart and vascular center two skilled nursing centers an outpatient center and a medical helicopter program. MetroHealth is owned by Ohio's Cuyahoga County.

Operations

More than 500 primary care and specialty care physicians and more than 1200 registered nurses practice within MetroHealth. On an annual basis MetroHealth Medical Center provides care to more than 28000 inpatients and delivers 2900 newborns. More than 950000 visits are recorded in the medical center's outpatient centers along with 17500 surgical cases and 100000 emergency room visits.

The system affiliates with Akron Children's Hospital to expand access to pediatric care throughout the region. Through the partnership Akron Children's provides specialty care at MetroHealth's main campus in the areas of pediatric cardiology gastroenterology cancer and blood disorders and critical care. The MetroHealth affiliation is Akron Children's fourth location in Cuyahoga County.

Geographic Reach

MetroHealth is one of the largest most comprehensive health care providers in Northeast Ohio serving the medical needs of the Greater Cleveland area through more than 15 locations.

Financial Performance

MetroHealth's revenue increased 9% to $855 in 2013 from $783 the year before.

Strategy

As emergency rooms continue to burst at the seams more hospitals are finding ways to divert non-emergency patients to more appropriate care settings. MetroHealth has done that with its MetroExpressCare unit for residents who need to see a doctor and would probably otherwise end up at the emergency room. The family medicine physicians who see patients at MetroExpressCare are also available to establish longer-term relationships with patients coming to MetroHealth for the first time. If the physician determines that it's a more serious problem the patient can be referred to MetroHealth's emergency department.

Having options such as MetroExpressCare available is especially important to MetroHealth because it is its region's safety net hospital. As such it receives the lion's share of uninsured patients many of whom end up in the ER because ERs are required to see all patients regardless of their ability to pay under the Emergency Medical Treatment and Active Labor Act. Being able to provide a less expensive option to those patients decreases MetroHealth's bad debt (or unpaid patient bills) and helps reduce crowding at its ER.

To serve non-ER patients Metrohealth opens a new clinic each year on average.

Background

MetroHealth has been serving the medical needs of the Greater Cleveland community since 1837. It has been a major affiliate of Case Western Reserve University since 1914.

EXECUTIVES

COO, Daniel K. Lewis
President and CEO, Akram Boutros
VP Marketing and Communications, Elizabeth Heller Allen, age 61
Chief Patient Experience Officer, Sara Laskey
Chief Nursing Officer, Mavis Bechtle
Chief Medical Officer and Chief Quality Officer, Alfred F. Connors
CFO, Craig Richmond
VP and Associate CIO, Donald Reichert
President Medical Staff, Sherrie Dixon-Williams
Infection Control Director, Kathleen Quealy
Medical Director, Carolyn Dziwis
Vice President Surgical and Perioperative Services, Chris Roker
Medical Director, Gary Clark
Vice Chairman, J. B. Silvers
Chairman, Thomas M. McDonald
Secretary, Nancy Koterba
Board Member, Mary Roach
Secretary Organizational Development, Tina Erickson
Auditors: MCGLADREY & PULLEN LLP CLEVE

LOCATIONS

HQ: THE METROHEALTH SYSTEM
2500 METROHEALTH DR, CLEVELAND, OH 441091900
Phone: 216 398-6000
Web: WWW.METROHEALTH.ORG

Selected locations

J. Glen Smith Health Center (In partnership with the City of Cleveland Cleveland)
MetroHealth Asia Town Health Center (Cleveland)
MetroHealth Beachwood Health Center (Beachwood Ohio)
MetroHealth Broadway Health Center (Cleveland)
MetroHealth Brooklyn Health Center (Cleveland)
MetroHealth Buckeye Health Center (Cleveland)
MetroHealth Center for Sleep Medicine South Campus (Independence Ohio)
MetroHealth Center for Sleep Medicine West Campus (Westlake Ohio)
MetroHealth Lakewood Health Center (Lakewood)
MetroHealth Lee-Harvard Health Center (Cleveland)
MetroHealth Medical Center Main Campus (Cleveland)
MetroHealth Old Brooklyn Campus (Cleveland)
MetroHealth Pepper Pike Health Center (Pepper Pike Ohio)
MetroHealth Premier Health Center (Westlake Ohio)
MetroHealth Rehabilitation Institute of Ohio (Cleveland)
MetroHealth Strongsville Health Center (Strongsville Ohio)
MetroHealth West 150th Health and Surgery Center (Cleveland)
MetroHealth Westlake Health Center (Westlake)
MetroHealth West Park Health Center (Cleveland)
The Elisabeth Severance Prentiss Center for Skilled Nursing Care at MetroHealth (Cleveland)
Thomas F. McCafferty Health Center (In partnership with the City of Cleveland Cleveland)

PRODUCTS/OPERATIONS

MetroHealth System Departments and Services

Aamoth Family Pediatric Wellness Center
Adolescent Clinic (Teen Health)
Advanced Gynecology (Center for Advanced Gynecology)
Advantage (MetroHealth Advantage)
Allergy & Immunology Clinic
Allergy Services (Department of Ear Nose & Throat)
Amigas Unidas Program
Anesthesiology
Art Therapy
Arthritis Center (Rheumatology)
Audiology
Bariatric Surgery (Weight Loss Surgery Program)
Behavioral Health (Child and Teen Mental Health Services)
Birth Control Procedures
Birthing Services
Bone Health and Surgery (Orthopaedics)
BREAST Program (Community Breast Cancer Outreach)
Burn Care Center
Cancer Care Center
Cardiology Cardiovascular (Heart & Vascular Center)
Center for Advanced Gynecology
Center for Behavioral Health (Child and Teen Mental Health Services)
Centers for Community Health
Center for Sleep Medicine
Cerebrovascular
Childbirth Education
Child Life and Education
Children's Health (Pediatrics)
Children's Health Specialties
Closing the Gap (MetroHealth Buckeye Health Center)
Comprehensive Care Program (Services for Children with Special Needs)
Concussion Clinic
Cosmetic Dermatology
Dentistry and Oral Health
Dermatology
Diabetes Self-Management Program
Digital Mammogram
Ear Nose and Throat (ENT/Otolaryngology)
Emergency Medicine/Emergency Department
Endocrinology
Endoscopy Suite (Gastroenterology)
ExpressCare (MetroExpressCare)
Family Medicine Clinic at MetroHealth Medical Center
Fertility Services
Freedom From Smoking
Gastroenterology and Endoscopy Suite
Genetics Clinic
Geriatrics (Senior Health & Wellness Center)
Gynecology
Gynecology Advanced (Center for Advanced Gynecology)
Gynecologic Oncology
Hand Center
Heart & Vascular Center
Hematology and Oncology (Cancer Care Center)
High-Risk Pregnancy Services
Hospital Medicine
Immunology (Allergy & Immunology Clinic)
Infectious Disease
Infertility Clinic
Infusion Therapy (Allergy & Immunology Clinic)
Internal Medicine Clinic at MetroHealth Medical Center
Internal Medicine and Pediatrics (Med-PEDS)
Kids' Health (Pediatrics)
Kids' Korner Free Daycare Service at MetroHealth Medical Center
Latina Clinic: English | En espa?ol
LGBT Pride Clinic (At Thomas F. McCafferty Health Center Health Center)
Life Flight (Metro Life Flight)
Long-Term/Skilled Nursing Care
Maternal-Fetal Medicine (High-Risk Pregnancy Services)
Medicine (Department of Medicine)
Mental Health (Psychiatry)
Metro Life Flight
MetroHealth Advantage
MetroExpressCare
MetroHealth Rehabilitation Institute of Ohio
MetroHealth Select Health Plan
MetroHealth Simulation Center
Mi MetroHealth Mi Comunidad
MyChart

Neonatology Neonatal Intensive Care Unit (NICU)
Nephrology
Neurology
Neurosciences
Northeast Ohio Chapter of the National Spinal Cord
    Injury Association (NSCIA)
Northeast Ohio Regional Spinal Cord Injury System
    (NORSCIS)
Nose Ear and Throat (ENT Otolaryngology)
Nursing
Nutrition
Obstetrics
Obstetrics and Gynecology
Occupational Medicine
Oncology (Cancer Care Center)
Opthalmologic (Eye) Surgery
Oral Health (Dentistry)
Oral and Maxillofacial Surgery
Orthopaedics
Osteopathic Medicine
Otolaryngology (Ear Nose and Throat)
Pain Management
Palliative Care
Pastoral Care
Pathology
Pediatrics
Permanent Birth Control Procedures
Pharmacy
Pregnancy Resources
Pride Clinic (At Thomas F. McCafferty Health Center
    Health Center)
Psychiatry (Behavioral/Mental Health)
Pulmonary and Critical Care
Quality Indicators
Radiology
Rehab Rehabilitation Services (MetroHealth
    Rehabilitation Institute of Ohio)
Reiki
Reproductive Endocrinology and Infertility Clinic
Rheumatology (Arthritis Center)

Select Health Plan

Senior Health and Wellness Center
Simulation Center
Skeletal (Orthopaedics)
Skilled Nursing/Long-Term Care
Sleep Medicine Sleep Studies
Spanish-language Information
Special Needs Services for Children (Comprehensive
    Care)
Spine Center
Stroke Stroke & Cerebrovascular Center
Surgery
Throat (Otolaryngology ENT)
Teen Health
Trauma Burns and Critical Care
Travel Clinic
Urgent Care (MetroExpressCare
Urology
Vascular Health and Surgery (Heart & Vascular Center
Weight Loss Surgery Program (Bariatric Surgery)
X-ray (Radiology)

COMPETITORS

AdCare	Lake Health
Catholic Health	OhioHealth
Initiatives	Premier Health
Cincinnati Children's	Partners
Hospital	Robinson Memorial
Community Health	Hospital
Systems	The Cleveland Clinic
Kettering Health	University Hospitals
Network	Health System

HISTORICAL FINANCIALS

Company Type: Private

Income Statement

FYE: December 31

	REVENUE ($ mil.)	NET INCOME ($ mil.)	NET PROFIT MARGIN	EMPLOYEES
12/13	813	41	5.1%	6,000
12/09	673	58	8.7%	—
12/08	642	(3)	—	—
12/07	1,941	0	—	—
Annual Growth	(13.5%)	—	—	—

2013 Year-End Financials

Return on assets: 5.0%   Cash ($ mil.): 3
Return on equity: 5.1%
Current ratio: 0.90

THE MIDDLE TENNESSEE ELECTRIC MEMBERSHIP CORPORATION

Middle Tennessee Electric Membership Corporation's service territory is smack dab in the middle of Tennessee. The utility cooperative distributes electricity to 190750 residential and business customers (member/owners) in four counties (Cannon Rutherford Williamson and Wilson) via more than 10470 miles of power lines connected to 34 electric distribution substations. Middle Tennessee Electric purchases its power supply from the Tennessee Valley Authority. The corporation is Tennessee's largest electric cooperative and the sixth largest in the US.

Geographic Reach

The cooperative serves customers in Cannon Rutherford Williamson and Wilson counties. According to a US Census report three of Tennessee's five fastest growing counties (Rutherford Williamson and Wilson) are in Middle Tennessee Electric's service area which also includes three of Tennessee's top five fastest-growing cities — LaVergne Smyrna and Franklin.

Strategy

To harness green energy as a way to limit fossil fuel power sources and reduce carbon emissions the utility cooperative is installing solar panels for customers. In 2012 the company completed a 850-panel solar field next to the City of Franklin's water plant. That year Middle Tennessee Electric had 70 solar projects operating across its service area and 30 more in the planning stages.

Company Background

Middle Tennessee Electric was formed in 1936 as part of a national rural electrification push.

EXECUTIVES

Vice President Human Resources, Shannon Kaprive
Vice President Engineering, Tom Suggs
Vice President Marketing Comms, Chris Jones
Vice President Of Information Systems, Gray Bateman
Vice President District Services, Dan Dement
Vice President Finance, Jack Maxey
Vice President Engineering, Thomas (Thom) Suggs
Auditors: WINNETT ASSOCIATES PLLC SHEL

LOCATIONS

HQ: THE MIDDLE TENNESSEE ELECTRIC MEMBERSHIP CORPORATION
555 NEW SALEM HWY, MURFREESBORO, TN 371293390
Phone: 615 890-9762
Web: WWW.MTEMC.COM

HISTORICAL FINANCIALS

Company Type: Private

Income Statement

FYE: June 30

	REVENUE ($ mil.)	NET INCOME ($ mil.)	NET PROFIT MARGIN	EMPLOYEES
06/13	524	27	5.3%	375
06/12	510	19	3.8%	—
06/11	525	31	6.0%	—
Annual Growth	(0.0%)	(5.9%)	—	—

2013 Year-End Financials

Return on assets: 8.4%   Cash ($ mil.): 58
Return on equity: 5.3%
Current ratio: 1.40

THE MITRE CORPORATION

Politicians try to engineer a better government but MITRE governs the country's best engineering. A private not-for-profit organization MITRE Corporation provides consulting engineering and technical research services primarily for agencies of the federal government. It employs more than 7000 scientists engineers and other specialists who work at primary research facilities in Massachusetts and Virginia. It also manages serveral federally funded research and development centers serving organizations such as the Department of Defense the Federal Aviation Administration the Internal Revenue Service and the Department of Veterans Affairs. MITRE was founded in 1958 by former MIT researchers.

Geographic Reach

In addition to primary research facilities in Bedford Massachusetts and McLean Virginia MITRE has international operations in Belgium Germany Japan the Netherlands South Korea Taiwan and the UK.

Operations

MITRE also supports the Department of Homeland Security (DHS) and the Administrative Office of the US Courts. For the DHS MITRE provides systems engineering practices and acquisition expertise while it helps the US Courts with state-of-the-art technology to benefit the federal judicial system. The company has also assisted the Intelligence Community in safeguarding classified information.

Strategy

The company is focusing on supporting the Department of Defense's operations and improving acquisition outcomes preserving an information advantage and addressing the government's enterprise IT consolidation. For the Intelligence Community it has been focusing on helping thwart cyber attacks to the nation's critical infrastructures.

In 2012 MITRE invested $51 million in research and development to advance military and civilian technologies. The investment is designed to provide more equipment and workspaces for the company's engineers and scientists. (Some 65% of its employees have advanced degrees.)

EXECUTIVES

Vice President, Stephen (Steve) Huffman
SVP CFO and Treasurer, Mark W. Kontos
SVP and COO, David H. Lehman
President and CEO, Alfred Grasso

Senior Vice President General Manager Center for
National Security, Raymond Haller
Senior Vice President Programs and Technology,
Richard J. Byrne
SVP and General Manager Center for Connected
Government, Jason F. Providakes
VP and Director Center for Enterprise
Modernization, James E. (Jim) Cook
VP and CIO, Joel Jacobs
VP and CTO, Mark T Maybury
VP and Director CMS Alliance to Modernize
Healthcare, Rob Jensen
SVP and General manager Center for Advanced
Aviation System Development, Lillian Zarelli Ryals
VP and Director Homeland Security Systems
Engineering and Development Institute, Barbara
Toohill
Senior Vice President And General Manager
Center For Air Force Command And Control
Systems, Raymond A Shulstad
Senior Vice President Chief Security Officer, Gary
Gagnon
Vice President, Peter Sherlock
Department Head, Steve Godin
Department Head, Bill Donaldson
Vice President Information Technology, Dwayne
Allain
Vice President Of Organizational Development,
Marc Levine
Vice President, Gary J Gagon
Vice President Information Technology, Greg
Crawford
Vice President, Kathy Saunders
Department Head, Dolores Derrinton
Senior Vice President and General Manager
Center for Advanced Aviation System
Development, Lillian Ryals
Department Head, Patrick Spivey
Department Head, David Hodulich
Department Head, Donna O'Neill
Chairman, James R. Schlesinger, age 86
Vice Chairman, Charles S. Robb, age 76
Secretary, Linda Wentworth
Auditors: PRICEWATERHOUSECOOPERS LLP MC

LOCATIONS

HQ: THE MITRE CORPORATION
  202 BURLINGTON RD, BEDFORD, MA 017301420
Phone: 781 271-2000
Web: WWW.MITRE.ORG

PRODUCTS/OPERATIONS

Selected Practice Areas:Agile & Adaptive Command
and ControlAnti-Access/Area-Denial TechnologyAvia-
tion & TransportationCritical Infrastructure Protec-
tionCyber-securityData to DecisionsHealth Transfor-
mationIntegrated Sensing Processing &
ExploitationTrans

COMPETITORS

Altarum
Battelle Memorial
Berkeley Lab
ComGlobal Systems
EDSI
General Atomics
Institute for Defense
  Analyses
Leidos
QinetiQ

SITA
SRI International
Sandia National
  Laboratories
SwRI
The Scripps Research
  Institute
Wyle Information
  Systems

HISTORICAL FINANCIALS
Company Type: Private

Income Statement
FYE: October 5

	REVENUE ($ mil.)	NET INCOME ($ mil.)	NET PROFIT MARGIN	EMPLOYEES
10/08	1,234	22	1.8%	7,000
10/07	1,113	23	2.1%	—
Annual Growth	10.9%	(4.6%)		

2008 Year-End Financials

Return on assets: —   Cash ($ mil.): 36
Return on equity: 1.8%
Current ratio: 0.80

THE MOSES H CONE MEMORIAL HOSPITAL

Auditors: DELOITTE & TOUCHE LLP RALEIGH

LOCATIONS

HQ: THE MOSES H CONE MEMORIAL HOSPITAL
  1200 N ELM ST, GREENSBORO, NC 274011020
Phone: 336 832-7000
Web: WWW.CONEHEALTH.COM

HISTORICAL FINANCIALS
Company Type: Private

Income Statement
FYE: December 31

	REVENUE ($ mil.)	NET INCOME ($ mil.)	NET PROFIT MARGIN	EMPLOYEES
12/14*	370	6	1.6%	7,000
09/14	1,403	78	5.6%	—
06/14	1,024	77	7.6%	—
09/13	1,139	0	—	—
Annual Growth	(67.5%)	—		

*Fiscal year change

2014 Year-End Financials

Return on assets: 17.1%   Cash ($ mil.): 21
Return on equity: 1.6%
Current ratio: 0.60

THE NEW LIBERTY HOSPITAL DISTRICT OF CLAY COUNTY MISSOURI

New Liberty Hospital District which operates as
Liberty Hospital hopes to liberate health care patients in northwestern Missouri. The facility is a
250-bed acute care hospital that serves communities located north of Kansas City. Founded in 1974
Liberty Hospital offers general and specialty health
care services including trauma care obstetrics cancer care diagnostics surgical services vascular and
cardiac medicine (including open-heart surgery)
rehabilitation and pediatrics. The not-for-profit
medical facility has more than 300 physicians on
staff and also operates a skilled nursing facility
and offers home health and hospice services.

Strategy
Liberty Hospital is expanding its facilities to improve services in the region. Recent openings include the new heart and vascular center and a 40-
room outpatient center (Liberty Clinic) that
includes a laboratory and diagnostic facilities.
In 2013 the hospital outsourced its IT operations
to Allscripts which also provides electronic health
records and physician order entries for Liberty.
The move helps to improve clinical financial and
operational outcomes.
Ownership
Liberty Hospital is a political subdivision district
hospital organized under the Revised Statues of
Missouri (Chapter 206). It is governed by board of
trustees consisting of six publicly elected members.

EXECUTIVES

Nursing Director, Shirley Heintz
Secretary, Julie Juarez
Secretary, Leslie Jenkins
Secretary, Cheryl Howard
Auditors: PAIGE COOPER

LOCATIONS

HQ: THE NEW LIBERTY HOSPITAL DISTRICT OF
  CLAY COUNTY MISSOURI
  2525 GLENN HENDREN DR, LIBERTY, MO
  640689625
Phone: 816 781-7200
Web: WWW.LIBERTYHOSPITAL.ORG

PRODUCTS/OPERATIONS

Selected Services
Breast Center
Cancer Center
Diagnostic Imaging
Emergency and Trauma
Gastroenterology
Heart and Vascular Center
Home Health
Hospice
Hyperbaric Medicine
Intensive Care
Interventional Radiology
Lung Cancer Clinic
Maternity
Neurology
Orthopedics
Pain Management
Palliative Care
Pediatrics
Pulmonary
Rehabilitation
Robotic Surgery
Sleep Lab
Surgery
WorkHealth Solutions
Wound Clinic

COMPETITORS

Ascension Health
Children's Mercy
  Hospital
Mercy Health
Saint Luke's Health
  System
Sisters of Charity of
  Leavenworth

Truman Medical Centers
University of Kansas
  Medical Center
Via Christi Health
  System

HISTORICAL FINANCIALS
Company Type: Private

Income Statement
FYE: June 30

	REVENUE ($ mil.)	NET INCOME ($ mil.)	NET PROFIT MARGIN	EMPLOYEES
06/08	157	17	11.0%	1,700
06/05	122	13	11.2%	—
06/04	2,010	0	0.0%	—
Annual Growth	(47.1%)	1690.1%		

2008 Year-End Financials

Return on assets: 9.5% Cash ($ mil.): 9
Return on equity: 11.0%
Current ratio: 0.70

THE NEW SCHOOL

When James Lipton asks you what your favorite swear word is you know you've made it. The New School's drama department (formerly called The Actor's Studio) was made famous by the cable show Inside the Actors Studio which features Lipton interviewing movie and television stars. The school offers degrees in theater for playwriting directing and acting and has taught "Method" acting to grads such as Marlon Brando and Robert De Niro. It is also home to Parsons The New School for Design and has schools devoted to general studies liberal arts social research management and urban policy and music. More than 10500 traditional students and 5600 continuing education students are enrolled at The New School.

Operations

The New School offers more than 90 degree and diploma programs and majors to a population of undergraduate and graduate students who come from all 50 states and more than 100 foreign countries (about one-quarter of its students hail from international locations). It boasts small class sizes and a student-teacher ratio of about 10:1.

The New School for Public Engagement is the university's founding division and is composed of five schools: Milano School of International Affairs Management and Urban Policy; School of Language Learning and Teaching; School of Media Studies; School of Undergraduate Studies; and School of Writing. It has since added six divisions: Drama Jazz Lang Mannes Parsons and Social Research.

Financial Performance

The New School's 2011 revenue grew by more than 5% vs. 2010. Net income increased 13% over the same period.

Strategy

Parsons' new academic center in Paris is slated to open in fall 2013. The Paris site will offer students a program that addresses the global nature of contemporary art and design practice and reflects Europe's culture and philosophy.

The New School was founded in 1919 by a group of university professors and intellectuals in New York City as place for students wanting to explore their creativity and engage in deep thought while studying liberal arts. Dozens of years later The New School has gained a reputation for its unconventional teaching methods as well as for being the home of many world-renowned institutes including the think tank The World Policy Institute. It also hosts the annual National Book Awards which has helped establish the careers of some of the country's most recognized authors including Richard Powers and Jonathan Franzen.

EXECUTIVES

Vice President Design Construction and Facilities Management, Lia Gartner
Auditors: KPMG LLP NEW YORK NY

LOCATIONS

HQ: THE NEW SCHOOL
66 W 12TH ST, NEW YORK, NY 100118871
Phone: 212 229-5600
Web: WWW.NEWSCHOOL.EDU

PRODUCTS/OPERATIONS

Selected Schools
Eugene Lang College The New School for Liberal Arts
Mannes College The New School for Music
Milano The New School for Management and Urban Policy
The New School for Drama
The New School for General Studies
The New School for Jazz and Contemporary Music
The New School for Public Engagement
The New School for Social Research
Parsons The New School for Design

HISTORICAL FINANCIALS

Company Type: Private

Income Statement

FYE: June 30

	REVENUE ($ mil.)	NET INCOME ($ mil.)	NET PROFIT MARGIN	EMPLOYEES
06/14	332	82	24.8%	855
06/13	313	11	3.6%	—
06/12	317	(3)	—	—
06/11	305	0	—	—
Annual Growth	2.9%	—	—	—

2014 Year-End Financials

Return on assets: 17.0% Cash ($ mil.): 3
Return on equity: 24.8%
Current ratio: —

THE NEW YORK AND PRESBYTERIAN HOSPITAL

The New York and Presbyterian Hospital is a learned institution: The hospital is affiliated with both the Columbia University College of Physicians & Surgeons and the Weill Cornell Medical College of Cornell University. Known as NewYork-Presbyterian Hospital the organization comprises two major medical centers Columbia University Medical Center and Weill Cornell Medical Center which conduct educational and research programs in partnership with the universities. The two facilities combined have about 2600 beds and offer specialized programs for burns digestive diseases pediatrics women's health and other conditions. NewYork-Presbyterian Hospital is part of the NewYork-Presbyterian Healthcare System.

Operations

Altogether the NewYork-Presbyterian Hospital campuses handle some 2 million patient visits each year (both on an inpatient and outpatient basis) including inpatient admissions and more than 311000 emergency room visits and about 14600 births. The facilities employ a total of more than 6500 physicians including residents and fellows in 2013. NewYork-Presbyterian Hospital provides more than $99 million in charity and community care services each year.

Geographic Reach

In addition to its flagship campuses NewYork-Presbyterian/Columbia and NewYork-Presbyterian/Weill Cornell NewYork-Presbyterian Hospital operates two small community hospitals in Manhattan –the Allen Hospital and the Lower Manhattan Hospital –and an inpatient mental health facility (the Westchester Division). The broader NewYork-Presbyterian Healthcare System oper-

ates facilities in other areas of New York as well as in New Jersey and Connecticut. The NewYork-Presbyterian Hospital/Columbia campus houses the Morgan Stanley Children's Hospital as well as other specialist units.

Sales and Marketing

Medicare and Medicaid recipients account for more than 60% of NewYork-Presbyterian Hospital's patients. Commercial managed care organizations and insurance firms as well as self-pay customers account for the rest.

Financial Performance

NewYork-Presbyterian Hospital's revenue increased 9% to $4.2 billion in 2013 on higher net patient service revenue and other income. Net income rose 23% to $866 million due to changes in beneficial interest in net assets held by related organizations.

Cash flow from operations slipped 26% to $390 million that year as patient accounts receivable and pension and post-retirement benefit liabilities increased as well as other factors such as changes in accrued salaries.

Strategy

NewYork-Presbyterian Hospital expands its facilities through regular construction programs. For instance in 2013 it opened an autism and brain development center on the Westchester campus; launched a center for precision medicine (individualized medical treatments) at the Weill Cornell campus; entered into a collaboration with the New York City Department of Education (along with Microsoft and City University of New York) to establish a technical education and career school for high school and early college students; and opened the Irving Radiation Oncology Center as part of its Herbert Irving Comprehensive Cancer Center. In 2014 NewYork-Presbyterian/Columbia opened the Irving Bone Marrow Transplant Unit which features 18 rooms high-tech patient monitoring and a specialized airflow system to help protect patients with weakened immune systems.

The system also partners with other organizations to expand access to health care. In 2014 it opened a space at New York City-based health tech accelerator Blueprint Health to help foster its collaboration with the technology and start-up sectors and gain access to new technologies.

Mergers and Acquisitions

The NewYork-Presbyterian/Lower Manhattan Hospital was added to the organization in 2013. The 180-bed community hospital extended NewYork-Presbyterian Hospital's patient reach in Manhattan; Lower Manhattan Hospital previously operated as New York Downtown Hospital.

Company Background

NewYork-Presbyterian Hospital was formed through the 1998 merger of the New York Hospital (founded in 1771) and the Presbyterian Hospital (founded in 1868). New York Hospital was known for advancing care in areas including women's health and surgery while the Presbyterian Hospital was known for its pediatric division and its cancer center.

EXECUTIVES

Vice President Insurance NYP Healthcare System, Eric Vorenkamp
Vice President of Safety, Karen Scott Collins
SVP and CIO, Aurelia G. Boyer
EVP CFO and Treasurer, Phyllis R. Lantos
SVP and Chief Medical Officer, Steven J. (Steve) Corwin
President, Robert E. Kelly
SVP Finance and Assistant Treasurer, Mark E. Larmore
SVP and Chief Nursing Officer, Wilhelmina Manzano
VP Medical Affairs, Laura L. Forese

VP Medical Affairs and Associate Chief Medical Officer, Richard S. Liebowitz
Vice President Planning, Jolie Singer
Medical Director, Neal Flomenbaum
Senior Vice President Chief Operating, Kevin Hammeran
Senior Vice President Strategy, Emme Deland
Vice President Real Estate, Cohen Martin
Vice President Human Resources, Shaun Smith
Vice President, Lori Armstrong
Vice President Compensation Benefits And Hris, Mary Falkowitz
Vice President Support Services and Patient Centered Care, Alan (Al) Lee
Nursing Vice President, Mary Brennan
Vice President Public Relations, Myrna A Mnners
Senior Vice President Strategic Planning, Joan Clark
Vice President Human Resources, Lorraine Orlando
Information Security Vice President, Kareen Jimenez
Chairman Board of Trustees, John J. Mack, age 71
Assistant Treasurer, Sedare Coradine
Secretary, Dawn Roberts

LOCATIONS

HQ: THE NEW YORK AND PRESBYTERIAN HOSPITAL
525 E 68TH ST, NEW YORK, NY 100654870
Phone: 212 746-5454
Web: WWW.NYP.ORG

PRODUCTS/OPERATIONS

2013 Patient Mix

	% of total
Commercial	37
Medicare	33
Medicaid	28
Other	2
Total	**100**

Selected Services

Cancer
Children' s Health
Digestive
Geriatrics
Heart
Mens Health
Neuroscience
Orthopedic
Psychiatry
Rehabilitation Medicine
Transplant
Vascular
Womens Health

COMPETITORS

Ascension Health
Beth Israel Medical Center
Bronx-Lebanon Hospital
Catholic Healthcare System
Continuum Health Partners
Lenox Hill Hospital
Lutheran HealthCare
Maimonides Medical Center
MediSys Health Network
Memorial Sloan-Kettering
Montefiore Medical
New York City Health and Hospitals
North Shore-Long Island Jewish Health System
Winthrop-University Hospital
Yale New Haven Health System

HISTORICAL FINANCIALS

Company Type: Private

Income Statement

FYE: December 31

	REVENUE ($ mil.)	NET INCOME ($ mil.)	NET PROFIT MARGIN	EMPLOYEES
12/13	4,264	595	14.0%	15,078
12/06	2,833	171	6.1%	—
12/04	2,427	56	2.3%	—
Annual Growth	**6.5%**	**29.9%**	**—**	**—**

2013 Year-End Financials

Return on assets: —
Return on equity: 14.0%
Current ratio: 0.90

Cash ($ mil.): 152

THE NEW YORK INDEPENDENT SYSTEM OPERATOR INC

Keeping the lights on in Times Square is only part of the job description of the New York Independent System Operator (New York ISO). The company which replaced the New York Power Pool manages and monitors wholesale activities on the state's transmission grid which consists of more than 11000 miles of high-voltage lines. The New York ISO is charged with providing fair access to the state's competitive wholesale power market while ensuring the reliable efficient and safe delivery of power to New York's 19.5 million residents. New York ISO had 37900 MW of generating capacity in 2013. The not-for-profit company is governed by a 10-person board of directors.

Geographic Reach
New York ISO administers the wholesale power market for New York State. It is responsible for the New York Control Area a part of the Eastern Interconnection interconnected power systems that cover most of the eastern US and Canada.

Sales and Marketing
New York ISO serves about 360 market participants.

Financial Performance
The ISO's revenue increased by 6% in 2012 due to higher revenues from grants planning studies fees and services partially offset by lower Rate Schedule 1 tariff charge revenues. The company's grant revenue of $15.3 million came from a 50% reimbursement received from Department of Energy for one of its projects that was being monitored by New York ISO. Planning studies revenues were offset by the corresponding study expenses.

Strategy
New York ISO's strategy includes adding new green power sources and improving plant efficiency to meet clean air regulations. Since 2000 the company has added more than 8600 MW of new power generation including renewable power generation (hydro and wind). In 2012 it had 1414 MW of wind generation in operation with plans for adding a further 4000 MW from renewable energy sources.

The company's 2012-2016 strategic plan calls for it to integrate gas operations and renewable power resources and expand wholesale electricity markets in addition to implementing Smart Grid

technology to enhance its core mission of providing power reliably across its transmission system.

With an eye towards using more natural gas as a power plant fuel in 2012 the company formed a working group to improve coordination between its market participants natural gas utilities pipelines and other industry players.

In a move to further increase operational efficiency and lower the costs of electric transmission congestion management in 2013 New York ISO and fellow ISO PJM Interconnection began jointly managing transmission limits that occur near the boundaries between their regions.

Company Background
In 2009 New York ISO was granted $37.8 million by the Department of Energy to support the reliability of the bulk electricity grid in New York and develop a Smart Grid infrastructure. This was supplemented in 2010 with a federal $76 million Smart Grid Investment Grant to enable the construction of a statewide Phasor Measurement Network to enhance New York ISO's ability to detect system vulnerabilities and avoid blackouts.

The company has it origins in the Northeast Blackout of 1965 following which New York's eight largest electric utilities joined to create the New York Power Pool in order to reduce the likelihood of another major power interruption. New York ISO was formed in 1998 as part of the ongoing restructuring of New York State's electric power industry.

EXECUTIVES

Vice President of Market Structures, Rana Mukerji
Vp Market Operations, Emilie Nelson

LOCATIONS

HQ: THE NEW YORK INDEPENDENT SYSTEM OPERATOR INC
10 KREY BLVD, RENSSELAER, NY 121449681
Phone: 518 356-6000
Web: WWW.NYISO.COM

HISTORICAL FINANCIALS

Company Type: Private

Income Statement

FYE: December 31

	REVENUE ($ mil.)	NET INCOME ($ mil.)	NET PROFIT MARGIN	EMPLOYEES
12/13	159	0	—	500
12/10	149	0	—	—
12/09	139	0	—	—
12/08	0	0	—	—
Annual Growth	**—**	**—**	**—**	**—**

2013 Year-End Financials

Return on assets: 205.6%
Return on equity: —
Current ratio: —

Cash ($ mil.): 651

THE NEWTRON GROUP L L C

Some contractors bomb but The Newtron Group keeps on ticking. Through subsidiaries The Newtron Group offers a variety of industrial electrical and other specialty construction and contracting services nationwide. Services include instrumentation and control systems installation and maintenance; fiber optic installation and testing; industrial pipe and panel fabrication; aviation services; and electrical heat tracing. Newtron serves clients in such industries as refining power generation mining pharmaceuticals and semiconductors. Subsidiaries include electrical contractor Triad Electric and Controls and fiber optics firm Com-Net Services. The Newtron Group has offices in California Louisiana and Texas.

EXECUTIVES

VP Marketing, Duff Schempf
President, Glen Redd
Auditors: HANNIS T BOURGEOIS LLP BATON

LOCATIONS

HQ: THE NEWTRON GROUP L L C
8183 W EL CAJON DR, BATON ROUGE, LA 708158093
Phone: 225 927-8921
Web: WWW.THENEWTRONGROUP.COM

PRODUCTS/OPERATIONS

Selected Subsidiaries
Com-Net Services Inc. (fiber optics)
Executive Aviation Inc. (hangar space fuel supplies)
Newtron Inc. (electrical and instrumentation)
Newtron Heat Trace (industrial heat tracing)
Newtron Mechanical (industrial mechanics)
Triad Electric and Controls Inc. (electrical and instrumentation)
Triad Control Systems Inc. (control panel fabrication)

Selected Industries
Cement
Electronics
Food processing
Gas transmission
Metals and mining
Petrochemical
Pharmaceuticals
Power generation
Pulp and paper
Refining
Semiconductors
Waste treatment

COMPETITORS

EMCOR
Fisk Electric
Industrial Specialty
  Contractors

Jelec
MMR Group
Motor City Electric
Pike Corporation

HISTORICAL FINANCIALS

Company Type: Private

Income Statement

	REVENUE ($ mil.)	NET INCOME ($ mil.)	NET PROFIT MARGIN	EMPLOYEES
06/14	366	0	—	2,000
06/13	443	0	—	—
06/12	296	2	0.7%	—
06/11	311	0	—	—
Annual Growth	5.6%	—	—	—

2014 Year-End Financials
Return on assets: 1.9%   Cash ($ mil.): 40
Return on equity: —
Current ratio: 0.70

THE NORTH CAROLINA MUTUAL WHOLESALE DRUG COMPANY

Auditors: THOMAS KNIGHT TRENT KING AN

LOCATIONS

HQ: THE NORTH CAROLINA MUTUAL WHOLESALE DRUG COMPANY
816 ELLIS RD, DURHAM, NC 277036019
Phone: 919 596-2151
Web: WWW.MUTUALDRUGCOMPANY.COM

HISTORICAL FINANCIALS

Company Type: Private

Income Statement

FYE: March 31

	REVENUE ($ mil.)	NET INCOME ($ mil.)	NET PROFIT MARGIN	EMPLOYEES
03/10	1,035	0	0.0%	160
03/09	1,024	0	0.1%	—
Annual Growth	1.1%	(68.7%)	—	—

2010 Year-End Financials
Return on assets: 9.1%   Cash ($ mil.): 53
Return on equity: —
Current ratio: 0.90

THE NORTH HIGHLAND COMPANY

The North Highland Company hopes its consulting services help its business clients chart a course toward improved operations. The employee-owned company provides management and technology consulting services through more than 900 professionals working out of 23 offices in 10 US states. Its services cover areas such as business strategy supply chain management marketing and customer service business process improvement and technology management. The company's partners include Big Insight Sourcing Group The Difference and True Bridge Resources.

Operations
North Highland operates through three divisions: Data and Analytics Managed Services and Sparks Grove.

Geographic Reach
North Highland's offices are located mainly in the southeastern US. It also operates more than 30 offices outside of the US. The company's US offices are located in Atlanta; Basking Ridge New Jersey; Charlotte North Carolina; Chicago; Dallas; Denver; Houston; Jacksonville; Los Angeles; Minneapolis; Nashville Tennessee; New York; Orlando Florida; Philadelphia; Richmond Virginia; San Francisco; Seattle; St. Louis Missouri; Tallahassee Florida; Tampa; and Washington DC.

Sales and Marketing
The company serves multiple industries including energy and utilities financial services health care life sciences media and telecommunications retail and travel and leisure.

Strategy
The company has grown organically over the years by opening offices in carefully chosen markets. North Highland's consultants typically work for clients in their home areas rather than traveling to engagements. The company believes that working locally gives it an edge in understanding clients' needs and in hiring qualified consultants who prefer to avoid the travel generally associated with the profession.

North Highland has also used product enhancement and innovation to grow its business. In 2013 North Highland expanded its capabilities to support retail pharmacies and health care-related re-

---

tailers. The following year it opened its Social Insights Lab in its Atlanta headquarters. The lab adds social media analysis and interaction to the firm's capabilities.

EXECUTIVES

CEO, Dan Reardon
CFO, Kirk Hancock
Co-President, David Deiters
President North Highland Division, Alex Bombeck
EVP, Michael Lee
CFO, David D. Cathcart, age 41
VP Information Systems, Roger Hardgrove
Vice President Data, Dwight Specht
Vice President, Teri Mendelovitz
Vice President, Vijay Desai
Vice President and Wealth Management Retirement Lead, Jill Jacques
Vice President of Charlotte Office, Keith Anthony
Vice President, Denise Sughrue
Vice President Media and Entertainment, Mike Carollo
Vice President Market Lead Chicago, Jose Martinez
Vice President and Office Lead Dallas Ft. Worth, Jim Schwalbe
Vice President, Chris Wilhelmi
Vice President and Houston Office Lead, Clark Varner
Chairman, Michael W. (Mike) Trapp, age 76

LOCATIONS

HQ: THE NORTH HIGHLAND COMPANY
3333 PIEDMON RD NE STE 10, ATLANTA, GA 303051811
Phone: 404 233-1015
Web: WWW.NORTHHIGHLAND.COM

PRODUCTS/OPERATIONS

Selected Practice Areas
Application integration
Business process improvement
Change management
Customer relationship management
Data management
Disaster recovery
Financial reporting and budgeting
Human resources strategy
Internet/intranet design
IT strategy
Lean manufacturing
Marketing strategy
Mergers and acquisitions integration
Organizational effectiveness
Risk management
Six Sigma
Supply chain assessment

COMPETITORS

A.T. Kearney
Bain & Company
Booz Allen
Boston Consulting

Deloitte Consulting
McKinsey & Company
PA Consulting

HISTORICAL FINANCIALS

Company Type: Private

Income Statement

FYE: December 31

	REVENUE ($ mil.)	NET INCOME ($ mil.)	NET PROFIT MARGIN	EMPLOYEES
12/08	170	8	4.7%	2,300
12/05	87	2	2.7%	—
12/04	59	57	96.4%	—
12/03	47	0	—	—
Annual Growth	29.0%	—	—	—

2008 Year-End Financials
Return on assets: 4.4%   Cash ($ mil.): 8
Return on equity: 4.7%
Current ratio: 1.50

THE NORTH HIGHLAND HOLDING COMPANY INC

Auditors: GRANTTHORNTON LLP ATLANTA GA

LOCATIONS

HQ: THE NORTH HIGHLAND HOLDING COMPANY INC
3333 PIEDMONT RD NE, ATLANTA, GA 303051811
Phone: 404 233-1015
Web: WWW.NORTHHIGHLAND.COM

HISTORICAL FINANCIALS
Company Type: Private

Income Statement
FYE: December 31

	REVENUE ($ mil.)	NET INCOME ($ mil.)	NET PROFIT MARGIN	EMPLOYEES
12/13	327	6	2.1%	1
12/12	318	11	3.5%	—
Annual Growth	2.9%	(38.3%)	—	—

2013 Year-End Financials
Return on assets: 6.6%
Return on equity: 2.1%
Current ratio: 0.70
Cash ($ mil.): 25

THE NORWALK HOSPITAL ASSOCIATION

Auditors: PRICEWATEHOUSECOOPERS LLP HAR

LOCATIONS

HQ: THE NORWALK HOSPITAL ASSOCIATION
34 MAPLE ST, NORWALK, CT 068503894
Phone: 203 852-2000
Web: WWW.NORWALKHOSPITAL.ORG

HISTORICAL FINANCIALS
Company Type: Private

Income Statement
FYE: September 30

	REVENUE ($ mil.)	NET INCOME ($ mil.)	NET PROFIT MARGIN	EMPLOYEES
09/13	351	(4)	—	1,660
09/12	388	28	7.4%	—
09/09	339	18	5.4%	—
09/08	319	0	—	—
Annual Growth	2.0%	—	—	—

2013 Year-End Financials
Return on assets: 8.3%
Return on equity: (-1.4%)
Current ratio: 1.60
Cash ($ mil.): 73

THE OLTMANS CONSTRUCTION CO

With projects ranging from the California Speedway to a distribution/warehouse building for TV retail giant HSN Oltmans Construction has done it all. The group offers preconstruction general contracting and design/build project delivery construction management tenant improvements and seismic retrofits among its services for commercial and industrial buildings throughout California Nevada and Arizona. The company also completes its own concrete work. Oltmans is one of the top general contractors in its home state as well as one of the top builders of distribution facilities in the US. The company was founded in 1932 and has been led by three generations of the Oltmans family.

EXECUTIVES
Chairman and CEO, Joseph O. (Joe) Oltmans
Secretary and Treasurer, John E (Jack) Rowe
Auditors: KPMG LLP LOS ANGELES CA

LOCATIONS

HQ: THE OLTMANS CONSTRUCTION CO
10005 MISSION MILL RD, WHITTIER, CA 906011739
Phone: 562 908-9578
Web: WWW.OLTMANS.COM

COMPETITORS

Bernards Brothers	Moorefield
DPR Construction	Construction
Duke Construction	Ryan Companies US
KPRS Construction	Swinerton
Menemsha Development	Webcor Builders

HISTORICAL FINANCIALS
Company Type: Private

Income Statement
FYE: March 31

	REVENUE ($ mil.)	NET INCOME ($ mil.)	NET PROFIT MARGIN	EMPLOYEES
03/08	326	5	1.6%	409
03/07	315	4	1.3%	—
03/06	317	3	1.1%	—
03/05	242	0	—	—
Annual Growth	10.4%	—	—	—

2008 Year-End Financials
Return on assets: 10.4%
Return on equity: 1.6%
Current ratio: 0.80
Cash ($ mil.): 18

THE PARADIES SHOPS LLC

For the frequent flyer this is retail paradise. The Paradies Shops operates 550-plus shops in more than 75 airports hotels and aquariums throughout the US and Canada. It serves more than half a billion passengers annually with retail sites that include bookstores gift shops jewelry stores ladies accessory shops newsstands sunglass stores and western stores among others. Paradies Shops is also the exclusive licensee of Brooks Brothers CNBC PGA Tour and the New York Times. The firm operates several hotel properties and the retail program for the Georgia Aquarium in Atlanta.

The company was founded by the Paradies family in 1960. In 2010 it sold a majority stake to Freeman Spogli & Co.

Geographic Reach
The Atlanta-based company operates stores at more than 75 locations including 17 of the top 25 airports in the US. It also has non-airport locations in Houston and Orlando Florida.

Strategy
Airport retail has experienced rapid growth in recent years as terminals become more akin to shopping malls with a captive audience. Flight delays and more stringent security requirements have increased waiting times for passengers many of whom turn to shopping for relief from the boredom. The Paradise Shops tailors its merchandise to regional tastes selling sports-related merchandise at its ACC (Atlantic Coast Conference) Shops in the Raleigh-Durham International Airport or Texas-themed goods and apparel at the Dallas-Fort Worth International Airport for example.

EXECUTIVES
President and CEO, Gregg Paradies
COO, Lou Bottino
CFO, Kevin Smith
Regional Vice President, Barry Young
Vice President General Counsel, Karen Suttle
Vice President Human Resources, Les Russell
Vice President Business Development, Bruce Feuer
Vice President Marketing, Lynn Bennett
Regional Vice President, Pat Wallace
Senior Vice President Fandb, William (Bill) Casey
Senior Vice President Stores Operations And Lp, Jeff Flowers
Senior Vice President Chief Financial Officer, Don Marek
Chairman, Dick Dickson
Vice Chairman, James N. (Jim) Paradies
Auditors: HABIF AROGETI & WYNNE LLP A

LOCATIONS

HQ: THE PARADIES SHOPS LLC
2849 PACES FERRY RD SE # 400, ATLANTA, GA 303396201
Phone: 404 344-7905
Web: WWW.THEPARADIESSHOPS.COM

PRODUCTS/OPERATIONS

Selected Licensed Brands
ACC Shops
Bass Pro Shops
Big 12 Conference
Big Ten Conference
Brighton Collectibles
Brooks Brothers
CNBC News
Dylan's Candy Bar
EA Sports
Harley-Davidson
KidZoo
Lettuce Entertain You
Pandora
PGA Tour Shops
The New York Times Bookstore
SPANX
TravelMart
Vera Bradley

COMPETITORS

Barnes & Noble	Puente Concessions
DFS Group	SkyMall
Hudson Group	

THE PENNSYLVANIA HOSPITAL OF THE UNIVERSITY OF PENNSYLVANIA HEAL

Early to bed early to rise may have made Ben Franklin healthy wealthy and wise. But for those not so healthy he (along with Dr. Thomas Bond) found it wise to establish Pennsylvania Hospital the nation's first such medical institution. The hospital is now a part of the University of Pennsylvania Health System (UPHS) and offers a comprehensive range of medical surgical and diagnostic services to the Philadelphia County area. Housing some 520 beds Pennsylvania Hospital offers specialized care in areas such as orthopedics vascular surgery neurosurgery and obstetrics; it is also a leading teaching hospital and a center for clinical research.

Operations

Pennsylvania Hospital has an average of about 29000 inpatient admissions per year including 5200 births as well as 115000 outpatient and emergency care visits. The medical center has more than 800 physicians on its medical staff. In addition to its extensive medical care services the company conducts medical training programs through its relationship with the University of Pennsylvania School of Medicine. Medical and clinical research programs are conducted with the school and with other research entities including government agencies. The hospital also collaborates with other UPHS entities including the Penn Presbyterian Medical Center and the Hospital of the University of Pennsylvania. The medical center also provides educational services across academic programs inlcuding Clinical Psychology Internship Program Medicine OB/GYN Pathology Radiology Sports Medicine Fellowship Surgery and Vascular Surgery Fellowship.

Financial Performance

For the fiscal year 2014 (ended June 30) Pennsylvania Hospital's revenues increased by 8.4% with a 9% increase in net patient service revenues 94% of total revenues); offset by a 1% decline in other revenues. The company's net loss for the year decreased by 38% due to higher revenues and a decline in employee benefits paid.

Strategy

To improve the quality of care in the region UPHS is expanding specialist programs at its facilities.

In 2014 Pennsylvania Hospital opened its new Well Mother & Baby Unit which will represent Philadelphia's first all-private maternity suite unit. The new unit is part of Pennsylvania Hospital's $61 million long-range facility master plan and expands the company's offerings by providing private rooms to all of their maternity patients along with an array of obstetrical services from conception to discharge from the hospital following childbirth.

In 2013 UPHS expanded the orthopedic surgery program at Pennsylvania Hospital. The medical center is also enhancing services in fields including stroke care and women's health.

Company Background

The hospital was founded in 1751 by Benjamin Franklin and Dr. Thomas Bond to care for the sick-poor and insane of Philadelphia.

EXECUTIVES

Managing Director, Mitchell Schnall
Director Of Radiology, Geoffrey A Agrons
Medical Director, Charles Orellana
Medical Records Director, Scott Gilyard
Vice President Finance and Human Resources Manager, Thomas E (Thom) Lawrence
Director of Pharmacy Pennsylvania Hospital, Suzanne Brown
Clinical Director, Tonya Johnson
Director Of Physical Therapy, Lisa Haney
Director of Radiology, Linda Bagley
Vice President Operations, Susan Small
Medical Director Department of Emergency Medicine, Kathleen Nasci
Vice President, Arthur (Art) Bartolozzi
Vice Chair Department of Neurology; Chief of Neur, Howard Hurtig
Treasurer, Ronald (Ron) Kotler
Auditors: PRICEWATERHOUSECOOPERS LLP PH

LOCATIONS

HQ: THE PENNSYLVANIA HOSPITAL OF THE UNIVERSITY OF PENNSYLVANIA HEAL
800 SPRUCE ST, PHILADELPHIA, PA 191076130
Phone: 215 829-3000
Web: WWW.VET.UPENN.EDU

PRODUCTS/OPERATIONS

Selected Centers
ALS Center
Birthing Suite
Center for Bloodless Medicine and Surgery
Crisis Response Center
CyberKnife
Diabetes Education Center
Joan Karnell Cancer Center
Pain Management Center
Parkinson's Disease and Movement Disorders Center
Penn Comprehensive Neurosciences Center
Penn Orthopaedic Institute
Penn Center for Voice
Sports Medicine and Rehabilitation Center
Sleep Disorders Center
Vascular Center
Women's Imaging Center

Selected Services
Behavioral health
Heart and vascular
Neonatology
Neurosurgery
Obstetrics (including high-risk maternal and fetal services)
Orthopedics
Otorhinolaryngology (ENT)
Urology
Vascular medicine/surgery

COMPETITORS
Abington Memorial Hospital
Albert Einstein Healthcare Network
Aria Health
Bryn Mawr Hospital
Children's Hospital of Philadelphia

Crozer-Keystone Health System
Fox Chase Cancer Center
North Philadelphia Health System
TUHS
The Magee Memorial Hospital for Convalescents
Thomas Jefferson University Hospital

THE PEPPER COMPANIES INC

Auditors: DELOITTE & TOUCHE LLP CHICAGO

LOCATIONS

HQ: THE PEPPER COMPANIES INC
643 N ORLEANS ST, CHICAGO, IL 606543608
Phone: 312 266-4703
Web: WWW.PEPPERCONSTRUCTION.COM

THE PEW CHARITABLE TRUSTS

Green is the grease The Pew Charitable Trusts uses to help not-for-profits run smoothly. Among the nation's largest private foundations it was established in 1948 in memory of Sun Oil founder Joseph Pew and his wife Mary by four of their children. Seven trusts were created between 1948 and 1979 to promote public health and welfare and to strengthen communities. With more than $5 billion in assets it distributes more than $100 million in grants annually to charitable organizations in culture education environment health and human services public policy and religion. The Pew Trusts has strong ties to Philadelphia and allocates a portion of its grants to programs in that area.

Geographic Reach

Pew has primary offices in Philadelphia and Washington DC.

Operations

The non-profit organization also operates through the Pew Center on the States; the Pew Environment Group; the Pew Health Group; and the Pew Research Center. The organization became an independent public charity in 2004.

Strategy

The Pew Charitable Trusts focuses its efforts on improving public policy informing the public of the latest topics and stimulating civic life mostly in the Philadelphia area. To that end in 2013 Pew announced it will provide almost $8.5 million over the next three years to 46 Philadelphia-area organizations serving some of the area's most disadvantaged children and their families. The aim is to improve the lives of poor children by offering support to instill social and learning skills thereby overcoming obstacles to academic success.

The non-profit organization has a broad reach beyond Philadelphia. Indeed its activities range from evaluating children's dental health policies across the 50 US states to investigating the impact of industrial-scale chicken farming on the nation's land and waterways. The Pew Environment Group is active in protecting boreal forest in Canada and the oceans' shark population through the establishment of shark sanctuaries.

EXECUTIVES

Executive Vice President, Susan (Sue) Urahn
Senior Vice President Communications, Melissa (Mel) Skolfield
Executive Vice President, Usha Chaudhary
Managing Director Communications, Melissa Mskolfieldpewtrustsorg
Board Of Directors, Patricia Bonney
Board Member, Matthew (Matt) Levy
Auditors: GRANT THORNTON LLP PHiLADELPH

LOCATIONS

HQ: THE PEW CHARITABLE TRUSTS
2005 MARKET ST STE 1700, PHILADELPHIA, PA
191037017
Phone: 215 575-9050
Web: WWW.PEWTRUSTS.ORG

PRODUCTS/OPERATIONS

Selected Program Areas
Arts and Culture
Children and Youth
Computers and the Internet
Sentencing and Corrections
Education
Elections
Environment
Family Financial Security
Government Performance
Health
Hispanics in America
Media and Journalism
National Civic Initiatives
Philadelphia Area
Public Opinion
Religion and Public Life
Science
State Policy and Performance

HISTORICAL FINANCIALS

Company Type: Private

Income Statement

FYE: June 30

	REVENUE ($ mil.)	NET INCOME ($ mil.)	NET PROFIT MARGIN	EMPLOYEES
06/14	874	585	66.9%	500
06/13	588	299	50.9%	—
06/12	85	(286)	—	—
06/11	991	0	—	—
Annual Growth	(4.1%)	—	—	—

2014 Year-End Financials

Return on assets: 1.3%
Return on equity: 66.9%
Current ratio: 0.20
Cash ($ mil.): 29

THE PLAZA GROUP INC

The Plaza Group (TPG) is an international distributor of petrochemical solvents and chemical intermediates. Established in 1994 TPG is the exclusive marketer of some products from companies such as Shell Oil and Frontier Oil. The company markets to FORTUNE 500 companies major international enterprises direct consumers and chemical distributors. Its products are used in the production of resins coatings and adhesives. TPG partners with global suppliers (like SABIC Innovative Plastics Total Petrochemicals and Alon) in Asia Australia Europe and the Americas. The company is owned by president Randy Velarde.

EXECUTIVES

Executive Vice President, John (Jack) Orlando
Vice Presidente Senior, Jerry Dunn
Board Member, John (Jack) Yanney
Auditors: UHY LLP CPAS HOUSTON TX

LOCATIONS

HQ: THE PLAZA GROUP INC
10375 RICHMOND AVE # 1620, HOUSTON, TX
770424143
Phone: 713 266-1059
Web: WWW.THEPLAZAGRP.COM

COMPETITORS

Cole Chemical
ICC Chemical
Sinochem

HISTORICAL FINANCIALS

Company Type: Private

Income Statement

FYE: December 31

	REVENUE ($ mil.)	NET INCOME ($ mil.)	NET PROFIT MARGIN	EMPLOYEES
12/13	288	1	0.4%	18
12/12	288	3	1.2%	—
12/11	271	4	1.6%	—
12/10	198	0	—	—
Annual Growth	13.3%	—	—	—

2013 Year-End Financials

Return on assets: 6.9%
Return on equity: 0.4%
Current ratio: 1.00
Cash ($ mil.): —

THE PRIDDY FOUNDATION

LOCATIONS

HQ: THE PRIDDY FOUNDATION
807 8TH ST STE 1010, WICHITA FALLS, TX
763013310
Phone: 940 723-8720
Web: WWW.PRIDDYFDN.ORG

HISTORICAL FINANCIALS

Company Type: Private

Income Statement

FYE: December 31

	REVENUE ($ mil.)	NET INCOME ($ mil.)	NET PROFIT MARGIN	EMPLOYEES
12/13	8,791	3	0.0%	4
12/12	3	(4)	—	—
12/10	32	27	86.7%	—
12/09	0	0	—	—
Annual Growth	—	—	—	—

2013 Year-End Financials

Return on assets: —
Return on equity: —
Current ratio: —
Cash ($ mil.): 14

THE RESEARCH FOUNDATION OF STATE UNIVERSITY OF NEW YORK

The Research Foundation of State University of New York (The Research Foundation) collects and administers research and education grants from state and federal governments corporations and foundations on behalf of the 24-campus State University of New York known as SUNY. The foundation has formed several affiliated divisions –including Long Island High Technology Incubator and NanoTech Resources —to operate research facilities encourage scientific collaboration and otherwise facilitate research for the university. It facilitates research for studies such as engineering and nanotechnology; physical sciences and medicine; life sciences and medicine; social sciences; and computer and information sciences.

Geographic ReachThe Research Foundation comprises a central office and operating units at 31 campus locations across New York State.

Operations The foundation manages SUNY's research portfolio. Research Foundation administrators help SUNY faculty students and staff through every step of the research grant process allowing them to focus on their work and ensuring compliance with university grant sponsor and government requirements.The Research Foundation protects SUNY's intellectual property (SUNY ranks among the nation's top faculty to commercialize their inventions for the public good).The organization makes strategic investments to maximize the collective impact of SUNY research to drive investment and job growth. SUNY's Networks of Excellence assemble scientists and scholars from all campuses to collaborate on research projects in areas ranging from advanced manufacturing and energy to health and the humanities.The Research Foundation is an integral partner in the execution and administration of the START-UP NY initiative to transform SUNY campuses and university communities across the state into tax-free communities for new and expanding businesses.

The organization funds its operations primarily from recoveries of indirect costs provided from grants and contracts.

Financial Performance

The Research Foundation reported $1 billion in revenues in 2014 compared to $1.07 billion in 2013. The primary reason for the decline was due to decreased sales from federal grants and contracts private grants and contracts and investment income.Investment income/loss included dividends and interest realized and unrealized gains and losses and equity adjustments from the foundation's investment in the Brookhaven Science Associates partnership.The organization's net income decreased by $30 million in 2014 due to lower revenues and increased other program expenses. Net cash provided by the operating activities increased by $127.7 million due to changes in interest payments on capital debts and other payments.

Strategy

In 2014 Iliad Neurosciences a company focused on the development of innovative approaches to diagnosing and treating Autism Spectrum Disorders entered into an Exclusive License Agreement with The Research Foundation for The State University of New York. Under this deal Iliad will provide a new biomarker to identify an abnormality in folate transport to the brain associated with susceptibility to Autism Spectrum Disorders. . The identification of this defect could lead to a targeted therapy that may improve the transport of folate to the brain in children and to the fetus in pregnant women who test positive for the folate receptor autoantibody.

Company Background

The Research Foundation was established in 1951 just three years after SUNY itself.

EXECUTIVES

Vice President For Finance, Chris Wade
Vice President Of Human Resources, Paul Kelly
Office Of The Vice President For Research,
 Edward Zablocki
Auditors: KPMG ALBANY NY

LOCATIONS

HQ: THE RESEARCH FOUNDATION OF STATE
 UNIVERSITY OF NEW YORK
 35 STATE ST, ALBANY, NY 122072826
Phone: 518 434-7000

PRODUCTS/OPERATIONS

2014 Revenues

	% of total
Federal grants & contracts	50
Private grants & contracts	23
State grants & contracts	17
Investments	2
Inventions & licenses	2
Local grants & contracts	2
Investment income	0
Gifts capital gifts & grants	0
Other	4
Total	**100**

HISTORICAL FINANCIALS

Company Type: Private

Income Statement

FYE: June 30

	REVENUE ($ mil.)	NET INCOME ($ mil.)	NET PROFIT MARGIN	EMPLOYEES
06/13	1,079	42	3.9%	8,000
06/12	1,114	12	1.2%	
06/09	985	(71)	—	
06/08	9	0	—	
Annual Growth	159.5%		—	—

2013 Year-End Financials

Return on assets: —
Return on equity: 3.9%
Current ratio: 0.70
Cash ($ mil.): —

THE ROCKEFELLER UNIVERSITY FACULTY AND STUDENTS CLUB INC

Rockefeller University sniffs out solid scientific evidence. The university is a leading US research institution and scientific graduate school providing training in biomedical and physical science fields such as biochemistry structural biology immunology neuroscience and human genetics. The university is centered around 76 research laboratories and a hospital and it runs M.D.-Ph.D. programs in conjunction with the Memorial Sloan-Kettering Cancer Center and the Weill Medical College at Cornell University. Rockefeller University's research is funded by entities such as the National Institutes of Health and the Howard Hughes Medical Institute as well as private gifts and endowments.

Operations

Rockefeller University maintains a small enrollment with only about 170 Ph.D. students and 25 M.D.-Ph.D. students. It also has some 200 research and clinical scientists on campus 350 postdoctoral researchers and 1000 clinicians technicians support staff and administrators.

The university doesn't charge tuition but instead relies on investment income research grants and contracts and private grants and gifts to fund its operations. It also provides its Ph.D. students with amenities such as scholarships subsidized housing and annual research budgets to encourage independent study and creativity.

Financial Performance

Rockefeller University reported a 68% decline in revenues to some $157 million in 2012 due to reduced government grants and contracts investment losses and depreciation of derivative instruments; these elements were partially offset by an increase in private grants and gifts. The university also posted a net income loss in 2012 due to lower revenues and increased research and academic expenses. Rockefeller University's earnings and profits tend to fluctuate from year to year due to the variability of its income sources.

Strategy

Harkening back to its famous entrepreneurial founder Rockefeller University's open structure encourages collaboration between disciplines and

empowers faculty members to take on high-risk high-reward projects. No formal departments exist bureaucracy is kept to a minimum and scientists are given resources support and unparalleled freedom to follow the science wherever it leads.

Company Background

Rockefeller University completed a $380 million renovation and construction program in 2010. The project included modernization of historical laboratory buildings and the construction of a new five-story Collaborative Research Center.

The school has been Rockefeller University since 1965 although it was originally founded by John D. Rockefeller in 1901 as The Rockefeller Institute for Medical Research. The Rockefeller University Hospital the first research-focused medical center in the US opened in 1910.

Over the course of its history some 24 of Rockefeller's scientists (including five current faculty) have won the Nobel Prize.

EXECUTIVES

President, Marc Tessier-Lavigne, age 55
VP Academic Affairs, Michael W. Young
VP University Strategy and Research Operations,
 Timothy P. OÂConnor
Vice Chairman, Henry R. Kravis, age 71
Vice Chairman, Richard E. Salomon, age 73
Chairman, Russell L. Carson
Vice Chairman, Marnie S. Pillsbury
Auditors: KPMG LLP NEW YORK NEW YORK

LOCATIONS

HQ: THE ROCKEFELLER UNIVERSITY FACULTY AND
 STUDENTS CLUB INC
 1230 YORK AVE, NEW YORK, NY 100656307
Phone: 212 327-8078
Web: WWW.RUCARES.ORG

HISTORICAL FINANCIALS

Company Type: Private

Income Statement

FYE: June 30

	REVENUE ($ mil.)	NET INCOME ($ mil.)	NET PROFIT MARGIN	EMPLOYEES
06/13	466	159	34.1%	1,700
06/06	413	271	65.5%	—
06/05	413	271	65.5%	—
Annual Growth	1.5%	(6.5%)	—	—

2013 Year-End Financials

Return on assets: —
Return on equity: 34.1%
Current ratio: 0.20
Cash ($ mil.): 133

THE RUDOLPH/LIBBE COMPANIES INC

The corporate model of a conglomerate composed of independent unrelated businesses is not for The Rudolph/Libbe Companies. The group of companies can build or oversee real estate projects (general contractor Rudolph/Libbe Inc.); perform mechanical electrical and structural work (GEM Industrial); and then represent those properties in the market (RLWest Properties). Operating in the Ohio/Michigan corridor the group provides site selection design/build and construction management. Its portfolio includes industrial retail municipal residential educational health care and mixed-use projects. Fritz and Phil Rudolph and their cousin Allan Libbe founded flagship subsidiary Rudolph/Libbe Inc. in 1955.

The Rudolph/Libbe Companies also has a partnership with Winter Construction. The contracting partnership Winter RLG specializes in industrial construction for the automotive food processing industrial manufacturing power generation and distribution industries. Clients have included Campbell Soup FedEx and Alcoa.

In 2009 Rudolph/Libbe's real estate development division merged with another Ohio-based firm Park West Management & Development. The resulting RLWest Properties offers property management build-to-suit for lease or purchase and land sites for sale in Ohio.

EXECUTIVES

President; CEO Rudolph/Libbe Inc., William D. (Bill) Rudolph
President Rudolph/Libbe Properties, Stephen Welly
EVP Rudolph/Libbe Inc., Scott W. Libbe
Auditors: REHMANN ROBSON TOLEDO OH

LOCATIONS

HQ: THE RUDOLPH/LIBBE COMPANIES INC
6494 LATCHA RD, WALBRIDGE, OH 434659788
Phone: 419 241-5000
Web: WWW.RUDOLPHLIBBE.COM

COMPETITORS

Albert M. Higley	Messer Construction
Atlas Industrial	Ruhlin
Holdings	Skanska USA Building
Danis	

HISTORICAL FINANCIALS

Company Type: Private

Income Statement

	REVENUE ($ mil.)	NET INCOME ($ mil.)	NET PROFIT MARGIN	EMPLOYEES
12/13	319	8	2.7%	600
12/12	375	13	3.6%	—
12/11	472	13	2.8%	—
12/10	237	0	—	—
Annual Growth	10.3%	—	—	—

2013 Year-End Financials

Return on assets: 9.8%
Return on equity: 2.7%
Current ratio: 0.30
Cash ($ mil.): 20

THE SALVATION ARMY

Auditors: ERNST & YOUNG LLP ATLANTA GE

LOCATIONS

HQ: THE SALVATION ARMY
1424 N EAST EXPY NE, ATLANTA, GA 303292088
Phone: 404 728-1300
Web: WWW.SALVATIONARMYUSA.ORG

HISTORICAL FINANCIALS

Company Type: Private

Income Statement

FYE: September 30

	REVENUE ($ mil.)	NET INCOME ($ mil.)	NET PROFIT MARGIN	EMPLOYEES
09/12	1,198	191	16.0%	16,168
09/09	830	(220)	—	—
09/08	533	(336)	—	—
09/07	1,185	0	—	—
Annual Growth	0.2%	—	—	—

2012 Year-End Financials

Return on assets: —
Return on equity: 16.0%
Current ratio: 0.80
Cash ($ mil.): 92

THE SALVATION ARMY

Auditors: GRANT THORNTON LLP NEW YORK

LOCATIONS

HQ: THE SALVATION ARMY
440 W NYACK RD OFC, WEST NYACK, NY 109941739
Phone: 845 620-7200
Web: WWW.DONATE.SALVATIONARMYUSA.ORG

HISTORICAL FINANCIALS

Company Type: Private

Income Statement

FYE: September 30

	REVENUE ($ mil.)	NET INCOME ($ mil.)	NET PROFIT MARGIN	EMPLOYEES
09/12	1,034	207	20.0%	15
09/09	782	(96)	—	—
09/08	288	(463)	—	—
09/07	1,036	0	—	—
Annual Growth	(0.0%)	—	—	—

2012 Year-End Financials

Return on assets: 2.5%
Return on equity: 20.0%
Current ratio: 0.20
Cash ($ mil.): 137

THE SALVATION ARMY NATIONAL CORPORATION

Battling to provide social services The Salvation Army is one of the world's largest faith-based charities with some 3550 officers and 3.3 million volunteers. Its Christian faith-based programs assist alcoholics drug addicts the homeless the elderly prison inmates people in crisis and the jobless through offerings such as community centers housing facilities and rehabilitation centers. The organization also provides disaster-relief services and operates more than 1300 thrift stores. Overall it serves nearly 30 million people and 58 million meals a year. The US organization is a unit of the London-based Salvation Army which oversees activities in more than 100 countries. US operations began in 1880.

Geographic Reach

The organization's structure incorporates both church and military themes. There are six separate Salvation Army corporations in the US: National Headquarters based in New Jersey; The Salvation Army World Service Office; Central Territory (an Illinois corporation); Eastern Territory (a New York corporation); Southern Territory (Georgia); and Western Territory (California).

Operations

The Salvation Army's 3600 US officers who are also ordained ministers are expected to wear their uniforms at all times work full-time for The Salvation Army and marry only other officers. They receive no salary; instead they are provided with room and board and given a limited stipend.

Financial Performance

Ringing bells at Christmas is just one of the ways The Salvation Army raises money. Besides cash dropped into red kettles and cash registers at its thrift stores (Family Stores) the group receives donations in response to direct mail campaigns; gifts from companies foundations and individuals; and fees from government agencies for providing social services under contract.

HISTORY

William Booth (1829-1912) started preaching the gospel as a Wesleyan Methodist in the UK but the church expelled him because he insisted on preaching outside and to everyone including the poor. In 1865 he moved to the slums of London's East End and attracted large crowds with his volatile sermons. Opposition to his message of universal salvation for drunks thieves prostitutes and gamblers often caused riots. In fact the first women in the organization wore bonnets designed with a dual purpose in mind —warmth and protection from flying objects.

At a meeting in 1878 a sign was used referring to the "Salvation Army." Booth adopted the reference as both the name and the style of his organization. Members became soldiers evangelists were officers and Booth was referred to as "General." Prayers became knee drills and contributions were called cartridges.

The Salvation Army marched across the Atlantic to the US in 1880 led by seven women and one man. Women have always played an active role in the Salvation Army both as officers and soldiers. Booth's wife Catherine Mumford was a leading suffragette and Booth advocated equal rights for women.

In 1891 a crab pot was placed on a San Francisco street to collect donations with a sign reading "Keep the Pot Boiling." The idea led to the Salvation Army's annual Christmas kettle program.

During WWI the organization became famous for the doughnuts that it served the doughboys fighting on the front lines. After some internal dissension The Salvation Army took its only public political stance in 1928 with the endorsement of Herbert Hoover for his support of Prohibition during his presidential campaign. The charity opened its first home for alcoholics in 1939 in Detroit.

After WWII The Salvation Army began using such radio and TV programs as Heartbeat Theater and Army of Stars to spread its message.

Over the years The Salvation Army has provided assistance to victims of hurricanes floods and earthquakes. Volunteers rendered almost 70000 service hours in the aftermath of the Oklahoma City bombing in 1995 counseling more than 1600 victims and family members helping with funeral arrangements and providing food clothing and travel assistance. Indicative of the organization's readiness and extensive reach its volunteers were helping victims in Guam within minutes of the 1997 Korean Air plane crash. The Salvation Army was quickly on the scene after a Jonesboro Arkansas shooting incident in 1998 when four students and one teacher were killed by fellow students. Late that year the organization received the largest donation in its history —$80 million from Joan Kroc wife of McDonald's co-founder Ray Kroc.

After the September 11 attacks on the US in 2001 The Salvation Army provided assistance to rescue workers and families affected by the tragedy through its Disaster Relief Fund.

Joan Kroc left The Salvation Army $1.5 billion in 2003. The money was earmarked for construction of community centers modeled on one in San

Diego named for her and her husband. By 2006 plans were underway to build community centers in Atlanta Honolulu Phoenix and San Francisco.

EXECUTIVES

Commander UK and Ireland, Shaw Clifton
CFO, Mark Knecht
Chairman National Advisory Board, Robert J. (Rob) Pace, age 53
Secretary, Allison Honsberger
Board Member, Gayle Horton
Board Member, Victor Doughty
Auditors: GRANT THORNTON LLP MCLEAN VI

LOCATIONS

HQ: THE SALVATION ARMY NATIONAL CORPORATION
615 SLATERS LN, ALEXANDRIA, VA 223141112
Phone: 703 684-5500
Web: WWW.SALVATIONARMYUSA.ORG

PRODUCTS/OPERATIONS

Selected Services
Alcohol and drug treatment centers
Clinics and hospitals
Convalescent homes
Counseling
Crisis counseling
Disaster services
Food distribution centers
Handicapped housing
Homeless shelters
Human trafficking awareness and eradication
Institutes for the blind
Leprosy clinics
Military canteens and hostels
Nurseries and day care centers
Occupational centers
Prison ministry
Probation housing
Refugee centers
Science and trade schools
Student housing
Welfare aid

HISTORICAL FINANCIALS

Company Type: Private

Income Statement
FYE: September 30

	REVENUE ($ mil.)	NET INCOME ($ mil.)	NET PROFIT MARGIN	EMPLOYEES
09/13	4,315	1,349	31.3%	60,000
09/12	42	2	5.6%	—
09/10	3	0	10.8%	—
09/09	36	0	—	—
Annual Growth	229.0%	—	—	—

2013 Year-End Financials

Return on assets: —
Return on equity: 31.3%
Current ratio: 0.10
Cash ($ mil.): 379

THE SAVANNAH COLLEGE OF ART AND DESIGN INC

With more than 11000 students Savannah College of Art and Design (SCAD) is one of the largest art and design schools in the US. It has undergraduate degrees in arts and fine arts as well as master's degrees in a range of subjects. The institution includes nine schools offering courses of study in fields such as architecture interior and graphic design fashion film and television painting dance and art history. The school also offers certificates in digital publishing digital publishing management historic preservation interactive design and typeface design.

Geographic Reach

SCAD has campuses in Atlanta and Savannah Georgia as well as in Hong Kong and Lacoste France. Students at the college hail from all 50 US states and more than 100 international countries.

Operations

Annual tuition runs at about $30000. The institution employs about 700 full- and part-time faculty members.

The school's most popular majors include animation fashion graphic design illustration and photography. In addition to regular coursework SCAD provides online distance education courses.

Company Background

The school was founded in 1978 and has taken an active role in restoring architectural landmarks in Savannah.

EXECUTIVES

Vice President for SCAD e Learning, Darrell Naylor-Johnson
Associate Vice President For Academic Support, Hannah (Hanna) Crockett
Offices of the Vice President for Student Services, Cathy Turbiville
Managing Director Trustees Theater, Christina Routhier
Vice President SCAD Atlanta, Teresa M Griffis
Vice President For Enrollment Management, Scott Linzey
Vice President Student Services, Philip Alletto
Board Member, Antoinette Parris
Auditors: MAULDIN & JENKINS LLC ATLANTA

LOCATIONS

HQ: THE SAVANNAH COLLEGE OF ART AND DESIGN INC
342 BULL ST, SAVANNAH, GA 314014518
Phone: 912 525-5000
Web: WWW.SCAD.EDU

PRODUCTS/OPERATIONS

Degrees Offered
Bachelor of Arts (B.A.)
Bachelor of Fine Arts (B.F.A.)
Master of Architecture (M.Arch.)
Master of Arts (M.A.)
Master of Fine Arts (M.F.A.)
Master of Urban Design (M.U.D.)
Master of Arts in Teaching Art (M.A.)

Selected Schools
School of Building Arts
School of Communication Arts
School of Design
School of Digital Media
School of Entertainment Arts
School of Fashion
School of Fine Arts
School of Foundation Studies
School of Liberal Arts

HISTORICAL FINANCIALS

Company Type: Private

Income Statement
FYE: June 30

	REVENUE ($ mil.)	NET INCOME ($ mil.)	NET PROFIT MARGIN	EMPLOYEES
06/10	314	10	3.2%	1,200
06/09	283	21	7.7%	—
06/08	0	0	—	—
Annual Growth	—32707.6%	—	—	—

2010 Year-End Financials
Return on assets: —
Return on equity: 3.2%
Current ratio: —
Cash ($ mil.): 5

THE SCOULAR COMPANY

The Scoular Company's business is a grind — and that's a good thing. Scoular is best known for buying selling storing handling and transporting agricultural products (mainly grains) worldwide. It deals in the mainstays of farming — corn hay millet rice sorghum soybeans and wheat —and gets them where they need to go. The company transports these products via rail barge and seagoing container vessels. Scoular's other divisions offer fishmeal products for farm-animal pet and aquaculture feeds; ingredients for food manufacturers; renewable fuels; and truck freight brokering. It has customers in Asia Africa the Americas and Europe. George Scoular founded the business in Nebraska in 1892.

Geographic Reach

Omaha-based Scoular has operations in 18 US states as well as in Calgary and Montreal Canada and in Mexico. The company has more than a dozen merchandising offices and some 60 grain-handling facilities in North America with a storage capacity topping 120 million bushels.

Operations

The company operates 90 independent units that together make up a grain marketing network that handles 332 million bushels of grain annually and includes facilities in 18 states Canada and Mexico. In addition to buying selling handling and transporting grain Scoular offers risk management services.

Sales and Marketing

Scoular serves customers in the aquaculture flour milling food processing and manufacturing grain production industrial ag processing livestock feeding and manufacturing pet food manufacturing and renewable fuels sectors. Its services include bagging blending cleaning containerizing organic certifying packaging sorting sourcing and storage.

Financial Performance

The Scoular Company's sales totaled $6.4 billion in 2013 compared with $6.1 billion in 2012.

Strategy

The company is actively expanding its grain handling capacity at home and internationally. To that end the firm is expanding its presence in Canada by increasing staffing levels at its office in Calgary and Montreal. It's also looking either to build or acquire grain collection facilities in western Canada. In the US Scoular in 2014 acquired a corn processing facility in Dexter New Mexico from Hi-Pro that produces steam-flaked and rolled corn and includes a shuttle train loop track connected to BNSF's Southwestern line. Even closer to home the company also opened a new grain origination and trading office in Rushville Nebraska.

Mergers and Acquisitions

In August 2013 Scouler acquired the assets of Kansas-based Tribune Grain which include a grain elevator in Tribune Kansas that's located on the Kansas and Oklahoma Railroad as well as two seasonally-operated rural truck facilities. (In addition to the Tribune area facilities Scoular operates 10 other grain elevators in Kansas and eastern Colorado.)

Scoular in 2012 acquired a grain-handling facility in Atlanta Nebraska as well as two grain facilities in Weiser Idaho. In 2011 the company formed a joint venture with Johnson Grain to own and manage two grain elevators and a loading facility in Illinois. Later that year Scoular acquired two grain elevators in Kansas from Ada Grain; during 2011 the facilities received operational upgrades (such as faster equipment and new scales) to speed up the unloading process. Scoular has also pumped up its holdings in the renewable energy market acquiring a 55 million-gallon ethanol plant and nearly 2 million-bushel train facility in Kansas in early 2011. Additionally Scoular is a minority investor in other ethanol production facilities.

Ownership

One of the US's largest private companies Scoular is owned by its employees.

EXECUTIVES

Vice President, Randall Foster
Ex V Pres, John (Jack) Heck
Vp Operations, George Schieber
CEO, Charles (Chuck) Elsea
COO, Robert (Bob) Ludington
Chairman and President, David M. Faith
CFO, Richard A. (Rick) Cogdill
Vice President Finance and Treasurer, Roger Barber, age 53
V Pres, Todd McQueen
Senior Vice President, Kurt Peterson
Vice President, Jim Konz
Vice President Manager Director, Damon Roush
Vice Chairman, Marshall E. Faith
Auditors: KPMG LLP OMAHA NE

LOCATIONS

HQ: THE SCOULAR COMPANY
2027 DODGE ST STE 200, OMAHA, NE 681021229
Phone: 402 342-3500
Web: WWW.SCOULAR.COM

PRODUCTS/OPERATIONS

Selected Customer Industries Products and Services
Aquaculture (feed ingredients)
  Animal fats
  Animal proteins
  Fish oil
  Fishmeal
  Grain byproducts
  Vegetable fats
  Vegetable proteins
Flour milling (buying selling storing and shipping)
  Durum
  Hard red spring
  Hard red winter
  Soft red winter
Food manufacturing and processing (conventional organic and functional ingredients blending packaging co-packing)
  Ingredients
  Proteins
  Dairy
  Pea
  Potato
  Rice
  Soy
  Specialty flours
  Soy
  Starches
  Pea
  Potato
  Rice
  Tapioca
  Textured proteins
  Soy
Grain production (marketing buying storing handling and shipping programs)
  Corn
  Hay
  Millet
  Rice
  Sorghum
  Soybeans
  Wheat
Industrial ag processing (feedstock supply byproduct marketing and crush risk management)

Products
  Citrus pulp
  Distillers grains
  Hominy feed
  Wheat mill feeds
  Whole cottonseed
Identity-preserved grain
  Corn
  Soybeans
  Wheat
  White corn
Livestock feeding and feed manufacturing (grain and feed ingredient sourcing risk management)
  Grains and oilseeds
  Barley
  Canola
  Corn
  Field peas
  Flax
  Lentils
  Rye
  Soybeans
  Wheat
  Other
  Canola meal
  Citrus pulp
  Distillers grains
  Hominy feed
  Wheat mill feed
  Whole cottonseed
Pet food manufacturing (ingredients)
  Products
  Fats
  Flours
  Gravy dust mix
  Proteins
  Starches
  Yellow corn
  Sourcing and solutions
  Animal oils
  Animal proteins
  Fish oil
  Fishmeal
  Frozen fish
  Fruits
  Grain products
  Pea protein fiber flour and starch
  Pomaces
  Specialty starches flours
  Variety meats
  Vegetable oils
  Vegetable proteins
  Vegetables
Transportation
  Container and vessel (freight forwarding logistics and documentation in more than 50 countries)
  Rail truck and barge (logistics for shipping agricultural products in North America)

COMPETITORS

ADM	Excel Maritime
Andersons	Carriers
Bartlett and Company	Louis Dreyfus Group
Bunge Limited	Syntroleum
CHS	TBS International
Cargill	TORM
DeBruce Grain	

HISTORICAL FINANCIALS

Company Type: Private

Income Statement

FYE: May 31

	REVENUE ($ mil.)	NET INCOME ($ mil.)	NET PROFIT MARGIN	EMPLOYEES
05/14	228	29	13.0%	800
05/13	211	27	12.9%	—
05/12	211	27	13.1%	—
05/11	203	0	—	—
Annual Growth	3.9%	—	—	—

2014 Year-End Financials

Return on assets: 73.4%   Cash ($ mil.): 11
Return on equity: 13.0%
Current ratio: 0.50

THE SCRIPPS RESEARCH INSTITUTE

The Scripps Research Institute (TSRI) is a not-for profit organization that performs basic biomedical research in molecular and cellular biology chemistry immunology neuroscience disease and vaccine development. TSRI receives the majority of its funding from federal agencies such as the National Institutes of Health. TRSI opened a second facility in Florida in 2009. Its staff includes more than 2900 scientists and lab technicians and the organization traces its history back to 1924 when philanthropist Ellen Browning Scripps founded Scripps Metabolic Clinic.

Geographic Reach

TRSI is located on campuses in La Jolla California and Jupiter Florida.

Financial Performance

TSRI reported revenue of $393.3 million in 2011. That figure was down slightly from the $406.3 million the organization claimed in revenue for 2010.

TSRI receives the majority of its funding from the National Institutes of Health. Other contributors include the American Cancer Society the American Heart Association the Cystic Fibrosis Foundation the Leukemia & Lymphoma Society and the Juvenile Diabetes Association.

EXECUTIVES

Executive Vice President Gen Cnsl, Douglas (Doug) Bingham
Vice President Office Of Sponsored Programs, Kaye Wynne
Auditors: DELOITTE TAX LLP SAN DIEGO C

LOCATIONS

HQ: THE SCRIPPS RESEARCH INSTITUTE
10550 N TORREY PINES RD, LA JOLLA, CA 920371000
Phone: 858 784-1000
Web: WWW.SCRIPPS.EDU

COMPETITORS

Argonne National Laboratory	MITRE Quintiles
Battelle Memorial	Transnational
Berkeley Lab	SRI International
Brookhaven Lab	SwRI
Lawrence Livermore Lab	
Life Technologies Corporation	

HISTORICAL FINANCIALS

Company Type: Private

Income Statement

FYE: September 30

	REVENUE ($ mil.)	NET INCOME ($ mil.)	NET PROFIT MARGIN	EMPLOYEES
09/09	375	(18)	—	99
09/08	464	137	29.7%	—
09/05	387	63	16.3%	—
09/04	326	0	—	—
Annual Growth	2.8%	—	—	—

2009 Year-End Financials

Return on assets: —   Cash ($ mil.): 28
Return on equity: (-5.0%)
Current ratio: 0.40

THE SHEPHERD GOOD HOSPITAL INC

Leading its citizens toward good health Good Shepherd Health System provides medical and surgical care to patients throughout the Piney Woods region of northeastern Texas. Its flagship facility is Good Shepherd Medical Center in Longview a more than 425-bed regional referral hospital providing specialty care in areas such as trauma cardiology neurology and pulmonology. Good Shepherd also has small inpatient facilities as well as a freestanding outpatient surgery center and several primary care Family Health Centers located throughout its service area. The hospital established in 1935 as the 50-bed Gregg Memorial Hospital is led by CEO Ed Banos.

Operations

The health system also operates the Institute for Healthy Living. The institute functions by offering patients two paths toward wellness. First it offers advanced outpatient rehabilitative services and educational programs for patients who require a medically guided continuum of care. Second it provides a comprehensive fitness and wellness facility for both patients and employers to help improve and maintain their health with the hope that preventative care will keep area residents from facing serious health problems that could land them in the hospital. The institute is also home to a full-service spa outdoor walking trail Healthy Living Hideaway children's play center and classrooms for community educational programs meetings and special events.

Strategy

As the health care landscape becomes increasingly complicated with regulations and new technologies and areas of expertise many health care systems have made moves to join together in order to expand care services and save on operating costs. In 2015 Good Shepherd Health System announced plans to consider such an alliance with another system; one possibility would be to establish an Accountable Care Organization (ACO).

EXECUTIVES

Operating Room Director, Joy Newton
Admissions Director, Allen Hold
Clinical Director, Kevin Lassen
Vice President of Patient Care, Paula Brandon
Director Of Health Information Management, Deborah (Deb) Stewart

LOCATIONS

HQ: THE SHEPHERD GOOD HOSPITAL INC
700 E MARSHALL AVE, LONGVIEW, TX 756015572
Phone: 903 315-2000
Web: WWW.GSMC.ORG

PRODUCTS/OPERATIONS

Selected Locations
Good Sheph
Good Sheph
Good Sheph
Good Shepherd Family Health Center Longview
Good Shepherd Family Health Center Gladewater
Good Shepherd Family Health Center Gilmer
Good Shepherd Family Health Center Henderson
Good Shepherd Glenn Garrett Clinic Hughes Springs
Good Shepherd Glenn Garrett Clinic Jefferson
Good Shepherd Family Health Center Kilgore
Good Shepherd Glenn-Garrett Clinic Linden
Good Shepherd Family Health Center White Oak
Good Shepherd Family Health Center Gilmer
Good Shepherd Family Health Center Henderson
Good Shepherd Glenn Garrett Clinic Hughes Springs
Good Shepherd Glenn Garrett Clinic Jefferson

Good Shepherd Family Health Center Kilgore
Good Shepherd Glenn-Garrett Clinic Linden
Good Shepherd Family Health Center White Oak

COMPETITORS

Community Health Systems
East Texas Medical Center Regional Healthcare
HCA
Memorial Health System of East Texas
Select Medical
Tenet Healthcare
Trinity Mother Frances Hospital and Clinics
Wadley Regional Medical Center
Woodland Heights Medical Center

HISTORICAL FINANCIALS

Company Type: Private

Income Statement

FYE: September 30

	REVENUE ($ mil.)	NET INCOME ($ mil.)	NET PROFIT MARGIN	EMPLOYEES
09/13	270	2	0.9%	2,200
09/12*	282	(11)	—	—
03/12	24	1	5.1%	—
09/11	267	0	—	—
Annual Growth	0.5%	—	—	—

*Fiscal year change

2013 Year-End Financials

Return on assets: 4.8%
Return on equity: 0.9%
Current ratio: 1.60
Cash ($ mil.): 9

THE SOUTHEASTERN CONFERENCE

LOCATIONS

HQ: THE SOUTHEASTERN CONFERENCE
2201 RICHARD ARRINGTN JR, BIRMINGHAM, AL 352031103
Phone: 205 458-3000

HISTORICAL FINANCIALS

Company Type: Private

Income Statement

FYE: August 31

	REVENUE ($ mil.)	NET INCOME ($ mil.)	NET PROFIT MARGIN	EMPLOYEES
08/13	314	(3)	—	30
08/12	273	2	0.9%	—
08/11	261	4	1.6%	—
08/10	244	0	—	—
Annual Growth	8.8%	—	—	—

2013 Year-End Financials

Return on assets: —
Return on equity: (-1.1%)
Current ratio: —
Cash ($ mil.): 18

THE STAMFORD HOSPITAL

LOCATIONS

HQ: THE STAMFORD HOSPITAL
30 SHELBURNE RD, STAMFORD, CT 069023628
Phone: 203 325-7000
Web: WWW.STAMFORDHOSPITAL.ORG

HISTORICAL FINANCIALS

Company Type: Private

Income Statement

FYE: September 30

	REVENUE ($ mil.)	NET INCOME ($ mil.)	NET PROFIT MARGIN	EMPLOYEES
09/13	491	7	1.5%	1,500
09/04	268	4	1.7%	—
09/03	233	(11)	—	—
09/02	2,121	0	—	—
Annual Growth	(12.4%)	—	—	—

2013 Year-End Financials

Return on assets: 14.3%
Return on equity: 1.5%
Current ratio: 1.40
Cash ($ mil.): 107

THE SUNDT COMPANIES INC

Sundt has put its stamp on the Southwest. Through Sundt Construction and other subsidiaries The Sundt Companies offers preconstruction construction management general contracting and design/build services for commercial government and industrial clients. Projects include commercial buildings military bases light rails airports and schools. It builds mostly in Arizona Nevada California New Mexico and Texas. Sundt has overseen some notable projects including the development of the top-secret town of Los Alamos New Mexico (where the first atomic bomb was built) and the relocation of the London Bridge to Arizona. Sundt Companies was formed in 1998 as a holding company for various company interests.

Operations

The Sundt Companies performs its work through various divisions: Industrial; concrete; building; heavy civil; and federal. The building division is divided into geographic regions: California; Southwest; and Texas; as well as a Federal Division.

Strategy

Like its peers Sundt is dealing with the lingering effects of the construction downturn that greatly impacted the Southwest. (The company lost more than $750 million in government projects due to state budget constraints.) Indeed Sundt anticipates that it may be 2015 before it sees a strong economy for construction. In the meantime the firm has relied on a healthy backlog of projects and diversification efforts to sustain its business. To that end it entered new geographic markets in 2012 including New Mexico where it is building new dorms at New Mexico State University. It also recently began construction of new schools in El Paso Texas its first in the city. The firm formed a new Criminal Justice Specialization group in 2012 to win courthouse and detention facility work.

Sundt also has focused on making investments in improving technology used in the preconstruction and construction process. It also grew its self-perform work capabilities when it acquired Foley Masonry and Tile Inc. in 2010. Also that year Sundt opened a new office in San Antonio as part of the company's growth plan. The company expanded once again in 2011. It opened new offices to support projects in New Mexico North Carolina and Texas.

Ownership

Sundt Companies is owned by its employees.

LOCATIONS

HQ: THE SUNDT COMPANIES INC
2015 W RIVER RD STE 101, TUCSON, AZ 857041676
Phone: 520 750-4600
Web: WWW.SUNDT.COM

PRODUCTS/OPERATIONS

Selected Projects
Aviation
Commercial buildings
Concrete construction
Courthouses
Federal government
Hospitality
Hospitals & health care
Infrastructure & site development
Juvenile detention facilities
K-12 schools
Mining
Mission critical/Data center
Municipal buildings
Parking structures
Power plants & alternative energy
Prisons
Research & development facilities
Residential
Retail
Roads & bridges
Student housing & dormitories
Universities & community colleges
Water & wastewater treatment

Selected Services
Build-to-suit
Construction manager at risk (CMAR)
Construction/program manager
Design-bid-build/general contractor (DBB)
Preconstruction
Self-perform contracting

COMPETITORS

Austin Industries	McCarthy Building
CORE Construction	Meadow Valley
Charles Pankow	O' Neil Industries
Builders	Peter Kiewit Sons'
DPR Construction	Swinerton
Granite Construction	Tutor Perini
Hunt Construction	Weitz
Kitchell	

HISTORICAL FINANCIALS

Company Type: Private

Income Statement

FYE: September 30

	REVENUE ($ mil.)	NET INCOME ($ mil.)	NET PROFIT MARGIN	EMPLOYEES
09/14	823	0	—	1,500
09/13	896	0	—	—
09/12	0	0	—	—
09/11	0	0	—	—
Annual Growth	—	—	—	—

2014 Year-End Financials

Return on assets: 15.6%
Return on equity: —
Current ratio: 0.80
Cash ($ mil.): 31

THE SUSAN G KOMEN BREAST CANCER FOUNDATION INC

Susan G. Komen For the Cure is dedicated to fighting breast cancer through education research screening and treatment programs. One of its well known fundraisers is an annual 5-K foot race called the Komen Race for the Cure which is conducted in numerous locations across the US and in other countries. The organization also operates a national help line and a website. Since its founding Komen for the Cure has invested more than $1.7 billion on screening education treatment and psychosocial support programs including more than $800 million to medical research as part of a broad campaign to combat breast cancer.

Geographic Reach

The organization operates in than 30 countries worldwide.

Operations

Susan G. Komen is the world's largest breast cancer organization funding more breast cancer research than any other nonprofit while providing real-time help to those facing the disease.

Financial Performance

The organization's revenues declined by 18% in 2013 primarily due to the decline in contribution revenues and Race for the Cure and 3 Days Walk series revenues.

Susan G. Komen's net assets decreased by $12.28 million (to $186.4 million) in 2013 was primarily due to a drop in revenues.

Strategy

The organization's fundraising has suffered in recent years after news of a plan to quit offering grants to Planned Parenthood broke in early 2012. Although it was quickly reversed the controversial decision led to the exit of several executives and a decline in a number of people taking part in its fundraising Race for the Cure events across the US. Current leadership is hoping to rebound and rebuild participation levels in upcoming fundraising races.

Company Background

Founded in 1982 by Nancy Brinker the organization is named in the memory of Brinker's sister Susan who died of breast cancer in 1980 at age 36. Brinker a breast cancer survivor herself promised her sister she would do everything she could to end breast cancer. Brinker stepped down as CEO in 2013.

EXECUTIVES

President and CEO, Judith A. Salerno
Chief Revenue and Marketing Officer, Norm Bowling
CFO, Bob Green
VP Information Technology, Eric Montgomery
Senior Vice President Affiliate Network, Carol Corcoran
Vice President, Julie Teer
Vice President, Nancy Macgregor
Chair, Linda Custard
Board Member, John Raffaelli
Board Member Board Of Directors, Elle Peji
Board Member, Fausta Nazaire
Board Of Directors Vice Chair 2014, D B Wienke
Board Member, Nathalie Johnson
Board Member, Jan Franke
Auditors: ERNST & YOUNG US LLP BIRMINGH

LOCATIONS

HQ: THE SUSAN G KOMEN BREAST CANCER FOUNDATION INC
5005 LYNDON B JOHNSON FWY # 250, DALLAS, TX 752446100
Phone: 972 855-1600
Web: WWW.KOMEN.ORG

PRODUCTS/OPERATIONS

2013 Spending

	% of total
Education	38
Screening	20
Research	18
Fundrasing	11
Treatment	7
Administration	6
Total	**100**

HISTORICAL FINANCIALS

Company Type: Private

Income Statement

FYE: March 31

	REVENUE ($ mil.)	NET INCOME ($ mil.)	NET PROFIT MARGIN	EMPLOYEES
03/09	159	3	2.2%	260
03/07	307	38	12.5%	—
03/06	0	0	—	—
Annual Growth	—	—	—	—

2009 Year-End Financials

Return on assets: —
Return on equity: 2.2%
Current ratio: 0.60
Cash ($ mil.): 117

THE TOLEDO HOSPITAL

One of the region's largest acute-care facilities The Toledo Hospital provides medical care to the residents of northwestern Ohio and southeastern Michigan. Boasting nearly 800 beds the facility offers several specialties and services including the Jobst Vascular Center which provides cardiac and vascular services in conjunction with The University of Michigan. The Toledo Hospital which shares a medical complex with the Toledo Children's Hospital also operates trauma emergency outpatient arthritis sleep disorder and women's health centers. The Toledo Hospital is a member of Toledo-based ProMedica Health System a mission-based not-for-profit healthcare organization formed in 1986.

Geographic Reach

The Toledo Hospital serves the residents of a 27-county area consisting of northwest Ohio and southeast Michigan.

Operations

The health care facility has expanded its footprint in Toledo in recent years. Besides its primary hospital it operates a stroke unit the Jobst Vascular Center a medical complex with the Toledo Children's Hospital and centers devoted to trauma emergencies arthritis sleep disorders and women's health. The Toledo Hospital and the Toledo Children's Hospital operate the Renaissance a 10-story medical complex that has enabled the pair to expand capacity with private rooms intensive and intermediate care units and pediatric hematology and oncology services.

Strategy

To address the needs of area residents The Toledo Hospital in late 2012 rolled out a program that makes a cardiologist available 24 hours a day seven days a week. It's the only hospital in the region to provide this service. In early 2012 the hospital opened a 20-bed stroke unit and a new 15-bed neuro intensive care unit on a newly developed floor of its Renaissance tower.

EXECUTIVES

Director Jobst Vascular Center, Anthony J. Comerota
Director Media Relations ProMedica Health System, Tedra White
President, Kevin Webb
Auditors: DELOITTE TAX LLP INDIANAPOLIS

LOCATIONS

HQ: THE TOLEDO HOSPITAL
2142 N COVE BLVD, TOLEDO, OH 436063896
Phone: 419 291-4000
Web: WWW.PROMEDICA.ORG

PRODUCTS/OPERATIONS

Selected Services
Arthritis and Osteoporosis Center
Bariatric Surgery
Behavioral Health and Psychiatric Services
Breast Care Center
Cancer Care
Critical Care
Diabetes
Dialysis
Emergency Services
Endoscopy Services
Fertility Services
Heart Care
Hemophilia Outpatient Clinic
Hyperbaric Medicine
Laboratory Services
Lactation Services
Maternal - Fetal Medicine
Mom & Me Boutique
Neurology
Neurophysiology
OccuHealth
Orthopaedics
Outpatient Surgery
Palliative Care
Radiology / Imaging Services
Rehabilitation Services
Respiratory Care
Sleep Medicine
Surgical Services
Trauma Services
 Urology /
Vascular Services
Women' s Services

COMPETITORS

Chelsea Community
 Hospital
Firelands Regional
 Health System
Mercy Health Partners
 Toledo
Oakwood Healthcare
Sylvania Franciscan
 Health

Tenet Healthcare
Trinity Health (Novi)
University of Toledo
 Medical Center
University of Michigan
 Health System

HISTORICAL FINANCIALS
Company Type: Private

Income Statement
FYE: December 31

	REVENUE ($ mil.)	NET INCOME ($ mil.)	NET PROFIT MARGIN	EMPLOYEES
12/09	635	19	3.0%	5,586
12/08	548	33	6.1%	—
12/05	518	28	5.5%	—
12/04	23	0	—	—
Annual Growth	93.6%	—	—	—

2009 Year-End Financials
Return on assets: —
Return on equity: 3.0%
Current ratio: 0.20
Cash ($ mil.): 30

THE TRUSTEES OF THE SMITH COLLEGE

Girl Power abounds at Smith. The nation's largest liberal arts college for women Smith College provides 1000 courses in some 50 academic areas including the arts humanities languages sciences and social sciences. It enrolls nearly 2900 undergraduate students and employs about 300 professors. Annually nearly half of Smith juniors study abroad. Founded in 1871 by Sophia Smith (who left funds in her will to create a women's college) and her minister John Greene the school also offers graduate degrees in areas such as education social work and fine arts. Smith's notable alumna include chef Julia Child author and political commentator Molly Ivins and feminist icon Gloria Steinem.

EXECUTIVES

Vice President Finance And Administration, Ruth Constantine
Vice President, Ileana Streinu
Vice President Advancement, Karin George
Secretary Receptionist Clark Science Center Office, Daryl Jett
Auditors: KPMG LLP HARTFORD CT

LOCATIONS

HQ: THE TRUSTEES OF THE SMITH COLLEGE
1 CHAPIN WAY, NORTHAMPTON, MA 010636302
Phone: 413 585-2700
Web: WWW.SMITH.EDU

HISTORICAL FINANCIALS
Company Type: Private

Income Statement
FYE: June 30

	REVENUE ($ mil.)	NET INCOME ($ mil.)	NET PROFIT MARGIN	EMPLOYEES
06/13	219	155	70.8%	1,300
06/12	218	(37)	—	—
06/11*	206	221	107.4%	—
12/08	0	0	—	—
Annual Growth	327.1%	—	—	—

*Fiscal year change

2013 Year-End Financials
Return on assets: —
Return on equity: 70.8%
Current ratio: —
Cash ($ mil.): 17

THE UNIVERSITY OF ARIZONA MEDICAL CENTER

Banner - University Medicine (formerly The University of Arizona Health Network) heals Arizonans and trains Wildcats. It operates three academic medical centers in Phoenix and Tucson serving as the primary teaching hospital for the University of Arizona (UA) and offering medical treatment research and education services. The not-for-profit center provides cancer cardiology geriatric respiratory transplant and dialysis care

as well as general practice and home health services. Specialty services include burn care behavioral health integrative medicine sports medicine and level I trauma care. The network merged with Banner Healthcare in 2015.

Operations
The University of Arizona Health Network merged with Banner Health to create Banner - University Medicine. The division includes three hospitals: Banner - University Medical Center Tucson Banner - University Medical Center South and Banner - University Medical Center Phoenix. The network also includes Banner - University Medical Group (formerly named University of Arizona Physicians) a group of Tucson-based physicians.

Geographic Reach
Banner - University Medicine serves patients in and around Phoenix and Tucson Arizona.

Strategy
In 2015 Banner - University Medical Center Phoenix broke ground on a new $160 million emergency department that will have the capacity to serve an additional 20000 patients each year. Expected to open in mid-2017 the new facility will include 60 private exam rooms a new trauma unit and 40 observation beds.

Company Background
The University of Arizona Health Network was formed in 2010 when University Physicians Hospital merged with University Medical Center.

EXECUTIVES

CFO, Jeff Buehrle
President, Kathy Bollinger
CEO, Tom Dickson
Auditors: RSM MCGLADREY INC MINNEAPOLIS

LOCATIONS

HQ: THE UNIVERSITY OF ARIZONA MEDICAL CENTER
1501 N CAMPBELL AVE, TUCSON, AZ 857240001
Phone: 520 694-0111
Web: WWW.UMCAZ.EDU

COMPETITORS

John C. Lincoln Health
 Network
Northern Arizona
 Healthcare
Phoenix Children' s
 Hospital

Scottsdale Healthcare
Sun Health
Yuma Regional Medical
 Center

HISTORICAL FINANCIALS
Company Type: Private

Income Statement
FYE: June 30

	REVENUE ($ mil.)	NET INCOME ($ mil.)	NET PROFIT MARGIN	EMPLOYEES
06/09	541	0	—	3,000
06/08	512	27	5.3%	—
06/05	708	0	0.0%	—
Annual Growth	(6.5%)	—	—	—

2009 Year-End Financials
Return on assets: 16.3%
Return on equity: —
Current ratio: —
Cash ($ mil.): 3

THE UNIVERSITY OF CHICAGO MEDICAL CENTER

It may have received its official dedication on Halloween but The University of Chicago Medical Center (UCMC) works hard to make visiting the hospital a little less spooky. UCMC is a complex of facilities located on The University of Chicago campus that include the acute care Bernard A. Mitchell Hospital the Comer Children's Hospital a women's health and maternity facility and an outpatient care center. Established in 1927 (and dedicated on Halloween of that year) the complex includes the affiliated University of Chicago Pritzker School of Medicine and forms the clinical arm of The University of Chicago Division of Biological Sciences. UCMC houses about 550 beds.

Geographic Reach

UCMC is located in Hyde Park on the south side of Chicago. Its main medical campus includes the Center for Care and Discovery Comer Children's Hospital Bernard A. Mitchell Hospital Chicago Lying-in Hospital and Duchossois Center for Advanced Medicine. UCMC also manages a network of area physicians and specialty clinics located in Chicago and its suburbs as well as in northwestern Indiana.

Operations

Its Bernard A. Mitchell Hospital includes helicopter transportation operations emergency level-one pediatric trauma services and regional burn and peri-natal units. The roughly 155-bed Comer Children's Hospital offers disease care education and research as well as expanded newborn intensive care services.

UCMC sees some 23000 inpatients and 75000 emergency room visits per year. The hospital is one of the largest providers of uncompensated care in Illinois providing millions of dollars in charity care every year.

As part of the university's Biological Sciences division UCMC operates medical research centers focused on cancer immunology diabetes cardiology and neurology. The cancer center is especially intent on discovering improved treatment and prevention measures using gene and protein-based treatments. The Gwen and Jules Knapp Center for Biomedical Discovery works on discovery programs for a variety of medical conditions including diabetes cancer and pediatrics.

Financial Performance

UCMC experienced a 9% increase in sales to some $1.3 billion in 2012 due to higher net patient service revenues. However the medical center reported a net income loss of some $35.6 million that year due to higher operating expenses from salary wage and benefit increases as well as supply costs physician service expenses other expenses and declined investment returns.

Strategy

UCMC is widening its service offerings through facility construction efforts. It completed a 1.2 million sq. ft. medical research and patient-centered care hospital pavilion on its main campus (named the Center for Care and Discovery) in 2012; the new facility opened its doors to 145 patients the following year.

Also in 2012 UCMC launched a new brand identity that encompasses the academic medical institution's operations: University of Chicago Medicine.

Company Background

First Lady Michelle Obama served as VP for community and external affairs at UCMC; she resigned from her post in early 2009 when she made the move to the White House.

EXECUTIVES

President, Sharon O'Keefe
EVP Medical Affairs; Dean Division of the Biological Sciences and Pritzker School of Medicine, Kenneth S. Polonsky
VP Legal and Government Affairs and General Counsel, Susan S. Sher
COO and Associate Dean, Carolyn S. Wilson
CFO, James M. Watson
Vice President, Jane Hagstrom
Vice President Global Marketing and Product Management, Stacey Brown
Director Of Pharmacy, Jennifer Tryon
Medical Director, John (Jack) Jacobson
Vice President Operations Integration And New Technology Deve, Michael (Mel) Millis
Vice Chairman, Craig J. Duchossois
Vice Chairman, James S. (Jim) Frank
Chairman, Emily Nicklin
Secretary III Medical Staff Executive Comm, Beverly Smith
Auditors: PRICEWATERHOUSECOOPERS LLP CH

LOCATIONS

HQ: THE UNIVERSITY OF CHICAGO MEDICAL CENTER
5841 S MARYLAND AVE MC6098, CHICAGO, IL 606371447
Phone: 773 702-1000
Web: WWW.UCHOSPITALS.EDU

PRODUCTS/OPERATIONS

Selected Services

Cancer
Endocrinology
Gastroenterology
Geriatrics
Heart
Kidney disease
Neurosciences
Orthopaedics
Respiratory disease
Surgery
Transplantation
Women's services

Selected Facilities

Bernard A. Mitchell Hospital
Center for Care and Discovery
Chicago Lying-in Hospital (Maternity and Women's Hospital)
Comer Children's Hospital
Duchossois Center for Advanced Medicine (outpatient care and diagnostics)
Gwen and Jules Knapp Center for Biomedical Discovery
LaRabida Children's Hospital (affiliated facility)
Mercy Hospital (affiliated facility)
University of Chicago Pritzker School of Medicine
Weiss Memorial Hospital (affiliated facility)

COMPETITORS

Advocate Health Care
Alexian Brothers Health System
Covenant Ministries
Elmhurst Memorial Healthcare
Loyola University Health System
Mercy Hospital and Medical Center
NorthShore University HealthSystem
Northwest Community Healthcare
Northwestern Memorial HealthCare
Rush System for Health
Silver Cross Hospital
Sinai Health System
St. Bernard Hospital and Health Care Center

HISTORICAL FINANCIALS

Company Type: Private

Income Statement

FYE: June 30

	REVENUE ($ mil.)	NET INCOME ($ mil.)	NET PROFIT MARGIN	EMPLOYEES
06/09	1,294	(190)	—	5,000
06/08	1,286	38	3.0%	—
06/07	1,092	234	21.5%	—
06/06	861	0	—	—
Annual Growth	**14.5%**	—	—	—

2009 Year-End Financials

Return on assets: —
Return on equity: (-14.7%)
Current ratio: 0.90
Cash ($ mil.): 100

THE UNIVERSITY OF DAYTON

More than 10000 students make the University of Dayton one of the nation's largest Catholic universities and the largest private university in Ohio. The institution offers some 70 majors. Students are recruited on a national basis and from foreign countries. The student population approximates 7300 undergraduate and 3000 graduate students. It has student and faculty ratio of 15:1 and charges tuition and fees of $33400 per annum. Well-known alumni include the late author and columnist Erma Bombeck and Super Bowl-winning NFL coaches Jon Gruden and Chuck Noll.

Geographic Reach

The university's students are primarily from Ohio and nine other Midwestern and Eastern US states.

Financial Performance

In 2012 the university saw a 4% increase in revenues due to higher student tuition and fees. Net income decreased by 120% in 2012 thanks to an increase in expenditures a decline in investment gains in the deficit of amounts designated for current operations a loss in the change in the net unrealized loss on interest rate swap agreements and a change in postretirement benefit obligations.

Company Background

The University of Dayton was founded in 1850 by the Society of Mary (the Marianists).

EXECUTIVES

Vice President Human Resources, Joyce Carter
Assistant Vice President Principal Gifts, Todd Imwalle
Assistant Vice President, Derrick Dukes
Vice President Student Development, William (Bill) Fischer
Assistant Vice President For Student Development, Cari Wallace
Vice President Athletics, Theodore Kissell
Associate Vice President For Athletics, Tim Wabler
Chair Department Of Communication, Donald (Don) Yoder
Assistant Vice President And Treasurer, Phillip (Phil) Chick
Vice President of Information Technology, Raymond Fitz
Director Board Of Directors, Robert Rosenfelder
Assistant Vice President and Treasurer, Philip Chick
Assistant Treasurer and Tax Manager, Ann Garcia
Secretary, Denise Quillen

LOCATIONS

HQ: THE UNIVERSITY OF DAYTON
  300 COLLEGE PARK AVE, DAYTON, OH 454690002
Phone: 937 229-1000
Web: WWW.DINING.UDAYTON.EDU

HISTORICAL FINANCIALS

Company Type: Private

Income Statement

FYE: June 30

	REVENUE ($ mil.)	NET INCOME ($ mil.)	NET PROFIT MARGIN	EMPLOYEES
06/14	460	126	27.4%	4,500
06/13	444	96	21.7%	—
06/12	418	(21)	—	—
06/11	402	0	—	—
Annual Growth	4.6%	—	—	—

2014 Year-End Financials

Return on assets: 3.0%   Cash ($ mil.): 39
Return on equity: 27.4%
Current ratio: —

THE UNIVERSITY OF HARTFORD

While its roots date back to 1877 The University of Hartford wasn't officially chartered until 1957 with the merger of the Hartford Art School the Hartt School of Music and Hillyer College. The modern-day university still has a strong arts and music programs and its Museum of American Political Life is home to what has been called the country's largest private collection of political memorabilia. University of Hartford which operates three campuses in West Hartford has about 7000 students enrolled in more than 80 undergraduate and 30 graduate programs including business nursing and engineering.

Geographic Reach

The University of Hartford's students hail from about 45 states and 50 international countries.

Operations

The University of Hartford consists of seven schools and colleges that offer programs in fields including arts architecture sciences business education nursing health engineering and technology. It employs 350 faculty members and has a student-to-faculty ratio of 13:1.

In addition to higher education the university operates two magnet schools (elementary and high school) on its campus as well as a community service center that coordinates volunteer opportunities for students staff and alumni members. In addition University of Hartford runs engineering design business development and professional development programs that work in partnerships with area businesses.

Hartford alumni include Broadway musical director Timothy Stella actress Marin Ireland and TV writer Kent McCray as well as a number of business entrepreneurs in medical scientific and technology fields.

Strategy

University of Hartford is improving its campus by investing in infrastructure enhancements. It is also working to improve its academic community through faculty recruitment and student recruitment efforts as well as through the development of interdisciplinary mission-centered and transformational learning programs.

EXECUTIVES

President, Walter Harrison
VP Finance and Administration, Arosha Jayawickrema
Provost, Sharon L. Vasquez
Director Media Relations, Dave Isgur
Executive Vice President, Cassandra Fowlie
Assistant Vice President For Student Affairs, Suzanne McNeil
Associate Vice President for Development, Marlisa Simonson
Vice President, Mason Paul
Vice President, Brandon Williams
Vice President, Ato Cudjoe
Finance Vice President, Nateka Scafe
Executive Vice President, Stillman Brown
Public Relations Vice President, Marianne Sayamath
Student Affairs Vice President, Landle Cheng
Academic Vice President, Ross Hart
Vice President Public Relations and Communications, Ben Cohn
Executive Vice President Activities, Rich Hoover
Vice President for Institutional Advancement, Christine Pina
Administrative Assistant Vice President Student Affairs Student Affairs, Marcia Suess
Chairman, Lucille M. Nickerson
Vice Chairman, Dominic Fulco
Vice Chairman, Arnold West
Board Member, Janell Carroll
Board Director, Bin Zhu
Treasurer, Samantha Cormier
Treasurer, Theresa Menhart
Secretary to the Dean Deans Office Department, Patsy Taylor
Auditors: PRICEWATERHOUSECOPPERS LLP HA

LOCATIONS

HQ: THE UNIVERSITY OF HARTFORD
  200 BLOOMFIELD AVE, WEST HARTFORD, CT
  061171599
Phone: 860 768-4393
Web: WWW.ADMISSION.HARTFORD.EDU

PRODUCTS/OPERATIONS

Selected Schools and Colleges

Barney School of Business
College of Arts and Sciences
College of Education Nursing and Health Professions
College of Engineering Technology and Architecture
Hartford Art School
The Hartt School
Hillyer College

HISTORICAL FINANCIALS

Company Type: Private

Income Statement

FYE: June 30

	REVENUE ($ mil.)	NET INCOME ($ mil.)	NET PROFIT MARGIN	EMPLOYEES
06/14	173	23	13.3%	950
06/13	170	21	12.7%	—
06/12	165	(10)	—	—
06/11	165	0	—	—
Annual Growth	1.7%	—	—	—

2014 Year-End Financials

Return on assets: 10.4%   Cash ($ mil.): 46
Return on equity: 13.3%
Current ratio: —

THE UNIVERSITY OF TULSA

If you're "Living on Tulsa Time" and looking for an education then the home of the Golden Hurricanes is the place to be. The University of Tulsa is a private university affiliated with the Presbyterian Church (USA) with an enrollment of about 5000 students. The school offers more than 60 undergraduate and about 35 graduate programs including a dozen doctoral degree programs at colleges of arts and sciences business and engineering and natural sciences. The University of Tulsa was founded in Muskogee in 1882 as the Presbyterian School for Indian Girls and was chartered as Henry Kendall College in 1894. The school moved to Tulsa in 1907 and became The University of Tulsa in 1920.

Operations

The University of Tulsa employs about 300 faculty members and has a student-to-teacher ratio of 12 to 1. About 84% of the students receive financial aid to help cover the annual costs of $35000.

Strategy

As part of its plan to increase enrollment The University of Tulsa in 2014 began construction to create a 300-bed student dormitory that it intends to open for the fall semester of 2015.

EXECUTIVES

Associate Vp And Controller, Michael (Mel) Thesenvitz
Assoc Vice President Enrollment Student Services, Yolanda Taylor
Vice President, Cary Taylor
Administrative Associate to the Executive Vice President, Devra McManus
Vice President Director of Athletics, Derrick Gragg
Vice President, Whitney House
Treasurer, Nicole Coppola
Secretary:, Brooke Boutwell
Auditors: HOGAN TAYLOR LLP TULSA OK

LOCATIONS

HQ: THE UNIVERSITY OF TULSA
  800 TUCKER DR, TULSA, OK 741049700
Phone: 918 631-2000
Web: WWW.UTULSA.EDU

PRODUCTS/OPERATIONS

Selected Colleges

College of Engineering and Natural Sciences
College of Law
Collins College of Business
Graduate School
Henry Kendall College of Arts and Sciences

HISTORICAL FINANCIALS

Company Type: Private

Income Statement

FYE: June 30

	REVENUE ($ mil.)	NET INCOME ($ mil.)	NET PROFIT MARGIN	EMPLOYEES
06/13	271	13	4.8%	1,033
06/12	173	(23)	—	—
06/11	180	134	74.7%	—
06/10	163	0	—	—
Annual Growth	18.5%	—	—	—

2013 Year-End Financials

Return on assets: 9.9%   Cash ($ mil.): 16
Return on equity: 4.8%
Current ratio: 0.20

THE VALLEY HOSPITAL INC

The Valley Hospital is second to none when it comes to its Same-Day Service program. More than one-third of the company's annual patients experience its longstanding continuum of one-day service; fully half the surgeries performed are same-day. The not-for-profit hospital is a 450-bed facility providing general and emergency services to residents of New Jersey's Bergen County. The hospital belongs to the Valley Health System which also includes subsidiaries Valley Home Care and Valley Health Medical Group and is an affiliate member of NewYork-Presbyterian Healthcare. The Valley Hospital New Jersey's second busiest has more than 800 physicians on its medical staff.

Geographic Reach

The hospital serves more than 440000 people in 32 towns in Bergen County and surrounding communities.

Operations

The Valley Hospital is well known for its cardiology cancer maternity and neonatal care programs (including its neonatal ICU). Its key services also include emergency care orthopedics and neurosciences. The hospital's emergency department treated more than 75000 patients in 2013. That year the hospital also admitted more than 49240 patients and the delivered almost 3200 babies.

The Valley Hospital's cardiac service includes a full range of diagnostic and interventional cardiac treatment services including cardiac surgery coronary angioplasty and electrophysiology studies. The hospital is also known for its work in lung cancer diagnosis and treatment radiation oncology (including tomotherapy) chemotherapy and infusion GYN oncology prostate cancer care and other clinical and support services.

Strategy

The medical system is looking to improve its facilities and technology in order to keep up with demand. The Valley Hospital is the first and only hospital in northern New Jersey to offer brain and spinal surgery with a state-of-the-art O-arm® surgical imaging system purchased through a $1 million grant from The Bolger Foundation. In 2012 The Valley Hospital Valley became the first hospital in northern New Jersey to offer the latest breast imaging technology —3D breast tomosynthesis.

That year it also enhanced its capacity to perform minimally invasive surgery with the acquisition of the robotic da Vinci® Surgical System funded by a $1.6 million donation from The Bolger Foundation.In 2012 the hospital opened a new Women's and Children's Resource Center to coordinate wide range of services for women and their families.

EXECUTIVES

Director Of Infection Control, Andrea Aluisi
Auditors: O'CONNOR DAVIES MUNNS & DOBBIN

LOCATIONS

HQ: THE VALLEY HOSPITAL INC
223 N VAN DIEN AVE, RIDGEWOOD, NJ 074502736
Phone: 201 447-8000
Web: WWW.VALLEYHEALTH.COM

PRODUCTS/OPERATIONS

Selected Services
Adoption Screening and Evaluation Program
Ambulatory Infusion Center
Anticoagulation Management Service
Autism Services

Auxiliary
Barrett' s Esophagus Center
Bariatric Surgery
Bereavement Services
Biplane
Bladder Cancer Care
Breast Center
Cancer Care
Capsule Endoscopy
Cardiac MRI
Cardiac Rehabilitation
Cardiac Surgery
Cardiology
Center for Childbirth
Kireker Center for Child Development
Center for Metabolic and Weight Loss Surgery
Center for Family Education
Center for Women' s Heart Health
Center for Youth Fitness
Clinical Trials Oncology
Clinical Trials Cardiology
Colonoscopy
Community Resources
Complementary Medicine
Concussion Management Program
Continence Services
Cosmetic Laser Treatment
Critical Care
Diabetes Support Services
Diagnostic Imaging
Doula Program
Emergency Services
Emergency Services Pediatric
Employee Recognition
Endoscopic Ultrasound
Epilepsy Monitoring Program Adult
Epilepsy Center Pediatric
ERCP
Esophagogastroduodenoscopy (EGD)
Extended Care

COMPETITORS

Barnabas Health
Bergen Regional Medical
Englewood Hospital and Medical Center
Hackensack University Medical Center
Jersey City Medical Center
Meridian Health
Newton Medical Center
Raritan Bay Medical Center
Robert Wood Johnson University Hospital at Rahway

HISTORICAL FINANCIALS

Company Type: Private

Income Statement

FYE: December 31

	REVENUE ($ mil.)	NET INCOME ($ mil.)	NET PROFIT MARGIN	EMPLOYEES
12/09	587	44	7.6%	2,900
12/08	531	33	6.4%	—
12/06	446	28	6.3%	—
12/05	419	0	—	—
Annual Growth	8.8%	—	—	—

2009 Year-End Financials

Return on assets: —
Return on equity: 7.6%
Current ratio: 0.30
Cash ($ mil.): —

THE WALDINGER CORPORATION

The Waldinger Corporation may actually do most of its work before the walls are even up. The company is an electrical mechanical and sheet metal contractor that primarily serves US customers across the Midwest and Southeast.

Through its work in more than 40 states Waldinger designs fabricates installs and maintains HVAC refrigeration electrical plumbing and piping for commercial institutional and industrial clients. Waldinger also operates a division devoted to the food service industry. The company has offices in Iowa Kansas Missouri and Nebraska. Austrian tinsmith Harry Waldinger founded the company as Capital City Tin Shop in 1906.

Geographic Reach

From its headquarters in Des Moines Iowa Waldinger caters to clients nationwide through its offices in the Midwestern states of Iowa Kansas Missouri and Nebraska.

Sales and Marketing

Waldinger serves several industries such as commercial industrial research and education government and civic healthcare and hospitality.

Financial Performance

The contractor generates about $200 million in annual revenues.

Operations

Waldinger has worked on projects throughout most of the US covering more than 40 states. Its projects portfolio includes a handful of nuclear power plants ethanol plants the Houston Astrodome the Louisiana Superdome and Cape Kennedy's Vehicle Assembly Building.

For commercial clients Waldinger works on corporate headquarters data centers office buildings and retail outlets. Industrial projects typically include alternative energy manufacturing water and waste water. Projects in the research and education sector include laboratories universities and schools and residence halls. Waldinger also serves the healthcare market through projects for hospitals and clinics and assisted living facilities as well as for arenas and casinos as part of the sports and entertainment market.

Strategy

The company has worked in recent years to expand its business through partnership agreements.

EXECUTIVES

Vice President, Dave Miller
Division President, Blaine Wilcoxson
Auditors: MCGLADREY & PULLEN LLP DES MO

LOCATIONS

HQ: THE WALDINGER CORPORATION
2601 BELL AVE, DES MOINES, IA 503211189
Phone: 515 284-1911
Web: WWW.WALDINGER.COM

PRODUCTS/OPERATIONS

Selected Capabilities
Pre-Construction
Design
Sheet Metal
Plumbing
Piping
Fabrication
Electrical
Service and Maintenance

Selected Sectors
Commercial
Healthcare
Hospitality
Industrial
Research and education
Sports and entertainment

COMPETITORS

ACCO
Duke Construction
EMCOR
F.A. Wilhelm
Fluor
Limbach Facility Services

Market & Johnson
MasTec
Siemens AG
Yates Companies

HISTORICAL FINANCIALS

Company Type: Private

Income Statement

FYE: December 31

	REVENUE ($ mil.)	NET INCOME ($ mil.)	NET PROFIT MARGIN	EMPLOYEES
12/13	207	0	—	900
12/12	186	0	—	—
12/11	160	0	—	—
12/10	155	0	—	—
Annual Growth	10.0%	—	—	—

2013 Year-End Financials

Return on assets: 9.4% Cash ($ mil.): 31
Return on equity: —
Current ratio: 1.90

THE WALSH GROUP LTD

The Walsh Group erects walls halls malls and more. Operating through subsidiaries Walsh Construction and Archer Western Contractors the family-owned group provides design/build general contracting and construction services for industrial public and commercial projects. Walsh provides complete project management services from demolition and planning to general contracting and finance. The company is involved in the construction of bridges highways water treatment facilities airports hotels convention centers correctional facilities and commercial industrial and residential buildings. It also renovates and restores buildings. The company was founded in 1898 by Matthew Myles Walsh.

Operations

Walsh Group frequently ranks within the top largest contractors in the US on Engineering News-Record's Top Contractors lists. In 2015 it ranked as ENR's 13th largest builder in the US. In 2014 it ranked as the nation's largest bridge builder the largest water treatment and desalination plant builder the second largest correctional facility domestic heavy contractor the fourth-largest transportation-sector contractor the 11th largest contractor by new contracts and the 35th largest contractor working abroad.

Geographic Reach

Walsh Construction is based in Chicago and has 19 regional offices nationwide. Archer Western is headquartered in Atlanta and has seven regional offices. Beyond the continental US the Walsh Group has operations in Hawaii Alaska and Puerto Rico.Sales and MarketingWalsh Group mostly works on projects in the commercial building transportation aviation water industrial and power sectors. These include wastewater and water treatment plants rapid transit highway and bridgework educational facilities warehouse/distribution facilities athletic facilities correctional facilities and offices.The company continued in 2016 its long history working with Travelers Casualty and Surety Company of America as its bonding company and Bank of America as its primary bank.

Financial Performance

One of America's largest private companies Walsh Group reported its annual revenue grew 12% to $4.6 billion during 2014 up from $4.1 billion in 2013. Its annual revenues are up nearly 30% since 2007 and have more than doubled since 2004 when they were at $1.95 billion.

Strategy

Walsh's geographic diversity and its wide range of project experience has helped it remain success-ful in recessions and in good times. Federal contracts have helped Walsh survive during times when private-sector building and construction were down.Walsh Group's aviation experience has grown substantially over the past decades. Indeed Walsh Group has performed work at some of the nation's largest airports including Chicago's O'Hare and Midway airports as well as Tom Bradley International Airport in Los Angeles. Notable projects for the firm include the $28 million 218-foot Air Traffic Control Tower at Chicago O'Hare (completed in early 2015; the Air Traffic Control Tower at Charlotte Douglas International Airport (planned in 2015); and the $1.3 billion international terminal work at Lax Tom Bradley International (completed in December 2013).The Walsh Group's Senior Housing Group also continued in 2016 to take advantage of long-term population trends in the US having completed more than $500 million in senior housing contracts for public and private sector clients. The unit has been working on renovations as well as new construction of independent living assisted living and skilled care facilities.

Company Background

In 2012 Walsh Group acquired California-based R&L Brosamer which specializes in heavy highway and other transportation projects. R&L Brosamer often works on projects for Bay Area Rapid Transit California Department of Transportation and Los Angeles World Airports. The deal helped Walsh strengthen its presence in California and bordering states including Nevada and Arizona.In 2011 Walsh was awarded its first overseas embassy project a $200 million contract to build the New American Embassy at Oslo Norway.

EXECUTIVES

Co-Chairman and CEO, Matthew M. (Matt) Walsh
President Building Division, Michael Whelan
President Heavy Civil Division, Don Gillis
CFO, Tim Gerken
VP Heavy/Civil Division, Daniel Walsh
VP Corporate Equipment, Michael Gibbons
VP Building Division, Matthew Walsh
President Walsh Construction, Sean Walsh
Co-Chairman, Daniel J. Walsh
Auditors: WOLF & COMPANY LLP OAKBROOK T

LOCATIONS

HQ: THE WALSH GROUP LTD
929 W ADAMS ST, CHICAGO, IL 606073021
Phone: 312 563-5400
Web: WWW.WALSHGROUP.COM

PRODUCTS/OPERATIONS

Projects

Airports
Athletic facilities
Bridges
Conference centers
Correctional facilities
Data centers
Educational facilities
Entertainment
Government
Health care
High rise residential
Highways and bridges
Hotels
Interiors
Laboratories
Parking garages
Renovations
Retail centers
Senior housing
Treatment plants
Warehouse and distribution

COMPETITORS

Bechtel	Jacobs Engineering
Black & Veatch	James McHugh

Brasfield & Gorrie	Lane Construction
C. G. Schmidt	MWH Global
CH2M HILL	McCarthy Building
Flatiron Construction	Peter Kiewit Sons'
Fluor	Skanska
Granite Construction	TIC Holdings
Hunt Companies	Turner Corporation
Hunt Construction	Vecellio & Grogan

HISTORICAL FINANCIALS

Company Type: Private

Income Statement

FYE: December 31

	REVENUE ($ mil.)	NET INCOME ($ mil.)	NET PROFIT MARGIN	EMPLOYEES
12/10	3,462	186	5.4%	5,000
12/09	3,316	191	5.8%	—
Annual Growth	4.4%	(3.0%)	—	—

2010 Year-End Financials

Return on assets: 9.8% Cash ($ mil.): 656
Return on equity: 5.4%
Current ratio: 1.50

THE WALTERS GROUP

Auditors: BDO USA LLP LAS VEGAS NV

LOCATIONS

HQ: THE WALTERS GROUP
2030 E FLAMINGO RD # 290, LAS VEGAS, NV
891190818
Phone: 702 450-8001

HISTORICAL FINANCIALS

Company Type: Private

Income Statement

FYE: December 31

	ASSETS ($ mil.)	NET INCOME ($ mil.)	INCOME AS % OF ASSETS	EMPLOYEES
12/12	382	(0)	—	20
12/05	288	12	4.5%	—
12/04	229	27	11.9%	—
12/02	135	0	—	—
Annual Growth	11.0%	—	—	—

2012 Year-End Financials

Return on assets: — Sales ($ mil): 426
Return on equity: (-0.1%)

THE WASHINGTON UNIVERSITY

Washington University also known as Washington University in St. Louis (WUSTL) is the gateway to higher education for more than 13000 students. Founded in 1853 the independent university offers 90 bachelor's master's and doctoral degrees and has about 3400 faculty members. It offers approximately 1500 courses in fields such as arts and sciences business design and visual arts engineering law medicine and social work. WUSTL which has multiple campuses in and near the city of St. Louis also offers associate degree and continuing education programs. The affiliated Washington University Medical Center is an acute-care hospital that also provides educational training and research services.

Operations

The Medical Campus conducts extensive collaborative studies between students faculty and hospital staff as well as external institutions. Areas of research include genome sequencing of cancer patients and children's developmental studies. The 2000-acre Tyson Research Center outside the city is a biological field station that conducts environmental studies and research activities including renewable energy and sustainability programs some of which is coordinated with outside groups.

The university has an 8:1 student-to-faculty ratio. Its libraries contain more than 3.6 million books journals and other print materials and have access to more than 65000 electronic journals and a half million e-books.

In the academic year ending spring 2015 annual undergraduate educational costs totaled $45700.

Geographic Reach

In addition to the main 170-acre Danforth Campus in St. Louis WUSTL's facilities include the nearby 165-acre Medical Campus (housing the School of Medicine and the hospital facilities). Other operations include three smaller satellite academic campuses and music research and art centers in the greater St. Louis area.

Financial Performance

In fiscal 2015 revenue increased 9% to $2.7 billion on higher tuition and fees endowment spending distribution gifts and patient services. However a decline in non-operating revenue such as investment returns led to a 71% drop in net income which fell to $270 million.

Cash flow from operations spiked 522% to $104 million as less cash was used in net gains on investments.

Strategy

WUSTL has made efforts to extend its collaborations with third parties which can help bring in academic and research funds. In addition the university has worked to attract more government research grants in recent years. It is also upgrading some classroom and student facilities as well as hiring more experienced teachers and medical staff members to maintain its tuition auxiliary enterprise (lodging and vending) health services and research income expectations.

EXECUTIVES

Executive Vice Chancellor Administration, Henry S. Webber

Executive Vice Chancellor Alumni and Development Programs, David T. Blasingame

Executive Vice Chancellor and General Counsel, Michael R. Cannon

Chancellor, Mark S. Wrighton, age 66

Vice Chancellor Finance and CFO, Barbara A. Feiner

Executive Vice Chancellor Medical Affairs and Dean School of Medicine, Larry J. Shapiro

Dean Olin Business School, Mahendra R. Gupta

Dean Sam Fox School of Design and Visual Arts, Carmon Colangelo

Dean George Warren Brown School of Social Work, Edward F. Lawlor

Dean School of Law, Kent D. Syverud

Provost and Executive Vice Chancellor Academic Affairs, H. Holden Thorp, age 51

Dean School of Engineering and Applied Science, Ralph S. Quatrano

Dean Faculty of Arts and Sciences, Barbara A. Schaal

Dean College of Arts and Sciences, Jennifer R. Smith

Dean Graduate School of Arts and Sciences, Richard J. Smith

CIO, Michael P. (Mike) Caputo

Director Of Admissions, Nanette Tambourini

Head Nurse, Barbara Faszl
Clinic Manager, Jeanne Thoma
Vice Chairman, John F. McDonnell, age 76
Chairman, David W. Kemper, age 64
Vice Chairman, Craig D. Schnuck, age 66
Vice Chairman, Stephen F. Brauer, age 70
Treasurer, Amy Kweskin
Secretary Football Department, Pat Smith
Auditors: PRICEWATERHOUSECOOPERS LLP S

LOCATIONS

HQ: THE WASHINGTON UNIVERSITY
1 BROOKINGS DR, SAINT LOUIS, MO 631304899
Phone: 314 935-8566
Web: WWW.WUSTL.EDU

PRODUCTS/OPERATIONS

2015 Sales

	% of total
Patient service	36
Grants	14
Tuition & fees	13
Endowment spending distribution	10
Gifts	7
Educational	6
Others	14
Total	**100**

Selected Schools and Colleges

College of Arts & Sciences
  Graduate School of Arts & Sciences
  University College and Summer School (Arts & Sciences)
George Warren Brown School of Social Work
Sam Fox School of Design & Visual Arts
School of Engineering & Applied Science
School of Law
School of Medicine
Olin Business School

COMPETITORS

Bucknell University
Missouri State University
Saint Louis University
Southeast Missouri State University
University of Missouri

HISTORICAL FINANCIALS

Company Type: Private

Income Statement

FYE: June 30

	REVENUE ($ mil.)	NET INCOME ($ mil.)	NET PROFIT MARGIN	EMPLOYEES
06/14	2,472	917	37.1%	9,600
06/13	2,393	557	23.3%	—
06/12	2,307	(49)	—	—
06/11	2,245	0	—	—
Annual Growth	**3.3%**	—	—	—

2014 Year-End Financials

Return on assets: 14.5%   Cash ($ mil.): 116
Return on equity: 37.1%
Current ratio: —

THE WATERBURY HOSPITAL

Where do broken hearts go? Waterbury Hospital hopes it's to its cardiologists. The community teaching hospital serving western Connecticut has been named one of the top hospitals in the nation for cardiac intervention. Of course hearts aren't the only body parts Waterbury Hospital treats; the full-service facility has nearly 370 beds and offers services that include behavioral health care an orthopedic center and an outpatient surgery center. Waterbury Hospital founded in 1890 forms the cornerstone of the Greater Waterbury Health Network which provides a range of outpatient health services from nursing care to hospice imaging and lab services. Prospect Medical Holdings is buying Waterbury Hospital.

Operations

As a teaching facility Waterbury Hospital is affiliated with the Yale School of Medicine the University of Connecticut School of Medicine and Connecticut Children's Medical Center. The hospital has been named a top provider of joint replacement surgery in Connecticut as well as one of the first hospitals in the nation to offer free HIV testing in its emergency room.

It boasts more than 400 physicians 13400 admissions 1125 births and 168400 outpatient visits.

Waterbury Hospital specializes in providing joint replacement services a Family Birthing Center Urgent Care and Cardiology. Its Harold Leever Regional Cancer Center operates through a partnership with St. Mary's Hospital. Its Heart Center of Greater Waterbury is a joint venture partnership between Waterbury Hospital St. Mary's Hospital and the University of Connecticut Medical Center.

Geographic Reach

Waterbury Hospital serves a regional population of about 280000 across Waterbury and its 11 surrounding communities in southern Connecticut's Fairfield County and New York State's Westchester County.

Strategy

Waterbury Hospital serves a large population of government-funded patients. More than 60% of its patients are covered by Medicare and Medicaid while only about 36% of its patient base is insured by private commercial payors. That can have far-reaching financial effects on a hospital since government payors tend to reimburse the hospital at a lower rate per patient than commercial payors.

In 2015 Waterbury Hospital agreed to be acquired by private health care company Prospect Medical Holdings; the deal will convert the hospital to a for-profit facility. (Recently passed legislation has made it easier for hospitals to operate on a for-profit basis in Connecticut.) The acquisition should help the struggling hospital strengthen its service offerings and reduce costs. The acquisition agreement follows on the heels of a couple of failed transactions —the hospital was nearly acquired by Tenet Healthcare in 2014 and a previous plan to partner up with other health care providers likewise fell apart.

EXECUTIVES

Pharmacy Manager, Saul Dunn
Director Of Health Information, Patricia Gentil
Vice President Of Operations, Thomas Burke
Medical Director, Scott Kurtzman
Auditors: MARCUM LLP HARTFORD CT

LOCATIONS

HQ: THE WATERBURY HOSPITAL
64 ROBBINS ST, WATERBURY, CT 067082600
Phone: 203 573-6000
Web: WWW.WATERBURYHOSPITAL.ORG

PRODUCTS/OPERATIONS

Selected Medical Services

Advanced Care Services
Auxiliary
Behavioral Health
Emergency Department
Family Birthing Center
Health Center Library
Laboratory Services
Orthopedic Services

Reed Cardiology
Sleep Lab
Specialty Programs & Services
The Hospitalist Program
The Stroke Center
Waterbury Hospital Pharmacy Program

COMPETITORS

Baystate Medical Center	MidHudson Regional Hospital
Bridgeport Hospital	MidState Medical Center
Bristol Hospital	
CSH	New Milford Hospital
Connecticut Children's Medical Center	Westchester Medical Center
Greenwich Hospital	Western Connecticut Health Network
Griffin Health	
Hartford Health Care	Yale New Haven Health System
Hospital of Central Connecticut	
Mather Memorial Hospital	

HISTORICAL FINANCIALS

Company Type: Private

Income Statement

FYE: September 30

	REVENUE ($ mil.)	NET INCOME ($ mil.)	NET PROFIT MARGIN	EMPLOYEES
09/13	207	(2)	—	1,625
09/09	251	(2)	—	—
09/08	237	(7)	—	—
Annual Growth	**(2.7%)**	—	—	—

2013 Year-End Financials

Return on assets: 10.0%
Return on equity: (-1.1%)
Current ratio: 1.60

Cash ($ mil.): 23

THE WHITING-TURNER CONTRACTING COMPANY

Whiting-Turner Contracting provides construction management general contracting and design/build services primarily for large commercial institutional and infrastructure projects conducted across the US. A key player in retail construction the employee-owned company also undertakes such projects as biotech cleanrooms theme parks historical restorations senior living residences educational facilities stadiums and corporate headquarters. Clients past and present include the US military AT&T General Motors and Texas A&M University. Whiting-Turner Contracting operates some 30 locations nationwide.

Geographic Reach

The company has offices in California Colorado Connecticut Delaware Florida Georgia Maryland Massachusetts Missouri Nevada New Jersey New York North Carolina Ohio Pennsylvania Texas Virginia and Washington DC.

Operations

Whiting-Turner Contracting's project portfolio includes the Joseph B. Whitehead Building at Emory University Vanderbilt Hall at Yale University projects at Universal Studios theme park and a vaccine facility at Chesapeake Biological Laboratories. Projects in the firm's hometown of Baltimore have included the city's convention center and the football stadium for the Baltimore Ravens.

More recent projects include the Horseshoe Casino Cleveland University of Maryland Baltimore County (UMBC) Performing Arts & Humanities Naval Facilities Engineering Command (NAV-FAC) Jacksonville Sentara Princess Anne Hospital Norwalk Community College Texas A&M University at Galveston Mary Moody Northen Student Center renovation Opry Mills the College of Business & Economics Vinson Hall Parking Garage a Coastal Studies Institute facility a Blue Diamond Growers building and a USPS Call Center.

Strategy

The company prefers to grow organically instead of making many acquisitions. It has been steadily expanding by opening new offices in places such as California Texas and Virginia.

In 2013 Whiting-Turner Contracting was awarded a $38.6 million contract for energy efficiency improvements at Marine Corps Base Camp Lejeune North Carolina. That year it was also awarded a $10.5 million project for an armory at Marine Corps Air Station Cherry Point in the same state.

In 2012 The Jackson Laboratory selected of Whiting-Turner Contracting to manage the design development phase of Institute for Genomic Medicine in Farmington Connecticut. The new facility on a 17-acres site will open in 2014.

Company Background

G.W.C. Whiting and LeBaron Turner classmates at MIT founded the company in 1909 to build sewer lines.

EXECUTIVES

VP Richmond, Dani Niccolucci
SVP Allentown, Jack DaSilva
Division VP Fort Lauderdale, Robert (Rob) Mitchell
Division VP Delaware and Maryland, James (Jim) Martini
SVP District of Columbia, Richard L. Vogel
Division VP Pleasanton, Troy Caldwell
SVP Irvine, Len Cannatelli
SVP Baltimore, Gino J. Gemignani
Division VP Dallas, Espen S. Brooks
VP Bridgewater, Chris Martinson
SVP Atlanta, Keith Douglas
VP, Daniel (Dan) Bauer
VP Boston, Kevin Shields
Division VP Las Vegas, Paul Schmitt
Division VP Chantilly, Kempton C. Haile
VP Tampa, Brent A. Voyles
Senior Project Manager (Denver), Mark Faul
VP San Diego, Steven Likins
VP Orlando, Robert Minutoli
Division VP Raleigh, Chris Carlson
VP White Plains, David Brickley
VP San Antonio, Daryl Steinbeck
VP Norfolk, John Berotti
Senior Project Manager Sacramento, Jack Stackalis
VP Cleveland, Jeff Maeder
Regional Manager Kansas City, Adam Eshelbrenner
Regional Manager Charlotte, Chris Woods
Regional Manager Houston, Michael Browning
President and CEO, Timothy J. Regan, age 59
Vice President, John Giovannone
Sr V Pres, Frank R Palmer
Vice President, Scott McMahon
Vice President, Ted Border
Vice President, Steve Lambertson
Division Vice President, Samuel (Sam) Wells
Vice President, Tony Moag
Vice President, David McGinnis
Vice President, Sam Abutaleb
Vice President San Diego, Steve Likins
Vice President, J Scott Breig

LOCATIONS

HQ: THE WHITING-TURNER CONTRACTING COMPANY
300 E JOPPA RD STE 800, BALTIMORE, MD 212863047
Phone: 410 821-1100
Web: WWW.WHITING-TURNER.COM

Selected Locations

Maryland - Baltimore (Headquarters)
California
California - Los Angeles
California
California
California - San Diego
Colorado
Connecticut - New Haven
Delaware -
District of Columbia
Florida - Ft. Lauderdale
Florida -
Florida -
Georgia -
Maryland -
Massachuse
Missouri - Kansas City
Nevada - Las Vegas
New Jersey
New York - White Plains
North Caro
North Caro
Ohio - Cle
Pennsylvan
Texas - Da
Texas - Ho
Texas - San Antonio
Virginia -
Virginia -
Virginia -

PRODUCTS/OPERATIONS

Selected Services

Construction management
    Agency
    At-risk
Design/build
General contracting
Preconstruction

Selected Markets

Biotechnology and pharmaceutical
Cleanroom and high-technology
Education
Entertainment
Federal/military
Food/beverage distribution
Health care
Historical restoration
Industrial and manufacturing
Interiors
Life sciences
Lodging and hospitality
Mission critical facilities
Mixed use
Offices and headquarters
Parking garages
Restaurants
Retail
Senior living
Sports
Sustainable
Technology
    Microelectronics
    Nano
Theme parks
Utilities
Warehouse and distribution

COMPETITORS

Barton Malow	J.E. Dunn Construction Group
Bechtel	
Choate Construction	Jacobs Engineering
Clark Construction Group	Kitchell
	McCarthy Building
DPR Construction	Peter Kiewit Sons'
Fisher Development	Skanska
Fluor	Suffolk Construction
Gilbane	Swinerton

Hensel Phelps Construction	Turner Corporation
Hoffman Corporation	Tutor Perini
	Weitz

HISTORICAL FINANCIALS
Company Type: Private

Income Statement
FYE: December 31

	REVENUE ($ mil.)	NET INCOME ($ mil.)	NET PROFIT MARGIN	EMPLOYEES
12/12	3,781	56	1.5%	1,839
12/11	3,897	57	1.5%	—
Annual Growth	(3.0%)	(1.9%)	—	—

2012 Year-End Financials
Return on assets: 22.8% Cash ($ mil.): 53
Return on equity: 1.5%
Current ratio: 0.70

THE WICHITA STATE UNIVERSITY

You are still in Kansas if you attend Wichita State University (WSU). The state-supported school enrolls more than 15000 students with more than 89% hailing from Kansas. Along with its main campus WSU provides classes at four additional campuses. The school offers 70 undergraduate degrees in more than 200 subjects. Its Graduate School offers more than 40 master's programs a dozen doctoral degree programs an educational specialist program and more than 20 graduate certificate programs as well as research opportunities. WSU colleges include business education engineering fine arts health professions and liberal arts and sciences. The school was founded in 1895 as a Congregational institution.

Geographic Reach

Besides its 330-acre main campus in Wichita Kansas WSU counts four other campuses that serve its traditional and non-traditional student body.

Operations

WSU offers undergraduate and graduate degrees from half a dozen colleges including Fairmount College of Liberal Arts and Sciences W. Frank Barton School of Business College of Education College of Engineering College of Fine Arts and College of Health Professions.

Enrolling students from 110 countries WSU employs some 450 full-time faculty members (75% of which hold the highest degrees in their field) and boasts a student/faculty ratio of 20:1.

The main campus is also home to a roughly 150 student organizations that cover a wide range of topics –from academics and multicultural interests to politics and special interests and more. The school also hosts 15 NCAA Division I teams and a wide range of intramurals and club teams.

WSU is the only research institution in Kansas in an urban area. WSU and Via Christi Health formed a joint venture in 2008 and founded The Center of Innovation for Biomaterials in Orthopaedic Research (CIBOR). The venture was restructured in 2012 to move CIBOR to the National Institute for Aviation Research (NIAR) on the university campus. CIBOR is managed by NIAR but remains a joint venture of WSU and Via Christi Health. Located on the WSU campus NIAR operates nearly 20 cutting-edge laboratories. It has partnered with Cisco Systems to provide one of the nation's best advanced-networking research centers.

Financial Performance

WSU logged a 6.1% revenue increase in 2013 from 2012.Tuition rose slightly while contracts from state and local sources increased by about $11 million. The university received less funding from the federal government for financial aid and research. Tuition and fees and state appropriations each account for 26% of WSU's revenue. Salaries and wages the university's biggest expense increased $3.8 million in 2013 from 2012.

EXECUTIVES

Vice President For Development, Terre Johnson
Vice President, John (Jack) Tomblin
Associate Vice President of Academic Affairs, Martha Shawver
Associate Vice President For Academic Data Systems And Strategic Planning, David (Dave) Wright
Vice President For Development, Joseph (Jo) Hunter
Vice President for Administration and Finance, Gary Brichacek
Department Chair Curriculum And Instruction, Shirley Lefever-Davis
Vice President Of Chapter Operations, Courtney Price
Department Chair, Janice Ewing
Vice President For Finance and Administrative Services, Patsy Selby
Vice President, Devin Roberts
Vice President Administration and Finance, Mary Herrin
Vice President and General Counsel, Ted Ayres
Managing Director, Mehmet Barut

LOCATIONS

HQ: THE WICHITA STATE UNIVERSITY
1845 FAIRMOUNT ST, WICHITA, KS 672600001
Phone: 316 978-3040
Web: WWW.HWS.WICHITA.EDU

Selected Campuses
Main
  Wichita Kansas
Satellite
  Eugene M. Hughes Metropolitan Complex Wichita Kansas
  WSU Downtown Center Wichita Kansas
  WSU South Campus Derby Wichita
  WSU West Campus Wichita Kansas

PRODUCTS/OPERATIONS

Selected Colleges and Schools
College of Education
College of Engineering
College of Fine Arts
College of Health Professions
Fairmount College of Liberal Arts and Sciences
Graduate School
W. Frank Barton School of Business

HISTORICAL FINANCIALS
Company Type: Private

Income Statement
FYE: June 30

	REVENUE ($ mil.)	NET INCOME ($ mil.)	NET PROFIT MARGIN	EMPLOYEES
06/14	178	5	2.9%	3,395
06/13	189	16	8.8%	—
06/12	184	10	5.8%	—
06/11	182	0	—	—
Annual Growth	(0.7%)	—	—	—

2014 Year-End Financials
Return on assets: 7.6% Cash ($ mil.): 108
Return on equity: 2.9%
Current ratio: 2.60

THE WILLS GROUP INC

The Wills Group willingly delivers petroleum products and related products and services to its customer base in southern Maryland and adjacent areas. The family-owned company operates four business subsidiaries: Dash-In Convenience Stores (with 35 locations including 18 franchises); DMO (provider of propane heating oil and HVAC equipment); and Southern Maryland Oil (SMO) and SMO Motor Fuels (distribution of diesel gasoline and kerosene products). More than 90% of SMO's gasoline products are Shell-branded fuels. The Wills Group supplies more than 300 dealer-operated gas stations in Delaware southern Maryland and Washington DC.

Operations

The Wills Group divides its business into four operations: Dash-In Convenience Stores (serving the Maryland; Delaware; and Tidewater Virgina regions); DMO (propane heating oil and HVAC equipment maker); and Southern Maryland Oil (SMO) and SMO Motor Fuels (distribution of diesel gasoline and kerosene products).

Company Background

The company was founded in 1926 by Jim Wills and Harold Swann. In 1942 The Wills Group was the first principal fuel supplier to the newly built Patuxent Naval Air Station. In 1972 the company developed the first branded self-service station in Maryland. In 2012 Lock Wills was serving as the president of The Wills Group.

EXECUTIVES

Vice President, Kris Demarr
Auditors: MCGLADREY LLP BALTIMORE MARY

LOCATIONS

HQ: THE WILLS GROUP INC
6355 CRAIN HWY, LA PLATA, MD 206464267
Phone: 301 932-3600
Web: WWW.WILLSGROUP.COM

COMPETITORS

Dixie Gas & Oil	Weis Markets
Petroleum Marketers	Woodfin Oil
Quarles Petroleum	

HISTORICAL FINANCIALS
Company Type: Private

Income Statement
FYE: September 30

	REVENUE ($ mil.)	NET INCOME ($ mil.)	NET PROFIT MARGIN	EMPLOYEES
09/13	933	24	2.7%	280
09/12	1,039	15	1.5%	—
09/11	1,052	17	1.7%	—
09/10	768	0	—	—
Annual Growth	6.7%	—	—	—

2013 Year-End Financials
Return on assets: 3.8% Cash ($ mil.): 39
Return on equity: 2.7%
Current ratio: 1.20

THEDACARE INC.

ThedaCare is a community health system that provides a wide range of health services to residents of nine central Wisconsin counties. It consists of five hospitals including Appleton Medical Center Theda Clark Medical Center New London

Family Medical Center Shawano Medical Center and Riverside Medical Center in Waupaca; more than 20 physician locations; and community health and wellness programs. The hospitals provide primary and acute care and offer many specialized diagnostic and medical services including behavioral health care and women's and children's services. ThedaCare also operates long-term care and assisted living facilities and provides occupational health and emergency transport services.

Geographic Reach

ThedaCare serves patients in more than nine counties in Eastern Wisconsin.

Operations

The health system operates five hospitals and 22 physician locations and manages 150000 patients per year.

Strategy

ThedaCare is expanding its facilities to keep pace with demand.

In 2013 it began construction on the ThedaCare Medical Center-Shawano which is being built to replace the 82-year-old Shawano Medical Center. The less-than-$50 million project is expected to open in 2015.

In 2012 the company opened a new outpatient unit (featuring five private rooms) at the New London Family Medical Center (renamed ThedaCare Medical Center-New London as part of a rebranding push in 2013).Expanding its insurance options in 2013 ThedaCare joined Anthem Blue Cross and Blue Shield's Blue Priority Network. Blue Priority is Anthem Blue Cross and Blue Shield's Accountable Care Organization network offering in eastern Wisconsin and was launched in 2012.

EXECUTIVES

Medical Director, Tom Nichols
Auditors: WIPFLI LLP GREEN BAY WI

LOCATIONS

HQ: THEDACARE INC.
122 E COLLEGE AVE STE 2A, APPLETON, WI 549115741
Phone: 920 735-5560
Web: WWW.THEDACARE.ORG

PRODUCTS/OPERATIONS

Selected Facilities and Programs
Appleton Medical Center
The Heritage Community (senior living)
ThedaCare Medical Center-New London
Peabody Manor (senior living)
Riverside Medical Center
Shawano Medical Center
Theda Clark Medical Center
ThedaCare at Home
ThedaCare at Work (occupational health services)
ThedaCare Behavioral Health
ThedaCare Physicians

COMPETITORS

Aspirus
Beaver Dam Community Hospitals
Beloit Health System
Benedictine Health System
Children' s Hospital and Health System
Columbia St. Mary' s
Dean Health Systems Inc.
Howard Young Health Care
Luther Midelfort
Marian Health System
Marshfield Clinic Health System
Sacred Heart Hospital
Tomah Memorial Hospital
UW Medical Foundation
University of Wisconsin Hospital and Clinics

HISTORICAL FINANCIALS
Company Type: Private

Income Statement
FYE: December 31

	REVENUE ($ mil.)	NET INCOME ($ mil.)	NET PROFIT MARGIN	EMPLOYEES
12/13	720	129	18.0%	5,900
12/12	276	(3)	—	—
12/08	3	0	—	—
12/06	0	0	—	—
Annual Growth	—	—	—	—

2013 Year-End Financials
Return on assets: 2.2%
Return on equity: 18.0%
Current ratio: 1.10
Cash ($ mil.): 42

THOMAS JEFFERSON UNIVERSITY

Thomas Jefferson University named after a founding father of diverse interests is itself diversifying the world of medical training. Its Jefferson Medical College boasts departments in surgery and specialized areas including obstetrics neurology and psychiatry. The Graduate Studies department offers programs in public health and biomedical studies. The College of Health Professions has programs in nursing pharmacy bioscience technologies and counseling. Founded as Jefferson Medical College in 1824 it has granted more than 30000 medical degrees. In late 2015 the school agreed to merge with Philadelphia University.

Operations

Thomas Jefferson University has six schools: Jefferson Graduate School of Biomedical Sciences; Sidney Kimmel Medical College; Jefferson School of Health Professions; Jefferson School of Nursing; Jefferson School of Pharmacy; and Jefferson School of Population Health. It also operates four centers: the Clinical Skills & Simulation Center; the Interprofessional Education Center; the Career Development Center; and the Center for Teaching & Learning. It also offers several continuing education programs.

With about 2600 students the university tests or treats 46000 inpatients and more than 1 million outpatients each year.

Geographic Reach

Thomas Jefferson University takes up 13 acres in the Center City area of downtown Philadelphia.

Financial Performance

Thomas Jefferson University reported that revenue edged up about 1.5% in 2014 from 2013. Patient revenue increased by about $13 million.

Strategy

In 2015 Thomas Jefferson University merged with Abington Health a Philadelphia health care organization with two hospitals and several clinics. The merger gives Abington access to the university's educational and training facilities and expands the university's reach to the Philadelphia suburbs. Other merger candidates include Aria Health of northeast Philadelphia and Philadelphia University a design-focused liberal arts school.

Seeking to increase its brand recognition Thomas Jefferson University paid almost $4 million to put its name on the transit station at its campus. The station previously the Market East Station will be the Jefferson Station for five years. The university has an option to renew for a total of nine years.

EXECUTIVES

VP Finance and CFO, Richard J. Schmid
President, Stephen K. Klasko
CIO, Doug Herrick
Dean Jefferson Medical College, Richard J. Tykocinski
Dean Graduate School of Biomedical Sciences, Gerald B. Grunwald
Dean School of Health Professions, Janice Burke
Dean School of Nursing, Beth A. Swan
Dean School of Pharmacy, Rebecca S. Finley
Dean School of Population Health, David Nash
Dean Students and Admissions, Clara A. Callahan
Vice President for Financial Operations, Andrew (Andy) Nathans
Senior Vice President, Mark L Tykocinski
Vice President Of Career Development, Natalie Chernets
Vice President Of Social Events, Maria Gubbiotti
Co Vice President, Thomas Neill
Medical Director, Anthony Prestipino
Vice President, Samantha Anderson
Executive Vice President, Ronald Bowlan
Vice President Finance, Kathleen Stinsman
Nursing Director, Edward (Ed) Tawyea
Vice President and University Counsel, Cristina G Cavalieri
Chairman, Richard C. Gozon, age 77
Vice Chair for Research, Neil Goldfarb
Auditors: PRICEWATERHOUSECOOPERS LLP PH

LOCATIONS

HQ: THOMAS JEFFERSON UNIVERSITY
1020 WALNUT ST STE 1, PHILADELPHIA, PA 191075567
Phone: 215 955-6000

PRODUCTS/OPERATIONS

Selected Research Centers and Institutes
Center for Translational Medicine
Daniel Baugh Institute
Delaware Health Science Alliance
Farber Institute for Neuroscience
Jefferson Coordinating Center for Clinical Research
Jefferson Vaccine Center
Kimmel Cancer Center

Selected Colleges and Schools
Sidney Kimmel Medical College
Jefferson Graduate School of Biomedical Sciences
Jefferson School of Health Professions
Jefferson School of Nursing
Jefferson School of Pharmacy
Jefferson School of Population Health

HISTORICAL FINANCIALS
Company Type: Private

Income Statement
FYE: June 30

	REVENUE ($ mil.)	NET INCOME ($ mil.)	NET PROFIT MARGIN	EMPLOYEES
06/14	776	131	17.0%	10,000
06/13	737	67	9.1%	—
06/12	731	(38)	—	—
06/11	714	0	—	—
Annual Growth	2.8%	—	—	—

2014 Year-End Financials
Return on assets: 7.0%
Return on equity: 17.0%
Current ratio: 0.20
Cash ($ mil.): 80

THOMAS JEFFERSON UNIVERSITY HOSPITALS INC.

Named after the "Man of the People" Thomas Jefferson University Hospitals serves the people of the Keystone State with a medical staff of more than 1200 and some 950 beds. Part of the Jefferson Health System it provides acute tertiary and specialty medical care. Aside from the main campus it operates through a Center City Campus Methodist Hospital Jefferson Voorhees and Jefferson Hospital for Neuroscience. The hospital also administers cardiac care at the Jefferson Heart Institute which provides everything from minimally invasive surgical procedures to heart transplants. It is also the teaching hospital for Thomas Jefferson University.

Operations

As part of its operations Thomas Jefferson University Hospital offers several premier programs to its patients as well as 35 different specialties. The hospital performed Delaware Valley's first liver transplant and designated a kidney transplant center for live and deceased donor transplants. In addition to transplantation the hospital provides surgical services heart and vascular digestive diseases and bones and joints in addition to its Kimmel Cancer Canter and Jefferson Hospital for Neuroscience. In 2014 the health system logged more than 470000 outpatient visits 45000 admissions and about 115000 emergency room visits.

Geographic Reach

Through a handful of locations Thomas Jefferson University Hospitals provides health care services to the residents of Philadelphia and the Delaware Valley. It shares a 13-acre campus with Thomas Jefferson University.

Strategy

In early 2016 Thomas Jefferson University Hospitals agreed to a merger with New Jersey-based Kennedy Health which operates three hospitals. The planned transaction followed closely on the heels of Jefferson's mergers with Aria Health and Abington Health.

In 2015 Jefferson Health hadded a new feature to its telemedicine program JeffConnect called On-Demand Virtual Care which allows patients to connect with an emergency medicine physician via computers and mobile devices.

That year the Philadelphia 76ers partnered with the Rothman Institute and Thomas Jefferson University Hospital. The Rothman Institute will provide the Official Orthopedics & Urgent Care of the Philadelphia 76ers as well as the Official Team Physicians; Thomas Jefferson University Hospital became an official hospital of the Philadelphia 76ers.In 2014 Thomas Jefferson University Hospitals opened the Jefferson Angioplasty Center the outpatient practice for Jefferson's interventional cardiologists. It is co-located with the Vascular Center allowing for streamlined consultations and convenience as the two specialties often see the same patients.That year it also introduced genomic analyses of breast cancer in house using the Prosigna Breast Cancer Prognostic Gene Signature Assay significantly reducing turn-around time for test results and allowing patients to begin effective treatment sooner.

Company Background

Thomas Jefferson University Hospital was founded in 1825.

EXECUTIVES

Vice President Clinical Resource Management, Patrice Miller
Chief Human Resources Officer and Senior Vice President, Pamela (Pam) Teufel
Vice President Financial Operations, Andrew (Andy) Nathans
Vice President Clinical Support Servicesneuroscience Service Line Administrator, Pamela (Pam) Kolb
Pharmacy Manager, Michael Roshko
Vice President Perioperative Services, Susan Kunkel
Senior Vice President and Chief Administrative Officer Methodist Hospital Division, James (Jamie) Robinson
Medical Records Director, Shinny George
Vice President Finance, Elizabeth Smith
Vice President Human Resources, Kimberly Evans
Senior Vice President Clinical Services, Rebecca O'shea
Vice Chairman Of Diagnostics, Christopher Roth
Board Member, Ron Lewis
Board Member, Joan Slobodzian

LOCATIONS

HQ: THOMAS JEFFERSON UNIVERSITY HOSPITALS INC.
111 S 11TH ST, PHILADELPHIA, PA 191074824
Phone: 215 955-5806
Web: WWW.NEMOURS.ORG

PRODUCTS/OPERATIONS

Selected Services
Cancer
Diabetes & Endocrinology
Ear Nose & Throat
Gastroenterology
Geriatrics
Gynecology
Nephrology
Orthopedics
Pulmonology
Rehabilitation
Urology

Selected University Locations
Jefferson at the Navy Yard
Jefferson Medical College
Jefferson College of Graduate Studies
Jefferson Radiology
Jefferson School of Health Professions
Jefferson School of Nursing
Jefferson School of Pharmacy
Jefferson School of Population Health
Jefferson Voorhees

COMPETITORS

Albert Einstein Healthcare Network
Bryn Mawr Hospital
Community Health Systems
Doylestown Hospital
Main Line Health
Mercy Health System
North Philadelphia Health System
Our Lady of Lourdes Medical Center
Pennsylvania Hospital
TUHS
Universal Health Services
University of Pennsylvania Health System

HISTORICAL FINANCIALS
Company Type: Private

Income Statement

	REVENUE ($ mil.)	NET INCOME ($ mil.)	NET PROFIT MARGIN	EMPLOYEES
06/10	1,250	49	4.0%	4,701
06/09	0	0	—	—
Annual Growth	781426.9%	—	—	—

FYE: June 30

2010 Year-End Financials
Return on assets: —
Return on equity: 4.0%
Current ratio: —
Cash ($ mil.): 206

THUNDERCAT TECHNOLOGY LLC

Auditors: GAFFEY DEANE TALLEY PLC RESTO

LOCATIONS

HQ: THUNDERCAT TECHNOLOGY LLC
1775 WIEHLE AVE STE 104, RESTON, VA 201905109
Phone: 703 657-7057
Web: WWW.THUNDERCATTECH.COM

HISTORICAL FINANCIALS
Company Type: Private

Income Statement

FYE: December 31

	REVENUE ($ mil.)	NET INCOME ($ mil.)	NET PROFIT MARGIN	EMPLOYEES
12/13	340	1	0.5%	44
12/12	216	2	1.0%	—
12/09	80	0	0.3%	—
Annual Growth	43.3%	60.0%	—	—

2013 Year-End Financials
Return on assets: —
Return on equity: 0.5%
Current ratio: 1.10
Cash ($ mil.): —

TIAA REAL ESTATE ACCOUNT

LOCATIONS

HQ: TIAA REAL ESTATE ACCOUNT
730 3RD AVE, NEW YORK, NY 100173206
Phone: 212 490-9000

HISTORICAL FINANCIALS
Company Type: Private

Income Statement

FYE: December 31

	REVENUE ($ mil.)	NET INCOME ($ mil.)	NET PROFIT MARGIN	EMPLOYEES
12/14	897	489	54.6%	2
12/13	540	2,046	378.5%	—
12/12	504	1,379	273.2%	—
12/11	544	0	—	—
Annual Growth	18.1%	—	—	—

2014 Year-End Financials
Return on assets: —
Return on equity: 54.6%
Current ratio: —
Cash ($ mil.): 36

TIFFIN MOTOR HOMES INC.

At Tiffin Motorhomes the family that stays together makes recreational vehicles together. The family-owned manufacturer builds a line of luxury recreational vehicles (RVs) including the Allegro Allegro Bus Phaeton and Zephyr models. RVs span 35 to 44 feet in length and offer amenities from washers and dryers to garden tubs to side-by-side refrigerators. Construction pluses feature thick glass windows added storage and reinforced steel crossbracing. Tiffin's vehicles are sold by dealers across the US and Canada. Spotlighting its nameplates the company owns the Allegro Club an organization of local US chapters that promotes race car rallies and RV events. Robert Tiffin founded the company in 1972.

A weak economy tight consumer credit markets and mounting fuel prices have combined to wipe out an estimated 50% of shipments by the Class A motor home builder. Since 2008 Tiffin has cut its workforce in half from its high in 2005 and slashed production by about 70% to four models a day from its former glory of 13. The belt-tightening fell on the heels of expanding the operations of its subsidiary Waterway Inc. Waterway manufactures the side and roof panels of Tiffin's motor homes.

EXECUTIVES

General Manager, Tim Tiffin
Manager Research and Development, Van Tiffin
Quality and Assistant Plant Manager, Lex Tiffin
Media Relations, Stephanie Umfress

LOCATIONS

HQ: TIFFIN MOTOR HOMES INC.
105 2ND ST NW, RED BAY, AL 355823859
Phone: 256 356-8661
Web: WWW.TIFFINMOTORHOMES.COM

COMPETITORS

Airstream	Motor Coach Industries
Forest River	Newmar Corporation
Gulf Stream Coach	Rexhall Industries
Jayco Inc.	Thor Industries
Keystone RV	Winnebago

HISTORICAL FINANCIALS
Company Type: Private

Income Statement
FYE: February 28

	REVENUE ($ mil.)	NET INCOME ($ mil.)	NET PROFIT MARGIN	EMPLOYEES
02/07	419	24	5.9%	545
02/05	286	(0)	—	—
02/04	1,280	0	—	—
Annual Growth	(31.1%)	28998.8%	—	—

2007 Year-End Financials
Return on assets: 7.7%
Return on equity: 5.9%
Current ratio: 0.70
Cash ($ mil.): 10

TIFT REGIONAL MEDICAL CENTER FOUNDATION INC.

Tift Regional Medical Center (TRMC) helps keep people healthy in the Peach State. The medical center with more than 125 physicians on staff representing some 30 specialties serves residents across a dozen counties in south central Georgia. TRMC offers its patients a wide range of services including cancer treatment cardiology neurology occupational and physical therapy obstetrics and surgical care. The not-for-profit medical center has a capacity of about 190 beds. It also operates an outpatient services clinic Cook Medical Center and Cook Senior Living Center. Tift County Hospital Authority owns and operates TRMC. The hospital is also affiliated with the Emory Healthcare network.

Mergers and Acquisitions
In 2012 Tift County Hospital Authority purchased Memorial Hospital of Adel and its affiliated nursing home and ancillary services from SunLink Health Systems. Memorial Hospital of Adel was renamed Cook Medical Center-A Campus of Tift Regional Medical Center (TRMC) and 95-bed Memorial Convalescent Center was renamed Cook Senior Living Center.
Auditors: DRAFFIN & TUCKER LLP ALBANY

LOCATIONS

HQ: TIFT REGIONAL MEDICAL CENTER FOUNDATION INC.
901 18TH ST E, TIFTON, GA 317943648
Phone: 229 382-7120
Web: WWW.TIFTREGIONAL.COM

PRODUCTS/OPERATIONS

Selected Services
Affinity Clinic
Allure Plastic & Reconstructive Surgery
Arthritis and osteoporosis Center of South GA
Breast Center
Cardio-pulmonary rehabilitation
Continuing Medical Education (CME)
Diabetes Learning Center
Dialysis Center
Endoscopy
HealthPlus Medical Office Centers
Heart and Vascular Center
Hospice of Tift Area
Infusion Center
Intensive Care Unit (ICU)
Lithotripsy
Neurodiagnostics Center
Oncology Center
Orthopedics
Outpatient therapy
Palliative care
Pediatrics
Primary care outreach clinics
Radiology
Respiratory care
Sleep Center
Spine Therapy Center
Tift Community Health Center
Tifton Physicians Center
Transitional Care Center
Women's health
WorkSmart Occupational Health

COMPETITORS

Doctors Hospital of Augusta
Liberty Regional Medical Center
MCG Health
Memorial Health University Medical Center
Redmond Regional Medical Center

South Georgia Medical Center
St. Joseph's/Candler Health System
University Health Services
Walton Rehabilitation Hospital

HISTORICAL FINANCIALS
Company Type: Private

Income Statement
FYE: September 30

	REVENUE ($ mil.)	NET INCOME ($ mil.)	NET PROFIT MARGIN	EMPLOYEES
09/09	216	30	14.1%	1,400
09/08	0	0	47.6%	
09/07	418	0	—	
Annual Growth	—33890.3%	—	—	

2009 Year-End Financials
Return on assets: 3.5%
Return on equity: 14.1%
Current ratio: 2.30
Cash ($ mil.): 25

TOM LANGE COMPANY INC.

Tom Lange Company wants you to eat your veggies. One of the largest purchasers and distributors of fresh fruits and vegetables in the US Tom Lange supplies its comestibles to clients in the retail wholesale and food service trades. The company also provides third party logistics services specializing in truckload freight movement. The company was founded in 1960 as a three-man operation in St. Louis Missouri Tom Lange has grown to encompass 35 offices in the US and Canada. Produce subsidiaries include Seven Seas M&M Marketing and Seven Seas Fruit.

EXECUTIVES

Vice President, Jim Griswold
Vice President, Mike Patton
Vice President Sales Indianapolis In Office, Rick Harsnett
Auditors: KERBER ECK & BRAECKEL LLP SP

LOCATIONS

HQ: TOM LANGE COMPANY INC.
755 APPLE ORCHARD RD, SPRINGFIELD, IL 627035914
Phone: 217 786-3300
Web: WWW.TOMLANGE.COM

COMPETITORS

A. Duda & Sons	FreshPoint
Caito Foods Service	Get Fresh Produce
Coast Citrus Distributors	The Oppenheimer Group
Cristina Foods	Wilson Farms

HISTORICAL FINANCIALS
Company Type: Private

Income Statement
FYE: August 31

	REVENUE ($ mil.)	NET INCOME ($ mil.)	NET PROFIT MARGIN	EMPLOYEES
08/13	431	1	0.4%	110
08/12	414	0	0.1%	—
08/11	445	1	0.4%	
08/08	407	0	—	
Annual Growth	1.1%	—	—	

2013 Year-End Financials

Return on assets: 8.1%   Cash ($ mil.): 15
Return on equity: 0.4%
Current ratio: 1.40

TORRANCE HEALTH ASSOCIATION INC.

Auditors: ERNST & YOUNG LLP LOS ANGELES

LOCATIONS

HQ: TORRANCE HEALTH ASSOCIATION INC.
3330 LOMITA BLVD, TORRANCE, CA 905055002
Phone: 310 325-9110
Web: WWW.TORRANCEMEMORIAL.ORG

HISTORICAL FINANCIALS

Company Type: Private

Income Statement

FYE: December 31

	REVENUE ($ mil.)	NET INCOME ($ mil.)	NET PROFIT MARGIN	EMPLOYEES
12/13	554	110	19.9%	5,700
12/09	5	(1)	—	—
12/05	341	0	—	—
12/02	222	0	—	—
Annual Growth	8.6%	—	—	—

2013 Year-End Financials

Return on assets: —   Cash ($ mil.): 29
Return on equity: 19.9%
Current ratio: 0.30

TORRANCE MEMORIAL MEDICAL CENTER

Back in 1925 Jared Sydney Torrance founded Torrance Memorial Medical Center in the southern California town that also bears his name. The not-for-profit medical center now includes 400 beds surgical suites clinical and diagnostic labs and specialist centers for cancer metabolic heart and other conditions. It is one of three burn centers in Los Angeles. Torrance Memorial Medical Center reaches beyond its walls and into the community with hospice care and home health care. The hospital also provides nursing residency programs and it offers staffing support services to physicians offices in the area.

Geographic Reach

Torrance Memorial serves residents of communities in the South Bay Peninsula and Harbor areas within the Los Angeles metropolitan area.

Operations

Torrance Memorial has about 1000 physicians on its medical staff. It is also supported by a volunteer organization with about 900 members.

The hospital provides more than $50 million in community benefits each year including subsidized care for Medicare and Medicaid patients and charity care for uninsured patients. Other programs include community outreach efforts including parenting and wellness classes.

Financial Performance

Torrance Memorial's revenues grew by 5% to $461 million in 2012 thanks to an increase in unrestricted revenues. HealthCare Partners and Torrance Hospital IPA (a non-profit multi-specialty physician network owned by Torrance Memorial) accounted for 38% of net patient revenues in 2012; Medicare 30%.

The company reported net income of $37 million in 2012 (compared to a net loss in 2011) primarily due to increase in unrealized gain from its trading portfolio.

Strategy

In order to accommodate the medical needs of a growing population the hospital is building a new 400000 sq. ft. $450 million patient tower featuring new medical technologies increased capacity and a modernized design. The seven-story tower will have more than 250 private rooms and about 20 surgical and interventional treatment rooms. The tower meets the hospital's needs for a growing customer base as a number of other area hospitals have closed in recent years. It is expected to open in late 2015. About $200 million of the construction costs is being procured through fundraising efforts.

Upgrading its technology to better serve patients in 2014 Torrance Memorial obtained the latest radiation therapy TrueBeam a state-of-the-art linear accelerator that helps zero in on tumors without harming surrounding normal tissue. In 2013 the Commission on Cancer of the American College of Surgeons granted the Torrance Memorial Hunt Cancer Institute a three-year accreditation with commendation.

Company Background

In 2012 Torrance Memorial earned the Magnet recognition from the American Nurses Credentialing Center which is given to top 6% of hospitals in the US.

Founded by Jared Torrance and his wife Helena in 1925 Torrance Memorial acquired the smaller Riviera Community Hospital in 1967. The medical center moved to its current location in 1971.

EXECUTIVES

Vice President Nursing, Peggy Burwald
President and CEO, Craig Leach
VP and CFO, Bill Larson
VP Information Technology and CIO, Bernadette Reid
VP Nursing, Barb LeQuire
Director Of Nursing, Armita Fenning
Vice President, Josh Luke
Vice President Ancillary and Support, Debby Kelley
Vice President, Mike Thomas
Director of Radiology and Radiation Oncology, Pat Baldivia
Vice President Administration, Sally Eberhird
Director of Pharmacy, Steve Thompson
SVP Patient Services, Peggy Berwald

LOCATIONS

HQ: TORRANCE MEMORIAL MEDICAL CENTER
3330 LOMITA BLVD, TORRANCE, CA 905055002
Phone: 310 325-9110
Web: WWW.TORRANCEMEMORIAL.ORG

PRODUCTS/OPERATIONS

Selected Centers and Services

Bariatric Surgery Program
Blood Donor Center
Breast Diagnostic Center
Burn Center
Cancer Institute
Cardiovascular Institute
Chemical Dependency
Diabetes
Eating Disorders Program
Emergency Care
Endoscopy Center and GI Lab
Home Health

Hospice
Laboratory Testing (includes Outpatient Lab)
Maternal Child Health Services
Nuclear Medicine
Orthopedics
Palliative Care
Pediatrics
Pharmacy
Radiation Oncology
Radiology
Rehabilitation
Sleep Disorders Center
Stroke Center
Surgical Services
Transitional Care Unit
Urgent Care
Wound Center

COMPETITORS

Brotman Medical Center
Cedars-Sinai Medical Center
Childrens Hospital Los Angeles
Dignity Health
Good Samaritan Hospital (Los Angeles)
HCA
Hollywood Presbyterian Medical Center
Long Beach Memorial
Los Angeles County Health Department
Providence Health System Southern California
Sisters of Charity of Leavenworth
Tenet Healthcare
Universal Health Services
White Memorial Medical Center

HISTORICAL FINANCIALS

Company Type: Private

Income Statement

FYE: December 31

	REVENUE ($ mil.)	NET INCOME ($ mil.)	NET PROFIT MARGIN	EMPLOYEES
12/14*	489	27	5.6%	3,500
09/14	362	17	4.9%	—
06/14	237	12	5.3%	—
12/13	476	0	—	—
Annual Growth	2.8%	—	—	—

*Fiscal year change

2014 Year-End Financials

Return on assets: 8.5%   Cash ($ mil.): 52
Return on equity: 5.6%
Current ratio: 0.50

TOURO COLLEGE & UNIVERSITY SYSTEM

Touro College is a Jewish university (the largest private Jewish-based educational institution in the US) and has sister institutions in France Germany Israel and Russia and branches in California Florida and Nevada. Some 19000 (Jewish and non-Jewish) students are enrolled in its 32 schools on 25 campuses which offer associate bachelor's and master's degrees in business education and law as well as professional degrees in osteopathic medicine pharmacy law and other fields. Touro also oversees the operations of New York Medical College. The institution claims some 75000 alumni.

Operations

Touro has more than 2200 full-time and about 1380 part-time faculty members.

The school has an annual operating budget of $460 million.

Strategy

The school is looking to expand its academic programs and research footprint.

Company Background

Dr. Bernard Lander a social behavior and Jewish studies scholar founded Touro College in 1971 to teach Jewish and secular subjects. The college is named after Judah and Isaac Touro who founded the Touro Synagogue in 1790.

Lander an orthodox rabbi died in 2010. He was one of the longest-serving college presidents in the country. Senior provost and medical doctor Alan Kadish was selected to replace Lander.

Under Lander's leadership Touro College grew quickly from a small school with 35 students to a multi-campus college with thousands of students. Touro continues to expand. It assumed control of New York Medical College in mid-2010. The Catholic-led medical school remains an independent institution. Some at the New York Medical College opposed the merger citing a well-publicized cash-for-grades scandal. In 2009 Touro's former director of admissions was found guilty of tampering with student transcripts and selling degrees. He was sentenced to two to eight years in prison. Nevertheless the deal went through and now New York Medical College is a member of the Touro College and University System.

EXECUTIVES

Director Of Admissions, Arthur Wigfall
Admissions Director, Steve Toplan
Executive Board Member, Kim Kandt
Auditors: PERELSON WEINER LLP NEW YORK

LOCATIONS

HQ: TOURO COLLEGE & UNIVERSITY SYSTEM
27 33 W 23RD ST, NEW YORK, NY 10010
Phone: 212 463-0400
Web: WWW.TOURO.EDU

HISTORICAL FINANCIALS

Company Type: Private

Income Statement

	REVENUE ($ mil.)	NET INCOME ($ mil.)	NET PROFIT MARGIN	EMPLOYEES
				FYE: June 30
06/13	334	42	12.8%	4,600
06/10	277	15	5.7%	—
06/09	145	0	—	—
06/08	2,037	0	—	—
Annual Growth	(30.3%)	—	—	—

2013 Year-End Financials

Return on assets: 8.7%   Cash ($ mil.): 7
Return on equity: 12.8%
Current ratio: 0.20

TOURO INFIRMARY

Auditors: LAPORTE METAIRE LA

LOCATIONS

HQ: TOURO INFIRMARY
1401 FOUCHER ST, NEW ORLEANS, LA 701153593
Phone: 504 897-7011
Web: WWW.TOURO.COM

HISTORICAL FINANCIALS

Company Type: Private

Income Statement

	REVENUE ($ mil.)	NET INCOME ($ mil.)	NET PROFIT MARGIN	EMPLOYEES
				FYE: December 31
12/12	306	31	10.4%	1,424
12/10	253	27	10.9%	—
12/09	213	5	2.5%	—
12/08	1,482	0	—	—
Annual Growth	(32.6%)	—	—	—

2012 Year-End Financials

Return on assets: 4.6%   Cash ($ mil.): 38
Return on equity: 10.4%
Current ratio: 1.00

TOWNSHIP HIGH SCHOOL DISTRICT 211 FOUNDATION

Township High School District 211 is the largest high school district in Illinois with some 12500 students attending its five high schools (grades 9 to 12) —James B. Conant William Fremd Hoffman Estates Palatine and Schaumburg —and two special education academies. The district's student-teacher ratio is nearly 14-to-1 and serves several suburban communities 25 miles northwest of Chicago. The school district started as one school (Palatine High School) in the Palatine-Schaumburg Township area in 1875 with the first graduating class in 1877.

Geographic Reach

Township High School District 211 serves the northwest suburbs of Chicago including the the communities of Hoffman Estates Inverness Palatine and Schaumburg as well as parts of Arlington Heights Elk Grove Village Hanover Park Rolling Meadows Roselle Streamwood and South Barrington.

Financial Performance

The school district reported revenue of nearly $240 million in 2012 nearly 85% of it coming from local property taxes.

HISTORY

All five district schools have been named among the top schools in the nation.

EXECUTIVES

School Board President, MUCIA BURKE
Auditors: BAKER TILLY VIRHOW KRAUSE LLP

LOCATIONS

HQ: TOWNSHIP HIGH SCHOOL DISTRICT 211 FOUNDATION
1750 S ROSELLE RD STE 100, PALATINE, IL 600677302
Phone: 708 359-3300
Web: WWW.D211.ORG

PRODUCTS/OPERATIONS

Schools
High Schools
James B. Conant High School
William Fremd High School
Hoffman Estates High School
Palatine High School

Schaumburg High School
Special Education Schools
District 211 Academy North
District 211 Academy South

HISTORICAL FINANCIALS

Company Type: Private

Income Statement

	REVENUE ($ mil.)	NET INCOME ($ mil.)	NET PROFIT MARGIN	EMPLOYEES
				FYE: June 30
06/14	280	(8)	—	1,909
06/13	268	19	7.2%	—
06/12	257	8	3.1%	—
06/11	250	0	—	—
Annual Growth	3.8%	—	—	—

TRAMMO INC.

Fertilizers liquefied petroleum gas (LPG) and petrochemicals are the "ammo" which international trader Trammo (formerly Transammonia) uses in its battle with competitors. The company trades distributes and transports these commodities around the world. Trammo's fertilizer business includes ammonia phosphates and urea. Its Sea-3 subsidiary imports and distributes propane to residential commercial and industrial customers in the northeastern US and Florida. The Trammochem unit trades in petrochemicals specializing in aromatics methanol methyltertiary butyl ether (MTBE) benzene and olefins. Its Trammo Gas trades LPG and propane as well as ethane butane and natural gas in the US.

Geographic Reach

Trammo has expanded its reach into the global market establishing merchandising and trading offices in Singapore China and the United Arab Emirates. Those offices complement its other global operations in Africa Asia Europe the Middle East and South America. It has major representative offices in Amman Beijing Cairo Dubai Hong Kong and Shanghai.

Its Fertilizers and Commodities Division's regional hubs are in Zurich Tampa Dubai Shanghai and Singapore; the Ammonia Division has hubs in Tampa and Dubai. The Chemicals Division maintains regional hubs in Zurich Darien (Connecticut) Dubai Shanghai and Singapore; while the Gas Division maintains hubs in Houston Tampa and Newington (New Hampshire).

Trammo has more than 30 offices worldwide.

Operations

The company operates three divisions: Chemicals Commodities and Gas. The Chemicals Division's annual sales volumes increased to 4.7 million metric tons in 2013. It key products include aromatics olefins and oxygenates. The Commodities Division accounted for two thirds of the Trammo Group's sales volumes and for 41% of its revenues; it's worldwide traded volume reached 27.7 million metric tons in 2013. The Gas Division's business areas include LPG business Trammo Gas and Petrochemicals Ltd and Sea-3 Inc. Trammo's international traded ammonia volume was more than 2.8 million metric tons in 2013.

Sea-3 is the largest importer and distributor of liquefied propane in the Northeastern US. It also supplies propane to the western and central portions of Florida. It moves 200000 metric tones of product per year.

Trammochem merchandises and trades in petrochemicals around the world.

Trammo Gas markets and trades LPG (primarily propane) in the US. Trammo Gas International Inc. operates two gas carriers which transport LPG worldwide for third parties. In 2013 the gas division traded 8 million metric tons of products.

Financial Performance

In 2013 Trammo had revenues of $12.5 billion.

Strategy

In 2015 the company's Ammonia Division and Fertilizers and Commodities Division merged into a new division —Commodities. The merger will allow Trammo to increase operational synergies use its global infrastructure to provide a larger portfolio of products and to more clearly present itself as a single company with different products.

Trammo opened offices in Ivory Coast and Dar Es Salaam in 2014 to strengthens its presence in the emerging African market.

In 2013 Transammonia changed its name to Trammo to more accurately represent the broad spectrum of products and services it provides.

Company Background

In 2010 the company's bulk carriers division entered the commodity shipping business. TA Bulk Carriers operates a fleet of 15 to 20 vessels which trade worldwide but focus on the handysize market (25000-35000 metric tons deadweight) in the Atlantic basin. In 2010 it transported about 2.9 million metric tons of cargo primarily fertilizers and grains.

Trammo is owned by founder Ronald Stanton who founded the company in 1965 as an international ammonia trader. It branched into fertilizer merchandising and trading in 1967 LPG trading in 1978 and petrochemicals trading in 1987.

EXECUTIVES

EVP and CFO, Edward G. Weiner
EVP and General Counsel, Fred Lowenfels
CEO Fertilizers & Commodities Division, Christian Wendel
CEO Chemicals Division, Ashok Kishore
CEO Ammonia Division, Jeffrey Minnis
CEO Gas Division, Dave Smothermon
President and CEO, Henk Dalfsen
Vice President Information Technology, Dudley Cox
Senior Vice President Ammonia Division, Bernard Rock
Assistant Vice President, Donald Madden
Vice President, Todd Matthes
Board Member, Oliver K Stanton, age 52
Auditors: DELOITTE & TOUCHE LLP NEW YOR

LOCATIONS

HQ: TRAMMO INC.
320 PARK AVE RM 1001, NEW YORK, NY 100226987
Phone: 212 223-3200
Web: WWW.GUIDE8480.GUIDECHEM.COM

PRODUCTS/OPERATIONS

Major SubsidiariesSea-3 (liquefied propane)Trammo Gas (LPG)Trammo Gas International Inc. (LPG transportation for third parties.Trammo Petroleum (crude oil and oil products)Trammochem (petrochemicals)Fertilizers and CommoditiesNitrogen BasedAnhydrous Ammo

COMPETITORS

Agrium	Dynegy
BASF SE	HELM
CF Industries	Koch Industries Inc.
Cargill	Magellan Midstream
ConAgra	Yara

HISTORICAL FINANCIALS

Company Type: Private

Income Statement   FYE: December 31

	REVENUE ($ mil.)	NET INCOME ($ mil.)	NET PROFIT MARGIN	EMPLOYEES
12/13	11,315	(11)	—	440
12/12	12,152	35	0.3%	—
12/11	11,303	31	0.3%	—
12/10	8,414	0	—	—
Annual Growth	10.4%	—	—	—

2013 Year-End Financials

Return on assets: 7.6%   Cash ($ mil.): 221
Return on equity: (-0.1%)
Current ratio: 1.00

TRANS-SYSTEM INC.

Freight hauler Trans-System operates through three main units: System Transport (flatbed); TW Transport (refrigerated and dry van); and James J. Williams (bulk commodities). The Trans-System trucking companies operate from some 10 terminals in the western US. Overall the company's fleet consists of about 1000 tractors and 1500 trailers. Trans-System also offers logistics services and runs a driver training school. Chairman and CEO Jim Williams founded the company in 1972 although it got its start when Williams' grandfather began transporting petroleum products throughout northern Idaho and eastern Washington.

Like its industry peers Trans-System has been traveling a rough road since 2008 when fuel prices soared to all-time highs only to be followed by a severe plunge in freight demand and an economic recession. The company implemented measures at some of its subsidiaries that included reducing idling time fitting trucks with mileage-improving tires and aligning trucks and trailers better.

But while other in the industry threw on the brakes Trans-System launched a $3.5 million expansion and remodeling project in 2009 at its headquarters. The project featured the addition of 10000 sq. ft. to its facility to house administrative offices a remodel of the maintenance shop and repurposing of a vacant space for showers and rest facilities for drivers.

Tran-System's range of companies provided some insulation from the sluggish economy —applications submitted since 2008 have reached historic heights at the company's professional truck driver school.

EXECUTIVES

CEO, James C. (Jim) Williams
Vice President Personnel, Jeff Benesch
Auditors: MCDIRMID MIKKELSEN & SECREST

LOCATIONS

HQ: TRANS-SYSTEM INC.
7405 S HAYFORD RD, CHENEY, WA 990049633
Phone: 509 623-4001
Web: WWW.TRANS-SYSTEM.COM

COMPETITORS

C.R. England	Quality Distribution
CRST International	Ruan Transportation
Comcar	Management Systems
Crete Carrier	Schneider National
Maverick USA	Werner Enterprises
Prime Inc.	

TRANSPERFECT TRANSLATIONS INTERNATIONAL INC.

You pick the language or languages and TransPerfect Translations International will aim to get your message through. In addition to translation and interpretation the company offers services such as document management multicultural marketing staffing subtitling and voiceover work. Its network of translators can handle more than 170 languages through offices located in 90 cities spanning six continents. TransPerfect serves a wide array of industries including advertising financial services legal life science technology retail and travel. Clients have include Sony American Airlines and Omnicom. TransPerfect was founded in 1992 by Liz Elting and Phil Shawe.

Geographic Reach

The global company's corporate headquarters are located in New York City. It also has regional headquarters in London and Hong Kong.

Sales and Marketing

The company has numerous partnerships it uses to fuel its business. Partners include Adobe and EMC.

Financial Performance

TransPerfect's annual revenue for fiscal 2014 was around $470 million.

Strategy

The firm has been steadily growing by opening new offices across the globe. In 2015 the company opened a discovery data center in Toronto. During 2014 it opened locations in Bangkok Thailand; Budapest Hungary; Luxembourg; and Taipei Taiwan.

During 2013 TransPerfect opened an office in Johannesburg South Africa which expanded the company's global footprint to six continents. Also during 2013 TransPerfect opened an office in Oslo Norway (its third Nordic office) and an office Vienna Austria. In 2012 it established locations in Buenos Aires Copenhagen Madrid and Rome.

Mergers and Acquisitions

During fiscal 2013 the company expanded when it merged with Vasont Systems. The combined organization is now best-in-class for language translation services. Back in 2012 the company acquired Boston-based Digital Reef which became a division of TransPerfect.

EXECUTIVES

Co-CEO, Phil Shawe

HISTORICAL FINANCIALS

Company Type: Private

Income Statement   FYE: March 31

	REVENUE ($ mil.)	NET INCOME ($ mil.)	NET PROFIT MARGIN	EMPLOYEES
03/14	209	6	3.1%	650
03/13	197	8	4.1%	—
03/12	191	8	4.6%	—
Annual Growth	4.8%	(13.8%)	—	—

2014 Year-End Financials

Return on assets: 1.9%   Cash ($ mil.): 1
Return on equity: 3.1%
Current ratio: 0.80

Co-CEO, Elizabeth (Liz) Elting
SVP North America, Kevin Obarski
CTO, Mark Hagerty
COO, Roy B. Trujillo
VP Quality Systems; President Crimson Life Sciences Division, Marc H. Miller
CIO, Yu-Kai Ng
VP Global Life Sciences, Jessica Eker
SVP Global Production, Jin Lee
EVP Global Sales and Marketing, A. Brooke Christian
Vice President Human Resources, Robert (Bob) DeNoia
Vice President Client Solutions, Michael (Mel) Edwards
Vice President of Quality Assurance, Mark Peeler
Vice President Content Solutions, Matt Hauser
Executive Vice President Global Sales Marketing Chief Sales Officer, Brooke Christian

LOCATIONS

HQ: TRANSPERFECT TRANSLATIONS INTERNATIONAL INC.
3 PARK AVE FL 39, NEW YORK, NY 100165934
Phone: 212 689-5555
Web: WWW.TRANSPERFECT.COM.HK

PRODUCTS/OPERATIONS

Selected Services
Brand research
Court reporting
Document management
Graphic services
Interpretation
Linguistic validation
Multilingual typesetting
Multicultural marketing
Software localization
Staffing
Subtitling
Technical writing
Translation
Virtual data rooms
Voiceovers
Website globalization

COMPETITORS

ALT Services
Albors & Associates
Eclipse Translations
JLS Language
  Corporation
Language Line
Linguistic Systems
Lionbridge
Mission Essential
  Personnel
Wordbank

HISTORICAL FINANCIALS

Company Type: Private

Income Statement

FYE: December 31

	REVENUE ($ mil.)	NET INCOME ($ mil.)	NET PROFIT MARGIN	EMPLOYEES
12/07	156	29	18.5%	950
12/06	79	11	14.8%	—
12/05	73	11	15.7%	—
Annual Growth	45.7%	58.5%	—	—

2007 Year-End Financials

Return on assets: —
Return on equity: 18.5%
Current ratio: 5.90
Cash ($ mil.): 11

TRAYLOR BROS. INC.

At Traylor Bros. building bridges and tunnels is a family affair. The family-owned heavy/civil construction company also works on dams and ports storm sewers and transmission lines. The company's new mining division focuses on copper gold and coal mine development in North America. Additionally the company offers used and surplus equipment for sale. Traylor Bros operates throughout the US through its heavy/civil underground/tunneling and Traylor Pacific divisions. Traylor Bros.' projects include work for the San Francisco's Bay Area Rapid Transit (BART) system and the I-10 span bridges over Lake Pontchartrain in Louisiana. Civil engineer William Traylor founded Traylor Bros. in Indiana in 1946.

HISTORY

Traylor Bros. operates from offices in Evansville Indiana and in Pleasanton and Irvine California.

EXECUTIVES

Chairman and CEO, Thomas W. (Tom) Traylor, age 75
Co-President and COO, Christopher S. Traylor
Co-President, Michael T. Traylor
Vice President, C Meagher
Auditors: BKD LLP EVANSVILLE IN

LOCATIONS

HQ: TRAYLOR BROS. INC.
835 N CONGRESS AVE, EVANSVILLE, IN 477152484
Phone: 812 477-1542
Web: WWW.TRAYLOR.COM

PRODUCTS/OPERATIONS

Selected Divisions
Heavy Civil
Traylor Mining
Traylor Pacific
Underground

COMPETITORS

American Bridge
  Company
American
  Infrastructure
Balfour Beatty
  Infrastructure
Barnard Construction
Garney Holding
Gohmann Asphalt &
  Construction
Granite Construction
MBC Holding
Milestone Contractors
Peter Kiewit Sons'
Rasmussen Group
Superior Construction
TIC Holdings
Walsh Group

HISTORICAL FINANCIALS

Company Type: Private

Income Statement

FYE: December 31

	REVENUE ($ mil.)	NET INCOME ($ mil.)	NET PROFIT MARGIN	EMPLOYEES
12/13	250	0	—	500
12/12	250	0	—	—
12/11	0	0	—	—
12/10	250	0	—	—
Annual Growth	(0.0%)	—	—	—

2013 Year-End Financials

Return on assets: 15.9%
Return on equity: —
Current ratio: 1.40
Cash ($ mil.): 226

TREE TOP INC.

Tree Top has towered over the Pacific Northwest's apple juice market for more than 50 years. The grower-owned cooperative's 1000 members cultivate and harvest thousands of tons of apples and pears each year to make a slew of juicy products. The co-op produces the Tree Top brand of apple and blended fruit juices and applesauce among many offerings for consumers and food service vendors. It also processes dehydrated and frozen fruit products for food makers worldwide through its ingredients unit. Tree Top operates production facilities in Washington Oregon and California and distributes its products through various channels including retailers and brokers in the US and several international markets.

Geographic Reach

The company has seven Tree Top manufacturing facilities located in Selah Wenatchee and Prosser Washington; Medford and Woodburn Oregon; and Oxnard California. Its wholly-owned subsidiary Northwest Naturals is located in Bothell Washington.

Operations

Beyond juice Tree Top supplies a wide variety of bulk dried chilled frozen apple and frozen cherry ingredients to food manufacturers. Reportedly it supplies ingredients to more than 20 of the top 25 US food companies for such applications as baked and frozen desserts cold and hot cereals yogurt fruit fillings and fruit smoothies. In this vein the co-op also owns Northwest Naturals a leading supplier of juice concentrates for the beverage industry and Sabroso Company which manufactures fruit purees concentrates flakes and bases used by food companies in the US.

Strategy

To grow Tree Top must compete with beverage giants Coca-Cola PepsiCo and Dr Pepper Snapple Group which have responded to consumers' health concerns with a stream of new juices and other noncarbonated beverages. Although Tree Top's apple juice and cider account for the majority of its sales it has stepped up its marketing efforts bringing out new product varieties including low-calorie and reduced-sugar selections blended juices flavored applesauce bagged fresh apple slices and fruit snacks as well as increasing its advertising.

EXECUTIVES

Senior Vice President of Ingredient and Foodservicand#8230, Tom Hurson
Vice President Human Resources, Nancy Buck
Auditors: MOSS ADAMS LLP YAKIMA WASHI

LOCATIONS

HQ: TREE TOP INC.
220 E 2ND AVE, SELAH, WA 989421408
Phone: 509 697-7251
Web: WWW.TREETOP.ORG

PRODUCTS/OPERATIONS

Selected Brands and Products
Consumer products
  Applesauce (Seneca and Tree Top)
  Juice and drinks
  Fiber rich
  Fresh pressed
  Fruit drinks
  Juice from concentrate
  Organic juice
  trim Functional Beverages
  Other
  Fruit Snacks
Food service products
  Beverages
  Cut produce
  Fruit bases
  Sauces
  Frozen fruit
Ingredient products
  Apple (dried chilled frozen and concentrate)
  Cherry (dried chilled frozen and concentrate)

COMPETITORS

Big Heart Pet Brands
Chiquita Brands
National Beverage
National Grape

Coca-Cola
Cranberries Limited
Dole Food
Dominion Citrus
Dr Pepper Snapple
  Group
Knouse Foods
Monster Beverage
Mott' s
Naked Juice

Cooperative
Ocean Spray
Odwalla
Old Orchard
PepsiCo
Snapple
Sun-Rype
Tropicana
Welch' s

HISTORICAL FINANCIALS
Company Type: Private

Income Statement
FYE: July 31

	REVENUE ($ mil.)	NET INCOME ($ mil.)	NET PROFIT MARGIN	EMPLOYEES
07/13	399	57	14.4%	1,100
07/10	364	26	7.4%	—
07/09	359	37	10.4%	—
07/08	350	0	—	—
Annual Growth	2.7%	—	—	—

2013 Year-End Financials
Return on assets: 4.7%
Return on equity: 14.4%
Current ratio: 0.30
Cash ($ mil.): —

TRI STAR ENERGY LLC

Auditors: LATTIMORE BLACK MORGAAN & CA

LOCATIONS
HQ: TRI STAR ENERGY LLC
  1740 ED TEMPLE BLVD, NASHVILLE, TN 372081850
Phone: 615 313-3600
Web: WWW.TRI-STARENERGY.COM

HISTORICAL FINANCIALS
Company Type: Private

Income Statement
FYE: December 31

	REVENUE ($ mil.)	NET INCOME ($ mil.)	NET PROFIT MARGIN	EMPLOYEES
12/12	749	1	0.2%	500
12/11	730	3	0.5%	—
12/10	635	4	0.7%	—
12/09	547	0	—	—
Annual Growth	11.0%	—	—	—

2012 Year-End Financials
Return on assets: 2.5%
Return on equity: 0.2%
Current ratio: 0.30
Cash ($ mil.): 1

TRI-WEST LTD

Tri-West tends to floor both residential and commercial customers with its broad selection of floor coverings. Founded in 1981 the company distributes floor coverings through about half a dozen warehouse facilities located in the western US and the Hawaiian Islands. In addition Tri-West also serves customers in Texas and Guam. Tri-West offers major manufacturers' products including carpets ceramic and specialty tile hardwood flooring laminate and vinyl flooring and eco-friendly items such as recycled rubber tiles and bamboo flooring.

As part of its business the company sells and distributes adhesives and tools from manufacturers such as Armstrong and California-based Taylor Adhesives.
  Geographic Reach
  Tri-West operates out of Santa Fe Springs California and has warehouses in San Diego California; Las Vegas Nevada; Phoenix Arizona; Albuquerque New Mexico; Salt Lake City Utah; and Waipahu Hawaii. It also serves Texas and Guam.
  Sales and Marketing
  The company serves several sectors such as commercial residential and environmentally friendly.
  Operations
  Tri-West sells commercial and residential flooring through manufactures the likes of Armstrong U.S. Rubber Recycling and VPI. The company sells eco-friendly flooring from Armstrong Kahrs USA LM Flooring Provenza Floors and Sound Seal among others.

EXECUTIVES
EVP, Jim Johnston
President, Dan Proctor
Controller, Tony Geiger
Vice President Technology, Naser Goyal
Vice President, Allen Gage
Auditors: KMJ CORBIN & COMPANY LLP IR

LOCATIONS
HQ: TRI-WEST LTD
  12005 PIKE ST, SANTA FE SPRINGS, CA 906706100
Phone: 562 566-1214

PRODUCTS/OPERATIONS

Selected Products
Adhesives & tools
Ceramic tile
Green products
Hardwood flooring
Laminate flooring
Luxury vinyl tile
Resilient flooring
Specialty products

COMPETITORS
Abbey Carpet	Florstar Sales
Adleta	HD Supply
B.R. Funsten	Lowe' s
CCA Global	

HISTORICAL FINANCIALS
Company Type: Private

Income Statement
FYE: December 31

	REVENUE ($ mil.)	NET INCOME ($ mil.)	NET PROFIT MARGIN	EMPLOYEES
12/13	162	14	8.7%	325
12/12	141	10	7.2%	—
12/11	117	7	6.1%	—
12/09	111	0	—	—
Annual Growth	9.8%	—	—	—

2013 Year-End Financials
Return on assets: 6.1%
Return on equity: 8.7%
Current ratio: 1.60
Cash ($ mil.): 8

TRIMEGA PURCHASING ASSOCIATION

Smart office products dealers pledge to buya lotta TriMega. The TriMega Purchasing Association is a product and services buying group made up of 590 independently owned office-supply dealers. TriMega in turn is a member of the larger Business Products Group International (BPGI) which gives TriMega's member dealers even more buying power and helps them compete with nationwide chains such as OfficeMax and Staples. TriMega also supplies its own Value Plus brand of office products. The not-for-profit cooperative was founded in 1987 and serves company's large and small from across the US.

EXECUTIVES
EVP Member Development, Grady Taylor
EVP Purchasing, Greg Fish
Vice Chairman, Lyle D. Dabbert
President, Charlie Cleary
Rebate Manager, Rachel Dorman
Accounting Manager, Gene Rigitano
Customer Service Supervisor, Diane Pakonen
Treasurer, Mark Porter
VP Marketing, Michael Morris
Credit Manager, Barbara Kraus
Marketing Manager, Kara Noble
Marketing Coordinator, LeeAna Theberg
Vice President Enterprise Technology, Lori Stevens
Executive Vice President Strategic Planning, Mark Hampton
Business Development Manager, Dan Fenton
Chairman, Bruce Eaton
Secretary, Tricia Burke

LOCATIONS
HQ: TRIMEGA PURCHASING ASSOCIATION
  5600 N RIVER RD STE 700, ROSEMONT, IL
  600185165
Phone: 847 699-3330
Web: WWW.TRIMEGA.ORG

COMPETITORS
BJ' s Wholesale Club	OfficeMax
Costco Wholesale	Staples
Office Depot	Wal-Mart

HISTORICAL FINANCIALS
Company Type: Private

Income Statement
FYE: June 30

	REVENUE ($ mil.)	NET INCOME ($ mil.)	NET PROFIT MARGIN	EMPLOYEES
06/13*	189	24	12.7%	19
12/11	387	36	9.4%	—
06/11	280	26	9.3%	—
03/09	90	0	—	—
Annual Growth	20.4%	—	—	—
*Fiscal year change

TRINITY HEALTH-MICHIGAN

LOCATIONS

HQ: TRINITY HEALTH-MICHIGAN
20555 VICTOR PKWY, LIVONIA, MI 481527031
Phone: 810 985-1500
Web: WWW.STJOESHEALTH.ORG

HISTORICAL FINANCIALS
Company Type: Private

Income Statement
FYE: June 30

	REVENUE ($ mil.)	NET INCOME ($ mil.)	NET PROFIT MARGIN	EMPLOYEES
06/13	2,475	138	5.6%	700
06/09	2,096	60	2.9%	—
Annual Growth	4.2%	23.0%	—	—

2013 Year-End Financials
Return on assets: 9.7%   Cash ($ mil.): 15
Return on equity: 5.6%
Current ratio: —

TRINITY MOTHER FRANCES HEALTH SYSTEM FOUNDATION

Trinity Mother Frances Health System Foundation (dba Trinity Mother Frances Hospitals and Clinics) has a complicated name but a simple mission: to improve patient health. Consisting of three general hospitals several specialist facilities and a large physicians' group Trinity Mother Frances serves northeastern Texas. Its largest acute-care facility is Mother Frances Hospital-Tyler with more than 400 beds offering comprehensive medical surgical trauma and cardiovascular care. Two smaller hospitals in Jacksonville and Winnsboro provide emergency diagnostic surgery and select specialty services. The Trinity Clinic is a multi-specialty physician group that includes 300 doctors in 36 community clinics.

Operations

Trinity Mother Frances Hospitals and Clinics' specialty facilities include the freestanding Trinity Mother Frances Rehabilitation Hospital in Tyler which has 75 beds and is operated through a joint venture with HealthSouth. It also operates the Tyler ContinueCARE Hospital a long-term acute care hospital located within the Mother Frances Hospital-Tyler as well as several urgent care centers.

Strategy

In 2010 the network added the 35-bed Mother Frances Hospital-Winnsboro facility when it took over control of the Texas Health Presbyterian Hospital Winnsboro from Texas Health Resources. The transfer was made to align the Winnsboro hospital with the main Tyler facility where the majority of specialized cases from Winnsboro were already being transferred.

The network also added a freestanding 72-bed cardiac facility the Louis and Peaches Owen Heart

Hospital in Tyler. The first phase of the center was added to the existing Mother Frances Hospital-Tyler facilities in 2010; the second stage is a six-story freestanding tower adjacent to the Tyler hospital. Construction on the tower started in early 2011 and was completed by the end of 2012.

Additionally Trinity Mother Frances Hospitals and Clinics is investing in information technology initiatives. It began installing electronic health record (EHR) systems at its facilities during 2012 as part of the US government's health care improvement initiatives.

Company Background

Trinity Mother Frances Hospitals and Clinics was established by the 1995 merger of Mother Frances Hospital and the Trinity Clinic both founded in the 1930s.

EXECUTIVES

President, J. Lindsey Bradley
EVP and COO, Ray Thompson
SVP Operations, Laura Owen
President and Chief Medical Officer TMF; President Trinity Clinic, Steven P. Keuer
EVP; Chief of Anesthesia Trinity Clinic, Gifford Eckhout
CEO Mother Frances Hospital - Jacksonville, Tom Cammack
CEO Mother Frances Hospital - Winnsboro, Janet Coates
CEO Louis and Peaches Owen Heart Hospital, John McGreevy
CEO ContinueCARE Hospital, Stephanie Hyde
CEO Trinity Mother Frances Rehabilitation Hospital, Sharla Anderson
VP and CIO, Jeff Pearson
Registered Nurse Clinical Director, Kelly Baggett
Senior Vice President Patient Care Services System Chief Nursing Officer, Robert (Bob) Rose
Vice President System Managed Care Regional Development, John (Jack) Webb
Vice President Finance, Elizabeth (Beth) Pulliman
Secretary, Terry Maddox

LOCATIONS

HQ: TRINITY MOTHER FRANCES HEALTH SYSTEM FOUNDATION
800 E DAWSON ST, TYLER, TX 757012036
Phone: 903 531-5057
Web: WWW.TMFHS.ORG

PRODUCTS/OPERATIONS

Selected Locations
DirectCARE (urgent care multiple sites)
Louis and Peaches Owen Heart Hospital Tyler
Mother Frances Hospital-Jacksonville
Mother Frances Hospital-Tyler
Mother Frances Hospital-Winnsboro
Trinity Clinics (physician practices multiple sites)
Trinity Mother Frances Rehabilitation Hospital-Tyler
Tyler ContinueCARE Hospital

Selected Services
Anesthesiology
Audiology
Bariatric Surgery Center
Cancer
Cardiac Services
Cardiothoracic Surgery
Critical Care Intensivists
Ear Nose & Throat
Emergency Medicine
Endocrinology
Gastroenterology Hepatology and Endoscopy
Family Medicine
General Surgeons
Genetics
Hospitalists
Imaging Radiology Mammography
Internal Medicine
Neonatology
Neuroscience Institute
Obstetrics & Gynecology

Occupational Medicine - Health At Work
Ophthalmology Optometry & Optical Services
Orthopedics
Pain Medicine
Pediatrics
Physical Medicine and Rehabilitation
Plastic Surgery
Podiatry
Psychiatry
Rehabilitation Hospital
Rheumatology
Sleep Medicine
Sports Medicine
Surgery Services
Trauma Services
Urgent Care
Urology Institute & Continence Center
Vascular Institute
Women & Children
WoundCARE

COMPETITORS

Community Health Systems
East Texas Medical Center Regional Healthcare
Good Shepherd Health System
HCA
Hunt Memorial
Memorial Health System of East Texas
Parkland Health & Hospital System
Southwestern Medical Center
Tenet Healthcare
The Methodist Health System
United Surgical Partners
Wadley Regional Medical Center
Woodland Heights Medical Center

HISTORICAL FINANCIALS
Company Type: Private

Income Statement
FYE: June 30

	REVENUE ($ mil.)	NET INCOME ($ mil.)	NET PROFIT MARGIN	EMPLOYEES
06/14	711	36	5.2%	3,551
06/13	653	21	3.3%	—
06/10	603	19	3.3%	—
06/09	562	0	—	—
Annual Growth	4.8%	—	—	—

2014 Year-End Financials
Return on assets: 5.5%   Cash ($ mil.): 74
Return on equity: 5.2%
Current ratio: 1.20

TROUT-BLUE CHELAN-MAGI INC.

Trout-Blue Chelan-Magi has a simpler and more apt name by which it does business –Chelan Fruit. The company is fruit growers' cooperative with some 420 member/growers located in Washington State. The co-op prepares packs and sells its members' apples pears cherries and other stone fruits including peaches apricots nectarines and plums. The fruit is shipped both domestically and internationally. Product marketing is conducted through Chelan Fresh Marketing. The co-op was formed through the 1995 merger of two cooperatives Trout and Blue Chelan; the combined company changed its name again in 2004 with the acquisition of Magi.

EXECUTIVES

Assistant General Manager, Jim Divis
CEO and General Manager, Reggie Collins
CFO, Todd Kamers

CEO Chelan Fresh Marketing, Steve Terry
Human Resources Director, Alissa Senyitko

LOCATIONS

HQ: TROUT-BLUE CHELAN-MAGI INC.
8 HOWSER RD, CHELAN, WA 988169590
Phone: 509 682-2591

PRODUCTS/OPERATIONS

Selected Member/Growers
Blue Chelan Inc.
Gebbers Farms
Mutual Apple Growers Inc. (MAGI)
Trout Incorporated
Trout-Blue Chelan Inc.
Trout-Blue Chelan-Magi Inc. - Chelan Fruit

COMPETITORS

Auvil Fruit	Graceland Fruit
Cherry Central	Greenridge Fruit
Cooperative Inc.	Hudson River Fruit
Chiquita Brands	Jack Brown Produce
Dole Food	Knouse Foods
Fresh Del Monte	Shoreline Fruit
Produce	Tree Top
Gold Digger Apples	

HISTORICAL FINANCIALS

Company Type: Private

Income Statement FYE: August 31

	REVENUE ($ mil.)	NET INCOME ($ mil.)	NET PROFIT MARGIN	EMPLOYEES
08/14	156	4	2.6%	675
08/13	180	5	2.8%	—
08/12	149	5	3.4%	—
08/11	138	0	—	—
Annual Growth	4.2%	—	—	—

2014 Year-End Financials

Return on assets: 4.0%
Return on equity: 2.6%
Current ratio: 0.30

Cash ($ mil.): 12

TROY UNIVERSITY

Troy University is not the topic of a Homeric poem but you'd probably find a Helen enrolled there. The school is a public institution comprised of a network of campuses throughout Alabama and worldwide. The network includes 60 campuses in some 7 US states and four other countries. Troy University has a total student enrollment of about 22000 and offers degrees in arts and sciences business communications and fine arts education and health and human services. The school also operates the Confucius Institute to promote understanding of Chinese language and culture.

Geographic Reach
Troy University has four campuses in Alabama and satellite locations in Florida Georgia North California South Carolina Tennessee Texas and Virginia as well as in Japan Korea Malaysia and Vietnam.

Operations
The university offers 110 undergraduate majors and minors 22 master's degree programs and one doctoral program as well as ROTC programs and research opportunities.

Company Background
Troy University was founded in 1887 by the Alabama Legislature as the State Normal School an institution to train teachers for Alabama's schools. The Troy University System was formed in 1982.

EXECUTIVES

Secretary, Sara Hester

LOCATIONS

HQ: TROY UNIVERSITY
600 UNIVERSITY AVE, TROY, AL 360820001
Phone: 334 670-3108
Web: WWW.TROY.EDU

COMPETITORS

Auburn University	University of Alabama
Birmingham-Southern	at Birmingham
College	University of Mobile
Miles College	University of South
Spring Hill College	Alabama
University of Alabama	

HISTORICAL FINANCIALS

Company Type: Private

Income Statement FYE: September 30

	REVENUE ($ mil.)	NET INCOME ($ mil.)	NET PROFIT MARGIN	EMPLOYEES
09/08	156	29	18.6%	3,000
09/07*	164	21	12.8%	—
12/06	2,023	0	—	—
Annual Growth	—35074.6%			

*Fiscal year change

2008 Year-End Financials

Return on assets: —
Return on equity: 18.6%
Current ratio: 1.70

Cash ($ mil.): 47

TRUE VALUE COMPANY

To survive against home improvement giants such as The Home Depot and Lowe's True Value Co. (TVC) is relying on the true value of service. Formed by the 1997 merger of Cotter & Company and ServiStar Coast to Coast the retailer-owned wholesale hardware cooperative serves some 4400 retail outlets in 58-plus countries. Stores offer home improvement and garden supplies as well as appliances housewares sporting goods and pet food. In addition to the flagship True Value banner members operate under the names of Taylor Rental Grand Rental Station Home & Garden Showplace Induserve Supply and Party Central among others. True Value also manufactures its own brand of paints.

Operations
Additional key cooperative members (which operate independently of TVC) include Leeway True Value Thomas Home Center Wilco Farm Stores Milwaukee Tool and Miami Home Centers.

In addition to its main chain hardware stores TVC operates several specialty franchise businesses. Grand Rental Station and Taylor Rental Centers rent tools party and event supplies and equipment and contractor equipment to amateurs and professional contractors. Home and Garden Showplace is a garden center cooperative offering products for homes gardens and landscaping projects. Induserve Supply sells hand and power tools paint janitorial supplies and many more products to commercial and industrial customers. Party Central franchises rent supplies for weddings backyard parties. Its customers include caterers and event planners.

TVC also manages national advertising and promotion efforts.

Geographic Reach

Chicago-based TVC operates about a dozen regional distribution centers across the US. TVC's goods and services are sold primarily in the US.
Sales and Marketing
TVC brands which can cost between 15 and 20 percent less than comparable national brands include True Value Master Mechanic Green Thumb and Master Plumber.

The company sells through retail and e-commerce outlets. Advertising expenses totaled $50025 in 2014 slightly up from $49943 in 2013.
Financial Performance
Sales have risen gradually for the past few years and in fiscal 2014 they rose 6% to $1.49 billion. The higher sales were largely due to increases in comparable sales and participating retailers. However net income dropped 26% to $41 million as selling general and administrative expenses –labor benefits etc. –rose 21%.

Operating cash outflow totaled $20.4 million in 2014 (versus an inflow of $44 million in 2013) as more cash was used toward inventory and other factors.
Strategy
TVC has decided on a number of initiatives to boost engagement and increase relevance. These include marketing analysis efforts dialogues with retailers and education.

Essential to the company's growth strategy has been the rollout of its Destination True Value (DTV) retail format which aims to simplify shopping in its hardware stores particularly for its female clientele (who hold sway when it comes to tackling home improvement projects). The format features a "racetrack" layout for easy navigation as well as color-coded signs brighter lighting and an expanded array of decorative hardware and paint. Also the format is relatively flexible and allows owners to customize their store layouts for their particular local markets. TVC estimates that stores operating under the DTV format average about 9% higher sales than their non-DTV counterparts. In 2014 TVC completed a review of DTV with plans to adjust as necessary.

In addition to the DTV plan the company is working to woo younger do-it-yourselfers into its stores through the reach of digital marketing. Stores produce area-specific online circulars and True Value's website offers a project library product guides and bargains of the month. The co-op is taking its marketing efforts forward with social media and an e-commerce site.

HISTORY

Noting that hardware retailers had begun to form wholesale cooperatives to lower costs John Cotter a traveling hardware salesman and associate Ed Lanctot started pitching the wholesale co-op idea in 1947 to small-town and suburban hardware retailers and by early 1948 they had enrolled 25 merchants for $1500 each. Cotter became chairman of the new firm Cotter & Company.

The co-op created the Value & Service (V&S) store trademark in 1951 to emphasize the advantages of an independent hardware store. Acquisitions included the 1963 purchase of Chicago-based wholesaler Hibbard Spencer Bartlett giving Cotter 400 new members and the well-known True Value trademark which soon replaced V&S signs. Four years later Cotter broadened its focus by buying the General Paint & Chemical Company (Tru-Test paint). The V&S name was revived in 1972 for a five-and-dime store co-op V&S Variety Stores.

In 1989 Cotter died and Lanctot retired. (Lanctot died in October 2003.) By 1989 there were almost 7000 True Value Stores. Cotter moved into Canada in 1992 by acquiring hardware distributor and store operator Macleod-Stedman (275 outlets).

Juggling variety-store and hardware merchandise and delivering very small amounts of merchandise to a lukewarm co-op membership did not allow for economies of scale so in 1995 the company quit its manufacturing operations and its US variety stores (though it still serves variety stores in Canada operating as C&S Choices) tightened membership requirements and introduced new services.

Two years later Cotter formed TruServ by merging with hardware wholesaler ServiStar Coast to Coast. ServiStar had its origins in the nation's first hardware co-op American Hardware Supply which was founded in Pittsburgh in 1910 by M. R. Porter John Howe and E. S. Corlett. By 1988 the year it changed its name to ServiStar the co-op topped $1 billion in sales.

ServiStar expanded in the upper Midwest and on the West Coast in 1990 when it acquired the assets of the Coast to Coast chain (founded in 1928 as a franchise hardware store in Minneapolis); ServiStar brought Coast to Coast out of bankruptcy two years later making it a co-op. Merging its 1992 acquisition of Taylor Rental Center with its Grand Rental Station stores in 1993 made ServiStar the #1 general rental chain. In 1996 it consolidated Coast to Coast's operations into its own and changed its name to ServiStar Coast to Coast.

President Don Hoye became CEO of the company in 1999. That year TruServ slashed 1000 jobs and declared it would convert all its hardware store chains to the True Value banner. But TruServ lost $131 million in 1999 over bookkeeping gaffes and co-op members received no dividends. Of 2800 ServiStar dealers only 1900 raised the True Value flag. Others either declined to switch or were never offered the change because other True Value stores already shared their market area. In addition stores began deserting the co-op because of inventory and other problems. In late 2000 the company sold its lumber and building materials business.

As competition continued to increase in 2001 the company was facing falling sales lawsuits from shareholders and accusations by retailers of unfair practices intended to pressure them into adopting the cooperative's flagship True Value banner. TruServ also had to confront a $200 million loan default. It made cuts in its corporate staff and divested its Canadian interests. In July 2001 Hoye resigned. The company's CFO and COO Pamela Forbes Lieberman was named the new CEO that November.

In April 2002 the company reported a net loss of $50.7 million during 2001 which it attributed to restructuring charges inventory write-downs and finance fees. Also that month the company announced that it had received $200 million in long-term financing. TruServ under SEC investigation for alleged inventory accounting and other internal-control problems was one of several companies that failed in August 2002 to meet a government requirement to swear by their past financial results.

In January 2003 TruServ received about $125 million in financing from investment firm W. P. Carey & Co. in a sale-leaseback deal on seven of TruServ's distribution centers. In March TruServ settled the SEC's allegations without admitting or denying them and agreed to follow measures intended to ensure compliance with securities laws.

TruServ changed its name to True Value in January 2005. In December the company sold its oil-based paint manufacturing operation in Chicago to Blackhawk/Halsted for about $10 million.

EXECUTIVES

SVP and CFO, David A. (Dave) Shadduck, $317,750 total compensation
VP Specialty Businesses, Eric Lane
VP and CIO, Rosalee Hermens
President and CEO, John Hartmann
Chief Merchandising Officer, Ken Goodgame
SVP and COO, Abhinav Shukla
Vice President, Ken Lanis
Vice President, Barbara Byrum
Senior Vice President and General Counsel Secretary, Cathy Anderson
Chairman, Brent A. Burger
Board Member, J George
Treasurer, Michael (Mel) Brixey
Auditors: MCGLADREY LLP SCHAUMBURG ILL

LOCATIONS

HQ: TRUE VALUE COMPANY
8600 W BRYN MAWR AVE 100S, CHICAGO, IL 606313505
Phone: 773 695-5000
Web: WWW.TRUEVALUE.COM

PRODUCTS/OPERATIONS

Selected Operations
Grand Rental Station (general rental)
Home & Garden Showplace (nursery and giftware)
Induserve Supply (commercial and industrial)
Party Central (parties and corporate events)
Taylor Rental (general rental)
True Value (hardware)

COMPETITORS

84 Lumber	Menard
Ace Hardware	Northern Tool
Akzo Nobel	Orgill
Benjamin Moore	Sears
Do it Best	Sherwin-Williams
Fastenal	Stock Building Supply
Hertz	Sutherland Lumber
Home Depot	United Rentals
Kmart	Valspar
Lowe's	Wal-Mart
McCoy Corp.	

HISTORICAL FINANCIALS
Company Type: Private

Income Statement
FYE: December 28

	REVENUE ($ mil.)	NET INCOME ($ mil.)	NET PROFIT MARGIN	EMPLOYEES
12/13	1,411	55	3.9%	3,000
12/12	1,399	74	5.4%	—
12/11*	1,864	60	3.2%	—
01/11	1,804	0	—	—
Annual Growth	(7.9%)	—	—	—

*Fiscal year change

2013 Year-End Financials

Return on assets: 15.9%   Cash ($ mil.): 4
Return on equity: 3.9%
Current ratio: 0.50

TRUMAN ARNOLD COMPANIES

It is not just jibber jabber —this jobber gets the job done by distributing wholesale petroleum across the US. Truman Arnold Companies (TAC) has more than 400 associates with fuel volume of more than 2 billion gallons a year and markets and distributes petroleum products to customers through its TAC Energy subsidiary. Through a partnership it operates two major petroleum terminals one in Arkansas and one in Texas which collectively have more than 1.3 million barrels of capacity. Through its TAC Air unit the company offers fixed-based operations (FBO) including aircraft fueling hangar and ground transportation services through 14 general aviation facilities located across the US.

Operations
TAC's Aviation Services Wholesale Petroleum Marketing Branded Petroleum Marketing and Petroleum Terminal Services operations function independently but take advantage of shared management and technical resources. The company's major subsidiaries include TAC Air TAC Energy Cowhorn Creek Fuel Base and Keystone Aviation.

The company's Aviation Services maintains a fleet of aircraft and is engaged in aircraft maintenance sales and brokerage and aircraft management.

Strategy
In 2015 TAC Energy launched ENERGIZE Online a new product that provides an improved user interface for managing fuel purchase transactions

Aviation Services is a growth market. In 2013 Keystone Aviation expanded its line of aviation products and services by making its Aurora Oregon shop a Cirrus Authorized Service Center to serve Cirrus owners in and around Oregon. In addition to Cirrus the Aurora location is an authorized service center for Daher-Socata. That year Keystone Aviation also became a Quest Aircraft (turboprops) distributor in California Colorado Nevada and Utah.

Mergers and Acquisitions In 2015 TAC Air purchased the facilities of Central Flying Service at the Bill and Hillary Clinton National Airport in Little Rock and will operate its fueling ground handling hangar operations and other related services as part of the TAC Air network. Also included is the purchase of Airport Services Inc. which provides airline fueling services.

Company Background
The company opened its 13th FBO in 2009 in the Spirit of St. Louis Airport in Chesterfield Missouri. It opened an executive terminal (its first at any FBO location) at Blue Grass Airport in Kentucky in July 2010. To raise cash in October 2010 TAC Air sold its Greenville South Carolina FBO operation to Greenville Jet Center for undisclosed terms.

TAC has also grown its wholesale energy segment. In 2009 TAC Energy acquired Fuel Managers (which has operations in 18 states) for an undisclosed price. The acquisition of the fuel wholesaler helped to boost TAC Energy's position in the supply market in the Central and Western US.

To keep up with the growth of the company in 2011 TAC expanded its Dallas sales office. The company anticipates doubling in size by 2016 and sees Dallas as a key operational/sales hub for managing its growth.

In 2012 to gain operational and financial support from another private energy company TAC Energy also combined its Caddo Mills Texas and North Little Rock Arkansas terminal operations into a master limited partnership with JP Energy Partners LP.

Expanding its fuel supply businesses in 2013 TAC Energy completed construction of a new diesel exhaust fluid distribution hub. The expansion at the terminal enabled TAC Energy to become a Tier 1 distributor of TerraCair Ultrapure Diesel Exhaust Fluid.

The family-owned and -operated company was founded in 1964 by Texarkana businessman Truman Arnold. It once operated a chain of 125 Road Runner convenience stores in eight states before selling this network to Total Petroleum in 1989. TAC revived the brand in 2003.

EXECUTIVES

General Counsel and Senior Vice President, James H (Jamie) Day
President and COO, Gregory A. (Greg) Arnold
SVP and CFO, Steve McMillen
VP and CIO, Michael Davis
Chairman and CEO, Truman Arnold
Auditors: THOMAS & THOMAS LLP TEXARKANA

LOCATIONS

HQ: TRUMAN ARNOLD COMPANIES
701 S ROBISON RD, TEXARKANA, TX 755016747
Phone: 903 794-3835
Web: WWW.TACENERGY.COM

COMPETITORS

Atlantic Aviation   Million Air
Getty Petroleum   Signature Flight
  Marketing   Sun Coast Resources
Gulf Oil   Warren Equities

HISTORICAL FINANCIALS
Company Type: Private

Income Statement
FYE: September 30

	REVENUE ($ mil.)	NET INCOME ($ mil.)	NET PROFIT MARGIN	EMPLOYEES
09/14	2,259	11	0.5%	550
09/13	2,172	54	2.5%	—
09/12	2,471	11	0.4%	—
Annual Growth	(4.4%)	3.4%	—	—

2014 Year-End Financials
Return on assets: 3.3%   Cash ($ mil.): 5
Return on equity: 0.5%
Current ratio: 0.80

TRUMAN MEDICAL CENTER INCORPORATED

If you're miserable in Missouri Truman Medical Center (TMC) can offer TLC and health care. TMC provides primary and mental health care at two not-for-profit hospitals in the Kansas City (Missouri) area with a combined total of about 540 beds. Its Hospital Hill runs one of the busiest emergency rooms in Kansas City and is known for treatments related to asthma diabetes obstetrics ophthalmology weight management and women's health. TMC Lakewood is a leading academic medical center providing a range of health care services to the greater Kansas City metropolitan area including uninsured patients.

OperationsThe hospital system has a combined capacity of more than 540 beds including 353 acute-care beds and 188 long-term-care beds. With a medical staff of more than 500 TMC admits more than 22000 patients and handles more than 322000 medical outpatient visits and more than 226000 mental health visits annually. It also treats more than 101000 emergency room patients every year.Truman Medical Center Hospital Hill provides an array of acute care and outpatient services. In addition to Emergency Medicine and Trauma TMC Hospital Hill is also noted for treatments of asthma and diabetes and for providing obstetrics ophthalmology weight management and women's health programs.TMC Lakewood is home to the University of Missouri Kansas City School of Medicine Community and Family Medicine Residency program.Truman Medical Centers Behavioral Health

is a leader in the treatment of mental health and substance abuse treatment. It serves more than 17000 patients a year and provides a comprehensive array of mental health and substance abuse treatment to persons living in the Kansas City Missouri metropolitan area.Sales and MarketingMedicare and Medicaid combined account for around half of TMC's net patient revenues; self-pay accounts represent about 35%.Financial PerformanceIn fiscal 2014 (ended June) net revenues totaled $422 million.Strategy

The system expands health care offerings by opening new care centers or by adding on to its existing ones. For example during 2014 it opened The Richard and Annette Bloch Cancer Center. It also opened Fairmount Family Medical Care in Western Independence Missouri a community that hadn't had a comprehensive health care facility since 2007.

It has also recently added a wound care center to its Hospital Hill campus.

Due to state and federal regulations TMC shut down the behavioral health emergency department at Hospital Hill in 2015. Going forward it will either treat incoming patients with acute mental health crises at its 47-bed standard emergency department or send them to another psychiatric facility.

EXECUTIVES

CFO, Allen (Al) Johnson
EVP Clinical Coordination, Mark S. McPhee
Chief Medical Officer, Mark T. Steele
COO Behavioral Health, Marsha L. Morgan
SVP Strategy Business Development and Performance Integration; CIO, Mitzi Cardenas
Corporate Quality Medical Director, Shauna R. Roberts
Chief Nursing Officer, Lynette Wheeler
COO Truman Medical Center Lakewood, Charles W. (Charlie) Shields
VP Professional Health Services, Lynda Donegan
Executive Director TMC Charitable Foundation, Karlyn Wilkins
Chief Nursing Officer, Amy Peters
Pharm D, Thomas Gregory
Rph, Eric Young
V Pres, Dmeter Dragovich
Director Of Pharmacy, Erin Pender
Vice President, Jerre Wiggans
Vice President Audit and Compliance, Barbara (Barb) Zubeck
Director of Radiology, Carole Jones
Auditors: BKD LLP KANSAS CITY MO

LOCATIONS

HQ: TRUMAN MEDICAL CENTER INCORPORATED
2301 HOLMES ST, KANSAS CITY, MO 641082677
Phone: 816 404-1000
Web: WWW.TRUMED.ORG

PRODUCTS/OPERATIONS

Truman Medical Center Hospital Hill
Asthma Center
The Birthplace
Cardiovascular Center
Chiropractic Services KC CORE
Dental Maxillofacial Surgery
Diabetes Center
Emergency Care
Eye Clinic
Eye Foundation
GI Gastrointestinal
Hospital Hill Medical Pavilion
Infectious Disease Clinic
Oncology
Orthopaedics
Pulmonary Fibrosis
Radiology Services
Rehabilitation Services
Sickle Cell Disease Center

Sleep Center
Trauma Services
TruMed Clinic
Weight Management
Women' s Care Breast Center
Women' s Health Services
TMC Lakewood
Family Medicine Center
Lakewood Family Birthplace
Chiropractic Services
Counseling Services Lakewood
Dental Services
Dental Services Elks Mobile
GI Gastrointestinal
Emergency Medicine
Eye Care Center
Lakewood Medical Pavilion
Longterm Care Center
Medical Detox
Orthopaedic Services
Outpatient Surgery Center
Podiatry
Rehabilitation Services
Sports Medicine
Women' s Health Services

COMPETITORS

Ascension Health   Shawnee Mission
Children' s Mercy   Medical Center
  Hospital   University of Kansas
CoxHealth   Medical Center
Saint Luke' s Health   Via Christi Health
  System   System

HISTORICAL FINANCIALS
Company Type: Private

Income Statement
FYE: June 30

	REVENUE ($ mil.)	NET INCOME ($ mil.)	NET PROFIT MARGIN	EMPLOYEES
06/13	493	(4)	—	3,000
06/10	439	5	1.2%	—
06/09	424	16	3.8%	—
06/08	4	0	—	—
Annual Growth	155.5%	—	—	—

2013 Year-End Financials
Return on assets: 25.5%   Cash ($ mil.): —
Return on equity: (-1.0%)
Current ratio: 0.40

TRUSTEES OF BOSTON COLLEGE

Students at Boston College (BC) get both academic excellence and the Red Sox. Located six miles from downtown Boston the university enrolls 14100 full- and part-time students (about a third of whom are graduate students) from every state in the US and 80 other countries. It has a student-teacher ratio of 13:1. BC offers degrees in more than 50 fields of study through its schools and colleges on four campuses. The university also has more than 20 research centers including the Institute for Scientific Research and the Center for International Higher Education. BC is one of the oldest Jesuit Catholic universities in the nation and has the largest Jesuit community in the world.

Geographic Reach

The university has campuses in Brighton Chestnut Hill Dover and Newton Massachusetts. It also operates a campus in Dublin Ireland.

Operations

About 70% of its undergraduate student body are self-identified as Roman Catholic.

The university is home to more than 20 centers and institutes designated for research and teaching. Research opportunities including participation in faculty research projects exist for both undergraduate and graduate students. It also houses 8 libraries with 2.9 million volumes.

The cost of tuition stood a $46670 for 2014-15.

Financial Performance

BC has enjoyed steady growth from voluntary giving by its alumni. Its endowment has grown to $2.2 billion placing it among the top 40 in the US. In 2014 it reported an operating budget of $917 million. Its revenues of $702.7 million were 5% up on the previous year due to growth in tuition and fees as well as auxiliary enterprises.

Strategy

BC's strategic plan includes adding 100 new faculty positions expanding research by faculty and graduate students increasing student financial aid to more than $128 million annually and extending undergraduate opportunities in international study internships and student formation. In 2013 it announced plans to build a $90 million residence hall near its Chestnut Hill campus.

Company Background

The university was founded by Jesuits in 1863. During its first seven decades BC was an exclusively undergraduate institution that served sons of the Irish working class. Its liberal arts emphasis was on the Greek and Latin classics English and modern languages and philosophy and religion. Development into the college it is today did not begin until the 1920s when the Graduate School of Arts and Sciences the Law School and the Evening College (known today as the James A. Woods S.J. College of Advancing Studies) were inaugurated. All classes became co-educational in the 1970s and today BC has a fairly equal split among male and female students.

EXECUTIVES

Vp Human Resources, Leo Sullivan
President, William P. Leahy
Chancellor, J. Donald Monan
Dean Carroll School of Management, Andrew C. Boynton
Dean School of Social Work, Alberto Godenzi
EVP, Patrick J. Keating
Associate VP Applications and Systems Services, Michael Bourque
Financial VP and Treasurer, John D. Burke
Provost and Dean of Faculties, David Quigley
Dean of Students, Tom Mogan
Dean School of Theology and Ministry, Mark Massa
Dean Connell School of Nursing, Susan Gennaro
Dean Lynch School of Education, Maureen E. Kenny
Dean Law School, Vincent Rougeau
Interim Dean Morrissey College of Arts and Sciences, Gregory Kalscheur
Dean Woods College of Advancing Studies, James Burns
Senior Vice President, James McIntyre
Assoc Vp Alumni Assoc, John Feudo
Assistant Vice President Inst Rsrch Plng Assess, Kelli Armstrong
Vice President Information Technology, Patricia McCormack
Vice President Special Assistant To PR, William (Bill) Neenan
Vice President Information Technology, Mark Ben
Vice President, John (Jack) Westman
Associate Vice President Information Technology, Mary Corcoran
Vice President, Michael (Mel) Forcier
Assistant Vice President, Ricardo Krulig
Vice President, Madeleine Moore
Vice President Assistant to President, Mary Lee Delong

Vice President, Donna Cullinan
Vice President For Finance And Administration, Christian Brand
Student Office Assistant For Senior Vice President Of University Advancement, Elizabeth Zappala
Vice President, John Westman
Department Chair, Richard Tresch
Vice President, Alicia Angeles
Associate Vice President of Facilities Services, Martin Dugal
Vice President, Robert (Bob) O'neill
Vice President, Pat Ryan
Department Chair, Susan (Sue) Shell
Vice President Engineering, David (Dave) Jellison
Chairman, John F. Fish
Vice Chairman, Peter K. Markell, age 59
Investment Officer Office Of The Associate Treasurer, Travis Looker
Assistant Treasurer Office Of The Associate Treasurer, Mark Conner
Secretary Palliative Care Grant School Of Nursing, Marybeth Crowley
Board Member, Marylou Sudders
Assistant Treasurer and Associate Director of Investmts Office of the Associate Treasurer, Johnathan Zona
Board Member, Barbara (Barb) Hebard
Executive Board Member, Wei Jingni
Auditors: PRICEWATERHOUSECOOPERS LLP BO

LOCATIONS

HQ: TRUSTEES OF BOSTON COLLEGE
140 COMMONWEALTH AVE, CHESTNUT HILL, MA 024673800
Phone: 617 552-8000
Web: WWW.BC.EDU

PRODUCTS/OPERATIONS

Selected Colleges and Schools
Carolyn A. and Peter S. Lynch School of Education
College of Arts and Sciences
Graduate School of Arts and Sciences
Graduate School of Social Work
James A. Woods S.J. College of Advancing Studies
School of Law
School of Theology and Ministry
Wallace E. Carroll School of Management
William F. Connell School of Nursing

HISTORICAL FINANCIALS

Company Type: Private

Income Statement FYE: May 31

	REVENUE ($ mil.)	NET INCOME ($ mil.)	NET PROFIT MARGIN	EMPLOYEES
05/14	702	221	31.5%	2,509
05/13	671	270	40.3%	—
05/12	653	(76)	—	—
05/11	643	0	—	—
Annual Growth	3.0%	—	—	—

TRUSTEES OF MEASE HOSPITAL INC.

Auditors: ERNST & YOUNG US LLP ATLANTA

LOCATIONS

HQ: TRUSTEES OF MEASE HOSPITAL INC.
601 MAIN ST, DUNEDIN, FL 346985848
Phone: 727 733-1111
Web: WWW.MPMHEALTH.COM

HISTORICAL FINANCIALS

Company Type: Private

Income Statement FYE: December 31

	REVENUE ($ mil.)	NET INCOME ($ mil.)	NET PROFIT MARGIN	EMPLOYEES
12/09	336	31	9.4%	2,000
12/08	231	15	6.7%	—
12/06	277	29	10.7%	—
12/05	256	0	—	—
Annual Growth	7.0%	—	—	—

2009 Year-End Financials

Return on assets: —
Return on equity: 9.4%
Current ratio: 1.20
Cash ($ mil.): —

TRUSTEES OF THE ESTATE OF BERNICE PAUAHI BISHOP

Kamehameha Schools provides an education fit for a king ... or queen. The private charitable trust was founded and endowed by Princess Bernice Pauahi Bishop great granddaughter and last royal descendant of Kamehameha the Great. One of the largest independent schools in the US Kamehameha educates more than 5000 elementary middle school and high school students many of whom board at one of its three Hawaii campuses. In addition it operates some 30 preschools with a total enrollment of about 1500. Kamehameha Schools is also the largest private property owner in the state of Hawaii and uses the proceeds from its real estate operations to support its schools.

The Kamehameha School for Boys was established in 1887 followed by the Kamehameha School for Girls which opened in 1894. By 1955 the schools consolidated onto a 600-acre campus with views of Honolulu that span from Pearl Harbor to Diamond Head.

To this day Kamehameha Schools gives preferential admissions treatment to students of Hawaiian decent a long-standing policy it is fighting to preserve despite the controversy it creates. The schools have successfully fought off several lawsuits aimed at opening its doors to other ethnicities including a close decision by an appeals court in 2009.

EXECUTIVES

Director of Admissions, Pua Fernandez
Vice President Human Resources, Winona White
Auditors: DELOITTE TAX LLP HONOLULU HI

LOCATIONS

HQ: TRUSTEES OF THE ESTATE OF BERNICE PAUAHI BISHOP
567 S KING ST STE 200, HONOLULU, HI 968133079
Phone: 808 523-6200
Web: WWW.KSBE.EDU

COMPETITORS

Edison Learning   Learning Care Group

Income Statement
FYE: June 30

	REVENUE ($ mil.)	NET INCOME ($ mil.)	NET PROFIT MARGIN	EMPLOYEES
06/13	519	109	21.1%	1,500
06/10	333	(21)	—	—
06/09	1	1	69.0%	—
Annual Growth	308.1%	203.6%		

2013 Year-End Financials
Return on assets: 11.8%   Cash ($ mil.): 22
Return on equity: 21.1%
Current ratio: —

TRUSTEES OF TUFTS COLLEGE INC.

Tufts University wants to light up the minds of New England scholars. The school offers undergraduate and graduate degrees in areas such as education engineering psychology art English music and medicine. The university enrolls some 11000 students and has 1300 faculty members and it offers classes in 70 fields at three campuses in Massachusetts (Boston Medford/Somerville and Grafton). It also has an international campus in Talloires France. Tufts University's Fletcher School of Law and Diplomacy is the oldest continuous international relations graduate program in the country. The school is also home to New England's only Veterinary School.

Operations

Tufts University has a number of research programs at all three campuses including clinical studies in medical dental veterinary and nutritional fields. It also has research programs in areas such as biology engineering and technology many of which are funded through grants and fellowship funds.

Financial Performance

Tufts University has an endowment of about $1.1 billion.

Strategy

Tufts University is working to expand the resources its School of Medicine. In 2012 it moved to add a new medical research lab to study serious infectious diseases (such as tuberculosis) within the Biomedical Research and Public Health Building. It also expanded the Cummings School of Veterinary Medicine by adding a new clinic for the care and study of pets with obesity problems. The university also expands by adding new degree programs such as a doctorate in mamalian genetics in 2011.

Company Background

Tufts was founded in 1852 through a land donation by Boston-area businessman Charles Tufts to the Universalist Church. The school adopted its motto Pax et Lux (Peace and Light) in 1857.

EXECUTIVES

Dean Tisch College of Citizenship and Public Service, Alan D. Solomont, age 66
VP Finance and Treasurer, Thomas S. McGurty
Dean The Fletcher School, James G. Stavridis
EVP, Patricia L. Campbell
VP Information Technology and CIO, David J. Kahle
President, Anthony P. Monaco

Provost and SVP, David R. Harris
Dean School of Dental Medicine, Huw F. Thomas
Dean School of Medicine, Harris Berman
Dean Cummings School of Veterinary Medicine, Deborah T. Kochevar
VP Communications and Marketing, Christine C. Sanni
Dean School of Arts and Sciences, James M. Glaser
Dean School of Engineering, Jianmin Qu
Dean Friedman School of Nutrition Science and Policy, Dariush Mozaffarian
Dean Sackler School of Graduate Biomedical Sciences, Naomi Rosenberg
Vice President Operations, Linda Snyder
Chairman, Peter R. Dolan, age 59
Vice Chairman, William R. (Bill) O'Reilly
Vice Chairman, Jonathan M. (Jon) Tisch
Auditors: PRICEWATERHOUSECOOPERS LLP

LOCATIONS

HQ: TRUSTEES OF TUFTS COLLEGE INC.
169 HOLLAND ST STE 318, SOMERVILLE, MA 021442401
Phone: 617 628-5000
Web: WWW.DENTAL.TUFTS.EDU

PRODUCTS/OPERATIONS

Schools & Colleges
Cummings School of Veterinary Science
Graduate School of Arts & Sciences
The Fletcher School
Friedman School of Nutrition Science and Policy
Sackler School of Graduate Biomedical Sciences
School of Arts & Sciences
School of Dental Medicine
School of Engineering
School of Medicine
Tisch College of Citizenship and Public Service

HISTORICAL FINANCIALS
Company Type: Private

Income Statement
FYE: June 30

	REVENUE ($ mil.)	NET INCOME ($ mil.)	NET PROFIT MARGIN	EMPLOYEES
06/13	768	127	16.6%	4,100
06/12	769	(100)		
06/11	851	83	9.8%	—
06/10	767	0	—	—
Annual Growth	0.0%			

2013 Year-End Financials
Return on assets: —   Cash ($ mil.): 64
Return on equity: 16.6%
Current ratio: —

TUDOR INVESTMENT CORPORATION

Auditors: ERNST & YOUNG LLP NEW YORK N

LOCATIONS

HQ: TUDOR INVESTMENT CORPORATION
1275 KING ST, GREENWICH, CT 068312936
Phone: 203 863-6700
Web: WWW.TUDORFUNDS.COM

Income Statement
FYE: December 31

	ASSETS ($ mil.)	NET INCOME ($ mil.)	INCOME AS % OF ASSETS	EMPLOYEES
12/13	905	486	53.7%	291
12/11	624	187	30.0%	—
12/10	584	(106)	—	—
Annual Growth	15.7%			

2013 Year-End Financials
Return on assets: —   Sales ($ mil): 946
Return on equity: 51.4%

TURTLE & HUGHES INC

Turtle & Hughes' longevity has demonstrated that slow and steady really does win the race when it comes to distributing electrical and industrial equipment. The company's exhaustive lineup is sold through three subsidiaries: Turtle & Hughes Integrated Supply Turtle Data (wire cable and power protection devices) and Turtle Ebay Store. Its customers include industrial and construction companies electrical contractors telecommunications servers utilities and various government agencies. Family-owned the company is led by its fourth generation Jayne Millard its third female CEO. One-third of Turtle & Hughes is employee-owned.

Geographic Reach
Turtle & Hughes operates through 17 branches across the US.

Operations
Turtle & Hughes provides electrical products such as alarms signals and annunciators; anchors and plugs; automation products; ballasts; batteries and flashlights; boxes and covers; breakers bus ducts panels and switchgears; programmable controls; time clocks; transformers; wires cables and cords; wiring accessories and devices; and others.

The company also offers industrial products such as adhesives/tapes and compounds brushes/brooms carbide tools cutting tools fasteners lubricating devices material handling products power transmissions precision tools soldering equipment solenoid valves struts/channels tooling accessories and other products.

Sales and Marketing
Turtle & Hughes' customers include industrial firms construction companies electrical contractors telecommunications servers utilities and various government agencies and municipalities.

Ownership
Turtle & Hughes is a family-owned employee-owned business and is certified as a Woman Business Enterprise.

Company Background
Turtle & Hughes was founded in 1923 as an electrical supply house.

EXECUTIVES

Vice President Finance, Kevin M Doyle
Vice President Export Sales, Abdul Hooda
Vice President, Norman Blumenthal
Vice President and General Manager of the Integrated Supply Division, Joseph (Jo) Drummond
Vice President Sales, Chuck Mitchell
Managing Director, Thomas Schoenborne
Executive Vice President, John (Jack) Mautone
Vice President Account Manager, John Bernhardt
Vice President Sales, Anthony Ventola

Vice President, Cory Szatkiewicz
Senior Vice President, Al Fernandes
Vice President, Richard (Dick) Reffler
Vice President Marketing, Jayne Clark
Vice President, Pete Landers
Board Member, Kathryn B Swintek
Auditors: EISNERAMPER LLP EDISON NEW J

LOCATIONS

HQ: TURTLE & HUGHES INC
 1900 LOWER RD, LINDEN, NJ 070366586
Phone: 732 574-3600
Web: WWW.TURTLE.COM

PRODUCTS/OPERATIONS

Selected Products
Datacom categories
 Anchors and fasteners
 Burial products/innerduct
 Cabinets and enclosures
 Cable management
 Cable tray/ladder rack
 Category rated and coax cable
 Connectivity
 Fiber-optic cable
 Hand tools
 Outside plant
 Power protection
 Raceway and duct systems
 Safety
 Security fencing
 Splices connectors and lugs
 Tools testers and safety
Electrical categories
 Alarms annunciators and signals
 Anchors and plugs
 Automation products
 Ballasts and transformers
 Batteries and flashlights
 Box enclosures
 Breakers panels and switchgears
 Cable trays and struts
 Conduit fittings
 Cord connectors
 Dimming controls
 Electrical tools
 Emergency lighting
 Enclosures
 Fans
 Fluorescent lighting
 Fuse holders and terminal blocks
 Generators
 Groundings
 Heat shrink
 Heating
 High-bay lighting
 Incandescent lighting
 Lamps
 Limit temp. and proximity switch
 Lugs and terminals
 Metering equipment
 Motor control
 Motors AC and DC drivers
 Outdoor lighting
 Pole line products
 Programmable controls
 Relays
 Strut/channel
 Test equipment
 Time clocks
 Transformers
 Wire cable and cord
 Wiring accessories
 Wiring devices
Industrial categories
 Adhesives and tapes
 Brushes and brooms
 Carbide tools
 Cutting fluid/lubricant
 Cutting tools
 Fasteners
 Hand tools
 Hoist chain and accessories
 Industrial abrasives
 Janitorial paper supplies
 Ladders
 Locks
 Lubricating devices
 Material handling
 MRO supplies
 Paint/markets
 Pipe hangers
 Pipe valves and fittings
 Pneumatics
 Pneumatic tools
 Power tools
 Safety equipment
 Saw blades
 Shim/shim stock
 Solenoid valves
 Strut/channel
 Tooling accessories

COMPETITORS

C. R. Laurence	Kennametal
CPAC	MSC Industrial Direct
Consolidated	Prime Advantage
Electrical	Rexel Inc.
Dillon Supply	Sonepar USA
Graybar Electric	Steiner Electric
Indoff	W.W. Grainger
Interline Brands	WESCO International

HISTORICAL FINANCIALS
Company Type: Private

Income Statement   FYE: September 30

	REVENUE ($ mil.)	NET INCOME ($ mil.)	NET PROFIT MARGIN	EMPLOYEES
09/13	555	21	3.8%	450
09/12	518	23	4.5%	—
09/11	452	17	4.0%	—
09/10	397	0		
Annual Growth 11.8%	—	—	—	—

2013 Year-End Financials
Return on assets: 12.1%   Cash ($ mil.): 10
Return on equity: 3.8%
Current ratio: 1.70

U G N INC

Buying a Japanese car? Sounds good. Especially if the vehicle has acoustic molding and other sound-dampening acoustic automotive trim products made by UGN. The company produces molding from a variety of materials including cotton fiber and foam for vehicles assembled in North America by US and Japanese auto makers. UGN also makes automotive interior trim and thermal management parts. Its products are used to reduce interior noise and fine tune acoustical signals. The company's clientele has included such heavy hitters as Honda Nissan and Toyota. UGN was established in 1986 and is a joint venture between Autoneum and Nihon Tokushu Toryo (Nittoku).

Geographic Reach
Stationed in Tinley Park Illinois UGH operates through six plants in the US and one in Guanajuato Mexico.

Sales and Marketing
UGN sells its products through its stores and distributors. The company's products are sold to large OEMs such as Honda Toyota and Nissan.

Financial Performance
UGN reports more than $375 million in annual revenue. It claims revenues have increased more than 50% in the past two years.

Strategy
UGN is focused on increasing its manufacturing capacity though the opening and expanding of new facilities. In 2013 it announced plans to open a new facility to serve Southern Indiana and parts of Ohio by investing $25 million and it expects the new location to be operational in 2014.

In 2013 it also opened a 60000 sq. ft. facility in Silao Guanajuato Mexico for the manufacturing products used in Mexican-produced vehicles. The expansion marked the company's entry into the South American market.

EXECUTIVES
Vice President Of Human Resources, Eric Kerkhoff

LOCATIONS

HQ: U G N INC
 18410 CROSSING DR STE C, TINLEY PARK, IL
 604876209
Phone: 773 437-2400
Web: WWW.UGNAUTO.COM

PRODUCTS/OPERATIONS

Selected Products
Carpet
Dampers
Dash Insulators
Headliners
Hood and Dash Outer Absorbers
Interior Applications
Textile Mudguards and Undercovers
Thermal Management System
Ultra Light

COMPETITORS

American Trim	Johnson Controls
DURA Automotive	Magna International
Delphi Automotive	Trim Masters
Systems	Visteon
Faurecia	

HISTORICAL FINANCIALS
Company Type: Private

Income Statement   FYE: December 31

	REVENUE ($ mil.)	NET INCOME ($ mil.)	NET PROFIT MARGIN	EMPLOYEES
12/08	225	11	5.1%	1,250
12/07	239	0	—	—
12/06	223	13	5.9%	—
12/05	213	0	—	—
Annual Growth 1.7%	—	—	—	—

2008 Year-End Financials
Return on assets: 3.7%   Cash ($ mil.): 14
Return on equity: 5.1%
Current ratio: 1.00

U.R.M. STORES INC.

URM Stores is a leading wholesale food distribution cooperative serving more than 160 grocery stores in the Northwest. Its member-owner stores operate under a variety of banners including Family Foods Harvest Foods Super 1 Foods Trading Co. Stores and Yoke's Fresh Market. It also owns the Rosauers Supermarkets chain. In addition to grocery stores URM supplies 1500-plus restaurants hotels and convenience stores; it also offers such services as merchandising store development consulting and technology purchasing. The cooperative was founded in 1921 as United Retail Merchants. The business is privately owned by its members.

Geographic Reach
Regional wholesaler URM Stores supplies stores and other customers in much of eastern Washington northern Idaho Oregon and Montana.

Operations

The company's Spokane Washington-based Peirone Produce distribution subsidiary supplies fresh produce including organic produce as well as specialty items source from Arizona California Florida Mexico and Texas. In addition to groceries and produce URM Stores sells insurance to its members and food service customers through URM Insurance Agency. Insurance products include business insurance for stores and personal lines of coverage for owns and their employees.

Financial Performance

URM Stores rings up sales of about $775 million employs more than 2700 people and has assets exceeding $100 million.

Strategy

In 2010 the company moved its Spokane Washington-based Peirone Produce distribution subsidiary into a larger facility boasting 70000 sq. ft. of warehouse space and 7000 sq. ft. of office space. It is equipped with about 15 docks for loading outgoing trucks and another dozen docks for unloading incoming trucks. The facility is more than twice the size of Peirone's previous building which had nearly 10 docks total. Because of the larger space and greater number of docks Peirone Produce said it has been able to improve its productivity.

EXECUTIVES

Vice President Of Information Technology, Rich Stuber
Vice President Of Human Resources, Linda Wilson
Auditors: BDO USA LLP SPOKANE WA

LOCATIONS

HQ: U.R.M. STORES INC.
7511 N FREYA ST, SPOKANE, WA 992178043
Phone: 509 467-3619
Web: WWW.URMSTORES.COM

PRODUCTS/OPERATIONS

Selected Banners
CenterPlace Market
Family Foods
Harvest Foods
Trading Co. Stores
Rosauers Supermarkets
Super 1 Foods
Yoke's Fresh Market

COMPETITORS

AMCON Distributing	McLane
Albertsons	SUPERVALU
Associated Food	Safeway
C&S Wholesale	Sysco
Core-Mark	US Foods
Farner-Bocken	Unified Grocers
Fred Meyer Stores	Wal-Mart

HISTORICAL FINANCIALS

Company Type: Private

Income Statement
FYE: August 2

	REVENUE ($ mil.)	NET INCOME ($ mil.)	NET PROFIT MARGIN	EMPLOYEES
08/08*	932	8	0.9%	2,100
07/07	859	7	0.8%	—
07/06	1,562	0	0.0%	—
Annual Growth	(22.7%)15808.9%	—	—	—

*Fiscal year change

2008 Year-End Financials

Return on assets: 4.7%   Cash ($ mil.): 2
Return on equity: 0.9%
Current ratio: —

U.S. VENTURE INC.

Smitten with the love of oil distribution the founding Schmidt family owns and operates U.S. Venture (formerly U.S. Oil). The company's U.S. Oil division (formerly U.S. Petroleum Operations) supplies refined oil products to residents in the Midwest and does a lot more. In addition to the wholesale distribution of oil products (its largest revenue generator) the company operates gas stations and installs gas pumps tanks and other petroleum-related equipment. U.S. Venture also provides plumbing and HVAC services (Design Air) collects used waste oil to be processed into burner fuel and has a metal custom manufacturing unit.

Geographic Reach

Under its U.S. AutoForce brand U.S. Oil also operates about a dozen warehouses in Illinois Minnesota Missouri Nebraska Iowa South Dakota and Wisconsin offering auto parts (for brakes exhausts and suspensions) and tires. U.S. Venture operates 12 refined products terminals across the Midwest (with a total storage capacity of about 127 million gallons at its bulk fuel storage tanks) including the Cheboygan 164000 barrels facility.

Operations

U.S. Venture's operating divisions are:
Design Air (serving commercial and residential HVAC contractors throughout Wisconsin and Upper Michigan);
Express Convenience Centers (gas stations and convenience stores throughout Wisconsin);
U.S. AutoForce (tires automotive parts and lubricants);
U.S. Custom Manufacturing (forming and supplying metal tubing for the automotive furniture and lawn and garden and other industries; it also makes frame components handles and rails);
U.S. Lubricants (lubricants for trucking industrial and commercial customers in the Upper Midwest);
U.S. Oil (bulk storage terminals wholesale and branded distribution of petroleum products multiple-brand C-store Jobbership and gas station-related real estate activities); and
U.S. Petroleum Equipment (tanks pumps and related equipment for petroleum-based products and vehicle lift equipment; it also offers installation and lighting services throughout Wisconsin and Upper Michigan).Strategy

The company has grown its geographic presence through complementary acquisitions.

Mergers and Acquisitions

Expanding its green fuel options in 2013 U.S. Oil bought six compressed natural gas fueling stations from We Energies (two in Milwaukee and one each in Appleton Franklin Racine and Waukesha) bring U.S. Oil's total to nine in Wisconsin. U.S. Oil plans to add a minimum of 50 additional GAIN Clean Fueling sites by 2018.

Growing is presence in North Central Wisconsin and the Upper Peninsula of Michigan in 2012 the bought Draeger Oil Company's branded dealer division. Under the terms of the deal U.S. Oil provides fuel supply to more than 50 retail gas stations while Draeger retained the transportation portion.

U.S. Ventures (U.S. Oil) also expanded its petroleum products distribution presence in Indiana in 2012 through the purchase of Farmersburg-based Trueblood Oil's branded wholesale fuel supply business.

Company Background

U.S. Oil was established in the 1950s as Schmidt Oil by the sons of local fuel distributor Albert Schmidt who landed his first job in the oil business in 1923. The company changed its name to U.S.

Venture in 2010 to reflect the company's increasingly diverse portfolio of entrepreneurial businesses.

EXECUTIVES

Vice President Sales and Marketing, Paul Kubic
Vice President Human Resources, Lori Hoersch
Secretary and Treasurer, Ray Schmidt
Auditors: DELOITTE & TOUCHE LLP MILWAU

LOCATIONS

HQ: U.S. VENTURE INC.
425 BETTER WAY, APPLETON, WI 549156192
Phone: 920 739-6101
Web: WWW.USVENTURE.COM

PRODUCTS/OPERATIONS

Selected Operations
Design Air (heating and air conditioning equipment)
Express Convenience Centers (gas stations and car washes)
U.S. AutoForce (exhaust pipe manufacturing and autoparts distribution)
U.S. Custom Manufacturing (tube bending and fabrication)
U.S. Lubricants (motor oil and related products)
U.S. Oil (gasoline fuel oil and natural gas)
U.S. Petroleum Equipment (petroleum-related equipment installation)

COMPETITORS

7-Eleven	Quality State Oil
Apex Oil	Company
Marathon Oil	QuikTrip
Motiva Enterprises	Sunoco

HISTORICAL FINANCIALS

Company Type: Private

Income Statement
FYE: July 31

	REVENUE ($ mil.)	NET INCOME ($ mil.)	NET PROFIT MARGIN	EMPLOYEES
07/14	9,088	49	0.5%	1,000
07/13	7,346	47	0.6%	—
07/12	5,906	60	1.0%	—
07/11	4,847	0	—	—
Annual Growth	23.3%	—	—	—

2014 Year-End Financials

Return on assets: 2.5%   Cash ($ mil.): 5
Return on equity: 0.5%
Current ratio: 0.90

UMASS MEMORIAL COMMUNITY MEDICAL GROUP INC.

Auditors: PRICEWATERHOUSECOOPERS LLP B

LOCATIONS

HQ: UMASS MEMORIAL COMMUNITY MEDICAL GROUP INC.
121 LINCOLN ST, WORCESTER, MA 016052429
Phone: 508 757-7745

HISTORICAL FINANCIALS

Company Type: Private

Income Statement
FYE: September 30

	REVENUE ($ mil.)	NET INCOME ($ mil.)	NET PROFIT MARGIN	EMPLOYEES
09/11	451	8	1.9%	3
09/09	400	7	1.8%	—
09/08	360	1	0.4%	—
Annual Growth	7.8%	79.8%	—	—

2011 Year-End Financials

Return on assets: —
Return on equity: 1.9%
Current ratio: 1.10

Cash ($ mil.): 25

UMASS MEMORIAL HEALTH CARE INC

Auditors: PRICEWATERHOUSECOOPERS LLP BO

LOCATIONS

HQ: UMASS MEMORIAL HEALTH CARE INC
365 PLANTATION ST STE 300, WORCESTER, MA 016052397
Phone: 508 754-6026
Web: WWW.UMASSMEMORIAL.ORG

HISTORICAL FINANCIALS

Company Type: Private

Income Statement
FYE: December 31

	REVENUE ($ mil.)	NET INCOME ($ mil.)	NET PROFIT MARGIN	EMPLOYEES
12/14*	555	6	1.3%	10,000
09/14	2,252	17	0.8%	—
09/13	2,186	253	11.6%	—
09/12	2,293	0	—	—
Annual Growth	(50.8%)	—	—	—

*Fiscal year change

2014 Year-End Financials

Return on assets: 24.3%
Return on equity: 1.3%
Current ratio: 0.80

Cash ($ mil.): 101

UMASS MEMORIAL HOSPITALS INC.

Auditors: PRICEWATERHOUSECOOPERS LLP B

LOCATIONS

HQ: UMASS MEMORIAL HOSPITALS INC.
119 BELMONT ST, WORCESTER, MA 016052903
Phone: 508 334-1000
Web: WWW.UMASSMEMORIAL.ORG

HISTORICAL FINANCIALS

Company Type: Private

Income Statement
FYE: September 30

	REVENUE ($ mil.)	NET INCOME ($ mil.)	NET PROFIT MARGIN	EMPLOYEES
09/08	332	9	2.9%	10,000
09/07	302	15	5.1%	—
09/06	0	0	—	—
Annual Growth	—	—	—	—

2008 Year-End Financials

Return on assets: —
Return on equity: 2.9%
Current ratio: 1.00

Cash ($ mil.): 29

UMASS MEMORIAL MEDICAL CENTER INC.

LOCATIONS

HQ: UMASS MEMORIAL MEDICAL CENTER INC.
55 LAKE AVE N, WORCESTER, MA 016550002
Phone: 508 334-1000
Web: WWW.UMASSMEMORIAL.ORG

HISTORICAL FINANCIALS

Company Type: Private

Income Statement
FYE: September 30

	REVENUE ($ mil.)	NET INCOME ($ mil.)	NET PROFIT MARGIN	EMPLOYEES
09/13	1,183	68	5.8%	1
09/12	1,209	23	1.9%	—
Annual Growth	(2.1%)	197.2%	—	—

2013 Year-End Financials

Return on assets: 9.6%
Return on equity: 5.8%
Current ratio: 0.70

Cash ($ mil.): 42

UNDERWRITERS LABORATORIES INC.

Products that pass the muster of this company get the UL symbol of approval. Underwriters Laboratories (UL) is one of the world's leading providers of product safety and certification testing services performing more than 90000 evaluations each year. Products that successfully navigate through its stringent tests are registered with the lab and can bear the UL Mark —a widely trusted symbol for product safety and assurance. Nearly 20 billion products from 72000 manufacturers bear the UL Mark each year. UL also offers commercial inspection and regulatory training services as well as consumer safety advice. William Merrill founded the not-for-profit lab in 1894.

Geographic Reach

UL mainly serves Asia North America and Europe. The company has been actively expanding its international operations and now has offices and affiliates in about 40 countries serving customers in nearly 105 different nations. It also represents US companies in gaining acceptance in foreign markets.

Operations

In addition to product testing UL serves as a leader in helping set regulatory and industry standards promoting conformity among companies and government agencies in establishing safety and performance requirements. UL is governed by a board of trustees elected by its corporate members (who are not manufacturers of products subject to UL coverage).

Strategy

UL restructured a couple of years ago to accommodate increased global demand as well as ramp up its "green" or environmentally friendly product services. Among the changes are the company's new sustainable products certification service and its environmental claims validation service which are the backbone of UL's Switzerland-based subsidiary UL Environment. Another new operating segment is Verification Services that expands the company's performance testing inspection and auditing offerings to a wider global audience.

The company uses partnerships acquisitions and subsidiaries to expand its business and geographic reach. During 2014 it expanded into Japan through an acquisition. Also during 2014 UL opened a new consumer products testing laboratory in Shanghai China.

Mergers and Acquisitions

During fiscal 2014 UL acquired Futuremark the market leading provider of performance benchmarking software. Based in Finland Futuremark develops the world's most widely used benchmarks for desktop computers notebooks tablets and smart phones. The acquisition marked UL's entry into the software development industry.

UL made several acquisitions in 2013 including Testtech Laboratorios a Brazil-based electrical safety and energy efficiency testing laboratory that is relied upon by many of the world's leading appliance manufacturers. The acquisition positions UL as a single trusted source of the appliance certification testing and follow-up services needed to access the Brazilian market. UL will also be able to serve global appliance manufacturers seeking access to Brazil and Brazilian manufacturers seeking access to the rest of the world.

UL acquired Overland Park Kansas-based Innovadex the leading search and information exchange platform for supplier chemicals ingredients and raw materials in 2013 as well. The strategic addition expands UL's search offering to fully serve several new product categories including paints coatings adhesives inks lubricants cosmetics cleaners food and beverages. UL expanded its capabilities in the food industry in 2013 with the acquisition of Everclean Services one of North America's leading food safety audit providers.

HISTORY

In 1893 the Chicago Board of Fire Underwriters asked William Merrill an expert electrical investigator to inspect a dazzling display called the Palace of Electricity at the World's Fair. This jolted him into the realization of the need for electrical industry standardization. He founded the Underwriters' Electrical Bureau in 1894 to furnish fire risk data to insurers. Incorporated in 1901 as Underwriters Laboratories (UL) it expanded into auto parts fire extinguishers telephone wiring and even airline pilot certification which the government later took over.

Since the end of WWII UL has worked to establish international standards to facilitate global trade. In 1993 the organization introduced the first UL designation outside the US —in Canada. UL Canada became a UL affiliate in 1995. That year

UL agreed with the Japan Quality Assurance Organization to exchange certification information. In 1996 UL opened offices in India and South Korea and acquired the Danish testing organization DEMKO. The company used its DEMKO subsidiary as a base to move into Sweden and Italy in 1998. It also opened a service center in China.

Alliances with organizations in Germany and Saudi Arabia followed in 1999 and Mexico in 2000. Also that year UL was recognized by the American National Standards Institute (ANSI) as one of only five organizations that can set standards without the need for ANSI review.

The company acquired Environmental Health Laboratories a leading public drinking water testing and analysis firm in 2001. Also that year UL agreed to exchange test data with the Water Quality Association (WQA) an independent water industry trade association.

In 2002 the organization acquired Eaton's Electromagnetic Compatibility (EMC) test laboratory. It also established offices in Chile and Switzerland and opened a new testing facility in Detroit. Knoblauch retired from UL in 2004.

EXECUTIVES

President and CEO, Keith E. Williams
SVP and CFO, Michael Saltzman
President Verification Services, Sajeev Jesudas
President Environmental Services, Sara A. Greenstein
President Europe and Latin America, Gitte Schjotz
SVP and Chief Commercial Officer, Weifang Zhou
SVP and CIO, Christian Anschuetz
President Knowledge Services, Patrick Boyle
SVP and President Enterprise Services, Clyde Kofman
SVP and President Product Safety, Ben Miller
SVP and President Life and Health Sciences, Hiroshi Yamaki
VP and Managing Director Asia Pacific, Jason Fischer
Vice President, Gary Savin
Vice President Customer Relations, Linda Zastrow
Vice President General Manager, Lisa Meier
Vice President General Manager, Jeff Smidt
Vice President Public Safety Advocacy Education And Outreach, Barbara Guthrie
Vice President and Corporate Controller, Ricardo Navarette
Senior Vice President, Steve Hewson
Board Member, Jeff Dornenburg
Auditors: PRICEWATERHOUSECOOPERS LLP PH

LOCATIONS

HQ: UNDERWRITERS LABORATORIES INC.
333 PFINGSTEN RD, NORTHBROOK, IL 600622096
Phone: 847 272-8800
Web: WWW.UL.COM

PRODUCTS/OPERATIONS

Selected Services and Operations
Architectural services
Components
Consulting
EMC services
Global field services
Hazardous locations services
Market access solutions
Product safety
UL Environment
UL University
Verification services

Selected Product Certifications and Industries Served
Appliances and HVAC/R
  Appliance switches
  Appliances
  Gas oil and solid fuel appliances and equipment
HVAC/R
  Infrared thermometers
Motors
Pool and spa safety
Building materials
  Fire safety engineering
  Sprinklers
  Chemicals
  Electrical insulation systems
  Flammable and combustible fluids
  Plastics
Energy
  Renewable energy
  Semiconductor equipment
Food and water
  Drinking water
  Food safety
Health sciences
  Medical devices
High Tech
  Communication circuits protectors
  Consumer electronics
  Information technology equipment
  Lasers
  Power supplies
  Printed wiring boards
  Telecommunications equipment
Life safety and security
  Alarm systems
  Fire equipment
  Personal flotation devices
  Personal protective equipment
  Security and signaling
Lighting
  Decorative lighting strings
  General lighting
  Sign listing
Power and controls
  Electric vehicle components
  Electrical/electronic control equipment
  Energy meters
  Industrial control equipment
  Programmable electronics and software
  Robots and robotic equipment
Wire and cable
  Appliance wiring material
  Marine shipboard cable
  Optical fiber
  Proprietary structured cabling

COMPETITORS

BSI Group	Methode Electronics
Bureau Veritas	National Technical
Canadian Standards	Systems
Association	Norske Veritas
Consumers Union	Quality Inspection
Exponent	Services
Intertek	SGS
J.D. Power	Silliker

HISTORICAL FINANCIALS
Company Type: Private

Income Statement
FYE: December 31

	REVENUE ($ mil.)	NET INCOME ($ mil.)	NET PROFIT MARGIN	EMPLOYEES
12/08	994	(23)	—	10,846
12/07	895	160	17.9%	—
12/06	792,081	0	0.0%	—
Annual Growth	**(96.5%)**	—	—	—

2008 Year-End Financials
Return on assets: 5.9%
Return on equity: (-2.3%)
Current ratio: 0.90
Cash ($ mil.): 46

UNION BANK AND TRUST COMPANY

Union Bank & Trust a subsidiary of financial services holding company Farmers & Merchants Investment operates more than 35 branches throughout Nebraska and in Kansas. As Nebraska's third-largest privately-owned bank it offers traditional deposit and trust services as well as insurance equipment finance and investment management services. Consumer loans account for the largest portion of the bank's portfolio followed by commercial real estate and farmland loans. Union Bank also originates business loans and residential mortgages. Affiliate company Union Investment Advisors manages the Stratus family of mutual funds. Another Farmers & Merchants unit Nelnet Capital offers brokerage services.

Geographic Reach
Union Bank operates mostly in Nebraska but also in Kansas.

Sales and Marketing
The bank primarily serves customers in Lincoln and Omaha as well as the Kansas City metropolitan area.

Operations
Union Bank has grown to become one of Nebraska's largest privately-owned banks. As of mid-2013 it boasted bank assets of $2.6 billion and trust assets of $11.8 billion.

Aside from its branches in Nebraska and Kansas Union Bank offers banking products and services through its online mobile and electronic banking services.

Strategy
Union Bank continues to expand its footprint in existing markets. The financial institution will have added three new Nebraska branches to its portfolio by 2014.

Company Background
The bank was originally founded in 1917 as Farmer's State Bank. It took on the Union Bank name in 1935 and became Union Bank & Trust in 1959.

Company Ownership
The company has been controlled by the Dunlap family since 1965.

EXECUTIVES

Vice President And Business Development Officer, Michael (Mel) Kulas

LOCATIONS

HQ: UNION BANK AND TRUST COMPANY
3643 S 48TH ST, LINCOLN, NE 685064390
Phone: 402 488-0941
Web: WWW.UBT.COM

PRODUCTS/OPERATIONS

Selected Services
Business banking
Investment & retirement
Personal banking
Wealth management

Selected Affiliates
InfoVisa
Nelnet Capital LLC
Nelnet Inc.
Union Agency Inc.
Union Equipment Finance LLC
Union Investment Advisors
Union Title Company LLC
Zelle

HISTORICAL FINANCIALS

Company Type: Private

Income Statement

FYE: December 31

	ASSETS ($ mil.)	NET INCOME ($ mil.)	INCOME AS % OF ASSETS	EMPLOYEES
12/13	2,862	35	1.3%	800
12/08	2,437	16	0.7%	—
12/06	1,518	18	1.2%	—
Annual Growth	9.5%	10.0%	—	—

2013 Year-End Financials

Return on assets: —
Return on equity: 22.6%

Sales ($ mil): 159

UNION COUNTY BOARD OF EDUCATION

Auditors: ANDERSON SMITH & WIKE PLLC CP

LOCATIONS

HQ: UNION COUNTY BOARD OF EDUCATION
400 N CHURCH ST, MONROE, NC 281124804
Phone: 704 296-4210
Web: WWW.UCPS.K12.NC.US

HISTORICAL FINANCIALS

Company Type: Private

Income Statement

FYE: June 30

	REVENUE ($ mil.)	NET INCOME ($ mil.)	NET PROFIT MARGIN	EMPLOYEES
06/14	324	7	2.4%	5,427
06/13	316	(8)	—	—
06/12*	318	2	0.7%	—
12/05	0	0	—	—
Annual Growth	—	—	—	—

*Fiscal year change

2014 Year-End Financials

Return on assets: 1.2%
Return on equity: 2.4%
Current ratio: —

Cash ($ mil.): 37

UNION HOSPITAL INC.

Union Hospital is the flagship facility of the Union Hospital Health Group a health care system that serves communities in western Indiana and eastern Illinois. The not-for-profit hospital has about 320 beds boasts an equal number of physicians and provides general medical and surgical care as well as specialty services in areas such as women's health newborn intensive care unit (Level II) cancer cardiovascular disease and sports medicine. It also offers occupational health and physical rehabilitation as well as medical training programs. Other facilities that comprise the Union system include Union Hospital Clinton physician practices specialty clinics and a home health agency.

Geographic Reach

The teaching hospital serves patients in west-central Indiana and eastern Illinois.

Operations

Besides the main Union Hospital which averages some 17000 patient admissions each year the hospital operates Union Hospital Clinton specialty clinics a home health agency and physician practices.

Strategy

Union Hospital's main campus underwent a nearly $180 million expansion project in recent years. The patient tower provides for private rooms instead of six- to eight-bed wards.

As part of a strategic focus to extend the reach of its operations Union Hospital partners with AP&S Clinic a multi-specialty physician group practice to expand the two entities' services. Operating as Union Health System the collaboration looks to increase coordination of care between physician specialists.

In 2015 Union Hospital partnered with the Ob Hospitalist Group to provide around-the-clock physician care for expectant mothers.

Company Background

Union Hospital's roots go back to 1892.

EXECUTIVES

Vice President Of Finance And Chief Financial Officer, Wayne R Hutson
V Pres, Sally Zuel
Medical Director, Ronald Leach
Clinical Director, Barbara (Barb) Gossett
Cota L, Karen Pharo
Medical Director, Ramesh Shatagopam
Medical Director, Neil Kabous
Medical Director, Grace Walker
Vice President and Administrator Union Hospital Clinton, Terri Hill
Director of Medical Records, Pamala Alexander
Vice President Physician Services, Jody Stoldt
Radiology Director, Gale Wilson
Director Of Nursing, Lea Camp
Medical Director and Emergency Department Physician, Ronald (Ron) Leach
Director of Pharmacy, Kristi Williams
Operating ROOM Director, Angela (Angie) Eggleston
Vice President of Information Technology, Yevette Cress
Vice President, Darwin Smith
Board Member, Steven (Steve) Mcdonald
Secretary, Mary Doti
Board Member, Dave Doerr
Auditors: BLUE & CO LLC INDIANAPOLIS I

LOCATIONS

HQ: UNION HOSPITAL INC.
1606 N 7TH ST, TERRE HAUTE, IN 478042780
Phone: 812 238-7000
Web: WWW.MYUNIONHOSPITAL.ORG

PRODUCTS/OPERATIONS

Selected Services

Acupuncture
Advanced Medical Technology
Asthma
Behavioral Healthcare
Breast Care
Cancer Care Services
Cardiovascular Testing
Clara Fairbanks Center for Women
Clay City Center for Family Medicine
Cork Medical Center
Family Medicine Center
Infections
Joint Replacement Center
Landsbaum Center

Lugar Center for Rural Health
Medical Rehabilitation Center
Neonatal Intensive Care Unit (NICU)
Pediatrics
Pulmonary and Lung Health
Wound Healing Center
Union Hospital Terre Haute
Union Hospital Clinton
Union Hospital Foundation

HISTORICAL FINANCIALS

Company Type: Private

Income Statement

FYE: August 31

	REVENUE ($ mil.)	NET INCOME ($ mil.)	NET PROFIT MARGIN	EMPLOYEES
08/10	400	(3)	—	1,960
08/09	408	18	4.5%	—
08/08	641	0	—	—
Annual Growth	—	—	—	—

2010 Year-End Financials

Return on assets: —
Return on equity: (-0.8%)
Current ratio: 0.30

Cash ($ mil.): 21

UNIPRO FOODSERVICE INC

UniPro Foodservice knows there's strength in numbers. As the largest US food service cooperative its members include more than 650 independent member companies that provide food and food-related products to more than 800000 food service customers including health care and educational institutions military installations and restaurants. UniPro provides training collective purchasing and marketing materials to all distributors. Its products —which include dry groceries and frozen and refrigerated foods —are sold under the brand names CODE ComSource Nifda and Nugget. Suppliers include Kraft Foods Reynolds Food Packaging Solo Cup Tyson Foods and Unilever Foodsolutions.

Geographic Reach

The Atlanta-based cooperative operates through more than 900 distribution centers across the US. Beyond the US it has distribution operations in Canada Mexico the Bahamas Australia Costa Rica Guam and Japan.

Operations

The cooperative's Multi-Unit Group (MUG) formed in 1985 to service multi-unit food service operators include some of the largest member distributors in the UniPro network. MUG members are like a one-stop shop for multi-unit operators offering fresh produce paper products and small wares from a single source in an effort to improve efficiency.

Sales and Marketing

Progressive Group Alliance a business unit distributes and supplies partners with sales marketing and advice to customers. Brands include Alliance Pro (non-food) Coral Princess (seafood) GourMates (condiments) Harvest Gold (cheese butter and dairy-related products) and Premium Recipe (prepared entrees salsas and sauces).

Financial Performance

While privately-owned Unipro Foodservice doesn't report its financial results collectively the cooperatives ring up an estimated $64 billion in sales annually.

Strategy

To enhance its members' competitiveness at home and abroad in 2013 UniPro formed a strategic alliance with Technomic a leading research and consulting firm to the food service industry. As part of the partnership UnPro joined the steering committee of Technomic's Foodservice Category Management Institute.

EXECUTIVES

Senior Vice President Logistics Redistribution, John (Jack) Burke

Departmental Vice President Accounting Services, Martin (Marti) Miller

Departmental Vice President Financial Services, Sharon Nesset

Regional Vice President of Sales, Edward (Ed) Delaney

Regional Vice President Sales, Gary Butler

Vice President Protein Beef and Pork, Phillip (Phil) Wilson

Executive Vice President Of Procurement, David Huch

Regional Vice President Sales Northeast, Jack Carlson

Regional Vice President Sales Southwest, Israel Vargas

Departmental Vice President Boxed Beef, Keith Jeanis

Vice President Saels West, Scott Strull

Regional Vice President Northeast, John (Jack) Stevens

Vice President of Sales and Marketing, Terry Fisher

Regional Vice President of Sales, Bob Bossong

Senior Vice President Sales East, Keith Durnell

Executive Vice President Marketing And Business Development, Don Gilligan

Regional Vice President, Robb Meath

Vice President Business Development, Dennis Urgo

Senior Vice President Logistics, Tom Brockman

Departmental Vice President Vendor Engagement, Dave Devlin

Regional Vice President MID Central, Bob Fannin

Vice President, Spencer Peterson

Treasurer, Dan Wolfram

LOCATIONS

HQ: UNIPRO FOODSERVICE INC
2500 CUMBRLD PKWY SE 60, ATLANTA, GA 30339
Phone: 770 952-0871
Web: WWW.UNIPROFOODSERVICE.COM

PRODUCTS/OPERATIONS

Selected Suppliers
Cargill Foodservice
Durable Packaging International
Handgards Inc.
Kraft Foods
Reynolds Foodservice Packaging
Solo Cup Company
Unilever Foodsolutions

COMPETITORS

Ben E. Keith
Foodbuy
Golden State Foods
Keystone Foods
MAINES
Martin-Brower
McLane Foodservice
Meadowbrook Meat Company
Services Group of America
Sysco
US Foods

HISTORICAL FINANCIALS
Company Type: Private

Income Statement
FYE: December 31

	REVENUE ($ mil.)	NET INCOME ($ mil.)	NET PROFIT MARGIN	EMPLOYEES
12/13	1,238	(0)	—	140
12/12	987	(0)	—	—
12/11	881	0	—	—
12/10	657	0	—	—
Annual Growth	23.5%	—	—	—

2013 Year-End Financials
Return on assets: 4.6%
Return on equity: —
Current ratio: 0.90
Cash ($ mil.): 17

UNITED COOPERATIVE

Auditors: CLIFTONLARSONALLEN LLP MIDDL

LOCATIONS

HQ: UNITED COOPERATIVE
N7160 RACEWAY RD, BEAVER DAM, WI 539169315
Phone: 920 887-1756
Web: WWW.UNITEDCOOPERATIVE.COM

HISTORICAL FINANCIALS
Company Type: Private

Income Statement
FYE: December 31

	REVENUE ($ mil.)	NET INCOME ($ mil.)	NET PROFIT MARGIN	EMPLOYEES
12/13	627	45	7.2%	358
12/12	641	34	5.4%	—
12/11	523	35	6.7%	—
12/10	324	0	—	—
Annual Growth	24.6%	—	—	—

2013 Year-End Financials
Return on assets: 2.5%
Return on equity: 7.2%
Current ratio: 0.20
Cash ($ mil.): 20

UNITED DAIRYMEN OF ARIZONA

Its name says it all: United Dairymen of Arizona (UDA) is a group of Arizona-based dairy farmers united together to stabilize and strengthen the market for milk products. Supplied by some 90-member producers the cooperative's plant has the capacity to process 10 million pounds of milk per day about 90% of the milk in the state. Products include sweet cream and butter fluid and condensed skim milk and non-fat dry milk among others. Customers include onsite cheese maker Schreiber Foods fluid milk processors and supermarket chains throughout The Grand Canyon State. UDA also makes dried lactose powder for food manufacturers. Started in 1960 the co-op was formed through a merger of two dairy associations.

Geographic Reach

Based in Arizona United Dairymen of Arizona serves other companies in the state as well as the US kosher niche. It exports products overseas.

Operations

UDA's Arizona-based manufacturing plant operates around the clock often serving as a balancing plant for other area processors. Its capacity handles a broad line of milk products shifting milk production according to dairy supply and market demand. The plant is the nation's largest supervised kosher milk facility with a weekly production capacity of more than 500 metric tons of kosher powder. UDA also produces blended dry products as part of a joint venture.

UDA's operations include providing emergency repair preventative maintenance installation and transportation services and related supplies to members. Since 2007 the co-op's service and supply division share a facility in Texas too.

Strategy

While UDA's business is concentrated in Arizona its member interests cross both eastern California and Texas. Beyond the US UDA has benefited from export assistance to sell cheese to customers in Asia North Africa and the Middle East. As a member of DairyAmerica (which is controlled by California Dairies) UDA further extends its international reach by selling non-fat dry milk skim milk powder and other products on the auction block known as GlobalDairyTrade developed by Fonterra.

The only milk marketing co-op in Arizona UDA is focused on improving production processing and marketing opportunities for member-producers. To that end it strategically joins with other daily cooperatives to expand global trade of dairy products and promote legislation that addresses issues such as surplus of milk low prices and volatile markets.

Sales and Marketing

To its benefit UDA enjoys long-term relationships with fluid milk processors which enables it to rely on a steady market for about 30% of its fluid milk. Schreiber Foods based in Tempe Arizona buys another 30% of its products.

EXECUTIVES

Vice President of Engineering Projects, James (Jamie) Hrusovszky

Vice President of Government Relations, Billotte Mike

Vice President, Gayle Lindsay

Auditors: HERBEIN & COMPANY INC READI

LOCATIONS

HQ: UNITED DAIRYMEN OF ARIZONA
2008 S HARDY DR, TEMPE, AZ 852821211
Phone: 480 966-7211
Web: WWW.UDA.COOP

PRODUCTS/OPERATIONS

Selected Products and Services
Products
Dried
Dry milk blends
Kosher powder
Lactose powder
Milk protein concentrate
Nonfat dry milk
Fluid
Butter
Cream
Condensed skim milk
Skim milk
Services
Emergency repair
Installation
Preventative maintenance
Transportation
Supplies
Chemical

Equipment
Pharmaceutical

COMPETITORS

Associated Milk	Main Street
Producers	Ingredients
Dairy Farmers of	Nestl©
America	Shamrock Foods
Dairy Manufacturers	Smucker
Dean Foods	Tate & Lyle
Goya	Ingredients
Land O' Lakes	

HISTORICAL FINANCIALS
Company Type: Private

Income Statement
FYE: September 30

	REVENUE ($ mil.)	NET INCOME ($ mil.)	NET PROFIT MARGIN	EMPLOYEES
09/11	825	21	2.6%	190
09/10	612	12	2.0%	—
09/09	51	0	0.0%	—
Annual Growth	300.9%	52	165.3%	—

2011 Year-End Financials
Return on assets: 0.9%   Cash ($ mil.): 30
Return on equity: 2.6%
Current ratio: 1.00

UNITED ELECTRIC SUPPLY COMPANY INC.

True to its name United Electric Supply distributes electrical parts such as lighting fasteners sensors wire connectors and voice data and fiber-optic products. The employee-owned company carries more than 23000 items from more than 250 manufacturers including Kyocera Panasonic Security and Schneider Electric. It sells to the building and industrial trades government and other markets. United Electric's wide range of services include design value engineering energy audits procurement training inventory management and E-commerce. It also offers value-added services such as next day delivery and Saturday-morning counter hours.

Geographic Reach

It has 17 branch locations in Delaware Maryland New Jersey Pennsylvania and Virginia.

Operations

United Electric divides its business into eight product groups: Data Comm; Electro-Mechanical; Energy Solutions; Gear and Control; Integrated Products; Lighting; Wire Cable and Conduit; and Solar Energy. Data Comm offers on-site consultation and assistance to deploy voice data and fiber optic technology. Electro-Mechanical provides project-specific quotations for such products as fittings boxes fasteners and tools.

Energy Solutions focuses on energy audits rebate studies lighting design and other services to increase the energy efficiency of lighting. Gear and Control offers project budgeting design and other services along with distributing products. Integrated Products markets programmable controllers operator interface products supervisory software drives and power conditioning equipment among other products. Lighting serves the construction and renovation markets with various lighting products and conducts audits of lighting systems to determine better energy efficiency. Wire Cable and Conduit offers items that range from

basic building wire to multi-conductor instrumentation cables. Solar Energy provides renewable power for a variety of structures from large commercial buildings to small houses.

United Electric additionally offers a program called Supplier Inventory Management System (SIMS) that includes such services as inventory reduction through analysis of each storeroom unit and bar-coding. United Electric is also an authorized supplier through Pennsylvania's COSTARS cooperative purchasing program which unifies local organizations to achieve more competitive pricing than individual businesses could obtain on their own.

Sales and Marketing

The company sells its products through its stores and via online marketing efforts.

Strategy

United Electric grows organically and through complementary acquisitions.

The company opened its 16th location in Easton Pennsylvania in 2013 and another branch location in Timonium Maryland to serve customers in Baltimore and the surrounding counties.

It uses an extensive in-house database to provide performance measures and analysis illustrate results and highlight best practices.

Mergers and Acquisitions

In 2012 United Electric acquired Easton-based Ealer Electric to serve the Lehigh Valley customers of Pennsylvania.

Company Background

The company which was founded in 1965 by Nick Gianoulis has been an employee-owned venture since 1996.

EXECUTIVES

VP Distribution and Control Products, Sal Muzzi
VP Finance and CFO, Rich Stagliano
VP Operations and COO, Bob Crawford
Director Information Technology, Luis Varela
Manager Energy Saving Products, Peggy Hill
VP Sales Maryland Washington DC and Virginia, George Vorwick
Manager Solar Products, Mike Howell
Product Manager Industrial Automation Group, Kurt Niehaus
Product Manager Electromechanical Products, Walt Opalach
Manager Wire and Cable Products, Dennis Risner
Auditors: PARENTEBEARD LLC PHILADELPHIA

LOCATIONS

HQ: UNITED ELECTRIC SUPPLY COMPANY INC.
10 BELLECOR DR, NEW CASTLE, DE 197201763
Phone: 800 322-3374
Web: WWW.UNITEDELECTRIC.COM

PRODUCTS/OPERATIONS

Selected Services
Consigned inventory
Design and build assistance
Electronic invoicing
Energy audits
Order staging
Post Order Focus
Procurement
Supplier Inventory Management Systems
Training
Value Engineering

COMPETITORS

Billows Electric	Gexpro
Supply	Graybar Electric
Consolidated	McCoy Group
Electrical	Rumsey Electric

HISTORICAL FINANCIALS
Company Type: Private

Income Statement
FYE: December 31

	REVENUE ($ mil.)	NET INCOME ($ mil.)	NET PROFIT MARGIN	EMPLOYEES
12/13	168	2	1.7%	292
12/12	171	3	1.8%	—
12/11	185	4	2.6%	—
12/10	164	0	—	—
Annual Growth	0.9%	—	—	—

2013 Year-End Financials
Return on assets: 12.1%   Cash ($ mil.): 5
Return on equity: 1.7%
Current ratio: 1.00

UNITED FOOD AND COMMERCIAL WORKERS UNIONS AND FOOD EMPLOYERS BEN

Auditors: HEMMING MORSE CPA'S AND CONSUL

LOCATIONS

HQ: UNITED FOOD AND COMMERCIAL WORKERS UNIONS AND FOOD EMPLOYERS BEN
6425 KATELLA AVE, CYPRESS, CA 906305246
Phone: 714 220-2297

HISTORICAL FINANCIALS
Company Type: Private

Income Statement
FYE: March 31

	REVENUE ($ mil.)	NET INCOME ($ mil.)	NET PROFIT MARGIN	EMPLOYEES
03/12	512	(34)	—	3
03/11	460	(74)	—	—
03/10	333	(165)	—	—
Annual Growth	24.0%	—	—	—

2012 Year-End Financials
Return on assets: —   Cash ($ mil.): 46
Return on equity: (-6.8%)
Current ratio: 0.50

UNITED HEALTH SERVICES HOSPITAL INC.

United Health Services Hospitals (UHS Hospitals) can service injuries from a slip in the snow or a slipped disc to health that's just plain slipping. The organization operates Binghamton General Hospital (about 200 beds) Wilson Medical Center (some 280 beds) and a group of primary and specialty care clinics in upstate New York. Specialty services include cardiology dialysis neurology rehabilitation pediatrics and psychiatry. The Wilson Medical Center serves as a teaching hospital offering residency and fellowship programs. UHS Hospitals is a subsidiary of United Health Services which operates a network of affiliated hospitals clinics long-term care centers and home health agencies in the region.

Geographic Reach

Binghamton General is located in Binghamton New York while Wilson Medical Center is located in Johnson City New York both within the boundaries of Broome County. UHS Hospitals also operates primary and specialty care clinics in Broome Chenango Delaware and Tioga counties in upstate New York.

Strategy

United Health Services Hospitals is investing in equipment upgrades and facility improvements at Binghamton General to help the facility remain at the forefront of medical technology and services. Wilson Medical Center which acts as a regional referral center in areas including emergency medicine newborn care neurology and heart surgery has also been the subject of enhancement measures. The hospital recently completed construction of the new Decker Center for Advanced Medical Treatment which offers high-tech diagnostic and acute care services.

EXECUTIVES

Senior Vice President Chief Financial Officer, Robert Gomulka

President and CEO; 2nd Vice Chair, Matthew J. Salanger

President and CEO Delaware Valley Hospital, David Polge

Chairman, Diana Bendz

Secretary, Susan Mistretta

VP Strategy and Business Development, Robin Kinslow-Evans

President CEO, Drake M. Lamen

EVP and COO, John Carrigg

President and CEO; 2nd Vice Chair, Matthew J. Salanger

1st Vice Chair, Bruce Bowling

Director, Barbara Chaffee

Director, William Craine

Director, Garabed Fattal

Director, Sara Gueldner

Director, Carol Miller

Director, Judith C. Peckham

Auditors: FUST CHARLES CHAMBERS LLP SYR

LOCATIONS

HQ: UNITED HEALTH SERVICES HOSPITAL INC.
10-42 MITCHELL AVE, BINGHAMTON, NY 139031617
Phone: 607 762-2200
Web: WWW.UHS.NET

COMPETITORS

Albany Medical Center
Guthrie Healthcare
Kaleida Health
Lifetime Health
Oneida Healthcare Center
SUNY Upstate Medical University
St. Joseph' s Hospital Health Center
Upstate University Hospital at Community General

HISTORICAL FINANCIALS

Company Type: Private

Income Statement

FYE: December 31

	REVENUE ($ mil.)	NET INCOME ($ mil.)	NET PROFIT MARGIN	EMPLOYEES
12/13	516	27	5.4%	5,000
12/12	496	18	3.8%	—
12/11	455	18	4.0%	—
12/10	442	0	—	—
Annual Growth	5.3%	—	—	—

2013 Year-End Financials

Return on assets: 4.4%
Return on equity: 5.4%
Current ratio: 1.00

Cash ($ mil.): 20

UNITED METHODIST RETIREMENT & HEALTH CARE CENTER INC

LOCATIONS

HQ: UNITED METHODIST RETIREMENT & HEALTH CARE CENTER INC
2316 W MODELLE AVE, CLINTON, OK 736013722
Phone: 580 323-0912
Web: WWW.UMRH.ORG

HISTORICAL FINANCIALS

Company Type: Private

Income Statement

FYE: June 30

	REVENUE ($ mil.)	NET INCOME ($ mil.)	NET PROFIT MARGIN	EMPLOYEES
06/09	331	19	6.0%	85
06/08	3	0	6.5%	—
06/99	2	0	2.4%	—
Annual Growth	65.8%	81.8%	—	—

2009 Year-End Financials

Return on assets: —
Return on equity: 6.0%
Current ratio: 1.10

Cash ($ mil.): —

UNITED NEGRO COLLEGE FUND INC.

A mind is a terrible thing to waste. In this spirit the United Negro College Fund (UNCF) offers financial assistance to students of color from low-to moderate-income families pursuing a higher education. UNCF the oldest and largest higher non-profit education assistance program for African-Americans enables some 60000 students to attend college each year. About 60% of the students are the first in their families to attend college. UNCF also provides operating funds and IT services to historically black colleges and universities such as Bethune-Cookman Morehouse Xavier and Voorhees College.

Geographic Reach

UNCF has offices in more than 25 US states.

Operations

The Fund's services include funding its 37 member colleges all of them small private historically black colleges and universities. In addition the fund has worked to upgrade and modernize technology provide computers to students and faculty as well as create an e-commerce site selling current hardware and software. UNCF drives an annual television public service announcement UNCF An Evening of Stars a national campaign that serves as an advocate and fundraiser for education. It also offers grants to help build capacity faculty development programs and assistance with teacher education programs.

More than 90% of UNCF students seeking higher education require financial aid. UNCF also provides scholarships internships and fellowships to support graduate and doctoral studies. To help prepare students for college UNCF has partnered with Teach For America and the KIPP Foundation to improve high school graduation rates.

Financial Performance

About 75% of UNCF's support in 2013 came through contributions for grants and scholarships; some 16% came from contributions and gifts.

In 2013 the Fund's revenues decreased by 4% due to a 30% decline in bequests and legacies and a more than $15 million drop in net realized and unrealized gains interests and dividends and amortization and investment premiums which more than offset higher revenues from gifts-in-kind and donated services a 1% increase from grants and scholarships and a 5% increase from contributions and gifts.

UNCF's net income dropped by 3% in 2013 due to a decline in revenues.In 2013 the organization posted cash outflow of $89.17 million (compared to cash outflow of $41.02 million in 2012) primarily due to a decline in net loss and a change in working capital.

Strategy

UNCF Scholarship Programs increase the likelihood that students will graduate. African American recipients of UNCF scholarships have a 70% six-year graduation rate 10% points higher than the national average and 30% higher than the average for all African Americans. A $5000 UNCF scholarship the likelihood that its recipient will graduate from college by 7%.

Its largest scholarship program the Gates Millennium Scholars Program a partnership with the Bill & Melinda Gates Foundation provides financial assistance to 1000 Hispanic American Asian/Pacific American Native American and African American students. Students receive a good-through-graduation scholarship to use at any US-based accredited college or university of their choice.

The recipients of the Gates Millennium Scholarships have average graduation rates of 90%.

Company Background

The not-for-profit organization was founded in 1944 by Dr. Frederick D. Patterson with 27 charter member colleges.

EXECUTIVES

EVP General Counsel and Secretary of the Corporation, Sydney M. Avent

EVP National Development, Maurice E. Jenkins

Executive Vice President at UNCF, John Donohue

Executive Director, Fred Mitchell

Senior Vice President Research Innovation And Member Engagement, Karl Reid

Vice President Marketing Communications, Richard (Dick) Shropshire

Vice President Operations and Technology, Robert (Bob) Rucker

Senior Vice President Public Policy Government Affairs, Cheryl Smith

Vice President Research and Member
Engagement, Brian Bridges

LOCATIONS

HQ: UNITED NEGRO COLLEGE FUND INC.
1805 7TH ST NW STE 100, WASHINGTON, DC
200013187
Phone: 703 205-3400
Web: WWW.UNCFSP.ORG

UNCF Member Institutions

Allen University Columbia SC
Benedict College Columbia SC
Bennett College for Women Greensboro NC
Bethune-Cookman University Daytona Beach FL
Claflin University Orangeburg SC
Clark Atlanta University Atlanta GA
Dillard University New Orleans LA
Edward Waters College Jacksonville FL
Fisk University Nashville TN
Florida Memorial University Miami FL
Huston-Tillotson University Austin TX
Interdenominational Theological Center Atlanta GA
Jarvis Christian College Hawkins TX
Johnson C. Smith University Charlotte NC
Lane College Jackson TX
LeMoyne-Owen College Memphis TN
Livingston College Salisbury NC
Miles College Birmingham AL
Morehouse College Atlanta GA
Morris College Sumter SC
Oakwood University Huntsville AL
Paine College Augusta GA
Paul Quinn College Dallas TX
Philander Smith College Little rock AR
Rust College Holly Springs MS
Saint Augustine' s College Raleigh NC
Saint Paul' s College Lawrenceville VA
Shaw University Raleigh NC
Spelman College Atlanta GA
Stillman College Tuscaloosa AL
Talladega College Talladega AL
Texas College Tyler TX
Tougaloo College Tougaloo MC
Tuskegee University Tuskegee AL
Virginia Union University Richmond VA
Voorhees College Denmark SC
Wilberforce University Wilberforce OH
Wiley College Marshall TX
Xavier University New Orleans LA

PRODUCTS/OPERATIONS

Selected Scholarship Programs

Corporate Scholars Program
Gates Millennium Scholars Program
UNCF/Merck Science Initiative

HISTORICAL FINANCIALS

Company Type: Private

Income Statement

FYE: March 31

	REVENUE ($ mil.)	NET INCOME ($ mil.)	NET PROFIT MARGIN	EMPLOYEES
03/14	208	40	19.2%	257
03/10	197	51	25.9%	—
03/09	240	89	37.3%	—
Annual Growth	(2.8%)	(14.9%)	—	—

2014 Year-End Financials

Return on assets: 5.4%   Cash ($ mil.): 83
Return on equity: 19.2%
Current ratio: 2.30

UNITED NETWORK FOR ORGAN SHARING

LOCATIONS

HQ: UNITED NETWORK FOR ORGAN SHARING
700 N 4TH ST, RICHMOND, VA 232191414
Phone: 804 782-4800
Web: WWW.TRANSPLANTLIVING.ORG

HISTORICAL FINANCIALS

Company Type: Private

Income Statement

FYE: September 30

	REVENUE ($ mil.)	NET INCOME ($ mil.)	NET PROFIT MARGIN	EMPLOYEES
09/09	35,111	340	1.0%	300
09/08	35	0	0.2%	—
Annual Growth	98509.7%	568121.7%	—	—

2009 Year-End Financials

Return on assets: —   Cash ($ mil.): 4
Return on equity: 1.0%
Current ratio: 1.30

UNITED REGIONAL HEALTH CARE SYSTEM INC.

If you take a fall in Wichita Falls United Regional Health Care System (URHCS) will be there. The health care provider serves the residents of northern Texas through two hospitals that combined have some 500 beds. Specialized services include emergency medicine cardiac care diagnostic imaging surgery obstetrics and pediatrics. The health care system also offers cancer treatment childbirth wound care and sleep diagnostic centers. It is the only comprehensive cardiac care facility and only Level II trauma center in the region. URHCS operates a Care Flight Helicopter to get those traumas to care quicker.

Geographic Reach

The hospital serves Wichita Falls and a surrounding nine-county area.

Operations

URHCS provides medical care including inpatient and outpatient services advanced diagnostics surgical specialties and life-saving emergency care and the area's only Level II Trauma Center. It also serves as the Primary Stroke Center for the region. Its centers of excellence include wound care center joint replacement program and stroke program; bariatric surgery program; breast imaging center of excellence; cardiovascular patient care. It has some 200 physicians on staff.In 2012 the medical system reported 14163 admissions; 74778 emergency department visits; 48890 outpatient visits/observations; 9211 surgeries and 2144 births.

Financial Performance

In 2012 URHCS provided $27 million in charity care.

Strategy

Along with building and technological expansions URHCS has been focused on increasing the number of specialists in its employ. To that end the system created a recruitment program that targets medical students residents and fellows who have ties to Wichita Falls and the surrounding areas. Hospital administration and members of the physician staff offer support and guidance to potential recruits as they progress in their medical education or as they consider making a move from another hospital.

In recent years URHCS has recruited physicians in the areas of cardiovascular surgery neurosurgery orthopedic surgery and minimally invasive general and bariatric surgery to meet the community's increased need for those medical specialties.

In 2013 it expanded the Barnett Road Medical Building to have office space for physicians. The system also added laboratory and radiology services to the building. In 2012 URHCS deployed Allscripts MDRX +1.09% Care Management's fully-integrated web-based solutions to help transform its administrative processes by streamlining and improving the quality of patient care enhancing operational efficiency and cutting costs. In addition new mobile access technology help physicians to securely access patient information and make care decisions for their patients via their iPhones and iPads.

Company Background

In 2011 URCHS initiated renovation of its Bethania Building and Administration Building and it relocated its Cardio-Pulmonary Rehab Facility. It also remodeled its United Regional Diagnostic building and extended the hospital's outpatient therapy space to accommodate more patients.

EXECUTIVES

Vice President Of Information Technology, Donnie Boydstun
Vice President Facilities Management, Rick Carpenter
Vice President Of Marketing, Stevie-Joe Brown
Auditors: BKD LLP DALLAS TEXAS

LOCATIONS

HQ: UNITED REGIONAL HEALTH CARE SYSTEM INC.
1600 11TH ST, WICHITA FALLS, TX 763014300
Phone: 940 764-3211
Web: WWW.UNITEDREGIONAL.ORG

PRODUCTS/OPERATIONS

Selected Medical Services

Advanced Technology
Bariatric Services
Cancer Care
Cardiac Services
Diabetes Education
Emergency and Trauma Services
ENT
Infusion Therapy
Neurology
Neurosurgery
Obstetrics
Orthopedics
Pediatrics
Pulmonary Rehabilitation
Radiology
Reference Laboratory
Respiratory
Stroke Program & Center of Distinction
Supportive Care
Surgical Services
Women' s Services
Wound Care

COMPETITORS

HCA	Tenet Healthcare
Jackson County Memorial Hospital	Texas Health Denton
Mercy Health	Texas Health Resources

HISTORICAL FINANCIALS
Company Type: Private

Income Statement
FYE: December 31

	REVENUE ($ mil.)	NET INCOME ($ mil.)	NET PROFIT MARGIN	EMPLOYEES
12/13	292	53	18.3%	1,950
12/12	279	41	15.0%	—
12/11	289	41	14.4%	—
12/10	287	0	—	—
Annual Growth	0.6%	—	—	—

2013 Year-End Financials
Return on assets: 1.6%
Return on equity: 18.3%
Current ratio: 1.60
Cash ($ mil.): 30

UNITED SPACE ALLIANCE LLC

United Space Alliance (USA) is a space-race heavyweight; the Houston-based prime contractor has run NASA's 173000 pound Shuttles –Discovery Atlantis and Endeavour. USA a joint venture between Lockheed Martin and Boeing was formed in response to NASA's move to consolidate multiple Space Shuttle contracts under a single entity. It is now wrapping up those contracts. USA has supported mission operations astronaut and flight controller training flight software development Shuttle payload integration and vehicle processing launch and recovery. It also has led training and planning for the International Space Station. USA served the Johnson and Kennedy Space Centers and Marshall Space Flight Center.

Geographic Reach

Based in Houston the company has another location in Titusville Florida.

Operations

The company has consolidated more than 30 heritage contracts which supported the Space Shuttle Program (including the Space Flight Operations contract the Space Program Operations Contract and the Integrated Mission Operations Contract).

Strategy

The company served as NASA's primary partner in human space operations for the management of the Space Shuttle fleet and worked together for 55 Space Shuttle missions and more than 35 International Space Station increments.

In 2014 the company had no active contracts and will not pursue future contracts. The company is currently operating in an administrative capacity to close-out its managed government contracts (a process that will take a further about 5-7 years).

Company Background

In 2012 NASA awarded a one-year extension of the Integrated Mission Operations Contract to USA to continue providing mission and flight crew operations support for the International Space Station and Exploration Programs. The deal includes a further option for 2014. Throughout 2012 and 2013 however USA laid off waves of workers that resided in its former Space Shuttle program.

The launch of space shuttle Atlantis in July 2011 marked the end of NASA's 30-year Space Shuttle program. The shuttles have transported astronauts launched recovered and repaired satellites as well as driven new research and built and stocked the International Space Station with parts and provisions.

The joint venture was formed in 1996.

EXECUTIVES

Vice President and General Counsel, Rochelle Cooper
Vice President Human Resources, Sherri K Lee
Vice President Space Shuttle Program Manager, Howard Decastro
Vice President Of Operations, Scott Hartwig
Vice President, Norman Gookins
Auditors: PRICEWATERHOUSECOOPERS LLP HO

LOCATIONS

HQ: UNITED SPACE ALLIANCE LLC
 600 GEMINI ST, HOUSTON, TX 770582783
Phone: 281 212-6200
Web: WWW.UNITEDSPACEALLIANCE.COM

PRODUCTS/OPERATIONS

Selected Capabilities
Flight software
Ground operations and processing
GSA (General Services Administration) services
Integrated logistics
Integration and program management
Mission operations
Safety

COMPETITORS

Air Traffic Alliance	Meggitt-USA
Airbus Group	Northrop Grumman
Arianespace	Raytheon
Astrotech	SGT
BAE SYSTEMS	Thales Aerospace
Honeywell Aerospace	

HISTORICAL FINANCIALS
Company Type: Private

Income Statement
FYE: December 31

	REVENUE ($ mil.)	NET INCOME ($ mil.)	NET PROFIT MARGIN	EMPLOYEES
12/07	1,859	168	9.0%	10,500
12/06	1,920	146	7.6%	—
Annual Growth	(3.2%)	14.8%	—	—

2007 Year-End Financials
Return on assets: 1.9%
Return on equity: 9.0%
Current ratio: 0.30
Cash ($ mil.): 57

UNITED STATES BEEF CORPORATION

This company has carved out a sandwich empire in the middle of the country. United States Beef Corporation is the largest franchisee of Arby's fast-food restaurants in the US with more than 280 locations in half a dozen states mostly in Kansas Missouri and Oklahoma. The restaurants franchised from Arby's Restaurant Group (part of Wendy's/Arby's Group) serve the chain's signature roast beef sandwiches and curly fries as well as ham chicken and turkey subs. Bob Davis and his wife Connie opened their first Arby's in 1969 and founded United States Beef in 1974. The Davis family continues to own the company.

Unlike many other fast food chains Arby's has not had much success expanding its product offerings beyond roast beef sandwiches and curly fries.

Regardless United States Beef Corporation plans to develop new Arby's restaurants in some of its existing markets while the company remodels older locations with modern and clean looking interiors and exteriors.

United States Beef Corporation has the exclusive franchise development rights for Arby's restaurants in Arkansas Colorado Illinois Kansas Missouri and Oklahoma.

EXECUTIVES

Vice President Operations, Bill Yerk
Vice President Human Resources, Kim Thompson
Vice President Operations, Bo Davis
Vice President Operations, Al Schiltz

LOCATIONS

HQ: UNITED STATES BEEF CORPORATION
 4923 E 49TH ST, TULSA, OK 741357002
Phone: 918 665-0740
Web: WWW.USBEEFCORP.COM

COMPETITORS

American Dairy Queen	Mazzio' s
Biglari Holdings	McDonald' s
Boddie-Noell	NPC Restaurant
Burger King	Holdings
Captain D' s	Panera Bread
Checkers Drive-In	Popeyes
Chick-fil-A	Quiznos
Chipotle	Sonic Corp.
Church' s Chicken	Subway
Hardee' s	Whataburger
Jack in the Box	YUM!
K-MAC	

HISTORICAL FINANCIALS
Company Type: Private

Income Statement
FYE: December 31

	REVENUE ($ mil.)	NET INCOME ($ mil.)	NET PROFIT MARGIN	EMPLOYEES
12/13	256	7	3.1%	2,000
12/12	246	7	3.0%	—
12/08	246	6	2.5%	—
12/07	246	0	—	—
Annual Growth	0.7%	—	—	—

2013 Year-End Financials
Return on assets: 1.4%
Return on equity: 3.1%
Current ratio: 0.10
Cash ($ mil.): 2

UNITED STATES FUND FOR UNICEF

The US Fund for UNICEF is one of about 40 committees in America that raises money for The United Nations Children's Fund (better known as UNICEF a not-for-profit organization that works for the human rights protection and development of children worldwide through education advocacy and fundraising. Among its dedicated programs are the five-year $100 million fundraising campaign for HIV/AIDS prevention and a campaign to protect mothers and newborns from tetanus. The US Fund for UNICEF derives revenue from public support –through its signature Trick-or-Treat for UNICEF program gifts corporate grants and the sale of greeting cards and educational materials. The organization was founded in 1947.Geographic ReachThe US Fund for UNICEF operates a handful of regional offices in Atlanta Boston Chicago Houston Los Angeles and San Francisco.Financial PerformanceThe organization's revenue increased by 1% in 2012 versus 2011 to more than $500 million. The US Fund attributed the gain to an increase in public support including major gifts Internet donations and gifts in kind. The increase in giving was partially offset by a decline in investment returns. Net income rose 7% over the same period despite an increase in expenses tied to program and support services.StrategyThe US Fund for UNICEF is rallying around its "Believe in Zero" campaign which aims to reduce the number of preventable deaths of children under five years of age to zero. The number of under-five child deaths has dropped more than 40 percent since 1990 to 19000.

EXECUTIVES

Vice President Corporate Partnerships, Deanna Helmig

Vice President Finance and Budget, Richard (Dick) Esserman

Vice President Public Advocacy and Strategic Communications, Lisa Szarkowski

Vice President Program & Community Engagement, Leslie Goldman

Vice President For Corporate And Found, Nicole Brown

LOCATIONS

HQ: UNITED STATES FUND FOR UNICEF
125 MAIDEN LN FL 11, NEW YORK, NY 100384999
Phone: 212 686-5522
Web: WWW.UNICEF.ORG

HISTORICAL FINANCIALS

Company Type: Private

Income Statement				FYE: June 30
	REVENUE ($ mil.)	NET INCOME ($ mil.)	NET PROFIT MARGIN	EMPLOYEES
06/14	606	67	11.2%	200
06/13	310	12	4.2%	—
Annual Growth	95.2%	423.1%	—	—

2014 Year-End Financials

Return on assets: —
Return on equity: 11.2%
Current ratio: 0.80
Cash ($ mil.): 65

UNITED STATES GOLF ASSOCIATION

Making sure golf stays clear of the rough is par for the course at this organization. The United States Golf Association is the governing body for golf in the US its territories and Mexico. The not-for-profit group writes and interprets the rules of the game provides handicap information offers turf consulting and funds equipment and course maintenance research and testing. It also holds several national championship events including the US Open the US Women's Open and the US Senior Open. The group generates most of its revenue from the sale of broadcast rights to championship tournaments and other matches as well as through membership fees. The USGA was founded in 1894.

Sales and Marketing

The organization has long-term television deals with ESPN and Bell Media's Canadian broadcasting outlets RDS and TSN.

Financial Performance

The USGA reported fiscal 2013 revenue of about $157 million up roughly 6% from the prior year on a rise in championships revenue (including broadcast rights) and corporate sponsorship revenue. It also saw net income of $51 million in fiscal 2013 an increase of 97% from $26 million in fiscal 2012 primarily because of unfunded Postretirement benefit obligation.

Strategy

The organization is working to combat the challenges posed by modern golf courses which aren't as inviting to average players take longer to play and are more expensive to maintain. Improving course sustainability is a key element of this work and the USGA has been consulting with courses across the nation to implement sustainable practices deal with reductions in water availability and protect the environment.

EXECUTIVES

Treasurer Executive Committee, Irving Fish
Secretary Executive Committee, James T. (Jim) Bunch
Chairman Women's Committee, Barbara Douglas
President Executive Committee, James F. Vernon
Director Communications and USGA Museum, Rand Jerris
Managing Director Digital Media, Alex Withers
Senior Director Hadicaping Regional Affairs Information Systems and Golf Handicaping and Information Network., Kevin O'Connor
VP Executive Committee, Cameron J. Rains
General Counsel Executive Committee, Joseph Anthony
Treasurer Executive Committee, John Kim
President, Glen D. Nager
Secretary and Member Executive Committee, Thomas J. O'Toole Jr.
Senior Director Finance, Pamela Martin
Controller, Suzanne Colon
Director Broadcasting, Mark Carlson
Chief Business Officer, Peter Bevacqua
Manager Business Operations, Zack Lang
Manager Web Developmant, Karen Keller
Senior Web Developer and Chief Systems Officer, Scott Kinne
Editor USGA Website, Kenneth Klavon
Manager Internet Services, William Lacey
Executive Director, David Fay
Software Engineer Golf Handicap and Information Network, Lisa Christie
Pregrammer Golf Handicap and Information Network Mainframe, Kevin Jorgensen
Assistant Manager Technical Support Golf Handicap and Information Network, John Stern
Managing Director Information Technologies, Jessica Carroll
Chief Marketing Officer, Barry Hyde
Manager Corporate Marketing, Amy Engel
Technical Support Specialist I, Vincent Capone
Assistant Manager Technical Support and Training, Nate Engel
Supervisor Data Entry, Nancy Fitzpatrick
Network Administrator I, Erik Keller
Network Administrator II, Paul Klein
Director Application Development and Database Administration, Michael Overhiser
Programmer and Analyst, Ken Roxbury
Manager Application Development, Eric Wolf
Director Members Program, Fiona Dolan
Director Licensing and U.S. Open Merchandising, Mary Lopuszynski
Senior Director Rules and Competitions, Michael Davis
Managing Director, Kimberly S. Erusha
Member Executive Committee, Christopher A. Liedel
Treasurer Executive Committee, Irving Fish

Secretary Executive Committee, James T. (Jim) Bunch
President Executive Committee, James F. Vernon
VP Executive Committee, Cameron J. Rains
Member Executive Committee, Christie Austin
Member Executive Committee, Pat Kaufman
Treasurer Executive Committee, John Kim
Member Executive Committee, Gene McClure
VP and Member Executive Committee, Glen D. Nager
Secretary and Member Executive Committee, Thomas J. O'Toole Jr.
Member Executive Committee, Brigid Shanley Lamb
Member Executive Committee, Steve Smyers
Member Executive Committee, Geoffrey Y. Yang

LOCATIONS

HQ: UNITED STATES GOLF ASSOCIATION
77 LIBERTY CORNER RD, FAR HILLS, NJ 079312570
Phone: 908 234-2300
Web: WWW.USGAMUSEUM.COM

COMPETITORS

Augusta National	Professional Bowlers
Major League Baseball	Association
NBA	The R&A
NFL	USA Track & Field
NHL	USSF
PGA	USTA
PGA TOUR	

HISTORICAL FINANCIALS

Company Type: Private

Income Statement				FYE: November 30
	REVENUE ($ mil.)	NET INCOME ($ mil.)	NET PROFIT MARGIN	EMPLOYEES
11/13	156	6	4.3%	350
11/12	147	13	9.3%	—
11/11	155	33	21.5%	—
11/10	131	0	—	—
Annual Growth	6.0%	—	—	—

2013 Year-End Financials

Return on assets: —
Return on equity: 4.3%
Current ratio: 1.60
Cash ($ mil.): 35

UNITED STATES OLYMPIC COMMITTEE INC

Friendship solidarity and fair play are the watchwords for this sports organization. United States Olympic Committee (USOC) is the governing body of the Olympic movement in the US and oversees the organization selection and training of the country's Olympic athletes and teams. The not-for-profit organization operates six training and education centers around the country where athletes prepare for the Olympic Games the Paralympic Games and the Pan American Games. The USOC is funded by corporate sponsorships private contributions and sales of licensed apparel. It also receives money from the International Olympic Committee (IOC). The USOC was formed in 1978.

EXECUTIVES

CEO, Scott Blackmun, age 58

Chief Financial Officer, Walter Glover
Managing Director Information Technology, Trevor Miller
Vice President, Paul George
Secretary, Charles Kaelin
Auditors: GRANT THORNTON LLP DENVER CO

LOCATIONS

HQ: UNITED STATES OLYMPIC COMMITTEE INC
27 S TEJON ST, COLORADO SPRINGS, CO 809031538
Phone: 719 632-5551
Web: WWW.TEAMUSA.ORG

HISTORICAL FINANCIALS
Company Type: Private

Income Statement
FYE: December 31

	REVENUE ($ mil.)	NET INCOME ($ mil.)	NET PROFIT MARGIN	EMPLOYEES
12/13	168	(27)	—	400
12/08*	280	0	—	—
08/08	2	0	1.8%	—
12/07	2,033	0	—	—
Annual Growth	(34.0%)	—	—	—

*Fiscal year change

2013 Year-End Financials
Return on assets: 19.2%
Return on equity: (-16.3%)
Current ratio: 0.80
Cash ($ mil.): 29

UNITED STUDENT AID FUNDS INC

Auditors: DELOITTE TAX LLP INDIANAPOLIS

LOCATIONS

HQ: UNITED STUDENT AID FUNDS INC
9998 CRNPINT BLVD STE 400, INDIANAPOLIS, IN 46256
Phone: 317 806-1200
Web: WWW.USAFUNDS.ORG

HISTORICAL FINANCIALS
Company Type: Private

Income Statement
FYE: September 30

	ASSETS ($ mil.)	NET INCOME ($ mil.)	INCOME AS % OF ASSETS	EMPLOYEES
09/10	1,082	56	5.2%	65
09/09	1,005	32	3.2%	—
09/07	946	53	5.6%	—
09/06	20	0	—	—
Annual Growth	168.7%	—	—	—

2010 Year-End Financials
Return on assets: —
Return on equity: 13.8%
Sales ($ mil): 407

UNIVERSITY AL HEALTH SVC FNDN PC

LOCATIONS

HQ: UNIVERSITY AL HEALTH SVC FNDN PC
500 22ND ST S STE 500, BIRMINGHAM, AL 352333110
Phone: 205 731-9600
Web: WWW.ALABAMAORGANCENTER.ORG

HISTORICAL FINANCIALS
Company Type: Private

Income Statement
FYE: September 30

	REVENUE ($ mil.)	NET INCOME ($ mil.)	NET PROFIT MARGIN	EMPLOYEES
09/13	520	10	1.9%	3,205
09/08*	466	(21)	—	—
06/06	0	0	—	—
09/00	0	0	—	—
Annual Growth	—	—	—	—

*Fiscal year change

2013 Year-End Financials
Return on assets: 17.0%
Return on equity: 1.9%
Current ratio: 0.30
Cash ($ mil.): 27

UNITED STEEL PAPER AND FORESTRY RUBBER MANUFACTURING ENERGY ALLI

Auditors: SCHNEIDER DOWNS & CO INC PITT

LOCATIONS

HQ: UNITED STEEL PAPER AND FORESTRY RUBBER MANUFACTURING ENERGY ALLI
5 GATEWAY CTR, PITTSBURGH, PA 15222
Phone: 412 562-2400
Web: WWW.USW.ORG

HISTORICAL FINANCIALS
Company Type: Private

Income Statement
FYE: December 31

	REVENUE ($ mil.)	NET INCOME ($ mil.)	NET PROFIT MARGIN	EMPLOYEES
12/13	489	83	17.0%	3
12/09	386	(28)	—	—
Annual Growth	6.1%	—	—	—

2013 Year-End Financials
Return on assets: 3.5%
Return on equity: 17.0%
Current ratio: 11.20
Cash ($ mil.): 191

UNIVERSAL COOPERATIVES INC.

Auditors: MCGLADREY & PULLEN LLP MINNE

LOCATIONS

HQ: UNIVERSAL COOPERATIVES INC.
1300 CORPORATE CTR CURV, EAGAN, MN 551212487
Phone: 651 239-1000
Web: WWW.UCPALLC.COM

HISTORICAL FINANCIALS
Company Type: Private

Income Statement
FYE: July 31

	REVENUE ($ mil.)	NET INCOME ($ mil.)	NET PROFIT MARGIN	EMPLOYEES
07/08	374	3	1.0%	250
07/07	305	(0)	—	—
07/06	310	0	—	—
Annual Growth	—17480.3%	—	—	—

2008 Year-End Financials
Return on assets: 9.4%
Return on equity: 1.0%
Current ratio: 0.60
Cash ($ mil.): 8

UNIVERSITY CORPORATION FOR ATMOSPHERIC RESEARCH

The University Corporation for Atmospheric Research (UCAR) is a not-for-profit corporation founded in 1960 to promote research in atmospheric and related environmental sciences. A consortium of more than 100 universities UCAR provides real-time weather data to universities educates weather forecasters and organizes international experiments through its Office of Programs. The organization also maintains radars aircraft and computer models for weather and climate through the National Center for Atmospheric Research (NCAR). UCAR is funded by sponsors such as the National Science Foundation the National Oceanic and Atmospheric Administration and NASA.

Geographic Reach

The University Corporation for Atmospheric Research (UCAR) and the National Center for Atmospheric Research (NCAR) are both based in Boulder Colorado. They have additional operations in Cheyenne Wyoming and Washington DC. Its affiliated Mauna Loa Solar Observatory is based in Hilo Hawaii.

Operations

The UCAR consortium consists of around 75 North American universities granting doctoral degrees related to atmospheric science 25 offering bachelor's and master's programs in this dame filed and roughly 50 international affiliates.

In addition to promoting research and professional development among academia UCAR provides educational resources to the public and advocates for strong federal science budgets on behalf of the geosciences community.

Strategy

To extend its reach in 2012 the UCAR opened NCAR-Wyoming Supercomputing Center which provides advanced computing services to scientists with expertise in air pollution climate oceanography space weather energy production seismology carbon sequestration computational science and other topics.

EXECUTIVES

Vice President Of Finance, Beverly Broach
Treas, Dan Wilson
Secretary, Steven (Steve) Rutledge
Auditors: KPMG LLP DENVER CO

LOCATIONS

HQ: UNIVERSITY CORPORATION FOR ATMOSPHERIC RESEARCH
3090 CENTER GREEN DR, BOULDER, CO 803012252
Phone: 303 497-1000
Web: WWW.UCAR.EDU

PRODUCTS/OPERATIONS

Selected Research Topics
Climate
Meterology/Weather
Societal impacts of weather and climate
Pollution and air chemistry
The whole Earth system
Sun & space weather

HISTORICAL FINANCIALS

Company Type: Private

Income Statement FYE: September 30

	REVENUE ($ mil.)	NET INCOME ($ mil.)	NET PROFIT MARGIN	EMPLOYEES
09/14	214	3	1.4%	1,565
09/13	221	8	3.8%	—
09/12	260	13	5.1%	—
09/11	269	0	—	—
Annual Growth	(7.3%)	—	—	—

2014 Year-End Financials

Return on assets: 2.9%   Cash ($ mil.): 36
Return on equity: 1.4%
Current ratio: 0.80

UNIVERSITY HOSPITALS HEALTH SYSTEM INC.

University Hospitals Health System (UHHS) is on a mission to teach research and administer good health throughout northeastern Ohio. Its flagship facility University Hospitals of Cleveland (UHC) which operates as University Hospitals Case Medical Center (UHCMC) is a more than 1000-bed tertiary care center serving Cleveland and other parts of northeastern Ohio. The teaching hospital which is affiliated with Case Western Reserve University is also home to Rainbow Babies & Children's Hospital Seidman Cancer Center and MacDonald Women's Hospital. the not-for-profit UHHS is also home to community hospitals outpatient health and surgery centers mental health facilities and senior care centers.

Geographic Reach

UHHS operates about 30 health centers and outpatient office buildings as well as more than 100 physician practice locations across the northeastern Ohio region. It serves 16 counties.

Operations

UHHS' eight community hospitals some of which are operated through affiliation agreements provide a full range of specialty and general acute care from anesthesia to vascular surgery. Along with those the system operates urgent care and neighborhood medical centers throughout the region. The UH Extended Care Campus includes a specialty hospital outpatient rehabilitation and extended care facility. UHHS also operates home health occupational health wellness and managed care (health plan) divisions. The UHHS facilities have a total of some 1800 beds.

Altogether the network's facilities handle some 65000 inpatient visits per year as well as 5.8 million outpatient procedures and 206000 emergency room visits. It delivered more than 5200 babies and conducted more than 60000 surgeries in 2013.

In addition to conducting education and training programs for Case Western Reserve University School of Medicine students UHHS partners with the university to operate the Center for Clinical Research and Technology. The center is the largest biomedical research facility in Ohio and focuses on translational research which connects laboratory research to clinical bedside care.

UHHS' physician network consists of 1700 physicians and 3000 affiliated members. The system provided $270 million for community benefit and provided $253 million for research in 2013.The hospital system is affiliated with three Cleveland-area health care providers: St. John Medical Center UH Rehabilitation Hospital (a joint venture with Center Healthcare) and Southwest General.

Financial Performance

UHHS' revenues increased by 4% to $2.3 billion in 2013 due to higher patient service revenues.

Operating income increased by 21% $78.6 million that year due to a change in fair value of derivative instruments and a growth in investment income partially offset by higher operating expenses.

UHHS' operating cash flow decreased by $143 million in 2013 due a change in beneficial interest in foundation and perpetual trusts pension liability adjustments and a change in operating assets and liabilities.

Strategy

The medical system is expanding by installing smaller regional and community hospitals and additional specialty care units within its larger facilities including a neonatal intensive care unit emergency care center and a cancer care center within UH Case Medical.

To strengthen its clinical capabilities it also expanded its established areas of excellence and developed new areas to improve access it has forged new hospital partnerships. To enhance care in the communities served by its new partners UHHS has opened satellites of some of its centers of excellence initially for cancer care cardiac care pediatrics and women's health. Pursuant to the growth strategy it has added two community hospitals that are now UHHS' largest: 387-bed UH Elyria Medical Center (formerly EMH Healthcare) and 332-bed UH Parma Medical Center (formerly The Parma Community General Hospital).

The company also plans to break ground on a $28 million state-of-the-art outpatient health center and freestanding emergency department in Broadview Heights with a projected completion date in late 2016. In 2013 University Hospitals Seidman Cancer Center expanded to Parma Community General Hospital providing integrated cancer care to residents in Parma and surrounding communities.

To expand in another neighboring community the system launched renovation of an office building that became the UH Solon Health Center in 2013. It also opened a new outpatient center the UH Aurora Health Center in 2012.

UHHS is also in the process of implementing an electronic health records (EHR) system across its facilities. The EHR system could make the network eligible for certain government incentives if they meet government guidelines for "meaningful use."

On the research front in 2014 UHHS Case Medical Center conducted a Phase 3 clinical trial to evaluate the safety and effectiveness of an investigational medicine called LMTX in people with a type of dementia known as behavioral-variant Frontotemporal Dementia (previously known as Pick's Disease).

Company Background

UHHS completed construction of the UH Ahuja Medical Center a new community hospital in 2011. The company was founded in 1866.

EXECUTIVES

Chairman, Alfred M. Rankin Jr., age 72
President University Hospitals Case Medical Center, Fred C. Rothstein
CEO, Thomas F. (Tom) Zenty III, age 59
COO; COO Clinical Operations, Achilles A. Demetriou
President Community Hospitals and Ambulatory Network, Richard A. (Dick) Hanson
CFO, Michael A. (Mike) Szubski
President University Hospitals Seidman Cancer Center, Nathan Levitan
Chief Medical Officer and President University Hospitals Accountable Care Organization, Eric J. Bieber
President University Hospitals Physician Services, Michael L. Nochomovitz, age 62
Chief Nursing Officer, Catherine S. (Cathy) Koppelman
Director Media Relations, Janice Guhl
Chief Legal Officer, Janet L. Miller
Chief Administrative Officer, Steven D. (Steve) Standley
President University Hospitals Bedford and Richmond Medical Centers Campuses of UH Regional Hospitals, Laurie S. Delgado
President University Hospitals Conneaut Medical Center; President University Hospitals Geneva Medical Center, Robert G. David
President University Hospitals Geauga Medical Center, M. Steven Jones
Chief Quality Officer and Director University Hospitals Quality Institute, William L. Annable
VP and Chief Compliance Officer, Cheryl Forino Wahl
President University Hospitals Rainbow Babies and Children?s Hospital and University Hospitals MacDonald Women?s Hospital, Patricia DePompei
President University Hospitals Ahuja Medical Center, Susan V. Juris
President St. John Medical Center, William A. Young Jr.
Chief Medical Officer, Amitabh Goel
Vice President, Joseph Shawi
Director, Henry L. Meyer III, age 64
Director, Paul G. Clark, age 60
Director, Richard W. Pogue
Director, Joseph (Joe) Lopez
Director, April M. Boise
Director, Brian E. Hall
Director, Ronald G. Harrington
Director, William E. Kamatz Sr.
Director, Robert A. Salata
Auditors: KPMG LLP CINCINNATI OH

LOCATIONS

HQ: UNIVERSITY HOSPITALS HEALTH SYSTEM INC.
3605 WARRENSVILLE CTR RD, SHAKER HEIGHTS,
OH 441225203
Phone: 216 844-1000
Web: WWW.UHHOSPITALS.ORG

PRODUCTS/OPERATIONS

Selected Facilities
Main Campuses
Case Medical Center
MacDonald Women's Hospital
Rainbow Babies & Children's Hospital
Seidman Cancer Center
Community Hospitals
Ahuja Medical Center
Bedford Medical Center (UH Regional Hospitals)
Conneaut Medical Center
Elyria Medical Center
Geauga Medical Center
Geneva Medical Center
Parma Medical Center
Richmond Medical Center (UH Regional Hospitals)

COMPETITORS

Akron Children's Hospital	Parma Community General Hospital
Akron General Health System	Robinson Memorial Hospital
Lake Health	Summa Health System
Mercy Medical Center (OH)	The Cleveland Clinic
MetroHealth System	Trinity Health System

HISTORICAL FINANCIALS

Company Type: Private

Income Statement

FYE: December 31

	REVENUE ($ mil.)	NET INCOME ($ mil.)	NET PROFIT MARGIN	EMPLOYEES
12/13	2,326	244	10.5%	30,000
12/12	2,266	54	2.4%	—
12/09	1,938	110	5.7%	—
12/08	1,800	0	—	—
Annual Growth	5.3%	—	—	—

2013 Year-End Financials

Return on assets: 13.3% Cash ($ mil.): 192
Return on equity: 10.5%
Current ratio: 0.30

UNIVERSITY MEDICAL CENTER INC

Auditors: ERNST & YOUNG LLP LOUISVILLE

LOCATIONS

HQ: UNIVERSITY MEDICAL CENTER INC
530 S JACKSON ST, LOUISVILLE, KY 402021675
Phone: 502 562-3000

HISTORICAL FINANCIALS

Company Type: Private

Income Statement

FYE: December 31

	REVENUE ($ mil.)	NET INCOME ($ mil.)	NET PROFIT MARGIN	EMPLOYEES
12/12	463	8	1.8%	2,000
12/11	450	(7)	—	—
12/10	448	13	3.0%	—
12/09	415	0	—	—
Annual Growth	3.7%	—	—	—

2012 Year-End Financials

Return on assets: 3.7% Cash ($ mil.): 60
Return on equity: 1.8%
Current ratio: 1.30

UNIVERSITY OF CHICAGO

LOCATIONS

HQ: UNIVERSITY OF CHICAGO
1414 E 59TH ST, CHICAGO, IL 606372916
Phone: 773 753-2270
Web: WWW.UCHICAGO.EDU

HISTORICAL FINANCIALS

Company Type: Private

Income Statement

FYE: June 30

	REVENUE ($ mil.)	NET INCOME ($ mil.)	NET PROFIT MARGIN	EMPLOYEES
06/13	3,091	182	5.9%	2
06/11	3,056	1,052	34.4%	—
Annual Growth	0.6%	(58.4%)	—	—

2013 Year-End Financials

Return on assets: 19.2% Cash ($ mil.): 45
Return on equity: 5.9%
Current ratio: —

UNIVERSITY OF CINCINNATI MEDICAL CENTER LLC

Auditors: DELOITTE TAX LLP CINCINNATI

LOCATIONS

HQ: UNIVERSITY OF CINCINNATI MEDICAL CENTER LLC
234 GOODMAN ST, CINCINNATI, OH 452192364
Phone: 513 584-1000
Web: WWW.UCHEALTH.COM

HISTORICAL FINANCIALS

Company Type: Private

Income Statement

FYE: June 30

	REVENUE ($ mil.)	NET INCOME ($ mil.)	NET PROFIT MARGIN	EMPLOYEES
06/10	633	28	4.6%	5,000
06/09	562	20	3.6%	—
Annual Growth	12.7%	42.0%	—	—

2010 Year-End Financials

Return on assets: — Cash ($ mil.): 3
Return on equity: 4.6%
Current ratio: 1.10

UNIVERSITY OF COLORADO

Operating independently from the University of Colorado the University of Colorado Foundation (CU Foundation) engages in not-for-profit fundraising on behalf of the University. It partners with the University to raise manage and invest private support for the University's benefit. The foundation manages more than $125 million annually from nearly 50000 donors; the funds it raises are used to support scholarships research athletics building construction and faculty and staff at the University. The CU Foundation also manages the University's Creating Futures fundraising campaign which aims to raise $1.5 billion.

Operations

In fiscal 2014 more than 46000 donors gave $148.9 million through the University of Colorado Foundation (a significant component of the nearly $300 million of private support for the University of Colorado that year. That year the Foundation's assets totaled $1.57 billion primarily made up of investments of $1.42 billion. It reported managed endowments of $1.06 billion.

Financial Performance

The revenue increased by 34% to $315 million in 2014 due to increase in contributions investment return and Change in value of split–interest agreements.Net income increased by 95% to $186 million in 2014 due to higher revenue.The company saw cash inflow of $40 million in 2014 over cash outflow in 2013 due to higher net income and cash generated from custodial funds.

Company Background

The CU Foundation was established by the University of Colorado in 1967.

EXECUTIVES

Vice President And Managing Director, David (Dave) Chadwick
Senior Assistant Vice President Chief Human Resources Officer, Jill Pollock
Assistant Vice President, Christen Woodburn
Associate Vice President Fortechnologytransfer(regional Director), David (Dave) Allen
Assistant Vice President, Andrea Wagner
Vice President Employee and Information Services, Kathy Nesbitt
Vice President Of Legislative Council, David (Dave) Gillis
Associate Vice President For Development, Maurin Anderson
Vice President Of Government Relations, Tanya Kelly-bowry
Board Member, Eileen Gordon
Assistant Treasurer, Joe Tinucci
Board Member, David Hinojosa
Auditors: EKS & H LLLP DENVER COLORADO

UNIVERSITY OF GEORGIA

Located in the quintessential college town of Athens The University of Georgia (UGA) offers a wide range of degree programs to nearly 35000 students. Forest resources veterinary medicine and law are a few of the school's academic programs. UGA which also runs 170-plus study-abroad and exchange programs administers the prestigious Peabody Awards which honors media achievements and boasts one of the nation's largest map collections. Famous alumni include former US Senator Phil Gramm TV journalist Deborah Norville and former PBS president Pat Mitchell. The University of Georgia was chartered by the State of Georgia in 1785 and graduated its first class in 1804.

Operations

As part of its business UGA offers nearly two dozen bachelor's degrees in about 140 fields and roughly 35 master's degrees in nearly 140 fields. Its doctorate or professional degrees cover a broad spectrum of disciplines such as law pharmacy veterinary medicine and 90 other areas. The university has a student-teacher ratio of about 12:1.

Strategy

Despite its annual endowment of more than $50 million UGA has logged decreases in state appropriations in recent years due to overall declines in Georgia's budget. The result spurred UGA to cut its budget increase undergraduate tuition fees institute a "Special Institutional" mandatory fee of $200 per semester reduce employer health insurance contributions and increase energy conservation measures. Going forward UGA has also not ruled out the possibility of hiking tuition further citing that an increase of up to 30% would help to replace all of the state funding the university has lost due to the recession.

Sales and Marketing

The university sources 80% of its students from the Peach State. Since 1851 25 Georgia governors have graduated from UGA. The institution also boasts nine Pulitzer Prize recipients 17 presidents or provosts of US colleges and universities and four members of the National Academy of Sciences.

EXECUTIVES

VP Marketing and Communications, Karri Hobson-Pape
Vp Information Technology, Timothy M (Tim) Chester
Vice President Information Technology, Timothy Chester
Vice President Finance And Administration, Ryan Nesbit
Auditors: GREG S GRIFFIN ATLANTA GEOR

LOCATIONS

HQ: UNIVERSITY OF GEORGIA
424 E BROAD ST, ATHENS, GA 306021535
Phone: 706 542-2786
Web: WWW.UGA.EDU

PRODUCTS/OPERATIONS

Selected Schools and Colleges
Agricultural and Environmental Sciences
Arts and Sciences Business
Ecology
Education
Environment and Design
Family and Consumer Sciences
Forest Resources
Graduate School
Journalism and Mass Communication
Law
Pharmacy
Public Health
Public and International Affairs
Social Work
Veterinary Medicine
The GHSU/UGA Medical Partnership
Engineering

HISTORICAL FINANCIALS
Company Type: Private

Income Statement
FYE: June 30

	REVENUE ($ mil.)	NET INCOME ($ mil.)	NET PROFIT MARGIN	EMPLOYEES
06/13	779	115	14.8%	17,800
06/12	776	72	9.3%	—
06/11	691	(12)	—	—
06/10	636	0	—	—
Annual Growth	7.0%	—	—	—

2013 Year-End Financials
Return on assets: 3.1%   Cash ($ mil.): 307
Return on equity: 14.8%
Current ratio: 2.60

UNIVERSITY OF ILLINOIS FOUNDATION

Auditors: DELOITTE TAX LLP CHICAGO IL

LOCATIONS

HQ: UNIVERSITY OF ILLINOIS FOUNDATION
1305 W GREEN ST, URBANA, IL 618012945
Phone: 217 333-0810

UNIVERSITY OF IOWA HOSPITALS AND CLINICS

Auditors: KPMG LLP DES MOINES IA

LOCATIONS

HQ: UNIVERSITY OF IOWA HOSPITALS AND CLINICS
200 HAWKINS DR, IOWA CITY, IA 522421009
Phone: 319 356-1616
Web: WWW.UICHILDRENS.ORG

HISTORICAL FINANCIALS
Company Type: Private

Income Statement
FYE: June 30

	REVENUE ($ mil.)	NET INCOME ($ mil.)	NET PROFIT MARGIN	EMPLOYEES
06/13	1,125	10	0.9%	7,638
06/10	943	52	5.6%	—
06/09	863	(11)	—	—
Annual Growth	6.9%	—	—	—

2013 Year-End Financials
Return on assets: —   Cash ($ mil.): 2
Return on equity: 0.9%
Current ratio: 0.90

UNIVERSITY OF KENTUCKY RESEARCH FOUNDATION

LOCATIONS

HQ: UNIVERSITY OF KENTUCKY RESEARCH FOUNDATION
102 KINKEAD HALL, LEXINGTON, KY 405060001
Phone: 859 257-4758

HISTORICAL FINANCIALS

Company Type: Private

Income Statement

FYE: June 30

	REVENUE ($ mil.)	NET INCOME ($ mil.)	NET PROFIT MARGIN	EMPLOYEES
06/10	345	12	3.6%	23
06/09	313	1	0.4%	—
06/08	1	(1)	—	—
06/06	271	0	—	—
Annual Growth	6.2%	—	—	—

2010 Year-End Financials

Return on assets: —   Cash ($ mil.): 17
Return on equity: 3.6%
Current ratio: 3.80

UNIVERSITY OF MAINE SYSTEM

University of Maine System is composed of seven public universities throughout Maine serving some 40000 students. It also operates eight regional outreach centers as well as distance education programs. The University of Maine System offers nearly 600 majors minors and concentrations; its flagship campus in Orono (UMaine) offers nearly 90 bachelor's degree programs more than 60 master's degree programs and about two dozen doctoral programs. UMaine was established in 1862 as the Maine College of Agriculture and Mechanic Arts; it adopted its current name in 1897. The University of Maine System was created in 1968 by the state legislature.

Financial Performance

In 2014 (ended June) the University of Maine System saw a $2 million increase in revenue vs. 2013. Net student fees remained at 36% of total revenue. Although money from tuition and fees dropped by $1 million residence and dining fees increased by $2 million. State appropriations the second biggest source of revenue remained at 29% of the total.

Strategy

The system acted to expand in Portland Maine and to maintain the number of campuses at the University of Southern Maine. It moved forward to on an opportunity to develop a professional and graduate center in Portland.The closing of campuses at USM had been proposed to save money but the system defended their value and kept them open.

EXECUTIVES

Assistant Vice President Finance Budget Services, Claire Strickland
Secretary, Karen Glidden

LOCATIONS

HQ: UNIVERSITY OF MAINE SYSTEM
16 CENTRAL ST, BANGOR, ME 044015106
Phone: 207 973-3300
Web: WWW.MAINE.EDU

PRODUCTS/OPERATIONS

System Universities
University of Maine
University of Maine at Augusta
University of Maine at Farmington
University of Maine at Fort Kent
University of Maine at Machias
University of Maine at Presque Isle
University of Southern Maine Maine Law School

HISTORICAL FINANCIALS

Company Type: Private

Income Statement

FYE: June 30

	REVENUE ($ mil.)	NET INCOME ($ mil.)	NET PROFIT MARGIN	EMPLOYEES
06/13	460	27	6.1%	5,379
06/12	476	37	8.0%	—
06/06	390	33	8.7%	—
06/05	381	0	—	—
Annual Growth	2.4%	—	—	—

2013 Year-End Financials

Return on assets: 3.6%   Cash ($ mil.): 1
Return on equity: 6.1%
Current ratio: 0.80

UNIVERSITY OF MARYLAND MEDICAL SYSTEM CORPORATION

The 12 academic specialty and community hospitals of the University of Maryland Medical System (UMMS) dot the map of the state's eastern half on both sides of Chesapeake Bay. UMMS one of the largest employers in the Baltimore area has more than 2300 acute care beds and attends to such specialties as trauma care coma emergence kidney transplants orthopedic rehabilitation stroke intervention and pediatric care. University of Maryland Medical Center the system's teaching hub is one of the oldest academic hospitals in the US. In addition to its hospitals UMMS also includes community clinics to address mental health rehabilitation and primary care. The system was established in 1984.

Operations

UMMC's members hospitals include the University of Maryland Medical Center Baltimore Washington Medical Center Chester River Health System Civista Health System Kernan Orthopaedics and Rehabilitation Maryland General Hospital Mt. Washington Pediatric Hospital Shore Health System University of Maryland St. Joseph Medical Center and Upper Chesapeake Health.

University of Maryland Medical Center which houses about 800 beds is staffed entirely by physicians who double as faculty members at the University of Maryland School of Medicine (SOM) the system's longtime partner. The hospital contains additional specialty facilities dedicated to such areas as pediatrics cancer treatment cardiac disease diabetes organ transplants Parkinson's disease and shock trauma. The shock trauma center was the first of its kind in the world when it was founded in 1968.

Aside from its integral partnership with SOM UMMS has in recent years been bolstering its network of member hospitals to reach new markets in Maryland. Having been affilated with Upper Chesapeake Health (UCH) UMMS merged the systems in 2013. UCH owns a pair of hospitals in northeastern Maryland an underserved corner of the state that UMMS hadn't yet entered.

Financial Performance

UMMS's revenue in fiscal 2012 was $2.8 billion.

Company Background

The system's flagship hospital began on its present site in 1823 as Baltimore Infirmary. It later was known for many years as University Hospital until Maryland's legislature changed it from a state-run single-building facility to a private not-for-profit medical system in 1984. In short order UMMS began expanding mainly by adding existing hospitals.

EXECUTIVES

Senior Vice President General Counsel, Megan M (Meg) Arthur
President and CEO University of Maryland Medical Center, Jeffrey A. Rivest
CEO Chester River Health System, James E. Ross
Senior Vice President Chief Information Officer, Jon P. Burns
President and CEO Maryland General Health Systems and Hospita, Sylvia Smith Johnson
SVP and COO Baltimore Washington Medical Center, Karen E. Olscamp, age 55
EVP and CFO, Henry J. Franey
Senior Vice President Government and Regulatory Affairs, Donna Jacobs
Senior Vice President and Chief Medical Informatics Officer, Mark Kelemen
Director Physician Recruitment, Susan Kamen
Medical Director Trauma Acute Care, Deborah M (Deb) Stein
Senior Vice President External Affairs, Mark Wasserman
Vice President Supply Chain Management, Gary Kane
Senior Vice President Corporate Operations, Jerry Wollman
System Vice President of Quality Management, Pat Ercolano
Medical Records Director, Robin Stults
Vice President Facilities, Leonard (Len) Jr
Senior Vice President Network Development and Associate Dean, John (Jack) Ashworth
Vice President Media Relations and Corporate Communications, Karen Lancaster
Chairman, Stephen A. Burch, age 65
Treasurer, Mary Caswell
Auditors: KPMG LLP BALTIMORE MD

LOCATIONS

HQ: UNIVERSITY OF MARYLAND MEDICAL SYSTEM CORPORATION
22 S GREENE ST, BALTIMORE, MD 212011544
Phone: 410 328-8667
Web: WWW.UMMS.ORG

PRODUCTS/OPERATIONS

Selected Facilities and Affiliates
Baltimore Washington Medical Center
Chester River Health System
Civista Medical Center
Kernan Orthopaedics and Rehabilitation
Maryland General Hospital

Mt. Washington Pediatric Hospital
Shore Health System
  Dorchester General Hospital
  The Memorial Hospital at Easton
University of Maryland Medical Center
  Marlene and Stewart Greenebaum Cancer Center
  R Adams Cowley Shock Trauma Center
  University of Maryland Hospital for Children
University of Maryland St. Joseph Medical Center
University Specialty Hospital
Upper Chesapeake Health
  Harford Memorial Hospital
  Upper Chesapeake Medical Center

COMPETITORS

Adventist HealthCare	Franklin Square
Anne Arundel Medical	Hospital Center
Center	GBMC
Ascension Health	Johns Hopkins Health
Bon Secours Health	System
Catholic Health	LifeBridge Health
Initiatives	MedStar Health
Dimensions Healthcare	

HISTORICAL FINANCIALS
Company Type: Private

Income Statement
FYE: June 30

	REVENUE ($ mil.)	NET INCOME ($ mil.)	NET PROFIT MARGIN	EMPLOYEES
06/13	2,571	139	5.4%	12,000
06/12*	2,504	(17)	—	—
09/11	0	0	—	—
Annual Growth	—	—	—	—

*Fiscal year change

2013 Year-End Financials
Return on assets: 9.3%   Cash ($ mil.): 252
Return on equity: 5.4%
Current ratio: 0.80

UNIVERSITY OF MINNESOTA PHYSICIANS

Auditors: KPMG LLP MINNEAPOLIS MN

LOCATIONS

HQ: UNIVERSITY OF MINNESOTA PHYSICIANS
720 WASHINGTON AVE SE # 200, MINNEAPOLIS, MN
554142924
Phone: 612 884-0600
Web: WWW.UMPHYSICIANS.ORG

HISTORICAL FINANCIALS
Company Type: Private

Income Statement
FYE: June 30

	REVENUE ($ mil.)	NET INCOME ($ mil.)	NET PROFIT MARGIN	EMPLOYEES
06/13	452	12	2.8%	200
06/12	415	5	1.3%	—
06/11	373	3	1.1%	—
06/10	368	0	—	—
Annual Growth	7.0%	—	—	—

2013 Year-End Financials
Return on assets: 13.6%   Cash ($ mil.): 53
Return on equity: 2.8%
Current ratio: 1.30

UNIVERSITY OF MISSISSIPPI

They call her "Ole Miss" and she really is old: The University of Mississippi was chartered in 1844 as the first public university in the state and opened in 1848. Starting with 80 students the school's enrollment has grown to more than 23000 with most students attending the main Oxford campus. Ole Miss has additional campuses in Southaven (Desoto County) and Tupelo and it operates the University of Mississippi Medical Center in Jackson. The school is home to more than 30 research centers that specialize in business engineering law and other disciplines. Its academic institutes include the Croft Institute for International Studies and the William Winter Institute for Racial Reconciliation.

Operations

The Medical Center campus includes Mississippi's only children's hospital a women and infants' hospital and a critical care hospital. It is also home to the state's only Level 1 trauma center Level 4 neonatal intensive care nursery and organ transplant programs. Enrollment has grown at the university by some 59% since 2004 (when the school enrolled 14497 students).

Ole Miss has an endowment of approximately $462 million.

Geographic Reach

Minorities make up almost a fourth of Ole Miss students and more than 60% of all students at the university come from within the state. The student-faculty ratio is 19:1.

EXECUTIVES

Vice President, Heather Chance
Vice President Department Of History, Jeffrey (Jeff) Watt
Secretary, Deborah (Deb) King
Board Of Directors, Bradley Baker
Secretary, Tami Barger

LOCATIONS

HQ: UNIVERSITY OF MISSISSIPPI
113 FALKNER, UNIVERSITY, MS 386779704
Phone: 662 915-7361
Web: WWW.OLEMISS.EDU

PRODUCTS/OPERATIONS

Selected Colleges and Schools
Colleges
  The College of Liberal Arts
  The Residential College
  The Sally McDonnell Barksdale Honors College
  The University of Mississippi
  Booneville (branch)
  Grenada (branch)
  Southaven Campus
  Tupelo Campus
  The University of Mississippi Graduate School
  The University of Mississippi Medical Center
Schools
  Meek School of Journalism and News Media
  Patterson School of Accountancy
  School of Applied Science
  School of Business Administration
  School of Education
  School of Engineering
  School of Law
  School of Nursing (at The University of Mississippi Medical Center)
  School of Pharmacy

Selected Research Centers
Center for Advanced Infrastructure Technology
Center for Applied Electromagnetic Systems Research
Center for Archaeological Research

Center for Community Earthquake Preparedness
Center for Educational Research and Evaluation
Center for Excellence in Literacy Instruction
Center for Excellence in Teaching and Learning
Center for Health Behavior Research
Center for Intelligence and Security Studies
Center for Manufacturing Excellence
Center for Marine Resources and Environmental Technology
Center for Mathematics and Science Education
Center for Pharmaceutical Marketing and Management
Center for Population Studies
Center for Speech and Hearing Research
Center for the Study of Southern Culture
Center for Water and Wetland Resources
Center for Wirelress Communications
INDO-US Joint Center for Research in Indian Systems of Medicine
Jamie Whitten National Center for Physical Acoustics
Magazine Innovation Center
National Center for Computational Hydroscience and Engineering
National Center for Justice and the Rule of Law
National Center for Natural Products Research
National Center for Remote Sensing Air and Space Law
National Sea Grant Law Center
Overby Center for Southern Journalism and Politics
Public Policy Research Center
Sarah Isom Center for Women' s Studies
Sino-U.S. Traditional Chinese Medicines Research Center
University of Mississippi Geoinformatics Center

HISTORICAL FINANCIALS
Company Type: Private

Income Statement
FYE: June 30

	REVENUE ($ mil.)	NET INCOME ($ mil.)	NET PROFIT MARGIN	EMPLOYEES
06/11	302	74	24.6%	8,700
06/10	278	63	22.8%	—
Annual Growth	8.5%	17.0%	—	—

2011 Year-End Financials
Return on assets: —   Cash ($ mil.): 45
Return on equity: 24.6%
Current ratio: 1.60

UNIVERSITY OF MONTANA SYSTEM

Sometimes referred to as the Harvard of the West The University of Montana's motto is Lux et Veritas (Light and Truth). The Big Sky Country certainly provides plenty of light for the university which is a leading producer of Rhodes Scholars. The University of Montana (UM) is a member of the Montana University System and offers associate's bachelor's master's first-professional and doctoral degrees as well as technical certificates. About 21000 undergraduate and graduate students enroll at UM's four campuses. Founded in 1893 UM also gets high marks for the physical beauty of its campus and nearby wilderness areas.

Geographic Reach

UM is located on a 200-acre campus containing about 65 buildings in Missoula Montana. It also has satellite campuses in Dillon (UM Western) Butte (Montana Tech) and Helena (Helena College of Technology). About two-thirds of students come from within the state.

Operations

UM has about 900 faculty members and a student-to-faculty ratio of 19:1. Of its student population of about 21000 some 15000 students attend class at the main campus in Missoula.

The university's colleges include arts and sciences technology education and human sciences health professions and biomedical sciences visual and performing arts forestry and conservation and an honors college. Its schools include journalism law business administration education pharmacy social work fine arts and more. UM also offers undergraduate research opportunities and study abroad programs as well as student organizations intramural sports and work-study opportunities.

Strategy

To increase enrollment of motivated students UM partners with area high schools to provide early college and recruitment programs. Other growth efforts include faculty and staff recruitment and development programs as well as curriculum enhancement efforts and procurement and technology improvements. Facility expansions also continue: In 2013 it selected a site for its new Missoula College satellite center.

EXECUTIVES

Dean School of Business Administration, Larry Gianchetta

VP Academic Affairs and Provost, Perry J. Brown

President, Royce C. Engstrom

VP Administration and Finance, Michael Reid

CIO, Matt Riley

Dean College of Visual and Performing Arts, Stephen Kalm

Dean College of Humanities and Sciences, Chris Comer

Dean School of Extended and Lifelong Learning, Roger Maclean

Dean Washington College of Education and Human Sciences, Roberta D. Evans

Dean of Libraries, Shali Zhang

Dean of Students, Rhondie Voorhees

Interim Dean College of Forestry and Conservation, Wayne Freimund

Dean College of Health Professions and Biomedical Sciences, Reed Humphrey

Interim Dean Missoula College, Jane Baker

Dean Davidson Honors College, Brock Tessman

Dean Graduate School, Sandy Ross

Dean School of Journalism, Larry Abramson

Dean Blewett School of Law, Paul F. Kirgis

President and CEO UM Foundation, Shane Giese

Vice President for Research and Creative Scholarship, Scott Whittenburg

Vice President Development, Ric Thomas

Department Chair, Cindy Garthwait

Chair Department of Anthropology Social Sciences Building, John (Jack) Douglas

Vice Chairman, Fran M. Albrecht

Chairman, Paul Tuss

Auditors: CINDY JORGENSON CPA HELENA

LOCATIONS

HQ: UNIVERSITY OF MONTANA SYSTEM
32 CAMPUS DR MAIN HALL, MISSOULA, MT 598120001
Phone: 406 243-0211
Web: WWW.UMT.EDU

PRODUCTS/OPERATIONS

2012 Revenue

	% of total
Student tuition & fees	47
Health care services	20
Auxiliary enterprises	6
Grants & contracts	4
Appropriated investment income	3
Contributions	3
Released net assets	2
Other	15
Total	**100**

Selected Colleges and Schools

College of Arts and Sciences
College of Education and Human Sciences
College of Forestry and Conservation
College of Health Professions and Biomedical Sciences
College of Technology
College of Visual and Performing Arts
Davidson Honors College
Graduate School
School for Extended and Lifelong Learning
School of Business Administration
School of Journalism
School of Law

HISTORICAL FINANCIALS

Company Type: Private

Income Statement

FYE: June 30

	REVENUE ($ mil.)	NET INCOME ($ mil.)	NET PROFIT MARGIN	EMPLOYEES
06/13	259	(8)	—	2,450
06/12	264	7	2.8%	—
06/09	246	27	11.2%	—
06/08	251	0	—	—
Annual Growth	**0.7%**	—	—	—

2013 Year-End Financials

Return on assets: —
Return on equity: (-3.3%)
Current ratio: 0.80
Cash ($ mil.): 55

UNIVERSITY OF NEBRASKA FOUNDATION

Auditors: KPMG LLP OMAHA NE

LOCATIONS

HQ: UNIVERSITY OF NEBRASKA FOUNDATION
1010 LINCOLN MALL STE 300, LINCOLN, NE 685082882
Phone: 402 458-1100
Web: WWW.NUFOUNDATION.ORG

HISTORICAL FINANCIALS

Company Type: Private

Income Statement

FYE: June 30

	REVENUE ($ mil.)	NET INCOME ($ mil.)	NET PROFIT MARGIN	EMPLOYEES
06/13	307	102	33.3%	80
06/09	119	(8)	—	—
06/08	262	109	41.7%	—
Annual Growth	**3.2%**	**(1.3%)**	—	—

2013 Year-End Financials

Return on assets: 0.3%
Return on equity: 33.3%
Current ratio: 28.90
Cash ($ mil.): 353

UNIVERSITY OF NORTH CAROLINA HOSPITALS

University of North Carolina Hospitals (UNCH) is at the heart of the UNC Health Care System (UNC HCS). The medical center provides acute care to the Tar Heel State through North Carolina Memorial Hospital North Carolina Children's Hospital North Carolina Neurosciences Hospital and North Carolina Women's Hospital. Combined the facilities have more than 800 beds. Specialties include cancer treatment at the North Carolina Cancer Hospital organ transplantation cardiac care orthopedics wound management and rehabilitation. Not-for-profit UNC HCS is owned by the state of North Carolina and is affiliated with the UNC-Chapel Hill School of Medicine.

Geographic Reach

UNCH not only serves patients from all North Carolina counties with about a third coming from the Research Triangle area it also serves patients from neighboring states.

OperationsUNCH operates under the umbrella of UNC HCS.

UNC HCS already extends beyond Chapel Hill and into the greater Triangle area through its network of primary care and specialty physician practices located in Orange Wake Durham Chatham and Lee counties. The system treats some 800000 people at UNC HCS practices and clinics annually.

UNCH handles more than 37000 patients each year and delivers 3500 babies annually.

North Carolina Children's offers 150 inpatient beds and a comprehensive children's outpatient center. Every year provides specialty care to more than 70000 children from all 100 North Carolina counties. The North Carolina Cancer Hospital is the clinical home of the UNC Lineberger Comprehensive Cancer Center. The state's only public cancer hospital the North Carolina Cancer Hospital treats patients from every county in North Carolina with more than 135000 patient visits a year.

Strategy

Being one of the primary health care providers in the area UNC HCS is nearly always expanding its services and service areas either through acquisitions or new construction.

In 2015 UNCH filed a petition with state regulators seeking the ability to add 42 acute-care beds at its Chapel Hill campus. If approved UNC estimates it will cost the hospital $17 million and would be completed by mid-2018.

UNC HCS planned to open a new 86-bed acute-care hospital in Hillsborough in 2015 as part of an effort to reduce pressure on its Chapel Hill campus. The construction of the hospital will cost about $200 million. The new facility will offer an emergency department outpatient surgery and a range of inpatient services to our patients in Alamance and Western Orange counties.

Dedicated cancer care and cancer research is another area in which UNC HCS is expanding. It opened a North Carolina Cancer Hospital at Rex Hospital in 2014.

The system is also building an Imaging Research Building expected to open in 2013 to house the Biomedical Research Imaging Center and serve as a state resource for handling the acquisition processing analysis storage and retrieval of scientific images.

In 2013 UNC HCS established the first stage of its Hillsborough campus with the opening of a 60000-square-foot medical office building. The building includes hospital services such as imaging laboratory pharmacy and medical and surgical oncology.

Company BackgroundIn 2011 the hospital opened a new wing of the Newborn Critical Care Unit in the North Carolina Children's Hospital that houses 10 new patient beds bringing the number of beds in the unit to 58.

UNCH was founded in 1952 under the name North Carolina Memorial Hospital. In 1989 the North Carolina General Assembly created UNCH.

EXECUTIVES

Vice President Finance, Barbara Aaron

LOCATIONS

HQ: UNIVERSITY OF NORTH CAROLINA HOSPITALS
101 MANNING DR BLDG 2, CHAPEL HILL, NC
275144423
Phone: 919 966-5111
Web: WWW.DENTISTRY.UNC.EDU

PRODUCTS/OPERATIONS

Selected Facilities
North Carolina Cancer Hospital (Chapel Hill)
  UNC Lineberger Comprehensive Cancer Center
North Carolina Children' s Hospital (Chapel Hill)
North Carolina Memorial Hospital (Chapel Hill)
North Carolina Neurosciences Hospital (Chapel Hill)
North Carolina Women' s Hospital (Chapel Hill)

COMPETITORS

Alamance Regional Medical Center	Emory Healthcare
	Grady Health System
Annie Penn Hospital	High Point Regional
Carolinas HealthCare System	Health System
	Morehead Memorial
Cone Health	Hospital
Cumberland County Hospital System	New Hanover Regional Medical Center
Danville Regional Medical Center	Rowan Regional Medical Center
Duke University Health System	Vidant Health
	WakeMed

HISTORICAL FINANCIALS

Company Type: Private

Income Statement

FYE: June 30

	REVENUE ($ mil.)	NET INCOME ($ mil.)	NET PROFIT MARGIN	EMPLOYEES
06/07	787	182	23.2%	6,000
06/06	652	36	5.6%	—
06/05	614	25	4.1%	—
06/04	550	0	—	—
Annual Growth	12.7%	—	—	—

2007 Year-End Financials

Return on assets: 5.6%
Return on equity: 23.2%
Current ratio: 2.50
Cash ($ mil.): 213

UNIVERSITY OF NORTH DAKOTA

Way up in the Upper Midwest is the University of North Dakota (UND) the largest and oldest institution of higher learning in the state with an enrollment of approximately 15000 students. It offers undergraduate and graduate programs in close to 225 fields through nine colleges and schools (aerospace sciences arts and sciences business and public administration education and human develop-

ment engineering and mines law medical and health sciences nursing and a graduate school). The university also has nearly 20 doctoral programs as well as certificate degree programs distance degree programs and a continuing education division. UND was founded in 1883 six years before North Dakota achieved statehood.

OperationsUND has an international reputation for research most notably in the health sciences nutrition energy and environmental protection aerospace and engineering. The university receives funding from various sources to perform research projects in areas that include neuroscience unmanned aerial systems vaccines advanced electronics nanotechnology high-tech coatings and alternative fuels.

EXECUTIVES

Assistant Vice President Of Wellness, Laurie Betting
Assoc Vice President Enrollment Management, Alice Hoffert

LOCATIONS

HQ: UNIVERSITY OF NORTH DAKOTA
264 CENTENNIAL DR, GRAND FORKS, ND
582026059
Phone: 701 777-2015
Web: WWW.UND.EDU

PRODUCTS/OPERATIONS

Selected Schools and Colleges
John D. Odegard School of Aerospace Sciences
College of Arts and Sciences
College of Business and Public Administration
College of Education and Human Development
School of Engineering and Mines
The Graduate School
School of Law
School of Medicine and Health Sciences
College of Nursing

HISTORICAL FINANCIALS

Company Type: Private

Income Statement

FYE: June 30

	REVENUE ($ mil.)	NET INCOME ($ mil.)	NET PROFIT MARGIN	EMPLOYEES
06/14	672	77	11.6%	2,756
06/11	278	27	9.8%	—
06/09	637	(40)	—	—
06/08	616	0	—	—
Annual Growth	1.5%	—	—	—

2014 Year-End Financials

Return on assets: 5.6%
Return on equity: 11.6%
Current ratio: 1.50
Cash ($ mil.): 149

UNIVERSITY OF NORTH TEXAS SYSTEM

LOCATIONS

HQ: UNIVERSITY OF NORTH TEXAS SYSTEM
1302 TEASLEY LN, DENTON, TX 762057946
Phone: 940 565-2281
Web: WWW.UNTSYSTEM.EDU

HISTORICAL FINANCIALS

Company Type: Private

Income Statement

FYE: August 31

	REVENUE ($ mil.)	NET INCOME ($ mil.)	NET PROFIT MARGIN	EMPLOYEES
08/13	530	(5)	—	23
08/09	463	47	10.2%	—
08/08	428	61	14.4%	—
08/06	361	0	—	—
Annual Growth	5.6%	—	—	—

2013 Year-End Financials

Return on assets: 4.0%
Return on equity: (-1.1%)
Current ratio: 0.90
Cash ($ mil.): 197

UNIVERSITY OF OKLAHOMA FOUNDATION INC

LOCATIONS

HQ: UNIVERSITY OF OKLAHOMA FOUNDATION INC
100 W TIMBERDELL RD RM 1, NORMAN, OK
730195016
Phone: 405 321-1174
Web: WWW.OU.EDU

HISTORICAL FINANCIALS

Company Type: Private

Income Statement

FYE: June 30

	ASSETS ($ mil.)	NET INCOME ($ mil.)	INCOME AS % OF ASSETS	EMPLOYEES
06/13	1,085	20	1.9%	20
06/11	1,041	108	10.4%	—
06/10	805	40	5.0%	—
06/09	776	0	—	—
Annual Growth	8.8%	—	—	—

2013 Year-End Financials

Return on assets: 6.6%
Return on equity: 15.6%
Sales ($ mil): 132

UNIVERSITY OF PITTSBURGH

Auditors: KPMG LLP PITTSBURGH PA

LOCATIONS

HQ: UNIVERSITY OF PITTSBURGH
7175 SALTSBURG RD, PITTSBURGH, PA 152352252
Phone: 412 795-6069

HISTORICAL FINANCIALS
Company Type: Private

Income Statement
FYE: June 30

	REVENUE ($ mil.)	NET INCOME ($ mil.)	NET PROFIT MARGIN	EMPLOYEES
06/14	2,005	570	28.4%	26
06/13	1,985	402	20.3%	
06/12	1,976	(90)	—	—
Annual Growth	0.7%	—	—	—

2014 Year-End Financials
Return on assets: 5.0% Cash ($ mil.): 60
Return on equity: 28.4%
Current ratio: 0.70

UNIVERSITY OF PUGET SOUND

The University of Puget Sound is a private liberal arts college located in the Pacific Northwest with an enrollment of some 2600 students and a student-faculty ratio of 12:1. It boasts more than 50 traditional and interdisciplinary programs and about 1200 courses. Based south of Seattle in Tacoma Washington the school offers a wide range of undergraduate degrees as well as graduate degrees in education occupational therapy and physical therapy. Students come from nearly 50 states and 15 countries. Founded in 1888 by the Methodist Church The University of Puget Sound divested its affiliation with the church in 1980. Notable alumni include Verio founder Justin Jaschke and Alaska governor Sean Parnell.

Geographic Reach

The University of Puget Sound operates its school on nearly 100 acres south of Seattle in the city of Tacoma Washington.

Sales and Marketing

The school sources its students from 49 states and 14 countries. Some 75% of its students arrive at The University of Puget Sound from outside Washington State. Its student population of 2600 students comprises 57% women and 43% men.

EXECUTIVES

President and Trustee, Ronald R. (Ron) Thomas
VP Finance and Administration, Sherry Mondou
Academic VP and Dean of University, Kristine (Kris) Bartanen
Associate VP Technology Services and CIO, William Morse
Academic Vice President, Jones Hall
Chair Elect, Robert C. Pohlad, age 60
Chairman, Richard M. Brooks
Vice Chair, Gwendolyn H. Lillis

LOCATIONS

HQ: UNIVERSITY OF PUGET SOUND
1500 N WARNER ST, TACOMA, WA 984160005
Phone: 253 879-3100
Web: WWW.PUGETSOUND.EDU

PRODUCTS/OPERATIONS

Selected Undergraduate Degrees
African American Studies
Art
Asian Languages & Cultures
Asian Studies
Biochemistry & Molecular Biology
Biology
Business & Leadership
Chemistry
Classics
Communication Studies
Comparative Sociology
Computer Science
Economics
Engineering Dual Degree
English
Environmental Policy & Decision Making
Exercise Science
Foreign Languages & Literature
Gender Studies
Geology
Global Development Studies
History
Honors
Humanities
International Political Economy
Latin American Studies
Mathematics & Computer Science
Music
Natural Science
Neuroscience
Philosophy
Physical Education
Physics
Politics & Government
Psychology
Religion
Science Technology & Society
Special Interdisciplinary Major
Theatre Arts

HISTORICAL FINANCIALS
Company Type: Private

Income Statement
FYE: June 30

	REVENUE ($ mil.)	NET INCOME ($ mil.)	NET PROFIT MARGIN	EMPLOYEES
06/13	171	16	9.6%	850
06/12	162	10	6.3%	—
06/11	147	1	1.2%	—
06/10	139	0	—	—
Annual Growth	7.0%			

2013 Year-End Financials
Return on assets: 10.3% Cash ($ mil.): 41
Return on equity: 9.6%
Current ratio: 0.40

UNIVERSITY OF RHODE ISLAND

The University of Rhode Island (URI) offers more than 80 undergraduate majors specializing in nursing psychology communication studies kinesiology and human development. It also offers master's doctoral and professional degrees from its nine colleges at four campuses across the state. URI's main campus is located in Kingston the W. Alton Jones Campus is in West Greenwich its Graduate School of Oceanography is located on Narragansett Bay and Providence is home to the university's Alan Shawn Feinstein College of Continuing Education. URI which has an enrollment of more than 16500 students was chartered as the state's agricultural school in 1888.

Geographic Reach

The University of Rhode Island spans four campus locations in Kingston Providence Narragansett Bay and West Greenwich. Its student population comes from 53 US territories and the District of Columbia.

Financial Performance

Revenue has increased for URI during the past three years due to increasing tuition and fees rising enrollment of out-of-state students and increasing grants and contracts. Tuition and fees contributed some 60% of revenue in fiscal 2012. Net income was flat in 2012 as compared to 2011 thanks to increased capital appropriations state contributed capital and capital gifts. These were partially offset however by rising expenses and declining non-operating revenues.

EXECUTIVES

Vice President Division Of Administration And Finance, Robert (Bob) Weygand
Vice President Research Economic Development, Gerald (Jerry) Sonnenfeld
Associate Vice President Of Research And, Mark Noll
Assistant Vice President Equity Diversity, Naomi Thompson
Auditors: O'CONNOR & DREW PC BRAINTREE

LOCATIONS

HQ: UNIVERSITY OF RHODE ISLAND
75 LOWER COLLEGE RD, KINGSTON, RI 028811966
Phone: 401 874-1000
Web: WWW.URI.EDU

PRODUCTS/OPERATIONS

Selected Schools and Colleges
College of Arts and Sciences
College of Business Administration
College of Continuing Education
College of Engineering
College of Environment and Life Sciences
College of Human Science and Services
College of Nursing
College of Pharmacy
Graduate School of Oceanography
University College

HISTORICAL FINANCIALS
Company Type: Private

Income Statement
FYE: June 30

	REVENUE ($ mil.)	NET INCOME ($ mil.)	NET PROFIT MARGIN	EMPLOYEES
06/14	402	47	11.9%	2,600
06/13	410	39	9.6%	—
06/11	392	58	14.9%	—
06/08	319	0	—	—
Annual Growth	3.9%	—	—	—

2014 Year-End Financials
Return on assets: 10.6% Cash ($ mil.): 127
Return on equity: 11.9%
Current ratio: 2.20

UNIVERSITY OF RICHMOND

Suffering from arachnophobia? You may want to steer clear of the more than 4300 Spiders who are enrolled at the University of Richmond (UR). UR consists of five schools: Jepson School of Leadership Studies Richmond School of Law Robins School of Business School of Arts and Sciences and School of Continuing Studies. The university offers some 60 undergraduate majors as well as graduate and master's programs in business accounting and law. UR also offers some 75 study-abroad programs in which more than half of its students participate. Founded in 1830 by Virginia Baptists as a seminary for men the school became Richmond College in 1840.

Geographic Reach

From its campus in Richmond Virginia UR serves students from nearly all 50 US states including Puerto Rico and Washington D.C. Its student population consists of more than 3000 undergraduates that come more than 70 countries.

Operations

UR with about 320 full-time undergraduate faculty members boasts a student-faculty ratio of 9:1. Through its Richmond Quadrangle LLC (a wholly controlled affiliate of UR) the university owns and operates a building and land located in Richmond. UR's Spider Management Company LLC is another wholly controlled affiliate that provides investment research advice counsel and management related to the university's endowment assets.

Financial Performance

Revenue for UR rose 8% in fiscal 2012 as compared to 2011 due to an increase in tuition and fees grants and contracts contributions endowment spending distribution and auxiliary enterprises. Net income for the same reporting period decreased by 112% thanks to rising operating expenses and declining contribution and net unrealized losses.

EXECUTIVES

Assoc Vice President Human Resources, Carl K Sorensen
Provost and VP Academic Affairs, Jacquelyn S. (Jacque) Fetrow
VP Business and Finance, David B. Hale
CIO, Kathy Monday
Vice President For Public Relations, Stefanie Mathew
Vice President For Public Relations, Mary Gardiner
Vice President Operations, Jason Hoogakker
Assistant Vice President, Elizabeth Curtler
Vice President Of Public Relations, Jesse Kedy
Vice President for Administration, Ethan Mcwilliams
Chief Associate Vice President Of Public Safety, David (Dave) Mccoy
Secretary, Ann Lloyd Breeden
Treasurer, Kristina Lam
Secretary, Jessica Miller
Secretary, Jessica Myers
Treasurer, Michael (Mel) Forsyth
Auditors: KPMG LLP

LOCATIONS

HQ: UNIVERSITY OF RICHMOND
28 WESTHAMPTON WAY, RICHMOND, VA 231730002
Phone: 804 289-8133
Web: WWW.RICHMOND.EDU

PRODUCTS/OPERATIONS

Selected Schools
Arts and Sciences
Business
Leadership Studies
Law
Professional and Continuing Studies

HISTORICAL FINANCIALS

Company Type: Private

Income Statement

FYE: June 30

	REVENUE ($ mil.)	NET INCOME ($ mil.)	NET PROFIT MARGIN	EMPLOYEES
06/14	264	287	108.6%	1,400
06/13	253	185	73.0%	—
06/10	210	83	39.7%	—
06/09	197	0	—	—
Annual Growth	6.1%	—	—	—

2014 Year-End Financials

Return on assets: 18.8%   Cash ($ mil.): 97
Return on equity: 108.6%
Current ratio: —

UNIVERSITY OF SAN DIEGO

The University of San Diego (USD) is private college located close to southern California's beaches and the Mexican border. The coeducational Roman Catholic university has an enrollment of more than 7750 full-time students (8350 if you count part-time students as well). USD offers roughly 75 bachelor's master's and doctoral degrees in areas such as arts and sciences business administration education engineering law and nursing. It has a faculty of more than 400 full time staff members. The university also home to the Joan B. Kroc School of Peace Studies established in 2003 by the wife of McDonald's founder Ray Kroc.

Operations

Adjacent to the USD campus is the St. Francis Seminary; young men studying for the priesthood attend the university for the academic portion of their course work. USD is a very residential college; more than 95% of its freshman class live on the school's grounds in 10 separate living areas with styles that range from shared rooms to apartments. About 7% of its students hail from outside of the US.

USD offers more than 40 bachelor's degrees 25 master's degrees in eight academic divisions as well as three doctoral degrees – two in nursing and one in leadership studies.

As a Carnegie-certified Doctoral/Research school the school is committed to graduate education through the doctorate awarding 50 or more doctoral degrees annually (USD regularly awards more than 360 doctoral degrees) and that it gives high priority to research receiving more than $40 million annually in federal research support.

Financial Performance

Higher tuition and fees helped to lift USD's revenues by 3% in 2014.

Strategy

The university undergoes a cycle of strategic initiatives every few years that shape the way it intends to move into the future. When school president Dr. Mary Lyons implemented the program in 2003 the first round of strategic initiatives included focusing on Catholic-based social studies inclusion and diversity integrated learning internationalization and sustainability. Those ideas were made into reality by focusing on enrollment management building out the school's technology infrastructure expanding undergraduate research developing USD's endowment and raising the university's branding and marketing standards. The Strategic Directions division's current goals included international expansion engaging alumni and assessing programs aimed at expressing the university's Catholic character.

In 2014 USD broke ground on a new health sciences building and opened a Madrid (Spain) location.

Company Background

USD was formed in 1972 by the merger of San Diego University and San Diego College for Women.

EXECUTIVES

EVP, Julie H. Sullivan, age 57
VP Finance and CFO, Terry Kalfayan
Vice Provost and CIO, Chris Wessells
VP and Provost, Andrew T. Allen
President, James T. Harris
Assistant Vice President Of Student Affairs For Pu, Larry Barnett
Vice President Student Affairs, Carmen Vazquez
Assistant Vice President Facilities Management Department, Mark Norita
Vice President Of Membership, Stephen Hilger
Vice President Of Administration, Kevin Ganley
Assistant Vice President Public Relations, Pamela (Pam) Gray
Vice President, Rommel Pinlac
Vice President Of Communications, Phillip Juarez
Vice President Of Programming, Chris Perry
Vice President of Tours Training, Sean Essex
Admissions Director, Kate Mickle
Vice President, Coral Anderson
Vice President Of Membership, Owen Buckley
Director Media Relations, Melissa Wagoner
Vice President, Steve Gauvin
Vice President University Relations, Tim O'Malley
Senior Management Senior Vice President GM Dire, Jonathan (Jon) Mack
Department Chair, Ann Garland
Vice President Of Customer Experience, Matthew (Matt) Tom
Vice President of Membership, Brandon Holm
Vice President of Programming, Aleczander Bangert
Vice President of Communications, Weston Preising
Vice President of Administration, Peter (Pete) Nelson
Senior Vice President, Liz Nutting
Vice President of Wellness and Standards, Kevin Karn
Auditors: MOSS ADAMS LLP SAN DIEGO CA

LOCATIONS

HQ: UNIVERSITY OF SAN DIEGO
5998 ALCALA PARK FRNT, SAN DIEGO, CA 921102492
Phone: 619 260-4600
Web: WWW.SANDIEGO.EDU

PRODUCTS/OPERATIONS

Selected Schools and Colleges
College of Arts and Sciences
School of Business Administration
Engineering
Hahn School of Nursing and Health Science
Joan B. Kroc School of Peace Studies
School of Law
School of Leadership and Education Sciences

HISTORICAL FINANCIALS

Company Type: Private

Income Statement

FYE: June 30

	REVENUE ($ mil.)	NET INCOME ($ mil.)	NET PROFIT MARGIN	EMPLOYEES
06/13	303	90	29.8%	1,600
06/10	347	21	6.2%	—
Annual Growth	(4.4%)	61.5%	—	—

2013 Year-End Financials

Return on assets: —   Cash ($ mil.): 110
Return on equity: 29.8%
Current ratio: —

UNIVERSITY OF SAN FRANCISCO INC

Known for their devotion to education as well as their investment portfolio the Jesuits are evident to all who visit the University of San Francisco (USF). One of 28 Jesuit Catholic colleges and universities in the US the main USF campus sits on 55 acres near Golden Gate Park in San Francisco. The school which was formed in 1855 as St. Ignatius Academy enrolls more than 10000 students. It operates five schools and colleges including the schools of business and management education law and nursing and the colleges of arts and sciences. In addition to its main campus the university operates five satellite sites in Northern and Southern California.

Operations

USF operates a handful of schools and colleges including schools of management education law nursing and the colleges of arts and sciences. More than 400 full-time faculty members offer 100-plus undergraduate and degree programs. With an undergraduate student-faculty ratio of 15:1 USF's 10000-plus student enrollment includes 6250 undergraduates 2950 graduates 670 law students and 150 non-degree students.

The independent private not-for-profit university is one of the nation's most ethnically diverse schools. Some 43% of its students are Asian African-American Latino Native Hawaiian/Pacific Islander or multi-ethnic.

Financial Performance

USF logged a slight decrease in revenue in 2014 (ended May) as compared to 203. Meanwhile expenses rose 6.6% during the same reporting period. The university ended 2014 with net assets of $625 million compared to the $577 million of net assets reported in 2013.

Strategy

To keep up with growth USF opened a campus in downtown San Francisco at 101 Howard Street. The university also changed the name of its school of nursing to the School of Nursing and Health Professions to reflect the institution's commitment and expansion of its master of public health degree.

EXECUTIVES

Vice President University Advancement, David (Dave) MacMillan
Assistant Vice President Community Counseling Services, Preston Walton
Vice President For Development, Peter Wilch
Associate Vice President Donor Engagement and Stewardship, Michelle (Mitch) Sklar
Vice President Finance Graduate Business Association Director of Finance Business Quarterly, Jeremy Lau
Assistant Vice President Marketing, Anneliese Mauch
Vice President Of Public Relations, Laureano Figueroa
Vice President Of Business Development, Jim Kovach
Analyst Office of the Vice President, Hien Pham
Associate Vice President University Advancement, Sally Dalton
Associate Vice President Of Developement, Chris Nicholson
Provost Vice President Academic Affairs, James (Jamie) Wiser
Chair Department Of Computer Science, Sami Rollins
Director Of Admissions, Michael Hughes

Assistant Vice President For Content Management, Angie Davis
Associate Vice President Corporate and Foundation, Marly Norris
Vice President Of Marketing, Lisa Nakasone
Vice President Finance And Budget, Jessica Sanchez-martinez
Finance Vice President, Eva Long
Vice President Of Business And Finance, Willard Nutting
Vice President Business Development, Derek Becker
Vice President, Aaron Moser
Vice President Public Relations, Kimura Goro
Vice President Online Communications, Jacqueline Look
Assistant Treasurer, Stacy Daher
Auditors: DELOITTE & TOUCHE LLP SAN FRA

LOCATIONS

HQ: UNIVERSITY OF SAN FRANCISCO INC
2130 FULTON ST, SAN FRANCISCO, CA 941171050
Phone: 415 422-5555
Web: WWW.CS.USFCA.EDU

PRODUCTS/OPERATIONS

Selected Schools and Colleges
College of Arts
College of Sciences
School of Education
School of Law
School of Management
School of Nursing

HISTORICAL FINANCIALS
Company Type: Private

Income Statement
FYE: May 31

	REVENUE ($ mil.)	NET INCOME ($ mil.)	NET PROFIT MARGIN	EMPLOYEES
05/13	375	71	19.0%	1,200
05/12	390	36	9.3%	—
05/11	380	55	14.5%	—
05/10	334	0	—	—
Annual Growth	4.0%	—	—	—

2013 Year-End Financials
Return on assets: —
Return on equity: 19.0%
Current ratio: —
Cash ($ mil.): 105

UNIVERSITY OF SCRANTON

The University of Scranton is a Catholic and Jesuit liberal arts university with a student population of 5900 including more than 600 graduate students. Its schools and colleges include the College of Arts & Sciences Panuska College of Professional Studies and Kania School of Management. It offers programs in areas such as theology music technology athletics nursing and continuing education and has some 300 faculty members. The University of Scranton offers 61 undergraduate and 25 graduate programs. It is overseen by the Society of Jesus (the Jesuits).

Operations

Some 85% of the University of Scranton's instructional faculty hold doctoral or other terminal degrees and the school has a student-to-faculty ratio of 11:1. It sponsors 18 NCAA Division III (non-scholarship) athletic programs (nine for men and nine for women).

The Harry and Jeanette Weinberg Memorial Library holds more than 512890 volumes and 21285 non-print items. The library has an integrated online catalog with a discovery layer that enables users to find books and journal in a single search.

Financial Performance

The university charged $37106 undergraduate tuition for 2012-13.

The school is supported by a $125 million endowment.

Strategy

The university focuses on integrating international study service and research opportunities for students faculty and staff and on upgrading campus facilities. Since 2003 it has invested more than $285 million in campus improvements.

In 2013 the school announced a $47.5 million project to build an eight-story rehabilitation center to provide a state-of-the-art facility for undergraduate and graduate programs in the Departments of Exercise Science Occupational Therapy and Physical Therapy.

The Loyola Science Center was completed in two phases in 2011 and 2012.

In 2011 the University of Scranton opened the Pilarz and Montrone Halls to house 400 upperclass students and a fitness center.

Company Background

The University of Scranton was founded in 1888 as Saint Thomas College.

The school's more than 45000 graduates are all members of the Alumni Society which has 20 clubs worldwide.

EXECUTIVES

Assistant Vice President of Finance, Robert (Bob) Thomas
Associate Vice President for Planning and Information Management, Robyn Dickinson
Secretary Information Res Vice President of Planning and Chief Information Officer, Karen Kuzmak
Secretary public Relations public Relations, Rosemary Corrigan
Secretary Information Technology Services, Jean Mastri
Auditors: GRANT THORNTON LLP PHILADELPH

LOCATIONS

HQ: UNIVERSITY OF SCRANTON
800 LINDEN ST, SCRANTON, PA 185104501
Phone: 570 344-6685
Web: WWW.SCRANTON.EDU

PRODUCTS/OPERATIONS

Schools and Colleges
College of Arts and Sciences
College of Graduate and Continuing Education
Kania School of Management
Panuska College of Professional Studies

HISTORICAL FINANCIALS
Company Type: Private

Income Statement
FYE: May 31

	REVENUE ($ mil.)	NET INCOME ($ mil.)	NET PROFIT MARGIN	EMPLOYEES
05/13	158	33	21.0%	1,050
05/12	212	16	7.6%	—
05/09	138	(1)	—	—
05/08	135	0	—	—
Annual Growth	3.3%	—	—	—

Return on assets: 4.3%   Cash ($ mil.): 14
Return on equity: 21.0%
Current ratio: —

UNIVERSITY OF SOUTH FLORIDA

The University of South Florida (USF) is bullishly educational. The school has some 48000 students at three campuses in Tampa St. Petersburg and Sarasota/Manatee. It offers some 180 undergraduate graduate specialty and doctoral degree programs through more than a dozen colleges including Arts and Sciences Business Education Engineering Marine Science Pharmacy and Public Health. USF also offers graduate certificates continuing education courses and teacher certifications and it is a major research institution among US universities. USF was founded in 1960; its mascot is the bull.

Operations

The university has some 2000 teaching faculty members and maintains a 24:1 student-to-faculty ratio. USF's core offerings include an extensive health sciences program including medical nursing pharmacy and public health colleges grouped under the USF Health banner. The health organization also includes patient care facilities such as family care practices emergency clinics and Alzheimer's centers.

USF Health also hosts medical research programs in areas such as neurological conditions cardiovascular care pediatrics infectious disease and biotechnology. The university also has research programs in a range of science engineering and arts fields such as veteran reintegration and photovoltaic energy technologies. Altogether USF's research programs were granted more than $400 million in awards and contracts during the fiscal 2014 year.

Extracurricular activities include 17 men's and women's varsity teams that participate in the American Athletics Conference at the NCAA level.

Geographic Reach

USF has more than 3100 international students or about 6% of the total student population. USF also supports study abroad programs. The university's campuses in Florida encompass some 1600 acres. The main Tampa campus includes the USF Health facilities and health-related schools

Financial Performance

USF has a budget of some $1.5 billion annually as well as an annual economic impact of some $4.4 billion. The university has an endowment of some $400 million.

EXECUTIVES

Associate Vp Information Technologies, George W Ellis
President and Corporate Secretary, Judy L. Genshaft
EVP and Provost, Ralph Wilcox
COO, John W. Long
SVP Research Innovation and Economic Development and President USF Research Foundation, Paul R. Sanberg
VP Information Technology and CIO, Sidney Fernandes
VP Business and Finance and CFO, Nick Trivunovich
Associate Vice President, Jay Wolfson
Vice President Research, Judith Lowry

Senior Vice President University Advancement, Joel Momberg
Senior Vice President For Research, Karen A Holbrook
Vice President Camp Executive Officer Sarasota Manatee, Arthur (Art) Guilford
Vice President Administrative Services, Sandy Lovins
Associate Vice President, Linda Whiteford
Vice President, David Williams
Associate Vice President, Phil Marty
Assistant Vice President For Research, Valerie McDevitt
Associate Vice President Faculty Affairs And Human Resources, Paula N Knaus
Senior Vice President, Chris Colaco
Sa Assistant Vice President For Wellness, Jennifer Larson
Clinic Manager, Karen Myers
Vice President Research, Scott Mann
Associate Vice President For Research And Innovation, Karen Liller
Vice President For Student Affairs, Thomas Miller
Vice President Research and Development, Don Clark
Associate Vice President Supplier, Ted Williams
Vice President, Ricci Allen
Director Of Clinical Services, Catherine Jahrsdorfer
Vice President Student Affairs, Carmen Goldsmith
Associate Vice President Educational Outreach, Kathleen Moore
Assistant Vice President, Guy Conway
Vice President, Maegan Fader
Assistant Vice President For Research Compliance, Cheryl Byers
Health Information Technology Consultant Vice President For Health Sciences, Gary Hendrickson
Search Committee Chair Department Of Geography, Phil Reeder
Vice President Acad Affairs Stpetersburg, Melanie Marquez
Assistant Vice President For Admissions Recruitment and Enrollment Planning, Robert (Bob) Spatig
Vice President, G Karolyi
Division Vice President, John (Jack) Yeates
Chair, Harold W. Mullis
Vice Chair, Brian D. Lamb
Secretary Finance, Amy Barbour
Board Of Directors; Chair Project Development and Evaluation Committee, Danielle Dennis
University Treasurer, Fell Stubbs
Auditors: DAVID W MARTIN CPA AUDITOR G

LOCATIONS

HQ: UNIVERSITY OF SOUTH FLORIDA
4202 E FOWLER AVE, TAMPA, FL 336208000
Phone: 812 974-2001
Web: WWW.HOUSING.USF.EDU

PRODUCTS/OPERATIONS

2013 Revenue

	% of total
Contracts & grants	26
Student financial aid	26
Tuition	16
General revenue	14
Auxiliary enterprises	11
Intercollegiate athletics	3
Lottery	2
Concessions & fees	2
Total	**100**

Selected Colleges

The Arts
Arts & Sciences
Behavioral & Community Sciences
Business
Education
Engineering
Global Sustainability
Honors College

Marine Science
Medicine
Nursing
Pharmacy
Public Health
University College (graduate school)

COMPETITORS

Florida Atlantic University	University of Central Florida
Florida International University	University of Florida
Florida State University	University of Miami
	University of North Florida

HISTORICAL FINANCIALS

Company Type: Private

Income Statement

FYE: June 30

	REVENUE ($ mil.)	NET INCOME ($ mil.)	NET PROFIT MARGIN	EMPLOYEES
06/09	892	42	4.7%	16,165
06/07	533	148	27.8%	—
Annual Growth	29.3%	(46.7%)	—	—

2009 Year-End Financials

Return on assets: 4.6%   Cash ($ mil.): 30
Return on equity: 4.7%
Current ratio: 0.70

UNIVERSITY OF SOUTHERN MISSISSIPPI

You don't have to be a belle to attend Southern Miss but it never hurts. The University of Southern Mississippi (USM or Southern Miss for short) was established by the state legislature in 1910 to educate Mississippi's teachers. The school has grown to boast an enrollment of more than 15000 students with a student-teacher ratio of 17:1. USM offers bachelor's master's doctoral and post-master's degrees through five colleges: College of Arts and Letters College of Business College of Education and Psychology College of Health and College of Science and Technology. Southern Miss also runs an Honors College and engages in extensive research in a range of disciplines including health and technology.

EXECUTIVES

Vice President Research Economic Devel, Cecil Burge
Associate Vice President Research and Economic Development, Julian Allen
Secretary, Catherine (Cathy) Herron

LOCATIONS

HQ: UNIVERSITY OF SOUTHERN MISSISSIPPI
118 COLLEGE DR BOX 5005, HATTIESBURG, MS 394060001
Phone: 601 266-4111
Web: WWW.USM.EDU

HISTORICAL FINANCIALS
Company Type: Private

Income Statement
FYE: June 30

	REVENUE ($ mil.)	NET INCOME ($ mil.)	NET PROFIT MARGIN	EMPLOYEES
06/14	192	20	10.8%	4,500
06/13	192	17	9.0%	—
06/11	193	13	7.2%	—
06/09	179	0	—	—
Annual Growth	1.4%	—	—	—

2014 Year-End Financials
Return on assets: 11.4%
Return on equity: 10.8%
Current ratio: 1.80
Cash ($ mil.): 42

UNIVERSITY OF ST. THOMAS

Far from any Bahamian beaches or Caribbean hot spots sits The University of St. Thomas (UST). The school is a Catholic university with campuses in Minneapolis and St. Paul Minnesota. It offers about 90 undergraduate and 60 graduate programs in seven academic divisions: education and philosophy arts and sciences business engineering divinity law and social work. The school has an enrollment of about 11000 undergraduate and graduate students with a student-to-teacher ratio of 14:1. UST along with military prep school St. Thomas Academy grew out of St. Thomas Aquinas Seminary which was founded in 1885 by Archbishop John Ireland.

Geographic Reach
UST has campuses in Minneapolis and St. Paul as well as the Daniel C. Gainey Conference Center in Owatonna Minnesota and the Bernardi Campus in Rome Italy.

Financial Performance
The university's revenues come from a mix of student tuition and fees sales and service enterprises grants gifts and contracts. The university has an annual operating budget of about $195 million and its tuition runs around $33000 per student. UST has an endowment of some $400 million.

EXECUTIVES
Vice President for Mission, John (Jack) Malone
Associate Vice President For Academic Affairs, Joseph (Jo) Kreitzer
Associate Vice President Academic Services and Special Programs, Eleni Roulis
Associate Vice President, James Brummer
Vice President, Adrienne F Geile
Associate Vice President of Human Resources, Amy Petruck
Vice President For Student Affairs, Jane Canney
Department Head, Gregory J Coulter
Vice President (Vizeprsident), Colin Bettis
Vice President, Trang Anh
Vice President Of Operations, Lukas Campbell
Associate Vice President Facilities, Gerald (Jerry) Anderley
Vice President, Julie Schuth
Senior Vice President, Dolores Hietpas
Vice President Enrollment Management, Daniel Meyer
Senior Vice President, Karen Pishko
Vice President, Max Shapiro
Secretary, John (Jack) Tauer

Treasurer, Matt Larson
Secretary, Amanda Fenolio
Treasurer, Tom Kalil
Auditors: CLIFTONLARSONALLEN LLP MINNE

LOCATIONS
HQ: UNIVERSITY OF ST. THOMAS
2115 SUMMIT AVE, SAINT PAUL, MN 551051096
Phone: 651 962-5000
Web: WWW.STTHOMAS.EDU

PRODUCTS/OPERATIONS

Academic Divisions
College of Arts and Sciences (Bachelor's and Master's)
College of Education Leadership and Counseling - Education (Bachelor's Master's Specialist Doctorate) and Professional Psychology (Master's and Doctorate)
Opus College of Business (Bachelor's and Master's)
Saint Paul Seminary School of Divinity (Master's)
School of Engineering (Bachelor's and Master's)
School of Law (Juris Doctor)
School of Social Work (Bachelor's and Master's)

HISTORICAL FINANCIALS
Company Type: Private

Income Statement
FYE: June 30

	REVENUE ($ mil.)	NET INCOME ($ mil.)	NET PROFIT MARGIN	EMPLOYEES
06/14	253	62	24.8%	1,900
06/13	260	69	26.7%	—
06/12	239	2	1.2%	—
06/11	56	0	—	—
Annual Growth	65.0%			

2014 Year-End Financials
Return on assets: 11.5%
Return on equity: 24.8%
Current ratio: —
Cash ($ mil.): —

UNIVERSITY OF TENNESSEE

Whether you want to learn the art of aviation or get ready for a career in public service the University of Tennessee System (UT) is here to help. The 200-year-old school provides undergraduate graduate and professional academic programs to about 50000 students; programs include business engineering law pharmacy medicine and veterinary medicine. It has a student-teacher ratio of about 16:1. Campuses include the flagship Knoxville location as well as the Health Science Center at Memphis the Space Institute at Tullahoma the statewide Institute for Public Service and the Institute of Agriculture. Other UT System campuses are located in Chattanooga and Martin. UT was founded in 1794 as Blount College.

Financial Performance
UT's funding comes from gifts grants and contracts (about 30%) state appropriations (roughly 28%) tuition and fees (20%) and a handful of auxiliary enterprises and independent operations (the remainder).

Company Background
Notable alumni include former Senate Majority Leader Howard Baker Nobel Prize-winning economist James Buchanan and author Cormac McCarthy.

EXECUTIVES
Vice President, Anthony Haynes
Auditors: ARTHUR A HAYES JR CPA NAS

LOCATIONS
HQ: UNIVERSITY OF TENNESSEE
1331 CIRCLE PARK DR, KNOXVILLE, TN 379163801
Phone: 865 974-2303
Web: WWW.TREASURER.TENNESSEE.EDU

PRODUCTS/OPERATIONS

Selected Colleges Schools and Institutes
College of Agricultural Sciences and Natural Resources
College of Allied Health Sciences
College of Architecture and Design
College of Arts and Sciences
College of Business Administration
College of Communication and Information
College of Dentistry
College of Education Health and Human Sciences
College of Engineering
College of Graduate Health Sciences
College of Health Science Engineering
College of Law
College of Medicine
College of Nursing
College of Pharmacy
College of Social Work
College of Veterinary Medicine
Graduate School of Medicine
School of Art
School of Music
Space Institute

HISTORICAL FINANCIALS
Company Type: Private

Income Statement
FYE: June 30

	REVENUE ($ mil.)	NET INCOME ($ mil.)	NET PROFIT MARGIN	EMPLOYEES
06/13	1,122	92	8.2%	12,000
06/12	1,092	60	5.5%	—
06/11*	1,034	296	28.7%	—
12/08	1	0	—	—
Annual Growth	443.8%	—	—	—

*Fiscal year change

2013 Year-End Financials
Return on assets: 9.0%
Return on equity: 8.2%
Current ratio: 0.90
Cash ($ mil.): 292

UNIVERSITY OF THE PACIFIC

Situated next to the largest body of water on earth the University of the Pacific holds a sizable body of knowledge. The school offers more than 80 undergraduate majors and about 20 graduate programs in such fields as art language biology business computer science engineering history and pharmacy. It offers undergraduate graduate and professional degree programs in nine colleges and enrolls about 7000 students at its main campus in Stockton California the McGeorge School of Law in Sacramento and the Arthur A. Dugoni School of Dentistry in San Francisco. California's first chartered institution of higher education University of the Pacific was founded in 1851.

Geographic Reach
More than 85% of University of the Pacific's students are California residents. The remainder of

the university's student base comes from 35 other US states as well as 25 international countries.

Operations

University of the Pacific has about 500 full-time faculty members and a student-to-teacher ratio of 13:1. Tuition at the university runs at about $38000 per year.

Financial Performance

University of the Pacific reported a 5% revenue rise to $331 million in 2012 due to increased tuition as well as from private grants gifts and bequests. Net income decreased by 53% to $21 million however due to increased expenses and lower investment returns.

Endowment funds contributed about $8 million of University of the Pacific's operating budget in fiscal 2012. The school has a total endowment of some $200 million.

Strategy

University of the Pacific is expanding its academic programs in targeted fields such as health-related education and training programs. It also is working to increase technology resources and implement related learning models as new high-tech generations join its ranks.

Other initiatives include recruiting teachers with scholarly experience attracting diverse and ambitious students and increasing job preparedness programs for students. University of the Pacific is also working to increase enrollment and fundraising efforts to generate new resources that will support its growth plans.

EXECUTIVES

VP Business and Finance, Patrick D. Cavanaugh
Dean Arthur A. Dugoni School of Dentistry, Patrick J. Ferrillo, age 63
Provost, Philip N. Gilbertson
Associate Provost and CIO, Larry Frederick
Dean McGeorge School of Law, Elizabeth Rindskopf Parker
President of University of the Pacific on, Pamela A. (Pam) Eibeck
Dean Library, C. Brigid Welch
Dean Eberhardt School of Business, Richard Flaherty
Dean Students, Joanna Royce-Davis
Dean College of the Pacific, Thomas Krise
Dean Conservatory of Music, Giulio Maria Ongaro
Dean Gladys L. Benerd School of Education, Lynn G. Beck
Dean School of Engineering and Computer Science, Ravi K. Jain
Dean School of International Studies and Associate Provost International Initiatives, Margee Ensign
Dean Thomas J. Long School of Pharmacy and Health Sciences, Phillip Oppenheimer
Dean Graduate Studies and Associate Provost Research and Collaborative Programs, Jin Gong
Clinic Manager, Elaine Hackenkamp
Vice President, Chris Chang
APhA ASP Vice President of Professional Affairs, Barrett Smith
Vice President, Laura Merry
Assistant Vice President Development Operations, Jeff Rhode
Clinic Supervisor, Charlene Pugh
Assistant Vice President Advancement Operations, Scott Rivinius
Assistant Vice President Corporate Foundation Relations and Principal Gifts, Scott Biedermann
Vice President For Student Life, Patrick Day
Rho Chi Honor Society Vice President, Danny Luu
Vice President Of Asuop, Elena Goldfoos
T C Gvpe, Karla Barbosa
Vice President Accounting Risk Management, Marcus Perrot
Associate Vice President for Planning, Linda Buckley

APhA ASP Vice President of Industry Affairs, M Harada
Chair, Tom Zuckerman
Auditors: KPMG LLP SAN FRANCISCO CA

LOCATIONS

HQ: UNIVERSITY OF THE PACIFIC
3601 PACIFIC AVE, STOCKTON, CA 952110197
Phone: 209 946-2401
Web: WWW.PACIFIC.EDU

PRODUCTS/OPERATIONS

Selected Schools and Colleges
Arthur A. Dugoni School of Dentistry
College of the Pacific (Arts and Sciences)
Conservatory of Music
Eberhardt School of Business
Gladys L. Benerd School of Education
McGeorge School of Law
School of Engineering and Computer Science
School of International Studies
Thomas J. Long School of Pharmacy and Health Sciences

HISTORICAL FINANCIALS

Company Type: Private

Income Statement

	REVENUE ($ mil.)	NET INCOME ($ mil.)	NET PROFIT MARGIN	EMPLOYEES
06/13	447	147	32.9%	1,500
06/12	330	20	6.3%	—
06/11	317	43	13.8%	—
06/10	354	0	—	—
Annual Growth	8.1%	—	—	—

FYE: June 30

2013 Year-End Financials

Return on assets: —
Return on equity: 32.9%
Current ratio: —
Cash ($ mil.): 13

UNIVERSITY OF WASHINGTON INC

The University of Washington (UW) is Husky indeed with an annual enrollment of more than 54000 students. Founded in 1861 as the Territorial University of Washington UW (pronounced "U-dub" by those on campus) has smaller branches in Tacoma and Bothell in addition to its main campus in downtown Seattle. The university whose mascot is a Husky offers more than 440 undergraduate graduate and professional degree programs through 16 colleges and schools. It also operates four hospitals: University of Washington Medical Center Harborview Medical Center Northwest Hospital and Valley Medical Center.

Operations

With more than 250 degree options the UW confers some 12000 bachelor's master's doctoral and professional degrees each year. Its graduates include about 135 Fulbright and 35 Rhodes scholars. The school's top five bachelor degree fields include biology psychology political science economics and communications.

Research is a cornerstone of the university which has more than 270 specialized research centers. The school's annual sponsored grant and contract research funding exceeds $1 billion and it has received more federal research funding than any other public university in the US since 1974.

Some 280 new companies have emerged based on UW research advances.

Financial Performance

In fiscal 2014 revenues for the school totaled $5.8 billion. UW has a diverse revenue base with no single source of fund representing more than 34% of revenues. Patient service revenues account for the largest amount of funds received (about 34%) followed by grants (about 23%).

The university lost half of its state funding between 2009 and 2013. However funding increased the following year so UW was able to free tuition rates for two years. Because of the recent state cuts tuition now accounts for 70% of its general operating fund resources (up from 34% in 2004).

EXECUTIVES

Dean School of Medicine, Paul G. Ramsey
SVP Finance and Facilities, V'Ella Warren
Chancellor Bothell Campus, Bjong Wolf Yeigh
Dean School of Law, Kellye Testy
Dean Libraries, Lizabeth A. (Betsy) Wilson
Interim Chancellor Tacoma Campus, Kenyon S. Chan
Dean School of Public Health, Howard Frumkin
President, Ana Mari Cauce
Dean Undergraduate Academic Affairs, Ed Taylor
VP Information Technology and CIO, Kelli Trosvig
Dean College of Arts and Sciences, Robert Stacey
Interim Dean College of Built Environments, John Schaufelberger
Dean School of Dentistry, Joel H. Berg
Dean College of Education, Tom Stritikus
Dean College of Engineering, Michael B. Bragg
Dean College of the Environment, Lisa Graumlich
Dean Evans School of Public Affairs, Sandra Archibald
Dean Foster School of Business, James Jiambalvo
Dean Graduate School, Dave Eaton
Dean Information School, Harry Bruce
Dean School of Nursing, Azita Emami
Dean School of Pharmacy, Thomas Baillie
Dean School of Social Work, Edwina (Eddie) Uehara
Associate Vice President, Clare Donahue
Associate Vice President General Manager, John (Jack) Haslam
Associate Vice President Facilities Services, Charles (Chas) Kennedy
Assistant Vice President For Labor Relations, Peter Denis
Assistant Vice President For Corporate A, Joanna Glickler
Assistant Vice President Brand Marketing Strategy, Nicole Dierks
Senior Vice President Chief Financial Officer, Barbara Smith
Medical Director, Chris Behrens
Department Chair, Rebecca Slayton
Vice President Of Marketing, Jason Trammell
Internal Vice President, Ian Lauth
External Vice President, Elliott Straube
Senior Vice President Ecommerce Mobile D, Brian Jones
Medical Director, Jean Haulman
Vice Chairman, William S. (Bill) Ayer
Chairman, Orin C. Smith, age 71
Secretary Supervisor, Melanie Kanna
Secretary Senior Community Standards And Amp Studen, Bobbi Offner
Board Member, Jacqueline Pruner
Secretary Senior Finance And Business Economics, Catherine (Cathy) Richardson
Secretary Senior Capital Projects Office, Chris Niblack
Auditors: KPMG LLP SEATTLE WA

LOCATIONS

HQ: UNIVERSITY OF WASHINGTON INC
4311 11TH AVE NE STE 600, SEATTLE, WA
981056369
Phone: 206 543-2100
Web: WWW.AA.WASHINGTON.EDU

PRODUCTS/OPERATIONS

Selected Colleges and Schools
College of Arts and Sciences
College of Built Environments
College of Education
College of Engineering
College of the Environment
Evans School of Public Affairs
The Graduate School
Information School
Michael G. Foster School of Business
School of Dentistry
School of Law
School of Medicine
School of Nursing
School of Pharmacy
School of Public Health
School of Social Work

HISTORICAL FINANCIALS

Company Type: Private

Income Statement			FYE: June 30
	REVENUE ($ mil.)	NET INCOME ($ mil.)	NET PROFIT MARGIN	EMPLOYEES
06/13	4,563	424	9.3%	27,228
06/12	4,258	5	0.1%	—
06/11	3	0	14.4%	—
06/09	2,902	0	—	—
Annual Growth	12.0%	—	—	—

2013 Year-End Financials
Return on assets: 4.0%   Cash ($ mil.): 131
Return on equity: 9.3%
Current ratio: 0.90

UNIVERSITY OF WISCONSIN FOUNDATION

Because even Badgers need help the University of Wisconsin Foundation raises funds receives gifts and manages assets for The University of Wisconsin-Madison and other donor-designated units of The University of Wisconsin System. (Bucky Badger is the school's mascot.) The foundation supports special programs and projects including professorships fellowships scholarships research efforts and building projects. The not-for-profit organization has received more than $2.4 billion in donations since it was founded in 1945.

EXECUTIVES

Managing Director Research And Prospect Management, Kari Stokosa
Associate Vice President For Development Office Of Gift Planning, Linda Halsey
Vice President Managing Group Leader, Anne Lucke
Asst Sec, Bridget Bush
Auditors: GRANT THORNTON LLP APPLETON

LOCATIONS

HQ: UNIVERSITY OF WISCONSIN FOUNDATION
1848 UNIVERSITY AVE, MADISON, WI 537264090
Phone: 608 263-4545
Web: WWW.UWHEALTH.ORG

HISTORICAL FINANCIALS

Company Type: Private

Income Statement				FYE: December 31
	REVENUE ($ mil.)	NET INCOME ($ mil.)	NET PROFIT MARGIN	EMPLOYEES
12/13	595	323	54.3%	150
12/12	434	183	42.3%	—
12/10	444	206	46.6%	—
12/09	423	0	—	—
Annual Growth	8.9%	—	—	—

2013 Year-End Financials
Return on assets: 0.4%   Cash ($ mil.): 173
Return on equity: 54.3%
Current ratio: 5.30

UNIVERSITY OF WISCONSIN SYSTEM

Unfortunately there is no School of Cheese in the University of Wisconsin System (UW System) but across its vast operations there are 13 four-year universities 13 two-year UW Colleges campuses and a statewide extension program that has offices in every Wisconsin county. The UW System is one of the largest public university systems in the US with more than 180000 students and 40000 faculty and staff members. Its top school is UW at Madison which offers more than 400 undergraduate majors master's degree programs and doctoral programs to some 43000 students. The system's other major campus is UW at Milwaukee with about 28000 students. The UW System has a student-teacher ratio of 17:1.

Operations
Combined the UW System's students have access to more than 250 undergraduate degree programs approximately 225 master's programs and 125 doctoral programs. More than 36000 degrees are conferred annually.

Geographic Reach
One of the nation's largest public universities the UW system boasts offices or campuses in every county in Wisconsin.

Strategy
The system operates with seven core strategies in mind: preparing students to thrive in the global society creating a stronger workforce building a stronger business environment building stronger communities growing its financial and human resources advancing its operational excellence and increasing collaborations between campuses and with other organizations.

As an increasing number of its students are working adults or students with nontraditional schedules the university has developed online accelerated and collaborative degree programs tailored to specific industries and emerging workforce needs.

Financial Performance
UW System reported a 5% increase in overall revenues to $4.7 billion in fiscal 2013. Gifts grants and contracts was the system's largest source of revenue that year ($1.6 billion or more than a third

of total revenue); this channel grew 5% during the year. Tuition and fees (which increased 6% in 2013) and state appropriations (which grew 6%) are among the other primary sources of funds followed by sales and services of auxiliary enterprises.

Sales and Marketing
About 85% of the system's students come from Wisconsin.

HISTORY

When Wisconsin became a state in 1848 its constitution called for the establishment of a state university. A board of regents was named and it first established a preparatory school because regents felt Wisconsin's secondary schools were not advanced enough to prepare students for university studies. The school began classes in 1849 with 20 students in the Madison Female Academy Building. The University of Wisconsin's first official freshman class began studies in the fall of 1850. A campus was established a mile west of the state capitol in Madison. By 1854 when it held its first commencement (with two graduates) the school had 41 students.

Enrollment dipped during the Civil War (all but one of the school's senior class joined the army) but soon rebounded and by 1870 the university had almost 500 students. Meanwhile it established a school of agriculture (1866) and a school of law (1868). The state established normal schools (teachers' colleges) in Platteville (1866) Whitewater (1868) Oshkosh (1871) and River Falls (1874).

There was also a teachers' course for women at the university in Madison. However when John Bascom became president in 1874 he transformed the university into a truly coeducational institution putting women "in all respects on precisely the same footing" with the men.

While the university at Madison remained Wisconsin's primary seat of learning the state continued to establish normal schools. It opened institutions in Milwaukee (1885) Superior (1893) Stevens Point (1894) La Crosse (1909) and Eau Claire (1916). The nine normal schools eventually became a system of state colleges called Wisconsin State Universities.

The university at Madison also continued to grow and by the late 1920s it had almost 9000 students. WWII brought a drop in enrollment but afterward it took off jumping from about 7000 in 1945 to over 22000 by the late 1950s. The University of Wisconsin-Milwaukee branch was founded in 1956. Other branch campuses were established in Green Bay (1965) and Kenosha (1968).

The Madison campus became a focal point for student protests during the Vietnam War. Events came to a head in 1970 when President Fred Harrington resigned during a four-day standoff between students and the National Guard. War protesters also placed a bomb outside Sterling Hall which housed the Army Math Research Center; the explosion killed one student and injured three others.

The state legislature merged the University of Wisconsin and the Wisconsin State Universities in 1971 to create The University of Wisconsin System.

EXECUTIVES

Associate Vice President, David (Dave) Brukardt
Vice President Of Sales, Hartley Murray
Associate Vice President For External Relations And Strategic Communications, John Diamond
Univ Executive Staff Assistant Vice President, Zayda Back
Assistant Vice President Assistant To Ch, Vicki Washington
Secretary Of The Academic Staff, Heather Daniels

LOCATIONS

HQ: UNIVERSITY OF WISCONSIN SYSTEM
   1220 LINDEN DR, MADISON, WI 537061525
Phone: 608 262-2321
Web: WWW.WISCONSIN.EDU

PRODUCTS/OPERATIONS

Selected Four-Year Campuses
UW-Eau Claire
UW-Green Bay
UW-La Crosse
UW-Madison
UW-Milwaukee
UW-Oshkosh
UW-Parkside
UW-Platteville
UW-River Falls
UW-Stevens Point
UW-Stout
UW-Superior
UW-Whitewater

Selected Two-Year Colleges
UW-Baraboo/Sauk County
UW-Barron County
UW-Fond du Lac
UW-Fox Valley
UW-Manitowoc
UW-Marathon County
UW-Marinette
UW-Marshfield/Wood County
UW-Richland
UW-Rock County
UW-Sheboygan
UW-Washington County
UW-Waukesha

HISTORICAL FINANCIALS
Company Type: Private

Income Statement   FYE: June 30

	REVENUE ($ mil.)	NET INCOME ($ mil.)	NET PROFIT MARGIN	EMPLOYEES
06/13	3,538	503	14.2%	31,992
06/11	3,331	411	12.4%	—
06/10	3,116	329	10.6%	—
06/07	2,541	0	—	—
Annual Growth	5.7%	—	—	—

2013 Year-End Financials
Return on assets: —
Return on equity: 14.2%
Current ratio: 3.50
Cash ($ mil.): 1,685

UNIVERSITY OF WYOMING

For folks who live in Wyoming the University of Wyoming (UW) is it –the only place offering baccalaureate and graduate degrees as well as research and outreach services that stretch across the state. The main campus is in Laramie but the school also has a campus in Casper (offering coordinated education programs with the Casper College) plus regional outreach education centers stationed throughout the state. Founded in 1887 UW has grown to serve more than 13000 students with about 200 programs of study through seven academic colleges as well as numerous schools and institutes. The university has a student-to-faculty ratio of 14:1.

Geographic Reach
Though most of its students come from Wyoming UW also attracts students from all 50 US states and about 90 countries. The university also offers a number of study abroad opportunities.

Strategy
In 2012 UW launched three construction projects to expand or upgrade a number of instructional research athletic and outreach facilities. One program will put about $10 million towards upgrading HVAC (heating ventilation and air conditioning) and lighting systems in the Biological Sciences building on the main Laramie campus. UW also completed construction of its new Visual Arts building in early 2012.

EXECUTIVES

Vice President Administration, Bill Mai
Vice President Academic Affairs Office Staff Assistant, Aneesa Anne McDonald
Vice President Research and Economic Development Office Project Coordinator Senior, Kelly Lynn Haigler Cornish
Associate Vice President for Fiscal Ad, JanetSue Lowe
Staff Assistant Vice President Student Affairs Office, RoxanneLee Rector
Vice President, Jean-pascal Planche
Foundation Associate Vice President, John (Jack) Stark
Vice President Academic Affairs Office Research Scientist Assistant, Justin McDonald
Vice President Gillette College, Mark Englert
Associate Vice President Fiscal Administration, Melanie Drever
Vice President Regional Technology, James Pew
Associate Vice President Vice President Academic Affairs Office, Myron Allen
Director of Pharmacy, Linda Martin
Vice President Technology, Jeffrey (Jeff) Hamerlinck
Vice President, Genee Vidakovich
Auditors: MCGEE HEARNE & PAIZ LLP LAR

LOCATIONS

HQ: UNIVERSITY OF WYOMING
   1000 E UNIVERSITY AVE # 3434, LARAMIE, WY 820712001
Phone: 307 766-3264
Web: WWW.WWWENG.UWYO.EDU

PRODUCTS/OPERATIONS

Selected Colleges and Schools
College of Agriculture and Natural Resources
College of Arts and Sciences
College of Business
College of Education
College of Engineering and Applied Science
College of Health Sciences
College of Law
Graduate Education
Outreach School
School of Energy Resources
School of Environment and Natural Resources

HISTORICAL FINANCIALS
Company Type: Private

Income Statement   FYE: June 30

	REVENUE ($ mil.)	NET INCOME ($ mil.)	NET PROFIT MARGIN	EMPLOYEES
06/14	215	47	21.9%	7,000
06/13	225	117	51.9%	—
06/10	195	31	16.2%	—
06/09	195	0	—	—
Annual Growth	2.0%	—	—	—

2014 Year-End Financials
Return on assets: 9.6%
Return on equity: 21.9%
Current ratio: 2.10
Cash ($ mil.): 128

UNIVERSITY PHYSICIANS HEALTHCARE

Auditors: BEACH FLEISCHMAN PC TUCSON A

LOCATIONS

HQ: UNIVERSITY PHYSICIANS HEALTHCARE
   2701 E ELVIRA RD, TUCSON, AZ 857567124
Phone: 520 874-3500
Web: WWW.UPH.ORG

HISTORICAL FINANCIALS
Company Type: Private

Income Statement   FYE: June 30

	REVENUE ($ mil.)	NET INCOME ($ mil.)	NET PROFIT MARGIN	EMPLOYEES
06/10	598	15	2.7%	1,818
06/08	320	(11)	—	—
06/07	309	(9)	—	—
06/05	248	0	—	—
Annual Growth	19.2%	—	—	—

2010 Year-End Financials
Return on assets: —
Return on equity: 2.7%
Current ratio: 0.50
Cash ($ mil.): 30

UNIVERSITY SYSTEM OF NEW HAMPSHIRE

The University of New Hampshire (UNH) is a liberal arts college that serves about 12600 undergraduate and more than 2200 graduate students. The institution offers more than 100 majors and academic programs of study at nine colleges and schools. The student-faculty ratio is 20:1. UNH is the flagship institution of the University System of New Hampshire. In 2007 the university graduated its first international class in Seoul under a program run by its Whittemore School of Business and Economics. Founded in 1866 as the New Hampshire College of Agriculture and the Mechanic Arts UNH is a designated land-grant sea-grant and space-grant chartered school.

Geographic Reach
In addition to its main campus in Durham UNH has a campus in Manchester and its School of Law is in Concord. Almost 60% of the school's student body comes from within state with a concentration of others coming from the northeastern region of the US. UNH is developing new academic programs expanding its online courses and opportunities and creating new international initiatives for faculty and students in Costa Rica Chile Ghana India South Korea and China.

Operations
UNH's most popular bachelor's programs include business administration undeclared liberal arts psychology English and communication followed by mechanical engineering biology biomedical science civil engineering and political science.

The University System of New Hampshire includes Keene State College Plymouth State University and Granite State College in addition to UNH.

Strategy

UNH is engaged in a strategic plan to support its growth through 2020. Its plan for creating a learning-centered environment includes such initiatives as establishing a New Venture Fund to promote collaborative research and teaching opportunities; developing new programs to support independent research and scholarship; commercializing UNH's intellectual capital; and promoting diversity and inclusiveness as well as international opportunities. It also includes making major capital investments in technology to build a high-capacity cyber-infrastructure and a learning portal to promote interdisciplinary collaboration; renovating restoring and adding on to facilities; and constructing a new center for the arts.

EXECUTIVES

Associate Vice President of Finance, Celine Austin
Secretary, Heidi Hedegard
Auditors: PRICEWATERHOUSECOOPERS LLP BO

LOCATIONS

HQ: UNIVERSITY SYSTEM OF NEW HAMPSHIRE
25 CONCORD RD, LEE, NH 038616659
Phone: 603 862-1800
Web: WWW.USNH.EDU

PRODUCTS/OPERATIONS

Selected Colleges and Schools

College of Engineering and Physical Sciences
College of Health and Human Services
College of Liberal Arts
College of Life Sciences and Agriculture
The Graduate School
Thompson School of Applied Science
University of New Hampshire at Manchester
University of New Hampshire School of Law
Whittemore School of Business and Economics
Special Academic Opportunities
Graduate Research Conference
Hamel Center for Undergraduate Reasearch
Honors program
International research opportunities program
Student internships
Study abroad
Undergraduate research opportunities program

HISTORICAL FINANCIALS

Company Type: Private

Income Statement

FYE: June 30

	REVENUE ($ mil.)	NET INCOME ($ mil.)	NET PROFIT MARGIN	EMPLOYEES
06/14	676	128	19.1%	3,800
06/13	800	111	14.0%	—
06/12	0	40	—	—
06/08	558	0	—	—
Annual Growth	3.3%	—	—	—

2014 Year-End Financials

Return on assets: 6.8%
Return on equity: 19.1%
Current ratio: 0.70
Cash ($ mil.): 80

UNMC PHYSICIANS

If you're in Nebraska and your doctor suddenly tells you to "Go Big Red!" —don't be shocked he's probably just a member of the not-for-profit UNMC Physicians (formerly University Medical Associates). Many of the more than 500 physicians in the UNMC group practice were trained and now teach at the University of Nebraska Medical Center. Additionally UNMC partners with The Nebraska Medical Center and the Olson Center for Women's Health to share best practices and resources. The physicians who also operate 10 family health clinics in the area provide services in about 50 specialties such as obstetrics cancer care family medicine cardiology and pediatrics.

Providers at UNMC also conduct and participate in a number of national and regional clinical research trials in a wide range of areas including cancer cardiovascular disease neurological sciences and infectious disease among many others.

EXECUTIVES

Chairman President and CEO, Rodney S. (Rod) Markin, age 53
Chairman Surgery, Byers W. Shaw Jr.
EVP and Chief Administrative Officer, Cory D. Shaw
Human Resources Director, Keli Royal
Media Relations, Cherie Lytle
Marketing and Media Relations, Genna Campbell
CFO, Troy Wilhelm
Chairperson Neuorsciences, Terri Mashek
Secretary Treasurer and Chairperson Radiation and Oncology, Charles Enke
Vice Chairman, Kevin Garvin
Secretary Treasurer and Chairperson Radiation and Oncology, Charles Enke
Vice Chairman, Kevin Garvin
Auditors: KPMG LLP OMAHA NE

LOCATIONS

HQ: UNMC PHYSICIANS
988101 NEBRASKA MED CTR, OMAHA, NE 681980001
Phone: 402 559-9700
Web: WWW.UNMCPHYSICIANS.COM

Selected Clinics (Omaha Nebraska)

Baker Place (family medicine/planning pediatrics)
Brentwood Village (internal medicine pain medicine)
Clarkson West (family medicine cardiology)
Durham Outpatient Center (houses a number of outpatient clinics/services)
Eagle Run (family medicine mental health)
Plattsmouth (internal medicine pediatrics)
Summit Plaza (family medicine cardiology)
Turner Park (internal medicine mental health)
UNMC Community Health Center (family planning midwifery mental health)
Village Pointe Specialties (ear nose throat pain medicine eye specialties)

COMPETITORS

CHI Health
Children's Hospital & Medical Center
Methodist Health System

HISTORICAL FINANCIALS

Company Type: Private

Income Statement

FYE: June 30

	REVENUE ($ mil.)	NET INCOME ($ mil.)	NET PROFIT MARGIN	EMPLOYEES
06/13	225	7	3.4%	1,200
06/12	218	(1)	—	—
06/11	219	5	2.7%	—
06/10	203	0	—	—
Annual Growth	3.4%	—	—	—

2013 Year-End Financials

Return on assets: 11.8%
Return on equity: 3.4%
Current ratio: 3.00
Cash ($ mil.): 38

USS POSCO INDUSTRIES

US and Korean steel manufacturing interests come together in the form of USS-POSCO Industries (UPI) a 50/50 joint venture between United States Steel (US Steel) and POSCO. The company operates a steel plant (formerly owned by US Steel) in Pittsburg Northern California. It manufactures flat-rolled steel sheets in various forms: cold-rolled steel galvanized steel and tinplate. In addition USS-POSCO churns out iron oxide which is used to make hard and soft ferrites. UPI sells its products to more than 150 customers in more than dozen states throughout the western US. End products include office furniture computer cabinets metal studs cans culverts and metal building materials.

Geographic Reach

The company markets its products primarily in the western US.

Operations

UPI's main product lines include cold rolled sheet galvanized sheet hot rolled pickled and oiled sheet and tin plate. It has the capacity to produce about 1.5 million tons of product per year.

Sales and Marketing

UPI ships steel products to more than 150 customers across North America. The company sells its products to a wide range of manufacturers whose end products include automotive parts computer cabinets culverts food packaging metal buildings metal studs and office furniture. About 1/3 of UPI's product line is tinplate for the canning industry.

Strategy

Its Korean co-owner supplied high quality raw materials for use at the plant. In order to stay competitive in the face of cheaper steel imports UPI jettisoned non-core product lines to focus on steel sheet and tin. However strong competition and poor market prices forced the company in 2011 to introduce furloughs at the plant and enforce temporary shutdowns of the facility.

Company Background

The company rebounded from a major fire in 2001. In 2010 UPI invested heavily in remediation measures to clean up soil and groundwater impacted by its plant activities.

US Steel teamed up with POSCO (then Pohang Iron & Steel Company) in 1986 as part of a major reorganization of the aging Pittsburg plant which first opened in 1910.

EXECUTIVES

Vice President Administration and Finance Treasurer, Alan (Al) Gardner
Senior Vice President, Sergey Korolev
Vice President Operations, Salvatore Sbranti

LOCATIONS

HQ: USS POSCO INDUSTRIES
900 LOVERIDGE RD, PITTSBURG, CA 945652808
Phone: 800 877-7672
Web: WWW.USSPOSCO.COM

PRODUCTS/OPERATIONS

Selected Steel Products

Cold Rolled Annealed
Hot Dipped Galvanized
Hot Rolled Pickled and Oiled
Tinplate

COMPETITORS

AK Steel Holding Corporation
ArcelorMittal USA
BlueScope Steel
Gerdau Ameristeel
Nucor
Steel Dynamics

HISTORICAL FINANCIALS
Company Type: Private

Income Statement
FYE: December 31

	REVENUE ($ mil.)	NET INCOME ($ mil.)	NET PROFIT MARGIN	EMPLOYEES
12/08	1,198	11	1.0%	759
12/07	998	(40)	—	—
12/06	1,034	14	1.4%	—
12/05	854	0	—	—
Annual Growth	11.9%	—	—	—

2008 Year-End Financials
Return on assets: 8.0%
Return on equity: 1.0%
Current ratio: 0.40
Cash ($ mil.): 1

UTAH HOUSING CORPORATION

Auditors: DELOITTE & TOUCHE LLP SALT L

LOCATIONS
HQ: UTAH HOUSING CORPORATION
2479 S LAKE PARK BLVD, WEST VALLEY CITY, UT 841208217
Phone: 801 902-8200
Web: WWW.B2B.UTAHHOUSINGCORP.ORG

HISTORICAL FINANCIALS
Company Type: Private

Income Statement
FYE: June 30

	ASSETS ($ mil.)	NET INCOME ($ mil.)	INCOME AS % OF ASSETS	EMPLOYEES
06/14	1,659	14	0.9%	77
06/13	1,596	7	0.5%	—
06/12	1,668	(0)	—	—
06/11	2,060	0	—	—
Annual Growth	(7.0%)	—	—	—

2014 Year-End Financials
Return on assets: —
Return on equity: 16.5%
Sales ($ mil): 86

UTAH STATE UNIVERSITY

Utah State University (USU) has more than 40 academic departments at colleges of agriculture arts business education and human services engineering science natural resources and humanities and social sciences. It offers more than 170 bachelor's degree programs and about 140 graduate degree programs. Biology elementary education mechanical and aerospace engineering and business administration are among the university's most popular majors. About 29000 students attend its main campus in northern Utah its three branch campuses or extension facilities located across the state. USU was established in 1888 as an agricultural college.
Geographic Reach

USU students hail from all 50 US states and some 80 international countries. The university's students have the opportunity to study abroad through partnerships with 140 other institutions located around the world. USU's main campuses or branch offices in Utah are located in Brigham City Logan San Juan Tooele and Uintah Basin.
Operations

USU has a student-to-faculty ratio of 18:1. Alumni of the university include Greg Carr founder of the Greg C. Carr Foundation and Charlie Denson former president of NIKE.
Financial Performance

Revenues increased at USU by 4% to some $340 million due to increased income from tuition and fees higher enrollment and increased state appropriations. The gain was offset by decreases in gifts grants and contracts. Net income fell 41% to $68 million due to higher operating expenses from salary benefit and other costs.
Strategy

To expand its facilities and meet growing student needs USU is adding a new school of business building and a new athletics center to its main campus. The university recently completed construction of a new $47 million agricultural building on the main campus as well as a new administration building on the USU Eastern campus. In addition USU is building a new distance education building on its Logan campus.

To further expand resources for students USU began offering a Master of Business Administration (MBA) program at the Brigham Young University's Idaho campus in 2013.

EXECUTIVES
Vice President Of Communications, Cade Robinson
Athletics Vice President, Corey Mikkelsen
Associate Vice President for Research, Jeff Broadbent

LOCATIONS
HQ: UTAH STATE UNIVERSITY
2400 OLD MAIN HL, LOGAN, UT 843222400
Phone: 435 797-1064
Web: WWW.USU.EDU

PRODUCTS/OPERATIONS

Selected Colleges
Caine College of the Arts
College of Agriculture
College of Engineering
College of Humanities and Social Sciences
College of Science
Emma Eccles Jones College of Education and Human Services
Jon M. Huntsman School of Business
S.J. & Jessie E. Quinney College of Natural Resources

HISTORICAL FINANCIALS
Company Type: Private

Income Statement
FYE: June 30

	REVENUE ($ mil.)	NET INCOME ($ mil.)	NET PROFIT MARGIN	EMPLOYEES
06/14	362	68	19.0%	6,000
06/13	350	44	12.7%	—
06/12	340	68	20.1%	—
06/11	328	0	—	—
Annual Growth	3.3%	—	—	—

2014 Year-End Financials
Return on assets: 1.7%
Return on equity: 19.0%
Current ratio: 0.70
Cash ($ mil.): 57

VALLEY MEDICAL FACILITIES INC.

Auditors: DELOITTE TAX LLP PITTSBURGH

LOCATIONS
HQ: VALLEY MEDICAL FACILITIES INC.
720 BLACKBURN RD, SEWICKLEY, PA 151431459
Phone: 724 728-7000
Web: WWW.HERITAGEVALLEY.ORG

HISTORICAL FINANCIALS
Company Type: Private

Income Statement
FYE: June 30

	REVENUE ($ mil.)	NET INCOME ($ mil.)	NET PROFIT MARGIN	EMPLOYEES
06/13	359	(1)	—	3,000
06/10	362	4	1.1%	—
06/09	432	7	1.8%	—
06/08	1,426	0	—	—
Annual Growth	—	—	—	—

2013 Year-End Financials
Return on assets: 15.7%
Return on equity: (-0.5%)
Current ratio: 0.50
Cash ($ mil.): 7

VALLEY PRESBYTERIAN HOSPITAL

LOCATIONS
HQ: VALLEY PRESBYTERIAN HOSPITAL
15107 VANOWEN ST, VAN NUYS, CA 914054597
Phone: 818 782-6600
Web: WWW.VALLEYPRES.ORG

HISTORICAL FINANCIALS
Company Type: Private

Income Statement
FYE: October 31

	REVENUE ($ mil.)	NET INCOME ($ mil.)	NET PROFIT MARGIN	EMPLOYEES
10/13	310	18	5.9%	1,600
10/12	318	25	7.9%	—
10/09	220	2	1.2%	—
10/08	185	0	—	—
Annual Growth	10.9%	—	—	—

2013 Year-End Financials
Return on assets: 16.7%
Return on equity: 5.9%
Current ratio: 0.80
Cash ($ mil.): 10

VALUE DRUG COMPANY

Value Drug Company sees a great deal of value in keeping independent pharmacies competitive. The company is a purchasing cooperative of hundreds of independent drugstores that provides wholesale pharmaceutical distribution services to its members primarily in the central Pennsylvania area. Its products include pharmaceuticals and non-prescription medications hospital and convalescent equipment health and beauty aids nutritional supplies and other health care-related products. The company works with some of the world's largest pharmaceutical makers. Value Drug was founded in 1934 and incorporated in 1936. The company is led by president Greg Drew a former Rite-Aid executive.

Operations

The company's private-label line includes nearly 1000 over-the-counter products. Value Drug participates in such retail initiatives as the federal 340B Drug Discount Program an adult immunization tracking program and competitive generic sourcing program OptiSource.

Geographic Reach

Value Drug is located in Pennsylvania and serves a market area covering 15 states.

EXECUTIVES

National Account Manager, Ellen Breitenbach
Auditors: DELOITTE & TOUCHE LLP PITTSBU

LOCATIONS

HQ: VALUE DRUG COMPANY
1 GOLFVIEW DR, ALTOONA, PA 166019398
Phone: 814 944-9316
Web: WWW.VALUEDRUGCO.COM

COMPETITORS

AmerisourceBergen	Kinray
Cardinal Health	McKesson
H. D. Smith Wholesale	Quality King
Drug	

HISTORICAL FINANCIALS

Company Type: Private

Income Statement

FYE: December 31

	REVENUE ($ mil.)	NET INCOME ($ mil.)	NET PROFIT MARGIN	EMPLOYEES
12/13	715	0	0.1%	107
12/09	751	0	0.0%	
12/08	732	0	0.0%	
12/07	1,599	0	—	
Annual Growth	(12.6%)	—	—	

2013 Year-End Financials

Return on assets: 10.5%   Cash ($ mil.): 1
Return on equity: 0.1%
Current ratio: 0.80

VANGUARD CHARITABLE ENDOWMENT PROGRAM

LOCATIONS

HQ: VANGUARD CHARITABLE ENDOWMENT PROGRAM
100 VANGUARD BLVD G19, MALVERN, PA 193552331
Phone: 888 383-4483
Web: WWW.VANGUARDCHARITABLE.ORG

Income Statement

FYE: June 30

	REVENUE ($ mil.)	NET INCOME ($ mil.)	NET PROFIT MARGIN	EMPLOYEES
06/13	1,117	608	54.4%	22
06/12	908	424	46.7%	
06/11	890	402	45.2%	
06/10	490	0	—	
Annual Growth	31.6%	—	—	

2013 Year-End Financials

Return on assets: —   Cash ($ mil.): 14
Return on equity: 54.4%
Current ratio: —

VASSAR BROTHERS HOSPITAL

Auditors: PRICEWATERHOUSECOOPERS LLP N

LOCATIONS

HQ: VASSAR BROTHERS HOSPITAL
45 READE PL, POUGHKEEPSIE, NY 126013990
Phone: 845 454-8500
Web: WWW.HEALTH-QUEST.ORG

HISTORICAL FINANCIALS

Company Type: Private

Income Statement

FYE: December 31

	REVENUE ($ mil.)	NET INCOME ($ mil.)	NET PROFIT MARGIN	EMPLOYEES
12/12	392	(0)	—	1,500
12/11	390	(12)	—	
12/07	317	10	3.3%	
12/06	287	0	—	
Annual Growth	5.3%	—	—	

2012 Year-End Financials

Return on assets: —   Cash ($ mil.): 13
Return on equity: (-0.1%)
Current ratio: 0.80

VASSAR COLLEGE INC

A cool nickname and certain heritage aren't enough to assure some students entrance into Vassar College. The highly selective school enrolls some 2400 students annually most of whom graduated in the top 20% of their high school class. It has a student-faculty ratio of 8:1 and a list of alumni that includes standouts in areas from business to philanthropy. Because Vassar has no core curriculum students may concentrate in a single discipline a multidisciplinary program or design an independent major. The only universal requirements for graduation are proficiency in a foreign language a freshman composition class and a quantitative class. Vassar was founded in 1861 as a women's school; it went coed in 1969.

Geographic Reach

From its campus in Poughkeepsie New York Vassar serves students globally. International students which comprise about 10% of its student body come from more than 50 countries. Typically juniors study for a year or semester in Vassar-sponsored programs in France Germany Ireland Italy Russia and Spain.

Operations

Vassar is considered one of the Seven Sisters seven women's liberal arts colleges founded in the northern US between 1837 and 1889. Besides Vassar they include Barnard Bryn Mawr Mount Holyoke Radcliffe Smith and Wellesley. Radcliffe is defunct and Vassar went co-ed; the rest remain women's schools.

With an annual cost of more than $49000 for tuition room and board and fees Vassar consistently ranks as one of the most expensive schools in the nation.

Strategy

As a way to further market itself and offer a place where military veterans can pick up an education Vassar in 2012 partnered with the Posse Foundation's Veterans Posse Program which is focused on boosting college attendance and graduation rates for military veterans at selective colleges and universities nationwide.

Sales and Marketing

Vassar sources its students from both public high schools (60%) and private schools (40%). For its tuition costs the college offers an impressive student-faculty ratio given its 290 faculty members.

Financial Performance

The New York college logged a 3% drop in revenue in fiscal 2012 as compared to 2011 due to decreases in net tuition fees room and board government grants and private gifts and grants. Net income for the same reporting period declined some 123%. Vassar points to non-operating activities for the drop attributable to decreases in investment returns and realized and unrealized gains spending on realized gains used to meet spending policy and increases in loss from adjustment for pension liability and post-retirement benefits changes other than net periodic benefits costs.

EXECUTIVES

Vice President For Finance and Administration, Robert (Bob) Walton
Associate Vice President of Alumnae i Affairs and Communications, Patricia (Pat) Lichtenberg
Treasurer, Carl Gaede
Auditors: PRICEWATERHOUSECOOPER LLP ALB

LOCATIONS

HQ: VASSAR COLLEGE INC
124 RAYMOND AVE BOX 12, POUGHKEEPSIE, NY 126040001
Phone: 845 437-7000
Web: WWW.ADMISSIONS.VASSAR.EDU

PRODUCTS/OPERATIONS

Selected Departments and Programs
Africana Studies Program
American Culture Program
Anthropology Department
Art Department
Asian Studies Program
Astronomy Department
Biology Department
Chemistry Department
Chinese and Japanese Department
Classics Department
Cognitive Science Program
College Courses
Computer Science Department
Dance Department
Drama (and Film) Department
Earth Science and Geography Department
Earth Science and Society Program
Economics Department
Education Department
English Department
Environmental Studies Program

Field Work Office
Film Department Drama and
French and Francophone Studies Department
Geography-Anthropology Program
Geography Department Earth Science and
German Studies Department
Hispanic Studies Department
History Department
Independent Program
Interdepartmental Courses
International Studies Program
Italian Department
Japanese Department Chinese and Jewish Studies
  Program
Latin American and Latino/a Studies Program
Mathematics Department
Media Studies Program
Medieval and Renaissance Studies Program
Music Department
Neuroscience and Behavior Program
Philosophy Department
Physical Education Department
Physics and Astronomy Department
Physics and Biochemistry Program
Political Science Department
Psychology Department
Religion Department
Russian Studies Department
Science Technology and Society Program
Self-Instructional Language Program
Sociology Department
Urban Studies Program
Victorian Studies Program
Women's Studies Program

HISTORICAL FINANCIALS
Company Type: Private

Income Statement
FYE: June 30

	REVENUE ($ mil.)	NET INCOME ($ mil.)	NET PROFIT MARGIN	EMPLOYEES
06/14	160	97	60.6%	974
06/13	175	103	58.7%	—
06/12	153	(33)	—	—
06/11	229	0	—	—
Annual Growth	(11.2%)	—	—	—

2014 Year-End Financials
Return on assets: 19.4%
Return on equity: 60.6%
Current ratio: —
Cash ($ mil.): 23

VCC LLC

LOCATIONS
HQ: VCC LLC
  600 LAS COLINAS BLVD E # 1525, IRVING, TX
  750395616
Phone: 501 376-0017
Web: WWW.VCCUSA.COM

HISTORICAL FINANCIALS
Company Type: Private

Income Statement
FYE: December 31

	REVENUE ($ mil.)	NET INCOME ($ mil.)	NET PROFIT MARGIN	EMPLOYEES
12/13	394	0	—	260
12/12	260	0	—	—
Annual Growth	51.7%	—	—	—

2013 Year-End Financials
Return on assets: 27.9%
Return on equity: —
Current ratio: 0.90
Cash ($ mil.): 18

VENTURE ELECTRICAL CONTRACTORS INC.

LOCATIONS
HQ: VENTURE ELECTRICAL CONTRACTORS INC.
  2110 PEWAUKEE RD STE 110, WAUKESHA, WI
  531882482
Phone: 262 542-2727
Web: WWW.VENTURE-ELECTRIC.COM

HISTORICAL FINANCIALS
Company Type: Private

Income Statement
FYE: December 31

	REVENUE ($ mil.)	NET INCOME ($ mil.)	NET PROFIT MARGIN	EMPLOYEES
12/13	16,837	68	0.4%	100
12/12*	16	181	1080.0%	—
06/10	4	0	7.4%	—
Annual Growth	668.5%	272.2%	—	—

*Fiscal year change

2013 Year-End Financials
Return on assets: 16.5%
Return on equity: 0.4%
Current ratio: 1.20
Cash ($ mil.): 518

VERST GROUP LOGISTICS INC.

Verst wants to be first when it comes to storing its customers' items. A warehousing and distribution specialist Verst Group Logistics maintains over 5 million sq. ft. of warehouse space. The company operates from facilities in the Cincinnati metropolitan area and in northern Kentucky. Verst Group Logistics uses its own trucking fleet to provide freight transportation services through subsidiary Zenith Logistics and a network of carriers to arrange long-distance transportation of customers' freight. It serves customers residing in the food and beverage retail and consumer products paper and automotive industries. William Verst the father of president and CEO Paul Verst founded the company in 1968.

EXECUTIVES
Vice President Information Technology, Brian Bockman
Vice President Packaging, Will Schretzman
Vice President It, Dennis Roell
Secretary Treasurer, James (Jamie) Stadtmiller

LOCATIONS
HQ: VERST GROUP LOGISTICS INC.
  300 SHORLAND DR, WALTON, KY 410949328
Phone: 859 485-1212
Web: WWW.VERSTGROUP.COM

COMPETITORS
DSC Logistics
GENCO Distribution System
Kenco Logistics Services
Ozburn-Hessey Logistics

HISTORICAL FINANCIALS
Company Type: Private

Income Statement
FYE: December 31

	REVENUE ($ mil.)	NET INCOME ($ mil.)	NET PROFIT MARGIN	EMPLOYEES
12/13	157	0	—	1,200
12/12	148	0	—	—
12/11	143	0	—	—
12/10	140	0	—	—
Annual Growth	4.0%	—	—	—

2013 Year-End Financials
Return on assets: 3.0%
Return on equity: —
Current ratio: 1.50
Cash ($ mil.): 5

VIKING YACHT COMPANY

Leif Eriksson's oceangoing Viking explorers could only dream of vessels like those made by the Viking Yacht Company. Viking Yacht can build more than 100 semi-custom fiberglass pleasure boats primarily used for sport fishing. About 90% of each yacht is made in-house. Its line of yachts vary in length from approximately 42 to 92 feet and include convertible and enclosed-bridge convertible vessels open sportfish models and a 52-foot sport yacht. The luxury boats are sold through a network of more than 40 dealers six of which are based outside the US. Founders and brothers Bob and Bill Healey own Viking Yacht Company.

Operations

Viking operates through several businesses and divisions. Atlantic Marine Electronics provides sales installation and service support for yacht electronics including navigation communication and entertainment systems equipment. Its Viking Yachting Center acts as a weather-protected storage area for boats up to 50 feet and provides full services to all brands of yachts including 250 deep-water slips a pool and pool house barbeque and picnic areas bathhouse fuel dock and nighttime security.

Palm Beach Towers designs and engineers aluminum tuna towers used aboard Viking yachts and other boats. In addition Palm Beach Towers produces fiberglass hardtops rod lockers and electronic boxes and other custom aluminum and fiberglass accessories. Palm Beach Towers has locations in New Jersey and Florida.

Sales and Marketing

The company has a sales network of waterfront locations across the US as well as in the Caribbean Central and South America Africa Asia Middle East and Australia.

Strategy

To attract additional customers Viking is focused on launching new models of yachts. It launched seven new models during 2011 and 2012 and in 2013 it launched sleek and sporty new generation 55 and 62 Convertibles ass had a 92 Convertible on the docket.

To help cut greenhouse gas emissions and control costs in 2012 Viking built a tri-generation power plant with six natural gas-fueled turbines at its New Jersey manufacturing facility enabling the company to produce its own electricity.

Company Background

Viking was founded in 1964 and has produced more than 4000 vessels.

EXECUTIVES

Vice President Sales, Joseph (Jo) Schwab
Vice President, John Kasinski, age 48
Auditors: ERNST & YOUNG LLP PHILADELPHI

LOCATIONS

HQ: VIKING YACHT COMPANY
ON THE BASS RIV RR 9, NEW GRETNA, NJ 08224
Phone: 609 296-6000
Web: WWW.VIKINGYACHTS.COM

PRODUCTS/OPERATIONS

Selected Models of Yachts
Enclosed Bridge Convertible
Motor Yachts
Open
Open Bridge Convertible
Sport Yacht

COMPETITORS

Brunswick Boat	Sea Fox Boats
Fountain Powerboat	Sea Ray Boats
Hatteras Yachts	Sunseeker
Marine Products Corp.	

HISTORICAL FINANCIALS

Company Type: Private

Income Statement				FYE: July 31
	REVENUE ($ mil.)	NET INCOME ($ mil.)	NET PROFIT MARGIN	EMPLOYEES
07/14	194	16	8.4%	775
07/13	154	10	6.7%	—
07/12	143	6	4.2%	—
07/11	142	0	—	—
Annual Growth 10.9%		—	—	—

2014 Year-End Financials

Return on assets: 4.0%
Return on equity: 8.4%
Current ratio: 0.80
Cash ($ mil.): 20

VILLANOVA UNIVERSITY IN THE STATE OF PENNSYLVANIA

The oldest and largest Roman Catholic institution of higher learning in Pennsylvania Villanova University offers more than 50 academic undergraduate programs at its six main colleges: Business Engineering Liberal Arts and Sciences Professional Studies and Nursing. The university also has a School of Law and it offers graduate programs in most of its disciplines. Villanova has an enrollment of more than 10730 full and part-time undergraduate and graduate students. It also reports a student-to-faculty ratio of 12:1. Average tuition is $45376 million per year.

Geographic Reach

Villanova is located on a 270-acre campus with 76 buildings located in Radnor Township in Delaware County Pennsylvania. It also operates a 30-acre conference center location in close proximity to the main campus. The university's enrollment includes students from most US states and 50 international countries.

Operations

While it is focused on providing a well-rounded Catholic-based liberal arts education to its students Villanova also strives to participate in the community of Philadelphia through outreach and service efforts. The school has 44 clubs and about 270 extracurricular activities and groups. In addition Villanova has some two dozen varsity sports offerings and prides itself on having produced about 60 Olympic athletes.

Student tuition and fees account for about two-thirds of sales. Other sources of income include auxiliary enterprises private gifts and grants endowment resources and government grants.

Financial Performance

Operating revenues in fiscal 2014 increased by 6% to $424.7 million on higher income from student tuition and fees private gifts and grants and other.

Strategy

The university has launched a long-term plan to upgrade the university's campus facilities. As part of the campus master plan in 2011 Villanova launched a $22.5 million project to enhance its landscape including adding aesthetic mobility and pedestrian solutions with the ultimate goal of making the campus vehicle-free. By 2013 the first two phases were completed with phase three efforts in progress including the redesign of the Alumni Quad. The university also plans to add more residence halls a performing arts center and retail and parking facilities.

In 2013 Villanova expanded its academic programs by adding new graduate programs in biochemical engineering and cybersecurity at the College of Engineering. In addition the School of Law opened a new center for law entrepreneurship and innovation as well as a clinic for interdisciplinary mental and physical health law.

Other strategic efforts include increasing the university endowment better defining its values and identity establishing national stature for scholarship and graduate offerings attracting high-quality students and revamping the undergraduate curriculum to enhance critical thinking and leadership skills among students.

In 2013 it launched a $600 million fundraising campaign aimed at cultivating academic innovation across its schools and colleges investing in recruiting and retaining quality teacher-scholars growing financial aid and student opportunities and continuing to improve the living-learning environment on Villanova's campus.

Company Background

Villanova was founded in 1842 by the friars of the Order of St. Augustine and named for St. Thomas of Villanova.

EXECUTIVES

Vp University Communication, Ann E Diebold
Vp University Advancement, Michael J (Mike) O'Neill
Assistant Vice President Annual Giving, HEATHER POTTS BROWN
Assoc Vice President For Development, Mary Mcrae
Associate Vice President Development Operations, Cathleen Parsons-nikolic
Assistant Vice President Athletics Development, George Kolb
Assistant Vice President, Christine Coleman
Nursing Director, Claire Devine
Vice President, Thomas (Thom) Southard
Associate Vice President for Facilities Management, Bob Morro
Vice President, PavanKumarRao Cheeti
First Vice President, John P (Jack) Kopesky
Vice President Of It, Steven Fugale
Vice President Communications, Christopher (Chris) Connors
Vice President For Student Life Art Gallery Dean, Teri O'Brien

Vice President Managed Services, David Henkin
Vice President, Michael (Mel) Carlone
Department Head, Wayne Bremser
Vice President, Seri Park
Vice President Of Technology, Emily Empel
Associate Vice President For Student Life, Kathleen Byrnes
Vice President, Brian Koller
Associate Vice President Instructnal Analysis, Robert (Bob) Devos
Executive Vice President, Christin Rodriguez
Vice President, Elizabeth Blunt
Co President, Dino Spadaccini
Vice President Of Human Resources, Ellen Lacorte
Vice President For Finance, KENNETH (Ken) VALOSKY
Vice President Student Life, John (Jack) Stack
Vice President Mission and Ministry, Barbara (Barb) Wall
Vice President Of Personnel, Lindsey Stinson
Vice President, Phaneendra Divakaruni
Associate Vice President Development Operations, Cathleen Nikolic
Vice Chair, Joseph V Topper, age 60
Secretary Treasurer, Douglas (Doug) Norton
Treasurer, Varun Dhanavantri
Treasurer, Blaise Sceski
Treasurer, Srikanth Marepalli
Secretary, Sri Kumar Kosaraju
Treasurer, Stephen (Steve) Tully
Secretary, Joan Davis
Board Member, George Pinchock
Treasurer, Nicole Perrelli
Executive Board Member, Rona Santos
Secretary, Maria Conway
Treasurer, Sue Stiner
Secretary, Anne Joyce
American Executive Committee Treasurer, Robert (Bob) Panis
Secretary to the Dean, Kathryn Johnson
Secretary, Molly Schreiber
Treasurer, Anne Hischar
Board Member, Jill Flanagan
Auditors: PRICEWATERHOUSECOOPERS LLP P

LOCATIONS

HQ: VILLANOVA UNIVERSITY IN THE STATE OF PENNSYLVANIA
800 E LANCASTER AVE, VILLANOVA, PA 190851603
Phone: 610 519-4500
Web: WWW.VILLANOVA.EDU

PRODUCTS/OPERATIONS

Selected Schools and Programs
Undergraduate
   College of Arts & Sciences
   College of Engineering
   College of Nursing
   College of Professional Studies
   Villanova School of Business
Graduate Studies
   Engineering
   Liberal Arts and Sciences
   Nursing
   School of Law
   Villanova School of Business
Other Offerings
   Continuing Studies
   Part-Time Studies

HISTORICAL FINANCIALS
Company Type: Private

Income Statement
FYE: May 31

	REVENUE ($ mil.)	NET INCOME ($ mil.)	NET PROFIT MARGIN	EMPLOYEES
05/14	424	152	35.9%	2,022
05/13	401	101	25.4%	—
05/12	385	(4)	—	—
05/11	378	0	—	—
Annual Growth	3.9%	—	—	—

2014 Year-End Financials
Return on assets: 3.0%
Return on equity: 35.9%
Current ratio: —
Cash ($ mil.): 158

VIRGINIA COMMUNITY COLLEGE SYSTEM OFFICE

LOCATIONS
HQ: VIRGINIA COMMUNITY COLLEGE SYSTEM OFFICE
101 N 14TH ST, RICHMOND, VA 232193665
Phone: 804 819-4901
Web: WWW.LFCC.EDU

HISTORICAL FINANCIALS
Company Type: Private

Income Statement
FYE: June 30

	REVENUE ($ mil.)	NET INCOME ($ mil.)	NET PROFIT MARGIN	EMPLOYEES
06/13*	544	97	18.0%	4,854
12/08	0	0	—	—
06/05	328	31	9.5%	—
06/04	326	0	—	—
Annual Growth	5.8%	—	—	—

*Fiscal year change

2013 Year-End Financials
Return on assets: 5.9%
Return on equity: 18.0%
Current ratio: 1.40
Cash ($ mil.): 245

VIRGINIA WEST UNIVERSITY FOUNDATION INC

The West Virginia University Foundation provides fund raising services and manages the assets of West Virginia University. The Foundation seeks support for faculty programs services equipment and facilities that the state of West Virginia might not be able to fund. The university founded the organization in 1954 as an independent non-profit corporation.

EXECUTIVES
VP Technology and Facilities, Mark Cottrill
VP Investments and Chief Investment Officer, Rick Kraich
COO CFO and Treasurer, Michael Augustine
President and CEO, Cindi Roth
Chairman, Robert L. Reynolds
Vice Chairman, Gary Pell
Auditors: DIXON HUGHES GOODMAN LLP MORG

LOCATIONS
HQ: VIRGINIA WEST UNIVERSITY FOUNDATION INC
1 WATERFRONT PL FL 7, MORGANTOWN, WV 265015978
Phone: 304 293-3708
Web: WWW.WVUF.ORG

HISTORICAL FINANCIALS
Company Type: Private

Income Statement
FYE: June 30

	ASSETS ($ mil.)	NET INCOME ($ mil.)	INCOME AS % OF ASSETS	EMPLOYEES
06/14	1,437	99	7.0%	70
06/13	1,245	75	6.1%	—
06/12	1,110	37	3.4%	—
06/11	1,085	0	—	—
Annual Growth	9.8%	—	—	—

2014 Year-End Financials
Return on assets: 2.6%
Return on equity: 57.4%
Sales ($ mil): 174

VIRGINIA WEST UNIVERSITY HOSPITALS INC

West Virginia University Hospitals (WVUH) has West Virginians covered. The health care system's 530-bed main campus includes the Ruby Memorial Hospital the WVU Children's Hospital and the behavioral health Chestnut Ridge Center as well as outpatient care centers. Other services include centers for eye and dental care cancer treatment and family medicine. WVUH's facilities serve as the primary teaching locations for the West Virginia University's health professions schools. Cheat Lake Physicians is the physicians group associated with the health system. WVUH is a member of the West Virginia United Health System.

Strategy
To increase its capacity for patient services WVUH launched a $230 million project to build a new tower addition at its main Ruby Memorial Hospital facility in 2012. The project will add about 115 general inpatient beds.

WVUH is also working to expand its community outreach capabilities and lower the cost of inpatient care through technology initiatives. The health system is adding a number of tele-health services including psychiatry and stroke programs that allow patients to communicate with doctors via video conferencing systems. These services especially help residents living in rural settings.

EXECUTIVES
Vice President Human Resources, Charlotte Bennett
Medical Director, Jeffery Carpenter
Medical Director, Leslie Willard

LOCATIONS
HQ: VIRGINIA WEST UNIVERSITY HOSPITALS INC
1 MEDICAL CENTER DR, MORGANTOWN, WV 26506
Phone: 304 598-4000
Web: WWW.WVUHEALTHCARE.COM

COMPETITORS
CAMC Health
HCA
West Penn Allegheny Health System

HISTORICAL FINANCIALS
Company Type: Private

Income Statement
FYE: December 31

	REVENUE ($ mil.)	NET INCOME ($ mil.)	NET PROFIT MARGIN	EMPLOYEES
12/13	703	97	13.8%	6,267
12/12	1,386	96	6.9%	—
12/06	0	0	—	—
12/05	0	0	—	—
Annual Growth	—	—	—	—

2013 Year-End Financials
Return on assets: 5.1%
Return on equity: 13.8%
Current ratio: 1.00
Cash ($ mil.): 12

VIRTUA MEMORIAL HOSPITAL BURLINGTON COUNTY INC

Virtua Memorial Hospital of Burlington County provides acute care to patients in southern New Jersey and the Philadelphia metropolitan area. Part of the Virtua Health network the hospital has more than 430 beds and is well-known for its women's and children's health services and stroke care. Other specialty programs include a sleep center cardiac rehabilitation diabetes treatment and wound care. Virtua Memorial provides a full range of cancer treatments through its collaboration with Philadelphia's Fox Chase Cancer Center and operates an in-hospital hospice center for terminally ill patients through a partnership with Samaritan Hospice.StrategyVirtua Memorial is part of Virtua Health's massive expansion plans which include technology upgrades through a partnership with GE. The health system is investing in new construction including a $9.5 million 13-bed pediatric pavilion scheduled to open on the Virtua Memorial campus in Mt. Holly New Jersey in the spring of 2013.

EXECUTIVES
Medical Records Director, Rudolf Santos
Secretary For Engineering, Cindy Derry

LOCATIONS
HQ: VIRTUA MEMORIAL HOSPITAL BURLINGTON COUNTY INC
175 MADISON AVE, MOUNT HOLLY, NJ 080602099
Phone: 609 267-0700
Web: WWW.VIRTUA.ORG

PRODUCTS/OPERATIONS

Selected Specialties
Cardiac care
Emergency care

General surgery
Maternal-fetal medicine
Obstetrics
Oncology
Orthopedics
Radiation oncology
Spine care
Stroke care

COMPETITORS

AtlantiCare
Atlantic Health
Crozer-Keystone Health System
Inspira Health Network
Kennedy Health System
Lourdes Health
Meridian Health
North Philadelphia Health System
Shore Memorial Hospital
The Cooper Health System
University of Pennsylvania Health System

HISTORICAL FINANCIALS

Company Type: Private

Income Statement

	REVENUE ($ mil.)	NET INCOME ($ mil.)	NET PROFIT MARGIN	EMPLOYEES
12/12	308	41	13.4%	1,450
12/08	328	25	7.9%	—
12/06	283	39	13.8%	—
12/05	0	0	—	—
Annual Growth	—	—	—	—

2012 Year-End Financials

Return on assets: 4.0%   Cash ($ mil.): —
Return on equity: 13.4%
Current ratio: 1.10

VIZIO INC.

VIZIO has done for HDTVs what Dell did for PCs and Southwest Airlines did for air travel: sell them for less. The company sells low-cost flat panel and plasma LCD HDTVs. It competes head-to-head with Japan's Sony and Samsung; its products however are made in China and Taiwan. VIZIO has logged large annual revenue gains by selling quality televisions for hundreds if not thousands of dollars less than its competitors. The company was founded by CEO William Wang in 2002 and initially its TVs were only sold at membership retailers such as Costco Wholesale BJ's Wholesale Club and Sam's Club. Since then it has extended its reach to discount retailers Wal-Mart and Sears. VIZIO entered the PC arena in 2012.

Operations

Best known for its TVs VIZIO also makes Blue-Ray disc players speakers headphones Internet routers and other consumer electronics products including PCs.

Financial Performance

One of America's largest private companies VIZIO ranG up an estimated $3.1 billion in sales in 2012. The bulk of the company's sales come from flat-screen TVs. Founder and CEO Wang owns the majority stake in VIZIO.

Strategy

With the market for flat TVs maturing VIZIO is working to become a diversified consumer electronics brand. To that end —and with home computers becoming an integral part of home entertainment systems —VIZIO entered the PC market in mid-2012 with a new line of laptops and desktops starting at about $890. By combining its entertainment know-how with the power of the latest Intel Core processors VIZIO hopes to set a new standard for the Windows experience. The line consists of the VIZIO Thin + Light Notebook and All-in-One PC. In a bid to enter the booming market for smartphones VIZIO is testing an Android-powered smartphone that was released in China in 2013.

Still VIZIO keeps innovating on its core HDTV product line. In 2014 it launched its new E-Series Full-Array LED backlit HDTV collection. It also debuted its 120-inch Reference Series Ultra HD Smart TV and sub-$1000 pricing on its 50-inch P-Series Ultra HD Smart TV at the Consumer Electronics Show in January. The TV maker entered after the market for smart TVs which are integrated with Internet functionality shipping its first model during the second half of 2011.

VIZIO controls the design and marketing of its products and partners with contract manufacturers to make TVs less expensively than its competitors. Its collaboration with AmTran Technology Co. based in Taipei has proven to be an integral part of the success of both VIZIO and AmTran. AmTran which has an ownership stake in VIZIO generates some 80% of its revenue from sales to VIZIO while VIZIO relies on AmTran as a supplier for most of its TVs.

VIZIO's low-cost business model and partnerships with high-volume retailers such as Wal-Mart has paid off for the company which was named the #1 shipper of LCD TVs in the US in 2009. Since 2002 VIZIO has sold more than 30 million TVs. To VIZIO having the top LCD TV in the US is a first step.

EXECUTIVES

Vice President Operations, Rob L Brinkman
CEO, William Wang
CFO, Kurt Binder
Senior Vice President Marketing, Bartholomew R Brown
National Account Manager, Stephanie Brandt
Vice President Sales and Marketing, Laynie Newsome
Vice President, Mark Nelson
Vice President Sales, Allen Powell
Vice President Of Support, Scott Patten
Vice President Direct Sales, Michelle Nguyen
Vice President Information Technology, Derrick Beard
Vice President Sales, Hernandez Paul

LOCATIONS

HQ: VIZIO INC.
 39 TESLA, IRVINE, CA 926184603
Phone: 949 428-2525
Web: WWW.VIZIO.COM

PRODUCTS/OPERATIONS

Selected Products
Cables and other accessories
Blue-ray disc players
HDTVs
HD home theater systems
Headphones
Internet routers
Personal computers
Tablet computers
Smartphones
Speakers

COMPETITORS

Acer	LG Electronics
Bose	Lenovo
Dell	Panasonic Corp
Funai Electric	Philips Electronics
Harman International	Pioneer Corporation
Hewlett-Packard	Samsung Electronics
Limited	Sony
Koss	Westinghouse

HISTORICAL FINANCIALS

Company Type: Private

Income Statement

FYE: December 31

	REVENUE ($ mil.)	NET INCOME ($ mil.)	NET PROFIT MARGIN	EMPLOYEES
12/08	2,006	10	0.5%	225
12/07	1,929	7	0.4%	—
12/06	671	1	0.2%	—
12/04	46	0	—	—
Annual Growth	155.8%	—	—	—

2008 Year-End Financials

Return on assets: 3.2%   Cash ($ mil.): 42
Return on equity: 0.5%
Current ratio: 0.90

VOLUNTEER ENERGY COOPERATIVE

In the strong tradition of volunteering in Tennessee Volunteer Energy Cooperative is voluntarily cooperating with its members to serve their energy needs. The distribution utility serves more than 109000 customers (who also own the cooperative) in 17 central and eastern Tennessee counties. It operates more than 9000 miles of power lines. Volunteer Energy purchases its power supply from the Tennessee Valley Authority. The company also provides metered natural gas and propane service and offers telecommunications (Internet access and long-distance phone) services. In addition Volunteer Energy offers its customer surge protection and security equipment.

The cooperative grows its customer base by about 2000 new accounts per year. It plans to add a number of electrical substations to keep pace with growing demand.

Volunteer Energy is governed by a board of 12 members who represent the 17 counties in its service area.

Higher rates and increased demand lifted the company's revenue and net income in 2011 despite the extra costs incurred by infrastructure damage caused by six tornados that ripped through the cooperative's service area in April 2011.

Volunteer Energy was formed as Meigs County Electric Membership Cooperative in 1935 largely at the prompting of Tennessee Agricultural Extension Agent for Meigs County Willis Shadow.

EXECUTIVES

Vice President Information Technology, Karen Zitek
Vice President Information Technology, Karen Davis
Auditors: HENDERSON HUTCHERSON & MCCULLO

LOCATIONS

HQ: VOLUNTEER ENERGY COOPERATIVE
 18359 STATE HIGHWAY 58 N, DECATUR, TN 373227825
Phone: 423 334-1020
Web: WWW.VEC.ORG

COMPETITORS

AGL Resources	Crestwood Equity
CenturyLink	

HISTORICAL FINANCIALS

Company Type: Private

Income Statement

FYE: June 30

	REVENUE ($ mil.)	NET INCOME ($ mil.)	NET PROFIT MARGIN	EMPLOYEES
06/14	244	12	5.1%	175
06/12	228	15	6.8%	—
06/11	235	13	5.5%	—
06/10	206	0	—	—
Annual Growth	4.3%	—	—	—

2014 Year-End Financials

Return on assets: 7.5%
Return on equity: 5.1%
Current ratio: 2.80

Cash ($ mil.): 33

W. DOUGLASS DISTRIBUTING LTD.

LOCATIONS

HQ: W. DOUGLASS DISTRIBUTING LTD.
325 E FOREST AVE, SHERMAN, TX 750908832
Phone: 903 893-1181
Web: WWW.DOUGLASSDIST.COM

HISTORICAL FINANCIALS

Company Type: Private

Income Statement

FYE: December 31

	REVENUE ($ mil.)	NET INCOME ($ mil.)	NET PROFIT MARGIN	EMPLOYEES
12/13	428	1	0.3%	130
12/12	422	0	0.1%	—
12/11	368	1	0.4%	—
12/10	275	0	—	—
Annual Growth	15.9%	—	—	—

2013 Year-End Financials

Return on assets: 3.3%
Return on equity: 0.3%
Current ratio: 0.80

Cash ($ mil.): —

W. K. KELLOGG FOUNDATION

Charitable grants from W.K. Kellogg Foundation are grrrrrrrrreat! Founded in 1930 by cereal industry pioneer Will Keith Kellogg the foundation provides more than $300 million in grants annually to programs focused on youth and education health food systems and rural development and philanthropy and volunteerism. About two-thirds of its grants go to initiatives in the US (mostly in Michigan Mississippi and New Mexico) although it also serves others through grants in Latin America Mexico the Caribbean Brazil and South Africa. The work of the W.K. Kellogg Foundation is supported by a related trust; together they have assets of more than $9 billion —mainly in Kellogg Company stock.

With a rise in Kellogg Company stock prices throughout 2009 the foundation stands to benefit. Although they share a founder and a home city the Kellogg Foundation and the Kellogg Company are governed independently.

Charity really does begin at home for the W.K. Kellogg Foundation which allocated about 18% of its US grant money to activities in Michigan in 2008.

W.K. Kellogg Foundation is guided by its founder's desire "to help people help themselves" and prefers to support programs that offer long-term solutions rather than quick handouts.

HISTORY

Born in 1860 Will Keith Kellogg began his career with jobs as a stock boy and traveling broom salesman. He also worked as a clerk (and later bookkeeper and manager) at the Battle Creek Sanitarium a renowned homeopathic hospital where his older brother John Harvey Kellogg was physician-in-chief. The brothers' experiments to improve vegetarian diets led to a happy accident in 1894 that resulted in the first wheat flakes. In 1906 W.K. Kellogg started the Battle Creek Toasted Corn Flake Company. Through marketing genius and innovative products Kellogg's company became a leader in the industry.

A philanthropist by inclination Kellogg established the Fellowship Corporation in 1925 to build an agricultural school and a bird sanctuary as well as to set up an experimental farm and a reforestation project. He also gave $3 million to hometown causes such as the Ann J. Kellogg School for disabled children and for the construction of an auditorium a junior high school and a youth recreation center.

After attending a White House Conference on Child Health and Protection Kellogg established the W.K. Kellogg Child Welfare Foundation in 1930. A few months later he broadened the focus of the charter and renamed the institution the W.K. Kellogg Foundation. That year the foundation began its landmark Michigan Community Health Project (MCHP) which opened public health departments in counties once thought too small and poor to sustain them. In 1934 Kellogg placed more than $66 million in Kellogg Company stock and other investments in a trust to fund his foundation.

During WWII the foundation expanded its programming to Latin America funding advanced schooling for dentists physicians and other health professionals. After the war it broadened its programming to include agriculture to help war-torn Europe. It funded projects in Germany Iceland Ireland Norway and the UK. Following Kellogg's death in 1951 the organization began providing support for graduate programs in health and hospital administration as well as for rural leadership and community colleges.

During the 1970s the foundation lent its support to the growing volunteerism movement and to aiding the disadvantaged with a special emphasis on programs for minorities. A review of operations in the late 1970s led the Kellogg Foundation to reassert its emphasis on health education agriculture and leadership. The foundation also expanded its programs to southern Africa.

In 1986 the Kellogg Foundation began funding the Rural America Initiative —a series of 28 projects meant to develop leadership train local government officials and revitalize rural areas. William Richardson became president and CEO of the foundation in 1995 leaving his post as president of The Johns Hopkins University. Also during the 1990s the foundation supported the Community-Based Public Health Initiative which assisted universities in educating public health professionals by

presenting community-based approaches to students and faculty.

In 1998 the organization announced a five-year $55 million plan to bring health care to the nation's poor and homeless. Also that year it gave Portland State University a $600000 grant to develop its Institute for Nonprofit Management. In 1999 the Kellogg Foundation started its first geographically based program pledging $15 million in grants for development of Mississippi River Delta communities in Arkansas Louisiana and Mississippi. In 2001 the foundation pledged an additional $20 million to support economic growth in the region through the Emerging Markets Partnership. In 2002 the Kellogg Foundation awarded about $2 million in grants to SPARK (Supporting Partnerships to Assure Ready Kids) to help prepare low-income children for school. The organization funded a national campaign to improve men's health in 2003.

After a decade as president and CEO Richardson stepped down in 2005. Sterling Speirn who had led the San Mateo California-based Peninsula Community Foundation since 1990 took over as president and CEO of the Kellogg Foundation in January 2006.

EXECUTIVES

Vice President Communications, Joanne Krell
Vice President For Programs, Dan Moore
Vp Integrated Services, Cindy Smith
Vice President Finance Treasurer Foundation Officer, Donald (Don) Williamson
Vice President for Programs, Rick Foster

LOCATIONS

HQ: W. K. KELLOGG FOUNDATION
1 MICHIGAN AVE E, BATTLE CREEK, MI 490174012
Phone: 269 968-1611
Web: WWW.WKKF.ORG

HISTORICAL FINANCIALS

Company Type: Private

Income Statement

FYE: August 31

	ASSETS ($ mil.)	NET INCOME ($ mil.)	INCOME AS % OF ASSETS	EMPLOYEES
08/13	428	92	21.5%	210
08/12	442	(106)	—	—
08/11	465	(13)	—	—
08/09	442	0	—	—
Annual Growth	(0.8%)	—	—	—

2013 Year-End Financials

Return on assets: 2.0%
Return on equity: 28.0%

Sales ($ mil): 329

W.S. BADCOCK CORPORATION

W.S. Badcock furnishes homes down in Dixie and beyond. As one of the largest privately-owned furniture retailers in the US the company sells furniture for every room in the house. It sells its furniture and accessories through more than 300 stores that operate under the banner names Badcock Home Furnishing Centers and Badcock &more. Aside from its e-commerce site Badcock's stores network extends to nearly 10 southeastern states. Stores also carry appliances lawn equipment electronics mattresses rugs bedding lighting wall art and other decorative accessories. The company was founded by Henry S. Badcock in 1904 as a general mercantile store. Today it is in its fourth generation of family management.

Geographic Reach

Headquartered in Mulberry Florida with more than 1200 corporate employees W.S. Badcock operates primarily in the southeastern US. Its operations span the states of Georgia Alabama Mississippi Tennessee and the Carolinas expanding into Virginia West Virginia and Kentucky.

Strategy

Through the company's dealer business model more than 80% of Badcock's stores are individually owned. As part of the model the company does not require a franchise fee but instead consigns merchandise to the dealers. As opposed to the typical franchise system startup this consignment method aims to allow for a quicker startup along with the benefits of business ownership.

Already established in half a dozen states Badcock has been expanding its store network in Virginia Kentucky and West Virginia. Despite a slowdown in its expansion plans amid the recession and downturn in furniture retailing the company aims to grow its stores network again throughout the Southeast.

EXECUTIVES

Vice President Corporate Administration, Robert (Bob) Burnette

Vice President Purchasing and International Logistics, Greg Anthony Brinkman

Vice President Human Resources, Lori Walsh

Vice President, Dave Gonyea

Vice President Retail Operations, Derrick Taylor

Vice President Of Merchandising, Cathy Allen

Executive Vice President Of Marketing, Bill Daughtrey

Vice President, Jan Baher

Executive Vice President Retail Operations, Bill Pou Jr

Auditors: KPMG LLP ORLANDO FL

LOCATIONS

HQ: W.S. BADCOCK CORPORATION
205 NW 2ND ST, MULBERRY, FL 338602405
Phone: 863 425-4921
Web: WWW.BADCOCK.COM

PRODUCTS/OPERATIONS

Selected Products
Accessories
Appliances
Electronics
Furniture
Mattresses

COMPETITORS

Aaron's Inc.	Ethan Allen
Ashley Furniture	Havertys
Baer's Furniture	Klaussner Furniture
Bassett Furniture	La-Z-Boy
City Furniture	Rooms To Go
El Dorado Furniture	Sealy

HISTORICAL FINANCIALS

Company Type: Private

Income Statement				FYE: June 30
	REVENUE ($ mil.)	NET INCOME ($ mil.)	NET PROFIT MARGIN	EMPLOYEES
06/14	518	11	2.3%	1,000
06/13	463	6	1.5%	—
06/12	455	12	2.6%	—
06/11	431	0	—	—
Annual Growth	6.3%	—	—	—

2014 Year-End Financials
Return on assets: 8.2%   Cash ($ mil.): 1
Return on equity: 2.3%
Current ratio: 3.10

WABASH VALLEY POWER ASSOCIATION INC

Auditors: DELOITTE & TOUCHE LLP INDIANA

LOCATIONS

HQ: WABASH VALLEY POWER ASSOCIATION INC
722 N HIGH SCHOOL RD, INDIANAPOLIS, IN 462143756
Phone: 317 481-2800
Web: WWW.WVPA.COM

HISTORICAL FINANCIALS

Company Type: Private

Income Statement				FYE: December 31
	REVENUE ($ mil.)	NET INCOME ($ mil.)	NET PROFIT MARGIN	EMPLOYEES
12/13	739	19	2.6%	65
12/10	750	14	1.9%	—
12/09	674	18	2.7%	—
12/08	1,335	0	—	—
Annual Growth	—	—	—	—

2013 Year-End Financials
Return on assets: 13.8%   Cash ($ mil.): 86
Return on equity: 2.6%
Current ratio: 1.10

WADA FARMS MARKETING GROUP LLC

The Wada folks have heard absolutely all the Mr. Potato Head jokes known to mankind; still they press resolutely on growing packing and supplying Idaho potatoes all of us meat-and-potatoes folks. And in addition to everyone's favorite starchy tuber Wada Farms Potatoes does the same with sweet potatoes and onions. It also offers value-added items such as Easy-Bakers and Easy-Steamers —potatoes packaged in special plastic that can be cooked right in their packaging. The Idaho company cultivates more than 30000 acres of farmland and operates a 140000-sq.-ft. processing facility. Wada's customers include retail food food wholesaler and foodservice companies throughout the US.

Through its Wada Farms Marketing Group the company has an exclusive marketing agreement for all potatoes (white and sweet) and onions sold under the Dole label in the US. It has been a Wal-Mart supplier for more than 15 years.

Wada formed a relationship with the Shoshone Bannock Tribe and in 2009 the company began growing more than 13000 acres of grain and potatoes on the Shoshone Bannock Tribe Reservation near Blackfoot Idaho.

EXECUTIVES

Vice President of Sales, Joe Esta
Auditors: VANORDEN LUND & CANNON PLLC

LOCATIONS

HQ: WADA FARMS MARKETING GROUP LLC
2155 PROVIDENCE WAY, IDAHO FALLS, ID 834044951
Phone: 208 542-2898
Web: WWW.WADAFARMS.COM

PRODUCTS/OPERATIONS

Selected Produce
Onions
  Red
  Sweet
  White
  Yellow
Potatoes
  Fingerling
  Idaho
  Red
  Red skin yellow flesh
  Russets
  Sweet
  White
  Yellow

COMPETITORS

Agrow Fresh Produce	JR Simplot
Appleton Produce	Jones Produce
Chiquita Brands	Larsen Farms
Fresh Del Monte Produce	MountainKing Potatoes
	Nonpareil Corporation
Idaho Fresh-Pak	O' Leary Potato
Idaho Supreme Potatoes	

HISTORICAL FINANCIALS

Company Type: Private

Income Statement				FYE: December 31
	REVENUE ($ mil.)	NET INCOME ($ mil.)	NET PROFIT MARGIN	EMPLOYEES
12/13	181	3	1.7%	30
12/12	165	1	1.2%	—
12/11	201	2	1.0%	—
12/10	150	0	—	—
Annual Growth	6.3%	—	—	—

2013 Year-End Financials
Return on assets: 8.6%   Cash ($ mil.): 2
Return on equity: 1.7%
Current ratio: 1.40

WAKE COUNTY PUBLIC SCHOOL SYSTEM

Auditors: CHERRY BEKAERT & HOLLAND LLP

LOCATIONS

HQ: WAKE COUNTY PUBLIC SCHOOL SYSTEM
5625 DILLARD DR, CARY, NC 275189226
Phone: 919 431-7343
Web: WWW.WCPSS.NET

HISTORICAL FINANCIALS
Company Type: Private

Income Statement
FYE: June 30

	REVENUE ($ mil.)	NET INCOME ($ mil.)	NET PROFIT MARGIN	EMPLOYEES
06/10	1,224	13	1.1%	17,000
06/09	1,425	(7)	—	—
Annual Growth	(14.1%)	—	—	—

2010 Year-End Financials
Return on assets: 2.1%
Return on equity: 1.1%
Current ratio: 1.00
Cash ($ mil.): 91

WAKE FOREST BAPTIST MEDICAL CENTER

Auditors: DIXON HUGHES GOODMAN LLP CHAR

LOCATIONS
HQ: WAKE FOREST BAPTIST MEDICAL CENTER
MEDICAL CENTER BLVD, WINSTON SALEM, NC
271570001
Phone: 336 713-8000
Web: WWW.WAKEHEALTH.EDU

HISTORICAL FINANCIALS
Company Type: Private

Income Statement
FYE: June 30

	REVENUE ($ mil.)	NET INCOME ($ mil.)	NET PROFIT MARGIN	EMPLOYEES
06/10	967	55	5.8%	7,612
06/09	992	(126)	—	—
Annual Growth	(2.5%)	—	—	—

2010 Year-End Financials
Return on assets: —
Return on equity: 5.8%
Current ratio: 0.40
Cash ($ mil.): 85

WAKEFERN FOOD CORP.

Grocery stores getting supplies from this co-op may be on the "Rite" track. Wakefern Food is the largest member-owned wholesale distribution cooperative in the US supplying groceries and other merchandise to more than 250 supermarkets under the ShopRite and The Fresh Grocer banners in New Jersey New York Connecticut Delaware Maryland Pennsylvania and Virginia. It also operates more than 50 PriceRite stores in these states plus Rhode Island and Massachusetts. Beyond supplying its member-owned stores Wakerfern distributes products to other supermarkets across the northeastern US and Bermuda. Founded by seven grocers in 1946 the coop now boasts 50 members 70000-plus employees and over $15 billion in annual sales.

Operations

Wakefern Food supplies retail and wholesale members mostly in the Northeast US. PriceRite a subsidiary of Wakefern Food and its nearly 50 supermarkets offer over 500 grocery items at dis-counted prices such as fresh fruits and vegetables breads prepackaged meat and seafood kosher products and national brands. Stores average about 35000 square feet in size which are smaller than traditional supermarkets. While the vast majority of ShopRite brand stores are member owned subsidiary ShopRite Supermarkets Inc operates nearly 35 company-owned stores.Sales and Marketing

The coop added its 50th member The Fresh Grocer in July 2013. Outside of its members the company also supplies grocery stores like Saker ShopRite (New Jersey) Village Super Market (New Jersey and Pennsylvania) and Inserra Supermarkets (New York and New Jersey).

Financial Performance

Wakern Food's revenues have been rising over the past several years thanks to new member additions and their store openings.The company's retail sales rose 4% to a record $14.7 billion in fiscal 2014 (ended September 27) thanks to the addition of six new ShopRite stores five new PriceRite discount supermarkets and six new The Fresh Grocer stores over the course of the year. The company also continued to expand its ShopRite from Home services store reach which would be provided from a total of 214 of its stores.

Strategy

Like other grocery wholesalers Wakefern Food's success depends on its ability to distribute goods at the lowest possible cost to its customers meaning the company focuses on keeping expenses low and improving efficiencies throughout its supply operation. But as a member-owned cooperative the company differs from other wholesalers such as Nash-Finch in that its primary focus is on its member stores. Wakefern Food also has the added responsibility of promoting its ShopRite retail chain and helping its member retailers expand the chain's footprint.

The ShopRite chain boasts a loyal following in its core markets but the supermarkets have been feeling the pinch from rivals in the price-competitive grocery business. The company is especially feeling pressure from non-supermarket chains such as Wal-Mart CVS Health and Wawa. To help boost customer loyalty Wakefern has turned to new technology in the form of mobile applications (developed in partnership with technology firm MyWebGrocer) for the Apple iPhone that allow users to get alerts about weekly store specials in their area. The company also rolled out an online pharmacy where customers can place orders through the Internet.

Company BackgroundWakefern Food announced in 2012 it was supplying New York-based Food Bazaar stores which had supermarkets in New York New Jersey and Connecticut. Wakefern will supply ShopRite private label brands along with non-private labels such as dairy frozen food grocery nonfoods and specialty products.

HISTORY

Company BackgroundWakefern Food was founded in 1946 by seven New York- and New Jersey-based grocers: Louis Weiss Sam and Al Aidekman Abe Kesselman Dave Fern Sam Garb and Albert Goldberg. The company got its name by taking the first letters of the last names of five of the original founders (Weiss Sam and Al Aidekman Kesselman and Fern). Like many cooperatives the association sought to lower costs by increasing its buying power as a group.

They each put in $1000 and began operating a 5000-sq.-ft. warehouse often putting in double time to keep both their stores and the warehouse running. The shopkeepers' collective buying power proved valuable enabling the grocers to stock many items at the same prices as their larger competitors.

In 1951 Wakefern members began pooling their resources to buy advertising space. A common store name —ShopRite —was chosen and each week co-op members met to decide which items would be sale priced. Within a year membership had grown to over 50. Expansion became a priority and in the mid-1950s co-op members united in small groups to take over failed supermarkets. One such group called the Supermarkets Operating Co. (SOC) was formed in 1956. Within 10 years it had acquired a number of failed stores remodeled them and given them the ShopRite name.

During the late 1950s sales at ShopRite stores slumped after Wakefern decided to buck the supermarket trend of offering trading stamps (which could then be exchanged for gifts) figuring that offering the stamps would ultimately lead to higher food prices. The move initially drove away customers but Wakefern cut grocery prices across the board and sales returned. The company did embrace another supermarket trend: stocking stores with nonfood items.

The co-op was severely shaken in 1966 when SOC merged with General Supermarkets a similar small group within Wakefern becoming Supermarkets General Corp. (SGC). SGC was a powerful entity with 71 supermarkets 10 drugstores six gas stations a wholesale bakery and a discount department store. Many Wakefern members opposed the merger and attempted to block the action with a court order. By 1968 SGC had beefed up its operations to include department store chains as well as its grocery stores. In a move that threatened to break Wakefern SGC broke away from the co-op and its stores were renamed Pathmark.

Wakefern not only weathered the storm it grew under the direction of chairman and CEO Thomas Infusino elected shortly after the split. The co-op focused on asserting its position as a seller of low-priced products. Wakefern developed private-label brands including the ShopRite brand. In the 1980s members began operating larger stores and adding more nonfood items to the ShopRite product mix. With its number of superstores on the rise and facing increased competition from club stores in 1992 Wakefern opened a centralized nonfood distribution center in New Jersey.

In 1995 30-year Wakefern veteran Dean Janeway was elected president of the co-op. The company debuted its ShopRite MasterCard co-branded with New Jersey's Valley National Bank in 1996. The following year the co-op purchased two of its customers' stores in Pennsylvania then threatened to close them when contract talks with the local union deteriorated. In 1998 Wakefern settled the dispute then sold the stores.

The company partnered with Internet bidding site Priceline in 1999 offering customers an opportunity to bid on groceries and then pick them up at ShopRite stores. Big V Wakefern's biggest customer filed for Chapter 11 bankruptcy protection in 2000 and said it was ending its distribution agreement with the co-op. In July 2002 however Wakefern's ShopRite Supermarkets subsidiary acquired all of Big V's assets for approximately $185 million in cash and assumed liabilities.

Infusino retired in May 2005 after 35 years with Wakefern Food. He was succeeded by former vice chairman Joseph Colalillo. The cooperative added to its footprint in 2007 when it acquired about 10 underperforming retail locations from Stop & Shop. The stores located mostly in South Jersey were rebranded under the ShopRite banner.

EXECUTIVES
Vice President Information Services Di, Alan (Al) Aront

Senior Vice President Technology Digital Innovation E Commerce And Wholesale, Natan Tabak

Vice President Deli And Seafood, Terry Sharkey

Vice President Compliance And Risk Management, Allison Berger

Vice President Of Production, Larry Kurz

Executive Vice President Of Retail Operations, Jason Ravitz

Vice President Advertising, Karen Gozzi

Vice President Quality Assurance, Mike Ambrosio

Vice President of LP, Steve Hoptay

Vice President Finance, Tom Cummiskey

Vice President Finance, Neil Falcone

Vice President Engineering And Purchasing, Dennis Daniels

Pharmacy Manager, Muhammed Khan

Vice President, Peter (Pete) Rolandelli

Treasurer, Doug Wille

Treasurer, Lawrence Inserra

Auditors: KPMG LLP SHORT HILLS NEW JER

LOCATIONS

HQ: WAKEFERN FOOD CORP.
5000 RIVERSIDE DR, KEASBEY, NJ 088321209
Phone: 908 527-3300
Web: WWW.WAKEFERN.COM

PRODUCTS/OPERATIONS

2012 Corporate Stores

	No.
PriceRite	48
ShopRite	40
Total	**88**

COMPETITORS

A&P	Krasdale Foods
Acme Markets	Pathmark Stores
Bozzuto's	SUPERVALU
C&S Wholesale	Stop & Shop
CVS	Wal-Mart
Hannaford Bros.	Wawa Inc.
IGA	

HISTORICAL FINANCIALS

Company Type: Private

Income Statement
FYE: September 28

	REVENUE ($ mil.)	NET INCOME ($ mil.)	NET PROFIT MARGIN	EMPLOYEES
09/13	11,455	0	0.0%	3,500
09/12*	11,010	5	0.0%	—
10/11	10,325	5	0.0%	—
09/08	8,396	0	—	—
Annual Growth	**6.4%**	—	—	—

*Fiscal year change

2013 Year-End Financials

Return on assets: —
Return on equity: —
Current ratio: 0.10

Cash ($ mil.): 129

WALSH BROTHERS INCORPORATED

This pair of Boston brothers has been building Beantown for more than a century. Walsh Brothers Incorporated a construction management and contracting company has worked on such iconic projects as Boston's Fenway Park and Faneuil Hall. The firm specializes in building cultural educational medical and research facilities throughout New England. It also offers historic renovation services and has refurbished places such as the Boston Symphony Orchestra and New England Conservatory of Music. Clients have included Harvard University Dana-Faber Cancer Institute Amgen Novartis and Proctor & Gamble. Founded in 1901 by brothers James and Thomas Walsh the company is now owned and led by the Walsh family.

Auditors: FEELEY & DRISCOLL PC NASHUA

LOCATIONS

HQ: WALSH BROTHERS INCORPORATED
210 COMMERCIAL ST, BOSTON, MA 021091463
Phone: 617 878-4800
Web: WWW.WALSHBROTHERS.COM

COMPETITORS

Clark Construction Group	Engelberth Construction
Commodore Builders	Gilbane
Cutler Associates	Morganti
Dimeo Construction	Shawmut Design and Construction
E.A. Colangeli Construction	Suffolk Construction

HISTORICAL FINANCIALS

Company Type: Private

Income Statement
FYE: December 31

	REVENUE ($ mil.)	NET INCOME ($ mil.)	NET PROFIT MARGIN	EMPLOYEES
12/09	408	6	1.5%	—
12/08	545	9	1.7%	—
12/07	383	0	0.0%	—
Annual Growth	**3.3%**	**4300**	**1.7%**	—

2009 Year-End Financials

Return on assets: 19.0%
Return on equity: 1.5%
Current ratio: 1.10

Cash ($ mil.): 22

WALSH CONSTRUCTION COMPANY

Auditors: WOLF & COMPANY LLP OAKBROOK

LOCATIONS

HQ: WALSH CONSTRUCTION COMPANY
929 W ADAMS ST, CHICAGO, IL 606073021
Phone: 312 563-5400
Web: WWW.WALSHCONSTRUCTIONCO.COM

HISTORICAL FINANCIALS

Company Type: Private

Income Statement
FYE: December 31

	REVENUE ($ mil.)	NET INCOME ($ mil.)	NET PROFIT MARGIN	EMPLOYEES
12/10	1,627	35	2.2%	3,000
12/09	1,711	56	3.3%	—
Annual Growth	**(4.9%)**	**(35.8%)**	—	—

2010 Year-End Financials

Return on assets: 12.0%
Return on equity: 2.2%
Current ratio: 1.30

Cash ($ mil.): 281

WALTON CONSTRUCTION COMPANY LLC

LOCATIONS

HQ: WALTON CONSTRUCTION COMPANY LLC
2 COMMERCE CT, NEW ORLEANS, LA 701233225
Phone: 504 733-2212

HISTORICAL FINANCIALS

Company Type: Private

Income Statement
FYE: December 31

	REVENUE ($ mil.)	NET INCOME ($ mil.)	NET PROFIT MARGIN	EMPLOYEES
12/08	695	0	—	700
12/07	626	0	—	—
12/06	0	0	—	—
12/05	0	0	—	—
Annual Growth	—	—	—	—

2008 Year-End Financials

Return on assets: 15.8%
Return on equity: —
Current ratio: 1.20

Cash ($ mil.): 4

WALTON ELECTRIC MEMBERSHIP CORPORATION

Good night John-Boy. This Walton family serves more than 118400 residential agricultural commercial and industrial customers in northeastern Georgia. The Walton Electric Membership Corporation (Walton EMC) operates 6840 miles of power lines spanning across all or portions of ten counties (Athens-Clarke Barrow DeKalb Greene Gwinnett Morgan Newton Oconee Rockdale and Walton). Subsidiary Walton EMC Natural Gas competes in the state's deregulated retail gas supply market and has about 64000 customers. Other operations include security systems installation and monitoring appliance sales and rebates and outdoor lighting services.

Like other energy co-ops Walton EMC is pushing energy conservation with its members in order to avoid wasteful energy use. This includes customer education tips for saving power (improving attic insulation turning down refrigerator thermostats using energy-efficient light bulbs) as well as the use of smart meters to reduce cooperative overhead. This strategy allows the co-op to continue offering some of the state's lowest electric rates.

Its Energy Solutions segment led by Walton EMC Natural Gas also offers the co-op an additional source of revenues and customer interaction beyond its core electric distribution business. In 2011 Walton EMC Natural Gas won the J.D Power and Associates' award for "highest in customer satisfaction" among retail natural gas providers in Georgia.

Extreme winter and summer weather temperatures spiked demand and lifted Walton EMC's revenues and gross margins in 2010.

Formed in 1936 as part of a nationwide drive to bring affordable electricity to rural areas Walton EMC is a not-for-profit cooperative owned by the members it serves.

EXECUTIVES

President CEO, Ronnie Lee
SVP Corporate Services, Russell DeLong
SVP Engineering and Operations, Ron Marshall
Executive Assistant, Kathy Joiner
Director Safety and Training, Larry Thompson
Communications Coordinator, Greg Brooks
EMC Security, Michael Morton
Director Natural Gas Operations, Allen Powers
VP Power Supply, Robert Rentfrow
Director Marketing and Member Services, Howard Turner
VP Finance, Marsha Shumate
Administrative Assistant, Debra Jackson
Account Executive, Keith Taylor
Account Executive, Scott Walker
Director, Warren Few
Director, Bud Wiley
Director, Jim Whitley
Director, Tommy Adcock
Director, Bobby Williams
Director, Sam Simonton
Director, Dan Chelko
Director, Johnny Allgood

LOCATIONS

HQ: WALTON ELECTRIC MEMBERSHIP CORPORATION
842 HIGHWAY 78 NW, MONROE, GA 306554475
Phone: 770 267-2505
Web: WWW.WALTONEMC.COM

COMPETITORS

AGL Resources   Piedmont Natural Gas
Georgia Power   SCANA

HISTORICAL FINANCIALS
Company Type: Private

Income Statement
FYE: December 31

	REVENUE ($ mil.)	NET INCOME ($ mil.)	NET PROFIT MARGIN	EMPLOYEES
12/13	243	0	—	273
12/09	227	6	2.7%	—
12/08	215	17	8.0%	—
12/07	212	0	—	—
Annual Growth	2.3%	—	—	—

2013 Year-End Financials
Return on assets: 12.1%   Cash ($ mil.): 1
Return on equity: —
Current ratio: 1.60

WALTON FAMILY FOUNDATION INC

LOCATIONS

HQ: WALTON FAMILY FOUNDATION INC
125 W CENTRAL AVE RM 218, BENTONVILLE, AR 727125248
Phone: 479 273-5605
Web: WWW.WALTONFAMILYFOUNDATION.ORG

HISTORICAL FINANCIALS
Company Type: Private

Income Statement
FYE: December 31

	REVENUE ($ mil.)	NET INCOME ($ mil.)	NET PROFIT MARGIN	EMPLOYEES
12/09	740	368	49.8%	7
12/08	421	244	58.0%	—
12/00	244	190	78.0%	—
Annual Growth	13.1%	7.6%	—	—

2009 Year-End Financials
Return on assets: —   Cash ($ mil.): 24
Return on equity: 49.8%
Current ratio: —

WARREN DISTRIBUTION INC.

Auditors: BKD LLP OMAHA NE

LOCATIONS

HQ: WARREN DISTRIBUTION INC.
727 S 13TH ST, OMAHA, NE 681023204
Phone: 402 341-9397
Web: WWW.WD-WPP.COM

HISTORICAL FINANCIALS
Company Type: Private

Income Statement
FYE: February 23

	REVENUE ($ mil.)	NET INCOME ($ mil.)	NET PROFIT MARGIN	EMPLOYEES
02/13	485	10	2.1%	600
02/12	470	5	1.1%	—
02/11	378	11	3.1%	—
02/10	315	0	—	—
Annual Growth	15.4%	—	—	—

2013 Year-End Financials
Return on assets: 5.7%   Cash ($ mil.): —
Return on equity: 2.1%
Current ratio: 1.00

WARREN RURAL ELECTRIC COOPERATIVE CORPORATION

This Warren needs no commission just a cooperative in order to deliver electric results to the people. Warren Rural Electric Cooperative Corporation (Warren RECC) provides its member customers with electricity security systems and surge suppression equipment as well as with floodlighting and street lighting. It offers propane through non-affiliated Propane Energy Partners. The co-op serves more than 55300 customers in an eight-county service area (Barren Butler Edmonson Grayson Logan Ohio Simpson and Warren counties) in rural south-central Kentucky. Warren RECC is affiliated with the Tennessee Valley

Authority and a member of Touchstone Energy a 600-member alliance of electricity co-ops.

After ice storms in early 2009 knocked out power to the area (Warren county was declared a disaster area) Warren RECC received a $6.5 million FEMA grant to help with associated repair costs. The coop spent about $15 replacing snapped poles and repair hundreds of miles of lines; it typically budgets about $200000 annually for repair work.

EXECUTIVES

Attorney, Keith Carwell
Chairman, Michael W. McGuirk
Secretary/Treasurer and Director, Dennis P. Ingram
President and CEO, Gary K. Dillard
Attorney, Keith Carwell
Director, Terry Garmon
Director, Joe B. Neely
Director, Kenneth H. Robbins
Director, Orville W. (Pete) Dotson
Director, Rebecca L. Goad
Secretary/Treasurer and Director, Dennis P. Ingram
Director, B.W. Lyons
Auditors: LATTIMORE BLACK MORGAN & CAIN

LOCATIONS

HQ: WARREN RURAL ELECTRIC COOPERATIVE CORPORATION
951 FAIRVIEW AVE, BOWLING GREEN, KY 421014937
Phone: 270 793-9857
Web: WWW.WRECC.COM

COMPETITORS

AmeriGas Partners   Kenergy
Duke Energy Kentucky

HISTORICAL FINANCIALS
Company Type: Private

Income Statement
FYE: June 30

	REVENUE ($ mil.)	NET INCOME ($ mil.)	NET PROFIT MARGIN	EMPLOYEES
06/13	177	4	2.7%	165
06/12	171	4	2.8%	—
06/09	170	2	1.3%	—
06/08	152	0	—	—
Annual Growth	3.1%	—	—	—

2013 Year-End Financials
Return on assets: —   Cash ($ mil.): 16
Return on equity: 2.7%
Current ratio: 0.30

WASHINGTON COUNTY BOARD OF EDUCATION

Auditors: SMITH ELLIOT KEARNS & COMPANY

LOCATIONS

HQ: WASHINGTON COUNTY BOARD OF EDUCATION
10435 DOWNSVILLE PIKE, HAGERSTOWN, MD 217401732
Phone: 301 766-2800
Web: WWW.WCPS.K12.MD.US

Income Statement
FYE: June 30

	REVENUE ($ mil.)	NET INCOME ($ mil.)	NET PROFIT MARGIN	EMPLOYEES
06/14	306	(1)	—	3,000
06/13	289	(3)	—	
06/12	289	3	1.2%	
06/11	301	0	—	
Annual Growth	0.5%	—	—	—

2014 Year-End Financials
Return on assets: 1.8%   Cash ($ mil.): 23
Return on equity: (-0.4%)
Current ratio: —

WASHINGTON REGIONAL MEDICAL CENTER

Washington Regional Medical System (formerly Washington Regional Medical Center) provides acute care services to the people of northwestern Arkansas. The system's main hospital has about 370 beds in Fayetteville and also includes assisted living facilities home health and hospice services and general practice and specialty clinics. Specialty services at the medical center include cardiac and vascular care (Walker Family Heart and Vascular Institute) emergency medicine kidney dialysis women's health services (Johnelle Hunt Women's Center) cancer treatment and rehabilitation.

Geographic Reach

Washington Regional Medical System's is the only not-for-profit community-owned and locally governed healthcare system in Northwest Arkansas.

Strategy

Upgrading its health record technology in 2013 the system contracted InteliChart Patient Portal and InteliChart Health Information Exchange (HIE). InteliChart's platform which includes interactive patient and HIE portals allows all of Washington Regional Medical System's providers to overcome interoperability challenges helping its care delivery teams to better manage patients as they transition between the health system's providers and care settings.

Company Background

Striving to expand its reach and attract additional patients Washington Regional Medical System in 2011 added Washington Regional Rheumatology Clinic Washington Regional Sleep Medicine and Harrison Family Practice Clinic to its network of clinics.

Washington Regional Medical System started out in 1950 as Washington County Hospital and moved into its modern facility in 2002. The system completed a $64 million expansion effort in 2008 that added over 100 beds and enhanced emergency senior support and pharmacy units.

EXECUTIVES

CFO, Dan Eckels
VP and CIO, Becky Magee
President and CEO, W. L. (Bill) Bradley
Chairman Medicine, Susan Portis Ferguson, age 48
Chairman Surgery, Randall D. Hightower, age 59
Chairman, Dorothy J. Hanby
Chief of Staff, Ted Fish
Chief Medical Officer, David Ratcliff

LOCATIONS

HQ: WASHINGTON REGIONAL MEDICAL CENTER
3215 N NORTHHILLS BLVD, FAYETTEVILLE, AR
727034424
Phone: 479 713-1000
Web: WWW.WREGIONAL.COM

PRODUCTS/OPERATIONS

Selected Medical Services
Assisted Living
Asthma
Bariatric
Bone Density
Cancer Services
Center for Exercise
Clinical Research
Diabetes Education
Dialysis
Emergency Services
Faith In Action
Gynecologic Oncology
Gynecology
Heart Health
Home Health
Hospice
Hyperbaric Oxygen Therapy
Imaging
IV Infusion
LIFELINE Personal Emergency Response System
Mammography
Neurology
Neurosurgery
Obstetrics
Pain Management
Pelvic Therapy
Senior Health
Senior Specialty Unit
Sleep Disorders
Urology
Women' s Health
Wound Care
Hospitals Facilities and Clinics
Cancer Support Home
  Cancer Sup
  Cancer Sup
Centers for Health
  Pat Walker Center for Seniors
  Springdale Center for Health
Dialysis
  Benton County Dialysis Center
  Dialysis Center of Siloam Springs
  North Hills Dialysis Center
Exercise Center
  Washington Regional Center for Exercise
Hospital
  Washington Regional Medical Center
Medical Clinics
  Crossroads Medical Clinic
  East Springdale Family Clinic
  Eureka Springs Family Clinic
  Farmington Family Clinic
  Fayetteville Family Clinic
  Har-Ber Family Clinic
  Harrison Family Practice Clinic
  HerHealth - Johnelle Hunt Women' s Center -
  Washington Regional Medical Center
  HerHealth
  Internal Medicine Associates
  Northwest Arkansas Neuroscience Institute
  Ozark Urology
  Rheumatology Clinic
  Shiloh Clinic
  Sleep Medicine Clinic
  Walker Heart Institute Cardiovascular Clinic
  Walker Heart Institute Harrison Cardiology Clinic
  Senior Health Clinic
  Washington Regional Diagnostic Clinic
  Washington Regional Memory Clinic
  Washington Regional Wound Care Clinic
Surgery Center
  North Hills Surgery Center

COMPETITORS

Baptist Health (Arkansas)	Community Health Systems
Baxter Regional Medical Center	Mercy Health Sparks Health System

Income Statement
FYE: December 31

	REVENUE ($ mil.)	NET INCOME ($ mil.)	NET PROFIT MARGIN	EMPLOYEES
12/12	205	33	16.4%	1,600
12/09	229	14	6.2%	
12/08	203	0	0.0%	
12/02	139	0	—	
Annual Growth	3.9%	—	—	—

2012 Year-End Financials
Return on assets: 3.7%   Cash ($ mil.): 12
Return on equity: 16.4%
Current ratio: 1.30

WATKINS AND SHEPARD TRUCKING INC.

Watkins & Shepard Trucking offers less-than-truckload (LTL) and truckload freight hauling throughout the US from about 20 terminals mainly west of the Rockies. (LTL carriers consolidate cargo from multiple shippers into a single trailer.) The company's fleet consists of about 630 tractors and 1600 trailers. Standard dry vans account for the majority of the company's trailers; Watkins & Shepard also uses flatbed trailers. In addition the company arranges intermodal transportation which involves hauling freight by multiple methods such as road and rail. CEO Ray Kuntz and president Steve Williamson own Watkins & Shepard which was founded in 1974 as Stan Watkins Trucking.

EXECUTIVES

Chairman and CEO, Ray Kuntz
President, Walt Ainsworth
Secretary and Treasurer, Daniel Brown
Auditors: EIDEBAILLY FARGO ND

LOCATIONS

HQ: WATKINS AND SHEPARD TRUCKING INC.
6400 US HIGHWAY 10 W, MISSOULA, MT 598089379
Phone: 406 532-6121
Web: WWW.WKSH.COM

COMPETITORS

Central Freight Lines	Saia
Crete Carrier	Swift Transportation
FedEx Freight	UPS Freight
J.B. Hunt	Werner Enterprises
Landstar System	YRC Worldwide
Oak Harbor Freight Lines	

HISTORICAL FINANCIALS
Company Type: Private

Income Statement
FYE: December 31

	REVENUE ($ mil.)	NET INCOME ($ mil.)	NET PROFIT MARGIN	EMPLOYEES
12/13	160	2	1.6%	950
12/12	157	3	1.9%	
12/00	102	0	0.9%	
12/99	95	0	—	
Annual Growth	3.8%	—	—	—

WATONWAN FARM SERVICE INC

Watonwan Farm Service which does business as WFS helps out its south central Minnesota and north central Iowa member-farmers with complete farm-management services and products. Offering marketing opportunities financial services and farming supplies such as chemicals fertilizers livestock feed petroleum products and seed the agricultural cooperative serves more than 4000 producers from its 22 locations. The primary crops of its members include corn soybean and specialty canning crops; most of its livestock farmers raise hogs and cattle. The co-op was called the Consumers Cooperative Oil Company of St. James when it was founded in 1937.

EXECUTIVES

Vice President Feed Division, Merlyn Kruger
Auditors: GARDINER THOMSEN PC DES MO

LOCATIONS

HQ: WATONWAN FARM SERVICE INC
233 W CIRO ST, TRUMAN, MN 560882018
Phone: 507 776-1244
Web: WWW.WFSAG.COM

COMPETITORS

ADM	Gold-Eagle Cooperative
Ag Processing Inc.	Heartland Co-op
CHS	Minn-Dak Co-op
Cargill	NEW Cooperative
Farm Service	United Farmers
Cooperative	Cooperative
Farmers Cooperative	
Society	

HISTORICAL FINANCIALS

Company Type: Private

Income Statement
FYE: July 31

	REVENUE ($ mil.)	NET INCOME ($ mil.)	NET PROFIT MARGIN	EMPLOYEES
07/14	468	7	1.7%	255
07/13	701	7	1.1%	—
07/12	592	6	1.1%	—
07/11	534	0	—	—
Annual Growth	(4.3%)	—	—	—

2014 Year-End Financials

Return on assets: 2.4%   Cash ($ mil.): 19
Return on equity: 1.7%
Current ratio: 0.60

WAUKESHA MEMORIAL HOSPITAL INC.

Waukesha Memorial Hospital is a 300-bed teaching hospital that provides health care services for Wisconsin's Milwaukee Waukesha and Dane counties. With about 670 physicians representing several specialties and 2700 employees the hospital operates centers for excellence focused on cardiology oncology neurology women's health and orthopedics as well as emergency neonatal and family practice services. Additionally Waukesha Memorial Hospital conducts a physician residency program. Established in 1914 the medical facility is a subsidiary of not-for-profit ProHealth Care a medical network that serves southeastern Wisconsin with acute care and specialty health services.

Operations

ProHealth Care runs Waukesha Memorial Hospital alongside its other critical-care hospital Oconomowoc Memorial Hospital. As part of its operations the hospital boasts a neuroscience center orthopedic center regional cancer center regional heart and vascular center and a women's center. Its newborn intensive care unit and its emergency department which averages more than 39000 visits are both Level III.

Geographic Reach

Despite its name Waukesha Memorial Hospital serves the residents of Milwaukee and Dane counties along with Waukesha County.

EXECUTIVES

CFO, Nancy (Nan) Nelson
Medical Director, James Gardner
Development Officer Waukesha Memorial Hospital Foundation, Kristin M. Freiberg
Auditors: PLANTE & MORAN PLLC GRAND RA

LOCATIONS

HQ: WAUKESHA MEMORIAL HOSPITAL INC.
725 AMERICAN AVE, WAUKESHA, WI 531885099
Phone: 262 544-2011
Web: WWW.WESTWOODFITNESS.ORG

PRODUCTS/OPERATIONS

Selected Services
Birthing
  Blood / Ly
Bones Joints & Muscles
Brain & Nerves
Cancer
Cancer Second Opinion
Children's Health
CyberKnife
Diabetes
Diagnostic Services
Digestive
Ear Nose & Throat
Emergency Services/Urgent Care
Eyes & Vision
General Surgery
Genetics
Heart & Vascular
Infections
Integrative Medicine
Kidneys & Urinary System
  Lungs / Br
Men's Health
Mental Health
Nutrition
Orthopedic
Pain
Rehabilitation Services
Senior's Health
Sleep
Stroke
Wellness & Lifestyle
Women's Health

COMPETITORS

Children's Hospital and Health System
Columbia St. Mary's
Froedtert Hospital
Hospital Sisters Health System
Ministry Health Care
SwedishAmerican Health System
University of Wisconsin Hospital and Clinics

HISTORICAL FINANCIALS
Company Type: Private

Income Statement
FYE: September 30

	REVENUE ($ mil.)	NET INCOME ($ mil.)	NET PROFIT MARGIN	EMPLOYEES
09/13	419	96	22.9%	2,071
09/12*	456	53	11.7%	—
06/07	277	48	17.6%	—
Annual Growth	7.1%	12.0%	—	—

*Fiscal year change

2013 Year-End Financials

Return on assets: 6.2%   Cash ($ mil.): 10
Return on equity: 22.9%
Current ratio: 1.30

WAUKESHA-PEARCE INDUSTRIES INC.

Waukesha-Pearce Industries (WPI) wants its customers to start their engines. Through its Engine Division the company designs and packages engine-driven equipment such as power generators pumps blowers control panels and switchgear. WPI also offers a slate of heavy construction and mining products including earth movers and demolition equipment made by such OEMs as Komatsu and Gradall Industries through its Construction Machinery Division. As part of its business the company sells used equipment and leases heavy earth-moving equipment. Founded as Portable Rotary Rig Co. in 1924 by Louis M. Pearce Sr. the company is owned and run by the Pearce family.

Geographic Reach

From its headquarters in Houston WPI serves customers through more than a dozen locations in Texas and another 15 across Louisiana Oklahoma New Mexico Arkansas Alabama Kansas California Rhode Island Pennsylvania and West Virginia. The company's training facility is located in Sugar Land Texas outside Houston.

Operations

WPI's Engine Equipment lineup includes its own Enginator used in field gas compression and power generation. Its Engine Division further supports WPI's performance by offering less economy-driven services such as certified remanufactured engines and revamping.

WPI's Construction Machinery arm benefits from a broad products portfolio paired with distributor affiliations. Such alliances include Bomag (compaction equipment) Allied/Rammer (demolition equipment) Esco Crushing (wearparts) Sennebogen (material handling) and Valmet (cranes). Like the Engine Equipment Division this segment is able to mitigate a recession's impact on capital equipment sales by providing repair and onsite maintenance services along with a multi-million-dollar inventory of used and rental equipment and parts.

The company also offers construction and mining products from equipment brands such as Komatsu Gradall Takeuchi Doppstadt NPK LaBounty and Vacall.

Sales and Marketing

Core markets for WPI include land clearing highway and heavy construction site development mining scrap petrochemical energy exploration and utility construction as well as a number of government agencies.

EXECUTIVES

President, Louis M. Pearce
Vice President Operations, Robert Lyde
Vice President, Jim Adian

LOCATIONS

HQ: WAUKESHA-PEARCE INDUSTRIES INC.
12320 MAIN ST, HOUSTON, TX 770356206
Phone: 713 723-1050
Web: WWW.WPI.COM

PRODUCTS/OPERATIONS

Selected Services
Earth moving
Gas compression
Mining
Power generation
Recycling
Service and replacement parts
Small engine and lawn

Selected Products
Engines
  Arrow VR engines
  BOB-CAT mowers
  Dresser Waukesha
  Generac Industrial
  Generac Residential
  HIPOWER generating sets
  Kohler engines
  Little Wonder products
  Mantis yard & garden products
  Powerhouse catalytic converters
  Remanufactured engines
  Revamp services
  Ryan turf renovation products
  WPI brand
Construction Machinery
  Allied/Rammer
  Bomag
  Bucyrus Blades
  Cummins Engines
  Dressta
  Esco
  Fleetguard Filters
  Gradall
  Hensley
  JRB
  Komatsu
  LaBounty
  Sennebogen
  Valmet

COMPETITORS

AGCO	Deere
Berry Companies	Dewey Electronics
Caterpillar	Emerson Electric
Connell Company	Kubota
Cummins Power	
Generation	

HISTORICAL FINANCIALS

Company Type: Private

Income Statement   FYE: March 31

	REVENUE ($ mil.)	NET INCOME ($ mil.)	NET PROFIT MARGIN	EMPLOYEES
03/13	369	10	2.9%	600
03/11	248	4	1.9%	—
03/10	197	1	0.8%	—
03/03	183	0	—	—
Annual Growth	7.3%	—	—	—

2013 Year-End Financials

Return on assets: —   Cash ($ mil.): —
Return on equity: 2.9%
Current ratio: —

WAYNE J. GRIFFIN ELECTRIC INC.

Wayne J. Griffin Electric brings a certain spark to New England and the Southeast. With offices in Massachusetts Georgia North Carolina and Alabama the electrical contractor offers construction and installation services on hospitals hotels industrial and high-tech buildings offices prisons research laboratories retirement communities and schools. The company's service division provides small project management and facility maintenance while its telecom division designs and installs fiber optics fire alarm and security systems as well as systems that control energy use from lighting to heating ventilation and air conditioning (HVAC). Founded in 1978 Wayne J. Griffin Electric is privately held.

Sales and Marketing

Since serving its first major customer the Coca-Cola Bottling Company at its Massachusetts plant Wayne J. Griffin Electric has been expanding into different commercial industrial and institutional sectors. It has worked for such clients as Boeing and EMC Corporation. It has also worked on electrical expansion projects for the Valley Creek Wastewater Treatment Facility in Alabama and the Raleigh-Durham International Airport in North Carolina.

Additional clients have included EMC Corporation TJX Companies Verizon and Liberty Mutual.

Strategy

Wayne J. Griffin Electric utilizes such tools as Building Information Modeling (BIM) technology to provide its customers with the best plans possible. The firm has continued to broaden its areas of expertise so that it can serve clients of many sectors from educational and institutional to industrial and corporate.

EXECUTIVES

President and CEO, Wayne J. Griffin
Auditors: KIRKLAND ALBRECHT & FREDICKSO

LOCATIONS

HQ: WAYNE J. GRIFFIN ELECTRIC INC.
116 HOPPING BROOK RD, HOLLISTON, MA
017461455
Phone: 508 429-8830
Web: WWW.WAYNEJGRIFFIN.COM

COMPETITORS

ADCO Electrical	Integrated Electrical
Bergelectric	Services
E-J Electric	J.F. White Contracting
Installation Co.	Mass Electric
EMCOR	Quanta Services

HISTORICAL FINANCIALS

Company Type: Private

Income Statement   FYE: December 31

	REVENUE ($ mil.)	NET INCOME ($ mil.)	NET PROFIT MARGIN	EMPLOYEES
12/13	291	17	6.0%	1,100
12/12	286	15	5.5%	—
12/11	286	15	5.5%	—
12/10	285	0	—	—
Annual Growth	0.7%	—	—	—

2013 Year-End Financials

Return on assets: 6.4%   Cash ($ mil.): 26
Return on equity: 6.0%
Current ratio: 0.30

WEBSTER UNIVERSITY

They have more than dictionaries at this Webster. Webster University is a private school that serves about 22000 undergraduate and graduate students through an international network of more than 100 campuses. Its main campus in St. Louis Missouri has an enrollment of more than 8000 students and 700 faculty and staff members. Other locations span the US and are also present in Europe Asia and other regions; many campuses are on military bases. Alumni include former shuttle commander Eileen Collins actress Marsha Mason and Indonesia's first democratically elected president Susilo Bambang Yudhoyono. Webster University was founded as a small Catholic women's college in 1915.

Geographic Reach

Students attending Webster hail from all 50 US states and about 150 countries. The university's main campus is located in St. Louis Missouri. It also has satellite campuses —including traditional military corporate and metropolitan-style locations —in more than 20 US states and in Africa (Ghana) Asia (China and Thailand) and Europe (Austria the Netherlands Switzerland and the UK) as well as an online presence.

Operations

The university has a faculty-to-student ratio of 1:9 and offers more than 100 program selections for majors and minors. Webster University's main campus serves students through five colleges and schools focusing on arts and sciences fine arts communications education and business and technology.

Financial Performance

Revenue fell 2% to some $210 million in fiscal 2013 due to lower student income (tuition and fees) and private contributions (gifts and grants). Net income rose by more than 200% to $23 million due to higher investment returns and changes in split-interest agreement values.

Webster University has an endowment of some $111 million. Full-time tuition runs at about $24000 per year.

Strategy

The strategic plan at Webster includes investments in infrastructure human resources and academic program improvements. In addition the university is working to enhance financial resources (including through fundraising efforts) increasing local and global partnerships building a stronger reputation and improving communication programs.

The organization expanded its geographic reach by establishing a campus in Ghana in 2013. Webster enhanced its network of global affiliates (called the Webster International Network of Schools or WINS) by adding Carroll University in 2012 and Mexico-based CETYS University in 2013.

Also in 2012 the university improved technology resources by launching a new online learning management system. In 2013 it introduced a new brand marketing campaign (including television and print advertisements) and added a new degree program in business management.

EXECUTIVES

Associate Vice President And Chief Communications Officer, Barbara (Barb) O'Malley
Associate Vice President Dean of Students, Ted Hoef
Vice President For Advancement, Charles Hahn
Associate Vice President, Matt Adrignola
Department Chair, John (Jack) Chappell
Interim Vice President Chief Information Officer, Kenneth (Ken) Freeman

Associate Vice President, Betsy Schmutz
Vice President of Enrollment Management and
  Student Affairs, Paul Carney
Associate Vice President For Undergraduate
  Admissions, Jim Myers
Board Member, Laura Arnold
Secretary, Kristi Evans
Board Member, Elizabeth Robb
Auditors: BKD LLP ST LOUIS MISSOURI

LOCATIONS

HQ: WEBSTER UNIVERSITY
  470 E LOCKWOOD AVE, SAINT LOUIS, MO
  631193194
Phone: 314 968-6900
Web: WWW.WEBSTER.EDU

PRODUCTS/OPERATIONS

Selected Schools and Colleges
College of Arts and Sciences
George Herbert Walker School of Business and
  Technology
Leigh Gerdine College of Fine Arts
School of Communications
School of Education

HISTORICAL FINANCIALS
Company Type: Private

Income Statement
FYE: May 31

	REVENUE ($ mil.)	NET INCOME ($ mil.)	NET PROFIT MARGIN	EMPLOYEES
05/13	209	22	10.8%	4,500
05/12	213	7	3.4%	—
05/11	202	21	10.4%	—
05/10	199	0	—	—
Annual Growth	1.6%	—	—	—

2013 Year-End Financials
Return on assets: —
Return on equity: 10.8%
Current ratio: 1.30
Cash ($ mil.): 28

WELCH FOODS INC. A COOPERATIVE

Welch Foods has a taste for the grape. An operating subsidiary of the 1000-plus-farmer owner National Grape Cooperative Welch produces the Welch's brand grape and white grape juices and jellies. Its beverage line includes refrigerated and sparkling juices and cocktails frozen and shelf-stable concentrates and single-serve drinks. Welch supplies fresh grapes as well as preserved offerings (jams and spreads) which are also sold under the BAMA label. The co-op licenses the Welch's name to other manufactures of frozen fruit confections dried fruit and carbonated beverages among many. Its 400-plus products are purchased by grocery retailers and food service operators in the US and 40 other countries.

Geographic Reach

Massachusetts-based Welch Foods has vineyards in Pennsylvania Michigan New York Ohio Washington and Ontario Canada. It sells its products in the US and some 40 other countries.

Financial Performance

National Grape Cooperative and Welch Foods's sales grew to $608.5 million in 2014. Volume grew 4% during the year with its Bottled 100% Juice product leading the way with 11% growth though all core product categories showed market share

and volume growth. Spread sales grew by 7% during the year while refrigerated juices grew by 8%. The cooperative's net proceeds jumped significantly to $84 million in FY2014 the second highest level in its history according to the company.

Strategy

Welch Foods and National Grape Cooperative regularly introduce new juices and grape-based products and in 2015 stated it was "committed to research and development that will meet the growing demand for products that address consumers' health and nutrition needs." During 2014 it increased investment in its successful Bottled 100% Juice line and launched Farmer's Pick a new 100% Juice line featuring unfiltered juice. In mid-2012 the coop launched four new flavors (lemonade strawberry lemonade raspberry limeade and mango) of its sparkling juice cocktails resulting in a 29% increase in volume during the summer months and market share gain during the holiday season. Welch Foods low-growth spreads business got a boost in 2012 with the launch of Welch's Nautrals an all natural no high fructose corn syrup formation that resonated with consumers. The co-op has also been making investments in efficiency to cut its overhead costs and boost proceeds for future growth. Its 2014 upgrade of its Sparkling line capacity and capabilities reduced material costs shortened lead teams eliminated waste and reduced overall costs by some $2 million per year. The new production line also doubled its processing speeds to up to 270 bottles per minute and introduced a new more efficient case configuration that allowed for more and better displays in retail stores.

EXECUTIVES

Vice President Operations and Technology, David
  (Dave) Engelkemeyer
Vice President Corporate Planning, Judy Carr
National Account Manager, Randy Holmes
Vice President Grocery Channel, Greg Malatesta
Auditors: KPMG LLP

LOCATIONS

HQ: WELCH FOODS INC. A COOPERATIVE
  300 BAKER AVE STE 101, CONCORD, MA 017422131
Phone: 978 371-1000
Web: WWW.WELCHS.COM

PRODUCTS/OPERATIONS

Selected Brands and Products
BAMA
  Jams jellies and preserves
  Peanut butter
Welch
  Bottled and canned juices
  Dried fruit
  Fresh table grapes
  Frozen juices
  Fruit juice bars
  Jams jellies and preserves
  Pourable concentrated juices
  Refrigerated juices
  Single-serve juices

COMPETITORS

Chiquita Brands	Old Orchard
Citrus World	Silver Springs
Coca-Cola	Smucker
Coloma Frozen Foods	Snapple
Dole Food	South Beach Beverage
Fresh Del Monte	Stapleton-Spence
Produce	Packing
Great Western Juice	Sun-Maid
Lion Raisins	Sunny Delight
Monster Beverage	Sunview Vineyards
Mott's	Tree Top
Naked Juice	Tropicana
National Raisin	Unilever NV
Ocean Spray	Wet Planet Beverages

Odwalla

HISTORICAL FINANCIALS
Company Type: Private

Income Statement
FYE: August 31

	REVENUE ($ mil.)	NET INCOME ($ mil.)	NET PROFIT MARGIN	EMPLOYEES
08/14	609	76	12.6%	1,000
08/13	608	65	10.7%	—
08/12	649	74	11.5%	—
08/11	640	0	—	—
Annual Growth	(1.6%)	—	—	—

2014 Year-End Financials
Return on assets: 3.7%
Return on equity: 12.6%
Current ratio: 0.60
Cash ($ mil.): 4

WELLMONT HEALTH SYSTEM

At Wellmont Health System wellness is paramount. Wellmont Health System provides general and advanced medical-surgical care to residents of northeastern Tennessee and southwestern Virginia. The health system consists of about a dozen owned and affiliated hospitals that collectively have more than 1000 licensed beds. One of its facilities is a rehabilitation hospital operated in partnership with HealthSouth. The system's Holston Valley Medical Center features a level I trauma center and a level III neonatal intensive care unit (NICU). Wellmont also operates numerous ancillary facilities including an assisted living center a mental health clinic home health care and hospice agencies and outpatient centers.

Operations

Today Wellmont is one of the region's largest employers with a staff of more than 6500 medical professionals. Nearly 600 physicians deliver care at Wellmont's facilities that include eight hospitals in Tennessee and Virginia. Other facilities include an outpatient surgery center a child development center a cancer center urgent care centers and a health network of physicians that include occupational health providers. The hospital also offers urgent care transportation with its Wellmont One Air Transport.

Wellmont is the only health system in Tennessee to offer two major trauma centers (at Holston Valley Medical Center in Kingsport and Bristol Regional Medical Center in Bristol).

Sales and Marketing

Medicare payments accounted for nearly 85% of Wellmont's net patient revenue in fiscal 2013 (ended June); Medicaid and TennCare (Tennessee's state Medicaid program) each accounted for nearly 10%.

Financial Performance

Revenue increased 1% to $798 million in fiscal 2013 (ended June) on higher net patient revenue. However patient volumes were mixed: Some categories declined while others increased. For example emergency department visits dropped 7% as more patients chose to visit the system's more affordable urgent care centers.

Net income rose significantly that year increasing 79% to $47 million. This was due to a change in net unrealized gains on investments and a change in the funded status of benefit plans. Cash flow from operations fell 5% to $74 million.

Strategy

Wellmont has expanded by opening new outpatient facilities including a new physical therapy clinic in 2013 and by acquiring existing medical facilities. For example in 2015 it agreed to buy out Adventist Health in their partnership owning Takoma Regional Hospital in Tennessee. The system also expands its service territory by partnering with other area care providers.

In 2014 the company migrated to a new electronic medical records (EMR) system replacing its four existing EHR platforms.

Company Background

Founded in 1996 Wellmont has grown over the years primarily through acquisitions including Lee Regional Medical Center Mountain View Regional Medical Center and Takoma Regional Hospital (through a partnership with Adventist Health).

EXECUTIVES

Vice President of Finance, Dale Poe
President and CEO, Margaret (Denny) DeNarvaez, age 59
Interim President Bristol Regional Medical Center, Greg Neal
Interim President and CEO Community Hospital Division, Fred Pelle
Executive Director Wellmont Foundation, Todd Norris
President Holston Valley Medical Center, Virginia Frank
President Takoma Regional Hospital, Daniel Wolcott
EVP Legal and Corporate Affairs; President and CEO Wellmont Medical Associates, John Howard
CFO, Alice Pope
Vice President, Thomas Mitoraj
Director Of Radiology, Sandra Pilkenton
Vice President Director of Project Management Office, Kim Whiteaker
Vice President of the Wellmont CVA, Tim Attebery

LOCATIONS

HQ: WELLMONT HEALTH SYSTEM
1905 AMERICAN WAY, KINGSPORT, TN 376605882
Phone: 423 230-8200
Web:
WWW.WELLMONT.NEWSROOM.MELTWATERPRESS.COM

PRODUCTS/OPERATIONS

Selected Facilities
Bristol Regional Medical Center (Bristol Tennessee)
Hancock County Hospital (Sneedville Tennessee)
Hawkins County Memorial Hospital (Rogersville Tennessee)
HealthSouth Rehabilitation Hospital of Kingsport (HealthSouth partnership; Kingsport Tennessee)
Holston Valley Medical Center (Kingsport Tennessee)
Lee Regional Medical Center (Pennington Gap Virginia)
Lonesome Pine Hospital (Big Stone Gap Virginia)
Mountain View Regional Medical Center (Norton Virginia)
Takoma Regional Hospital (Greeneville Tennessee)

Selected Services
Cancer Care
Children
Diabetes
Emergency and Trauma
Family Medicine
Hearing Services
Heart Care
Home Care
Hospice
Hospitalists
Marsh Regional Blood Center
Neurology
Occupational Medicine
Orthopedics
Palliative Care
Psychiatry
Radiology
Rehabilitation and Therapy
Sleep Medicine
Stroke Care
Surgical Services
Weight Loss
Women's Health

COMPETITORS

Ascension Health
Baptist Memorial Health Care
Community Health Systems
Cookeville Regional Medical Center
Kindred Healthcare
LifePoint Health
Mountain States Health
Tenet Healthcare

HISTORICAL FINANCIALS
Company Type: Private

Income Statement
FYE: June 30

	REVENUE ($ mil.)	NET INCOME ($ mil.)	NET PROFIT MARGIN	EMPLOYEES
06/10	622	33	5.5%	6,114
06/09	2	0	—	—
06/08	1,771	0	0.0%	—
Annual Growth	(40.8%)	4451.4%	—	—

2010 Year-End Financials
Return on assets: —
Return on equity: 5.5%
Current ratio: —
Cash ($ mil.): 29

WELLS REAL ESTATE INVESTMENT TRUST II

Auditors: DELOITTE & TOUCHE LLP ATLANT

LOCATIONS

HQ: WELLS REAL ESTATE INVESTMENT TRUST II
1 GLENLAKE PKWY STE 1200, ATLANTA, GA 303287267
Phone: 404 465-2200
Web: WWW.WELLSREITII.COM

HISTORICAL FINANCIALS
Company Type: Private

Income Statement
FYE: December 31

	REVENUE ($ mil.)	NET INCOME ($ mil.)	NET PROFIT MARGIN	EMPLOYEES
12/12	576	48	8.3%	—
12/11	613	56	9.2%	—
Annual Growth	(5.9%)	(15.2%)	—	—

2012 Year-End Financials
Return on assets: —
Return on equity: 8.3%
Current ratio: 0.10
Cash ($ mil.): —

WELSPUN PIPES INC.

Auditors: HUDSON CISNE & CO LLP LITTL

LOCATIONS

HQ: WELSPUN PIPES INC.
9301 FRAZIER PIKE, LITTLE ROCK, AR 722069280
Phone: 501 301-8800
Web: WWW.WELSPUN.COM

HISTORICAL FINANCIALS
Company Type: Private

Income Statement
FYE: March 31

	REVENUE ($ mil.)	NET INCOME ($ mil.)	NET PROFIT MARGIN	EMPLOYEES
03/13	335	5	1.7%	507
03/12	354	46	13.0%	—
Annual Growth	(5.2%)	(87.5%)	—	—

2013 Year-End Financials
Return on assets: 10.3%
Return on equity: 1.7%
Current ratio: 0.50
Cash ($ mil.): 20

WESLEYAN UNIVERSITY (INC)

Wesleyan University is a private institution offering liberal arts and sciences education from its 360-acre campus in Middleton Connecticut. Some 3500 undergraduate and graduate students attend the university which has programs in academic areas including American studies film studies and psychology. Notable alumni include television producer Joss Whedon and educational writer Ted Fiske. Founded in 1831 Wesleyan was the first of several US colleges and universities to be named after John Wesley founder of the Methodist church; it ended its formal affiliation with the church in 1937.

EXECUTIVES

V Pres, John C Meerts
Group Managing Director, Darren Kapelus
Medical Director, Thomas McLarney
Senior Vice President Sportscenter And News Espn, Robert King
Vice President For University Relations, Barbara-Jan Wilson
Vice Chair, Irma Gonzalez
Auditors: KPMG LLP HARTFORD CT

LOCATIONS

HQ: WESLEYAN UNIVERSITY (INC)
45 WYLLYS AVE, MIDDLETOWN, CT 064593211
Phone: 860 685-2000
Web: WWW.WESLEYAN.EDU

HISTORICAL FINANCIALS
Company Type: Private

Income Statement
FYE: June 30

	REVENUE ($ mil.)	NET INCOME ($ mil.)	NET PROFIT MARGIN	EMPLOYEES
06/07	179	90	50.3%	900
06/06	172	95	55.2%	—
Annual Growth	4.4%	(4.9%)	—	—

2007 Year-End Financials
Return on assets: —
Return on equity: 50.3%
Current ratio: —
Cash ($ mil.): 19

WEST TEXAS GAS INC.

With a deep understanding the utility of natural gas natural gas utility West Texas Gas distributes more than 25 billion cu. ft. of natural gas propane and other petroleum products to more than 25000 residential commercial agricultural and governmental customers in Texas and Oklahoma Panhandle region. The company the fourth-largest investor-owned public utility in Texas also operates retail gasoline stations and convenience stores and has gas gathering production transmission and marketing operations. West Texas Gas is 100%-owned by CEO J. L. Davis.

Like other energy companies West Texas Gas saw its revenues drop on 2009 as the global recession hammered commodity prices and weakened demand. A rebounding economy and a rise in oil and gas prices helped the company's sales and income in 2010.

West Texas Gas was founded in 1976 by J. L. Davis a midstream oil and gas industry veteran with more than 50 years of experience in the business. He began his professional career in 1949 with Magnolia Oil Company.

Seeking to expand its gas distribution into Mexico in 2008 the company acquired Reef International a marketer of gas to Mexico and which controlled a natural gas pipeline that ties the US-Mexico border to intrastate gas facilities on the US side of the Rio Grande. West Texas Gas subsequently acquired the pipeline from Reef International.

EXECUTIVES

Sec-treas, Nancy Chandler

LOCATIONS

HQ: WEST TEXAS GAS INC.
211 N COLORADO ST, MIDLAND, TX 797014607
Phone: 432 682-4349
Web: WWW.WESTTEXASGAS.COM

COMPETITORS

Atmos Energy	Oncor Electric
Gateway Energy	Delivery
Martin Midstream	Southwestern Energy
Partners	Texas New Mexico Power

HISTORICAL FINANCIALS
Company Type: Private

Income Statement
FYE: December 31

	REVENUE ($ mil.)	NET INCOME ($ mil.)	NET PROFIT MARGIN	EMPLOYEES
12/07	889	40	4.5%	600
12/06	745	65	8.8%	—
12/05	795	36	4.6%	—
12/04	625	0	—	—
Annual Growth 12.4%	—	—	—	—

2007 Year-End Financials
Return on assets: 13.0%
Return on equity: 4.5%
Current ratio: 1.50
Cash ($ mil.): 73

WEST VIRGINIA UNITED HEALTH SYSTEM INC.

West Virginia United Health System (WVUHS) helps residents in the Mountain State stay on top of their health. The system operates United Hospital Center (in Clarksburg) as well as hospitals in the West Virginia University Hospitals (WVUH) system including City Hospital (Martinsburg) Jefferson Memorial Hospital (Ranson) and WVUH's home hospital in Morgantown. In addition WVUHS operates WVUH's Cheat Lake physicians ambulatory center as well as a network of about a dozen primary care clinics located throughout central and northern West Virginia. Combined the system's hospitals and clinics have more than 1000 beds and treat approximately 1.4 million patients annually.

WVUHS was formed in 1997 after United Hospital Center merged with WVUH; the system added City Hospital and Jefferson Memorial Hospital in 2004.

LOCATIONS

HQ: WEST VIRGINIA UNITED HEALTH SYSTEM INC.
1000 TECH DR STE 2320, FAIRMONT, WV 26554
Phone: 304 368-2700

PRODUCTS/OPERATIONS

Selected facilities
Barbour Country Family Medicine
Bridgeport Physicians Care
Chestnut Ridge Center
City Hospital
Doddridge Family Medicine
Elk Memorial Clinic
Harrisville Medical Center
Jefferson Memorial Hospital
Lumberport Family Medicine
Oakland Family Medicine Center
Pennsboro Medical Center
Pinewood Medical Center
Shinnston Healthcare Clinic
United Hospital Center
United Summit Center
WVU Hospitals

COMPETITORS

CAMC Health	West Penn Allegheny
HCA	Health System

HISTORICAL FINANCIALS
Company Type: Private

Income Statement
FYE: December 31

	REVENUE ($ mil.)	NET INCOME ($ mil.)	NET PROFIT MARGIN	EMPLOYEES
12/13	703	97	13.8%	13
12/12	1,386	96	6.9%	—
12/09	4	(0)	—	—
12/08	4	0	—	—
Annual Growth 179.1%	—	—	—	—

2013 Year-End Financials
Return on assets: —
Return on equity: 13.8%
Current ratio: 1.00
Cash ($ mil.): 12

WESTAT INC.

Survey the market research business and you'll find Westat among the leaders of the pack. A statistical survey organization the company provides research and consulting services including study design and analysis data collection program evaluation and communications campaign development. It has technical expertise in survey and analytical methods computer systems technology biomedical science and clinical trials. Westat serves US state and local government clients in addition to businesses and foundations. It has offices in six US states as well as international locations around the world. The company was founded in 1963 and is employee-owned.

Geographic Reach
Westat has offices in Bethesda Maryland; Atlanta; Cambridge Massachusetts; Raleigh/Durham North Carolina; Philadelphia; and Houston. International offices are located in Beijing Costa Rica Ethiopia India South Africa and Thailand.

Strategy
In 2013 Westat partnered with the Bill & Melinda Gates Foundation. In the same year the company received a $7 million federal contract from the US Department of Education's Contracts and Acquisitions Management for data collection.

Mergers and Acquisitions
In late 2012 Westat expanded through the acquisition of Atlanta-based GeoStats a research and technology firm. Because of the advanced technology Geostats uses the deal enhanced Westat's expertise in collecting and analyzing geospatial mobility and physical activity data.

EXECUTIVES

President, James E. Smith
VP Planning and Finance, Patricia Espey-English
Executive Vice President Application Development, Vasudha Narayanan
Vice President Of Human Resources, Randy Yu
Vice President, Laurie May
Vice President Health Studies, William Frey
Vice President, Steve Durako
Vice President Associate Director, Garrett Moran
Senior Vice President, Renee Slobasky
Vice President Of Information Systems, Greg Binzer
Senior Vice President Administration, Martha Palan
Vice President, Doreen Deleonardis
First Vice President, Liz Jansky
Vice President, Michael Brick
Vice President, Jane Shepherd
Vice President, Kerry Levin
Vice President, Susan Mountford
Vice President of Sales, Bruce Vivari
Vice President, Sue Connor
Vice President, Ron Hirschhorn
Vice President, Roger Tourangeau
Vice President, Brad Edwards
Vice President, Nancy Dianis
Vice President, Dianne F Walsh
Vice President Accounting Contracts, Peter (Pete) Gill
Vice President, Andrea Sedlak
Board Member, Kay Gallagher
Auditors: RUBINO & COMPANY BETHESDA MD

LOCATIONS

HQ: WESTAT INC.
1600 RESEARCH BLVD, ROCKVILLE, MD 208503129
Phone: 301 251-1500
Web: WWW.WESTAT.COM

PRODUCTS/OPERATIONS

Selected Operations and Services
Program areas
- Alcohol tobacco and other drug studies
- Consulting services and marketing research
- Customer satisfaction
- Education
- Employment and training
- Energy
- Environmental protection
- Health and medical studies
- Housing
- Military human resources
- Organizational and personnel studies
- Science and technology
- Social services and community development
- Transportation

Research services
- Clinical trials management
- Conference planning and support
- Data analysis and reporting
- Data preparation and processing
- Focus groups
- Program evaluation
- Qualitative studies
- Statistical sample design
- Study design

Survey Services
- Data collection from institutions and businesses
- Data preparation and processing
- Design
- In-field measurement and biospecimen collection
- Interviewing
- Mail surveys
- On-site data collection coordination
- Telephone surveys
- Web-based surveys

COMPETITORS

Gallup	Nielsen
GfK	ORC International
Harris Interactive	QinetiQ
IMS Health	SDI Health
Ipsos	Social & Scientific
J.D. Power	Systems
Kantar Group	Walker Information
Maritz Research	

HISTORICAL FINANCIALS

Company Type: Private

Income Statement

FYE: December 31

	REVENUE ($ mil.)	NET INCOME ($ mil.)	NET PROFIT MARGIN	EMPLOYEES
12/13	582	23	4.1%	2,000
12/12	495	28	5.8%	—
12/11	506	27	5.4%	—
12/10	455	0	—	—
Annual Growth	8.6%			

2013 Year-End Financials

Return on assets: 1.3%
Return on equity: 4.1%
Current ratio: 1.40

Cash ($ mil.): 16

WESTERN CONSOLIDATED COOPERATIVE

Auditors: CARLSON HIGHLAND & CO LLP

LOCATIONS

HQ: WESTERN CONSOLIDATED COOPERATIVE
101 RAND ST, HOLLOWAY, MN 562491107
Phone: 320 394-2171
Web: WWW.WEST-CON.COM

HISTORICAL FINANCIALS

Company Type: Private

Income Statement

FYE: December 31

	REVENUE ($ mil.)	NET INCOME ($ mil.)	NET PROFIT MARGIN	EMPLOYEES
12/07	311	7	2.3%	130
12/06	169	3	2.0%	—
12/05	1,364	0	—	—
Annual Growth	—18243.6%			

2007 Year-End Financials

Return on assets: 5.4%
Return on equity: 2.3%
Current ratio: 0.10

Cash ($ mil.): 7

WESTERN FARMERS ELECTRIC COOPERATIVE

Power also comes sweeping down the plain in Oklahoma thanks to the Western Farmers Electric Cooperative. Led by its coal- and natural gas-fueled generating plants –three in Anadarko one in Mooreland and one in Hugo (all in Oklahoma) –the generation and transmission co-op produces more than 1845 MW of capacity. It pipes power over 3700 miles of transmission lines to two-thirds of rural Oklahoma and parts of New Mexico. It also operates 264 substations and 59 switch stations. Western Farmers Electric Cooperative which is owned by its member distribution cooperatives supplies 22 distribution co-ops and Altus Air Force base which serve a total of a half million members.

Geographic Reach

Western Farmers Electric Cooperative's members consist of 22 distribution cooperatives (serving customers in Kansas Oklahoma New Mexico and Texas) and the Altus Air Force Base in Oklahoma.

Operations

The company maintains a well-balanced and diversified portfolio of generation resources reflecting a mix of technologies and fuel types. In 2013 coal represented 33% of Western Farmers Electric Cooperative's energy production with natural gas at 12 percent. Power generated from wind resources represents about 14% of the coop's energy mix hydro 7%. Economy purchases energy imbalance purchases and contract power (primarily natural gas) made up the balance.

Financial Performance

In 2013 the company's revenues increased by 15% to $525.3 million due to a 7.7% energy sales increase. (Its average MWh sales growth rate of 5.5% over the past three year is above the national average). Western Farmers Electric Cooperative also gets a small amount of off-system sales from three of its four New Mexico members. Power sales increased $64 million in 2013 due to higher MWh sales a slight increase in wholesale power rates and a 40% rise in natural gas prices.Western Farmers Electric Cooperative's net income increased by 61% in 2013 due to higher sales and an increase in noninterest income.That year the company's operating cash inflow increased to $53.3 million (compared to $21.2 million in 2012) primarily due to higher net income and increased coal and oil inventory.

Strategy

Western Farmers Electric Cooperative has diversified its fuel mix to meet green energy regulations and boasts one of the state's largest renewable energy portfolios. The diversity in generation mix helps reduce exposure to changing market conditions helping to keep rates competitive.

In 2013 the company signed a purchase with Apex Clean Energy through its subsidiary Balko Wind LLC for 100 MW of wind energy from the Balko Wind Project. With this agreement Apex has sold all the capacity of 300 MW project which will produce enough electricity to power over 110000 U.S. homes. This new site represents the fifth Oklahoma wind farm development that is a part of an ongoing commitment to diversify Western Farmers Electric Cooperative's portfolio of generation sources.That year it also entered into a purchase and sale agreement with community-wind developer National Renewable Solutions to acquire the development assets for the Broadview Wind Projects in New Mexico. The two projects with a combined 19.8 MW capacity will each sell power over the next 20 years to Western Farmers Electric Cooperative. This wind farm site is in the service territory of Western Farmers Electric Cooperative member Farmers' Electric Cooperative.

In 2012 the company teamed up with Enel Green Power which that year began operating the 150-MW Rocky Ridge Wind Project in Kiowa and Washita counties Oklahoma. The energy generated by the wind farm will be bought by Western Farmers Electric Cooperative.In 2012 Calpine Corporation agreed to supply Western Farmers Electric Cooperative with electric generation capacity and power (up to 280 MW) from Calpine's gas-fired Oneta Energy Center from June 2014 through 2035.

Company Background

Growing its geographic coverage in late 2010 Western Farmers Electric Cooperative added four New Mexico-based cooperatives (Farmers' Central Valley Lea County and Roosevelt County with a total of 400 MW of load) to its membership.

Responding to a growing demand for power in 2009 the power co-op completed an expansion project at its gas-fueled Anadarko plant adding some 145 MW of power generating capacity.

Western Farmers Electric Cooperative was organized in 1941 by western Oklahoma rural electric distribution cooperatives in order to secure power generation and distribution at an affordable rate. The co-op began generating power in 1950.

EXECUTIVES

Vice President Legal Corporate Services, Brian Hobbs
Secretary, Ray Smith
Auditors: KPMG LLP OKLAHOMA CITY OKLAH

LOCATIONS

HQ: WESTERN FARMERS ELECTRIC COOPERATIVE
701 NE 7TH ST, ANADARKO, OK 730052297
Phone: 405 247-3351
Web: WWW.WFEC.COM

COMPETITORS

Empire District Electric	OGE Energy
Entergy	ONEOK
Grand River Dam Authority	PG&E Corporation

Income Statement

FYE: December 31

	REVENUE ($ mil.)	NET INCOME ($ mil.)	NET PROFIT MARGIN	EMPLOYEES
12/13	525	21	4.1%	378
12/12	457	13	2.9%	—
12/11	462	10	2.3%	—
12/10	455	0	—	—
Annual Growth	4.9%	—	—	—

2013 Year-End Financials

Return on assets: —
Return on equity: 4.1%
Current ratio: 0.60

Cash ($ mil.): 10

WESTERN MARYLAND HEALTH SYSTEM REHAB

Auditors: KPMG LLP BALTIMORE MD

LOCATIONS

HQ: WESTERN MARYLAND HEALTH SYSTEM REHAB
600 MEMORIAL AVE, CUMBERLAND, MD 215023778
Phone: 301 723-4200

HISTORICAL FINANCIALS

Company Type: Private

Income Statement

FYE: June 30

	REVENUE ($ mil.)	NET INCOME ($ mil.)	NET PROFIT MARGIN	EMPLOYEES
06/13	301	17	5.9%	2,200
06/11	296	15	5.2%	—
06/10	277	(2)	—	—
06/09	272	0	—	—
Annual Growth	2.5%	—	—	—

2013 Year-End Financials

Return on assets: —
Return on equity: 5.9%
Current ratio: 2.10

Cash ($ mil.): 51

WESTERN OREGON UNIVERSITY

LOCATIONS

HQ: WESTERN OREGON UNIVERSITY
345 MONMOUTH AVE N, MONMOUTH, OR 973611329
Phone: 503 838-8000
Web: WWW.WOU.EDU

Income Statement

FYE: June 30

	REVENUE ($ mil.)	NET INCOME ($ mil.)	NET PROFIT MARGIN	EMPLOYEES
06/08	1,251	80	6.4%	706
06/06*	0	(0)	—	—
12/05	1	0	30.1%	—
06/04	1	0	—	—
Annual Growth	483.6%	—	—	—

*Fiscal year change

2008 Year-End Financials

Return on assets: —
Return on equity: 6.4%
Current ratio: 0.70

Cash ($ mil.): 355

WESTERN STATES FIRE PROTECTION COMPANY INC

Western States Fire Protection (WSFP) is sprinkling its own brand of safety west of the Mississippi. The company a division of APi Group installs water-based fire sprinklers and other fire suppression systems for the commercial residential and industrial markets primarily in the western US. It designs installs and maintains fire protection systems at defense gaming high-tech institutional medical processing and sports facilities. Specific projects include installing systems at the Colorado Convention Center and Microsoft's data storage facility in Washington. WSFP also manufactures fire sprinklers at its own fabrication workshops. The company was founded in 1985.

In addition to its water-based fire sprinklers WSFP serves hazardous facilities with FM-200 and carbon dioxide systems. FM-200 is a dry chemical that extinguishes fire through a combination of chemically-based inhibition and cooling. These systems are used in facilities where water damage must be avoided such as art galleries historical libraries and record and storage facilities.

EXECUTIVES

Executive Vice President, Jeff Daane
V P., Rick Charles
Auditors: KPMG LLP MINNEAPOLIS MN

LOCATIONS

HQ: WESTERN STATES FIRE PROTECTION COMPANY INC
7026 S TUCSON WAY, CENTENNIAL, CO 801123921
Phone: 303 792-0022
Web: WWW.WSFP.COM

COMPETITORS

COSCO Fire Protection
China Fire
Sharpfibre
SimplexGrinnell

Tyco Fire & Security
UTC Climate Controls & Security

Income Statement

FYE: December 31

	REVENUE ($ mil.)	NET INCOME ($ mil.)	NET PROFIT MARGIN	EMPLOYEES
12/13	225	19	8.5%	1,429
12/12	202	17	8.5%	—
12/11	165	12	7.3%	—
12/10	150	0	—	—
Annual Growth	14.4%	—	—	—

2013 Year-End Financials

Return on assets: 1.2%
Return on equity: 8.5%
Current ratio: 0.80

Cash ($ mil.): —

WESTERN WASHINGTON UNIVERSITY

If you're in the West and you're looking for a liberal arts education look no further than Western Washington University. The university is located in northwest Washington state and is one of a handful of state-funded four-year institutions of higher education in Washington. The school has an enrollment of about 15000 students; roughly 95% of those are undergraduate students. Western Washington University has a student-teacher ratio of roughly 21:1. The university has students from almost every other state and from three dozen other countries. Western which began as a teachers college accepting its first students in 1899 became a full university in 1977.

Geographic Reach

The university serves mostly undergraduate students in northwest Washington state.

Operations

Western Washington University offers its students five colleges with more than 160 academic programs. Students can also design their own degrees such as some recent choices: Medicine and Social Justice Eco-Cultural Studies in Education and Law Diversity & Public Policy.

Financial Performance

The university has been growing in recent years. New enrollment and improved retention have helped Western Washington University post an 8% increase in revenue in 2012 as compared to 2011. Attracting students through scholarship allowances eroded some of its 13% increases in tuition revenue. The educational institution also generated revenue from state and local grants and contracts as well as sales services of educational activities. Net income meanwhile dropped some 46% during the same reporting period. Non-operating revenue such as declines in income from state appropriation loss on endowments and rental property expenses all contributed toward the net income slip.

Strategy

Western Washington University works to regularly provide additional programs. In 2013 the school's College of Sciences and Technology and Whatcom Community College partnered to offer a bachelor's degree in Computer and Information Systems Security. It also introduced a Bachelor's Degree Program in Nursing.

To provide a more flexible education option for students Western Washington University's Woodring College of Education offers a Master of

Education in Continuing and College Education degree program through an online-only basis. It has also rolled out an online-only TESOL Certificate Program.

The university provides for studying abroad through its Center for International Studies. Students enrolled in this program generally learn a foreign language and have the opportunity to immerse themselves in their chosen culture. Conversely the school offers international students the opportunity to learn English through the International Students at Western program.

Western Washington University also runs a program called Query a faculty research database that allows other faculty members and students to keep tabs on what the university's teachers are interested in and possibly looking to teach. Members can look up who researched specific subjects. Query which can be used to search by subject area last name or by department gives members the ability to find out what Western Washington University's faculty are working on.

EXECUTIVES

Avp-student Affairs, Susanna Yunker
Vice President, Janet Xing
Auditors: TROY KELLEY OLYMPIA WASHINGT

LOCATIONS

HQ: WESTERN WASHINGTON UNIVERSITY
516 HIGH ST, BELLINGHAM, WA 982255996
Phone: 360 650-3000
Web: WWW.WWU.EDU

PRODUCTS/OPERATIONS

Selected Colleges
College of Business and Economics
College Of Fine and Performing Arts
College of Humanities and Social Sciences
College ot Sciences and Technology
Fairhaven College of Interdisciplinary Studies
Graduate School
Huxley College of the Environment
Woodring College of Education

HISTORICAL FINANCIALS
Company Type: Private

Income Statement
FYE: June 30

	REVENUE ($ mil.)	NET INCOME ($ mil.)	NET PROFIT MARGIN	EMPLOYEES
06/14	200	3	1.9%	466
06/13	196	5	2.8%	—
06/12	181	14	8.0%	—
06/11	167	0	—	—
Annual Growth	6.1%	—	—	—

2014 Year-End Financials
Return on assets: 5.7%
Return on equity: 1.9%
Current ratio: 1.40
Cash ($ mil.): 41

WEXFORD HEALTH SOURCES INC.

Wexford Health Sources provides health care services to inmates doing time in the big house. The company has contracts at more than 100 government-run facilities including county jails state and federal prisons juvenile detention centers substance abuse treatment centers psychiatric hospitals and correctional centers for sex offenders.

Wexford Health staffs professionals that perform medical and mental health care dentistry pharmacy services and administration services and serves about 90000 inmates and patients through contracts in five states —Illinois Mississippi Ohio Pennsylvania and West Virginia. Wexford Health was founded in 1992.

EXECUTIVES

Senior Vice President Human Resources Risk Management, Elaine Gedman
Senior Vice President Operations Strategic Development, Darius Holmes
Vice President Quality Compliance and Business Affairs, Nicholas Little
Vice President, Diana Malloy
Vice President Of Finance, John Froehlich

LOCATIONS

HQ: WEXFORD HEALTH SOURCES INC.
425 HOLI DR FOST PLZ TWO FOSTER, PITTSBURGH, PA 15220
Phone: 888 633-6468
Web: WWW.WEXFORDHEALTH.COM

COMPETITORS

Conmed Healthcare
Corizon
Corrections Corporation of America
GEO Group
MHM Services
PHS Correctional Healthcare

HISTORICAL FINANCIALS
Company Type: Private

Income Statement
FYE: December 31

	REVENUE ($ mil.)	NET INCOME ($ mil.)	NET PROFIT MARGIN	EMPLOYEES
12/08	159	16	10.4%	1,525
12/05	160	6	4.0%	—
12/01	1,793	0	—	—
Annual Growth	—	168.8%		

2008 Year-End Financials
Return on assets: 2.3%
Return on equity: 10.4%
Current ratio: 1.60
Cash ($ mil.): 5

WHEATON FRANCISCAN

LOCATIONS

HQ: WHEATON FRANCISCAN
3070 N 51ST ST STE 601, MILWAUKEE, WI 532101663
Phone: 414 447-2000
Web: WWW.MYWHEATON.ORG

HISTORICAL FINANCIALS
Company Type: Private

Income Statement
FYE: June 30

	REVENUE ($ mil.)	NET INCOME ($ mil.)	NET PROFIT MARGIN	EMPLOYEES
06/11	347	12	3.7%	—
06/10	0	0	39.1%	—
Annual Growth	37414.8%	3443.6%	—	—

2011 Year-End Financials
Return on assets: —
Return on equity: 3.7%
Current ratio: —
Cash ($ mil.): —

WHEATON FRANCISCAN HLTHCRE-FRANKLIN INC

LOCATIONS

HQ: WHEATON FRANCISCAN HLTHCRE-FRANKLIN INC
3070 N 51ST ST STE 601, MILWAUKEE, WI 532101663
Phone: 414 447-2209
Web: WWW.MYWHEATON.ORG

HISTORICAL FINANCIALS
Company Type: Private

Income Statement
FYE: June 30

	REVENUE ($ mil.)	NET INCOME ($ mil.)	NET PROFIT MARGIN	EMPLOYEES
06/09	314	0	—	154
06/02	248	18	7.3%	—
Annual Growth	3.4%	—	—	—

WHEATON FRANCISCAN SERVICES INC.

Wheaton Franciscan Services Inc. (WFSI) is the not-for-profit parent company for more than 100 health care housing and social service organizations in Colorado Illinois Iowa and Wisconsin. Also known as Wheaton Franciscan Healthcare WFSI operates about 15 hospitals including Affinity Health System Rush Oak Park Hospital and United Hospital System with more than 1600 beds total. WFSI also includes long-term care centers home health agencies and physician offices. Its Franciscan Ministries division provides affordable housing units including assisted-living facilities and low-income dwellings. The health system is sponsored by The Franciscan Sisters Daughters of the Sacred Hearts of Jesus and Mary.

Operations

Many of WFSI's hospitals are operated in partnership with other area providers. For instance the Affinity Health System in Wisconsin is jointly sponsored by Wheaton Franciscan Sisters and Ministry Health Care while the Rush Oak Park Hospital in Illinois is operated through a partnership between WFSI and the Rush System for Health.

The health system partners with the YMCA of Milwaukee to try to address chronic health concerns of area residents. The two organizations converted a local YMCA campus into the YMCA Healthy Lifestyle Village. The center offers health screenings health education outpatient therapy and fitness services. WFSI and the YMCA have more Healthy Lifestyle Village campuses planned for other locations within their service areas.

The organization had a total of 1656 beds and 2620 housing units at the end of 2014.

In fiscal 2013 WSFI delivered more than 8000 babies and had more than 330000 emergency department visits. It reported more than 1580000 outpatient visits and some 64000 hospital admissions. It employs more than 500 physicians and has some 2000 affiliated physicians.

Geographic Reach

WFSI operates in Wisconsin Iowa Colorado and Illinois.

Financial Performance

The not-for-profit system's revenues were flat in fiscal 2014 at $1.8 billion. Net income totaled $184 million.

Strategy

To increase the scope of specialty health care services it can provide to the community WFSI recruits new physicians and specialists to the Wheaton Franciscan Medical Group. The system also works to improve communication among its physicians and facilities by adding electronic health record (EHR) systems.

In 2013 the system opened a new 80000-sq.-ft. outpatient center specializing in neurology services.

Company Background

The Franciscan Sisters Daughters of the Sacred Hearts of Jesus and Mary (also known as the Wheaton Franciscan Sisters) founded WSFI in 1983 as a holding company for their ministry operations. The health system traces its roots back to the founding of the St. Mary's Hospital in Racine Wisconsin in 1882.

EXECUTIVES

Senior Vice President Human Resources, David Smith
Senior Vice President And Chief Administrative Officer, Michael (Mel) Lepore
Vice President Of Physician Network, Jeffrey Halverson
Medical Director Cancer Care, Jonathan (Jon) Treisman
Vice President Finance, Timothy Masek
Vice President, Joanne Biesterfeld
Vice President Accounting and Finance, Jim Simaris
Auditors: KPMG LLP CHICAGO ILLINOIS

LOCATIONS

HQ: WHEATON FRANCISCAN SERVICES INC.
26W 171 ROOSEVELT RD, WHEATON, IL 60189
Phone: 414 465-3000
Web: WWW.WFHEALTHCARE.ORG

PRODUCTS/OPERATIONS

Selected Operations

Franciscan Ministries Inc. (housing in Colorado Illinois Iowa and Wisconsin)
Illinois
  Marianjoy Rehabilitation Hospital (Wheaton)
  Rush Oak Park Hospital (affiliate Oak Park)
Iowa (Wheaton Franciscan Healthcare of Iowa)
  Covenant Medical Center (Waterloo)
  Mercy Hospital (Oelwein)
  Sartori Memorial Hospital (Cedar Falls)
Wisconsin
  Affinity Health System (partnership with Minstry Health Care)
  Calumet Medical Center (Chilton)
  Mercy Medical Center (Oshkosh)
  St. Elizabeth Hospital (Appleton)
  Wheaton Franciscan Healthcare of Southeast Wisconsin
  All Saints Hospital (two campuses in Racine)
  Elmbrook Memorial Hospital (Brookfield)
  Franklin Hospital (Franklin)
  St. Francis Hospital (Milwaukee)
  St. Joseph Hospital (Milwaukee)
  Wisconsin Heart Hospital (Wauwatosa)
  United Hospital System Inc. (affiliated system)
  Kenosha Medical Center (Kenosha)
  St. Catherine' s Medical Center (Pleasant Prairie)

COMPETITORS

Advocate Health Care	KishHealth
Alden Management Services	Loyola University Health System
Children' s Hospital and Health System	Ministry Health Care
	Morris Hospital

Columbia St. Mary' s	NorthShore University
Elmhurst Memorial	HealthSystem
Healthcare	OSF Healthcare System
FHN	ProHealth Care
Froedtert Hospital	Rockford Health System
Hospital Sisters	SwedishAmerican Health
Health System	System

HISTORICAL FINANCIALS

Company Type: Private

Income Statement

FYE: June 30

	REVENUE ($ mil.)	NET INCOME ($ mil.)	NET PROFIT MARGIN	EMPLOYEES
06/14	1,754	128	7.3%	18,000
06/13	1,763	177	10.1%	—
06/12	1,723	(112)	—	—
06/11	1,710	0	—	—
Annual Growth	0.9%	—	—	—

2014 Year-End Financials

Return on assets: 13.5% Cash ($ mil.): 58
Return on equity: 7.3%
Current ratio: 0.80

WHEELING HOSPITAL INC.

Auditors: DELOITTE & TOUCHE LLP

LOCATIONS

HQ: WHEELING HOSPITAL INC.
1 MEDICAL PARK, WHEELING, WV 260036300
Phone: 304 243-3000
Web: WWW.WHEELINGHOSPITAL.ORG

HISTORICAL FINANCIALS

Company Type: Private

Income Statement

FYE: September 30

	REVENUE ($ mil.)	NET INCOME ($ mil.)	NET PROFIT MARGIN	EMPLOYEES
09/14	321	35	11.2%	1,228
09/13	297	15	5.2%	—
09/12	315	24	7.6%	—
09/11	298	0	—	—
Annual Growth	2.5%	—	—	—

2014 Year-End Financials

Return on assets: 4.5% Cash ($ mil.): 81
Return on equity: 11.2%
Current ratio: 2.60

WHEELING-NISSHIN INC.

Wheeling-Nisshin a subsidiary of Nisshin Steel produces a variety of hot-dip coated steels such as stainless steel. The company's output includes 400000 tons produced at its aluminizing and galvanizing line facility and 300000 tons produced at its continuous galvanizing line facility. Both of the facilities are located at the company's headquarters site in West Virginia. Its primary customers are in the automotive appliance and construction industries. Wheeling-Nisshin was founded in 1986. It had been a joint venture between Nisshin and US

---

steel producer Wheeling Pitt (now operating as Severstal Wheeling) until the Japanese steel company bought out its partner in early 2008.

EXECUTIVES

Vice President Sales And Marketing, Brian Petrella
Vice President, Ricky Onishi
Auditors: ERNST & YOUNG LLP COLUMBUS O

LOCATIONS

HQ: WHEELING-NISSHIN INC.
400 PENN ST, FOLLANSBEE, WV 260371412
Phone: 304 527-2800
Web: WWW.NISSHIN-STEEL.CO.JP

COMPETITORS

Dofasco	United States Steel
ThyssenKrupp Stainless	

HISTORICAL FINANCIALS

Company Type: Private

Income Statement

FYE: December 31

	REVENUE ($ mil.)	NET INCOME ($ mil.)	NET PROFIT MARGIN	EMPLOYEES
12/13	391	2	0.7%	175
12/12	426	6	1.6%	—
12/11	489	9	2.0%	—
12/10	434	0	—	—
Annual Growth	(3.4%)	—	—	—

2013 Year-End Financials

Return on assets: 5.5% Cash ($ mil.): 27
Return on equity: 0.7%
Current ratio: 2.10

WHITE COUNTY MEDICAL CENTER

If you're sick in Searcy you may want to visit White County Medical Center (WCMC). The organization provides health care to Central Arkansas' residents. It has about 440 licensed inpatient beds on two hospital campuses (WCMC North and WCMC South) as well as a number of outpatient surgery centers primary care clinics and a retirement community called River Oaks Village. The WCMC South campus features an inpatient rehabilitation center that helps patients recover from injury and illness as well as a long-term acute care hospital for patients needing extended general care. In addition WCMC provides home health care services and runs a training program for certified nurse assistants.

Geographic Reach

The hospital serves patients in Independence Jackson Lonoke Prairie White and Woodruff Counties.

Operations

The Center's operations include Family Practice Associates Orthopaedic and Spine Center of Central Arkansas Searcy Medical Center and Searcy Medical Center – West Clinic Westside Family Medical Clinic WCMC Cardiology Clinic and White County Oncology.

WCMC employs some 1700 health care professionals including 150 physicians. Most of its general and specialty acute care services are provided at the main WCMC North Campus location including critical care cardiac rehabilitation and radiology. Its specialty services include cancer care diabetes education diagnostic imaging and labor and delivery services. It also operates a 31-bed inpatient rehabilitation center.

Strategy

In 2013 the Center created a comprehensive center to better care for patients with orthopaedic and spine needs –the Orthopaedic and Spine Center of Central Arkansas in Searcy.

In 2012 the Arkansas Department of Health made WCMC a Level III Trauma Center an integral part of the statewide trauma system.

Company Background

Founded in 1967 WCMC later acquired fellow health care provider Central Arkansas Hospital also located in Searcy and subsequently renamed it WCMC South. The South campus was expanded in 2008 with the opening of Compass an inpatient psychiatric facility for adults.

EXECUTIVES

Clinical Director, Glenda Light
Pharmacy Manager, Dennis Milner
Director of Pharmacy, Jon Simmons
Infection Control Director, Marylou Adams
Ast. Vice President Specialty Services, Ramona Staton
Nursing Director, Janet Spotts
Assistant Vice President of Fiscal Services, Bj Roberts
Clinic Manager, Andrea Pankey
Auditors: BKD LLP LITTLE ROCK AR

LOCATIONS

HQ: WHITE COUNTY MEDICAL CENTER
3214 E RACE AVE, SEARCY, AR 721434810
Phone: 501 268-6121
Web: WWW.WCMC.ORG

PRODUCTS/OPERATIONS

Selected Centers and Services

Advanced Care Hospital of White County (long term acute care hospital)
Cancer care
Cardiac care
Clearview Geriatrics (senior psychiatric care)
Compass (adult psychiatric care)
Critical care
Diabetes education
Durable medical equipment
Emergency services
Healthworks (industrial and occupational medicine)
Home health
Imaging Center (X-ray ultrasound cath lab)
Inpatient rehabilitation unit
Inpatient hospice
New Life Center (labor delivery)
Outpatient rehabilitation
Pharmacy program
PrimeTimes (seniors' program)
River Oaks Village (retirement center offering independent and assisted living)
Searcy Medical Center (physician practice locations)
Sleep study
Sports medicine
Weight loss surgery
White County Outpatient Surgery Center
Wound care

COMPETITORS

Arkansas Children's Hospital
Arkansas Heart Hospital
Baptist Health (Arkansas)
Community Health Systems
Conway Regional Health System
Jefferson Regional Medical Center of Arkansas
St. Vincent Health System
WRMC

HISTORICAL FINANCIALS
Company Type: Private

Income Statement
FYE: September 30

	REVENUE ($ mil.)	NET INCOME ($ mil.)	NET PROFIT MARGIN	EMPLOYEES
09/13	177	17	9.7%	1,010
09/09	482	11	2.5%	—
09/08	415	8	2.1%	—
09/06	365	0	—	—
Annual Growth	(9.8%)	—	—	—

2013 Year-End Financials
Return on assets: 2.9%
Return on equity: 9.7%
Current ratio: 3.60
Cash ($ mil.): 55

WICKED FASHIONS INC.

LOCATIONS

HQ: WICKED FASHIONS INC.
222 BRIDGE PLZ S, FORT LEE, NJ 070245703
Phone: 201 242-5909
Web: WWW.SOUTHPOLE-USA.COM

HISTORICAL FINANCIALS
Company Type: Private

Income Statement
FYE: December 31

	REVENUE ($ mil.)	NET INCOME ($ mil.)	NET PROFIT MARGIN	EMPLOYEES
12/08	411	32	7.9%	400
12/07	408	55	13.6%	—
12/06	314	36	11.6%	—
12/05	302	0	—	—
Annual Growth	10.8%	—	—	—

2008 Year-End Financials
Return on assets: 2.3%
Return on equity: 7.9%
Current ratio: 2.40
Cash ($ mil.): 2

WIDENER UNIVERSITY

You probably won't find any narrow-minded students at Widener. A private co-educational liberal arts college Widener University offers a curriculum that emphasizes social awareness and civic engagement. It has an enrollment of some 6500 students and a student-to-faculty ratio of 12:1. The university grants undergraduate and graduate degrees in about 60 different fields; its programs are divided into eight schools and colleges that cover areas including arts and sciences business engineering law hospitality human services and nursing. Widener University has had its current name since 1979 but its roots reach back to a group of 19th century boys' military academies.

Geographic Reach

In addition to its main 110-acre campus located about 20 miles outside of Philadelphia in Chester Pennsylvania Widener operates three auxiliary campuses in Pennsylvania (Harrisburg and Exton) and Delaware (Wilmington) including the University College campus geared towards part-time adult undergraduates. The university's students come from more than 20 states and 25 countries. About 35% of its student base participates in study abroad programs.

Financial Performance

Widener reported a 2% increase in revenues in fiscal 2011 to some $155 million. Operating income was also up $5 to nearly $7 million.

Strategy

Widener has enhanced its attractiveness to students and faculty alike in recent years by expanding and upgrading facilities including the completion of a new nursing school building. In 2012 it opened a new international study center to help non-US students acclimate.

As part of its civic engagement curriculum Widener encourages students to participate in community service activities volunteer programs and internships. To help facilitate such activities as well as to enhance community relations in 2012 Widener opened a new science learning center wing on its Widener Partnership Charter School (a partnership with Chester Pennsylvania) and it established an early career and college partnership with the Sussex Technical School District.

EXECUTIVES

Senior Vice President University Advancement, Linda Durant
SVP Administration and Finance, Joseph J. Baker
CIO, Peter D. Shoudy
President, Julie Wollman
Interim Provost, Jerry M. Greiner
Assistant Vice President University Relations, Lou Bulik
Associate Vice President University Deve, Amy Wilson
Associate Vice President, Lawrence Lesick
Vice Chairman, Paul S. Beideman, age 65
Vice Chairman, James J. Mack
Chairman, John H. Tilelli
Treasurer of Biomedical Engineering Society, David (Dave) Waller
Secretary, Marianne Zane
Board Member, Diana Vecchio
Secretary, Yvonne Williams
Auditors: CLIFTONLARSONALLEN LLP PLYMO

LOCATIONS

HQ: WIDENER UNIVERSITY
1 UNIVERSITY PL, CHESTER, PA 190135792
Phone: 610 499-4000
Web: WWW.WIDENER.EDU

PRODUCTS/OPERATIONS

Selected Colleges and Schools

College of Arts and Sciences
School of Business Administration
School of Engineering
School of Hospitality Management
School of Human Service Professions
School of Law
School of Nursing
University College

HISTORICAL FINANCIALS
Company Type: Private

Income Statement
FYE: June 30

	REVENUE ($ mil.)	NET INCOME ($ mil.)	NET PROFIT MARGIN	EMPLOYEES
06/13	155	8	5.5%	1,021
06/11	200	9	4.9%	—
06/10	188	5	2.7%	—
06/09	184	0	—	—
Annual Growth	(4.3%)	—	—	—

2013 Year-End Financials
Return on assets: —
Return on equity: 5.5%
Current ratio: —
Cash ($ mil.): 28

WILBUR SMITH ASSOCIATES INC.

For many cities around the world where there's a Wilbur there's a roadway. Wilbur Smith Associates provides engineering design planning construction and economic consulting services for municipal works and infrastructure jobs including highways bridges railroads waterways airports and public buildings. Wilbur Smith is active throughout the US Europe Central America the UK the Middle East and Asia. Pioneer transportation engineer Wilbur Smith founded the firm in 1952. The company was acquired by Camp Dresser & McKee (CDM) in 2011. The deal helped broaden both firms' service capabilities and geographic reach.

EXECUTIVES

Exec V Pres, Thierry Desmaris, age 69
Vice President Mid South Region, Michael (Mel) McGuire
Vice President Marketing, Bob Ferrell
Vice President, Eugene Ryan
Senior Vice President and Director of Asia Intl Aviation and Rail and US Gov Intl Programs, Santhosh Nair
Vice President Infrastructure Civil Design, Bryan Cully
Auditors: PRICEWATERHOUSECOOPERS LLP SP

LOCATIONS

HQ: WILBUR SMITH ASSOCIATES INC.
1301 GERVAIS ST STE 1600, COLUMBIA, SC
292013361
Phone: 803 758-4500

COMPETITORS

AECOM
David Evans
Jacobs Engineering

Michael Baker
Parsons Brinckerhoff

HISTORICAL FINANCIALS

Company Type: Private

Income Statement

FYE: December 25

	REVENUE ($ mil.)	NET INCOME ($ mil.)	NET PROFIT MARGIN	EMPLOYEES
12/09	182	1	0.7%	1,217
12/08	183	3	1.8%	—
12/07	436	0	—	—
Annual Growth	—	789.0%	—	—

2009 Year-End Financials

Return on assets: 7.8%
Return on equity: 0.7%
Current ratio: 1.10
Cash ($ mil.): 1

WILBUR-ELLIS COMPANY

Seed 'em weed 'em and feed 'em could be the motto of San Francisco's Wilbur-Ellis Co. (aka WECO). Through its agribusiness division WECO sells fertilizer herbicides insecticides seed and farm machinery in North America. The Connell Bros. unit exports and distributes food ingredients and specialty chemicals throughout the Pacific Rim. Its feed division serves international customers in the livestock pet food and aquaculture industries. Additionally WECO provides consulting pesticide application and other agriculture-related services. Beyond North America WECO has operations in about 15 countries in the Asia/Pacific Region. WECO was founded in 1921 by Brayton Wilbur Sr. and Floyd Ellis.

Operations
WECO's Agribusiness division is one of the top marketers and distributors of agricultural products in the US with sales of $2 billion. Connell Bros. is the largest marketer and distributor of specialty chemicals and ingredients with about three dozen offices across the Asia/Pacific region and annual sales of about $815 million. The $500-million-in-sales Feed division supplies value-added feed ingredients and markets for customers' by-products.

Geographic Reach
The San Francisco-based company has agribusiness operations in the West Southwest and Midwest regions on the US. Connell Bros. has offices in 17 countries across the Asia/Pacific Region including Australia China and Vietnam. The Feed unit has operations in North America and in Australia and New Zealand.

Sales and Marketing
WECO's ProMarket business serves such markets as nurseries greenhouses forests and golf courses and sporting facilities. The Connel Bros. division sells ingredients and specialty chemicals to the coatings food personal care plastics paper construction and other industries.

Financial Performance
WECO's annual sales continue to exceed $3 billion.

Strategy
WECO employs a strategy of acquiring successful businesses and integrating them into its existing operations. Geography is no barrier when it comes to buying companies: The group has acquired operations in such faraway places as Malaysia Taiwan the Philippines China Australia and New Zealand. WECO continues to expand both through acquisitions and organically across its three divisions.

Mergers and Acquisitions
The company continued its acquisitive streak in 2014 and 2015. In early 2014 it acquired one of its alliance partners New Horizons Ag Service an agricultural retail business in Elgin North Dakota. New Horizons became part of Wilbur-Ellis Midwest. The company also acquired Accu-Rate Services a full-service agricultural retailer in Sedgwick Kansas and Advanced Ag located in Creston Iowa. Other agribusinesses added in 2014 included retail facility Poynter's Ag Supply (North Dakota) and feed provider Allied Premium Protein.

Also that year WECO's Connell Brothers unit purchased Enzyme Solutions of Melbourne Australia extending its capabilities in enzymes. Furthering its Asia/Pacific business it acquired Bioworld Fine Chemical (Shanghai) which distributes upscale botanical oils and plant extracts.

Agribusiness purchases in 2015 include The Seed House a Nebraska-based professional seed company; Lacey's Farmacy a South Dakota-based agriculture retail outfit and Aero Spray Services an aerial spraying and fire-fighting firm also based in South Dakota.

Ownership
Family-owned WECO is transitioning to the fourth generation of family ownership. CEO and president John Thacher is the grandson of founder Brayton Wilbur Sr.

EXECUTIVES

VP Treasurer and CFO, James D. Crawford
President Agribusiness Division, Daniel R. (Dan) Vradenburg
President and CEO, John P. Thacher
VP South Central Operations, Steven J. Dietze
VP Western Operations, Scott Hushbeck
President Feed Division, Rob Fullerton
President Wilbur-Ellis Japan, Iguchi Shinichi
President Connell Brothers, Azita Owlia
Vice President, Jeff Streblow
Vice President, Gene Gauss
Vice President Finance, Steve Flowers
Chairman, Herbert B. Tully
Treasurer, Alison Amonette
Vice Chairman, Vaughn Goodman
Auditors: PRICEWATERHOUSECOOPERS

LOCATIONS

HQ: WILBUR-ELLIS COMPANY
345 CALIFORNIA ST FL 27, SAN FRANCISCO, CA
941042644
Phone: 415 772-4000
Web: WWW.WILBUR-ELLIS.COM

PRODUCTS/OPERATIONS

Selected Products and Services
Agribusiness Division
  Agricultural chemicals
  Fertilizers
  Fungicides
  Herbicides
  Insecticides
  Machinery
  Pesticides
  Seed protectants
  Seed treatments
  Sprayers
  Supply-chain management
Connell Bros. Division
  Industrial chemicals
Feed Division
  Aquaculture products
  Feed ingredients
  Food oils
  Forage products
  Pet food
Professional Products
  Forestry
  Fungicides
  Herbicides
  Golf
  Fungicides
  Landscape
  Fungicides
  Nursery/Greenhouse
  Fungicides
  Vegetation Management
  Selective and nonselective growth regulators

COMPETITORS

ADM
AGRI Industries
Ag Processing Inc.
Agrium
Andersons
BASF SE
Bayer CropScience
CF Industries
CHS
Cargill
Dow AgroSciences

DuPont Agriculture
Frontier Agriculture
GROWMARK
Goulding Chemicals
Ingredion
JR Simplot
Land O' Lakes Purina
Feed
Monsanto Company
Southern States

HISTORICAL FINANCIALS

Company Type: Private

Income Statement

FYE: December 31

	REVENUE ($ mil.)	NET INCOME ($ mil.)	NET PROFIT MARGIN	EMPLOYEES
12/11	2,812	0	—	3,200
12/10	2,342	0	—	—
12/09	0	0	—	—
12/00	1,100	0	—	—
Annual Growth	8.9%	—	—	—

WILDLIFE CONSERVATION SOCIETY

From Congo gorillas to humpback whales off the coast of Gabon all life is worth conserving to the Wildlife Conservation Society (WCS). The group founded in 1895 works to protect wildlife and lands throughout the world and to instill in humans a concern about nature. The not-for-profit organization operates New York City's Bronx Zoo New York Aquarium Central Park Zoo Prospect Park Zoo and the Queens Zoo. WCS's environmental education programs are used in US schools as well as those in other nations. The society has ongoing efforts in more than 60 countries to protect endangered species and ecosystems. About a quarter of the funding for its work comes from visitors at its handful of parks.Geographic ReachThe society operates country programs across four continents including Africa Asia Latin America and North America. It boasts ongoing efforts in 60-plus countries.OperationsWCS manages about 500 conservation projects nationwide and works to educate millions of visitors at its handful of living institutions: the Bronx Zoo New York Aquarium Central Park Zoo Prospect Park Zoo and Queens Zoo. As part of its operations WCS manages more than 200 million acres of protected lands globally and retains a staff of 200-plus scientists.Financial PerformanceDespite the anemic economy in recent years WCS has logged healthy attendance of about 4 million visitors across its five New York City parks. As Americans chose to vacation at home WCS has benefited. With those visitors came a noteworthy boost in income from gate admissions exhibits and contributions from visitor services such as food merchandising and parking. Attendance-driven revenues reach more than $50 million.The conservation group points to its operational diversity for being able to keep its head above water when funding from the state and other entities it had relied on had slimmed.Sales and MarketingWCS is working to ramp up its construction. The group's revised Master Plan includes enhancements at the Bronx Zoo's C.V. Starr Science Campus with the Special Care Unit and LaMattina Wildlife Ambassador Center the Queens Zoo's jaguar exhibit and the Ocean Wonders exhibit.During the past decade WCS has spent $243 million to fund physical plant improvements on its five campuses. They were financed through grants from New York City and the federal government private gifts and the proceeds from WCS's Series 2004 tax-exempt bond issue.

EXECUTIVES

Executive Vice President Public Affairs, John (Jack) Calvelli
Executive Vice President Conservation & Science, John G. Robinson
Executive Vice President for Administration & Chief Financial Officer, Patricia Calabrese
SVP Living Institutions; Director Bronx Zoo, James J. Breheny
EVP Global Resources, Bertina Ceccarelli
President Chief Executive Officer, Cristi ?n Samper
Vice President Human Resources, Herman D Smith
Vice President Communications Public Affairs, Mary Dixon
Vice President Program Development, Susan (Sue) Tressler
Vice President Species Conservation, Elizabeth (Beth) Bennett

Vice President of Planning and Design and Chief Architect, Susan (Sue) Chin
Auditors: KPMG NEW YORK NY

LOCATIONS

HQ: WILDLIFE CONSERVATION SOCIETY
2300 SOUTHERN BLVD, BRONX, NY 104601090
Phone: 718 220-5100
Web: WWW.WCS.ORG

PRODUCTS/OPERATIONS

2014 Sales

	% of total
Contributed	26
Gate-and-exhibit admissions	15
Federal agencies	14
Visitor services	11
City of New York	10
Investment income	8
Membership dues	6
Non-governmental-organization grants	6
New York State	1
Education programs	1
Sponsorship licensing & royalties	0
Insurance proceeds	0
Other	1
Total	**100**

Selected Areas of Focus
Climate change
Natural resource exploitation
Sustainable development of human livelihoods

HISTORICAL FINANCIALS
Company Type: Private

Income Statement
FYE: June 30

	REVENUE ($ mil.)	NET INCOME ($ mil.)	NET PROFIT MARGIN	EMPLOYEES
06/10	228	9	4.1%	4,000
06/09	197	0	—	—
06/06	2,125	0	—	—
Annual Growth	—	388.5%		

2010 Year-End Financials

Return on assets: 12.3% Cash ($ mil.): 61
Return on equity: 4.1%
Current ratio: —

WILLIAM MARSH RICE UNIVERSITY INC

You have to be as wise as an owl to attend Rice University and have really good SAT scores. Often referred to as the "Ivy League of the South" Rice — with mascot "Sammy the Owl" —consistently appears at the top of college academic rankings including those published by U.S. News & World Report. The private university has an enrollment of more than 6000 and about 1100 full-time part-time and adjunct faculty members (giving it a student-teacher ratio of about 6:1). Rice offers programs through eight schools in areas such as engineering computer science economics music and architecture. The university opened in 1912 with funds from the estate of William Marsh Rice.OperationsRice's research programs span a dizzying array of disciplines that include energy health and tax policy science and technology conflict resolution and border policy. About 80% of Rice students are from the US including about 45% from Texas.StrategyThe school is in the process of increasing the number of its undergrad-

uates to 3800 students while still maintaining its very low student-faculty ratio. The change which began in 2008 and will take place over 10 years could involve building two new residential colleges the expansion of existing colleges and a possible Rice-affiliated off-campus facility to house both undergraduate and graduate students.

EXECUTIVES

Vice President Finance, Kathy Collins
Vice President for Public Affairs, Linda Thrane
Vice President Resource Development, Darrow Zeidenstein
Investment Analyst Vice President for Investments Treasurer, Darren Britt
Assistant Vice President Of Facilities, Russell Price
Vice President, Patricia Reiff
Assistant to the Vice President Vice President for Investments Treasurer, Ann Wise
Vice President, Matthias Heinkenschloss
Assistant Treasurer Trust Manager Vice President for Investments Treasurer, Susan (Sue) Castanza
Vice President Investments And Treasurer, Allison Thacker
Vice President, Denis Leahy
Vice President, J D Dornell
Vice President, Elizabeth Barre
Minerals Manager Vice President For Investments T, Roy Buckley
Vice President, Jennifer Tang
Associate Vice President For Investmen, Claire Nelson
Vice President, Lilly Chen
Vice President For Enrollment Office Of Enrollment, Chris Munoz
Assistant Vice President Project Management And Engineer Facilities Engineering And Planning, Doug Tomlinson
Associate Vice President For Investments Associate Treasurer Vice President For Investmen, Ronald (Ron) Long
Vice President, Patricia (Pat) Reiff
Associate Vice President for Development, Benjamin R (Ben) Renberg
Vice President, Emily Hendryx
Vice President, Elizabeth (Beth) Barre
Vice President, JD Dornell
Board Member, Andrew Barros
Auditors: PRICEWATERHOUSECOOPERS LLP HO

LOCATIONS

HQ: WILLIAM MARSH RICE UNIVERSITY INC
10300 TOWN PARK DR, HOUSTON, TX 770725236
Phone: 713 348-4055
Web: WWW.RICE.EDU

PRODUCTS/OPERATIONS

Selected Departments and Interdisciplinary Programs
Air Force Science
Ancient Mediterranean Civilizations
Anthropology
Applied Physics Graduate Program
Architecture
Art History
Asian Studies
Bioengineering
Biosciences
Center for Digital Learning and Scholarship
Center for the Study of Languages
Chemical Engineering
Chemistry
Civil and Environmental Engineering
Classical Studies
Cognitive Sciences
Computational and Applied Mathematics
Computer Science
Earth Science
Economics
Education
Education Certification
Electrical and Computer Engineering

English
Environmental Analysis and Decision Making
Environmental Studies
French Studies
German and Slavic Studies
Hispanic Studies
History
Kinesiology
Leadership Rice
Lifetime Physical Activity Program
Linguistics
Management and Accounting
Managerial Studies
Master of Liberal Studies
Mathematics
Mechanical Engineering and Materials Science
Medieval Studies
Military Science
Music
Nanoscale Physics
Naval Science
Neurosciences
Philosophy
Physics and Astronomy
Policy Studies
Political Science
Psychology
Religious Studies
Sociology
Statistics
Subsurface Geoscience
The Program for the Study of Women and Gender

HISTORICAL FINANCIALS
Company Type: Private

Income Statement
FYE: June 30

	REVENUE ($ mil.)	NET INCOME ($ mil.)	NET PROFIT MARGIN	EMPLOYEES
06/14	599	657	109.8%	2,600
06/13	568	459	80.9%	—
06/12	551	(33)	—	—
06/11	550	0	—	—
Annual Growth	2.8%	—	—	—

2014 Year-End Financials
Return on assets: 15.6%
Return on equity: 109.8%
Current ratio: —
Cash ($ mil.): 12

WILLIS-KNIGHTON MEDICAL CENTER

Auditors: COLE EVANS & PETERSON SHREVEP

LOCATIONS
HQ: WILLIS-KNIGHTON MEDICAL CENTER
2600 GREENWOOD RD, SHREVEPORT, LA 711033908
Phone: 318 212-4000
Web: WWW.CAREERS.WKHS.COM

HISTORICAL FINANCIALS
Company Type: Private

Income Statement
FYE: September 30

	REVENUE ($ mil.)	NET INCOME ($ mil.)	NET PROFIT MARGIN	EMPLOYEES
09/12	849	83	9.8%	3,089
09/11	807	76	9.4%	—
09/10	818	47	5.8%	—
09/09	768	0	—	—
Annual Growth	3.4%	—	—	—

2012 Year-End Financials
Return on assets: —
Return on equity: 9.8%
Current ratio: 0.80
Cash ($ mil.): 156

WILMED NURSING CARE CENTER

LOCATIONS
HQ: WILMED NURSING CARE CENTER
1705 TARBORO ST SW, WILSON, NC 278933428
Phone: 252 399-8998
Web: WWW.WILMED.ORG

HISTORICAL FINANCIALS
Company Type: Private

Income Statement
FYE: September 30

	REVENUE ($ mil.)	NET INCOME ($ mil.)	NET PROFIT MARGIN	EMPLOYEES
09/09	586	(3)	—	110
09/08	5	0	2.9%	—
Annual Growth	9876.3%	—	—	—

2009 Year-End Financials
Return on assets: —
Return on equity: (-0.5%)
Current ratio: 1.60
Cash ($ mil.): —

WINCHESTER MEDICAL CENTER AUXILIARY INC.

Winchester Medical Center is the flagship facility of Valley Health System a not-for-profit health care organization serving the residents of Virginia's Shenandoah Valley. The full-service general hospital which has more than 400 inpatient beds serves as a regional referral center for the system's smaller community hospitals. It provides medical services across a number of specialties (including neuroscience heart disease and cancer) and offers surgical diagnostic and rehabilitative care. The hospital's campus also features outpatient diagnostic and surgical facilities an adult psychiatric facility and doctors' offices. Winchester Medical Center opened its doors in 1903.The hospital opened a new $160 million tower in 2012 that replaces many of the aging equipment and parts of the building that were nearly two decades old. The tower opened in stages starting in 2009. The site includes a Heart & Vascular Center and a clinical lab expansion an expanded Emergency Department and a nearly 50-bed critical care unit. It also includes a larger labor and delivery unit and an all-private room Neonatal ICU increasing Winchester Medical Center's licensed beds from 411 to 445.The new tower was designed to give medical providers and their patients more room and work spaces for better patient care. The three year construction project produced more than 350000 square feet of new space and 78000 square feet of renovated space. The two top floors of the North Tower are shelled for future growth.Winchester Medical Center began with with just 36-beds; today

it is a full-service referral center offering a range of medical surgical diagnostic and rehabilitative services to roughly 400000 residents in the tri-state area.

EXECUTIVES
SVP and CFO, J. Craig Lewis
Chairman, Harry F. Byrd III
President and CEO, Reese Jackson
President Medical Staff, Sherif Kaiser
Vice President of Operations, Tonya Smith
Vice President of Information Systems & Chief Information Officer, Joan Roscoe
Vice President of Clinical Operations, George Goldman
Vice President of Human Resources, Elizabeth Savage-Tracy
Auditors: ARNETT & FOSTER PLLC CHA

LOCATIONS
HQ: WINCHESTER MEDICAL CENTER AUXILIARY INC.
190 CAMPUS BLVD STE 220, WINCHESTER, VA 226012872
Phone: 540 536-8000
Web: WWW.VALLEYHEALTHLINK.COM

COMPETITORS
Ascension Health
Carilion Clinic
Fauquier Hospital
Georgetown University Hospital
HCA
Inova
Johns Hopkins Health System
Loudoun Healthcare
Martha Jefferson Hospital
MedStar Health
Novant Health
Prince William Health System
Providence Hospital (Washington DC)
Rockingham Memorial Hospital
Sentara Northern Virginia Medical Center

HISTORICAL FINANCIALS
Company Type: Private

Income Statement
FYE: December 31

	REVENUE ($ mil.)	NET INCOME ($ mil.)	NET PROFIT MARGIN	EMPLOYEES
12/07	453	48	10.8%	2,046
12/06	413	61	14.9%	—
12/05	134	0	0.0%	—
Annual Growth	83.9%	40861.4%	—	—

2007 Year-End Financials
Return on assets: —
Return on equity: 10.8%
Current ratio: 1.70
Cash ($ mil.): 18

WINCO HOLDINGS INC.

Auditors: KPMG LLP BOISE ID

LOCATIONS
HQ: WINCO HOLDINGS INC.
650 N ARMSTRONG PL, BOISE, ID 837040825
Phone: 208 377-0110
Web: WWW.WINCOFOODS.COM

HISTORICAL FINANCIALS

Company Type: Private

Income Statement

	REVENUE ($ mil.)	NET INCOME ($ mil.)	NET PROFIT MARGIN	EMPLOYEES
03/09	4,104	225	5.5%	14,000
03/08	3,515	132	3.8%	—
Annual Growth	16.8%	69.7%	—	—

FYE: March 28

2009 Year-End Financials

Return on assets: 3.8%
Return on equity: 5.5%
Current ratio: 0.50

Cash ($ mil.): 146

WINSTON-SALEM/FORSYTH COUNTY SCHOOLS

Auditors: DIXON HUGHES GOODMAN LLP WINS

LOCATIONS

HQ: WINSTON-SALEM/FORSYTH COUNTY SCHOOLS
4801 BETHANIA STATION RD, WINSTON SALEM, NC 271051202
Phone: 336 727-2635
Web: WWW.WSFCS.K12.NC.US

HISTORICAL FINANCIALS

Company Type: Private

Income Statement

	REVENUE ($ mil.)	NET INCOME ($ mil.)	NET PROFIT MARGIN	EMPLOYEES
06/08	484	0	0.1%	6,841
06/07	451	0	—	—
06/06	0	0	—	—
Annual Growth	—	7367.5%	—	—

FYE: June 30

2008 Year-End Financials

Return on assets: 5.7%
Return on equity: 0.1%
Current ratio: 0.40

Cash ($ mil.): 12

WINTHROP-UNIVERSITY HOSPITAL INC

From providing it to teaching it Winthrop-University Hospital is focused on health care. The medical center boasts some 590 beds and offers a full range of acute and tertiary health care services. Services include pediatric women's health and cancer care as well as home health services. Winthrop-University Hospital is also a leading provider of cardiovascular surgeries in the region. The hospital is a member of Winthrop-South Nassau University Health System along with sister facility South Nassau Communities Hospital. Winthrop-University Hospital serves as a teaching hospital for the SUNY at Stony Brook School of Medicine.

Geographic Reach

Based in Mineola New York Winthrop-University Hospital serves patients in New York's Nassau Suffolk and Queens counties.

Operations

Overall Winthrop-University Hospital logs more than 66000 emergency visits and 33000-plus in-patient visits each year.

Specialty divisions within the Winthrop-University Hospital include the Minstretta Emergency Diagnostic Imaging Center and a pediatric emergency unit both located within the emergency department as well as centers for dialysis digestive disorders neuroscience and diabetes education. Other specialty programs include orthopedics sports medicine wound healing radiosurgery (CyberKnife) and bariatric surgery.

Its services include an expanded Emergency Department including a 9-bed Fast Track Unit comprehensive 15-bed Chest Pain Rule-Out Unit a separate 10-bed Pediatric Emergency Unit equipped with the latest technology and an emergency diagnostic imaging center – the

Its Phyllis & Nathan J. Mistretta Emergency Diagnostic Imaging Center includes a dedicated CT scanner and additional x-ray and digital imaging technology for fast and accurate diagnoses of emergency room patients. The Institute for Heart Care offers advanced diagnostics and disease prevention programs as well as sophisticated medical treatment and rehabilitation and a superior cardiac surgery program.

The hospital is a New York State Department of Health-designated Stroke Center New York State-designated Regional Trauma Center and a New York State Regional Perinatal Center.

Winthrop-University Hospital is also a member of the Long Island Health Network which comprises 10 hospitals in Nassau and Suffolk counties. Member hospitals include Brookhaven Memorial Hospital Medical Center John T. Mather Memorial Hospital and South Nassau Communities Hospital among others.

Strategy

To expand its outpatient care services to community residents the hospital opened a family dental practice in 2013.

That year Winthrop-University Hospital teamed up with Cablevision to launch an interactive video on-demand television channel offering 24/7 health-related content to Cablevision's nearly 3 million viewers in New York New Jersey and Connecticut. Winthrop HealthTV (on Optimum TV channel 652) provides viewers with health and wellness content including videos from Winthrop's leading medical experts on specific health conditions. It also offers information about a variety of community programs classes and events at the hospital.

In 2012 Winthrop-University Hospital began an $80 million construction project to add a research and academic center on the main hospital campus.

The first hospital on Long Island to acquire the daVinci Si HD Surgical System Winthrop-University Hospital is one of the top hospitals for minimally invasive surgeries. It is also the first hospital in the New York City metropolitan area to perform CyberKnife radiosurgery procedures. In 2012 it expanded specialist services in fields including orthopedics neurology and cardiac care procedures.

Mergers and Acquisitions

To improve the treatment of diabetes in 2013 the hospital acquired the Diabetes Core Curriculum Workshop a four day multidisciplinary diabetes course given in a dynamic ‘live' venue that provides participants with the specialized knowledge and skills needed to educate and care for people with diabetes.

Company Background

Winthrop-University Hospital was founded in 1896.

EXECUTIVES

Vice President, Barbara (Barb) Kohart-Kleine
Vice President Administration, Garry Schwall
Senior Vice President Chief Nursing Officer, Valerie (Val) Terzano
President and CEO, John F. Collins
Treasurer, Palmira M. Cataliotti
VP Marketing and Advertising, J. Edmund (Ed) Keating
Assistant Director Of Pharmacy, Brian Malone
CMIO and Senior Vice President Patient Care Services, Maureen Gaffney
Senior Vice President Human Resources and Organizational Development, Stacey Pfeffer
Director Of Infection Control, Valsamma Thekkel
Medical Director, Joseph Rotolo
Vice President, Evelyn Sirena
Vice President Of Information Technology, Feliks Koyfman
Vice President of Facilities and Engineering, Joe Burke
Vice President Human Resources, George Rainer
Operating Room Director, Diane Bendelier
Assistant Vp Case Management And Quality Metrics, Ann Hanford
Medical Director of Transfusion Services, Joseph (Jo) Chiofolo
Assistant Vice President Financial Planning and Reimbursement, Timothy C (Tim) Reilly
Medical Director, Joseph (Jo) Greensher
Vice President of Sales, Barbara (Barb) Eisenkraft
Vice President Marketing Advertising and Public Relations, J Edmund Keating
Assistant Vice President Human Resources, Sphr Chad Hoffman-Fragale
Vice Chairman, Joan Cox
Chairman, Charles M. Strain
Vice Chairman, John H. Treiber
Vice Chairman, Kevin T. Curran

LOCATIONS

HQ: WINTHROP-UNIVERSITY HOSPITAL INC
259 1ST ST, MINEOLA, NY 115013987
Phone: 516 663-0333
Web: WWW.WINTHROP.ORG

PRODUCTS/OPERATIONS

Selected Services
Angioplasty
Arthritis
Asthma
Bariatric Surgery
Breast Cancer
Cancer Care
Cardiology
Childhood Cancer
Children's Health
Clinical Trials
CyberKnife
Diabetes
Dialysis
Digestive Care
Education
Emergency Dept.
Family Care
Gastroenterology
Heart Care
Home Health Care
Hyperbarics
Joint Replacement
Kidney Disease
Lung Cancer
Lung Care
Maternity
Neurology
Neurosciences
Neurosurgery
OB/GYN
Open Heart Surgery
Orthopedics
Pediatric Cancer
Pediatrics
Physicians

Prostate Cancer
Pulmonary Care
Research
Sleep Disorders
Stroke
Trauma Center
Urology
Weight Loss

COMPETITORS

Barnabas Health
Bronx-Lebanon Hospital
Catholic Health Services of Long Island
Continuum Health Partners
Franklin Hospital
HealthSouth
Long Island Jewish Medical Center
Lutheran HealthCare
MediSys Health Network
New York City Health and Hospitals
NewYork-Presbyterian Healthcare
Newark Beth Israel Medical Center
North Shore-Long Island Jewish Health System
Queens-Long Island Medical Group
SUNY Downstate

HISTORICAL FINANCIALS

Company Type: Private

Income Statement

FYE: December 31

	REVENUE ($ mil.)	NET INCOME ($ mil.)	NET PROFIT MARGIN	EMPLOYEES
12/08	725	(134)	—	6,000
12/07	669	0	0.0%	—
12/06	610	15	2.5%	—
12/05	0	0	—	—
Annual Growth	—	—	—	—

2008 Year-End Financials

Return on assets: 11.3%   Cash ($ mil.): 74
Return on equity: (-18.5%)
Current ratio: 0.80

WISCONSIN ALUMNI RESEARCH FOUNDATION

LOCATIONS

HQ: WISCONSIN ALUMNI RESEARCH FOUNDATION
614 WALNUT ST FL 13, MADISON, WI 537262336
Phone: 608 263-2500
Web: WWW.WARF.ORG

HISTORICAL FINANCIALS

Company Type: Private

Income Statement

FYE: June 30

	ASSETS ($ mil.)	NET INCOME ($ mil.)	INCOME AS % OF ASSETS	EMPLOYEES
06/12	2,586	206	8.0%	27
06/11	2,516	259	10.3%	—
06/10	2,198	340	15.5%	—
06/09	1,680	0	—	—
Annual Growth	15.5%	—	—	—

2012 Year-End Financials

Return on assets: —   Sales ($ mil.): 316
Return on equity: 65.2%

WITHLACOOCHEE RIVER ELECTRIC COOPERATIVE INC

Auditors: PURVIS GRAY & COMPANY GAINESV

LOCATIONS

HQ: WITHLACOOCHEE RIVER ELECTRIC
COOPERATIVE INC
14651 21ST ST, DADE CITY, FL 335232920
Phone: 352 567-5133
Web: WWW.WREC.NET

HISTORICAL FINANCIALS

Company Type: Private

Income Statement

FYE: December 31

	REVENUE ($ mil.)	NET INCOME ($ mil.)	NET PROFIT MARGIN	EMPLOYEES
12/10	487	44	9.1%	99
12/09	454	25	5.7%	—
Annual Growth	7.4%	72.9%	—	—

2010 Year-End Financials

Return on assets: —   Cash ($ mil.): 20
Return on equity: 9.1%
Current ratio: 0.20

WITHLACOOCHEE RIVER ELECTRIC COOPERATIVE INC

Withlacoochee River Electric Cooperative keeps the power flowing to the residences and businesses of more than 200360 member-owners in five counties along the central Florida Gulf Coast. The power distribution utility which was originally set up in 1941 receives wholesale generation and transmission services from the Seminole Electric Cooperative. Withlacoochee River Electric a non-profit organization returns any funds remaining at the end of each year to its membership. The cooperative has returned more than $190 million to its member-owners.

Pushing green energy and recycling in 2008 the company reported that in addition to supplying reliable electricity it was seeking to reduce carbon emissions through providing its members with compact fluorescent bulbs. That year Withlacoochee River Electric also recycled more than 442000 pounds of materials installed a 3.15 kV solar panel display at its corporate headquarters in Dade City and added more than 3220 new customers.

"Withlacoochee River" was chosen as the name for the organization because the river was the common link for the cooperative's original service region (Citrus Hernando and Pasco counties).

EXECUTIVES

Secretary, Cindy Rizer

LOCATIONS

HQ: WITHLACOOCHEE RIVER ELECTRIC
COOPERATIVE INC
14651 21ST ST, DADE CITY, FL 335232920
Phone: 352 567-5133
Web: WWW.WREC.NET

HISTORICAL FINANCIALS

Company Type: Private

Income Statement

FYE: December 31

	REVENUE ($ mil.)	NET INCOME ($ mil.)	NET PROFIT MARGIN	EMPLOYEES
12/13	433	16	3.8%	458
12/12	421	25	6.1%	—
12/11	423	28	6.7%	—
12/09	0	0	—	—
Annual Growth	578.7%	—	—	—

2013 Year-End Financials

Return on assets: 8.3%   Cash ($ mil.): 179
Return on equity: 3.8%
Current ratio: 6.10

WOLVERINE POWER SUPPLY COOPERATIVE INC.

Named after a voracious carnivore Wolverine Power Supply Cooperative makes sure that that voracious consumer of electricity —the American public —gets the power its needs. The non-profit company is an electric generation and transmission utility that provides services to five member distribution cooperatives in Michigan. Wolverine Power Supply Cooperative monitors and operates 1600 miles of bulk transmission lines and owns five power plants that generate 200 megawatts of capacity. It also maintains about 130 distribution substations and 36 transmission stations as well as purchases power (including windpower energy) from other utilities and marketers to distribute to its customers.

Wolverine Power Supply Cooperative's five members are Cherryland Electric Cooperative Great Lakes Energy Home Works Tri-County Electric Cooperative Presque Isle Electric & Gas Co-op and Wolverine Power Marketing Cooperative.

The cooperative is developing a coal-fired power plant near Rogers City Michigan and plans to build two 300W units and a wind turbine farm. It also expanded in late 2009 with an agreement to buy a generation facility in Michigan from FirstEnergy.

EXECUTIVES

Vice President Finance and Accounting, Richard (Dick) Kehl
Vice President Human Resources, Craig S Borton
Vice President Generation, Dan Decoeur
Vice President Rates And Administrativ, Kim Molitor
Vice President, Eric Baker
Auditors: PLANTE & MORAN PLLC

LOCATIONS

HQ: WOLVERINE POWER SUPPLY COOPERATIVE INC.
10125 W WATERGATE RD, CADILLAC, MI 496018458
Phone: 231 775-5700
Web: WWW.WPSCI.COM

COMPETITORS

ITC Holdings Corp.
Lansing Board of Water and Light
Midland Cogeneration Venture

HISTORICAL FINANCIALS

Company Type: Private

Income Statement

	REVENUE ($ mil.)	NET INCOME ($ mil.)	NET PROFIT MARGIN	EMPLOYEES
12/10	294	(16)	—	110
12/09	256	13	5.2%	—
12/07	164	0	0.0%	—
Annual Growth 21.3%	—	—	—	—

2010 Year-End Financials

Return on assets: 25.7%
Return on equity: (-5.8%)
Current ratio: 0.30
Cash ($ mil.): 2

WOMAN'S HOSPITAL FOUNDATION INC

Woman's Hospital is a 170-bed hospital catering to the needs of women and infants in southern Louisiana. Founded in 1968 the hospital was one of the nation's first women's specialty hospitals. The not-for-profit hospital offers women's health classes as well as other educational resources and delivers about 8500 babies each year. Services include breast care cosmetic surgery general surgery genetics counseling occupational therapy and speech therapy. Woman's Hospital moved to a new 225-acre campus in 2012 to replace its aging facilities. It boasts a five-story hospital building medical office buildings and increased capacity for its inpatient rooms and neonatal intensive care unit.

Strategy
Woman's Hospital which logged 11500 adult admissions in 2012 is working to grow its core business and expanding strategically. The hospital's $330 million relocation project —which was put on hold for about a year in the wake of the global recession —was restarted in 2010 and completed in 2012. It has also added a 20-bed unit that features areas for patients on bed rest.

Woman's Hospital also conducts clinical and molecular biology and genetic research. The organization collaborates with researchers at a range of institutions around the US including the American College of Surgeons Oncology Group and Louisiana State University.

Sales and Marketing
Woman's Hospital markets its services through TV advertising.

Financial Performance
The Baton Rouge Louisiana hospital logged $217.7 million in net patient service revenues in 2012 up from its $204.4 million in 2011.

The hospital receives more than half of its gross revenue from managed care contracts (HMO PPO) the rest from a mixture of Medicaid and Medicare and self-pay patients. Woman's Hospital's largest

---

inpatient service segment is neonatal ICU followed by obstetrics and gynecology.

EXECUTIVES

Vice President Medical Staff Services, Nancy Crawford
Vice President Of Campus Development, Stanley (Stan) Shelton
Vice President Support Services, Stan Shelton
Director Of Infection Control, Jennifer Freeny
Anesthesia Scheduling and Secretary, Claudia Venezia
Board Member, Renee Harris

LOCATIONS

HQ: WOMAN' S HOSPITAL FOUNDATION INC
100 WOMANS WAY, BATON ROUGE, LA 708175100
Phone: 225 927-1300
Web: WWW.WOMANS.ORG

PRODUCTS/OPERATIONS

Selected Services

Audiology
Breast Care
Breastfeeding
Cancer Care
Childbirth
Day Spa
Diabetes Care
Fertility
Fitness Club
Genetics
Health Screenings
Heart Health
Mammography
Metabolic Health
Nutrition
Philanthropy
Pregnancy
Social Services
Weight Loss

COMPETITORS

Amedisys
Baton Rouge General
General Health System
LSU System
Lane Regional Medical Center
Our Lady of the Lake
RMC
River Parishes
Hospital
Tenet Healthcare

HISTORICAL FINANCIALS

Company Type: Private

Income Statement

FYE: September 30

	REVENUE ($ mil.)	NET INCOME ($ mil.)	NET PROFIT MARGIN	EMPLOYEES
09/13	217	(12)	—	1,850
09/12	217	22	10.3%	—
09/11	219	46	21.0%	—
Annual Growth	(0.4%)	—	—	—

WOMEN & INFANTS HOSPITAL OF RHODE ISLAND

Auditors: ERNST & YOUNG US LLP GREENVIL

LOCATIONS

HQ: WOMEN & INFANTS HOSPITAL OF RHODE ISLAND
101 DUDLEY ST, PROVIDENCE, RI 029052499
Phone: 401 274-1100
Web: WWW.WOMENANDINFANTS.ORG

HISTORICAL FINANCIALS

Company Type: Private

Income Statement

FYE: September 30

	REVENUE ($ mil.)	NET INCOME ($ mil.)	NET PROFIT MARGIN	EMPLOYEES
09/13	411	14	3.6%	2,800
09/09	388	15	4.0%	—
09/08*	365	18	5.1%	—
12/05	0	0	—	—
Annual Growth 235.0%				

*Fiscal year change

2013 Year-End Financials

Return on assets: 10.9%
Return on equity: 3.6%
Current ratio: 1.70
Cash ($ mil.): 62

WORLD FINER FOODS INC

Fine food is quite a find for this company and its customers. World Finer Foods distributes more than 900 specialty food items to US supermarkets and gourmet food stores. Its inventory boasts some 40 brands including Blanchard & Blanchard La Vie Mrs. Leeper's Pasta and Panni. The company also markets its own food products under such names as DaVinci London Pub Pritikin and Reese. Its InterNatural Foods unit represents its natural foods division while its Liberty Richter division distributes domestic and imported gourmet food items. Founded as VIP Foods in 1971 World Finer Foods is a cooperative owned by food distributors Millbrook Distribution (a unit of United Natural Foods) and Kehe Food.

Geographic Reach
Based in New Jersey World Finer Foods serves supermarkets and gourmet food stores nationwide and internationally with its vast menu of specialty food items.

Operations
Through past acquisitions the company provides specialized natural foods thanks to its InterNatural Foods division and premium gourmet specialty items via its Liberty Richter division which has expertise in distributing both domestic and imported gourmet food items.

It sells markets and distributes specialty food products including cookies candies crisp bread crackers mustards spices herbs and oils sauces soups pasta cereals pickles vinegar products oatmeal jellies berries instant meals chutney and curry powders among others.

Sales and Marketing
World Finer Foods sells its products through a network of specialty food distributors that supply supermarket retailers as well as through its online store.

Strategy
As part of its business World Finer Foods has become an experienced global sourcing expert. To this end the company is well-versed in several functions such as purchasing inventory management freight forwarding and consolidation issues related

to the US Food and Drug Administration US Customs clearance warehousing and food labeling.

Some of its new products include the Reese line of fine foods Panda Candy Coated Licorice Pieces Bonne Maman French preserves and organic-certified and natural Spice Grinders from Drogheria & Alimentari.

Company Ownership

A cooperative World Finer Foods is owned by Millbrook Distribution (a unit of United Natural Foods) and Kehe Food both food distributors.

EXECUTIVES

Vice President Marketing, Marybeth Depersio
Vice President Of Finance, Barry O'Brien
Managing Director, Dimitrios Stratakis
Auditors: EISNERAMPER LLP NEW YORK NY

LOCATIONS

HQ: WORLD FINER FOODS INC
1455 BROAD ST STE 4, BLOOMFIELD, NJ 070033039
Phone: 973 338-0300
Web: WWW.WORLDFINER.COM

PRODUCTS/OPERATIONS

Selected Brands
Allegro
Bahlsen
Bonne Maman
Candoni
Colman's
DaVinci
Dr. Woods
Drogheria & Alimentari
Eddie's
El Rio
Familia
Felix
Fifty50
Honeycup Gourmet Mustards
Jules Destrooper
LaVie
McCann's
Monari Federzoni
Mrs. Leeper's
Panda
Panni
Pritkin
Reese
Ryvita
Storehouse Foods
Sun Brand
Sylvia's
Ty Ling
Wellington

COMPETITORS

Associated Wholesale Grocers	Kroger
C&S Wholesale	Performance Food Group
DPI Specialty Foods	SUPERVALU
European Imports	Wal-Mart
Haddon House	atalanta

HISTORICAL FINANCIALS

Company Type: Private

Income Statement

FYE: December 31

	REVENUE ($ mil.)	NET INCOME ($ mil.)	NET PROFIT MARGIN	EMPLOYEES
12/10	161	0	0.0%	78
12/08	125	0	0.6%	—
Annual Growth	13.2%	(68.7%)	—	—

2010 Year-End Financials

Return on assets: 8.7% Cash ($ mil.): —
Return on equity: —
Current ratio: 0.10

WORLD OF JEANS & TOPS

EXECUTIVES

VP Marketing, Cheryl A. Rudich, age 52
President CEO and Director, Daniel (Dan) Griesemer, age 53
VP Real Estate, John Burgess, age 60
Chairman and Chief Strategy Officer, Hezy Shaked, age 58
SVP and CFO, William (Bill) Langsdorf, age 56
VP COO and Chief Information Officer, Craig DeMerit, age 43
VP and General Merchandising Manager, Debbie Anker-Boetes, age 54
VP General Counsel and Secretary, Patrick Grosso, age 40
VP Stores, Shelly Johnson, age 43
VP Vendor Relations, Tilly Levine, age 57
VP Merchandise Planning and Allocation, Carolyn S. McNamara, age 48
VP Finance and Controller, Rochelle Myers, age 46
Founder, Chet Thomas
Director, Seth R. Johnson, age 59
Director, Bernard Zeichner, age 69
President CEO and Director, Daniel (Dan) Griesemer, age 53
Director, Jerold H. Rubinstein, age 74
Director, Janet E. Kerr, age 58
Auditors: DELOITTE & TOUCHE LLP COSTA M

LOCATIONS

HQ: WORLD OF JEANS & TOPS
10 WHATNEY, IRVINE, CA 926182807
Phone: 949 609-5599
Web: WWW.TILLYS.COM

COMPETITORS

Abercrombie & Fitch	Hot Topic
Aeropostale	Pacific Sunwear
American Eagle Outfitters	The Buckle
Forever 21	Urban Outfitters
	Wet Seal
	Zumiez

HISTORICAL FINANCIALS

Company Type: Private

Income Statement

FYE: January 29

	REVENUE ($ mil.)	NET INCOME ($ mil.)	NET PROFIT MARGIN	EMPLOYEES
01/11	332	24	7.3%	4,000
01/10	282	20	7.3%	—
01/09	1,486	0	—	—
Annual Growth	—67773.4%	—	—	—

2011 Year-End Financials

Return on assets: 4.4% Cash ($ mil.): 29
Return on equity: 7.3%
Current ratio: 0.80

WORLD WILDLIFE FUND INC.

A fuzzy-wuzzy with kung fu strength the panda embodies mission of the World Wildlife Fund (WWF). The conservation organization has worked on more than 13000 projects in about 100 countries to save endangered species and natural areas as well as to address threats such as global warming and the exploitation of forests. By 2020 WWF aims to conserve 15 of the world's more ecologically important regions. Its work crosses Africa Asia Latin America North America and Eurasia through national affiliates in about 100 countries. The group publishes data on wildlife wild places and global environmental challenges. Founded in 1961 WWF is joined by 1.1 million members in the US and some 5 million overseas.

Geographic Reach

While the Anchorage Alaska-based WWF is active in some 100 countries the organization targets the world's most ecologically important regions for conservation including the Arctic Amazon Congo Basin the Galapagos eastern Himalayas and the Northern Great Plains in the US.

Financial Performance

The conservation organization's total revenue including pledges for future years remained flat from 2013 to 2014 hovering around the $266 million mark. The consistent revenue was due to the success of the Arctic Home campaign with The Coca-Cola Company. Support from individual donors remained the single largest source of WWF's unrestricted revenue.

Strategy

In 2014 WWF opened its new Myanmar office in an effort to develop a green economy and help conserve the country's diverse species such as tigers elephants and Irrawaddy dolphins.

EXECUTIVES

Senior Vice President Forest and Freshwater, Tom Dillon
Senior Vice President Communications and Marketing, Terry Macko
Senior Vice President Market Transformations, Jason Clay
Vice President Climate Change, Lou Leonard
Managing Director Northern Great Plains Program, Martha Kauffman
Vice President Human Resources, Elaine Bowman
Vice President Travel Tourism and Conservation, Jim Sano
Special Assistant to the Senior Vice President of Development, Katy Lai
Vice President for U.S. Government Relations, Todd Shelton
Auditors: BDO USA LLP BETHESDA MD

LOCATIONS

HQ: WORLD WILDLIFE FUND INC.
1250 24TH ST NW FL 2, WASHINGTON, DC 200371193
Phone: 202 293-4800
Web: WWW.WORLDWILDLIFE.ORG

PRODUCTS/OPERATIONS

2015 Expenses

	% of total
Program	84
Fundraising	11
Finance & administration	5
Total	**100**

2015 Revenue

	% of total
Individual contributions	32
In-Kind & other revenues	19
Government grants & contracts	19
Foundation contributions	9
Network revenues	7
Corporations	4
Other/non-operating contributions	10
Total	**100**

Selected Goals

Ensure that the value of nature is reflected in the decisions made by individuals communities governments and businesses

Mobilize hundreds of millions of people to support conservation

Protect and restore species and their habitats

Strengthen local communities' ability to conserve the natural resources they depend upon

Transform markets and policies to reduce the impact of the production and consumption of commodities

HISTORICAL FINANCIALS
Company Type: Private

Income Statement
FYE: June 30

	REVENUE ($ mil.)	NET INCOME ($ mil.)	NET PROFIT MARGIN	EMPLOYEES
06/13	229	25	11.1%	2,500
06/12	208	16	8.1%	—
06/11	182	(1)	—	—
06/09	151	0	—	—
Annual Growth 10.9%	—	—	—	—

2013 Year-End Financials
Return on assets: —
Return on equity: 11.1%
Current ratio: 1.60
Cash ($ mil.): 62

WORLEY & OBETZ INC.

Auditors: TROUT EBERSOLE & GROFF LLP L

LOCATIONS
HQ: WORLEY & OBETZ INC.
85 WHITE OAK RD, MANHEIM, PA 175458550
Phone: 717 665-6891
Web: WWW.WORLEYOBETZ.COM

HISTORICAL FINANCIALS
Company Type: Private

Income Statement
FYE: August 31

	REVENUE ($ mil.)	NET INCOME ($ mil.)	NET PROFIT MARGIN	EMPLOYEES
08/14	466	1	0.4%	68
08/13	383	1	0.3%	—
08/12	417	1	0.3%	—
08/11	478	0	—	—
Annual Growth (0.8%)	—	—	—	—

2014 Year-End Financials
Return on assets: 2.4%
Return on equity: 0.4%
Current ratio: 1.20
Cash ($ mil.): —

WOROCO MANAGEMENT LLC

Auditors: AJ SANTYE & CO SOMERVILLE N

LOCATIONS
HQ: WOROCO MANAGEMENT LLC
40 WOODBRIDGE AVE STE 3, SEWAREN, NJ
070771335
Phone: 732 855-7720

HISTORICAL FINANCIALS
Company Type: Private

Income Statement
FYE: December 31

	REVENUE ($ mil.)	NET INCOME ($ mil.)	NET PROFIT MARGIN	EMPLOYEES
12/13	339	1	0.6%	14
12/12	274	2	0.7%	—
12/11	267	1	0.6%	—
12/10	169	0	—	—
Annual Growth 26.0%	—	—	—	—

2013 Year-End Financials
Return on assets: 0.9%
Return on equity: 0.6%
Current ratio: 0.60
Cash ($ mil.): 2

WRIGHT STATE UNIVERSITY

Wright State University named after aviation pioneers the Wright Brothers has an enrollment of some 18000 students and offers more than 100 undergraduate degrees and about 90 graduate and professional degrees. It consists of eight colleges (including education and human services business engineering and computer science liberal arts nursing and health and science and mathematics) and three schools (graduate studies medicine professional psychology). Wright State has about 900 faculty members. Originally a branch campus of Ohio State University and Miami University Wright State became an independent university in 1967.

Geographic Reach

Along with its main campus in Dayton Ohio Wright State also offers classes at its smaller Lake Campus in Celina Ohio.

Operations

The university's tuition fees are $16500 per annum for non-residential students and $8700 for residential students. Some 10% of its students are international (from about 70 countries).

Wright State's libraries include the Paul Laurence Dunbar Library the Lake Campus Learning Center the Student Technology Assistance Center (STAC) and Special Collections and Archives.

Financial Performance

Wright State reported a 11% decrease in revenues in fiscal 2014 due to lower sales and services led by a drop in conference and events income grants and contracts (related to the transition of the OhioLINK program to The Ohio State University); and reductions in the volume and amount of federal grants and auxiliary revenues due to expenses related to hospitality services. This was partially offset by higher student tuition and fees. The university's net loss decreased by 63% in fiscal 2014 due to higher investment return and capital appropriation. Wright State's cash outflow in fiscal 2014 declined by 15% due to a lower net loss and a decrease in receivables.

Strategy

The university's 2013-2018 Strategic Plan aims at enhancing academic quality and program distinctiveness; improving student access and educational achievement by increasing enrollment and retention and attaining national prominence in research scholarship and entrepreneurial activities. In 2015 Wright State announced plans to grow STEM education (science technology engineering and mathematics) in the region in order to help prepare workers for jobs in intelligence aerospace and defense through the creation of The Center for Workforce Development.

In addition the university is adopting a new budgeting model that it hopes will provide more transparency while allowing academic units to strategically identify new revenue sources. The system also aims to help divisions identify programs that are not adding academic or financial value.

Company Background

In 2012 Wright State issued $55 million in bonds to pay for construction and renovation efforts on academic and administrative buildings both on new and existing facilities. It is also upgrading campus infrastructures and student recreation and athletic facilities.

EXECUTIVES

VP Business and Finance, Mark Polatajko
President, David R. Hopkins
EVP Planning, Robert J. Sweeney
Dean Graduate School, Robert E. Fyffe
Provost, Sundaram Narayanan
Dean College of Education and Human Services, Charlotte Harris
Dean College of Engineering and Computer Science, Nathan Klingbeil
Dean Raj Soin College of Business, Joanne Li
Dean College of Science and Mathematics, Yi Li
Dean College of Nursing and Health, Rosalie O'Dell Mainous
Dean Lake Campus, Bonnie K. Mathies
Dean College of Liberal Arts, Kristin D. Sobolik
Dean Boonshoft School of Medicine, Marjorie Bowman
Interim Dean School of Professional Psychology, LaPearl L. Winfrey
CIO, Craig Woolley
Second Vice President, Lewis Shupe
Associate Vice President Development, Rebecca Cole
Assistant Vice President for Advancement, Robert (Bob) Copeland
Vice President Technology, Amit Sheth
Assc Vice President Facilities Plng Development, Vicky L Davidson
Assistant Vice President For Advancement, Cindy Young
Vice President Enrollment Management, Jacqueline McMillan
Executive Vice President, Gary Leroy
Vice President Research, Benjamin Salisbury
Vice President, Connie James
Vice President For Academic Affairs, Molly Hall
Vice President, Elizabeth Richardson
Vice President Student Affairs, Jill Sink
Assistant Vice President, Bill Shepard
Vice President For Enrollment Management, Mary Ashley
Vice President University Advancement, Bryan Rowland
Associate Vice President for Human Resources and Chief Human Resources Officer, Shari Mickey-Boggs
Vice President Curriculum and Instruction, Tamarus L Stokes
Vice President of Marketing, Amy Jones
Senior Vice President Business And Fiscal Affairs, Matt Filipic
Associate Vice President Public Affairs, Robert (Bob) Hickey
Chairman, Larry R. Klaben
Vice Chairman, Michael C. Bridges
Club Treasurer, Anne Tormey
Secretary, Lisa Duke
Auditors: CROWE HORWATH LLP COLUMBUS

LOCATIONS

HQ: WRIGHT STATE UNIVERSITY
3640 COLONEL GLENN HWY, DAYTON, OH
454350002
Phone: 937 775-3333
Web: WWW.WRIGHT.EDU

PRODUCTS/OPERATIONS

2014 sales

	% of total
Student tuition and fees	61
Grants and contracts	31
Sales and services	3
Auxiliary enterprises	4
Other	1
Total	**100**

Selected Schools and Colleges

Colleges
Education and Human Services
Engineering and Computer Science
Liberal Arts
Nursing and Health
Raj Soin College of Business
Professional Psychology
Science and Mathematics
University College
WSU-Lake Campus
Schools
Boonshoft School of Medicine
Graduate Studies
Professional Psychology

HISTORICAL FINANCIALS

Company Type: Private

Income Statement

FYE: June 30

	REVENUE ($ mil.)	NET INCOME ($ mil.)	NET PROFIT MARGIN	EMPLOYEES
06/14	235	(3)	—	2,748
06/13	272	0	0.2%	
06/12	267	(10)	—	
06/11	263	0	—	
Annual Growth	(3.7%)	—	—	—

2014 Year-End Financials

Return on assets: 7.2%   Cash ($ mil.): 13
Return on equity: (-1.4%)
Current ratio: 0.70

WTG GAS PROCESSING L.P.

LOCATIONS

HQ: WTG GAS PROCESSING L.P.
211 N COLORADO ST, MIDLAND, TX 797014607
Phone: 432 682-6311

HISTORICAL FINANCIALS

Company Type: Private

Income Statement

FYE: December 31

	REVENUE ($ mil.)	NET INCOME ($ mil.)	NET PROFIT MARGIN	EMPLOYEES
12/07	588	85	14.5%	25
12/06	498	64	13.0%	—
12/05	484	69	14.4%	—
12/04	342	0	—	—
Annual Growth	19.7%	—	—	—

2007 Year-End Financials

Return on assets: 8.6%   Cash ($ mil.): 45
Return on equity: 14.5%
Current ratio: 2.60

WYCKOFF HEIGHTS MEDICAL CENTER

Wyckoff Heights is taking health care to new levels. Serving the New York boroughs of Brooklyn and Queens Wyckoff Heights Medical Center maintains some 350 beds and provides a comprehensive range of specialized services including diagnostics radiology cardiology obstetrics pediatrics surgery and rehabilitative care. The hospital also provides educational services through a partnership with the Weill Medical College of Cornell University and it offers outpatient services through several family health clinics in the area. The not-for-profit medical center is an affiliated member of the New York-Presbyterian Healthcare System but is governed by an independent board of trustees.

OperationsThe hospital has 75000 visits a year at its Pediatric/Adult Emergency Departments. Every year it also delivers 2000 babies offers outpatient services to thousands through a network of community ambulatory care centers and conducts extensive community health education and screening programs.StrategyWyckoff Heights is responding to the growing healthcare needs of the communities they serve by acquiring new equipment and expanding clinical programs. The center has added an on-site MRI to ensure that community residents do not have to travel outside the neighborhood to access advanced radiologic procedures the center established a cardiac catheterization lab for definitive diagnostic tests that assess coronary circulation and overall heart function implemented a a bloodless medicine and surgery program to accommodate those individuals who for religious or other reasons choose treatment options that do not include blood installed hyperbaric chambers to aid in the healing of wounds encountered by diabetic patients and burn victims and access to a discrete Women's Health Center that offers a comprehensive range of obstetrical and gynecological services in maximum privacy and comfort for female patients of all ages.

Company Background
Wyckoff Heights was founded in 1889.

EXECUTIVES

Vp Regulatory Services, Karen Carey
Acting Vice President Nursing, Margaret (Peg) Pelkowski
Vice President Of Information Technology, Jebashini Jesursa
Assistant Vice President Of Ambulatory Care, Sonia Mercado
Vice President Health Information Management, Teresa Silversmith
Vice President, Kenneth Freiberg
Medical Director, Harry Boparai
Vice President Nursing, Rosetta Melvin
Director Of Nursing, Joy Mitchell
Vice President Of It, Cletis Earl
Vice President Nursing, Renee Herskowitz-mauriello

LOCATIONS

HQ: WYCKOFF HEIGHTS MEDICAL CENTER
374 STOCKHOLM ST, BROOKLYN, NY 112374006
Phone: 718 963-7272
Web: WWW.WYCKOFFHOSPITAL.ORG

PRODUCTS/OPERATIONS

Selected Services

Anesthesiology
Asthma
Breast Surgery
Cardiology/Heart
Colorectal Surgery
Dermatology
Ear Nose & Throat (ENT)
Emergency Medicine
Endocrinology (Diabetes)
Family Medicine
Gastroenterology
General Surgery
Genetics
Geriatrics
Head & Neck Surgery
Hyperbaric Medicine/Wound Care
Infectious Diseases
Internal Medicine
Medical Oncology
Nephrology
Neurology/Designated Stroke Center
Neurosurgery
Nursing
Obstetrics & Gynecology
Ophthalmology/Eye
Orthopedics
Otolaryngology
Pain Management
Pathology
Pediatrics
Physical Medicine & Rehabilitation
Plastic Surgery
Podiatry
Psychiatry
Pulmonary Medicine
Radiation Oncology
Radiology
Respiratory Therapy
Rheumatology
Thoracic Surgery
Urology

COMPETITORS

Catholic Healthcare System
Continuum Health Partners
Kingsbrook Jewish Medical Center
Maimonides Medical Center
MediSys Health Network
Memorial Sloan-Kettering
Montefiore Medical
New York City Health and Hospitals
North Shore-Long Island Jewish Health System

HISTORICAL FINANCIALS

Company Type: Private

Income Statement

FYE: December 31

	REVENUE ($ mil.)	NET INCOME ($ mil.)	NET PROFIT MARGIN	EMPLOYEES
12/12	246	4	1.9%	1,900
12/09	286	8	3.0%	—
12/08*	233	(32)	—	—
11/08	2	0	—	—
Annual Growth	207.5%	—	—	—

*Fiscal year change

2012 Year-End Financials

Return on assets: 6.9%   Cash ($ mil.): 5
Return on equity: 1.9%
Current ratio: 0.30

WYOMING MEDICAL CENTER INC.

Wyoming Medical Center is The Cowboy State's largest medical facility. The hospital founded in 1911 offers those who live in and around Wyoming's Natrona County more than 50 medical specialties thanks to its 150 physicians. The health care services provider boasts nearly 1300 skilled staff members and more than 190 beds. It offers services such as an emergency air transport system trauma care diagnostic services diabetes care center nephrology and surgical care. The facility is a community-owned not-for-profit hospital.that also operates the Heart Center of Wyoming the Wyoming Neuroscience and Spine Institute and a network of about a dozen community clinics throughout Wyoming.

Geographic Reach

The health care provider serves the Wyoming communities of Natrona County and its surrounding counties.

EXECUTIVES

Medical Director Emergency Department, Ron Iverson
Director Of Nursing Services, Jan Backus
Assistant Vice President Of Nursing, Andrew Bertapelle
Secretary, Eugene Duquette
Auditors: EIDE BAILLY LLP FARGO NORTH

LOCATIONS

HQ: WYOMING MEDICAL CENTER INC.
1233 E 2ND ST, CASPER, WY 826012988
Phone: 307 577-7201
Web: WWW.WYOMINGMEDICALCENTERFOUNDATION.ORG

PRODUCTS/OPERATIONS

Selected Services

AHA Training
Casper Pulmonary
da Vinci System
Diabetes Care Center
Heart Center of Wyoming
Hometown Specialty Clinics
Professional Lab Services
Sage Primary Care
Weight Management Program
Wyoming Brain & Spine Associates
Wyoming Life Flight
Wyoming Nephrology
Wyoming Relay Health

COMPETITORS

Banner Health
Billings Clinic
Evanston
LifePoint Health
North Colorado Medical Center
Poudre Valley Health System
Universal Health Services

HISTORICAL FINANCIALS

Company Type: Private

Income Statement FYE: June 30

	REVENUE ($ mil.)	NET INCOME ($ mil.)	NET PROFIT MARGIN	EMPLOYEES
06/13	239	15	6.5%	1,033
06/11	227	14	6.3%	—
06/10	236	8	3.7%	—
06/09	204	0	—	—
Annual Growth	4.1%	—	—	—

2013 Year-End Financials

Return on assets: 7.4%
Return on equity: 6.5%
Current ratio: 2.40
Cash ($ mil.): 51

XANTERRA HOLDING CORP

LOCATIONS

HQ: XANTERRA HOLDING CORP
6312 S FIDDLERS GREEN CIR # 600, GREENWOOD VILLAGE, CO 801114943
Phone: 303 600-3400
Web: WWW.XANTERRA.COM

HISTORICAL FINANCIALS

Company Type: Private

Income Statement FYE: December 25

	REVENUE ($ mil.)	NET INCOME ($ mil.)	NET PROFIT MARGIN	EMPLOYEES
12/13	336	4	1.3%	3,500
12/12	335	7	2.2%	—
12/11	328	1	0.5%	—
12/10	316	0	—	—
Annual Growth	2.0%	—	—	—

2013 Year-End Financials

Return on assets: —
Return on equity: 1.3%
Current ratio: 0.30
Cash ($ mil.): 19

XANTERRA INC.

LOCATIONS

HQ: XANTERRA INC.
6312 S FIDDLERS GREEN CIR 600N, GREENWOOD VILLAGE, CO 801114943
Phone: 303 600-3400
Web: WWW.XANTERRA.COM

HISTORICAL FINANCIALS

Company Type: Private

Income Statement FYE: December 25

	REVENUE ($ mil.)	NET INCOME ($ mil.)	NET PROFIT MARGIN	EMPLOYEES
12/13	304	11	3.7%	3,500
12/12	305	13	4.3%	—
12/11	301	7	2.4%	—
12/10	305	0	—	—
Annual Growth	(0.1%)	—	—	—

2013 Year-End Financials

Return on assets: —
Return on equity: 3.7%
Current ratio: 0.30
Cash ($ mil.): 18

XAVIER UNIVERSITY

Xavier University is a not-for-profit Jesuit Catholic institution that operates from a single campus located in Cincinnati Ohio. The private school which has recently grown its enrollment numbers to about 7000 students offers nearly 90 undergraduate programs and about 20 graduate programs. Xavier University's programs range from arts and sciences to social sciences and business. Boasting small class sizes the university's student-to-faculty ratio is a noteworthy 12:1. Known among sports circles as having a highly respected men's basketball program Xavier University also manages to graduate every member of its men's Musketeers group. Xavier University was founded in 1831.

Geographic Reach

The university serves about 7000 students from its 190-acre campus located in Cincinnati Ohio.

Operations

The university is the nation's sixth-oldest Catholic university as compared to 27 other Jesuit colleges in the US. Xavier University's enrollment of about 7000 students includes 4540 undergraduates. Across its three colleges the university offers 87 undergraduate majors 55 minors and 19 graduate programs.

Sales and Marketing

Xavier University is the top school in the Midwest for graduation and approximately 77% of its student population is accepted to medical school. Across the university's sports disciplines it has 16 Division I teams.

Financial Performance

For the reporting period of 2012 vs. 2011 Xavier University posted flat revenue due to an increase in tuition and fees and auxiliary enterprise revenue. This was offset however by a decrease in government grants as well as a decline in contracts private gifts grants and endowment income. Net income for 2012 as compared to 2011 declined by 199% thanks to contributions and change in contributions receivable for non-operating purpose and investment return net of amounts in operations.

EXECUTIVES

Vice President, Mary Walker
Assistant Vice President Fin Admin, KEITH BALDWIN
Vice President for Student Enrollment, Terry Richards
Vice President for Financial Administration, Richard (Dick) Hirte
Vice President, Gary Massa
Senior Vice President Chief Financial Officer, Maribeth Amyor
Secretary Actuarial Science, Teresa Hardin
Auditors: DELOITTE & TOUCHE LLP CINCINN

LOCATIONS

HQ: XAVIER UNIVERSITY
3800 VICTORY PKWY UNIT 1, CINCINNATI, OH 452071092
Phone: 513 745-3000
Web: WWW.XAVIER.EDU

PRODUCTS/OPERATIONS

Selected Colleges

College of Arts& Sciences
College of Social Sciences Health & Education
Williams College of Business

Income Statement

FYE: June 30

	REVENUE ($ mil.)	NET INCOME ($ mil.)	NET PROFIT MARGIN	EMPLOYEES
06/14	166	37	22.3%	940
06/13	163	14	8.7%	—
06/12	166	(22)	—	—
06/11	167	0	—	—
Annual Growth	(0.2%)	—	—	—

2014 Year-End Financials

Return on assets: 4.4% Cash ($ mil.): 24
Return on equity: 22.3%
Current ratio: —

YAKIMA VALLEY MEMORIAL HOSPITAL ASSOCIATION INC

Whether you're a major yakker or quiet as a mouse Yakima Valley Memorial Hospital serves the health care needs of patients of all types. The health provider's acute-care hospital skilled-nursing facilities and outpatient specialty treatment facilities serve patients in and around Yakima in Washington State. The hospital has about 225 beds and provides a variety of services such as heart care orthopedics pediatrics cancer treatment women's health and mental health care. It also offers sleep and wound care and provides home health and hospice services. The organization is a not-for-profit group governed by a board of directors.

Geographic Reach

In addition to its main 26-acre campus in Yakima Washington the organization has 15 locations throughout Yakima County.

Operations

Yakima Valley Memorial Hospital sees about 15000 inpatients each year as well as 77000 emergency room visits and 3100 births. It serves a total of more than 130000 patient per year.

The organization provides a full range of inpatient and outpatient services that include critical care surgery diagnostics cancer care heart care orthopedics a family birthplace a neonatal intensive care unit pediatrics physical therapy and psychiatric care. Its Children's Village provides care for kids with special health or development needs. Other specialty units include the Garden Village skilled nursing center and the Cottage in the Meadow hospice facility. The organization also runs a community education program and a maternal health preventative care program.

Among its staff are 330 physicians representing 35 medical specialties.

Financial Performance

During 2012 the hospital provided $73.7 million in Community Benefits (22% more than in 2011). Included in this number was more than $33 million to cover a shortfall from Medicare funding. Net patient revenue in 2012 was $286 million.

Strategy

Yakima Valley Memorial Hospital is upgrading its infrastructure and its technologies to better serve area residents. In 2013 for instance it added digital breast screening systems to its mammography center and in 2012 the facility invested $1.3 million to replace aging beds.

In 2013 the hospital announced that it was looking for a partner to help it with several challenges including Medicare reimbursement cuts state Medicaid funding woes and the high costs of health information technology. The three prospective groups (which submitted proposals) included Virginia Mason Medical Center in Seattle; Seattle-based Swedish Health Services and Renton-based Providence Health & Services; and Vancouver (Washington)-based PeaceHealth and the University of Washington Medicine Medicine in Seattle.

Company Background

Yakima Valley Memorial Hospital was founded in 1950.

EXECUTIVES

Director of Home Healthcare, Carolyn Nieswender
Senior Vice President, Mely Davenport
Vice President Nursing, Sandy Dahl
Medical Records Director, Jamie Beaman
Director of Physical Therapy, Jackie Ray
Cota l, Rachael Monahan
Vice President Communications and Development, Anne Caffery
Medical Director Sleep Center, Susan (Sue) Rausch
Vice President Of Medical Staff, Judy Harvey
Vice President, Aberle Jim
Board Member, Gail Weaver
Auditors: MOSS-ADAMS LLP YAKIMA WASHIN

LOCATIONS

HQ: YAKIMA VALLEY MEMORIAL HOSPITAL ASSOCIATION INC
2811 TIETON DR, YAKIMA, WA 989023761
Phone: 509 249-5129
Web: WWW.YAKIMAMEMORIAL.ORG

PRODUCTS/OPERATIONS

Selected Services and Locations

16th Avenue Pavilion
Apple Valley Family Medicine
Cardiac Rehabilitation and Wellness Center
Cascade Surgical Partners
Children' s Village
Family Medicine of Yakima
Garden Village
Home Health and Hospice
Memorial Cornerstone Medicine
Memorial Hospitalist Program
Memorial' s Valley Imaging
North Star Lodge Cancer Center
' Ohana Mammography Center
Pacific Crest Family Medicine
Selah Family Medicine
Sleep Center at Memorial
Surgi-Center at Memorial
The Springs Rehabilitation and Occupational Medicine
Water' s Edge Pain Relief Institute
Yakima Gastroenterology Associates
Yakima Internal Medicine
Yakima Neurosurgery Associates
Yakima Plastic Surgery Associates
Yakima Vascular Associates

COMPETITORS

Adventist Health	Overlake Hospital
Catholic Health Initiatives	PeaceHealth
Franciscan Health System	Providence Health & Services
HCA	Sacred Heart Medical Center
Harrison Medical Center	Swedish Health Services
MultiCare Health System	Watson Institute

Income Statement

FYE: October 31

	REVENUE ($ mil.)	NET INCOME ($ mil.)	NET PROFIT MARGIN	EMPLOYEES
10/13	361	39	10.9%	1,150
10/12	309	(6)	—	—
10/09	276	(18)	—	—
10/08	245	0	—	—
Annual Growth	8.1%	—	—	—

2013 Year-End Financials

Return on assets: 3.7% Cash ($ mil.): 11
Return on equity: 10.9%
Current ratio: 1.30

YESHIVA UNIVERSITY

Yeshivas are traditional Jewish schools and Yeshiva University believes strongly in following tradition. The Jewish higher education institution serves more than 7000 undergraduate and graduate students at four campuses in New York City. Subjects taught include liberal arts sciences medicine law business social work and psychology. It also has extensive Jewish studies and education programs including study abroad opportunities. Yeshiva University also known as YU has an undergraduate student-to-teacher ratio of 6:1. Its graduate programs include medicine law psychology and Jewish education.

Geographic Reach

Yeshiva University's four New York City campuses consist of the Brookdale Center the Israel Henry Beren Campus and the Wilf Campus in Manhattan and the Jack and Pearl Resnick Campus in the Bronx. It also has a campus in Jerusalem that coordinates its study abroad programs.

Operations

Yeshiva University operates three undergraduate schools: Yeshiva College Stern College for Women and Sy Syms School of Business. Undergraduates may also enroll in the Joint Israel Program a formal arrangement between Yeshiva University and more than 45 yeshivot and seminaries in Israel. Enrolled students get to spend a year studying at Israeli institutions in fields including Talmud Bible Jewish Law and Jewish thought Philosophy Zionism Jewish History and oral and written Hebrew.

Beyond undergraduate education the university operates the Albert Einstein School of Medicine which provides medical training and research opportunities. With roughly 1000 students Albert Einstein School of Medicine is a major biomedical and clinical research facility and receives some $200 million in annual funding from the National Institutes of Health. Areas of research include diabetes cancer liver disease and HIV/AIDS.

Other graduate programs include schools and affiliate institutions in areas including law social work psychology Jewish studies and theology.

Company Background

The university traces its roots to the 1915 merging of two schools from New York's Lower East Side: Yeshiva Eitz Chaim founded in 1886 and the Rabbi Isaac Elchanan Theological Seminary (RIETS) founded in 1896.

EXECUTIVES

Vice President Information Technology Cio, Marc Milstein

Provost and VP Academic Affairs, Selma Botman
President, Richard M. Joel
Dean Einstein College of Medicine, Allen M. Spiegel
Dean University Libraries, Pearl Berger
VP Business Affairs and CFO, Jacob (Jake) Harman
Dean Yeshiva College, Barry Eichler
Dean Syms School of Business, Moses Pava
Dean Center for the Jewish Future, Rabbi Yaakov Glasser
Dean Azrieli Graduate School of Jewish Education and Administration, Rona M. Novick
Dean Elchanan Theological Seminary, Rabbi Menachem Penner
Dean Stern College for Women, Karen Bacon
Dean Revel Graduate School of Jewish Studies, David Berger
Dean Cardozo School of Law, Matthew Diller
Vice President, Daniel Forman
Vice President University Community Life, Kenneth (Ken) Brander
Vice President for Enrollment Management, MJKnoll Finn
Chairman, Moshael J. Straus
Secretary to Chairman, Maura Gabriele
Auditors: PRICEWATERHOUSECOOPERS LLP NE

LOCATIONS

HQ: YESHIVA UNIVERSITY
500 W 185TH ST, NEW YORK, NY 100333299
Phone: 212 960-5400
Web: WWW.YUHSB.ORG

PRODUCTS/OPERATIONS

Schools and Colleges
Albert Einstein College of Medicine-MS MD
Azrieli Graduate School of Jewish Education and Administration-MS EdD
Benjamin N. Cardozo School of Law-JD LLM
Bernard Revel Graduate School of Jewish Studies- MA PhD
Ferkauf Graduate School of Psychology-MA MS PhD PsyD
Stern College for Women-BA
Sue Golding Graduate Division of Medical Sciences-MS PhD
Sy Syms School of Business-BS
Wurzweiler School of Social Work-MSW CJCS PhD
Yeshiva College-BA
Special Institutions
Marsha Stern Talmudical Academy for Boys
Rabbi Isaac Elchanan Theological Seminary
Samuel H. Wang Yeshiva University High School for Girls
Yeshiva University High Schools
Yeshiva University Museum
Centers/Institutions
Center for Israel Studies at Yeshiva University
Center for Jewish Law and Contemporary Civilization
Center for the Jewish Future
Graduate Program in Advanced Talmudic Studies at Stern College for Women
Institute for Public Health Sciences
Rabbi Arthur Schneier Center for International Affairs
The Center for Ethics at Yeshiva University

HISTORICAL FINANCIALS

Company Type: Private

Income Statement

FYE: June 30

	REVENUE ($ mil.)	NET INCOME ($ mil.)	NET PROFIT MARGIN	EMPLOYEES
06/13	704	(98)	—	4,500
06/11	674	(85)	—	
06/10	657	(94)	—	
06/09	541	0	—	
Annual Growth	6.8%	—	—	—

2013 Year-End Financials

Return on assets: 13.2%   Cash ($ mil.): 20
Return on equity: (-13.9%)
Current ratio: —

YORK HOSPITAL

York Hospital operating as WellSpan York Hospital takes its name from the community whose health it seeks to preserve. Part of WellSpan Health the medical center has about 570 beds and serves residents of York and surrounding area of south-central Pennsylvania. It is a regional leader in cardiovascular and orthopedic care and has programs in other specialty areas including oncology behavioral health and geriatrics. Additionally WellSpan York Hospital operates a Level 1 trauma center offers outpatient surgery emergency home health and diagnostic imaging services. It is also has teaching and research programs. The hospital was founded in 1880.

Operations
WellSpan York Hospital has been recognized as a top 100 US hospital by US News for more than five years in a row. It is also recognized for its cardiovascular and orthopedic programs. The center employs about 700 doctors.

The hospital's education programs include five allied health schools and seven residency programs. Affiliated organizations include the medical schools of Drexel University Pennsylvania State University and University of Maryland.

Strategy
WellSpan York Hospital is working to improve its specialist programs to meet the growing medical needs of area residents. In 2011 for instance it collaborated with technology firm Cerner and pharmaceuticals firm Hospira to form an infusion management program for its intensive care unit; the program aims to reduce infusion-related errors. In addition it launched a urinary catheter removal protocol to reduce infection rates and it implemented an aortic valve replacement program (making it one of three facilities in Pennsylvania to offer the open-heart surgery alternative).

EXECUTIVES

Medical Director, Cathy Penton Carpenter

LOCATIONS

HQ: YORK HOSPITAL
1001 S GEORGE ST, YORK, PA 174033645
Phone: 717 337-4123
Web: WWW.YORKHOSPITAL.EDU

COMPETITORS

Ascension Health
Catholic Health Initiatives
Geisinger Health System
Guthrie Healthcare
Hanover Healthcare
Hershey Medical Center
Holy Spirit
Lancaster General
Memorial Hospital (PA)
PinnacleHealth System

HISTORICAL FINANCIALS

Company Type: Private

Income Statement

FYE: June 30

	REVENUE ($ mil.)	NET INCOME ($ mil.)	NET PROFIT MARGIN	EMPLOYEES
06/14	853	136	16.0%	6,200
06/13	840	103	12.3%	
06/12	806	27	3.4%	
06/11	807	0	—	
Annual Growth	1.8%	—	—	

2014 Year-End Financials

Return on assets: 1.6%   Cash ($ mil.): 76
Return on equity: 16.0%
Current ratio: 3.10

YOSEMITE FARM CREDIT ACA

LOCATIONS

HQ: YOSEMITE FARM CREDIT ACA
800 W MONTE VISTA AVE, TURLOCK, CA 953827242
Phone: 209 667-2366
Web: WWW.YOSEMITEFARMCREDIT.COM

HISTORICAL FINANCIALS

Company Type: Private

Income Statement

FYE: December 31

	ASSETS ($ mil.)	NET INCOME ($ mil.)	INCOME AS % OF ASSETS	EMPLOYEES
12/13	1,993	37	1.9%	100
12/12	1,879	37	2.0%	
12/11	1,676	54	3.2%	
12/10	1,609	0	—	
Annual Growth	7.4%	—	—	

2013 Year-End Financials

Return on assets: —   Sales ($ mil.): 80
Return on equity: 46.6%

YOUNG LIFE

Young Life is focused on promoting Christianity among teenagers in the US and in more than 50 other countries. Founded in 1941 the not-for-profit organization provides activities and support for junior high middle school and high school students located in rural and urban communities. Young Life also operates week-long summer camp programs at about 20 locations throughout North America as well as retreats held throughout the year. The group has grown throughout the years from a single club in Texas to about 600 international Young Life ministries dotting the globe. The organization boasts about 3000 staffers and more than 27000 volunteers.

EXECUTIVES

Senior Vice President North, Lee Infrastructure Corder
Senior Vice President North, Gail Infrastructure Ebersole
Vice President Field Ministries, Jan Marable
Vice President Of Human Resources, Reid Estes
Senior Vice President Western Division, John Franklin
Senior Vice President South, Marty Infrastructure Caldwell
Senior Vice President West, Ty Saltzgiver
Vice President of Field Ministries Southern Division, Bebe Hobson
Vice President Of Information Technology, Jeff Mawhirter
Vice President of Field Ministries Western Division, Angel Ruiz
Auditors: CAPIN CROUSE LLP COLORADO SPR

LOCATIONS

HQ: YOUNG LIFE
420 N CASCADE AVE, COLORADO SPRINGS, CO 809033352
Phone: 719 381-1800
Web: WWW.YOUNGLIFE.ORG

Company Type: Private

Income Statement FYE: September 30

	REVENUE ($ mil.)	NET INCOME ($ mil.)	NET PROFIT MARGIN	EMPLOYEES
09/14	311	31	10.3%	3,100
09/13	276	17	6.5%	—
09/12	237	0	0.1%	—
09/11	245	0	—	—
Annual Growth	8.2%	—	—	—

2014 Year-End Financials

Return on assets: 6.1% Cash ($ mil.): 51
Return on equity: 10.3%
Current ratio: 2.40

YUMA REGIONAL MEDICAL CENTER INC

Yuma Regional Medical Center (YRMC) is an acute care hospital that provides medical services for Yuma Arizona and its surrounding communities. The not-for-profit hospital which has more than 400 beds and 300 doctors provides general medical surgical and emergency services as well as 40 specialties through units including a cardiac catheterization lab children's and women's health centers a weight loss department and a cancer treatment center as well as outpatient care divisions. YRMC also offers home health care school health care medical equipment rentals (through First Health Medical Supply) and cardiac and pulmonary rehabilitation services off-site.

Sales and Marketing

Medicare and Arizona Health Care Cost Containment System (AHCCCS) accounted for 35% and 11% respectively of YRMC's net patient service revenue in 2014. Other third-party payors accounted for 41% and self-pay accounted for 13%.

Financial Performance

Net sales increased 12% to $343.4 million in 2014 as patient service revenues rose. That led to an increase in net income which rose 7% to $368.9 million. Operating cash flow more than doubled rising 120% to $38.2 million.

Strategy

Being a regional hospital YRMC works hard to recruit physicians who might otherwise be drawn to larger teaching hospitals with more advanced technological equipment and complex patient cases. In order to lure in such specialists the hospital offers extended medical education career weekends and a number of specialized centers in which physicians can perform procedures solely in their specialty such as a neonatal ICU and a pediatric sub-specialty unit. It opened a new cardiovascular operating room in 2013 and it broke ground on a new cancer care center.

YRMC also offers a free program called Silver Care in which patients who are 55 and older are encouraged to live active and healthy lives by being offered a number of benefits such as discounts at local stores specially reduced rates on selected lab tests including cholesterol and blood glucose screenings. Additionally Silver Care members are eligible for free membership in the Fit for Life cardiac wellness program.

The hospital's medical personnel have completed advanced procedures such as a tran-scatheter aortic valve replacement and a one-level cervical disc replacement using Mobi-C technology.

Ownership

The not-for-profit YRMC organization is governed by a 12-member board composed of community volunteers. The hospital is funded by the Foundation of Yuma Regional Medical Center which raises money through various means including donations bequests and special events. Since it is located on property leased from the area hospital district it is also eligible to receive financial support from tax-exempt revenue bonds for construction projects.

EXECUTIVES

Vice President Information Technology, Gene Shaw
Vice President, Carl F Myers
Pharmd, Jody Agena
Medical Librarian, Leone Neegan
Vice President Marketing and Communications, Machele Headington
Physical Therapy Director, Jennifer (Jen) Breen
Vice President Of Human Resources, Marshall Jones
Vice President Patient Care Services Cno, Karen Jensen
Vice President Professional and Support Services, Jim Hall
Board Member, Wayne Steffey
Secretary, Phillip (Phil) Richemont
Auditors: MOSS ADAMS LLP SCOTTSDALE AR

LOCATIONS

HQ: YUMA REGIONAL MEDICAL CENTER INC
2400 S AVENUE A, YUMA, AZ 853647170
Phone: 928 344-2000
Web: WWW.YUMAREGIONAL.ORG

PRODUCTS/OPERATIONS

2014

	$ mil	%
Net patient service revenue	368	98
Other revenue	6	2
Provision for doubtful accounts	(31.6)	-
Total	**343**	**100**

Selected Services

Children
Cancer Care
Children's Rehabilitative Services
Critical Care
Diabetes Education
Diagnostic Imaging
Emergency Department
First Health Medical Supply
Gastroenterology
Heart
Hospitalist Program
Lab
Medical Staff Services
Nursing Units
Outpatient Surgical Center
Pharmacy
Spiritual Care and Patient Advocacy
Surgical Services
Weight Loss
Women's Services
Wound Care Center

COMPETITORS

Banner Health	Phoenix Children's Hospital
Community Health Systems	Poudre Valley Health System
Dignity Health	
HCA	Providence Health & Services
Iasis Healthcare	
Inova	Scottsdale Healthcare
John C. Lincoln Health Network	St. Joseph Health System
Northern Arizona Healthcare	University of Arizona Health Network

Company Type: Private

Income Statement FYE: September 30

	REVENUE ($ mil.)	NET INCOME ($ mil.)	NET PROFIT MARGIN	EMPLOYEES
09/13	291	11	3.9%	1,600
09/12	346	22	6.6%	—
09/11	330	4	1.2%	—
09/10	317	0	—	—
Annual Growth	(2.8%)	—	—	—

2013 Year-End Financials

Return on assets: 4.7% Cash ($ mil.): 14
Return on equity: 3.9%
Current ratio: 0.50

Z GALLERIE

Cain and Abel they're not! Brothers and executives Joe and Mike Zeiden founded Z Gallerie in 1979 using their parents' garage for a warehouse and production facility. Initially Z Gallerie (later joined by sister Carole Malfatti) sold poster art but in the 1980s the trio added home furnishings and accessories to the merchandising mix. Today Z Gallerie stores which span some 10000 sq. ft. on average feature bedding and pillows dinnerware glassware rugs lamps candleholders clocks frames and albums games and gifts. The company's eclectic pieces are sold through its website and about 55 US retail locations in nearly 20 states. Z Gallerie is privately owned.

Geographic Reach

California-based Z Gallerie has stores in about 20 states. Its biggest markets —California Florida and Texas —are home to more than half of its 55-plus stores. The furniture retailer has buying offices in Berkeley.

Sales and Marketing

Besides its retail locations Z Gallerie caters to professional and amateur interior designers through its website.

Strategy

After a six-month stint in bankruptcy ending in 2009 Z Gallerie is spending its time prudently shopping for new locations for its stores while the company keeps a close eye on performance. The retailer has been expanding in Texas Colorado and Illinois. The housing crisis in California was particularly painful for the home furnishings retailer due to its heavy presence there.

EXECUTIVES

Vice President Of Information Technology, Gary Zorko
Senior Executive Vice President Merchandising and Marketing, Carole Malfatti
Vice President Human Resources, Mara Roitman
Auditors: MARCUM LLP LOS ANGELES CA

LOCATIONS

HQ: Z GALLERIE
1855 W 139TH ST, GARDENA, CA 902493013
Phone: 310 630-1200
Web: WWW.ZGALLERIE.COM

2013 Stores

	No
Alabama	1
Arizona	4
California	14
Colorado	2
Florida	8
Georgia	2

Illinois	3
Indiana	1
Kansas	1
Kentucky	1
Louisiana	1
Nevada	1
North Carolina	1
Oregon	1
Tennessee	1
Texas	10
Utah	2
Virginia	1
Washington	1
Total	**56**

PRODUCTS/OPERATIONS

Selected Products

Accessories
Area Rugs
Art
  Abstract
  Canvas
  Lanscapes
  Vintage
Bedding
Drapery Panels
Furniture
  Bedroom
  Dining Room
  Office
  Outdoor
Lamps
  Floor Lamps
  Hanging Lamps
  Table Lamps
Mirrors
Tabletop items

COMPETITORS

Amazon.com	Macy's
Bed Bath & Beyond	Pier 1 Imports
Cost Plus	Provide Gifts
Euromarket Designs	Restoration Hardware
Four Hands	Room & Board
Hanover Direct	Williams-Sonoma
IKEA	

HISTORICAL FINANCIALS

Company Type: Private

Income Statement
FYE: December 31

	REVENUE ($ mil.)	NET INCOME ($ mil.)	NET PROFIT MARGIN	EMPLOYEES
12/13	194	26	13.8%	950
12/12	176	25	14.5%	—
12/11	154	20	13.4%	—
Annual Growth	**12.3%**	**14.2%**	**—**	**—**

2013 Year-End Financials

Return on assets: —
Return on equity: 13.8%
Current ratio: 0.70
Cash ($ mil.): 15

ZEN-NOH GRAIN CORPORATION

Auditors: KPMG LLP NEW ORLEANS LA

LOCATIONS

HQ: ZEN-NOH GRAIN CORPORATION
1127 HWY 190 E SERVICE RD, COVINGTON, LA
704334929
Phone: 985 867-3500
Web: WWW.CGB.COM

HISTORICAL FINANCIALS

Company Type: Private

Income Statement
FYE: May 31

	REVENUE ($ mil.)	NET INCOME ($ mil.)	NET PROFIT MARGIN	EMPLOYEES
05/14	7,550	56	0.7%	213
05/13	7,704	51	0.7%	—
05/12	6,306	33	0.5%	—
05/11	6,217	0	—	—
Annual Growth	**6.7%**	**—**	**—**	**—**

2014 Year-End Financials

Return on assets: 0.6%
Return on equity: 0.7%
Current ratio: 0.10
Cash ($ mil.): 4

ZOOLOGICAL SOCIETY OF SAN DIEGO

Talk about animal magnetism! The Zoological Society of San Diego is a not-for-profit organization that operates the 100-acre San Diego Zoo which cares for more than 4000 individual animals as well as a collection of some 3500 species of plants. The Zoological Society also manages the 1800-acre San Diego Zoo Safari Park and the center for Conservation and Research. The zoo entertains all with its daily shows in-park restaurants guided tours and special events. The society also supports conservation education and efforts such as planned travel adventure-tours to exotic destinations in Mexico and Africa. It was founded by Dr. Harry Wegeforth in 1916 and is managed by a 12-member board.

Operations

The society is the largest zoological membership group in the world with more than half a million members (including 130000 children). Members receive free zoo and safari park admission a subscription to the society's magazine and other benefits.

EXECUTIVES

Vice President Retail Management, Don Leiker
Board Member, Lance Aubrey
Auditors: ERNST & YOUNG LLP SAN DIEGO

LOCATIONS

HQ: ZOOLOGICAL SOCIETY OF SAN DIEGO
2920 ZOO DR, SAN DIEGO, CA 921011646
Phone: 619 231-1515
Web: WWW.SANDIEGOZOO.ORG

HISTORICAL FINANCIALS

Company Type: Private

Income Statement
FYE: December 31

	REVENUE ($ mil.)	NET INCOME ($ mil.)	NET PROFIT MARGIN	EMPLOYEES
12/13	259	29	11.5%	2,300
12/10	193	(6)	—	—
12/09*	173	(15)	—	—
01/06	483	0	—	—
Annual Growth	**(7.5%)**	**—**	**—**	**—**

*Fiscal year change

2013 Year-End Financials

Return on assets: 12.7%
Return on equity: 11.5%
Current ratio: 1.10
Cash ($ mil.): 91

Hoover's Handbook of

Private Companies

Index of Executives

Index of Executives

A

Aaron, Carol 401
Aaron, Todd 512
Aaron, Barbara 610
Abadessa, Virginia 389
Abbeele, Annick D. Van den 157
Abbott, Alice 58
Abbott, Justin 263
Abbott, Cal 533
Abed, Mary 120
Abell, Deborah 58
Abiera, Henry (Hal) 112
Abiri, Michael 368
Aboubaker, Aziza 377
Abraham, Karen 77
Abraham, Nirmala 287
Abrams, Jon F. 270
Abrams, Jim 270
Abramson, Richard (Dick) 494
Abramson, Larry 609
Abu, Mary 316
Abutaleb, Sam 576
Acampuzano, Guillermo 160
Achenbach, John (Jack) 74
Acker, Claud 92
Acosta, Miguel 379
Adams, Greg 66
Adams, Kevin D. 111
Adams, Pam 258
Adams, David (Dave) 263
Adams, Gregory A. 279
Adams, Martin L. 309
Adams, Archie 353
Adams, Lori 417
Adams, Marylou 641
Adcock, Tommy 630
Adepeder, Suzanne 160
Adian, Jim 633
Adkins, Steve 188
Adkins, Joanne 250
Adkins, Shaundra 406
Adkisson, Gary 400
Adler, Neil 314
Adoremos, Anthony R 3
Adrick, Jay 399
Adrignola, Matt 633
Advises, Evan 526
Afnan, Jamshid A. 267
Agena, Jody 654
Ager, Gary 24
Agrons, Geoffrey A 562
Agtmael, Antoine W. van 358
Aguiniga, Julie 167
Aguirre, Manuel E. 112
Ahern, Gregory 197
Ahlem, Karl 342
Aho, Patty 34
Aho, Karla 342
Aibe, Sono 543
Aichele, William S 223
Aiello, Frank 377
Aiken, Leah 543
Ainsworth, Walt 631
Akabane, Angel 474

Akers, David (Dave) 90
Akey, Jason 375
Akridge, John 339
Alam, Danesh 107
Alaniz, Carol 470
Alarie, Kathy 492
Albers, Keith 126
Albert, John (Jack) 391
Albrecht, Fran M. 609
Albro, George 552
Alcala, Michael J. 414
Aldersley, Stephen (Steve) 439
Aldrich, Al 109
Aldrich, William (Bill) 298
Aldrich, Peter D (Pete) 462
Aldridge, Mary 5
Aldridge, Susan C. 171
Alessandrini, Robert G. 550
Alexander, Nick 5
Alexander, Joel 127
Alexander, Andrew F (Andy) 150
Alexander, Lisa 304
Alexander, James 349
Alexander, Cathy 456
Alexander, Melanie 470
Alexander, John (Jack) 513
Alexander, Kim 533
Alexander, Pamala 596
Alexiades, Alexander 423
Alfred, Richard L. 470
Alfrey, Alan 207
Algoe, Eric 534
Alhadeff, Ginger 307
Alibrandi, Vincent 450
Alicea, Marisa 159
Alinea, Mario 353
Allain, Dwayne 557
Allard, Tania 10
Alldian, David P. 77
Allegretti, Bart 57
Alleman, Merlin 490
Allen, Ken 20
Allen, Amy 32
Allen, William 121
Allen, Diane 139
Allen, Paul H. 181
Allen, Delcina 197
Allen, Ilene 245
Allen, Michael (Mel) 245
Allen, Gove 284
Allen, Jeff 290
Allen, Clay M. 295
Allen, Jare 310
Allen, Steve 360
Allen, Ralph E. 399
Allen, Peggy 401
Allen, Kim 474
Allen, Melvin 482
Allen, Chuck 489
Allen, Paul 513
Allen, Elizabeth Heller 555
Allen, David (Dave) 605
Allen, Andrew T. 612
Allen, Ricci 614
Allen, Julian 614
Allen, Myron 618

Allen, Cathy 627
Alles, Brandon 171
Alletto, Philip 566
Alley, C Thomas 182
Allgood, Johnny 630
Allison, Debra 340
Allison, Julie 362
Allore, Gary 231
Allport, Jeff 501
Allred, William (Bill) 500
Almgren, Ake 409
Alonzo, Ralph 126
Alpert, Chuck 551
Alston, Prissana 85
Alston, Kal 526
Alstrom, Ray 9
Altaras, June 524
Altman, Steven J. 147
Altobella, Michelle 259
Altruda, Melanie 98
Aluisi, Andrea 573
Alvarez, Stanley 130
Alves, Uanna 487
Alwani, Shawn 99
Alyea, Mark 16
Amankonah, Thomas 524
Amante, Jerry 389
Amaral, Ev 305
Ambrose, Marilyn 31
Ambrose, Kelly 307
Ambrosio, Lucille 308
Ambrosio, Mike 629
Amer, Muhieddin 439
Americo, Peter (Pete) 114
Amonette, Alison 642
Amos, Harold 431
Amprey, Walter G. 305
Amyor, Maribeth 651
Ana, Coleen Santa 467
Anand, Nishant (Shaun) 46
Anatol, Algernon 58
Ancker, Walt 176
Anda, Gabriela De 310
Anderley, Gerald (Jerry) 615
Andersen, David 26
Andersen, H. A. (Andy) 26
Andersen, Nicki 236
Anderson, Charles 43
Anderson, Rhonda 46
Anderson, Lisa Stevens 46
Anderson, Tom 64
Anderson, Craig 73
Anderson, Lois 83
Anderson, Linda 99
Anderson, Jackie 106
Anderson, Jennifer (Jen) 191
Anderson, C. Colt 204
Anderson, Paul 225
Anderson, Kory 263
Anderson, A. Scott 263
Anderson, Todd 287
Anderson, Carl A. 291
Anderson, Allyson 302
Anderson, Curtis G. 330
Anderson, Melissa 417
Anderson, Cary 450

Anderson, Sasha 479
Anderson, Ernie 513
Anderson, Gregory 530
Anderson, Stephanie J 534
Anderson, Brian T. 550
Anderson, Samantha 578
Anderson, Sharla 586
Anderson, Cathy 588
Anderson, Maurin 605
Anderson, Coral 612
Andolino, Frank 483
Andraws, Richard 120
Andrews, Abigail 95
Andrews, Eddie 181
Andrews, Deborah 434
Andrews, Harold W. 446
Anello, Neil 262
Angeles, Alicia 590
Angelichio, Mick J. 550
Angelides, Susan (Sue) 461
Angelini, Michael P. 323
Angerbauer, Spencer 90
Anglin, Francis X. 323
Anglin, Michael 432
Angstadt, John 330
Anh, Trang 615
Aniston, Lisa 113
Ankenbrandt, Russell (Russ) 197
Anker-Boetes, Debbie 648
Ankrum, Jim 82
Anna, Ted 319
Annable, William L. 604
Annunziato, Frank 530
Anschuetz, Christian 595
Ansel, Dana 209
Anspach, Ma 275
Antenucci, Thomas (Thom) 367
Anthony, Taylor 277
Anthony, Keith 560
Anthony, Joseph 602
Anton, Michael E (Mel) 114
Anton, Christopher 464
Antonellis, Dan 516
Antonino, John R. 423
Antonio, Juan 40
Antonio, Juan 40
Ao'brien, Kathryn 160
Apea, Abena 160
Apeagyei, Eric 99
Apperson, Kevin 324
Appiah, Chelsea 340
Apple, Harrison 100
Appleby, Terry P. 36
Applestein, Gerald (Jerry) 528
Arakelian, John (Jack) 362
Aramaki, Teresa 315
Arasa, Pedro 40
Araujo, Lisa 5
Araujo, Jaeleen 463
Arbuckle, Barry 307
Archibald, Sandra 616
Area, Ronald 320
Arellano, Margarita 534
Arendt, Arleen 372
Arens, Jeanne 256
Argo, Linda 24

Arguijo, Jessica 121
Argyropoulos, Christos 166
Armada, Anthony A. (Tony) 524
Armbruster, Neil 176
Armbruster, Elif 517
Armitage, Sherry 175
Armstrong, Shelly 197
Armstrong, Shelly 197
Armstrong, Lori 197
Armstrong, Georgine 257
Armstrong, Kevin 259
Armstrong, William 334
Armstrong, Lori 559
Armstrong, Kelli 590
Armsworthy, Richard 516
Arn, Peter 305
Arner, Barbara 429
Arnold, Dennis 55
Arnold, Joseph 112
Arnold, Bill 349
Arnold, Justin 380
Arnold, Dean 381
Arnold, Jarvie 515
Arnold, Gregory A. (Greg) 589
Arnold, Truman 589
Arnold, Laura 634
Arnone, Ronald 332
Aronhalt, Steven (Steve) 1
Aronhalt, Steve 1
Aront, Alan (Al) 628
Arosteguy-Brown, Lisa 389
Arsenault, Matt 47
Arsenault, Julie 437
Arshi, Arash 386
Arthur, Bill 76
Arthur, Megan M (Meg) 607
Artman, Lynn 342
Arx, Jeffrey P. von 191
Asarian, Armand 87
Ashbrook, Bradley 54
Ashford, Brytain 538
Ashkar, Ziad 295
Ashley, Mary 649
Ashline, Michael 83
Ashman, Tim 26
Ashworth, John (Jack) 607
Aspery, Daniel (Dan) 77
Assaf, Ronald G. 380
Astle, Angela 123
Atherlay, Peggy 25
Atkinson, Lisa 139
Atkinson, Charlene M 526
Atkinson, Kerry 526
Attebery, J 119
Attebery, Tim 635
Attilio, Patrick G. 514
Attridge, Joshua (Josh) 119
Aubele, Jim 445
Aubrey, Lance 655
Aucker, Kendra 189
Aucreman, Christine 352
Audett, John (Jack) 285
Audiffred, Doug 327
Auer, John (Jack) 267
Auery, Larry 412
Aufman, Mathew A. 357
Augustine, Michael 624
Augustino, Philip 186
Aulakh, Sudeep 58
Ault, Craig 153
Auman, Theodore W. 429
Aurilio, Lisa 119
Austin, Russell 54
Austin, Timothy (Tim) 172
Austin, Wanda M. 534
Austin, Christie 602
Austin, Celine 619
Ausubel, Eric 153
Auteri, Joseph 169
Autry, Jimmy 202
Auw, Lori 504
Avent, Sydney M. 599
Averna, Lennie 431
Averso, Martha 200
Avery, Steven B. 167

Avery, Jonathan 302
Avila, Kirk 389
Awbrey, Michael (Mel) 213
Awells, Rebecca 160
Awuah, Leonard (Len) 340
Axelson, David (Dave) 360
Axenson, Tanya 6
Axtell, Tom 420
Aycock, Ben 407
Ayer, William S. (Bill) 616
Ayers, William L. (Bill) 423
Aylsworth, Heidi 524
Aynardi, J. Marc 429
Ayork, Richard (Dick) 189
Ayres, Ted 577
Azarela, Michael (Mike) 516
Azaren, John 307

B

Baber, Jan 627
Babington, Lynn 191
Babyak, Dawna 166
Bachand, Deborah 313
Bache-Wiig, Ben 15
Bachman, Maria 342
Bachman, Page 500
Back, Justin 3
Back, Zayda 617
Backus, Shane 215
Backus, Jan 651
Bacon, Karen 653
Badavas, Robert P. (Bob) 64
Bader, Mary 418
Badowska, Eva 204
Baer, Jerome I 44
Baer, Ira J 44
Baer, Bob 109
Baer, Donald A. (Don) 420
Baeseman, Jody 34
Baggett, Kelly 586
Bagley, Linda 562
Bagwell, Leah 17
Bahr, Leticia 160
Bailey, Glen 55
Bailey, Mike 109
Bailey, David E. 130
Bailey, Cindy 133
Bailey, Kris 246
Bailey, Matt 259
Bailey, Larry 259
Bailey, Thaddeus (Thad) 275
Bailey, Don 432
Baillie, Thomas 616
Baird, Donna 55
Bakaletz, Lauren 360
Baker, Kathryn 77
Baker, Nicholas 88
Baker, Tom 90
Baker, Nichole 93
Baker, Charles 133
Baker, Johnna 236
Baker, John 247
Baker, David (Dave) 256
Baker, Daniel 392
Baker, Glen 423
Baker, Gary 461
Baker, Gretchen 526
Baker, Bradley 608
Baker, Jane 609
Baker, Joseph J. 641
Baker, Eric 646
Balas, Egon 100
Balcavage, Thomas J. 283
Balcer, Holly 96
Baldivia, Pat 581
Baldwin, Richard 155
BALDWIN, KEITH 651
Balinsky, Sharon 80
Balke, Byron 78
Balke, Byron 78
Ball, Jon W. 240
Ball, Ryan 401
Ball, Andrew J. (Andy) 516

Ballentine, Brad 431
Ballman, David 224
Balloch, Michael Ann 227
Balmat, Bruce 408
Balthazor, Steve 235
Bammann, Deb 246
Banas, Arlene 246
Bangert, Aleczander 612
Bankowski, Jessica 437
Banks, Walter 212
Banse, Kristin 95
Banu, Dana 65
Barajas, Maria 307
Baraldi, Raymond L. 542
Barash, Andrew 112
Barb, Michael 487
Barba, James J. 10
Barba, Peter (Pete) 253
Barbee, Kenneth A. 171
Barber, Desiree 2
Barber, Dennis 146
Barber, Gene 163
Barber, Dave 461
Barber, Sandy 501
Barber, Roger 567
Barbosa, Karla 616
Barbour, Amy 614
Barch, Frank 467
Barchenger, Ed 371
Barclay, Duane 162
Bardier, Catherine 183
Barger, Tricia 46
Barger, Tami 608
Barham, David (Dave) 49
Barker, Bethany 224
Barker, Sphr B 225
Barker, Karen 305
Barker, William G. (Bill) 357
Barkley, Jamie 391
Barkley, Sandra 505
Barlok, Tracy 133
Barlows, Ted 244
Barnard, John 360
Barnes, Laura 174
Barnes, Rose 426
Barnes, Christopher 492
Barnes, Jack 518
Barnes, Maureen P. 542
Barnett, Larry 612
Barone, Nancy 427
Barr, Bret 144
Barr, Barbara 272
Barr, Hannah (Hanna) 380
Barr, Laurie 453
Barre, Elizabeth 643
Barre, Elizabeth (Beth) 643
Barrett, Maggie 24
Barrett, Bill 80
Barrett, Barbara M. 534
Barron, Kathleen 530
Barros, Andrew 643
Barrow, Henry 128
Barrows, Karen 439
Barry, Amy 297
Barry, Thomas 487
Barta, William 405
Bartanen, Kristine (Kris) 611
Bartel, Sylvia 157
Bartel, Trish 247
Bartelmay, Tina 280
Bartholomew, Vernon 47
Bartlett, Robert 554
Barto, Jack 364
Bartoli, Andrea 469
Bartolozzi, Arthur (Art) 562
Bartolucci, Tony 6
Barut, Mehmet 577
Barycki, Elvera 307
Barzansky, Barbara (Barb) 22
Barzilay, Jonathan 419
Baskel, Christopher (Chris) 492
Basmadjian, Kevin 423
Basom, Jean 448
Bass, Scott A. 24
Bass, William L. 106

Bass, Steven 358
Bassett, Mary Beth 76
Bassett, Dorothy 172
Bateman, Gray 556
Bates, Jonathan R. (Jon) 31
Bates, Michael (Mel) 91
Bates, Peter W. 313
Bates, Patricia (Pat) 389
Bates, Patricia (Pat) 389
Bates, Wesley C. 509
Bates, Steve 530
Batiste, Doris 272
Batman, Mary Ellen 429
Batshaw, Mark 118
Batten, Geri 466
Battenfield, Keith 105
Battle, Adell 21
Battle, Lee 214
Battles, Rachel 539
Baty, Darren 255
Baublis, Dan 112
Bauchner, Howard C. 22
Baudanza, Anthony J. 423
Bauer, Ted 55
Bauer, Elizabeth 90
Bauer, Julie 198
Bauer, Paul 278
Bauer, Wayne 510
Bauer, Richard 546
Bauer, Daniel (Dan) 576
Baugh, Travis E. 165
Baughn, Charles M. 245
Bauhs, Timothy 135
Bauman, Mark 258
Baumgarten, Patrick 423
Baumgarten, Patrick 423
Baus, Steve 110
Baxley, Thomas 96
Baxter, Janna 197
Baxter, Rob 471
Bayer, Michelle 506
Bayliss, Philip 551
Baynes, Linda 284
Beach, David 492
Beal, Steven (Steve) 329
Beam, Mildred 391
Beam, Lauris 497
Beaman, Jamie 652
Beane, Ray 278
Bear, Liz 447
Beard, Derrick 625
Bearman, Robert M. (Bob) 399
Beasley, Mark 226
Beason, Samuel 218
Beatrice, Dennis 494
Beattie, Jeff 13
Beatty, Ellen M. 534
Bebermeyer, Jon 437
Beccaro, Mark A. Del 464
Bechler, David (Dave) 112
Bechtel, Kathleen 211
Bechtle, Elizabeth (Beth) 449
Bechtle, Mavis 555
Bechtold, Polly 48
Beck, Doug 60
Beck, Brian 60
Beck, Dean 60
Beck, Gretchen 99
Beck, Ann 101
Beck, Steve 148
Beck, Rebecca 263
Beck, Dana 509
Beck, Lynn G. 616
Beckemeyer, Curt A 30
Becker, Derek 613
Beckham, Sarah 373
Beckius, Larry 32
Beckman, Lee 60
Beckstead, Ian 431
Beckwith, Brian 8
Bedard, Jean 64
Bedessem, Mike 146
Bedford, Craig 263
Beeler, Jim 128
Beeler, Rodney 160
Beeman, William 155

Beeman, William 155
Beeman, Thomas E. (Tom) 551
Beenders, Gene 233
Beenenga, Cari 200
Beeny, David 199
Beeter, Evelyn 9
Beetle, Brian 136
Beetson, Deborah 170
Begley, Marybeth 82
Behrens, Matt 266
Behrens, Chris 616
Beideman, Paul S. 641
Beil, Mary Ann Bowman 330
Belemjamin, Michael (Mel) 10
Belflower, Paul 355
Belk, Kurt 15
Belknap, Chris 445
Bell, Douglas (Doug) 71
Bell, Alastair 82
Bell, Steve 114
Bell, Gus H. 330
Bell, Renee 349
Bell, Greg 409
Bell, Douglas (Doug) 523
Bellamy, Bill 112
Bellamy, Billie 437
Bellanti, Tim 36
Bellas, Ron 173
Bellingham, Hope 68
Belton, Paul 473
Ben, Mark 590
Benamati, Robert (Bob) 551
Bendel, Rosemarie 495
Bendelier, Diane 645
Bender, Randy 112
Bender, Judy 439
Bendz, Diana 599
Beneby, Doyle N. 126
Benedetto, Michael (Mel) 536
Benenati, James (Jamie) 47
Benesch, Jeff 583
Bengtson, Bruce P. 429
Benko, Amy 254
Benner, Kevin 110
Bennett, Susan (Sue) 96
Bennett, Jean 197
Bennett, Brad 198
Bennett, Shelia 203
Bennett, W. Bradley (Brad) 324
Bennett, Mark 340
Bennett, Thomas 355
Bennett, Tim 370
Bennett, Lynn 561
Bennett, Charlotte 624
Bennett, Elizabeth (Beth) 643
Bennion, TY 245
Benns, Kimberly 530
Benoit, Michel 201
Benoit, Rebecca (Becki) 295
Benson, Kathryn 112
Benthuysen, Maureen Van 313
Bentley, Jennifer 437
Benton, Mike 362
Benvenuto, Joe 52
Benyo, David 95
Benz, Edward J. 157
Berdanier, Bruce 191
Berek, Jonathan S 307
Berg, Scott 195
Berg, Joel H. 616
Bergener, Jennifer 389
Berger, Jerry 67
Berger, Helen 83
Berger, Allison 629
Berger, Pearl 653
Berger, David 653
Bergeson, Steven (Steve) 15
Bergeson, Robert (Bob) 531
Berglund, Kay 337
Bergman, William (Bill) 530
Bergmann, Johannes D. (Hans) 423
Berigan, Bret 120
Berkowitz, Gale 543
Berlin, Steven D (Steve) 61
Berman, Ira P. 330

Berman, Harris 591
Bernard, David (Dave) 68
Bernard, Lewis W. 536
Bernard, David P (Dave) 554
Bernardo-sousa, Marie 277
Bernd, David L. 467
Bernhardt, John 591
Bernier, Jane (Ginny) 485
Bernstein, Brian 19
Bernstein, Michael 386
Bernthal, Eric L. 548
Berotti, John 576
Berra, Mickey 275
Berrios, Joena 265
Berry, David T. 31
Berry, Gale 75
Berry, Brice 75
Berry, Mark 111
Berry, Jordana 543

Bershadker, Matthew 23
Bertapelle, Andrew 651
Bertke, Monika 131
Bertolozzi, Melissa 95
Bertrand, Diane 449
Berwald, Peggy 581
Besse, Kimberly 118
Betro, Darryl 193
Betting, Laurie 610
Bettis, Mark 522
Bettis, Colin 615
Betts, Steven (Steve) 112
Betz, Robert 327
Beutin, Brian 46
Bevacqua, Peter 602
Bevins, Dale 509
Bezdek, Joe 425
Bezich, Louis S. 542
Bezy, Linda 292
Bhavanishankar, Chinmayi 99
Bia, Frank 25
Biats, David 517
Bibbins, Kathleen 317
Bichsel, Terrance (Terry) 66
Bieber, Eric J. 604
Biedermann, Scott 616
Biedron, Gregory 548
Bielarski, Edward 212
Biernbaum, Robert 353
Biesterfeld, Joanne 640
Bigelow, Teresa 524
Bigger, Jeffrey 163
Billingsley, Emily 55
Binder, Kurt 625
Binford, Jim 30
Bingham, Jacob 321
Bingham, Douglas (Doug) 567
Binzer, Greg 636
Biocini, Pete 424
Bird, Michael 119
Bird, Mike 119
Bird, Jim 204
Bird, James B. (Jim) 204
Bird, William C. 217
Birnbrauer, Robert 530
Birren, Susan J. 83
Bishof, Edward J. 364
Bishop, C. Donald 260
Bishop, John 447
Bison, Michael (Mel) 14
Bitter, Genevieve 167
Biuso, Joe 203
Bixby, David E. 42
Bixby, David (Dave) 46
Black, John 127
Black, Rochelle 382
Black, Jami 414
Black, Phil 441
Blackburn, Elijah 272
Blackford, Martha 119
Blackledge, Laura 110
Blackman, Louise 482
Blackmon, Steve 82
Blackmun, Scott 602
Blackney, Kenneth S. 171

Blad, Paul 263
Blagden, Robert (Bob) 280
Blair, Cynthia 527
Blair, Randy 545
Blake, M. Brian 171
Blake, Kathy 517
Blakely, Cameron 222
Blakey, Marion C. 369
Blanchard, William B (Bill) 363
Blanchard, Denise 501
Blanchfield, Molly 194
Blanco, Maria 93
Bland, Judy 102
Blanda, Michael 534
Blanks, Richard 447
Blasingame, David T. 575
Blasko, Brian 550
Blass, Chris 280
Blaylock, Tom 105
Blazier, Rick 489
Bleicken, Linda M. 217
Blessing, Sarah 215
Blickenstaff, Scott 535
Bligh, Margaret M. 429
Block, Susan D. 157
Blom, David P. 386
Bloom, Stephanie 39
Bloom, Joel S. 364
Blower, Judy 539
Blubaugh, Sue 109
Blue, Janet 246
Bluhm, Neil 402
Blum, Dan 404
Blumenfeld, Barry 313
Blumenthal, Norman 591
Blunt, Roshawn 307
Blunt, Mary L. 467
Blunt, Elizabeth 623
Boals, Richard L. (Rich) 76
Boardman, Shelby J. 99
Boardman, David 530
Bockenfeld, Todd 518
Bockhorst, Thomas A. 357
Bockman, Brian 622
Bockstaele, Elisabeth Van 171
Bode, Hank 42
Bodnar, Amanda 100
Boedigheimer, Mark 112
Boeding, Jim 220
Boehme, Linda M 490
Boehms, Dennis 181
Boese, Christine 430
Bogard, Tom 389
Bogenberger, Vicki 112
Boggs, Thomas Hale 399
Boggs, Douglas C. (Doug) 399
Bogue, Greg 317
Bohbrink, Marshall 226
Boice-pardee, Heath 439
Boise, April M. 604
Boivin, Ryan 342
Boken, Paul R. 246
Bolander, Sherry 389
Bolch, Allison 316
Bolen, Michael D. (Mike) 327
Boller, Judy 460
Bollinger, Kathy 45
Bollinger, Kathy 570
Bolton, Linda Burnes 104
Bolyard, Joe 318
Bombeck, Alex 560
Bomesberger, Blake 484
Bonaparte, Donna 43
Bond, William (Bill) 303
Bond, Jeffrey C. (Jeff) 304
Bone, Wm 55
Bonetti, Elizabeth 86
Bonin, Donald 230
Bonkowski, Angela 46
Bonner, Karen 121
Bonner, Olin 482
Bonner, Olin 482
Bonnett, John W (Jack) 238
Bonney, Patricia 563
Bonnot, Joanne 504

Bonsall, Mark B. 405
Bonstrom, Jeanette 391
Bonwich, Steve 24
Booher, Lisa 175
Booker, Sonia 229
Booker, Toni L 281
Boom, Marc L. 554
Boon, Ron 195
Boone, Diana 150
Boone, Melissa 153
Boone, Elwood B. (Bernie) 467
Booth, Kathryn Ryan 258
Boozang, Kathleen M. 470
Boparai, Harry 650
Border, Ted 576
Borders, Denise Glyn 494
Borek, Mark 276
Borgeson, Jon 518
Born, Leann 192
Boroughs, Philip L. 133
Borth, Randi 41
Borton, Craig S 646
Bos, Hans 22
Boschini, Victor J. 532
Bosco, John 208
Bosio, Amy 171
Bosley, Barry 208
Bosso, Ed 213
Bossong, Bob 597
Boston, W. Terry 408
Bostrom, Brent 226
Bothmann, Larry 519
Botman, Selma 653
Bottino, Lou 561
Bottoms, William (Bill) 257
Bottorff, Jeff 464
Bottrill, Lorry 489
Bouchard, Mark 313
Bouchard, Lorraine 486
Boudewyns, Mary 158
Boulais, Nicole 439
Bourgeois, Shauneen 529
Bourgeois, Eugene J. (Gene) 534
Bourgoine, Michael C. (Mike) 36
Bourque, Michael 590
Boushey, Richard A. 357
Boutros, Akram 555
Boutwell, Brooke 572
Bouvier, Daniel 103
Bova, Joseph 308
Bove, Lane 310
Boven, Isaac 175
Bowen, Doug 46
Bowen, Russell 112
Bowen, Terri 263
Bowen, John J. 277
Bower, Bruce 425
Bowers, Ruth 24
Bowers, Rodney 91
Bowers, Joanne Delgiorno 145
Bowie, Paul J. 14
Bowlan, Ronald 578
Bowling, Douglas 96
Bowling, Doug 96
Bowling, Norm 569
Bowling, Bruce 599
Bowman, Rick 90
Bowman, Helen Y. 171
Bowman, Jamie 352
Bowman, Julie 405
Bowman, Elaine 648
Bowman, Marjorie 649
Boyce, Tom 3
Boyce, Jodi 492
Boyd, Stephen (Steve) 57
Boyd, Bryan 132
Boyd, Michael (Mel) 204
Boyd, Diane 272
Boyd, Christopher (Chris) 280
Boyd, Donald 439
Boyd-Pugh, Jennifer (Jen) 51
Boydstun, Donnie 600
Boyer, Cheryl 305
Boyer, Gloria 533
Boyer, Aurelia G. 558

Boyett, James 503
Boyette, Jon 297
Boyette, Scott 362
Boylan, Stuart (Stu) 397
Boyle, Patrick 595
Boynton, Andrew C. 590
Bozard, John 391
Bozeman, Keith 529
Braatz, Jay 159
Braccio, Christine 24
Bracken, Mike 112
Brackett, Jeffrey 316
Brackett, Geoffrey 316
Brackin, D. Wayne 47
Bradfield, Shannon 340
Bradford, Carol 93
Bradley, Leslie 32
Bradley, Allen 181
Bradley, Carol 302
Bradley, Maureen A 302
Bradley, Timothy (Tim) 551
Bradley, J. Lindsey 586
Bradley, W. L. (Bill) 631
Brady, Jennifer (Jen) 236
Brady, Jodie 254
Brady, Linda 289
Bragg, Michael B. 616
Braithwaite, Melinda 513
Brakhage, Lori 487
Braman, April 95
Brand, Joe 236
Brand, Michelle (Mitch) 321
Brand, Christian 590
Brandenburg, Lisa 464
Brandenburg, Julie 532
Brander, Kenneth (Ken) 653
Brandien, Peter (Pete) 267
Brandon, David 266
Brandon, Paula 568
Brandt, Earl 220
Brandt, Stephanie 625
Branies, John (Jack) 44
Branigan, Tim 426
Brannon, Jim 45
Branyan, Luke 445
Bras, Barbara (Barb) 66
Brauer, Rod 112
Brauer, Mark 255
Brauer, Stephen F. 575
Braun, Harland 233
Braun, Robert (Bob) 549
Braveman, Peter (Pete) 104
Braveman, Carla 183
Breeden, Ann Lloyd 612
Breen, Jennifer (Jen) 654
Breheny, James J. 643
Breier, Barbara 534
Breig, J Scott 576
Breitenbach, Ellen 621
Brekhus, Louann 59
Bremser, Brett 255
Bremser, Wayne 623
Brenan, Kathryn 534
Brennan, Mary 559
Breon, Richard C. (Rick) 492
Breshears, Betty 304
Breslin, Susan (Sue) 162
Bressler, Gregory 351
Brett, Anne Liners 304
Brichacek, Gary 577
Brick, Michael 636
Bricker, J. Douglas 172
Bricker, Jason 290
Brickley, David 576
Brickner, Julianna 231
Bridegroom, Eileen 20
Bridges, Brian 600
Bridges, Michael C. 649
Briesacher, Steve 227
Briesacher, Mark 263
Briesemeister, Eric 266
Briggs, Steve 484
Briley, Dennis 504
Brill, David (Dave) 74
Brill, Karen 218

Brilli, Richard J. 360
Brim, Laura 431
Bringle, Charlie 109
Brinkman, Chelsea 89
Brinkman, Kristina 377
Brinkman, Rob L 625
Brinkman, Greg Anthony 627
Briscoe, Kathy 495
Britt, Darren 643
Brixey, Michael (Mel) 588
Brizzolara, Sarah 340
Broach, Beverly 604
Broadbent, Jeff 620
Brocini, Pete 424
Brock, Jason 153
Brockelbank, Russ 170
Brockman, Tom 597
Broda, Elsie 137
Broerman, Robert A. (Rob) 467
Broker, Linda K. 423
Bromley, Sharon 330
Brooker, Michael (Mel) 54
Brooks, Jo 259
Brooks, Charles M. 423
Brooks, Tim 510
Brooks, Espen S. 576
Brooks, Richard M. 611
Brooks, Greg 630
Brophy, Beth 254
Brosnan, Gerard 369
Brotcke, Kurt 389
Browder, Caroline 554
Brower, Carrie 355
Brown, Cynthia 22
Brown, Pamela (Pam) 32
Brown, Roger H. 65
Brown, David 71
Brown, Charles H. 80
Brown, Tracy 90
Brown, Courtney 112
Brown, Hannah 113
Brown, Scott 131
Brown, Tom 153
Brown, Alexander 159
Brown, Jeff 161
Brown, Scott 198
Brown, William L. 202
Brown, Heidi 209
Brown, Charles (Chas) 212
Brown, Thomas R. 212
Brown, Jerry L 245
Brown, Rocky 245
Brown, Winnie 247
Brown, Bill C. 258
Brown, Douglas T (Doug) 271
Brown, George J. 302
Brown, David 307
Brown, Marion 340
Brown, Luke 360
Brown, Carl D. 364
Brown, Rodger 373
BROWN, STEPHANIE G 379
Brown, Arthur C. (Art) 389
Brown, Clarence 391
Brown, Danny 422
Brown, Robin B. 462
Brown, Jeff 464
Brown, Venessa 470
Brown, James 473
Brown, Rhonda 530
Brown, Daniel A. 534
Brown, Suzanne 562
Brown, Stacey 571
Brown, Stillman 572
Brown, Stevie-Joe 600
Brown, Nicole 602
Brown, Perry J. 609
BROWN, HEATHER POTTS 623
Brown, Bartholomew R 625
Brown, Daniel 631
Brownell, Jayne 340
Browning, Michael 576
Broyles-Aplin, Teresa 181
Bruce, Andrea L 516
Bruce, Harry 616

Bruciak, John S. 420
Bruciak, John S. 420
Brueck, Margaret (Peg) 470
Brukardt, David (Dave) 617
Brummer, James 615
Brumsted, John R. 201
Brunner, Laura 46
Bruno, Michael 511
Bruno, Rick 520
Bruse, Michael (Mel) 280
Brushwood, Amy 34
Bruski, Georgann 512
Brussow, Julie 466
Brustein, Lawrence 240
Bryan, Jay 231
Bryant, Randall E. (Randy) 99
Bryant, Elizabeth (Beth) 112
Bryant, Leah 160
Bryant, Dawn L 449
Bryant, Brigette 470
Bryant, Carla 470
Buchanan, Herbert C. 259
Buchanan, Carrie 355
Bucher, Al 188
Bucher, Ron 338
Buchhammer, Rene 233
Buchholz, Gwendolyn 112
Buchwald, Gail 23
Buck, Karen 299
Buck, Nancy 584
Buckalew, Steve 226
Buckholdt, David (Dave) 319
Buckingham, David (Dave) 411
Buckley, Erin 183
Buckley, Adam P. 201
Buckley, John (Jack) 204
Buckley, Gerard J. 439
Buckley, John 530
Buckley, Owen 612
Buckley, Linda 616
Buckley, Roy 643
Budd, Michele 401
Buddendeck, Michael (Mel) 21
Budig, David H. 340
Buehrle, Jeff 570
Buescher, John 327
Buffa, Peter 389
Buffa, Christopher 391
Bugg, Sylvia 147
Buhler, Maxine 263
Buhrig, Melissa M. 375
Buie, James C. (Jim) 245
Buie, Jim 245
Bulik, Lou 641
Bulinski, Jeff 222
Bull, Donald (Don) 315
Bullard, Coby 90
Bullis, Gene 528
Bumgarner, Gail 443
Bunch, James T. (Jim) 602
Bunch, James T. (Jim) 602
Bundock, Peter (Pete) 204
Bunin, Stacy 369
Bunis, David A. 83
Bunn, Gary 434
Bunnell, Ronald R. (Ron) 45
Bunnell, Ron 46
Bunnell, Mike 90
Bunnell, Craig A. 157
Bunner, Mark 509
Bunten, Suzanne 506
Bunyard, Steve 386
Buongiorno, Michael (Mel) 312
Buoni, James (Jamie) 240
Burbrink, Steve 111
Burch, John (Jack) 92
Burch, John 92
Burch, Curtis 134
Burch, Stephen A. 607
Burcham, David (Dave) 310
Burdick, Twila 46
Burge, Neil 346
Burge, Cecil 614
Burger, Terry 303
Burger, Brent A. 588

Burgess, Michael (Mel) 293
Burgess, Patrice 447
Burgess, John 648
Burgett, June 280
Burke, Michael W (Mel) 11
Burke, Brenton 113
Burke, Patrick (Paddy) 208
Burke, Kevin Joseph 246
Burke, John 290
Burke, Tessa 352
Burke, James (Jamie) 461
Burke, Thomas 575
Burke, Janice 578
BURKE, MUCIA 582
Burke, Tricia 585
Burke, John D. 590
Burke, John (Jack) 597
Burke, Joe 645
Burkey, Daniel E (Dan) 150
Burlington, Fletcher 399
Burmahln, John 309
Burnett, Janice 80
Burnett, Michael (Mel) 254
Burnett, Nancy Packard 543
Burnett, Nancy Packard 543
Burnette, Robert (Bob) 627
Burney, Mike 3
Burnham, Elizabeth 263
Burnley, Cynthia Sue 175
Burns, Eric 43
Burns, Russ 129
Burns, Katherine (Kate) 242
Burns, Helene 283
Burns, Terry 286
Burns, Kathleen 324
Burns, Moira 437
Burns, Paulette 532
Burns, Steve 554
Burns, James 590
Burns, Jon P. 607
Burrell, Steve 217
Burrin, Stephen 534
Burriss, Steve 432
Bursch, Lowell 492
Burstein, Sanders 158
Burton, Don 176
Burton, Ellen S. 389
Burwald, Peggy 581
Busby, Ramonda 118
Busch, Joe 36
Busch, Johannes 277
Buschiazzo, John (Jack) 419
Buschman, John E. 470
Buschmann, Arthur (Budd) 40
Bush, Dina 352
Bush, Richard 437
Bush, Bridget 617
Bushey, Eric 510
Bushnell, Lynn M. 423
Bushong, Amelie 43
Buss, Timothy A. 357
Bussone, Mary Z. 267
Buswell, Lori 157
Butler, Margaret 15
Butler, Susan (Sue) 49
Butler, Gary P. 83
Butler, Pete 112
Butler, Amy 383
Butler, Steve 407
Butler, Linda 432
Butler, Donna 500
Butler, Gary 597
Butterfield, Patricia (Pat) 160
Butterfield, Brad 311
Button, Sigrid 390
Buttrey, Karen 158
Buttry, Jill 160
Butts, Sean 342
Buxton, Lisa 421
Buzachero, Vic 462
Byers, Andrew 74
Byers, Cheryl 614
Byerwalter, Mariann 494
Byington, Tony 255
Bykowski, Bruce 490

Byrd, Lu 71
Byrd, Jane 432
Byrd, Harry F. 644
Byrne, Kerry 288
Byrne, Richard J. 557
Byrnes, Kathleen 623
Byrum, Fred 232
Byrum, Barbara 588
Byun, Hyuk 24
Byun, Dae Gyu 253
Byus, Fred 54

C

Cabibbo, Steven 442
Cabral, Jv 121
Cabrejos, Jason 364
Cacheria, Ray Ann 445
Cachofa, Al 522
Caesar, Brett 208
Cafarelli, Mike 109
Cafferillo, Nick 446
Caffery, Anne 652
Cagle, Philip 554
Caglioti, Sally 76
Cagney, Phil 153
Cahill, Kevin 215
Cain, Lawrence 81
Cain, Debbie 304
Cain, Jean 369
Cairns, Michael (Mel) 197
Calabrese, Gary 19
Calabrese, Patricia 643
Calahan, Walter 24
Calame, John 355
Calbert, Robert (Bo) 327
Calcagnini, Donald P. 423
Caldarelli, Brian 419
Calderon, Larry A 379
Caldwell, Dave 317
Caldwell, Helen 418
Caldwell, Troy 576
Caldwell, Marty Infrastructure 653
Calhoun, Jay 100
Caliandro, Richard 416
Call, Dawn 315
Callahan, Harry 24
Callahan, Phyllis 340
Callahan, Clara A. 578
Callecod, David L. 295
Calloway, Valerie (Val) 229
Calman, Albi 118
Calnon, Wanda 42
Calvelli, John (Jack) 643
Calvert, Mike 77
Cameron, Hazel 395
Cameron, Rick 543
Camille, Marc 310
Cammack, Tom 586
Camp, David 509
Camp, Lea 596
Campagna, Margo 103
Campanella, George 200
Campbell, Rocky 90
Campbell, Scott 184
Campbell, Linda 268
Campbell, Dave 285
Campbell, Carla 332
Campbell, Clark 382
Campbell, Bill 389
Campbell, Susan 392
Campbell, Robert (Bob) 405
Campbell, Joseph (Jo) 420
Campbell, Todd 506
Campbell, Carol 532
Campbell, Patricia L. 591
Campbell, Lukas 615
Campbell, Genna 619
Campese, Mike 188
Campot, Peter 516
Candanoza, Emilio 112
Candia, Gary R 2
Candullo, Carl 137
Caneris, Anthony 171

Cann, Michael 219
Cannatelli, Len 576
Canney, Steven 74
Canney, Jane 615
Canning, Josh 105
Cannon, Wayne 263
Cannon, Eric 263
Cannon, Diana 534
Cannon, Michael R. 575
Canosa, Albert 423
Cantey, Carolyn 96
Canty, Tara D. 392
Capecci, Pam 222
Capitelli, Robert 452
Caplin, Stacie 208
Capone, Vincent 602
Capossela, Nicole 358
Capps, Kendall 271
Capps, Kenneth 322
Cappucci, Lou 529
Capuano, Terry 303
Caputo, Michael P. (Mike) 575
Caraballo, Kelvin 511
Carageorge, Adrianne 439
Caratenuto, Isabel 437
Caravati, Charles M. 117
Carberry, Claudia 272
Carbone, Raymond (Ray) 324
Carbone, Valerie 423
Carbuto, Judy 308
Cardali, Mike 483
Cardenas, Mitzi 589
Carey, Arlene 83
Carey, Helen 360
Carey, Judith 449
Carey, Karen 650
Carl, David (Dave) 37
Carleton, Alice M 383
Carlin, Greg 402
Carlone, Michael (Mel) 623
Carls, Rod 481
Carlson, Wanda 299
Carlson, Pamela J. 405
Carlson, Brian 505
Carlson, Carolyn 551
Carlson, Chris 576
Carlson, Jack 597
Carlson, Mark 602
Carlton, Frank 330
Carmichael, Lawson 21
Carmichael, William P. 258
Carnaghi, Jill 451
Carney, Daniel (Dan) 118
Carney, Paul 634
Carol, Wood 360
Carolan, Susan (Sue) 159
Carolis, Donna De 171
Carollo, Mike 560
Caron, William L. 313
Carpenter, Jane 267
Carpenter, Jolana 405
Carpenter, Stan 534
Carpenter, Rick 600
Carpenter, Jeffery 624
Carpenter, Cathy Penton 653
Carr, Curtis 188
Carr, Joanne 271
Carr, Joseph (Jo) 418
Carr, Judy 634
Carracher, Craig 470
Carreiro, Manuel 423
Carreras, Felica 47
Carrico, Stephen J. (Steve) 240
Carrigg, John 599
Carrillo, Jesse 245
Carrillo, Joseph (Jo) 422
Carrington, John E. 366
Carroll, Allen 96
Carroll, David (Dave) 177
Carroll, Kevin 226
Carroll, Alan 298
Carroll, Dale 468
Carroll, Janell 572
Carroll, Jessica 602
Carruth, Janet 530

Carscaddon, Michael (Mike) 230
Carscaddon, Mike 230
Carson, Steven (Steve) 530
Carson, Russell L. 564
Carstens, Earl 186
Carter, Robert 24
Carter, William 36
Carter, Dorothy 162
Carter, Kelli 175
Carter, Tom 280
Carter, Allison 342
Carter, Jason 342
Carter, Mike 524
Carter, Joyce 571
Cartier, Karen 155
Cartwright, Nancy 280
Cartwright, Carol A. 358
Caruso, Thomas 77
Caruso, Dave 513
Carvallo, Jorge 100
Carvana, John (Jack) 310
Carwell, Mark 139
Carwell, Keith 630
Carwell, Keith 630
Cary, Alan 112
Casadonte, Jane 209
Case, Barbara 103
Casella, Sergio 398
Casente, Salvador 182
Casey, Rose 389
Casey, William (Bill) 561
Cassell, Jack C. 24
Cassella, Pat 296
Castanza, Susan (Sue) 643
Castle, Don 403
Castor, Tory C 259
Castro, Ivette 133
Caswell, Mary 607
Cataliotti, Palmira M. 645
Catel, Mark S 525
Catena, Lillian 309
Cathcart, David D. 560
Catlin, Ray 186
Catsavas, Debora 280
Cauce, Ana Mari 616
Cavagnaro, Charles E. 58
Cavalieri, Cristina G 578
Cavanaugh, Patrick D. 616
Cavecche, Carolyn V. 389
Caven, Brad 408
Caver, Steven 415
Cavins-Tull, Kathy 532
Cazares, Joe 112
Cecava, Eric 5
CECCANECCHIO, DOMENIC 171
Ceccarelli, Bertina 643
Cecil, Kristine 99
Cecil, Kim 464
Cedergreen, Chris 129
Cederholm, Wayne 90
Cerio, Sigrid 95
Cerutti, Frank L. 358
Cervini, August 539
Cha, Andrew 332
Chadalavada, Vamsi 267
Chadwich, Jerry 228
Chadwick, Gloria A. 225
Chadwick, Gloria A. 225
Chadwick, David (Dave) 605
Chaffee, Lisa 360
Chaffee, Barbara 599
Chahin, Jaime 534
Chakalis, Nicole 135
Chalke, Dennis W. 58
Challinor, Bob 510
Chalmers, Eileen 342
Chamberlain, Gail 112
Chamberlain, David R. 155
Chamberlain, David R. 155
Chambers, Barry 394
Chan, Kenyon S. 616
Chance, Lucindia 217
Chance, Heather 608
Chancey, Mark 487
Chandler, H 77

Chandler, Rodney 270
Chandler, Nancy 636
Chandley, Bonnie 175
Chaney, Curtis 339
Chang, Daniel 43
Chang, Florence 353
Chang, Chris 616
Chant, Rick 530
Chanthasene, Phillip (Phil) 360
Chanthasene, Phillip 360
Chantry, Rhonda 338
Chapel, Edward P. 351
Chapman, Janet 50
Chapman, Robert H. (Bob) 52
Chapman, Warren K 135
Chapman, Craig 222
Chapman, Thomas 259
Chapman, Theresa 410
Chappell, Debbie 447
Chappell, John (Jack) 633
Chaput, Katie 43
Charles, Steve 257
Charles, Rick 638
Charsha, Dianne 542
Chase, Brenda 20
Chase, Linda 259
Chasteen, Carol 251
Chatman, Mary 330
Chaudhary, Usha 563
Chavira, Tony 389
Cheal, Catheryn 383
Cheatham, Ollie 365
Check, Jerome 542
Checketts, Lannie 448
Cheeti, PavanKumarRao 623
Chelko, Dan 630
Chen, Jiamei 43
Chen, Yin 43
Chen, Timothy (Tim) 96
Chen, Leo 245
Chen, Patrick (Paddy) 321
Chen, Ji 444
Chen, Lilly 643
Cheney, Dave 45
Cheng, Landle 572
Cheong, Hoe Wai 73
Chermak, Jerome 379
Chernets, Natalie 578
Cherrick, Lorraine 153
Cherry, Michael 46
Chertoff, Michael 369
Cherwony, Karen 530
Chester, Timothy M (Tim) 606
Chester, Timothy 606
Cheung, Teresa 17
Cheung, Yan 17
Cheves, Brad 487
Chevreaux, Pamela (Pam) 307
Chevrette, John 73
Chew, Roy 286
Chick, Phillip (Phil) 571
Chick, Philip 571
Chidester, Paul 468
Childers, Susan 9
Childers, Scott 48
Childress, Ronald (Ron) 320
Childs, Joe 174
Childs, Craig 339
Chilton, Penny 134
Chin, Susan (Sue) 643
Chinn, Jeff 82
Chiofolo, Joseph (Jo) 645
Chism, Jim 194
Chitemerere, Tatenda 18
Chiusolo, Brittany 231
Cho, Christine 233
Choi, Vicky 280
Choi, Jill 360
Chopnak, Charlene 526
Chopra, Rupal 10
Chou, Lisa 487
Choutka, Michael J. 240
Chow, Allan 112
Chow, Wendy 244
Chowdhry, Vimal 238

Chrestay, Joan 450
Chrisman, George 487
Christen, Tim L. 21
Christenberry, Reid 340
Christensen, Tom 73
Christensen, Austin 316
Christensen, Heather 492
Christian, Dan 1
Christian, A. Brooke 584
Christian, Brooke 584
Christie, Lisa 602
Christoforo, John 67
Christophel, Randy 259
Christopher, Norman C. 119
Chu, David S.C. 261
Chu, Benjamin K. 279
Chulick, Michele 118
Chun, Gregory H. (Greg) 328
Church, Leah 263
Church, Dean 409
Ciambrone, Regina 437
Ciencewicki, Michael (Mel) 427
Ciervo, Carman A. 283
Ciesinski, Stephen J. (Steve) 494
Cima, Laura 231
Cimino, MaryJo 542
Cinar, Ali 256
Cintron, Rocky D. 204
Cioffi, George A. (Jack) 301
Cioffi, Jack 302
Cipullo, Donald D. 351
Cirksena, Mark 170
Cirricione, Mary 104
Cisneros, Henry G. 230
Citron, Andrew M 427
Claase, Julianna 5
Clark, Doug 14
Clark, Roger S. 35
Clark, Rodney L. 111
Clark, Leofwin 112
Clark, Robert G. (Bob) 129
Clark, Paul 137
CLARK, ELAINE 141
Clark, Lynda 154
Clark, Jeffrey (Jeff) 157
Clark, Wayne 301
Clark, Darryl 347
Clark, Jack 360
Clark, Michael 425
Clark, Terry 482
Clark, Gerard 517
Clark, Dana 542
Clark, Gary 555
Clark, Joan 559
Clark, Jayne 592
Clark, Paul G. 604
Clark, Don 614
Clarke, Clinton 46
Clarke, Richard L. (Dick) 121
Clarke, Chris 230
Clauser, Allan 110
Clavelle, Joanne 461
Clay, Sharon Ten 130
Clay, Jason 648
Clayton, Philip A. (Phil) 144
Clayton, Laurie 263
Cleary, Gerry 2
Cleary, Charlie 585
Clegg, Charlotte 89
Cleland, Robert 311
Clement, Linda 9
Clemente, Paul 64
Clemente, Roderick 231
Clements, Deb 82
Clemmer, Terry 263
Clemons, Marianne 360
Clendenen, Marsa 137
Clerc, Phil 451
Cleveland, Karrie 71
Cleveland, David H. 202
Clifford, Suzanne 137
Clifford, Chad 348
Clifton, Jim 213
Clifton, Mark A. 494
Clifton, Shaw 566

Clinton, Brenden 340
Clinton, Deoarn 476
Clinton, Malissia 534
Cloe, Martin 26
Cloutier, Dagan 487
Coari, John 108
Coates, Janet 586
Cobb, William (Bill) 268
Coccaro, Alfred 418
Cochran, Deanna 51
Cochran, Jeffrey (Jeff) 103
Cochran, Clarke 148
Cochran, Robert W. 298
Cochran, Dan 429
Cochrane, Andy 372
Cody, Kenneth B. 64
Coen, Bill 339
Coffey, Susan S. 21
Coffey, Patrick 214
Coffey, Jim 224
Coffey, Dick 392
Coffin, Joanne 68
Coffin, Mark W. 470
Cogan, Scott 518
Cogdill, Richard A. (Rick) 567
Coggans, Chris 112
Cogwin, Jack 518
Cohen, Philip 98
Cohen, Paula Marantz 171
Cohen, Howard 180
Cohen, Eric 280
Cohen, Sarah 414
Cohen, Louise 420
Cohen, Jay 479
Cohen, Marvin 518
Cohn, David (Dave) 462
Cohn, Ben 572
Cohon, Jared L. 99
Colaco, Chris 614
Colangelo, Carmon 575
Colby, Tony 5
Colcord, Dan 176
Cole, Charles T. 96
Cole, Susan A. 351
Cole, Rebecca 649
Colella, Carmine 351
Coleman, David 133
Coleman, Terrance R 308
Coleman, Brendan 362
Coleman, Christine 623
Colgan, Gary 112
Colgate, Ken 186
Colineri, Lori 437
College, Craig 92
Collignon, David (Dave) 3
Collins, Jeff 5
Collins, Mark 83
Collins, David D (Dave) 175
Collins, Jodi R. 217
Collins, Joseph L (Jo) 236
Collins, Karen Scott 558
Collins, Reggie 586
Collins, Kathy 643
Collins, John F. 645
Collura, Corren 516
Colon, Suzanne 602
Colpaert, Gary 211
Colvin, Jeff 6
Colvin, Garren 448
Colwell, Willanne 391
Combe, Paul 323
Comber, Peter J. 388
Combs, Michelle 1
Combs, Randy 333
Combs, Bobby 528
Comer, Diane 280
Comer, Chris 609
Comerota, Anthony J. 570
Compton, Al 225
Compton, Barry 229
Compton, Craig 398
Comstock, Ross 167
Conaghan, David (Dave) 105
Conard, Todd 21
Concepcion, Theresa 246

Concordel, Gilles 145
Conder, Don 110
Condron, P. Kevin 133
Cone, Alex 163
Confalone, Pat N. 19
Conforme, Veronica 133
Congdon, David (Dave) 245
Conklin, Carla 48
Conklin, George S. 121
Conley, Sophie 379
Conley, Elizabeth (Beth) 517
Connelly, Thomas M. (Tom) 19
Connelly, James (Jamie) 239
Connely, Michael 368
Conner, Mark 590
Connolly, Landon 105
Connolly, Lois 211
Connolly, Meg 451
Connor, Sue 636
Connors, Dennis 14
Connors, Robert H. (Bob) 492
Connors, Alfred F. 555
Connors, Christopher (Chris) 623
Conover, Duke 400
Conrad, Heidi 430
Conrad, Scott 525
Conrad, Jerry 539
Considine, William H. (Bill) 119
Constan, Louis 149
Constantine, Tim 112
Constantine, Ted 112
Constantine, Ruth 570
Constantino, Tawnya 263
Constantino, Vincent 427
Conti, Kurt G. 143
Conway, Chin 215
Conway, William A (Bill) 238
Conway, Guy 614
Conway, Maria 623
Cook, Marvin 82
Cook, Larry 215
Cook, Gayle C. 258
Cook, Jeanne 424
Cook, Lydia 517
Cook, Dillon 532
Cook, James E. (Jim) 557
Coolidge, Kathryn 313
Coombs, Albert 379
Cooney, Michael 352
Cooper, Mark 6
Cooper, Alan 17
Cooper, Joel 99
Cooper, Mark A. 105
Cooper, Jennifer (Jen) 202
Cooper, Chris 428
Cooper, Mark 529
Cooper, Rochelle 601
Coopwood, Kenneth (Ken) 347
Copeland, Robert (Bob) 649
Coppola, Nicole 572
Coppolo, Carolina 389
Cora-Bramble, Denice 118
Coradine, Sedare 559
Corao, Diana 363
Corcoran, Carol 569
Corcoran, Mary 590
Cordano, Roberta J. (Bobbi) 213
Cordeiro, Anne 330
Corder, Lee Infrastructure 653
Core, Ronald J. 217
Corell, Kemp 394
Corgan, Emily 353
Corlew, Teresa 181
Corley, William E. (Bill) 137
Corley, Bill 551
Corliss, Frank 51
Cormier, Samantha 572
Cornell, Kathleen 310
Cornish, Kelly Lynn Haigler 618
Cornuejols, Gerard 100
Coronado, Janet 424
Corrigan, Rosemary 613
Cors, Allen D. 358
Corse, William (Bill) 169
Corwin, Steven J. (Steve) 558

Coryat, Catherine A. 351
Cosme, Lydia 85
Costa, Frank 131
Costantini, Otto 517
Costantino, Vincent 427
Costanzo, Ronald 169
Costella, Margaret F (Peg) 551
Costello, Danny 543
Cottingham, Joyce 456
Cottrell, Cicely 547
Cottrill, Mark 624
Coulter, Gregory J 615
Counts, Lori 363
Courneya, Patrick (Paddy) 280
Court, Adrianne 445
Courtney, Richard 181
Courtright, Henry A (Hal) 182
Cousineau, Courtney 316
Coutilish, Theodore 177
Cover, Mark 245
Covi, Gina 284
Covington, Billy 534
Cow, Jay 409
Cowley, Daron 263
Cowley, Matt 489
Cox, Julie 98
Cox, Edward G. 208
Cox, Julie 305
Cox, Linda 307
Cox, Sonja M. 322
Cox, Chris W. 358
Cox, Scott 523
Cox, Michael (Mel) 526
Cox, Curtis 528
Cox, Dudley 583
Cox, Joan 645
Coyne, Sean 89
Cozart, Kevin M 337
Crabtree, Robbin 191
Craft, Blount 485
Craghead, Todd 263
Craig, Karen 31
Craig, Tommy 245
Craig, James 307
Craig, Ulanders 418
Craighead, Donora 99
Crain, Mark 153
Craine, Brenda 22
Craine, William 599
CRAMB, ALAN W (Al) 256
Cramer, Joe 510
Crane, Larry 441
Crawford, Brian 19
Crawford, Greg 557
Crawford, Bob 598
Crawford, James D. 642
Crawford, Nancy 647
Creach, Rod 52
Creamer, David 339
Creech, Denise 19
Creech, Michael 345
Creevey, Tom 207
Creevy, William 82
Creger, Phil 96
Creighton, Mark 189
Cress, Yevette 596
Creveling, Mark 551
Crews, Kimberly 242
Cribari, Lisa 143
Criger, Sara 15
Cripps, Tom 113
Crisci, Nick 290
Crocker, Janet 255
Crocker, Pat 443
Crockett, Tom 234
Crockett, Hannah (Hanna) 566
Crocquet, Marc C 379
Croken, Kenneth (Ken) 215
Cron, William (Bill) 109
Cronin, Paula 94
Crook, Anne 417
Crosby, James G. (Jim) 36
Crosley, Pascal 162
Crossland, Christopher (Chris) 151
Croston, J. Kevin 372

Crovesi, Marco 253
Crowder, Otis A. 151
Crowder, Andy 462
Crowell, Diana 77
Crowell, Edward (Ed) 132
Crowell, Eric 266
Crowell, Patricia 396
Crowley, Diane 150
Crowley, Dick 290
Crowley, Timothy (Tim) 512
Crowley, Marybeth 590
Crowson, Niel 173
Croy, Stanley (Stan) 405
Croymans, Ed 127
Cruickshank, Jay 552
Cruise, Rodney (Rod) 185
Crumby, Douglas 64
Crumley, John (Jack) 36
Cruse, Marc 111
Crutcher, Jared 365
Cruts, Adam 149
Cruz, Mike De La 226
Cruzd, Adrienne 321
Csj, Jane Gerard (Ginny) 160
Csont, Dan 419
Cudina, Christopher C. 254
Cudjoe, Ato 572
Culbert, John 159
Culbert, Doug 436
Cullen, Roxanne 197
Cullinan, Donna 590
Culling, Robert (Doug) 467
Cully, Bryan 642
Cummings, Mark 245
Cummings, Jay 363
Cummings, Jeff 426
Cummins, Frank 275
Cummiskey, Tom 629
Cuneo, Marie 379
Cunningham, Marsha 47
Cunningham, Trace 311
Cunningham, Michael R. 359
Cunningham, Morla 534
Cuomo, Lori 284
Curesky, Maria 191
Curley, Matthew (Matt) 487
Curphy, Rona 46
Curran, Kevin T. 645
Curren, Tammy 283
Currie, John (Jack) 362
Currier, Rand 224
Curry, Maridee 328
Curry, Kevin 426
Curtis, Carrie 197
Curtis, David 433
Curtis, Brad 529
Curtler, Elizabeth 612
Cushing, Robert 10
Cushman, Floyd 348
Custard, Linda 569
Custis, Sheree L 163
Cutler, Scott M. 442
Cutrone, Paul S. 377
Cuzzola, Anthony 541
Cvetas, Joseph G. 489
Cwalina, Marianne 83
Czarnecki, Gerald M. 359
Czebotar, Jerry A. 357
Czernik, Gabrielle 511
Czernikowski, Roy 439
Czink, Debra 107

D

Daane, Jeff 638
Dabbert, Lyle D. 585
Dacey, Michael (Mel) 285
Dadlez, Christopher M. (Chris) 449
Dafilou, David (Dave) 96
Daher, Stacy 613
Dahl, Deb 46
Dahl, Cheri W. 117
Dahl, Sandy 652
Dahlen, Dennis 45

Dahlstrom, Krista 163
Dahlstrom, Richard (Rick) 328
Dai, Hai-Lung 530
Dailey, Krisoula 198
Dake, Stephan H. (Steve) 457
Dakovich, Bob 193
Dalal, Kosha 198
Dalal, Ardeshir J 347
Daleo, Robert D. (Bob) 204
Dalfsen, Henk 583
Dallala, Daniel 100
Dalton, Robert 227
Dalton, Chuck 377
Dalton, William J. (Bill) 389
Dalton, Sally 613
Dameron, John 307
Dammon, Robert M. 99
Damon, Lisa J. 470
Damon-Scherer, Carol 425
Dana, Phillips 321
Dandes, Jonathan 434
Dandes, Jonathan (Jon) 434
Danes, Mike 37
Daniel, Karen L. 73
Daniel, Mark 157
Daniel, Joseph R. (Joe) 272
Daniel, Joseph R. (Josh) 272
Daniel, William T. (Bill) 330
Daniel, June 470
Daniels, Hovannes 280
Daniels, Clifford (Cliff) 337
Daniels, Heather 617
Daniels, Dennis 629
Danilowicz, Bret S. 217
Dansie, Scott 70
Dantley, Michael 340
Daprano, Corinne 572
Darneille, Wallace L. (Wally) 409
Darnell, Gail 55
Darrington, Jim 263
Darst, David M. 423
Dasaro, George 310
DaSilva, Jack 576
Dassance, Charles 138
Datte, Deborah 2
Daugherty, Suzanne 408
Daugherty, Michael 534
Daughtrey, Bill 627
Dave, Sachin 137
Davenport, Jamie 113
Davenport, John 233
Davenport, Mely 652
David, Rich 360
David, Robert G. 604
Davidoff, Ravin 82
Davidoff, Andrew 503
Davidson, Thomas 160
Davidson, Bruce 247
Davidson, Marty 488
Davidson, Gary 551
Davidson, Vicky L 649
Davies, Kevin 19
Davies, Antony 172
Davies, Susan Braxton 217
Davis, James C. (Jim) 14
Davis, Robert (Bob) 22
Davis, Maxine 109
Davis, Paul 112
Davis, Richard K. (Ricky) 128
Davis, Paulette 175
Davis, Larry 176
Davis, Hervey 208
Davis, Kimberly 226
Davis, Michael (Mel) 239
Davis, Darcy J. 330
Davis, Morgan 342
Davis, Robert 346
Davis, Karen 375
Davis, Richard E. 379
Davis, Jeff 411
Davis, Lee 412
Davis, Gary 412
Davis, Eric 414
Davis, Lynette 427
Davis, Karen 432

Davis, Kent 432
Davis, Jonathan S. 467
Davis, Matthew (Matt) 471
Davis, Anne 473
Davis, Matt 492
Davis, Dewey 500
Davis, Glenn W. 514
Davis, Eric 532
Davis, Glenn 534
Davis, Christopher 536
Davis, Bill 538
Davis, Joan S. 542
Davis, Julie 543
Davis, Charlotte 554
Davis, Michael 589
Davis, Bo 601
Davis, Michael 602
Davis, Angie 613
Davis, Joan 623
Davis, Karen 625
Davison-wilson, Sand 197
Dawson, Mary 256
Day, Kristina 46
Day, James (Jamie) 198
Day, Kim 333
Day, Danyel 393
Day, Scott 460
Day, James H (Jamie) 589
Day, Patrick 616
Days, Karen 360
Dayton, Mindy 534
Deal, Thomas M. 217
Dean, Clint 186
Dean, Kathy 401
Dean, Chana 425
DeAngelis, Christine 305
Debenedetti, Barby 47
Deberry, Herb 181
DeBerto, Joann 470
Deborah, Ferguson 540
Debruin, Chris 516
DeBrunner, Alexis 340
DeCardy, Chris 543
Decaro, James (Jamie) 439
Decastro, Howard 601
Decker, Jan 104
Decker, Lisa 207
Decoeur, Dan 646
Decook, Daniel (Dan) 247
DeCoudreaux, Alecia A. 258
Deek, Fadi P. 364
DeFrank, Jay 64
Degaetano, Joseph P 379
Degenhart, William J. 330
DeGeorge, Peter R. 423
Degraff, Michelle 502
DeGroote, Christina 516
Degruttola, John (Jack) 467
Deibel, Chris 209
Deiters, David 560
Deitz, Michelle 425
Dejgaard, Anders 411
Delagardelle, Pam 266
Deland, Emme 559
Delaney, Edward (Ed) 597
Delatorre, Sarah 524
Deleo, Cary 240
Deleonardis, Doreen 636
Delgado, Laurie S. 604
Delgiorno, Christopher 316
Delisle, Dennis 10
Delmont, Brad 151
Delohery, Andrew 423
Delong, Mary Lee 590
DeLong, Russell 630
Delproposto, Zachary S (Zach) 238
DeLuca, Tony 298
Demarco, Victor 85
Demarinis, Patrick (Paddy) 149
Demarr, Kris 577
Demartino, Richard 439
Dement, Dan 556
DeMerit, Craig 648
Demers, John 95
Demetriades, James 429

Demetriou, Achilles A. 604
Demme, Missy 100
Demmer, Vicki 387
DeMoss, Ruby 175
Dempsey, Lorcan 384
DeNarvaez, Margaret (Denny) 635
denBoer, Marten 159
Dench, Anne 279
Dendinger, Jim 272
Dengg, Robert 263
Denham, Glenn 91
DeNichilo, Nicholas 233
Denicholas, Joseph (Jo) 38
Denis, Peter 616
Dennis, Valerie (Val) 149
Dennis, Roger J. 171
Dennis, Kristin 478
Dennis, Danielle 614
Denny, Susan 278
DeNoia, Robert (Bob) 584
DePalma, Stephen P. 364
DePell, Fred (Fred) 379
Depersio, Marybeth 648
DePiano, Frank 379
Depiero, David (Dave) 139
DePompei, Patricia 604
Depugh-landrum, Peggy 5
Derbyshire, Geri 191
Derr, John (Jack) 200
Derrick, Opal 433
Derrick, Brian 517
Derrinton, Dolores 557
Derry, Cindy 624
Derusso, Patricia 539
Desai, Chirag 82
Desai, Vijay 560
Desguin, Michael (Mel) 245
Deshaies, Roger 201
Deshpande, Jayant K. 31
Desmaris, Thierry 642
DeSocio, Susan M. 487
Deson, Chip 153
Destler, William W. (Bill) 439
Detering, Paul J. 522
DeTore, Arthur W. 449
Dettelbach, Michael (Mel) 83
Deuschle, James R. (Jim) 434
Deutsch, Jonathan 171
Devarajan, Raj 185
Devens, Michael 170
Devine, Joseph W. 283
Devine, Claire 623
Devlin, Dave 597
Devon, Susan 298
Devos, Robert (Bob) 623
Dhanavantri, Varun 623
Diamond, Brent 143
Diamond, John 617
Dianis, Nancy 636
Diaz, Rubin 86
Diaz, Natalia 437
Diblasio, Kerry 171
Dicenso, Darren 105
Dick, Russell A. 463
Dickerson, Staci 474
Dickert-scherr, Carole 420
Dickey, Kevin 252
Dickinson, Tyler 149
Dickinson, Robyn 613
Dickson, Tom 45
Dickson, Dick 561
Dickson, Tom 570
Dickstein, Janice S 267
Didiano, Brian 158
Didier, Bridgett 337
Didur, Chris 342
Diebold, Raymond J. 155
Diebold, Ann E 623
Diede, Shannon 524
Diemer, Brent 112
Dierks, Nicole 616
Dietze, Steven J. 642
Diffee, Vic 196
Diffley, George 191
Dijulia, Dominick J 450

Dilek, Erhan 224
Dillard, Enid 289
Dillard, Gary K. 630
Diller, Matthew 653
Dillis, Mike 269
Dillon, Steve 83
Dillon, Timothy (Tim) 165
Dillon, Tom 648
Dimeo, Bradford S. 167
Dimon, Jamie 399
DiNapoli, Mark L. 516
DiNapoli, Michael (Mike) 516
DiNapoli, Mike 516
Dinaue, Cathy 101
Dingman, Ward 453
Dinon, Nancy 391
Dipace, Brian S 178
Diparlo, Mark 201
Dipasqua, Gaetano 232
Dipietro, Joseph 285
Direnna, James 237
Dittenber, Jody 109
Divakaruni, Phaneendra 623
Divanni, Alison 197
Divis, Jim 586
Dixon, Greg 229
Dixon, Richard T. 389
Dixon, Mary 643
Dixon-Williams, Sherrie 555
Dobbins, Sandra 495
Dodd, David 511
Dodds, Rick 287
Dodge, Richard E. 379
Dodgen, Claudia 151
Dodson, Laura 77
Doehner, George 431
Doering, Richard 247
Doerr, Dave 596
Doherty, Paul 474
Dohm, Faith-Anne 191
Dohm, Thomas 332
Dohman, David 370
Dohzen, Shirley 534
Dolan, John 171
Dolan, Patricia 202
Dolan, Peter R. 591
Dolan, Fiona 602
Dolen, Jim 170
Doliber, Peter 330
Doll, John (Jack) 494
Dolling, Lisa M. 511
Doll☐r, Marek 339
Dombrowski, H. Timothy 283
Domersant, Rachmani 204
Dominy, Michele D 51
Donahue, Tom 188
Donahue, Nancy 237
Donahue, Clare 616
Donald, Clay 414
Donaldson, Randy 210
Donaldson, Bill 557
Donato, Greg 388
Donavanberry, Lisa 147
Donegan, Lynda 589
Donelson, Jennifer (Jen) 380
Doninger, Clarence H. 258
Donley, Jeffrey S. (Jeff) 538
Donnell, Barbara 393
Donnelly, Gloria F. 171
Donnelly, David 423
DONOHOE, KIMBERLY A 271
Donohue, John 599
Donough, E. Merritt 449
Donovan, Douglas (Doug) 245
Donovan, Cary 454
Donovan, R. Nowell 532
Dooley, Paige 137
Dooley, Shawna 543
Doolin, James 323
Doran-Collins, Marianne 277
Dorchester, Wendy 307
Dori, Holnagel 247
Dorman, H. Paul 165
Dorman, Rachel 585
Dormo, Cindy 119

Dornell, J D 643
Dornell, JD 643
Dornenburg, Jeff 595
Dorsa, Daniel M 390
DORSEY, LISA 451
Dostal, Drew 46
Doti, Mary 596
Dotson, Pam 503
Dotson, Pamela (Pam) 503
Dotson, Orville W. (Pete) 630
Dougherty, Blaire 124
Dougherty, Charles J. 172
Doughty, Victor 566
Douglas, Nikki 153
Douglas, Marian 202
Douglas, Rob 255
Douglas, Joseph (Jo) 280
Douglas, Keith 576
Douglas, Barbara 602
Douglas, John (Jack) 609
Douglass, Travis 407
Doukas, Peter 530
Dove, Kent 258
Dow, John 275
Dow, Laura 330
Dowdle, Deedie 339
Dowey, Ed 518
Dowling, Dorothy 66
Downes, Terry 463
Downey, Douglas C (Doug) 337
Downing, Helen Dean 330
Downing, James 503
Doyle, Arthur (Art) 133
Doyle, James 160
Doyle, Lori 171
Doyle, Kevin 179
Doyle, Kevin M 591
Drago, William 224
Dragovich, Dmeter 589
Drake, James L 30
Drake, Rhonda 342
Dralle, Laurie 491
Draper, Suzie 263
Draper, Alfred C. 377
DReed, David (Dave) 342
Drees, Barbara (Barb) 544
Drees-Jones, Barbara (Barb) 544
Dreiling, Rick 59
Dresen, Scott 492
Dressen, Jessi 379
Drever, Melanie 618
Drewry, Richard (Dick) 49
Drews, Penny 88
Drolshagen, Colleen 107
Druckenmiller, Fiona 536
Druga, Greg 227
Drummond, Joseph (Jo) 591
Drushella, Joanie 94
Dryden, Ken 415
Dube, Cynthia 540
Dubea, Cynthia K. 423
Dubois, Erin 224
DuCharme, Duane 445
Duchossois, Craig J. 571
DuCloux, Harold P. 330
Dudley, Michael M. 467
Dudley-hart, Paul 332
Duduit, Dustin 481
Dueland, Dave 267
Dueppengiesser, Arnold 155
Dufault-Hunter, David (Dave) 42
Duff, John 304
Duffett, Richard 197
Duffy, Dorothy 542
Dugal, Martin 590
Dugent, Paul 188
Duguay, William G. (Bill) 270
Duhaime, Bob 103
Duke, Lee M. 551
Duke, Lisa 649
Dukes, Derrick 571
Dullea, Jeanne 218
Dumay, Ida 380
Dumonceaux, John (Jack) 449
Duncan, Jim 71

Duncan, Donna 227
Duncan, Jon 463
Dunlap, David L. 96
Dunlap, Edward B. 105
Dunlap, Timothy M. 105
Dunlap, Ron 222
Dunn, Carolyn 109
Dunn, Laurie 141
Dunn, Brent 347
Dunn, Jerry 563
Dunn, Saul 575
Dunne, Thomas (Thom) 204
Dunne, Liz 401
Duquette, Eugene 651
Durako, Steve 636
Durand, Bob 37
Durant, Linda 641
Durgan, Bob 26
Durma, Mary 183
Durnell, Keith 597
Durst, Lisa 2
Duteau, Mike 293
Duttenhaver, John R. 330
Duvall, Sister Judith Ann 392
Dwight, Mary 154
Dworkin, Darren 104
Dwyer, Thomas L. G. 277
Dwyer, Shannon 501
Dyal, Herman 128
Dyamenahalli, Shashi 32
Dyer, Halie 175
Dyer, Cathy 482
Dyke, William R. (Bill) Van 73
Dykehouse, Rod 211
Dykehouse, Rodney C (Rod) 211
Dykens, Jeff 94
Dykes, Bradford W. 259
Dykes, Pamela 372
Dymond, Mary 222
Dymond, Robert 525
Dyson, Kenneth L. (Kenny) 322
Dyson, Kenneth L. (Kenny) 322
Dzamashvili, Konstantin 107
Dzielecki, Debbie 316
Dziwis, Carolyn 555
D'Agostino, Jim 516
D'Ambra, Diane 277
D'Angelo, Andrea 236
D'Anna, Theodore 319
D'Arcy, Thomas (Thom) 245
D'Arienzo, Annette Marino 77

E

Eager, Pamela (Pam) 100
Earl, Cletis 650
Early, Philip 81
Early, Betsy 468
Early, Betsy 468
Earnest, Dianna 517
Earp, Wyatt 392
Easley, Thomas J. 22
Easley, Paul 490
Easterday, Tim 13
Easterly, Mark 554
Eastham, Catherine (Cathy) 211
Eaton, Bruce 585
Eaton, Dave 616
Eberhird, Sally 581
Eberly, Jeff 171
Ebersole, Gail Infrastructure 653
Echols, Lee 377
Eck, Cheryl 184
Eckberg, Stephen 501
Eckels, Dan 631
Ecker, Christian 374
Eckhardt, Bill 26
Eckhart, Paul 226
Eckhout, Gifford 586
Eddowes, Geoffrey W. 551
Eddy, Helen 255
Edeker, Randy 255
Edelen, Donald (Don) 207
Edelman, Marc 418

Edgington, Jerry 263
Edginton, Emilee 112
Edholm, Craig 311
Ediger, Scott 279
Edleman, Peter (Pete) 24
Edmonds, Jane (Ginny) 43
Edmonds, Jennifer 551
Edney, Jerry 37
Edwards, Steven L. 73
Edwards, Austin 224
Edwards, Gordon 302
Edwards, Steven D. (Steve) 304
Edwards, Marcie L. 309
Edwards, Ellie 347
Edwards, Dave 358
Edwards, Scott 372
Edwards, Teresa L. (Terrie) 467
Edwards, Michael (Mel) 584
Edwards, Brad 636
Edwin, Shirin 253
Efurd, Richard 518
Egeland, Juli 255
Eger, Ydelia 49
Eggers, Drew 379
Eggleston, Angela (Angie) 596
Egidi, Kenneth A. (Ken) 402
Egrican, Korkud 112
Ehrlich, Elizabeth 429
Eibeck, Pamela A. (Pam) 616
Eichler, Barry 653
Eigen, Joel 208
Eisel, Tim 370
Eisenberger, Gary 154
Eisenkraft, Barbara (Barb) 645
Eisenstein, Bruce 171
Eiss, Steve 46
Eker, Jessica 584
Ekren, Brandie 298
Ekstrand, Diane 46
Eladoumikdachi, Firas 215
Elberfeld, Adrienne 542
Elder, J 23
Elder, Rachel 347
Eldridge, Greg 112
Elices, Simone 532
Elliott, J 554
Ellis, Mike 239
Ellis, Barnes 332
Ellis, David (Dave) 340
Ellis, Heidie 425
Ellis, George W 614
Ellish, Patti 452
Ellison, David 96
Ellison, Edward 279
Ellison, David 503
Ellison-Taylor, Kimberly N. 21
Ellsworth, Kathryn 215
Ellwanger, Dina 448
Elmore, Bill 153
Elmore, David G. 258
Elrod, David 170
ElSawy, Amr A. 369
Elsea, Charles (Chuck) 567
Elswick, Shannon 391
Elting, Elizabeth (Liz) 584
Eltringham, Natasha 69
Elwood, Audrey L 321
Elyea, Mike 473
Emami, Azita 616
Emerson, Lawrence 58
Emerson, Michael 225
Emerson, Cal 311
Emerson, Delta 445
Emery, Robert 201
Emison, Kevin 225
Emmons, Christopher W. 313
Emo, Diane 149
Emond, Lawrence M. (Larry) 213
Emore, Doug 430
Empel, Emily 623
Endres, John J (Jack) 546
Endsley, Samantha 46
Engel, Gretchen 112
Engel, Amy 602
Engel, Nate 602

Engelberg, Barry 389
Engelkemeyer, David (Dave) 634
Engels, John 66
England, Todd D. 90
England, Corey D. 90
England, Chad 90
England, Josh 90
England, Zach 90
England, Dustin 90
England, Daniel E. (Dan) 90
England, Dean D. 90
Englert, Mark 618
English, John (Jack) 91
English, Lars 166
English, David 445
English, John 491
Engstrom, Royce C. 609
Enis, Terry 185
Enke, Charles 619
Enke, Charles 619
Ensign, Margee 616
Epke, Barbara 305
Epke, Barbara 481
Epmeier, Bruce 161
Epps, Donna 300
Epps, JoAnne A. 530
Epstein, Leon G. 27
Epstein, Frederick (Fred) 55
Epstein, Doug 240
Erbes, Troy 158
Ercolano, Pat 607
Erden, Dale Van 155
Erekson, O. Homer 532
Eriamiato, Eseosa 364
Erickson, Sue 335
Erickson, Tina 555
Ericson, Brent 226
Erinjeri, Veena 254
Ernest, Cindi 111
Ertle, Alan (Al) 395
Erusha, Kimberly S. 602
Erwin, Dary 271
Erwin, Terry 317
Escamilla, Paul 126
Escano, Richard 95
Escasa-Haigh, Jo 501
Escobedo, Efrain 93
Escobedo, Brook 414
Esfahani, Sam 419
Eshelbrenner, Adam 576
Esipova, Neli 213
Eskandarian, Romic 219
Esker, Jerry 456
Eslick, Rob 255
Espey-English, Patricia 636
Espinoza, Patricia 404
Espy, Kevan 132
Espy, Julie 389
Esquina, Linda 238
Esrael, Craig 419
Esserman, Richard (Dick) 602
Essex, Sean 612
Esta, Joe 627
Esteban, A. Gabriel 469
Esteban, Gabriel 470
Esterheld, Paul 442
Estes, Rob W. 188
Estes, David (Dave) 317
Estes, Reid 653
Esther, Chet 226
Estus, Maureen 201
Ethier, Robert 267
Ethridge, Craig 22
Etneier, Bruce 160
Etter, Carl J. 462
Eubanks, Susan 46
Eugster, Cris 126
Eulberg, Patrick J (Paddy) 29
Eulberg, Patrick 29
Evans, Dave 54
Evans, Sharene 158
Evans, Pam 242
Evans, David C. 258
Evans, Daniel F. (Dan) 259
Evans, Fred 306

Evans, David (Dave) 362
Evans, Melinda 501
Evans, Kimberly 579
Evans, Roberta D. 609
Evans, Kristi 634
Everett, Daniel L. 64
Everett, Linda Q. 258
Everett, Linda Q. 259
Everett, Brad 270
Everhart, Martin 437
Ewell, Cris V. 464
Ewers, Ron 138
Ewing, A. Hugh 117
Ewing, Janice 577
Exler, Michael (Mel) 171
Eynon, Matthew 208

F

Faas, Sidney A (Sid) 112
Faber, Amy 100
Fache, Marsha 376
Fache, Jane (Ginny) 503
Fader, Maegan 614
Fagan, Michael 366
Fagan, Mary 425
Fagan, Shiraz M. 462
Fahland, Richard 25
Fahrlander, Jason 137
Fairall, Kathleen 318
Faith, David M. 567
Faith, Marshall E. 567
Fajardo, Jose A. 358
Falaguerra, Robert J. (Bob) 449
Falb, Derek 123
Falcone, Joseph C. 357
Falcone, Anthony J. 357
Falcone, Joseph C. 357
Falcone, Anthony J. 357
Falcone, Neil 629
Falken, Tim 434
Falkowitz, Mary 559
Fallin, Jesse 460
Fallon, Mark D. 112
Fallon, Shawna 473
Falsey, Ann 552
Fannin, Stephen (Steve) 517
Fannin, Bob 597
Farber, Greg 213
Farber, Scott 423
Farberman, Daniel (Dan) 281
Farberman, Daniel 281
Farhangpour, Amir 380
Farkas, Andrew 542
Farley, John (Jack) 317
Farmer, Gerard 77
Farmer, Bill 112
Farmer, Dennis 226
Farr, Rich 90
Farr, David (Dave) 513
Farrar, Jerry 112
Farrell, James G. 392
Farrell, Martin F (Marti) 450
Farrow, Alan (Al) 118
Farvardin, Nariman 511
Fassezke, Mike 510
Fasula, Joyce A. 218
Fasula, Joseph (Joe) 218
Faszl, Barbara 575
Fattal, Garabed 599
Faturos, David (Dave) 434
Faucette, Bill 131
Faul, Mark 576
Faulkner, Ryan 501
Faust, Devan 342
Fauteux, Greg 252
Fawcett, George 490
Fay, Jody 461
Fay, David 602
Featherly, Walter T. 399
Featherston, Marcus 261
Featherstone, Craig 306
Feaver, Charles (Chas) 520
Federenko, Garvin 9

Fedie, Joe 342
Feed, Mike 492
Feekes, Stan 195
Feenstra, Randall 99
Feghali, Imad 112
Fehringer, Rich 379
Fehser, Kathy 513
Feigelman, Theodor 39
Feiner, Barbara A. 575
Felis, Sandra L. 201
Felleson-ilko, Beret 49
Felton, Stephen 36
Felton, Tom 327
Felty, Craig 259
Fennessey, Mike 253
Fenning, Armita 581
Fenolio, Amanda 615
Fenton, Dan 585
Ferando, Jim 45
Ferchland-Parella, Joanne 379
Ferebee, Ellen 470
Ferencz, Steven M. 105
Ferer, Fernando 536
Ferguson, Stewart 9
Ferguson, Paul W. 44
Ferguson, David (Dave) 44
Ferguson, Chris 171
Ferguson, Stephen L. (Steve) 258
Ferguson, Richard C. 423
Ferguson, Susan Portis 631
Fern, Francine 419
Fernandes, Paul A. 514
Fernandes, Al 592
Fernandes, Sidney 614
Fernandez, Robert (Bob) 158
Fernandez, Miguel 236
Fernandez, Alfonso (Al) 270
Fernandez, David 437
Fernandez, Pua 590
Ferndinand, Norma 551
Fernstrum, Lisa 342
Ferrando, Carrie 113
Ferranti, Richard M. 434
Ferrara, Phylis 517
Ferrara, Raymond 551
Ferrarelli, Alan (Al) 462
Ferrari, Dan 518
Ferrari, Mauro 554
Ferraro, Madeline 39
Ferre, Fernando 536
Ferrell, Bob 642
Ferren, Brent 74
Ferrenberg, Alan (Al) 340
Ferrillo, Patrick J. 616
Ferrucci, Gabriel 423
Ferrymd, Jane 223
Fetrow, Jacquelyn S. (Jacque) 612
Feudo, John 590
Feuer, Bruce 561
Few, Warren 630
Fey, Charles J (Chas) 364
Fhfma, Steven (Steve) 302
Fiaksel, Michael 112
Fickett, Joel 198
Fidorowicz, Elaine 152
Fiedler, Peter (Pete) 82
Fielding, Dave 513
Fields, Kathy 10
Fields, James P. (Jim) 408
Fiereck, Ken 141
Figueroa, Carolina 83
Figueroa, Laureano 613
Filipic, Matt 649
Filipov, Douglas 98
Fillhaber, Mitchell (Mitch) 476
Fillhaber, Mitch 476
Filtz, Joe 105
Fimiano, Andrew A. 489
Finch, Mike 127
Fine, Kim 10
Fine, Peter S. 45
Fine, Susan (Sue) 548
Finkel, Louis 23
Finkelstein, Arthur 95
Finlayson, Krista 46

Finley, Tim 411
Finley, Rebecca S. 578
Finley-Hazle, Gabrielle 506
Finn, Michael 323
Finn, MJKnoll 653
Finnagan, Joe 153
Firdaus, Dave 77
Fireman, Howard 18
Fischer, Alexander (Al) 54
Fischer, Steven 67
Fischer, Alex 360
Fischer, William (Bill) 571
Fischer, Jason 595
Fish, John F. 516
Fish, Greg 585
Fish, John F. 590
Fish, Irving 602
Fish, Irving 602
Fish, Ted 631
Fisher, Lauren 119
Fisher, William (Bill) 137
Fisher, Scott 188
Fisher, Todd 218
Fisher, Morris 313
Fisher, Jacquelyn 380
Fisher, Mark 489
Fisher, Terry 597
Fitz, Kevin 35
Fitz, Raymond 571
Fitzpatrick, James 191
Fitzpatrick, Jerry 311
Fitzpatrick, Mike 388
Fitzpatrick, Donna 449
Fitzpatrick, Nancy 602
Fitzsimmons, Bill 142
Flaherty, Ellen 158
Flaherty, Richard 616
Flaherty-Oxler, Karen 551
Flanagan, Dennis P. 423
Flanagan, Jill 623
Flanigan, John 6
Flannery, Terry 24
Flathers, Kristina 363
Flathman, Christian H. 217
Flax, Tim 343
Fleekop, Kenneth 421
Fleming, Russ 32
Fleming, William (Bill) 98
Fleming, Karen 447
Fleming, Thomas (Thom) 523
Fleming, John 534
Fleming, Horace 543
Flemming, Mark 100
Flencher, Ben 78
Flencher, Ben 78
Fletcher, Andrew 167
Fletcher, Lou 201
Flick, Tim 113
Flickinger, Donald (Don) 197
Flomenbaum, Neal 559
Flood, David L. 263
Flood, Rebecca 366
Flores, Debbie 46
Flores, Eduardo 126
Flores, Hector 439
Flores, Debra A. 467
Flores, Eloisa 470
Flowers, Jeff 561
Flowers, Steve 642
Floyd, P 96
Floyd, Kathy 271
Floyd, Ben 412
Flury, Elizabeth 119
Flynn, Cheryl 338
Flynn, Eric 340
Flyte, Jonathan (Jon) 492
Fogarty, John 67
Fogel, Jeri 320
Fohrer, Jon 137
Foley, Brian 137
Foley, Michele 158
Foley, Marie 470
Folkerts, John (Jack) 54
Folsom, Laurie 423

Fong, Peter L. 550
Font, Yvette 175
Foran, Christine 365
Forbes, Clarett 85
Forbes, Kay 245
Forbes, Caleb 407
Forbush, David (Dave) 383
Forcier, Michael (Mel) 590
Ford, Mike 170
Ford, Gary 198
Ford, Brad 199
Ford, Richard E. 258
Ford, Kay A. 330
Ford, Kay A. 330
Ford, Chris 409
Ford, Henri 540
Fore, Ken 106
Fore, Stephanie 245
Forese, Laura L. 558
Foris, Nico 228
Forman, Daniel 653
Formica, Richard (Dick) 92
Forraht, Douglas R. 357
Forsgard, Fred 508
Forster, James (Jamie) 234
Forster, Michael L. 363
Forstner, Jim 162
Forsyth, Michael (Mel) 612
Fort, Bob 468
Fortney, John 5
Foss, Taylor 305
Foss, Taylor 481
Fossett, Diana 369
Foster, Ken 88
Foster, Dennis 110
Foster, Gregory 230
Foster, Marlene 280
Foster, Paul L. 375
Foster, Jean 407
Foster, Mary-Jane 423
Foster, Edward (Ed) 511
Foster, Eric 526
Foster, Randall 567
Foster, Rick 626
Fostyk, Irene 453
Fournier, Marc 486
Foust, Lawrence L 540
Fowler, Pat 80
Fowler, Laura 144
Fowler, Bob 188
Fowlie, Cassandra 572
Fox, Lisa 36
Fox, Kellie 95
Fox, Greg 205
Fox, Peter 205
Fox, Beth 215
Fox, Kim 226
Fox, Harry 279
Fox, Russell 290
Fox, Jan I. 320
Fox, Timothy (Tim) 343
Fox, Joanne 542
Foyo, George W. 47
Frady, Brandon 377
Frame, Thomas (Tom) 457
Francis, Robert (Bob) 171
Francis, Paige 191
Francis, Pauline 442
Franco, Mary 94
Francois, Paul 402
Frandsen, Mike 383
Franey, Henry J. 607
Frank, Isabelle 204
Frank, Ken 206
Frank, Norman 226
Frank, John (Jack) 245
Frank, James S. (Jim) 571
Frank, Virginia 635
Franke, Jan 569
Frankhart, Katie 109
Franklin, Dan 506
Franklin, John 653
Franks, Dennis 318
Franzen, Ron 505
Frazer, Gregory 172

Frazier, Bryan 519
Frear, David 428
Frederick, Larry 616
Fredericks, Raymond F. 274
Frederiksen, Derik 463
Freed, Michael P. (Mike) 492
Freedman, Stephen 204
Freeman, Richard (Dick) 68
Freeman, Alan (Al) 132
Freeman, Shawn 280
Freeman, Robert 307
Freeman, Jillian 310
Freeman, Kenneth (Ken) 633
Freeny, Jennifer 647
Freese-Decker, Tina 492
Frehse, Todd 263
Freiberg, Dan 342
Freiberg, Kristin M. 632
Freiberg, Kenneth 650
Freije, Margaret N. 133
Freimund, Wayne 609
Freitas, Christopher (Chris) 490
French, Peter 83
French, Elizabeth 112
French, Constance 390
Freni, Edward C. 323
Frey, Pamela 504
Frey, William 636
Frias, Richard 280
Frick, Dean 254
Friday, Rashad 240
Friday, Gary 312
Fried, Ehud 65
Frieder, Elliott J. 399
Friedlander, Ezra H. (Zeke) 258
Friedman, Steve 80
Friedman, Jennifer 246
Friedman, Tessa 347
Friedman, Jack 390
Friend, Katherine 32
Friend, Gwyn 160
Friend, Laurence 321
Friese, Ron 59
Friloux, David 373
Frisch, Steven M. 10
Frisch, Stephen (Steve) 10
Frisch, Harry 60
Frisch, Mark 60
Frisko, Pete 171
Fritsch, Billy D. (Bill) 101
Fritz, Laura 179
Fritz, Steven 490
Frix, Matthew 464
Froehlich, John 639
Froman, Sandra (Sandy) 358
Fromm, Bernard 429
Frost, Scott 295
Frost, Cherilynn 342
Frost, Claire 524
Fruchter, Eleanor 83
Fruin, John 226
Frumkin, Howard 616
Fry, John A. 171
Frysh, Frank 510
Fu, Belinda 524
Fuemmeler, Patty 339
Fuerst, James 64
Fugale, Steven 623
Fulco, Dominic 572
Fulginiti, Lisa 242
Fuller, Dan 153
Fuller, John D. (Jack) 364
Fullerton, Rob 642
Fullington, Bob 300
Fulton, Tork A. 109
Funderburk, William W. 309
Funk, Dan 36
Funkhouser, Cameron 198
Futter, Ellen V. 535
Fybel, Gary G. 462
Fyffe, Robert E. 649

G

Gabel, Pamela 95
Gabel, Timothy J. (Tim) 432
Gaboury, David 531
Gabriel, Ariel 30
Gabriel, Gloria 166
Gabriele, Maura 653
Gabrys, Gerard T. 228
Gaden, Nancy 82
Gadre, Aniruddha 95
Gaede, Carl 621
Gaffney, Maureen 645
Gage, Steve 173
Gage, Emma 316
Gage, Allen 585
Gagnon, Gary 557
Gagon, Gary J 557
Gaharan, George 129
Gahr, Freddie 433
Gajan, J. U. 490
Gajjar, Amar 503
Galaid, Edward (Ed) 96
Galarza, Adrian 99
Gale, Nigel 490
Galindo, Norma Sierra 257
Gallagher, Duncan P. 15
Gallagher, Kevin 100
Gallagher, Kelly 270
Gallagher, Susan (Sue) 332
Gallagher, Sandra 390
Gallagher, Ellen 536
Gallagher, Kay 636
Gallant, Gregory 169
Gallegos, Chris 518
Gallik, Mary 296
Gallo, Robert (Bob) 237
Gallo, Young 296
Galloway, Jon 218
Galloway, Heather C. 534
Galovich, Daniel 12
Galvao, Louis 445
Galvin, Sue 239
Gambert, Steven 481
Gamble, John (Jack) 9
Gammiere, Tom 462
Gandia, Melodee 308
Gandre, Tom 419
Gandy, Patrick W. 295
Ganesh, Deo 483
Ganley, Kevin 612
Garbini, Dennis 469
Garcia, Mandy 324
Garcia, William 364
Garcia, Carlos 409
Garcia, Leandro G. 420
Garcia, Al 467
Garcia, Lauren 539
Garcia, Ann 571
Gardiner, Mary 612
Gardner, Alan (Al) 619
Gardner, James 632
Gares, Donna 554
Garigliano, Frank 245
Garland, Ann 612
Garman, Matthew 89
Garmon, Terry 630
Garner, Cynthia 325
Garnett, Valerie (Val) 340
Garoff, Stephen 100
Garrett, James H. 99
Garrett, Kathy 421
Garrish, Ted 112
Garten, Michael 37
Garthwait, Cindy 609
Gartner, Lia 558
Garvin, Theresa 253
Garvin, Kevin 619
Garvin, Kevin 619
Garza, Rudy 126
Garza, Eva 534
Gasal, John (Jack) 141
GaskellBsnRn, Rose 211
Gaskins, Sherman L. 105

Gasper, William (Bill) 82
Gasstrom, Glen 155
Gaston, Octavia 393
Gaston, Denise 418
Gates, Robert M. 83
Gates, John 228
Gatlin, Shatiek 43
Gatlin, Greg 517
Gatmaitan, Al W. 259
Gaul, Steve 242
Gaul, Veera S 277
Gauss, Gene 642
Gautreaux, Cindy 487
Gauvin, Steve 612
Gavens, Mark R. 104
Gavin, Veronica 470
Gavish, Bezalel 487
Gavulic, Melanie 254
Gayman, Grant 322
Gazaway, Brad 461
Gazecki, Cindy Evans 464
Geannacopulos, Nick C. 470
Gebhard, J. Scott 274
Geddes, Deanna 530
Gedman, Elaine 639
Gee, Jeff 526
Geertsen, Tyler 43
Geidt, Steve 447
Geiger, James (Jamie) 303
Geiger, Eric 306
Geiger, Tony 585
Geile, Adrienne F 615
Geisendorfer, Emery O. 35
Gelber, Brian 214
Gellings, Clark 182
Gelman, Steve 112
Gemignani, Gino J. 576
Genebach, Michael L 3
Gennaro, Susan 590
Genshaft, Judy L. 614
Gentil, Patricia 575
Gentry, Dwight 144
Gentry, Michael 467
Geoghegan, Lisa 542
George, Karin 570
George, Shinny 579
George, J 588
George, Paul 603
Gephart, George W. 171
Gerard, Alice 56
Gerard, Matthew (Matt) 150
Gerber, Hilary 380
Gerken, Tim 574
Germain, John 149
Germek, Maryjane 437
Gerow, Cheryl 98
Gerstner, Louis V. 536
Gerwig, Kathy 280
Getchell, Charles M. 423
Geyman, Jennifer (Jen) 208
Ghaffarian, Kam 471
Ghanem, Salma 159
Ghanim, Isam M. 117
Ghormely, Larry 30
Giacobone, Chris 222
Giamalis, John N. 449
Gianchetta, Larry 609
Gianelli, Patricia (Pat) 302
Gibble, Robert J. 429
Gibbons, Andrew (Andy) 189
Gibbons, Michael 574
Gibbs, Leanne 174
Gibbs, Jeanette 547
Gibson, Sandra Lee 76
Gibson, Donald E. 191
Gibson, Richard (Dick) 301
Gibson, James J. (Jim) 432
Gibson, Valerie 517
Gibson, Rodney C (Rod) 534
Gies, Douglas J. (Doug) 355
Giese, Shane 282
Giese, Shane 609
Gigliotti, Mike 471
Gilardi, Corinne 340
Gilbert, Jerome A. 320

Gilbert, Ronnie 421
Gilbertson, Richard J. 503
Gilbertson, Philip N. 616
Giles, Alyson Pitman 103
Gilkey, Douglas 551
Gill, Johnson 33
Gill, Jack M. 258
Gill, Margaret (Maggie) 330
Gill, Margaret (Maggie) 330
Gill, Peter (Pete) 636
Gillean, John A. 121
Gilles, Patrick 449
Gilley, Patricia Boatright (Pat) 377
Gilliam, Craig 31
Gilligan, Jeff 271
Gilligan, Don 597
Gilliland, Terry 467
Gillis, Robert (Bob) 25
Gillis, Don 574
Gillis, David (Dave) 605
Gillula, E. William (Bill) 153
Gilman, Robert (Bob) 18
Gilman, Fred 99
Gilmore, Thomas W. 378
Gilrain, Kevin R. 25
Gilray, Jeff 297
Giltne, F 471
Giltner, F. Phillips (Phil) 471
Gilyard, Scott 562
Gingerich, Willard P. 351
Ginsberg, Ava 89
Ginsburg, J 189
Gionet, Tina 481
Giordon, Ron 188
Giovannone, John 576
Gipson, Sid 47
Gir, Roopa 256
Giron, Juan 450
Girouard, Marylynn 363
Girouard, Linney 554
Gisel, William G. (Bill) 434
Gisi, Richard 125
Givant, Steven 37
Glaab, Paul G. 389
Glanvill, Derek W. 327
Glanzman, Michael 5
Glaser, David 218
Glaser, David 218
Glaser, James M. 591
Glass, Cynthia 448
Glasser, Judy 83
Glasser, Rabbi Yaakov 653
Glatch, Lisa 112
Glatt, Aaron E. 334
Glawe, Sue 77
Glazer, Matt 317
Glazier, Steve 391
Gleason, Bonnie 191
Gleisner, Martha 417
Glenn, Richard K. 31
Glenn, Rose 238
Glenn, Pamela (Pam) 254
Glenning, Robert L (Bob) 231
Glickler, Joanna 616
Glidden, Karen 607
Glime, Garry 410
Glitsch, William 280
Gloggner, Peter (Pete) 278
Gloria, Doriane 365
Gloss, Ken 311
Glotfelty, Robert (Bob) 483
Glover, Mary 82
Glover, Renee 230
Glover, Walter 603
Gluth, Larry 230
Glynn, Mary 285
Glynn, Thomas P. 323
Goad, Michael 479
Goad, Rebecca L. 630
Goble, Jonathan 259
Gochnour, Gregory 263
Goddard, Anne Lynam 117
Godenzi, Alberto 590
Godfrey, Ellie 280
Godin, Steve 557

Godoy, Johanna 213
Godsey, Tracy 50
Godwin, John T. 105
Goebel, Rick 386
Goedecke, Nancy Collat 325
Goedecke, Glenn 325
Goedecke, Nancy Collat 325
Goehl, Athena 470
Goel, Amitabh 604
Goelzer, Angela 198
Goering, Richard 150
Goetsch, Timothy (Tim) 7
Goffredo, John 209
Golato, Andrea 534
Goldberg, Kenneth 359
Goldberg, Michael (Mel) 427
Goldfarb, Neil 578
Goldfoos, Elena 616
Goldman, Leslie 602
Goldman, George 644
Goldsmith, Carmen 614
Goldstein, Steve A. N. 83
Goldstick, Jonathan 112
Golightly, William (Bill) 551
Gollihue, Tiffani 54
Goltara, Ken 280
Golub, Jerel T. (Jerry) 546
Golub, Mona J. 546
Golub, David 546
Golub, Neil M. 546
Gomez, Melva 253
Gomez, Jess 263
Gomez, Denise 335
Gomez, Albert 420
Gomez, Genoveva G. 420
Gomez, Bobbi 425
Gomez, Diana 470
Gomulka, Robert 599
Gondringer, Nancy 448
Gong, Jin 616
Gonsalves, Linda 495
Gonyea, Dave 627
Gonzales, Raul 189
Gonzalez, Susan (Sue) 18
Gonzalez, Raul 189
Gonzalez, Naldo 200
Gonzalez, Catalina 380
Gonzalez, Will 518
Gonzalez, Shawn 546
Gonzalez, Irma 635
Goodell, Phil 343
Goodfellow, Daniel 221
Goodfellow, Dan 221
Goodfellow, Chad 221
Goodgame, Ken 588
Goodgion, Sean 111
Goodman, Wayne H. 534
Goodman, Vaughn 642
Goodstine, Sarah 23
Goodwin, Tarina 32
Goodwin, Sarah 215
Goodwin, Terry W. 423
Gookins, Norman 601
Goot, Stephen (Steve) 476
Gopalani, Radhan 47
Gopffarth, Lance 186
Gorder, Chrisoph 25
Gorder, Christopher D. Van 462
Gordon, Jeffrey 10
Gordon, Susan (Sue) 24
Gordon, Scott R. 31
Gordon, Larry 34
Gordon, Bob 49
Gordon, Robert 49
Gordon, Ora 104
Gordon, Thomas D (Thom) 104
Gordon, Rob 358
Gordon, Eileen 605
Gore, Jeremiah 247
Gorham, James (Jamie) 112
Gorman, Kathleen E. Chavanu 119
Gorman, Donna 307
Gorney, David J. 534
Goro, Kimura 613
Gorski, Al 389

Gosnell, Doug 24
Gossett, Barbara (Barb) 596
Gostick, Adrian 382
Gottesman, David S. 536
Gottlieb, Katherine 9
Gough, Patrick 389
Gould, Rob 45
Gouveia, Jeffrey (Jeff) 516
Gouveia, Jeffrey 516
Gow, Aileen 298
Goyal, Naser 585
Gozon, Richard C. 578
Gozzi, Karen 629
Grace, Robin 94
Gradin, Fredrik 23
Graebel, William (Bill) 222
Graebel, David (Dave) 222
Graf, Don 73
Gragg, Derrick 572
Graham, Rilus 189
Graham, Katie 255
Graham, Randolph H. 357
Graham, Stephen A. 469
Graham, William 532
Gralike, David M. 227
Gralike, Dave 227
Gram, Dwight 434
Grambart, Sean 98
Granata, Jessica 380
Grande, Alexandra 99
Granick, Mel 334
Grant, Duane 535
Grass, Linda 530
Grassi, R 150
Grassinger, Maxine 475
Grasso, Alfred 556
Grasty, Kevin 24
Gratz, Robert (Bob) 534
Grauer, Steve M 240
Graumlich, Lisa 616
Graves, Bob 247
Graves, Jennifer 524
Gravlin, Nick 342
Gray, James (Jamie) 83
Gray, Chip 128
Gray, Jeffrey (Jeff) 204
Gray, Celeste 235
Gray, Moses W. 258
Gray, Eric 379
Gray, Geoff 479
Gray, Bill 508
Gray, Jarrod 553
Gray, Pamela (Pam) 612
Graybeal, Carol 189
Greaney, Michael (Mike) 204
Greck, Sonya 345
Gredler, Frank 527
Green, Warren 248
Green, Louise 263
Green, Warren 305
Green, Andrea 347
Green, Thomas (Thom) 359
Green, Jane 432
Green, John 497
Green, Doug 503
Green, Beth 542
Green, Stephen D. 550
Green, Bob 569
Greenawalt, Richard A. 171
Greenberg, Henry 5
Greenberg, Harry 83
Greenberg, Lawrence 534
Greene, Sandy 175
Greene, Michael (Mel) 245
Greene, Joseph J. 277
Greene, Mary 505
Greene, Randy L. 511
Greene, Anastasia 511
Greenip, Debbie 65
Greenlee, Billy 32
Greensher, Joseph (Jo) 645
Greenstein, Scott 428
Greenstein, Sara A. 595
Greenwell, John 227
Greer, Gerald (Jerry) 3

Greer, Robert G. (Bobby) 364
Greer, Jeanne 542
Gregorian, Myra 307
Gregory, Alexandra 172
Gregory, Raymond 198
Gregory, Willis 397
Gregory, Bryan 409
Gregory, Thomas 589
Greiner, Brooke 43
Greiner, Jerry M. 641
Grench, Meghan 396
Grennan, M. Joseph 429
Gresh, Gary 310
Greubel, Scott 170
Grieco, Chrysanthy M. 470
Grier, Timothy (Tim) 42
Grier, Rosa 530
Griesemer, Daniel (Dan) 648
Griesemer, Daniel (Dan) 648
Griffin, Bill 49
Griffin, James D. 157
Griffin, Mark 435
Griffin, Wayne J. 633
Griffis, Mark 1
Griffis, Carri 197
Griffis, William I. 217
Griffis, Teresa M 566
Griffith, Darrell 286
Griffith, J. Brian 339
Griffith, Brian 339
Grigsby, Todd 91
Grimes, Robert R. 204
Grimes, Theresa 276
Grisez, Todd 119
Griswold, Jim 580
Groff, Stacey 255
Groff, Greg 362
Gronbach, Kort M 5
Gronevelt, Russell A 342
Gronski, Paul 450
Groom, Gary W. 457
Crosby, Karen 379
Gross, Frank C. 112
Gross, Peter (Pete) 231
Gross, Barry L 436
Gross, Joseph W. 448
Gross, Daniel L. (Dan) 473
Grossenbacher, Charles (Chas) 365
Grosser, Joy M. 266
Grossman, Marsha 182
Grossman, Orin 191
Grosso, Patrick 648
Grosveld, Gerard 503
Grote, Emma 206
Grottenthaler, Bob 52
Groves, Diahann 46
Groves, Meg 414
Grow, Timothy E. 357
Grow, Timothy E. 357
Grube, Bruce 217
Gruber, Seth 13
Gruber, Karen 542
Gruenthal, Michael 10
Grunley, Martin 227
Grunley, Kenneth (Ken) 227
Grunwald, Gerald B. 578
Guanowsky, Glenn 303
Guarini, Andrew (Andy) 247
Guarracino, Joseph J 86
Gubbiotti, Maria 578
Gudavalli, Prasad 366
Gueldner, Sara 599
Guenther, Stuart 321
Guenther, Rick 379
Guenther, Roger 411
Guerci, Alan D. 334
Guerin, Vera S. 104
Guerra, Emilia 420
Guerra, Juan 534
Guess, Charlie 389
Guez, Shirel 83
Guglielmo, Michael 530
Guhl, Janice 604
Guilander, Rick 153
Guilford, Arthur (Art) 614

Gulley, R. Michael 392
Gullicksrud, Lynn 446
Gumba, Rosemarie 112
Gumbs, Milton 85
Gumiela, Mike 149
Gumpel, Stephen (Steve) 18
Gunaratne, Pradeep 389
Gunn, George 112
Gunn, Deborah 126
Gunn, Laurie 201
Gunnink, Brett 350
Gupta, Mahendra R. 575
Guralnick, Sidney 256
Gurin, Joel 143
Gusler, Tim 337
Gustafson, Lynn 83
Gustke, John 74
Guter, Donald 172
Guthrie, Barbara 595
Gutierrez, Brian G. 532
Gutmann, Jim 245
Gutridge, Doug 290
Gutthann, Susana 432
Guy, Kip 503
Guyette, Kathy 345
Guyette, Kathleen Culhane 345
Guzicki, Mark 492
Guzman, Manuel 19
Guzman, Jolene 391

H

Haake, Anne 439
Haber, Rebecca 113
HABERBERGER, PATTY 451
Haberstroh-nelke, Kathie 153
Habingreither, Robert 534
Hackenkamp, Elaine 616
Hackert, Roy 116
Hackett, Dan 352
Hackett, Pete 477
Hackworth, David 112
Haddad, Gabriel G. 425
Haddican, James 218
Haden, James (Jamie) 467
Haecker, Matt 126
Haefner, Jeremy A. 439
Hagan, Julie 442
Hage, J%2ER%2E 454
Hagen, Bruce 386
Hagerty, Denise M. 22
Hagerty, Mark 584
Hagstrom, Jane 571
Hahn, Charles 633
Haider, Susan 266
Haile, Kempton C. 576
Hain, Judith 351
Haj, Ray 525
Haj, Ray 526
Hajewski, Cherona J 160
Haken, Jean T 139
Halagan, Kevin 342
Halamka, John D. 67
Halas, Wally 191
Halcomb, Peggy 286
Haldeman, Greg 170
Hale, Robert T. (Rob) 224
Hale, David F. 425
Hale, David B. 612
Haley, Michael 259
Hall, Rick 44
Hall, Marc 68
Hall, Bob 110
Hall, Bob 110
Hall, Aaron 112
Hall, Doug 139
Hall, Christopher 186
Hall, Tom 194
Hall, Kendall 213
Hall, Ken 265
Hall, Brenda 273
Hall, Peter J. 311
Hall, Craig 311
Hall, Lonnie 315

Hall, David 419
Hall, Jim 432
Hall, Vera 448
Hall, Brian E. 604
Hall, Jones 611
Hall, Molly 649
Hall, Jim 654
Hallada, Tony 130
Haller, Raymond 557
Halloran, Owen 293
Halm, Ted 197
Halonen, Eric 342
Halpin, Jean 386
Halsey, Drew 186
Halsey, Andrew (Andy) 441
Halsey, Linda 617
Halverson, Jeffrey 640
Halvorsen, Kathy 342
Halvorson, Bob 345
Hambleton, Margaret 501
Hamerlinck, Jeffrey (Jeff) 618
Hamil, Randy 500
Hamilton, Mark 31
Hamilton, Shanna 148
Hamilton, Stephen G. (Steve) 153
Hamilton, Pete 215
Hamilton, Ann H. 217
Hamilton, Mike 233
Hamilton, William 263
Hamilton, Heather 423
Hamilton, Kerry-Ann 547
Hamlin, Stephen E. 528
Hammel, Charles L. (Chuck) 408
Hammel, Victor 429
Hammer, David 218
Hammer, Doug 263
Hammeran, Kevin 559
Hammett, Samuel J. (Jack) 322
Hammett, Troy 386
Hammond, Patti 183
Hammond, Al 358
Hammond, Ruby 530
Hampton, Mark 585
Han, Jenny 204
Hanahan, Jane 152
Hanbury, George L. 379
Hanby, Dorothy J. 631
Hancock, Frank 44
Hancock, Myra 391
Hancock, Kirk 560
Handwerk, Emily 331
Handwerk, Thomas P. 429
Hanes, Lesley 447
Haney, Lisa 562
Hanford, Ann 645
Hanks, Steven (Steve) 252
Hanly, Donna 386
Hanna, Kathryn 474
Hannah, William (Bill) 112
Hannon, Rita 323
Hanscom, Morgan 112
Hanscom, Lisa 513
Hansen, Mike 6
Hansen, Lonnie 194
Hansen, Scott 263
Hansen, Don 389
Hansen, Thomas N. 464
Hanson, Gail 24
Hanson, Shawna 35
Hanson, Cathy 353
Hanson, David 483
Hanson, Richard A. (Dick) 604
Haque, Ihsan 518
Harada, M 616
Haralson, Jason 457
Harbuck, Tom 272
Harden, Joy 190
Harden, Chris 267
Hardgrove, Roger 560
Hardin, Jeffrey 551
Hardin, Teresa 651
Harding, Scott 98
Harding, Patrick (Paddy) 436
Hardman, Elaine 320
Hardy, Charles J. 217

Hardy, Angela (Angie) 407
Harewood, Joan 427
Hargesheimer, Elbert 126
Hargett, Ken 554
Hargis, Bob 355
Harkey, Kathleen 157
Harkness, Gordon 263
Harlowe, Michael 259
Harman, Jacob (Jake) 653
Harmon, Lovell 236
Harmon, Tracy 422
Harmon, Pam 497
Harmon, Rebecca 530
Harned, Glenda 448
Harnly, Chris 234
Harp, Larry 199
Harper, Acey 24
Harper, Thomas J 103
Harper, Thomas (Thom) 103
Harper, Joe 226
Harper, Donna L 272
Harpool, Dennis 76
Harrington, Richard (Dick) 24
Harrington, Starla 71
Harrington, John 204
Harrington, Ronald G. 604
Harris, Cris 10
Harris, Peter (Pete) 42
Harris, Todd 137
Harris, Jay R. 157
Harris, Peter 160
Harris, Michael 197
Harris, Bruce 229
Harris, Debbie 304
Harris, Mark A. 313
Harris, Liberache 370
Harris, Richard 379
Harris, Alan 459
Harris, Richard P. (Rick) 463
Harris, Henry (Sandy) 468
Harris, Dan 524
Harris, David R. 591
Harris, James T. 612
Harris, Renee 647
Harris, Charlotte 649
Harrish, Laurel 530
Harrison, John (Jack) 22
Harrison, Brandon 90
Harrison, Ann L. 258
Harrison, Brad 346
Harrison, Dan 431
Harrison, Katherine 468
Harrison, Kay 468
Harrison, Cole 518
Harrison, Walter 572
Harshbarger, Catherine 46
Harsnett, Rick 580
Hart, Todd 47
Hart, Dan 89
Hart, Linda 152
Hart, Joy 370
Hart, Chet 467
Hart, Michael J. 524
Hart, Ross 572
Hartig, Jeanne 256
Hartis, Karen 363
Hartley, Chris 449
Hartline, Sally L 119
Hartman, Chris 14
Hartman, Kurt 245
Hartman, Donna 307
Hartman, Philip S. 532
Hartmann, John 588
Hartwick, Bryan 120
Hartwig, Scott 601
Harve, Shruthi 43
Harvey, Deborah 22
Harvey, Judy 652
Harwood, Theodore 135
Harwood, Alycia 353
Harwood, David 531
Haskins, Scott 112
Haslam, Harry 330
Haslam, John (Jack) 616
Hasselbarth, William C. 10

Hassen, Pamela (Pam) 368
Hassler, Jeffrey (Jeff) 75
Hastings, Elizabeth (Beth) 191
Hastings, Rick 375
Hatcher, Mel 112
Hatfield, Mark 3
Hatfield, Weston W 271
Hathaway, Richard (Rick) 230
Hathorn, Todd 155
Hatler, Doug 160
Hatridge, Victor L. (Vic) 181
Hattrich, Deborah (Debbie) 330
Hau, Leola 474
Haulcy, Braxton 218
Haulman, Jean 616
Haungs, Terese 190
Hause, Chris 280
Hauser, Eduardo 358
Hauser, Robert J. 423
Hauser, Ruth 540
Hauser, Matt 584
Hausman, Alice 530
Havlisch, Rebecca 46
Hawkins, R. Erick 432
Hawley, Rick 210
Hayden, Robert 112
Hayden-Cook, Melissa 473
Hayes, Nelson 90
Hayes, Gaynelle 213
Hayes, Joseph (Jo) 429
Hayes, Kay 456
Haynes, Thomas 351
Haynes, Joan E. 379
Haynes, Jenna 473
Haynes, Anthony 615
Haywood, Kimberly 316
Hazel, Rich 70
Hazel, Andrew (Andy) 340
Hazen, Verna 439
Heacock, Steven (Steve) 492
Head, Arthur 202
Headington, Machele 654
Headley, Thor 245
Healy, Thomas (Thom) 22
Healy, Patrick J. 423
Heap, Richard 448
Heater, Betty 417
Heath, Pat 80
Heath, Christine 119
Heath, David 392
Heath, Susan 464
Heath, Joan 534
Hebard, Barbara (Barb) 590
Hebda, Martin (Marti) 332
Hebda, Bernard A. 470
Hebert, Adam W. 258
Hebert, Katie 295
Hebert, Cathy 449
Hebert, Theresa 487
Heck, John (Jack) 567
Heckler, Lynn 419
Heckman, Cathy 487
Heckt, Jason 515
Hedde, Charles (Chas) 292
Hedegard, Heidi 619
Hedgpeth, Bob 24
Hedlund, Jamie 266
Heiden, Kay 47
Heidt, Thomas J. 411
Heikens, Laird 240
Heil, Marti 258
Heilbrun, Kirk 171
Heilman, Allen (Al) 386
Heiman, Steven (Steve) 276
Hein, Karen 117
Hein, Dan 401
Heineke, Emily 292
Heinemann, Tom 112
Heinkenschloss, Matthias 643
Heinold, Clint 146
Heintz, Shirley 557
Heiser, Karen 360
Heisey, John L. 105
Heist, Richard H (Dick) 185
Helgesen, Roald 9

Heller, William G. 258
Heller, Dora 307
Hellinger, Alex 208
Hellums, Larry 346
Helmick, Jack A. 375
Helmig, Deanna 602
Helmke, Rhonda 321
Hemstead, Louise 146
Hemstreet, Rame 280
Henck, Dan 449
Henderson, Mary G. 22
Henderson, Sharon 179
Henderson, Carol 461
Henderson, Laura 470
Hendricks, Todd 23
Hendricks, James B. 464
Hendricksen, Theresa 140
Hendrickson, Gary 614
Hendryx, Emily 643
Hengesbaugh, Bernard L. 22
Henion, Brad 224
Henkin, David 623
Henley, Dale 426
Hennessy, James J. 204
Hennessy, Michael J. 534
Henney, Cheryl 190
Henning, Donna 121
Henrichs, Robert J. 9
Henrichsen, Kim 263
Henrikson, Mary 473
Henry, Cassie 271
Henry, Richard A. (Rich) 327
Hensing, John 45
Hensley, Amanda 248
Henson, Judith (Judi) 5
Herbert, Nanette 79
Herbert, James 171
Herbert, Cheryl 386
Herbst, Lawrence 544
Herd, Tammy 448
Hergenroether, Craig 52
Herman, Brian 179
Hermann, Cheryl 15
Hermens, Rosalee 588
Hernandez, Amanda 128
Hernandez, Joe 270
Hernandez, Lucila Cano 420
Hernando, Roberto 47
Heron, W. David 379
Heron, David 380
Heron, David (Dave) 380
Herr, Rosemary E. 358
Herrera, Jesus 43
Herrera, Frank 393
Herrick, Timothy (Tim) 94
Herrick, Beth 485
Herrick, Doug 578
Herrin, Mary 577
Herring, Cameron 340
Herrington, Mary 150
Herrison, Gary 412
Herrmann, John A. 358
Herron, Catherine (Cathy) 614
Hershman, George W 525
Herskowitz-mauriello, Renee 650
Herting, Roger R. 531
Hertz, George K 323
Hertzson, Joyce 439
Herzog, Chris 216
Heskett, Todd 112
Hess, Jan 504
Hessert, Pete 34
Hester, Michael 360
Hester, Sara 587
Hetzer, Tom 362
Heupler, Stephen (Steve) 517
Heuton, Mary E. 320
Hewett, Charles E. 549
Hewitt, Michelle (Mitch) 154
Hewson, Steve 595
Hiatt, Wendy 255
Hibbitts, Paul E. 202
Hickey, Timothy (Tim) 83
Hickey, Cathy 112
Hickey, Wayne 516

Hickey, John 539
Hickey, Patricia (Pat) 539
Hickey, Robert (Bob) 649
Hickman, George T. 10
Hickman, Cheryl 406
Hicks, Lee 128
Hicks, Deborah (Deb) 157
Hicks, Harold 173
Hicks, Kelly 197
Hicks, Tish 316
Hicks, Lisa Winston 355
Hicks, David 378
Hietpas, Dolores 615
Higgins, Cornelius J 30
Higgins, Maura 89
Higgins, Thomas 112
Higgins, Tom 133
Higgins-bouers, Shir 274
Higginson, David 405
Highsmith, Carlton L. 422
Highsmith, Carlton L. 423
Hightower, Randall D. 631
Hildebrandt, Larry 55
Hildebrandt, Magdalina 342
Hildebrandt, James (Jamie) 456
Hilgendorf, Ellen 91
Hilger, Stephen 612
Hill, Cindy L 31
Hill, Joseph (Jo) 211
Hill, Terry 244
Hill, Tim 306
Hill, Mark 337
Hill, Lyn 366
Hill, Sam 409
Hill, Rob 422
Hill, Dwight 433
Hill, Tom 501
Hill, Terri 596
Hill, Peggy 598
Hill-davis, Nancy 332
Hille, James R. 532
Hillenbrand, Michelle (Mitch) 419
Hiller, Dawn 254
Hills, Linda 254
Hills, Malina M 534
Hiltibidal, John (Jack) 448
Hilton, Eric 229
Hilton, Thomas 390
Himes, Vicky 404
Hinckley, Robert (Bob) 95
Hines, Jackie 71
Hines, Gerald D. 245
Hines, Grace 467
Hinger, Douglas 544
Hinkelman, Jon B. 357
Hinkelman, Jon B. 357
Hinkle, Craig M 292
Hinkle, Donna 518
Hinkleman, Jon B. 357
Hinman, Jacqueline C. 112
Hinn, Gregory 432
Hinojosa, David 605
Hirsch, Richard (Dick) 73
Hirsch, Ronnie 77
Hirschbiel, Paul 117
Hirschhorn, Ron 636
Hirsekorn, Rick 112
Hirte, Richard (Dick) 651
Hischar, Anne 623
Hiscoe, Les 474
Hisey, Richard M. 65
Hite, Patricia (Pat) 82
Hitt, Anne 383
Hitter, Paul 337
Ho, Brenda A. 233
Hoag, Jo Ann 505
Hobart, Robert (Bob) 22
Hobbs, Timothy L. 137
Hobbs, Brian 637
Hobson, James 329
Hobson, Bebe 653
Hobson-Pape, Karri 606
Hochberg, Stanley 82
Hochstetler, Robert (Bob) 251
Hockenson, Tod 255

Hodge, Heath 325
Hodge, David C. 339
Hodge, Karen 448
Hodges, Jack 427
Hodgkins, Michael L. 22
Hodgson, Marvin 194
Hodgson, Deborah 470
Hodulich, David 557
Hoef, Ted 633
Hoekema, Dale 279
Hoekstra, Jason 195
Hoersch, Lori 593
Hof, Amber 383
Hofelich, Kurt 467
Hoff, Joel 207
Hoffa, James P. (Jim) 265
Hoffert, Alice 610
Hoffman, G E 183
Hoffman, Dean 315
Hoffman, Ethel 405
Hoffman, Brad 475
Hoffman-Fragale, Sphr Chad 645
Hoffmeister, Susan 275
Hofman, Paul 108
Hogan, Noel 10
Hogan, Chris 77
Hogan, Sean M. 172
Hogan, Gail 369
Hogan, Carolyn 382
Hogsett, John 355
Hogue, Polly 476
Hoh, Andrew 150
Hohmann, Paul 471
Holbrook, Karen A 614
Hold, Allen 568
Holden, Kenneth (Ken) 68
Holden, Sharon 349
Holden, E. Wayne 432
Holder, Tim 187
Holder, Judy 464
Holder, Adriene 552
Holdn, Wayne 432
Holfelner, Barbara (Barb) 393
Holford, Will 78
Holladay, Tom 95
Holland, Cristie 95
Hollenbeck, Ron 194
Hollingsworth, Joe A. 248
Hollins, Tara 342
Holloway, John B. 96
Hollowood, Judith (Judi) 272
Holm, Ryan 90

Holm, Dennis 202
Holm, Brandon 612
Holmes, Chip 201
Holmes, Frank 253
Holmes, Briana 316
Holmes, Scott 389
Holmes, Ruth 417
Holmes, Nicholas 425
Holmes, Randy 634
Holmes, Darius 639
Holstein, Bob 22
Holt, Patrick 76
Holthaus, Matt 127
Holton, Bill 156
Holtschneider, Dennis H. 159
Holtzclaw, Sandra 459
Homberger, Scott 545
Honsberger, Allison 566
Hood, Rob 112
Hood, Daniel (Dan) 340
Hood, Rodney 363
Hood, Les 386
Hooda, Abdul 591
Hoogakker, Jason 612
Hook, Frank 217
Hooper, Joe 386
Hoopes, Barry 326
Hooten, Alvin 253
Hoover, Rich 572
Hopkins, Mark 386
Hopkins, Mike 448
Hopkins, David R. 649

Hoppe, Beth 420
Hoptay, Steve 629
Horgan, Ralph 100
Horikami, Brian 469
Horn, George A. 217
Horn, Rebecca 293
Horn, Teresa 297
Horn, Rodney 513
Horne, Larry E. 128
HORNE, GREG 379
Horner, Lynn 343
Horsford, Thomas W. 421
Horst, Joanna 542
Horswell, Bruce 114
Horton, Eileen 96
Horton, Sheilah Shaw 310
Horton, Gayle 566
Horvath, Finn 160
Horvath, Alex 554
Hoskins, William (Bill) 330
Hottendorf, Catherine 208
Houghton, Nicole 263
Houlton, Andrew 372
Hourigan, Michael 198
House, Sherry 342
House, Whitney 572
Houston, Don 339
Howard, Randy 44
Howard, Chris 98
Howard, Deanna 158
Howard, James 167
Howard, Samuel 181
Howard, Samuel 181
Howard, Randy 185
Howard, Edward 320
Howard, Tom 379
Howard, Cheryl 557
Howard, John 635
Howard-Gomez, Caitlin 43
Howe, Louise M. 423
Howe, Kenneth F. 487
Howc, Jim 510
Howell, Rebecca 89
Howell, Mike 598
Howse, Jennifer L. 316
Hoyer, Glen 358
Hoyne, James B 290
Hradsky, Robert (Bob) 24
Hrina, Sharon 119
Hrina, Sharin 119
Hrountas, Stacey 473
Hrusovszky, James (Jamie) 597
Hubbard, Skip 80
Hubbard, Kenneth W. (Ken) 245
Hubble, Julie 524
Hubenthal, Mary 46
Huberlie, Fred 14
Huch, David 597
Huck, Deron 112
Huddleson, David (Dave) 391
Hudecek, Paul G. 514
Hudgens, Carol 31
Hudis, Wayne 421
Hudson, John 21
Hudson, Duane 160
Hudson, Trish 434
Huff, Diane 240
Huff, Nancy 513
Huff, Joe 535
Huffer, Linda R. 467
Huffman, Jeffrey 13
Huffman, Stephen (Steve) 556
Hughes, Emily 9
Hughes, Gregg 112
Hughes, Joseph 171
Hughes, Mike 197
Hughes, Michael (Mel) 197
Hughes, Christopher D. 245
Hughes, Amy H. 330
Hughes, Mark 403
Hughes, Elizabeth (Beth) 498
Hughes, Mark 534
Hughes, Michael 613
Hulahan, Shannon 153
Hulburd, Jon 405

Hulett, Federica H 380
Hull, Nancy 470
Hulse, Allan 36
Hulse, Mark 229
Hulstein, Kevin 195
Humenik, Del 2
Huml, Jeffrey (Jeff) 107
Hummel, Dennis 317
Humphrey, Mike 170
Humphrey, Reed 609
Hung, Benjamin J (Ben) 449
Hunt, David 1
Hunt, Pamela (Pam) 137
Hunt, William 231
Hunt, Jay B. 258
Hunt, V. William 258
Hunter, Jim 112
Hunter, Jim 134
Hunter, Joseph (Jo) 577
Huntley, Mike 226
Hupp, Billy 188
Hurd, John D 109
Hurd, Paul 303
Hurley, Marty 434
Hurney, Carol 271
Hurson, Tom 584
Hurst, Ann 363
Hurst, Ron 409
Hurt, George A. 106
Hurt, Michele 118
Hurt, Jim 362
Hurtig, Howard 562
Hushbeck, Scott 642
Huson, Jennifer 155
Hussey, Lynn 291
Husted, Jean 423
Huston, Stephanie 99
Hutchinson, Beverly 162
Huth, Steven K. (Steve) 99
Huth, F Robert 414
Hutson, Wayne R 596
Huval, Carolyn 295
Hyatt, Sandra 47
Hyde, Gail 230
Hyde, Stephanie 586
Hyde, Barry 602
Hyder, S 498
Hyland, John 299
Hyman, Craig 144
Hynes, Don 26
Hynes, James 219

I

Ian, Beckstead 431
Iannarelli, Rocco 367
Ibeh, Nnadozie 530
Ibison, Meg 112
Icenhower, Janice 316
Ierace, Joe 198
Ignash, Joe 510
Ihle, James 503
Ilderice, Boez 249
Iler, Mark 517
Ilseng, Rodney 518
Imm, Teresa 31
Imwalle, Todd 571
Incarnati, Philip A. 56
Ingram, George 530
Ingram, Dennis P. 630
Ingram, Dennis P. 630
Ingrum, Jeff 98
Inks, Samantha 115
Inmon, Lataydria 391
Inouye, Glenn 469
Inserra, Lawrence 629
Ip, Eric 330
Ippolito, Dennis 487
Ipson, David 159
Irizarry, George 85
Irvin, Lisa 96
Irwin, Joe 110
Irwin, Tom 269

Irwin, Robert (Bob) 437
Isaac, Kim 464
Isaacson, Jon F. 109
Isakower, Kyle 23
Isgur, Dave 572
Isha, Julie 539
Ismail, Khalil 179
Ismail, Amid I. 530
Ispass, Alan (Al) 112
Israel, Dan 531
Isreal, Toni 302
Isyk, Ronald J. (Ron) 364
Iton, Anthony 538
Ivanikiw, Alex 52
Ivers, Lewis 463
Iverson, Ron 651
Ives, Stephanie 530
Ivy, Dianne 533

J

Jabara, Amer 247
Jablonski, Sue 386
Jack, Kelly 421
Jackson, Justin J 54
Jackson, Teresa 154
Jackson, Kathryn J. (Kate) 267
Jackson, L. Duane 323
Jackson, Jolinda 324
Jackson, Jill 368
Jackson, Joy 536
Jackson, Debra 630
Jackson, Reese 644
Jacob, Gregg 297
Jacob, Cheryl 307
Jacobs, Richard F. 31
Jacobs, Stephen H 65
Jacobs, Richard (Dick) 104
Jacobs, Brian 119
Jacobs, Joel 557
Jacobs, Donna 607
Jacobs-Jones, Brandi 320
Jacobsen, Craig 263
Jacobson, Zachary (Zach) 43
Jacobson, John (Jack) 571
Jacques, Jill 560
Jacquez, Dorothy 303
Jaeger, Kurt 129
Jaehrling, Matt 135
Jaffe, Harry J 376
Jaffe, David E. 524
Jagger, Hal 477
Jahanian, Farnam 99
Jahrsdorfer, Catherine 614
Jain, Sahil 100
Jain, Ravi K. 616
Jalil, Qamar 107
Jamerson, Megan 175
James, Jonathan (Jon) 112
James, Mark 114
James, Dula C. 117
James, Paul 121
James, Fred 126
James, Frank 253
James, Margaret 260
James, Scott 467
James, Rita A 472
James, Catherine A (Cathy) 534
James, Connie 649
Jameson, Eileen 2
Jamzadeh, Nahid 259
Janes, Arthur R. (Art) 401
Janeway, Weslie R. 549
Janger, Michael (Mel) 213
Janis, Robert (Bob) 159
Janklow, Erin 43
Jankowski, Heidi 259
Jankowski, Joseph 427
Jannace, William (Bill) 198
Janowicz, Mike 145
Jansen, Roger E. 492
Jansky, Liz 636
Janssens, Patrick 18
Jantz, Barry 225

Jantz, Barry 225
Janus, Michael (Mel) 54
Jany, Barb 417
Jarry, Timothy M. 133
Jarve, Robert K (Bob) 492
Jarvis, Patrick (Paddy) 54
Jaskuta, Eileen 336
Javorka, Tony 137
Jayawickrema, Arosha 572
Jeanis, Keith 597
Jeffcoat, Stuart 112
Jeffers, Lewis 412
Jeffrey, William 494
Jeffries, Stuart 30
Jelle, Lorraine 71
Jellison, David (Dave) 590
Jelski, Martha 548
Jendzejec, Mark 514
Jenkins, Decosta E. 181
Jenkins, A. Dale 432
Jenkins, Kathy 539
Jenkins, Leslie 557
Jenkins, Maurice E. 599
Jennings, Gary 36
Jennings, Stephen 425
Jenrette, John 473
Jensen, Chris 280
Jensen, Karen 391
Jensen, Linda 549
Jensen, Rob 557
Jensen, Karen 654
Jepson, Brian D. 386
Jerris, Rand 602
Jesudas, Sajeev 595
Jesursa, Jebashini 650
Jett, Daryl 570
Jetty, Sathish 5
Jhaveri, Vishu 77
Jiambalvo, James 616
Jim, Aberle 652
Jimenez, Kareen 559
Jimmie, Andrew (Andy) 9
Jinar, Dan 38
Jingni, Wei 590
Jocelyn, Danielle 175
Joel, Richard M. 653
Joffrion, Barry 409
Johanneman, Ben 327
Johanning, Eckardt 95
Johansen, Bob 42
Johansen, Robert L (Bob) 42
Johns, Byron 24
Johnson, Dawn Bennett 5
Johnson, Charlotte 32
Johnson, Norm 35
Johnson, James (Jim) 36
Johnson, George 41
Johnson, John (Jack) 73
Johnson, Bret 96
Johnson, Beth 107
Johnson, Steven (Steve) 109
Johnson, Dale 110
Johnson, Dale 110
Johnson, Mark 112
Johnson, Aaron 124
Johnson, Bruce E. 157
Johnson, Paul H. 165
Johnson, Cyndee 171
Johnson, William (Bill) 171
Johnson, Cassie 175
Johnson, Tessa 175
Johnson, Karen 182
Johnson, Kirk 194
Johnson, Geri 197
Johnson, Russell 234
Johnson, C. Hastings (Hasty) 245
Johnson, Robert P. 246
Johnson, Brent 263
Johnson, Beth 263
Johnson, Kent 263
Johnson, Mark 266
Johnson, Ron 299
Johnson, Scott 302
Johnson, Diane 305
Johnson, Desmond 309

Johnson, Twila 321
Johnson, Kirk 359
Johnson, Theodore (Theo) 364
Johnson, Diane 376
Johnson, Darrell 389
Johnson, Janice 400
Johnson, Tamara 405
Johnson, John 409
Johnson, Daniel 423
Johnson, Lisa 426
Johnson, Scott 433
Johnson, Rick 434
Johnson, Sandra 439
Johnson, Robert (Rob) 463
Johnson, Diane 481
Johnson, Walter 482
Johnson, Charles 488
Johnson, Shawn 517
Johnson, Calvin B. 530
Johnson, Mark L. 532
Johnson, Tonya 562
Johnson, Nathalie 569
Johnson, Terre 577
Johnson, Allen (Al) 589
Johnson, Sylvia Smith 607
Johnson, Kathryn 623
Johnson, Shelly 648
Johnson, Seth R. 648
Johnston, Christine 297
Johnston, Lisa 377
Johnston, Katie 482
Johnston, Jim 585
Joiner, Kathy 630
Jolley, Jason 347
Jonas, John F. 399
Jones, Joanne 2
Jones, Greg 6
Jones, Beverly 23
Jones, Edson 40
Jones, Tina 47
Jones, Michael (Mel) 94
Jones, John Paul (Jack) 106
Jones, Howard 110
Jones, William (Bill) 118
Jones, Angie 132
Jones, Joy 135
Jones, Amy 154
Jones, David 156
Jones, Jim 171
Jones, Marie M. 172
Jones, Wes 186
Jones, Chip 198
Jones, Herb 204
Jones, Mike 211
Jones, John 225
Jones, Ronnie 257
Jones, Sheri 263
Jones, Brian 266
Jones, Rhonda 298
Jones, Calvin 298
Jones, Jack M. 330
Jones, Boomesma 332
Jones, Carolyn 336
Jones, Debra 337
Jones, Barbara 340
Jones, Tommy 346
Jones, Hugh 352
Jones, Kevin 362
Jones, Mark A 379
Jones, Ben 383
Jones, Mark A. 391
Jones, Richard W. 429
Jones, Ken 436
Jones, Bobbi 448
Jones, Sterling 509
Jones, Douglas 515
Jones, Warren 527
Jones, Joy 536
Jones, Caitlin 539
Jones, Chris 556
Jones, Carole 589
Jones, M. Steven 604
Jones, Brian 616
Jones, Amy 649
Jones, Marshall 654

Jordahl, Mark S. 15
Jordan, Randy 405
Jordan, Sharon 470
Jordan, Shawn 481
Jorgensen, Rosie 197
Jorgensen, Mary 307
Jorgensen, Kevin 602
Joseph, Satheesh 86
Joseph, Robert (Bob) 137
Joseph, Christopher 284
Joslyn, Scott 307
Joyce, Jon 199
Joyce, Janie 253
Joyce, Anne 623
Jr, Gerry 445
Jr, Leonard (Len) 607
Jr, Bill Pou 627
Juan, Steve 227
Juarez, Alfonso 257
Juarez, Julie 557
Juarez, Phillip 612
Judd, Rodney (Rod) 362
Judge, Kenan 255
Judge, Martin E. 550
Judge, Dennis F. 550
Judge, John 550
Judy, Franklin 112
Julian, Steve 467
Juliana, Denise 179
Julien, Mae St 323
Julien, Jared 342
Jumonville, Lydia W 460
Jung, Brian 233
Jungers, Natasha 379
Junk, Lori 215
Jura, James J. 35
Jurczyk, Andrew D. 470
Jurczyk, John (Jack) 513
Juris, Susan V. 604
Jury, Victor R. 518
Jusko, James (Jamie) 534
Justice, Peggy 406
Justice, Lorraine 439
Juusela, Kari 65

K

Kabbaz, Michael (Mel) 340
Kabous, Neil 596
Kading, Douglas 90
Kaelin, Michael H. (Mike) 432
Kaelin, Charles 603
Kafle, Patricia 212
Kahanek, Sheila 519
Kahle, David J. 591
Kai, Marilyn 100
Kaigelak, Bernice 9
Kail, Marilyn 99
Kaiser, Laura S. 263
Kaiser, Jan 321
Kaiser, Tracy 473
Kaiser, Larry R. 530
Kaiser, Ken 530
Kaiser, Sherif 644
Kalfayan, Terry 612
Kalil, Tom 615
Kall, Gregory 517
Kalm, Stephen 609
Kalsbeek, David 159
Kalscheur, Gregory 590
Kalwinsky, David (Dave) 503
Kamel, Hany 76
Kamen, Susan 607
Kamensky, Bo 487
Kamers, Todd 586
Kaminski, Scott 292
Kamlet, Mark S. 99
Kamlet, Lee 423
Kamphuis, Bob 326
Kana, Elizabeth 78
Kanable, Jim 370
Kandt, Kim 582
Kane, Patrick J (Paddy) 94
Kane, Jeffrey 308

Kane, Gary 607
Kangas, Karen 342
Kanna, Melanie 616
Kantor, Hans 240
Kanyoro, Musimbi 543
Kanzawa, Mark 81
Kapadia, Dipak 227
Kapelus, Darren 635
Kaplan, Michael (Mel) 176
Kaplan, Willy 240
Kaplan, Alan S. 266
Kaplon, Sari 494
Kaprive, Shannon 556
Karas, Gail 140
Karawan, Oleh 381
Kari, Doug 30
Karn, Kevin 612
Karns, Steve 296
Karolyi, G 614
Kashevaroff, Don 9
Kashevaroff, Don 9
Kasicki, Kirk 153
Kasinski, John 623
Kaska, Tony 255
Kasman, Glenn 353
Kasturi, Srinath Pai 91
Katsianis, John 120
Katz, Brian 382
Katz, Ken E. 545
Katz, Elizabeth H (Beth) 551
Katzmann, Rich 362
Kauffman, Martha 648
Kaufman, Irvin A. 425
Kaufman, Gary 510
Kaufman, Pat 602
Kautz, Rhonda 138
Kay, Brian 56
Kay, Stephen B. 67
Kaylor, Shawn 316
Kayser, Laura 193
Keach, Camillia 530
Keag, W. Ken 40
Keagy, Gregory 215
Kearns, Richard (Dick) 36
Kearns, Paul 54
Kearns, Donald 425
Keating, Patricia 349
Keating, Patrick J. 590
Keating, J. Edmund (Ed) 645
Keating, J Edmund 645
Keaton, Sheba 175
Kedy, Jesse 612
Keefe, Pamela (Pam) 182
Keefe, Hugh F. 423
Keegel, C Thomas 265
Keehan, Effie Mc 544
Keel, Pat 503
Keeler, Scott 545
Keeler, Diane Fishel 545
Keeley, Brian E. 47
Keenan, Kathleen 27
Kees, Tom 426
Kehl, Richard (Dick) 646
Keightley, Rebecca 330
Keiper, Joel 238
Keita, Maghan 133
Keith, Elizabeth 80
Keith, Dahlen 551
Kelch, Mercedes 14
Kelemen, Mark 607
Kellar, Brian 46
Kelleher, Winifred 518
Kellenberger, Jack 340
Keller, Neal 129
Keller, Karen 602
Keller, Erik 602
Kellerhouse, James (Jamie) 10
Kelley, H. Lynn 304
Kelley, Richard G. 423
Kelley, Debby 581
Kellner, Lawrence 554
Kelly, John J. 2
Kelly, Thomas B. (Tom) 6
Kelly, Stephen E. 54
Kelly, William M. 77

Kelly, Mark 238
Kelly, Riley 340
Kelly, Michael J. (Mike) 419
Kelly, Linda 426
Kelly, Lyn 439
Kelly, Alan (Al) 461
Kelly, John 466
Kelly, Chad 479
Kelly, Kathleen 501
Kelly, Becca 524
Kelly, Glenna 526
Kelly, Patrick 526
Kelly, Robert E. 558
Kelly, Paul 564
Kelly-bowry, Tanya 605
Kelsey, Katie 150
Kelsheimer, Bradley 163
Kemp, Kristian 263
Kemper, Jeffrey H. (Jeff) 385
Kemper, David W. 575
Kempf, Robert 358
Kemppel, Denali 31
Kempton, Will 389
Kenagy, John 302
Kenchel, Kurt T 103
Kendall, Anthony 47
Kendall, Randolph L. (Randy) 534
Kennedy, Brad 6
Kennedy, Charles A 99
Kennedy, Leroy 256
Kennedy, Barbara 554
Kennedy, Charles (Chas) 616
Kenner, Shane 225
Kennett, Karen 103
Kenney, Dianne 99
Kenney, George 530
Kenny, John (Jack) 200
Kenny, Maureen E. 590
Kent, Robert 517
Kenyon, Jay 132
Keohane, Ellen J. 133
Kephart, Kevin D. 483
Kerger, Paula A. 419
Kerkhoff, Eric 592
Kern, Howard P. 467
Kern, Mark 510
Kernick, Inez 121
Keroack, Mark A. 58
Kerr, Janet E. 648
Kerrigan, Susanne 518
Kerschen, Susan (Sue) 460
Kershaw, James B. 78
Kershaw, James B. 78
Kersten, Rebecca 31
Kersting, Matt 153
Kerwin, Cornelius M. 24
Kessler, Joe 137
Kessler, John 417
Kester, Alexandra 532
Ketchum, Joe 386
Ketola, Todd 52
Ketter, Don 36
Keuer, Steven P. 586
Key, George 226
Keyack, Robin 478
Keyes, Tracie 329
Kezirian, Wayne 277
Khaleghi, Trisha 473
Khan, Shafaat 43
Khan, Karen 100
Khan, Saeed 112
Khan, Iqtidar 121
Khan, Muhammed 629
Khoshreza, Kathy 406
Kibby, Brian 355
Kiblawi, Nazeeh 227
Kidd, Edwin 451
Kieffer, Jeanette 275
Kiener, Mary 434
Kientz, Kevin 545
Kilby, Andrew L. 431
Kildisas, Irena 362
Killgore, John B. 35
Killham, William 24
Killian, Martin 183

Killion, Kathleen 497
Killoren, Robert A. 385
Kilpatrick, Brian 109
Kilzer, Frank 498
Kim, Hans 2
Kim, James 30
Kim, T.H. 254
Kim, John 602
Kim, John 602
Kimmons, Herb 425
Kindseth, Lon 428
King, Terry S. 44
King, Barbara (Barb) 68
King, Shawn 73
King, Jeffrey 131
King, Edgar A. 155
King, Lisa 252
King, Patrick 275
King, Terese 383
King, Victoria 401
King, Kenneth 518
King, Deborah (Deb) 608
King, Robert 635
King-davis, Lynette 427
Kingsmore, Stephen 425
Kinne, Scott 602
Kinneary, Bill 260
Kinsella, Dan 107
Kinslow-Evans, Robin 599
Kirby, Karla 137
Kirby, Kevin A. 267
Kirby, Tracy 372
Kirby, Stan 409
Kirby, Rex B. 516
Kirby, Adrienne 542
Kirch, Nicole 342
Kirchhoff, Mary 19
Kirchoff, Victor 292
Kirgis, Paul F. 609
Kiriazis, Michael 472
Kirk, Dana 225
Kirkland, John W. 427
Kirkland, Annette K. 427
Kirkpatrick, Sean 342
Kirtley, Karen 320
Kiser, Janice 114
Kishan, Neel 99
Kishore, Ashok 583
Kisiel, Steven 46
Kiskaddon, Robert T 98
Kissell, Theodore 571
Kissling, Ginny Buckner 445
Kitchell, Ryan C. 259
Kitchens, Andrew (Andy) 245
Kitchings, Chester 300
Kitson, Jay 254
Kittell, Patricia (Pat) 104
Kitto, David (Dave) 275
Kittrell, Clinton 89
Kitts, Stan 311
Kitz, Kristopher 401
Klaben, Larry R. 649
Klaiber, Robert 225
Klapper, David I. 258
Klasko, Stephen K. 578
Klavon, Kenneth 602
Kleess, Eric 18
Kleiman, Michael 274
Klein, Tammy 292
Klein, Jan 348
Klein, Julia H. 429
Klein, Michael L. 530
Klein, Paul 602
Klein-Gitelman, Marisa S. 27
Kleinman, Paola 308
Kleitz, Shawn 530
Klemp, Thomas 518
Kletzel, Morris 27
Kleynen, Barbara (Barb) 162
Klika, Kevin A. 355
Kline, Sam 224
Kline, Sidney D. 429
Klingbeil, Nathan 649
Klingen, Patti 34
Klinkhammer, Skip 428

Klockenga, Kevin 501
Kludt, Todd 195
Kluemper, Steve 225
Kluzinski, James (Jamie) 137
Knapp, Cheryl 85
Knapp, Fred 146
Knapp, Spencer 201
Knasel, Teresa 321
Knauf, Ron 492
Knaus, Paula N 614
Knecht, Mark 566
Kneisel, Geoff 25
Knichel, Thomas 208
Knight, Sherry 109
Knight, Thomas W 554
Knights, Martin 112
Knobloch, George 287
Knock, Brad 195
Knoll, Rolf W. 449
Knopf, Keith 426
Knoth, Kurt 492
Knotts, Chris 204
Knowles, Wendy 389
Knowlton, Carla May 423
Knox, D. L. (Pete) 482
Knudsen, Brian 26
Knudson, Lisa 197
Knudson, Peter 307
Knutel, Phillip G. 64
Koch, Gary 36
Koch, Matt 379
Kochem, Gary J. 10
Kocher, Edward 172
Kochevar, Deborah T. 591
Kodama, Hugh 353
Koehler, Debra 383
Koelkebeck, Debbie 210
Koelker, June 532
Koelmel, John R. 367
Koerner, Spencer 104
Koerner, Ryan 340
Kofman, Clyde 595
Kohart-Kleine, Barbara (Barb) 645
Kohl, Rebecca 236
Kohn, Julie 89
Kohne, John C. 259
Kolb, Bob 73
Kolb, Rick 516
Kolb, Pamela (Pam) 579
Kolb, George 623
Kolisz, Karin 502
Kolker, Eugene 464
Koller, Brian 623
Kolni, Harold 338
Kolruss, Chuck 247
Kompkoff, Lloyd 116
Konda, Damodar 363
Kong, David T. 66
Konishi, Kathleen 263
Konkel, Kevin 425
Kons, Pat 397
Konst, Dave 434
Kontos, Mark W. 556
Konz, Jim 567
Koob, Beth 530
Koocher, Gerald P. 159
Koogler, David 426
Kookesh, Albert M. 463
Koop, Steven 218
Koop, Steven 218
Kopaczewski, Mike 355
Kopesky, John P (Jack) 623
Koppelman, Catherine S. (Cathy) 604
Koppen, Roger 194
Korfiatis, George P. 511
Kormos, Michael J. 408
Korolev, Sergey 619
Korry, Edward (Ed) 277
Korstanje, Doug 506
Korten, Patrick 291
Kosaraju, Sri Kumar 623
Kosiyangkakul, Tai 447
Koski, Jim 510
Kosoko-Lasaki, Sade 150
Koss, Gail 34

Koterba, Nancy 555
Kothari, Rashmikant 81
Kothari, Manish 494
Kotler, Christine 47
Kotler, Ronald (Ron) 562
Kotsol, Carolyn 54
Koudouris, Maria 126
Kovach, Andrew L (Andy) 39
Kovach, Jim 613
Kovalcik, James (Jamie) 112
Kovoch, Dan 52
Kowaloff, Harvey 512
Koyfman, Feliks 645
Kozak, Charlie 31
Kozak, John 160
Kozak, Dave 255
Kozoman, Robert L. (Bob) 159
Kraeve, Igor 183
Kraft, Blount 485
Kraich, Rick 624
Krajewski, David 305
Krajewski, David 481
Krakowsky, Robin 277
Kramer, Jennifer 46
Kramer, David A. 90
Kramer, Peter W. 298
Kramer, Karen 304
Kramer, Megan (Meg) 352
Kramer, Jim 389
Krampe, Edward J. 295
Kran, Bob 341
Kraras, Chris G. 429
Kratzert, Niki 291
Kraus, John (Jack) 312
Kraus, Barbara 585
Krause, Rick 545
Krauss, Jim 467
Kravis, Henry R. 564
Krebsbach, Larry 88
Kreitzer, Joseph (Jo) 615
Krell, Joanne 626
Krenke, Brian 294
Krenz, William C. (Willie) 534
Kreuger, Adam 419
Krichels, Ted 147
Kricun, Robert (Bob) 303
Krieger, James (Jim) 213
Krieger, Kenneth F. (Ken) 550
Kring, Gail 421
Krinsky, Susan 83
Kripke, Donald 359
Krise, Thomas 616
Krishnan, Ramayya 99
Kristiansen, Thomas 201
Krmpotic, Deb 46
Krohman, Barbara (Barb) 448
Kroll, Jason 349
Krouse, Michael 386
Krueger, Kimberly 296
Krueger, Roger 484
Kruger, Isaak 497
Kruger, Merlyn 632
Kruggel, Thomas (Thom) 245
Krugman, Michael (Mel) 81
Krulig, Ricardo 590
Krupp, Jason 46
Kruse, Shelly 226
Kruse, Karl 255
Kruse, Kathy 275
Krywanski, Polly M 492
Kubic, Paul 593
Kubicek, Alex 150
Kubow, Phil 98
Kucija, Barbara (Barb) 495
Kuczer, David 487
Kuczmanski, John D. 328
Kudravetz, Douglas 24
Kuelbs, Cynthia 425
Kuenzle, Sheila 80
Kuhlman, Michael 54
Kuhn, Rebecca (Becky) 45
Kuhn, Michael 137
Kuhnley, Nick 372
Kuk, Linda 197
Kulas, Michael (Mel) 595

Kulma, Maria 176
Kumar, Shoba 329
Kun, Larry E. 503
Kunkel, Denise 35
Kunkel, Kavin 426
Kunkel, Susan 579
Kuntschik, David (Dave) 362
Kuntz, Louann 10
Kuntz, Kevin 327
Kuntz, Richard (Dick) 349
Kuntz, Ray 631
Kunz, Ricky W. 411
Kupec, Jess 449
Kupfer, Lawrence J. (Larry) 253
Kurichi, Jaison 530
Kurlinski, Seth 43
Kurmaskie, Dan 472
Kurtzman, Scott 575
Kurz, Larry 629
Kushner, Michael 539
Kussin, Karl 185
Kuszmar, Susie 447
Kuzas, Betsy 405
Kuzmak, Karen 613
Kvaternik, Davor 513
Kweskin, Amy 575
Kyner, Tom 82

L

LA, Hao 64
Labbe, Marc 43
LaBelle, James 462
Labriola, Albert 172
Lacertosa, Tyler 380
Lacey, William 602
Lackey, Kristina 487
Lackmann, Andrew (Andy) 5
Laconsay, Croix 316
Lacorte, Ellen 623
Lacy, Robert 421
Lacy, Joe 533
Ladouceur, Danny 445
Laffey, Brian 256
Lagutaine, Francesco 123
Lahey, John L. 422
Lahey, John L. 423
Lai, Ngoc 344
Lai, Michelle (Mitch) 530
Lai, Katy 648
Lain, Frank B. 298
Laing, Sheila 255
Laird, Timothy (Tim) 236
Lal, Rohan 83
Lam, Kristina 612
Lamanna, Susan 502
Lamb, Michael 76
Lamb, Eric 170
Lamb, Carol 549
Lamb, Brigid Shanley 602
Lamb, Brian D. 614
Lambert, Richard 169
Lambertson, Steve 576
Lambright, Dawn 176
Lambright, Keith 311
Lamen, Drake M. 599
Lamp, David L. (Dave) 375
Lanahan, Martha 270
Lancaster, George 245
Lancaster, Karen 607
Lance, Ryan M. 23
Land, Tom 47
Land, Alison 203
Land, Edward J. 358
Landers, Pete 592
Landes, Barbara L. 419
Landis, Tess 311
Landis, John 535
Landry, Stephen G. 469
Lane, Tim 79
Lane, Raymond J. (Ray) 100
Lane, Philip 191
Lane, Barbara (Barb) 307
Lane, Mark L. 368

Lane, Eric 588
Lang, Zack 602
Langberg, Michael L. 104
Lange, Paul 81
Langenberg, David (Dave) 234
Langerot, Danny 151
Langlais, Tracy 95
Langley, W. John 324
Langley, Janet 533
Langman, Craig B. 27
Langridge, Nicholas 271
Langsdorf, William (Bill) 648
Lanier, Bo 113
Lanier, Jeff 427
Lanier, Andrea 447
Lanis, Ken 588
Lanius, Joe 417
Lankford, Joel 497
Lanspa, Stephen (Steve) 150
Lantos, Phyllis R. 558
Lanum, Robert W. 258
Laphan-morad, Lisa 542
LaPierre, Wayne 358
Lappe, Donald (Don) 263
Laque, Jim 490
Lareau, Doug 474
Larimer, Bob 79
Lark, J. Peter 298
Larmore, Mark E. 558
Larrick, Rob 92
Larsen, Christian 182
Larson, Steve 16
Larson, John (Jack) 58
Larson, Gloria Cordes 64
Larson, Andrew 274
Larson, Carol S. 543
Larson, Carol S. 543
Larson, Bill 581
Larson, Jennifer 614
Larson, Matt 615
Larsson, John (Jack) 362
Larsson, Randi 473
Larwood, Charlie 389
Laskey, Sara 555
LaSpaluto, Tim 21
Lassen, Kevin 568
Lasseter, Aline 364
Lassetter, Jessi 53
Latimore, Ronny 197
Lau, Luther 494
Lau, Jeremy 613
Laubach, Harold E. 379
Laubacher, Ned 501
Lauderdale, Lindy 148
Laueau, Douglas (Doug) 474
Laur, James (Jamie) 104
Laurel, Marty 77
Lauria, Dorothy M. 423
Laurie, Robert 367
Lauth, Ian 616
Lavallee, Andrea 47
Lavelle, Larna 339
Lavin, David 99
Lawler, Cae 22
Lawlor, Jan 157
Lawlor, Kevin 191
Lawlor, Jill 542
Lawlor, Edward F. 575
Lawn, John 241
Lawrence, Heather 307
Lawrence, Sarah 437
Lawrence, Elizabeth A. (Beth) 457
Lawrence, Thomas E (Thom) 562
Lawson, Linda 36
Lawson, Ralph E. 47
Lawson, James W. (Jim) 52
Lawson, Jennifer (Jen) 147
Lawson, Michael 386
Lawson, Paul E. 402
Lawson, Jason 402
Lawton, Joseph S 504
Lax, David (Dave) 23
Laxton, Mary 379
Lay, Jeri 263
Lazarus, Larry S. 46

Le, Ha 33
Le, Brendan 113
Le, Tram 464
Lea, Katie 32
Lea, Jerrold P. 245
Lea-Maijala, Barb 147
Leach, Craig 581
Leach, Ronald 596
Leach, Ronald (Ron) 596
Leahey, Joe 168
Leahy, Mary 80
Leahy, Debra 543
Leahy, William P. 590
Leahy, Denis 643
Leaman, J 184
Leaning, Jennifer 548
Leanse, Annie 340
Leary, Timothy (Tim) 464
Leary, Angus 516
Leaver, Bill 266
LeBaron, Dawn 201
Leblaburley, Jelynne 126
LeBlanc, Stephen 158
Lebolt, James (Jamie) 492
Lechy, Robert 312
Leckman, Linda C. 263
Lecompte, Seth 253
Ledbetter, David (Dave) 46
Ledet, Happie 308
Ledford, Patricia 120
Ledington, Meghan 393
Ledyard, Robin 137
Lee, Connie 14
Lee, Carrie 32
Lee, Randall 47
Lee, Angela 112
Lee, Terrie 114
Lee, Milton B 126
Lee, Louis 131
Lee, Wanda 132
Lee, Vivian 133
Lee, Sally 175
Lee, Wen-yu 206
Lee, Alec 316
Lee, J Douglas D 321
Lee, William (Bill) 330
Lee, Gary 412
Lee, Aline 447
Lee, Richard 451
Lee, Jay 460
Lee, Jenny L. 470
Lee, Thai 477
Lee, Celeste 477
Lee, Simon S. 514
Lee, Charles 549
Lee, Alan (Al) 559
Lee, Michael 560
Lee, Jin 584
Lee, Sherri K 601
Lee, Ronnie 630
Leech, Thomas 200
Leer, Pete 304
Lefebvre, David (Dave) 73
Lefever-Davis, Shirley 577
Leff, Dale Ellen 258
Leffler, Stephen 201
LeFrak, Richard S. 536
Legan, Debra 247
Lehman, Harold 293
Lehman, John (Jack) 342
Lehman, David H. 556
Lehmann, Bonnie 504
Lehn, Chuck 46
Lehne, Kathy 519
Lehne, Kyle 519
Lehoczky, John 99
Leiber, Phil 309
Leiderman, Roni 379
Leiker, Don 655
Leineweber, Mark 126
Leiva, Michele 170
Lekkala, Maneesh 100
Lelievre, Phil 17
Lella, Louise 112
Lemen, Todd 82

Lemieux, Karen 345
Lemke, Dave 194
Lemler, Scott 117
Lemmer, Peter 224
Lemon, Tyson 224
Lemonde, Jane 369
Lenahan, Sarah 165
Lencioni, Kathi 473
Lender, Murray 423
Lenh, Ned 194
Lennen, Anthony 137
Lennie, Daniel (Dan) 3
Lennon, Timothy 248
Lentenbrink, Laura 81
Lenti-Ponsetto, Jean 159
Lentz, Edward T. 429
Leo, Rose 80
Leo, Koguan 477
Leon, Alfonso 186
Leonard, James C. 98
Leonard, John 377
Leonard, Lou 648
Leone, Mitchell (Mitch) 68
Leonhardt, Darrell T. 31
Leopold, Jay 170
Lepore, Michael (Mel) 640
Lepper, David 197
Lepto, John 119
Lepzinski, Julie 492
LeQuire, Barb 581
Lerose, Danielle 64
Leroy, Gary 649
Lesick, Lawrence 641
Lesneski, Gary J. 542
Lesser, John 15
Lesser, Eugene 487
Lessing, Tim C. 452
Lester, Ronald 221
Lester, Patrick 554
Letson, Douglas 229
Lettera, Frank T 276
Letts, Hanna 43
Levasseur, Rita 249
Levengood, Debra 429
Lever, Brian K. 253
Levin, Ruth 68
Levin, Kerry 636
Levine, Mel 309
Levine, Jane (Ginny) 420
Levine, Elliot 442
Levine, Marc 557
Levine, Tilly 648
Levino, Evelyn 160
Levitan, Nathan 604
Levoy, Rob 340
Levy, Scott S 169
Levy, Robert 362
Levy, Ann 362
Levy, Lester A 362
Levy, Walter 362
Levy, Andy 533
Levy, Sharon 539
Levy, Matthew (Matt) 563
Lewellen, Mitch 212
Lewis, James R. (Jim) 73
Lewis, Stephen 99
Lewis, Lisa 126
Lewis, Myron 137
Lewis, Phyllis 171
Lewis, Linda 179
Lewis, Georj L. 217
Lewis, Allen (Al) 271
Lewis, Rebecca 287
Lewis, Mike 441
Lewis, Ky 473
Lewis, Rayburn S. 524
Lewis, Daniel K. 555
Lewis, Ron 579
Lewis, J. Craig 644
Lewissecretary, Don 112
Lewit, Ari 380
Leyhane, James 95
Li, Chuang 4
Li, Yan 439

Li, Joanne 649
Li, Yi 649
Liang, Lorrie 481
Libbe, Scott W. 565
Lichtblau, Dale 261
Lichtenberg, Patricia (Pat) 621
Lidstone, Rhonda 543
Liebow, Elizabeth 157
Liebowitz, Richard S. 559
Liebson, Mike 243
Liedel, Christopher A. 602
Liekar, John (Jack) 105
Liesegang, Skip 257
Light, Glenda 641
Lihota, Gerald M. (Jerry) 442
Likins, Steven 576
Likins, Steve 576
Liller, Karen 614
Lillis, Gwendolyn H. 611
Lilly, Susan (Sue) 175
Lilly, Edward (Ed) 432
Lin, Stella 389
Lin, Jay 434
Lincoln, Butch 31
Lincoln, Steve 518
Lind, Sharon 46
Linda, Mattson 7
Lindberg, Larry 377
Linden, Stacy 23
Lindenbaum, Herman 65
Lindenmeyer, Mary 333
Lindholm, Wayne S. 240
Lindner, Rand 342
Lindner, Doug 431
Lindsay, Gayle 597
Lindsey, Lawrence B. 399
Lindsey, Carol 533
Lingerfelt, Lisa 170
Link, Mary 119
Linker, George 167
Linnehan, Frank 171
Linskey, Chris 232
Linville, Corey 521
Linzey, Scott 566
Lipkin, Gary 198
Lipner, Zachary (Zach) 368
Lipomi, Jack D 94
Lipomi, Jack D 94
Lippert, Norbert 389
Lippman, Frederick 379
List, Alan 229
Litschi, Michael 389
Little, Robert 95
Little, Nicholas 639
Littlejohn, Bill 473
Liu, Wei 404
Liu, Edison T. 549
Livesay, Jackie 147
Livingood, Jack 70
Lloyd, Karen Ann 137
Lloyd, Lisa Kay 534
Loar, Theresa 112
Lobaugh, Mike 232
Lochhead, Michael J. 133
Locke, Justin 126
Locke, Justin M. 212
Locken, Dale 484
Loderhose, Brian 545
Loeffler, Art 510
Loehr, Steve 295
Loesberg, Jonathan 24
Loewengart, Victoria 54
Loewenstein, Peter (Pete) 358
Lofland, Rrt 542
Lofton, Helyn R. 364
Logan, Lyle L. 358
Logan, Roger 405
Logemann, Cari 34
Loh, Marcel 524
London, Pam 137
Long, Carlton M 174
Long, Michael T. 225
Long, John 321
Long, William (Bill) 360
Long, Eva 613

Long, John W. 614
Long, Ronald (Ron) 643
Longobardy, Sandy 329
Longoria, Janiece M. 411
Look, Jacqueline 613
Looker, Travis 590
Loomis, Greg 231
Loomis, Gregory A 231
Loomis, Anna 353
Lopes, Richard T 460
Lopez, Orlando 33
Lopez, Ana 47
Lopez, Val 49
Lopez, Tony 226
Lopez, Karen 254
Lopez, Ann 324
Lopez, Joseph (Joe) 604
Lopman, Abe 391
Lopresti, Joseph 176
Lopuszynski, Mary 602
Lorenz, Vikki 467
Lorenzo, Heather N 336
Lori, William E. 291
Loshin, David S. 379
Louge, Michael W. (Mike) 386
Loughran, Michael 284
Louis, Karen St. 36
Loukus, Josh 342
Loutsch, Richard 147
Louttit, Gordon L 534
Love, Heather 175
Lovell, Tabitha 543
Loven, Rachael 175
Lovett, Kevin 144
Lovins, Sandy 614
Lovvorn, Jonathan 548
Low, Lewis 302
Lowe, Terril 138
Lowe, Jeff 432
Lowe, JanetSue 618
Lowenfels, Fred 583
Lowery, David 113
Lowman, Mark 47
Lowman, Tim 422
Lowrey, Ray 355
Lowry, Judith 614
Loyd, Joe 163
Lozada, Pete 457
Lozano, Ana I. 420
LU, Ziqian 83
Lu-Beker, Mei 359
Lubkowski, John (Jack) 468
Lubrano, Emily 316
Lucas, Paul 48
Lucas, John 124
Lucas, Bryan 532
Lucke, Anne 617
Lucks, Cheryl W. 360
Luddeke, Dale E. 514
Ludeking, Jim 220
Ludington, Robert (Bob) 567
Ludlow, Robert C. 267
Ludwig, Dennis 184
Ludwig, Logan T. 291
Ludwig, Tom 311
Luff, Paula 160
Lukach, Jaclynn 408
Luke, Josh 581
Lukiewski, David J. 357
Lukovits, Timothy (Tim) 158
Lum, Andrew 280
Lumbard, Sarah 358
Lumpkins, Luanne 391
Lumsden, Chris A. 467
Luna, Michael 451
Lunardi, Joe 450
Lund, Kenny 14
Lund, Ed 14
Lund, Dennis P. 405
Lundberg, Janet 280
Lunde, Beth 342
Lundeen, Christi 489
Lupisella, Melissa (Mel) 484
Lurie, Robert F. 367
Lushkevich, Patricia 95

Luther, Lori 259
Luttinger, Raymond 276
Luu, Danny 616
Lux, Robert H. 530
Lyde, Robert 633
Lyden, Shawn 119
Lydon, Christopher (Chris) 539
Lyght, William L. (Bill) 330
Lyles, William 447
Lynam, Terry 208
Lynch, Lisa M. 83
Lynch, Anne 112
Lynch, Cece 183
Lynch, Jack 419
Lynch, Ted 489
Lyon, Courtney 44
Lyon, Marlene 206
Lyons, Scott 170
Lyons, Kailey 316
Lyons, Althea 374
Lyons, B.W. 630
Lytle, Cherie 619

M

Mable, Richard 429
Macaione, Katheryn B. 423
Macan, Drew 414
Macaulay, Linda R. 536
Macbeth, Douglas (Doug) 549
MacConnell, John (Jack) 29
Macdonald, George 127
MacDonald, Mott 233
MacDonald, Joyce 358
Macdonald, Doug 377
MacDougall, Harriett 379
Mace, Bridget 236
Macgregor, Nancy 569
Machones, Melinda 505
Macias, Deb 522
Macina, Scott 151
Macina, Robert P. 551
Maciver, Lloyd 47
Mack, Timothy P. 217
Mack, John J. 559
Mack, Jonathan (Jon) 612
Mack, James J. 641
Mackay, Elizabeth F 118
Mackey, Amy 2
Mackey, Neosha 347
Mackey, Sarah 460
Mackey, Sandra 532
Macko, Terry 648
Mackown, Jennifer 437
Maclean, Roger 609
MacMillan, David (Dave) 613
Madara, James L. 22
Madden, Donald 583
Maddern, Rhonda 305
Maddox, Terry 586
Madek, Gerald A (Jerry) 64
Madia, John A. 112
Madigan, James 155
Madsen, Jan 150
Madsen, Tammy 263
Maeder, Jeff 576
Magauran, Brendan 82
Magee, Becky 631
Maggelakis, Sophia 439
Maggio, Mariah 342
Magit, Anthony 425
Magness, Bill 182
Magoon, Patrick M. 27
Magrid, Bruce 83
Maguire, Kimberly A 231
Mahana, Brent 111
Maher, John 320
Maher, Tom 400
Mahlich, Ben 225
Mahoney, Thomas J. (Tom) 267
Mahoney, Joanne M. 367
Mai, Bill 618
Mainoe, Kevin 226
Mainous, Rosalie O'Dell 649
Maione, Kevin 226
Majer, Ted 92
Majerus, Michelle (Mitch) 387
Makaroff, Chris 340
Makoid, Michael 150
Maksymowicz, Zygmunt 285
Malanga, Benjamin (Ben) 460
Malanowski, John (Jack) 158
Malasky, Beth 448
Malasto, Thomas A. 137
Malatesta, Greg 634
Malav□©, Andr□©s 379
Malchoff, Kevin R. 434
Maldonado, Liliana 112
Maley, Christopher 551
Malfatti, Carole 654
Malin, John 194
Malitzis, John 198
Mallery, Edwina 295
Mallett, Belinda 287
Mallott, Anthony 463
Malloy, Diana 639
Malm, Kathleen 513
Malone, Lisa 324
Malone, Thomas 517
Malone, John (Jack) 615
Malone, Brian 645
Mals, Deb 340
Manahan, Richard (Dick) 175
Mancewicz, Joel 342
Mancheski, Frederick J. 423
Manchur, Fred 286
Mancoridis, Spiros 171
Mandell, Joyce 449
Mandich, Sandy 305
Mandri, Daniel 47
Maneker, Amy 119
Manera, Lisa 157
Manfredi, Steven P. 64
Manganello, Ed 392
Mangano, Rob 303
Mangel, Allen W. 432
Mangram, Alicia 275
Manigault, Pierre 96
Mankin, Eric 530
Mann, Scott 614
Manner, Bob 460
Manning, John (Jack) 24
Manning, Marykay 445
Manning, Danielle 517
Mano, Steven 83
Mansfield, Douglas A. 290
Mansh, Steven H 165
Manso, Annette 470
Mansoor, Allan 389
Manter, Wendy 313
Mantoani, Jessica 280
Manzano, Wilhelmina 558
Mao, Bill 389
Marable, Jan 653
Marazano, John (Jack) 391
Marcheschi, Michael 378
Marchino, Rex 110
Marchuk, Rob 219
Marden, Brian 313
Marek, Don 561
Marepalli, Srikanth 623
Maresco, Martha 404
Margules, Gary 379
Marimon, Victor 136
Marimon, Vivian 136
Marinelli, Fred 240
Maringer, Michalene 499
Marinkoski, Robert 105
Marinzel, Ron 471
Maritz, W. Stephen (Steve) 317
Mark, William 494
Mark, Joe 501
Markell, Peter K. 590
Markey, Jeff 255
Markin, Rodney S. (Rod) 619
Markovski, Veni 266
Marks, Sandra 129
Marksteiner, Dave 466
Marlow, Gary 374
Maroc, Genny 304
Marquardt, James A (Jamie) 80
Marquardt, R. Scott 314
Marquardt, Robert 315
Marquez, Melanie 614
Marquis, Jeffrey A. 228
Marr, Tommy 248
Marriott, Bob 226
Marrs, Sherry 353
Marsh, Bill 279
Marsh, Allen 456
Marshall, Robert 105
Marshall, Jay 255
Marshall, James (Jamie) 362
Marshall, Jeff 363
Marshall, William 462
Marshall, Joretta 532
Marshall, Deann 540
Marshall, Ron 630
Martel, Ron 277
Martelly, Peter (Pete) 485
Martin, Curtis 74
Martin, Symansky 95
Martin, Dan 99
Martin, Michelle 100
Martin, Glen 114
Martin, Gerard R. 119
Martin, Stephen (Steve) 142
Martin, Whitney 175
Martin, Michael M. 204
Martin, Richard (Dick) 247
Martin, Jane Halagiere 258
Martin, Steve 290
Martin, Frank 311
Martin, Frank (Guy) 311
Martin, Shereen 336
Martin, Kelley 357
Martin, Charissa 390
Martin, Kevin J. 399
Martin, Grady 409
Martin, Ron 440
Martin, Larry 526
Martin, Earl 543
Martin, Cohen 559
Martin, Pamela 602
Martin, Linda 618
Martinez, Roxanne 64
Martinez, John-Bauer 112
Martinez, Nancy 227
Martinez, Norma 419
Martinez, Gioconda 501
Martinez, Diana 516
Martinez, Jose 560
Martini, Jimmy 90
Martini, James (Jim) 576
Martinson, Chris 576
Marty, Phil 614
Marulli, Michael (Mel) 254
Marusek, Paul 142
Marvuglio, Matt 65
Marx, Carol 190
Mascharka, William L. 209
Mascioli, Carol 47
Masek, Timothy 640
Mash, David S. 65
Mashburn, Alan 64
Mashek, Terri 619
Maslak, Joseph 36
Maslen, Eric 271
Mason, Julia 10
Mason, Patti 48
Mason, Randy 67
Mason, Andrew 77
Mason, Dan 362
Mason, Ronald 423
Mason, Brenda 482
Mason, Brenda 482
Massa, Mark 590
Massa, Gary 651
Massey, Berns 144
Massey, Jerry 176
Massey, Jane E. 316
Massey, Mary 490
Massiet, Jill 47
Masters, Chuck 14
Masterson, David J. (Dave) 467
Mastri, Jean 613
Mastro, Kari 437
Matagi, Iosefa 112
Mateja, Lynne 470
Matesic, Edith 98
Matheny, Lynn 47
Mathew, Soni 85
Mathew, Jody 207
Mathew, Stefanie 612
Mathews, Gwen 219
Mathews, Jack 409
Mathias, Ann 100
Mathias, Karen 202
Mathias, David (Dave) 236
Mathias, Steven (Steve) 419
Mathies, Bonnie K. 649
Matros, Richard K. 446
Matsuda, Noboru 100
Matsunaga, Amy 464
Matthes, Todd 583
Matthew, Cooper 10
Matthews, Bill 82
Matthews, Gwen 219
Matthews, Michael (Mel) 247
Matthews, Clint 429
Matthews, Ted 543
Mattiacci, John A. 530
Mattingly, Paul P. 470
Mattke, Roger 295
Mattox, Wayne 128
Mattson, Linda 7
Mattson, Gayle 372
Matz, Jason 99
Matzke, Richard (Dick) 235
Mauch, Anneliese 613
Mauermayer, Henry (Hal) 364
Maughan, James (Jamie) 112
Mauk, Tary 393
Mauldin, Gary 458
Mauldin, Vance 545
Maupin, Debbie 222
Maurer, Marsha 67
Mauri, Ross A 316
Mauskopf, Josephine 432
Mautone, John (Jack) 591
Mawhirter, Jeff 653
Maxcy, Stephanie 373
Maxey, Margie 162
Maxey, Jack 556
Maxwell, Mark 128
Maxwell, Annie 167
Maxwell, Edwin 215
May, Debbie 131
May, Michael 200
May, Kenneth A. (Ken) 316
May, Grace M. 469
May, Laurie 636
Mayberry, Katherine (Kate) 439
Maybury, Mark T 557
Mayefskie, Jerry 471
Mayer, Matt 207
Mayer, Louis 450
Mayeux, Gary 321
Mayhew, Joe 545
Mayland, Ed 195
Maylath, Gina 147
Mayo, Janet 331
Mays, William G. 258
Mazadoorian, Lynne 439
Mazo, James 449
Mcalester, Lanny 173
McAllister, Lon 209
McAnder, Michael (Mel) 280
McAnear, Matthew 89
McArthur, Gary L. 112
Mcarthur, John (Jack) 317
McAuliffe, Stephanie 543
McAvoy, Karen 252
McCabe, Michael 171
McCabe, Robert A. (Rob) 181
McCabe, Robert A. (Rob) 181
Mccabe, John (Jack) 267
McCaffrey, Maura C. 58

McCain, Richard B (Dick) 551
Mccall, Gerald (Jerry) 280
McCallum, Greg 481
McCalmon-bailey, Briana 83
Mccandless, Barbara (Barb) 507
McCann, Andy 255
McCann, Kay 360
McCann, James 420
McCarthy, William 75
McCarthy, Patsy 99
Mccarthy, Jeffrey (Jeff) 105
Mccarthy, Mary 245
McCarthy, Ellen 369
McCarthy, Heather 379
McCarthy, William J. (Bill) 402
McCarthy, Suzanne 539
Mccarty, Larry J 245
McCarver, Rena 118
McCaskill, Don 433
Mccauley, Lisa A 54
McChesney, Jack 30
McClellan, Scott 464
McClelland, Norman 471
McClelland, Kent 471
McClenahan, Abbe 389
McClernon, Mike 317
McClintock, Wendy 241
McClung, Linda 121
McClure, Kenneth (Ken) 347
McClure, Gene 602
McCollum, Robert 424
McComas, Randy 311
McComish, Dick 483
McConnell, Donald P. 360
McConnell, John P. 386
McCormack, Patricia 590
McCormick, Bob 159
McCormick, Beth 389
McCormick, C. Clair 551
McCoy, R. Craig 80
McCoy, Thomas M. (Tom) 112
McCoy, Julie 473
Mccoy, David (Dave) 612
McCraven, Marcus R. 423
McCreedy, John 535
McCulloch, Mike 110
McCullough, Samuel A. 429
McCurdy, Jacquie 280
McCurry, Michael 333
McDanel, Joyce 266
McDaniel, Eric 118
McDaniel, James 309
Mcdermott, Mark 74
McDermott, Sandra 118
McDermott, Ann 133
McDevitt, Valerie 614
McDonald, Carol 10
McDonald, Glen 30
McDonald, Alan 110
McDonald, Joan 171
Mcdonald, Jim 240
McDonald, Jeff 267
McDonald, Robert (Bob) 372
McDonald, Fredda 419
McDonald, John J. 423
McDonald, Jerome 468
McDonald, Thomas M. 555
Mcdonald, Steven (Steve) 596
McDonald, Aneesa Anne 618
McDonald, Justin 618
McDonnell, John F. 575
McDonough, Eileen 51
McDonough, Robert 430
McDonough, Kevin 516
McDowell, Debra 487
McElaney, Michael (Mel) 63
McElravy, Deborah 225
McElroy, Brian 367
Mcelwee, James K (Jamie) 516
McEvoy, Victoria 323
McFall, Don 263
McFarren, Timothy (Tim) 101
McGahren, John 399
McGarity, Sean 513
McGee, Genemarie 467

McGeean, TJ 90
McGhee, Craig 119
McGibbon, Michael C (Mel) 256
McGinness, Brenden 419
Mcginnis, Debbie 75
McGinnis, Bob 409
McGinnis, David 576
McGinty, Daniel 15
McGlinn, Terrence J. 429
McGlynn, Cindy 74
McGoldrick, Margaret M. (Meg) 2
Mcgowan, Matthew (Matt) 112
McGowan, Patrick J 381
McGowan, Pat 381
McGowan, Marion A. 551
McGranaghan, Mark F 182
McGrath, Greg 245
McGrath, Robert T. 385
McGraw, Tom 20
McGraw, Kari 317
McGreevy, John 586
McGregor, Robert 119
Mcguire, Deborah (Deb) 191
McGuire, Troy L. 464
McGuire, Michael (Mel) 642
McGuirk, Michael W. 630
McGurty, Thomas S. 591
McHenry, Christina 363
McHollan, Bruce 128
McIlvaine, James 518
McIntire, Eric 187
McIntire, Larry 210
McIntosh, Chris 93
Mcintosh, Glenn 382
McIntyre, Gregory T. (Greg) 112
McIntyre, James 590
McKee, Chris 129
McKee, Page W. 170
McKeehan, Effie 544
McKeever, Clare 215
Mckellar-Jones, Kearlinc 236
McKendree, Rodney (Rod) 363
McKenna, Dennis 10
McKenna, Joann 64
McKenna, Kevin 129
McKenzie, Craig 245
Mckenzie, Stanley D (Stan) 439
McKibben, Bill 414
Mckibben, William (Bill) 414
McKinley, Rayna 135
McKinley, Lee 258
McKinney, Andrea 175
McKinney, David 253
Mckinnon, Ted 534
Mckissick, Michelle (Mitch) 360
McKnelly, Cindy 304
McKnight, Virginia (Ginny) 342
McKnight, Craig L. 405
McKnight, Arlene 437
McLain, Ginny 280
McLane, Jeffrey 43
McLarney, Thomas 635
McLaughlin, Patricia (Pat) 277
McLean, Angie 7
McLean, Chris 119
McLenithan, Amanda 95
MCLURE, KEN 347
McMahan, Chris 481
McMahon, Marybeth 154
McMahon, Heidi 215
McMahon, Scott 576
McManus, Richard 377
McManus, Devra 572
McMillan, Charles F. 330
McMillan, George 396
McMillan, Jacqueline 649
McMillen, Steve 589
Mcmullen, Marshall 114
McMullen, Ronald B. (Ron) 120
McNabb, David W. 35
McNabb, Forrest 70
McNabb, Mike 156
McNamara, Thomas (Thom) 133
McNamara, Carolyn S. 648

McNaney, Michael 429
McNaughton, Jarrod 287
Mcnealis, Anne 280
McNeely, James 54
McNeil, Stan 156
McNeil, Chris E. 463
McNeil, Suzanne 572
McNulty, Tim 99
McNulty, Timothy (Tim) 100
McPhee, Debra M. 204
McPhee, Mark S. 589
Mcpherson, James (Jamie) 112
McPherson, Lon 137
McPherson, Lon H. 138
McPherson, John (Jack) 419
McQueen, Todd 567
McRae, Jay 112
McRae, Tom 218
Mcrae, Mary 623
McShane, Joseph M. 204
McShane, Gerald J. 392
McTaggart, Jon R. 358
McTigue, Tim 224
McWay, Jacob 304
McWay, Michael J. 327
Mcwilliams, Ethan 612
Meadows, Steve 66
Meadows, Charles 137
Meadows, Sheila 345
Meadows, Randall G. 482
Meagher, C 584
Meares, Ron 17
Meath, Robb 597
Mecham, Rex 32
Medina, Karla 47
Meegan, Robert (Bob) 224
Meek, Julie 279
Meerts, John C 635
Mefford, Roger 209
Megibben, John 337
Meguiar, Ramon V. 330
Mehindru, Vinay 202
Meibergen, Joey 277
Meier, Gretchen 95
Meier, Lisa 595
Meindl, Nympha 289
Meininger, Steve 112
Meisner, Laurie 528
Meissner, Doris 145
Mejia, Gerald (Jerry) 526
Melancon, Barry C. 21
Melanson, Nancy 58
Melaragno, Tony 302
Mele, Cheryl 182
Mellace, Debbie 84
Mellowes, Charles (Chas) 115
Melmed, Shlomo 104
Melnick, Jeffrey 180
Melnick, Samantha 450
Melski, John (Jack) 321
Melton, Debbie 390
Meltzer, Neil M. 305
Meltzer, Neil M. 481
Melvin, Pat 442
Melvin, Rosetta 650
Menard, Didier 112
Menas, Bob 1
Menassian, Julianne 420
Mendel, Elisa 279
Mendelovitz, Teri 560
Mendelsohn, Dave 73
Menders, Chuck 114
Mendez, Alex 49
Mendez, Martha 487
Mendoza, Ted 518
Menes, Robin 22
Menhart, Theresa 572
Menichini, Leslie 441
Merav, Avraham 404
Meraz, Juan 347
Mercado, Sonia 650
Mercer, Julie 80
Mercer, Richard 391
Mercier, Denise 485
Mercier, Andrew B. (Andy) 553

Meredith, Christopher (Chris) 154
Meriano, John J. 423
Merkel, Mike 111
Merrell, Scott 432
Merrill, Sharon 280
Merry, Laura 616
Mertzlufft, Douglas (Doug) 227
Messina, Elizabeth A. 76
Messina, Scott 151
Messner, Garret 185
Metcalf, Peter 215
Metcalf, Michael 401
Metcalf, Ben 425
Metsker, Ron 419
Metzen, Dan 554
Meuser, John F. 423
Meyer, Alan 110
Meyer, Gary 133
Meyer, Peter 222
Meyer, Steve 255
Meyer, Peter (Pete) 321
Meyer, Robert L. 405
Meyer, Brian 405
Meyer, Christopher 524
Meyer, Henry L. 604
Meyer, Daniel 615
Meyers, Tony W 25
Meyers, Steve 278
Miceli, Charles (Chas) 201
Michaelis, Nicole 113
Michaelis, Brian L. 470
Michalet, Elizabeth 345
Michaud, Gregory 489
Michel, Euclid 91
Michel, Butch 423
Michel, Mike 423
Michell, Pam 137
Miciak, Alan 172
Mickeleit, Dennis 294
Mickells, Adrienne 73
Mickey-Boggs, Shari 649
Mickle, Kate 612
Mieden, Gregory 242
Mignone, Roberto 536
Mike, Billotte 597
Mikeska, Robert 78
Mikkelsen, Corey 620
Milano, Karen 87
Miles, John 196
Miles, Mark 439
Mileti, Joe 445
Milian, Carlos 153
Millan, Juan 302
Millen, Robert P 386
Miller, Karen 49
Miller, Adam 60
Miller, Jennifer 95
Miller, Ken 112
Miller, Scott 127
Miller, Marc J. 137
Miller, David 159
Miller, Kathleen 171
Miller, William 175
Miller, Carla 197
Miller, Jane E. 213
Miller, Justin 240
Miller, Edwin (Glen) 240
Miller, Gary 253
Miller, Robert (Bob) 260
Miller, Rudy 305
Miller, Sean 307
Miller, Scott 320
MILLER, PETER C (Pete) 340
Miller, Patti 342
Miller, Rick 360
Miller, H. Gilbert 369
Miller, Dan 383
Miller, Charles P. (Charlie) 399
Miller, Ron 423
Miller, Marlin 439
Miller, James 439
Miller, Derek 447
Miller, Rudy 481
Miller, Mike 489
Miller, Michael 489

Miller, Pamela 551
Miller, Dave 573
Miller, Patrice 579
Miller, Marc H. 584
Miller, Ben 595
Miller, Martin (Marti) 597
Miller, Carol 599
Miller, Trevor 603
Miller, Janet L. 604
Miller, Jessica 612
Miller, Thomas 614
Miller-phipps, Julie 280
Milles, Ellen 284
Millhollin, Jeff 397
Millikan, J. Scott 71
Millikan, Charles (Chas) 554
Millis, Michael (Mel) 571
Millner, Ann 263
Mills, E N 135
Mills, Bryan A. 137
Mills, Don 339
Mills, Michael 379
Mills, Claudia 473
Mills, Nicole 516
Millsap, Mark 255
Milner, Dennis 641
Milstein, Marc 652
Milton, Kerry 452
Mimm, Nancy 542
Minatra, Terri 358
Miner, Lenny 36
Miner, Mark 194
Miner, Jim 345
Miner, Thomas 477
Miner, James D. 550
Mingle, Regina 551
Minnis, Jeffrey 583
Minopoli, Anthony 291
Minor, Mike 227
Minshew, Tony 144
Minteer, Dinah 389
Minutoli, Robert 576
Miracle, Phoenicia 330
Mirza, Sohail 158
Mishina, Craig 469
Mistretta, Susan 599
Misura, Alex 252
Mitchell, Ken 70
Mitchell, Martha 126
Mitchell, Marjo 139
Mitchell, Shondra 213
Mitchell, James S (Jamie) 248
Mitchell, Benjamin 342
Mitchell, Kendra 400
Mitchell, Thomas 530
Mitchell, Robert (Rob) 576
Mitchell, Chuck 591
Mitchell, Fred 599
Mitchell, Joy 650
Mitola, Joseph (Jo) 511
Mitoraj, Thomas 635
Mjos, Lisa 263
Mnners, Myrna A 559
Moag, Tony 576
Mock, Robert C. 277
Moczygemba, Crystal 490
Modell, Mitchell B. (Mitch) 240
Modisett, Tom 299
Moehling, John H. 543
Moffat, Anne J.M. 385
Moffatt, Kevin 261
Moffet, Brian L. 481
Moffett, Bryan 358
Moffitt, John 339
Mofor, Lapah 100
Mogan, Tom 590
Mogler, Devin 194
Mohney, Tami 240
Mohr, Todd M. 6
Mohr, Joan Isaac 423
Molberg, Peter J 158
Molbert, Paul 295
Molina, Sergio 314
Molitor, Kim 646
Mollere, Ben 47

Molloy, Kevin 289
Molosky, Amberly 46
Mom, Sherrie 391
Momberg, Joel 614
Monaco, Anthony P. 591
Monahan, Rachael 652
Monan, J. Donald 590
Monday, Kathy 612
Mondello, Judith (Judi) 215
Mondou, Sherry 611
Mongar, Mark 150
Monk, Wade 203
Monnin, Matt 337
Monson, Dale D 132
Montague, Norma 364
Montalvo, Jose 112
Montalvo, Juan 230
Montalvo, Darren 501
Monteiro, Manuel 82
Montesino, Becky 49
Montgomery, Alan (Al) 100
Montgomery, Mellodee 160
Montgomery, Keith 245
Montgomery, Mark 501
Montgomery, Eric 569
Monti, Philip 479
Montoya, Marcus 77
Montreuil, Eugene 126
Moody, Chris 24
Moon, Deborah 99
Mooney, Frances 320
Moore, Steven (Steve) 43
Moore, Rob 70
Moore, Kyle 80
Moore, Jeffrey 110
Moore, Ginger 112
Moore, Dolores 175
Moore, Todd 201
Moore, Darrel 215
Moore, Sue M. 217
Moore, Timothy (Tim) 247
Moore, Mark E. 259
Moore, Mikelle 263
Moore, Towana 271
Moore, Benjamin 308
Moore, David (Dave) 339
Moore, William M. 432
Moore, Edward (Ed) 434
Moore, Brendan F. 445
Moore, Madeleine 590
Moore, Kathleen 614
Moore, Dan 626
Moorehead, Alexander A. (Alex) 253
Moorehead, Donald V. 399
Moorlach, John 389
Moorman, Kathy 47
Moos, Walter H. 494
Mooz, John (Jack) 245
Morales, Melanee Jo 217
Morales, David S. 420
Moran, Michael F. 58
Moran, Mike 91
Moran, Erin 160
MORAN, STEPHANIE 517
Moran, Garrett 636
Morcott, Southwood J. (Woody) 330
Morehouse-Reynolds, Alexandra 45
Moreland, Linda 504
Morell, Abelardo 24
Morelli, John (Jack) 439
Moretto, Jill 512
Morgan, Kayla 175
Morgan, Randall C. 258
Morgan, Lori 301
Morgan, Lori 302
Morgan, David L. 325
Morgan, Dianna 391
Morgan, James 503
Morgan, Marsha L. 589
Morgenstern, Moises 100
Moriarity, Bridget 6
Mork, Lee 15
Mormando, Karin 530
Mormann, James J. 392
Moro, Karen 526

Morray, Jeffrey P. 405
Morris, Howell 10
Morris, Julie 23
Morris, John (Jack) 136
Morris, Beverly 287
Morris, Tony 305
Morris, Don 330
Morris, Doug 463
Morris, Gary R. 550
Morris, Michael 585
Morrison, Karen 386
Morro, Bob 623
Morrow, W. Robert 31
Morrow, W. Robert (Bob) 118
Morrow, Joseph T. 258
Morrow, Grant 360
Morse, Elizabeth 323
Morse, Ted 351
Morse, William 611
Mortazavi, Kia 389
Morton, Tony 421
Morton, Michael 630
Morway, Joe 471
MORYCZ, BARBARA (Barb) 99
Moschell, Paul 40
Moschell, Paul 40
Moser, Joseph (Jo) 28
Moser, Len 52
Moser, Aaron 613
Moses, Dave 129
Mosley, Mark 128
Mosley, John B. 492
Mosley, Steven 543
Moss, Jeffrey 266
Moss, R. Lawrence 360
Most, Kevin 107
Mostofi, Ann 179
Mott, Howard 128
Moudry, Gwen 500
Moughan, Tara 302
Moulton, Leigh 492
Mountford, Susan 636
Mounty, Lauren 5
Mourad, Sam 477
Mouret, Ralph 518
Movva, Sandeep 99
Mowbray, Brad 242
Mowe, Will 302
Mowll, Kevin 95
Moyes, Michael (Mel) 65
Moyes, Fiona 470
Moynahan, Paula 423
Mozaffarian, Dariush 591
Mozrall, Jacqueline 439
Mskolfieldpewtrustso, Melissa 563
Mucha, John (Jack) 239
Muchnok, Charles (Chas) 215
Mueller, Christopher (Chris) 74
Mueller, George 226
Mueller, Ken 426
Mueller, Bryan 524
Muellner, Gen. George K. 534
Muessig, Geoffrey (Geoff) 408
Mueth, Melanie 120
Mukerji, Rana 559
Mula, Lu 103
Mulcahy, Joe 445
Mulhall, Marty 158
Mulla, Lu 103
Mullady, Alexa 191
Mullen, Gerard 542
Mullenix, Elizabeth R. 340
Mullert, Drew 224
Mullican, Charles 237
Mulligan, Richard E. 316
Mullin, Shelly 353
Mullings, Sharon 377
Mullins, Alvin 433
Mullis, Harold W. 614
Mulvehill, Mitch 118
Muncaster, Karen 83
Mundhenk, Katherine 437
Mundy, Mark J. 366
Munford, Thedosia 418
Munoz, Alex 487

Munoz, Chris 643
Munro, Doug 245
Munsch, Frank 317
Munson, Robb 280
Murasko, Donna 171
Murdoch, Brian 131
Murdoch, Susan (Sue) 198
Murfin, Ross 487
Murillo, Jose 554
Murin, Bill 501
Murphey, Connie Griggs 217
Murphy, Thomas (Thom) 10
Murphy, Kristen 24
Murphy, Maureen 27
Murphy, Ronald H. 35
Murphy, John E. 73
Murphy, David 83
Murphy, Anne 137
Murphy, Kathy 169
Murphy, Dennis 182
Murphy, Teresa 201
Murphy, Dennis M. 259
Murphy, John 265
Murphy, Janice 280
Murphy, Mike 314
Murphy, Mark E. 330
Murphy, Barbara 337
Murphy, Michael 401
Murphy, Michael W. (Mike) 473
Murphy, Kevin 501
Murphy, Mark 502
Murphy, Laurie 510
Murphy, Chris 513
Murphy, Vin 516
Murphy, Teresa 518
Murphy, Sheriann 526
Murphy, Charles J 542
Murr, Emily 175
Murr, Lilianne 441
Murray, Donald 126
Murray, Kerri 167
Murray, John E. 172
Murray, Robert (Bob) 183
Murray, Michael 208
Murray, Scott 245
Murray, Kevin 276
Murray, Robin 384
Murray, Jean 450
Murray, Bill 529
Murray, Michael 545
Murray, Hartley 617
Murril, Antoinette 256
Murry, Velma McBride 117
Musgrave, Beverly 204
Musial, Cora 98
Musick, William 554
Musselman, Kathy I 342
Musso, Stephen 23
Mutarelli, Richard D. (Rich) 137
Mutscher, Kenneth (Ken) 78
Muzzi, Sal 598
Mycek, John (Jack) 281
Myers, Jerry 73
Myers, Marcy 114
Myers, Douglas T. 119
Myers, Frank 132
Myers, Kevin 213
Myers, Christy 255
Myers, R 271
Myers, J 272
Myers, John 311
Myers, Matthew B. 340
Myers, Diana 457
Myers, John J. 470
Myers, Emily 543
Myers, Jessica 612
Myers, Karen 614
Myers, Jim 634
Myers, Rochelle 648
Myers, Carl F 654
Mysore, Ashwin 43

N

Nachreiner, Carol 307
Nadol, Anne 530
Nadolny, Stephanie 94
Nagel, Andrew 110
Nager, Glen D. 602
Nager, Glen D. 602
Nagourney, Robert 329
Nahrgang, Jim 52
Naidoo, Shirley 379
Naik, Guruprasad 321
Nair, Mohnish 530
Nair, Auro 549
Nair, Santhosh 642
Naito, Tomo 520
Nakano, Tom 379
Nakasone, Lisa 613
Nama, Veeresh 239
Namazi, Cyrus 266
Nance, Norman (Norm) 294
Nance, William 533
Nance, William A (Bill) 534
Nantais, Tom 238
Nantz, Mark S. 80
Napier, Laine 261
Nappi, Bob 14
Narang, Steve 46
Narayanan, Vasudha 636
Narayanan, Sundaram 649
Narcisso, Deborah (Deb) 37
Narinesingh, Sandra 171
Narisety, Chalapathy 273
Narla, Mohandas 365
Nasci, Kathleen 562
Nash, Bruce D 95
Nash, David 578
Naspinski, Ed 528
Nassif, Tony 18
Natale, J. Peter 339
Nathans, Andrew (Andy) 578
Nathans, Andrew (Andy) 579
Nathanson, Martha 305
Nauert, Gary 170
Naugle, Dennis 432
Nava, Gustavo 252
Navarette, Ricardo 595
Navran, Susan H. 76
Naylor-Johnson, Darrell 566
Nazaire, Fausta 569
Nazarian, Marita 31
Nazarian, Simon 280
Nazarko, Michael 237
Ndong, Juan A. 40
Ndong, Juan A. 40
Neal, Doug 58
Neal, Frederick (Fred) 153
Neal, Greg 635
Nealon, Jackie 308
Nearhood, Richard (Dick) 445
Neary, Francis (Fran) 432
Nece, Carl 105
Neegan, Leone 654
Neely, Joe B. 630
Neenan, William (Bill) 590
Neeper, Jarral 92
Neeson, Bill 245
Neill, Thomas 578
Neilsen, Yasmin 349
Nelsen, Suzanne 487
Nelson, Wendell 32
Nelson, Shelby 45
Nelson, Dennis 54
Nelson, Scott M. 76
Nelson, Sheila 95
Nelson, Carrie 100
Nelson, Rob 215
Nelson, Rick 226
Nelson, Torre 230
Nelson, Leah 280
Nelson, Keith 329
Nelson, Walt 347
Nelson, David R. 423
Nelson, Brock D. 430

Nelson, Jacqueline 483
Nelson, Gregory V 554
Nelson, Emilie 559
Nelson, Peter (Pete) 612
Nelson, Mark 625
Nelson, Nancy (Nan) 632
Nelson, Claire 643
Nelson-mustard, Ruth 432
Nembhard, Nicole 68
Nenaber, Pam 45
Nenzel, Andrea 401
Nepper, Justin 194
Ner, Ryan 47
Nerkar, Hemchandra 21
Nesbit, Ryan 606
Nesbitt, Mark 110
Nesbitt, Kathy 605
Nesset, Sharon 597
Nester, Brian 303
Neubert, A. George 429
Neubert, A. George 429
Neumen, Gary 127
Nevers, Rick 34
Nevo-Hacohen, Talya 446
Newbrough, James P. 386
Newbury, Robert 425
Newcomb, Mike 302
Newell, David 530
Newman, Kurt D. 119
Newman, Eric 146
Newman, Steve 382
Newport, Frank M. 213
Newschaffer, Craig 171
Newsome, Laynie 625
Newton, Bryan 210
Newton, Joy 568
Neyman, Craig 543
Ng, Paul 477

Ng, Yu-Kai 584
Nguyen, Ted 389
Nguyen, Janet 389
Nguyen, Mimi 524
Nguyen, Michelle 625
Niblack, Chris 616
Niccolucci, Dani 576
Nichols, Mike 150
Nichols, Rodney 227
Nichols, Gretchen 302
Nichols, Charlie M 431
Nichols, Laurie 483
Nichols, Tom 578
Nicholson, Earl 362
Nicholson, Chris 613
Nichter, Mike 153
Nickerson, Steven Cash 401
Nickerson, Lucille M. 572
Nickles, Jessica 518
Nicklin, Emily 571
Nickolas, Mike 370
Nickolay, Brittany 350
Nicol, Peter G. 112
Nicol, Kathleen 360
Nicolle, Brittnee 109
Nidiffer, Doug 89
Nidiffer, Alan 90
Niederhoffer, Debbie 86
Niehaus, Jason 517
Niehaus, Kurt 598
Nielsen, Milt 534
Nieswender, Carolyn 652
Nieves, Doris 95
Nikolic, Cathleen 623
Nilsson, Ted 276
Nimmo, Tammy 506
Nisley, Fred 13
Nitecki, Danuta 171
Nixon, Mark 298
Nizza, Arthur 266
Noble, Paula 27
Noble, Steve 130
Noble, Kara 585
Nobles, Anne 259
Noce, Walter W. (Bill) 501
Nochomovitz, Michael L. 604

Nokes, Gloria 227
Nolan, Bill 193
Nolan, Carrie 317
Nolan, Joseph 523
Noland, Jeff 487
Nolde-morrissey, Paul 46
Noll, Mark 611
Nollner, Charlene 9
Nomoto, Michael 522
Noonan, Anna 201
Noorani, Adil 245
Norbrun, Joanna 82
Norcross, George E. 542
Nordin, Brandon 19
Norgaard, Kris 195
Norita, Mark 612
Norkus, Gerard K. (Gerry) 369
Norkus, Stephen J. 369
Norkus, Mark 369
Norman, Karen Van 470
Norotsky, Mitch 201
Norris, John (Jack) 47
Norris, David 236
Norris, Charez 275
Norris, Marly 613
Norris, Todd 635
Norton, Connie 179
Norton, Andrew J (Andy) 211
Norton, Rick 226
Norton, Robert (Bob) 347
Norton, Margareta E. (Meg) 425
Norton, Anthony 482
Norton, Anthony 482
Norton, Alan (Al) 506
Norton, Douglas (Doug) 623
Nothmann, David 54
Notte, Jerry 112
Novak, Derek 18
Novell, Javier 208
Novick, Rona M. 653
Novitski, Michael 294
Novo, Sergio 233
Nowlan, Thomas (Thom) 381
Noyes, Vikki 461
Nubel, Anna 150
Nucci, John 517
Nuchamovitz, Eyal 222
Nugent, Bryan 46
Nugent, Cchea 487
Nunley, Julie 45
Nusbaum, Nancy 534
Nussbaum, Mark 479
Nutting, Liz 612
Nutting, Willard 613
Nye, Steven J. 112
Nygaard, Kristina 112
Nzinkeu, Tatiana 282

O

Oakley, Bruce 87
Oakley, Ronald W (Ron) 405
Oaks, Kenneth 288
Oates, Justin 511
Obanner, Doreen 191
Obarski, Kevin 584
Oberg, Ed 13
Obray, Bob 35
Obrist, Mary 502
Ochoa, Arthur (Art) 104
OConnor, Dan 138
Oden, Robert A. 99
Oden, Bill 118
Odle, Samuel (Sam) 259
Odom, Bill 385
Odom, Jim 385
Oertli, Frederick J. (Rick) 227
Oertli, Roger 227
Oeters, Phillis 47
Offinger, Walter E 215
Offner, Bobbi 616
Offutt, Christi J. 428
Offutt, Ryan 428
Offutt, Ronald (Ron) 428

Oftelie, Andrew 389
Ogden, Keith 112
Ogden, Ken 153
Ogg, Tom 119
Ogrinc, Mary 296
Okafo, Nneka 480
Okamoto, Wesley 501
Okano, Bob 26
Oldfield, Thomas (Thom) 197
Olejniczak, Agnes 245
Oleksy, Jill 119
Olem, Matt 224
Olhava, Marty 245
Oliva, Harvey 52
Oliveira, Victor 94
Oliver, Daquan 43
Oliver, Rhea 137
Oliver, Carlos 209
Oliver, Wendy 232
Oller, Robert S. 379
Olmos, Maribel 263
Olscamp, Karen E. 607
Olsen, Becky 90
Olsen, Tom 195
Olson, Dan 37
Olson, Carl 100
Olson, Gayle 225
Olson, Bill 245
Olson, Skip 260
Olson, Carol 292
Olson, Gerald (Jerry) 307
Olson, Cory 372
Olson, Kathy 470
Olson, Ryan 530
Oltmans, Joseph O. (Joe) 561
Omobono, Tony 112
Ondieki, Irene 273
Ondreyka, Terry 534
Oneill, Martin 485
Ongaro, Giulio Maria 616
Oniel, Daniel 513
Onishi, Ricky 640
Ontiveros, Gregg 226
Ontiveros, Matt 226
Ontiveros, Robert (Bob) 226
Oot, David (Dave) 457
Opalach, Walt 598
Opalinski, Michael (Mel) 467
Opalinski, Mike 467
Ophaug, Courtney 46
Oppenheimer, Phillip 616
Oppmann, Andrew (Andy) 342
Orellana, Charles 562
Oriol, Albert 425
Oris, Jim 340
Orkin, Stuart H. 157
Orlando, Charles (Chuck) 305
Orlando, Charles (Chuck) 481
Orlando, Chuck 481
Orlando, Don 546
Orlando, Lorraine 559
Orlando, John (Jack) 563
Orlich, Nada 554
Orme, James 263
Ormiston, Gayle 320
Ornt, Daniel B. 439
Orourke, Brian J 3
Orozco, Gerard 112
Orr, Mark 226
Orr, Susan Packard 543
Orris, Keith 171
Orris, Keith 208
Ort, Shirley A. 133
Orta, Jesse 126
Ortega, Ivette 68
Ortega, Rebecca 470
Ortego, Craig 295
Ortlip, Debra 134
Oshiro, Mabel 534
Oskvig, O. H. (Dean) 73
Ostendorf, Todd 372
Oster, Mike 327
Ostrander, R 160
Osullivan, Joe 362
Oswald, Kathy 238

Otellini, Marissa 526
Ott, Susan (Sue) 36
Ott, Andrew L. 408
Ottolini, Mary 119
Ousley, Glenna 160
Overall, Travis 245
Overhiser, Michael 602
Overmyer, Cindy 280
Owen, Laura 586
Owens, Tom 245
Owens, Thomas (Thom) 245
Owens, Melissa (Mel) 321
Owlia, Azita 642
Owusu-ansah, Albert (Al) 88
Oxholm, Carl 171
Ozdamar, Ayse 47
O'Boyle, Ed 213
O'Boyle, Andrew (Andy) 464
O'Brien, Laura 10
O'Brien, Carolyn 25
O'Brien, Tom 73
O'Brien, Beth 401
O'Brien, Thomas F. 408
O'Brien, Keith 414
O'Brien, Gary 429
O'Brien, Teri 623
O'Brien, Barry 648
O'Casek, Jim 40
O'Connell, Kathleen 389
O'Connor, Thomas (Tom) 15
O'Connor, Timothy 92
O'Connor, Dan 137
O'Connor, James (Jamie) 238
O'Connor, Michael J. 291
O'Connor, Edward R. 423
O'Connor, Patrick J. (Pat) 530
O'Connor, Kevin 602
O'Dea, Edward 303
O'Dell, Allen 518
O'Donnell, Deb 107
O'Hara, Curt 36
O'Hare, Patrick J. 492
O'Keefe, Patrick 112
O'Keefe, Peggy 116
O'Keefe, Sharon 571
O'Leary, Rand 401
O'Leary, Thomas M. (Tom) 402
O'Loughlin, Pat 88
O'Malley, Tim 612
O'Malley, Barbara (Barb) 633
O'Meara-mckinney, Colette 150
O'Neal, Pat 346
O'Neil, William 418
O'Neil, Julie 532
O'Neill, Tim 317
O'Neill, Donna 557
O'neill, Robert (Bob) 590
O'Neill, Michael J (Mike) 623
O'Reilly, William R. (Bill) 591
O'Rourke, Susan 157
O'Rourke, Elizabeth 526
O'Rourke, Timothy C. 530
O'shea, Rebecca 579
O'Sullivan, Paul 331
O'Toole, Thomas J. 602
O'Toole, Thomas J. 602
OÂ'Connor, Timothy P. 564
OÂ'Neal, Fred 153

P

Pablo, Rubinstein 365
Pace, Robert J. (Rob) 566
Pacelle, Wayne 548
Pacey, Amy 460
Pacheco, Diego 43
Packard, Julie E. 543
Packard, Julie E. 543
Packer, Roger J. 119
Packer, Barbara 379
Padgett, Ricky 201
Pagano, Stephen 183
Page, Michael J. 64
Page, Kerry 128

Page, Peter (Pete) 260
Page, Michael 494
Pagelow, Terri 279
Pagorek, Bob 355
Painter, Ginny 320
Pakkala, Karen 492
Pakonen, Diane 585
Palan, Martha 636
Palkoski, Linda 437
Palla, Rukhsar 464
Palmer, Richard M. 429
Palmer, Harvey 439
Palmer, David 499
Palmer, Frank R 576
Palmieri, Judy 126
Palmucci, John (Jack) 310
Pamer, Dawn 518
Panik, Anne 303
Panis, Robert (Bob) 623
Pankey, Lance 460
Pankey, Andrea 641
Panneton, Kirk 95
Panzino, Jodi 139
Pao, Sun 112
Paoletti, Rich 551
Papacostas, Arthur 530
Paparone, Bruce J. 283
Papp, Harry A. 77
Pappert, P. David 172
Paquette, Jim 310
Paradies, Gregg 561
Paradies, James N. (Jim) 561
Paradis, Jim 312
Paradise, Edward (Ed) 129
Paradowski, Ed 326
Parikh, Purvish M. 25
Parikh, Sudip 54
Paris, Jerry 364
Parish, Annette 346
Parizeau, Ernie 414
Park, Mike 400
Park, Seri 623
Parke, Pat 343
Parker, Cathy 88
Parker, Vicki 305
Parker, Dean 431
Parker, Harry 532
Parker, Elizabeth Rindskopf 616
Parks, Crockett 113
Parks, Jasmine 239
Parks, Richard H. 501
Parma, Ben 160
Parmelee, Ferole 296
Parnell, Tim 506
Parris, Antoinette 566
Parrish, Mike 346
Parrish, Mike 372
Parsel, Lori 389
Parsons, John (Jack) 534
Parsons-nikolic, Cathleen 623
Partch, Judy Gerrard 167
Pasch, Leo 225
Pascualy, Ralph 524
Paseaur, Jeff 188
Passafaro, David (Dave) 516
Passaro, Karen 470
Patchen, Paul 473
Pate, Steve 515
Pate, Kevin 515
Pategas, Dianna 423
Patel, Manish 472
Patel, Nehal 477
Patel, Hiral 543
Pater, Mary 297
Patete, Daniel L. 227
Patkotak, Crawford 31
Paton, John 423
Patrick, Becky 260
Patrick, Debby 303
Patrick, Wesley 490
Patten, Scott 625
Patterson, James (Jamie) 189
Patterson, Summer 263
Patterson, Robert 287
Patterson, Jeff 471

Patterson, Gary 481
Patterson, John (Jack) 543
Patton, Jeannie 21
Patton, Susannah 279
Patton, Andrea 383
Patton, Mike 580
Paul, Chausse 313
Paul, Mason 572
Paul, Hernandez 625
Paulakos, Kimberly 252
Pauley, William E. (Bill) 545
Paulikas, George 534
Paulino, Lewis 526
Paustian, Dan 59
Pava, Moses 653
Pavlovich, Roger 91
Pavone, Bob 434
Paw, Tom 219
Pawlak, Mark 247
Paxton, James F. (Jim) 400
Paxton, Richard E. 400
Payson, Susan Healey (Sue) 374
Peach, Anne 391
Pearce, Louis M. 633
Pearson, Laura 34
Pearson, Ralph L. 172
Pearson, Chris 194
Pearson, David P. 377
Pearson, Reggie 407
Pearson, David 409
Pearson, Chris 484
Pearson, Eric 494
Pearson, Douglas 543
Pearson, Jeff 586
Peck, Lori 34
Peck, David (Dave) 42
Peckham, Michael P. (Mike) 425
Peckham, Judith C. 599
Peckinpaugh, David 317
Pecoraro, Frank 131
Pedersen, John (Jack) 314
Pederson, Peter E (Pete) 246
Pedlow, Bernadette 10
Pedone, Peter 550
Peeler, Mark 584
Peeters, Clare 42
Peffley, Dick 298
Peji, Elle 569
Pelkowski, Margaret (Peg) 650
Pell, Gary 624
Pelle, Fred 635
Pellegrino, Thomas (Thom) 191
Pelletier, Mark 459
Pelton, James (Jamie) 395
Pena, Richard (Dick) 126
Pender, Erin 589
Pendergast, Mike 69
Peniston, John 2
Penman, Candyce 263
Pennella, Thomas L. 112
Penner, Rabbi Menachem 653
Penney, Robert T. 105
Pennington, Karen 351
Penno, D B 414
Pepe, Heather 118
Peperissa, Kenneth (Ken) 36
Pepper, J. David (Dave) 402
Peralta, Pennie 96
Perda, Michael J. 357
Perea, Jennifer Rosato 159
Pereira, Daisy 164
Perera, Jaime 327
Perez, Roberta 403
Perfect, Jane W. 202
Perin, James P. (Jim) 258
Perkins, Lucian 24
Perkins, James 366
Perlewitz, Kathleen 211
Perlish, Joel 551
Perlowitz, Bill B. 514
Perlowski, Kevin 222
Perlroth, Donald L. 423
Perrelli, Nicole 623
Perren, Katharine 379
Perring-mulligan, John 501

Perrone, Michael (Mel) 224
Perrot, Marcus 616
Perry, Nancy 23
Perry, Steve 42
Perry, Sabrina 68
Perry, Amy 305
Perry, Amy 481
Perry, Keith 503
Perry, Chris 612
Perryman, Margaret E. 218
Perryman, Margaret E. 218
Pesco, Janice J 96
Peters, Dolores 506
Peters, Amy 589
Petersen, Andy Kramer 46
Petersen, Richard W. (Rich) 313
Petersen, Whitney 342
Peterson, Mark G. 21
Peterson, Jacqueline D. 133
Peterson, Lawrence 245
Peterson, Wally 245
Peterson, John D. 258
Peterson, Carol J. 483
Peterson, Douglas (Doug) 498
Peterson, Gary 505
Peterson, Kurt 567
Peterson, Spencer 597
Petlak, Beth 32
Petrella, Brian 640
Petrow, Angela 389
Petruck, Amy 615
Petruzzelli, Guy 330
Petty, Meredith L 160
Petzel, Jim 222
Pew, James 618
Peyton, Kurt 234
Pezzoli, Robert E. 530
Pfau, N. E. (Ned) 258
Pfeffer, George 170
Pfeffer, Stacey 645
Ph, Hemang 487
Pham, Hien 613
Pharo, Karen 596
Pharris, Jeff 326
Phelps, Vicki 258
Phiffer, Cynthia 342
Philbrick, Karen 343
Philip, May 90
Philipose, Betsy 319
Phillips, Pam 80
Phillips, Joan 114
Phillips, Bill 128
Phillips, Sherman 128
Phillips, Andrew 227
Phillips, Margie 419
Phillips, John E. 545
Phipps, Ken 389
Phipps, Sean 503
Phong, Sam 100
Phyllis, Sweeney 385
Picha, Douglas 464
Picken, William 143
Pickerill, Bob 37
Pickett, Joan Joan Pickett 97
Pickett, Gary 113
Pidhurney, James (Jamie) 43
Pieper, Karen J. 258
Pierce, Phil 41
Pierce, John E (Jack) 150
Pierce, Kevin 173
Pierce, Jeff S. 202
Pierce, Roger 211
Pierce, Jeff 255
Pierce, Dan 290
Pierce, Leslie 338
Pierce, Morgan 405
Pierce, Ken 534
Pierrotti, Craig 112
Piersma, Howie 402
Pierson, Susan (Sue) 21
Pierson, Lynn 89
Pietris, Timos 316
Pietryka, Lori 95
Pietrykowski, Robert (Bob) 379
Pifer, Susan 298

Pike, Mike 113
Pilafas, Penny 408
Pilates, Joseph 505
Pilkenton, Sandra 635
Pillsbury, Marnie S. 564
Pilusa, Chris 511
Pina, Christine 572
Pinchock, George 623
Pinlac, Rommel 612
Pinsky, David 437
Pintcke, T 74
Piorko, Jennifer (Jen) 198
Piper, Krista 155
Piper, Daniel 199
Pipkins, Christopher (Chris) 271
Pirov, Elana 495
Pirro, Thomas H (Thom) 108
Pisano, Kerry 404
Pish, Al 38
Pishko, Karen 615
Piskun, Matt 478
Pistoresi, Ronda 447
Pitts, David (Dave) 24
Pitz, James (Jamie) 208
Pizzini, Chris 113
Pizzuto, Michael 542
Place, Brock 263
Planche, Jean-pascal 618
Planz, John (Jack) 516
Plass, Mary Ellen 10
Plecenik, Jeanie 316
Pleeter, Joel 481
Pleiman, Diane 340
Plumback, Jay 431
PLUMMER, ROBERT (Bob) 175
Plummer, Bill 311
Pobjoy, Peter 489
Podesta, Charles (Chuck) 201
Podsednik, J 528
Poe, Dale 635
Pogue, Richard W. 604
Pohl, Ron A 66
Pohl, Ron 66
Pohlad, Robert C. 611
Polatajko, Mark 649
Polep, Jeffrey M. (Jeff) 142
Polge, David 599
Pollack, Murray M. 405
Polley, Greg 203
Pollock, E. Kears 100
Pollock, Jill 605
Polonsky, Kenneth S. 571
Pombo, David (Dave) 263
Pombo, Tammy 510
Pomeroy, Jim 121
Ponds, Theresa 470
Ponterio, Elaine 349
Pool, James (Jamie) 57
Pope, Deborah 80
Pope, Leslie 162
Pope, Alan (Al) 393
Pope, Alice 635
Popien, Toni 425
Porat, M. Moshe 530
Port, Joel 312
Porter, Terry 66
Porter, Cindy Long 423
Porter, Holly 423
Porter, Julie 442
Porter, Stephen D. 467
Porter, Mark 585
Porterfield, Kent 451
Posillico, Angela (Angie) 198
Poskanzer, Jane 99
Poskanzer, Steven 99
Post, Kim 461
Postrozny, Hank 112
Poteet, LaVonne 89
Pothen, Daniel 501
Potter, Patricia (Pat) 359
Potterton, Kent 419
Poulliott, Joe 419
Poulsen, Gregory Pou 263
Powell, Robert 27
Powell, Erika 112

Powell, George 112
Powell, John 201
Powell, Kenneth 304
Powell, Chris 324
Powell, Hall 330
Powell, Mary Lou 432
Powell, Jeff 437
Powell, Allen 625
Powers, Bill 4
Powers, Shannon 214
Powers, Monica 475
Powers, Mamon 554
Powers, Allen 630
Pradia, Marsha 534
Praeger, Jaime 232
Pranckevicius, John 323
Prastacos, Gregory 511
Prather, Sharon 148
Pratt, Don 153
Pratt, Donald (Don) 153
Pratt, Dan 224
Pratt, G. Michael 340
Prausa, John W. 494
Preising, Weston 612
Preiss, Tammy 126
Prenger, Ron 304
Prescher, Mike 73
Prescott, Heidi 548
President, Rocky Campbell ?????? Vice 90
Presnell, Rick 448
Presnell, Richard (Dick) 448
Pressendo, Mike 117
Prestipino, Anthony 578
Presto, Jim 442
Prewitt, Connie F. 71
Price, Tom 112
Price, Sarah 113
Price, Cynthia 117
Price, Jay 143
Price, Mary Jo 181
Price, Joseph (Jo) 198
Price, David (Dave) 204
Price, David (Dave) 275
Price, Randy 482
Price, Roger 484
Price, Courtney 577
Price, Russell 643
Pricken, Stephanie 450
Principe-crockett, Nan 209
Pringle, Rebecca 356
Pringle, Curt 389
Prioleau, Florence 547
Prior, Andy 95
Prior, Matt 442
Priselac, Thomas M. (Tom) 104
Pricheta, Anne 231
Pritchett, Anne 231
Probst, Marc 263
Probst, Larry 481
Proctor, Dan 585
Profetto, Mike 220
Proffitt, Julie 255
Proia, Jillian 64
Prokosch, Brian 15
Pronk, Thom 90
Propf, Peter 133
Prosono, Marvin 347
Prosser, Jim 167
Provenzano, Susan (Sue) 439
Providakes, Jason F. 557
Provost, Helene 342
Pruessing, Peter (Pete) 211
Pruitt, Chris 19
Prunchunas, Edward M. 104
Pruner, Jacqueline 616
Pryor, William 154
Puckett, Jeffrey M. (Jeff) 121
Pugh, Charlene 616
Pugliese, Anthony J. 21
Puhl, Frances 36
Puhy, Dorothy E. 157
Pui, Ching-Hon 503
Puleo, Pamela (Pam) 139
Pulido, Michael (Mel) 237

Pulido, Miguel A. 389
Pulley, Kathy J 347
Pulliam, Gary P 534
Pulliman, Elizabeth (Beth) 586
Pum, Michael (Mel) 294
Pumpian, Ann 473
Pupo, Timothy (Tim) 198
Purington, Christine 133
Purkey, Jeffrey (Jeff) 137
Purohit, Nidhi 43
Purtle, Mark 266
Purves, Stephen A. (Steve) 137
Puryear, Bridget 209
Puskar, Joseph (Jo) 551
Putnam, Jean 137

Q

Qu, Jianmin 591
Quade, Bill 37
Quatrano, Ralph S. 575
Quealy, Kathleen 555
Quibell, Ed 230
Quigley, David 590
Quillen, Denise 571
Quillty, Allison 450
Quin, Rob 266
Quiniones, Gil C. 367
Quinlivan, Pete 420
Quinn, Joseph (Jo) 204
Quinn, Brandi 318
Quinn, Don 456
Quinones, Miguel 487
Quintanilla, Katie 417
Quintero, Suzzanne 47
Quinton, Jody 170
Quon, Cindy 389

R

R-CA, Mary 399
Raab, Andy 515
Rabinowitz, Jacqueline 330
Race, Taylor 511
Racine, Scott 303
Radek, Matthew (Matt) 112
Radford, Marsha 453
Radibush, Sharon 271
Radley, Mary 539
Raffaelli, John 569
Raftevold, Dan 309
Ragsdale, John 32
Raikes, Deborah (Deb) 316
Raikes-Colbert, Deborah (Deb) 316
Rainer, Thom S. 306
Rainer, George 645
Rains, Cameron J. 602
Rains, Cameron J. 602
Rainwater, Tom 173
Rajan, Raunak 43
Rakowitz, Susan 191
Ralp, Kevinh 94
Ramer, Larry 335
Ramm, Greg 457
Ramos, Raymond 121
Ramos, Rick 317
Ramos, Rebecca 437
Ramos, Mark 522
Ramsay, Nancy 532
Ramser, Jordan 213
Ramsey, Sid 266
Ramsey, Beryl 554
Ramsey, Paul G. 616
Ramthun, Lisa 501
Randall, Joellen 75
Randall, Jeff 499
Randi, Hornback 54
Randolph, Kerry 304
Randolph, Mary Lou 456
Randopoulos, Anthoula 167
Raney, Carolyn 400
Rankin, Alfred M. 604

Rapaccioli, Donna 204
Rapaport, Marc H. 104
Rapp, Peter F. 390
Raska, Billy 89
Rasmussen, Paul 220
Rasmussen, Steve 386
Rasnick, Bill 175
Ratcliff, David 631
Rath, Connie 213
Ratley, Warren 144
Ratliff, William (Bill) 30
Ratliss, Maggie 456
Rauch, Todd 339
Raughton, Dana 112
Rauner, John 497
Rausch, Susan (Sue) 652
Rauscher, Bob 150
Rautio, Julie 436
Ravitz, Jason 629
Ray, Amy G. 106
Ray, Joel 432
Ray, Jackie 652
Raymond, Susan 263
Raymond, Dennis 265
Reardon, Dan 560
Reavis, Mack 297
Rebel, Vivian 239
Rechtiene, James 218
Rechtine, Linda 102
Reckford, Jonathan T. M. 230
Rectenwald, Richard S. (Dick) 457
Rector, Nancy 47
Rector, Drew 236
Rector, RoxanneLee 618
Recupero, Patricia 285
Redd, Glen 560
Reddan, Taylor 310
Reddington, Brian J. 420
Reddy, Brian 176
Reddy, Gautam 208
Redetzke, Rick 492
Rediger, Mary 511
Reece, Nell M 178
Reece, Edwina 253
Reece, Eddy 427
Reed, Johnna S 80
Reed, Tom 116
Reed, Stephanie 150
Reed, Mark C. 191
Reed, Natalie 198
Reed, LaVonda 526
Reed, Rick 546
Reeder, Phil 614
Reel, Gina 258
Reese, Kirk 32
Reese, Cindy 137
Reese, Bruce T. 263
Reese, Bertram S. (Bert) 467
Reetz, Jodi 56
Reeves, Elise 263
Reeves, Jonathan M. 423
Reffler, Richard (Dick) 592
Refolo, Cynthia 542
Regan, Timothy J. 576
Rege, Umesh 95
Reger, Michael (Mike) 483
Rego, Arely 47
Rehm, Dana D. 358
Reich, Marti 46
Reicher, Terri 198
Reichert, Brian 242
Reichert, Donald 555
Reichfield, Mike 386
Reid, Shannan 313
Reid, Walter 543
Reid, Bernadette 581
Reid, Karl 599
Reid, Michael 609
Reidy, Kara 399
Reifer, William (Bill) 404
Reiff, Patricia 643
Reiff, Patricia (Pat) 643
Reifsteck, John 226
Reigler, Thea 492
Reilly, Bill 222

Reilly, Joseph R. 469
Reilly, Timothy C (Tim) 645
Reiman, Eric (Bill) 46
Reimche, Brenda E 526
Reiner, Mark 483
Reinhardt, David 49
Reinhart, Dale 35
Reisert, Denise 427
Reistrup, Leslie 419
Reiten, Randi 302
Reiter, Donald W. (Don) 101
Relling, Mary 503
Renberg, Benjamin R (Ben) 643
Rench, Jerry 432
Reney, Michael L. 157
Rengel, Michael 112
Renna, Rose 502
Renner, Rob 197
Rentfrow, Robert 630
Repp, Philip 44
Resch, Richard J. (Dick) 294
Resner, Jason 546
Resnick, Alice R. 494
Restivo, Joseph (Jo) 517
Revere, Charles R. 436
Rew, Michael (Mel) 105
Rey, Aixa 47
Reyes, Laura 20
Reyes, Donna 307
Reynaga, Victor S 364
Reynolds, John C. 42
Reynolds, Jeffrey 48
Reynolds, Neil 112
Reynolds, Johnathon 245
Reynolds, G. David 429
Reynolds, Leah 532
Reynolds, Robert L. 624
Rezendes, Kelsey 94
Rhode, Jeff 616
Rhodes, David (Dave) 48
Rhue, Deborah 215
Rhymer, Ernie 422
Rhyne, Jerry 306
Ribeiro, Mimi 245
Ricco, Kathy 417
Rice, Jim 246
Rice, Larry 277
Rice, Larry 388
Rice, Arthur H. 423
Rice, Craig 506
Rich, John 171
Rich, Melinda R. (Mindy) 434
Rich, Paul 434
Rich, Ted 434
Rich, Robert E. (Bob) 434
Richards, Robert 52
Richards, Jesse 113
Richards, Patricia R. 263
Richards, David (Dave) 397
Richards, Allwyne 432
Richards, Terry 651
Richardson, Kenneth (Ken) 18
Richardson, Todd 34
RICHARDSON, SARAH 150
Richardson, Mark 390
Richardson, Terry L 433
Richardson, Julie 503
Richardson, Catherine (Cathy) 616
Richardson, Elizabeth 649
Richemont, Phillip (Phil) 654
Richer, Alvin 32
Richey, Mike 512
Richmond, Cindy 42
Richmond, Craig 555
Richner, Scott 311
Richter, Karen 119
Richter, Jennifer L. 399
Ricker, Bob 432
Rickertson, Bruce 13
Ridderman, Ruth 197
Riddle, Margaret 134
Ridenour, Mark E. 340
Rideout, Deb 485
Ridgely, Gerry L. 445

Ridinger, Loren 318
Ridley, Wadell 450
Ridlon, Kevin 434
Riebling, Antoinette 470
Riel, Kevin 379
Riemer, Jeff 260
Riewe, Paul R. 545
Rigas, Warren A. (Sonny) 203
Rigger, Kathy 304
Riggs, Teresa L 1
Rigitano, Gene 585
Rigsby, Katy Dalton 386
Riker, Rick 112
Riksen, Mike 358
Riles, Warren 217
Riley, William (Bill) 72
Riley, Donna 112
Riley, John 456
Riley, Matt 609
Rinaldi, Paul 68
Rinehart, Rick 98
Rinehart, Lucy 159
Rinehart, Brenda 395
Rinehart, Timm 530
Rinehart, Doug 551
Ringelstein, Bill 173
Rios, Art 23
Rios, Jesus 213
Risk, James K. (JIm) 290
Risner, Dennis 598
Risser, Donald 155
Ristanovic, Petar 93
Ritchey, Lori 448
Ritchie, Samantha 318
Ritschdorff, John T (Jack) 316
Ritter, Barbara (Barb) 541
Ritz, Robert P. (Bob) 496
Rivard, Elizabeth (Betty) 218
Rivas, Ronna 267
Rivera, Frank 175
Rivera, Pete 490
Rivero, Marita 358
Rivers, Jill 280
Rivest, Jeffrey A. 607
Rivinius, Scott 616
Rizco, Lorin 437
Rizer, Cindy 646
Rizzi, Philip 92
RN, Janet Bagley 157
RN, Baird 189
Rn, D 542
Roach, Alan (Al) 338
Roach, Mary 555
Robb, Charles S. 557
Robb, Elizabeth 634
Robbins, Keith 263
Robbins, Kenneth H. 630
Robert, Tracey 191
Roberto, Len 191
Roberts, Samuel 61
Roberts, Dave 73
Roberts, Peter W. 118
Roberts, Brad 146
Roberts, Teresa Y 163
Roberts, J. William 246
Roberts, Teri 263
Roberts, M. Parker 313
Roberts, Patricia (Pat) 485
Roberts, Hillary 532
Roberts, Dawn 559
Roberts, Devin 577
Roberts, Shauna R. 589
Roberts, Bj 641
Robertson, Emily 43
Robertson, Laura 45
Robertson, Rick 112
Robertson, Mike G. 137
Robertson, Chad 233
Robertson, Martha 307
Robertson, William G. (Bill) 353
Robertson, Joseph (Joe) 390
Robertson, Bruce 467
Robertson, Debbie 479
Robinette, Julie 175
Robinette, Steve 346

Robinson, Garry 10
Robinson, Carol 46
Robinson, David (Dave) 54
Robinson, Benjamin 95
Robinson, Daniel (Dan) 100
Robinson, Robin 107
Robinson, Patricia 188
Robinson, Jackie 202
Robinson, David (Dave) 245
Robinson, Nina B 247
Robinson, William 253
Robinson, Jan 325
Robinson, Kayne 358
Robinson, Timothy C. 360
Robinson, Bradley 363
Robinson, Patricia 397
Robinson, Barbara (Barb) 444
Robinson, Lisa 448
Robinson, Kevin W 450
Robinson, Larry A. 469
Robinson, Susan (Sue) 506
Robinson, David (Dave) 527
Robinson, Jana 549
Robinson, James (Jamie) 579
Robinson, Cade 620
Robinson, John G. 643
Robison, Bruce 304
Robison, Les 503
Roby, Scott 15
Rocci, Anna 95
Rocco, Ellen 358
Roche, Kathleen M. (Kate) 449
Rock, Rex A. 31
Rock, Ann 505
Rock, Bernard 583
Rockett, Kathryn 308
Rockett, Kitty 308
Rode, ED 227
Rodeghero, Margaret 480
Rodenbaugh, Jeffrey 379
Rodgers, Mark 230
Rodgers, Stephen 271
Rodgers, Christopher (Chris) 437
Rodgers, Mary Anne 543
Rodocker, Julee M. 298
Rodriguez, Elaine 107
Rodriguez, Jerry 121
Rodriguez, Arnaldo 153
Rodriguez, Alex 448
Rodriguez, Carmen 484
Rodriguez, David 540
Rodriguez, Christin 623
Rodts, Duncan 340
Roell, Dennis 622
Roemer, Dennis R. 551
Roetzel, Frank 457
Roever, Carol 237
Roever, Carol 238
Rogers, Jed 23
Rogers, Frederick A. (Fred) 99
Rogers, Randy 163
Rogers, John 188
Rogers, Sarah 197
Rogers, William R 201
Rogers, Julie 203
Rogers, Melissa (Mel) 225
Rogers, Rob 261
Rogers, Betty 275
Rogers, Warren 299
Rogers, Erin 389
Roggie, Brent J. 357
Rohan, Nikki 316
Roheim, John (Jack) 362
Rohr, James E. (Jim) 100
Rohrbaugh, James W (Jamie) 418
Rohrer, Mary 342
Roitman, Mara 654
Rojas, Marcela 42
Roker, Chris 555
Roland, David H. 429
Roland, John 429
Rolandelli, Peter (Pete) 629
Rolfe, Lauren 323
Rolleston, Keith 419
Rollins, Barrett J. 157

Rollins, Paul 546
Rollins, Sami 613
Roloff, Maria 345
Romero, Benjamin 112
Romero, Susan (Sue) 239
Romero, Javier 309
Ronthal, Berenice 157
Rooke, Anne S 39
Rooy, Jean-Pierre Van 449
Rorex, Rick 433
Rosamilia, Thomas (Thom) 65
Rosati, Rebecca 450
Roscoe, Joan 644
Rose, Mark 78
Rose, John 267
Rose, Michael 324
Rose, Michael S. 487
Rose, Vera 506
Rose, Vivian 554
Rose, Robert (Bob) 586
Rosen, Harris 441
Rosen, Sharon 481
Rosenbach, Lynn 46
Rosenbach, Edward 357
Rosenbaum, Clint 299
Rosenberg, Ken 176
Rosenberg, Michael 231
Rosenberg, Naomi 591
Rosenberger, Angie 255
Rosenblum, Don 379
Rosenfeld, Alan (Al) 512
Rosenfelder, Robert 571
Rosenlund, Stuart (Stu) 90
Rosenstein, David (Dave) 198
Roshko, Michael 579
Rosner, Margaret 467
Ross, Samuel L. 80
Ross, Tony 383
Ross, Valerie 464
Ross, Vernell 530
Ross, James E. 607
Ross, Sandy 609
Rossetti, Anthony 82
Rossi, Richard (Dick) 150
Rosso, Clar 21
Rotenberg, Lesli 420
Roth, Theodore D. (Ted) 425
Roth, Ben 442
Roth, Adam 442
Roth, Brett 442
Roth, Christopher 579
Roth, Cindi 624
Rothberger, Richard K. 462
Rothermel, Elizabeth B. 429
Rothstein, Fred C. 604
Rothwell, Dustin 170
Rotolo, Joseph 645
Rotty, Dirk 156
Rougeau, Vincent 590
Roughton, Keith 217
Roulis, Eleni 615
Round, Garry 445
Rountree, Gordon 295
Rourke, Stephen 267
Rourke, Sheri 383
Rouseff, Maribeth 47
Roush, Damon 567
Rousseau, Jeffrey L (Jeff) 153
Routhier, Christina 566
Routly, Kathy 439
Roux, Ana Diez 171
Roux, David J. 549
Row, Maggie 46
Rowan, Andrew N. 548
Rowe, Matt 171
Rowe, Steve 378
Rowe, Steven (Steve) 475
Rowe, Margie 482
Rowe, T Cay 534
Rowe, John E (Jack) 561
Rowland, Margie 316
Rowland, David J. 470
Rowland, Bryan 649
Rowlett, Rocky 193
Roxbury, Ken 602

Roy, Steve 1
Roy, Lynne 104
Royal, Keli 619
Royce-Davis, Joanna 616
Rozanski, Robert K (Bob) 309
Rozett, Linda 23
Rubalcava, Dominick 309
Rubenstein, Ira 419
Rubertone, Joseph D. 423
Rubin, Allan 257
Rubinstein, Jerold H. 648
Rucker, Robert (Bob) 599
Rudavsky, Sue 536
Ruddle, Christopher (Chris) 74
Ruddock, Val 360
Rudich, Cheryl A. 648
Rudolf, Steve 48
Rudolph, Ronald (Ron) 112
Rudolph, Eric 400
Rudolph, William D. (Bill) 565
Rudy, John 6
Rudy, Jim 389
Rudzik, Robert J. 105
Rudzik, John (Jack) 105
Ruedrich, Lillian 46
Ruesterholz, Virginia P. 511
Ruge, Mike 7
Ruggeri, Tony 153
Ruggles, Andrea 197
Ruhl, Terry A. 112
Ruhlman, Phil 213
Ruiz, Ileana 112
Ruiz, Mauricio 528
Ruiz, Angel 653
Rumans, Mark C. 71
Rumer, Richard (Dick) 530
Runck, Cathy 15
Runey, Mim L. 277
Runge, Margaret 95
Rus, Steven 73
Rush, Thomas D. 258
Rusk, Craig 518
Russ, John 388
Russell, Thomas 26
Russell, Samantha 150
Russell, Kerry 171
Russell, Dee B. 203
Russell, Caroline 236
Russell, Les 561
Russelli, Deborah 204
Russo, Maggie 64
Ruth, John 59
Rutledge, Stephen F. 167
Rutledge, Steven (Steve) 604
Rutz, Bill 337
Ruwe, Steve 419
Ryals, Lillian Zarelli 557
Ryals, Lillian 557
Ryan, Ellen 135
Ryan, Barbara 171
Ryan, G. Brint 445
Ryan, Mary 502
Ryan, Morrow 512
Ryan, Pat 590
Ryan, Eugene 642
Ryckman, Diane 287
Ryman, David (Dave) 110
Ryser, Phillip P. 509

S

Sabinson, Allen 171
Sabistina, Chona 426
Sabitoni, Che 277
Saccone, Robert 470
Sachs, Robert 280
Sachs, Lainey 284
Sackett, Wally 287
Sackett, Neil C. 538
Sadau, Ernie W. 121
Saddul, Joon 501
Sadro, Cheryl 329
Sadvary, Thomas (Thom) 461
Saenz, Fernando 420

Safady, Randolph W. 121
Saguil, Linda 273
Sahin, Mustafa 539
Salandra, Michael (Mike) 14
Salanger, Matthew J. 599
Salanger, Matthew J. 599
Salas, Debbie 501
Salata, Robert A. 604
Salazar, Nathan 534
Salerno, Judith A. 569
Salina, Annette 252
Salisbury, Lois 543
Salisbury, Benjamin 649
Salley, Karla 284
Salomanson, Kisten 197
Salomon, Robert 530
Salomon, Richard E. 564
Salter, Carmen 96
Saltz, Jeff 526
Saltzgiver, Ty 653
Saltzman, Michael 595
Salvati, Peter A. 170
Salvioli, Brigida 191
Salzberg, Ron 447
Salzer, Steve 419
Samak, Laura 34
Samet, Ida 481
Sammy, Stubblefield 434
Samper, Cristiァn 643
Sams, Pam King 119
Samuels, Aliza L 97
Samuels, Deborah (Deb) 336
Sanberg, Paul R. 614
Sanborn, Mark 516
Sanchez, Debra 147
Sanchez-martinez, Jessica 613
Sandberg, Ellen 112
Sandberg, Susan (Sue) 137
Sandefur, David W (Dave) 251
Sandefur, Gwen G. 492
Sandeno, Greg 89
Sanders, Johnny 78
Sanders, Jeffrey D. (Jeff) 313
Sanders, Brenda 362
Sanders, Alberta 432
Sandler, Anthony 119
Sands, Debra J 163
Sanger, Jim 302
Sanichar, Sabrina 511
Sanni, Christine C. 591
Sano, Jim 648
Santiago, Luisa 121
Santiago, Conrad 391
Santilli, Ann 309
Santoro, Frank 550
Santos, Cheryse Burgos 47
Santos, Barbara (Barb) 349
Santos, Frank A. 441
Santos, Rona 623
Santos, Rudolf 624
Santulli, Deborah 95
Sanyal, Neil 99
Saperstein, Karen 465
Sapp, Allen (Al) 325
Sapyta, Tim 98
Sargeant, Isabelle 201
Sargent, Sarah 197
Sarow, Roger 358
Sarsfield, Sally 42
Sartorelli, Kennith 201
Sass, Wayne 329
Sasser, Gary D. 40
Sassus, Suzanne 501
Satele, Evelyn 307
Sattan, Ron 234
Sattler, Levi 393
Sauer, Glenn 191
Saul, J. Philip 360
Saul, Michael G (Mel) 447
Saunders, Lee A. 20
Saunders, Melissa (Mel) 197
Saunders, Kathy 557
Savage, Joe 198
Savage-Tracy, Elizabeth 644
Savic, Marizela 313

Savin, Gary 595
Sawczuk, Ihor S 231
Sawicki, David 129
Sawicki, Robert 392
Sawin, Robert S. 464
Sawyer, Peggy 278
Sawyer, Ryan 393
Sawyer, Jonathan (Jon) 539
Sawyers, Gregory 124
Saxton, Brad 423
Sayamath, Marianne 572
Sayen, Gina 342
Sayles, Andy 422
Sayre, Michelle 33
Sbranti, Salvatore 619
Scaer, Robert (Bob) 200
Scafe, Nateka 572
Scalone, Edward L. 423
Scanlon, John P. 105
Scanlon, Dennis 168
Scanlon-mcginity, Anne 554
Scarantino, Charles (Chas) 432
Scarboro, Lynne 310
Scarboro, Evelynne 310
Scarborough, Fred 31
Scazzero, Jim 14
Sceski, Blaise 623
Schaal, Barbara A. 575
Schachter, Alan (Al) 176
Schachter, Alan 176
Schaefer, Brenda 46
Schaefer, Michele 333
Schaefer, Don 369
Schaeffer, Joel 160
Schaffler, Harvey 365
Schager, Marty 6
Schapiro, Howard 201
Schapiro, Benjamin S. 305
Schapker, Dennis 73
Scharbauer, Clarence 532
Scharf, Kristin 419
Schatz, Jay 249
Schaufelberger, John 616
Schautz, Lisa 319
Schawaroch, Regina 379
Schecter, Carol 504
Scheer, Dan 66
Scheer, Todd 194
Scheerer, Daniel 215
Scheirman, Kathy 280
Schellman, Julie 134
Schempf, Duff 560
Schenkenberger, Tom 209
Schepker, James (Jim) 449
Schepker, Jim 449
Scherbarth, Kathy 319
Scherpbier, Harm 312
Schidlow, Daniel V. 171
Schieber, George 567
Schilling, Don 209
Schillo, Stephen 172
Schiltz, Al 601
Schjotz, Gitte 595
Schlatterer, William (Bill) 431
Schleif, John 239
Schleper, Denny 130
Schlesinger, James R. 557
Schmid, Lauren 98
Schmid, Richard J. 578
Schmidt, Diane Grob 19
Schmidt, Brian 73
Schmidt, Richard 78
Schmidt, Pamela 80
Schmidt, Chris 153
Schmidt, Bill 215
Schmidt, Todd 379
Schmidt, Leigh 437
Schmidt, Ray 593
Schmit, Annett 98
Schmitt, David (Dave) 79
Schmitt, Eric 93
Schmitt, Joseph (Jo) 238
Schmitt, Paul 576
Schmitz, Jhan 112
Schmutz, Betsy 634

Schnall, Mitchell 562
Schneider, Mark 22
Schneider, Jill 340
Schneider, Bill 350
Schneider, Howard 409
Schneider, Amy 447
Schneider, Judy 448
Schneider, Jennifer J (Jen) 449
Schneider, Jeff 509
Schnirring, Greg 147
Schnuck, Craig D. 575
Schoch, Ellen 470
Schoenberger, Anja 112
Schoenborne, Thomas 591
Schoenfeld, Michael 414
Schoeplein, Kevin D. 392
Schofield, Tony 129
Schokmiller, Steve 153
Scholten, Patrick (Paddy) 64
Scholtz, Jennifer 80
Schon, Christine 158
Schonlau, Dan 448
Schooler, Rick 391
Schoolmaster, F. Andrew 532
Schorer, Emily 94
Schramke, Todd 342
Schreiber, John R. 58
Schreiber, Molly 623
Schretzman, Will 622
Schrock, Bonnie 48
Schroeder, Connie 75
Schroeder, Andrew 167
Schroyer, Tom 129
Schubert, Marian 422
Schubert, Marian 501
Schuerman, Janice 339
Schultz, Karl 211
Schultz, Betty 261
Schultz, Kerry 497
Schulz, Kelly 503
Schulz, Kathy 511
Schulz, Kathryn 511
Schuman, Michael 139
Schumann, Andrea 448
Schurz, Scott C. 258
Schussler, Russ 217
Schuster, Nancy 95
Schuster, Benjamin (Ben) 287
Schuth, Julie 615
Schutz, Holly 160
Schwab, Jamie 246
Schwab, Joseph (Jo) 623
Schwalbe, Jim 560
Schwall, Garry 645
SchwanzlBsnMba, Shari 492
Schwartz, Jordana 365
Schwartz, Robert (Bob) 464
Schwartz, Thomas E (Thom) 554
Schwartz, Lee 554
Schwieterma, Rick 384
Schwoeble, Walt 119
Scirica, Anthony J. 530
Scofield, Clay 1
Scott, Sam 90
Scott, Anne 117
Scott, Marycarroll 133
Scott, Anoush 183
Scott, Chip 227
Scott, Eric 247
Scott, Roland 342
Scott, Larry 428
Scott, Peter M. 432
Scott, Joan 497
Scott, Ronald 501
Scott, Sandra 517
Scott, Jack 531
Scoville, Joshua (Josh) 245
Scoville, Spencer 263
Scozzafava, Samuel 526
Scribano, Philip 360
Scribner, Steve 204
Sczudlo, Raymond S. 119
Searles, Richard C. 258
Sears, Katherine A. 25
Sears, David (Dave) 310

Seastrom, Dave 170
Seaton, Scott 494
Seay, Thomas 377
Sebastian, Roland 233
Sebastian, Donald H. 364
Seckinger, Mark 386
Secrist, Richard A. 77
Secrist, Ryan 77
Seder, David (Dave) 313
Sedey, Ray 327
Sedlak, Andrea 636
Segal, Richard 453
Segev, Amir 180
Sehi, John (Jack) 236
Seid, Lynette 280
Seidel, Victor 43
Seidl, Carl 429
Seidler, Rick 266
Seip, Jan 2
Sekerka, Robert (Bob) 100
Selby, Patsy 577
Sellards, Michael G. 320
Sellards, Michael G. 506
Selman, Thomas (Thom) 198
Selvaraj, Saravanan 167
Selvey, Barbara (Barb) 137
Semenza, Patrick S. 86
Senese, Jeffrey 277
Senyitko, Alissa 587
Seplveda, Juan 420
Serioharney, Angela 325
Serpico, Donna 473
Sessoms, Vickie 236
Sethi, Satinder 432
Setterdahl, Jon 194
Sevenikar, Gerilynn 473
Severance, Matthew 96
Severino, Diane 478
Sexauer, Pam 442
Sexton, Dorothy 133
Sexton, Janice M 208
Seybert, David 172
Sfeir, Nicolas 489
Shackelford, Paul 407
Shadduck, David A. (Dave) 588
Shaeffer, Carrie 52
Shafer, Niki 360
Shaffer, Evelyn 280
Shaffer, Lynne 335
Shaffer, Lynn 386
Shah, Ashish 39
Shah, Yash 43
Shah, Vaibhav 43
Shah, Vijay 443
Shah, Natasha 489
Shah, Hiral 511
Shaikh, Zakir 338
Shaked, Hezy 648
Shaker, Mena 280
Shalakhti, Shadi 80
Shallash, Anthony 208
Shane, Craig 263
Shanko, Bill 105
Shanks, Laura 98
Shanley, Kevin 39
Shanley, Linda 449
Shannahan, C. Kevin 245
Shannahan, Kevin 245
Shannon, John T. (Jack) 351
Shapiro, Steven 96
Shapiro, Larry J. 575
Shapiro, Max 615
Share, Christopher J. 118
Share, Douglas G. 118
Sharieff, Ghazala 425
Sharkey, Terry 629
Sharp, Mike 215
Sharp, Myron 265
Sharp, Milton 363
Sharp, Joseph 482
Sharp, Joseph 482
Sharp, Matthew D. (Matt) 543
Shatagopam, Ramesh 596
Shattuck, Carol 25
Shatz, Lauren 390

Shaver, Lee 336
Shaw, Milton 78
Shaw, Terri 133
Shaw, Ella 197
Shaw, Mark 340
Shaw, Suzanne 347
Shaw, Randy 482
Shaw, Wiley 518
Shaw, Byers W. 619
Shaw, Cory D. 619
Shaw, Gene 654
Shawe, Phil 583
Shawi, Joseph 604
Shawver, Martha 577
Shay, Gregory 280
Shaye, Gary 457
Shea, Chris 112
Shea, Dennis 160
Shea, Billy 171
Shea, Suzanne 280
Shea, Agnes A 340
Shearer, James 154
Shearer, Alan 171
Shearer, Brad 457
Shearer, Jim 477
Sheeran, Jane 152
Sheeran, Nathan 279
Sheerin, Rick 203
Sheets, Wayne 358
Sheikh, Shanza 43
Sheils, David 506
Shell, Susan (Sue) 590
Shelley, Tom 263
Shellman, Carolyn E. 126
Shelton, Jeff 46
Shelton, Stanley (Stan) 647
Shelton, Stan 647
Shelton, Todd 648
Shen, Fredy 239
Shendell-Falik, Nancy 58
Shenfeld, Michele 365
Shepard, William (Bill) 59
Shepard, Bill 649
Shepardson, J. Andrew 64
Shepheard, Hillary 532
Shepherd, Samson 171
Shepherd, Colin 245
Shepherd, Jane 636
Sheppard, Mark 400
Sheppard, Grant 445
Sher, Susan S. 571
Sherard, Daniel 240
Sheridan, Richard (Dick) 462
Sheridan, John P. 542
Sherlock, Peter 557
Sherman, Julie 46
Sherman, Malcolm L. 83
Sherman, Les 119
Sherman, Julie 267
Sherman, Violet 272
Sherman, Mark 471
Sherr, Charles 503
Sheth, Amit 649
Shields, Toni 546
Shields, Kevin 576
Shields, Charles W. (Charlie) 589
Shiffler, Ronald E. 217
Shin, Megan 83
Shindler, Emily 340
Shinichi, Iguchi 642
Shirakata, Kyle 469
Shirk, Michael F (Mel) 242
Shirley, Douglas E. 542
Shoemate, Jack 299
Shoudy, Peter D. 641
Shoulders, Patrick A. 258
Shows, Chip 518
Shropshire, Richard (Dick) 599
Shub, Mitchell (Mitch) 405
Shukla, Abhinav 588
Shulkin, David J (Dave) 39
Shull, Chris 171
Shulman, Mona 396
Shulman, Brian B. 469

Shulstad, Raymond A 557
Shumaker, Nancy W. 217
Shumate, Marsha 630
Shumway, William (Bill) 46
Shupe, Lewis 649
Shurbaji, Salah 175
Shute, Kyle 43
Shuter, Mark H. 5
Siderowicz, Joe 530
Sides, Dale 173
Sidhu, Ranjit 133
Sidhu, Jay S. 429
Sidwell, Sherry 137
Siebenaler, Chris 554
Siebert, Brian 245
Sieckhaus, Steven R. (Steve) 129
Sieckhaus, Tom 129
Siegel, Louis 171
Siegel, Donald (Don) 265
Siegfried, Thomas A. 117
Sielak, George 31
Siemer, Robert (Bob) 307
Siemer, Julie 448
Siemon, George 146
Sierra, Rodrigo A. 22
Sierra, Chris 419
Sigler, John C. 358
Sikes, Scott 476
Sikowitz, Peter (Pete) 396
Silbar, Ean 83
Silber, Steven 366
Siler, Brad 222
Silk, Barb 99
Silva, Alex 230
Silva, Joseph M (Jo) 238
Silva-ortiz, Aidy 391
Silvagni, Anthony J. 379
Silver, Kenneth 309
Silver, Kevin H 517
Silveria, Richard 81
Silverman, Daniel 305
Silverman, Barry J. 380
Silvers, Mara 464
Silvers, J. B. 555
Silversmith, Teresa 650
Silvey, Ray 412
Simaris, Jim 640
Simerly, Rick 268
Simic, Laura 150
Simic, Curtis R. 258
Simic, Curtis R. 258
Siminoff, Laura A. 530
Simio, Frank 204
Simione, Mark A. 369
Simmons, Alvin 32
Simmons, Ron 194
Simmons, Linda 391
Simmons, Jon 641
Simon, Randall (Randy) 110
Simon, Donald R. (Don) 144
Simon, Esther 144
Simon, Debbie 266
Simon, Nancy 338
Simon, Linda 501
Simonson, Jennifer Jech (Jen) 442
Simonson, Marlisa 572
Simonton, Sam 630
Simpson, Gerald 112
Simpson, Julie Inskeep 258
Sims, Amber 176
Sims, Demarlo 309
Sims, Adelia 372
Sinatra, Barbara (Barb) 179
Sinclair, James G. 258
Sindel, Bruce 125
Sine, Jeffrey A. 24
Singer, Jeremy 133
Singer, Steven 157
Singer, Cheryl 376
Singer, Jolie 559
Singh, Bhupindarpal (Bhupi) 167
Singla, Anjali 10
Singleton, Alan 111
Singleton, Terri L. 298
Singleton, H. Wells 379

Singleton, Tom 431
Sini, Frank 276
Sink, Jill 649
Sinkevich, Doris 67
Sirena, Evelyn 645
Sirianni, Frank 204
Sisk, Chip 248
Sisson, Rick 432
Sizemore, Thomas (Thom) 317
Sizer, Judith (Judi) 83
Skabelund, Hoyt 46
Skeen, Richard (Dick) 315
Skelton, Scott 15
Skiermont, Darla 368
Skinner, Stephen 516
Skjodt, Cynthia Simon (Cindy) 258
Sklar, Louis 245
Sklar, Michelle (Mitch) 613
Skogen, Ginny 295
Skokan, Mike 255
Skolfield, Melissa (Mel) 563
Slade, Bert 165
Slade, William 367
Sladich, Harry 543
Slate, Jim 422
Slater, Austin J. 322
Slater, Mark 461
Slayton, Rebecca 616
Slepian, Steve 363
Slinkard, John (Jack) 520
Sloan, Marie 495
Sloane, Scott 139
Slobasky, Renee 636
Slobodzian, Joan 579
Slocum, Joyce 358
Slocum, Joyce 358
Slominski, Donald D. (Don) 328
Slon, Dennis 310
Slosberg, Meridith 119
Slovak, Michelle 118
Slusser, Kimberly 439
Small, Richard G. 129
Small, Mark T. 129
Small, James (Jamie) 129
Small, Toni 501
Small, Susan 562
Smallwood, Michelle 247
Smallwood, Pamela 530
Smart, Kacey 515
Smart, Denise T. 534
Smelser, Linda 379
Smid, Joe 149
Smidt, Jeff 595
Smilde, Renee 462
Smiley, Cari 24
Smit, Brian 46
Smit, Brian 275
Smith, H. Sally 9
Smith, Gil 14
Smith, Joseph L (Jo) 30
Smith, David 36
Smith, Ryan 46
Smith, Gerald (Jerry) 61
Smith, Shane 87
Smith, Patrick (Paddy) 90
Smith, Amy 95
Smith, Barbara (Barb) 99
Smith, Terrance B. (Terry) 101
Smith, Michael (Mel) 111
Smith, Dale 121
Smith, Hubert 126
Smith, Patrick (Paddy) 150
Smith, John (Jack) 170
Smith, Sheri S 174
Smith, Richard S (Dick) 184
Smith, Marty 185
Smith, Drew 186
Smith, Dan 204
Smith, Judy 236
Smith, Sanford 247
Smith, Mary Anne 256
Smith, James E. 258
Smith, Sheila 259
Smith, Albert E. 283
Smith, Mark 286

Smith, Jeff 305
Smith, David R. 316
Smith, Wes 325
Smith, Judy 342
Smith, Pat 347
Smith, Michael 353
Smith, Travis 353
Smith, Margaret Low 358
Smith, Matt 362
Smith, Steve 379
Smith, Michelle (Mitch) 382
Smith, Howard 391
Smith, Henderson 419
Smith, Cecilia M. 429
Smith, Cecilia M. 429
Smith, Norman 431
Smith, Craig 439
Smith, Lloyd 447
Smith, Linda 447
Smith, Jody 451
Smith, Bo 457
Smith, Kenneth 457
Smith, Tim 473
Smith, Andrea 487
Smith, Klyne 487
Smith, Gary 490
Smith, Nils 490
Smith, Phyllis 526
Smith, Dillon 532
Smith, Joanne 534
Smith, Barbara H (Barb) 542
Smith, Joe 543
Smith, Shaun 559
Smith, Kevin 561
Smith, Beverly 571
Smith, Jennifer R. 575
Smith, Richard J. 575
Smith, Pat 575
Smith, Elizabeth 579
Smith, Darwin 596
Smith, Cheryl 599
Smith, Barrett 616
Smith, Barbara 616
Smith, Orin C. 616
Smith, Cindy 626
Smith, James E. 636
Smith, Ray 637
Smith, David 640
Smith, Herman D 643
Smith, Tonya 644
Smithers, Westwood 147
Smithson, John 450
Smittle, Brenda 509
Smothermon, Dave 583
Smullen, Richard (Dick) 253
Smyers, Steve 602
Smyth, Mattie 150
Snekvik, Rick 167
Snitcher, Ann 284
Snodgrass, Cyndi 332
Snow, Laura 46
Snowberger, Thomas 54
Snowden, Guy B. 277
Snyder, Donna 251
Snyder, Timothy L 310
Snyder, Sam 419
Snyder, Linda 591
Sobolik, Kristin D. 649
Soby, Lynn 432
Socha, Josh 342
Sock, Shannon 333
Sockwell, James 482
Sodano, Carol 51
Solaro, Chris 75
Solberg, Jeff 226
Solberg, Jeffrey (Jeff) 226
Soldo, Stephen 447
Solecki, Greg 239
Solitaire, Diane 420
Solliday, Mary 495
Sollmann, Justin 194
Solomon, Patrick (Paddy) 145
Solomon, Lisa 309
Solomont, Alan D. 591
Somers, Rick 490

Sommers, Susan (Sue) 377
Son, John 188
Song, Norman 73
Songer, Nancy Butler 171
Songstad, Jaci 329
Sonnenfeld, Gerald (Jerry) 611
Sonnier, Leland M. 518
Sontheimer, Dan 303
Sorensen, Dawn 352
Sorensen, Carl K 612
Sorenson, Charles W. 263
Sorenson, Carrie 498
Soroka, Dina 368
Sortwell, Christopher T (Chris) 361
Sosebee, Hugh 543
Soto, Madelyn 517
Sotolongo, David M (Dave) 432
Sousa, Pat 185
Southam, Arthur (Art) 279
Southard, Thomas (Thom) 623
Sowers, Chuck 489
Sowinski, Jordan 310
Spadaccini, Dino 623
Spain, Wayne 41
Spain-Remy, Claire 353
Spallino, Jon 489
Spallucci, Maryanne 152
Spatig, Robert (Bob) 614
Speaker, John 448
Spears, Keith 320
Spears, William G. 423
Specht, Dwight 560
Speer, Richard (Dick) 43
Spellman, Becky 511
Spencer, Terry 90
Spencer, Scott 121
Spencer, Kate 204
Spencer, Kathleen 208
Spencer, Jason 240
Spencer, Scott 359
Spenst, Brett 287
Speranza, Elisa 112
Sperring, Jeff 259
Spickler, Eric 239
Spiegel, Allen M. 653
Spielman, Stephen 554
Spires, Roger 481
Spiro, Barbara (Barb) 171
Spitale, Emily 530
Spitulnik, Aric 305
Spitulnik, Aric 481
Spitzer, John 81
Spivey, Gregory 245
Spivey, Patrick 557
Splaine, Kevin 492
Spoelman, Roger W. 231
Spoler, J Al 310
Spong, Bernadette 391
Spong, Bernadette 432
Spooner, William A. (Bill) 473
Spoor, David 515
Sporing, Eileen 539
Sposato, Anthony 513
Spotts, Janet 641
Spradlin, Jim 226
Spragg, Anna M. 423
Sprague, Robert (Bob) 80
Sprague, Kelly 89
Sprague, F. Remington 231
Spriggs, Danny 536
Springmann, Tressa 305
Springmann, Tressa 481
Sprunger, Tracy 137
Sr., Lincoln A. Bean 9
Sr., Lincoln A. Bean 9
Sr., Charles A. Collat 325
Sr., William E. Kamatz 604
Srinivasan, Rajesh 213
Srivastava, Bharati 436
Sroufe, Daniel 396
Stacey, Brandon 379
Stacey, Robert 616
Stack, Steven J. 22
Stack, Jeff 337
Stack, John (Jack) 623

Stackalis, Jack 576
Stadnyk, Sheldon G. 45
Stadtmiller, James (Jamie) 622
Stafford, Kevin 95
Stafford, Deborah 215
Stafford, Deborah (Deb) 215
Stafford, Dave 419
Stafura, Paul 172
Stagliano, Rich 598
STAHLER, SHERI 530
Stallings, Jay 46
Stallworth, Nicole 383
Stambula, Nick 434
Stamm, Jeffrey (Jeff) 73
Stamp, Diane 271
Stanard, Patricia 309
Standish, Marion 538
Standley, Bonnie 98
Standley, Chuck 481
Standley, Steven D. (Steve) 604
Stanfield, Margot 543
Stanford, Johnny 49
Stanley, William 299
Stansbury, Shannon 121
Stansfield, Gill 277
Stanton, Mark E. 42
Stanton, Tamie 432
Stanton, Lowell 554

Stanton, Oliver K 583
Staples, Susan 362
Stapleton, Maureen A 462
Stapleton, F. Bruder 464
Stapleton, F 464
Starbuck, William 269
Stark, Jared 295
Stark, John (Jack) 618
Starling, Mike 358
Starner, Wendy 208
Start, David 492
Stastney, Eric 185
State, Scott E. 377
Staton, Ramona 641
Statuto, Richard J. (Rich) 80
Staudt, Tom 339
Staudt, Mark 457
Stauffer, Sanford 155
Stavridis, James G. 591
Stayer, Rhett 129
Stearns, Terry 183
Steck, Jim 481
Steele, Athornia 379
Steele, Erik 517
Steele, Mark T. 589
Steffey, Wayne 654
Steidle, Ian 175
Steier, Kate 150
Steiger, Nancy 401
Steimel, Ron 334
Stein, Deborah M (Deb) 607
Steinback, Kenneth B. (Ken) 153
Steinbauer, Rick 224
Steinbeck, Daryl 576
Steingraber, Fred G. 258
Steinhauser, Barbara (Barb) 307
Stelnik, Jeff 77
Stencel, Lindsay 49
Stencel, Lindsay 50
Stenehjem, Jerome 473
Stepe, Betty 433
Stephen, Emily 172
Stephens, Robert 16
Stephens, Dana 96
Sterling, Sharon 353
Sterling, Melvyn 501
Stern, Alan (Al) 490
Stern, John 602
Sternberger, Lee 271
Sterner, Jeffery L. 243
Stesny, Anne 510
Stetzer, Ed 306
Stevens, Chris 71
Stevens, Bruce R 80
Stevens, Scott L. 375
Stevens, John 524

Stevens, Lori 585
Stevens, John (Jack) 597
Stevenson, Doreen 497
Steves, Sonya 302
Steward, Palmer 215
Stewart, Cheryl Ann 14
Stewart, John 157
Stewart, Milton R. (Milt) 258
Stewart, Robin 360
Stewart, John 421
Stewart, Scott 512
Stewart, Craig 513
Stewart, Mark 513
Stewart, Maureen 517
Stewart, Inez 539
Stewart, Deborah (Deb) 568
Stichter, Don 10
Stiehr, Jack 317
Stiger, Jeffrey 280
Stimpert, John 163
Stinebaugh, Louis 7
Stiner, Sue 623
Stinger, Harold 471
Stinnett, Hester 530
Stinsman, Kathleen 578
Stinson, Wade 127
Stinson, Lindsey 623
Stirling, Steve 117
Stith, Melanie 96
Stitle, Stephen A. 258
Stitt, Carrol 38
Stiver, Ron 259
Stobak, Michael (Mel) 52
Stobak, Mike 52
Stock, Ann 275
Stock, Steve 280
Stocker, Oliver 342
Stoebner, Jeff 41
Stoebner, Joe 41
Stofko, Larry 501
Stojic, George 298
Stokes, Charles D. (Chuck) 331
Stokes, Tamarus L 649
Stokosa, Kari 617
Stoldt, Jody 596
Stolicker, Melissa (Mel) 224
Stoll, Carol 149
Stollsteimer, Terry 382
Stone, Jeanette 49
Stone, Kim 161
Stone, Terry 239
Stone, Mike 266
Stone, Joseph V. (Joe) 322
Stone, Susan 473
Stone, Danny 482
Stone, Jan 492
Stone, W Wes 523
Stonecypher, Michael (Mel) 541
Stopper, Joshua 473
Storey, Debbie 226
Storrs, Ed 82
Story, Greg 432
Story, Edward (Ed) 432
Story, G 432
Stoudt, James R. 429
Stoutland, Judith 506
Stover, Ricky 90
Stoverock, Linda 360
Strachan, Ron 137
Strain, Charles (Chas) 160
Strain, Charles M. 645
Straley, Donna 551
Strand, Shawnee 15
Strang, Garland 286
Strange, John 505
Strasbaugh, George 442
Straszynski, Mark 66
Stratakis, Dimitrios 648
Stratten, Gary A. 258
Stratton, Lori 75
Straube, Elliott 616
Strauss, Moshael J. 653
Strauss, Natalie 307
Strawn, Chris 17
Strawser, Joyce 470

Streblow, Jeff 642
Street, Nikki 393
Streeter, Edwin 302
Streeter, Bill 339
Streeter, Al 437
Streeter, Debra 490
Streif, Mary 451
Streinu, Ileana 570
Streletzky, Donna 61
Stribling, Hanah 175
Strickland, David 5
Strickland, Claire 607
Strickler, Patty 398
Strickler, Susan (Sue) 551
Stritikus, Tom 616
Stroker, Robert T. 530
Strom, Jessica 175
Stroman, Jay 543
Strong, David W. 391
Strosnider, Preston 144
Stroubakis, Demetri 18
Stroud, Cindy 448
Strovers, David 59
Stroz, Edward M. 204
Struby, Neil 361
Strull, Scott 597
Strumwasser, Todd 524
Strykowski, Jill 15
Stubbs, Fell 614
Stuber, Rich 593
Studebaker, Kyle 310
Studer, James 534
Stueber, Shelly 321
Stuenkel, Kurt 203
Stukane, Edward 511
Stulken, Judy 484
Stults, Robin 607
Stumf, Kathy 231
Stump, Mike 311
Sturk, Dawn 254
Sturt, David (Dave) 382
Sucher, Therese 429
Sudders, Marylou 590
Sudheendra, Vijay 513
Suer, Bernie 337
Suess, Marcia 572
Suggs, Tom 556
Suggs, Thomas (Thom) 556
Sughrue, Denise 560
Suits, Scott 102
Suits, Bryan 342
Suldan, Joel 305
Sullivan, John 19
Sullivan, Thomas J. 27
Sullivan, Sean 48
Sullivan, John 96
Sullivan, Lynn 97
Sullivan, Mike 121
Sullivan, Janet 179
Sullivan, Kelly 278
Sullivan, Susan (Sue) 362
Sullivan, Scott R. 408
Sullivan, Kevin 474
Sullivan, Kimberly 501
Sullivan, Scott A. 532
Sullivan, Leo 590
Sullivan, Julie H. 612
Summerlin, Jim 325
Summers, Curtis 32
Summers, Barbara (Barb) 137
Summers, Cynthia 160
Summerville, Gregg T. 258
Sun, Yue 511
Sundborg, Stephen (Steve) 464
Surbaugh, Michael 83
Suriano, Beth 278
Surprenant, Stephen T 449
Sussman, Betsy 201
Sutela, Kyle 342
Sutley, Nancy 309
Suttle, Jim 518
Suttle, Karen 561
Sutton, Richard O. (Rick) 45
Sutton, Denise 324
Sutton, Ben 517

Sutton, Benjamin (Ben) 517
Sutton, Jaqueline 542
Sveilich, Norman 208
Swan, Beth A. 578
Swango, Gary 226
Swanson, Gary 112
Swanson, Scott J. 157
Swanson, Marleen 277
Swanson, James T (Jim) 290
Swanstrom, Ronald 470
Swapp, Russell B. 470
Swartz, David G. 24
Swartz, Brian 405
Swearingen, Fritz 215
Swearingen, Angie 506
Sweeney, Tara 31
Sweeney, Sean 450
Sweeney, Robert J. 649
Sweet, Stephen J. 58
Sweet, Jon C. 445
Sweet, Bill 546
Sweitzer, Dan 203
Swenson, Paul 280
Swierczek, Stephen (Steve) 502
Swindle, Greg 362
Swindle, Richard (Dick) 543
Swintek, Kathryn B 592
Sydnor, Walker P. 106
Syed, Mamoon 425
Sylvain, Larry 224
Syverud, Kent D. 575
Szarkowski, Lisa 602
Szatkiewicz, Cory 592
Szczesny, Jeff 425
Szomjassy, Michael A. 112
Szubski, Michael A. (Mike) 604
Szymanski, Jennifer 95

T

Tabak, Natan 629
Tabb, Kevin 67
Tadje, Rob 263
Taffe, Pat 372
Taggart, Richard (Rich) 477
Taheri, Paul 201
Tahtinen, Dale 342
Tait, Raymond 451
Tak, Laurens 112
Takla, Magdy 542
Talbott, Sandra 325
Talib, Javid 73
Tallent, William (Bill) 512
Talley, Linda 119
Talton, Neal L. 202
Talton, Neal L. 202
Tambourini, Nanette 575
Tamburini, Kristen 530
Tamby, Jeyant 182
Tammaro, Suzanne 487
Tamporello, Glenn 490
Tan, Vivian 280
Tande, Brett 107
Tang, Ryan 233
Tang, Jennifer 643
Tanne, Frederick 23
Tannert, Silvio 100
Tarbet, Michele 473
Tarca, Fred 423
Tart, Edward 151
Tarves, Paul 189
Tate, Harry 423
Tauber, David W. 528
Tauber, Richard E. 528
Tauer, John (Jack) 615
Taugher, Damon 167
Tawyea, Edward (Ed) 578
Taylor, Mimi 47
Taylor, Bill 60
Taylor, Aaron 60
Taylor, Mike 96
Taylor, John 110
Taylor, Steve 277
Taylor, Becky 282

Taylor, Vernon (Vern) 359
Taylor, Vance 371
Taylor, Jim 409
Taylor, Mimi 442
Taylor, Michael (Mel) 467
Taylor, Christopher 489
Taylor, Lee 506
Taylor, Leslie 543
Taylor, Patsy 572
Taylor, Yolanda 572
Taylor, Cary 572
Taylor, Grady 585
Taylor, Ed 616
Taylor, Derrick 627
Taylor, Keith 630
Teahen, Roberta (Bobbi) 197
Teare, Alan 112
Tech, Georgia 100
Tedesco, Michael 550
Teel, Michael J. (Mike) 425
Teel, Joyce Raley 426
Teer, Harold 271
Teer, Julie 569
Telatovich, Joyce 189
Telles, Lisa M 525
Telles, Lisa M 526
Tenaglia, Christine 405
Tenhaken, Jean 139
Tennant, Lance 102
Tennis, Karen 15
Tennison, George 206
Terpylak, Mark 517
Terrell, Seth 421
Terronez, Tony 275
Terry, Lisa 73
Terry, Paul 382
Terry, Steve 587
Terterian, Rita 540
Terzano, Valerie (Val) 645
Tessier-Lavigne, Marc 564
Tessman, Brock 609
Testy, Kellye 616
Teuber, Andrew (Andy) 9
Teufel, Pamela (Pam) 579
Thacher, John P. 642
Thacker, Melissa (Mel) 406
Thacker, Krista 500
Thacker, Allison 643
Thames, Thomas B. 467
Thangam, Siva 511
Thareererg, Karen 233
Tharp, Beth 137
Theberg, LeeAna 585
Theis, Anne 453
Thekkel, Valsamma 645
Theobald, Neil D. 530
Theophilus, Don 524
Thersen, Tom 222
Thesenvitz, Michael (Mel) 572
Thibodeau, Tami 150
Thiboutot, Paul 99
Thiel, Donald 101
Thiriot, Kenna 263
Thoma, Jeanne 575
Thomas, Arleen R. 21
Thomas, Troy 35
Thomas, Christopher (Chris) 112
Thomas, Howard 112
Thomas, Karen 304
Thomas, Beverly 340
Thomas, Mark 405
Thomas, Pamela 448
Thomas, Shirley 449
Thomas, Dean 461
Thomas, Bill 463
Thomas, Brad 482
Thomas, Brad 482
Thomas, Mike 581
Thomas, Huw F. 591
Thomas, Ric 605
Thomas, Ronald R. (Ron) 611
Thomas, Robert (Bob) 613
Thomas, Chet 648
Thomason, George 331
Thomason, Joel D. 402

Thompson, Gregg 112
Thompson, Dean 127
Thompson, Bill 128
Thompson, Ashley 151
Thompson, Michelle 153
Thompson, Timothy 198
Thompson, Timothy (Tim) 198
Thompson, Kim 217
Thompson, Teresa E. 217
Thompson, Elizabeth 259
Thompson, Sue 266
Thompson, Steve 283
Thompson, Martin J 342
Thompson, Fulton 372
Thompson, Richard L. (Dick) 399
Thompson, Patty 406
Thompson, Charles T. 411
Thompson, John (Jack) 419
Thompson, Mark A. 423
Thompson, Todd 433
Thompson, Kristin 450
Thompson, Penny 472
Thompson, Donna 473
Thompson, James D 476
Thompson, Dennis 482
Thompson, Christina 518
Thompson, Steve 581
Thompson, Ray 586
Thompson, Kim 601
Thompson, Naomi 611
Thompson, Larry 630
Thordarson, G. Thor 259
Thorne, Debbie Marie 534
Thornhill, Hugh 386
Thornock, Cody 263
Thornton, Rhonda 32
Thorp, H. Holden 575
Thorpe, Linda 45
Thrane, Linda 643
Throne, Beth 208
Thun, David L. 429
Thunberg, Robert 46
Thurman, Patricia 470
Thurston, Mark 112
Tibbitts, Betsy 215
Tibbs, E. W. 106
Tichenor, Sherry 121
Tidwell, Laura S. 181
Tiedeken, MJ 542
Tielke, Lori 20
Tietzsch, Roberto 43
Tiffin, Tim 580
Tiffin, Van 580
Tiffin, Lex 580
Tighe, Thomas 167
Tikka, Kirsi 18
Tilchin, Mike 112
Tilelli, John H. 641
Tiley, Susan (Sue) 383
Tilford, Tim 321
Tilghman, Richard H. (Rich) 402
Tillett, Jamie 286
Tillman, Linda 398
Tilton, Colette D. 487
Tim, Pickett 431
Timpone, Leonard 208
Tinney, Steve 26
Tinucci, Joe 605
Tippets, Amy 263
Tirrell, Mary 303
Tiry, Michael 342
Tisch, Jonathan M. (Jon) 591
Toburen, Paul 429
Todd, Janine 153
Todeasa, Sophia 316
Toffey, Bryan 6
Tokad, Murat 321
Tokarczyk, Peter 25
Token, Eric 441
Toll, David (Dave) 171
Tom, Walker 227
Tom, Matthew (Matt) 612
Tomaino, Mary 380
Tomblin, John (Jack) 577
Tomlinson, Tommy 128

Tomlinson, Doug 643
Tomshack, Ramona 456
Toni-Jean, Lisa 324
Tonjum, Kurt 127
Tonkin, Bruce 266
Toohill, Barbara 557
Tooker, Jeanie 494
Tooker, Jean 494
Toomajian, Marty 54
Toombs, Elizabeth 95
Topham, Michael J. G. 245
Toplan, Steve 582
Topper, Joseph V 623
Toppin, Bruce 372
Topping, Shane 511
Torcom, Lance 467
Tormey, Anne 649
Torosian, Jennifer (Jen) 103
Torrance, Kelly 239
Torres, Kevin 307
Torres, George 533
Torrone, John (Jack) 312
Tortora, Robert D. 213
Toscano, Dan 153
Totemoff, Charles W. 153
Totten, Glenda 280
Totzke, Jim 193
Totzke, Ned R. 357
Tougas, Roger C. 474
Toulme, Patrick 376
Toups, Sharon A. 452
Tourangeau, Roger 636
Tourkaman, Ali 179
Toussaint, Don 302
Townsend, Ronald D. (Ron) 54
Townsend, Ron 54
Townsend, Craig 124
Townsend, Ted 266
Trachtman, Les 204
Tracy, Russell 201
Tracy, Thomas (Tom) 379
Trafecante, Michael 191
Trainer, Michael 119
Trainer, Nancy 171
Trainham, James (Jamie) 432
Trammell, Jason 616
Tramontana, Anthony 273
Tran, Peter 100
Tran, Tri 446
Tran, Hong 530
Tranchon, Harold 276
Trapp, John J 88
Trapp, Paul 156
Trapp, Michael W. (Mike) 560
Trapper, Ryan 434
Trauth, Denise M. 534
Travers, Martin G. 73
Travis, Troy 340
Travis, Theresa 450
Travisano, Jacqueline A. 379
Traylor, Thomas W. (Tom) 584
Traylor, Christopher S. 584
Traylor, Michael T. 584
Trebesch, Butch 25
Tregaskis, Gay 263
Treiber, John H. 645
Treisman, Jonathan (Jon) 640
Treml, Carl 225
Trentacosta, Joseph 322
Tresch, Richard 590
Tressler, Susan (Sue) 643
Trice, Barry G. 228
Trick, Mike 100
Trilla, Maura 107
Tripi, John 25
Triplett, Larry 284
Tripp, Gayla 206
Tripp, Katie 418
Tritch, James 242
Trivunovich, Nick 614
Trobiano, Jackie 231
Troike, Jeffrey (Jeff) 110
Troski, Janet 103
Trosvig, Kelli 616
Trotta, Dan 388

Trotter, Chris 506
Trout, Tina 77
Trowbridge, Andy 245
Trowbridge, Rick 457
Truitt, Blake 358
Trujillo, Tate N 259
Trujillo, Roy B. 584
Trumble, James (Jamie) 209
Trumpower, Melissa (Mel) 221
Trusch, Kathy 79
Tryon, Jennifer 571
Tseng, Vivian S. Y. 357
Tseng, Judy 484
Tsuboi, Kenneth (Ken) 543
Tubb, Marga 362
Tubb, Joe 409
Tubbs, Dorothy 226
Tubbs, Jeff 269
Tucci, James M. 492
Tuchman, Mendel 119
Tucker, Archie 109
Tucker, Tim 153
Tucker, James 171
Tucker, Richard G. 240
Tucker, Jeff 421
Tuite, James M. 117
Tully, Stephen (Steve) 623
Tully, Herbert B. 642
Tune, Jim 499
Tuomanen, Elaine 503
Turbiville, Cathy 566
Turina, Mary 390
Turley, John (Jack) 232
Turner, Paul 1
Turner, Beth 49
Turner, Casey 171
Turner, Chris 287
Turner, Thomas (Thom) 335
Turner, Wanda 373
Turner, Howard 630
Turver, John 541
Turvey, Lavona 506
Tuss, Paul 609
Tussing, Laura 190
Tussing, Janet 360
Tuttle, Cathy 191
Tuzzolo, Karen 276
Tveekrem, Susan 51
Tveitnes, Tim 131
Tveten, Karen 258
Tweeten, Donna 255
Twiford, Lise 303
Twining, John R. 423
Twisdale, Lawrence A 30
Twitchell, David (Dave) 82
Tykocinski, Richard J. 578
Tykocinski, Mark L 578
Tynan, Robert 330
Tyrell, James E. 399
Tyrell, Chris 479
Tyrrell, Edward (Ed) 554
Tyson, James T (Jamie) 186
Tyson, Michael (Mel) 232
Tyson, Michael 232

U

Uchin, Robert A. 379
Udager, Mark 28
Udovic, Edward (Ed) 160
Uehara, Edwina (Eddie) 616
Uhl, Melissa (Mel) 150
Ullman, David F. 364
Ullrich, George 30
Ulmer, Andrew 93
Ulozas, Catherine (Cathy) 171
Ulrich, Clayton 245
Umali, Lana 495
Umfress, Stephanie 580
Underwood, John 405
Underwood, David M. 554
Ungaro, Pe 171
Unger, Mark 5
Unger, Shan Del 110

Ungerman, Bill 131
Uniat, Lois 461
Unruh, David 530
Unsworth, John 83
Urahn, Susan (Sue) 563
Urban, Larry 225
Urban, Thomas (Thom) 225
Urban, Brian 242
Urgo, Dennis 597
Urofsky, JoAnn 358
Urquhart, Kenneth (Ken) 10
Urushihara, Takuo 43
Usher, Chris 24
Utkov, George 487
Uttermark, Anne 15

V

Vacco, Dennis C. 357
Vadella, Jamie 189
Vaidya, Archana 74
Vaidya, Vinay 405
Vail, Matthew (Matt) 386
Vaillette, Lisa 550
Vakharia, Harish 441
Valadez, Therese 46
Valadez, David (Dave) 135
Valenti, Robert (Bob) 191
Valentine, Daniel 170
Valentine, Denise 349
Valentine, Mike 419
Valigorsky, Maryjean 368
VALOSKY, KENNETH (Ken) 623
Vance, Richard (Dick) 163
Vance, Rick 245
Vance, Richard (Dick) 245
Vandenberg, Marnie 379
Vanderhoff, Bruce 386
VanderWaal, Brent 267
Vandevelde, Jim 447
Vandeventer, Larry 551
Vandezande, Vicki 321
Vandort, Patti 247
VanDriel, Mary Kay 492
Vanfleteren, Bob 306
Vanhyfte, Ted 41
VanNess, William C. (Bill) 137
VanWyhe, Brenda 443
Varela, Luis 598
Vargas, Israel 597
Varkey, Alex 554
Varlan, Danni 174
Varnado, Darryl 119
Varner, Deanne 533
Varner, Clark 560
Vasche, Sybil 494
Vasil, Lee 310
Vasquez, Anthony 43
Vasquez, Jose 240
Vasquez, Sharon L. 572
Vassall, John H. 524
Vastine, Julie 166
Vath, Rick 394
Vats, Trib 330
Vaughan, Jefferson R 278
Vaughan, Marylou 470
Vaughn, Donnie 113
Vaupel, Christian 5
Vaux, Keith 425
Vazquez, Carmen 612
Veale, Dick 233
Vecchi, Mario 420
Vecchio, Diana 641
Veeraganti, Shourya 83
Vehige, Monica 338
Velasquez, David 66
Velazquez, Mary 246
Velazquez, Ralph R. 392
Velez, Patsy 126
Velez, Pablo 473
Vellaccio, Frank 133
Velonias, George 83
Venard, Paul 572
Venema, Robert (Bob) 280

Venezia, Claudia 647
Vengco, Joel L. 58
Venters, Beverly 407
Ventola, Anthony 591
Venus, Sam 391
Vera, George A. 543
Verde, Peter J. (Pete) 163
Verdile, Vincent 10
Verhoff, John (Jack) 146
Verma, Sudhir 204
Verma, Dinesh 511
Vermeer, Kevin 266
Vernon, James F. 602
Vernon, James F. 602
Versace, Enrico 524
Verslues, Ernie 339
Verst, Robert (Bob) 337
Vicente, Joeseph 389
Vickerie, Grace 65
Vickery, Michael (Mel) 198
Vidakovich, Genee 618
Vincent, Mary Ann 501
Vincenti, Claude 517
Vineyard, Tim 306
Vining, Marvin D. 357
Violette, Michael J. (Mike) 36
Visner, Gary 539
Vitale, Joe 129
Vitale, David J (Dave) 256
Vitanza, Alfred 500
Vitelli, Tom 263
Vivari, Bruce 636
VLACK, VALERIE R (Val) VAN 534
Vlassis, Christine 551
Vleet, Marlin 131
Voegtli, Josh 227
Vogel, Nicholas 333
Vogel, Rick 401
Vogel, Charles C. 477
Vogel, Stuart L. 477
Vogel, Joanne 487
Vogel, Richard L. 576
Voiss, James (Jamie) 543
Voit, Jennifer 360
Volk, Christopher H. (Chris) 46
Vollmar, Ken 347
Vonderohe, Eric 137
Voorhees, Karyn 153
Voorhees, Rhondie 609
Vorenkamp, Eric 558
Vorwick, George 598
Vosburgh, Kristen 432
Voss, Jim 457
Voss, Wayne 554
Voyles, Margie 297
Voyles, Brent A. 576
Voytek, Frank 47
Vrabel, Sheryl 189
Vradenburg, Daniel R. (Dan) 642
Vranken, Matthew G. (Matt) Van 492
Vries, Brad De 195
Vyas, Veena 329

W

Wabler, Tim 571
Wachira, Grace 112
Wade, John (Jack) 54
Wade, Kim 373
Wade, Chris 564
Wadsworth, Barbara (Barb) 2
Wadsworth, Jeffrey (Jeff) 54
Wagenfeld, Evan 310
Waggoner, Hank 298
Waggoner, Brad 306
Wagner, Hudlin 99
Wagner, Paige 222
Wagner, Karen 235
Wagner, Loretta 276
Wagner, Heidi 379
Wagner, Brent J. 429
Wagner, Brent J. 429
Wagner, Gerilynn 473
Wagner, Gary 554

Wagner, Andrea 605
Wagoner, Melissa 612
Wahl, Cheryl Forino 604
Wahlman, Mark 396
Wainwright, Jeff 202
Waite, G. Thomas 548
Waite-O'Brien, Nancy 179
Wakefield, John (Jack) 528
Wakim, Nada 47
Wakulchik, Grace 119
Walden, Crystal 437
Waldron, Jay 390
Waling, Randy 110
Walker, Jane 150
Walker, Kevin 218
Walker, Kevin 218
Walker, Tom 227
Walker, Kenneth 307
Walker, Bart 311
Walker, Susan 420
Walker, H. Fred 439
Walker, Annette M. 501
Walker, William S. (Bill) 545
Walker, Grace 596
Walker, Scott 630
Walker, Mary 651
Wall, Thomas 337
Wall, James 539
Wall, Barbara (Barb) 623
Wallace, Jon R. 42
Wallace, Frank 46
Wallace, Kathleen 65
Wallace, Brent E. 263
Wallace, Nikki 272
Wallace, Karen 342
Wallace, Tom 342
Wallace, Kelly 464
Wallace, Steve 467
Wallace, Betsy 522
Wallace, Allen (Al) 543
Wallace, Pat 561
Wallace, Cari 571
Waller, Rachel 151
Waller, Ken 255
Waller, David (Dave) 641
Wallis, Lee 245
Wallis-Lage, Cindy 73
Walls, Cynthia 77
Walsh, Kate E. 82
Walsh, Geraldine 198
Walsh, Matt 238
Walsh, Kathy 252
Walsh, Matthew M. (Matt) 574
Walsh, Daniel 574
Walsh, Matthew 574
Walsh, Sean 574
Walsh, Daniel J. 574
Walsh, Lori 627
Walsh, Dianne F 636
Walstrom, Jan 112
Walter, Paul 148
Walters, Patrick 13
Walters, Bob 90
Walters, Leigh 255
Walton, Peter 83
Walton, Lewis 212
Walton, Preston 613
Walton, Robert (Bob) 621
Walz, George 198
Wambold, Keith 311
Wampler, Dan 255
Wamsley, Cheryl 353
Wanahita, Anna 500
Wandoloski, Matthew (Matt) 77
Wang, Peter 17
Wang, Emily 43
Wang, Shen 83
Wang, Roxanne F. 92
Wang, Ernest 113
Wang, Xia 238
Wang, William 625
Wanik, Jillian 252
Waninger, Karen 137
Wann, Tara 342
Ward, Brook 85

Ward, Eugene W. 181
Ward, Norman (Norm) 201
Ward, Scott 219
Ward, Rory 340
Ward, Howard 439
Ward, James 459
Ward, Lesli 472
Ward, Paul 487
Ward, Lanie 517
Ward, Christa 543
Ward, Jared (JW) 545
Warden, P. Kirk 129
Wardrop, Kathryn J. 218
Ware, Pam 369
Ware, Jonathan (Jon) 391
Warehime, Val 379
Waress, Brett 330
Wargo, Mary E. 423
Waring, Darlene 197
Wark, Nicole 43
WARNER, TONY 175
Warner, Rene 263
Warner, Craig 487
Warren, Sue 298
Warren, Galen 446
Warren, V'Ella 616
Warrick, Paula 24
Wasan, Darsh 256
Waschitsch, Wendie 429
Wascom, David 518
Wasdovich, Andrea 296
Washa, Brian 376
Washington, Alton J. 77
Washington, Lewis 482
Washington, Vicki 617
Washinski, Micah 419
Wasserman, Mark 607
Watanabe, August M. (Gus) 258
Watanabe, August M. (Gus) 258
Waterbor, Robert (Bob) 179
Waters, Mickey 144
Waterston, Judith (Judi) 513

Watkins, Chuck 113
Watkins, Judy 118
Watson, James 18
Watson, Joni 175
Watson, Charlie 287
Watson, Jeff 305
Watson, Anita 404
Watson, Jeff 481
Watson, James M. 571
Watt, Andrew 487
Watt, Jeffrey (Jeff) 608
Watters, James H. 439
Watts, Jeff 24
Watts, Bruce 256
Wayland, Rick 228
Wayson, Amy M 390
Weaner, Lisa 317
Weatherall, Maureen 511
Weaver, Ron 315
Weaver, Gail 652
Webb, Tammy 32
Webb, Richard 235
Webb, Yvonne 279
Webb, Maryjo 473
Webb, Kevin 570
Webb, John (Jack) 586
Webber, Matthew 73
Webber, Harris 530
Webber, Henry S. 575
Weber, Barb 6
Weber, Joe 109
Weber, Dan 110
Weber, Russell 268
Weber, Ron 326
Weber, William (Bill) 420
Weber, Donna 429
Weber, Keith 510
Webster, Kathleen 307
Webster, Jeff 533
Wedge, Kim 512
Wedge, Kimberly 513
Weed, Matt 263

Weekly, Stephanie 171
Weeks, Lionel 305
Wehrle, Bill 280
Weikert, Scott 112
Weil, Amy 43
Weil, Laura 92
Weiler, Nathan 34
Weiman, Robin 481
Weimer, Linn 5
Weinbach, Donald J. 423
Weinberg, Zach 99
Weinberger, Steve 141
Weiner, Robert (Bob) 540
Weiner, Edward G. 583
Weinstein, Charles (Charly) 180
Weiser, Anna 540
Weisert, Marvin 226
Weisner, Thomas 117
Weiss, Emily 23
Weiss, George 49
Weiss, Tamara 276
Weiss, Gary 376
Weiss, Gregory S 445
Weiss, Philippe 470
Weiss, Janice 510
Weiss, Jason 518
Weissberg, Jed 280
Weitz, Sue D 543
Welborn, Ruth B. 534
Welch, John K. 54
Welch, Bill 148
Welch, Olga 172
Welch, Kevin 360
Welch, Mark 419
Welch, C. Brigid 616
Welde, Brittney 450
Weldon, William C. (Bill) 423
Weldon, Stephanie 437
Welie, Gordon van 267
Welkie, Katherine A. (Katy) 263
Wellborn, Sam M. 202
Welle-Powell, Debbie 460
Welling, Curtis R. (Curt) 25
Welliver, Dave 8
Wells, Brooks 6
Wells, Michael 175
Wells, W. Michael (Mike) 258
Wells, James 307
Wells, Samuel (Sam) 576
Welly, Stephen 565
Welsh, Peter 516
Welt, John (Jack) 134
Welz, Edward A. (Ed) 367
Wenaas, Jeffrey K. (Jeff) 240
Wendel, Jon S. 255
Wendel, Christian 583
Wendt, Barry 448
Wendy, Warring 539
Wenger, Philip R. 551
Wentworth, Linda 557
Werlein, Ewing 554
Werner, Todd S. 45
Wernette, Terry 149
Wertman, Jessica 391
Wertman, Linda 550
Wescott, Elizabeth 319
Wesemann, Jeannie 7
Wesner, Bradley 253
Wessel, David 119
Wessells, Chris 612
Wessler, Alan 339
West, Steven 259
West, Karl 263
West, Barbara 280
West, Steve 346
West, Tom 379
West, Arnold 572
Westermeier, Stephanie 448
Westlund, Jessie 137
Westman, John (Jack) 590
Westman, John 590
Weston, Nancy 417
Wetherell, Russ 286
Wetstein, Daniel 112
Wetzel, Charles 226

Wetzel, Kathleen 429
Wexler, Erik G. 305
Wexner, Abigail S. 360
Weydig, Arlene 308
Weygand, Robert (Bob) 611
Whalen, Jimmy 30
Whalen, Andrew 95
Whalen, Thomas 303
Whalen, Donna 448
Wharton, Peggy 71
Wheat, Charles E. (Chuck) 457
Wheeler, Penny Ann 15
Wheeler, Bobbi 237
Wheeler, Keeley 346
Wheeler, Ronnie 431
Wheeler, Mary 511
Wheeler, Melanie 537
Wheeler, Lynette 589
Wheeleri, Mary 511
Whelan, Mike 507
Whelan, Michael 574
Whelehon, Chuck 269
Whelton, Deborah L (Deb) 517
Wherry, Robert 474
Whetsone, Jim 321
Whetstone, Jim 321
Whillock, David 532
Whinnery, Ellie 117
Whitaker, Cathy 395
Whitaker, Candace 479
Whitbread, Mary 238
White, Tom 5
White, Rev. William W. 47
White, Cooper 119
White, David 155
White, Rebecca 162
White, Louise 179
White, Carolyn 222
White, Brian 305
White, Jacqueline 418
White, Brian 457
White, Brian 481
White, James I. 482
White, Stephen 503
White, Craig 529
White, Tedra 570
White, Winona 590
Whiteaker, Kim 635
Whiteford, Linda 614
Whitehead, Jayne 339
Whiteman, Jeffrey S. (Jeff) 187
Whitener, C. Cleve 299
Whiteside, Tom 69
Whiting, Douglas 277
Whitley, Jim 630
Whitlock, Susan (Sue) 353
Whitmarsh, Alana 450
Whitmore, Colleen 119
Whitney, Tom 128
Whitney, Jack 383
Whitson, Mark 170
Whitt, Frederick K. 217
Whittall, Jeffrey J (Jeff) 353
Whittenburg, Scott 609
Whittington, Ray 159
Whittle, Scott 263
Wical, Beverly 219
Wicker, Joanna 175
Wickham, Gregory I. (Greg) 155
Wicklander, Jeff 372
Wicks, Cynthia 95
Wiegand, Jason 227
Wieland, Robert A. 15
Wieland, John 52
Wieland, Lisa 323
Wiemelt, Karen Wiemelt Karen 112
Wienke, D B 569
Wiercinski, Katy A. 550
Wiernicki, Christopher J. (Chris) 18
Wiesen, Wayne 124
Wigfall, Arthur 582
Wiggans, Jerre 589
Wiggin, Pete 112
Wiggins, Roy A. (Chip) 64
Wiggins, Rondi 377

Wiggs, David H. 309
Wigington, Jarnett W. 482
Wilch, Peter 613
Wilcox, Don 420
Wilcox, Ralph 614
Wilcoxson, Blaine 573
Wild, Mary 456
Wildberg, Pam 34
Wildenthal, Kern 118
Wildermuth, Heather 360
Wiley, Leslie 182
Wiley, Susan (Sue) 303
Wiley, Bud 630
Wilhelm, Troy 619
Wilhelmi, Chris 560
Wilhelmsen, Thomas E. (Tom) 487
Wilhoite, Charles A. 390
Wilke, Lydia 353
Wilkens, Don 255
Wilkin, Maria 100
Wilkins, Robert 54
Wilkins, Karlyn 589
Wilkinson, Kate 90
Wilkinson, Thomas G. 357
Willard, Leslie 624
Wille, James (Jamie) 229
Wille, Doug 629
Willenbrink, Robert (Bob) 347
Willey, John (Jack) 197
Williams, Carol 46
Williams, James (Jamie) 137
Williams, Brett 167
Williams, Wendy 175
Williams, Lisa 183
Williams, Sheri 215
Williams, Theodore E. 217
Williams, Rod 261
Williams, Mike 266
Williams, Lauren 300
Williams, William (Bill) 313
Williams, Monique 330
Williams, Dwight 338
Williams, Brad 379
Williams, Aaron S. 432
Williams, Tom 432
Williams, Ed 433
Williams, Gary W 462
Williams, Lydia 476
Williams, Ryan 526
Williams, Linda 542
Williams, Carol 543
Williams, Denene 554
Williams, Brandon 572
Williams, James C. (Jim) 583
Williams, Keith E. 595
Williams, Kristi 596
Williams, David 614
Williams, Ted 614
Williams, Bobby 630
Williams, Yvonne 641
Williamson, Jeff 25
Williamson, Alan (Al) 179
Williamson, Corey 434
Williamson, Tony 525
Williamson, Donald (Don) 626
Williamson-hughes, Andrea 457
Williford, S. Hart 330
Willis, Diane H. 117
Willis, Willie 421
Willis, Linda 540
Willman, Ed 60
Wilmot, Kenneth S. 35
Wilmoth, Donna 468
Wilmshurst, Neil 182
Wilson, Modena H. 22
Wilson, Gail 32
Wilson, Patrick (Paddy) 46
Wilson, Kristianne 71
Wilson, Gary 95
Wilson, Matthew T 104
Wilson, Elka 135
Wilson, Brad 151
Wilson, David 155
Wilson, Gary 199
Wilson, Thomas (Thom) 225

Wilson, Eric L. 240
Wilson, Christopher 253
Wilson, Michael (Mel) 255
Wilson, James C. 268
Wilson, Linda 278
Wilson, Larry 280
Wilson, Selma 306
Wilson, Tom 317
Wilson, Kinsey 358
Wilson, Allen 401
Wilson, Ruth 425
Wilson, Charlton 489
Wilson, James (Jim) 492
Wilson, Karen 501
Wilson, Karen 506
Wilson, Sam 533
Wilson, Carolyn S. 571
Wilson, Linda 593
Wilson, Gale 596
Wilson, Phillip (Phil) 597
Wilson, Dan 604
Wilson, Lizabeth A. (Betsy) 616
Wilson, Barbara-Jan 635
Wilson, Amy 641
Winebrake, James J. 439
Winegard, Tanya 150
Winfrey, LaPearl L. 649
Wing, Craig 43
Winger, Brenda 263
Wingerning, William (Bill) 64
Wingfield, Gena G. 31
Wining, Pat 118
Winship, Nancy 83
Winstead, Bill 481
Winston, Patricia 86
Winter, Maridith 470
Winterbottom, Gregory T. 389
Winterfield, Curt 164
Winters, Lonnie 409
Wireman, Dan 129
Wirth, Dave 33
Wise, Ann 643
Wiser, James (Jamie) 613
Withers, Alex 602
Witherspoon, Djuna 530
Witschen, Pete 379
Witt, Edward (Ed) 344
Witte, Rob 245
Wittkop, Scott 327
Wittman, Stephen E (Steve) 234
Wobma, Paul 112
Wohlschlegel, Eric 23
Woike, David (Dave) 177
Wojtowicz, Sarah 316
Wolcott, Daniel 635
Wold, Lynn 266
Wolf, Stacy 23
Wolf, George 347
Wolf, Eric 602
Wolf-Rosenblum, Stephanie 487
Wolfe, Carolyn J 99
Wolfe, Kate 255
Wolfe, Brian 426
Wolfe, Ron 463
Wolff, Barbara (Barb) 175
Wolfman, Barry A 280
Wolfram, Dan 597
Wolfson, Amy 310
Wolfson, Jay 614
Wolk, Seth W. 492
Wollan, Kathy 342
Wollen, Allison 444
Wollman, William 198
Wollman, William (Bill) 198
Wollman, Jerry 607
Wollman, Julie 641
Wolt, Dave 471
Wolter, Nicholas J. 71
Wolterman, Daniel J. 331
Wolz, Lyle L. 78
Womack, Ashley 178
Wong, Jimmy 171
Wong, Desmond C. 258
Wong, Dorothy 337
Wong, Irene 543

Wood, Gary 112
Wood, John J (Jack) 112
Wood, Terry F. 131
Wood, Calvin 155
Wood, Calvin 155
Wood, Heather 202
Wood, Doug 298
Wood, Nancy 524
Wood, Cathy 539
Woodall, Pamela 163
Woodard, Elizabeth (Beth) 412
Woodburn, Christen 605
Woodland, Mark 113
Woodruff, Lawrence 155
Woodruff, David 295
Woods, Eugene A. 121
Woods, Douglas E. (Doug) 170
Woods, Mike 226
Woods, Keith 358
Woods, Athena 393
Woods, Ruby 482
Woods, Christopher 516
Woods, Chris 576
Woodward, Keith 423
Woodward, Charles 482
Woodworth, Gregory A. (Greg) 457
Woolen, Jim 197
Woolley, Craig 649
Woolsey, Suzanne H. (Sue) 261
Woolsey, Christine 460
Woomer, Kasey 340
Woosnam, Richard E. 258
Worcester, Peter 431
Work, C. Thomas 429
Worl, Rosita F. 463
Worrell, Judy 66
Worrell, Larry 70
Worrell, C. P. (Pat) 270
Worrell, C 270
Worrell, Doug 491
Worth, Denny 226
Worth, Eugene 263
Wortham, Tom 248
Worthy, Lee 426
Wray, Tim F. 23
Wrede, Linda 163
Wright, Ernie 73
Wright, Joseph 119
Wright, Dean 119
Wright, Susan (Sue) 297
Wright, David H. (Dave) 309
Wright, Jean 330
Wright, David (Dave) 577
Wrighton, Mark S. 575
Wrona, Jim 198
Wu, Lena 43
Wuellner, James (Jim) 505
Wuertz, Greg 92
Wulf, Tom 389
Wurman, Richard 224
Wyatt, Christa 176
WYATT, CARL V VAN 534
Wyatt, C Van 534
Wyels, Mary 247
Wyhe, Brenda Van 443
Wykoff, Phyllis 340
Wykpisz, Elizabeth 497
Wyllieandrews, Victoria 377
Wynia, Marvin 195
Wynn, Jimmy R 133
Wynne, Craig 481
Wynne, Susan 551
Wynne, Kaye 567
Wyper, Jay 245
Wyrens, Marcy 88

X

Xing, Janet 639

Y

Yako, Osamu 111
Yamaki, Hiroshi 595
Yamamoto, Terrina 76
Yaney, Eileen 494
Yang, Honggang 379
Yang, Geoffrey Y. 602
Yanney, John (Jack) 563
Yanoschak, John 437
Yardley, Scott 263
Yates, Teresa 166
Yates, Vinson M. 386
Yates, Deirdre 470
Yau, Joe 170
Yaw, Quincy 240
Yeager, Fair 112
Yeager, Scott 201
Yeates, John (Jack) 614
Yedvab, Lauren 366
Yeigh, Bjong Wolf 616
Yen, Chen 200
Yena, Donna 277
Yenzer, Scott 112
Yerby, Bob 239
Yerk, Bill 601
Yetman, Matt 471
Yochum, Alice 100
Yoder, Lamont 46
Yoder, Suzi MacDonald 66
Yoder, Suzi 66
Yoder, Donald (Don) 571
Yoders, David 265
Yoia, Dominic R. 423
Yoon, Heather 83
York, Allen (Al) 30
Yorkis, Kathleen 64
Yost, Shannon 197
Youmans, Kevin 215
Young, Lisa 31
Young, Bob 66
Young, Lynn 100
Young, Matthew 129
Young, G. Douglas 155
Young, Gary 196
Young, Anne 310
Young, Ann 345
Young, Ron 385
Young, Lydia 530
Young, Gary S. 542
Young, Barry 561
Young, Michael W. 564
Young, Eric 589
Young, William A. 604
Young, Cindy 649
Younger, Jon 524
Youngs, Gary R. 357
Yount, Dave 400
Yu, Haoren 530
Yu, Randy 636
Yunker, Susanna 639
Yusi, Jerlyn 473

Z

Zablocki, Edward 564
Zacharius, Sherrie 534
Zacharof, Mike 9
Zaharis, Chris 187
Zahm, Kevin 311
Zaiss, Stephen 310
Zaki, Jill 548
Zalucki, Paula 278
Zalupski, Dennis A. 283
Zambardi, Victor 382
Zammit, Wade 463
Zane, Marianne 641
Zanni, Dave 5
Zapata, Rafael 418
Zappala, Elizabeth 590
Zar, Neville 513
Zarubi, Kathi 461
Zastrow, Linda 595

Zavarella, Min 516
Zawistowski, Stephen L. 23
Zdziarski, Eugene 160
Zeichner, Bernard 648
Zeidel, Mark L. 67
Zeidenstein, Darrow 643
Zeien, Leon 200
Zender, Dale 401
Zeno, Brian 386
Zenty, Thomas F. (Tom) 604
Zepp, Evelyn 618
Zerkle, Sandra 298
Zerkle, Sandra 298
Zerrudo, Lourdes 309
Zetena, Chris 362
Zetter, Bruce 539
Zeyrek, Birsen 112
Zhang, Jiaying 83
Zhang, Grace 204
Zhang, Shali 609
Zhou, Huan 83
Zhou, Weifang 595
Zhu, Bin 572
Ziegler, Keith 129
Ziegler, John 172
Ziegler, Jeff 360
Zierath, Stacey 401
Zietlow, Donald P. (Don) 295
Zietlow, Steve 295
Ziffer, Jack A. 47
Zigic, Filip 310
Zikmund, Joe 370
Zillmer, Eric 171
Zimmerli, Bert R. 263
Zimmerman, Melissa (Mel) 296
Zimmerman, Gail 424
Zimmerman, Gean 428
Zimmerman, Mark 468
Zimmerman, Jim 533
Zingale, Daniel (Dan) 538
Zingeser, Joel 227
Zinner, Michael J. 47
Zinsmeister, Stephen C 321
Zionts, Paul 159
Zitek, Karen 625
Zito, Julie 24
Zmich, Kenneth W. 105
Zmolek, Pat 194
Zoilo, John 119
Zoller, Richard (Dick) 337
Zollinger, Lance 379
Zona, Johnathan 590
Zone, Christine 432
Zorko, Gary 654
Zou, Cathy 112
Zrepskey, Kim 416
Zubeck, Barbara (Barb) 589
Zuckerman, Tom 616
Zuel, Sally 596
Zuhlke, Dan 263
Zuhlke, Sue 389
Zulick, Clarissa 30
Zumstein, Larry 287
Zungolo, Eileen 172
Zuniga, Anita 280
Zuschlag, John 3
Zuschlag, John (Jack) 3
Zuzich, David 396
Zwolak, Robert (Bob) 158
Zygmont, Dolores 530